GOALS!!!

C000183444

BW

KC

KC

GW

AC

PB

AC

GW

PB

What happened next?

Once again a huge thank you to Peter Barnes (PB), Keith Clayton (KC), Alan Coomes (AC), Roger Turner (RT) and Bill Wheatcroft (BW). A special mention to Gordon Whittington (GW), who tells me he's not ready to move into the digital era and apologises for sending 'old skool' prints - but I love opening up Gordon's envelopes and seeing the latest batch of behind the goal shots which capture 'goals! goals! goals!' better than any other - thank you.

Again I haven't captioned the photographs so as to fit more action shots in. Each photographer as been credited with their photo and should you be interested in obtaining a copy we can put you in touch with the photographer in question.

NON-LEAGUE CLUB DIRECTORY 2018-19

(41st Edition)

EDITORS
MIKE & TONY WILLIAMS

NON-LEAGUE CLUB DIRECTORY 2018-19
ISBN 978-1-869833-71-8

Editors
Mike Williams
(Tel: 01548 531 339)
mwpublishing@btconnect.com
Tony Williams
Email: t.williams320@btinternet.com

Published by MW Publishing
(Tel: 01548 531 339)
Email: mwpublishing@btconnect.com

Printed and bound by
CPI Group (UK) Ltd, Croydon, CR0 4YY

Sales & Distribution
MWPublishing (01548 531 339)

Front Cover: Bond (Fylde) and Horsfall (Kidderminster) challenge for the ball during this FA Cup First
Round Proper match, which AFC Fylde won 4-2 to set up a Second Round tie against League One
Wigan Athletic. Photo: Keith Clayton.

Non-League Day was set up by James Doe in 2010 as a social media experiment, after being inspired by a pre-season trip to Devon to watch Queens Park Rangers play at Tavistock. It has now grown to become an annual part of the football calendar, backed by Premier League and Football League clubs, MPs, celebrities, media organisations, charities and most importantly the non-league clubs themselves and the fans who turn up on the day.

Always scheduled to coincide with an international break, Non-League Day provides a platform for clubs to promote the importance of affordable volunteer led community football while giving fans across the country the chance to show support for their local non-league side.

NON LEAGUE DAY
13.10.18
Support your
LOCAL
FOOTBALL CLUB
nonleagueday.co.uk

Many non-league clubs are almost exclusively volunteer run, with money taken at the turnstiles often funding thriving youth set-ups, projects and facilities which are of benefit to the whole community. The level of skill on offer at non-league grounds will never compare to that at the Emirates Stadium or Old Trafford, for example, but there are other sides to the experience, from which the smaller club will always win hands down. The vast majority of games still kick off at 3pm, ticket prices are realistic, you can often stand (and drink!) anywhere in the ground and will always be guaranteed a warm welcome by people who run their clubs for a love of the game.

Whether you're a Premier League or Championship fan without a game, a League One or League Two supporter who can't make an away trip, or just someone who is curious about what their local club has to offer, there is sure to be something to interest everyone.

CONTENTS

GOING THROUGH A TRANSITIONAL PERIOD...

Like the recent restructuring of our beloved National League System, the Directory too is undergoing a slight change in format. Over the next two editions I hope to move the Directory towards a clear 'book of two halves' - a look back at the season just gone followed by a club directory that will help you through the coming campaign.

I have listened to your comments and I hope the improved index and the addition of the player sections meet with your approval. Again, in time, I hope to develop the players section further, with adding National North and South the first phase of this development. Hopefully the 'restructuring' will enhance the Directory further and keep it alive for a few more years to come. As ever, please get in touch with your comments, it certainly helps to know if I'm on the right track, or not!

Here's to a successful 2018-19 let's hope the new National League System structure is a great success!

SPECIAL ACKNOWLEDGMENTS

'OUR TEAM' OF PHOTOGRAPHERS
Peter Barnes, Keith Clayton, Alan Coomes,
Roger Turner, Bill Wheatcroft and Gordon Whittington.

FA COMPETITIONS DEPARTMENT
Chris Darnell and Scott Bolton

CONTRIBUTORS
Arthur Evans (Photographer & reports).
Richard Rundle (Football Club History Database).
The many league and club officials that have been kind enough to supply the necessary information.

And finally thank you, as always to Dad. We published his memoirs 'Arguably a Love Story' in March and it astounds me how much he has done for the game of football in this country. For over 70 years he has dedicated his life to the game we all love and, although he is left bemused by some of the going's on in the game today, he is as passionate about the sport as he ever has been!

If you're interested in purchasing a copy of the his book '**Arguably a Love Story**' please email mwpublishing@btconnect.com for further details.

Thank you one and all

Mike Williams

YOU CAN'T BUY PASSION AND LOYALTY

How the Non-League Football world has changed since we launched our first little annual in 1978.

The number of ex non-league clubs now proudly competing in the Football League underlines the importance of all those years in which promotion for the non-league champions was suggested, and was eventually accepted.

Looking at the membership of the senior non-league competitions, it can also be seen that, with determination and hard work on and off the field, the smallest and sometimes the youngest of clubs can achieve promotion up the pyramid.

What a wonderful change from the old days in which new ideas for development of the game and its competitions regularly appeared to be blocked.

It is clear to see that clubs with ambition to improve their facilities and their playing standards have achieved promotion right through the ranks, and this has encouraged more and more financial involvement for the very ambitious.

The importance of finance, has often been criticised by the traditional non-league football lover, but we have seen wonderful changes in club facilities, playing surfaces and training areas, all of which can attract good players and bring impressive results.

Looking back through our first 40 publications, the loyalty that the non-league world has shown to clubs, leagues and even football in general has been uplifting. We take great pleasure and satisfaction from compiling and publishing books concerning a sport we love, and to see so many of you also dedicated to the game in general has been inspirational.

Sometimes, the incredible transfer fees and the influx of foreign players at the top levels of the English game can be confusing to the mature football fan. Modern non-league followers of the game will realise there is now much more money available on and off the field, but we have to hope the spirit of the game at grass roots levels can still be admired.

So hopefully, 'non-league' competitions will continue to give enjoyment and satisfaction to all involved. The rewards may be greater but hopefully the traditional spirit and standards will still be respected.

Tony Williams

Non-League Pyramid (Steps 1-7) 2018-19

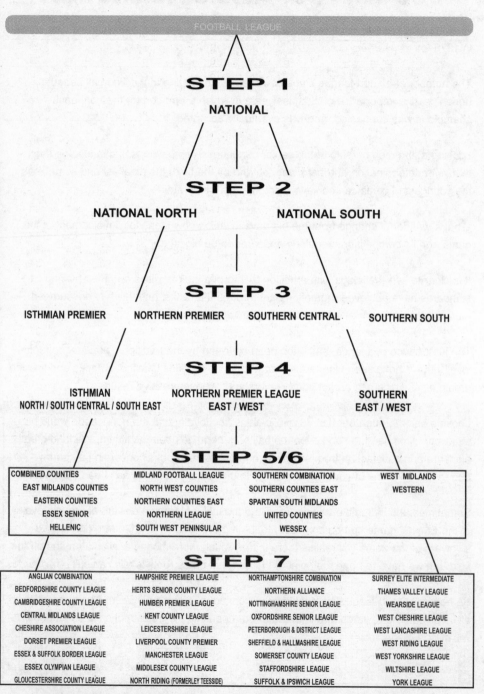

FOOTBALL LEAGUE

STEP 1
NATIONAL

STEP 2
NATIONAL NORTH   NATIONAL SOUTH

STEP 3
ISTHMIAN PREMIER   NORTHERN PREMIER   SOUTHERN CENTRAL   SOUTHERN SOUTH

STEP 4
ISTHMIAN
NORTH / SOUTH CENTRAL / SOUTH EAST   **NORTHERN PREMIER LEAGUE**
EAST / WEST   **SOUTHERN**
EAST / WEST

STEP 5/6

COMBINED COUNTIES	MIDLAND FOOTBALL LEAGUE	SOUTHERN COMBINATION	WEST MIDLANDS
EAST MIDLANDS COUNTIES	NORTH WEST COUNTIES	SOUTHERN COUNTIES EAST	WESTERN
EASTERN COUNTIES	NORTHERN COUNTIES EAST	SPARTAN SOUTH MIDLANDS	
ESSEX SENIOR	NORTHERN LEAGUE	UNITED COUNTIES	
HELLENIC	SOUTH WEST PENINSULAR	WESSEX	

STEP 7

ANGLIAN COMBINATION	HAMPSHIRE PREMIER LEAGUE	NORTHAMPTONSHIRE COMBINATION	SURREY ELITE INTERMEDIATE
BEDFORDSHIRE COUNTY LEAGUE	HERTS SENIOR COUNTY LEAGUE	NORTHERN ALLIANCE	THAMES VALLEY LEAGUE
CAMBRIDGESHIRE COUNTY LEAGUE	HUMBER PREMIER LEAGUE	NOTTINGHAMSHIRE SENIOR LEAGUE	WEARSIDE LEAGUE
CENTRAL MIDLANDS LEAGUE	KENT COUNTY LEAGUE	OXFORDSHIRE SENIOR LEAGUE	WEST CHESHIRE LEAGUE
CHESHIRE ASSOCIATION LEAGUE	LEICESTERSHIRE LEAGUE	PETERBOROUGH & DISTRICT LEAGUE	WEST LANCASHIRE LEAGUE
DORSET PREMIER LEAGUE	LIVERPOOL COUNTY PREMIER	SHEFFIELD & HALLMASHIRE LEAGUE	WEST RIDING LEAGUE
ESSEX & SUFFOLK BORDER LEAGUE	MANCHESTER LEAGUE	SOMERSET COUNTY LEAGUE	WEST YORKSHIRE LEAGUE
ESSEX OLYMPIAN LEAGUE	MIDDLESEX COUNTY LEAGUE	STAFFORDSHIRE LEAGUE	WILTSHIRE LEAGUE
GLOUCESTERSHIRE COUNTY LEAGUE	NORTH RIDING (FORMERLEY TEESSIDE)	SUFFOLK & IPSWICH LEAGUE	YORK LEAGUE

NATIONAL LEAGUE TABLE 2017-18

		P	W	D	L	F	A	GD	Pts
1	Macclesfield Town	46	27	11	8	67	46	21	92
2	Tranmere Rovers	46	24	10	12	78	46	32	82
3	Sutton United	46	23	10	13	67	53	14	79
4	Boreham Wood	46	20	15	11	64	47	17	75
5	Aldershot Town	46	20	15	11	64	52	12	75
6	Ebbsfleet United	46	19	17	10	64	50	14	74
7	AFC Fylde	46	20	13	13	82	56	26	73
8	Dover Athletic	46	20	13	13	62	44	18	73
9	Bromley	46	19	13	14	75	58	17	70
10	Wrexham	46	17	19	10	49	39	10	70
11	Dagenham & Redbridge	46	19	11	16	69	62	7	68
12	Maidenhead United	46	17	13	16	65	66	-1	64
13	Leyton Orient	46	16	12	18	58	56	2	60
14	Eastleigh	46	13	17	16	65	72	-7	56
15	Hartlepool United	46	14	14	18	53	63	-10	56
16	FC Halifax Town	46	13	16	17	48	58	-10	55
17	Gateshead	46	12	18	16	62	58	4	54
18	Solihull Moors	46	14	12	20	49	60	-11	54
19	Maidstone United	46	13	15	18	52	64	-12	54
20	Barrow	46	11	16	19	51	63	-12	49
21	Woking	46	13	9	24	55	76	-21	48
22	Torquay United	46	10	12	24	45	73	-28	42
23	Chester	46	8	13	25	42	79	-37	37
24	Guiseley	46	7	12	27	44	89	-45	33

Play-Offs: Aldershot Town 1-1 4-5p Ebbsfleet United. Boreham Wood 2-1 AFC Fylde
Semi Finals: Tranmere Rovers 4-2 Ebbsfleet United. Sutton United 2-3 Boreham Wood
Final: Boreham Wood 1-2 Tranmere Rovers

		1	2	3	4	5	6	7	8	9	10	11	12	13	14	15	16	17	18	19	20	21	22	23	24
1	AFC Fylde		7-1	1-0	2-2	2-2	1-1	2-2	3-1	2-2	1-1	2-0	0-0	2-1	3-3	0-1	6-0	1-4	3-0	1-1	2-1	2-0	5-2	1-2	2-0
2	Aldershot Town	2-1		1-1	2-0	1-1	1-2	1-1	0-2	0-2	0-0	0-1	1-0	6-0	2-1	2-2	1-2	1-0	1-1	1-0	2-2	3-2	2-1	3-1	2-0
3	Barrow	1-3	3-1		2-1	0-3	1-2	0-1	0-0	3-2	0-1	0-0	1-1	0-0	1-2	2-2	0-2	1-1	0-1	1-2	1-1	1-1	1-1	3-0	1-1
4	Boreham Wood	1-0	2-1	0-0		2-2	4-2	1-2	2-3	1-0	0-1	1-1	2-1	3-1	0-0	2-0	0-2	1-1	1-0	4-1	0-4	2-0	2-1	2-1	0-1
5	Bromley	0-1	0-2	0-0	3-2		1-1	3-1	2-2	4-2	3-0	0-0	2-1	2-0	6-1	1-1	2-3	2-2	1-0	0-1	3-1	0-1	2-0	1-1	
6	Chester	1-1	0-0	3-2	1-2	3-2		0-4	0-2	3-1	1-1	0-0	1-3	0-2	1-1	0-1	0-2	1-0	2-3	0-2	0-2	0-2	0-1		
7	Dagenham & Redbridge	2-0	0-2	2-1	2-3	5-1	3-2		1-0	1-2	3-3	3-1	3-1	3-2	4-2	0-0	1-0	1-0	2-1	1-3	1-2	1-0	0-4	1-1	0-1
8	Dover Athletic	0-1	1-2	1-1	0-1	1-2	4-0	1-0		2-0	1-1	0-0	3-2	2-1	4-0	1-0	2-0	1-1	2-2	1-0	0-1	1-0	0-1	3-1	1-0
9	Eastleigh	2-2	0-0	0-2	0-2	4-4	2-2	2-2	2-1		0-1	0-0	3-2	4-2	4-3	0-0	0-2	2-2	0-1	1-2	1-0	1-1	2-0	2-2	1-1
10	Ebbsfleet United	3-3	0-2	3-2	0-3	2-1	1-1	2-1	2-2			2-0	0-0	4-0	3-0	2-1	2-2	1-1	2-0	1-0	0-1	0-0	0-1	2-1	3-0
11	FC Halifax Town	2-1	0-2	0-1	2-1	2-1	4-0	2-1	1-2	3-3	1-2		2-2	2-0	2-0	1-2	1-4	3-2	0-2	2-2	0-2	1-1	0-2	0-0	0-0
12	Gateshead	1-2	0-1	1-2	1-1	1-2	3-2	0-0	0-0	2-0	2-5	0-0		1-0	2-2	1-3	3-0	7-1	2-1	2-2	0-2	3-0	1-0	1-1	0-0
13	Guiseley	1-0	1-1	0-1	0-0	0-1	1-1	3-5	1-1	0-0	2-2	1-1	0-1		0-1	1-3	1-2	1-3	0-0	4-2	0-2	3-2	0-0	1-2	0-2
14	Hartlepool United	0-2	0-2	1-0	0-0	2-1	1-1	1-0	0-1	1-1	4-0	2-2	0-1		1-2	1-2	3-1	1-1	1-1	1-1	1-1	3-2	0-2		
15	Leyton Orient	1-2	2-3	4-1	0-0	0-1	2-2	2-0	1-1	1-1	1-1	0-3	0-2	4-1	1-2		0-1	0-1	2-0	3-1	4-1	0-1	1-1	3-0	0-2
16	Macclesfield Town	2-1	2-0	3-1	0-0	0-0	1-0	2-0	1-0	1-2	1-0	2-1	1-0	2-1	1-1	1-1		1-0	1-0	0-0	1-0	1-1	2-2	1-3	4-1
17	Maidenhead United	1-2	3-3	0-1	2-1	5-2	3-0	1-1	3-2	3-1	1-1	0-0	0-3	3-0	2-1	0-1	1-1		0-0	1-0	2-1	1-2	1-0	2-1	1-2
18	Maidstone United	1-0	1-1	0-1	0-4	0-2	1-0	0-0	2-2	2-3	1-2	0-0	2-2	1-1	1-2	0-2	2-2	1-1		1-1	1-0	1-0	2-3	3-1	2-1
19	Solihull Moors	0-4	0-0	3-3	0-0	2-0	2-0	2-2	3-2	1-4	1-3	0-1	1-1	3-1	1-2	1-0	0-1	3-1	1-0		0-2	1-1	0-2	3-0	0-0
20	Sutton United	2-1	2-1	3-2	1-1	0-3	3-2	2-1	2-2	2-0	0-0	3-2	1-1	4-0	1-1	2-0	0-2	1-3	1-0		0-1	1-3	2-0	2-1	1-1
21	Torquay United	1-3	0-0	3-1	2-4	0-4	1-1	0-3	0-2	1-2	1-1	1-0	1-1	3-4	0-2	3-0	0-1	4-0	0-1	1-2	2-3		0-0	2-1	0-0
22	Tranmere Rovers	4-1	2-0	1-0	2-2	1-0	0-0	2-0	0-1	3-1	3-0	4-2	4-2	4-0	1-2	2-1	1-4	3-2	4-0	1-2	0-1	3-0		3-1	0-1
23	Woking	1-0	1-2	1-2	0-0	0-2	1-0	1-0	1-2	2-1	1-0	1-3	2-1	2-3	1-1	0-2	2-3	1-1	4-4	2-1	2-0	4-1	0-1		2-2
24	Wrexham	0-0	2-2	3-3	0-1	2-0	2-0	1-2	0-0	2-1	2-0	1-1	1-0	1-1	0-0	2-2	0-1	2-0	1-0	1-0	1-1	4-0	2-2	1-0	

AFC FYLDE

Club Contact Details 01772 682 593
Mill Farm, Coronation Way, Wesham, Preston PR4 3JZ
info@afcfylde.co.uk

Founded: 1988   **Nickname:** The Coasters   **Manager:** Dave Challinor - Nov 2011
Previous Names: Wesham FC and Kirkham Town amalgamated in 1988 to form Kirkham & Wesham > 2008.
Previous Leagues: West Lancashire > 2007. North West Counties 2007-09. Northern Premier 2009-14.

Club Colours (change): White

Ground Capacity: 6,000   **Seats:** 6,000   **Covered:** Yes   **Clubhouse:** Yes   **Shop:** Yes
Previous Grounds: Coronation Road > 2006. Kellamergh Park 2006-2016.
Record Attendance: 3,858 v Chorley, National League North, 26/12/2016.
Nearest Railway Station Kirkham & Wesham half a mile away.   **Bus Route** No. 61

RECORDS
Victory: 8-1 v Oxford City, Conference North, 06/09/14. 9-2 v (H) Boston United, Conference North, 19/11/16.
Goalscorer: Danny Rowe - 132 - August 2014 - 01/12/2017 (still playing)

HONOURS
FA Comps: FA Vase 2007-08.
League: West Lancashire League 1999-2000, 00-01, 01-02, 03-04, 04-05, 05-06, 06-07.
North West Counties League 2008-09. Northern Premier Division One North 2011-12. National North 2016-17.
County FA: Lancashire FA Challenge Trophy 2010-11, 12-13, 13-14. Lancashire Amateur Shield 2000-01, 03-04, 04-05, 05-06.
Northern Inter Counties Cup 2004-05, 05-06, 06-07.

08-09		09-10		10-11		11-12		12-13		13-14		14-15		15-16		16-17		17-18	
NWCP	1	NP1N	13	NP1N	5	NP1N	1	NP P	5	NP P	2	Conf N	2	Nat N	3	Nat N	1	Nat	7
FAC	Pr	FAC	2Q	FAC	P	FAC	2Qr	FAC	1P	FAC	2Q	FAC	1P	FAC	1P	FAC	2Q	FAC	2Pr
FAV	4P	FAT	3Qr	FAT	P	FAT	1Q	FAT	3Q	FAT	3Q	FAT	3P	FAT	3P	FAT	1Pr	FAT	1P

2017-18 STATS   **Goals Total** 93   **Games Without Scoring** 7 (2)   **Total No. of Scorers** 12   **Total Clean Sheets** 14
Most Consecutive Scoring Games 13   **Best Unbeaten Run** 7   **Most Consecutive Clean Sheets** 4
Best Att: 3,351 v Wigan Athletic, FA Cup 2P   Number in brackets denotes consecutive runs.

2017-18 MATCH LINE-UPS

Match Number	1	2	3	4	5	6	7	8	9	10	11	12	13	14	15	16	17	18	19	20	21	22	23	24	25	26	27	28	29	30	31	32	33	34	35	36	37	38	39	40	41	42	43	44	45	46	47	48	49	50	51	52	Total
Taylor (1)	x	x	x	x	x	x	x	x	x	x	s					s		s			s		s		s	x																											11
Ezewele	xs	s	sx	sx	s		s	s	sx	xs	s	s		s		s				sx			xs		xs	x	s		s	s																							9
Tunnicliffe	x	x	x	x	x	x	x	x	x	x	x	x	x	x	x	xs		x	x	x	xs	x	x	x	x	x	x	x	x	x	x	x	x	x	x	x	x	x	x	x	x	x	x	x	x	x	x	x	xs	x			50
Langley	x	x	x	xr																																																	4
Francis-Angol	x	x	x	x	x	xs		x	x	x	x	x	x	x	x	x	x	x	x	x	x	x	x		x	x	x	x	x	x	x	x	x	x	x	x	x	x	x	x		xs			x	x	x	x	x	x		48
Montrose	x	x	x	x	x	x	x	x	xs	x	x	xr		xr			sx	sx	sx	x	x	x	x	y	s	x	x	x	x	x	x	x	x	x	x	xs	x	x	x	x	x	x	x	x	x	x	x	x	x	xs			48
Bond	x	x	x	x	x	x	xs	xs	x	xs	x		x	x	x			x	x	x	x	xs	xs		xs	sx	sx	x	sx	x	x	xs	x		s	s	x			x	x	xs		x	x	x	x					48
Finley	x	x	x	xs	x	x	x	x					xs	x	xs	xs	xs	x			xs	xs	x	x		xr		xr		x	xs	x			xs	x	x	xr			x	x	x					x	x			38
Hardy	xs	sx	s	sx	xs	xs	xs	s					xs	xs	xs	s														sx	xs	sx	xs	xs	xs	x	xs	x	xs	xs	x	xs	x			sx	sx					25
Muldoon	x	x	xs	x	x	x	x	x	xs	x	xs	xs	sx	sx	xs	x	x		xr				xs	sx	xs	sx	xs	x	sx	sx	xs	xs	xs	xs	sx	x	xs	x		xs	x	x	xs	sx	xs	x	x	sx	x			49
Rowe	x	xs	x	xs	x	x	x	x	x	x	x	x	x	xs	x	x		x	xs	x			x	x		sx	x	x	xs	xs	x	x		x	x	x	x		xs	x		xs	xs	x	xs	x						52
Smith	sx	x	xs	x	sx	sx	sx	sx	xs	x	xs	sx	xs	x	sx	sx	sx	xs		sx	xs		x	x		x	x	x	s	s	s	s	sx	x	x		s	s	s		sx	x	s		x	s					50
Jones																																		sx	xs	x	sx	xs	s	s	sx	sx	s			x	s	x	s	sx			24
Lynch	s	s	s	s	s	s			s	s		x	x	x	x												x	x	x	x	x	x	x	x	x	x	x	x	x	x	x	x	x	x		x	x		x	x			41
Grand	s	sx	sx	sx	x	x	x	x	x	x	x	x			s	s	s	s	s	sx	s	sx	s	sx	s	x	x	x		sx	x	x	s	s	s	x	xs	x	x	x	x	x	x		x	xs	sx	x	xs			41
Blinkhorn	x	s	sx	s	sx	s	sx	sx	xr				sx	sx	s	s	s	s	s	s	sx	s	sx	s	sx	x	s	xs	s	x	x	sx			s		sx	sx		s	s	s	sx	s	s	xs	s					25
Tasdemir				s						sx	sx	sx	sx	s			sx	sx	sx	xs	sx	sx		s	sx	xs	s	sx	s	sx	sx	sx	sx				xs	xs	sx	sx	sx	sx	sx	s								28
McCready						sx			sx	s	s	xs	s	x	xs	s						s		s	x		sx			s																							10
Richards							sx			s	s	sx	x	xs				sx	xs	x	x		x	x	x	x	x	x																									14
Burke															sx	sx	x	xs	x	x		x				s		sx	x	sx	x	x	x				xs	xs	xs	x		x	x	s	x	x	xr					35
Taylor (12)															s	sx	xs	x	x	xs	sx	xs	xs	s	s	s	sx	s				sx	sx	x	xs	s		s		sx	sx	s	s	s	s	x						21
Edmundson																	x	x	x	x	x	x	x	x		x	x	x	x	x	x																						14
Stott																	sx			s																																	1
Mangan																	x	x		xs		xs	sx																														5
Chettle																													xs	xs	sx	sx	sx	xs	s	s			sx	xs	s												9
Stubbs																													sx	s	x	x	x	x	xs	s		x											s				7
Flores (L)																																				xs																	1
Lawlor																																				s	sx	sx	sx	sx	xs	sx	x										7
RESULT	D	D	D	L	D	W	W	L	D	L	D	L	W	D	L	W	W	W	W	L	W	W	D	L	L	L	L	D	L	W	W	W	D	W	W	W	L	D	W	L	L	W	W	W	W	L	D	D	L				

AFC FYLDE MATCH RESULTS 2017-18

Date	Comp	H/A	Opponents	Att:	Result		Goalscorers	Pos	No.
Aug 5	Nat Lg	H	Boreham Wood	1641	D	2 - 2	Woodards 17 (og) Smith 74	7	1
8	Nat Lg	A	Chester	2223	D	1 - 1	Muldoon 43	14	2
12	Nat Lg	A	Ebbsfleet United	1270	D	3 - 3	Jones 6 Rowe 15 Finley 34	15	3
15	Nat Lg	H	Maidenhead United	1657	L	1 - 4	Montrose 45	18	4
19	Nat Lg	H	Dagenham & Redebridge	1590	D	2 - 2	Jones 14 Grand 85	20	5
26	Nat Lg	A	Hartlepool United	2954	W	2 - 0	Jones 40 Rowe 84	17	6
28	Nat Lg	H	Barrow	2234	W	1 - 0	Hardy 56	12	7
Sept 2	Nat Lg	A	FC Halifax Town	1775	L	1 - 2	Rowe 56	17	8
9	Nat Lg	H	Bromley	1514	D	2 - 2	Tasdemir 67 Rowe 69	18	9
12	Nat Lg	A	Macclesfield Town	1065	L	1 - 2	Muldoon 49	20	10
16	Nat Lg	A	Eastleigh	3312	D	2 - 2	Jones 45 Tunnicliffe 60	20	11
23	Nat Lg	H	Woking	1532	L	1 - 2	Tunnicliffe 18	20	12
30	Nat Lg	A	Leyton Orient	4357	W	2 - 1	Rowe 15 48	19	13
Oct 2	Nat Lg	H	Gateshead	1494	D	0 - 0		16	14
7	Nat Lg	A	Sutton United	2127	L	1 - 2	Grand 85	19	15
14	**FAC 4Q**	**H**	**Wrexham**	**1390**	**W**	**1 - 0**	**Rowe 37**		16
24	Nat Lg	H	Wrexham	1816	W	2 - 0	Smith 8 Muldoon 77	18	17
28	Nat Lg	A	Solihull Moors	668	W	4 - 0	Smith 44 Rowe 45 Finley 76 Muldoon 87	18	18
Nov 4	**FAC 1**	**H**	**Kidderminster Harriers**	**1480**	**W**	**4 - 0**	**Rowe 14 46 Smith 54 Finley 64**		19
11	Nat Lg	H	Aldershot Town	2011	L	1 - 2	Rowe 56	18	20
18	Nat Lg	H	Torquay United	1552	W	2 - 0	Rowe 34 69	16	21
25	Nat Lg	A	Dover Athletic	2860	W	1 - 0	Rowe 78	16	22
Dec 1	**FAC 2**	**H**	**Wigan Athletic**	**3351**	**D**	**1 - 1**	**Rowe 70 (pen)**		23
9	Nat Lg	A	Boreham Wood	401	L	0 - 1		17	24
12	**FAC2r**	**A**	**Wigan Athletic**	**3124**	**L**	**2 - 3**	**Grand 40 Rowe 65**		25
16	**FAT 1**	**A**	**Chester**	**886**	**D**	**2 - 2**	**Tasdemir 90 Rowe 94 (Lost 4-5 on pens)**		26
23	Nat Lg	H	Ebbsfleet United	1512	D	1 - 1	Rowe 89	17	27
26	Nat Lg	A	Tranmere Rovers	6669	L	1 - 4	Smith 58		28
30	Nat Lg	A	Maidenhead United	1315	W	2 - 1	Montrose 71 Muldoon 83	15	29
Jan 1	Nat Lg	H	Tranmere Rovers	3065	W	5 - 2	Rowe 21 Muldoon 28 Francis-Angol 36 Tunnicliffe 55 Smith 90	13	30
6	Nat Lg	A	Bromley	1239	W	1 - 0	Muldoon 43	11	31
9	Nat Lg	A	Chester	1531	D	1 - 1	Rowe 55	11	32
13	Nat Lg	H	Guiseley	1535	W	2 - 1	Smith 18 Rowe 88	11	33
20	Nat Lg	H	Macclesfield Town	1982	W	6 - 0	Montrose 6 Muldoon 23 Finley 34 52 Smith 45 Bond 81	9	34
23	Nat Lg	H	Maidstone United	1408	W	3 - 0	Bond 12 Rowe 42 Tunnicliffe 84	6	35
27	Nat Lg	A	Woking	1856	L	0 - 1		9	36
Feb 3	Nat Lg	H	Eastleigh	1626	D	2 - 2	Francil-Angol 54 Jones 85	9	37
10	Nat Lg	A	Gateshead	752	W	2 - 1	Rowe 16 37	7	38
17	Nat Lg	H	Leyton Orient	2206	L	0 - 1		7	39
20	Nat Lg	A	Guiseley	1584	L	0 - 1		9	40
24	Nat Lg	H	Dover Athletic	1622	W	3 - 1	Rowe 69 Tasdemir 77 Hardy 90	9	41
Mar 10	Nat Lg	H	Aldershot Town	2018	W	7 - 1	ROWE 3 (2 18 19) Finlay 10 62 Grand 45 Muldoon 65	7	42
17	Nat Lg	A	Hartlepool United	1753	D	3 - 3	Bond 46 55 Hardy 77	8	43
24	Nat Lg	A	Dagenham & Redbridge	1168	L	0 - 2		8	44
30	Nat Lg	H	FC Halifax Town	2230	W	2 - 0	Smith 47 Hardy 54	8	45
Apr 3	Nat Lg	A	Barrow	901	W	3 - 1	Smith 24 Rowe 54 Tasdemir 90	7	46
7	Nat Lg	H	Sutton United	1789	W	2 - 1	Smith 77 Rowe 80	7	47
10	Nat Lg	A	Torquay United	1416	W	3 - 1	Muldoon 24 Tunnicliffe 28 78	5	48
14	Nat Lg	A	Maidstone United	2254	L	0 - 1		5	49
21	Nat Lg	H	Solihull Moors	2045	D	1 - 1	Bond 50	5	50
28	Nat Lg	A	Wrexham	3931	D	0 - 0		7	51
May 3	**P-O**	**A**	**Boreham Wood**	**1244**	**L**	**1 - 2**	**Montrose 30**		52

GOALSCORERS	SG	CSG	Pens	Hat tricks	Total		SG	CSG	Pens	Hat tricks	Total
2016-17 Rowe					*50*	Montrose	4				4
Rowe	24	6	1	1	30	Tasdemir	3				4
Smith	11	3			11	Francil-Angol	2				2
Muldoon	10	2			10	Opponents	1				1
Finley	6	2			7						
Tunnicliffe	5	2			6						
Bond	5	2			5						
Jones	4				5						
Grand	4	2			4						
Hardy	4				4						

ALDERSHOT TOWN

Club Contact Details 01252 320 211
EBB Stadium, High street, Aldershot, GU11 1TW
admin@theshots.co.uk

Founded: 1992 **Nickname:** Shots **Manager:** Gary Waddock
Previous Names: None
Previous Leagues: Isthmian 1992-2003. Conference 2003-2008. Football League 2008-13.

Club Colours (change): Red & blue

Ground Capacity: 7,025 **Seats:** 2,676 **Covered:** 5,975 **Clubhouse:** Yes **Shop:** Yes
Previous Grounds: None
Record Attendance: 7,500 v Brighton & Hove Albion, FA Cup 1st Round, 18/11/2000

RECORDS
Victory:	8-0 v Bishop's Stortford (A) Isthmian Premier 05/09/1998
Defeat:	0-6 v Worthing (A) Isthmian League Cup 02/03/99
Goalscorer:	Mark Butler - 155 (1992-98)
Appearances:	Jason Chewings - 489 (August 1994 - May 2004)
Additional:	Paid an undisclosed record fee to Woking for Marvin Morgan (05/2008)
	Received £130,000 from Crewe Alexandra for Joel Grant (11/2008)

HONOURS
FA Comps: N/A

League: Isthmian League Division Three 1992-93, Division One 97-98, Premier Division 2002-03.
Conference 2007-08.
County FA: Hampshire Senior Cup 1998-99, 99-2000, 01-02, 02-03, 06-07.

08-09		09-10		10-11		11-12		12-13		13-14		14-15		15-16		16-17		17-18	
FL 2	15	FL 2	6	FL 2	14	FL 2	11	FL 2	24	Conf	19	Conf	18	Nat	15	Nat	5	Nat	5
FAC	2P	FAC	2Pr	FAC	2P	FAC	2P	FAC	4P	FAC	4Qr	FAC	2Pr	FAC	1Pr	FAC	4Q	FAC	1P
FLC	1P	FLC	1P	FLC	1P	FLC	4P	FLC	1P	FAT	QF	FAT	1P	FAT	1P	FAT	1Pr	FAT	1P

2017-18 STATS **Goals Total** 67 **Games Without Scoring** 12 (3) **Total No. of Scorers** 19 **Total Clean Sheets** 17
Most Consecutive Scoring Games 8 **Best Unbeaten Run** 9 **Most Consecutive Clean Sheets** 4
Best Att: 4,358 v Macclesfield Town, National League *Number in brackets denotes consecutive runs.*

2017-18 MATCH LINE-UPS

Match Number	1	2	3	4	5	6	7	8	9	10	11	12	13	14	15	16	17	18	19	20	21	22	23	24	25	26	27	28	29	30	31	32	33	34	35	36	37	38	39	40	41	42	43	44	45	46	47	48	49	50	Total
Cole	x	x	x	x	x	x	x	x	x	x	x	x	x	x	x	x	x	x	s						s		x	s	s	s	s	s		s	s	s	s	x	x	x	x	s	s	s	s	s	s	s	s	s	23
Arnold	x	x	sx	x	x	sx	xs																																												7
Alexander	x	x	xs	x	x		x	x	x	x	x	x	x	x	x	x	x	x	x	x	x	x	xs		x	x	x	x	x	x	x	x	x	x		x		x	x	x	x	x	x	x	x	x	x	x	xs	x	46
De Havilland	x	x	x	x	x	x								xs	s	sx	x	s	s																																8
Reynolds	x	x	x	x	x	x	x	x	x	x	x	x	x	x	x	x	x	xs	x	x	x	x	x		x	x		x					x	x	x	x	sx	s	x	x	x	x	x	x	x	x	x	x	x	x	42
Oyeleke	x	x	x	x	x	xs		x	x	x		sx	xs	x	x	x	x	x	xs	sx		x	x	x	x	sx	sx	x	x	x	x	x	x	x	x	xs	6x	x	x	x	x	x	x	x	xs	x	x	x	x	x	44
Gallagher	x	x	sx	sx	xs		sx	xs	x	x	x	x	xr		xs	sx	sx	sx	sx	sx	x	xs	sx	x		x	x	xs	x	x	x	sx	sx	s		xs	s	sx	xs	xs	xs		s	xs	xs	sx	sx	s			38
Rowe	x	x	xs	x	x	x	x	x	x	x	x	x	xs	sx	sx	sx	sx	x	x	xs	xs	x	x					sx	xs	s	sx	xs	x	x	x	x	xs	sx	sx	s	sx				sx	sx	x	sx			43
Taylor	xs	xs	x	xs	xs	x	x	x											sx	x	x	xs	x	x	x	s			xs	sx	sx	sx	sx	s		sx			sx	x	x	s									26
Fenelon	x	x	xs	x	x	sx	x	xs						xs	xs	xs	x	xs	xs		xs	x	xs	xs	xs	x		x	x	xs	xs	xs		sx	x	xs	s					sx	xs	x		xs	x	x			38
Rendell	xs	sx	sx			sx	x		x	x	x	sx	x		x	x	x	x	x	sx	sx	sx	sx			x	x	x	xs	sx	x	xs	x	sx	x	x	x	s	sx	sx	sx	x			x	x	x	x			41
Kellerman	sx	s	x	xs	sx	xs	x	x	xs	x	s	x	xs	x	s	x	x	x	x	x	x	x	xs		x	x	x	x				xs	xs			sx			sx	xs	xs	xs	s	x	x	x	sx	x		sxs	41
Okojie	sx	sx	s	sx	sx	xs	s					s			sx	xs	s		sx	xs	s																														9
Smith	s	s	s	s	s	s	s	s	s	s	s	s	s	s	s	s	s	s	s	x	x																														2
Lyons-Foster	s	s		s	s	s	s	x	xr			sx	s											sx	s	sx	s	sx	sx	sx	s	s	s	s	sx	s															7
McClure	s	xs	x	xs	xs	x	sx	xs	x	x	xs	sx	x	xs		sx	sx				sx	sx	x	x		sx	sx	sx	sx	sx	sx	s	s		sx	sx	sx	xs	sx	x	x	sx	sx	sx	xs					xs	36
Arthur		x	sx	xs	xs	x	x	xs	x	x		x	xs			xs	s																																		13
McDonnell				x	x	x	x	x	x	xs	x	x	x	x	x	x	x	x	xr		x	x								x	x	x	x	xs	xs	x	x	x	xs	x	x	x	sx	sx	x						34
Fowler					x	xs	x	x	xs		s	sx		s	s	sx	xs	x	x	x	x	x	x	x												x	x	x	s	s			s	s								27
Wrightman								s	sx	sx	sx	s	s																											0												2
Bozier										sx	sx	s										s		sx		s																									3
Robert (L)						sx	sx	sx	sx	sx	sx	x		x	sx		x	x	sx	xs	xs	xs									sx	sx	sx	sx		xs			sx	xs	sx				sx	sx					25
Kirwan								s	s																																										0
Evans													sx	x	x	x	x	x	x	x	x	x	x	x	x	x	x	x	x	x	x	x	xr	x	x	x	x	x	x	x	x		x	x	x	x	x	x	x	x	37
Mensah														sx	xs	sx	x	x	x	x	x	x	x	x	x	xs	x	xs	x	x																					17
Pring													s	sx	sx	s		s																																	1
Ward																	x	x	x	x	x	x	s	x	x	x	x	x	x	x	x	x			x	x	x	x	x	x	x	x	x	x	x						25
Skinner																	s	s	s	s	s	s		s																											0
Blanchfield																						s	sx	s																											1
Kinsella																							xs	x	x	x	x	x	x	x	x	x	x	x	x	x		x	x	x	x		x		x	x				x	19
Kabamba																								sx	sx	sx	sx	sx	s			sx			sx	x	s	sx	x	s	x										11
McQuiod																	xs	x	xs	xs	xs	xs	x	x	x	x	sx	sx	sx	xs	s																				16
RESULT	W	W	W	D	L	L	D	W	L	W	W	D	L	D	D	W	D	W	D	L	L	W	W	W	W	D	L	L	D	W	D	W	D	W	W	D	W	W	L	D	D	W	L	W	D	W	D	L	W	D	

ALDERSHOT TOWN MATCH RESULTS 2017-18

Date	Comp	H/A	Opponents	Att	Result	Goalscorers	Pos	No.
Aug 5	Nat Lg	A	FC Halifax Town	2108	W 2 - 0	Fenelon 59 Rowe 90 (pen)	1	1
8	Nat Lg	H	Torquay United	2662	W 3 - 2	Fenelon 5 Taylor 48 Okojie 85	1	2
12	Nat Lg	H	Guiseley	1938	W 6 - 0	McClure 20 74 Reynolds 37 Kellerman Fenelon 45 Ross 53	1	3
15	Nat Lg	A	Maidstone United	2524	D 1 - 1	Gallagher 76	1	4
19	Nat Lg	A	Boreham Wood	809	L 1 - 2	Alexander 51	3	5
26	Nat Lg	H	Chester	2056	L 1 - 2	McClure 34	5	6
28	Nat Lg	A	Eastleigh	2525	D 0 - 0		5	7
Sept 2	Nat Lg	H	Solihull Moors	1803	W 1 - 0	Fenelon 9	5	8
9	Nat Lg	H	Dover Athletic	1862	L 0 - 2		7	9
12	Nat Lg	A	Ebbsfleet United	1402	W 2 - 0	Rowe 14 Rendell 67	3	10
16	Nat Lg	A	Gateshead	654	W 1 - 0	Robert 83	1	11
23	Nat Lg	H	Leyton Orient	3060	D 2 - 2	Alexander 9 McClure 20	2	12
30	Nat Lg	A	Macclesfield Town	1350	L 0 - 2		7	13
Oct 2	Nat Lg	H	Dagenham & Redbridge	1903	D 1 - 1	McDonnell 23	8	14
7	Nat Lg	A	Maidenhead United	2425	D 3 - 3	Kellerman 16 90 McDonnell 47	8	15
14	**FAC 4Q**	**H**	**Torquay United**	**1563**	**W 1 - 0**	**Rendell 79**		16
21	Nat Lg	H	Tranmere Rovers	2714	W 2 - 1	Robert 80 Rendell 90	7	17
24	Nat Lg	H	Sutton United	2259	D 2 - 2	Mensah 15 Rendell 43	6	18
28	Nat Lg	A	Barrow	1128	L 1 - 3	Rendell 47	9	19
Nov 4	**FAC 1**	**A**	**Shrewsbury Town**	**3859**	**L 0 - 5**			20
11	Nat Lg	H	AFC Fylde	2011	W 2 - 1	Fenelon 20 Evans 86	7	21
18	Nat Lg	A	Hartlepool	3732	W 2 - 0	Mensah 44 Kelleman 87	5	22
25	Nat Lg	H	Wrexham	2377	W 2 - 0	Mensah 15 Fenelon 33	6	23
28	Nat Lg	A	Bromley	1171	W 2 - 0	Mensah 28 Rendell 68	4	24
Dec 2	Nat Lg	A	Torquay United	1851	D 0 - 0		4	25
8	Nat Lg	H	FC Halifax Town	1912	L 0 - 1		6	26
16	**FAT 1**	**A**	**East Thurrock United**	**252**	**L 0 - 4**			27
23	Nat Lg	A	Guiseley	620	D 1 - 1	McClure 90	5	28
26	Nat Lg	H	Woking	4181	W 3 - 1	Fenelon 11 27 Fowler 41	3	29
30	Nat Lg	H	Maidstone United	2287	D 1 - 1	Kellerman 90	2	30
Jan 1	Nat Lg	A	Woking	3790	W 2 - 1	Rendell 28 89	2	31
6	Nat Lg	A	Dover Athletic	1237	W 2 - 1	Kellerman 45 Kabamba 67		32
20	Nat Lg	H	Ebbsfleet United	2457	D 0 - 0		2	33
27	Nat Lg	A	Leyton Orient	5728	W 3 - 2	Fenelon 44 Evans 48 McDonald 78	2	34
Feb 10	Nat Lg	A	Dagenham & Redbridge	1509	W 2 - 1	Kellerman 4	2	35
17	Nat Lg	H	Macclesfield Town	4358	L 1 - 2	Rendell 68 (pen)	3	36
20	Nat Lg	H	Bromley	1909	D 1 - 1	Oyeleke 90	3	37
24	Nat Lg	A	Wrexham	4662	D 2 - 2	Fenelon 42 Reynolds 75	4	38
Mar 5	Nat Lg	H	Hartlepool United	1665	W 2 - 1	Rendell 13 Oyeleke 60	3	39
10	Nat Lg	A	AFC Fylde	2018	L 1 - 7	McQuoid 5	4	40
17	Nat Lg	A	Chester	1612	D 0 - 0		6	41
24	Nat Lg	H	Boreham Wood	2448	W 2 - 0	Gallagher 11 McClure 75	5	42
30	Nat Lg	A	Solihull Moors	1734	D 0 - 0		4	43
Apr 2	Nat Lg	H	Eastleigh	2853	L 0 - 2		4	44
7	Nat Lg	H	Maidenhead United	2318	W 1 - 0	Kabamba 89	3	45
14	Nat Lg	A	Tranmere Rovers	5444	L 0 - 2		6	46
17	Nat Lg	H	Gateshead	1893	W 1 - 0	Rendell 45	3	47
21	Nat Lg	H	Barow	2947	D 1 - 1	Rendell 90	4	48
28	Nat Lg	A	Sutton United	3541	L 1 - 2	Rendell 57	3	49
May 2	**P-O**	**H**	**Ebbsfleet United**	**3319**	**D 1 - 1**	**Kabamba 106 (Lost 4-5 on pens)**		50

GOALSCORERS	SG	CSG	Pens	Hat tricks	Total		SG	CSG	Pens	Hat tricks	Total
2016-17 Mensah					13	Gallagher	2				2
Rendell	12	4	1		13	Oyeleke	2				2
Fenelon	8	3			9	Reynolds	2				2
Kellerman	7	2			8	Robert	2				2
McClure	7				6	Rowe	2		1		2
McDonnell	4	2			4	Fowler					1
Mensah	4	3			4	McQuoid					1
Kabamba	3				3	Okojie					1
Alexander	2				2	Ross					1
Evans	1				2	Taylor					1

BARROW

Club Contact Details 01229 823 061
Furness Building Society Stadium, Wilkie Road, Barrow-in-Furness LA14 5UW
office@barrowafc.com

Founded: 1901   **Nickname:** Bluebirds   **Manager:** Ian Evatt - June 2018
Previous Names: None
Previous Leagues: Lancashire Combination 1901-21. Football League 1921-72. Northern Premier 1972-79, 83-84, 86-89, 92-98, 99-04.
Conference 1979-83, 84-86, 89-92, 98-99.
Club Colours (change): Blue & white

Ground Capacity: 5,045   **Seats:** 1,000   **Covered:** 2,200   **Clubhouse:** Yes   **Shop:** Yes
Previous Grounds: Strawberry & Little Park, Roose.
Record Attendance: 16,854 v Swansea Town - FA Cup 3rd Round 1954
Nearest Railway Station Barrow-in-Furness half a mile away.

RECORDS
Victory: 12-0 v Cleator - FA Cup 1920
Defeat: 1-10 v Hartlepool United - Football League Division 4 1959
Goalscorer: Colin Cowperthwaite - 282 (December 1977 - December 1992)
Appearances: Colin Cowperthwaite - 704
Additional: Paid £9,000 to Ashton United for Andy Whittaker (07/94)
       Received £40,000 from Barnet for Kenny Lowe (01/91)

HONOURS
FA Comps: FA Trophy 1989-90, 2009-10.
League: Northern Premier League 1983-84, 88-89, 97-98.
     Conference North 2014-15.
County FA: Lancashire Senior Cup 1954-55.
     Lancashire Challenge Trophy 1980-81.

08-09		09-10		10-11		11-12		12-13		13-14		14-15		15-16		16-17		17-18	
Conf	20	Conf	15	Conf	18	Conf	13	Conf	22	Conf N	11	Conf N	1	Nat	11	Nat	7	Nat	20
FAC	3P	FAC	3P	FAC	4Q	FAC	1P	FAC	2Pr	FAC	4Qr	FAC	2Q	FAC	4Q	FAC	3P	FAC	4Q
FAT	2P	FAT	F	FAT	1P	FAT	1P	FAT	2P	FAT	QF	FAT	2P	FAT	3Q	FAT	2P	FAT	QF	FAT	2Pr

2017-18 STATS
Goals Total	53	**Games Without Scoring**	15 (2)	**Total No. of Scorers**	16	**Total Clean Sheets**	13
Most Consecutive Scoring Games	7	**Best Unbeaten Run**	5	**Most Consecutive Clean Sheets**	2

Best Att: 1,796 v Leyton Orient, National League   *Number in brackets denotes consecutive runs.*

2017-18 MATCH LINE-UPS

Match Number	1	2	3	4	5	6	7	8	9	10	11	12	13	14	15	16	17	18	19	20	21	22	23	24	25	26	27	28	29	30	31	32	33	34	35	36	37	38	39	40	41	42	43	44	45	46	47	48	49	50	Total
Moore	x	x	x	x	x	x	x	x	x	x	x	s		s		s	s	s	s	x	x	x	x	x	x	s	s					s																				18
Diarra	x	x	x	x	x	x	x	x	x									x	x	x		x	x	x	x	x	x	x	x	x	x	x	x	x	x	x	x	x	x	x	x	x	x	x	x	x	x	x	x	x	41
Audel	x	s	s	sx	x	xs			sx	x															s		s	s		x	x	x		s	s										s						9
Jones (3)	x	x	x	x	x	x	x	x	x	x	x													xs	xs	x	xs	x	xs	x		x	xs	xs	xs	x	s	s	sx	s	sx	x	xr			x	x	x	x	xs	35
Bartrham	x	xs	x	xs	s	s	x	x	x	x	xs			x	x	xs		x	x	x	x	xs		x	sx		x	x	x	x	x	x	x	x	x	x	x	s				x	s									33
Dunne	x	x	x	xr			x	x	x	x	x	x	x	xr			x	x	x	x	x	x	x		x	x	x	x	x																							23
Hall	xs	x	x	x		s		x	x	x	x	xs			x	x		x	x		x	x	x		x	x	x				x	x	x	x	x	x	x	x	xs		s	x	xs	x	x	x	x				38
Gomis	x	x	xs	x	x	x	x	x	x	xs	x		x	xs	xs	sx	x	xs	x	x	x	x	x	x	x	sx	x	x	sx	x	x	x	x	x	x	xs	xs	xr		x	x	sx	xs	xs	sx	s	sx	x	x		47
Harvey	x	xs	x	xs	x	x	x	xr				x	x	x	x	xs																																			14
White	x	xs	xs	x	x	xs	xs	xs	xs	sx	sx		s	sx	s	sx	sx	sx	xs	sx	xs	xs	xs	xs	x	s	x	xs	sx	xs	x	sx	sx	sx	sx	sx	sx	sx	sx	sx	sx	sx	x	x	x	x	x				48
Yussuf	x	x	xs					sx	x	xs	xs	xs	xs								sx	sx	xs	xs	xs	xs	x	xs	sx	sx		sx	x	s	sx	x															25
Panayiotou	sx	s	sx	sx	xs	xs	sx	sx	sx	sx	s	sx	s		s	s	sx	sx	xs	s	xs	x	x	x		sx	s	s	xs	x	sx	x	xs	sx	s	sx	s			s	sx		s			sx	sx	sx	sx		33
Cockerline	sx	sx	sx	xs	sx		s								.																																				5
Bauress	s	sx		sx	x	x	xs	x	xs	x	xs			s		sx	xs	sx	x	x	x	xs	xs	xs	x					sx	x	sx	sx	sx	sx	sx	s	sx	x	sx	s			sx	s	s	sxr				32
Hughes	s	sx	s	s	x	x	sx							s	x	x		s	xs	x	x																														9
Nieskens	s	x	x	x	x	x	xs																																												8
Makoma			sx	s	s	s	xs	s	s			s	s	s	s		s	s		sx	sx	s				xs	sx	xs	sx	xs	s	x	xs			s		x	xs	x	x	x	s	x	x	xr					19
Ramsbottom				s	s	s																																													0
Harrison				sx	sx	xs	x	xs	x	x	x		x	x		x	x	x	xs	xs	xs		x	x	xs	sx	x	x	s	sx	sx																				29
Dixon					s	s	s	s	x	x	x	x	x	x		x	x	s	s	s	s	s	s	s	x	x	x	x	x	x	x	xs	s				0									s					15
Fitzpatrick						s	x	s	s											s						sx											sx	sx						s	s	sx					5
Bignot									sx	x	s	s	sx	x	x	x				s						x			s																						14
Thompson										x	x	x	x	x		xs	x																																		9
Diagne									sx	sx	x	x	x	xs	x	s									x	s			s					s					s	s				x	s	sx	xs	x	x		19
Clements												x		x	x	x	x	xs	s	s	x																														8
Holt																sx	sx	sx	xs	x	s	xs			xs	xs	x	xs	xs		xs	xs	x	xs	xs		xs	xs	xs	xs	sx			s	xs	xs	s	xs			23
MacDonald																	x	x	x	x	x	x	x	x		x	x	x	x	s	x			x	x	x	x	x		x	x	x	xs	xs	xs						24
Walters																	sx	x	xs											sx	xs	sx	xs	xs	x	xs	sx	xs	xs	x	x	sx	sx	x							16
Humphrey																										xs	sx	xs	s	sx																					4
Arnold																											x	x	x	x	x	x	x	x	x	x	x	x	x	x	x	x	x		x						17
Cook																											x	x	x	x	x	x	x	x	x	x	x	x	x	x	s	s	s	s							13
James (24)																											x	xs	x	x	x	x	x	x	x	x	x	x	x	x	x	x									17
James (4) (L)																													sx	x	x	x	x	x	x	x	x	x	x	x	x	x	x								14
Waterston																												sx	xs	xs	s	s			xs	xs	x	xs						xs	sx						9
RESULT	L	D	W	D	D	D	L	W	L	D	D	L	L	L	D	L	L	L	W	L	W	W	W	L	W	L	W	W	D	L	D	D	D	L	L	D	W	D	L	W	L	W	L	D	D	L	L	W	L	W	D	D	L

BARROW MATCH RESULTS 2017-18

Date	Comp	H/A	Opponents	Att:	Result	Goalscorers	Pos	No.
Aug 5	Nat Lg	A	Dagenham & Redbridge	1362	L 1 - 2	Jones 86	19	1
8	Nat Lg	H	FC Halifax Town	1410	D 0 - 0		20	2
12	Nat Lg	H	Woking	1075	W 3 - 0	Yussuf 20 White 47 83	12	3
15	Nat Lg	A	Solihull Moors	558	D 3 - 3	Neskens 20 Jones 31 Panayiotou 90	13	4
19	Nat Lg	A	Dover Athletic	937	D 1 - 1	White 53	12	5
25	Nat Lg	H	Maidenhead United	1154	D 1 - 1	Diarra 56	16	6
28	Nat Lg	A	AFC Fylde	2234	L 0 - 1		19	7
Sept 2	Nat Lg	H	Boreham Wood	1159	W 2 - 1	Gomis 3 Barthram 37	16	8
9	Nat Lg	A	Tranmere	4269	L 0 - 1		20	9
12	Nat Lg	H	Guiseley	1072	D 0 - 0		18	10
16	Nat Lg	H	Torquay United	1190	D 1 - 1	Harrison 90	18	11
23	Nat Lg	A	Sutton United	1909	L 2 - 3	Harrison 39 62	19	12
30	Nat Lg	H	Maidstone United	1097	L 0 - 1		20	13
Oct 3	Nat Lg	A	Hartlepool United	3082	L 0 - 1		20	14
7	Nat Lg	H	Leyton Orient	1796	D 2 - 2	Gomis 23 White 41	20	15
14	FAC 4Q	A	Shaw Lane	864	L 1 - 2	Harrison 47 (pen)		16
21	Nat Lg	A	Ebbsfleet United	1402	L 2 - 3	Gomis 71 90	20	17
24	Nat Lg	A	Chester	1548	L 2 - 3	Yussuf 44 Harrison 45	22	18
27	Nat Lg	H	Aldershot Town	1128	W 3 - 1	YUSSUF 3 (5 39 65)	21	19
Nov 11	Nat Lg	H	Macclesfield Town	1614	L 0 - 1		21	20
18	Nat Lg	A	Eastleigh	1708	W 2 - 0	Harrison 32 Dunne 55	20	21
21	Nat Lg	A	Gateshead	663	W 2 - 1	Harrison 34 Panayiotou 56	19	22
25	Nat Lg	H	Bromley	941	L 0 - 2		19	23
Dec 2	Nat Lg	A	FC Halifax Town	1618	W 1 - 0	White 69	18	24
8	Nat Lg	H	Dagenham & Redbridge	917	L 0 - 1		19	25
16	FAT 1	A	Nuneaton Town	415	W 1 - 0	Harrison 90		26
23	Nat Lg	A	Woking	1816	W 2 - 1	Diarra 2 Dunne 28	19	27
26	Nat Lg	H	Wrexham	1648	D 1 - 1	Diarra 3	20	28
30	Nat Lg	H	Solihull Moors	1315	L 1 - 2	Hall 35	20	29
Jan 1	Nat Lg	A	Wrexham	4390	D 3 - 3	White 31 Jones 37 McDonald 90	20	30
6	Nat Lg	H	Tranmere Rovers	1470	D 1 - 1	Harrison 5 (pen)	20	31
13	FAT 2	A	Brackley Town	512	D 0 - 0			32
16	FAT2r	H	Brackley Town	430	L 0 - 2			33
Feb 3	Nat Lg	A	Torquay United	1563	L 1 - 3	Harrison 74 (pen)	20	34
13	Nat Lg	H	Sutton United	643	D 1 - 1	Gomis 10	20	35
17	Nat Lg	A	Maidstone United	2338	W 1 - 0	James 31	20	36
20	Nat Lg	H	Gateshead	860	D 1 - 1	James 18 (pen)	20	37
Mar 10	Nat Lg	A	Macclesfield Town	1748	L 1 - 3	James 11	20	38
17	Nat Lg	A	Maidenhead United	1030	W 1 - 0	James 31	19	39
21	Nat Lg	H	Hartlepool United	1018	L 1 - 2	James 19	20	40
24	Nat Lg	H	Dover Athletic	908	D 0 - 0		20	41
30	Nat Lg	A	Boreham Wood	623	D 0 - 0		20	42
Apr 2	Nat Lg	H	AFC Fylde	901	L 1 - 3	Waterston 29	20	43
7	Nat Lg	A	Leyton Orient	3979	L 1 - 4	James 7	21	44
10	Nat Lg	H	Eastleigh	817	W 3 - 2	Hall 15 Makoma 62 Walters 79	20	45
14	Nat Lg	H	Ebbsfleet United	1189	L 0 - 1		21	46
17	Nat Lg	A	Guiseley	611	W 1 - 0	Hall 51	20	47
21	Nat Lg	A	Aldershot Town	2947	D 1 - 1	James 72	20	48
24	Nat Lg	A	Bromley	1331	D 0 - 0		20	49
28	Nat Lg	H	Chester	1788	L 1 - 3	White 54	20	50

GOALSCORERS	SG	CSG	Pens	Hat tricks	Total		SG	CSG	Pens	Hat tricks	Total
2016-17 Bennett					22	Panayiotou	2				2
Harrison	8	2	3		10	Barthram					1
James	7	5			7	Makoma					1
White	6				7	McDonald					1
Gomis	4				5	Neskens					1
Yussuf	3	2	1		5	Walters					1
Diarra	3	2			3	Waterston					1
Hall	3				3						
Jones	3				3						
Dunne	2				2						

BOREHAM WOOD

Club Contact Details 0208 953 5097
Meadow Park, Broughinge Road, Boreham Wood WD6 5AL
matt@borehamwoodfootballclub.co.uk

Founded: 1948   **Nickname:** The Wood   **Manager:** Luke Garrard
Previous Names: Boreham Wood Rovers and Royal Retournez amalgamated in 1948 to form today's club
Previous Leagues: Mid Herts 1948-52, Parthenon 1952-57, Spartan 1956-66, Athenian 1966-74, Isthmian 1974-2004, Southern 2004-10

Club Colours (change): White & black

Ground Capacity: 4,502   **Seats:** 1,700   **Covered:** 2,800   **Clubhouse:** Yes   **Shop:** Yes
Previous Grounds: Eldon Avenue 1948-63
Record Attendance: 4,030 v Arsenal - Friendly 13/07/2001
Nearest Railway Station Elstree & Boreham Wood.

RECORDS
Goalscorer: Mickey Jackson
Appearances: Dave Hatchett - 714
Additional: Received £5,000 from Dagenham & Redbridge for Steve Heffer

HONOURS
FA Comps: N/A
League: Athenian League Div. Two 1968-69, Div.One 73-74. Isthmian League Division Two 1976-77, Division One 1994-95, 2000-01, Premier Division Play-off 2009-10. Southern Div. One East 2005-06, Conference South Play-off 2014-15.
County FA: Herts Senior cup 1971-72, 98-99, 2001-02, 07-08, 13-14. Herts Charity Cup 1980-81, 83-84, 85-86, 88-89, 89-90. London Challenge Cup 1997-98.

08-09		09-10		10-11		11-12		12-13		13-14		14-15		15-16		16-17		17-18	
Isth P	18	Isth P	4	Conf S	14	Conf S	8	Conf S	9	Conf S	13	Conf S	2	Nat	19	Nat	11	Nat	4
FAC	3Q	FAC	2Q	FAC	4Q	FAC	2Q	FAC	1P	FAC	1Pr	FAC	4Q	FAC	1Pr	FAC	1Pr	FAC	2P
FAT	2Q	FAT	1P	FAT	1P	FAT	1P	FAT	1Pr	FAT	3Q	FAT	3Q	FAT	1P	FAT	QF	FAT	2Pr

2017-18 STATS

Goals Total 82	**Games Without Scoring** 14 (2)	**Total No. of Scorers** 20	**Total Clean Sheets** 18
Most Consecutive Scoring Games 8	**Best Unbeaten Run** 12	**Most Consecutive Clean Sheets** 3	
Best Att: 1,920 v Leyton Orient, National League		Number in brackets denotes consecutive runs.	

2017-18 MATCH LINE-UPS

Match Number	Total
Smith.G (1)	56
Smith.K (2)	51
Woodards	40
Ricketts	51
Stephens	49
Shakes	50
Champion	52
Benson	14
Murtagh	53
Turley (L)	37
Balanta	42
Andrade	55
Johnson (L)	2
Jeffers	31
Sach	7
Keita	1
Bozkurt	0
Gordon	0
Wells	20
Turgott	17
Thomas	6
Holman (L)	17
Burbidge	0
Chesmain (L)	4
Jarvis (L)	4
Davey	14
Quigley (L)	14
Folivi (L)	18
Harfield (L)	1
Ferrier (L)	15
Doe	4
RESULT	

RESULT: D L W W W W D L L W W L L D W D W D D W D D W W L W D W D L W D D W D D W D L L W W W W D D D W L D W L L W L W W W L

BOREHAM WOOD MATCH RESULTS 2017-18

Date	Comp	H/A	Opponents	Att:	Result	Goalscorers	Pos	No.
Aug 5	Nat Lg	A	AFC Fylde	1641	D 2 - 2	Shakes 45 Smith 56	8	1
8	Nat Lg	H	Dagenham & Redbridge	635	L 1 - 2	Andrade 7 (pen)	16	2
12	Nat Lg	H	Solihull Moors	319	W 4 - 1	Turley 34 Andrade 40 Benson 44 Balanta 59	11	3
15	Nat Lg	A	Torquay United	1864	W 4 - 2	Balanta 50 Andrade 57 Jeffers 73 Sach 90	6	4
19	Nat Lg	H	Aldershot Town	809	W 2 - 1	Andrade 27 Jeffers 40	4	5
26	Nat Lg	A	Tranmere Rovers	4295	D 2 - 2	Andrade 53 (pen) Balanta 68	3	6
28	Nat Lg	H	Wrexham	765	L 0 - 1		7	7
Sept 2	Nat Lg	A	Barrow	1159	L 1 - 2	Andrade 38	10	8
9	Nat Lg	H	Leyton Orient	1920	W 2 - 0	Woodards 35 Murtagh 50	8	9
12	Nat Lg	A	Dover Athletic	1012	W 1 - 0	Turgott 44	4	10
16	Nat Lg	A	Maidenhead United	1351	L 1 2	Ricketts 90	8	11
23	Nat Lg	H	Ebbsfleet United	622	L 0 - 1		12	12
30	Nat Lg	A	Gateshead	606	D 1 - 1	Shakes 87	11	13
Oct 3	Nat Lg	H	Eastleigh	404	W 1 - 0	Andrade 77	11	14
7	Nat Lg	H	FC Halifax	562	D 1 - 1	Andrade 7	11	15
14	FAC 4Q	A	St Albans City	1418	W 3 - 1	Andrade 14 38 Jeffers 42		16
21	Nat Lg	A	Chester	1501	W 2 - 1	Jeffers 31 Andrade 38	8	17
24	Nat Lg	A	Guiseley	706	D 0 - 0		9	18
27	Nat Lg	H	Bromley	1128	D 2 - 2	Holman 25 Turley 38	10	19
Nov 4	FAC 1	H	Blackpool	1041	W 2 - 1	Turgott 68 Holman 88		20
11	Nat Lg	A	Hartlepool United	773	D 0 - 0		10	21
18	Nat Lg	A	Macclesfield	1324	D 0 - 0		10	22
21	Nat Lg	A	Maidstone United	1945	W 4 - 0	Smith 13 Turgott 28 77 Holman 53	9	23
25	Nat Lg	H	Woking	543	W 2 - 1	Champion 32 Andrade 82	7	24
Dec 3	FAC 2	A	Coventry City	2983	L 0 - 3			25
8	Nat Lg	H	AFC Fylde	401	W 1 - 0	Balanta 6	7	26
16	FAT 1	A	Dartford	807	D 1 - 1	Shakes 56		27
19	FAT 1r	H	Dartford	173	D 2 - 2	Andrade 73 Jeffers 90 (Won 3-1 on pens)		28
23	Nat Lg	A	Solihull Moors	410	D 0 - 0		7	29
27	Nat Lg	H	Sutton United	455	L 0 - 4		8	30
30	Nat Lg	H	Torquay United	627	W 2 - 0	Balanta 11 Andrade 81	7	31
Jan 1	Nat Lg	A	Sutton United	2007	D 1 - 1	Balanta 90	7	32
6	Nat Lg	A	Leyton Orient	4094	D 0 - 0		7	33
9	Nat Lg	A	Dagenham & Redbridge	1117	W 3 - 2	Andrade 12 48 (pen) Balanta 59	5	34
13	FAT 2	A	Gateshead	284	D 3 - 3	Murtagh 51 Chesmain 55 Andrade 90 (pen)		35
16	FAT 2r	H	Gateshead	183	L 1 - 2	Quigley 20		36
20	Nat Lg	H	Dover Athletic	523	L 2 - 3	Stephens 70 Davey 87	8	37
27	Nat Lg	A	Ebbsfleet United	1366	W 3 - 0	Andrade 35 Turley 48 Quigley 66	8	38
Feb 10	Nat Lg	A	Eastleigh	1751	W 2 - 0	Ferrier 58 Andrade 67 (pen)	6	39
17	Nat Lg	H	Gateshead	464	W 2 - 1	Andrade 35 75	6	40
20	Nat Lg	H	Maidstone United	428	W 1 - 0	Andrade 36	4	41
24	Nat Lg	A	Woking	1744	D 0 - 0		5	42
Mar 10	Nat Lg	A	Hartlepool	2538	D 0 0		4	43
13	Nat Lg	H	Maidenhead United	401	D 1 - 1	Ferrier 4	5	44
17	Nat Lg	H	Tranmere Rovers	801	W 2 - 1	Balanta 45 Andrade 78	3	45
24	Nat Lg	A	Aldershot Town	2448	L 0 - 2		6	46
30	Nat Lg	H	Barrow	623	D 0 0		6	47
Apr 2	Nat Lg	A	Wrexham	4746	W 1 - 0	Andrade 10		48
7	Nat Lg	A	FC Halifax Town	1480	L 1 - 2	Ferrier 53	5	49
10	Nat Lg	H	Macclesfield	602	L 0 - 2		6	50
14	Nat Lg	H	Chester	331	W 4 - 2	Folivi 66 Andrade 44(pen) Ferrier 58 Shakes 90	4	51
21	Nat Lg	A	Bromley	1282	L 2 - 3	Ferrier 3 25	6	52
28	Nat Lg	H	Guiseley	701	W 3 - 1	Andrade 3 Ferrier 16 Smith 69	4	53
May 3	P-O	H	AFC Fylde	1244	W 2 - 1	Turley 6 Andrade 17		54
6	P-O S-F	A	Sutton United	2,730	W 3 - 2	Balanta 42 Lafayette 53 (og) Folivi 88		55
12	P-O Final	N	Tranmere Rovers	16,306	L 1 - 2	Andrade 45		56

GOALSCORERS	SG	CSG	Pens	Hat tricks	Total		SG	CSG	Pens	Hat tricks	Total
2016-17 Ferrier					16	Murtagh	2				2
Andrade	25	5	5		28	Quigley	2				2
Balanta	9	2			9	Benson					1
Ferrier	6				7	Champion					1
Jeffers	5	2			5	Chesmain					1
Shakes	4				4	Davey					1
Turgott	2				4	Opponents			1		
Turley	4				4	Ricketts					1
Holman	2	2			3	Sach					1
Smith	3				3	Stephens					1
Folivi	2				2	Woodards					1

BRAINTREE TOWN

Club Contact Details 01376 345 617
Cressing Road Stadium, off Clockhouse Way, Braintree CM7 3DE
braintreeTFC@aol.com

Founded: 1898   **Nickname:** The Iron   **Manager:** Brad Quinton
Previous Names: Manor Works 1898-1921, Crittall Athletic 1921-68, Braintree and Crittall Athletic 1968-81, Braintree 1981-83.
Previous Leagues: N.Essex 1898-1925, Essex & Suffolk Border 1925-29, 55-64, Spartan 1928-35, Eastern Co. 1935-37, 38-39, 52-55, 70-91, Essex Co. 1937-38, London 1945-52, Gt London 1964-66, Met 1966-70, Southern 1991-96, Isthmian 1996-2006

Club Colours (change): Orange & blue

Ground Capacity: 4,222   **Seats:** 553   **Covered:** 1,288   **Clubhouse:** Yes   **Shop:** Yes
Previous Grounds: The Fiar Field 1898-1903, Spalding Meadow 1903-23.
Record Attendance: 4,000 v Tottenham Hotspur - Testimonial May 1952
Nearest Railway Station Braintree - less than a mile from the ground.

RECORDS
Victory:	12-0 v Thetford - Eastern Counties League 1935-36
Defeat:	0-14 v Chelmsford City (A) - North Essex League 1923
Goalscorer:	Chris Guy - 211 (1963-90). Gary Bennett scored 57 goals during season 1997-98
Appearances:	Paul Young - 524 (1966-77)
Additional:	Received £10,000 from Brentford for Matt Metcalf and from Colchester United for John Cheesewright

HONOURS
FA Comps: None
League: North Essex 1905-06, 10-11, 11-12. Eastern Counties League 1936-37, 83-84, 84-85. Essex & Suffolk Border 1959-60. Isthmian League Premier Division 2005-06. Conference South Champions 2010-11.
County FA: Essex Senior Cup 1995-96.
Essex Senior Trophy 1986-87.

08-09	09-10	10-11	11-12	12-13	13-14	14-15	15-16	16-17	17-18
Conf S 14	Conf S 7	Conf S 1	Conf 12	Conf 9	Conf 6	Conf 14	Nat 3	Nat 22	Nat S 6
FAC 2Q	FAC 2Qr	FAC 3Q	FAC 3Q	FAC 4Q	FAC 1P	FAC 1Pr	FAC 1P	FAC 1Pr	FAC 2P	FAC 3Q
FAT 3Qr	FAT 3Q	FAT 1P	FAT 2Pr	FAT 1Pr	FAT 2P	FAT 3Pr	FAT 2P	FAT 3Pr	FAT 1Pr

2017-18 STATS	**Goals Total**	81	**Games Without Scoring**	7 (3)	**Total No. of Scorers**	17	**Total Clean Sheets**	14
Most Consecutive Scoring Games	20	**Best Unbeaten Run**	5			**Most Consecutive Clean Sheets**	2	
Best Att:	1,631 v Dartford, National League South					Number in brackets denotes consecutive runs.		

Worzel Gummidge, and friends, can't quite believe how his team (Hemel Hempstead) haven't scored against Weston-Super-Mare in this National South match. Photo: Peter Barnes.

BRAINTREE TOWN MATCH RESULTS 2017-18

Date	Comp	H/A	Opponents	Att:	Result	Goalscorers	Pos	No.
Aug 5	Nat South	A	Eastbourne Borough	598	W 3 - 2	Shulton 28 Roberts 48 Crook 54	4	1
8	Nat South	H	Dartford	1631	D 2 - 2	Oliyide 34 Crook 43	6	2
12	Nat South	H	Chippenham Town	550	W 2 - 0	Oliyide 20 Roberts 45	4	3
15	Nat South	A	East Thurrock United	442	L 3 - 5	Roberts 16 Crook 33 Wynter 90	8	4
19	Nat South	H	Hampton & Richmond	472	W 2 - 1	Roberts 45 Crook 53	4	5
26	Nat South	A	Whitehawk	237	D 1 - 1	Allen 58	4	6
28	Nat South	H	St Albans City	706	W 1 - 0	Okoye 64	5	7
Sept 2	Nat South	A	Oxford City	312	W 2 - 1	Crook 43 Roberts 75	5	8
5	Nat South	H	Welling United	505	D 1 - 1	Roberts 26	4	9
9	Nat South	A	Hemel Hempstead Town	469	L 3 - 4	Miles 26 (og) Shulton 42 Roberts 75	7	10
12	Nat South	A	Concord Rangers	275	W 1 - 0	Roberts 11	6	11
16	FAC 2Q	H	Royston Town	256	D 2 - 2	Allen 52 Olyide 60		12
19	FAC 2Qr	A	Royston Town	251	W 2 - 1	Roberts 21 Muleba 36		13
23	Nat South	H	Hungerford Town	475	W 5 - 0	Michael-Percil 31 35 Roberts 40 67 Wyatt 86	2	14
30	FAC 3Q	A	Brackley Town	383	L 1 - 4	Olyide 89		15
Oct 7	Nat South	A	Gloucester City	346	W 3 - 1	Roberts 47 51 Olyide 90	1	16
21	Nat South	A	Bath City	842	D 1 - 1	Olyide 85	1	17
28	Nat South	H	Havant & Waterlooville	551	L 1 - 3	Barrington 66	4	18
Nov 4	Nat South	H	Bognor Regis Town	497	W 3 - 0	Wynter 1 Olyide 53 Barrington 90	2	19
11	Nat South	A	Poole Town	470	W 3 - 0	Wynter 59 Bettache 75 Crook 78		20
18	Nat South	H	Weston-s-Mare	452	L 0 - 1		2	21
21	Nat South	H	Truro City	466	D 1 - 1	Michael-Percilo 49	2	22
25	FAT 3Q	H	Cray Wanderers	214	W 3 - 0	Olyidi 60 Barrington 76 Baxter 83		23
Dec 2	Nat South	A	Wealdstone	861	L 1 - 3	Ellul 65	2	24
9	Nat South	A	Eastbourne Borough	389	W 3 - 2	Roberts 38 62 Crook 77 (pen)	2	25
16	FAT 1	H	Brackley Town	249	D 0 - 0			26
19	FAT 1r	A	Brackley Town	235	L 0 - 2			27
23	Nat South	A	Dartford	936	D 1 - 1	Barrington 44	4	28
26	Nat South	H	Chelmsford City	1465	D 2 - 2	Roberts 10 Barrington 90	4	29
Jan 1	Nat South	A	Chelmsford City	1662	D 2 - 2	Roberts 35 Michael-Percil 83	6	30
6	Nat South	H	East Thurrock United	445	W 4 - 0	Crook 24 Grant 38 67 Allen 39	2	31
13	Nat South	A	Chippenham Town	470	D 1 - 1	Grant 10	4	32
20	Nat South	H	Hemel Hempstead T	432	L 1 - 2	Roberts 18	4	33
27	Nat South	A	Welling United	528	L 0 - 3		5	34
Feb 3	Nat South	A	Havant & Waterlooville	654	D 0 - 0		7	35
10	Nat South	H	Bath City	430	L 0 - 2		8	36
17	Nat South	A	Bognor Regis Town	558	L 1 - 2	Crook 64	8	37
24	Nat South	H	Poole Town	368	W 1 - 0	Thompson 31	6	38
Mar 10	Nat South	H	Wealdstone	510	D 2 - 2	Allen 42 Crook 45	7	39
24	Nat South	A	Hampton & Richmond	874	D 1 - 1	Barrington 78	9	40
27	Nat South	A	Weston-s-Mare	424	W 2 - 1	Allen 81 Wyatt 85	8	41
Apr 2	Nat South	A	St Albans City	812	L 1 - 2	Hill 2	8	42
7	Nat South	A	Hungerford Town	233	W 1 - 0	Thompson 58	7	43
14	Nat South	H	Concord Rangers	446	W 2 - 1	Thompson 87 Allen 90	7	44
17	Nat South	H	Whitehawk	389	W 4 - 3	Okoye 20 Muleba 74 Grant 85 90	7	45
21	Nat South	A	Truro City	521	W 2 - 1	Wyatt 8 Thompson 63	6	46
24	Nat South	A	Oxford City	466	D 0 - 0		6	47
28	Nat South	H	Gloucester City	616	W 3 - 0	Grant 50 77 Hill 77	6	48
May 2	PO	A	Hemel Hempstead Town	1165	D 0 - 0	(won 3-1 on pens)		49
6	PO SF	A	Dartford	1704	W 1 - 0	Crook 72		50
13	PO Final	A	Hampton & Richmond		D 1 - 1	Grant 45 (Won 4-3 on pens)		51

GOALSCORERS	SG	CSG	Pens	Hat tricks	Total		SG	CSG	Pens	Hat tricks	Total
2016-17 Cheek					23	Wynter	3	2			3
Roberts	15	4			18	Hill	2				2
Crook	11	2	1		11	Muleba					2
Grant	5	2			8	Okoye					2
Oliyide	8	3			8	Shulton	2				2
Allen	6				6	Baxter					1
Barrington	6	2			6	Bettache					1
Michael-Percil	3				4	Ellul					1
Thompson	4				4	Opponents					1
Wyatt	3				3						

BROMLEY

Club Contact Details 020 8460 5291
The Stadium, Hayes Lane, Bromley, Kent BR2 9EF
info@bromleyfc.net

Founded: 1892 **Nickname:** The Lillywhites **Manager:** Neil Smith
Previous Names: None
Previous Leagues: South London, Southern, London, West Kent, South Surburban, Kent, Spartan 1907-08, Isthmian 1908-11, 52-2007, Athenian 1919-1952

Club Colours (change): White and black

Ground Capacity: 5,000 **Seats:** 1,300 **Covered:** 2,500 **Clubhouse:** Yes **Shop:** Yes
Previous Grounds: White Hart Field. Widmore Road. Plaistow Cricket Ground.
Record Attendance: 10,798 v Nigeria - 1950

RECORDS
Victory:	13-1 v Redhill - Athenian League 1945-46
Defeat:	1-11 v Barking - Athenian League 1933-34
Goalscorer:	George Brown - 570 (1938-61)
Appearances:	George Brown
Additional:	Received £50,000 from Millwall for John Goodman

HONOURS
FA Comps: Amateur Cup 1910-11, 37-38, 48-49.
League: Spartan 1907-08. Isthmian League 1908-09, 09-10, 53-54, 60-61. Athenian League 1922-23, 48-49, 50-51. Conference South 2014-15.
County FA: Kent Senior Cup 1949/50, 76-77, 91-92, 96-97, 2005-06, 06-07. Kent Amateur Cup x12. London Senior Cup 1909-10, 45-46, 50-51, 2002-03, 12-13.

08-09	09-10	10-11	11-12	12-13	13-14	14-15	15-16	16-17	17-18
Conf S 13	Conf S 12	Conf S 11	Conf S 17	Conf S 15	Conf S 3	Conf S 1	Nat 14	Nat 10	Nat 9
FAC 2Q	FAC 1P	FAC 3Qr	FAC 1P	FAC 1P	FAC 3Q	FAC 1P	FAC 4Q	FAC 4Q	FAC 1P
FAT 3Q	FAT 3Q	FAT 3Q	FAT 3Q	FAT 3P	FAT 3Q	FAT 2P	FAT 1P	FAT 2P	FAT F

2017-18 STATS **Goals Total** 99 **Games Without Scoring** 14 (2) **Total No. of Scorers** 19 **Total Clean Sheets** 19
Most Consecutive Scoring Games 7 **Best Unbeaten Run** 6 **Most Consecutive Clean Sheets** 3
Best Att: 3,346 v Leyton Orient, National League *Number in brackets denotes consecutive runs.*

2017-18 MATCH LINE-UPS

Player	Total
Gregory	58
Chorley	28
Wynter	16
Sterling	55
Wanadio	48
Mekki	44
Holland	57
Raymond	47
Rees	54
Williams	30
Dennis	53
Allen	15
Dunne	19
Johnson D	26
Porter	46
Sutherland	40
Higgs	42
Campbell	2
Enver	0
Johnson R	28
Adeyinka (L)	3
Anderson	0
Tulian	0
Baskerville	0
Vose	7
Woolfenden (L)	26
Bugiel (L)	22
Hanlan (L)	22
McLoughlin	2
Huxter	0

RESULT: D W D W W L L L D W W L L W W D W W L D L W D W L D D W D L W W L W W W W D W D L D D W W W L D L D W D W L W W W D L D

BROMLEY MATCH RESULTS 2017-18

Date	Comp	H/A	Opponents	Att:	Result		Goalscorers	Pos	No.
Aug 5	Nat Lg	H	Eastleigh	1228	D	0 - 0		13	1
8	Nat Lg	A	Dover Athletic	1145	W	2 - 1	Rees 33 Dennis 71	5	2
12	Nat Lg	A	Macclesfield Town	1281	D	0 - 0		9	3
15	Nat Lg	H	Leyton Orient	3346	W	6 - 1	Porter 11 Holland 39 75 Rees 55 Mekki 62 Williams 88	4	4
19	Nat Lg	H	Hartlepool United	1709	W	2 - 0	Rees 36 Wanadio 58	2	5
25	Nat Lg	A	Dagenham & Redbridge	1415	L	1 - 5	Wanadio 26	4	6
28	Nat Lg	H	Sutton United	2239	L	0 - 1		8	7
Sept 2	Nat Lg	A	Wrexham	4032	L	0 - 2		13	8
9	Nat Lg	A	AFC Fylde	1514	D	2 - 2	Sutherland 8 Rees 50	13	9
12	Nat Lg	H	Torquay United	1029	W	3 - 1	WILLIAMS 3 (20 58 88)	12	10
16	Nat Lg	H	Solihull Moors	1003	W	1 - 0	Porter 88	5	11
23	Nat Lg	A	FC Halifax	1760	L	1 - 2	Porter 62	10	12
30	Nat Lg	H	Tranmere Rovers	2056	L	0 - 1		12	13
Oct 3	Nat Lg	A	Maidstone United	2541	W	2 - 0	Okuonghae (og) 38 Dennis 90	13	14
7	Nat Lg	A	Gateshead	853	W	2 - 1	Dennis 84 Williams 90	7	15
14	**FAC 4Q**	**A**	**Dover Athletic**	**923**	**D**	**0 - 0**			16
17	**FAC 4Qr**	**H**	**Dover Athletic**	**828**	**W**	**3 - 0**	**Rees 70 Mekki 73 Dennis 90**		17
21	Nat Lg	H	Woking	1577	W	2 - 0	Holland 42 Rees 45	6	18
24	Nat Lg	H	Maidenhead United	1056	L	2 - 3	Wanadio 10 Rees 23	8	19
27	Nat Lg	A	Boreham Wood	1128	D	2 - 2	Turley 32 Wanadio 38	7	20
Nov 4	**FAC 1**	**A**	**Rochdale**	**2241**	**L**	**0 - 4**			21
11	Nat Lg	A	Guiseley	1074	W	1 - 0	Allen 90	6	22
18	Nat Lg	H	Chester	1129	D	1 - 1	Dennis 15	8	23
25	Nat Lg	A	Barrow	941	W	3 - 0	Raymond 24 Wanadio 58 Vose 81	8	24
28	Nat Lg	H	Aldershot Town	1171	L	0 - 2			25
Dec 2	Nat Lg	H	Dover Athletic	1201	D	2 - 2	Dennis 33 42	7	26
8	Nat Lg	A	Eastleigh	1751	D	4 - 4	Rees 26 Williams 37 Daniels 50 87	8	27
16	**FAT 1**	**A**	**Hartley Wintney**	**482**	**W**	**2 - 0**	**Rees 68 Porter 82**		28
23	Nat Lg	H	Macclesfield Town	1445	D	1 - 1	Dennis 70	8	29
26	Nat Lg	A	Ebbsfleet United	1567	L	1 - 2	Dennis 19	10	30
30	Nat Lg	A	Leyton Orient	5227	W	1 - 0	Dennis 22	9	31
Jan 1	Nat Lg	H	Ebbsfleet United	1302	W	4 - 2	Holland 17 Porter 28 Wanadio 36 Dennis 85	9	32
6	Nat Lg	H	AFC Fylde	1239	L	0 1		9	33
13	**FAT 2**	**A**	**Blyth Spartans**	**647**	**W**	**4 - 1**	**Rees 15 72 Dennis 40 90**		34
20	Nat Lg	A	Torquay United	1547	W	4 - 0	Dennis 41 Mekki 65 Wanadio 73 Rees 80	7	35
27	Nat Lg	H	FC Halifax Town	1524	W	3 - 0	Dennis 50 Rees 54 58	7	36
Feb 3	**FAT 3**	**A**	**Workington**	**897**	**D**	**1 - 1**	**Holland 70**	**7**	37
6	**FAT 3 r**	**H**	**Workington**	**604**	**W**	**7 1**	**Hanlan 4 Dennis 43 69 Porter 53 Wanadio 77 Higgs 84 Holland 88**		38
10	Nat Lg	H	Maidstone United	2027	D	2 - 2	Rees 5 Porter 45	8	39
17	Nat Lg	A	Tranmere Rovers	5536	L	0 - 1		8	40
20	Nat Lg	A	Aldershot Town	1909	D	1 - 1	Woolfender 23	8	41
24	FAT 4	H	Spennymoor Town	830	D	0 - 0			42
10	Nat Lg	H	Guiseley	906	W	2 - 1	Rees 73 Bugiel 90	9	43
Mar 14	**FAT 4r**	**A**	**Spennymoor Town**	**802**	**W**	**2 - 1**	**Dennis 7 Raymond 55**		44
17	**FAT S-F 1**	**H**	**Gateshead**	**1250**	**W**	**3 - 2**	**Hanlan 15 (pen) Dennis 15 81**		45
20	Nat Lg	A	Solihull Moors	624	L	0 - 2		10	46
24	**FAT S-F 2**	**A**	**Gateshead**	**2264**	**D**	**1 - 1**	**Kerr 5 (og)**		47
27	Nat Lg	A	Hartlepool United	3041	L	1 - 2	Rees 45	10	48
30	Nat Lg	H	Wrexham	1403	D	1 - 1	Hanlan 66	10	49
Apr 2	Nat Lg	A	Sutton United	2233	W	3 - 0	Hanlan 5 Mekki 45 (pen) Rees 80	9	50
7	Nat Lg	H	Gateshead	1035	D	0 - 0		10	51
10	Nat Lg	A	Chester	754	L	2 - 3	Rees 65 Bugiel 80	10	52
14	Nat Lg	A	Woking	2027	W	2 - 0	Higgs 32 Johnson 68	10	53
17	Nat Lg	H	Dagenham & Redbridge	1007	W	3 - 1	Holland 37 71 Raymond 90	10	54
21	Nat Lg	H	Boreham Wood	1282	W	3 - 2	Higgs 35 Hanlan 56 (pen) Bugiel 90	9	55
24	Nat Lg	H	Barrow	1331	D	0 - 0		9	56
28	Nat Lg	A	Maidenhead United	1418	L	2 - 5	Porter 22 Bugiel 68	9	57
May 20	**FAT Final**	**W**	**Brackley Town**	**31430**	**L**	**1 - 1**	**Bugiel 19 (Lost 4-5 on pens aet)**		58

GOALSCORERS	SG	CSG	Pens	Hat tricks	Total		SG	CSG	Pens	Hat tricks	Total
2016-17 Turgott					14	Higgs					3
Dennis	16	4			20	Raymond					3
Rees	15	3			19	Daniels	2				2
Holland	6				8	Opponents					2
Porter	8	2			8	Allen					1
Wanadio	8	2			8	Johnson					1
Williams	4			1	6	Sutherland					1
Bugiel	4	2			5	Turley					1
Hanlan	3		2		5	Vose					1
Mekki	4		1		4	Woolfender					1

DAGENHAM & REDBRIDGE

Club Contact Details 0208 592 1549
Chigwell Construction Stadium, Victoria Road, Dagenham, Essex RM10 7XL
info@daggers.co.uk

Founded: 1992 **Nickname:** The Daggers **Manager:** Peter Taylor - 05/06/2018
Previous Names: Formed by the merger of Dagenham and Redbridge Forest
Previous Leagues: Football Conference 1992-96, 2000-2007. Isthmian 1996-2000. Football League 2007-16.

Club Colours (change): Red & blue

Ground Capacity: 6,078 **Seats:** 2,200 **Covered:** Yes **Clubhouse:** Yes **Shop:** Yes
Previous Grounds: None
Record Attendance: 5,949 v Ipswich Town (05/01/2002) FA Cup Third Round Proper
Nearest Railway Station Dagenham East Underground (District line), exit left **Bus Route** The 103 runs from Romford Station and
and take fifth turning on the left 400 metres away. stops outside the ground.

RECORDS
Victory: 8-1 v Woking, Football Conference, 19.04.94
Defeat: 0-9 v Hereford United, Football Conference, 27.02.04.
Goalscorer: Danny Shipp - 105
Appearances: Tony Roberts - 507
Additional: Transfer fee received: £470,000 Dwight Gayle to Peterborough United

HONOURS
FA Comps: N/A
League: Isthmian League Premier Division 1999-2000. Football Conference 2006-07.
Football League Two Play-offs 2009-10.
County FA: Essex Senior Cup 1997-98, 2000-01.

	08-09		09-10		10-11		11-12		12-13		13-14		14-15		15-16		16-17		17-18	
	FL 2	8	FL 2	7	FL 1	21	FL 2	19	FL 2	22	FL 2	9	FL 2	14	FL 2	23	Nat	4	Nat	11
	FAC	2P	FAC	1P	FAC	1Pr	FAC	3Pr	FAC	1P	FAC	1P	FAC	1Pr	FAC	3P	FAC	1Pr	FAC	4Qr
	FLC	1P	FLC	1P	FLC	1P	FLC	1P	FLC	1P	FLC	1P	FLC	1P	FLC	1P	FAT	1P	FAT	1P

2017-18 STATS
Goals Total 71 **Games Without Scoring** 14 (4) **Total No. of Scorers** 17 **Total Clean Sheets** 13
Most Consecutive Scoring Games 6 **Best Unbeaten Run** 8 **Most Consecutive Clean Sheets** 3
Best Att: 3,144 v Leyton Orient, National League

Number in brackets denotes consecutive runs.

2017-18 MATCH LINE-UPS

Player	Total
Cousins	49
N'Gala	9
Ling	32
Lokko (L)	28
Pennell	22
Robson	46
Whitely	29
Boucaud	44
Ferrier	33
Okenabirhie	39
Cheek	36
Hawkins	7
Justham	0
Robinson	35
Wheeler	1
Howells	43
Doe	20
Romain	12
McNamara	0
White	3
Howell	35
Nunn	25
Adams	24
Kandi	18
Enigbokan-Bloomfield	26
Moore	0
Bloomfield	3
Chapman	0
Sparkes	26
Bonos	5
Gordon	2
Mongoy	1

RESULT: W W D D D W D W L L W D W D L D L L W D L W W W W L L L D D W L L L L W L W L L W D W D W L W W W L

DAGENHAM & REDBRIDGE MATCH RESULTS 2017-18

Date	Comp	H/A	Opponents	Att:	Result	Goalscorers	Pos	No.
Aug 5th	Nat Lg	H	Barrow	1362	W 2 - 0	Whitely 18 (pen) Cheek 21	3	1
8	Nat Lg	A	Boreham Wood	635	W 2 - 1	Okenabirhie 2 Whitely 18	2	2
12	Nat Lg	A	Eastleigh	1614	D 2 - 2	Whitely 13 74 (pen)	2	3
15	Nat Lg	H	Ebbsfleet United	1686	D 3 - 3	Whitely 22 Lokko 45 Ferrier 64	5	4
19	Nat Lg	A	AFC Fylde	1590	D 2 - 2	Ferrier 45 Ling 90	7	5
25	Nat Lg	H	Bromley	1415	W 5 - 1	Cheek 15 29 Lokko 44 Ferrier 74 Whitely 81	1	6
28	Nat Lg	A	Maidstone United	2544	D 0 - 0		2	7
Sept 2	Nat Lg	H	Gateshead	1358	W 3 - 1	White 13 Romaine 87 Ferrier 90	1	8
9	Nat Lg	A	Hartlepool United	3366	L 0 - 1		2	9
12	Nat Lg	H	Sutton United	1261	L 1 - 2	Whitely 22	8	10
16	Nat Lg	H	FC Halifax Town	1282	W 3 - 1	Robson 17 Whitely 22 Garner 45 (og)	3	11
23	Nat Lg	A	Solihullo Moors	625	D 2 - 2	Bloomfield 6 Howell 90	7	12
30	Nat Lg	H	Torquay United	1421	W 1 - 0	Okenabirhie 2	2	13
Oct 3	Nat Lg	A	Aldershot Town	1903	D 1 - 1	Ling 86	4	14
7	Nat Lg	A	Woking	2509	L 0 - 1		6	15
14	**FAC 4Q**	**H**	**Leyton Orient**	**2529**	**D 0 - 0**			16
17	**FAC 4Qr**	**A**	**Leyton Orient**	**2013**	**L 0 - 1**			17
21	Nat Lg	H	Wrexham	1492	L 0 - 1		9	18
24	Nat Lg	H	Macclesfield Town	1185	W 1 - 0	Ferrrier 50	7	19
27	Nat Lg	A	Maidenhead United	1384	D 1 - 1	Cheek 55	10	20
Nov 11	Nat Lg	A	Tranmere Rovers	5227	L 0 - 2			21
18	Nat Lg	H	Guiseley	1116	W 3 - 2	Ferrier 29 Doe 45 Howell 80	8	22
21	Nat Lg	H	Dover Athletic	1263	W 1 - 0	Ferrier 23	5	23
25	Nat Lg	A	Chester	1638	W 4 - 0	Ling 56 Howell 75 Cheek 79 90	4	24
Dec 8	Nat Lg	A	Barrow	917	W 1 - 0	Ferrier 56	5	25
17	**FAT 1**	**A**	**Hereford**	**1518**	**L 2 - 3**	**Deaman 30 (og) Cheek 70**		26
23	Nat Lg	A	Eastleigh	1263	L 1 - 2	Cheek 17	8	27
26	Nat Lg	A	Leyton Orient	5125	L 0 - 2		8	28
30	Nat Lg	A	Ebbsfleet United	1684	D 1 - 1	Bloomfield 86	8	29
Jan 1	Nat Lg	H	Leyton Orient	3144	D 0 - 0		8	30
6	Nat Lg	H	Hartlepool United	1290	W 4 - 2	Sparkes 39 81 Cheek 65 Okenabirhie 79	6	31
9	Nat Lg	H	Boreham Wood	1117	L 2 - 3	Cheek 55 Sparkes 90	7	32
20	Nat Lg	A	Sutton United	2071	L 1 - 2	Okenabirhie 84	10	33
27	Nat Lg	H	Solihull Moors	2217	L 1 - 3	Okenabirhie 40	10	34
Feb 10	Nat Lg	H	Aldershot Town	1509	L 0 - 1		11	35
17	Nat Lg	A	Torquay United	1931	W 3 - 0	Okenabirhie 50 90 Robson 76	11	36
20	Nat Lg	A	Dover Athletic	677	L 0 1		11	37
24	Nat Lg	H	Chester	1254	W 3 - 2	Okenbabirie 11 85 Halls 88 (og)	11	38
Mar 10	Nat Lg	H	Tranmere Rovers	1431	L 0 - 4		11	39
13	Nat Lg	A	FC Halifax Town	1315	L 1 - 2	Adams 40	11	40
24	Nat Lg	H	AFC Fylde	1168	W 2 - 0	Kandi 33 Bloomfield 42	11	41
30	Nat Lg	A	Gateshead	764	D 0 - 0		11	42
Apr 2	Nat Lg	H	Maidstone United	1633	W 2 - 1	Okenabirhie 25 Robson 64	10	43
7	Nat Lg	H	Woking	1391	D 1 - 1	Sparkes 9	11	44
14	Nat Lg	A	Wrexham	4193	W 2 - 1	Okenabirhie 49 Raven 75 (og)	11	45
17	Nat Lg	A	Bromley	1007	L 1 - 3	Howell 54	11	46
19	Nat Lg	A	Guiseley	311	W 5 - 3	CHEEK 3 (16 36 67) Gordon 26 Okenabirhie44 (pn)	11	47
21	Nat Lg	H	Maidenhead United	1433	W 1 - 0	Cheek 11	11	48
28	Nat Lg	A	Macclesfield Town	4201	L 0 - 2		11	49

GOALSCORERS	SG	CSG	Pens	Hat tricks	Total		SG	CSG	Pens	Hat tricks	Total
2016-17 Hawkins					19	Sparkes	3				3
Cheek	10	2		1	14	Lokko		2			2
Okenabirhie	10	2	1		12	Adams					1
Ferrier	8	3			8	Doe					1
Whitely	7	4	2		8	Gordon					1
Howell	4				4	Kandi					1
Opponents	4				4	Romaine					1
Bloomfield	3				3	Sparkes					1
Ling	3				3	Whitely					1
Robson	3				3						

DOVER ATHLETIC

Club Contact Details 01304 822 373
Crabble Athletic Ground, Lewisham Road, Dover, Kent CT17 0JB
enquiries@doverathletic.com

Founded: 1983   **Nickname:** The Whites   **Manager:** Chris Kinnear
Previous Names: Dover F.C. until club folded in 1983
Previous Leagues: Southern 1983-93, 2002-04, Conference 1993-2002, Isthmian 2004-2009

Club Colours (change): White & black

Ground Capacity: 6,500   **Seats:** 1,010   **Covered:** 4,900   **Clubhouse:** Yes   **Shop:** Yes
Previous Grounds: None
Record Attendance: 4,186 v Oxford United - FA Cup 1st Round Proper November 2002

RECORDS
Victory: 7-0 v Weymouth - 03/04/1990
Defeat: 1-7 v Poole Town
Goalscorer: Lennie Lee - 160
Appearances: Jason Bartlett - 520+
Additional: Paid £50,000 to Farnborough Town for David Lewworthy August 1993
Received £50,000 from Brentford for Ricky Reina 1997

HONOURS
FA Comps: None
League: Southern League Southern Division 1987-88, Premier Division 1989-90, 92-93.
Isthmian League Division 1 South 2007-08, Premier Division 2008-09. Conference South Play-offs 2013-14.
County FA: Kent Senior Cup 1990-91, 2016-17.

08-09		09-10		10-11		11-12		12-13		13-14		14-15		15-16		16-17		17-18	
Isth P	1	Conf S	2	Conf S	7	Conf S	7	Conf S	3	Conf S	5	Conf	8	Nat	5	Nat	6	Nat	8
FAC	3Qr	FAC	4Q	FAC	3P	FAC	4Q	FAC	3Qr	FAC	2P	FAC	3P	FAC	1P	FAC	1Pr	FAC	4Qr
FAT	2Q	FAT	3P	FAT	3Q	FAT	3Q	FAT	3Qr	FAT	3P	FAT	QFr	FAT	QF	FAT	1Pr	FAT	3P

2017-18 STATS

Goals Total 72	**Games Without Scoring** 11 (2)	**Total No. of Scorers** 18	**Total Clean Sheets** 20
Most Consecutive Scoring Games 6	**Best Unbeaten Run** 7		**Most Consecutive Clean Sheets** 4
Best Att: 2,860 v AFC Fylde, National League			Number in brackets denotes consecutive runs.

2017-18 MATCH LINE-UPS

Match Number	1	2	3	4	5	6	7	8	9	10	11	12	13	14	15	16	17	18	19	20	21	22	23	24	25	26	27	28	29	30	31	32	33	34	35	36	37	38	39	40	41	42	43	44	45	46	47	48	49	50	51	Total
Walker	x	x	x	x	x	x	x	x	x	x	x	x	x	x	x	x	x	x	x	x	x	x	x	x	x	x	x	x	x	x	x	x	x	x	x	x	x	x	x	x	x	x	x	x	x	x	x	x	x	x	x	51
Passley	x	x	x		x	x	x	x	x	x	x	x	x	xs	x	x	x	xs									xs	x	x	x	x	x	x	s	xs	xs	xs	s	s	s	sx	x	s	s	sx	x	s	s	sx	s		38
Gallifuoco	x		x	x	xs	x	x	x	x	x	x	x	x	x	xs		x	x	x	x	x	x	x	x		x	x	x	x	x	x	x	x	x	x	x	x	x	x	x	x	x	x	x	x	x	x	x	x			49
Parry	x	xs	x	x	x	x	xs	x	x	x	x	x	x	x	x	x	x	x	x	x	x	x	x	x		x	x	x	x	x	x	x	x	x	x	xs	sx	x	x	x	xs	x	x	x	x	x	x	x	xs			51
Essam	x	x	x	x	x	x	x	x	x	x	x	x	x	x	x	x	x	x	x	x	x	x	x	x		x	xs	x	x	x	x	x	x	x	x	x	x	x	x	x	x	x	x	x	x	x	x	xs	x			51
Ilesanmi	x	x	x	x	x	x	xs	x	x	xs	xs	x	x	x	x	x	x		x	x	x	x	x	x	x	x	x	x	x	x	x	x	x	x	x	x	x	x	x	x	x	x	x	x	x	x	x	x	x			50
Richards	xs	x	xs	xs	xs	xs	s	s	s	sx	s	xs	s	xs	s	sx	s	xs	s	s	s	s	s	sx	s	sx	s		s	xs	xs	s	s								s	s	s	s	x	xs						17
Nortey	xs	x	x	x	x	x	xs	x	x	xs	x	s	s	s	x	xs	s	x	x	x	xs	xs	xs	x	x	x	x	xs	xs	xs	xs	xs	s	xs	s					s	x	s	s	x	xs							38
Brundle	x	xs	x	x	x	x	xs	x	x	xs	x	x	x	x	x	x	x	x	x	x	x	x	x	x		x	x	x	x	x	x	x	x	x	x	x	x	x	x	x	x	x	x	x	x	x	x	x	x			51
Allen	xs	x	x	x	xs			xs	xs	xs	s	s	sx	sx	xs	x	s	s																																		12
Bird	xs	x	x	xs	x	x	x	x	xs	x		x	xs			x	xs	x	x	x	x	x	xs	x		x	x	x	xs	x	xs	sx	sx	xs	x	x	sx	x	x	sx	xs		x	x	sx	xs	xs				51
Sho-Silva	sx	sx	sx	sx	sx	x	x	x	sx	sx	sx	sx	sx	sx	sx																																					14
Pinnock	sx	sx	s	sx	s	sx	xs	x	xs	x	x	xs	sx	sx	x	x	xs	x	x	x	x	x	x	x		x	xs	sx	x	xs	x	x	x	x	x	xs	xs	xs	x	xs	s	xs	xs	xs	x	s	xs	xs	sx	x		48
Daniel	sx	s	sx	sx	sx	sx	sx	sx	sx	xs	xs	sx	sx		x	sx	sx	sx	sx	sx	sx	sx	sx	sx	sx	sx	sx	sx	sx	sx	sx	sx	sx	sx	sx	sx	sx	sx	s	sx	sx	s	s	s	sx	sx	s	s				44
Essuman	s		s	s	sx	s	s																			s		s																									1
Adebowale	s	s	s	s	s													s	s																																	0
Barnard		s																																																		0
Fazakerley			x	s	s	sx	sx	s		s	sx	s	s	sx	x	s	x	s	sx	x	xs	xs	s	sx	s	sx	s	s	s	s	s	s	s	s		s	s															13
Deen-Conteh					sx	sx	s		sx			s	s	sx	s	s	s	s			s	sx	s	s	s	s	s	s	s																							5
Lewington							s	s	s			sx			s	s											s		s																							0
Lewis (L)									sx	xs	sx	x	x		x	x																																				6
Alabi (L)														xs	xs	xs	xs	x	xs	xs	s	sx	s	s	s	sx	sx	sx						sx	sx	s	s															13
Okosieme									sx	s	s			s	s	s	s	s	sx	x	xs								sx	sx	s	x	sx	sx			s		s	s		sx										9
Jeffrey (L)										s	sx	sx	sx	xs	xs	xs	xs								sx	xs	xs	xs			xs	xs	s	s	sx	sx	sx	sx	sx	xs	xs	x	x									24
Bellamy																								sx	sx	sx	sx	s	sx	sx	s	sx	x	x	sx	x	x		x	x	x	s	x	sx								18
Lokko (L)																																s	sx	x	x	x	x	x	x	x	x	x	x	x								12
Azeez																															xs	x	x	xs	xs	x	x	sx	sx	sx	sx											12
Marsh-Brown (L)																																							xs	xs	s	sx	s		sx	sx	sx					6
RESULT	W	L	W	W	D	W	D	L	D	W	W	L	W	D	W	D	W	D	L	D	W	D	W	D	L	L	D	W	W	D	D	D	D	L	W	W	W	L	L	L	W	L	W	W	W	D	L	L	W	L	L	W	W	

DOVER ATHLETIC MATCH RESULTS 2017-18

Date	Comp	H/A	Opponents	Att:	Result	Goalscorers	Pos	No.
Aug 5	Nat Lg	A	Hartlepool United	3954	W 1 - 0	Allen 29	5	1
8	Nat Lg	H	Bromley	1145	L 1 - 2	Gregory 75 (og)	10	2
12	Nat Lg	H	Wrexham	1012	W 1 - 0	Bird 18	6	3
15	Nat Lg	A	FC Halifax Town	1486	W 2 - 1	Brundle 87 Sho-Silva 90	3	4
19	Nat Lg	H	Barrow	937	D 1 - 1	Bird 72	5	5
25	Nat Lg	A	Macclesfield Town	1270	L 0 - 1		7	6
28	Nat Lg	H	Ebbsfleet United	1625	D 1 - 1	Bird 17	7	7
Sept 2	Nat Lg	A	Tranmere Rovers	4101	W 1 - 0	Bird 79	6	8
9	Nat Lg	A	Aldershot Town	1862	W 2 - 0	Gallifuoco 25 Daniel 65	1	9
12	Nat Lg	H	Boreham Wood	1012	L 0 - 1		5	10
16	Nat Lg	H	Chester	1102	W 4 - 0	Gallifuoco 22 Pinnock 62 Nortey 70 Brundle 83	2	11
23	Nat Lg	A	Guiseley	805	L 1 - 2	Nortey 40	3	12
30	Nat Lg	H	Solihull Moors	2795	W 1 - 0	Bird 80	1	13
Oct 3	Nat Lg	A	Sutton United	2206	D 2 - 2	Gallifuoco 36 Parry 90	2	14
7	Nat Lg	A	Torquay United	1915	W 2 - 0	Lewis 5 Bird 63	2	15
14	**FAC 4Q**	**H**	**Bromley**	**923**	**D 0 - 0**			16
17	**FAC 4Qr**	**A**	**Bromley**	**828**	**L 0 - 3**			17
21	Nat Lg	H	Maidenhead United	837	D 1 - 1	Bird 76	2	18
24	Nat Lg	H	Woking	1017	W 3 - 1	Bird 6 21 Parry 56	1	19
27	Nat Lg	A	Gateshead	816	D 0 - 0		1	20
Nov 11	Nat Lg	H	Eastleigh	1273	W 2 - 0	Alabi 31 Essam 57	1	21
18	Nat Lg	A	Leyton Orient	4548	D 1 - 1	Nortey 23	1	22
21	Nat Lg	A	Dagenham & Redbridge	1263	L 0 - 1		2	23
25	Nat Lg	H	AFC Fylde	2860	L 0 - 1		5	24
Dec 2	Nat Lg	A	Bromley	1201	D 2 - 2	Brundle 55 Richards 90	5	25
8	Nat Lg	H	Hartlepool United	1083	W 4 - 0	Pinnock 3 25 Bird 79 90	4	26
16	**FAT 1**	**H**	**Eastbourne Borough**	**424**	**W 3 - 0**	**Pinnock 46 Bird 57 Alabi 87**		27
23	Nat Lg	A	Wrexham	4980	D 0 - 0		3	28
26	Nat Lg	H	Maidstone United	2078	D 2 - 2	Bird 2 80	5	29
30	Nat Lg	H	FC Halifax Town	1127	D 0 - 0		4	30
Jan 1	Nat Lg	A	Maidstone United	2502	D 2 - 2	Ilesanmi 27 Nortey 76	4	31
6	Nat Lg	H	Aldershot Town	1237	L 1 - 2	Parry 45	5	32
13	**FAT 2**	**H**	**Marine**	**565**	**W 4 - 3**	**Parry 6 Bird 27 Brundle 81 Pinnock 52**		33
20	Nat Lg	A	Boreham Wood	527	W 3 - 2	Parry 52 Daniel 72 Ilesanmi 85	6	34
27	Nat Lg	H	Guiseley	2327	W 2 - 1	Brundle 5 Pinnock 88	6	35
Feb 3	**FAT 3**	**H**	**Leyton Orient**	**1016**	**L 3 - 4**	**Bird 57 83 Pinnock 81**		36
10	Nat Lg	H	Sutton United	1027	L 0 - 1		9	37
17	Nat Lg	A	Solihull Moors	679	L 2 - 3	Bird 22 Pinnock 60	9	38
20	Nat Lg	H	Dagenham & Redbridge	677	W 1 - 0	Pinnock 30	7	39
24	Nat Lg	A	AFC Fylde	1622	L 1 - 3	Pinnock 57	9	40
Mar 3	Nat Lg	H	Leyton Orient	1348	W 1 - 0	Pinnock 82	7	41
5	Nat Lg	A	Chester	1182	W 2 - 0	Lokko 64 Astles 71 (og)	6	42
17	Nat Lg	H	Macclesfield Town	837	W 2 - 0	Marsh-Brown 2 36	7	43
24	Nat Lg	A	Barrow	908	D 0 - 0		7	44
27	Nat Lg	A	Eastleigh	1450	L 1 - 2	Bird 22	7	45
Apr 2	Nat Lg	A	Ebbsfleet United	1735	L 1 - 2	Marsh-Brown 90	8	46
7	Nat Lg	H	Torquay United	1128	W 1 - 0	Bird 57 (pen)	8	47
14	Nat Lg	A	Maidenhead United	1155	L 2 - 3	Jeffrey 49 Parry 54	8	48
17	Nat Lg	H	Tranmere Rovers	1231	L 0 - 1		9	49
21	Nat Lg	H	Gateshead	1424	W 3 - 2	Gallifuoco 36 Bird 68 Azeez 89	8	50
28	Nat Lg	A	Woking	2593	W 2 - 1	Gallifuoco 26 Marsh-Brown 90	8	51

GOALSCORERS	SG	CSG	Pens	Hat tricks	Total		SG	CSG	Pens	Hat tricks	Total
2016-17 Miller					46	Isanmi	2				2
Bird	17	2	1		21	Opponents					2
Pinnock	10	4			11	Allen					1
Parry	5				6	Azeez					1
Brundle	5				5	Essam					1
Gallifuoco	5				5	Jeffrey					1
Marsh-Brown	3				4	Lewis					1
Nortey	4				4	Lokko					1
Alabi	2				2	Richards					1
Daniel	2				2	Sho-Silva					1

EASTLEIGH

Club Contact Details 02380 613 361
The Silverlake Stadium 'Ten Acres', Stoneham Lane, Eastleigh SO50 9HT
admin@eastleigh-fc.co.uk

Founded: 1946   **Nickname:** The Spitfires   **Manager:** Andy Hessenthaler
Previous Names: Swaythling Athletic 1946-59, Swaythling 1973-80
Previous Leagues: Southampton Junior & Senior 1946-59, Hampshire 1950-86, Wessex 1986-2003, Southern 2003-04, Isthmian 2004-05

Club Colours (change): Blue & white

Ground Capacity: 3,000   **Seats:** 2,700   **Covered:** Yes   **Clubhouse:** Yes   **Shop:** Yes
Previous Grounds: Southampton Common. Walnut Avenue >1957.
Record Attendance: 5,250 v Bolton Wanderers, FA Cup Third Round 09/01/2016

RECORDS
Victory: 12-1 v Hythe & Dibden (H) - 11/12/1948
Defeat: 0-11 v Austin Sports (A) - 01.01.1947
Goalscorer: Johnnie Williams - 177
Appearances: Ian Knight - 611
Additional: Paid £10,000 to Newport (I.O.W.) for Colin Matthews

HONOURS
FA Comps: None
League: Southampton Senior League (West) 1949-50. Hampshire League Division Three 1950-51, 53-54, Division Two 1967-68. Wessex League Division One 2002-03. Conference South 2013-14.
County FA: Hampshire Intermediate Cup 1950-51, Senior Cup 2011-12.

	08-09	09-10	10-11	11-12	12-13	13-14	14-15	15-16	16-17	17-18
	Conf S 3	Conf S 11	Conf S 8	Conf S 12	Conf S 4	Conf S 1	Conf 4	Nat 7	Nat 15	Nat 14
FAC	3Q	1P	4Q	3Q	3Q	3Q	2P	3Pr	3P	4Q
FAT	3Q	3Q	3P	3Q	3Q	QF	1P	2P	1P	1P

2017-18 STATS   **Goals Total** 67   **Games Without Scoring** 14 (3)   **Total No. of Scorers** 18   **Total Clean Sheets** 8
Most Consecutive Scoring Games 10   **Best Unbeaten Run** 8   **Most Consecutive Clean Sheets** 2
Best Att: 3,312 v AFC Fylde, National League   *Number in brackets denotes consecutive runs.*

2017-18 MATCH LINE-UPS

Match Number	Total
Stack	28
Hoyte	33
Green	18
Johnson	13
Boyce	40
Togwell	22
Wood	37
Yeates	47
Hollands	34
McCallum	28
Williamson	37
Stearn	5
McAllister	24
Zebroski	39
Constable	27
Obileye	34
Matthews (L)	39
Miley	38
Flintney	21
Howe (L)	28
Strevens	8
McSheffrey	12
Reid (15)	0
Cresswell	13
Dennett	1
Shaw	6
Read (23)	1
Heslop (L)	5
Hudson-Odoi (L)	7
Broom (L)	13
Childs	1
RESULT	D W D L W D D D D L D W L L L W L W D L L D D L D L W D D W W W W D L L L D D L W W D L L L L W

EASTLEIGH MATCH RESULTS 2017-18

Date	Comp	H/A	Opponents	Att:	Result	Goalscorers	Pos	No.
Aug 5	Nat Lg	A	Bromley	1228	D 0 - 0		14	1
8	Nat Lg	H	Sutton United	1744	W 1 - 0	Williamson 59	7	2
12	Nat Lg	H	Dagenham & Redbridge	1614	D 2 - 2	Williamson 44 45 (pen)	8	3
15	Nat Lg	A	Woking	1796	L 1 - 2	Obileye	15	4
19	Nat Lg	H	Tranmere Rovers	1906	W 2 - 0	Williamson 64 McAllister 79	10	5
26	Nat Lg	A	Leyton Orient	4373	D 1 - 1	Obileye 46	10	6
28	Nat Lg	H	Aldershot Town	2525	D 0 - 0		11	7
Sept 2	Nat Lg	A	Ebbsfleet Uited	1423	D 2 - 2	Constable 19 McAllister 80	15	8
9	Nat Lg	A	Guiseley	735	D 0 - 0		12	9
12	Nat Lg	H	Maidstone United	1820	L 0 - 1		15	10
16	Nat Lg	H	AFC Fylde	3312	D 2 - 2	Johnson 26 McSheffery 54	16	11
23	Nat Lg	A	Hartlepool United	3374	W 2 - 1	Howe 48 Yeates 52	15	12
Oct 2	Nat Lg	A	Boreham Wood	404	L 0 - 1		17	13
7	Nat Lg	A	Wrexham	3907	L 1 - 2	Williamson 43	18	14
14	FAC 4Q	H	Hereford	1345	L 1 - 2	Howe 78		15
21	Nat Lg	H	Gateshead	1597	W 3 - 2	Williamson 4 Constable 62 Strevens 90	16	16
24	Nat Lg	H	Solihull Moors	2577	L 1 - 2	Williamson 59	17	17
27	Nat Lg	A	Macclesfield Town	1352	W 2 - 1	Yeates 45 50	18	18
Nov 4	Nat Lg	H	Chester	1868	D 2 - 2	Williamson 2 McSheffery 53	16	19
11	Nat Lg	A	Dover Athletic	1273	L 0 - 2		17	20
18	Nat Lg	H	Barrow	1708	L 0 - 2		18	21
21	Nat Lg	H	Maidenhead United	1525	D 2 - 2	Obileye 84 Williamson 90	18	22
25	Nat Lg	A	FC Halifax Town	1407	D 3 - 3	Matthews 16 Zebroski 22 Heslop 63	18	23
Dec 2	Nat Lg	A	Sutton United	1967	L 0 - 2		19	24
8	Nat Lg	H	Bromley	1751	D 4 - 4	McCALLUM 3 (10 19 58) Matthews 88	18	25
16	FAT 1	H	Ebbsfleet United	733	L 1 - 2	Miley 79		26
23	Nat Lg	H	Dagenham & Redbridge	1263	W 2 - 1	Zebroski 32 McCallum 60	18	27
26	Nat Lg	H	Torquay United	2092	D 1 - 1	Miley 15	17	28
30	Nat Lg	H	Woking	2067	D 2 - 2	Zebroski 64 Howe 90	18	29
Jan 6	Nat Lg	H	Guiseley	2001	W 4 - 2	May 2 Zebroski 36 Yeates 56 Howe 65	15	30
13	Nat Lg	A	Torquay United	1486	W 2 - 1	Matthews 9 Hoyle 70	14	31
20	Nat Lg	A	Maidstone United	2132	W 3 - 2	Obileye 11 86 Broom 79	12	32
27	Nat Lg	H	Hartlepool United	2163	W 4 - 3	Obileye 23 ZEBROSKI 3 (42 685 75)	12	33
Feb 3	Nat Lg	A	AFC Fylde	1626	D 2 - 2	Broom 23 67	11	34
10	Nat Lg	H	Boreham Wood	1751	L 0 2		12	35
17	Nat Lg	A	Chester	1604	L 1 - 3	Yeates 19	13	36
20	Nat Lg	A	Maidenhead United	1055	L 1 - 3	Obileye 45 (pen)	14	37
24	Nat Lg	H	FC Halifax Town	1852	D 0 - 0		13	38
Mar 17	Nat Lg	H	Leyton Orient	2013	D 0 - 0		14	39
24	Nat Lg	A	Tranmere Rovers	4619	L 1 - 3	Zebroski 88	16	40
27	Nat Lg	H	Dover Athletic	1450	W 2 - 1	McCallum 84 90	14	41
Apr 2	Nat Lg	A	Aldershot Town	2853	W 2 - 0	Zebroski 42 McCallum 63	13	42
7	Nat Lg	H	Wrexham	1765	D 1 - 1	Cresswell 90	13	43
10	Nat Lg	A	Barrow	817	L 2 - 3	Zebroski 60 Williamson 90	13	44
14	Nat Lg	A	Gateshead	612	L 0 - 2		16	45
17	Nat Lg	H	Ebbsfleet United	1614	L 0 - 1		16	46
21	Nat Lg	H	Macclesfield Town	2372	L 0 - 2		16	47
28	Nat Lg	A	Solihull Moors	1014	W 4 - 1	MATTHEWS 3 (34 51 53) McCallum 68	14	48

GOALSCORERS	SG	CSG	Pens	Hat tricks	Total		SG	CSG	Pens	Hat tricks	Total
2016-17 Mandron					15	McAllister	2				2
Williamson	9	2	1		10	McSheffery	2				2
Zebroski	8	2		1	10	Miley	2				2
McCallum	5			1	8	Cresswell					1
Obileye	6		1		7	Heslop					1
Matthews	4			1	6	Hoyle					1
Yeates	4				5	Johnson					1
Howe	4				4	May					1
Broom	2				3	Strevens					1
Constable	2				2						

EBBSFLEET UNITED

Club Contact Details 01474 533 796
Stonebridge Road, Northfleet, Kent DA11 9GN
info@eufc.co.uk

Founded: 1946	**Nickname:** The Fleet	**Manager:** Daryl McMahon

Previous Names: Gravesend United and Northfleet United merged in 1946 to form Gravesend and Northfleet > 2007
Previous Leagues: Southern 1946-79, 82-97. Alliance (FM) 1979-82. Isthmian 1997-2002.

Club Colours (change): Red & white

Ground Capacity: 4,184 **Seats:** 2,300 **Covered:** 3,000 **Clubhouse:** Yes **Shop:** Yes
Previous Grounds: Gravesend United: Central Avenue
Record Attendance: 12,036 v Sunderland - FA Cup 4th Round 12/02/1963
Nearest Railway Station Northfleet - 300 yards from the ground. **Bus Route** 480/490 or FASTRACK 'B' Service

RECORDS
Victory: 8-1 v Clacton Town - Southern League 1962-63
Defeat: 0-9 v Trowbridge Town - Southern League Premier Division 1991-92
Goalscorer: Steve Portway - 152 (1992-94, 97-2001)
Appearances: Ken Burrett - 537
Additional: Paid £8,000 to Wokingham Town for Richard Newbery 1996 and to Tonbridge for Craig Williams 1997
Received £35,000 from West Ham United for Jimmy Bullard 1998

HONOURS
FA Comps: FA Trophy 2007-08.
League: Southern League 1957-58, Division One South 1974-75, Southern Division 1993-94.
Isthmian League Premier 2001-02. Southern Premier Play-offs 2016-17.
County FA: Kent Senior Cup 1948-49, 52-53, 80-81, 99-00, 00-01, 01-02, 07-08, 13-14.

08-09		09-10		10-11		11-12		12-13		13-14		14-15		15-16		16-17		17-18	
Conf	14	Conf	22	Conf S	3	Conf	14	Conf	23	Conf S	4	Conf S	8	Nat S	2	Nat S	2	Nat	6
FAC	1P	FAC	4Q	FAC	1Pr	FAC	4Q	FAC	1P	FAC	4Qr	FAC	3Q	FAC	2Qr	FAC	4Q	FAC	1P
FAT	SF	FAT	1P	FAT	2P	FAT	3P	FAT	1P	FAT	3P	FAT	QF	FAT	1P	FAT	2P	FAT	2Pr

2017-18 STATS	**Goals Total**	73	**Games Without Scoring**	14 (4)	**Total No. of Scorers**	14	**Total Clean Sheets**	16
Most Consecutive Scoring Games	11	**Best Unbeaten Run**	9			**Most Consecutive Clean Sheets**		3
Best Att: 2,852 v Sutton United, National League						Number in brackets denotes consecutive runs.		

2017-18 MATCH LINE-UPS

Match Number	1	2	3	4	5	6	7	8	9	10	11	12	13	14	15	16	17	18	19	20	21	22	23	24	25	26	27	28	29	30	31	32	33	34	35	36	37	38	39	40	41	42	43	44	45	46	47	48	49	50	51	52	53	54				Total
Ashmore	x	x	x	x	x	x	x	x	x	x	x	x	x	x	x		x	x	x	x	x	x	x	x	x	x	x	x	x	x	x	x	x	x	x	x	x	x	x	x	x	x	x	x	x	x	x	x	x	x	x	x	x	x				54
Coulson	x	x	x	x	x	x	xs	sx	x	x	xs	sx	xs	xs	sx	sx	sx	sx	sx	x	xs	x	xs	xs	xs	xs	x	x	xs	xs	x	x	x	xs	x	xs	xs	x	x	xs	xs	x	xs	xs	x	xs	xs	x	xs	xs	x	x	xs	xs				54
Weston	x	xs	xs	xs	sx	xs	xs			sx	x	x	x	xs	x	xs	sx	x	sx	x	x	x	x	x	sx	x	sx	x	xs	sx	sx	x	x	xs	x	sx	x	sx		sx	sx	sx	sx	sx	sx	sx	sx	sx	x	sx	x	xf				48
Winfield	x	xs																		sx	x	x	x	x	x	x	x	xs	x						x	x	x	x	x	x	x	x	x							x	x	x	xr				31
Magri	x	x	x	x	x	x			x	x	xs	x	x			x	x	x	sx	x	xs	x							xs	x					x	x	x	x	x	x	x	x	x	x	x	xs											39
Clark	x	x	x						sx	x	x	x	x	x	x		x	x	x	x			xs	x	x	x	x	x	x										x	x	x	x	x	x	x	x	x	x	x	x	x	x	x	x				44
Drury	x	x	x	xs	sx	x			x	x	x	xs													x	x	x	x	x	x	x	sx	x	x	x	x	x	x	x	x	x	x	x	x	x	x	xs	x	x							46
Payne	x	x	x	x	xs	x	x	x	x	x	x	xs																		sx	x	sx	x	x	x	x	x	x	sx																		25
Powell	x	x	xs	sx	x	xs	x	x	xs	x	x	x	x		x	xs	x	x	x	sx	x	sx	x		x	xs	xs	xs	x	xs	xs	sx	xs	s	xs	sx	xs	sx	x	s	xs	s	sx	x	xs	s	sx	x	xs	xs	x	xs				49
Kedwell	x	x	x	xs	xs	xs	x	x	sx	xs	x	x		x	x		x	x		x	xs	x		x		x	x	x	x	x	x		x	xs	x	x	xs	x	x	x	x	x	x	x	x	xs	x	x							53
McQueen	x	xs		sx	sx	sx	x	x	sx	xs	sx	xs																																											12
McCoy	s	sx	x	x	x	x	s	x					s	x	x				s	xs	sx	sx		s			s	s	s	s	s	s	s		s			x	xs	x						x	xs	x		s	s	s	s	sx	sx				22
McLean	s	sx	s	sx	xs		s	sx					xs	s	sx	xs	sx			s				sx	sx	s	s	s	s	s		s	x																										11
Miles	s	s	s	s	s	s	s	s	s	s	s	s	s	s	s	s			s	s	s	s	s	s	s													s	s	s	s	s	s	s	s	s	s	s	s	s	s				0
Shields	s	sx	sx	sx	s	sx	sx	x	xs					sx	xs	xs	s		sx	sx	sx	sx	x		x	sx	x		x	x	xs	x	x		sx				x	sx	sx	x	sx	x	x	xs	xs										38
Mills	s	s	sx	sx	s	sx	s	sx	xs	xs	s	sx	xs	xs	s	x	xs	x	xs	xs	s	s	s	s		sx																																12
Connors			xs	x	x					s	x	x	x	xs	x	sx	x	x	xs			s	x	x	x	xs	sx	x	xs					sx	xs				s	xs		x	x	x	x	x	x	s	s			sx	x	xs				31
Mambo				x	x	x	x	xs					s	s		s	s	s	s			x	x	xs																																			10
Bush			x	x	x	xs	x	x			x	x	x	x	x	xs	x	x						xr									x	sx	x	x	x		x	s	x	x	x	x	x	x	xs	x	xs	s	x						40
Graham				xs	x	x	x							sx	s	s	s																																										5
Cook				sx	s		xs							sx	sx	s		x	xs	x	xs	xs	sx	s																																			11
Rance					sx	x	xs	s	sx	x	x	x	x		x	xs	x	x	x	x	x	x	x	xs		sx	x	x	x	x	x	sx	xs		sx	x	x	x	x	x	x	x					x	x	x	x	x	x	x					41
German																		sx																																								1
Brandy																						sx	sx																																				2
Bubb																					s	sx											sx	sx	sx	sx	s																					7
Jordan																					s	s	s		s	s	s	s	s																														0
Wilson																									x	x	xs	xs	x	x	xs						x											sx	x	x	xs	x	x	x				17
Whitely																																	x			sx	x	xs	x	xs	xs	xs	x	xs	x	xs	x	xs	x									15
Wabo																																		s	sx	sx	sx		sx	s	s	sx	sx	s	s	sx	sx										8
RESULT	D	W	D	D	D	D	D	D	L	D	W	W	W	L	D	W	W	L	D	L	W	L	L	W	W	W	D	W	D	L	L	W	D	L	D	L	L	W	W	W	W	D	D	W	D	W	W	W	W	L	W	D	D	L				

EBBSFLEET UNITED MATCH RESULTS 2017-18

Date	Comp	H/A	Opponents	Att:	Result	Goalscorers	Pos	No.
Aug 5	Nat Lg	A	Guiseley	848	D 2 - 2	Weston 63 McQueen 66	9	1
8	Nat Lg	H	Maidstone United	2519	W 2 - 0	Coulson 65 Kedwell 76	3	2
12	Nat Lg	H	AFC Fylde	1270	D 3 - 3	Clark 18 Kedwell 28 Drury 89	7	3
15	Nat Lg	A	Dagenham & Redbridge	1686	D 3 - 3	Powell 59 Coulson 67 Kedwell 80	8	4
18	Nat Lg	A	Maidenhead United	1628	D 1 - 1	Coulson 50	11	5
25	Nat Lg	H	Gateshead	1446	D 0 - 0		12	6
28	Nat Lg	A	Dover Athletic	1625	D 1 - 1	McQueen 76	13	7
Sept 2	Nat Lg	H	Eastleigh	1423	D 2 - 2	Powell 45 Kedwell 68	15	8
9	Nat Lg	A	Chester	1591	L 1 - 1	Powell 58	17	9
12	Nat Lg	H	Aldershot Town	1402	L 0 - 2		19	10
16	Nat Lg	H	Tranmere Rovers	1525	D 0 - 0		18	11
23	Nat Lg	A	Boreham Wood	622	W 1 - 0	Kedwell 78	16	12
30	Nat Lg	H	Halifax Town	1643	W 2 - 0	Shields 47 71	13	13
Oct 3	Nat Lg	A	Solihull Moors	579	W 3 - 1	Weston 27 Kedwell 31 Mills 83	11	14
7	Nat Lg	A	Macclesfield Town	1635	L 0 - 1		14	15
14	FAC 4Q	A	**East Thurrock United**	669	D 0 - 0			16
17	FAC 4Qr	H	**East Thurrock United**	866	W 3 - 0	**Drury 60 McLean 63 Weston 88**		17
21	Nat Lg	H	Barrow	1402	W 3 - 2	McLean 25 Drury 71 Powell 80	10	18
24	Nat Lg	H	Torquay United	1525	L 0 - 1		12	19
27	Nat Lg	A	Sutton United	2197	D 0 - 0		13	20
Nov 4	FAC 1	H	**Doncaster Rovers**	2069	L 2 - 6	**Kedwell 35 (pen) Coulson 37**		21
11	Nat Lg	H	Leyton Orient	2021	W 2 - 1	Drury 6 Kedwell 40	11	22
18	Nat Lg	A	Wrexham	4150	L 0 - 2		12	23
21	Nat Lg	A	Woking	1580	L 0 - 1		15	24
25	Nat Lg	H	Hartlepool	1416	W 3 - 0	Weston 22 Kedwell 67 Coulson 81	12	25
Dec 9	Nat Lg	H	Guiseley	1127	W 4 - 0	Powell 21 Kedwell 43 (p) Bush 77 Weston 79	10	26
16	FAT 1	H	**Eastleigh**	733	W 2 - 1	**Kedwell 78 Weston 90**		27
23	Nat Lg	A	AFC Fylde	1512	D 1 - 1	Kedwell 53	10	28
26	Nat Lg	H	Bromley	1567	W 2 - 1	Powell 15 Kedwell 30	9	29
30	Nat Lg	H	Dagenham & Redbridge	1684	D 1 - 1	Powell 33	10	30
Jan 1	Nat Lg	A	Bromley	1302	L 2 - 4	Drury 39 Shields 54	10	31
6	Nat Lg	H	Chester	1389	L 0 - 1		10	32
9	Nat Lg	A	Maidstone United	2396	W 2 - 1	Powell 46 61	10	33
13	FAT 2	H	**Warrington Town**	911	D 1 - 1	**Shields 90**		34
16	FAT 2r	A	**Warrington Town**	334	L 0 - 2			35
20	Nat Lg	A	Aldershot Town	2457	D 0 - 0		11	36
27	Nat Lg	H	Boreham Wood	1306	L 0 - 3		11	37
Feb 3	Nat Lg	A	Tranmere Rovers	5138	L 0 - 3		12	38
10	Nat Lg	H	Solihull Moors	1117	W 1 - 0	Coulson 72	10	39
17	Nat Lg	A	FC Halifax Town	1762	W 2 - 1	Whitely 55 Coulson 60	10	40
20	Nat Lg	H	Woking	1146	W 2 - 1	Kedwell 42 (pen) 49	10	41
24	Nat Lg	A	Hartlepool United	2893	W 1 - 0	Rance 17	8	42
Mar 10	Nat Lg	A	Leyton Orient	4127	D 1 1	Whitely 15	8	43
24	Nat Lg	H	Maidenhead United	1503	D 1 - 1	Coulson 4	9	44
Apr 2	Nat Lg	H	Dover Athletic	1735	W 2 - 1	Shields 55 Drury 90	9	45
7	Nat Lg	H	Macclesfield Town	1501	D 2 - 2	Kedwell 70 (pen) Rance 78	9	46
10	Nat Lg	H	Wrexham	1376	W 3 - 0	Whiteley 50 Kedwell 84 Coulson 90	9	47
14	Nat Lg	A	Barrow	1189	W 1 - 0	Rance 32	9	48
17	Nat Lg	A	Eastleigh	1614	W 1 - 0	Clark 82	8	49
21	Nat Lg	H	Sutton United	2852	L 0 - 1		8	50
24	Nat Lg	A	Gateshead	411	W 5 - 2	KEDWELL 3 (33p 62 71) Coulson 74 Powell 83	5	51
28	Nat Lg	A	Torquay United	1728	D 1 - 1	Connors 69	6	52
May 2	P-O	A	**Aldershot Town**	3319	D 1 - 1	**Winfield 119 (Won 5-3 on pens)**		53
5	P-O SF	A	**Tranmere Rovers**	6898	L 2 - 4	**Coulson 16 Weston 51**		54

GOALSCORERS	SG	CSG	Pens	Hat tricks	Total		SG	CSG	Pens	Hat tricks	Total
2016-17 McQueen					20	McLean	2				2
Kedwell	17	5	4	1	20	McQueen	2				2
Coulson	10	2			11	Bush					1
Powell	8	2			10	Connors					1
Drury	6				6	Mills					1
Weston	6	2			6	Weston					1
Shields	4				5	Winfield					1
Rance	3				3						
Whitely	3				3						
Clark	2				2						

FC HALIFAX TOWN

Club Contact Details 01422 341 222
The Shay Stadium, Shay Syke, Halifax HX1 2YT
mikesharman@fchalifaxtown.com

Founded: 1911 **Nickname:** Shaymen **Manager:** Jamie Fullarton
Previous Names: Halifax Town 1911-2008 then reformed as F.C. Halifax Town
Previous Leagues: Yorkshire Combination 1911-12, Midland 1912-21, Football League (FM Division Three North)1921-93, 98-2002, Conference 1993-98, 2002-08

Club Colours (change): Blue and white trim

Ground Capacity: 10,401 **Seats:** 5,830 **Covered:** Yes **Clubhouse:** Yes **Shop:** Yes
Previous Grounds: Sandhall Lane 1911-15, Exley 1919-21.
Record Attendance: 36,885 v Tottenham Hotspur - FA Cup 5th Round 14/02/1953
Nearest Railway Station Halifax - 5-10min walk from the ground.

RECORDS
Victory: 12-0 v West Vale Ramblers - FA Cup 1st Qualifying Road 1913-14
Defeat: 0-13 v Stockport County - Division 3 North 1933-34
Goalscorer: Ernie Dixon - 132 (1922-30)
Appearances: John Pickering - 402 (1965-74)
Additional: Recorded a 30 game unbeaten run at The Shay between 18/04/2009 - 20/11/2010 (W 24 D 6 F 79 A 20). Fee paid - £150,000 for Chris Tate, July 1999. Fee Received - £350,000 for Geoff Horsfield, October 1998.

HONOURS
FA Comps: FA Trophy 2015-16.
League: Conference 1997-98, Conference North Play-offs 2012-13, 16-17. Northern Premier League Division One North 2009-10, Premier Division 2010-11.
County FA: West Riding County Cup 2012-13.

	08-09	09-10	10-11	11-12	12-13	13-14	14-15	15-16	16-17	17-18
	NP1N 8	NP1N 1	NP P 1	Conf N 3	Conf N 5	Conf 5	Conf 9	Nat 21	Nat N 3	Nat 16
	FAC 2Q	FAC 4Q	FAC 4Q	FAC 1P	FAC 4Qr	FAC 1P	FAC 1P	FAC 1P	FAC 2Pr	FAC 4Q
	FAT P	FAT 3Q	FAT 2Q	FAT 3Qr	FAT QFr	FAT 1P	FAT QF	FAT F	FAT 3Qr	FAT 2P

2017-18 STATS **Goals Total** 49 **Games Without Scoring** 18 (3) **Total No. of Scorers** 16 **Total Clean Sheets** 16
Most Consecutive Scoring Games 5 **Best Unbeaten Run** 6 **Most Consecutive Clean Sheets** 3
Best Att: 3,113 v Tranmere Rovers, National League
Number in brackets denotes consecutive runs.

2017-18 MATCH LINE-UPS

Player	Total
Johnson	47
Duckworth	18
Wilde	37
Brown	42
Garner	33
Hotte	33
Oliver	33
MacDonald	32
Kosylo	35
Tomlinson	35
Denton	33
Clarke	19
Charles (L)	12
Nicholson	3
Riley	3
McManus	39
Cheidu Dixon	4
Morgan	21
Moyo	24
Lynch	14
King	3
Hibbs	27
Waring (L)	10
Batty (L)	5
Middleton (L)	5
Clackstone (L)	5
Atkinson	0
Collins	23
Barrows	0
Khan	2
Tuton (L)	7
Fondop-Talom (L)	12
Hanley (L)	7
Maher	9
Thomson	11
Hanson (L)	2
Graham (L)	7

RESULT: L D D L W W D W W W L W L D D L D L L D L L D L W W L D L D W L L L L D L W D W W D D L W W D L L L D

FC HALIFAX MATCH RESULTS 2017-18

Date	Comp	H/A	Opponents	Att:	Result	Goalscorers	Pos	No.
Aug 5	Nat Lg	H	Aldershot Town	2108	L 0 - 2		23	1
8	Nat Lg	A	Barrow	1410	D 0 - 0		23	2
12	Nat Lg	A	Chester	2082	D 0 - 0		19	3
15	Nat Lg	H	Dover Athletic	1486	L 1 - 2	Denton 90	20	4
19	Nat Lg	A	Solihull Moors	684	W 1 - 0	Morgan 28	16	5
25	Nat Lg	H	Guiseley	1777	W 2 - 0	Kosylo 25 Brown 78	13	6
28	Nat Lg	A	Gateshead	1609	D 0 - 0		16	7
Sept 2	Nat Lg	H	AFC Fylde	1775	W 2 - 1	Denton 58 77	8	8
9	Nat Lg	H	Maidenhead United	1727	W 3 - 2	Morgan 29 Kosylo 55 67	6	9
12	Nat Lg	A	Leyton Orient	3600	W 3 - 0	Morgan 5 Denton 29 Kosylo 74	2	10
16	Nat Lg	A	Dagenham & Redbridge	1282	L 1 - 3	Brown 70	8	11
23	Nat Lg	H	Bromley	1760	W 2 - 1	Kosylo 55 Denton 70	4	12
30	Nat Lg	A	Ebbsfleet United	1643	L 0 - 2		8	13
Oct 3	Nat Lg	H	Wrexham	2136	D 0 - 0		10	14
7	Nat Lg	A	Boreham Wood	562	D 1 - 1	Morgan 81	10	15
14	**FAC 4Q**	**H**	**Tranmere Rovers**	**1630**	**L 1 - 3**	**McNulty 20 (og)**		**16**
21	Nat Lg	H	Torquay United	1764	D 1 - 1	Waring 68	11	17
24	Nat Lg	H	Maidstone United	1410	L 0 - 2		13	18
27	Nat Lg	A	Tranmere Rovers	4826	L 2 - 4	Brown 51 Batty 65	15	19
Nov 11	Nat Lg	H	Woking	1710	D 0 - 0		16	20
18	Nat Lg	A	Sutton United	1968	L 2 - 3	Denton 64 Garner 85	17	21
21	Nat Lg	A	Hartlepool United	2755	L 0 - 4		17	22
25	Nat Lg	H	Eastleigh	1407	D 3 - 3	McManus 39 (pen) Denton 74 Batty 90		23
Dec 2	Nat Lg	H	Barrow	1618	L 0 - 1		17	24
9	Nat Lg	A	Aldershot Town	1912	W 1 - 0	McManus 39	16	25
23	Nat Lg	H	Chester	2040	W 4 - 0	Denton 6 McManus 28 Clarke 33 MacDonald 38	14	26
26	Nat Lg	A	Macclesfield Town	2313	L 1 - 2	Denton 11		27
30	Nat Lg	A	Dover Athletic	1127	D 0 - 0		14	28
Jan 1	Nat Lg	H	Macclesfield Town	1962	L 1 - 4	Waring 70	16	29
6	Nat Lg	A	Maidenhead United	1229	D 0 - 0		16	30
9	**FAT 1**	**H**	**Macclesfield Town**	**503**	**W 1 - 0**	**Kosylo 37**		**31**
13	**FAT 2**	**H**	**Maidenhead United**	**602**	**L 1 - 4**	**Kosylo 1**		**32**
27	Nat Lg	A	Bromley	1524	L 0 - 3		18	33
30	Nat Lg	H	Leyton Orient	1352	L 1 - 2	Denton 33	18	34
Feb 10	Nat Lg	A	Wrexham	4998	D 1 - 1	McManus 45	18	35
17	Nat Lg	H	Ebbsfleet United	1762	L 1 - 2	Kosylo 37 (pen)	20	36
20	Nat Lg	H	Hartlepool United	1584	W 2 - 0	Hotte 74 Tomlinson 78	18	37
24	Nat Lg	A	Eastleigh	1852	D 0 - 0		17	38
Mar 10	Nat Lg	A	Woking	1619	W 3 - 1	Kosylo 33 (pen) 66 Thomson 80	17	39
13	Nat Lg	H	Dagenham & Redbridge	1315	W 2 - 1	Hanley 67 Fondop-Talom 69	15	40
17	Nat Lg	A	Guiseley	1106	D 1 - 1	Tomlinson 68	15	41
24	Nat Lg	H	Solihull Moors	1849	D 0 - 0		15	42
30	Nat Lg	A	AFC Fylde United	2230	L 0 - 2		17	43
Apr 7	Nat Lg	H	Boreham Wood	1480	W 2 - 1	Brown 20 Fondop-Talom 64	15	44
10	Nat Lg	A	Sutton United	1274	W 2 - 1	Fondop-Talum 18 Tomlinson 89	14	45
12	Nat Lg	A	Gateshead	1302	D 2 - 2	Hanley 81 Fondop-Talom 90		46
14	Nat Lg	A	Torquay United	1567	L 0 - 1		15	47
21	Nat Lg	H	Tranmere Rovers	3113	L 0 - 2		15	48
28	Nat Lg	A	Maidstone United	2632	D 0 - 0		16	49

GOALSCORERS	SG	CSG	Pens	Hat tricks	Total		SG	CSG	Pens	Hat tricks	Total
2016-17 Denton					*19*	Waring	2				2
Denton	9	2			10	Clarke					1
Kosylo	8	2	1		10	Garner					1
Brown	4				4	Hotte					1
Fondop-Talom	4				4	MacDonald					1
McManus	4		1		4	Opponent					1
Morgan	4	2			4	Thomson					1
Tomlinson	3				3						
Batty	2				2						
Hanley	2				2						

GATESHEAD

Club Contact Details 01914 783 883
The International Stadium, Neilson Road, Gateshead NE10 0EF
info@gateshead-fc.com

Founded: 1930   **Nickname:** Tynesiders, The Heed   **Manager:** Steve Watson
Previous Names: Gateshead AFC (formerly South Shields)1930-73. Gateshead Town 1973-74. Gateshead Utd (formerly South Shields) 1974-77.
Previous Leagues: Football League 1930-60, Northern Counties East 1960-62, North Regional 1962-68, Northern Premier 1968-70, 73-83, 85-86, 87-90, Wearside 1970-71, Midland 1971-72, Northern Combination 1973-74. Alliance/Conf 1983-85, 86-87, 90-98.

Club Colours (change): White & black

Ground Capacity: 11,795 **Seats:** 11,795 **Covered:** 7,271 **Clubhouse:** Yes **Shop:** Yes
Previous Grounds: Redheugh Park 1930-71
Record Attendance: 11,750 v Newcastle United - Friendly 07/08/95
Nearest Railway Station Gateshead Stadium Metro stop 5min walk away.

RECORDS
Victory: 8-0 v Netherfield - Northern Premier League
Defeat: 0-9 v Sutton United - Conference 22/09/90
Goalscorer: Paul Thompson - 130
Appearances: James Curtis - 506 (2003-present)
Additional: Record transfer fee paid; £9,000 - Paul Cavell, Dagenham & Redbridge 1994
Record transfer fee received; £150,000 Lee Novak, Huddersfield Town 2009

HONOURS
FA Comps: N/A
League: Northern Regional 1963-64. Northern Premier League 1982-83, 85-86, NPL Premier Division play-offs 2007-08,
Conference North play-offs 2008-09.
County FA: Durham Senior Professional Cup 1930-31, 48-49, 501-51, 54-55, 58-59.
Durham Challenge Cup 2010-11 (Reserve Team)

08-09		09-10		10-11		11-12		12-13		13-14		14-15		15-16		16-17		17-18	
Conf N	2	Conf	20	Conf	15	Conf	8	Conf	17	Conf	3	Conf	10	Nat	9	Nat	8	Nat	17
FAC	3Q	FAC	1Pr	FAC	1P	FAC	2P	FAC	4Q	FAC	1Pr	FAC	3P	FAC	4Q	FAC	4Qr	FAC	2P
FAT	3Q	FAT	3Pr	FAT	SF	FAT	QF	FAT	2P	FAT	3Pr	FAT	3Pr	FAT	QFr	FAT	2P	FAT	SF

2017-18 STATS   **Goals Total** 87   **Games Without Scoring** 12 (2)   **Total No. of Scorers** 14   **Total Clean Sheets** 17
Most Consecutive Scoring Games 12   **Best Unbeaten Run** 8   **Most Consecutive Clean Sheets** 5
Best Att: 3,538 v Hartlepool United, National League   Number in brackets denotes consecutive runs.

2017-18 MATCH LINE-UPS

Match Number	Total
Montgomery	34
Vassell	40
Barrow	46
Kerr F	38
Byrne	51
Fyfield	41
Penn	52
McLaughlin	57
Preston	54
Johnson	44
Burrow	56
Tinkler (L)	17
Peniket	50
Hanford	26
Green	8
Mellish	10
Williams (L)	23
Horsfall (L)	0
York	42
O'Donnell	12
Hannant	23
Macleod	0
Happe (L)	1
Langstaff	4
Maxwell	12
Fox (L)	12
Bell	2
McNall (L)	11
Greenwood	11

RESULT: L W W W L W D D L D W L W L W D W W W W L D D L W D D L D W W D W D D L W L W D D W W W D L D L D D L D W L L L L

GATESHEAD MATCH RESULTS 2017-18

Date	Comp	H/A	Opponents	Att:	Result	Goalscorers	Pos	No.
Aug 5	Nat Lg	A	Woking	1705	L 1 - 2	Johnson 26	20	1
8	Nat Lg	H	Guiseley	629	W 1 - 0	Byrne 53	11	2
12	Nat Lg	H	Torquay United	756	W 3 - 0	Higgins 19 (og) Peniket 78 Anderson 82 (og)	3	3
15	Nat Lg	A	Wrexham	4097	L 0 - 1		9	4
19	Nat Lg	H	Macclesfield Town	633	W 3 - 0	Kerr 5 Burrow 45 Preston 72	6	5
25	Nat Lg	A	Ebbsfleet United	1446	D 0 - 0		6	6
28	Nat Lg	H	FC Halifax Town	1609	D 0 - 0		6	7
Sept 2	Nat Lg	A	Dagenham & Redbridge	1358	L 1 - 3	Lokko 24 (og)	11	8
9	Nat Lg	A	Sutton United	1805	D 1 - 1	Johnson 15	13	9
12	Nat Lg	H	Chester	657	W 3 - 2	Halls 41 (og) Peniket 46 Mitchell 90 (og)	11	10
16	Nat Lg	H	Aldershot Town	654	L 0 - 1		14	11
23	Nat Lg	A	Maidstone United	2530	D 2 - 2	Peniket 69 Johnson 80	14	12
30	Nat Lg	H	Boreham Wood	606	D 1 - 1	York 30	14	13
Oct 2	Nat Lg	A	AFC Fylde	1494	D 0 - 0		18	14
7	Nat Lg	H	Bromley	853	L 1 - 2	Johnson 68	16	15
14	FAC 4Q	A	Buxton	653	W 2 - 1	McLaughlin 26 Burrow 44 (pen)		16
21	Nat Lg	A	Eastleigh	1597	D 2 - 2	Preston 74 Vassell 87	17	17
24	Nat Lg	H	Leyton Orient	3468	W 2 - 0	Burrow 9 80	15	18
27	Nat Lg	H	Dover Athletic	816	D 0 - 0		17	19
Nov 4	FAC 1	H	Chelmsford City	732	W 2 - 0	Burrow 30 Johnson 34		20
11	Nat Lg	A	Maidenhead United	1377	W 3 - 0	Hannant 5 50 Johnson 8	14	21
18	Nat Lg	H	Tranmere Rovers	1140	W 1 - 0	Sutton 90 (og)	11	22
21	Nat Lg	H	Barrow	663	L 1 - 2	York 43	13	23
25	Nat Lg	A	Solihull Moors	534	D 1 - 1	Burrow 12	15	24
Dec 3	FAC 2	H	Luton Town	1339	L 0 - 4			25
12	Nat Lg	A	Torquay United	1405	D 1 - 1	Preston 27	15	26
20	FAT 1	H	Guiseley	290	W 2 - 1	Peniket 29 Vassell 121 (aet)		27
26	Nat Lg	H	Hartlepool United	3538	D 2 - 2	Barrow 49 59	16	28
Jan 1	Nat Lg	A	Hartlepool United	3241	D 2 - 2	Peniket 41 York 79	17	29
6	Nat Lg	A	Sutton United	493	L 0 - 2		18	30
13	FAT 2	H	Boreham Wood	284	D 3 - 3	BURROW 3 (77 84 90)		31
16	FAT 2r	A	Boreham Wood	183	W 2 - 1	McLaughlin 68 Hannant 76		32
20	Nat Lg	A	Chester	1580	W 3 - 1	McLaughlin 45 Burrow 45 Preston 52	15	33
23	Nat Lg	H	Woking	470	D 1 - 1	Fox 80	15	34
27	Nat Lg	H	Maidstone United	771	W 2 - 1	McNall 3 Fox 87	14	35
30	Nat Lg	H	Wrexham	658	D 0 - 0		14	36
Feb 3	FAT 3	A	Maidstone United	1186	D 2 - 2	McNall 77 Peniket 82		37
6	FAT 3r	H	Maidstone United	771	W 3 - 0	Byrne 15 Mclaughlin Peniket		38
10	Nat Lg	H	AFC Fylde	752	L 1 - 2	Peniket 90	16	39
13	Nat Lg	A	Guiseley	541	W 1 - 0	York 6	13	40
17	Nat Lg	A	Boreham Wood	464	L 1 - 2	York 55	14	41
20	Nat Lg	A	Barrow	860	D 1 - 1	Preston 80	13	42
24	FAT 4	A	Leyton Orient	3771	D 3 - 3	Johnson 68 78 Peniket 90		43
Mar 6	FAT4r	H	Leyton Orient	685	W 3 - 2	Johnson 2 16 (pen) Peniket 80		44
10	Nat Lg	H	Maidenhead United	581	W 7 - 1	Peniket 22 Fyfield 27 JOHNSON 3 (59 766 79) McLaughlin 81 Burrow 90	12	45
13	Nat Lg	H	Solihull Moors	486	D 2 - 2	McLaughlin 26 Daly 94 (og)	12	46
17	FAT S-F 1	A	Bromley	1254	L 2 - 3	Peniket 1 Johnson 41		47
24	FAT S-F 2	H	Bromley	2264	D 1 - 1	Burrow 69		48
27	Nat Lg		Macclesfield Town	1537	L 0 - 1		12	49
30	Nat Lg	H	Dagenham & Redbridge	764	D 0 - 0		12	50
Apr 7	Nat Lg	A	Bromley	1035	D 0 - 0		14	51
10	Nat Lg	A	Tranmere Rovers	4328	L 2 - 4	York 39 Barrow 43	14	52
12	Nat Lg	A	F.C.Halifax Town	1302	D 2 - 2	Burrow 37 90	14	53
14	Nat Lg	H	Eastleigh	612	W 2 - 0	Johnson 45 Burrow 52	13	54
17	Nat Lg	H	Aldershot Town	1893	L 0 - 1		13	55
21	Nat Lg	A	Dover Athletic	1424	L 2 - 3	Vassell 20 Johnson 84	14	56
24	Nat Lg	H	Ebbsfleet United	422	L 2 - 5	Johnson 45 66	15	57
28	Nat Lg	A	Leyton Orient	1056	L 1 - 3	Johnson 90 (pen)	17	58

GOALSCORERS	SG	CSG	Pens	Hat tricks	Total		SG	CSG	Pens	Hat tricks	Total
2016-17 Johnson					18	Vassell	3				3
Johnson	14	3	2	1	19	Byrne	2				2
Burrow	12	2	1	1	15	Fox	2				2
Peniket	12	3			12	McNall	2				2
Opponents					7	Fyfield	1				1
McLaughlin	6	2			6	Kerr	1				1
York	6				6						
Preston	5				5						
Barrow	2				3						
Hannant	3				3						

HARROGATE TOWN

Club Contact Details 01423 880 675
The CNG Stadium, Wetherby Road, Harrogate HG2 7SA
enquiries@harrogatetownafc.com

Founded: 1914   **Nickname:** Town and Sulphurites   **Manager:** Simon Weaver
Previous Names: Harrogate AFC 1914-32. Harrogate Hotspurs 1935-48.
Previous Leagues: West Riding 1919-20, Yorkshire (FM) 1920-21, 22-31, 57-82, Midland 1921-22, Northern 1931-32,
     Harrogate & Dist. 1935-37, 40-46, W.Riding Co.Am. 1937-40, W.Yorks. 1946-57, N.C.E. (FM) 1982-87, N.P.L. (FM) 1987-2004

Club Colours (change): Yellow & black

Ground Capacity: 3,800   **Seats:** 500   **Covered:** 1,300   **Clubhouse:** Yes   **Shop:** Yes
Previous Grounds: Starbeck Lane 1919-20.
Record Attendance: 4,280 v Railway Athletic - Whitworth Cup Final 1950
Nearest Railway Station Harrogate - 25min walk from the ground.   **Bus Route** 770 / 771 TransDev from Town Centre.

RECORDS
Victory: 13-0 v Micklefield
Defeat: 1-10 v Methley United - 1956
Goalscorer: Jimmy Hague - 135 (1956-58 and 1961-76)
Appearances: Paul Williamson - 428 (1980-81, 1982-85, and 1986-93)

HONOURS
FA Comps: None
League: Yorkshire 1926-27. Northern Premier League Division One 2001-02.

County FA: West Riding Challenge Cup 1924-25, 31-32, 62-63, 72-73, 85-86, 2001-02, 02-03, 07-08.

08-09		09-10		10-11		11-12		12-13		13-14		14-15		15-16		16-17		17-18	
Conf N	9	Conf N	21	Conf N	12	Conf N	15	Conf N	6	Conf N	9	Conf N	15	Nat N	4	Nat N	11	Nat N	2
FAC	3Qr	FAC	2Q	FAC	3Q	FAC	2Qr	FAC	2Pr	FAC	2Q	FAC	2Q	FAC	4Q	FAC	4Q	FAC	4Q
FAT	1P	FAT	1Pr	FAT	1P	FAT	1P	FAT	1P	FAT	3Qr	FAT	1P	FAT	3Q	FAT	1Pr	FAT	3Pr

2017-18 STATS   **Goals Total** 126   **Games Without Scoring** 3   **Total No. of Scorers** 19   **Total Clean Sheets** 20
Most Consecutive Scoring Games 31   **Best Unbeaten Run** 8   **Most Consecutive Clean Sheets** 4
Best Att: 3,000 v Brackley Town, Play-off Final   Number in brackets denotes consecutive runs.

The Boston United player shields the ball from the Nuneaton attacker during their 1-1 National North draw, which was played at Alfreton Town FC. Photo: Bill Wheatcroft.

HARROGATE TOWN MATCH RESULTS 2017-18

Date	Comp	H/A	Opponents	Att:	Result	Goalscorers	Pos	No.
Aug 5	Nat North	H	Nuneaton Town	663	W 4 - 0	Thomson 17 Thewlis 60 66 Ainge 82 (pen)	2	1
8	Nat North	A	North Ferriby Town	274	W 2 - 0	Ainge 59 (pen) Leesley 64	1	2
12	Nat North	A	Stockport County	3107	D 2 - 2	Ainge 24 30	4	3
15	Nat North	H	Chorley	676	W 4 - 1	Ainge 3 43 Thewlis 64 90	2	4
19	Nat North	A	Gainsborough Trinity	517	W 5 - 4	Jones 33 (og) Knowles 49 Leesley 54 60 Kennedy 83	2	5
26	Nat North	H	Tamworth	669	W 3 - 0	AINGE 3 (2 63 73)	1	6
28	Nat North	A	Blyth Spartans	829	W 2 - 0	Kennedy 41 Falkingham 90	1	7
Sept 2	Nat North	H	Brackley Town	1081	D 1 - 1	Leesley 9	1	8
5	Nat North	H	Salford City	1137	L 1 - 2	Leesley 47 (pen)	2	9
9	Nat North	A	AFC Telford United	1018	W 5 - 1	Wright 26 75 Parker 55 Thomson 72 Emmett 85	1	10
12	Nat North	A	Southport	868	W 4 - 1	THEWLIS 3 (118 73) Leesley 81	1	11
16	FAC 2Q	H	Penistone Church	653	W 3 - 0	Kennedy 57 Emmett 70 Parker 75		12
23	FAC 3Q	A	York City	2800	W 2 - 0	Leesley 15 (pen) Agnew 51		13
30	FAC 3Q	H	Bradford PA	911	D 0 - 0			14
Oct 3	FAC 3Qr	A	Bradford PA	393	W 2 - 0	Leesley 71 Boshell (og) 88		15
7	Nat North	A	Curzon Ashton	508	W 2 - 1	Leesley 10 Curry 87	1	16
14	FAC 4Q	H	Gainsborough Trinity	928	L 1 - 2	Falkingham 31		17
21	Nat North	H	Leamington	1021	D 2 - 2	Thomson 34 English 57 (og)	1	18
24	Nat North	H	Bradford PA	745	D 1 - 1	Emmett 29	1	19
28	Nat North	A	Alfreton Town	569	W 2 - 1	Leesley 3 Emmett 7	1	20
Nov 11	Nat North	A	Spennymoor Town	1085	L 1 - 3	Nelson 34	2	21
18	Nat North	H	Boston United	1388	W 3 - 1	Leesley 32 Thomson 38 Thewlis 58	2	22
25	FAT 3Q	A	Darlington	1,127	W 3 - 2	Leesley 15 (pen) 89 Barr 59		23
Dec 2	Nat North	A	FC United of Manchester	2.394	L 2 - 3	Vann 25 Ainge 90	3	24
5	Nat North	A	Kidderminster Harriers	854	D 2 - 2	Kennedy 45 Ainge 90	2	25
16	FAT 1	A	Wrexham	1370	W 2 - 0	Beck 41 69		26
23	Nat North	H	North Ferriby United	1209	W 3 - 0	Kennedy 32 53 Leesley 67	2	27
26	Nat North	A	Darlington	1759	L 1 - 3	Ainge 65	2	28
Jan 1	Nat North	A	Darlington	1648	W 3 - 0	Emmett 48 Thewlis 54 Leesley 90	2	29
6	Nat North	A	Chorley	1257	W 1 - 0	Thewlis 80	2	30
9	Nat North	A	Nuneaton Town	364	L 1 - 2	Kennedy 45	2	31
13	FAT 2	A	St Albans City	634	D 1 - 1	Leesley 80		32
16	FAT 2r	H	St Albans City	362	W 5 - 0	Burrell 12 72 Knowles 64 Leesley 74 Thomson 90		33
20	Nat North	A	Salford City	1931	L 1 - 2	Knowles 63	2	34
23	Nat North	H	Stockport County	882	W 4 - 1	Emmett 24 Thomson 39 Knowles 58 Kennedy 67	2	35
27	Nat North	A	AFC Telford United	1034	W 2 - 1	Leesley 33 Ainge 51	2	36
Feb 3	FAT 3	H	Billericay Town	846	D 2 - 2	Leesley 11 64		37
6	FAT 3r	A	Billericay Town	820	L 2 - 3	Ainge 38 (Pen) Beck 88		38
10	Nat North	A	Leamington	412	W 3 - 1	Beck 30 Kitching 55 Knowles 75	2	39
17	Nat North	A	Kidderminster Harriers	1739	W 2 - 0	Leesley 15 Knowles 46	2	40
20	Nat North	H	Alfreton Town	688	W 4 - 3	Knowles 18 Kitching 30 Beck 33 34	1	41
Mar 10	Nat North	H	FC United of Manchester	1547	W 6 - 0	Emmett 7 Kitching 20 THOMSON 3 (37 76 90) Wright 78	1	42
17	Nat North	A	Tamworth	662	D 1 - 1	Thomson 26	2	43
24	Nat North	A	Gainsborough Trinity	1179	W 2 - 0	Emmett 18 Beck 66	2	44
27	Nat North	H	Spennymoor Town	1001	L 1 - 2	Beck 83	2	45
30	Nat North	A	Brackley Town	750	D 0 - 0		2	46
Apr 2	Nat North	H	Blyth Spartans	1944	W 5 - 1	McCombe 19 Wright 36 69 Knowles 44 Thomson 53	2	47
7	Nat North	H	York City	3564	W 2 - 0	Wright 51 Beck 67	2	48
14	Nat North	H	Southport	1386	W 2 - 0	Beck 4 Thomson 58	2	49
17	Nat North	A	Boston United	875	L 0 - 3		2	50
21	Nat North	A	Bradford PA	581	L 1 - 3	Wright 84	2	51
28	Nat North	H	Curzon Ashton	1170	W 5 - 0	KNOWLES 5 (24 46 50 89 90)	2	52
May 4	P-O S-F	H	Chorley	2307	W 2 - 0	Knowles 51 (pen) 90		53
13	P-O Final	H	Brackley Town	3000	W 3 - 0	Knowles 26 40 Leesley 71		54

GOALSCORERS	SG	CSG	Pens	Hat tricks	Total		SG	CSG	Pens	Hat tricks	Total
2016-17 Ainge					*23*	Opponents	3				3
Leesley	19	2	3		22	Burrell	1				2
Knowles	11	3	1.	1	17	Falkingham	2				2
Ainge	9	4	3	1	14	Parker	2				2
Thomson	9	3		1	12	Agnew					1
Beck	10	2			10	Barr					1
Thewlis	7	2		1	10	Curry					1
Emmett	8	2			8	McCombe					1
Kennedy	7				8	Nelson					1
Wright	5				7	Vann					1
Kitching	2				3						

HARTLEPOOL UNITED

Club Contact Details 01429 272 584
Victoria Park, Clarence Road, Hartlepool TS24 8BZ
enquiries@hartlepoolunited.co.uk

Founded: 1908 **Nickname:** Monkey Hangers **Manager:** Matthew Bates - 04/05/2018
Previous Names: Hartlepools United 1908-68. Hartlepool 1968-77.
Previous Leagues: North Eastern 1908-21. Football League 1921-2017.

Club Colours (change): White & blue

Ground Capacity: 7,865 **Seats:** 4,359 **Covered:** Yes **Clubhouse:** Yes **Shop:** Yes
Previous Grounds: None
Record Attendance: 17,264 v Manchester United, FA Cup Third Round Proper, 1957
Nearest Railway Station Hartlepool is about half a mile away.

RECORDS
Goalscorer: Joshie Fletcher - 111
Appearances: Ritchie Humphreys - 543 (Includes a run of 234 consecutive appearances)

HONOURS
FA Comps: None

League: None

County FA: None

08-09		09-10		10-11		11-12		12-13		13-14		14-15		15-16		16-17		17-18	
FL 1	19	FL 1	20	FL 1	16	FL 1	13	FL 1	23	FL 2	19	FL 2	22	FL 2	16	FL 2	23	Nat	15
FAC	4P	FAC	1P	FAC	3P	FAC	1P	FAC	1P	FAC	2Pr	FAC	2P	FAC	3P	FAC	2P	FAC	1P
FLC	3P	FLC	2P	FLC	2P	FLC	1P	FLC	1P	FLC	1P	FLC	1P	FLC	2P	FLC	1P	FAT	1P

2017-18 STATS

Goals Total	55	Games Without Scoring	16 (3)	Total No. of Scorers	20	Total Clean Sheets	9
Most Consecutive Scoring Games	9	Best Unbeaten Run	7			Most Consecutive Clean Sheets	2

Best Att: 6,833 v Wrexham, National League

Number in brackets denotes consecutive runs.

2017-18 MATCH LINE-UPS

Match Number	1	2	3	4	5	6	7	8	9	10	11	12	13	14	15	16	17	18	19	20	21	22	23	24	25	26	27	28	29	30	31	32	33	34	35	36	37	38	39	40	41	42	43	44	45	46	47	48	49	Total
Loach	x	x	x	x	x	x	x	x	x	x	x	x	x	x	x	x	x	x	x		x	x	x	x	x	x		x	x	x	x	x	x	x	x	x	x	x	x	x	x	x	x	x	x	x	x	x	x	49
Magnay	x	x	x	x	x			x	x	x	x					x	xs			x	x							x	x			x	x	x	xr		x	x	x	x	x	x	x	x	x		x			35
Laing	x	x	x	x	xs						sx	sx	x	x	x	x	x	x				x	x	x	x	x	x	s	sx	x	x	x		s	sx		x	x												42
Harrison	x	x	x	x	x	x	xs	xs			s	x	x	x	s		sx	s	x	x	x	x	x		x	sx			s	s	x	x	x	x	x	xr		xs					sx	sx	sx	x	x	sx		29
Donnelly	x	x	xs	sx	x	x			sx	s	x	x	x			x	x	x	x	x	x	x	x	x	x					x	x	x			x	x	x											x		29
Newton	x	x	x	x	x	xs	s	s	s	s	s		s				s	s	s	x	x	x	x	x	s	x			s	s	x	x	x	xs	xs	xs	x	x	x	xs	x	x	xs	x						28
Woods	xs	s	sx	s	s	s	s	x	x	x	x	x		x	x	x	xs	xs	xs	xs	s	sx	x	x	xs	x		x	x	x	x	x	x	x	x	x	xs	x	x	x	x	x	xs	xs						42
Hawkins	xs	x	xs	s	sx	x	x	x	x	xs	x	x	xs	sx	x	x	s	s		s	s	sx	s	x		x	x	xs	x	s	sx	s	sx	x	xs	x	xs	x	x	x	x	x	x	x						37
Munns	xs	xs	s	sx	s	x	s	s	s	s	s	sx	sx	xs	xs	s	s	sx	sx	x	s	sx	sx	xs	x	s	s		sx	s		s	s					sx	s	sx	s	s	s	s	sx					19
Amond	x	x	x	x																																														4
Donaldson	x	x	xs	x	x	x	xs	xs	sx	sx		x	xs	xs	xs																							sx	sx	xs	xs	x	xs							19
Cassidy	sx	x	x	x	x	x	x														sx	x	xs	x	x	x		sx	x	xs	x	x	x																	36
Oates	sx							sx	sx	xs	xs	xs	sx	xs	sx	sx	x		xs	x					sx	xs	x	x	xs	sx	x	x	xs			xs	x	x	xs	x	xs	xs	sx	sx	xs	xs	sx			39
Deverdics	sx	s	sx	xs	xs	s	x	x	xs	x	x	x	x	x	x	x	x	x	xs	x	sx	x	sx	x	xr	xs	x	x	x	x	x	x																		32
Catterick	s																									s		s	s	s		s	s	s	s	s	s	s	s	s	s	s	s	s	s	s	s	s	0
Richardson	s				sx	sx	s					s				s	s			sx	x	x	x			s		xs																							7
Adams	sx	x	xs	x	x						s		s	sx	sx	x	sx	sx	x	x	xs			s	sx	x	xs	xr		xs	x	x	x	x	x	x	sx	x	x	x	x	x	x	x	x	x	x			36
Rodney	s	sx	xs	sx	xs	xs	xs	xs	sx	sx	xs	xs	xs	xs	xs		sx	x	xs	xs	xs	s	sx	xs	xs	sx	x	xs	xs	sx	x	xs	sx	sx	sx	sx	sx	sx	sx	sx	sx	sxr			xs					44
Featherstone	s	s	xs	x	x	x	x	x	x	x	x	x	x	x	x	x	x	x	xs		x	x	x	xs			xs	x	x	x	x	x	x	x	x	x	x	x	xs											38
Franks				sx	x	x	x	x	x	x	x	x	x	x	x	xs	x	x	x	x					sx	x	x	x																						23
Watson				x	x	x	x	xs																	sx	x	x																							9
Simpson						s	xs	xs			s		s	sx	s	s									sx	s	sx																							7
Ledger				x	x	x	x										x	x	sx	xs				s	sx	s	s	xs			x	x																		12
Thorne								xs	s	xs	s																		s																					2
George									s	sx	s	x	sx	xs	x	xs	s	s																	xs	s	xs	xs												8
Adeloye																			sx			sx	sx	sx	sx	sx	s	s			s	sx	sx	xs																10
Hawkes																													s	s	s	sx	s	s	s	sx	s	sx	xs	x	xs	x	xs	xs	x	sx			11
Pritchard																															s	s																		0
Owen																													s		s				s				s										s	1
Orrell																																							s	s				s	s					0
Cunningham																																																sxr			1
RESULT	L	D	L	D	L	L	W	W	W	D	W	L	D	W	W	W	D	D	W	L	D	L	W	L	L	L	L	D	D	L	L	D	L	W	L	L	L	D	D	W	W	W	L	L	D	W	D	W		

HARTLEPOOL UNITED MATCH RESULTS 2017-18

Date	Comp	H/A	Opponents	Att:	Result	Goalscorers	Pos	No.
Aug 5	Nat Lg	H	Dover Athletic	3954	L 0 - 1		21	1
8	Nat Lg	A	Macclesfield Town	1519	D 1 - 1	Cassidy 58	21	2
12	Nat Lg	A	Maidenhead United	1491	L 1 - 2	Amond 87 (pen)	20	3
15	Nat Lg	H	Chester	3071	D 1 - 1	Cassidy 71	19	4
19	Nat Lg	A	Bromley	1709	L 0 - 2		20	5
25	Nat Lg	H	AFC Fylde	2,954	L 0 - 2		23	6
28	Nat Lg	A	Guiseley	1723	W 1 - 0	Franks 49	23	7
Sept 2	Nat Lg	H	Maidstone United	4137	W 3 - 1	Watson 19 Franks 57 Simpson 68	20	8
9	Nat Lg	H	Dagenham & Redbridge	3366	W 1 - 0	Franks 75	19	9
12	Nat Lg	A	Wrexham	4144	D 0 - 0		17	10
16	Nat Lg	A	Leyton Orient	3867	W 2 - 1	Franks 45 Oates 47	15	11
23	Nat Lg	H	Eastleigh	3374	L 1 - 2	Munns 990	17	12
30	Nat Lg	A	Woking	2479	D 1 - 1	Donaldson 26	17	13
Oct 3	Nat Lg	H	Barrow	3082	W 1 - 0	Woods 90	14	14
7	Nat Lg	A	Solihull Moors	2658	W 2 - 1	Oates 47 Franks 90	13	15
14	FAC 4Q	A	South Shields	2887	W 2 - 1	Rodney 52 Deverdics 58		16
21	Nat Lg	H	Sutton United	4526	D 1 - 1	Oates 39	14	17
24	Nat Lg	H	Tranmere Rovers	3371	D 1 - 1	Deverdics 52	14	18
27	Nat Lg	A	Torquay United	1987	W 2 - 0	Oates 54 Francis 68	12	19
Nov 4	FAC 1	A	Morecambe	2004	L 0 - 3			20
11	Nat Lg	A	Boreham Wood	773	D 0 - 0		11	21
18	Nat Lg	H	Aldershot Town	3732	L 0 - 2		11	22
21	Nat Lg	H	FC Halifax Town	2755	W 4 - 0	Deverdics 4 Donnelly 7 Oates 31 Newton 89	11	23
25	Nat Lg	A	Ebbsfleet United	1416	L 0 - 3		13	24
Dec 2	Nat Lg	H	Macclesfield Town	3082	L 1 - 2	Woods 39		25
8	Nat Lg	A	Dover Athletic	1083	L 0 - 4		14	26
16	FAT 1	A	Workington	771	L 0 - 1			27
23	Nat Lg	H	Maidenhead United	2756	L 1 - 2	Cassidy 28	15	28
26	Nat Lg	A	Gateshead	3538	D 2 - 2	Donnelly 17 (pen) Woods 72	15	29
Jan 1	Nat Lg	H	Gateshead	3241	D 2 - 2	Watson 7 64	15	30
6	Nat Lg	A	Dagenham & Redbridge	1290	L 2 - 4	Woods 59 64	17	31
20	Nat Lg	H	Wrexham	6833	L 0 2		18	32
23	Nat Lg	A	Chester	1421	D 1 - 1	Woods 62	18	33
27	Nat Lg	A	Eastleigh	2153	L 3 - 4	Woods 9 29 Newton 88	19	34
Feb 10	Nat Lg	H	Woking	3018	W 3 - 2	Rooney 19 Cassidy 34 Oates 44	18	35
20	Nat Lg	A	FC Halifax Town	1584	L 0 - 2		19	36
24	Nat Lg	H	Ebbsfleet United	2895	L 0 - 1		19	37
Mar 6	Nat Lg	A	Aldershot Town	1665	L 1 - 2	Adams 45	19	38
10	Nat Lg	H	Boreham Wood	2538	D 0 - 0		19	39
17	Nat Lg	A	AFC Fylde	1753	D 3 - 3	Tunnicliffe 39 (og) Cassidy 85 Rodney 90	20	40
21	Nat Lg	A	Barrow	1018	W 2 - 1	Newton 45 Magnay 50	19	41
24	Nat Lg	H	Bromley	3041	W 2 - 1	Hawkes 10 Newton 45	18	42
30	Nat Lg	A	Maidstone United	2559	W 2 - 1	Woods 25 89 (pen)	16	43
Apr 2	Nat Lg	H	Guiseley	2634	L 0 - 1		16	44
7	Nat Lg	H	Solihull Moors	2782	L 0 - 1		17	45
14	Nat Lg	A	Sutton United	2272	D 1 - 1	Hawkes 26	19	46
17	Nat Lg	H	Leyton Orient	2656	W 1 - 0	Laing 38	17	47
21	Nat Lg	H	Torquay United	3252	D 1 - 1	Donaldson 14	17	48
28	Nat Lg	A	Tranmere Rovers	5499	W 2 - 1	Donnelly 45 (pen) Oates 74	15	49

GOALSCORERS	SG	CSG	Pens	Hat tricks	Total		SG	CSG	Pens	Hat tricks	Total
Woods	7	2	1		10	Rodney	2				2
Oates	7				7	Adamas					1
Cassidy	5				5	Almond			1		1
Franks	5	3			5	Francis					1
Newton	4				4	Laing					1
Deverdics	2				3	Magnay					1
Watson	3				3	Munns					1
Donaldson	2				2	Opponents					1
Donnelly	2		1		2	Rooney					1
Hawkes	2				2	Simpson					1

HAVANT AND WATERLOOVILLE

Club Contact Details 02392 787 822
Westleigh Park, Martin Road, West Leigh, Havant PO9 5TH
mail@havantandwaterlooville.net

Founded: 1998 **Nickname:** Hawks	**Manager:** Lee Bradbury

Previous Names: Havant Town and Waterlooville merged in 1998
Previous Leagues: Southern 1998-2004. Conference/National 2004-16. Isthmian 2016-17.

Club Colours (change): White & sky blue

Ground Capacity: 4,800 **Seats:** 562 **Covered:** 3,500 **Clubhouse:** Yes **Shop:** Yes
Previous Grounds: None
Record Attendance: 4,400 v Swansea City - FA Cup 3rd Round 05/01/2008
Nearest Railway Station Havant - within 2 miles of the ground.

RECORDS
Victory: 9-0 v Moneyfields - Hampshire Senior Cup 23/10/2001
Defeat: 0-5 v Worcester City - Southern Premier 20/03/2004
Goalscorer: James Taylor - 138
Appearances: James Taylor - 297
Additional: Paid £5,000 to Bashley for John Wilson
Received £15,000 from Peterborough United for Gary McDonald

HONOURS
FA Comps: None
League: Southern League Southern Division 1998-99.
Isthmian League Premier Division 2016-17. National South 2017-18.
County FA: Hampshire Senior Cup 2015-16, 17-18.

08-09	09-10	10-11	11-12	12-13	13-14	14-15	15-16	16-17	17-18
Conf S 15	Conf S 6	Conf S 9	Conf S 19	Conf S 10	Conf S 6	Conf S 5	Nat S 20	Isth P 1	Nat S 1
FAC 1P	FAC 3Q	FAC 1P	FAC 3Q	FAC 2Q	FAC 2Qr	FAC 1P	FAC 4Qr	FAC 3Q	FAC 4Q
FAT QF	FAT 1P	FAT 1P	FAT 3Qr	FAT 2P	FAT SF	FAT 2P	FAT 3P	FAT 3Q	FAT 1P

2017-18 STATS	Goals Total	78	Games Without Scoring	9	Total No. of Scorers	13	Total Clean Sheets	23
Most Consecutive Scoring Games	23		Best Unbeaten Run	8		Most Consecutive Clean Sheets		2
Best Att:	2,270 v Concord Rangers, National League South					Number in brackets denotes consecutive runs.		

National League action between AFC Fylde and Solihull Moors - FT: 1-1.
The point taken by Solihull that day was enough to secure their National League place for 2018-19 season.
Photo: Bill Wheatcroft.

HAVANT & WATERLOOVILLE MATCH RESULTS 2017-18

Date	Comp	H/A	Opponents	Att:	Result	Goalscorers	Pos	No.
Aug 5	Nat South	A	Chippenham Town	668	D 0 - 0			1
8	Nat South	H	Eastbourne Borough	644	W 3 - 2	Widdrington 1 Williams 22 Prior 35		2
12	Nat South	H	Dartford	775	D 0 - 0			3
14	Nat South	A	Wealdstone	922	W 1 - 0	Lewis 37		4
19	Nat South	H	Bath City	633	L 1 - 2	Prior 35		5
26	Nat South	A	Hampton & Richmond B	426	W 1 - 0	Fogden 90		6
28	Nat South	H	Whitehawk	838	W 4 - 0	Prior 8 22 (pen) Rutherford 15 Barker 59		7
Sept 2	Nat South	A	Weston-s-Mare	467	W. 4 - 1	Prior 1 Williams 14 53 Lewis 24		8
5	Nat South	H	Truro City	698	L 1 - 2	Rutherford 65		9
9	Nat South	A	Gloucester City	322	W 1 - 0	Widdrington 73		10
12	Nat South	H	St Albans City	403	L 1 - 2	Tarbuck 67		11
16	FAC 2Q	H	Merthyr Town	296	W 2 - 1	Prior 53 Hayter 77		12
23	Nat South	H	Welling United	826	L 2 - 3	Fogden 41 Prior 90		13
30	FAC 3Q	A	Hayes & Yeading United	241	W 4 - 0	Williams, Prior Woodford Hayter		14
Oct 7	Nat South	A	Concord Rangers	228	D 1 - 1	Prior 17		15
14	FAC 4Q	A	Maidenhead United	753	L 1 - 2	Prior 50		16
21	Nat South	H	Poole Town	830	D 2 - 2	Prior 31 Rutherford 88		17
28	Nat South	A	Braintree Town	551	W 3 - 1	PRIOR 3 (48 53pen 79)		18
Nov 4	Nat South	A	Hungerford Town	345	W 1 - 0	Prior 72		19
11	Nat South	H	Hemel Hempstead Town	886	D 1 - 1	Woodford 40		20
18	Nat South	A	East Thurrock	203	W 1 - 0	Rutherford 54		21
21	Nat South	H	Chelmsford City	577	D 1 - 1	Prior 26		22
28	FAT 3Q	H	Dorking Wanderers	233	W 3 - 1	Prior 18 (pen) Rose 47 62		23
Dec 9	Nat South	H	Chippenham Town	648	W 4 - 0	Woodford 6 Fogden 10 64 Widdington 82		24
16	FAT 1	A	Billericay Town	705	L 1 - 3	Tubbs 64		25
23	Nat South	A	Eastbourne Borough	487	W 4 - 1	Lewis 11 Rose 46 Fogden 56 Tubbs 70		26
26	Nat South	H	Bognor Regis Town	1010	D 0 - 0			27
Jan 1	Nat South	A	Bognor Regis Town	1015	W 3 - 0	Tubbs 19 84 Hayter 76		28
9	Nat South	H	Oxford City	601	W 3 - 2	Tubbs 8 78 Lewis 54		29
13	Nat South	A	Dartford	1278	L 0 - 1			30
Feb 3	Nat South	A	Braintree Town	654	D 0 - 0			31
10	Nat South	A	Poole Town	454	W 3 - 1	Williams 22 Lewis 84 Fogden 90		32
17	Nat South	H	Hungerford Town	967	W 2 - 0	Prior 35 50		33
24	Nat South	A	Hemel Hempstead	508	D 0 - 0			34
27	Nat South	H	Gloucester City	572	W 2 - 1	Prior 65 Lewis 77		35
Mar 10	Nat South	A	Oxford City	410	W 1 - 0	Prior 45		36
13	Nat South	A	Wealdstone	806	W 1 - 0	Rutherford 81		37
17	Nat South	H	Hampton & Richmond B	958	D 0 - 0			38
20	Nat South	A	Truro City	413	L 0 - 1			39
24	Nat South	A	Bath City	922	W 2 - 1	Fogdon 45 Lewis 84		40
30	Nat South	H	Weston-s-Mare	1063	W 2 - 0	Fogden 47 Prior 62		41
Apr2	Nat South	A	Whitehawk	277	D 0 - 0			42
7	Nat South	A	Welling United	603	W 1 - 0	Strugnell 72		43
14	Nat South	H	St Albans City	1051	W 2 - 0	Fogden 25 Prior 38		44
21	Nat South	H	Chelmsford City	1160	W 2 - 0	Prior 4 Fogden 36		45
25	Nat South	H	East Thurrock United	1153	W 6 - 1	Williams 16 Tubbs 61 Scott 75 (og) P		46
28	Nat South	H	Concord Rangers	2270	W 3 - 2	Lewis 8 Tubbs 25 Prior 89		47

GOALSCORERS	SG	CSG	Pens	Hat tricks	Total		SG	CSG	Pens	Hat tricks	Total
2016-17 Prior					23	Rose	1				2
Prior	22	8	3	1	25	Barker	2				2
Fogden	8	2			10	Opponents					1
Lewis	9				8	Strugnell	1				1
Tubbs	8				8	Tarbuck	1				1
Williams	6				6						
Rutherford	4				5						
Widdrington	2				3						
Woodford	3				3						
Hayter	3				3						

LEYTON ORIENT

Club Contact Details 0871 310 1881
Matchroom Stadium, Brisbane Road, Leyton, London E10 5NF
info@leytonorient.net

Founded: 1881 **Nickname:** O's	**Manager:** Justin Edinburgh - 29/11/2017

Previous Names: Glyn Cricket Club 1881-86. Eagle C.C. 1886-88. Orient 1888-98. Clapton Orient 1898-46.
Previous Leagues: Clapton & District 1893-96. London 1896-05. Football League 1905-2017. London Combination 1915-19.

Club Colours (change): All red

Ground Capacity: **Seats:** 9,271 **Covered:** Yes **Clubhouse:** Yes **Shop:** Yes
Previous Grounds: Whittles Athletic Ground 1896-1900. Millfields Road 1900-46 (name changed to Brisbane Road).
Record Attendance: 37,615 v Tottenham Hotspur, Division Two, 16/03/1929

RECORDS
Victory: 8-0 v Crystal Palace, D3S, 12/11/55. v Rochdale, D4, 14/10/87. v Colchester Utd, D4, 15/10/88. v Doncaster Rov, D3, 28/12/97.
Defeat: 0-8 v Aston Villa, FA Cup Fourth Round Proper, January 1929.
Goalscorer: Tommy Johnston - 121, 1956-58, 59-61, also holds the record for most in a season having scored 35 during 57-58.
Additional: Paid £200,000 to Oldham Athletic for Liam Kelly, July 2016.
Received £1,000,000 from Fulham for Gabriel Zakuani, July 2006 and from Brentford for Moses Odubajo, June 14.

HONOURS
FA Comps: None

League: Clapton & District 1895-96. League Division Three South 1955-56, Division Three 69-70.

County FA: Middlesex County Cup 1901-02.

08-09	09-10	10-11	11-12	12-13	13-14	14-15	15-16	16-17	17-18
FL 1 14	FL 1 17	FL 1 7	FL 1 20	FL 1 7	FL 1 3	FL 1 23	FL 2 8	FL 2 24	Nat 13
FAC 3P	FAC 1Pr	FAC 5Pr	FAC 2P	FAC 3Pr	FAC 3P	FAC 1P	FAC 2Pr	FAC 1P	FAC 1P
FLC 1P	FLC 2P	FLC 2P	FLC 3P	FLC 2P	FLC 2P	FLC 3P	FLC 1P	FLC 1P	FAT 4Pr

2017-18 STATS	Goals Total	73	Games Without Scoring	16 (3)	Total No. of Scorers	15	Total Clean Sheets	14
Most Consecutive Scoring Games	8	Best Unbeaten Run	6			Most Consecutive Clean Sheets		2

Best Att: 5,729 v Aldershot Town, National League   Number in brackets denotes consecutive runs.

2017-18 MATCH LINE-UPS

Match Number	1	2	3	4	5	6	7	8	9	10	11	12	13	14	15	16	17	18	19	20	21	22	23	24	25	26	27	28	29	30	31	32	33	34	35	36	37	38	39	40	41	42	43	44	45	46	47	48	49	50	51	52	53	54			Total
Grainger	x	x	x	x	x	x	x	x	x	x	x	x	x	x	x	x						xs	s	s	s	s	s	s	s						s	s	s	s	s	s	s				s	s	s	s	s	s				23
Caprice	x	x	x	x	x	x	x	x	x	x	x	x	xs	xs	xs	x	x	x	xs	x	x	x	xr			x	x	x	x	x	x	x	x	x	x	x	x	xs	x	x	xs											42
Elokobi	x	x	x	x	x	x	x	x	x																	xs	xs	x			xs	x		sx			x	x	x	x	x	x	xs									23
Coulson	x	x	x	x	x	x	x	x	xs				xs										xs	x	x	x	x	x	x			x	x	x	x	x	x	x	x	x	x	x	x	x	x	xs						31
Widdowson	x	x	x	x	x	x	x	x	x	x	x	x		x	x	x	x	xs		xr		x	x	x	x	x	x	x	x	x	x	x	x	x		x	x	x	x	x	x	x		sx	x	x	x	x	x		s			44
Dayton	xs	xs	xs	xs	x	xs	x	xs	x	xs		s	xs	x	xs	xs	x	x	sx	x	x	x	xs	x	x	x	xs	xs	xs	x	x	x		xs																			32
Lee	xs	xs	x	x	xs																																											sx	sx	xs			8
Lawless	x	x	x	x	x	x	x	x	xs	x	xs	x	x	xs		sx	xs	xs		x	xs	x	x	x	x		sx	sx	sx	s									s														30
McAnuff	xs	xs	xs	sx	xs	xs	sx	x	x	x	x	x	x	xs			xs		sx	x	x	x	x	x	x	x	x	x	x			x	x	x				xs	xs	x	x	x	x	x	x	x							40
Mooney	x	x	xs	x	x	xs	xs	xs	x	xs	x		xs	xs	x	xs	x	xs	xs	xs	x	x	s	sx	s	sx	sx	x	xs	xs	xs	xs	sx	s		s	sx		sx		x	sx	x	s	sx	sx	sx	sx	sx	x			42
Bonne	x	x	x	x	x	x	x	x	xs	x	x	x	x	x	x	x	x	x	x	x	x	x	x	x	x	x	xs	x	x	x	x	x	x	x	xs	x	x	x	sx	sx	x	x	x	x	x	x							52
Koroma	sx	sx	xs	xs	sx	sx	sx	sx	sx	sx			x	x	s								xs		sx	x	s	s	s	s				sx	sx	x	s	x	xs	xs	xs	x	x	xs	sx	sx	sx	x	x	x			34
Clay		x	x	x	x	x	x	x	x	x	x	x	x									xs	x	xs	x	x	x	x	x	x	x	x	x	x	x	x	x	x	x	x	x	xs	x	x	x	xs	x	xs	xs	x	xs	s		48
Boco	sx	sx	sx	xs	sx	xs	sx	xs			xs	sx	sx	sx	sx	sx	s	sx	xs	xs	sx	sx	sx		sx																													20
Sargeant	s	s	s	s	s	s	s	s	s	s	s	s	s	s	s	s	s	s	s	s	s	s	x	x	sx										s	s	s																3
Clark	s	s	s	s										x	s							xs	x																														3
Sendles-White					s	s	s	sx	x	x	x	s	xs	xs	x				x	x	x	x	xr																														16
Ochieng				s	s	xs	xs	xs	xs	s	sx		s	s	x																																							6
Harrold									sx	xs	xs			sx	xs				sx	x	sx	x	x	sx	x	xs	xs	sx	sx	sx	sx	xs	sx	x	xs	sx	x	xs	x	sx	x	sx	x	x	xs									30
Judd							s							x	x	sx	x	x	sx	x	x	x		x	x	x					sx															s	s	s	s	s	s			15
Happe							x	s	sx	x	x	sx	x	x		sx	x	x	x		x	xs	x	x	x	x	x		s	sx	x	sx	x	s	sx	sx	x	x			xs						s	sx	x	x	x			32
Dalby										sx	s		s		s	s										sx									s																			2
Brophy																		sx	x	x												sx	xs	x	x	xs	x	x	x	x	x	xs	xs	x	x	x	xs	xs	xs					27
Ellis (L)														x	x	x			x	x	x						x	s	s	s																								7
Westbrooke																			sx	xs	x	x	x	x	sx	x	xs	xs	s																									8
Sotiriou																			sx	x	sx	sx	s															s		sx														6
Barker																			s																																			0
Pollock																						s						s	s																									0
Brill															s	s			x	x	sx	x	x	x	x	x	x	x	x	x	x	x	x	x	x	x	x	x	x	x	x	x	x	x	x	x	x	x	x	x	x	x	29
N'Gala (L)																			x	x	x	x	x	sx			xr		sx	x																								7
Moncur																												s	s				s																					0
Reynolds																											sx	s	xs	xs	sx	s	x	x	sx	s	x	xs	xs		x				sx		sx	x	sx	x				12
Holman																											s			x	x	x		x	xs	xs	x			x	s	xs	sx	xs									10
Adams																									xs	s	s	x	xs	x	xs	xs	x	x	x	x	x	sx	x	x	x	xs	x	x	x								20
Ling																																	sx				xs									s	s	sx						13
Clayden																																					s											s	s	sx				1
Ekpiteta																																													s	x	x	x	x	x	x			6
Janata																																									s													0
RESULT	L	W	W	W	L	W	D	W	W	L	L	L	D	L	L	L	D	D	W	L	L	D	D	L	L	W	W	W	W	D	D	W	L	W	W	D	W	W	W	D	L	L	D	L	D	W	W	W	D	L	W	L	W			

LEYTON ORIENT MATCH RESULTS 2017-18

Date	Comp	H/A	Opponents	Att:	Result	Goalscorers	Pos	No.
Aug 5	Nat Lg	A	Sutton United	3198	L 0 - 2		24	1
8	Nat Lg	H	Solihull Borough	4411	W 3 - 1	Leer 21 Mooney 47 Elokobi 78	9	2
12	Nat Lg	H	Maidstone United	5085	W 2 - 0	Mooney 60 Boco 90	4	3
15	Nat Lg	A	Bromley	3346	L 1 - 6	Bonne 67	11	4
19	Nat Lg	A	Woking	2885	W 2 - 0	Bonne 50 86	8	5
25	Nat Lg	H	Eastleigh	4373	D 1 - 1	Clay 90	8	6
28	Nat Lg	A	Maidenhead United	2544	W 1 - 0	Bonne 67	3	7
Sept 2	Nat Lg	H	Guiseley	4323	W 4 - 1	BONNE 3 (43 45 82) Harrold 65	2	8
9	Nat Lg	A	Boreham Wood	1920	L 0 - 2		4	9
12	Nat Lg	H	FC Halifax Town	3600	L 0 - 3		9	10
16	Nat Lg	H	Hartlepool United	3867	L 1 - 2	McAnuff 19	13	11
23	Nat Lg	A	Aldershot Town	3060	D 2 - 2	Clay 39 Boco 82	13	12
30	Nat Lg	H	AFC Fylde	4357	L 1 - 2	McAnuff 72	15	13
Oct 4	Nat Lg	A	Tranmere Rovers	4145	L 1 - 2	Harrold 22	16	14
7	Nat Lg	A	Barrow	1796	D 2 - 2	Mooney 19 Clay 27	17	15
14	FAC 4Q	A	Dagenham & Red	2529	D 0 - 0			16
17	FAC 4Qr	H	Dagenham & Red	2013	W 1 - 0	Bonne 23		17
21	Nat Lg	A	Macclesfield Town	4662	L 0 - 1		18	18
24	Nat Lg	H	Gateshead	3468	L 0 - 2		19	19
27	Nat Lg	A	Wrexham	4432	D 2 - 2	Bonne 20 Ellis 85	19	20
Nov 4	FAC 1	A	Gillingham	3659	L 1 - 2	Dayton 79		21
11	Nat Lg	A	Ebbsfleet United	2021	L 1 - 2	Dayton 87	19	22
18	Nat Lg	H	Dover	4548	D 1 - 1	Clay 78	16	23
21	Nat Lg	A	Chester	3352	D 2 - 2	Bonne 6 McAnuff 60	20	24
25	Nat Lg	A	Torquay United	1913	L 0 - 3		20	25
Dec 2	Nat Lg	A	Solihull Moors	1118	L 0 - 1		20	26
8	Nat Lg	H	Sutton United	4180	W 4 - 1	Bonne 7 (pen) 81 Harrold 54 Dayton 85	20	27
16	FAT 1	A	Haringey United	1133	W 2 - 1	Coulson 59 Harrold 79		28
23	Nat Lg	A	Maidstone United	3225	W 2 - 0	N'Gala 36 Bonne 52	20	29
26	Nat Lg	H	Dagenham & Red	5125	W 2 - 0	Coulson 49 Bonne 59	18	30
30	Nat Lg	H	Bromley	5227	L 0 - 1		19	31
Jan 1	Nat Lg	A	Dagenham & Red	3144	D 0 - 0		19	32
6	Nat Lg	H	Boreham Wood	4094	D 0 - 0		19	33
13	FAT 2	A	Bognor Regis Town	1371	W 2 - 1	Bonne 83 Koroma 105 (aet)		34
27	Nat Lg	H	Aldershot Town	5,729	L 1 - 2	Bonne 1 Elokobi 52	19	35
30	Nat Lg	A	FC Halifax Town	1,352	W 2 - 1	Bonne 19 Koroma 39	17	36
Feb 3	FAT 3	A	Dover Athletic	1.016	W 4 - 3	Elokobi 34 Bonne 48 Harrold 53 Mooney 90		37
10	Nat Lg	H	Tranmere Rovers	4631	D 1 - 1	Harrold 52	17	38
17	Nat Lg	A	AFC Fylde	2206	W 1 - 0	Bonne 42 (pen)	16	39
20	Nat Lg	A	Chester	1935	W 1 - 0	Brophy 68	15	40
24	FAT 4	H	Gateshead	3771	D 3 - 3	Karoma 35 Adams 52 Coulson 57		41
Mar 3	Nat Lg	A	Dover	1348	L 0 - 1		16	42
6	FAT 4r	A	Gateshead	685	L 2 - 3	Brophy 52 Mooney 70		43
10	Nat Lg	H	Ebbsfleet United	4127	D 1 - 1	Clark 32 (og)	15	44
13	Nat Lg	H	Torquay United	2900	L 0 - 1		16	45
17	Nat Lg	A	Eastleigh	2013	D 0 - 0		17	46
24	Nat Lg	H	Woking	5673	W 3 - 0	Bonne 10 17 (pen) Brophy 80	14	47
30	Nat Lg	A	Guiseley	1216	W 3 - 1	McAnuff 48 75 Mooney 90	12	48
Apr 7	Nat Lg	H	Barrow	3929	W 4 - 1	Jones 28 (og) Koroma 72 Bonne 89 90	12	49
14	Nat Lg	A	Macclesfield Town	3110	D 1 - 1	Koroma 42	14	50
17	Nat Lg	A	Hartlepool United	2656	L 0 - 1		14	51
21	Nat Lg	H	Wrexham	5166	W 1 - 0	Bonne 29	13	52
24	Nat Lg	H	Maidenhead United	3145	L 0 - 1		13	53
28	Nat Lg	A	Gateshead	1056	W 3 - 1	Bonne 17 McAnuff 53 Karoma 60	13	54

GOALSCORERS	SG	CSG	Pens	Hat tricks	Total		SG	CSG	Pens	Hat tricks	Total
Bonne	18	4	3	1	25	Boco	2				2
Harrold	16				6	Opponent		2			2
Koroma	6				6	Adams					1
McAnuff	5				6	Ellis					1
Mooney	5	2	–		6	Leer					1
Clay	4				4	N'Gala					1
Brophy	3				3						
Coulson	3				3						
Dayton	3				3						
Elokobi	3				3						

MAIDENHEAD UNITED

Club Contact Details 01628 636 314
York Road, Maidenhead, Berkshire SL6 1SF
kenneth.chandler@btinternet.com

Founded: 1870   **Nickname:** Magpies   **Manager:** Alan Devonshire - May 2015
Previous Names: After WWI Maidenhead F.C and Maidenhead Norfolkians merged to form Maidenhead Town >1920.
Previous Leagues: Southern (FM) 1894-1902, 2006-07, West Berkshire 1902-04, Gr. West Suburban 1904-22, Spartan 1922-39, Gr. West Comb. 1939-45, Corinthian 1945-63, Athenian 1963-73, Isthmian 1973-2004, Conference 2004-06.

Club Colours (change): Black & white

Ground Capacity: 4,500   **Seats:** 550   **Covered:** 2,000   **Clubhouse:** Yes   **Shop:** Yes
Previous Grounds: Kidwells Park (Norfolkians)
Record Attendance: 7,989 v Southall - FA Amateur Cup Quarter final 07/03/1936
Nearest Railway Station Maidenhead - 200 yards from the ground.

RECORDS
Victory: 14-1 v Buckingham Town - FA Amateur Cup 06/09/1952
Defeat: 0-14 v Chesham United (A) - Spartan League 31/03/1923
Goalscorer: George Copas - 270 (1924-35). Most goals in a season: Jack Palethorpe - 65 in 39 apps (1929-30).
Appearances: Bert Randall - 532 (1950-64)
Additional: Received £5,000 from Norwich City for Alan Cordice 1979

HONOURS
FA Comps: None
League: West Berkshire 1902-03. Spartan 1926-27, 31-32, 33-34. Corinthian 1957-58, 60-61, 61-62. National South 2016-17.
County FA: Berks & Bucks Senior Cup 1894-95, 95-96, 1911-12, 27-28, 29-30, 30-31, 31-32, 38-39, 45-46, 55-56, 56-57, 60-61, 62-63, 65-66, 69-70, 97-98, 98-99, 2001-02, 02-03, 09-10, 14-15, 16-17. Wycombe Senior Cup 1999-2000.

08-09	09-10	10-11	11-12	12-13	13-14	14-15	15-16	16-17	17-18
Conf S 6	Conf S 16	Conf S 19	Conf S 20	Conf S 19	Conf S 18	Conf S 18	Nat S 7	Nat S 1	Nat 12
FAC 2Q	FAC 2Q	FAC 4Q	FAC 1Pr	FAC 3Q	FAC 2Q	FAC 3Qr	FAC 1Pr	FAC 2Q	FAC 1P
FAT 3Q	FAT 2P	FAT 3Q	FAT 1Pr	FAT 1P	FAT 3P	FAT 2Pr	FAT 2P	FAT 3Q	FAT 3Pr

2017-18 STATS   **Goals Total** 76   **Games Without Scoring** 12 (2)   **Total No. of Scorers** 17   **Total Clean Sheets** 9
Most Consecutive Scoring Games 8   **Best Unbeaten Run** 5   **Most Consecutive Clean Sheets** 2
Best Att: 2,544 v Leyton Orient, National League   Number in brackets denotes consecutive runs.

2017-18 MATCH LINE-UPS

Match Number	Total
Pentney	52
Clerima	38
Odametey	50
Massey	50
Inman	13
Tarpey	6
Comley	37
Marks	38
Pritchard	47
Upward	44
Kilman	38
Clifton	41
Barratt	35
Goodman	43
Smith	36
Mulley	17
Hyde	37
Peters	15
McKenzie	2
Steer	37
Emmanuel	23
Hamann	0
Hammond	0
Owusu	10
Osho	3

RESULT: D L W W W D D L W L W W L W L D W D W D L L D D D D L D W W W L L D W L W D L L W W L L D L D L W W W W L W W W

MAIDENHEAD UNITED MATCH RESULTS 2017-18

Date	Comp	H/A	Opponents	Att:	Result	Goalscorers	Pos	No.
Aug 5	Nat Lg	A	Maidstone United	2298	D 1 - 1	Barrett 88	11	1
8	Nat Lg	H	Wrexham	1632	L 1 - 2	Tarpey 42	18	2
12	Nat Lg	H	Hartlepool United	1491	W 2 - 1	Tarpey 34 58	14	3
15	Nat Lg	A	AFC Fylde	1657	W 4 - 1	TARPEY 3 (26 pen 37 pen 58) Barrett 78	7	4
19	Nat Lg	H	Ebbsfleet United	1628	D 1 - 1	Pritchard 26	9	5
25	Nat Lg	A	Barrow	1154	D 1 - 1	Clifton 28	9	6
28	Nat Lg	H	Leyton Orient	2544	L 0 - 1		14	7
Sept 2	Nat Lg	A	Sutton United	2158	W 2 - 0	Upward 73 Odametey 90	7	8
9	Nat Lg	A	FC Halifax Town	1727	L 2 - 3	Goodman 79 Marks 90	10	9
12	Nat Lg	H	Tranmere Rovers	1483	W 1 - 0	Pritchard 88	10	10
16	Nat Lg	H	Boreham Wood	1351	W 2 - 1	Clifton 43 Upward 61	6	11
23	Nat Lg	A	Chester	1839	L 0 - 2		11	12
30	Nat Lg	H	Guiseley	1224	W 3 - 0	Upward 3 Pritchard 5 Comley 35	8	13
Oct 3	Nat Lg	A	Torquay United	1567	L 0 - 4		12	14
7	Nat Lg	A	Aldershot	2425	D 3 - 3	Clifton 18 Inman 63 Pritchard 86 (pen)	12	15
14	FAC 4Q	H	Havant & Waterlooville	793	W 2 - 1	Barrett 23 Upward 90		16
21	Nat Lg	A	Dover Athletic	837	D 1 - 1	Hyde 90	13	17
24	Nat Lg	A	Bromley	1056	W 3 - 2	CLIFTON 3 (17 21pen 35)		18
27	Nat Lg	H	Dagenham & Redbridge	1384	D 1 - 1	Clerima	11	19
Nov 5	FAC 1	A	Coventry City	3370	L 0 - 2			20
11	Nat Lg	H	Gateshead	1377	L 0 - 3		13	21
18	Nat Lg	A	Woking	1878	D 1 - 1	Clifton 10	12	22
21	Nat Lg	A	Eastleigh	1525	D 2 - 2	Odametey 41 Pritchard 51	14	23
25	Nat Lg	A	Macclesfield Town	1165	D 1 - 1	Hyde 68	14	24
Dec 2	Nat Lg	A	Wrexham	3968	L 0 - 2		14	25
9	Nat Lg	H	Maidstone United	1313	D 0 - 0		13	26
16	FAT 1	A	Woking	648	W 2 - 0	Moses 50 Hyde 90		27
23	Nat Lg	A	Hartlepool United	2756	W 2 - 1	Markis 52 78	11	28
26	Nat Lg	H	Solihull Moors	1261	W 1 - 0	Smith 60	11	29
30	Nat Lg	H	AFC Fylde	1315	L 1 - 2	Pritchard 42 (pen)	11	30
Jan 1	Nat Lg	A	Solihull Moors	602	L 1 - 3	Emmanuel 53	12	31
6	Nat Lg	H	FC Halifax Town	D	D 0 - 0		12	32
13	FAT 2	H	FC Halifax Town	802	W 4 - 1	Moses 45 59 Pritchard 53 73 (pen)		33
20	Nat Lg	A	Tranmere Rovers	4980	L 2 - 3	Barrett 55 Clerima 84	13	34
27	Nat Lg	H	Chester	1510	W 3 - 0	Pritchard 12 (pen) 14 Barrett 35	13	35
Feb 3	FAT 3	H	Stockport County	856	D 1 - 1	Upward 57		36
6	FAT 3r	A	Stockport County	1121	L 2 - 3	Hyde Barrett (aet)		37
10	Nat Lg	H	Torquay United	1433	L 1 - 2	Upward 69	23	38
17	Nat Lg	A	Guiseley	777	W 3 - 1	Hyde 30 Pritchard 43 48	12	39
20	Nat Lg	H	Eastleigh	1055	W 3 - 1	Emmanuel 21 Marks 56 Pritchard 59		40
24	Nat Lg	A	Macclesfield Town	1668	L 0 - 1		12	41
Mar 10	Nat Lg	A	Gateshead	581	L 1 - 7	Hyde 25	13	42
13	Nat Lg	A	Boreham Wood	401	D 1 - 1	Emmanual 29	12	43
17	Nat Lg	H	Barrow	1030	L 0 - 1		13	44
24	Nat Lg	A	Ebbsfleet United	1503	D 1 - 1	Pritchard 81	12	45
Apr 7	Nat Lg	A	Aldershot	2318	L 0 - 1		16	46
10	Nat Lg	H	Woking	1301	W 2 - 1	Clifton 81 Marks 88	16	47
14	Nat Lg	H	Dover Athletic	1155	W 3 - 2	Hyde 52 Upward 60 Kilman 90	12	48
17	Nat Lg	H	Sutton United	2201	W 2 - 1	Pritchard 25 Goodman 34	12	49
21	Nat Lg	A	Dagenham & Redbridge	1433	L 0 - 1		12	50
24	Nat Lg	A	Leyton Orient	3145	W 1 - 0	Upward 5	12	51
28	Nat Lg	H	Bromley	1418	W 5 - 2	Barrett 3 49 Smith 5 Owusu 32 Marks 61	12	52

GOALSCORERS	SG	CSG	Pens	Hat tricks	Total		SG	CSG	Pens	Hat tricks	Total
2016-17 Tarpey					44	Clerima	2				2
Pritchard	12	2	4		15	Goodman	2				2
Barrett	6				8	Odameter	2				2
Clifton	6		1	1	8	Smith	2				2
Upward	8				8	Comley	1				1
Hyde	7				7	Inman	1				1
Tarpey	3	3	2	1	6	Kilman	1				1
Marks	5				6	Owusu					1
Emmannual	3				3						
Moses	2				3						

MAIDSTONE UNITED

Club Contact Details 01622 753 817
The Gallagher Stadium, James Whatman Way, Maidstone, Kent ME14 1LQ
info@maidstoneunited.co.uk

Founded: 1992 **Nickname:** The Stones **Manager:** Jay Saunders
Previous Names: Maidstone Invicta > 1997
Previous Leagues: Kent County 1993-2001, Kent 2001-06. Isthmian 2006-15.

Club Colours (change): Amber & black

Ground Capacity: 3,030 **Seats:** 792 **Covered:** 1,850 **Clubhouse:** Yes **Shop:** Yes
Previous Grounds: London Rd 1993-2001, Central Pk 2001-02 & Bourne Pk 2002-09 (S'bourne), 11-12, The Homelands (Ashford) 2009-11.
Record Attendance: 3,030 v Sutton United, National League South, 05/04/2016.
Nearest Railway Station Maidstone East & Maidstone Barracks a walk away **Bus Route** Nos. 101 or 155 from the Mall Bus Station

RECORDS
Victory: 12-1 v Aylesford - Kent League 1993-94
Defeat: 2-8 v Scott Sports - 1995-96
Goalscorer: Richard Sinden - 98
Appearances: Tom Mills
Additional: Paid £2,000 for Steve Jones - 2000

HONOURS
FA Comps: None
League: Kent County Division Four 1993-94, Div. Two 1994-95, Div. One 1998-99, Premier 2001-02. Kent 2000-02, 05-06. Isthmian Division One South 2006-07, Premier 2014-15. National League South Play-offs 2015-16.
County FA: Kent Junior Cup 1994-95, Weald of Kent Charity Cup 1999-00, 00-01, Kent Senior Trophy 2002-03. Kent Senior Cup 2017-18

08-09	09-10	10-11	11-12	12-13	13-14	14-15	15-16	16-17	17-18
Isth P 15	Isth P 18	Isth P 20	Isth1S 6	Isth1S 2	Isth P 7	Isth P 1	Nat S 3	Nat 14	Nat 19
FAC 4Q	FAC 3Q	FAC 1Q	FAC 2Q	FAC 3Q	FAC 3Q	FAC 2P	FAC 1P	FAC 1Pr	FAC 2P
FAT 2Q	FAT 2P	FAT 3Q	FAT P	FAT 2P	FAT 3Q	FAT 2Q	FAT 1P	FAT 1P	FAT 3Pr

2017-18 STATS
Goals Total 70 **Games Without Scoring** 16 (2) **Total No. of Scorers** 22 **Total Clean Sheets** 13
Most Consecutive Scoring Games 8 **Best Unbeaten Run** 8 **Most Consecutive Clean Sheets** 2
Best Att: 3,225 v Leyton Orient, National League

Number in brackets denotes consecutive runs.

2017-18 MATCH LINE-UPS

Match Number	Total
Worgan	53
Hare	33
Finney (L)	31
Prestedge	36
Lewis	49
Sam-Yorke	39
Paxman	28
Anderson	50
Ofori-Twumasi	38
Willard	3
Pigott	34
Phipps	3
Wraight	25
Wynter	49
Reason	50
Richards	14
Taylor	0
Okuonghoe	27
Hines	24
ter Horst	22
Sodeinde	0
Capel	0
Muldoon	7
Loza	36
McCorkell	0
Bartlett	1
Collins (39)	6
Osei	9
Healy	0
Coker (L)	8
Beckwith	4
Turgott (L)	14
Lafayette	10
De Havilland (L)	10
Phillips	8
Luer	6

RESULT: D L L D W W D L W W W D W L D D W W W W D L L L D W L D D D D L W L L L L D L D L L L W W D L L L D L W W W D

MAIDSTONE UNITED MATCH RESULTS 2017-18

Date	Comp	H/A	Opponents	Att:	Result	Goalscorers	Pos	No.
Aug 5	Nat Lg	H	Maidenhead United	2298	D 1 - 1	Wozencroft-Pigott 32	12	1
8	Nat Lg	A	Ebbsfleet United	2519	L 0 - 2		22	2
12	Nat Lg	A	Leyton Orient	5085	L 0 - 2		22	3
15	Nat Lg	H	Aldershot Town	2524	D 1 - 1	Hare 90	21	4
19	Nat Lg	H	Wrexham	2192	W 2 - 1	Wynter 15 Richards 33	17	5
25	Nat Lg	A	Sutton United	2312	W 3 - 1	Okuonghoe 68 Paxman 74 Pigott 82	14	6
28	Nat Lg	H	Dagenham & Redbridge	2544	D 0 - 0		17	7
Sept 2	Nat Lg	A	Hartlepool United	4137	L 1 - 3	Te Horst 90	19	8
9	Nat Lg	H	Woking	2527	W 3 - 1	Hines 34 Sam-Yorke 67 Pigott 77	15	9
12	Nat Lg	A	Eastleigh	1820	W 1 - 0	Hines 89	13	10
16	Nat Lg	A	Macclesfield Town	1347	W 4 - 1	Hines 11 65 Wynter 24 Pigott 74	7	11
23	Nat Lg	H	Gateshead	2530	D 2 - 2	Hines 11 (pen) Wynter 67	9	12
30	Nat Lg	A	Barrow	1097	W 1 - 0	Pigott 52	5	13
Oct 3	Nat Lg	A	Bromley	2541	L 0 - 2		9	14
7	Nat Lg	H	Guiseley	2552	D 1 - 1	Hines 12	9	15
14	FAC 4Q	H	Enfield	1495	D 2 - 2	Wynter 45 Pigott 90		16
17	FAC 4Qr	A	Enfield	820	W 3 - 1	Hines 47 Finney 102 Reason 107 (aet)		17
24	Nat Lg	A	FC Halifax Town	1410	W 2 - 0	Pigott 15 Reason 61 (pen)	10	18
27	Nat Lg	H	Chester	2351	W 1 - 0	Finney 90	5	19
Nov 5	FAC 1	A	Cheltenham Town	2799	W 4 - 2	Sam-Yorke 20 53 Pigott 21 Hines 43		20
11	Nat Lg	A	Torquay United	1799	W 1 - 0	Pigott 30	5	21
18	Nat Lg	H	Solihull Moors	2463	D 1 - 1	Pigott 1	6	22
21	Nat Lg	H	Boreham Wood	1945	L 0 - 4		7	23
25	Nat Lg	A	Tranmere Rovers	4126	L 0 - 4		10	24
Dec 2	FAC 2	A	MK Dons	4804	L 1 - 4	Okuonghoe 25		25
8	Nat Lg	A	Maidenhead United	1313	D 0 - 0		11	26
16	FAT 1	A	Torquay United	604	W 4 - 0	Ofori-Twurnasi 14 Prestedge 4 Pigott 55 Wraight 90		27
23	Nat Lg	H	Leyton Orient	3225	L 0 - 2		12	28
26	Nat Lg	A	Dover Athletic	2078	D 2 - 2	Wozencroft-Pigott 36 39	12	29
30	Nat Lg	A	Aldershot Town	2287	D 1 - 1	Collins 48	12	30
Jan 1	Nat Lg	H	Dover Athletic	2502	D 2 - 2	Wraight 69 Anderson 90	12	31
6	Nat Lg	A	Woking	1874	D 4 - 4	Lewis 25 53 Reason 41 (pen) Pigott 42	13	32
9	Nat Lg	H	Ebbsfleet United	2396	L 1 - 2	Anderson 54	13	33
13	FAT 2	H	Heybridge Swifts	1278	W 2 - 1	Loza 29 Osei 43		34
20	Nat Lg	H	Eastleigh	2130	L 2 - 3	Te Horst 11 Lewis 34	14	35
23	Nat Lg	A	AFC Fylde	1408	L 0 - 3		15	36
27	Nat Lg	A	Gateshead	771	L 1 - 2	Reason 19 (pen)	16	37
Feb 3	FAT 3	H	Gateshead	1186	D 2 - 2	Loza 59 Reason 90		38
6	FAT 3r	A	Gateshead	771	L 0 - 3			39
10	Nat Lg	A	Bromley	2027	D 2 - 2	Loza 35 Turgott 77	16	40
17	Nat Lg	H	Barrow	2328	L 0 - 1		17	41
20	Nat Lg	A	Boreham Wood	428	L 0 - 1		17	42
24	Nat Lg	H	Tranmere Rovers	2502	L 2 - 3	Finney 27 Lafayette 41 (pen)	18	43
Mar 10	Nat Lg	A	Torquay United	2211	W 1 - 0	Hare 89	17	44
17	Nat Lg	H	Sutton United	2065	W 1 - 0	Lewis 75	16	45
21	Nat Lg	H	Macclesfield Town	1994	D 2 - 2	Wynter 19 Lafayette 83	15	46
24	Nat Lg	A	Wrexham	4443	L 0 - 1		17	47
30	Nat Lg	H	Hartlepool United	2559	L 1 - 2	Lafayette 90	18	48
Apr 1	Nat Lg	A	Dagenham & Redbridge	1633	L 1 - 2	Wynter 82	18	49
7	Nat Lg	A	Guiseley	957	D 0 - 0		18	50
10	Nat Lg	A	Solihull Moors	665	L 0 - 1		18	51
14	Nat Lg	H	AFC Fylde	2254	W 1 - 0	Turgott 23	18	52
21	Nat Lg	A	Chester	1728	W 3 - 1	Turgott 19 Phillips 32 Hare 74	18	53
28	Nat Lg	H	FC Halifax Town	2832	D 0 - 0		19	54

GOALSCORERS	SG	CSG	Pens	Hat tricks	Total		SG	CSG	Pens	Hat tricks	Total
2016-17 Loza					10	Okuonghoe	2				2
Wozencroft-Pigott	9	3			13	Te Horst	2				2
Hines	7	4	1		8	Wraight	2				2
Wynter	6	2			6	Collins					1
Reason	5	2	3		5	Osei					1
Lewis	3				4	O-Twurmasi					1
Finney	3				3	Paxman					1
Hare	3				3	Phillips					1
Lafayette	3				3	Prestedge					1
Lewis	2				3	Richards					1
Loza	3				3						
Sam-Yorke	2				3						
Turgott	3				3						

SALFORD CITY

Club Contact Details 07762 386 337
Peninsula Stadium, Moor Lane, Kersal, Salford, Manchester M7 3OZ
enquiries@salfordcityfc.co.uk

Founded: 1940   **Nickname:** Ammies   **Manager:** Graham Alexander - 14/05/2018
Previous Names: Salford Central 1940-63, Salford Amateurs 1963 until merger with Anson Villa, Salford F.C. > 1990
Previous Leagues: Local leagues 1940-63. Manchester 1963-80. Cheshire County 1980-82. North West Counties 1982-2008.

Club Colours (change): Red/white/black

Ground Capacity: 8,000   **Seats:** 1,300   **Covered:** 600   **Clubhouse:** Yes   **Shop:** Yes
Previous Grounds: None
Record Attendance: 3,000 v Whickham, FA Vase, 1980. 4,058 (at The Willows) v FC United, North West Counties Div.1,
Nearest Railway Station Manchester Victoria - 3 miles from the ground.   **Bus Route** First Bus No.98 from Manchester Victoria.

RECORDS
Best FA Cup   Second Round Proper Replay 2015-16
FA Trophy   Third Qualifying Round 2009-10, 16-17(r)
FA Vase   Fourth Round Proper 1980-81

HONOURS
FA Comps: None
League: Manchester League Premier Division 1974-75, 75-76, 76-77, 78-79.
     Northern Premier Division One North 2014-15. National North 2017-18.
County FA: Lancashire Amateur Cup 1972-73, 74-75, 76-77. Manchester Premier Cup 1977-78, 78-79.

08-09		09-10		10-11		11-12		12-13		13-14		14-15		15-16		16-17		17-18	
NP1N	20	NP1N	11	NP1N	12	NP1N	13	NP1N	16	NP1N	12	NP1N	1	NP P	3	Nat N	4	Nat N	1
FAC	2Q	FAC	3Q	FAC	1Q	FAC	Pr	FAC	2Q	FAC	P	FAC	2Q	FAC	2Pr	FAC	3Q	FAC	2Q
FAT	1Q	FAT	3Q	FAT	P	FAT	2Q	FAT	P	FAT	P	FAT	P	FAT	1Q	FAT	3Qr	FAT	3Q

2017-18 STATS   **Goals Total** 80   **Games Without Scoring** 4   **Total No. of Scorers** 17   **Total Clean Sheets** 15
Most Consecutive Scoring Games 19   **Best Unbeaten Run** 10   **Most Consecutive Clean Sheets** 3
Best Att: 2,937 v FC Utd of Manchester , National League North   Number in brackets denotes consecutive runs.

National League North action between Alfreton Town and Salford City - FT: 2-3. Photo: Bill Wheatcroft.

SALFORD CITY MATCH RESULTS 2017-18

Date	Comp	H/A	Opponents	Att:	Result	Goalscorers	Pos	No.
Aug 5	Nat North	H	Darlington	1777	L 0 - 2		19	1
8	Nat North	A	Chorley	1352	W 1 - 0	Nottingham 36	15	2
12	Nat North	A	AFC Telford United	1335	W 2 - 0	Beesley 10 Phenix 77	7	3
15	Nat North	H	Stockport County	2358	W 2 - 1	Nottingham 5 Dudley 26	6	4
19	Nat North	H	Kidderminster Harriers	1320	W 3 - 0	REDSHAW 3 (47 51 80)	4	5
26	Nat North	A	Spennymoor Town	687	D 1 - 1	Touray 82	5	6
28	Nat North	H	Southport	1757	W 2 - 1	Dieseruvwe 63 Kpohomouh (og)	3	7
Sept 2	Nat North	A	Curzon Ashton	723	D 1 - 1	Maynard 65	4	8
5	Nat North	A	Harrogate Town	1137	W 2 - 1	Phenix 2 Maynard 77	3	9
9	Nat North	H	Brackley Town	1117	W 2 - 0	Redshaw 43 53	2	10
12	Nat North	H	Nuneaton Town	902	W 3 - 0	Maynard 9 Dudley 13 Askew 33	2	11
16	FAC 2Q	H	York City	1350	L 1 - 2	Hogan 45		12
23	Nat North	A	Gainsborough Trinity	706	W 1 - 0	Phenix 44	2	13
Oct 7	Nat North	H	Leamington	1582	L 2 - 3	Phenix 29 65	2	14
21	Nat North	H	York City	1874	W 3 - 2	Hogan 22 50 Redshaw 27	2	15
28	Nat North	A	Bradford PA	533	W 2 - 1	Phenix 70 Mafuta 73	2	16
31	Nat North	A	Boston United	1019	W 1 - 0	Dudley 30	2	17
Nov 4	Nat North	H	Alfreton Town	2074	W 1 - 0	Dieseruvwe 90	1	18
11	Nat North	A	Tamworth	1233	W 2 - 1	Shelton 30 Phenix 72	1	19
18	Nat North	H	North Ferriby United	1712	W 4 - 0	REDSHAW 4 (56 78 (pen) 83 90)	1	20
25	FAT 3Q	A	Brackley Town	426	L 0 - 4			21
Dec 2	Nat North	A	Blyth Spartans	1040	W 1 - 0	Redshaw 36	1	22
22	Nat North	H	Chorley	1760	L 0 - 3		1	23
26	Nat North	A	FC United of Manchester	3041	L 2 - 3	Allen 9 Maynard 31	1	24
Jan 1	Nat North	H	FC United of Manchester	2937	D 2 - 2	Dudley 15 Redshaw 49	1	25
6	Nat North	A	Stockport County	5002	D 2 - 2	Redshaw 48 Nottingham 90	1	26
10	Nat North	A	Darlington	1350	W 2 - 1	Phenix 55 Dudley 89	1	27
13	Nat North	H	AFC Telford United	1626	W 2 - 0	Redshaw 72 Nottingham 90	1	28
20	Nat North	A	Harrogate Town	1931	W 2 - 1	Phenix 14 Walker 28	1	29
27	Nat North	A	Brackley Town	1010	L 1 - 2	Beesley 90	1	30
Feb 10	Nat North	A	York City	3366	L 0 - 1		1	31
17	Nat North	A	Alfreton Town	984	W 3 - 2	Livesey 5 Redshaw 25 Mafuta 45	1	32
20	Nat North	H	Bradford PA	982	D 2 - 2	Dudley 78 90	1	33
Mar 5	Nat North	H	Tamworth	1096	W 2 - 1	Dudley 71 Redshaw 90	1	34
17	Nat North	H	Spennymoor Town	1237	W 3 - 2	Piergianni 5 Walker 67 75	1	35
20	Nat North	A	North Ferriby United	470	D 1 - 1	Dudley 39	1	36
24	Nat North	A	Kidderminster Harriers	2524	D 4 - 4	Askew 81 Haughton 89 Dieseruvwe 90 Walker90	1	37
27	Nat North	H	Blyth Spartans	804	W 4 - 1	Haughton 44 Walker 50 (p) Dudley 58 Hogan 61	1	38
30	Nat North	H	Curzon Ashton	1541	W 2 - 1	Maynard 47 Redshaw 90	1	39
Apr 7	Nat North	H	Gainsborough Trinity	1288	W 1 - 0	Piergianni 45	1	40
14	Nat North	A	Nuneaton Town	937	W 2 - 0	Haughton 19 Piergianni 43	1	41
17	Nat North	A	Southport	1165	W 1 - 0	Walker 67	1	42
21	Nat North	H	Boston United	2466	L 1 - 2	Maynard 70	1	43
28	Nat North	A	Leamington	1275	W 4 - 0	Dudley 19 64 Phenix 38 48	1	44

GOALSCORERS	SG	CSG	Pens	Hat tricks	Total		SG	CSG	Pens	Hat tricks	Total
2016-17 Phenix					15	Piergianni	3				3
Redshaw	11	2	1	2	17	Askew	2				2
Dudley	10	2			12	Beesley	2				2
Phenix	10	2			11	Mafuta	2				2
Maynard	6	2	1		6	Allen					1
Walker	4		1		6	Livesey					1
Hogan	3				4	Opponents					1
Nottingham	4				4	Shelton					1
Diesenuvwe	2				3	Touray					1
Haughton	3				3						

SOLIHULL MOORS

Club Contact Details 0121 705 6770
The Automated Technology Group Stadium, Damson Park, Damson Parkway, Solihull B91 2PP
info@solihullmoorsfc.co.uk

Founded: 2007	**Nickname:** Moors	**Manager:** Tim Flowers - 20/06/2018

Previous Names: Today's club was formed after the amalgamation of Solihull Borough and Moor Green in 2007.
Previous Leagues: None

Club Colours (change): Blue with yellow trim

Ground Capacity: 3,050 **Seats:** 770 **Covered:** 1,000 **Clubhouse:** Yes **Shop:** Yes
Previous Grounds: None
Record Attendance: 2,658 v Hartlepool United, National League, 07/10/2017 (Non-League Day)
Nearest Railway Station Solihull & Birmingham within 3 miles away. **Bus Route** Nos. X12 or 966 from Town Centre.

RECORDS
Victory: 7-2 v Corby Town, Conference North, 12/02/2011.
Defeat: 0-6 v Harrogate Town, Conference North, 23/01/2016.
Appearances: Carl Motteram - 71 (2007-08)

HONOURS
FA Comps: None
League: National North 2015-16.
County FA: Birmingham Senior Cup 2015-16.

08-09	09-10	10-11	11-12	12-13	13-14	14-15	15-16	16-17	17-18
Conf N 16	Conf N 17	Conf N 7	Conf N 19	Conf N 9	Conf N 8	Conf N 12	Nat N 1	Nat 16	Nat 18
FAC 2Q	FAC 3Q	FAC 3Q	FAC 4Q	FAC 3Q	FAC 4Q	FAC 2Q	FAC 3Q	FAC 2P	FAC 1P
FAT 3Q	FAT 3Q	FAT 3Q	FAT 1P	FAT 2P	FAT 3Q	FAT 1P	FAT 1P	FAT 1P	FAT 2P

2017-18 STATS
Goals Total 54 **Games Without Scoring** 20 (3) **Total No. of Scorers** 18 **Total Clean Sheets** 12
Most Consecutive Scoring Games 6 **Best Unbeaten Run** 10 **Most Consecutive Clean Sheets** 5
Best Att: 2,658 v Hartlepool United, National League *Number in brackets denotes consecutive runs.*

2017-18 MATCH LINE-UPS

Match Number	Total
Trueman	4
Green K	37
Kelleher	42
Carter	49
Murombedzi	32
Cullinane-Liburd	13
Carline	38
Afolayan	33
Edwards	10
Thomas (3)	6
Tonks	3
Kettle	18
Dunkley	10
Vaughan	13
Cleary	2
Benbow	3
Campbell	14
Green P	24
Westbrooke	2
Daly	43
Fox	5
Richards	12
McDonald	5
Payne	3
Brodie	5
Maye	3
Bannister	3
Hylton	32
Bowen	10
Asante	11
Townsend	5
Camwell	4
Sammons	2
Higgs	1
Martin	4
St Ledger	1
Coyle	0
Acton	1
Thomas (37)	27
O'Leary	25
Atkinson	3
Osborne	24
Reckord	19
Storer	19
Frempah	1
Martinez	2
Yussuf	13
Reid	15
Williams	14
Lait	6
Sterling-James	8
RESULT	

RESULT: L L D L W L L W L D L L L D W L W L L D L D W L W D L W W D L W W L W D L D D W D D W W W D W L

SOLIHULL MOORS MATCH RESULTS 2017-18

Date	Comp	H/A	Opponents	Att:	Result	Goalscorers	Pos	No.
Aug 8	Nat Lg	A	Leyton Orient	4411	L 1 - 3	Afolayan 76	18	1
12	Nat Lg	A	Boreham Wood	319	L 1 - 4	Kelleher 32	24	2
15	Nat Lg	H	Barrow	558	D 3 - 3	Kettle 61 Afolayan 70 Carter 73	23	3
19	Nat Lg	H	FC Halifax Town	684	L 0 - 1		23	4
26	Nat Lg	A	Torquay United	1862	W 2 - 1	Campbell 47 Vaughan 74	22	5
28	Nat Lg	H	Tranmere Rovers	1312	L 0 - 2		22	6
Sept 2	Nat Lg	A	Aldershot Town	1803	L 0 - 1		23	7
5	Nat Lg	H	Chester	651	W 2 - 0	Afolayan 17 77	21	8
9	Nat Lg	H	Macclesfield United	808	L 0 - 1		22	9
12	Nat Lg	A	Woking	1402	L 1 - 2	Carter 74	22	10
16	Nat Lg	A	Bromley	1003	L 0 - 1		23	11
23	Nat Lg	H	Dagenham & Redbridge	625	D 2 - 2	Carter 11 Afolayan 40	23	12
30	Nat Lg	A	Dover Athletic	2795	L 0 - 1		23	13
Oct 3	Nat Lg	H	Ebbsfleet United	579	L 1 - 3	Maye 56	23	14
7	Nat Lg	H	Hartlepool	2658	L 1 - 2	Carter 86 (pen)	23	15
14	FAC 4Q	H	**Ossett Town**	415	D 1 - 1	Murombedzi 20		16
17	FAC 4Q	A	**Ossett Town**	1176	W 2 - 1	Kettle 8 Carter 45 (pen)		17
21	Nat Lg	A	Guiseley	812	L 2 - 4	Afolayan 34 67	24	18
24	Nat Lg	A	Eastleigh	2577	W 2 - 1	Hylton 4 Afolayan 56	24	19
27	Nat Lg	H	AFC Fylde	668	L 0 - 4		24	20
Nov 5	FAC 1	H	**Wycombe Wanderers**	1544	L 0 - 2			21
11	Nat Lg	H	Sutton United	729	L 0 - 2		24	22
18	Nat Lg	A	Maidstone United	2463	D 1 - 1	Thomas 64	23	23
21	Nat Lg	A	Wrexham	3896	L 0 - 1		24	24
25	Nat Lg	H	Gateshead	634	D 1 - 1	Atkinson 65	24	25
Dec 2	Nat Lg	H	Leyton Orient	1118	W 1 - 0	Daly 58	24	26
9	Nat Lg	A	Chester	1430	L 0 - 1		24	27
18	FAT 1	H	**Tranmere Rovers**	215	W 2 - 0	Osborne 7 Hylton 40		28
23	Nat Lg	H	Boreham Wood	419	D 0 - 0		24	29
26	Nat Lg	A	Maidenhead United	1261	L 0 - 1		24	30
30	Nat Lg	A	Barrow	1315	W 2 - 1	Carter 57 Reckord 84 pen	24	31
Jan 1	Nat Lg	H	Maidenhead United	602	W 3 - 1	Afolayan 63 72 Carter 64	21	32
6	Nat Lg	A	Macclesfield Town	1229	D 0 - 0		22	33
13	FAT 2	A	**Spennymoor Town**	570	L 0 - 2			34
20	Nat Lg	H	Woking	638	W 3 - 0	Thomas 6 Hylton 57 72	21	35
27	Nat Lg	A	Dagenham & Redbridge	2217	W 3 - 1	Yussuf 11 12 Afolayan 77	21	36
Feb 10	Nat Lg	A	Ebbsfleet United	1117	L 0 - 1			37
17	Nat Lg	H	Dover Athletic	679	W 3 - 2	Storer 29 Thomas 75 pen Reid 84	21	38
20	Nat Lg	H	Wrexham	1228	D 0 - 0		21	39
Mar 10	Nat Lg	A	Sutton United	1990	L 0 - 1		21	40
13	Nat Lg	A	Gateshead	486	D 2 - 2	Reid 46 Lait 87	21	41
17	Nat Lg	H	Torquay United	781	D 1 - 1	Yussuf 82	21	42
20	Nat Lg	H	Bromley	624	W 2 - 0	Thomas 13 Reid 90	21	43
24	Nat Lg	A	F.C.Halifax Town	1849	D 0 - 0		21	44
30	Nat Lg	H	Aldershot Town	1734	D 0 - 0		20	45
Apr 7	Nat Lg	A	Hartlepool	2782	W 1 - 0	Yussuf 88	20	46
10	Nat Lg	H	Maidstone United	665	W 1 - 0	Williams 25	19	47
14	Nat Lg	H	Guiseley	915	W 3 - 1	Frempah (og) 6 Osborne 19 Kelleher 60	17	48
21	Nat Lg	A	AFC Fylde	2045	D 1 - 1	Sterling-James 5	16	49
24	Nat Lg	A	Tranmere Rovers	418	W 2 - 1	Osborne 32 Reid 64	14	50
28	Nat Lg	H	Eastleigh	1014	L 1 - 4	Yussuf 75	18	51

GOALSCORERS	SG	CSG	Pens	Hat tricks	Total		SG	CSG	Pens	Hat tricks	Total
2016-17 Asante					12	Campbell					1
Afolayan	8	2			11	Daly					1
Carter	7	2	2		7	Lait					1
Yussuf	4				5	Maye					1
Hylton	3				4	Murombedzi					1
Reid	4				4	Opponents					1
Thomas	4		1		4	Reckord		1			1
Osborne	3				3	Sterling-James					1
Kelleher	2				2	Storer					1
Kettle	2				2	Vaughan					1
Atkinson					1	Williams					1

SUTTON UNITED

Club Contact Details 0208 644 4440
Borough Sports Ground, Gander Green Lane, Sutton, Surrey SM1 2EY
info@suttonunited.net

Founded: 1898   **Nickname:** The U's   **Manager:** Paul Doswell - 2008
Previous Names: Club formed after the merger of Sutton Guild Rovers and Sutton Association (formerley Sutton St Barnabas FC).
Previous Leagues: Sutton Junior, Southern Suburban, Athenian 1921-63, Isthmian 1963-86, 91-99, 2000-04, 2008-11, Conference 1999-2000, 04-08

Club Colours (change): Amber

Ground Capacity: 7,032   **Seats:** 765   **Covered:** 1,250   **Clubhouse:** Yes   **Shop:** Yes
Previous Grounds: Western Road, Manor Lane, London Road, The Find
Record Attendance: 14,000 v Leeds United - FA Cup 4th Round 24/01/1970
Nearest Railway Station West Sutton a few minutes walk from the ground.

RECORDS
Victory: 11-1 v Clapton - 1966 and v Leatherhead - 1982-83 both Isthmian League
Defeat: 0-13 v Barking - Athenian League 1925-26
Goalscorer: Paul McKinnon - 279
Appearances: Larry Pritchard - 781 (1965-84)
Additional: Received £100,000 from AFC Bournemouth for Efan Ekoku 1990

HONOURS
FA Comps: None
League: Athenian League 1927-28, 45-46, 57-58. Isthmian League 1966-67, 84-85, 85-86, 98-99, 2010-11. National League South 2015-16.
County FA: London Senior Cup 1957-58, 82-83. Surrey Senior Cup 1945-46, 64-65, 67-68, 69-70, 79-80, 82-83, 83-84, 84-85, 85-86, 86-87, 87-88, 92-93, 94-95, 98-99, 2002-03.

08-09		09-10		10-11		11-12		12-13		13-14		14-15		15-16		16-17		17-18	
Isth P	5	Isth P	2	Isth P	1	Conf S	4	Conf S	6	Conf S	2	Conf S	15	Nat S	1	Nat	12	Nat	3
FAC	1P	FAC	1P	FAC	1Q	FAC	2P	FAC	2Q	FAC	1P	FAC	3Q	FAC	4Q	FAC	5P	FAC	1P
FAT	3Qr	FAT	1Q	FAT	1Q	FAT	1Pr	FAT	3Q	FAT	3Q	FAT	1P	FAT	3Pr	FAT	3Pr	FAT	3P

2017-18 STATS
Goals Total 77   **Games Without Scoring** 9 (2)   **Total No. of Scorers** 20   **Total Clean Sheets** 15
Most Consecutive Scoring Games 12   **Best Unbeaten Run** 8   **Most Consecutive Clean Sheets** 2
Best Att: 3,541 v Aldershot Town, National League   *Number in brackets denotes consecutive runs.*

2017-18 MATCH LINE-UPS

Match Number	1	2	3	4	5	6	7	8	9	10	11	12	13	14	15	16	17	18	19	20	21	22	23	24	25	26	27	28	29	30	31	32	33	34	35	36	37	38	39	40	41	42	43	44	45	46	47	48	49	50	51	52				Total
Butler	x	x	x	x	x	x	x	x	x	x	x	x	x	x	x	x	x	x	x	x	x	x	x	x	x	x	x	x	x					x	x	x	x	x	x	x	x	x	x	x	x	x	x	x	x	x	x				48
Spence	x	xs	s	sx	x			s	s	sx	x	x	x	s	xs		s	s	s	s				s	x	x	x	s	sx	s	sx			x	s																					17
Beckwith	x	x	x	x												s	x	x	x	x	x					s			sx		s									s	x	x	s	s	s	x	s	s	x	s				14
Collins	x	x	x	x	x	x	x	x			x	x	x	x	x	x	x	x	x	x	x		x	x	x	x	x	x	x	x			x	x	x	x	x	x	x	x	x	x	xs	xr		x	x	x	x				46
Thomas (3)	x	x	x	x	x	x	x	x	x	x	x	x	x	x	x	x		sx	xs	x	x			x	x	s	x		x	x	x	s	x	x	x	x	x	x	x	sx	s	x	x	x	x	x				xs				41
Bailey	xs	x	x	x	x	x	x	xs			x	sx	x	x	x	xs		sx	sx	x	x	x	x	x	x		s	xs	xs												x	x	x	x	x								34
Davis	x	xs	x	xs	xs	s	sx	s	x	x	xs		s		sx	xs	x	x	x	x	xs	xs			x	xs	x	x	x		s	xs	x	xs	sx	x	x	x	x	x	xs	x		xs	x				xs	s				42
Eastmond	x	x	x	x	x	x	x	x							xs	x	xs	x	xs	x	x			sx	xs	x	xs	xs	x	x			xs	xs	x	x	x	x	x	xs	x	x	x		xs	x								41
Cadogan	x	x	sx	sx	sx	sx	x	x	xs	xs	xs	xs	s	x	xs		s	x	xs	x		x	xs	x	x	x	xs	sx	x	sx	s	xs	sx			x		xs	x	xs	xs	xs	xs	xs	sx	s	s	x	xs	sx				45
Dundas	x	x	x	sx	x	sx	x	sx	x	sx	x	sx	s	sx	s	xs	x	x	x	x	xs	xs	x	xs	x	s	x	sx	s	s	xs	s	x	x	sx	x	sx		sx	sx	sx	sx	sx	sx	x	s	xs							41
Lafayette	x	x	xs	xs	sx						x	x	x	xs			xs	x	sx	x					x	xs	sx	sx	sx	sx	s	s							sx	x	x	sx	sx	sx										32
Wright	sx	xs	x	x	x	xs					xs	sx	xs	xs	s	x	xs	sx	xs	x	xs	xs	xs		s	sx		sx	x	x	xs	sx	sx	x	x	xs	x	x	xs	x	s	xs	xs	xs	xs	xs	xs	xs	xs	x	xs				46
John	x	x	x	x	s	x	x	x	x	x	x	x	x	x	x	x	x	x		sx	x	s	x			x		x	xs	x	x	x	x	x		x		x	x	x	x	x	x	x			s	s	x	x	x				39
Monakana	s	s	x	s	s																																																		1
Emmanuel	s	xs	s	s	sx	sx	xs	xs	x	s	sx	xs	xs	s	sx	sx																																						11
Taylor	s	sx				x	x	x	sx	xs	x	x	x	xs	sx	x	s	xs	x	sx	xs	xs		s	sx	sx	s	sx	x	s	sx	x						s	s						sx	sx	x	x	x					32
Amankwaah			x	x	s	x	s																																															3
Jeffrey				s	s		sx	sx	sx	sx	s	sx	xs	sx	sx		sx	sx	6x	s																																			12
Walton				sx	x	x	xs	x	sx	x	xs	x	x				xs	s			s	s	x	x	x	x	x		x	x	xs	x	s		s	xs	xs	x	x		sx	x	xs	s	x	xs								32
Brown				s		s	s										s		s		s					s			s												s														0
Downer											xs	s		x		s	s				s	sx	x	x	x	x	x	s	xs	x		x	xs	x	x	s	xs	x	s	s	s	sx					xs	x				s		18
Thomas (30)											xs				x		s																																					3
Bentley											s	s			s																																							0
Coombes									sx								s	sx	sx	sx	sx	s				sx	sx	sx	xs	xs	s	x			s	sx	sx	sx	xs	s														16
Bolarinwa																	x	xs	x	xs	sx	x	xs	x	x	s	x	xs	sx	xs	sx	xs	x	xs	sx	x	xs	x	x			x		x	xs				x	x	x			27
Egan																	sx	sx	sx	sx	s																																	4
Stearn																	sx	s			sx	xs													sx	s			sx	sx	sx	sx	s	sx	sx	s	s							11
Morris																	s																																					0
Lema																	s																																					0
Thomas (19)																							x	x	x	x		x	x	x	x	x	x		x	x	x	x	x	x	x	x	x		x						x				21
Evans																							x	x	x	x		s																											4
Beautyman																							x	xs	x	x	xr								sx	xs	xs	xs	xs	xs	s	x	x	xs	sx	xs	sx	xs						17
Hudson-Odoi																																										s	sx	sx	s										2
Harrison																														x	x	xs	x	x	x	s	x	xs	sx	xs	xs	s		sx	s									13
RESULT	W	L	W	W	W	L	W	L	D	W	L	W	D	D	W	W	D	D	D	L	W	W	L	W	W	L	W	L	W	L	W	L	D	W	W	W	L	W	D	D	W	W	W	W	L	L	L	D	L	W	W	L				

SUTTON UNITED MATCH RESULTS 2017-18

Date	Comp	H/A	Opponents	Att:	Result	Goalscorers	Pos	No.
Aug 5	Nat Lg	H	Leyton Orient	3,198	W 2 - 0	Collins (pen) Beckwith	2	1
8	Nat Lg	A	Eastleigh	1,744	L 0 - 1		8	2
12	Nat Lg	A	Tranmere Rovers	5,050	W 1 - 0	Dundas 32	5	3
15	Nat Lg	H	Macclesfield Town	1,986	W 2 - 1	Emmanuel 85 Wright 86	2	4
19	Nat Lg	A	Chester	1,670	W 3 - 2	John 5 Wright 44 Cadogan 90	1	5
25	Nat Lg	H	Maidstone United	2,312	L 1 - 3	Wright 35	2	6
28	Nat Lg	A	Bromley	2,239	W 1 - 0	Eastmond 24	1	7
Sept 2	Nat Lg	H	Maidenhead United	2,158	L 0 - 2		4	8
9	Nat Lg	H	Gateshead	1,805	D 1 - 1	Walton 28	5	9
12	Nat Lg	A	Dagenham & Redbridge	1,261	W 2 - 1	Dundas 45 Davis 90	1	10
16	Nat Lg	A	Woking	2,193	L 0 - 2		4	11
23	Nat Lg	H	Barrow	1,909	W 3 - 2	Thomas 26 Taylor 49 Emmanuel 52	1	12
30	Nat Lg	A	Wrexham	4.815	D 1 - 1	Lafayette 90	5	13
Oct 3	Nat Lg	H	Dover Athletic	2,206	D 2 - 2	Wright 70 Cadogan 80	5	14
7	Nat Lg	H	AFC Fylde	2,127	W 2 - 1	Dundas 41 Grand 42 (og)	5	15
14	FAC 4Q	A	**Paulton Rovers**	601	W 3 - 2	**Cadogan 10 49 John 54**		16
21	Nat Lg	A	Hartlepool United	4526	D 1 - 1	Wright 90	5	17
24	Nat Lg	A	Aldershot Town	2259	D 2 - 2	John 5 Dundas 31	4	18
27	Nat Lg	H	Ebbsfleet United	2197	D 0 - 0		4	19
Nov 5	FAC 1	A	**Cambridge United**	3070	L 0 - 1			20
11	Nat Lg	A	Solihull Moors	729	W 2 - 0	Jeffrey 29 Dundas 86	4	21
18	Nat Lg	H	FC Halifax Town	1968	W 3 - 2	Lafayette 45 73 Dundas 58	3	22
21	Nat Lg	H	Torquay United	1970	L 0 - 1		4	23
25	Nat Lg	A	Guiseley	929	W 2 - 0	Dundas 12 Bolarinwa 36	1	24
Dec 2	Nat Lg	H	Eastleigh	1967	W 2 - 0	Bolarinwa 33 Wright 82	1	25
8	Nat Lg	A	Leyton Orient	4180	L 1 - 4	Wright 83	2	26
16	FAT 1	H	**Truro City**	576	W 1 - 0	**Dundas 89**		27
23	Nat Lg	H	Tranmere Rovers	2237	L 1 - 3	Davis 25	4	28
26	Nat Lg	A	Boreham Wood	455	W 4 - 0	Bailey 2 45 Collins 32 Eastmond 73	2	29
30	Nat Lg	A	Macclesfield Town	2246	L 0 - 1		3	30
Jan 1	Nat Lg	H	Boreham Wood	2007	D 1 - 1	Collins 57 (pen)	3	31
6	Nat Lg	A	Gateshead	493	W 2 - 0	Wright 74 81	3	32
13	FAT 2	H	**Hendon**	785	W 3 - 0	**Cadogan 35 Coombes 74 Wright 88**		33
20	Nat Lg	H	Dagenham & Redbridge	2071	W 2 - 1	Wright 57 Bolarinwa 62	2	34
Feb 3	FAT 3	A	**Brackley Town**	767	L 1 - 3	**Wright 90**		35
10	Nat Lg	A	Dover Athletic	1027	W 1 - 0	Cadogan 26	4	36
13	Nat Lg	A	Barrow	643	D 1 - 1	Wright 72	3	37
17	Nat Lg	H	Wrexham	2621	D 1 - 1	Walton 47	5	38
20	Nat Lg	A	Torquay United	1302	W 3 - 2	Harrison 6 Walton 45 Collins 90	2	39
24	Nat Lg	H	Guiseley	1915	W 4 - 0	Thomas 34 Harrison 50 Eastmond 56 Coddington 75 (og)	2	40
Mar 6	Nat Lg	H	Woking	2019	W 2 - 1	Harrison 33 Bolarinwa 54	2	41
10	Nat Lg	H	Solihull Moors	1990	W 1 - 0	Bolarinwa 37	2	42
17	Nat Lg	A	Maidstone United	2065	L 0 - 1		3	43
24	Nat Lg	H	Chester	2195	W 3 - 2	Beautyman 13 Harrison 45 Stearn 79	1	44
Apr 2	Nat Lg	H	Bromley	2233	L 0 - 3		2	45
7	Nat Lg	A	AFC Fylde	1789	L 1 - 2	Wright 20	2	46
10	Nat Lg	A	FC Halifax Town	1274	L 1 - 2	Lafayette 82	3	47
14	Nat Lg	H	Hartlepool United	2272	D 1 - 1	Lafayette 9	3	48
17	Nat Lg	A	Maidenhead United	2201	L 1 - 2	Eastmond 87	3	49
21	Nat Lg	A	Ebbsfleet United	2852	W 1 - 0	Bolarinwa 77	3	50
28	Nat Lg	H	Aldershot Town	3541	W 2 - 1	Wright 49 Lafayette79	3	51
May 4	P-O S-F	H	**Boreham Wood**	2730	L 2 - 3	Bolarinwa 82 Lafayette 90		52

GOALSCORERS	SG	CSG	Pens	Hat tricks	Total		SG	CSG	Pens	Hat tricks	Total
2016-17 Blamou					13	Bailey					2
Wright	14	4			15	Davis					2
Dundas	7				8	Emmanuel					2
Bolarinwa	6	2			7	Opponents					2
Lafayette	6				7	Thomas					2
Cadogan	5				6	Beautyman					1
Collins	4		2		4	Beckwith					1
Eastmond	4				4	Coombes					1
Harrison	4				4	Jeffrey					1
John	3				3	Stearn					1
Walton	3				3	Taylor					1

WREXHAM

Club Contact Details 01978 891 864
Racecourse Ground, Mold road, Wrexham LL11 2AH
info@wrexhamfc.tv

Founded: 1864   **Nickname:** The Robins   **Manager:** Sam Ricketts - 02/05/2018
Previous Names: Wrexham Athletic for the 1882-83 season only
Previous Leagues: The Combination 1890-94, 1896-1906, Welsh League 1894-96, Birmingham & District 1906-21,
     Football League 1921-2008

Club Colours (change): Red & white

Ground Capacity: 15,500   **Seats:** 10,771   **Covered:** 15,500   **Clubhouse:** Yes   **Shop:** Yes
Previous Grounds: Rhosddu Recreation Ground during the 1881-82 and 1882-83 seasons.
Record Attendance: 34,445 v Manchester United - FA Cup 4th Round 26/01/57
Nearest Railway Station Wrexham General is right next to the ground.

RECORDS
Victory: 10-1 v Hartlepool United - Division Four 03/03/62
Defeat: 0-9 v v Brentford - Division Three
Goalscorer: Tommy Bamford - 201 (1928-34)
Appearances: Arfon Griffiths - 591 (1959-61 & 62-79)
Additional: Paid £800,000 to Birmingham City for Bryan Hughes March 1997
       Received £212,000 from Liverpool for Joey Jones October 1978

HONOURS
FA Comps: Welsh FA Cup a record 23 times. FAW Premier Cup 1997-98, 99-00, 00-01, 02-03, 03-04. FA Trophy 2012-13.
League: Welsh Senior League 1894-95, 95-96. Combination 1900-01, 01-02, 02-03, 04-05.
     Football League Division Three 1977-78.
County FA: Denbighshire & Flintshire (Soames) Charity Cup 1894-95, 98-99, 1902-03, 04-05, 05-06, 08-09.

08-09	09-10	10-11	11-12	12-13	13-14	14-15	15-16	16-17	17-18
Conf 10	Conf 11	Conf 4	Conf 2	Conf 5	Conf 17	Conf 11	Nat 8	Nat 13	Nat 10
FAC 4Qr	FAC 2P	FAC 4Q	FAC 3Pr	FAC 1P	FAC 2P	FAC 3P	FAC 4Q	FAC 4Qr	FAC 4Q
FAT QFr	FAT 1Pr	FAT 2P	FAT 1P	FAT 1P	FAT F	FAT 2P	FAT 2P	FAT 1P	FAT 1P

2017-18 STATS   **Goals Total** 49   **Games Without Scoring** 16 (2)   **Total No. of Scorers** 12   **Total Clean Sheets** 22
Most Consecutive Scoring Games 5   **Best Unbeaten Run** 16   **Most Consecutive Clean Sheets** 5
Best Att: 6,511 v Chester, National League   Number in brackets denotes consecutive runs.

2017-18 MATCH LINE-UPS

Match Number	1	2	3	4	5	6	7	8	9	10	11	12	13	14	15	16	17	18	19	20	21	22	23	24	25	26	27	28	29	30	31	32	33	34	35	36	37	38	39	40	41	42	43	44	45	46	47	48	Total
Dunn	x	x	x	x				s							s	s		x	x	x	x	x	x	x	x	s	x	x	x	x	x	x	x	x	x	x	x	x	x	x	x	x	x	x	x	x	x	x	36
Jennings	x	x	x	x	x	x	x	x	x			x	x	x	x	x	x	x	xs	xs			x	x		x	x	xs	x	xs	x	x	x	x	x	x			x	x	x	x	x	x	x	x	x	x	41
Smith M (4)	x	x	x	x	xr	x	x	x	xs	x	x		x	x	x	x	x	x	x	x	x	x	x		x	x	x	x	x	x	x	x	x	x	x	xs		x	x	x	x	x	x	x	x	x	x	x	45
Pearson	x	x	x	x	x	x	x	x	x	x	x			x		x		x	x	x	x	x	x		x	xs	x	x	x	x	x	x	x	x	x	x	x	x	x	x		x	x	x	x	x	x	x	45
Wedgbury	x	x	x	x	x	x	x	x	x	x	x	x	xr		x	x	x		x	x	x	x	xs			x	x	x	x	x	x	x	x	x	x	x	x	x	x	x			x	x	x	x			42
Holroyd	xs								s	sx	xs	xs	x	x	xs	xs	x	xs	x	xs	x	x	x	x	x		x	x	x	x	x	x	x	xs	x	x	x	xs	x	x	x	x	x	xs					35
Carrington	xs	x	xs	x	xr		s		sx	x		sx	x	xs	x	sx	xs	sx	sx	x	x		x	sx	x		s	x	s	sx						sx	x				sx	s	s						28
Rutherford	xs	xs	xs	sx	xs	xs	sx	x	x	x	x	x	x	xs	xs	x	sx	x	x	x	x	x	x		x	xs	xs	x	xs	x	x	xf		x	s	xs	x	xs	s	x	xs	xs	x	x					44
Kelly	x	x	x	x	x	s	s	xs					xs	xs	x	x	x	x	x	x	xs	x	x	xs	xs	xs	xs	x		x	xs	x	x	x	xs	x	x	xs	x	x	xs	x							44
Roberts	x	x	x	x	x	s	sx	x	x	x	x	x		x	x	x	x	x	x	xs	x	x	x	x	x		x	x	x	x	x	x	x	x	x	x	x	x	x	xr			x	x					40
Boden	x	xs	xs	xs	xs	sx	sx	sx	sx	xs	s	s	sx	xs	xs	x	s	sx	s	s	sx			x		x	xs	x	x	xs	xs				s	sx	s	sx	xs	sx	x	sx	x						36
Massanka	sx	sx	sx	sx	xs	xs	xs	sx	sx	sx	s	s	sx	sx	s		sx	sx	sx	sx	sx	sx	sx	sx	s	xs	sx	sx	s																				25
Wright	sx	sx	x	s	sx	x	x	x	x	s	sx				sx	x					s						sx	s	sx	sx	sx	s		sx	sx	s	s	x	xs	s	sx	x							31
Mackreth	sx	sx	x	xs	s	s				sx	sx	sx	sx	sx	sx	sx	s	sx		s	sx	x	s	sx	x		x	s	sx	sx	s	sx	sx	s	sx	sx	s				sx	s	sx	x	xs	sx			34
Dibble	s	s	s	s	x	x	x	x	x	x					s	s	s	s	s	s	s		x	s	s	s	s	s	s	s	s	s	s	s			s			s	s	s	s	s					6
Hurst		s	sx	sx	sx	x	x	x	xs				sx	s	sx	xs	s			s	s		sx	s	s	x	x	s	sx		sx	sx	s	s	s														19
Smith L		s				sx	x	sx	x	xs		x					sx				sx				s	xs			s																				8
Marx			s		s	s		s		s							x			x																													2
Reid			sx	x	x	x	x	x	x	xs	x	xs	sx		xs	xs	sx										xs	xs	sx	x	xs	xs	xs																18
Preston						s	s	x	s	x	s	s																													0								1
Tharme								s										s																			x												1
Coddington											x	x	x	x	x	x																																	5
Miller																				sx	x	xs	xs	x	x																								6
McGregor																				sx																													1
Burrows																				sx																													1
Takyi																				sx																													1
Williams																				x																													1
Barratt																				s																													0
Quigley (L)																											xs	xs	xs			xs	xs	sx	x	x	x	xs	xs	xs	xs	sx	x	x	x	xs			17
Raven																											sx	s	s	s	s	s	s	s	x	x	s	s	sx	x	x	x	s	s					7
Deverdics																													x	xs	x	x	xs	xs	sx			x	sx	x	s	sx							12
Franks																											sx	sx	sx	x	s	s	sx	xs	sx	s													7
Ainge																											sx	sx	sx	sx	sx	sx	sx	sx	x	sx	sx												10
RESULT	L	W	L	W	L	W	W	W	D	D	D	W	D	D	W	L	W	L	D	W	W	W	L	W	L	L	D	D	D	W	D	D	W	D	D	W	D	L	D	L	L	L	L	D					

WREXHAM MATCH RESULTS 2017-18

Date	Comp	H/A	Opponents	Att:	Result	Goalscorers	Pos	No.
Aug 5	Nat Lg	H	Macclesfield Town	6118	L 0 - 1		22	1
8	Nat Lg	A	Maidenhead United	1632	W 2 - 1	Smith 40 77	12	2
12	Nat Lg	A	Dover Athletic	1012	L 0 - 1		16	3
15	Nat Lg	H	Gateshead	4097	W 1 - 0	Reid 70	10	4
19	Nat Lg	A	Maidstone United	2192	L 1 - 2	Reid 10	13	5
25	Nat Lg	H	Woking	3875	W 1 - 0	Jennings 43	11	6
28	Nat Lg	A	Boreham Wood	765	W 1 - 0	Reid 61	4	7
Sept 2	Nat Lg	H	Bromley	4032	W 2 - 0	Massanka 46 70	3	8
9	Nat Lg	A	Torquay United	1814	D 0 - 0		3	9
12	Nat Lg	H	Hartlepool United	4144	D 0 - 0		6	10
16	Nat Lg	H	Guiseley	3916	D 1 - 1	Wedgbury 90	9	11
23	Nat Lg	A	Tranmere Rovers	1835	W 1 - 0	Holroyd 58	5	12
30	Nat Lg	H	Sutton United	4815	D 1 - 1	Kelly 16	6	13
Oct 3	Nat Lg	A	FC Halifax Town	2136	D 0 - 0		6	14
7	Nat Lg	H	Eastleigh	3907	W 2 - 1	Pearson 73 Holroyd 78	5	15
14	**FAC 4Q**	**A**	**AFC Fylde**	**1390**	**L 0 - 1**			16
21	Nat Lg	A	Dagenham & Redbridge	1492	W 1 - 0	Roberts 90 (og)	3	17
24	Nat Lg	A	AFC Fylde	1816	L 0 - 1		3	18
27	Nat Lg	H	Leyton Orient	4432	D 2 - 2	Holroyd 1 71	3	19
Nov 7	Nat Lg	A	Chester	4079	W 1 - 0	Pearson 43	2	20
18	Nat Lg	H	Ebbsfleet United	4150	W 2 - 0	Holroyd 26 74	2	21
21	Nat Lg	H	Solihull Moors	3896	W 1 - 0	Rutherford 39	1	22
25	Nat Lg	A	Aldershot Town	2377	L 0 - 2		2	23
Dec 2	Nat Lg	H	Maidenhead United	3968	W 2 - 0	Holroyd 18 Jennings 75	2	24
8	Nat Lg	A	Macclesfield Town	2402	L 1 - 4	Boden 74	3	25
16	**FAT 1**	**H**	**Harrogate Town**	**1370**	**L 0 - 2**			26
23	Nat Lg	H	Dover Athletic	4980	D 0 - 0		2	27
26	Nat Lg	A	Barrow	1648	D 1 - 1	Pearson 25	4	28
Jan 1	Nat Lg	H	Barrow	4390	D 3 - 3	Holroyd 19 Jennings 45 Boden 76	5	29
6	Nat Lg	H	Torquay United	4242	W 4 - 0	HOLROYD 3 (9 37 89) Smith 30	4	30
20	Nat Lg	A	Hartlepool United	6833	W 2 - 0	Quigley 54 78	4	31
27	Nat Lg	H	Tranmere Rovers	6471	D 2 - 2	Quigley 12 Holroyd 16 (pen)	3	32
30	Nat Lg	A	Gateshead	658	D 0 - 0		3	33
Feb 3	Nat Lg	A	Guiselley	1338	W 2 - 0	Holroyd 16 Pearson 72	1	34
10	Nat Lg	H	FC Halifax Town	4998	D 1 - 1	Boden 19		35
17	Nat Lg	A	Sutton United	2621	D 1 - 1	Quigley 20	3	36
20	Nat Lg	H	Solihull Moors	1228	D 0 - 0		5	37
24	Nat Lg	H	Aldershot Town	4662	D 2 - 2	Quigley 21 57	6	38
Mar 11	Nat Lg	H	Chester	6511	W 2 - 0	Quigley 63 Deverdicks 69	4	39
17	Nat Lg	A	Woking	1458	D 2 - 2	Rutherford 33 Kelly 60	5	40
24	Nat Lg	H	Maidstone United	4443	W 1 - 0	Pearson 75	4	41
30	Nat Lg	A	Bromley	1403	D 1 - 1	Jennings 51	3	42
Apr 2	Nat Lg	H	Boreham Wood	4746	L 0 - 1		3	43
7	Nat Lg	A	Eastleigh	1785	D 1 - 1	Quigley 20	6	44
10	Nat Lg	A	Ebbsfleet United	1376	L 0 - 3		6	45
14	Nat Lg	H	Dagenham & Redbridge	4193	L 1 - 2	Rutherford 23	7	46
21	Nat Lg	A	Leyton Orient	5166	L 0 - 1		10	47
28	Nat Lg	H	AFC Fylde	3931	D 0 - 0		10	48

GOALSCORERS	SG	CSG	Pens	Hat tricks	Total		SG	CSG	Pens	Hat tricks	Total
2016-17 Rooney					11	Massanka	1				2
Holroyd	9	2		1	13	Deverdicks					1
Quigley	6				8	Opponents					1
Pearson	5				5	Wedgbury					1
Jennings	4				4						
Boden	3				3						
Reid	3	2			3						
Rutherford	3				3						
Smith	2				3						
Kelly	2				2						

MACCLESFIELD TOWN

Club Contact Details 01625 264 686
Moss Rose Ground, London Road, Macclesfield SK11 7SP
reception@mtfc.co.uk

Founded: 1874 **Nickname:** The Silkmen **Manager:** John Askey
Previous Names: Macclesfield Football & Athletic Club, Hallifield FC, Macclesfield FC - Current name since 1946.
Previous Leagues: Manchester. Cheshire County 1946-68. Northern Premier 1968-87. Conference 1987-97. Football League 1997-2012.

Club Colours (change): Blue & white

Ground Capacity: 6,335 **Seats:** 2,599 **Covered:** Yes **Clubhouse:** Yes **Shop:** Yes
Previous Grounds: Rostron Field 1874-1891.
Record Attendance: 9,008 v Winsford United - Cheshire Senior Cup 04.02.1948.
Nearest Railway Station Macclesfield - roughly 20min walk away. **Bus Route** Nos. 9 & 14 from the bus station.

RECORDS
Victory: 15-0 v Chester St Marys - Cheshire Senior Cup Second Round 16.02.1886.
Defeat: 1-13 v Tranmere Rovers Reserves - 03.05.1929.
Goalscorer: Albert Valentine scored the most goals in a season when he recorded 83 during 1933-34.
Appearances: John Askey - 700+ (1984-2003).
Additional: Paid: £40,000 for Danny Swailes from Bury, 2004-05.
Received: £300,000 for Rickie Lambert from Stockport County, 2002-03.

HONOURS
FA Comps: FA Trophy 1969-70, 95-96.
League: Manchester 1908-09, 10-11. Cheshire County 1931-32, 32-33, 53-54, 60-61, 63-64, 67-68.
Northern Premier League 1968-69, 69-70, 86-87. Conference 1994-95, 96-97. National 2017-18.
County FA: Cheshire Senior 1889-90, 90-91, 93-94, 95-96, 1910-11, 29-30, 34-35, 50-51, 51-52, 53-54, 59-60, 63-64, 68-69, 70-71, 72-73, 82-83, 90-91, 91-92, 97-98, 1999-00, 14-15. Staffordshire Senior Cup 1992-93, 95-96.

	08-09		09-10		10-11		11-12		12-13		13-14		14-15		15-16		16-17		17-18	
FL 2	20	FL 2	19	FL 2	15	FL 2	24	Conf	11	Conf	15	Conf	6	Nat	10	Nat	9	Nat	1
FAC	3P	FAC	1P	FAC	2P	FAC	3Pr	FAC	4P	FAC	3Pr	FAC	4Qr	FAC	1P	FAC	2Pr	FAC	1P
FLC	2P	FLC	1P	FLC	1P	FLC	2P	FAT	1P	FAT	1P	FAT	1P	FAT	3Pr	FAT	F	FAT	1P

2017-18 STATS **Goals Total** 72 **Games Without Scoring** 9 (3) **Total No. of Scorers** 18 **Total Clean Sheets** 19
Most Consecutive Scoring Games 12 **Best Unbeaten Run** 11 **Most Consecutive Clean Sheets** 3
Best Att: 4,201 v Dagenham & Redbridge, National League *Number in brackets denotes consecutive runs.*

2017-18 MATCH LINE-UPS

Match Number	1	2	3	4	5	6	7	8	9	10	11	12	13	14	15	16	17	18	19	20	21	22	23	24	25	26	27	28	29	30	31	32	33	34	35	36	37	38	39	40	41	42	43	44	45	46	47	48	49	Total
Jalal	x	x	xs			x	x	x	x	x	x	x	x	x	x	xs			x		x	x	x	x	x	x	x	xr				sx	x	x	x	x	x	x	x	x	x	x	x	x	x	x	x			43
Yates	x	x	x	s	x	x	x	x																																										7
Baba	x	x	x	x	xs	sx	sx	s	x	x	x	s				sx	s	s	s	xs	s						s				x	sx	xs							s										15
Fitzpatrick	x	x	x		x	x	x	x	x	xs	x	x	x	xs	x	x	x	x	x	x	x	x	x	x	x	x	x	x	x	x	s	x	x	x	x	x	x	x	x	x	x	x	x	x	x	x	x			48
Lowe	x	x	x		x	x	x	x	x	x	x	x	x	x	x	x	x	x	x	x	x	x	x	x			x	x	x	x	x	x	x	x	x	x	x	x	x	x	x	x	x	x	x	x	x			48
Pilkington	x	xs				s	s	x	x	x	x	xs	x	x	sx	x	x	x	x		s	s	sx	x	x	x		x	sx	x		x	s	s	x	x	x	s	x	x	x					s				35
Durrell	xs	xs			xs	xs	x	xs	x	x	xs	xs	xs	xs	x	x	x	xs	x	x	sx		sx	xs	sx	x	x	x	xs	xs	xs	xs	x	xs	x	xs	x	x												38
Lloyd	x	x	xs	sx	s	x			sx	xs	x	x	x		x	x	x	x	x	x	x	x	x	xs	x	x	s	x																		s				28
Burgess	x	xs	s	x	xs	x	x	xs	sx	xs	xs	sx	s	sx	x	s	s	s	s	x	xs	x	xs	x	xs	xs	s	x		x	x	s	sx	s	sx	s	sx	s	sx	s	s	sx	xs	s	sx	s	sx			33
Whitaker	x	x	x	xs	x	x	x	x	x	xs	xs	x	s	x	xs	sx	x	x	xs	x	x	x	x	x	s	x		x	x	x	x	x	x	x	x	x	x	x	x	x	x	x	x							45
Marsh	x	x	x	xs	x	xs	xs	x		sx	s	sx	sx	sx	xs	sx	sx	sx	x	sx		sx	x	x	x	x	sx	x	sx	xs	xs	xs	xs	s	sx	s	xs	x	xs	xs	x	x	x							44
Richards	sx	x	s	xs	sx	s	sx	xs	s																s	s	xs				sx					sx														7
Wilson	sx	sx	sx	xs	x	sx	x	x	xs	xs	xs	xs	xs	s	xs	xs	x	x		sx	xs	sx	x	x		s	x	s	sx	x	xs	x	s	sx	s	s	x	s	sx	sx	sx	sx	s	x						37
Kennedy	s	sx	x	x	x	x	x	x	x	sx	xs	sx	x	x	x	s			m		sx	x	sx	x	x	x	x	xs	x	x	sx	sx	s	s	s	s	s	sx	sx	sx	sx	s	x							35
Hancox	s	s	sx	x	s	x	x	x	x	xs	x	x	x	sx	x	xs	s	sx	xs	x	xs	x	s	sx	sx	xs	x	xs	x	s	sx	x	x	xs	xs	xs	x	x	x	x	x									41
Arthur	s	sx	xs	xs	sx		s	sx	sx	xs	s	sx	x	s	x	xs	xs	xs		s	sx	s	s	s	s	s	sx	x																						16
O'Brien			sx	x	x	s	s	s																																										3
Toure		x	x	x	x	xs	xs	x	xs	xs		s			sx		sx		s	s	sx																													12
Thompson			s			s																																												0
Whitehead					sx	x	x	x	x	x	x	x			xs	x	x	x	x	x	x		xs	x	x	x	x	x	x	x	x	x	xs		xs	xs	x	xs												37
Hodgkiss							x	x	x	x	x				x	x	x	x	x	x	x	x	xs		sx				x	x	x	x	x	xs	x	x	x	x	xs	xs	x	xs								32
Ramsbottom									s	s	s	sx	x	s		s		s	s	s	s	s	s	s	x	x	xs	s	s	s	s	s	s	s	s	s	s	s	s	s	s	s	s	s						7
Blissett																							sx	x	x	x	x	x	x	x	x	x	xr	x	x	xs														16
Evans																							s	xs	s	sx	xs	sx		sx	x	sx	x	x	x	xs	x	xs												14
Del Girolamo																																									s	s	s	s	s	s				0
RESULT	W	D	D	L	L	W	W	W	W	W	W	L	W	W	W	W	W	L	L	L	W	D	D	D	W	W	D	W	W	W	D	L	D	W	W	W	W	L	D	W	W	W	D	W	D	W	W			

MACCLESFIELD TOWN MATCH RESULTS 2017-18

Date	Comp	H/A	Opponents	Att:	Result		Goalscorers	Pos	No.
Aug 5	Nat Lg	A	Wrexham	6118	W	1 - 0	Baba 12	6	1
8	Nat Lg	H	Hartlepool United	1519	D	1 - 1	Cassidy 58	10	2
12	Nat Lg	H	Bromley	1281	D	0 - 0		10	3
15	Nat Lg	A	Sutton United	1986	L	1 - 2	Wilson 2	16	4
19	Nat Lg	A	Gateshead	633	L	0 - 3		18	5
25	Nat Lg	H	Dover Athletic	1270	W	1 - 0	Marsh 49	15	6
28	Nat Lg	A	Chester	2363	W	2 - 0	Hancox 7 Kennedy 62	10	7
Sept 2	Nat Lg	H	Woking	1289	L	1 - 3	Durrell 18	14	8
9	Nat Lg	A	Solihull Moors	808	W	1 - 0	Wilson 62	9	9
12	Nat Lg	H	AFC Fylde	1065	W	2 - 1	Wilson 14 90	7	10
16	Nat Lg	H	Maidstone United	1345	L	1 - 4	Arthur 80	12	11
23	Nat Lg	A	Torquay United	1835	W	1 - 0	Wilson 49	11	12
30	Nat Lg	H	Aldershot Town	1350	W	2 - 0	Lloyd 1 Durrell 58	3	13
Oct 3	Nat Lg	H	Guiseley	812	W	2 - 1	Whitaker 16 Durrell 86	1	14
7	Nat Lg	H	Ebbsfleet United	1635	W	1 - 0	Hancox 42	1	15
14	**FAC 4Q**	**A**	**Stourbridge**	**1152**	**W**	**5 - 0**	**Whitehead 10 Marsh 13 Durrell 45 Arthur 67 Burgess 78**		**16**
21	Nat Lg	A	Leyton Orient	4662	W	1 - 0	Wilson 45	1	17
24	Nat Lg	A	Dagenham & Redbridge	1185	L	0 - 1		2	18
28	Nat Lg	H	Eastleigh	1352	L	1 - 2	Whitehead 90	2	19
Nov 4	**FAC 1**	**A**	**Forest Green Rovers**	**1387**	**L**	**0 - 1**			**20**
11	Nat Lg	A	Barrow	1614	W	2 - 0	Hodgkiss 27 Durrell 61	4	21
18	Nat Lg	H	Boreham Wood	1324	D	0 - 0		4	22
21	Nat Lg	H	Tranmere Rovers	1709	D	2 - 2	Wilson 40 Marsh 90	3	23
25	Nat Lg	A	Maidenhead United	1165	D	1 - 1	Hyde 88	3	24
Dec 2	Nat Lg	A	Hartlepool United	3082	W	2 - 1	Lloyd 85 Lowe 90	1	25
9	Nat Lg	H	Wrexham	2402	W	4 - 1	WILSON 3 (6 78 82) Fitzpatrick 90	1	26
23	Nat Lg	A	Bromley	1445	D	1 - 1	Lloyd 39	1	27
26	Nat Lg	H	FC Halifax Town	2313	W	2 - 1	Whitehead 45 Marsh 78	1	28
30	Nat Lg	H	Sutton United	2246	W	1 - 0	Whitaker 10 (pen)	1	29
Jan 1	Nat Lg	A	FC Halifax Town	1962	W	4 - 1	HANCOX 3 (45 48 72) Wilson 60	1	30
6	Nat Lg	H	Solihull Moors	1771	D	0 - 0		1	31
9	**FAT 1**	**H**	**FC Halifax Town**	**503**	**L**	**0 - 1**			**32**
20	Nat Lg	A	AFC Fylde	1982	L	0 - 6		1	33
27	Nat Lg	H	Torquay United	1510	D	1 - 1	Whitehead 72	1	34
Feb 10	Nat Lg	H	Guiseley	1646	W	2 - 1	Blissett 61 Marsh 72	1	35
17	Nat Lg	A	Aldershot Town	4358	W	2 - 1	Whitaker 3 (pen) Blissett 48	1	36
20	Nat Lg	A	Tranmere Rovers	7385	W	4 - 1	Whitaker 45 62 (pen) Durrell 55 66	1	37
24	Nat Lg	H	Maidenhead United	1668	W	1 - 0	Wilson 90	1	38
Mar 10	Nat Lg	H	Barrow	1748	W	3 - 1	Hancox 35 Whitaker 70 Durrell 77	1	39
17	Nat Lg	A	Dover Athletic	837	L	0 - 2		1	40
21	Nat Lg	A	Maidstone United	1994	D	2 - 2	Whitehead 52 Durrell 75	1	41
27	Nat Lg	H	Gateshead	1537	W	1 - 0	Blissett 89	1	42
30	Nat Lg	H	Woking	2158	W	3 - 2	Blissett 35 Marsh 54 Whitehead 90	1	43
Apr 2	Nat Lg	H	Chester	2996	W	1 - 0	Whitehead 53	1	44
7	Nat Lg	A	Ebbsfleet United	1501	D	2 - 2	Blissett 29 Marsh 59	1	45
10	Nat Lg	A	Boreham Wood	602	W	2 - 0	Marsh 20 58	1	46
14	Nat Lg	H	Leyton Orient	3110	D	1 - 1	Whitaker 17	1	47
21	Nat Lg	A	Eastleigh	2372	W	2 - 0	Marsh 3 Hancox 60	1 (C)	48
28	Nat Lg	H	Dagenham & Redbridge	4201	W	2 - 0	Wilson 79 82	1	49

GOALSCORERS	SG	CSG	Pens	Hat tricks	Total		SG	CSG	Pens	Hat tricks	Total
2016-17 Holroyd					14	Baba					1
Wilson	9	2		1	14	Burgess					1
Marsh	9	2			10	Cassidy					1
Durrell	7	2			9	Fitzpatrick					1
Hancox	5			1	7	Hodgkiss					1
Whitehead	7				7	Hyde					1
Whitaker	7		3		7	Kennedy					1
Blissett	5	2			5	Lowe					1
Lloyd	3				3						
Arthur	2				2						

TRANMERE ROVERS

Club Contact Details 03330 144 452
Prenton Park, Prenton Road West, Birkenhead, Merseyside, CH42 9PY
timr@tranmererovers.co.uk

Founded: 1884   **Nickname:** Superwhite Army / Rovers   **Manager:** Micky Mellon
Previous Names: Belmont FC 1884-85.
Previous Leagues: West Lancashire 1889-97. The Combination 1897-1910. Lancashire Combination 1910-19. Central 1919-21. Football League 1921-2015.

Club Colours (change): White with blue trim

Ground Capacity: 16,567   **Seats:** 16,567   **Covered:** Yes   **Clubhouse:** Yes   **Shop:** Yes
Previous Grounds: Steeles Field 1884-87. Ravenshaws Field 1887-1912.
Record Attendance: 24,424, for an FA Cup tie against Stoke City on 5 February 1972

RECORDS
Victory: 13-4 v Oldham Athletic, Football League Division Three North, 26 December 1935
Goalscorer: Ian Muir - 180 (In 351+42 appearances). Bunny Bell scored 57 goals during the 1933-34 season.
Appearances: Ray Mathias - 637

HONOURS
FA Comps: Welsh FA Cup 1934-35.
League: The Combination 1907-08. Lancashire Combination 1913-14, 18-19. League Division Three North 1937-38.
County FA: Liverpool Senior Cup 1948-49, 49-50, 54-55, 69-70, 73-73, 73-74, 91-92, 94-95, 2011-12, 13-14.

	08-09	09-10	10-11	11-12	12-13	13-14	14-15	15-16	16-17	17-18
	FL 1 7	FL 1 19	FL 1 17	FL 1 12	FL 1 11	FL 1 21	FL 2 24	Nat 6	Nat 2	Nat 2
	FAC 2Pr	FAC 3P	FAC 1P	FAC 1P	FAC 3P	FAC 2P	FAC 3P	FAC 4Qr	FAC 4Q	FAC 1Pr
	FLC 1P	FLC 2P	FLC 2P	FLC 1P	FLC 2P	FLC 3P	FLC 1P	FAT 1P	FAT SF	FAT 1P

2017-18 STATS   **Goals Total** 88   **Games Without Scoring** 12 (3)   **Total No. of Scorers** 17   **Total Clean Sheets** 19
Most Consecutive Scoring Games 25   **Best Unbeaten Run** 7   **Most Consecutive Clean Sheets** 2
Best Att: 7,385 v Macclesfield Town, National League   Number in brackets denotes consecutive runs.

2017-18 MATCH LINE-UPS

Player	Total
Davies	45
Buxton	41
Ridehalgh	42
McNulty	47
McEveley	13
Harris	42
Hughes	35
Norburn	47
Jennings	48
Norwood	48
Alabi	9
Sutton	49
Cook	47
Pilling	2
Dunn	9
Mangan	14
Waring	3
Gumbs	4
Duggan	12
Wharton	0
Clarke	16
Tollitt	12
Mottley-Henry	16
McDonagh	11
Cole	17
Kirby	3
Rokka	1
Drysdale	1
Soloman-Davies	1
Banks	9
Green	3
Kay	2
Taylor	6
Ginnelly	12
Wallace	2
Monthe	6
Traore	3
Spellman	1
Walker-Rice	1

RESULT: D W L D L D W L W L W D W L L W D W L L L W D W W L W D W D W D W L W W L W W W W W W W L L W W

TRANMERE ROVERS MATCH RESULTS 2017-18

Date	Comp	H/A	Opponents	Att:	Result	Goalscorers	Pos	No.
Aug 5	Nat Lg	A	Torquay United	3162	D 0 - 0		16	1
8	Nat Lg	H	Woking	4698	W 3 - 1	Cook 18 Norburn 31 McEverley 60	4	2
12	Nat Lg	H	Sutton United	5050	L 0 - 1		13	3
15	Nat Lg	A	Guiseley	1231	D 0 - 0		14	4
19	Nat Lg	A	Eastleigh	1906	L 0 - 2		15	5
25	Nat Lg	H	Boreham Wood	4295	D 2 - 2	Cook 82 Mangan 90	19	6
28	Nat Lg	A	Solihull Moors	1312	W 2 - 0	Norburn 19 Cook 82	15	7
Sept 2	Nat Lg	H	Dover Athletic	4191	L 0 - 1		18	8
9	Nat Lg	H	Barrow	4269	W 1 - 0	Norburn 90	14	9
12	Nat Lg	A	Maidenhead United	1483	L 0 - 1		12	10
16	Nat Lg	A	Ebbsfleet United	1525	D 0 0		17	11
23	Nat Lg	H	Wrexham	1835	L 0 - 1		18	12
30	Nat Lg	A	Bromley	2056	W 1 - 0	Norwood 90	17	13
Oct 4	Nat Lg	H	Leyton Orient	4145	W 2 - 1	Cook 25 Norwood 70	14	14
7	Nat Lg	H	Chester	7172	D 0 - 0		15	15
14	**FAC 4Q**	**A**	**FC Halifax Town**	**1630**	**W 3 - 1**	**Jennings 5 Norwood 45 Ridehalgh 57**		16
21	Nat Lg	A	Aldershot Town	2714	L 1 - 2	McNulty 17	15	17
24	Nat Lg	A	Hartlepool United	3371	D 1 - 1	McEverley 57	15	18
28	Nat Lg	H	FC Halifax Town	4826	W 4 - 2	Norwood 5 14 Cole 42 Mottley-Henry 58	14	19
Nov 4	**FAC 1**	**A**	**Peterborough United**	**3750**	**D 1 - 1**	**Cook 72**		20
11	Nat Lg	H	Dagenham & Redbridge	5227	W 2 - 0	Norwood 4 Norburn 41	12	21
15	**FAC 1r**	**H**	**Peterborough United**	**4199**	**L 0 - 5**			22
18	Nat Lg	A	Gateshead	1140	L 0 - 1		15	23
21	Nat Lg	A	Macclesfield Town	1709	D 2 - 2	Cole 19 Cook 42	14	24
25	Nat Lg	H	Maidstone United	4126	W 4 - 0	Norwood 7 83 Cook 16 Norburn 77	11	25
Dec 9	Nat Lg	H	Torquay United	4569	W 3 - 0	Jennings 35 Cook 79 82	9	26
18	**FAT 1**	**A**	**Solihull Moors**	**215**	**L 0 - 2**			27
23	Nat Lg	A	Sutton United	2237	W 3 - 1	Buxton 10 Jennings 14 Cook 90	9	28
26	Nat Lg	H	AFC Fylde	6669	W 4 - 1	Sutton 37 43 Jennings 52 68	6	29
30	Nat Lg	H	Guiseley	5271	W 4 - 0	Norwood 65 Jennings 70 78 Cook 86	6	30
Jan 1	Nat Lg	A	AFC Fylde	3065	L 2 5	Banks 58 Jennings 90 (pen)	6	31
6	Nat Lg	A	Barrow	1470	D 1 - 1	Norwood 90	7	32
13	Nat Lg	A	Woking	2115	W 1 - 0	Cook	5	33
20	Nat Lg	H	Maidenhead United	4980	W 3 - 2	Norwood 4 Ginnelly 49 Hughes 78	5	34
27	Nat Lg	A	Wrexham	8471	D 2 - 2	Sutton 10 Cook 45.	5	35
Feb 3	Nat Lg	H	Ebbsfleet United	5138	W 3 - 0	Cook 16 Norwood 35 63	4	36
10	Nat Lg	A	Leyton Orient	4631	D 1 1	Sutton 43	4	37
17	Nat Lg	H	Bromley	5536	W 1 0	Jennings 35	2	38
20	Nat Lg	H	Macclesfield Town	7385	L 1 - 4	Cook 49	2	39
24	Nat Lg	A	Maidstone United	2502	W 3 - 2	Cook 39 Finney 85 (og) Buxton 88 (pen)	3	40
Mar 10	Nat Lg	A	Dagenham & Redbridge	1411	W 4 - 0	Cook 47 69 Norwood 68 90	3	41
17	Nat Lg	A	Boreham Wood	801	L 1 - 2	Norwood 66	4	42
24	Nat Lg	H	Eastleigh	4619	W 3 - 1	Sutton 9 Cook 78 90	3	43
Apr 5	Nat Lg	A	Chester	3103	W 2 - 0	Cook 45 Norwood 64	4	44
10	Nat Lg	H	Gateshead	4328	W 4 - 2	COOK 4 (45 53 60 69)	2	45
14	Nat Lg	H	Aldershot Town	5444	W 2 - 0	Norwood 70 80	2	46
17	Nat Lg	A	Dover Athletic	1231	W 1 - 0	Cook 39	2	47
21	Nat Lg	A	FC Halifax Town	3113	W 2 - 0	Cook 4 Norwood 23	2	48
24	Nat Lg	H	Solihull Moors	1007	L 1 - 2	Green 67	2	49
28	Nat Lg	H	Hartlepool United	5499	L 1 - 2	Hughes 76	2	50
May 5	**P O S-F**	**H**	**Ebbsfleet United**	**6898**	**W 4 - 2**	**Norwood 33 102 Ginelly 56 Cole 106 (aet)**		51
12	**P O Final**	**A**	**Boreham Wood**	**16,306**	**W 2 - 1**	**Cook 6 Norwood 81**		52

GOALSCORERS	SG	CSG	Pens	Hat tricks	Total		SG	CSG	Pens	Hat tricks	Total
2016-17 Cook					23	McEverley	2				2
Cook	22	3	1		28	Banks					1
Norwood	17	2			23	Bromley					1
Jennings	5	3	1		8	Green					1
Norburn	5				5	M-Henry					1
Sutton	5				5	Mangan					1
Cole	3		1		3	McNulty					1
Buxton	2				2	Opponents					1
Ginnelly	2				2	Ridehalgh					1
Hughes	2				2						

Relegated from League Two

BARNET

Club Contact Details 020 8381 3800

The Hive, Camrose Avenue, Edgware, Middlesex, HA8 6AG

tellus@thehivelondon.com

Founded: 1885	**Nickname:** The Bees	**Manager:** John Still - 18/05/2018

Previous Names: New Barnet 1885-88. Barnet 1888-1902 (folded). Barnet Alston 1904-19.

Previous Leagues: Post 1945 - Athenian 1945-65. Southern 1965-79. Conference 1979-91, 2001-05, 13-15. Football League 1991-2001, 05-13.

Club Colours (change): Amber and black

Ground Capacity: 5,176 **Seats:** 3,434 **Covered:** 5,176 **Clubhouse:** Yes **Shop:** Yes

Previous Grounds: Underhill 1907-2013

Record Attendance: 11,026 v Wycombe Wanderers FA Amateur Cup 01/01/1953

Nearest Railway Station Canons Park Underground (Jubilee line) is a 5 min **Bus Route** 340, 186 & 79 from Edgware to Canons Pk.
walk away.

RECORDS

Victory:	7-0 v Blackpool Division 3 11/11/2000
Defeat:	1-9 v Peterborough Division 3 05/09/1998
Goalscorer:	Arthur Morris - 403 (1927-36)
Appearances:	Les Eason - 648 (1965-74, 77-78)

HONOURS

FA Comps: Amateur Cup 1945-46.

League: Athenian League 1931-32, 32-33, 46-47, 58-59, 63-64, 64-65. Southern League Division One 1965-66, Division One South 1977-78. Football Conference 1990-91, 2004-05, 2014-15.

County FA: Herts Senior Cup 1985-86, 90-91, 91-92, 92-93, 95-96, 2006-07, 10-11.

08-09	09-10	10-11	11-12	12-13	13-14	14-15	15-16	16-17	17-18
FL 2 17	FL 2 11	FL 2 22	FL 2 22	FL 2 23	Conf 8	Conf 1	FL 2 15	FL 2 15	FL 2 23
FAC 1Pr	FAC 2Pr	FAC 1Pr	FAC 2P	FAC 1P	FAC 1P	FAC 1P	FAC 2P	FAC 1P	FAC 1P
FLC 1P	FLC 1P	FLC 1P	FLC 2P	FLC 1P	FAT 2P	FAT 1Pr	FLC 2P	FLC 1P	FLC 2P

2017-18 STATS	Goals Total	N/A	Games Without Scoring	N/A	Total No. of Scorers	N/A	Total Clean Sheets	N/A
Most Consecutive Scoring Games		N/A	Best Unbeaten Run	N/A		Most Consecutive Clean Sheets		N/A
Best Att:	N/A				Number in brackets denotes consecutive runs.			

The Brackley Town player gets up highest to head towards goal during their 1-0 win over Bradford Park Avenue in the National North Play-off Semi Final. Photo: Peter Barnes.

CHESTERFIELD

Club Contact Details 01246 269 300
The Proact Stadium, 1866 Sheffield Road, Whittington Moor, Chesterfield S41 8NZ
reception@chesterfield-fc.co.uk

Founded: 1866   **Nickname:** The Spireites   **Manager:** Martin Allen - 15/05/2018
Previous Names: Chesterfield Town 1891-1915, Chesterfield Municipal 1915-20.
Previous Leagues: Sheffield & District 1892-96. Midland 1896-99, 1909-15, 19-20. Football League 1899-1909, 1921-2018.

Club Colours (change): Blue & white

Ground Capacity: 10,000 **Seats:** 10,000 **Covered:** Yes   **Clubhouse:** Yes **Shop:** Yes
Previous Grounds: Athletic Ground 1866-72. Saltergate (Recreation Ground) 1872-2010.
Record Attendance: 30,561 (Saltergate) v Tottenham, 12/02/1938. 10,089 (1866 Sheffield Rd) v Rotherham United.
Nearest Railway Station Chesterfield

RECORDS
Appearances: Mark Allott - 385 (League) 2001-12.
Goalscorer: Jack Lester - 92 (League) 2007-13.
Victory: 8-1 v Barrow 13/11/1926 and v Gateshead 25/04/1931.

HONOURS
FA Comps: None
League: Midland 1909-10, 19-20.
     League Division Three North 1930-31, 35-36, Division Four/League Two 69-70, 84-85, 2010-11, 13-14.
County FA: Derbyshire Senior Cup 1898-99, 1920-21, 21-22, 24-25, 32-33, 36-37, 2017-18.

08-09	09-10	10-11	11-12	12-13	13-14	14-15	15-16	16-17	17-18
FL 2 10	FL 2 8	FL 2 1	FL 1 22	FL 2 8	FL 2 1	FL 1 6	FL 1 18	FL 1 24	FL 2 24
FAC 3P	FAC 1P	FAC 2P	FAC 1P	FAC 2P	FAC 2P	FAC 4P	FAC 2Pr	FAC 2P	FAC 1P
FLC 1P	FLC 1P	FLC 1P	FLC 1P	FLC 1P	FLC 1P	FLC 1P	FLC 1P	FLC 1P	FLC 1P

2017-18 STATS	Goals Total	N/A	Games Without Scoring	N/A	Total No. of Scorers	N/A	Total Clean Sheets	N/A
Most Consecutive Scoring Games		N/A	Best Unbeaten Run	N/A		Most Consecutive Clean Sheets		N/A
Best Att:	N/A							

Number in brackets denotes consecutive runs.

The Chesterfield number nine gets in front of his marker to head home Chesterfield's winning goal in the Derbyshire Senior Cup Final. Photo: Bill Wheatcroft.

CHESTER MATCH RESULTS 2017-18

Date	Comp	H/A	Opponents	Att:	Result	Goalscorers	Pos	No.
Aug 8	Nat Lg	H	AFC Fylde	2223	D 1 - 1	Dawson 45	17	1
12	Nat Lg	H	FC Halifax Town	2082	D 0 - 0		18	2
15	Nat Lg	A	Hartlepool United	3071	D 1 - 1	Akintunde 1	17	3
19	Nat Lg	H	Sutton United	1670	L 2 - 3	Mahon 45 Dawson 63	21	4
26	Nat Lg	A	Aldershot Town	2056	W 2 - 1	Dawson 45 (pen) James 82	18	5
28	Nat Lg	H	Macclesfield Town	2363	L 0 - 2		20	6
Sept 2	Nat Lg	A	Torquay United	1455	D 1 - 1	Hánnah 90	20	7
5	Nat Lg	A	Solihull Moors	651	L 0 - 2		22	8
9	Nat Lg	H	Ebbsfleet United	1591	D 1 - 1	Akintunde 82	21	9
12	Nat Lg	A	Gateshead	657	L 2 - 3	Hannah 73 Waters 90	21	10
16	Nat Lg	A	Dover Athletic	1102	L 0 - 4		21	11
23	Nat Lg	H	Maidenhead United	1839	W 2 - 0	Astles 6 Hannah 73	21	12
Oct 3	Nat Lg	H	Woking	1658	L 0 - 2		21	13
7	Nat Lg	A	Tranmere Rovers	7172	D 0 - 0		21	14
14	**FAC 4Q**	**A**	**Kidderminster Harriers**	**1896**	**L 0 - 2**			15
21	Nat Lg	H	Boreham Wood	1501	L 1 - 2	Bell 77	22	16
24	Nat Lg	H	Barrow	1548	W 3 - 2	Archer 11 Hall-Johnson 25 Dawson 90	20	17
28	Nat Lg	A	Maidstone United	2351	L 0 - 1			18
Nov 4	Nat Lg	A	Eastleigh	1868	D 2 - 2	Dawson 59 Akintunde 60	22	19
8	Nat Lg	H	Wrexham	4079	L 0 - 1		22	20
18	Nat Lg	A	Bromley	1129	D 1 - 1	Hannah 14	21	21
21	Nat Lg	A	Leyton Orient	3352	D 2 - 2	Akintunde 15 Hannah 40	21	22
25	Nat Lg	H	Dagenham & Redbridge	1638	L 0 - 4		21	23
Dec 9	Nat Lg	H	Solihull Moors	1430	W 1 - 0	Hannah 77	21	24
16	**FAT 1**	**H**	**AFC Fylde**	**886**	**D 2 - 2**	**Hannah 51 Dawson (Won 5-4 on pens)**		25
23	Nat Lg	A	FC Halifax Town	2040	L 0 - 4		21	26
26	Nat Lg	H	Guiseley	1643	L 0 - 2		22	27
Jan 1	Nat Lg	A	Guiseley	855	D 1 - 1	James 61	22	28
6	Nat Lg	A	Ebbsfleet United	1389	W 1 - 0	White 20	21	29
9	Nat Lg	A	AFC Fylde	1531	D 1 - 1	White 20	21	30
13	**FAT 2**	**A**	**East Thurrock United**	**347**	**L 0 - 1**			31
20	Nat Lg	H	Gateshead	1580	L 1 - 3	White 70	22	32
23	Nat Lg	A	Hartlepool United	1421	D 1 - 1	White 77	22	33
27	Nat Lg	A	Maidenhead United	1510	L 0 - 3		22	34
Feb 10	Nat Lg	A	Woking	1367	L 0 - 1			35
17	Nat Lg	A	Eastleigh	1604	W 3 - 1	Hannah 19 43 Akintunde 90	22	36
20	Nat Lg	H	Leyton Orient	1935	L 0 - 1		22	37
24	Nat Lg	H	Dagenham & Redbridge	1254	L 2 - 3	Archer 31 Waters 62	22	38
Mar 4	Nat Lg	H	Dover Athletic	1182	L 0 - 2		22	39
11	Nat Lg	A	Wrexham	6511	L 0 2		22	40
17	Nat Lg	H	Aldershot Town	1612	D 0 - 0		23	41
24	Nat Lg	A	Sutton United	2195	L 2 - 3	Akintunde 60 White 87	23	42
30	Nat Lg	H	Torquay United	1830	L 0 - 2		23	43
Apr 2	Nat Lg	A	Macclesfield Town	2996	L 0 - 1		23	44
7	Nat Lg	H	Tranmere Rovers	3103	L 0 - 2		23 (R)	45
10	Nat Lg	H	Bromley	754	W 3 - 2	Vose 45 Archer 77 Brown 90	23	46
14	Nat Lg	A	Boreham Wood	551	L 2 - 4	Akintunde 73 90	23	47
21	Nat Lg	H	Dagenham & Redbridge	1728	L 1 - 3	Noble 58	23	48
28	Nat Lg	A	Barrow	1788	W 2 - 1	Archer 20 Crawford 76	23	49

GOALSCORERS	SG	CSG	Pens	Hat tricks	Total		SG	CSG	Pens	Hat tricks	Total
2016-17 Alabi					*18*	Brown					1
Hannah	8	2			9	Crawford					1
Akintunde	6	2			8	Hall-Johnson					1
Dawson	5	2	1		6	Mahon					1
White	4	4			5	Noble					1
Archer	4				4	Vose					1
James	2				2						
Waters	2				2						
Asties					1						
Bell					1						

GUISELEY MATCH RESULTS 2017-18

Date	Comp	H/A	Opponents	Att:	Result		Goalscorers	Pos	No.
Aug 5	Nat Lg	H	Ebbsfleet United	848	D	2 - 2	Rooney 16 Thompson 77	10	1
8	Nat Lg	A	Gateshead	629	L	0 - 1		17	2
12	Nat Lg	A	Aldershot	1938	L	0 - 6		23	3
15	Nat Lg	H	Tranmere Rovers	1231	D	0 - 0		22	4
19	Nat Lg	H	Torquay United	791	W	3 - 2	Lawlor 13 Hurst 86 Molyneux 90	19	5
25	Nat Lg	A	FC Halifax Town	1777	L	0 - 2		21	6
28	Nat Lg	H	Hartlepool United	1723	L	0 - 1		21	7
Sept 2	Nat Lg	A	Leyton Orient	4323	L	1 - 4	Odejayi 36	22	8
9	Nat Lg	H	Eastleigh	735	D	0 - 0		21	9
12	Nat Lg	A	Barrow	1072	D	0 - 0		23	10
16	Nat Lg	A	Wrexham	3916	D	1 - 1	Correia 27	22	11
23	Nat Lg	A	Dover Atrhletic	805	D	1 - 1	Rooney 29	22	12
30	Nat Lg	A	Maidenhead United	1224	L	0 - 3		22	13
Oct 3	Nat Lg	H	Macclesfield Town	812	L	1 - 2	Fondop-Talom 42	22	14
7	Nat Lg	A	Maidstone United	2552	D	1 - 1	Mulhern 90 (pen)	22	15
14	FAC 4Q	H	Shildon	772	W	6 - 0	Fondop-Talem 52 90 Haworth 55 Rooney 61 Hatfield 70 81		16
21	Nat Lg	H	Solihull Moors	812	W	4 - 2	Molyneux 23 Liburd 65 Lawlor 68 Rooney 86	21	17
24	Nat Lg	H	Boreham Wood	706	D	0 - 0		21	18
27	Nat Lg	A	Woking	1783	W	3 - 2	Liburd 33 49 Fondop-Talom 74	20	19
Nov 5	FAC 1	H	Accrington Stanley	1611	D	0 - 0			20
11	Nat Lg	A	Bromley	1074	L	0 - 1		20	21
14	FAC 1r	A	Accrington Stanley	1166	D	1 - 1	Rooney (pen) (Won 4-3 on pens)		22
18	Nat Lg	A	Dagenham & Redbridge	1116	L	2 - 3	Molyneux 18 Fondiop-Talom 23	22	23
25	Nat Lg	H	Sutton United	929	L	0 - 2		23	24
Dec 3	FAC 2	A	Mansfield Town	4081	L	0 - 3			25
8	Nat Lg	A	Ebbsfleet United	1127	L	0 - 4		23	26
19	FAT 1	A	Gateshead	290	L	1 - 2	Liburd 59		27
23	Nat Lg	H	Aldershot Town	820	D	1 - 1	Purver 9	23	28
26	Nat Lg	A	Chester	1643	W	2 - 0	McFadzean 12 Roberts 15	21	29
30	Nat Lg	A	Tranmere Rovers	5271	L	0 - 4		22	30
Jan 1	Nat Lg	H	Chester	855	D	1 - 1	Palmer 90	23	31
6	Nat Lg	A	Eastleigh	2001	L	2 - 4	Liburd 18 Roberts 79	23	32
13	Nat Lg	A	AFC Fylde	1535	L	1 - 2	Roberts 30	23	33
27	Nat Lg	A	Dover Athletic	2327	L	1 - 3	Southwell 63	23	34
Feb 3	Nat Lg	H	Wrexham	1338	L	0 - 2		23	35
10	Nat Lg	A	Macclesfield Town	1646	L	1 - 2	Liburd 10	23	36
13	Nat Lg	H	Gateshead	541	L	0 - 1		23	37
17	Nat Lg	H	Maidenhead United	777	L	1 - 3	Southwell 19	24	38
20	Nat Lg	A	AFC Fylde	613	W	1 - 0	Rooney 86	24	39
24	Nat Lg	A	Sutton United	1915	L	0 - 4		24	40
Mar 10	Nat Lg	A	Bromley	906	L	1 - 2	Rooney 88	24	41
17	Nat Lg	H	F.C.Halifax Town	1106	D	1 - 1	Odejayi 13	24	42
30	Nat Lg	H	Leyton Orient	1216	L	1 - 3	Widdowson 76 (og)	24	43
Apr 1	Nat Lg	A	Hartlepool United	2634	W	1 - 0	Southwell 90	24	44
7	Nat Lg	H	Maidstone United	957	D	0 - 0		24	45
14	Nat Lg	A	Solihull Moors	915	L	1 - 3	Southwell 49 (pen)	24	46
17	Nat Lg	H	Barrow	61	L	0 - 1		24 (R)	47
19	Nat Lg	A	Dagenham & Redbridge	311	L	3 - 5	Purver 27 Hudson 33 Lenighan 38	24	48
21	Nat Lg	H	Woking	552	L	1 - 2	Southwell 61	24	49
24	Nat Lg	A	Torquay United	3496	W	4 - 3	Southwell 5 Hatfield 38 Liburd 60 80	24	50
28	Nat Lg	A	Boreham Wood	701	L	1 - 3	Southwell 21	24	51

GOALSCORERS	SG	CSG	Pens	Hat tricks	Total		SG	CSG	Pens	Hat tricks	Total
2016-17 Cassidy					*8*	Correia					1
Liburd	6	2	1		8	Haworth					1
Rooney	7	2	1		7	Hudson					1
Southwell	6	3	1		7	Hurst					1
Fondop-Talom	4				5	Lenighan					1
Hatfield	2				3	McFadzean					1
Molyneux	3				3	Mulhern		1			1
Roberts	3				3	Opponents					1
Lawler	2				2	Palmer					1
Odejayi	2				2	Thompson					1
Purver	2				2						

TORQUAY UNITED MATCH RESULTS 2017-18

Date	Comp	H/A	Opponents	Att:	Result	Goalscorers	Pos	No.
Aug 5	Nat Lg	H	Tranmere Rovers	3162	D 0 - 0		15	1
8	Nat Lg	A	Aldershot Town	2662	L 2 - 3	Young 9 (pen) Pittman 90	19	2
12	Nat Lg	A	Gateshead	756	L 0 - 3		21	3
15	Nat Lg	H	Boreham Wood	1864	L 2 - 4	Effiong 43 Hoyte 54 (og)	24	4
19	Nat Lg	A	Guiseley	791	L 2 - 3	McGinty 36 Keating 40	24	5
25	Nat Lg	H	Solihull Moors	1862	L 1 - 2	Pittman 75	24	6
28	Nat Lg	A	Woking	1936	L 1 - 4	Gray 45	24	7
Sept 2	Nat Lg	H	Chester	1455	D 1 - 1	Dowling 12	24	8
9	Nat Lg	H	Wrexham	1814	D 0 - 0		24	9
12	Nat Lg	A	Bromley	1029	L 1 - 3	Pittman 24	24	10
16	Nat Lg	A	Barrow	1190	D 1 - 1	Gray 6	24	11
23	Nat Lg	H	Macclesfield Town	1835	L 0 - 1		24	12
30	Nat Lg	A	Dagenham & Redbridge	1421	L 0 - 1		24	13
Oct 3	Nat Lg	H	Maidenhead United	1567	W 4 - 0	McQuoid 4 Young 12 Murphy 21 Reid 44	24	14
7	Nat Lg	H	Dover	1915	L 0 - 2		24	15
14	**FAC 4Q**	**A**	**Aldershot Town**	**1583**	**L 0 - 1**			**16**
21	Nat Lg	A	FC Halifax Town	1764	D 1 - 1	Reid 76	23	17
24	Nat Lg	A	Ebbsfleet United	1525	W 1 - 0	Reid 63	23	18
27	Nat Lg	H	Hartlepool United	1987	L 0 - 2		23	19
Nov 11	Nat Lg	H	Maidstone United	1799	L 0 - 1		23	20
18	Nat Lg	A	AFC Fylde	1552	L 0 - 2		24	21
21	Nat Lg	A	Sutton United	1970	W 1 - 0	Keating 10	23	22
25	Nat Lg	H	Leyton Orient	1913	W 3 - 0	McQuoid 16 Young 29 Reid 47	22	23
Dec 2	Nat Lg	H	Aldershot Town	1851	D 0 - 0		21	24
9	Nat Lg	A	Tranmere Rovers	4569	L 0 - 4		22	25
13	Nat Lg	H	Gateshead	1405	D 1 - 1	McGinty 90	22	26
16	**FAT 1**	**H**	**Maidstone United**	**604**	**L 0 - 4**			**27**
26	Nat Lg	A	Eastleigh	2092	D 1 - 1	Reid 47	23	28
30	Nat Lg	A	Boreham Wood	627	L 0 - 2		23	29
Jan 6	Nat Lg	A	Wrexham	4242	L 0 - 4		23	30
13	Nat Lg	H	Eastleigh	1486	L 1 - 2	Young 34	23	31
20	Nat Lg	H	Bromley	1547	L 0 - 4		24	32
27	Nat Lg	A	Macclesfield Town	1510	D 1 - 1	Romaine 79	24	33
Feb 3	Nat Lg	H	Barrow	1563	W 3 - 1	McGinty 52 Dowling 55 Young 66	23	34
10	Nat Lg	A	Maidenhead United	1433	W 2 - 1	Barnes 35 Romain 85	22	35
17	Nat Lg	H	Dagenham & Redbridge	1931	L 0 - 3		23	36
20	Nat Lg	H	Sutton United	1302	L 2 - 3	McGinty 12 Williams 45	23	37
Mar 10	Nat Lg	A	Maidstone United	2211	L 0 - 1		23	38
13	Nat Lg	A	Leyton Orient	200	W 1 - 0	Romain 37	23	39
17	Nat Lg	A	Solihull Moors	781	D 1 - 1	Williams 41 (pen)	22	40
30	Nat Lg	A	Chester	1830	W 2 - 0	Healey 3 Romaine 66	22	41
Apr 2	Nat Lg	H	Woking	1837	W 2 - 1	Williams 14 (pen) Lemonheigh-Evans 68	22	42
7	Nat Lg	A	Dover Athletic	1128	L 0 - 1		22	43
10	Nat Lg	H	AFC Fylde	1416	L 1 - 3	Williams 5 (pen)	22	44
14	Nat Lg	H	FC Halifax Town	1567	W 1 - 0	Reid 60	22	45
21	Nat Lg	A	Hartlepool United	3254	D 1 - 1	Healey 82	22	46
24	Nat Lg	H	Guiseley	3496	L 3 - 4	HEALEY 3 (16 72 86)	22	47
28	Nat Lg	H	Ebbsfleet United	1728	D 1 - 1	Healey 71 (pen)	22	48

GOALSCORERS	SG	CSG	Pens	Hat tricks	Total		SG	CSG	Pens	Hat tricks	Total
2016-17 Williams					10	Keating	2				2
Healey	4	3	1	1	6	McQuoid	2				2
Reid	6	2			6	Barnes					1
Young	5		1		5	Effiong					1
McGinty	4				4	L-Evans					1
Romaine	4				4	Murphy					1
Williams	4		2		4	Opponents					1
Pittman	3				3						
Dowling	2				2						
Gray	2				2						

WOKING MATCH RESULTS 2017-18

Date	Comp	H/A	Opponents	Att:	Result	Goalscorers	Pos	No.
Aug 5	Nat Lg	H	Gateshead	1705	W 2 - 1	Effiong 18 Ward 44	4	1
8	Nat Lg	A	Tranmere Rovers	4698	L 1 - 3	Carter 43	13	2
12	Nat Lg	A	Barrow	1075	L 0 - 3		17	3
15	Nat Lg	H	Eastleigh	1796	W 2 - 1	Effiong 43 Hoyte 54 (og)	12	4
19	Nat Lg	H	Leyon Orient	2884	L 0 - 2		14	5
25	Nat Lg	A	Wrexham	3875	L 0 - 1		20	6
28	Nat Lg	H	Torquay United	1936	W 4 - 1	Ward 23 Ferdinand 33 Carter 51 Bawling 58	18	7
Sept 1	Nat Lg	A	Macclesfield Town	1289	W 3 - 1	Banton 27 Ward 41 Effiong 89	9	8
9	Nat Lg	A	Maidstore United	2527	L 1 - 3	Ward 23	16	9
12	Nat Lg	H	Solihull Borough	1402	W 2 - 1	Banton 30 Carter 82	14	10
16	Nat Lg	H	Sutton United	2192	W 2 - 1	Charles-Cook 49 90	10	11
23	Nat Lg	A	AFC Fylde	1532	W 2 - 1	Ward 53 Philpot 54	6	12
30	Nat Lg	H	Hartlepool United	2479	D 1 - 1	Philpot 45	7	13
Oct 3	Nat Lg	A	Chester	1658	W 2 - 0	Ferdinand 10 Philpot 71	3	14
7	Nat Lg	H	Dagenham & Redbridge	2509	W 1 - 0	Charles-Cook 78	3	15
14	**FAC 4Q**	**H**	**Concord Rangers**	**1004**	**D 1 - 1**	**Philpot 87**		**16**
17	**FAC 4Qr**	**A**	**Concord Rangers**	**382**	**W 2 - 1**	**Charles-Cook 7 Carter 117 (aet)**		**17**
21	Nat Lg	A	Bromley	1577	W 2 - 0	Holland 42 Rees 45	4	18
24	Nat Lg	A	Dover	1017	L 1 - 3	Ward 54	5	19
27	Nat Lg	H	Guiseley	1783	L 2 - 3	Appau 14 Charles-Cook 65	8	20
Nov 5	**FAC 1**	**H**	**Bury**	**1858**	**D 1 - 1**	**Philpot 25**		**21**
11	Nat Lg	A	FC Halifax Town	1710	D 0 - 0		8	22
14	**FAC 1r**	**A**	**Bury**	**1513**	**W 3 - 0**	**Charles-Cook 30 Effiong 71 Philpot 86**		**23**
18	Nat Lg	H	Maidenhead United	1878	D 1 - 1	Carter 39	9	24
21	Nat Lg	A	Ebbsfleet United	1580	W 1 - 0	Effiong 30	8	25
25	Nat Lg	A	Boreham Wood	543	L 1 - 2	Effiong 90	9	26
Dec 3	**FAC 2**	**H**	**Peterborough United**	**3032**	**D 1 - 1**	**Ward 84**		**27**
12	**FAC 2r**	**A**	**Peterborough United**	**3022**	**L 2 - 5**	**Effiong 19 Young 68**		**28**
16	**FAT 1**	**H**	**Maidenhead United**	**648**	**L 0 - 2**			**29**
23	Nat Lg	H	Barrow	1816	L 1 - 2	Carter 21	13	30
26	Nat Lg	A	Aldershot Town	4181	L 1 - 3	Effiong 14	13	31
30	Nat Lg	A	Eastleigh	2067	D 2 - 2	Carter 70 Effiong 83	13	32
Jan 1	Nat Lg	H	Aldershot Town	3790	L 1 - 2	Ferdinand 47	14	33
6	Nat Lg	A	Maidstone United	1874	D 4 - 4	Ferdinand 21 Effiong 24 Carter 50 Banton 60	14	34
13	Nat Lg	H	Tranmere Rovers	2115	L 0 - 1		15	35
20	Nat Lg	A	Solihull Moors	638	L 0 - 3		16	36
23	Nat Lg	A	Gateshead	470	D 1 - 1	Grego-Cox 52	16	37
27	Nat Lg	H	AFC Fylde	1856	W 1 - 0	Stojsavljevic 49	15	38
Feb 10	Nat Lg	H	Chester	1367	W 1 - 0	Staunton 23	13	39
17	Nat Lg	A	Hartlepool United	3018	L 2 3	Grego-Cox 85 90	13	40
20	Nat Lg	A	Ebbsfleet United	1146	L 1 - 2	Carter 61	16	41
24	Nat Lg	H	Borehan Wood	1744	D 0 - 0		15	42
Mar 5	Nat Lg	A	Sutton United	2019	L 0 - 2		15	43
10	Nat Lg	H	FC Halifax Town	1619	L 1 - 3	Carter 50	15	44
17	Nat Lg	H	Wrexham	1458	D 2 - 2	Staunton 12 Jones 80	18	45
24	Nat Lg	A	Leyton Orient	5673	L 0 - 3		18	46
30	Nat Lg	H	Macclesfield Town	2158	D 2 - 2	Carter 20 Grego-Cox 83	18	47
Apr 2	Nat Lg	A	Torquay United	1837	L 1 - 2	Grego-Cox 65	19	48
7	Nat Lg	H	Dagenham & Redbridge	1391	D 1 - 1	Staunton 47	19	49
10	Nat Lg	A	Maidenhead United	1301	L 1 - 2	Edwards 76	19	50
14	Nat Lg	H	Bromley	2027	L 0 - 2		21	51
21	Nat Lg	A	Guiseley	552	W 2 - 1	Carter 25 Orlu 85	21	52
28	Nat Lg	H	Dover Athletic	2592	L 1 - 2	Carter 38	21	53

GOALSCORERS	SG	CSG	Pens	Hat tricks	Total		SG	CSG	Pens	Hat tricks	Total
2016-17 Ugwu					20	Bawling					1
Carter	13	2			13	Edwards					1
Effiong	10	2			10	Ferdinand					1
Ward	7	3			7	Holland					1
Charles-Cook	5				6	Jones					1
Philpot	6	3			6	Opponents					1
Ferdinand	4				4	Orlu					1
Grego-Cox	4				4	Rees					1
Banton	3				3	Stojsavljevic					1
Staunton	3				3	Ward					1
Appau					1						

National League Play-off Final 2018-19

At Wembley, 12/05/17 - Att: 16,306

Tranmere Rovers 2-1 Boreham Wood

Photo: Peter Barnes

Right: Norwood (Tranmere) crosses under pressure from Champion (Boreham Wood) for Cook to score.
Below: The ball in the net, the referee awards a goal, the fans celebrate.
Photos: Keith Clayton

Photo: Peter Barnes

2017-18 NATIONAL LEAGUE APPEARANCES AND GOALS

Surname	First name	Club	Lge St	Lge S	Lge Np	FAC St	FAC S	FAC Np	Oth St	Oth S	Oth Np	G Lg	G FC	G Oth	T St	T S	T Np	T Ap	T Gls	Y	R
Acton	Darren	Solihull Moors									1						1				
Adams	Blair	Hartlepool	27	6	3	1	1		1			1			29	7	3	36	1	4	1
Adams	Charlee	Dagenham & Redbridge	16	5	8	2			1			1		1	19	5	8	24	2	4	
Adams	Ebou	Leyton Orient (L)	16		1				4						20		1	20		9	
Adebowale	Emmanuel (Manny)	Dover Athletic		6						2							8		8			
Adeloye	Tomi	Hartlepool	1	8	1				1						2	8	1	10			
Adeyinka	Tashan	Bishop's Stortford																			
Afolayan	Oladapo	Solihull Moors	21	7	2	3			2			11			26	7	2	33	11	4	
Ainge	Simon	Wrexham (L)	1	9	1										1	9	1	10		1	
Akintunde	Oluwaseun (James)	Chester	34	7	2				2			8			36	7	2	43	8	1	
Alabi	James	Tranmere	4	5	4										4	5	4	9			
		Dover Athletic (L)	7	4	6					2					7	6	6	13			
Alexander	Cheye	Aldershot Town	42			2			2						46			46			
Allen	Ifeanyi (Iffy)	Bromley	3	10	11		1	2	1			1			4	11	13	15	1	1	
Allen	Jamie	Dover	10	2	1			2				1			10	2	3	12	1	2	
Amankwaah	Kevin	Sutton United	3		2										3		2	3		1	
Amond	Padraig	Hartlepool	4									1			4			4	1		
Anderson	Joe	Maidstone United	41	1	3	4			4			2			49	1	3	50	2	3	
Anderson	Tahjay	Bromley								2						2		2			
Andrade	Bruno	Boreham Wood	44	1		3			6	1		22	2	4	53	2		55	28	9	
Anderson	Myles	Torquay United	7	2	4										7	2	4	9		1	
		Chester (L)	1	1	2				1						2	1	2	3			
		Chester	15		1										15		1	15		6	
Andresson	Axel	Torquay United (L)	4	1					1						5	1		6			
Appau	Declan	Woking	3	7	13		2	4				1			3	9	17	12	1	1	
Archer	Jordan	Chester	12	8	1							4			12	8	1	20	4	2	
Arnold	Nick	Aldershot Town	5	2											5	2		7			
Arnold	Steve	Barrow	17												17			17			
Arthur	Chris	Aldershot Town	10	3							1				10	3	1	13			
Arthur	Koby	Macclesfield Town	3	10	14	2			1			1	1		6	10	14	16	2	1	
Asante	Akwasi	Solihull Moors (L)	7	3	2	1									8	3	2	11		1	
Ashmore	Nathan	Ebbsfleet United	46			3			5						54			54		4	
Astles	Ryan	Chester	39	1		1			2			2			42	1		43	2		
Atkinson	Jack	Halifax		1												1					
Atkinson	Rob	Guiseley	11							4					11	4		11			
Atkinson	Wesley	Solihull Moors (L)	3								1	1			3		1	3	1	1	
Audel	Thierry	Barrow	5	2	7				2		1				7	2	8	9		1	
Azeez	Ade	Dover Athletic (L)	8	4								1			8	4		12	1	1	
Baba	Noe	Macclesfield Town (L)	9	3	8	1	1		1						11	4	8	15			
Bailey	Nicky	Sutton United	27	3		2			2		1	1			31	3	1	34	1	7	
Balanta	Angelo	Boreham Wood	26	6	2	2	1		6	1		11		1	34	8	2	42	12	2	
Balatoni	Conrad	Torquay United	16		2										16		2	16		1	
Banks	Oliver	Tranmere Rovers (L)	8						1			1			9			9	1	2	
Bannister	Charlie	Solihull Moors		1	6	2									2	1	6	3			
Banton	Jason	Woking	17	8	3		3	2		1		3			17	12	5	29	3		
Barker	Charley	Leyton Orient						1									1				
Barnard	Christopher	Dover Athletic			1												1				
Barnes	Aaron	Torquay United (L)	16		1							1			16		1	16	1	1	

2017-18 NATIONAL LEAGUE
APPEARANCES AND GOALS

			Lge Apps			FAC Apps			Other Apps			Goals			Totals						
			St	S	Np	St	S	Np	St	S	Np	Lg	FC	Oth	St	S	Np	Ap	Gls	Y	R
Barnum-Bobb	Jazzi	Torquay United (L)	7						1						8			8		1	
Barratt	Ben	Wrexham						1									1				
Barratt	Sam	Maidenhead United	19	11	7	2			2	1		5	1	1	23	12	7	35	7	2	
Barrow	Scott	Gateshead	34			3			8			3			45			45	3	5	
Barrows	Ross	Halifax			2						1							3			
Barthram	Jack	Barrow	29	2	3				2		1	1			31	2	4	33	1	3	
Bartlett	Rhys	Maidstone United		1													1	1			
Baskerville	Guy	Bromley						1									1				
Batty	Daniel	Halifax (L)	4	1								2			4	1		5	2		
Bauress	Bradley	Barrow	17	13	7	1			1		1				19	13	8	32		2	1
Bawling	Bobson	Woking	9	2	5	1									10	2	5	12			
Baxter	Nathan	Woking (L)	42		1	6									48		1	48		3	
Beautyman	Harry	Sutton United	10	4	1				3			1			13	4	1	17	1	1	1
Beckwith	Dean	Sutton United	12		7	1				1	2	1			13	1	9	14	1	4	
		Maidstone United (L)	4												4			4		2	1
Bell	Nyal	Chester (L)	4	9	4		1					1			4	10	4	14	1	2	
		Gateshead			2				1	1					1	1	2	2			
Bellamy	Liam	Dover Athletic	9	7	4					2					9	9	4	18		4	
Benbow	Luke	Solihull Moors	1	2											1	2		3		1	
Benson	Paul	Boreham Wood	4	10	7			3				1			4	10	10	14	1	1	
Bentley	Jordan	Sutton United (L)			2												2				
Bignot	Paul	Barrow	11	1	4		1		1		1				12	2	5	14			
Bird	Ryan	Dover Athletic	43	3		2			3			16		4	48	3		51	20	4	
Blanchfield	James	Aldershot Town		1	2											1	2	1			
Blinkhorn	Matt	AFC Fylde	1	20	20		2	2	1	1					2	23	22	25			1
Blissett	Nathan	Macclesfield	15	1								5			15	1		16	5		1
Bloomfield	Mason	Dagenham & Redbridge	10	16	3		2			1		3			10	19	3	29	3		
Boco	Romuald	Leyton Orient	5	12		2	1					2			7	13		20	2		
Boden	Scott	Wrexham	23	11	9	1			1			3			25	11	9	36	3		
Bolarinwa	Tom	Sutton United (L)	22	1	1				3	1		7		1	25	2	1	27	8	4	
Bond	Andy	AFC Fylde	40	3	1	4			1			5			45	3	1	48	5	9	
Bonne	Macauley	Leyton Orient	43	1		3			5			22	1	2	51	1		52	25	7	
Bonos	Elliott	Dagenham & Redbridge	1	4	4										1	4	4	5			
Boucaud	Andre	Dagenham & Redbridge	40	1	1	2			1						43	1	1	44		6	
Bowen	James	Solihull Moors	9	1	4										9	1	4	10		5	
Boyce	Andrew	Eastleigh	38		5	1			1						40		5	40		6	1
Bozhurt	Erbil	Boreham Wood			9			3									12				
Bozier	Matt	Aldershot Town		3	3											3	3	3			
Brandy	Febian	Ebbsfleet United		1			1										2		2		1	
Brill	Dean	Leyton Orient	24		2				5						29		2	29			
Brodie	Richard	Solihull Moors (L)	3	2	1										3	2	1	5			
Broom	Ryan	Eastleigh (L)	10	3	2							3			10	3	2	13	3		
Brophy	James	Leyton Orient (L)	23	2					1	1		2		1	24	3		27	3	1	
Brown	Connor	Guiseley	20		4	4			1						25		4	25		15	
Brown	Matt	Halifax	39			1			2			4			42			42	4	8	
Brown	Nathan	Chester	1	5	1							1			1	5	1	6	1		
Brown	Sebastian	Sutton United			6			2									8				
Brundle	Mitch	Dover Athletic	46			2			3			4		1	51			51	5	7	

Key: St - Started; S - Sub on; Np - Non-playing Sub; Oth - FA Trophy/League Play-offs; Y - Yellow Cards; R - Red Cards.

2017-18 NATIONAL LEAGUE APPEARANCES AND GOALS

			Lge Apps			FAC Apps			Other Apps			Goals			Totals						
			St	S	Np	St	S	Np	St	S	Np	Lg	FC	Oth	St	S	Np	Ap	Gls	Y	R
Bubb	Bradley	Ebbsfleet United		7	2											7	2	7		1	1
Bugiel	Omar	Bromley (L)	7	9					4	2	1	4		1	11	11	1	22	5	2	
Burbidge	Fred	Boreham Wood			5						4						9				
Burgess	Scott	Macclesfield Town (L)	20	11	14	1		1	1				1		22	11	15	33	1		
Burke	Luke	AFC Fylde	29	3	5	2			1						32	3	5	35		3	1
Burrow	Jordan	Gateshead	34	10	2	3			4	5		10	2	4	41	15	2	56	16	4	
Burrows	Brandan	Wrexham								1						1		1			
Bush	Chris	Ebbsfleet United	29	5	5	3			2	1	2	1			34	6	7	40	1	6	1
Butler	Jamie	Sutton United	44			2			2						48			48	2		
Buxton	Adam	Tranmere Rovers	35	2	1	1	1	1	2			2			38	3	2	41	2	4	
Byrne	Neill	Gateshead	39		3	3			9			1		1	51		3	51	2	6	
Cadogan	Kieron	Sutton United	29	11	4	2			1	2		3	2	1	32	13	4	45	6	1	
Campbell	Kristian	Bromley	1	1	2			1							1	1	3	2			
Campbell	Tahvon	Solihull Moors (L)	8	5			1					1			8	6		14	1		
Camwell	Chris	Solihull Moors (L)		1	1	2	1								2	2	1	4			
Capel	Elliott	Maidstone United			2						1						3				
Caprice	Jake	Leyton Orient	35			3			4						42			42		3	1
Carline	George	Solihull Moors	22	11	7	1	2			2					23	15	7	38		2	
Carrington	Mark	Wrexham	17	9	5	1			1						19	9	5	28		3	1
Carter	Charlie	Woking	32	9	1	3	1	1		1		12			35	11	2	46	12	3	
Carter	Darren	Solihull Moors	44	1		3				1		7	1		47	2		49	8	6	1
Cassidy	Jake	Hartlepool	33	2					1			5			34	2		36	5	11	
Catterick	Ryan	Hartlepool			21			2			1						24				
Champion	Tom	Boreham Wood	42		1	3			7			1			52		1	52	1	5	
Chaney	Sam	Torquay United	6												6			6			
Chapman	Louie	Dagenham & Redbridge						2									2				
ChapPell	Jordan	Chester	3	6	1		1								3	7	1	10			
Charles	Dion	Halifax	5	6	5		1								5	7	5	12		1	
Charles-Cook	Regan	Woking (Lx2)	19	4		5			1			5	1		25	4		29	6	4	
Cheek	Michael	Dagenham & Redbridge	27	7	2		1		1			13		1	28	8	2	36	14	1	
Cheidu Dixon	Bohan	Halifax	3	1											3	1		4		2	
Chesmain	Noah	Boreham Wood (L)	2	1	3				1		1			1	3	1	4	4	1		
Chettle	Callum	AFC Fylde (L)	4	5	3										4	5	3	9			
Childs	Mark	Eastleigh	1		1										1		1	1			
Chorley	Ben	Bromley	17	6	7				3	2	3				20	8	10	28		2	
Clackstone	Josh	Halifax (L)	5												5			5			
Clark	Kenny	Ebbsfleet United	37	1		3			3			2			43	1		44	2	4	
Clark	Michael	Leyton Orient	1		7	2		1							3		8	3			
Clarke	Danny	Halifax	10	7	4				2			1			12	7	4	19	1	4	1
Clarke	Eddie	Tranmere Rovers	12	2	5			1	1	1					13	3	6	16			
Clarke	Ryan	Torquay United	10		24				1						11		24	11			
Clay	Craig	Leyton Orient	38	4	3	2		1	4			4			44	4	4	48	4	8	
Clayden	Charles	Leyton Orient		1	2						1					1	3	1			
Cleary	Dan	Solihull Moors	1	1	5			2							1	1	7	2		1	
Clements	Chris	Barrow	7		2	1									8		2	8		2	
Clerima	Remy	Maidenhead United	33					2	3			2			38			38	2	2	
Clifton	Adrian	Maidenhead United	20	16	4	2			1	2		8			23	18	4	41	8	4	1
Cockerline	Daniel	Barrow	1	4											1	4		5			

2017-18 NATIONAL LEAGUE APPEARANCES AND GOALS			Lge Apps			FAC Apps			Other Apps			Goals			Totals						
			St	S	Np	St	S	Np	St	S	Np	Lg	FC	Oth	St	S	Np	Ap	Gls	Y	R
Coddington	Luke	Wrexham (L)	5												5			5			
		Guiseley (L)	11		5										11		5	11			1
Coker	Andre	Maidstone United (L)	4	2	1					2					4	4	1	8			
Cole	Chinua	Torquay United	3												3			3			
Cole	Jake	Aldershot Town	21		19	1			1			1			23		20	23			
Cole	Larnell	Tranmere Rovers	9	4	1		2		1	1		3		1	10	7	1	17	4		
Collins	Aaron	Maidstone United (L)	3	1			1			1		1			3	3		6	1		
Collins	Jamie	Sutton United	41			2			3			4			46			46	4	8	1
Collins	Michael	Halifax	22						1						23			23		8	
Comley	James	Maidenhead United	30	2	3	2			2	1		1			34	3	3	37	1	10	
Connors	Jack	Ebbsfleet United	22	2	6	2		1	3	2		1			27	4	7	31	1	2	
Constable	James	Eastleigh	14	11	10		1			1		2			14	13	10	27	2	2	
Cook	Anthony	Ebbsfleet United	5	4	2	2		1							7	4	3	11	1		
		Woking	14	2	1										14	2	1	16	3		
Cook	Andy	Tranmere Rovers	37	4	2	1	2		3			27	1	1	41	6	2	47	29	7	1
Cook	Ollie	Barrow (L)	13		4										13		4	13	4		
Coombes	Adam	Sutton United	2	11	3		1	1	1	1				1	3	13	4	16	1	3	
Correia	Raul	Guiseley (L)	6	5	2					1		1			6	6	2	12	1		
Coulson	Josh	Leyton Orient	27						4			1		1	31			31	2	1	
Coulson	Luke	Ebbsfleet United	40	6		1	2		4	1		11	1	1	45	9		54	13	1	
Cousins	Mark	Dagenham & Redbridge	46			2			1						49			49			
Coyle	Callum	Solihull Moors	1		3			1							1		4	1			
Crawford	Tom	Chester	15	2	4						1	1			15	2	5	17	1	5	
Cresswell	Ryan	Eastleigh	12	1	2			1				1			12	1	3	13	1	3	
Crookes	Adam	Guiseley	13	2					1						14	2		16		2	
Crump	Ryan	Chester						1									1				
Cullinane-Liburd	Jordan	Solihull Moors	11	1	3	1		2							12	1	5	13		3	
Cunningham	Aaron	Hartlepool		1												1		1			1
Cunningham	Karl	Chester		2	4											2	4	2			
Dalby	Sam	Leyton Orient		2	3						3					2	6	2			
Daly	Liam	Solihull Moors	38			3			2			1			43			43	1	4	1
Daniel	Kadell	Dover Athletic	5	34	7	2				3		2			7	37	7	44	2	4	
Davey	Alex	Torquay United (L)	7						1						8			8		3	
		Boreham Wood (L)	9	4	6					1	2	1			9	5	8	14	1	1	
Davies	Liam	Chester	1	1	11			1							1	1	12	2			
Davies	Scott	Tranmere Rovers	40			3			2						45			45		3	
Davis	Kenny	Sutton United	36	2		1	1		1	1		2			38	4	2	42	2	7	
Davis	Liam	Torquay United	33		1	1									34		1	34		4	
Dawson	Lucas	Chester	31	4	6	1			2			4		1	34	4	6	38	5	5	1
Dayton	James	Leyton Orient	25	3		3			1			2	1		29	3		32	3	2	
De Havilland	Will	Aldershot Town	7	1											7	1		8		2	
		Maidstone United (L)	9	1											9	1		10			
Deen-Conteh	Aziz	Dover Athletic		4	14		1	1			1					5	16	5			
Del Girolamo	Diego	Macclesfield Town			6												6				
Dennet	Oliver	Eastleigh		1	4											1	4	1			
Dennis	Louis	Bromley	30	12	1	2	1		8			13	1	7	40	13	1	53	21	5	
Denton	Tom	Halifax	28	3	6				2			10			30	3	6	33	10	7	1
Devericks	Nicky	Hartlepool	27	2	2	2			1			2			30	2	2	32	2	2	1

Key: St - Started; S - Sub on; Np - Non-playing Sub; Oth - FA Trophy/League Play-offs; Y - Yelow Cards; R - Red Cards.

2017-18 NATIONAL LEAGUE APPEARANCES AND GOALS

Surname	First	Club	Lge Apps St	S	Np	FAC Apps St	S	Np	Other Apps St	S	Np	Goals Lg	FC	Oth	Totals St	S	Np	Ap	Gls	Y	R
		Wrexham	10	2	2							1			10	2	2	12	1	1	
Diagne	Tony	Barrow	12	5	13	1			1		1	1			14	5	14	19		1	
Diarra	Moussa	Barrow	38						3			3			41			41	3	7	
Dibble	Christian	Wrexham	5		28			1	1						6		29	6			
Dixon	Joel	Barrow	11		13	1			3						15		13	15		2	
Doe	Scott	Dagenham & Redbridge	15	2	2	2			1			1			18	2	2	20	1	1	
		Boreham Wood	1	1	9				2		1				3	1	10	4		1	
Donaldson	Ryan	Hartlepool	14	5								2			14	5		19	2		
Donnelly	Liam	Hartlepool	25	2	2	1			1			3			27	2	2	29	3	10	
Dorel	Vincent	Torquay United	33	1	3	1					1				34	1	4	35			
Dowling	George	Torquay United (L)	15	6	2				1			2			16	6	2	22	2	3	1
Downer	Simon	Sutton United	12	4	8			2	2		1				14	4	11	18		5	
Downes	Alex	Chester		1	2											1	2	1			
Drury	Andy	Ebbsfleet United	37	3	2	1			4	1		5	1		42	4	2	46	6	5	
Drysdale	Declan	Tranmere Rovers	1					1							1		1	1		1	
Duckworth	Michael	Halifax	16	2	5										16	2	5	18		1	
Duggan	Mitch	Tranmere Rovers	9	2			1	1							9	3	1	12		2	
Dundas	Craig	Sutton United	25	12	5	2			1	1	1	7		1	28	13	6	41	8	2	
Dunkley	Tristan	Solihull Moors	3	7	1										3	7	1	10		3	
Dunn	Chris	Wrexham	35		3	1					1				36		4	36			
Dunn	Jack	Tranmere Rovers	3	3	3										3	3	3	6			
Dunne	Alan	Bromley	14	2	11	3					1				17	2	12	19		4	
Dunne	Jimmy	Barrow	21			1			1			2			23			23	2	5	2
Durrell	Elliott	Macclesfield Town	31	4		2			1			8	1		34	4		38	9	7	
East	Danny	Guiseley	4	1	7										4	1	7	5			
Eastmond	Craig	Sutton United	35	1		1			4			5			40	1		41	5	10	
Edmundson	Samuel George	AFC Fylde (L)	10			3			1						14			14		3	
Edwards	Jack	Solihull Moors	3	3											3	3		6			
Edwards	Jonathan	Woking (L)	3	11	1							2			3	11	1	14	2	3	
Edwards	Opanin	Solihull Moors (L)		4	1											4	1	4			
Efete	Michee	Torquay United (L)	24	2	6		1								24	3	6	27		1	
Effiong	Inih	Woking	19	9		6			1			10	2		26	9		35	12	2	
Egan	Alfie	Sutton United (L)		4	1											4	1	4			
Ekpiteta	Marvin	Leyton Orient	5	1	4										5	1	4	6			
Ellis	Mark	Leyton Orient	7		3							1			7		3	7	1		
Elokobi	George	Leyton Orient	21	1					1			2		1	22	1		23	3	1	
Enver	Aiden	Bromley		2				2										4			
Essam	Connor	Dover Athletic	46			2			3			1			51			51	1	5	
Essuman	George	Dover Athletic		1	5											1	5	1			
Evans	Callum	Torquay United (L)	10			1							1		11	1		12			
		Macclesfield Town (L)	9	5											9	5		14		2	
Evans	Owen	Sutton United (L)	2		1				2						4		1	4			
Evans	Will	Aldershot Town	32	1		2			2			2			36	1		37	2	3	1
Ezewele	Josh	AFC Fylde	2	3	10	2	1		1						5	4	10	9		2	
Fallon	Rory	Torquay United	1	4	5										1	4	5	5			
Fazakerley	Loui	Dover Athletic	4	5	17		1	1		1	1				4	7	19	11		1	
Featherstone	Nicky	Hartlepool	36		3	2									38		3	38		6	
Fenelon	Shamir	Aldershot Town	31	4	1	2			1			10			34	4	1	38	10	2	

			Lge Apps			FAC Apps			Other Apps			Goals			Totals						
			St	S	Np	St	S	Np	St	S	Np	Lg	FC	Oth	St	S	Np	Ap	Gls	Y	R
Ferdinand	Kane	Woking	41	3		5			1			4			47	3		50	4	4	1
Ferrier	Morgan	Dagenham & Redbridge	27	3		2			1			8			30	3		33	8	5	
		Boreham Wood	14	1								7			14	1		15	7	2	
Finley	Sam	AFC Flyde	33			4			1			6	1		38			38	7	12	3
Finney	Alex	Maidstone United (L)	24	2	7	4			1			2	1		29	2	7	31	3	3	
Firth	Andrew	Chester	11		5										11		5	11			
Fitzpatrick	David	Barrow	1	3	6					1					1	4	6	5			
Fitzpatrick	David	Macclesfield Town	46			2					1	1			48		1	48	1		
Fletcher	Alex	Torquay United (L)	2	1											2	1		3			
Flintney	Ross	Eastleigh	18	2	8	1									19	2	8	21		2	1
Flores	Jordan	AFC Fylde (L)	1												1			1			
Flowers	Harry	Guiseley	13												13			13		6	1
Folivi	Michael	Boreham Wood (L)	1	12	4				4	1		2		1	5	13	4	18	3	2	
Fondop-Talom	Mike	Guiseley (L)	8	11		4						3			12	11		23	3	2	
		Halifax (L)	10	2								4			10	2		12	4	4	
Fox	Ben	Solihull Moors (L)	2	3											2	3		5			
		Gateshead (L)	11	1								2			11	1		12	2		
Fowler	George	Aldershot Town	24		7	1	1		1						26	1	7	27		1	
Francis-Angol	Zaine	AFC Fylde	43			4			1			2			48			48	2	3	
Franks	Jonathan	Hartlepool	19	1		2				1		6			21	2		23	6	1	
		Wrexham	2	5	3										2	5	3	7			
Freestone	Lewis	Peterborough	2	2											2	2		4			
Frempah	Ben	Solihull Moors		1	6											1	6	1			
		Guiseley	3		4										3		4	3		1	
Fyfield	Jamal	Gateshead	32	1	3			1	7		1	1			39	1	5	40	1	10	1
Gallagher	Jake	Aldershot Town	23	12	4		1		2			2			25	13	4	38	2	4	1
Gallifuoco	Giancarlo	Dover Athletic	44			2			3			5			49			49	5	6	
Garner	Scott	Halifax	30		1	1			2			2			33		1	33	2	10	1
George	Luke	Hartlepool	6	1	4	1		1							7	1	5	8		1	
Ginnelly	Josh	Tranmere Rovers (L)	9	1	3				2		1	2			11	1	3	12	3	1	
Gnabouyou	Guy Kassa	Torquay United		5	1				1						1	5	1	6		1	
Gomis	Bedsente	Barrow	39	4	1	1			2	1		5			42	5	1	47	5	13	1
Goodman	Jake	Maidenhead United	34	4	5	1		1	4			2			39	4	6	43	2	3	
Gordon	Liam	Dagenham & Redbridge	1	1	3							1			1	1	3	2	1	1	
Gordon	Quba	Boreham Wood			1												1				
Gosling	Jake	Torquay United	9	5							1				9	5	1	14			
Gough	Jordan	Chester	15	1	1				2						17	1	1	18		2	
Gowling	Josh	Torquay United	24	1	1	1									25	1	1	26		3	
Graham	Bagasan	Ebbsfleet United	4	1	1			2							4	1	3	5			
Graham	Sam	Halifax (L)	6	1											6	1		7		1	
Grainger	Charlie	Leyton Orient	20		21	3					4				23		25	23		1	
Grand	Simon	AFC Fylde	35		11	2	2		2			3	1	1	39	2	11	41	5	4	
Gray	James	Torquay United	7	6				1				2			7	6	1	13	2	2	
Green	Devarn	Tranmere Rovers	2	1								1			2	1		3	1		
Green	Elliot	Guiseley	2		1										2		1	2			
Green	Joe	Guiseley	18	1											18	1		19		1	
Green	Kieran	Gateshead	5	3	6										5	3	6	8		2	
Green	Kristian	Solihull Moors	30	1	11	2			2						34	1	11	35		1	

Key: St - Started; S - Sub on; Np - Non-playing Sub; Oth - FA Trophy/League Play-offs; Y - Yelow Cards; R - Red Cards.

2017-18 NATIONAL LEAGUE APPEARANCES AND GOALS

			Lge Apps			FAC Apps			Other Apps			Goals			Totals						
			St	S	Np	St	S	Np	St	S	Np	Lg	FC	Oth	St	S	Np	Ap	Gls	Y	R
Green	Mike	Eastleigh	11	6	4	1									12	6	4	18		1	
Green	Paul	Solihull Moors	15	8	12	1	1		1		1				17	9	13	26		5	
Greenwood	Rees	Gateshead	4	4	7				2	1	1				6	5	8	11			1
Grego-Cox	Reece	Woking (L)	16	2								4			16	2		18	4	4	
Gregory	David	Bromley	46			3			9						58			58		2	
Gumbs	Evan	Tranmere Rovers	2	2	10										2	2	10	4			
Hall	Asa	Barrow	37		3			1	1			3			38		4	38	3	6	
Hall-Johnson	Reece	Chester (L)	11						1			1			12			12	1	3	
Halls	Andy	Chester																			
Hamann	Nick	Maidenhead United		1			1									2					
Hammond	James	Maidenhead United			5												5				
Hancox	Mitch	Macclesfield Town	31	8	7		1	1	1			7			32	9	8	41	7	4	
Hanford	Dan	Gateshead	21	1	23	2		1	2		4				25	1	28	26		2	1
Hanlan	Brandon	Bromley (L)	11	4					6	1		3		2	17	5		22	5		
Hanley	Raheem	Halifax (L)	4	3											4	3		7		1	
Hannah	Ross	Chester	21	9	2				2			8		1	23	9	2	32	9	6	
Hannant	Luke	Gateshead	18	1		3			1	1		2		1	22	2		24	3	3	
Hanson	Jacob	Halifax (L)	1	1											1	1		2			
Happe	Daniel	Leyton Orient	21	5	3	2			2	2	1				25	7	4	32			
		Gateshead (L)		1													1	1			
Hardy	James	AFC Fylde	18	6				1		1					18	7	1	25			
Hare	Josh	Maidstone United	26	2	10	2		1	3		1	3			31	2	12	33	3		
Harfield	Ollie	Boreham Wood (L)		1	11						3					1	14	1			
Harris	Jay	Tranmere Rovers	26	12		1		1		3					27	15	1	42		11	1
Harrison	Byron	Barrow	21	5		1			2		1	8			24	5	1	29	8		
		Sutton United (L)	9	3	2					1		3			9	4	2	13	3	1	
Harrison	Scott	Hartlepool	22	5	4	1		1	1						24	5	5	29		5	1
Harrold	Matt	Leyton Orient	9	15	3		1		3	2		3		2	12	18	3	30	5	2	
Harvey	Alex-Ray	Barrow	12			2									14			14		1	1
		Guiseley	19		1				1						20		1	20		3	
Hatfield	Will	Guiseley	26	3		1						1	2		27	3		30	3	7	
Hawkes	Josh	Hartlepool	7	4	7							2			7	4	7	11	2		
Hawkins	Lewis	Hartlepool	31	4	7		1		1						32	5	7	37		4	
Hawkins	Oliver	Dagenham & Redbridge	2	5											2	5		7			
Haworth	Andy	Torquay United	3	3	3										3	3	3	6			
		Guiseley	1	6	9	1	2	1							2	8	10	10		1	
Healey	Rhys	Torquay United (L)	7	1								6			7	1		8	6	1	1
Healy	Joe	Maidstone United		2												2					
Hellawell	Rhain	Chester		1												1					
Heslop	Simon	Eastleigh (L)	5									1			5			5	1	1	
Hibbs	Jake	Halifax	17	8				1	2						19	8	1	27		7	
Higgins	Ryan	Torquay United	16	1	4	1									17	1	4	18		1	
Higgs	Jordan	Bromley	22	10	9	3			5	2	1	2		1	30	12	10	42	3	4	1
Higgs	Kieran	Solihull Moors (L)		1													1	1			
Hines	Zavon	Maidstone United	16	4		4					1	6	2		20	4	1	24	8	7	
Hobson	Shaun	Chester (L)	13												13			13		1	
Hodgkiss	Jared	Macclesfield Town	29	1		2						1			31	1		32	1	1	
Holden	Darren	Guiseley	16	2	3	4									20	2	3	22		2	1

2017-18 NATIONAL LEAGUE APPEARANCES AND GOALS

			Lge Apps			FAC Apps			Other Apps			Goals			Totals						
			St	S	Np	St	S	Np	St	S	Np	Lg	FC	Oth	St	S	Np	Ap	Gls	Y	R
Holland	Jack	Bromley	45			3			9			7		2	57			57	9	1	
Hollands	Danny	Eastleigh	29	4	8				1						30	4	8	34		5	
Holman	Dan	Boreham Wood (L)	9	3	1	1	2				2	4			10	7	1	17	4		
Holman	Dan	Leyton Orient (L)	9	1	2							1			9	1	2	10	1	1	
Holroyd	Chris	Wrexham	33	1	1	1						13			34	1	1	35	13	4	
Holt	Grant	Barrow	15	8	3										15	8	3	23		4	
Hornby	Sam	Chester (L)	13						2						15			15			
Horsfall	Fraser	Gateshead		1													1				
Hotte	Nathan	Halifax	30	2	3	1					2	1			31	2	5	33	1	8	
Howe	Callum	Eastleigh (L)	26			1			1			3	1		28			28	4	4	
Howell	Luke	Dagenham & Redbridge	26	7	2		1		1			4			27	8	2	35	4	2	
Howells	Jake	Dagenham & Redbridge	38	5	4	2			1						41	5	4	46		3	
Hoyte	Gavin	Eastleigh	31			1			1			1			33			33	1	7	
Hudson	Ellis	Guiseley (L)	2	1											2		1	2			
Hudson-Odoi	Bradley	Eastleigh (L)	5	1	2				1						6	1	2	7		1	
Hudson-Odoi	Bradley	Sutton United		2	2											2	2	2		1	
Hughes	Jeff	Tranmere Rovers	24	7	7	2			2			2			28	7	7	35	2	4	
Hughes	Liam	Barrow	7	2	5										7	2	5	9		1	
Hughes	Liam	Guiseley	4	1	4	1									5	1	4	6		1	
Humphrey	Chris	Barrow	1	1	1				1	1					2	2	1	4		2	
Hunter	Max	Bromley		1							1						2				
Hurst	James	Wrexham	6	11	9	1			1						8	11	9	19		3	
Hurst	Kevan	Guiseley	16	5	4	2	2					1			18	7	4	25	1	3	
Hyde	Jake	Maidenhead United	16	16	4		2		1	2		5		2	17	20	4	37	7	1	
Hyde	Tyrique	Dagenham & Redbridge																			
Hylton	Jermaine	Solihull Moors	23	4	1	3			2			3		1	28	4	1	32	4	1	
Ilesanmi	Femi	Dover Athletic	45			2			3			2			50			50	2	9	
Inman	Dean	Maidenhead United	7	5	5	1						1			8	5	5	13		1	
Isaac	Chez	Woking	33	5	1	5			1						39	5	1	44		9	1
Jaaskelainen	Will	Chester (L)			6												6				
Jalal	Shwan	Macclesfield Town	40	1		2									42	1		43		3	1
James	Kingsley	Chester	30			1			2			2			33			33	2	3	
James	Kingsley	Barrow (L)	13	1											13		1	14		2	
James	Luke	Barrow (L)	17									7			17			17	7	1	
Janata	Arthur	Leyton Orient		1												1					
Jarvis	Aaron	Boreham Wood (L)	1	3	2						2				1	3	4	4			
Jeffers	Shaun	Boreham Wood	14	12	4	2	1		2		2	3	1	1	18	13	6	31	5	3	
Jeffrey	Anthony	Sutton United	2	8	4		2								2	10	4	12			
Jeffrey	Anthony	Dover Athletic (L)	13	8	3				2	1		1			15	9	3	24	1	2	
Jennings	Connor	Tranmere Rovers	39	4		3			1	1		8	1		43	5		48	9	10	
Jennings	James	Wrexham	40			1						4			41			41	4	12	
John	Louis	Sutton United	33	1	7	2			3			2	1		38	1	7	39	3	2	
Johnson	Dan	Bromley	17	5	23	2	1			1	7				19	7	30	26		3	
Johnson	Danny	Gateshead	26	9	6	2		1	6	2	1	14	1	6	34	11	8	45	21	2	
Johnson	Reda	Eastleigh	11	2	1							1			11	2	1	13	1	4	
Johnson	Roger	Bromley	17	1	4	3			6	1	2	1			26	2	6	28	1		1
Johnson	Ryan	Boreham Wood (L)	2	6											2		6	2			
Johnson	Sam	Halifax	44			1			2						47			47		3	1

Key: St - Started; S - Sub on; Np - Non-playing Sub; Oth - FA Trophy/League Play-offs; Y - Yelow Cards; R - Red Cards.

Surname	Firstname	Club	Lge Apps St	S	Np	FAC Apps St	S	Np	Other Apps St	S	Np	Goals Lg	FC	Oth	Totals St	S	Np	Ap	Gls	Y	R
Jones	Dan	Barrow	31	2					2			3			33	2		35	3	4	1
Jones	Henry	AFC Fylde	14	9	10			2		1		5			14	10	12	24	5	3	
Jones	James	Chester	15		7			1	2						17		8	17		2	1
Jones	Joseph	Woking	25	6	2	4	1	1			1	1			29	7	4	36	1	4	
Jordan	Michael	Ebbsfleet United			7						2						9				
Joyce	Wade	Chester	6	5	5										6	5	5	11		1	
Judd	Myles	Leyton Orient	7	3	1	3			1	1					11	4	1	15		2	
Justham	Elliot	Dagenham & Redbridge			11												11				
Kabamba	Nike	Aldershot Town (L)	3	7	3				1			3			4	7	3	11	3		
Kandi	Chike	Dagenham & Redbridge	5	13	2							1			5	13	2	18	1		
Kay	Josh	Tranmere Rovers (L)		2	1											2	1	2			
Keating	Ruairi	Torquay United	16	23	3		1				1	4			16	25	3	41	4	5	
Kedwell	Danny	Ebbsfleet United	43	2		3			5			19	1	1	51	2		53	21	3	
Keita	Frank	Boreham Wood		1	10											1	10	1			
Kelleher	Fiacre	Solihull Moors (L)	37	1		2		1	2			2			41	1	1	42	2	3	
Kellerman	Jim	Aldershot Town	32	5	2	2			1	1		7			35	6	2	41	7	8	
Kelly	Marcus	Wrexham	42	1	1	1						2			43	1	1	44	2	6	
Kennedy	Kieran	Macclesfield Town	21	11	12	2			1			1			24	11	12	35	1	2	
Kerr	Fraser	Gateshead	24	3	1	2	1		7	1	1	1			33	5	2	38	1	2	
Kettle	Joel	Solihull Moors	14	2		1	1	1				1	1		15	3	1	18	2	1	
Khan	Shiraz	Halifax		1						1						2		2			
Kilman	Max	Maidenhead United	27	6		1		1	2	2		1			30	8	1	38	1	5	
King	Liam	Halifax		2	1	1										3	1	3			
Kinsella	Lewis	Aldershot Town (L)	18						1						19			19		5	
Kirby	Jake	Tranmere Rovers	1	2	4			1							1	2	5	3			
Kirwan	Eoin	Aldershot Town		2												2					
Klukowski	Yan	Torquay United	7	1	12										7	1	12	8			
Koroma	Josh	Leyton Orient	16	15	3			1	2	1	2	4		2	18	16	6	34	6	1	
Kosylo	Matt	Halifax	30	3					2			9		2	32	3		35	11	12	1
Koue Niate	Jean-Yves	Guiseley	3	3	2	1		2			1				4	3	5	7		1	
Lafayette	Ross	Sutton United	21	6	2		1		2	2		8			23	9	2	32	8	4	
		Maidstone United (L)	9	1								3			9	1		10	3	3	
Laing	Louis	Hartlepool	35	4		2			1			1			38	4		42	1	6	
Lait	Chris	Solihull Moors	1	5	6							1			1	5	6	6	1	
Langley	Josh	AFC Fylde	4												4			4		1	1
Langstaff	Macaulay	Gateshead	1	3	1			1							1	3	2	4			
Lathrope	Damon	Torquay United	16	3	4	1									17	3	4	20		2	
		Woking	3	1	1										3	1	1	4			
Lavercombe	Dan	Torquay United (L)	2												2			2			
Lawless	Alex	Leyton Orient	23	3	3	1	1		1	1					25	5	3	30		10	
Lawlor	Jake	Guiseley	20	1	3	4						2			24	1	3	25	2	1	
		AFC Fylde (L)	1	5					1						2	5		7			
Ledger	Michael	Hartlepool	9	2	3	1									10	2	3	12			
Lee	Charlie	Leyton Orient	6	2								1			6	2		8	1	3	
Lee	Jordan	Torquay United (L)	1	1											1	1		2			
Lema	Crossley	Sutton United		1												1					
Lemonheigh-Evans	Connor	Torquay United (L)	11	4								1			11	4		15	1	1	
Lenighan	Simon	Guiseley	17	3		4					1	1			21	3	1	24	1	5	

2017-18 NATIONAL LEAGUE APPEARANCES AND GOALS

			Lge Apps			FAC Apps			Other Apps			Goals			Totals						
			St	S	Np	St	S	Np	St	S	Np	Lg	FC	Oth	St	S	Np	Ap	Gls	Y	R
Lewington	Chris	Dover Athletic			3			2			2						7				
Lewis	Paul	Dover Athletic (L)	5	1					2			1			7	1		8	1	2	
Lewis	Stuart	Maidstone United	41			4			4			4			49			49	4	9	2
Liburd	Rowan	Guiseley	19	9					1			7		1	20	9		29	8		
Ling	Sam	Dagenham & Red	28	1		2			1			3			31	1		32	3	2	1
		Leyton Orient	12	1											12	1		13			
Lloyd	Ryan	Macclesfield Town	25	2	1	1					1	4			26	2	2	28	4		
Loach	Scott	Hartlepool United	46			2			1						49			49			
Lokko	Kevin	Dagenham & Redbridge (L)	23	2	1	2			1			2			26	2	1	28	2	5	1
		Dover Athletic (L)	11	1	1							1			11	1	1	12	1	1	
Lowe	Daniel	Guiseley	14		1		1	2							14	1	3	15		2	
Lowe	Keith	Macclesfield Town	45			2			1			1			48			48	1	1	
Loza	Jamar	Maidstone United	16	12	1		4		4			1		2	20	16	1	36	3	2	
Luer	Greg	Maidstone United (L)	2	4	1										2	4	1	6			
Lynch	Alex	Chester	14		13	1					2				15		15	15			
Lynch	Dave	Halifax	6	7	2		1								6	8	2	14		1	
Lynch	Jay	AFC Fylde	36		9	4			1						41		9	41		3	
Lyons-Foster	Kodi	Aldershot Town	1	5						1					1	6		7		1	1
M'Boungou	Chris	Guiseley	4	1	2	3	1								7	2	2	9			2
MacDonald	Calum	Barrow (L)	21						3			1			24			24	1	2	
MacDonald	Josh	Halifax	25	4	1	1			2			1			28	4	1	32	1		
Mackreth	Jack	Wrexham	7	25	8	1			1						9	25	8	34		2	
MacLeod	Ian	Gateshead			6			1			5						12				
MagnAy	Carl	Hartlepool	35									1			35			35	1	9	1
Magri	Sam	Ebbsfleet United	32	1		3			3						38	1		39		5	
Maher	Niall	Halifax	9		1										9		1	9		1	
Mahon	Craig	Chester	23	9	3					1	1	1			23	10	4	33	1	2	
Makoma	Donovan	Barrow	11	5	16			1	3			1			14	5	17	19	1		1
Mambo	Yado	Ebbsfleet United	9		4	1		2							10		6	10		2	
Mangan	Andy	Tranmere Rovers	3	11	14			1			2	1			3	11	17	14	1		
		AFC Fylde (L)	3	1					1						4	1		5			
Marks	Sean	Maidenhead United	23	11	2			1	3	1		6			26	12	3	38	6	2	
Marsh	Tyrone	Macclesfield Town	28	13	3	2				1		9	1		30	14	3	44	10	2	
Marsh-Brown	Keanu	Dover Athletic (L)	2	4	2							4			2	4	2	6	4		
Marsh-Hughes	Lloyd	Chester		1												1					
Martin	Romario	Solihull Moors		2	4					2						4	4	4			
Martinez	Sheridan	Solihull Moors	2		6										2		6	2			
Marx	Oliver	Wrexham	1		5	1									2		5	2			
Mason	Sam	Woking	3		33			6			1				3		40	3			
Massanka	Ntumba	Wrexham (L)	8	15	4		1		1			3			9	16	4	25	3	1	
Massey	Alan	Maidenhead United	44			2			4						50			50		7	
Matthews	Sam	Eastleigh (L)	20	18	2				1			6			21	18	2	39	6	4	
Maxted	Jonathan	Guiseley	17		4	3			1						21		4	21		3	
Maxwell	Luke	Gateshead (L)	6	2	4	1	2								7	4	4	11		3	
Maye	Simeon	Solihull Moors	1	2											1	2		3			
McAllister	Craig	Eastleigh	2	21	3	1						2			3	21	3	24	2	1	
McAnuff	Jobi	Leyton Orient	34	3					3			6			37	3		40	6	6	
McCallum	Paul	Eastleigh	23	3				1				8			24	4		28	8	3	

Key: St - Started; S - Sub on; Np - Non-playing Sub; Oth - FA Trophy/League Play-offs; Y - Yellow Cards; R - Red Cards.

2017-18 NATIONAL LEAGUE APPEARANCES AND GOALS

			Lge Apps			FAC Apps			Other Apps			Goals			Totals						
			St	S	Np	St	S	Np	St	S	Np	Lg	FC	Oth	St	S	Np	Ap	Gls	Y	R
McClure	Matt	Aldershot Town	19	15	3		1		1			6			20	16	3	36	6	2	
McCombe	John	Chester	22	1		1									23	1	2	24		5	
McCorkell	Andrew	Maidstone United			4												4				
McCoy	Marvin	Ebbsfleet United	15	4	14		1			2	2				15	7	16	22		2	
McCready	Tom	AFC Fylde	3	6	2			3	1						4	6	5	10			
McDonagh	Gerry	Tranmere Rovers (L)	2	6	3	2	1				1				4	7	4	11		1	
McDonald	Wesley	Solihull Moors (L)	3	2											3	2		5			
McDonnell	Adam	Aldershot Town (L)	28	2	2	2			2			4			32	2	2	34	4	7	1
McEveley	James	Tranmere Rovers	9	2	3	2		1			1	2			11	2	5	13	2	2	1
McFadzean	Callum	Guiseley	16	8	1		1	2	1			1			17	9	3	26	1		
McGinty	Sean	Torquay United	46			1			1			4			48			48	4	8	
McGregor	Callum	Wrexham								1							1		1		
McKenzie	Chinedu	Maidenhead United		2							1					2	1	2			
McLaughlin	Patrick	Gateshead	42	4		3			8			3	1	2	53	4		57	6	2	
McLean	Aaron	Ebbsfleet United	2	7	8		1	2	1		1	1	1		3	8	11	11	2		
McLoughlin	Shane	Bromley (L)	1	1											1	1		2			
McManus	Scott	Halifax	32	5	6	1			1		1	3			34	5	7	39	3	8	
McNall	Lewis	Gateshead (L)	3	4	6				1	3	1			1	4	7	7	11	2		
McNamara	Ben	Dagenham & Redbridge			1												1				
McNulty	Steve	Tranmere Rovers	41		1	3			3			1			47		1	47	1	7	1
McQueen	Darren	Ebbsfleet United	9	3								2			9	3		12	2	1	
McQuoid	Josh	Torquay United (L)	13	1		1				1		2			14	2		16	2	3	
		Aldershot Town (L)	13	3							1	1			13	3	1	16	1	5	
McSheffrey	Gary	Eastleigh	11				1					2			11	1		12	2	1	
Mekki	Adam	Bromley	30	7	1	2	1		3	1	1	3	1		35	9	2	44	4	3	
Mellish	Jon	Gateshead	9	1	3										9	1	3	10		1	
Mensah	Bernard	Aldershot Town	14			1	1		1			4			16	1		17	4	2	
Middleton	Harry	Halifax (L)	3	2	1				1						4	2	1	6		3	
Miles	Jonathan	Ebbsfleet United			40			3			3						46				
Miley	Cavanagh	Eastleigh	34	3	7			1	1			2		1	35	3	8	38	3	4	
Miller	George	Wrexham (L)	4	1					1						5	1		6			
Mills	Danny	Ebbsfleet United	3	7	9	1	1	1				1			4	8	10	12	1		
Mitchell	Conor	Chester (L)	8												8		3	8			
Mitchell	Tallen	Torquay United		2	3											2	3	2			
Molyneux	Lee	Guiseley	18	3		3						2			21	3		24	2	1	
Monakana	Jeffrey	Sutton United		1	3											1	3	1			
Moncur	Freddy	Leyton Orient			3												3				
Mongoy	Jordy	Dagenham & Redbridge		1												1		1			
Montgomery	James	Gateshead	25	1	9	1		1	7						33	1	10	34		1	
Monthe	Emmanuel	Tranmere Rovers (L)	4		4				1	1					5	1	4	6			
Montrose	Lewis	AFC Fylde	42	2		2	1		1		1	3			45	3	1	48	3	11	2
Mooney	David	Leyton Orient	22	13	5	3			2	2	1	4		2	27	15	6	42	6	3	
Moore	Lewis	Dagenham & Redbridge			34						1						35				
Moore	Stuart	Barrow	18	5			1				2				18		8	18			
Moses	Ademola	Sutton United (L)	6	4	5		1					2			6	5	5	11	2	1	
		Maidenhead United (L)	16	5	8				2			3			18	5	8	23	3	3	
Morgan	Adam	Halifax	12	8	4	1						4			13	8	4	21	4	2	
Morris	Chad	Sutton United			1												1				

Surname	First	Club	Lge St	Lge S	Lge Np	FAC St	FAC S	FAC Np	Oth St	Oth S	Oth Np	Gls Lg	Gls FC	Gls Oth	Tot St	Tot S	Tot Np	Ap	Gls	Y	R
Morrison	Curtis	Guisley	3												3			3			
Mottley-Henry	Dylan	Tranmere Rovers (L)	11	1		3			1			1			15	1		16	1	2	
Moyo	Cliff	Halifax	19	3	8	1			1						21	3	8	24		4	
Muldoon	Jack	AFC Fylde	35	9		2	1		2			10			39	10		49	10	2	1
Muldoon	Oliver	Maidstone United	2	3	6	2		2			3				4	3	11	7			
Mulhern	Euan (Frank)	Guiseley	2	9	6			1				2			2	9	7	11	2		
Mulley	James	Maidenhead United	5	10	5		1			1					5	12	5	17		3	1
Munns	Jack	Hartlepool	5	12	21	1	1				1	1			6	13	22	19	1	1	
Murombedzi	Shepherd	Solihull Moors		2	25	3			1	1					4	3	25	7		6	
		Chester	2												2			2		1	
Murphy	Rhys	Torquay United (L)	6	2		1						1			7	2		9	1	2	
Murtagh	Keiran	Boreham Wood	44			3			6			1		1	53			53	2	12	1
Myrie-Williams	Jennison	Torquay United	3	7	8		1		1						4	8	8	12		1	
N'Gala	Bondz	Dagenham & Red	9		25			2							9		27	9			
		Leyton Orient (L)	5		1				2						7		1	7			1
Newton	Conor	Hartlepool	26	1	11			1	1			3			27	1	12	28	3	6	
Nicholson	Tom	Halifax	2	1	42			1			2				2	1	45	3			
Nieskens	Dave	Barrow	8		1							1			8		1	8	1	1	
Nirennold	Victor	Fleetwood							1	2					1	2		3			
Noble	Cain	Chester	1		1										1		1	1			
Norburn	Oliver	Tranmere Rovers	42		1	3			2			4			47		1	47	4	10	
Nortey	Nortei	Dover	32	1	10	2			3			5			37	1	10	38	5		
Norwood	James	Tranmere Rovers	40	2		3			3			23	1	3	46	2		48	27	5	1
Nsimbi	Ivan	Woking			2			1									3				
Nunn	Ben	Dagenham & Redbridge	24	1	2			2							24	1	4	25		2	
O'Brien	Billy	Macclesfield Town	2	1	4										2	1	4	3			
O'Donnell	Jonathan	Gateshead	6	4	8	1		2		1	2				7	5	12	12		1	
O'Leary	Max	Solihull Moors (L)	23						2						25			25			
O'Sullivan	Tommy	Torquay United (L)	5	2	2										5	2	2	7		1	
Oates	Rhys	Hartlepool	25	11		2				1		7			27	12		39	7		
Obileye	Ayo	Eastleigh	23	11	6			1			1	7			23	11	8	34	7	3	
Ochieng	Henry	Leyton Orient	3	2	4		1	1							3	3	5	6			
Odametey	Harold	Maidenhead United	44	1		1		1	4			2			49	1	1	50	2	6	
Odejayi	Kayode	Guiseley	27	9	6	4			1			2			32	9	6	41	2		
Ofori-Twumasi	Nathan	Maidstone United	32	1	6	1		1	4					1	37	1	7	38	1	9	
Okenabirhie	Fejiri	Dagenham & Redbridge	34	4	1		1	1				12			34	5	2	39	12	2	
Okojie	Shaun	Aldershot Town	1	8	3			2				1			1	8	5	9	1	1	
Okosieme	Ejiro	Dover Athletic	2	6	10			2	1		1				3	6	13	9		1	
Okuonghoe	Magnus	Maidstone United	21	2	5	1		1	3		1	1	1		25	2	7	27	2	1	
Oliver	Connor	Halifax	25	6	11	1			1		1				27	6	12	33		2	
Orlu	Richard	Woking	22	4	7	5			1			1			28	4	7	32	1	5	
Orrell	Lewis	Hartlepool			4												4				
Osborn	Neal	Torquay United			18			1									19				
Osborne	Jamey	Solihull Moors	22						2			2		1	24			24	3	6	1
Osei	Darius	Maidstone United	3	3					1	2				1	4	5		9	1		
Osho	Gabriel	Maidenhead United (L)	2	1	2										2	1	2	3			
Owen	Jacob	Hartlepool		1	9											1	9	1			
Owusu	Nana	Maidenhead United	2	8	10						4	1			2	8	14	10	1		

Key: St - Started; S - Sub on; Np - Non-playing Sub; Oth - FA Trophy/League Play-offs; Y - Yelow Cards; R - Red Cards.

2017-18 NATIONAL LEAGUE APPEARANCES AND GOALS

			Lge Apps			FAC Apps			Other Apps			Goals			Totals						
			St	S	Np	St	S	Np	St	S	Np	Lg	FC	Oth	St	S	Np	Ap	Gls	Y	R
Oyeleke	Emmanuel	Aldershot Town	34	6		2			2			3			38	6		44	3	7	1
Palmer	Ashley	Guiseley	36	1		3			1			1			40	1		41	1	5	1
Panayiotou	Harrison (Harry)	Barrow	10	21	11			1	1	1		2			11	22	12	33	2		
Parry	Immanuel (Manny)	Dover Athletic	45	1		2			3			5		1	50	1		51	6	4	
Passley	Josh	Dover Athletic	31	3	7	2			2						35	3	7	38		3	
Paxman	Jack	Maidstone United	10	13	12	1	1	1	1	2		1			12	16	13	28	1	3	
Payne	Jack	Ebbsfleet United	21	2					1	1					22	3		25		2	
Payne	Joe	Solihull Moors (L)	3												3			3			
Pearson	Shaun	Wrexham	45									5			45			45	5	9	
Peniket	Richard	Gateshead	30	10	1	1	1	1	7	1		6		6	38	12	2	50	12	3	
Penn	Russell	Gateshead	36	5	4	2			9						47	5	4	52		6	1
Pennell	Luke	Dagenham & Redbridge	22		2						1				22		3	22		2	
Pentney	Carl	Maidenhead United	46			2			4						52			52		4	
Peters	Ryan	Maidenhead United	10	3	17		1	1	1		1				11	4	19	15		2	
Phillips	Michael	Maidstone United	6	2								1			6	2		8	1	1	
Philpot	Jamie	Woking (L)	14	12		1	5				1	4	3		15	18		33	7	3	
Phipps	Harry	Maidstone United	1	1	7						1				1	1	8	2			
Pigott	Joe	Maidstone United	28			4			1	1		11	2	1	33	1		34	14		
Pilkington	George	Macclesfield Town	31	2	6	1	1	1	1						32	3	7	35		7	
Pilling	Luke	Tranmere Rovers		1	26	2			1						1	3	26	4			
Pinnock	Mitchell	Dover Athletic	39	4	3	2			3			8		3	44	4	3	48	11	6	
Pittman	Jon-Paul	Torquay United	8	10	4				1			3			9	10	4	19	3		
Pollock	Aron	Leyton Orient			2			1									3				
Porter	George	Bromley	29	9	2				7	1		6		2	36	10	2	46	8	4	1
Powell	Jack	Ebbsfleet United	33	8	5	3			4	1					40	9	5	49			
Prestedge	Reece	Maidstone United	25	8		1	1	2	1		1			1	27	9	3	36	1	3	
Preston	Callum	Wrexham	1		5										1		5	1			
Preston	Jordan	Gateshead	24	18	2	1	2		6	3		5			31	23	2	54	5	3	
Pring	Cameron	Aldershot Town (L)		1	3											1	3	1		1	
Pritchard	Harry	Maidenhead United	41	2		1			3		1	13		2	45	2	1	47	15	4	
Pritchard	Liam	Hartlepool			2												2				
Purver	Alex	Guiseley	24	4	6		1		1			2			25	5	6	30	2	5	
Quigley	Joe	Boreham Wood (L)	5	4	6				2	3		1		1	7	7	6	14	2	1	
Quigley	Scott	Wrexham (L)	16	1								8			16	1		17	8	2	
Rainey	Ryan	Chester (L)	2		1										2		1	2			
Ralph	Nathan	Woking	32			6			1						39			39		8	
Ramsbottom	Sam	Barrow			2												2				
		Macclesfield Town	4	2	27			1	1						5	2	28	7			
Ramsey	Louis	Woking (L)	23	5	2	2									25	5	2	30			
Rance	Dean	Ebbsfleet United	30	4	3	3			3	1	1	3			36	5	4	41	3	6	
Raven	David	Wrexham	5	2	10										5	2	10	7		1	
Raymond	Frankie	Bromley	32	4	5	3			8			2		1	43	4	5	47	3	10	
Read	Harvey	Eastleigh	1		7						1				1		8	1			
Reason	Jai	Maidstone United	37	5	2	2	2		4			3	1	1	43	7	2	50	5	7	
Reckord	Jamie	Solihull Moors	17		1				2			1			19		1	19	1	3	
Rees	Josh	Bromley	38	5	3	3			5	3		16	1	3	46	8	3	54	20	3	
Reid	Alex	Wrexham (L)	14	4	1							3			14	4	1	18	3		
		Solihull Moors (L)	3	12								4			3	12		15	4	1	

2017-18 NATIONAL LEAGUE APPEARANCES AND GOALS

Surname	First	Club	Lge St	Lge S	Lge Np	FAC St	FAC S	FAC Np	Oth St	Oth S	Oth Np	Gls Lg	Gls FC	Gls Oth	Tot St	Tot S	Tot Np	Tot Ap	Tot Gls	Y	R
Reid	Jamie	Torquay United (L)	33	8	5	1			1			6			35	8	5	43	6	3	
Reid	Paul	Eastleigh			1												1				
Rendell	Scott	Aldershot Town	25	13	1	2			1			12	1		28	13	1	41	13	1	
Reynolds	Callum	Aldershot Town	38	1	1	2			1			2			41	1	1	42	2	6	
Reynolds	Lamar	Leyton Orient (L)	2	7	5				3		1				5	7	6	12			
Richards	Courtney	Macclesfield Town	2	4	7				1						3	4	7	7		1	
		Solihull Moors (L)	10			2									12			12		2	
Richards	Jack	Maidstone United	3	11	7			3				1			3	11	10	14	1		
Richards	Jordan	AFC Fylde	7	3	4	3			1						11	3	4	14		1	
Richards	Kane	Dover	8	6	16		2		1		1	1			9	8	17	17	1	4	
Richardson	Kenton	Hartlepool	3	3	5	1		1							4	3	6	7			
Ricketts	Mark	Boreham Wood	43	2		2			6			1			51		2	51	1	7	
Ridehalgh	Liam	Tranmere Rovers	35	2	1	3			2					1	40	2	1	42	1	2	1
Riley	Martin	Halifax	2	1	2										2	1	2	3		1	
Robert	Fabien	Aldershot Town	12	11		1				1		2			13	12		25	2	3	
Roberts	Gary	Chester	12	1							1				12	1	1	13		6	
Roberts	James	Oxford United		1	2				1	1	1				1	2	3	3			
Roberts	Kevin	Wrexham	38	1	3				1		1			—	39	1	4	40		4	1
Robinson	Matt	Dagenham & Redbridge	25	9	5			2		1					25	10	7	35		3	
Robson	Craig	Dagenham & Redbridge	44			2						3			46			46	3	1	
Rodney	Devante	Hartlepool	22	19	2	1	1			1		2	1		23	21	2	44	3	7	1
Rokka	Elliot	Tranmere Rovers	1					1			1				1		2	1			
Romaine	Elliott	Dagenham & Redbridge	1	9		2						1			3	9		12	1	1	
		Torquay United (L)	13									4			13			13	4	2	1
Rooney	John	Guiseley	24	7	2	1	2				1	6	2		25	9	3	34	8	6	1
Rowe	Danny M	AFC Fylde	46			4			1	1		24	5	1	51	1		52	30	4	
Rowe	James	Aldershot Town	30	10	2	1	1			1		3			31	12	2	43	3	1	
Rowe-turner	Lathaniel	Chester	27	2	3	1				1					28	3	3	31		3	1
Rutherford	Paul	Wrexham	40	3	2		1					2			40	4	2	44	2	4	1
Sach	Bradley	Boreham Wood		7	8			1			2	1				7	11	7	1		
Sam-Yorke	Delano	Maidstone United	32			4			1	2		1	2		37	2		39	3	5	1
Sammons	Ashley	Solihull Moors	1		3	1		2							2		5	2			
Saraiva	Fabio	Woking	7	11	10	1	1	2							8	12	12	20			
Sargeant	Sam	Leyton Orient	2	1	21			3			1				2	1	25	3			
Sendles-White	Jamie	Leyton Orient	8	5	6	2				1					10	6	6	16			1
Shakes	Ricky	Boreham Wood	36	6	2	2			4	2	1	3		1	42	8	3	50	4	3	
Shaw	Frazer	Eastleigh	5	1	8						1				5	1	9	6		2	
Shaw	Tom	Chester	9	4	1			1	2						11	4	2	15		4	
Sheppard	Jack	Reading U21							2					1	2			2	1		
Sheron	Nathan	Chester (L)	3		3										3		3	3		1	
Shields	Sean	Ebbsfleet United	17	15	5	2	1		3			4		1	22	16	5	38	5	1	
Sho-Silva	Tobi	Dover Athletic	2	12								1			2	12		14	1		
Simpson	Connor	Hartlepool	2	5	5			2				1			2	5	7	7	1		
Skinner	Luke	Aldershot Town			5			1									6				
Slew	Jerome	Chester		2												2		2			
Smith	Christian	Maidenhead United	17	14	10	1	1		1	2		2			19	17	10	36	2	5	
Smith	Emanuel	Wrexham	44			1						2			45			45	2	4	1
Smith	Grant	Boreham Wood	46			3			7						56			56		3	

Key: St - Started; S - Sub on; Np - Non-playing Sub; Oth - FA Trophy/League Play-offs; Y - Yelow Cards; R - Red Cards.

2017-18 NATIONAL LEAGUE APPEARANCES AND GOALS

			Lge Apps			FAC Apps			Other Apps			Goals			Totals					Y	R
			St	S	Np	St	S	Np	St	S	Np	Lg	FC	Oth	St	S	Np	Ap	Gls		
Smith	Jonathan	AFC Fylde	30	14	1	3	1		1	1		9	1		34	16	1	50	10	1	
Smith	Kane	Boreham Wood	43			3			5			3			51			51	3	6	
Smith	Leo	Wrexham	4	3	4			1	1						5	3	5	8		2	
Smith	Mark	Aldershot Town	1		17	1		1							2		18	2			
Sodeinde	Victor	Maidstone United			1												1				
Sokolik	Jakub	Torquay United	5		1										5		1	5		1	
Soloman-Davies	Josh	Tranmere Rovers	1		1			1							1		2	1			
Sotiriou	Ruel	Leyton Orient		3	1		2	1		1	1					6	3	6			
Southwell	Dayle	Guiseley	18									7			18			18	7	2	
Sparkes	Daniel	Dagenham & Redbridge	21	4	3					1		4			21	5	3	26	4		
Spellman	Carl	Tranmere Rovers		1												1		1			
Spence	Daniel	Sutton United	10	5					2		2				12	5	2	17		2	
St Ledger	Sean	Solihull Moors			1	1									1		1	1			
		Guiseley	6	1											6	1		7			
Stack	Graham	Eastleigh	27						1						28			28			
Staunton	Joshua	Woking	40		1			2	1			3			41		3	41	3	8	
Stearn	Ross	Eastleigh	1	4	4										1	4	4	5			
		Sutton United		10	4				1			1			1	10	4	11	1		
Steer	Rene	Maidenhead United	31	1	5	1			4		1				36	1	6	37		5	
Stephens	Dave	Boreham Wood	41			3			5			1			49			49	1	7	
Sterling	Tyrone	Bromley	44			2			9			3			55			55	3		
Sterling-James	Omari	Solihull Moors (L)	4	4								1			4	4		8	1	1	
Stojsavljevic	Lazar	Woking	2	4	5			3				1			2	4	8	6	1	1	
Storer	Jack	Solihull Moors (L)	17	1	2				1						18	1	2	19			
Stott	Jamie	AFC Fylde (L)				1		1							1		1	1			
Strevens	Ben	Eastleigh	1	6	4	1						1			2	6	4	8	1	2	
Stubbs	Sam	AFC Fylde (L)	6	1	2						1				6	1	3	7		1	
Sutherland	Frankie	Bromley	26	7	3		1		4	2	1	1			30	10	4	40	1	7	
Sutton	Richard	Tranmere Rovers	41	2	1	3			3			5			47	2	1	49	5	1	
Takyi	Ferdinand	Wrexham									1						1				
Tarpey	Dave	Maidenhead United	6									7			6			6	7		
Tasdemir	Serhat	AFC Fylde	6	20	6		1	3		1		4		1	6	22	9	28	5		
Taylor	Bobby-Joe	Aldershot Town	17	8	1				1			1			18	8	1	26	1	4	
Taylor	Jason	AFC Fylde	5	12	13	2	1	1	1		1	1			8	13	15	21	1	3	
Taylor	Josh	Sutton United	18	10	5	2			1	1	1	1			21	11	6	32	1	4	
Taylor	Rhys	AFC Fylde	10		1				1		4				11		5	11			
		Tranmere Rovers (L)	6		13						2				6		15	6			
Taylor	Tommy	Maidstone United		6			1									7		7			
ter Horst	Johan	Maidstone United	9	9	4		1	2		3		2			9	13	6	22	2	2	
Tharme	Douglas	Wrexham			1												1				
Theophanous	Louie	Woking	7	4											7	4		11			
Thomas	Aswad	Sutton United	34	3		1			3			1			38	3		41	1	6	
Thomas	Kalern	Solihull Moors	3	3											3	3		6			
Thomas	Kwame	Sutton United (L)	1	1	2	1									2	1	2	3			
		Solihull Moors (L)	24	1	1				2			4			26	1	1	27	4	4	
Thomas	Sorba	Boreham Wood		3	12			2		3	1					6	15	6			
Thomas	Terell	Sutton United (L)	19						2			1			21			21	1	3	
Thompson	Jordan	Barrow (L)	7	1		1									8	1		9		1	

2017-18 NATIONAL LEAGUE APPEARANCES AND GOALS

			Lge Apps			FAC Apps			Other Apps			Goals			Totals						
			St	S	Np	St	S	Np	St	S	Np	Lg	FC	Oth	St	S	Np	Ap	Gls	Y	R
Thompson	Josh	Macclesfield			2												2				
Thompson	Reece	Guiseley	6	6			1					1			6	7		13	1	3	
Thomson	Connor	Halifax	8	3								1			8	3		11	1	1	
Thomson	Matthew	Chester	2												2			2			
Thorne	James	Hartlepool	2		1						1				2		2	2			
Tinkler	Robbie	Gateshead (L)	11	4	3	1			1						13	4	3	17		4	
Togwell	Sam	Eastleigh	19	2	4	1									20	2	4	22		4	
Tollitt	Ben	Tranmere Rovers	6	6											6	6		12		1	
Tomlinson	Ben	Halifax	19	14	6	1				1	1	3			20	15	7	35	3	5	1
Tonks	Tom	Solihull Moors	2	1	3										2	1	3	3			
Toure	Gime	Macclesfield	8	3			1	1							8	4	1	12		3	
Townsend	Nick	Solihull Moors (L)	5												5			5			
Traore	Drissa	Tranmere Rovers	2	1	2										2	1	2	3			
Trueman	Connal	Solihull Moors (L)	4		3										4		3	4			
Tulian	Santi	Bromley			3												3				
Tunnicliffe	Jordan	AFC Fylde	46			3			1		1	6			50		1	50	6	7	
Turgott	Blair	Boreham Wood (L)	10	3	10	1	2		1		1	3			12	5	11	17	3	3	
		Maidstone (L)	13	1								2			13	1		14	2	2	
Turley	Jamie	Boreham Wood (L)	29	2	5		1	2	4	1		4		1	33	4	7	37	5	7	
Turnbull	Paul	Chester	17	4	2	1			1	1					19	5	2	24		5	
Tuton	Shaun	Halifax (L)	4	3	2										4	3	2	7		1	
Udoh	Daniel	Chester (L)	2	1	1					1					2	2	1	4		1	
Upward	Ryan	Maidenhead United	33	6	1	2			3			6	1	1	38	6	1	44	8	9	2
Vassell	Theo	Gateshead	29	5	6	1	1	1	3	2	1	2		1	33	8	8	41	3	2	1
Vaughan	Nathan	Solihull Moors	12		3	1		1				1			13		4	13	1		
		Chester			5												5				
Vose	Dominic	Bromley	1	5	4				1			1			2	5	4	7	1		
		Chester	10	1	1							1			10	1	1	11	1	3	
Wabo	Norman	Ebbsfleet United (L)		6	4				2							8	4	8			
Walker	Mitch	Dover Athletic	46			2			3						51			51			
Walker-Rice	Danny	Tranmere Rovers		1												1		1			
Wallace	James	Tranmere Rovers		2	3											2	3	2			
Walters	Lewis	Barrow (L)	11	4					1			1			12	4		16	1	1	
Walton	Simon	Sutton United	24	4	7	1			2	1		3			27	5	7	32	3	6	
Wanadio	Luke	Bromley	38	2		2	1		3	2	2	7		1	43	5	2	48	8	3	
Ward	Joe	Woking	25	2		6			1			7	1		32	2		34	8	1	
Ward	Lewis	Aldershot Town	24		1				1		1				25		2	25		1	
Waring	George	Tranmere Rovers (L)		3	7											3	7	3			
		Halifax (L)	5	5	2							2			5	5	2	10	2		
Waters	Matty	Chester	3	4	7	1						2			4	4	7	8	2		
Waterston	Nathan	Barrow	7	2								1			7	2		9	1	2	
Watson	Keith	Hartlepool	8	1								3			8	1		9	3	1	
Wedgbury	Samuel	Wrexham	41			1						1			42			42	1	11	1
Wells	Dean	Boreham Wood	16		2	2			2						20		2	20		1	
Wells	William	Guiseley			1												1				
Wesolowski	James	Guiseley	2	5	3						1				2	5	4	7			
Westbrooke	Zain	Solihull Moors (L)	1	1											1	1		2			1
		Leyton Orient (L)	3	2	4	1	2								4	4	4	8			

Key: St - Started; S - Sub on; Np - Non-playing Sub; Oth - FA Trophy/League Play-offs; Y - Yelow Cards; R - Red Cards.

			Lge Apps			FAC Apps			Other Apps			Goals			Totals						
			St	S	Np	St	S	Np	St	S	Np	Lg	FC	Oth	St	S	Np	Ap	Gls	Y	R
Weston	Myles	Ebbsfleet United	13	17	2	2	1		3	2		5	1	2	18	20	2	38	8	5	
Wharton	Patrick	Tranmere Rovers			5			1			1						7				
Wheeler	Nick	Dagenham & Redbridge		1	2											1	2	1			
Whitaker	Dan	Macclesfield Town	43	1	2		1	1			1	9			43	2	4	45	9		
White	Harry	Chester	20	10	4	1			1			5			22	10	4	32	5	3	
White	Joe	Dagenaham & Redbridge		3	2							1				3	2	3	1		
White	Jordan	Barrow	22	22	2	1			3			7			26	22	2	48	7	2	
Whitehead	Danny	Macclesfield Town	33	1		2				1		5	1		35	2		37	6	1	
Whitely	Corey	Dagenham & Redbridge	22	4	2	2			1			8			25	4	2	29	8	2	
		Ebbsfleet United	12	1					2			3			14	1		15	3	1	
Widdowson	Joe	Leyton Orient	35	1	1	3			5						43	1	1	44		6	1
Wilde	Josh	Halifax	32	2		1			2						35	2		37		6	
Willard	Harley	Maidstone United	1	2	3										1	2	3	3		1	
Williams	Brett	Bromley	11	15		2			1	1		6			14	16		30	6	4	1
		Torquay United (L)	14	2								4			14	2		16	4	1	
Williams	Callum	Gateshead	18	2	5	2		1	1	1	2				21	3	8	24		2	
Williams	Marcus	Guiseley	8		3										8		3	8			
Williams	Ryan	Wrexham							1						1			1			
Williams	Tyrone	Solihull Moors	14		1							1			14		1	14	1	1	
Williamson	Ben	Eastleigh	24	12		1						10			25	12		37	10	1	
Wilson	Lawrie	Ebbsfleet United	12	1					4						16	1		17		2	
Wilson	Scott	Macclesfield Town	23	12	11		1	1	1			14			24	13	12	37	14	3	
Winfield	Dave	Ebbsfleet United	25	1					5			1		1	30	1		31	2	2	1
Wollacott	Jojo	Woking (L)	1		4				1						2		4	2			
Wood	Sam	Eastleigh	34	1	3	1			1						36	1	3	37		3	
Woodards	Danny	Boreham Wood	25	7	9	1	1	1	6			1			32	8	10	40	1	3	
Woods	Michael	Hartlepool	37	2	5	2			1			11			40	2	5	42	11	3	
Woolfenden	Luke	Bromley (L)	17	3	1				6			1			23	3	1	26	1	2	
Worgan	Lee	Maidstone United	46			4			3						53			53		2	
Wraight	Tom	Maidstone United	10	11	5	1	1	2	1	1		1		1	12	13	7	25	2	3	
Wright	Akil	Wrexham	19	11	10		1								19	12	10	31		2	
Wright	Tommy	Sutton United	26	14	3	2			4			13		2	32	14	3	46	15	2	
Wrightman	Luca	Aldershot Town		2	3											2	3	2			
Wynter	Alex	Maidstone United	40	1	1	4			4			5	1		48	1	1	49	6	4	1
Wynter	Ben	Bromley	12	2	8		2	1							12	4	9	16			
Wynter	Jordan	Woking	24		4	6			1						31		4	31		1	
Yates	Adam	Macclesfield Town	7		1										7		1	7			
Yeates	Mark	Eastleigh	37	8	1	1					1	5			38	9	1	47	5	5	
York	Wesley	Gateshead	18	12	8	1	1	1	8	1		6			27	14	9	41	6	2	
Young	Luke	Torquay United	46			1			1			5			48			48	5	6	
Young	Matt	Woking	31	3	10	4	2		1			1	1		36	5	10	41	2	6	1
Young	Reggie	Woking			1												1				
Yussuf	Adi	Barrow	16	5	1		1				3	5			16	9	1	25	5	3	
		Solihull Moors	12	1	1							5			12	1	1	13	5	1	1
Zanzala	Offrande	Chester	1	3			1								1	4		5			
Zebroski	Chris	Eastleigh	29	9	6			1	1			10			30	9	7	39	10	7	

NATIONAL NORTH LEAGUE TABLE 2017-18

		P	W	D	L	F	A	GD	Pts
1	Salford City	42	28	7	7	80	45	35	91
2	Harrogate Town	42	26	7	9	100	49	51	85
3	Brackley Town	42	23	11	8	72	37	35	80
4	Kidderminster Harriers	42	20	12	10	76	50	26	72
5	Stockport County	42	20	9	13	75	57	18	69
6	Chorley	42	18	14	10	52	39	13	68
7	Bradford Park Avenue	42	18	9	15	66	56	10	63
8	Spennymoor Town	42	18	9	15	71	67	4	63
9	Boston United	42	17	9	16	67	66	1	60
10	Blyth Spartans	42	19	2	21	76	69	7	59
11	York City	42	16	10	16	65	62	3	58
12	Darlington	42	14	13	15	58	58	0	55
13	Nuneaton Town	42	14	13	15	50	57	-7	55
14	AFC Telford United	42	16	5	21	55	69	-14	53
15	Southport	42	14	8	20	60	72	-12	50
16	FC United of Manchester	42	14	8	20	58	72	-14	50
17	Alfreton Town	42	14	7	21	67	71	-4	49
18	Curzon Ashton	42	12	13	17	52	66	-14	49
19	Leamington	42	13	10	19	51	65	-14	49
20	Gainsborough Trinity	42	14	4	24	47	73	-26	46
21	Tamworth	42	11	9	22	55	77	-22	42
22	North Ferriby United	42	4	9	29	25	101	-76	21

Play-Offs: Stockport County 0-1 Chorley. Kidderminster Harriers 0-2 Bradford Park Avenue
Semi Finals: Harrogate Town 2-1 Chorley. Brackley Town 1-0 Bradford Park Avenue
Final: Harrogate Town 3-0 Brackley Town

		1	2	3	4	5	6	7	8	9	10	11	12	13	14	15	16	17	18	19	20	21	22
1	AFC Telford United		1-2	2-3	2-1	1-3	1-4	1-2	0-3	0-0	1-0	3-2	1-5	0-0	3-2	3-0	1-2	0-2	1-1	3-2	3-2	2-0	3-5
2	Alfreton Town	0-1		2-0	2-3	1-1	1-3	0-2	4-0	1-1	1-0	4-1	1-2	0-2	4-1	1-0	1-1	2-3	0-1	1-4	1-3	2-1	2-3
3	Blyth Spartans	0-1	0-1		5-2	3-0	3-0	2-0	2-1	3-1	1-1	4-0	0-2	1-2	1-0	0-1	6-3	0-1	2-0	2-3	0-1	4-2	0-2
4	Boston United	1-0	3-1	2-1		2-3	1-2	2-0	3-3	1-1	4-4	2-0	3-0	3-2	0-1	2-1	1-1	0-1	3-2	0-3	2-2	3-1	2-1
5	Brackley Town	1-1	1-3	3-1	4-1		0-1	1-2	2-2	3-0	2-1	2-0	0-0	2-0	1-1	3-0	1-0	2-1	4-0	2-0	3-2	0-0	2-0
6	Bradford Park Avenue	2-1	3-3	4-1	2-1	2-0		0-0	3-1	0-1	3-0	5-0	3-1	1-1	1-0	0-1	1-1	1-2	1-2	2-3	3-4	0-5	
7	Chorley	3-2	1-0	2-0	0-1	0-0	2-0		1-1	4-1	1-0	1-0	0-1	0-0	2-0	2-2	2-2	0-1	0-0	3-1	1-1	1-1	2-0
8	Curzon Ashton	1-0	2-2	0-3	2-1	0-2	1-1	0-2		1-0	1-0	2-0	1-2	1-2	1-1	4-0	2-2	1-1	2-2	1-0	1-1	1-0	4-1
9	Darlington	0-1	4-1	3-0	1-2	0-3	2-1	2-2	1-0		3-0	4-3	3-1	2-1	0-0	6-0	0-0	1-2	2-4	1-1	1-1	0-1	1-2
10	FC United of Manchester	3-1	3-2	1-3	2-1	1-1	4-0	0-0	2-0	1-2		1-0	3-2	1-2	1-2	0-2	2-1	3-2	1-0	2-3	0-1	3-1	1-0
11	Gainsborough Trinity	3-2	2-1	2-4	1-1	1-2	0-3	1-0	1-0	3-1	1-0		4-5	1-0	1-2	2-0	0-1	0-1	0-3	4-1	2-3	3-0	1-0
12	Harrogate Town	2-1	4-3	5-1	3-1	1-1	1-1	4-1	5-0	3-0	6-0	2-0		2-2	2-2	3-0	4-0	1-2	2-0	1-2	4-1	3-0	2-0
13	Kidderminster Harriers	2-0	2-1	5-4	1-1	2-1	1-2	0-1	2-2	3-3	4-0	3-0	0-2		2-0	4-0	3-0	4-4	3-0	2-2	3-1	2-0	2-1
14	Leamington	0-3	2-3	1-0	0-2	2-2	2-1	2-0	0-0	2-3	1-0	3-0	1-3	1-1		3-0	1-0	0-4	0-1	4-0	2-3	1-2	2-2
15	North Ferriby United	0-2	0-3	1-0	1-5	0-5	0-1	0-2	0-1	1-1	3-3	0-1	0-2	1-3	1-1		0-2	1-1	0-3	0-6	1-3	0-0	1-4
16	Nuneaton Town	0-2	2-2	2-2	1-1	0-2	0-0	1-1	1-1	2-1	1-0	0-1	2-1	1-0	4-0	2-2		0-2	3-0	0-1	1-3	4-1	1-0
17	Salford City	3-0	1-0	4-1	1-2	2-0	2-2	0-3	2-1	0-2	2-2	1-0	2-1	3-0	2-3	4-0	3-0		2-1	3-2	2-1	2-1	3-2
18	Southport	3-0	1-3	0-3	4-0	0-1	0-4	3-0	3-1	2-0	3-3	2-2	1-4	0-3	2-0	2-2	0-1	0-1		1-2	3-1	3-0	1-1
19	Spennymoor Town	1-2	2-1	3-1	0-0	0-3	3-0	1-0	2-4	1-2	4-4	1-1	3-1	1-1	1-0	1-1	0-1	1-1	2-1		1-0	1-0	2-4
20	Stockport County	1-0	1-0	1-3	1-0	0-1	0-0	1-1	3-0	1-1	4-1	1-0	2-2	1-2	4-0	4-1	0-1	2-2	6-0	3-2		3-2	2-0
21	Tamworth	2-2	2-3	0-3	2-1	1-1	0-1	3-4	4-1	0-0	0-2	1-2	1-1	2-1	0-3	4-1	2-0	1-3	3-3	3-1	3-1		1-1
22	York City	0-1	1-1	2-3	1-0	2-1	2-1	1-1	2-1	0-0	0-2	1-1	0-2	1-0	2-2	2-0	4-3	1-0	3-2	2-2	2-0	2-3	

AFC TELFORD UNITED MATCH RESULTS 2017-18

Date	Comp	H/A	Opponents	Att:	Result	Goalscorers	Pos	No.
Aug 5	Nat North	A	York City	2951	W 1 - 0	Barnes-Homer 44	8	1
8	Nat North	H	Brackley Town	1225	L 1 - 3	Myles-Tebbutt (og)	14	2
12	Nat North	H	Salford City	1335	L 0 - 2		18	3
14	Nat North	A	Curzon Ashton	380	L 0 - 1		18	4
19	Nat North	A	Darlington	1532	W 1 - 0	Dinanga 47	15	5
26	Nat North	H	Bradford PA	1130	L 1 - 4	Dinanga 70	17	6
28	Nat North	A	Leamington	711	W 3 - 0	Reid 11 Styche 76 87	11	7
Sept 2	Nat North	A	Blyth Spartans	1078	L 2 - 3	Dinanga 64 Newby 78	15	8
5	Nat North	H	Nuneaton Town	569	W 2 - 0	Dwyer 25 Heaton 63 (og)	14	9
9	Nat North	H	Harrogate Town	1018	L 1 - 5	Dwyer 20	15	10
12	Nat North	H	Stockport County	853	W 3 - 2	Marsden 11 Dwyer 41 Murphy 71	12	11
16	FAC 2Q	H	Barwell	541	W 2 - 0	Gough 17 Murphy 73		12
23	Nat North	A	Chorley	1125	L 2 - 3	Dinanga 52 (pen) 55	15	13
30	FAC 3Q	A	Stafford Rangers	1137	D 1 - 1	Marsden 84		14
Oct 2	FAC 3Qr	H	Stafford Rangers	869	W 4 - 1	Dinanga 6 57 Dwyer 78 Murphy 78		15
7	Nat North	H	Boston United	1097	L 1 - 2	Sutton 49 (og)	13	16
14	FAC 4Q	H	FC United	1451	W 3 - 1	Dinanga 52 90 Lussey 90		17
21	Nat North	A	North Ferriby United	250	W 2 - 0	Lussey 45 Newby 78	11	18
24	Nat North	A	Gainsborough Trinity	412	L 2 - 3	Newby 34 Lussey 45	11	19
28	Nat North	H	Southport	1082	D 1 - 1	Dinanga 40	11	20
Nov 4	FAC 1	A	Hereford	4712	L 0 - 1			21
11	Nat North	A	FC United of Manchester	2079	L 1 - 3	Cowans 3	14	22
18	Nat North	H	Alfreton Town	913	L 1 - 2	Newby 44	16	23
21	Nat North	H	Tamworth	747	W 2 - 0	Marsden 62 Newby 88	12	24
25	FAT 3Q	H	Droylesden	522	W 4 - 2	Ebanks-Blake 26 32 Marsden 72 Dinanga 80		25
Dec 19	FAT 1	A	Blyth Spartans	476	L 0 - 1			26
13	Nat North	A	Brackley Town	440	D 1 - 1	Dinanga 33	13	27
26	Nat North	H	Kidderminster Harriers	1995	D 0 - 0		15	28
Jan 1	Nat North	A	Kidderminster Harriers	2201	L 0 - 2		16	29
13	Nat North	A	Salford City	1628	L 0 - 2		19	30
16	Nat North	A	York City	1852	L 3 - 5	Ebanks-Blake 21 60 Johnson 71	19	31
27	Nat North	H	Harrogate Town	1034	L 1 - 2	Murphy 90	21	32
Feb 10	Nat North	H	North Feriby United	919	W 3 - 0	Marsden 19 Morgan-Smith 77 Dinanga 92	21	33
13	Nat North	A	Curzon Ashton	747	L 0 - 3		21	34
17	Nat North	A	Tamworth	736	D 2 - 2	Morgan-Smith 68 Kettle 75 (og)	20	35
24	Nat North	H	FC United of Manchester	1186	W 1 - 0	McAtee 33	20	36
27	Nat North	H	Nuneaton Town	336	L 1 - 2	Morgan-Smith 38	20	37
Mar 13	Nat North	A	Southport	784	L 0 - 3		20	38
20	Nat North	A	Alfreton Town	381	W 1 - 0	Dinanga 12	20	39
24	Nat North	H	Darlington	1318	D 0 - 0		20	40
26	Nat North	A	Bradford PA	334	L 1 - 2	Dinanga 43	20	41
Apr 5	Nat North	H	Spennymoor Town	1212	W 3 - 2	Dinanga 9 Giles 53 Newby 73	19	42
7	Nat North	H	Chorley	1048	L 1 - 2	Newby 86	19	43
12	Nat North	H	Leamington	977	W 3 - 2	Dinanga 6 Sutton 34 Smith 54	19	44
14	Nat North	A	Stockport County	3546	L 0 - 1		19	45
17	Nat North	A	Blyth Spartans	486	W 1 - 0	Dinanga 28	15	46
21	Nat North	H	Gainsborough Trinity	1495	W 3 - 2	Sutton 61 Dinanga 67 75	15	47
24	Nat North	A	Spennymoor Town	418	W 2 - 1	Dinanga 30 Giles 68	14	48
28	Nat North	A	Boston United	1075	L 0 - 1		14	49

GOALSCORERS	SG	CSG	Pens	Hat tricks	Total		SG	CSG	Pens	Hat tricks	Total
2016-17 Wilson					*9*	Styche	1				2
Dinanga	17	2	1		21	Sutton	2				2
Newby	7	2			6	Barnes-Homer					1
Marsden	5	2			5	Cowans					1
Dwyer	4	3			4	Gough					1
Ebanks-Blake	2				4	Johnson					1
Murphy	3	2			4	McAtee					1
Opponents	4				4	Murphy					1
Lussey	3	3			3	Reid					1
Morgan-Smith	3				3	Smith					1
Giles	2				2						

ALFRETON TOWN MATCH RESULTS 2017-18

Date	Comp	H/A	Opponents	Att:	Result	Goalscorers	Pos	No.
Aug 5	Nat North	H	Blyth Spartans	596	W 2 - 0	Shiels 38 Johnson 64	4	1
8	Nat North	A	Boston United	1107	L 1 - 3	Westcarr 21	9	2
12	Nat North	A	Darlington	1547	L 1 - 4	Sharp 1	17	3
15	Nat North	A	North Ferriby United	371	W 1 - 0	Priestley 70	12	4
19	Nat North	H	Southport	479	L 0 - 1		14	5
26	Nat North	A	Kidderminster Harriers	1613	L 1 - 2	Allan 17	15	6
28	Nat North	H	Curzon Ashton	405	W 4 - 0	Smith 12 Westcarr 64 Platt 89 Daniels 90	12	7
Sept 2	Nat North	A	Nuneaton Town	632	D 2 - 2	Sharp 11 Westcarr 53	12	8
6	Nat North	A	Leamington	435	W 3 - 2	Westcarr 20 Shiels 44 Platt 90	11	9
9	Nat North	H	Gainsborough Trinity	454	W 4 - 1	Platt 7 Westcarr 12 German 17 Daniels 25	8	10
12	Nat North	H	Brackley Town	383	D 1 - 1	Westcarr 18	9	11
16	**FAC 2Q**	**H**	**AFC Rushden**	**403**	**D 2 - 2**	**Robertson 43 Priestley 81**		12
19	**FAC 2Qr**	**A**	**AFC Rushden**	**609**	**W 3 - 1**	**Allan German Andrews**		13
23	Nat North	A	Spennymoor Town	634	L 1 - 2	Allan 90	11	14
30	**FAC 3Q**	**A**	**Stourbridge**	**646**	**L 1 - 3**	**Westcarr 64 (pen)**		15
Oct 7	Nat North	H	Chorley	620	L 0 - 2		14	16
21	Nat North	H	Tamworth	583	W 3 - 2	Robertson 18 40 Westcarr 89	12	17
28	Nat North	A	Harrogate Town	569	L 1 - 2	Allan 35	14	18
Nov 4	Nat North	A	Salford City	2074	L 0 - 1		15	19
11	Nat North	H	York City	997	L 2 - 3	Keane 33 Daniels 55	16	20
14	Nat North	A	FC United of Manchester	1548	L 2 - 3	Westcarr 22 Daniels 45	16	21
18	Nat North	A	AFC Telford United	913	W 2 - 1	Westcarr 26 Allan 31	13	22
25	**FAT 3Q**	**H**	**Altrincham**	**329**	**L 0 - 2**			23
Dec 2	Nat North	H	Bradford PA	435	L 1 - 3	Ross 24 (og)	14	24
23	Nat North	H	Boston United	518	L 2 3	Mulhern 59 Watson 63	18	25
26	Nat North	A	Stockport County	3453	L 0 - 1		19	26
Jan 1	Nat North	H	Stockport County	949	L 1 - 3	Daniels 90 (pen)	20	27
6	Nat North	A	North Ferriby United	297	W 3 - 0	Shiels 17 Sharp 20 Bird 45	17	28
13	Nat North	H	Darlington	727	D 1 - 1	Daniels 90	18	29
20	Nat North	H	Leamington	479	W 4 - 1	Daniels 34 Keane 43 57 Jennings 47	15	30
23	Nat North	A	Blyth Spartans	541	W 1 - 0	Daniels 30	14	31
27	Nat North	A	Gainsborough Trinity	483	L 1 - 2	Shiels 59	14	32
Feb 10	Nat North	H	Tamworth	449	W 2 - 1	Daniels 35 Westcarr 87	13	33
17	Nat North	H	Salford City	984	L 2 - 3	Shiels 21 Marshall 90	16	34
20	Nat North	A	Harrogate Town	688	L 3 - 4	Sharp 40 Bell 65 67	16	35
24	Nat North	A	York City	2397	D 1 - 1	Allan 38	16	36
Mar 10	Nat North	A	Bradford PA	434	D 3 - 3	Platt 29 Sharp 39 Daniels 73	16	37
20	Nat North	H	AFC Telford United	381	L 0 - 1		17	38
24	Nat North	A	Southport	1614	W 3 1	Allan 2 Daniels 38 Bell 76	16	39
27	Nat North	H	Kidderminster Harriers	433	L 0 - 2		16	40
30	Nat North	H	Nuneaton Town	535	D 1 - 1	Daniels 42	16	41
Apr 5	Nat North	A	Curzon Ashton	206	L 2 - 2	Allan 50 Platt 56	19	42
7	Nat North	H	Spennymoor Town	441	L 1 - 4	Bell 61	19	43
14	Nat North	A	Brackley Town	495	W 3 - 1	Sharp 2 40 Daniels 30	16	44
21	Nat North	H	FC United of Manchester	911	W 1 - 0	Platt 23	16	45
28	Nat North	A	Chorley	1053	L 0 - 1		17	46

GOALSCORERS	SG	CSG	Pens	Hat tricks	Total		SG	CSG	Pens	Hat tricks	Total
2016-17 Westcarr					18	Andrews					1
Daniels	13	3	1		13	Bird					1
Westcarr	11	5	1		11	Daniels					1
Allan	8	2			8	German					1
Sharp	6				7	Jennings					1
Platt	6	2			6	Johnson					1
Shiels	5				5	Marshall					1
Bell	3				4	Mulhern					1
Keane	2				3	Opponents					1
Robertson	2				3	Smith					1
Priestley					2	Watson					1

BLYTH SPARTANS MATCH RESULTS 2017-18

Date	Comp	H/A	Opponents	Att:	Result	Goalscorers	Pos	No.
Aug 5	Nat North	A	Alfreton Town	596	L 0 - 2		21	1
8	Nat North	H	York City	1373	L 0 - 2		21	2
12	Nat North	H	Tamworth	654	W 4 - 2	Hutchinson 13 Maguire 27 Rivers 56 Hopson 66	14	3
15	Nat North	A	Gainsborough Trinity	559	W 4 - 2	Hopson 8 Buddle 16 Reid 64 Maguire 86	10	4
19	Nat North	H	North Ferriby United	562	L 0 - 1		11	5
26	Nat North	A	Curzon Ashton	284	W 3 - 0	Regan 65 (og) Maguire 81 Reid 85	9	6
28	Nat North	H	Harrogate Town	829	L 0 - 2		13	7
Sept 2	Nat North	A	AFC Telford United	1078	W 3 - 2	Dale 28 Maguire 31 Hopson 35 (pen)	8	8
5	Nat North	A	FC United of M	1491	W 3 - 1	Maguire 38 82 Reid 61	6	9
9	Nat North	H	Boston United	773	W 5 - 2	MAGUIRE 3 (3 14 37) Buddle 10 Rivers 79	4	10
12	Nat North	A	Chorley	617	W 2 - 0	Buddle 56 Maguire 84	4	11
16	FAC 2Q	H	Shaw Lane	573	L 1 - 2	Wrightson 57	-	12
23	Nat North	A	Kidderminster Harriers	1524	L 4 - 5	Hopson 15 85 Harrison 19 McTiernan 25	5	13
Oct 7	Nat North	H	Nuneaton Town	901	W 6 - 3	HOPSON 3 (39 67 82) Maguire 37 41 McTiernon 69	3	14
14	Nat North	A	Stockport County	3423	W 3 - 1	Wrightson 33 Liddle 90 Rivers 90	3	15
21	Nat North	A	Brackley Town	473	L 1 - 3	Maguire 18	3	16
28	Nat North	H	Darlington	1554	W 3 - 1	Wrighton 48 Reid 57 Dale 82	3	17
Nov 4	Nat North	A	Bradford PA	395	L 1 - 4	Dale 68	5	18
11	Nat North	H	Leamington	541	W 1 - 0	English 19 (og)	5	19
18	Nat North	A	Southport	905	W 3 - 0	Liddle 55 Rutherford 61 Reid 90		20
25	FAT 3Q	H	Stalybridge Celtic	482	W 2 - 1	Reid 79 Watson 84		21
Dec 2	Nat North	H	Salford City	1040	L 0 - 1		4	22
19	FAT 1	H	AFC Telford United	476	W 1 - 0	Hopson		23
22	Nat North	A	York City	2751	W 3 - 2	Reid 26 Wrightson 35 Rutherford 71	4	24
26	Nat North	H	Spennymoor Town	1179	L 2 - 3	Buddle 22 Green 44	4	25
Jan 1	Nat North	A	Spennymoor Town	1066	L 1 - 3	Hopson 15	6	26
6	Nat North	H	Gainsborough Trinity	591	W 4 - 0	Rutherford 32 82 Reid 58 62	5	27
13	FAT 2	H	Bromley	647	L 1 - 4	Rutherford 82		28
20	Nat North	H	FC United of Manchester	985	D 1 - 1	Reid 56	6	29
23	Nat North	H	Alfreton Town	541	L 0 - 1		6	30
27	Nat North	A	Boston United	1203	L 1 - 2	Maguire 77	7	31
Feb 3	Nat North	A	Darlington	1526	L 0 - 3		7	32
10	Nat North	H	Brackley Town	621	W 3 - 0	Maguire 3 37 Rivers 5	7	33
13	Nat North	H	Tamworth	501	W 3 - 0	DALE 3 (20 59 90)	5	34
17	Nat North	H	Bradford PA	306	W 3 - 0	Hopson 14 Rivers 44 Dale 77	4	35
24	Nat North	A	Leamington	524	L 0 - 1		4	36
Mar 24	Nat North	A	North Ferriby United	367	L 0 - 1		6	37
27	Nat North	A	Salford City	804	L 1 - 4	Reid 20	7	38
Apr 2	Nat North	A	Harrogate Town	1044	L 1 - 5	Reid 39	8	39
7	Nat North	H	Kidderminster Harriers	738	L 1 - 2	Reid 87	9	40
14	Nat North	A	Chorley	1165	L 0 - 2		10	41
17	Nat North	H	FC Telford United	486	L 0 - 1		11	42
19	Nat North	H	Southport	1045	W 2 - 0	Rivers 10 Wrightson 90	11	43
21	Nat North	H	Stockport County	1045	L 0 - 1		11	44
24	Nat North	H	Curzon Ashton	610	W 2 - .1	Buddle 22 Mullen 63	9	45
28	Nat North	A	Nuneaton Town	597	D 2 - 2	Dale 76 Reid 88	10	46

GOALSCORERS	SG	CSG	Pens	Hat tricks	Total		SG	CSG	Pens	Hat tricks	Total
2016-17 Maguire					36	McTiernan	2				2
Maguire	11	4		1	16	Opponents					2
Reid	12	3			14	Green					1
Hopson	8	2	1	1	11	Harrison					1
Dale	5	2		1	8	Hutchinson					1
Rivers	6				6	Mullen					1
Buddle	5	2			5	Watson					1
Rutherford	4				5						
Wrightson	5				5						
Liddle	2				2						

BOSTON UNITED MATCH RESULTS 2017-18

Date	Comp	H/A	Opponents	Att:	Result	Goalscorers	Pos	No.
Aug 5	Nat North	A	Southport	886	L 0 - 4		20	1
8	Nat North	H	Alfreton Town	1107	W 3 - 1	Warren 16 Keane 40 Smith 77	16	2
15	Nat North	A	Tamworth	702	L 1 - 2	Tshimanga 47	16	3
19	Nat North	H	Chorley	934	W 2 - 0	Hemmings 37 Tshimanga 47	12	4
22	Nat North	H	Spennymoor Town	1048	L 0 - 3		14	5
26	Nat North	A	FC United	1688	L 1 - 2	Chapman 89	16	6
28	Nat North	H	Nuneaton Town	1020	D 1 - 1	McGowan 90	15	7
Sept 2	Nat North	A	Kidderminster Harriers	1463	D 1 - 1	Horsfall 49 (og)	16	8
5	Nat North	H	North Ferriby United	859	W 2 - 1	Rollins 48 90	16	9
9	Nat North	A	Blyth Spartans	773	L 2 - 4	Vince 45 Hawley 71	17	10
11	Nat North	A	Bradford PA	358	L 1 - 2	McGowan 30	17	11
16	FAC 2Q	H	Haughmond	726	D 1 - 1	Yeomans 54		12
19	FAC 2Qr	A	Haughmond	768	W 5 - 0	Clifton 20 60 Rollins 30 Smith 63 Tshiminga (p) 90		13
23	Nat North	H	Darlington	1051	D 1 - 1	Tshimanga 78	18	14
30	FAC 3Q	A	AFC Mansfield	613	W 2 - 0	Broadhead 13 Tshimanga 90		15
Oct 7	Nat North	A	AFC Telford United	1097	L 1 - 2	Sutton 40 (og)	19	16
14	FAC 4Q	A	Chorley	1204	D 0 - 0			17
17	FAC 4Qr	H	Chorley	1132	L 3 - 4	Clifton 23 Tshimanga 51 Smith 82 (aet)		18
21	Nat North	A	Curzon Ashton	234	L 1 - 2	Tshimanga 54	20	19
28	Nat North	H	Brackley Town	950	L 2 - 3	Hemmings 54 (pen) Rollins 73	21	20
31	Nat North	H	Salford City	1019	L 0 - 1		21	21
Nov 4	Nat North	A	Leamington	592	W 2 - 0	McGowan 34 Hemmings 37 (pen)	20	22
11	Nat North	H	Stockport County	1211	D 2 - 2	Smith 30 Rollins 54	21	23
18	Nat North	H	Harrrogate Town	1358	L 1 - 3	Hemmings 4 (pen)	21	24
25	FAT 3Q	H	Kidderminster Harriers	732	D 2 - 2	Curry 78 Tshimanga 80		25
28	FAT 3Qr	A	Kidderminster Harriers	604	L 0 - 2			26
Dec 2	Nat North	H	York City	1126	W 2 - 1	Keane 54 Hemmings 74	21	27
16	Nat North	H	Southport	784	W 3 - 2	Hemmings 22 (pen) Tshimanga 80 McGowan 88	18	28
23	Nat North	A	Alferton Town	518	W 3 - 2	Hemmings 1 (pen) 13 (pen) Keane 80	16	29
26	Nat North	H	Gainsborough Trinity	1491	W 2 - 0	Rollins 44 Abbott 73	14	30
Jan 1	Nat North	A	Gainsborough Trinity	1022	D 1 - 1	Thompson 49	14	31
6	Nat North	H	Tamworth	1056	W 3 - 1	Thompson 23 Hemmings 52 62 (pen)	12	32
20	Nat North	A	North Ferriby United	546	W 5 - 1	Hemmings 1 Smith 5 Thompson 12 Abbott 45 Tshimanga 82	11	33
27	Nat North	H	Blyth Spartans	1203	W 2 - 1	Hemmings 62 (pen) Tshimanga 84	11	34
Feb 10	Nat North	H	Curzon Ashton	1009	D 3 - 3	Abbott 63 75 Thompson 66	11	35
17	Nat North	H	Leamington	1107	L 0 - 1		11	36
Mar 10	Nat North	A	York City	2461	L 0 - 1		14	37
17	Nat North	H	FC United	1052	D 4 - 4	Thompson 3 McGuire 8 Hemmings 30 (pen) 73	15	38
20	Nat North	A	Stockport County	2244	L 0 - 1		15	39
24	Nat North	A	Chorley	1022	W 1 - 0	Thompson 10	15	40
27	Nat North	A	Brackley Town	405	L 1 - 4	Keane 90	15	41
30	Nat North	H	Kidderminster Harriers	1158	W 3 - 2	Keane 24 Middleton 30 Wafula 90	15	42
Apr 2	Nat North	A	Darlington	1286	W 2 - 1	Thompson 35 Hemmings 39	11	43
10	Nat North	A	Spennymoor United	479	D 0 - 0		11	44
14	Nat North	H	Bradford PA	992	L 1 - 2	Keane 3	13	45
17	Nat North	H	Harrogate Town	875	W 3 - 0	Beesley 29 Thompson 35 Tshimanga 84	12	46
21	Nat North	A	Salford City	2456	W 2 - 1	Thompson 26 Keane 34	10	47
25	Nat North	A	Nuneaton Town	154	D 1 - 1	Johnson 58 (og)	10	48
28	Nat North	H	AFC Telford United	1075	W 1 - 0	Hemmings 59	9	49

GOALSCORERS	SG	CSG	Pens	Hat tricks	Total		SG	CSG	Pens	Hat tricks	Total
2016-17 Rollins					12	Beesley					1
Hemmings	11	3	9		16	Broadhead					1
Tshimanga	10	3	1		12	Chapman					1
Thompson	9				9	Curry					1
Keane	6				7	Hawley					1
Rollins	6				6	McGuire					1
Smith	5				5	Middleton					1
Abbott	3				4	Vince					1
McGowan	4				4	Wafula					1
Clifton	2				3	Warren					1
Opponents					3	Yeomans					1

BRACKLEY TOWN MATCH RESULTS 2017-18

Date	Comp	H/A	Opponents	Att:	Result	Goalscorers	Pos	No.
Aug 5	Nat North	H	FC Utd of Manchester	654	W 2 - 1	Armson 50 Brown 77	6	1
8	Nat North	A	AFC Telford United	1225	W 3 - 1	Brown 31 Gough 33 (og) Ndlovu 47	3	2
12	Nat North	A	North Ferriby United	167	W 5 - 0	Graham 35 ARMSON 4 (72 75 84 86)	1	3
15	Nat North	H	Nuneaton Town	530	W 1 - 0	Myles-Tebbutt 11	1	4
19	Nat North	H	Spennymoor Town	400	W 2 - 0	Ndlovu 40 Lowe 90	1	5
26	Nat North	A	Chorley	732	D 0 - 0		2	6
28	Nat North	H	Kidderminster Harriers	690	W 2 - 0	Ndlovu 26 Armson 68	2	7
Sept 2	Nat North	A	Harrogate Town	1081	D 1 - 1	Williams 3	2	8
5	Nat North	H	Tamworth	430	D 0 - 0		1	9
9	Nat North	A	Salford City	1117	L 0 - 2		3	10
12	Nat North	A	Alfreton Town	383	D 1 - 1	Ndlovu 15	3	11
16	FAC 2Q	A	Kingstonian	289	W 3 - 0	Ndlovu 24 Brown 47 Lowe 73		12
Sept 23	Nat North	A	Curzon Ashton	473	D 2 - 2	Walker 24 Williams 44	3	13
30	FAC 3Q	A	Braintree Town	383	W 4 - 1	Walker 3 Graham50 Myles-T 58 Williams 66		14
Oct 7	Nat North	A	York City	2732	L 1 - 2	Williams 70	5	15
14	FAC 4Q	H	Billericay Town	731	D 3 - 3	Williams 2 Walker 76 Byrne 90		16
17	FAC 4Qr	A	Billericay Town	1464	L 1 - 2	Williams 41		17
21	Nat North	H	Blyth Spartans	473	W 3 - 1	Williams 46 85 Byrne 51	4	18
28	Nat North	A	Boston United	950	W 3 - 2	Brown 10 Williams 15 48	4	19
Nov 4	Nat North	A	Darlington	1267	W 3 - 0	Brown 18 Williams 42 Myles-Tebbutt 80	3	20
11	Nat North	H	Gainsborough Trinity	482	W 2 - 0	Williams 75 Armson 79	3	21
14	Nat North	H	Southport	343	W 4 - 0	Dean 35 Williams 45 (pen) 60 Byrne	2	22
18	Nat North	A	Bradford PA	341	L 0 - 2		3	23
25	FAT 3Q	H	Salford City	426	W 4 - 0	WILLIAMS 3 Walker 85		24
Dec 2	Nat North	H	Stockport County	585	W 3 - 2	Byrne 16 Williams 57 70	2	25
8	Nat North	A	FC United	1893	D 1 - 1	Armson 58	2	26
16	FAT 1	H	Braintree Town	249	D 0 - 0			27
19	FAT 1r	H	Braintree Town	235	W 2 - 0	Lowe 51 Byrne 78		28
23	Nat North	A	AFC Telford United	440	D 1 - 1	Walker 90	3	29
26	Nat North	A	Leamington	645	D 2 - 2	Walker 47 Williams 73	3	30
Jan 1	Nat North	H	Leamington	522	D 1 - 1	Williams 78 (pen)	3	31
6	Nat North	A	Nuneaton Town	532	W 2 - 0	Walker 8 Armson 59	3	32
13	FAT 2	H	Barrow	512	D 0 - 0			33
16	FAT 2r	A	Barrow	430	W 2 - 0	Williams 41 Armson 62		34
20	Nat North	H	Tamworth	588	D 1 - 1	Armson 84	3	35
27	Nat North	H	Salford City	1010	W 2 - 1	Williams 4 Gudger 17	3	36
Feb 3	FAT 3	H	Sutton United	767	W 3 - 1	Ndlovu 29 Williams 40 (pen) Armson 56		37
10	Nat North	A	Blyth Spartans	521	L 0 - 3		3	38
13	Nat North	A	North Ferriby United	225	W 3 - 0	Williams 4 Gudger 22 Armson 70	3	39
17	Nat North	H	Darlington	675	W 3 - 0	Ndlovu 13 Williams 74 Armson 77	3	40
24	FAT 4	A	Stockport County	2213	D 1 - 1	Ndlovu 69		41
Mar 6	FAT 4r	H	Stockport County	506	W 2 - 1	Williams 4 Byrne 51		42
10	Nat North	A	Stockport County	3060	W 1 - 0	Williams 89	3	43
13	Nat North	A	Gainsborough Trinity	374	W 2 - 1	Williams 30 Murombedzi 44	3	44
17	FAT S-F 1	H	Wealdstone	1250	W 1 - 0	Gudger 85		45
24	FAT S-F 2	A	Wealdstone	2008	W 2 - 0	Byrne 55 Williams 81		46
27	Nat North	H	Boston United	405	W 4 - 1	Murombedzi 71 Nicholson 75 Williams 78 Armson 90	3	47
30	Nat North	H	Harrogate Town	750	D 0 - 0		3	48
Apr 2	Nat North	A	Kidderminster Harriers	1935	L 1 - 2	Dean 82	3	49
7	Nat North	A	Curzon Ashton	180	W 2 - 0	Murombedzi 12 Walker 59	3	50
12	Nat North	A	Spennymoor Town	409	W 3 - 0	Ndlovu 17 Armson 30 (pen) Byrne 90	3	51
14	Nat North	H	Alfreton Town	495	L 1 - 3	Williams 61	3	52
17	Nat North	H	Bradford PA	290	L 0 - 1		3	53
21	Nat North	H	Southport	1004	W 1 - 0	Williams 75	3	54
25	Nat North	H	Chorley	275	L 1 - 2	Armson 18 (pen)	3	55
28	Nat North	H	York City	670	W 2 - 0	Armson 52 80	3	56
May 6	P-O S-F	H	Bradford PA	923	W 1 - 0	Williams 10		57
13	P.O Final	A	Harrogate Town	3000	L 0 - 3			58
20	FAT Final	W	Bromley	31430	D 1 - 1	R Johnson 90+6 (og) (Won 5-4 on pens)		59

GOALSCORERS	SG	CSG	Pens	Hat tricks	Total		SG	CSG	Pens	Hat tricks	Total
2016-17 Armson					25	Myles-Tebbutt	3				3
Williams	28	10	3	1	34	Dean	2				2
Armson	15	2	2	1	19	Graham	2				2
Ndlovo	9	2			9	Opponents					2
Byrne	8	2			8	Nicholson					1
Walker	8	2			8						
Brown	6	2			5						
Gudger	3				3						
Lowe	3				3						
Murombedzi	3				3						

BRADFORD PARK AVENUE MATCH RESULTS 2017-18

Date	Comp	H/A	Opponents	Att:	Result	Goalscorers	Pos	No.
Aug 5	Nat North	A	Tamworth	564	W 1 - 0	Boyes 90	9	1
7	Nat North	H	Southport	574	L 1 - 2	Boyes 10	10	2
12	Nat North	H	York City	1123	L 0 - 4		20	3
15	Nat North	A	Spennymoor Town	755	L 0 - 3		20	4
19	Nat North	H	FC United of Manchester	546	W 3 - 0	Boyes 17 Brooksby 55 65	16	5
26	Nat North	A	AFC Telford United	1130	W 4 - 1	Havern 12 Johnson 34 78 Nowakowski 41	12	6
28	Nat North	H	Chorley	466	D 0 - 0		12	7
Sept 2	Nat North	A	Stockport County	3018	D 0 - 0		11	8
5	Nat North	A	Gainsborough Trinity	523	W 3 - 0	Johnson 14 Boyes 29 Brooksby 85	10	9
9	Nat North	H	Nuneaton Town	319	D 1 - 1	Johnson 20	11	10
11	Nat North	H	Boston United	358	W 2 - 1	Ross 34 Boyes 52	4	11
16	FAC 2Q	A	Southport	496	W 3 - 0	Boyes Johnson Vidal		12
23	Nat North	A	Leamington	502	L 1 - 2	Knowles 5	8	13
30	FAC 3Q	A	Harrogate Town	911	D 0 - 0			14
Oct 2	FAC 3Qr	H	Harrogate Town	393	L 0 - 2			15
7	Nat North	H	Kidderminster Harriers	397	D 1 - 1	Nowakowski 37	9	16
21	Nat North	A	Darlington	1312	L 1 - 2	Johnson 89	15	17
24	Nat North	A	Harrogate Town	745	D 1 - 1	Boyes 50	14	18
28	Nat North	H	Salford City	533	L 1 - 2	Johnson 17 (pen)	15	19
Nov 4	Nat North	H	Blyth Spartans	395	W 4 - 1	Brooksby 3 Johnson 45 Spencer 52 Boyes 66	10	20
11	Nat North	A	North Ferriby United	389	W 1 - 0	Johnson 19	7	21
18	Nat North	H	Brackley Town	341	W 2 - 0	Boyes 41 Kelly 63	7	22
25	FAT 3Q	H	Stourbridge	256	D 1 - 1	Clee 57		23
27	FAT3Qr	A	Stourbridge	385	L 1 - 2	Boyes 75		24
Dec 2	Nat North	A	Alfreton Town	435	W 3 - 1	Boyes 48 Killock 60 Johnson 68	6	25
16	Nat North	H	Tamworth	354	L 3 - 4	Johnson 9 81 (pen) Nowakowski 78	6	26
23	Nat North	A	Southport	635	W 4 - 0	Boyes 24 33 Clee 43 Knight 69		27
26	Nat North	H	Curzon Ashton	334	W 3 - 1	Brooksby 83 89 Johnson 90	5	28
Jan 1	Nat North	A	Curzon Ashton	286	D 1 - 1	Johnson 61	5	29
6	Nat North	H	Spennymoor Town	446	L 1 - 2	Clee 79	7	30
13	Nat North	A	York City	2542	L 1 - 2	Boyes 90		31
27	Nat North	A	Nuneaton Town	513	D 0 - 0		8	32
Feb 6	Nat North	H	Gainsborough Trinity	311	W 5 - 0	Brooksby 4 55 Boyes 19 47 Johnson 66	7	33
10	Nat North	H	Darlington	733	L 0 - 1		8	34
17	Nat North	A	Blyth Spartans	806	L 0 - 3		8	35
21	Nat North	A	Salford City	982	D 2 - 2	Wroe 44 Nowakoski 53	9	36
24	Nat North	H	North Ferriby United	423	L 0 - 1		9	37
Mar 10	Nat North	H	Alfreton Town	434	D 3 - 3	Hill 15 Johnson 63 87	8	38
24	Nat North	A	FC United of Manchester	2084	L 0 - 4		12	39
26	Nat North	H	AFC Telford United	334	W 2 - 1	Mulhern 54 87	9	40
30	Nat North	H	Stockport County	1044	L 2 - 3	Vidal 71 Mulhern 81	12	41
Apr 2	Nat North	A	Chorley	1724	L 0 - 2		12	42
7	Nat North	H	Leamington	338	W 1 - 0	Boyes 10	10	43
14	Nat North	A	Boston United	992	W 2 - 1	Boyes 36 90	9	44
17	Nat North	A	Brackley Town	290	W 1 - 0	Toulson 80	8	45
21	Nat North	H	Harrogate Town	581	W 3 - 1	Boyes 24 88 Mulhern 84	7	46
28	Nat North	A	Kidderminster Harriers	1642	W 2 - 1	Mulhern 81 Boyes 90	7	47
May 2	P.O.	A	Kidderminster Harriers	2291	W 2 - 0	Boyes 10 Johnson 78		48
6	P.O. S-F	A	Brackley Town	923	L 0 - 1			49

GOALSCORERS	SG	CSG	Pens	Hat tricks	Total		SG	CSG	Pens	Hat tricks	Total
2016-17 Wroe					6	Kelly					1
Boyes	19	2			23	Killock					1
Johnson	15	3	2		18	Knight					1
Brooksby	5				8	Knowles					1
Mulhern	4				5	Ross					1
Nowakowski	4				4	Spencer					1
Clee	3				3	Toulson					1
Vidal	2				2	Wroe					1
Havern					1						
Hill					1						

CHORLEY MATCH RESULTS 2017-18

Date	Comp	H/A	Opponents	Att:	Result	Goalscorers	Pos	No.
Aug 5	Nat North	A	Kidderminster Harriers	1793	W 1 - 0	Williams 78 (og)	10	1
8	Nat North	H	Salford City	1352	L 0 - 1		13	2
12	Nat North	H	Curzon Ashton	804	D 1 - 1	Leather 27	10	3
15	Nat North	A	Harrogate Town	676	L 1 - 4	Carver 53	14	4
19	Nat North	A	Boston United	934	L 0 - 2		17	5
26	Nat North	H	Brackley Town	732	D 0 - 0		18	6
28	Nat North	A	Bradford PA	466	D 0 - 0		18	7
Sept 2	Nat North	H	York City	1294	W 2 - 0	Wilson 20 37	14	8
5	Nat North	H	Darlington	1011	W 4 - 1	Walker 3 (p) 43 Challoner 32 Haughton76	13	9
9	Nat North	A	North Ferriby United	280	W 2 - 0	Walker 4 Wilson 79	10	10
12	Nat North	A	Blyth Spartans	617	L 0 - 2		11	11
16	FAC 2Q	A	Stalybridge Celtic	551	W 3 - 1	Carver 24 Wilson 50 Walker 90		12
23	Nat North	A	AFC Telford United	1125	W 3 - 2	Wilson 11 Carver 32 66	9	13
30	FAC 3Q	A	Ashton Athletic	610	W 1 - 0	Haughton 83		14
Oct 7	Nat North	A	Alfreton Town	620	W 2 - 0	Haughton 11 85	7	15
14	FAC 4Q	H	Boston United	1204	D 0 - 0			16
17	FAC 4Qr	A	Boston United	1132	W 4 - 3	HAUGHTON 3 (50 61 111) Teague 57 (aet)		17
21	Nat North	H	FC United	1440	W 1 - 0	Haughton 72	6	18
28	Nat North	A	Spennymoor Town	753	L 0 - 1		6	19
31	Nat North	H	Tamworth	961	D 1 - 1	O'Keefe 52	6	20
Nov 6	FAC 1	H	Fleetwood Town	3526	L 1 - 2	Carver 58		21
11	Nat North	H	Nuneaton Town	1306	D 2 - 2	O'Keefe 61 Hughes 83	8	22
18	Nat North	A	Stockport County	3674	D 1 - 1	Haughton 83	8	23
25	FAT 3Q	A	Grantham Town	361	W 4 - 3	Walker 19 Wilson 56 63 Blakeman 89		24
Dec 2	Nat North	H	Leamington	823	W 2 - 0	Teague 39 Carver 45	8	25
16	FAT 1	H	Marine	704	L 1 - 3	Hughes 2		26
23	Nat North	A	Salford City	1760	W 3 - 0	Haughton 32 Carver 32 O'Keefe 595	8	27
26	Nat North	H	Southport	1517	D 0 - 0		8	28
Jan 1	Nat North	A	Southport	1309	L 0 - 3		10	29
6	Nat North	H	Harrogate Town	1257	L 0 - 1		10	30
9	Nat North	H	Kidderminsterr Harriers	790	D 0 - 0		10	31
13	Nat North	A	Curzon Ashton	466	W 2 - 0	O'Keefe 13 Haughton 76	9	32
20	Nat North	A	Darlington	1168	D 2 - 2	Blakeman 23 Walker 75	9	33
27	Nat North	H	North Ferriby United	1011	D 2 - 2	Walker 21 O'Keefe 56	10	34
30	Nat North	A	Gainsborough Trinity	386	L 0 - 1		10	35
Feb 9	Nat North	A	FC United	2288	L 0 - 1		9	36
17	Nat North	H	Gainsborough Trinity	1084	W 1 - 0	Wilson 54	8	37
24	Nat North	A	Nuneaton Town	535	D 1 - 1	Wilson 41	8	38
Mar 20	Nat North	A	Spennymoor United	596	W 3 - 1	Carver 18 20 O'Keefe 81	8	39
24	Nat North	H	Boston United	1022	L 0 - 1		9	40
31	Nat North	H	York City	2721	D 1 - 1	Newby 10	9	41
Apr 2	Nat North	H	Bradford PA	1724	W 2 - 0	Carver 44 Walker 51	9	42
7	Nat North	A	AFC Telford United	1048	W 2 - 1	Newby 68 Carver 80	8	43
14	Nat North	H	Blyth Spartans	1165	W 2 - 0	Newby 42 Carver 64	6	44
17	Nat North	H	Stockport County	1983	D 1 - 1	Leather 27	6	45
19	Nat North	A	Leamington	407	L 0 - 2		6	46
21	Nat North	A	Tamworth	732	W 4 - 3	Burns 50 (og) O'Keefe 62 65 Carver 77	6	47
25	Nat North	H	Brackley Town	275	W 2 - 1	Carver 26 Whitham 50	6	48
28	Nat North	H	Alfreton Town	1053	W 1 - 0	Walker 51	6	49
May 2	P.O.	A	Stockport County	6230	W 1 - 0	Walker 69		50
6	P.O. S.F.	A	Harrogate Town	2307	L 1 - 2	O'Keefe 36		51

GOALSCORERS	SG	CSG	Pens	Hat tricks	Total		SG	CSG	Pens	Hat tricks	Total
2016-17 Walker					14	Opponents					2
Carver	12	3		1	14	Teague	2				2
Haughton	9	2			11	Challoner					1
Walker	9	2	1		10	Whitham					1
O'Keefe	8				9						
Wilson	7	2			9						
Newby	3				3						
Blakeman	2				2						
Hughes	2				2						
Leather	2				2						

CURZON ASHTON MATCH RESULTS 2017-18

Date	Comp	H/A	Opponents	Att:	Result	Goalscorers	Pos	No.
Aug 5	Nat North	H	North Ferriby United	290	W 4 - 0	Leonard 3 7 Cummins 53 Crowthers 86	1	1
8	Nat North	A	Stockport County	3002	L 0 - 3		7	2
12	Nat North	A	Chorley	804	D 1 - 1	Guest 9	9	3
14	Nat North	H	AFC Telford United	380	W 1 - 0	Cummins 49	8	4
19	Nat North	A	Tamworth	606	L 1 - 4	Cummins 90	10	5
26	Nat North	H	Blyth Spartans	284	L 0 - 3		13	6
28	Nat North	A	Alfreton Town	405	L 0 - 4		18	7
Sept 2	Nat North	H	Salford City	723	D 1 - 1	Leonard 35	18	8
5	Nat North	A	Kidderminster Harriers	1281	D 2 - 2	Regan 52 Cummins 89	17	9
9	Nat North	H	FC United of Manchester	726	W 1 - 0	Leonard 42	16	10
11	Nat North	H	Leamington	233	D 1 - 1	Wharton 28	15	11
16	FAC 2Q	A	Stockport County	1922	L 0 - 1			12
23	Nat North	A	Brackley Town	473	D 2 - 2	Baker 37 Guest 90	16	13
30	Nat North	H	Darlington	292	W 1 - 0	McKenzie 86	14	14
Oct 7	Nat North	H	Harrogate Town	608	L 1 - 2	Rowney 24	15	15
14	Nat North	A	Spennymoor Town	745	W 4 - 2	CUMMINS 3 (49 66 69) Wharton 78	9	16
21	Nat North	H	Boston United	234	W 2 - 1	Wright 8 Baker 64	7	17
28	Nat North	A	Gainsborough Trinity	527	L 0 - 1		8	18
Nov 4	Nat North	A	York City	2146	L 1 - 2	Guest 57	11	19
11	Nat North	H	Southport	519	D 2 - 2	Wharton 9 Cummins 45	11	20
18	Nat North	H	Nuneaton Town	481	D 1 - 1	Cummins 57	11	21
25	FAT 3Q	A	Leamington	249	L 1 - 3	Cummins 6		22
Dec 19	Nat North	A	North Ferriby United	194	W 1 - 0	Brooke 6	11	23
23	Nat North	H	Stockport County	1473	D 1 - 1	Cummins 70 (pen)	12	24
26	Nat North	A	Bradford PA	334	L 1 - 3	Cummins 88	12	25
Jan 1	Nat North	H	Bradford PA	286	D 1 - 1	Madeley 90	12	26
13	Nat North	H	Chorley	466	L 0 - 2		14	27
27	Nat North	A	FC United of Manchester	2140	L 0 - 2		19	28
Feb 5	Nat North	H	Kidderminster Harriers	200	L 1 - 2	Hunt 71	19	29
10	Nat North	A	Boston United	1009	D 3 - 3	Dunwoody 4 Shaw 47 McKenna 61	19	30
13	Nat North	A	AFC Telford United	747	W 3 - 0	McKenna 18 Dunwoody 61 Cummins 69	17	31
17	Nat North	H	York City	892	W 4 - 1	CUMMINS 3 (6 35 38) Walker 58	17	32
24	Nat North	A	Southport	863	L 1 - 3	Regan 14	17	33
Mar 10	Nat North	A	Darlington	1292	L 0 - 1		18	34
24	Nat North	H	Tamworth	1022	W 1 - 0	Walker 53	18	35
30	Nat North	A	Salford City	1541	L 1 - 2	Guest 90	19	36
Apr 5	Nat North	H	Alfreton Town	206	D 2 - 2	Dunwoody 15 McKenna 27	19	37
7	Nat North	H	Brackley Town	180	L 0 - 2		19	38
11	Nat North	H	Gainsborough Trinity	244	W 2 - 0	Shaw 45 Guest 90	17	39
14	Nat North	A	Leamington	531	D 0 - 0		17	40
16	Nat North	H	Nuneaton Town	173	D 2 - 2	Thornley 16 Baille 68 (pen)	17	41
21	Nat North	H	Spennymoor Town	309	W 1 - 0	Guest 41	17	42
24	Nat North	A	Blyth Spartans	610	L 1 - 2	McKenna 90 (pen)	17	43
28	Nat North	A	Harrogate Town	1170	L 0 - 5		18	44

GOALSCORERS	SG	CSG	Pens	Hat tricks	Total		SG	CSG	Pens	Hat tricks	Total
2016-17 Cummins					*16*	Walker					2
Cummins	12	3	1	2	16	Baille					1
Guest	6				6	Brooke					1
Leonard	3				4	Crowthers					1
McKenna	3		1		4	Hunt					1
Dunwoody	3	2			3	Madeley					1
Wharton	3				3	McKenzie					1
Baker	2				2	Rowney					1
Regan	2				2	Thornley					1
Shaw	2				2	Wright					1

DARLINGTON 1883 MATCH RESULTS 2017-18

Date	Comp	H/A	Opponents	Att:	Result	Goalscorers	Pos	No.
Aug 5	Nat North	A	Salford City	1777	W 2 - 0	Ferguson 43 90	5	1
9	Nat North	H	Gainsborough Trinity	1682	W 4 - 3	Beck 23 Syers 43 Galbraith 49 Gillies 73	1	2
12	Nat North	H	Alfreton Town	1847	W 4 - 1	Caton 3 Gillies 37 63 Ferguson	2	3
15	Nat North	A	York City	3944	D 0 - 0		3	4
19	Nat North	H	AFC Telford United	1532	L 0 - 1		6	5
26	Nat North	A	North Ferriby United	479	D 1 - 1	Gillies 9	7	6
28	Nat North	H	Spennymoor Town	2050	D 1 - 1	Brown 57	6	7
Sept 2	Nat North	A	Southport	1059	L 0 - 2		7	8
5	Nat North	A	Chorley	1011	L 1 - 4	Saunders 57	12	9
9	Nat North	H	Leamington	1277	D 0 - 0		14	10
13	Nat North	A	FC United	1178	W 3 - 0	Cartman 52 Ferguson 77 Wheatley 85	11	11
16	FAC 2Q	H	South Shields	1814	L 0 - 3			12
23	Nat North	A	Boston United	1051	D 1 - 1	Thompson 60	12	13
30	Nat North	A	Curzon Ashton	292	L 0 - 1		12	14
Oct 7	Nat North	H	Stockport County	1758	D 1 - 1	Oswell 90	11	15
14	Nat North	H	Nuneaton Town	694	L 1 - 2	Syers 90	12	16
21	Nat North	H	Bradford PA	1312	W 2 - 1	Havern 2 (og) Gillies 56	10	17
28	Nat North	A	Blyth Spartans	1554	L 1 - 3	Syers 30	13	18
Nov 4	Nat North	H	Brackley Town	1267	L 0 - 3		14	19
11	Nat North	A	Kidderminster Harriers	1879	D 3 - 3	Taylor 45 (og) Galbraith 79 Syers 89	14	20
18	Nat North	H	Tamworth	1246	L 0 - 1		14	21
25	FAT 3Q	H	Harrogate Town	1127	L 2 - 3	Styche 10 (pen) 81		22
Dec 22	Nat North	A	Gainsborough Trinity	773	L 1 - 3	Gillies 67	19	23
26	Nat North	H	Harrogate Town	1759	W 3 - 1	Styche 8 (pen) 26 Thompson 87	17	24
Jan 1	Nat North	A	Harrogate Town	1648	L 0 - 3		18	25
6	Nat North	H	York City	2405	L 1 - 2	Styche 43	19	26
10	Nat North	H	Salford City	1350	L 1 - 2	Mills 65	19	27
13	Nat North	A	Alfreton Town	727	D 1 - 1	Styche 5	20	28
20	Nat North	H	Chorley	1168	D 2 - 2	Styche 16 Thompson 48	19	29
27	Nat North	A	Leamington	845	W 3 - 2	THOMPSON 3 (9pen 74 90)	17	30
Feb 3	Nat North	H	Blyth Spartans	1528	W 3 - 0	Thompson 45 (pen) Styche 58 Syers 73	15	31
10	Nat North	A	Bradford PA	733	W 1 - 0	Syers 56	14	32
17	Nat North	A	Brackley Town	675	L 0 - 3		17	33
24	Nat North	H	Kidderminster Harriers	1427	W 2 - 1	Heaton 10 Thompson 90	14	34
Mar 10	Nat North	A	Curzon Ashton	1292	W 1 - 0	Syers 58	13	35
13	Nat North	A	Tamworth	584	D 0 - 0		13	36
17	Nat North	H	North Ferriby United	1087	W 6 - 0	Syers 16 Thompson 28 (p) 41 Styche 37 Gillies 45 69	10	37
24	Nat North	A	AFC Telford United	1318	D 0 - 0		10	38
Apr 7	Nat North	H	Boston United	1286	L 1 - 2	Styche 45	13	39
14	Nat North	A	FC United	2269	W 2 - 1	Gillies 26 Styche 65	12	40
19	Nat North	A	Spennymoor Town	1661	W 2 1	Styche 23 Tait 59 (og)	12	41
21	Nat North	H	Nuneaton Town	1409	D 0 - 0		12	42
25	Nat North	H	Southport	1019	L 2 - 4	Gillies 18 Saunders 86	12	43
28	Nat North	A	Stockport County	6163	D 1 - 1	Cowan 63	12	44

GOALSCORERS	SG	CSG	Pens	Hat tricks	Total		SG	CSG	Pens	Hat tricks	Total
2016-17 Beck					19	Brown					1
Styche	10	2	2		12	Caton					1
Gillies	8	2			10	Cowan					1
Thompson	7	3	2	1	10	Ferguson					1
Syers	8	2			8	Heaton					1
Ferguson	2				4	Mills					1
Opponents					3	Oswell					1
Galbraith					2	Wheatley					1
Saunders	2				2						
Beck					1						

FC UNITED OF MANCHESTER MATCH RESULTS 2017-18

Date	Comp	H/A	Opponents	Att:	Result		Goalscorers	Pos	No.
Aug 5	Nat North	A	Brackley Town	654	L	1 - 2	Gilchrist 73	12	1
8	Nat North	H	Spennymoor Town	1602	L	2 - 3	Gilchrist 36 Wisdom 52	19	2
12	Nat North	H	Kidderminster Harriers	1946	L	1 - 2	Wisdom 6	19	3
15	Nat North	A	Southport	1270	D	3 - 3	Hooper 8 Lowe 33 Lindfield 72	22	4
19	Nat North	A	Bradford Park Avenue	546	L	0 - 3		22	5
26	Nat North	H	Boston United	1688	W	2 - 1	Lowe 8 McCarthy 37	19	6
28	Nat North	A	York City	3411	W	2 - 0	Greaves 78 Gilchrist 90	17	7
Sept 2	Nat North	H	Leamington	2380	L	1 - 2	Kay 84	20	8
5	Nat North	H	Blyth Spartans	1491	L	1 - 3	Gilchrist 70	20	9
9	Nat North	A	Curzon Ashton	726	L	0 - 1		19	10
13	Nat North	H	Darlington	1178	L	0 - 3		21	11
16	FAC 2Q	A	Handsworth Parramore	434	D	1 - 1	Irwin 35 (pen)		12
19	FAC 2Qr	H	Handsworth Parramore	623	W	6 - 2	Connor Gilchrist Logan McCARTHY 3		13
24	Nat North	A	Tamworth	1770	W	3 - 1	Gilchrist 18 65 Irwin 89	20	14
30	FAC 3Q	A	Stockport County	3034	D	3 - 3	Gilchrist 57 Greaves 71 Irwin 83 (pen)		15
Oct 3	FAC 3Qr	H	Stockport County	1688	W	1 - 0	Greaves 55		16
7	Nat North	A	North Ferriby United	402	D	3 - 3	Walker 41 Greaves 63 Irwin 73	20	17
14	FAC 4Q	A	AFC Telford United	1451	L	1 - 3	Lindfield 76		18
21	Nat North	A	Chorley	1440	L	0 - 1		21	19
28	Nat North	H	Nuneaton Town	1781	W	2 - 1	Greaves 36 Fagbola 62	20	20
Nov 4	Nat North	A	Stockport County	4076	L	1 - 4	Gilchrist 55	21	21
11	Nat North	H	AFC Telford United	2079	W	3 - 1	Greaves 28 Gilchrist 53 73	19	22
14	Nat North	A	Alfreton Town	1548	W	3 - 2	Glynn 49 Gilchrist 87 (pen) Logan 89	15	23
18	Nat North	A	Gainsborough Trinity	738	L	0 - 1		19	24
25	FAT 3Q	A	Marine	778	L	0 - 1			25
Dec 2	Nat North	H	Harrogate Town	2394	W	3 - 2	Lindfield 49 Greaves 83 90	15	26
6	Nat North	H	Brackley Town	1893	D	1 - 1	Irwin 83	14	27
22	Nat North	A	Spennymoor United	795	D	4 - 4	Fagbola 28 McCarthy 58 76 Lindfield 72	15	28
26	Nat North	H	Salford City	3041	W	3 - 2	McCarthy 29 Corbett 74 Greaves 81	13	29
Jan 1	Nat North	A	Salford City	2937	D	2 - 2	Lindfield 36 Corbett 87	13	30
7	Nat North	H	Southport	2863	W	1 - 0	Greaves 12	12	31
20	Nat North	A	Blyth Spartans	985	L	1 - 1	Greaves 69	13	32
23	Nat North	A	Kidderminster Harriers	1375	L	0 - 4		13	33
27	Nat North	H	Curzon Ashton	2140	W	2 - 0	Irwin 51 McCarthy 72	12	34
Feb 3	Nat North	A	Nuneaton Town	720	L	0 1		13	35
9	Nat North	H	Chorley	2286	D	0 - 0		12	36
17	Nat North	H	Stockport County	3084	L	0 - 1		14	37
24	Nat North	A	AFC Telford United	1186	L	0 - 1		18	38
Mar 10	Nat North	H	Harrogate Town	1547	L	0 - 6		18	39
17	Nat North	A	Boston United	1052	D	4 - 4	Lindfield 52 90 King 71 Garner 88	18	40
20	Nat North	H	Gainsborough Trinity	1557	W	1 - 0	Lindfield 16	16	41
24	Nat North	H	Bradford Park Avenue	2084	W	4 - 0	KING 3 (45 58 71pen) Garner 68	14	42
31	Nat North	A	Leamington	1005	L	0 - 1		15	43
Apr 7	Nat North	H	Tamworth	962	W	2 - 0	Lindfield 65 Garner 90	15	44
14	Nat North	H	Darlington	2269	L	1 - 2	Kay 45	15	45
17	Nat North	H	York City	1816	W	1 - 0	McCarthy 61	14	46
21	Nat North	A	Alfreton Town	911	L	0 - 1		14	47
28	Nat North	H	North Ferriby United	2580	L	0 - 2		16	48

GOALSCORERS	SG	CSG	Pens	Hat tricks	Total		SG	CSG	Pens	Hat tricks	Total
2016-17 Thomson					17	Kay	2				2
Gilchrist	10	3	1		12	Logan	1				2
Greaves	10	3			11	Lowe	2				2
Lindfield	8				9	Wisdom	2				2
McCarthy	6			1	9	Connor	1				1
Irwin	6	2	2		6	Glynn	1				1
King	2		1	1	4	Hooper	1				1
Garner	3				3	Walker	1				1
Corbett	2				2						
Fagbola	2				2						

GAINSBOROUGH TRINITY MATCH RESULTS 2017-18

Date	Comp	H/A	Opponents	Att:	Result	Goalscorers	Pos	No.
Aug 5	Nat North	H	Leamington	648	L 1 - 2	Worsfold 17	13	1
9	Nat North	A	Darlington	1682	L 3 - 4	Worsfold 10 Evans 51 Jarman 64	22	2
12	Nat North	A	Nuneaton Town	559	W 1 - 0	Jacklin 14	11	3
15	Nat North	H	Blyth Spartans	559	L 2 - 4	Jacklin 30 Wells 65	15	4
19	Nat North	H	Harrogate Town	517	L 4 - 5	Worsfold 13 Wells 45 King 70 Clarke 73	18	5
26	Nat North	A	Stockport County	3006	L 0 - 1		21	6
28	Nat North	H	North Ferriby United	737	W 2 - 0	Jacklin 28 Jarman 44	18	7
Sept 2	Nat North	A	Spennymoor Town	746	D 1 - 1	Tait 10 (og)	17	8
5	Nat North	H	Bradford PA	523	L 0 - 3		18	9
9	Nat North	A	Alfreton Town	454	L 1 - 4	Wells 85	20	10
12	Nat North	A	York City	2196	D 1 - 1	Wafula 68	19	11
16	FAC 2Q	A	Spennymoor Town	403	W 2 - 1	Worsfold 60 Evans 89		12
23	Nat North	A	Salford City	706	L 0 - 1		20	13
30	FAC 3Q	A	Leamington	459	D 0 - 0			14
Oct 2	FAC 3Qr	H	Leamingtion	370	W 2 - 0	Jarman 75 Wells 90		15
7	Nat North	A	Tamworth	762	W 2 - 1	Jarman 46 Wells 83	21	16
14	FAC 4Q	A	Harrogate Town	928	W 2 - 1	Johnson 45 Jacklin 60		17
21	Nat North	A	Southport	771	D 2 - 2	Davie 2 King 90	19	18
24	Nat North	H	AFC Telford United	412	W 3 - 2	Jacklin 9 56 Wells 50	18	19
28	Nat North	H	Curzon Ashton	527	W 1 - 0	Rowney 75	18	20
Nov 4	FAC 1	H	Slough Town	1630	L 0 - 6		18	21
11	Nat North	A	Brackley Town	482	L 0 - 2		18	22
18	Nat North	H	FC United	728	W 1 - 0	Worsfold 6	17	23
25	FAT 3Q	H	Stafford Rangers	299	W 2 - 0	Worsfold 55 Jarman 80		24
Dec 2	Nat North	A	Kidderminster Harriers	1381	L 0 - 3		18	25
23	Nat North	H	Darlington	773	W 3 - 1	Worsfold 11 Clarke 21 Jarman 83	17	26
26	Nat North	A	Boston United	1491	L 0 - 2		18	27
Jan 1	Nat North	H	Boston United	1022	D 1 - 1	Worsfold 10	19	28
6	Nat North	A	Blyth Spartans	591	L 0 - 4		20	29
9	FAT 1	A	Spennymoor Town	360	L 4 - 4	Worsfold 19 64 Bateson 31 Simmons 97 (Lost 3-5 on pens)		30
13	Nat North	H	Nuneaton Town	463	L 0 - 1		21	31
23	Nat North	A	Leamington	372	L 0 - 3		21	32
27	Nat North	H	Alfreton Town	483	W 2 - 1	Jarman 31 King 79	20	33
30	Nat North	H	Chorley	386	W 1 - 0	King 48	19	34
Feb 5	Nat North	A	Bradford PA	311	L 0 - 5		20	35
10	Nat North	H	Southport	532	L 0 - 3		20	36
17	Nat North	A	Chorley	1084	L 0 - 1		21	37
Mar 10	Nat North	H	Kidderminster Harriers	547	W 1 - 0	Syers 88	21	38
13	Nat North	H	Braintree Town	374	L 1 - 2	Walker 9	21	39
17	Nat North	H	Stockport County	474	L 2 - 3	Jarman 27 Stanfield 74	21	40
20	Nat North	A	FC United of Manchester	1557	L 0 - 1		21	41
24	Nat North	A	Harrogate Town	2524	L 0 - 2		21	42
30	Nat North	H	Spennymoor Town	686	W 4 - 1	Clarke 22 Worsfold 38 Simmons 49 Jarman 83	21	43
Apr 7	Nat North	A	Salford City	1288	L 0 - 1		21	44
11	Nat North	H	Curzon Ashton	244	L 0 - 2		21	45
14	Nat North	H	York City	1014	W 1 - 0	Worsfold 54	21	46
17	Nat North	A	North Ferriby United	399	W 1 - 0	Worsfold 29 (pen)	20	47
21	Nat North	A	AFC Telford United	1494	L 2 - 3	Worsfold 41 56	20	48
28	Nat North	H	Tamworth	589	W 3 - 0	Walker 4 Jarman 30 57	20	49

GOALSCORERS	SG	CSG	Pens	Hat tricks	Total		SG	CSG	Pens	Hat tricks	Total
2016-17 Worsfold					12	Bateson					1
Worsfold	13	3	1		15	Davie					1
Jarman	10	2			11	Johnson					1
Jacklin	5	2			6	Opponents					1
Wells	6	2			6	Rowney					1
King	4				4	Stanfield					1
Clarke	3				3	Syers					1
Evans	2				2	Wafula					1
Simmons	2				2						
Walker	2				2						

KIDDERMINSTER HARRIERS MATCH RESULTS 2017-18

Date	Comp	H/A	Opponents	Att:	Result	Goalscorers	Pos	No.
Aug 5	Nat North	H	Chorley	1793	L 0 - 1		14	1
8	Nat North	A	Nuneaton Town	781	L 0 - 1		20	2
12	Nat North	A	FC Utd of Manchester	1946	W 2 - 1	Sonupe 19 80	13	3
15	Nat North	H	Leamington	1465	W 2 - 0	Ironside 64 Sonupe 90	9	4
19	Nat North	A	Salford City	1320	L 0 - 3		13	5
26	Nat North	H	Alfreton Town	1613	W 2 - 1	Ironside 60 Ngwatala 62	11	6
28	Nat North	A	Brackley Town	690	L 0 - 2		14	7
Sept 2	Nat North	H	Boston United	1463	D 1 - 1	Sonupe 7	13	8
5	Nat North	H	Curzon Ashton	1281	D 2 - 2	Croasdale 43 Ironside 60	15	9
9	Nat North	A	Southport	901	W 3 - 0	Longbottom 26 Brown 52 87	13	10
12	Nat North	A	Tamworth	723	L 1 - 3	Ironside 80	14	11
16	FAC 2Q	A	Deeping Rangers	696	W 4 - 2	Brown 33 Sonupe 40 44 Wright 60		12
23	Nat North	H	Blyth Spartans	1524	W 5 - 4	Brown 3 Pearson 23 58 Sonupe 56 Wright 78	13	13
30	FAC 3Q	A	Newcastle Benfield	403	W 1 - 0	Ironside 67		14
Oct 7	Nat North	A	Bradford PA	397	D 1 - 1	Sonupe 45	12	15
14	FAC 4Q	H	Chester	1896	W 2 - 0	Sonupe 19 Ironside 79		16
21	Nat North	H	Spennymoor	1406	D 2 - 2	McQuilken 62 Brown 78	14	17
28	Nat North	A	Stockport County	3016	W 2 - 1	Ironside 58 90	10	18
Nov 4	FAC 1	A	AFC Fylde	1480	L 2 - 4	Taylor 74 Brown 90		19
11	Nat North	H	Darlington	1879	D 3 - 3	Brown 15 McQuilkin 38 Ngwatala 54	11	20
18	Nat North	A	York City	2507	D 1 - 1	Croasdale 20	12	21
21	Nat North	H	North Ferriby United	1198	W 4 - 0	Ironside 8 Croasdale 16 40 Ngwatala 32	8	22
25	FAT 3Q	A	Boston United	732	D 2 - 2	Brown 56 Ironside 66		23
29	FAT 3Qr	H	Boston United	604	W 2 - 0	Ngwatala 10 Ironside 59		24
Dec 2	Nat North	A	Gainsborough Trinity	1381	W 3 - 0	Ironside 47 Horsfall 61 Weeks 82	7	25
4	Nat North	A	Harrogate Town	854	D 2 - 2	Ironside 68 90	7	26
15	FAT 1	H	York City	1138	W 2 - 1	Pearson 35 Sonupe 38		27
23	Nat North	H	Nuneaton Town	1510	W 3 - 0	Sonupe 32 Ironside 52 Truslove 87	7	28
26	Nat North	A	AFC Telford United	1995	D 0 - 0		7	29
Jan 1	Nat North	H	AFC Telford United	2201	W 2 - 0	Brown 40 74	7	30
6	Nat North	A	Leamington	912	D 1 - 1	Brown 27		31
9	Nat North	A	Chorley	790	D 0 - 0		6	32
13	FAT 2	H	Stockport County	1348	D 2 - 2	Horsfall 77 Sonupe 80		33
16	FAT 2r	A	Stockport County	883	L 0 - 3			34
23	Nat North	H	FC Utd of Manchester	1375	W 4 - 0	Croasdale 54 Ironside 60 Waring 77 Ngwatala 77	7	35
27	Nat North	H	Southport	1968	W 3 - 0	Sonupe 15 Horsfall 20 Ironside 28	5	36
Feb 5	Nat North	A	Curzon Ashton	200	W 2 1	Croasdale 49 Waring 80	4	37
17	Nat North	H	Harrogate Town	1739	L 0 - 2		5	38
24	Nat North	A	Darlington	1427	L 1 - 2	Ironside 78	6	39
Mar 10	Nat North	A	Gainsborough Trinity	547	L 0 - 1		6	40
13	Nat North	A	York City	1244	W 2 - 1	Bradley 58 72	4	41
24	Nat North	H	Salford City	2524	D 4 - 4	Sonupe 21 Ironside 33 Vaughan 54 Bradley 56	4	42
27	Nat North	A	Alfreton Town	433	W 2 - 0	Ironside 55 Bradley 71	4	43
30	Nat North	H	Boston United	1158	L 2 - 3	Bradley 15 Waring 72	4	44
Apr 2	Nat North	H	Brackley Town	1935	W 2 - 1	Horsfall 83 Bradley 88	4	45
5	Nat North	H	Blyth Spartans	738	W 2 - 1	Croasdale 64 Sonupe 71	4	46
10	Nat North	H	Stockport County	1722	W 3 - 1	Ironside 4 McQuilkin 20 Beradley 59	4	47
14	Nat North	H	Tamworth	1821	W 2 - 0	Ironsmith 62 Ngwatala 65	4	48
17	Nat North	A	Spennymoor United	415	D 1 - 1	Ngwatala 57	4	49
21	Nat North	H	North Ferriby United	331	W 3 - 1	Waring 18 Ironside 25 Vaughan 62	4	50
28	Nat North	H	Bradford PA	1642	L 1 - 2	Bradley 15	4	51
May 2	PO	H	Bradford PA	2291	L 0 - 2			52

GOALSCORERS	SG	CSG	Pens	Hat tricks	Total		SG	CSG	Pens	Hat tricks	Total
2016-17 Gnahoua					15	Pearson	2				3
Ironside	20	5			23	Vaughan	2				2
Sonupe	13	2			15	Wright	2	2			2
Brown	9	2			11	Longbottom	1				1
Bradley	6	5			8	Taylor	1				1
Croasdale	6	2			7	Truslove	1				1
Ngwatala	7				7	Weeks	1				1
Horsfall	4				4						
Waring	4				4						
McQuilken	3				3						

LEAMINGTON MATCH RESULTS 2017-18

Date	Comp	H/A	Opponents	Att:	Result	Goalscorers	Pos	No.
Aug 5	Nat North	A	Gainsborough Trinity	648	W 2 - 1	Bishop 33 Obeng 72	7	1
8	Nat North	H	Tamworth	625	L 1 - 2	English 24	10	2
12	Nat North	H	Southport	711	L 0 - 1		13	3
15	Nat North	A	Kidderminster Harriers	1465	L 0 - 1		17	4
19	Nat North	H	Stockport County	844	L 2 - 3	Thompson-Brown 37 Canavan 82	19	5
26	Nat North	A	Nuneaton Town	731	L 0 - 4		22	6
28	Nat North	H	AFC Telford United	711	L 0 - 3		22	7
Sept 2	Nat North	A	FC United of Manchester	2380	W 2 - 1	Dunbar 70 Bishop 77	21	8
5	Nat North	H	Alfreton Town	435	L 2 - 3	Breeden 13 (pen) Moore 23	21	9
9	Nat North	A	Darlington	1277	D 0 - 0		21	10
11	Nat North	A	Curzon Ashton	233	D 1 - 1	Edwards 71	19	11
16	FAC 2Q	A	Westfields	365	W 2 - 0	Bishop 89 Thompson-Brown 89 (pen)		12
23	Nat North	H	Bradford PA	502	W 2 - 1	Dunbar 21 Revan 87	19	13
30	FAC 3Q	H	Gainsborough Trinity	459	D 0 - 0			14
Oct 3	FAC 3Qr	A	Gainsborough Trinity	370	L 0 - 2			15
7	Nat North	A	Salford City	1582	W 3 - 2	Thompson-Brown 19 Gudger 45 Revan 86	17	16
14	Nat North	H	York City	965	D 2 - 2	English 85 Canavan 88	18	17
21	Nat North	A	Harrogate Town	1021	D 2 - 2	English 24 Thompson-Brown 70	17	18
28	Nat North	H	North Ferrriby United	529	W 3 - 0	Edwards 7 Thompson-Brown 30 (pen) 56	16	19
Nov 4	Nat North	A	Boston United	592	L 0 - 2		17	20
11	Nat North	A	Blyth Spartans	541	L 0 - 1		17	21
18	Nat North	H	Spennymoor United	456	W 4 - 0	BISHOP 3 (27pen 52 77pen) Dunbar 85	15	22
25	FAT 3Q	H	Curzon Ashton	249	W 3 - 1	Magunda 40 Ballie 52 (og) Canavan 78 (pen)		23
Dec2	Nat North	A	Chorley	823	L 0 - 2		17	24
16	FAT 1	H	Stourbridge	404	L 0 - 1			25
22	Nat North	A	Tamnworth	708	W 3 - 0	Bishop 31 52 Gittings 44	14	26
26	Nat North	H	Brackley Town	645	D 2 - 2	Bishop 44 Hood 90	16	27
Jan 1	Nat North	A	Brackley Town	522	D 1 - 1	Moore 43	15	28
6	Nat North	H	Kidderminster Harriers	912	D 1 - 1	Obeng 57	15	29
13	Nat North	A	Southport	848	L 0 - 2		17	30
20	Nat North	H	Alfreton Town	479	L 1 - 4	Canavan 88	18	31
23	Nat North	H	Gainsborough Trinity	372	W 3 - 0	Udoh 4 90 King 46 (og)	15	32
27	Nat North	H	Darlington	845	L 2 - 3	Gittings 17 (pen) Edwards 60	16	33
Feb 3	Nat North	A	North Ferriby United	214	D 1 - 1	Udoh 13	17	34
10	Nat North	H	Harrogate Town	412	L 1 - 3	Canavan 53	18	35
17	Nat North	A	Boston United	1107	W 1 - 0	Obeng 53	19	36
24	Nat North	H	Blyth Spartans	524	W 1 - 0	Udoh 50	15	37
Mar 17	Nat North	H	Nuneaton Town	353	W 1 - 0	Dodd 34	14	38
22	Nat North	A	Spennymoor Town	635	L 0 - 1		15	39
24	Nat North	A	Stockport County	3673	L 0 - 4		17	40
31	Nat North	H	FC United of Manchester	1005	W 1 - 0	Hood 43	16	41
Apr 7	Nat North	A	Bradford PA	338	L 0 - 1		16	42
12	Nat North	A	AFC Telford United	977	L 2 - 3	English 9 Udoh 23	18	43
14	Nat North	H	Curzon Ashton	531	D 0 - 0		18	44
19	Nat North	H	Chorley	407	W 2 - 0	Breeden 70 Gittings 90	18	45
21	Nat North	A	York City	2350	D 2 - 2	Kempster 42 (og) Dodd 89	18	46
28	Nat North	A	Salford City	1275	L 0 - 4		19	47

GOALSCORERS	SG	CSG	Pens	Hat tricks	Total		SG	CSG	Pens	Hat tricks	Total
2016-17 *Baker-Richardson*					17	Opponents					3
Bishop	6	2	2	1	9	Breeden	2		1		2
T-Brown	5	2	2		6	Dodd	2				2
Canavan	5		1		5	Hood	2				2
Udoh	4				5	Moore	2				2
English	4	2			4	Revan	2				2
Dunbar	3				3	Gudger					1
Edwards	3				3	Magunda					1
Gittings	3		1		3						
Obeng	3				3						

NORTH FERRIBY UNITED MATCH RESULTS 2017-18

Date	Comp	H/A	Opponents	Att:	Result	Goalscorers	Pos	No.
Aug 5	Nat North	A	Curzon Ashton	290	L 0 - 4		21	1
8	Nat North	H	Harrogate Town	274	L 0 - 2		22	2
12	Nat North	H	Brackley Town	167	L 0 - 5		22	3
15	Nat North	A	Alfreton Town	371	L 0 - 1		21	4
19	Nat North	A	Blyth Spartans	678	W 1 - 0	Francis 62	21	5
26	Nat North	H	Darlington	479	D 1 - 1	Bateson 51	20	6
28	Nat North	A	Gainsborough Trinity	737	L 0 - 2		21	7
Sept 2	Nat North	H	Tamworth	261	D 0 - 0		22	8
5	Nat North	A	Boston United	859	L 1 - 2	Pugh 38	22	9
9	Nat North	H	Chorley	280	L 0 - 2		22	10
12	Nat North	H	Spennymoor Town	206	L 0 - 6		22	11
17	FAC 2Q	A	1874 Northwich	439	L 0 - 1			12
23	Nat North	A	Stockport County	3071	L 1 - 4	Bailey-King 47	22	13
Oct 7	Nat North	H	FC United	492	D 3 - 3	Muskwe 43 86 Brogan 56	22	14
14	Nat North	H	AFC Telford United	250	L 0 - 2		22	15
28	Nat North	A	Leamington	529	L 0 - 3		22	16
Nov 4	Nat North	A	Southport	635	D 2 - 2	Gray 30 Muskwe 60	21	17
11	Nat North	H	Bradford PA	389	L 0 - 1		22	18
18	Nat North	A	Salford City	1712	L 0 - 4		22	19
21	Nat North	A	Kidderminster Harriers	1198	L 0 - 4		22	20
25	FAT 3Q	A	Nuneaton Town	360	L 1 - 5	Rzonka 60		21
Dec 2	Nat North	H	Nuneaton Town	311	L 0 - 2		22	22
19	Nat North	H	Curzon Ashton	194	L 0 - 1		22	23
23	Nat North	A	Harrogate Town	1,209	L 0 - 3		22	24
26	Nat North	H	York City	1001	L 1 - 4	Stewart 48	22	25
Jan 1	Nat North	A	York City	2523	L 0 - 2		22	26
6	Nat North	H	Alfreton Town	297	L 0 - 3		22	27
20	Nat North	H	Boston United	546	L 1 - 5	Bolder 79 (pen)	22	28
27	Nat North	A	Chorley	1011	D 2 - 2	Agnew 19 Harrison 76	22	29
Feb 3	Nat North	H	Leamington	214	D 1 - 1	Agnew 2	22	30
10	Nat North	A	AFC Telford United	919	L 0 - 3		22	31
13	Nat North	A	Brackley Town	225	L 0 - 3		22	32
17	Nat North	H	Southport	309	L 0 - 3		22	33
24	Nat North	H	Bradford PA	423	L 0 - 1		22	34
Mar 10	Nat North	A	Nuneaton Town	478	D 2 - 2	Mail 20 Johnson 71	22	35
17	Nat North	A	Darlington	1087	L 0 - 6		22	36
20	Nat North	H	Salford City	470	D 1 - 1	Nicholls 86	22	37
24	Nat North	H	Blyth Spartans	367	W 1 - 0	Cooke 60	22	38
30	Nat North	A	Tamworth	665	L 1 - 4	Nichols 57	22	39
Apr 7	Nat North	H	Stockport County	480	L 1 - 3	Collins 41	22	40
17	Nat North	H	Gainsborough Trinity	399	L 0 - 1		22	41
21	Nat North	H	Kidderminster Harriers	331	L 1 - 3	Mail 76	22	42
26	Nat North	A	Spennymoor Town	629	D 1 - 1	Harrison 63	22	43
28	Nat North	A	FC United	2580	W 2 - 0	Lofts 49 70	22	44

GOALSCORERS	SG	CSG	Pens	Hat tricks	Total		SG	CSG	Pens	Hat tricks	Total
2016-17 Thompson					12	Brogan					1
Muskwe	2				3	Collins					1
Agnew	2	2			2	Cooke					1
Harrison	2				2	Francis					1
Lofts	1				2	Gray					1
Mail	2				2	Johnson					1
Nicholls	2				2	Pugh					1
Bailey-King					1	Rozonka					1
Bateson					1	Stewart					1
Bolder					1						

NUNEATON TOWN MATCH RESULTS 2017-18

Date	Comp	H/A	Opponents	Att:	Result	Goalscorers	Pos	No.
Aug 5	Nat North	A	Harrogate Town	663	L 0 - 4		22	1
8	Nat North	H	Kidderminster Harriers	781	W 1 - 0	Chambers 90	17	2
12	Nat North	H	Gainsborough Trinity	559	L 0 - 1		19	3
15	Nat North	A	Brackley Town	530	L 0 - 1		19	4
19	Nat North	A	York City	2430	L 3 - 4	Chambers 68 83 Nicholson 89	20	5
26	Nat North	H	Leamington	731	W 4 - 0	Nicholson 9 29 Henshall 20 Hickey 75	14	6
28	Nat North	A	Boston United	1020	D 1 - 1	Glover 89	16	7
Sept 2	Nat North	H	Alfreton Town	632	D 2 - 2	Nicholson 3 Gascoigne 62	16	8
5	Nat North	H	AFC Telford United	569	L 0 - 2		18	9
9	Nat North	A	Bradford PA	319	D 1 - 1	Elliott 6	18	10
12	Nat North	A	Salford City	902	L 0 - 3		18	11
16	FAC 2Q	H	Kings Lynn Town	627	W 3 - 1	CHAMBERS 3 (57 69 89)		12
23	Nat North	H	Southport	553	W 3 - 0	CHAMBERS 3 (37 68 88)	17	13
30	FAC 3Q	A	Nantwich Town	479	L 1 - 3	Mills 75		14
Oct 7	Nat North	A	Blyth Spartans	601	L 3 - 6	Chambers 16 64 Dielna 52	18	15
14	Nat North	H	Darlington	694	W 2 - 1	Chambers 7 Nicholson 47		16
21	Nat North	H	Stockport County	737	L 1 - 3	Nti 80	18	17
28	Nat North	A	FC United	1781	L 1 - 2	Ball 81	19	18
Nov 4	Nat North	H	Spennymoor United	491	L 0 - 1		19	19
11	Nat North	H	Chorley	106	D 2 - 2	Nicholson 6 Chambers 47	11	20
18	Nat North	H	Curzon Ashton	481	D 1 - 1	Chambers 18	20	21
25	FAT 3Q	H	North Ferriby United	360	W 5 - 1	Nicholson 16 85 Nti 30 Chambers 38 43		22
Dec 2	Nat North	A	North Ferriby United	311	W 2 - 0	Elliott 62 Chambers 65	20	23
16	FAT 1	H	Barrow	415	L 0 - 1			24
23	Nat North	A	Kidderminster Hariers	1510	L 0 3		21	25
26	Nat North	H	Tamworth	929	W 4 - 1	Elliott 11 Nicholson 21 Chambers 26 28	20	26
Jan 1	Nat North	A	Tamworth	1023	L 0 - 2		21	27
6	Nat North	H	Brackley Town	542	L 0 - 2		21	28
9	Nat North	A	Harrogate Town	365	W 2 - 1	Nicholson 18 Chambers 56	18	29
13	Nat North	A	Gainsborough Trinity	463	W 1 - 0	Nicholson 17	15	30
27	Nat North	H	Bradford PA	513	D 0 - 0		18	31
Feb 3	Nat North	H	FC United of Manchester	730	W 1 - 0	Chambers 29	16	32
17	Nat North	A	Spennymoor United	852	W 1 - 0	Chambers 24	18	33
20	Nat North	A	Stockport County	2629	W 1 - 0	Hinchcliffe 41 (og)	12	34
24	Nat North	H	Chorley	535	D 1 - 1	Chambers 84	12	35
27	Nat North	A	AFC Telford United	336	W 2 - 1	Ferry 30 Wildin 52	11	36
Mar 10	Nat North	H	North Ferriby United	478	D 2 - 2	Green 5 Nti 44	11	37
17	Nat North	A	Leamington	353	L 0 - 1		13	38
30	Nat North	A	Alfreton Town	535	D 1 - 1	Nti 79	13	39
Apr 7	Nat North	A	Southport	814	W 1 - 0	Nti 26	12	40
10	Nat North	H	York City	479	W 1 - 0	Chambers 74	12	41
14	Nat North	H	Salford City	937	L 0 - 2		11	42
17	Nat North	A	Curzon Ashton	173	D 2 - 2	Wildin 40 Langmead 90	11	43
21	Nat North	A	Darlington	1409	D 0 - 0		13	44
25	Nat North	H	Boston United	154	D 1 - 1	Ferry 21	13	45
28	Nat North	H	Blyth Spartans	597	D 2 - 2	Chambers 24 Green 80	13	46

GOALSCORERS	SG	CSG	Pens	Hat tricks	Total		SG	CSG	Pens	Hat tricks	Total
2016-17 Ironside					18	Gascoigne					1
Chambers	17	4	2		25	Glover					1
Nicholson	9	2			11	Henshall					1
Nti	5				5	Hickey					1
Elliott	3				3	Langmead					1
Ferry	2				2	Mills					1
Green	2				2	Opponents					1
Wildin	2				2						
Ball					1						
Dielna					1						

SOUTHPORT MATCH RESULTS 2017-18

Date	Comp	H/A	Opponents	Att:	Result	Goalscorers	Pos	No.
Aug 5	Nat North	H	Boston United	886	W 4 - 0	Schumaster 14 Martin 35 C.Jones 54 Roberts 81	3	1
8	Nat North	A	Bradford Park Avenue	574	W 2 - 1	White 29 Roberts 89	2	2
12	Nat North	A	Leamington	711	W 1 - 0	Jones 75	3	3
15	Nat North	H	FC Utd of Manchester	1270	D 3 - 3	Martin 62 Dugdale 87 Sampson 90	4	4
19	Nat North	A	Alfreton Town	479	W 1 - 0	Schumacher 57	2	5
26	Nat North	H	York City	1177	D 1 - 1	Roberts 51	3	6
28	Nat North	A	Salford City	1757	L 1 - 2	Jennings 18	5	7
Sept 2	Nat North	H	Darlington	1059	W 2 - 0	Sang 459 Merrie 90	3	8
5	Nat North	A	Stockport County	2702	L 0 - 6		4	9
9	Nat North	H	Kidderminster Harriers	901	L 0 - 3		7	10
12	Nat North	H	Harrogate Town	868	L 1 - 4	Roberts 55	10	11
16	FAC 2Q	H	Bradford Park Avenue	496	L 0 - 3			12
23	Nat North	A	Nuneaton Town	553	L 0 - 3		14	13
Oct 7	Nat North	H	Spennymoor	838	L 1 - 2	Sampson 88	16	14
21	Nat North	H	Gainsborough Trinity	771	D 2 - 2	Sampson 55 Anderson 86	16	15
28	Nat North	A	AFC Telford United	1082	D 1 - 1	Lowe 90 (pen)	17	16
Nov 4	Nat North	H	North Ferriby United	635	D 2 - 2	Schumacher 39 Hallam 51	16	17
11	Nat North	A	Curzon Ashton	519	D 2 - 2	Schumacher 18 (pen) Hallam 23	15	18
14	Nat North	A	Brackley Town	343	L 0 - 4			19
18	Nat North	H	Blyth Spartans	905	L 0 - 3		18	20
25	FAT 3Q	A	Stockport County	1215	D 2 - 2	White 14 Gilchrist 70		21
29	FAT 3Qr	H	Stockport County	424	L 0 - 3			22
Dec 2	Nat North	A	Tamworth	564	D 3 - 3	GILCHRIST 3 (5 46 75)	19	23
16	Nat North	H	Boston United	784	L 2 - 3	Gilchrist 39 35 (pen)	19	24
23	Nat North	H	Bradford Park Avenue	635	L 0 - 4		20	25
26	Nat North	A	Chorley	1517	D 0 - 0		21	26
Jan 1	Nat North	H	Chorley	1309	W 3 - 1	Morgan 20 Sharon 85 Sampson 90	17	27
7	Nat North	A	FC Utd of Manchester	2863	L 0 - 1		18	28
13	Nat North	H	Leamington	848	W 2 - 0	Sampson 7 Gilchrist 70	13	29
20	Nat North	A	Stockport County	1652	W 3 - 1	Sampson 46 73 Gilchrist 71	16	30
27	Nat North	H	Kidderminster Harriers	1968	L 0 - 3		17	31
Feb 10	Nat North	A	Gainsborough Trinity	532	W 3 - 0	GILCHRIST 3 (42 47 51)	16	32
17	Nat North	A	North Ferriby United	309	W 3 - 0	Gilchrist 38 (pen) Morgan 41 Sampson 48	13	33
24	Nat North	H	Curzon Ashton	863	W 3 - 1	Gilchrist 25 Shaw 32 (og) Osborne 90	12	34
Mar 10	Nat North	H	Tamworth	849	W 3 - 0	Gilchrist 22 Charles 60 Priestley 70	10	35
13	Nat North	H	AFC Telford United	784	W 3 - 0	Osborne 48 Charles 72 Sampson 76	8	36
24	Nat North	H	Alfreton Town	1614	L 1 - 3	Gilchrist 80	11	37
27	Nat North	A	York City	2169	L 2 - 3	Gilchrist 78 (pen) Osborne 86	11	38
Apr 2	Nat North	H	Nuneaton Town	814	L 0 - 1		14	39
14	Nat North	A	Harrogate Town	1385	L 0 - 2		14	40
17	Nat North	H	Salford City	1165	L 0 - 1		15	41
19	Nat North	A	Blyth Spartans	398	L 0 - 2		19	42
21	Nat North	H	Brackley Town	1004	L 0 - 1		19	43
25	Nat North	A	Darlington	1019	W 4 - 2	Hannah 34 Charles 63 79 Smith 86	15	44
28	Nat North	A	Spennymoor Town	891	L 1 - 2	Hannah 9	15	45

GOALSCORERS	SG	CSG	Pens	Hat tricks	Total		SG	CSG	Pens	Hat tricks	Total
2016-17 Allen					11	Anderson					1
Gilchrist	11	4	3	2	16	Dugdale					1
Sampson	8	2			9	Jennings					1
Charles	3				4	Lowe			1		1
Roberts	4	2			4	Merrie					1
Schumaker	4	2	1		4	Opponents					1
Osborne	3				3	Priestley					1
Hallam	2				2	Sang					1
Hannah	2				2	Sharon					1
Jones	2				2	Smith					1
Martin	2				2						
Morgan	2				2						
White	2				2						

SPENNYMOOR TOWN MATCH RESULTS 2017-18

Date	Comp	H/A	Opponents	Att:	Result	Goalscorers	Pos	No.
Aug 5	Nat North	H	Stockport County	1337	W 1 - 0	Foley 41	11	1
8	Nat North	A	FC United of Manchester	1602	W 3 - 2	Griffiths 14 Johnson 28 Taylor 62	4	2
15	Nat North	H	Bradford PA	755	W 3 - 0	Taylor 36 38 Johnson 39	5	3
19	Nat North	A	Brackley Town	400	L 0 - 2		7	4
22	Nat North	A	Boston United	1048	W 3 - 0	Taylor 42 74 Johnson 87		5
26	Nat North	H	Salford City	687	D 1 - 1	Johnson 74	4	6
28	Nat North	A	Darlington	2050	D 1 - 1	Foley 23	4	7
Sept 2	Nat North	H	Gainsborough Town	746	D 1 - 1	Tait 36 (pen)	5	8
5	Nat North	H	York City	1306	L 2 - 4	Tait 61 (pen) Anderson 84	5	9
9	Nat North	A	Tamworth	721	L 1 - 3	Griffiths 48	9	10
12	Nat North	A	North Ferriby United	206	W 6 - 0	ANDERSON 3 (2 32 75) Mason 7 Taylor 18 Griffiths 50	6	11
16	FAC 2Q	H	Gainsborough Trinity	403	L 1 - 2	Taylor 20	6	12
23	Nat North	H	Alfreton Town	634	W 2 - 1	Henry 35 Tait 63 (pen)	4	13
Oct 7	Nat North	A	Southport	838	W 2 - 1	Foley 39 Taylor 90	4	14
14	Nat North	H	Curzon Ashton	745	L 2 - 4	Anderson 17 Taylor 23	4	15
21	Nat North	A	Kidderminster Harriers	1406	D 2 - 2	English 24 Thompson-Brown 70	5	16
28	Nat North	H	Chorley	753	W 1 - 0	Johnson 63	5	17
Nov 4	Nat North	A	Nuneaton Town	491	W 1 - 0	Taylor 83	4	18
11	Nat North	H	Harrogate Town	1085	W 3 - 1	Foley 2 Taylor 18 Ramshaw 39	4	19
18	Nat North	A	Leamington	455	L 0 - 4		5	20
25	FAT 3Q	A	Cleethorpes Town	306	W 2 - 1	Hall 35 Johnson 82		21
Dec 9	Nat North	A	Stockport County	3379	L 2 - 3	Taylor 21 (pen) Ramshaw 61	5	22
23	Nat North	H	FC United of Manchester	795	D 4 - 4	Hall 5 43 Ramshaw 23 Taylor 52	6	23
26	Nat North	A	Blyth Spartans	1179	W 3 - 2	Taylor 38 Anderson 73 Mason 90	6	24
Jan 1	Nat North	H	Blyth Spartans	1066	W 3 - 1	Griffiths 36 Ramshaw 46 Taylor 69	4	25
6	Nat North	A	Bradford PA	448	W 2 - 1	Foley 14 Mason 74		26
9	FAT 1	H	Gainsborough Trinity	360	W 4 - 4	Foley 14 Anderson 28 Hall 86 Taylor 93 (Won 5-3 on pens)		27
13	FAT 2	H	Solihull Moors	570	W 2 - 0	Anderson 34 Johnson 79		28
20	Nat North	A	York City	2976	D 2 - 2	Hall 52 Johnson 77	5	29
27	Nat North	H	Tamworth	832	W 1 - 0	Taylor 25	4	30
Feb 3	FAT 3	H	East Thurrock United	743	D 1 - 1	Johnson 66		31
6	FAT 3r	A	East Thurrock United	238	W 5 - 2	JOHNSON 3 (34 59 62) Taylor 45 Griffiths 49		32
17	Nat North	H	Nuneaton Town	852	L 0 - 1		7	33
24	FAT 4	A	Bromley	850	D 0 - 0			34
Mar 14	FAT 4r	H	Bromley	802	L 1 - 2	Taylor 5		35
17	Nat North	A	Salford City	1287	L 2 - 3	Lowe 7 Hall 31	7	36
20	Nat North	A	Chorley	596	L 1 - 3	Teague 60 (og)		37
22	Nat North	H	Leamington	635	W 1 - 0	Hall 79		38
27	Nat North	A	Harrogate Town	1001	W 2 - 1	Curtis 54 Mason 63	5	39
30	Nat North	H	Gainsborough Town	686	L 1 - 4	Johnson 15	8	40
Apr 5	Nat North	A	AFC Telford United	1212	L 2 - 3	Lowe 13 Johnson 23	6	41
7	Nat North	A	Alfreton Town	441	W 4 - 1	Lowe 35 TAYLOR 3 (45 78 90)	6	42
10	Nat North	H	Boston United	479	D 0 - 0		6	43
12	Nat North	H	Brackley Town	409	L 0 - 3		6	44
17	Nat North	H	Kidderminster Harriers	415	D 1 - 1	Taylor 73	6	45
19	Nat North	H	Darlington	1661	L 1 - 2	Chamdler 2	6	46
21	Nat North	A	Curzon Ashton	309	L 0 - 1		8	47
24	Nat North	A	AFC Telford United	418	L 1 - 2	Anderson 3	8	48
26	Nat North	H	North Ferriby United	629	D 1 - 1	Foley 27	8	49
28	Nat North	H	Southport	891	W 2 - 1	Anderson 57 Ramshaw 63	8	50

GOALSCORERS	SG	CSG	Pens	Hat tricks	Total		SG	CSG	Pens	Hat tricks	Total
2016-17 Taylor					*18*	Tait	3	2	3		3
Taylor	19	4	1	1	23	Chandler					1
Johnson	11	2		1	14	Curtis					1
Anderson	9	2		1	10	English					1
Foley	3	2			7	Henry					1
Hall	6				7	Opponents					1
Griffiths	4				5	T-Brown					1
Ramshaw	4				5						
Mason	4				4						
Lowe	3				3						

STOCKPORT COUNTY MATCH RESULTS 2017-18

Date	Comp	H/A	Opponents	Att:	Result	Goalscorers	Pos	No.
Aug 5	Nat North	A	Spennymoor Town	1337	L 0 - 1		15	1
8	Nat North	H	Curzon Ashton	3002	W 3 - 0	Winter 21 Warburton 48 Oswell 55	5	2
12	Nat North	H	Harrogate Town	3107	D 2 - 2	Oswell 53 72	8	3
15	Nat North	A	Salford City	2358	L 1 - 2	Hampson 41	13	4
19	Nat North	A	Leamington	844	W 3 - 2	OSWELL 3 (16 86 90)	9	5
26	Nat North	H	Gainsborough Trinity	3006	W 1 - 0	Oswell 54	8	6
28	Nat North	A	Tamworth	1120	L 1 - 3	Miniham 5	11	7
Sept 2	Nat North	H	Bradford PA	3018	D 0 - 0		10	8
5	Nat North	H	Southport	2702	W 6 - 0	Warburton 2 23 Winter 40 Oswell 45 59 Ball 52	7	9
9	Nat North	A	York City	3011	L 0 - 2		12	10
12	Nat North	A	AFC Telford United	853	L 2 - 3	Warburton 23 Dixon 44	13	11
16	FAC 2Q	H	Curzon Ashton	1922	W 1 - 0	Thomas 52		12
23	Nat North	H	North Ferreiby United	3071	W 4 - 1	Oswell 30 48 Minihan 39 Duxbury 57	10	13
30	FAC 3Q	H	FC United of Manchester	3034	D 3 - 3	Warburton 19 31 Oswell 41		14
Oct 3	FAC 3Qr	A	FC United of Manchester	1688	L 0 - 1			15
7	Nat North	A	Darlington	1758	D 1 - 1	Oswell 90	10	16
14	Nat North	H	Blyth Spartans	3423	L 1 - 3	Warburton 39 (pen)	11	17
21	Nat North	H	Nuneaton Town	737	W 3 - 1	Oswell 36 Stopforth 45 Ball 68	9	18
28	Nat North	H	Kidderminster Harriers	3015	L 1 - 2	Warburton 45	12	19
Nov 4	Nat North	A	FC United of Manchester	4078	W 4 - 1	Warburton 6 60 (p) Oswell 10 Mantack 42	8	20
11	Nat North	A	Boston United	1211	D 2 - 2	Warburton 59 Ball 90		21
18	Nat North	H	Chorley	3674	D 1 - 1	Oswell 90	10	22
25	FAT 3Q	H	Southport	1215	D 2 - 2	Dixon 12 Stephenson 86		23
28	FAT 3Qr	A	Southport	424	W 3 - 0	Oswell 18 Warburton 31 (pen) 65		24
Dec 2	Nat North	H	Brackley Town	585	L 2 - 3	Smalley 21 Warburton 42	11	25
8	Nat North	H	Spennymoor Town	3379	W 3 - 2	OSWELL 3 (34 (pen) 59 69)	9	26
16	FAT 1	A	Lancaster City	578	W 3 - 1	Oswell 26 Stopforth 38 Dixon 90		27
23	Nat North	A	Curzon Ashton	1473	D 1 - 1	Stephenson 7	10	28
26	Nat North	H	Alfreton Town	3453	W 1 - 0	Mantack 41	9	29
Jan 1	Nat North	A	Alfreton Town	949	W 3 - 1	Smalley 7 50 Elliott 74 (og)	8	30
6	Nat North	H	Salford City	5002	D 2 - 2	Oswell 31 Dixon 82	10	31
13	FAT 2	A	Kidderminster Harriers	1348	D 2 - 2	Oswell 4 Stephenson 70		32
16	FAT 2r	H	Kidderminster Harriers	883	W 3 - 0	Turner 25 McKenna 75 Dixon 90 (pen)		33
20	Nat North	A	Southport	1652	L 1 - 3	Turner 9	10	34
23	Nat North	A	Harrogate Town	882	L 1 - 4	Smalley 35	10	35
27	Nat North	H	York City	4,407	W 2 - 0	Stephenson 24 Warburton 31	9	36
Feb 3	FAT 3	A	Maidenhead United	855	D 1 - 1	Warburton 8		37
6	FAT 3r	H	Maidenhead United	1,121	W 3 - 2	Stephenson 81 West 90 Ball 95 (aet)		38
17	Nat North	A	FC United of Manchester	3084	W 1 - 0	Warburton 10	10	39
20	Nat North	H	Nuneaton Town	2629	L 0 - 1		12	40
24	FAT 4	A	Brackley Town	2213	D 1 - 1	Ball 73		41
Mar 6	FAT 4r	H	Brackley Town	506	L 1 - 2	Oswell 48		42
10	Nat North	H	Brackley Town	3060	L 0 - 1		12	43
17	Nat North	A	Gainsborough Trinity	474	W 3 - 2	Turner 16 Thomas 48 Ball 66	9	44
20	Nat North	H	Boston United	2244	W 1 - 0	Warburton 85	7	45
24	Nat North	A	Leamington	3673	W 4 - 0	Ball 2 31 Turner 19 Duxbury 83	7	46
30	Nat North	H	Bradford PA	1044	W 3 - 2	Oswell 7 59 Ball 90	5	47
Apr 3	Nat North	H	Tamworth	2854	W 3 - 2	Oswell 28 58 Warburton 32	5	48
7	Nat North	A	North Ferriby United	490	W 3 - 1	Oswell 8 Warburton 38 77	5	49
10	Nat North	A	Kidderminster Harriers	1722	L 1 - 3	Ball 9	5	50
14	Nat North	H	AFC Telford United	3546	W 1 - 0	Stephenson 74	5	51
17	Nat North	A	Chorley	1983	D 1 - 1	Duxbury 71	5	52
21	Nat North	A	Blyth Spartans	1045	W 1 - 0	Ball 47	5	53
28	Nat North	H	Darlington	6163	D 1 - 1	Cowan 63	5	54
May 2	PO	H	Chorley	6230	L 0 - 1			55

GOALSCORERS	SG	CSG	Pens	Hat tricks	Total		SG	CSG	Pens	Hat tricks	Total
2016-17 Lloyd					29	Minihan	2				2
Oswell	20	3	1	2	29	Stopforth	2				2
Warburton	16	3	3		21	Thomas	2				2
Ball	10		1		11	Winter	2				2
Stephenson	6				6	Cowan					1
Dixon	5				5	Hampson					1
Smalley	3				4	McKenna					1
Turner	4				4	Opponents					1
Duxberry	3				3	West					1
Mantack	2				2						

TAMWORTH MATCH RESULTS 2017-18

Date	Comp	H/A	Opponents	Att:	Result	Goalscorers	Pos	No.
Aug 5	Nat North	H	Bradford PA	564	L 0 - 1		16	1
8	Nat North	A	Leamington	625	W 2 - 1	Burns 4 Verma 73	11	2
12	Nat North	A	Blyth Spartans	654	L 2 - 4	Styche 14 58 (pen)	15	3
15	Nat North	H	Boston United	702	W 2 - 1	Styche 22 Knights 71	11	4
19	Nat North	H	Curzon Ashton	606	W 4 - 1	Morley 17 25 Knights 79 Reid 80	8	5
26	Nat North	A	Harrogate Town	669	L 0 - 3		10	6
28	Nat North	H	Stockport County	1120	W 3 - 1	Reid 11 Styche 26 87	7	7
Sept 2	Nat North	A	North Ferriby United	261	D 0 - 0		6	8
5	Nat North	A	Brackley Town	430	D 0 - 0		9	9
9	Nat North	H	Spennymoor Town	721	W 3 - 1	Reid 10 Knights 54 86	6	10
12	Nat North	H	Kidderminster Harriers	723	W 2 - 1	Knights 40 Reid 53	5	11
16	FAC 2Q	A	Stafford Rangers	782	L 0 - 1			12
24	Nat North	A	FC United	1770	L 1 - 3	Taylor 52	6	13
Oct 7	Nat North	H	Gainsborough Town	762	L 1 - 2	Styche 41	8	14
21	Nat North	H	Alfreton Town	563	L 2 - 3	Styche 30 45	13	15
28	Nat North	A	York City	2605	W 3 - 2	Styche 34 48 Knights 90	7	16
31	Nat North	A	Chorley	961	D 1 - 1	Knights 47	7	17
Nov 11	Nat North	H	Salford City	1233	L 1 - 2	Verma 26	10	18
18	Nat North	A	Darlington	1246	W 1 - 0	Knights 71	9	19
21	Nat North	H	AFC Telford United	747	L 0 - 2		10	20
25	FAT 3	H	Warrington Town	468	D 2 - 2	Verma 11 41		21
Nov 28	FAT 3r	A	Warrington Town	223	L 0 - 3			22
Dec 2	Nat North	A	Southport	564	D 3 - 3	Jones 71 (og) Reid 82 Taylor 90	10	23
16	Nat North	A	Bradford PA	354	W 4 - 3	Taylor 2 Powell 36 Verma 52 Kotwica 75	8	24
22	Nat North	H	Leamington	708	L 0 - 3		9	25
26	Nat North	A	Nuneaton Town	929	L 1 - 4	Ashton 73 (og)	11	26
Jan 1	Nat North	H	Nuneaton Town	1023	W 2 - 0	Taylor 27 Powell 33	11	27
6	Nat North	A	Boston United	1050	L 1 - 3	Reid 74	11	28
20	Nat North	A	Brackley Town	588	D 1 - 1	Powell 37	12	29
27	Nat North	A	Spennymoor Town	832	L 0 - 1		13	30
Feb 3	Nat North	A	York City	764	D 1 - 1	Knights 89	12	31
10	Nat North	A	Alfreton Town	449	L 1 - 2	Knights 24	15	32
13	Nat North	H	Blyth Spartans	501	L 0 - 3		15	33
17	Nat North	H	AFC Telford United	736	D 2 - 2	Asante 73 Shaw 90	15	34
Mar 5	Nat North	A	Salford City	1096	L 1 - 2	Verma 58	15	35
10	Nat North	A	Southport	849	L 0 - 3		18	36
13	Nat North	H	Darlington	584	D 0 - 0		17	37
17	Nat North	H	Harrogate Town	662	D 1 - 1	Taylor 34	16	38
24	Nat North	A	Curzon Ashton	323	L 0 - 1		19	39
30	Nat North	H	North Ferriby United	665	W 4 - 1	Angus 19 Verma 27 Asante 45 Lane 65	17	40
Apr 2	Nat North	A	Stockport County	2854	L 2 - 3	Davies 20 Angus 86	17	41
7	Nat North	H	F.C.United	962	L 0 - 2		18	42
14	Nat North	A	Kidderminster Harriers	1821	L 0 - 2		21	43
21	Nat North	H	Chorley	732	L 3 - 4	Angus 16 Asante 56 (pen) Jones 60	21	44
28	Nat North	A	Gainsborough Trinity	589	D 0 - 0		21	45

GOALSCORERS	SG	CSG	Pens	Hat tricks	Total		SG	CSG	Pens	Hat tricks	Total
2016-17 Newton					29	Opponents					2
Knights	8	2			10	Burns					1
Styche	6	3	1		10	Davies					1
Verma	5				7	Jones					1
Reid	6	2			6	Kotwica					1
Taylor	4				5	Lane					1
Angus					3	Shaw					1
Asante					3						
Powell	3				3						
Morley	1				2						

YORK MATCH RESULTS 2017-18

Date	Comp	H/A	Opponents	Att:	Result	Goalscorers	Pos	No.
Aug 5	Nat North	H	AFC Telford United	2951	L 0 - 1		17	1
8	Nat North	A	Blyth Spartans	1373	W 2 - 0	Parkin 15 Newton 22	8	2
12	Nat North	A	Bradford Park Avenue	1133	W 5 - 0	Parslow 5 Morgan-Smith 12 25 Newton 32 Havern 69 (og)	5	3
15	Nat North	A	Darlington	3944	D 0 - 0		7	4
19	Nat North	H	Nuneaton Town	2430	W 4 - 3	Rankine 1 70 Heslop 23 52	5	5
26	Nat North	A	Southport	1177	D 1 - 1	Newton 82	6	6
28	Nat North	H	FC United of Manchester	3411	L 0 - 2		9	7
Sept 2	Nat North	A	Chorley	1294	L 0 - 2		9	8
5	Nat North	A	Spennymoor Town	1306	W 4 - 2	Parkin 28 (pen) 37 (pen) Almond 40 Felix 90	8	9
9	Nat North	H	Stockport County	3011	W 2 - 0	Heslop 17 Morgan-Smith 28	5	10
12	Nat North	A	Gainsborough Trinity	2196	D 1 - 1	Law 75	7	11
16	FAC 2Q	A	Salford City	1350	W 2 - 1	Parkin 54 85	7	12
23	Nat North	A	Harrogate Town	2800	L 0 - 2		7	13
30	FAC 3Q	A	South Shields	2806	L 2 - 3	Newton 78 Parkin 78		14
Oct 7	Nat North	H	Brackley Town	2732	W 2 - 1	Parkin 20 86	6	15
14	Nat North	A	Leamington	965	D 2 - 2	Ferguson 9 Parkin 52	6	16
21	Nat North	A	Salford City	1874	L 2 - 3	Almond 84 Connolly 90	8	17
28	Nat North	H	Tamworth	2605	L 2 - 3	Parkin 56 Rowe 68	9	18
Nov 4	Nat North	H	Curzon Ashton	2146	W 2 - 1	Parkin 18 Parslow 33	6	19
11	Nat North	A	Alfreton Town	997	W 3 - 2	Connolly 13 Parkin 52 70 (pen)	6	20
18	Nat North	H	Kidderminster Harriers	2507	D 1 - 1	Parkin 37	6	21
25	FAT 3Q	H	Coalville Town	1001	W 3 - 1	Martin 44 Parkin 62 (pen) 77 (pen)		22
Dec 2	Nat North	A	Boston United	1126	L 1 - 2	Moke 19	9	23
15	FAT 1	A	Kidderminster Harriers	1138	L 1 - 2	Morgan-Smith 76		24
22	Nat North	A	Blyth Spartans	2751	L 2 - 3	Parkin 33 89	11	25
26	Nat North	A	North Ferriby United	1001	W 4 - 1	PARKIN 3 (19 40 87) Burn 46	10	26
Jan 1	Nat North	H	North Ferriby United	2523	W 2 - 0	Parkin 31 76	9	27
6	Nat North	A	Darlingtobn	2405	W 2 - 1	Newton 46 Parkin 53 (pen)	8	28
13	Nat North	H	Bradford P A	2642	W 2 - 1	Parkin 41 Morgan-Smith 65	6	29
16	Nat North	A	AFC Telford United	1852	W 5 - 3	Newton 9 34 Connolly 10 Moke 43 Burn 52	5	30
20	Nat North	H	Spennymoor Town	2976	D 2 - 2	Burn 11 Connolly 72	4	31
27	Nat North	A	Stockport County	4407	L 0 - 2		6	32
Feb 3	Nat North	A	Tamworth	764	D 1 - 1	Connolly 73	6	33
10	Nat North	H	Salford City	3366	W 1 - 0	Connolly 27	5	34
17	Nat North	A	Curzon Ashton	892	L 1 - 4	Kempster 67	6	35
24	Nat North	H	Alfreton Town	2397	D 1 - 1	Heslop 5	5	36
Mar 10	Nat North	H	Boston United	2461	W 1 - 0	Ferguson 73	4	37
13	Nat North	A	Kidderminster Harriers	1244	L 1 - 2	Newton 90	5	38
27	Nat North	A	Southport	2169	W 3 - 2	Kempster 9 Connolly 45 Gray 90	4	39
31	Nat North	H	Chorley	2721	D 1 - 1	Smith 72	5	40
Apr 2	Nat North	H	Harrogate Town	3554	L 0 - 2		7	41
10	Nat North	A	Nuneaton Town	479	L 0 - 1		7	42
14	Nat North	A	Gainsborough Trinity	1014	L 0 - 1		8	43
17	Nat North	A	FC United of Manchester	1816	L 0 - 1		9	44
21	Nat North	H	Leamington	2350	D 2 - 2	Newton 56 86	9	45
28	Nat North	A	Brackley Town	670	L 0 - 2		11	46

GOALSCORERS	SG	CSG	Pens	Hat tricks	Total		SG	CSG	Pens	Hat tricks	Total
2016-17 Parkin					16	Moke	2				2
Parkin	16	5x2	6	1	25	Parslow	2				2
Newton	8	2			10	Rankine	1				2
Connolly	7	2			7	Felix					1
Morgan-Smith	5				5	Gray					1
Heslop	3				4	Law					1
Burn	3				3	Martin					1
Almond	2				2	Opponents					1
Kempster	2				2	Rowe					1
Kempster	2				2	Smith					1

AFC TELFORD UNITED

Club Contact Details 01952 640 064
New Bucks Head Stadium, Watling Street, Wellington, Telford TF1 2TU
enquiries@afctu.co.uk

Founded: 1892   **Nickname:** The Bucks   **Manager:** Gavin Cowan
Previous Names: Wellington Town 1892-1969. AFC Telford United was formed when Telford United folded in May 2004
Previous Leagues: Shropshire 1892-98. Birmingham & District 1898-1901, 02-06, 08-38, 39-45. The Combination 1901-02. Cheshire County 1938-39, 45-58. Southern 1958-79. Alliance/Conference 1979-2004. Northern Premier 2004-06.
Club Colours (change): White and navy

Ground Capacity: 6,380   **Seats:** 2,200   **Covered:** 4,800   **Clubhouse:** Yes   **Shop:** Yes
Previous Grounds: None - Renovation of the old Bucks Head started in 2000 and was completed in 2003.
Record Attendance: 5,710 vs Burscough 28/04/2007
Nearest Railway Station Wellington (Shropshire) - 20min walk to ground.   **Bus Route** 44 - every 10 mins from Town centre.

RECORDS
Victory: 7-0 v Runcorn (A) - Northern Premier League Division One, 17/04/06.
Defeat: 1-6 v Guiseley (A) - Conference North, 01/04/14.
Goalscorer: Andy Brown - 56 (2008-12)
Appearances: Ryan Young - 367 (2007-14)
Additional: Paid £5,000 to Tamworth for Lee Moore 08/12/06
Received £25,000 from Burnley for Duane Courtney 31/08/05

HONOURS
FA Comps: Welsh FA Cup 1901-02, 05-06, 39-40. FA Trophy 1970-71, 82-83.
League: Birmingham & District 1920-21, 34-35, 35-36, 39-40. Cheshire County 1945-46, 46-47, 51-52.
NPL Div. 1 Play-off 2004-05, Premier Division Play-off 2006-07. Conference North Play-off 2010-11, Champions 13-14.
County FA: Birmingham Senior Cup 1946-47. Walsall Senior Cup 1946-47. Shropshire Senior Cup 2008-09, 13-14, 16-17.

08-09		09-10		10-11		11-12		12-13		13-14		14-15		15-16		16-17		17-18	
Conf N	4	Conf N	11	Conf N	2	Conf	20	Conf	24	Conf N	1	Conf	22	Nat N	18	Nat N	17	Nat N	14
FAC	1Pr	FAC	1P	FAC	3Qr	FAC	1P	FAC	4Qr	FAC	2Q	FAC	2P	FAC	2Q	FAC	2Qr	FAC	1P
FAT	SF	FAT	3Qr	FAT	3P	FAT	2P	FAT	2P	FAT	1Pr	FAT	2P	FAT	1P	FAT	1P	FAT	1P

2017-18 STATS	**Goals Total**	68	**Games Without Scoring**	12 (2)	**Total No. of Scorers**	19	**Total Clean Sheets**	13
Most Consecutive Scoring Games	16	**Best Unbeaten Run**	3		**Most Consecutive Clean Sheets**			1
Best Att:	1,995 v Kidderminster Harriers, National South					Number in brackets denotes consecutive runs.		

ALFRETON TOWN

Club Contact Details 01773 830 277
The Impact Arena, North Street, Alfreton, Derbyshire DE55 7FZ
a.raisin@alfretontownfc.com

Founded: 1959   **Nickname:** The Reds   **Manager:** Billy Heath - May 2018
Previous Names: Formed when Alfreton Miners Welfare and Alfreton United merged.
Previous Leagues: Central Alliance 1959-61. Midland 1961-82. Northern Counties East 1982-87, 99-02. Northern Premier 1987-99, 02-04.

Club Colours (change): All red

Ground Capacity: 3,600   **Seats:** 1,500   **Covered:** 2,600   **Clubhouse:** Yes   **Shop:** Yes
Previous Grounds: None
Record Attendance: 5,023 v Matlock Town - Central Alliance 1960
Nearest Railway Station Alfreton - Approx. 15min walk from the ground

RECORDS
Victory: 15-0 v Loughbrough Midland League 1969-70
Defeat: 1-9 v Solihull - FAT 1997. 0-8 v Bridlington - 1992
Goalscorer: John Harrison - 303
Appearances: John Harrison - 561
Additional: Paid £2,000 to Worksop Town for Mick Goddard
Received £150,000 from Swindon Town for Aden Flint, January 2011

HONOURS
FA Comps: None
League: Midland 1969-70, 73-74, 76-77. Northern Counties East 1986-87, 2001-02
Northern Premier League Division One 2002-03. Conference North 2010-11
County FA: Derbyshire Senior Cup 1960-61, 69-70, 72-73, 73-74, 81-82, 94-95, 2001-02, 02-03, 15-16

08-09		09-10		10-11		11-12		12-13		13-14		14-15		15-16		16-17		17-18	
Conf N	3	Conf N	3	Conf N	1	Conf	15	Conf	13	Conf	11	Conf	21	Nat N	10	Nat N	18	Nat N	17
FAC	2P	FAC	3Qr	FAC	2Qr	FAC	1P	FAC	2P	FAC	1P	FAC	4Qr	FAC	4Q	FAC	1Pr	FAC	3Q
FAT	1P	FAT	3Qr	FAT	3Qr	FAT	3Pr	FAT	3P	FAT	1P	FAT	2P	FAT	3Q	FAT	2P	FAT	3Q

2017-18 STATS	**Goals Total**	73	**Games Without Scoring**	8	**Total No. of Scorers**	20	**Total Clean Sheets**	6
Most Consecutive Scoring Games	11	**Best Unbeaten Run**	7		**Most Consecutive Clean Sheets**			1
Best Att:	997 v York City, National South					Number in brackets denotes consecutive runs.		

ALTRINCHAM

Club Contact Details 0161 928 1045
The J Davidson Stadium, Moss Lane, Altrincham, Cheshire WA15 8AP
office@altrinchamfootballclub.co.uk

Founded: 1891   **Nickname:** The Robins   **Manager:** Phil Parkinson
Previous Names: Rigby Memorial Club 1891-93. Merged with the 'Grapplers' to form Broadheath FC 1893-1903.
Previous Leagues: Manchester (Founder members) 1893-1911. Lancashire Combination 1911-19. Cheshire County (FM) 1919-68. Northern Premier (FM) 1968-79, 97-99, 00-04, 17-18. Alliance/Conference/National (FM) 1979-97, 99-00, 04-17.
Club Colours (change): Red & white stripes

Ground Capacity: 6,085   **Seats:** 1,154   **Covered:** Yes   **Clubhouse:** Yes   **Shop:** Yes
Previous Grounds: Pollitts Field 1903-10.
Record Attendance: 10,275 - Altrincham Boys v Sunderland Boys English Schools Shield 28/02/1925.
Nearest Railway Station Altrincham - Approx. 10min walk from the ground   **Bus Route** Arriva 263 & Stagecoach X41

RECORDS

Victory:	14-2 v Sale Holmfield, Cheshire Amateur Cup, 05/12/1903
Defeat:	1-13 v Stretford (H) - 04.11.1893
Goalscorer:	Jack Swindells - 252 (1965-71)
Appearances:	John Davison - 677 (1971-86)
Additional:	Transfer fee paid - £15k to Blackpool for Keith Russell. Received - £50k from Leicester for Kevin Ellison

HONOURS
FA Comps: FA Trophy 1977-78, 85-86
League: Manchester 1904-05, 06-07. Cheshire 1965-66, 66-67. Football Alliance Champions 1979-80, 80-81. N.P.L. Premier Division 1998-99, 2017-18.
County FA: Cheshire Amateur Cup 1903-04. Cheshire Senior Cup Winners 1904-05, 33-34, 66-67, 81-82, 98-99, 04-05, 08-09.

	08-09		09-10		10-11		11-12		12-13		13-14		14-15		15-16		16-17		17-18	
	Conf	15	Conf	14	Conf	22	Conf N	8	Conf N	4	Conf N	3	Conf	17	Nat	22	Nat N	22	NP P	1
	FAC	1Pr	FAC	4Q	FAC	4Q	FAC	2Q	FAC	1Pr	FAC	2Q	FAC	1P	FAC	2P	FAC	1P	FAC	3Q
	FAT	1P	FAT	2P	FAT	2P	FAT	3Q	FAT	1P	FAT	1P	FAT	3P	FAT	2P	FAT	1Pr	FAT	1Pr

2017-18 STATS	**Goals Total** 114	**Games Without Scoring** 8	**Total No. of Scorers** 17	**Total Clean Sheets** 25
Most Consecutive Scoring Games 17	**Best Unbeaten Run** 17		**Most Consecutive Clean Sheets**	4
Best Att: 1,856 v Hednesford Town, NPL Premier Division			Number in brackets denotes consecutive runs.	

ASHTON UNITED

Club Contact Details 0161 339 4158
Hurst Cross, Surrey Street, Ashton-u-Lyne OL6 8DY
ashtonunitedfc@gmail.com

Founded: 1878   **Nickname:** Robins   **Manager:** Jody Banim
Previous Names: Hurst 1878-1947
Previous Leagues: Manchester, Lancashire Combination 1912-33, 48-64, 66-68, Midland 1964-66, Cheshire County 1923-48, 68-82, North West Counties 1982-92
Club Colours (change): Red and white

Ground Capacity: 4,500   **Seats:** 250   **Covered:** 750   **Clubhouse:** Yes   **Shop:** Yes
Previous Grounds: Rose Hill 1878-1912
Record Attendance: 11,000 v Halifax Town - FA Cup 1st Round 1952
Nearest Railway Station Ashton-under-Lyne - 1.4km   **Bus Route** Kings Road - stop 50m away

RECORDS

Victory:	11-3 v Stalybridge Celtic - Manchester Intermediate Cup 1955
Defeat:	1-11 v Wellington Town - Cheshire League 1946-47
Appearances:	Micky Boyle - 462
Additional:	Paid £9,000 to Netherfield for Andy Whittaker 1994
	Received £15,000 from Rotherham United for Karl Marginson 1993

HONOURS
FA Comps: None
League: Manchester League 1911-12. Lancashire Combination 1916-17. North West Counties Division Two 1987-88, Division One 1991-92.
County FA: Manchester Senior Cup 1894-95, 1913-14, 75-76, 77-78. Manchester Premier Cup 1979-80, 82-83, 91092, 2000-01, 01 -02, 02-03. Manchester Challenge Shield 1992-93.

	08-09		09-10		10-11		11-12		12-13		13-14		14-15		15-16		16-17		17-18	
	NP P	9	NP P	12	NP P	14	NP P	12	NP P	10	NP P	5	NP P	3	NP P	3	NP P	11	NP P	2
	FAC	1Q	FAC	2Q	FAC	2Q	FAC	2Q	FAC	2Q	FAC	3Q	FAC	3Q	FAC	3Q	FAC	3Q	FAC	2Q
	FAT	2Q	FAT	1Q	FAT	1Qr	FAT	1Q	FAT	1Q	FAT	1Q	FAT	1Q	FAV	1P	FAT	1Q	FAT	2Pr

2017-18 STATS	**Goals Total** 95	**Games Without Scoring** 5	**Total No. of Scorers** 20	**Total Clean Sheets** 12
Most Consecutive Scoring Games 12	**Best Unbeaten Run** 12		**Most Consecutive Clean Sheets**	2
Best Att: 546 v Altrincham, NPL Premier Division			Number in brackets denotes consecutive runs.	

BLYTH SPARTANS

Club Contact Details 01670 352 373
Croft Park, Blyth, Northumberland NE24 3JE
generalmanager@blythspartans.com

Founded: 1899   **Nickname:** Spartans   **Manager:** Alun Armstrong
Previous Names: None
Previous Leagues: Northumberland 1901-07, Northern All. 1907-13, 46-47, North Eastern 1913-39, Northern Com. 1945-46, Midland 1958-60,
     Northern Counties 1960-62, Northern 1962-94, Northern Premier 1994-2006, 13-17. Conference 2006-13.
Club Colours (change): Green and white

Ground Capacity: 4,435   **Seats:** 563   **Covered:** 1,000   **Clubhouse:** Yes   **Shop:** Yes
Previous Grounds: None
Record Attendance: 10,186 v Hartlepool United - FA Cup 08/12/1956

RECORDS
Victory: 18-0 v Gateshead Town - Northern Alliance 28/12/1907
Defeat: 0-10 v Darlington - North Eastern League 12/12/1914
Appearances: Eddie Alder - 605 (1965-68)
Additional: Received £30,000 from Hull City for Les Mutrie

HONOURS
FA Comps: None
League: North Eastern 1935-36. Northern 1972-73, 74-75, 75-76, 79-80, 80-81, 81-82, 82-83, 83-84, 86-87, 87-88.
     Northern Division 1 1994-95. Northern Premier Premier Division 2005-06, 16-17.
County FA: Northumberland Senior Cup 2014-15, 16-17.

08-09	09-10	10-11	11-12	12-13	13-14	14-15	15-16	16-17	17-18
Conf N 15	Conf N 13	Conf N 9	Conf N 21	NP P 16	NP P 8	NP P 6	NP P 2	NP P 1	Nat N 10
FAC 3P	FAC 4Qr	FAC 2Q	FAC 1P	FAC 2Qr	FAC 1Q	FAC 3P	FAC 1Q	FAC 2Q	FAC 2Q
FAT 3Q	FAT 2P	FAT QF	FAT 3Q	FAT 3Q	FAT 2Q	FAT 2Qr	FAT 3Q	FAT 3Qr	FAT 2P

2017-18 STATS	**Goals Total** 81	**Games Without Scoring** 12 (2)	**Total No. of Scorers** 15	**Total Clean Sheets** 10
Most Consecutive Scoring Games 14	**Best Unbeaten Run** 4		**Most Consecutive Clean Sheets** 3	
Best Att: 1,554 v Darlington, National North				Number in brackets denotes consecutive runs.

BOSTON UNITED

Club Contact Details 01205 364 406
Jakemans Stadium, York Street, Boston PE21 6JN
admin@bufc.co.uk

Founded: 1933   **Nickname:** The Pilgrims   **Manager:** Adam Murray
Previous Names: Reformed as Boston United when Boston Town folded in 1933
Previous Leagues: Midland 1933-58, 62-64, Southern 1958-62, 98-2000, United Counties 1965-66, West Midlands 1966-68,
     Northern Premier 1968-79, 93-98, 2008-10, Alliance/Conference 1979-93, 2000-02, 07-08, Football League 2002-07.
Club Colours (change): Amber and black

Ground Capacity: 6,778   **Seats:** 5,711   **Covered:** 6,645   **Clubhouse:** Yes   **Shop:** Yes
Previous Grounds: None
Record Attendance: 11,000 v Derby County, FA Cup Third Round Proper Replay, 09/01/1974
Nearest Railway Station Boston - less than 1 mile from the ground

RECORDS
Victory: 12-0 v Spilsby Town - Grace Swan Cup 1992-93
Defeat: 2-9 v AFC Fylde - (A) National North, 19/11/2017
Goalscorer: Chris Cook - 181
Appearances: Billy Howells - 500+
Additional: Paid £30,000 to Scarborough for Paul Ellender, 08/2001
HONOURS
              Received £50,000 from Bolton Wanderers for David Norris 2000
FA Comps: None
League: Central Alliance League 1961-62. United Counties League 1965-66. West Midlands League 1966-67, 67-68.
     Northern Premier League 1972-73, 73-74, 76-77, 77-78. Southern League 1999-2000. Conference 2001-02.
County FA: Lincolnshire Senior Cup 1934-35, 36-37, 37-38, 45-46, 49-50, 54-55, 55-56, 56-57, 59-60, 76-77, 78-79, 85-86, 87-88, 88
     -89, 05-06. East Anglian Cup 1960-61.

08-09	09-10	10-11	11-12	12-13	13-14	14-15	15-16	16-17	17-18
NP P 16	NP P 3	Conf N 3	Conf N 11	Conf N 16	Conf N 6	Conf N 3	Nat N 5	Nat N 15	Nat N 9
FAC 4Q	FAC 2Q	FAC 2Q	FAC 2Qr	FAC 4Q	FAC 3Q	FAC 3Q	FAC 2Q	FAC 3Q	FAC 4Qr
FAT 1P	FAT 2Qr	FAT 2P	FAT 2P	FAT 2P	FAT 1Pr	FAT 2P	FAT 1Pr	FAT 3Q	FAT 3Qr

2017-18 STATS	**Goals Total** 80	**Games Without Scoring** 9	**Total No. of Scorers** 20	**Total Clean Sheets** 10
Most Consecutive Scoring Games 11	**Best Unbeaten Run** 9		**Most Consecutive Clean Sheets** 1	
Best Att: 1,491 v Gainsborough Trinity, National North				Number in brackets denotes consecutive runs.

BRACKLEY TOWN

Club Contact Details 01280 704 077
St James Park, Churchill Way, Brackley NN13 7EJ
janenebutters@brackleytownnfc.co.uk

Founded: 1890   **Nickname:** Saints   **Manager:** Kevin Wilkin - Sept 2015
Previous Names: N/A
Previous Leagues: Oxfordshire Senior. North Bucks & District. Banbury & District. Hellenic 1977-83, 94-97, 99-2004. United Counties 1983-84. Southern 1997-99.
Club Colours (change): Red and white stripes

Ground Capacity: 3,500   **Seats:** 300   **Covered:** 1,500   **Clubhouse:** Yes   **Shop:** Yes
Previous Grounds: Manor Road 1890-1968. Buckingham Road 1968-74.
Record Attendance: 2,604 v FC Halifax Town, Conference North Play-off final, 12/05/13.
Nearest Railway Station Banbury - Approx. 10 miles from the ground.   **Bus Route** Stagecoach No. 500 from Banbury.

RECORDS
Goalscorer: Paul Warrington - 320
Appearances: Terry Muckelberg - 350
Additional: Received £2,000 from Oxford City for Phil Mason 1998

HONOURS
FA Comps: FA Trophy 2017-18.
League: United Counties Division One 1983-84. Hellenic Premier Division 1996-97, 2003-04.
Southern Division One Midlands 2006-07, Premier Division 2011-12.
County FA: Northamptonshire Senior Cup 2010-11, 11-12, 14-15.

	08-09	09-10	10-11	11-12	12-13	13-14	14-15	15-16	16-17	17-18
	SthP 11	SthP 5	SthP 9	SthP 1	Conf N 3	Conf N 7	Conf N 18	Nat N 19	Nat N 7	Nat N 3
FAC	1P	2Q	2Q	1Q	3Q	2P	3Q	1Pr	2P	4Qr
FAT	1P	2Qr	3Q	3Q	1P	3Qr	3Q	3Q	QF	F

2017-18 STATS   **Goals Total** 102   **Games Without Scoring** 9   **Total No. of Scorers**   **Total Clean Sheets** 27
Most Consecutive Scoring Games 12   **Best Unbeaten Run** 14   **Most Consecutive Clean Sheets** 5
Best Att: 1,250 v Wealdstone, FA Trophy Semi Final 1st Leg   Number in brackets denotes consecutive runs.

BRADFORD PARK AVENUE

Club Contact Details 07863 180 787
Horsfall Stadium, Cemetery Road, Bradford, West Yorkshire BD6 2NG
colinbarker7@outlook.com

Founded: 1863   **Nickname:** Avenue   **Manager:** Mark Bower - Sept 2016
Previous Names: Bradford FC. 1863-1907. Reformed as a Sunday club in 1974, then as a Saturday club in 1988.
Previous Leagues: West York. 1895-98. Yorkshire 1898-99. Southern 1907-08. Football Lge 1908-70. NPL 1970-74, 95-04, 05-12. Bradford Am Sun. 1974-76. Bradford Sun.All. 1976-92. W. Riding Co. Am. 1988-89. Central Mids 1989-90. N.W. Co. 1990-95. Conf 2004-05
Club Colours (change): Green and white

Ground Capacity: 5,000   **Seats:** 1,800   **Covered:** 2,000   **Clubhouse:** Yes   **Shop:** Yes
Previous Grounds: Park Ave 1907-73, 87-88, Valley Parade 73-74, Bingley Rd, Hope Ave, Avenue Rd, Bramley, M'nt Pleasant
Record Attendance: 2,100 v Bristol City - FA Cup 1st Round 2003
Nearest Railway Station Bradford Foster Square or Bradford Interchange   **Bus Route** From Interchange - 681 (682 Eve & Sun)

RECORDS
Victory: 11-0 v Derby Dale - FA Cup 1908
Defeat: 0-7 v Barnsley - 1911
Goalscorer: Len Shackleton - 171 (1940-46)
Appearances: Tommy Farr - 542 (1934-50)
Additional: Paid £24,500 to Derby County for Leon Leuty 1950
Received £34,000 from Derby County for Kevin Hector 1966

HONOURS
FA Comps: N/A
League: West Yorkshire 1895-96 (Shared). Football League Division Three North 1927-28. North West Counties Div.One 1994-95 Northern Premier Division One 2000-01, Division One North 2007-08, Premier Division Play-offs 2011-12.
County FA: West Riding Senior Cup x9. West Riding County Cup 1990-91, 2014-15, 15-16.

	08-09	09-10	10-11	11-12	12-13	13-14	14-15	15-16	16-17	17-18
	NP P 7	NP P 2	NP P 3	NP P 4	Conf N 7	Conf N 10	Conf N 13	Nat N 14	Nat N 16	Nat N 7
FAC	2Q	3Qr	1Q	1P	1P	4Qr	2Qr	3Q	2Q	3Qr
FAT	1Q	1Q	1Q	1Qr	3Q	2P	1P	2Pr	3Q	3Qr

2017-18 STATS   **Goals Total** 71   **Games Without Scoring** 12 (2)   **Total No. of Scorers** 17   **Total Clean Sheets** 14
Most Consecutive Scoring Games 16   **Best Unbeaten Run** 8   **Most Consecutive Clean Sheets** 3
Best Att: 1,123 v York City, National North   Number in brackets denotes consecutive runs.

CHESTER

Club Contact Details 01244 371 376
Swansway Chester Stadium, Bumpers Lane, Chester CH1 4LT
info@chesterfc.com

Founded: 1885   **Nickname:** Blues   **Manager:** Anthony Johnson & Bernard Morley 16/05/18
Previous Names: Chester > 1983, Chester City 1983-2010
Previous Leagues: Cheshire 1919-31, Football League 1931-2000, 2004-09, Conference 2000-04, 09-10 (Did not finish the season). Northern Premier League 2010-12.
Club Colours (change): Blue & white stripes

Ground Capacity: 6,012   **Seats:** 4,170   **Covered:** Yes   **Clubhouse:** Yes   **Shop:** Yes
Previous Grounds: Faulkner Street 1885-98, The Old Showground 98-99, Whipcord Lane 1901-06, Sealand Road 06-90, Macclesfield FC 90-92
Record Attendance: 20,378 v Chelsea - FA Cup 3rd Round replay 16/01/1952
Nearest Railway Station Chester - 2.5 miles away.   **Bus Route** No.10A from City Centre Bus Exchange.

RECORDS
Victory: 12-0 v York City - 01/02/1936
Goalscorer: Stuart Rimmer - 135
Appearances: Ray Gill - 406 (1951-62) New Chester Craig Mahon, still playing.
Additional: Paid £100,000 to Rotherham for Gregg Blundell.
                 Received £300,000 from Liverpool for Ian Rush

HONOURS
FA Comps: Welsh Cup 1907-08, 32-33, 46-47.
League: Conference 2003-04, Conference North 2012-13.
           Northern Premier League Division One North 2010-11, Premier Division 2011-12.
County FA: Cheshire Senior Cup 1894-95, 96-97, 1903-04, 07-08, 08-09, 30-31, 31-32, 2012-13.
           Herefordshire Senior Cup 1991-92 (shared).

08-09		09-10		10-11		11-12		12-13		13-14		14-15		15-16		16-17		17-18	
FL 2	23	Conf	dnf	NP1N	1	NP P	1	Conf N	1	Conf	21	Conf	12	Nat	17	Nat	19	Nat	23
FAC	1P	FAC	4Qr					FAC	3Qr	FAC	4Q	FAC	2Pr	FAC	4Q	FAC	4Q	FAC	4Q
FLC	1P	FAT	1P			FAT	2P	FAT	3Qr	FAT	1P	FAT	1Pr	FAT	3P	FAT	2P	FAT	2P

2017-18 STATS	**Goals Total**	44	**Games Without Scoring**	22 (3)	**Total No. of Scorers**	15	**Total Clean Sheets**	6
Most Consecutive Scoring Games	4	**Best Unbeaten Run**	3		**Most Consecutive Clean Sheets**			1
Best Att:	4,079 v Wrexham, National League					Number in brackets denotes consecutive runs.		

CHORLEY

Club Contact Details 01257 230 007
Victory Park Stadium, Duke Street, Chorley, Lancashire PR7 3DU
webmaster@chorleyfc.com

Founded: 1875   **Nickname:** Magpies   **Manager:** Jamie Vermiglio - 23/06/2018
Previous Names: Founded as a Rugby Union side in 1875 then switched to football in 1883.
Previous Leagues: Lancashire Junior 1889-90. Lancashire Alliance 1890-94. Lancashire 1894-1903. Lancashire Combination 1903-68, 69-70. Northern Premier (founder member) 1968-69, 70-72, 82-88, 90-2014. Cheshire County 1972-82. Conference 1988-90.
Club Colours (change): Black and white stripes

Ground Capacity: 3,550   **Seats:** 900   **Covered:** 2,800   **Clubhouse:** Yes   **Shop:** Yes
Previous Grounds: Dole Lane 1883-1901, Rangletts Park 1901-05, St George's Park 1905-20.
Record Attendance: 9,679 v Darwen, FA Cup Fourth Qualifying Round, 15/11/1932.
Nearest Railway Station Chorley - half a mile from the ground.   **Bus Route** Bus station half a mile from the ground.

RECORDS
Victory: 14-1 v Morecambe, April 1946.
Goalscorer: Peter Watson - 372 (1958-66).
Additional: Received £30,000 from Newcastle United for David Eatock 1996.

HONOURS
FA Comps: None
League: Lancs All. 1892-93. Lancashire 1896-97, 98-99. Lancs Comb. 1919-20, 22-23, 27-28, 28-29, 32-33, 33-34, 39-40, 45-46, 59
           -60, 60-61, 63-64. Cheshire County 1975-76, 76-77, 81-82. NPL 1987-88, 2013-14, Div. One North P-off 2010-11.
County FA: Lancashire FA Trophy (Record 18 times) 1893-94, 1908-09, 23-24, 39-40, 45-46, 57-58, 58-59, 60-61, 63-64, 64-65, 75
           -76, 79-80, 81-82, 82-83, 2011-12, 14-15, 15-16, 17-18.

08-09		09-10		10-11		11-12		12-13		13-14		14-15		15-16		16-17		17-18	
NP1N	14	NP1N	16	NP1N	3	NP P	3	NP P	8	NP P	1	Conf N	4	Nat N	8	Nat N	6	Nat N	6
FAC	P	FAC	3Q	FAC	P	FAC	1Qr	FAC	2Q	FAC	2Q	FAC	4Qr	FAC	4Qr	FAC	3Q	FAC	1P
FAT	Pr	FAT	1Q	FAT	3Q	FAT	1Q	FAT	1Q	FAT	3P	FAT	2Pr	FAT	3Qr	FAT	1P	FAT	1P

2017-18 STATS	**Goals Total**	66	**Games Without Scoring**	14 (3)	**Total No. of Scorers**	12	**Total Clean Sheets**	19
Most Consecutive Scoring Games	8	**Best Unbeaten Run**	7		**Most Consecutive Clean Sheets**			3
Best Att:	3,526 v Fleetwood Town, FA Cup 1P					Number in brackets denotes consecutive runs.		

CURZON ASHTON

Club Contact Details 0161 330 6033
Tameside Stadium, Richmond Street, Ashton-u-Lyme OL7 9HG
rob@curzon-ashton.co.uk

Founded: 1963   **Nickname:** The Nash   **Manager:** John Flanagan
Previous Names: Club formed when Curzon Road Methodists and Ashton Amateurs merged, and were initially known as Curzon Amateurs.
Previous Leagues: Manchester Amateur. Manchester > 1978. Cheshire (FM of Div.2) 1978-82. North West Counties (FM) 1983-87, 98-2007.
Northern Premier (FM) 1987-97, 2007-15. Northern Counties East 1997-98.
Club Colours (change): Royal blue and white

Ground Capacity: 4,000   **Seats:** 527   **Covered:** 1,100   **Clubhouse:** Yes   **Shop:** Yes
Previous Grounds: National Park 1963-2004. Stalybridge Celtic FC 2004-05.
Record Attendance: 3,210 v FC United of Manchester, North West Counties Challenge Cup Final, 03/05/07.
Nearest Railway Station Ashton-under-Lyne - Approx. one mile from ground.   **Bus Route** Also 5mins from Ashton West Metrolink.

RECORDS
Victory:	10-1 v Wakefield, 2012-13
Defeat:	0-8 v Bamber Bridge
Goalscorer:	Rod Lawton - 376
Appearances:	Alan Sykes

HONOURS
FA Comps: None
League: Manchester Amateur Division One 1963-64, 65-66. Manchester Premier Division 1977-78.
Northern Premier Division One North 2013-14, Premier Division Play-off 2014-15.
County FA: Manchester Premier Cup 1981-82, 83-84, 85-86, 87-87, 89-90.

	08-09	09-10	10-11	11-12	12-13	13-14	14-15	15-16	16-17	17-18
	NP1N 4	NP1N 3	NP1N 4	NP1N 2	NP1N 7	NP1N 1	NP P 4	Nat N 11	Nat N 14	Nat N 18
FAC	2P	Pr	1Qr	Pr	2Q	3Q	3Q	2Q	1Pr	2Q
FAT	Pr	P	1P	1P	3Q	1P	2Q	2P	2P	3Q

2017-18 STATS   **Goals Total** 53   **Games Without Scoring** 11 (2)   **Total No. of Scorers** 19   **Total Clean Sheets** 10
Most Consecutive Scoring Games 8   **Best Unbeaten Run** 4   **Most Consecutive Clean Sheets** 2
Best Att: 1,473 v Stockport County, National North   *Number in brackets denotes consecutive runs.*

DARLINGTON 1883

Club Contact Details 01325 363 777
Blackwell Meadows, Grange Road, Darlington DL1 5NR
rob.jones@darlingtonfc.org

Founded: 1883   **Nickname:** The Quakers   **Manager:** Tommy Wright
Previous Names: Darlington FC 1883-2012
Previous Leagues: Northern League 1883-1908, 2012-13, North Eastern 1908-21, Football League 1921-89, 91-2010,
Conference 1989-90, 10-12.
Club Colours (change): Black and white

Ground Capacity: 3000   **Seats:** 280   **Covered:** Yes   **Clubhouse:** Yes   **Shop:**
Previous Grounds: Feethams 1883-2003. Darlington Arena 2003-12. Bishop Auckland 2012-16.
Record Attendance: 21,023 v Bolton Wanderers - League Cup 3rd Round 14/11/1960
Nearest Railway Station Darlington - 1.5 miles away

RECORDS
Victory:	13-1 v Scarborough, FA Cup, 24/10/1891
Defeat:	0-10 v Doncaster Rovers - Division 4 25/01/1964
Goalscorer:	Alan Walsh - 100, Jerry Best - 80
Appearances:	Ron Greener - 490, John Peverell - 465, Brian Henderson - 463
Additional:	Paid £95,000 to Motherwell for Nick Cusack January 1992. Received £400,000 from Dundee United for Jason Devos October 1998

HONOURS
FA Comps: FA Trophy 2010-11.
League: Northern 1895-96, 99-1900, 2012-13. North Eastern 1912-13, 20-21. Football League Division Three North 1924-25,
Division Four 1990-91. Conference 1989-90. NPL Division One North Play-off 2014-15, Premier Division 2015-16.
County FA: Durham Challenge Cup 1884-85, 90-91, 92-93, 96-97, 1919-20, 99-2000.

	08-09	09-10	10-11	11-12	12-13	13-14	14-15	15-16	16-17	17-18
	FL 2 12	FL 2 24	Conf 7	Conf 22	NL 1 1	NP1N 2	NP1N 2	NP P 1	Nat N 5	Nat N 12
FAC	1Pr	1P	2P	4Qr			1Qr	1Q	2Q	2Q
FAT			F	1P		1Qr	2Q	2Q	3Qr	3Q

2017-18 STATS   **Goals Total** 60   **Games Without Scoring** 13 (2)   **Total No. of Scorers** 16   **Total Clean Sheets** 11
Most Consecutive Scoring Games 7   **Best Unbeaten Run** 5   **Most Consecutive Clean Sheets** 4
Best Att: 2,405 v York City, National North   *Number in brackets denotes consecutive runs.*

FC UNITED OF MANCHESTER

Club Contact Details 0161 769 2005
Broadhurst Park, 310 Lightbowne Road, Moston, Manchester, M40 0FJ
office@fc-utd.co.uk

Founded: 2005   **Nickname:** F.C.   **Manager:** Tom Greaves - 22/10/2017
Previous Names: N/A
Previous Leagues: North West Counties 2005-07. Northern Premier 2007-15.

Club Colours (change): Red/white/black

Ground Capacity: 4,400   **Seats:** 696   **Covered:** Yes   **Clubhouse:** Yes   **Shop:** Yes
Previous Grounds: Gigg Lane(Bury FC) 2005-14. Bower Fold (Stalybridge Celtic FC) Aug-Dec'14. Tameside Stadium (Cuzon Ashton).
Record Attendance: 6,731 v Brighton & Hove Albion, FA Cup 2nd Round 08/12/2010 (Gigg Lane)
Nearest Railway Station Moston - 11min walk from the ground.   **Bus Route** Matchday Special and Shuttle Bus

RECORDS
Victory: 10-2 v Castleton Gabriels 10/12/2005. 8-0 v Squires Gate 14/10/06, Glossop N.E. 28/10/06 & Nelson 05/09/10
Defeat: 0-5 v Harrogate Town, 20 February 2016
Goalscorer: Rory Patterson - 99 (2005-08)
Appearances: Jerome Wright - 400
Additional: Simon Carden scored 5 goals against Castleton Gabriels 10/12/2005.
Longest unbeaten run (League): 22 games 03/12/2006 - 18/08/2007.
HONOURS
FA Comps: None
League: North West Counties League Division Two 2005-06, Division One 2006-07.
Northern Premier League Division One North Play-off 2007-08, Premier Division 2014-15.
County FA: Manchester Premier Cup 2016-17, 17-18.

	08-09	09-10	10-11	11-12	12-13	13-14	14-15	15-16	16-17	17-18
	NP P 6	NP P 13	NP P 4	NP P 6	NP P 3	NP P 2	NP P 1	Nat N 13	Nat N 13	Nat N 16
FAC	1Qr	4Q	2Pr	2Q	4Q	1Q	2Q	1P	3Qr	4Q
FAT	3Q	3Q	3Q	1P	2Q	1Qr	QF	3Q	3Q	3Q

2017-18 STATS				
Goals Total	70	Games Without Scoring 15 (5)	Total No. of Scorers 17	Total Clean Sheets 9
Most Consecutive Scoring Games	7	Best Unbeaten Run 6	Most Consecutive Clean Sheets	1
Best Att:	3,084 v Stockport County, National North			Number in brackets denotes consecutive runs.

GUISELEY

Club Contact Details 01943 873 223 (Office) 872 872 (Club)
Nethermoor Park, Otley Road, Guiseley, Leeds LS20 8BT
admin@guiseleyafc.co.uk

Founded: 1909   **Nickname:** The Lions   **Manager:** Marcus Bignot & Russ O'Neill - 16/05/18
Previous Names: None
Previous Leagues: Wharfedale, Leeds, West Riding Counties, West Yorkshire, Yorkshire 1968-82,
Northern Counties East 1982-91, Northern Premier 1991-2010
Club Colours (change): White and navy

Ground Capacity: 4,200   **Seats:** 500   **Covered:** 1,040   **Clubhouse:** Yes   **Shop:** Yes
Previous Grounds: None
Record Attendance: 2,486 v Bridlington Town - FA Vase Semi-final 1st Leg 1989-90
Nearest Railway Station Nethermoor is about 5 min walk away.   **Bus Route** There are two bus stops directly outside.

RECORDS
Misc: Highest points total gained - 93 - NPL 1 (1st) 1993-94 and NPL P (3rd) 1994-95.

HONOURS
FA Comps: FA Vase 1990-91.
League: Wharfedale 1912-13. Yorkshire Division Two 1975-76. Northern Counties East 1990-91.
NPL Division One 1993-94, Premier Division 2009-10. Conference North Play-off 2014-15.
County FA: West Riding County Cup 1978-79, 79-80, 80-81, 93-94, 95-96, 2004-05, 10-11, 11-12.

	08-09	09-10	10-11	11-12	12-13	13-14	14-15	15-16	16-17	17-18
	NP P 3	NP P 1	Conf N 5	Conf N 2	Conf N 2	Conf N 5	Conf N 5	Nat 20	Nat 20	Nat 24
FAC	3Qr	3Qr	1P	3Q	1Pr	2Q	4Q	4Qr	4Qr	2P
FAT	1Q	3P	QF	3P	2P	3P	1P	3Pr	2P	1P

2017-18 STATS				
Goals Total	52	Games Without Scoring 20 (3)	Total No. of Scorers 19	Total Clean Sheets 10
Most Consecutive Scoring Games	4	Best Unbeaten Run 6	Most Consecutive Clean Sheets	2
Best Att:	1,723 v Hartlepool United, National League			Number in brackets denotes consecutive runs.

HEREFORD

Club Contact Details 01432 268 257
Edgar Street, Hereford HR4 9JU
info@herefordfc.co.uk

Founded: 2014   **Nickname:** The Bulls   **Manager:** Pete Beadle
Previous Names: Formed in 2014 after the demise of Hereford United who folded during the 2014-15 season.
Previous Leagues: Midland 2015-16. Southern 2016-18.

Club Colours (change): White and black

Ground Capacity: 8,843   **Seats:** 2,761   **Covered:** 6,082   **Clubhouse:** Yes   **Shop:** Yes
Previous Grounds: None
Record Attendance: 4,712 v AFC Telford United, FA Cup 1P, 04/11/2017.
Nearest Railway Station Hereford - 0.6km

RECORDS
Victory: 8-0 v Heanor Town - Midland League 23/04/16 & v Godalming Town (H), FAC 1Q, 02/09/2017.
Defeat: 4-5 v Coleshill Town - Midland League 2015-16.
Goalscorer: John Mills

HONOURS
FA Comps: None
League: Midland League 2015-16. Southern Division One South & West 2016-17, Premier Division 17-18.

County FA: Herefordshire County Cup 2015-16, 17-18.

08-09	09-10	10-11	11-12	12-13	13-14	14-15	15-16		16-17		17-18	
							MidL	1	Sthsw	1	SthP	1
									FAC	3Q	FAC	2P
							FAV	F	FAT	P	FAT	1P

2017-18 STATS	**Goals Total**	139	**Games Without Scoring**	5	**Total No. of Scorers**	22	**Total Clean Sheets**	29
Most Consecutive Scoring Games	13	**Best Unbeaten Run**	19			**Most Consecutive Clean Sheets**		6
Best Att:	4,712 v AFC Telford United, FA Cup 1P					Number in brackets denotes consecutive runs.		

KIDDERMINSTER HARRIERS

Club Contact Details 01562 823 931
Aggborough Stadium, Hoo Road, Kidderminster DY10 1NB
info@harriers.co.uk

Founded: 1886   **Nickname:** Harriers   **Manager:** Neil MacFarlane
Previous Names: Kidderminster Harriers and Football Club 1886-90. Kidderminster FC 1890-1891.
Previous Leagues: Birmingham & District (FM) 1889-90, 91-1939, 47-48, 60-62. Midland 1890-91. Southern 1939-45, 48-60, 72-83.
       Birmingham Combination 1945-47. West Midlands (Regional) 1962-72. Conference 1983-2000. Football League 2000-05.
Club Colours (change): Red and white

Ground Capacity: 6,444   **Seats:** 3,140   **Covered:** 3,062   **Clubhouse:** Yes   **Shop:** Yes
Previous Grounds: Chester Road 1886-87.
Record Attendance: 9,155 v Hereford United, FA Cup First Round Proper, 27/11/48
Nearest Railway Station Kidderminster - half a mile from the ground.

RECORDS
Victory: 25-0 v Hereford (H), Birmingham Senior Cup First Round, 12/10/1889
Defeat: 0-13 v Darwen (A), FA Cup First Round Proper, 24/01/1891
Goalscorer: Peter Wassell - 448 (1963-74)
Appearances: Brendan Wassell - 686 (1962-74)
Additional: Paid £80,000 to Nuneaton Borough for Andy Ducros July 2000
                    Recieved £380,000 from W.B.A. for Lee Hughes July 1997
HONOURS
FA Comps: FA Trophy 1986-87.
League: Birmingham & District 1937-38. West Midlands (Regional) 1964-65, 68-69, 69-70, 70-71.
       Conference 1993-94, 1999-2000.
County FA: Worcestershire Senior Cup (27 times) Firstly in 1895-96 and most recently 2016-17. Birmingham Senior Cup (7x) Firstly in 1933-34 and
       most recently in 1966-67. Staffordshire Senior Cup (4x) Firstly in 1980-81 and most recently in 1984-85.

08-09		09-10		10-11		11-12		12-13		13-14		14-15		15-16		16-17		17-18	
Conf	6	Conf	13	Conf	6	Conf	6	Conf	2	Conf	7	Conf	16	Nat	23	Nat N	2	Nat N	4
FAC	3P	FAC	4Qr	FAC	4Q	FAC	4Qr	FAC	1P	FAC	4P	FAC	4Q	FAC	4Q	FAC	1P	FAC	1P
FAT	3Pr	FAT	SF	FAT	1P	FAT	3P	FAT	2P	FAT	1P	FAT	2P	FAT	1P	FAT	3Q	FAT	2Pr

2017-18 STATS	**Goals Total**	93	**Games Without Scoring**	9	**Total No. of Scorers**	16	**Total Clean Sheets**	15
Most Consecutive Scoring Games	21	**Best Unbeaten Run**	14			**Most Consecutive Clean Sheets**		3
Best Att:	2,524 v Salford City, National North					Number in brackets denotes consecutive runs.		

LEAMINGTON

Club Contact Details 01926 430 406
Phillips 66 Community Stadium, Harbury Lane, Whitmarsh, Leamington CV33 9QB
info@leamingtonfc.co.uk

Founded: 1892   **Nickname:** The Brakes   **Manager:** Paul Holleran
Previous Names: Leamington Town 1892-1937, Lockheed Borg & Beck 1944-46 , Lockheed Leamington 1946-73, AP Leamington 1973-88
Previous Leagues: Birmingham Combination, Birmingham & District, West Midlands Regional, Midland Counties, Southern, Midland Combination, Midland Alliance 2005-07. Southern 2007-13, 15-17. Football Conference 2013-15.
Club Colours (change): Gold and black

Ground Capacity: 5,000   **Seats:** 700   **Covered:** 720   **Clubhouse:** Yes   **Shop:** Yes
Previous Grounds: Old Windmill Ground
Record Attendance: 1,380 v Retford United - 17/02/2007
Nearest Railway Station Leamington Spa - 3 miles away   **Bus Route** Nos. 65 & 66

RECORDS
Goalscorer: Josh Blake - 187
Appearances: Josh Blake - 406

HONOURS
FA Comps: None
League: Birmingham & Dist 1961-62. West Mids Regional 1962-63. Midland Co 1964-65. Southern League 1982-83, 2012-13, Division One Midlands 2008-09. Midland Comb Div Two 2000-01, Premier Div 2004-05. Midland All 2006-07. Southern Prem Play-offs 2016-17.
County FA: Birmingham Senior Cup 2016-17.

	08-09		09-10		10-11		11-12		12-13		13-14		14-15		15-16		16-17		17-18	
	SthM	1	SthP	10	SthP	5	SthP	7	SthP	1	Conf N	13	Conf N	21	SthP	3	SthP	2	Nat N	19
	FAC	1Q	FAC	1Q	FAC	1Qr	FAC	2Q	FAC	2Q	FAC	2Qr	FAC	3Qr	FAC	1Qr	FAC	1Q	FAC	3Qr
	FAT	1Q	FAT	1Q	FAT	3Q	FAT	1Q	FAT	1Qr	FAT	2P	FAT	3Q	FAT	1Pr	FAT	1Q	FAT	1P

2017-18 STATS	**Goals Total**	56	**Games Without Scoring**	17 (2)	**Total No. of Scorers**	16	**Total Clean Sheets**	13
Most Consecutive Scoring Games	8	**Best Unbeaten Run**	5			**Most Consecutive Clean Sheets**		1
Best Att:	1,275 v Salford City, National North						Number in brackets denotes consecutive runs.	

NUNEATON BOROUGH

Club Contact Details 024 7638 5738
Liberty Way, Nuneaton CV11 6RR

Founded: 1889   **Nickname:** The Boro / The Town   **Manager:** Nicky Eaden
Previous Names: Nuneaton St. Nicholas 1889-1894. Nuneaton Town 1894-37. Nuneaton Borough 1937-2008. Nuneaton Town 2008-18.
Previous Leagues: Local 1894-1906. Birmingham Junior/Combination 1906-15, 26-33, 38-52. Birmingham 1919-24, 33-37. Central Am. 1937-38. Birmingham 1952-58. Southern 1924-25, 58-79 81-82, 87-99, 2003-04, 08-10. Conference 1979-81, 82-87, 99-03, 04-08.
Club Colours (change): Blue and white

Ground Capacity: 4,500   **Seats:** 514   **Covered:** Yes   **Clubhouse:** Yes   **Shop:** Yes
Previous Grounds: Higham Lane/Rose Inn/Arbury Rd/Edward St. 1889-1903. Queens Rd 03-08. Newdegate Arms 08-15. Manor Pk 19-07.
Record Attendance: 22,114 v Rotherham Utd, FAC 3P 28/01/1967 (Manor Park). 3,480 v Luton Town, Conf. Prem., 22/02/14
Nearest Railway Station Nuneaton - approx. 35min walk from the ground.

RECORDS
Victory: 11-1 - 1945-46 and 1955-56
Defeat: 1-8 - 1955-56 and 1968-69
Goalscorer: Paul Culpin - 201 (55 during season 1992-93)
Appearances: Alan Jones - 545 (1962-74)
Additional: Paid £35,000 to Forest green Rovers for Marc McGregor 2000
HONOURS   Received undisclosed from Peterborough United for Alex Penny July 2017
FA Comps: None
League: Coventry & Dist. 1902-03. Coventry & North Warwicks' 1904-05. Birmingham Junior 1906-07, Combination 1914-15, 28-29, 30-31. Birmingham League North 1954-55, Div.One 55-56. Southern League Midland Div. 1981-82, 92-93, 95-96, Premier Division 1988-99.
County FA: Birmingham Senior Cup 1930-31, 48-49, 54-55, 59-60, 77-78, 79-80, 92-93, 2001-02, 09-10.

	08-09		09-10		10-11		11-12		12-13		13-14		14-15		15-16		16-17		17-18	
	SthE	2	SthP	2	Conf N	6	Conf N	5	Conf	13	Conf	13	Conf	24	Nat N	6	Nat N	12	Nat N	13
	FAC	2Qr	FAC	1P	FAC	1P	FAC	4Q	FAC	1Pr	FAC	4Q	FAC	4Qr	FAC	3Q	FAC	2Q	FAC	3Q
	FAT	Pr	FAT	1P	FAT	3Q	FAT	1P	FAT	1P	FAT	2Pr	FAT	1P	FAT	1P	FAT	3P	FAT	1P

2017-18 STATS	**Goals Total**	59	**Games Without Scoring**	14 (2)	**Total No. of Scorers**	15	**Total Clean Sheets**	12
Most Consecutive Scoring Games	7	**Best Unbeaten Run**	9			**Most Consecutive Clean Sheets**		5
Best Att:	937 v Salford City, National North						Number in brackets denotes consecutive runs.	

SOUTHPORT

Club Contact Details 01704 533 422
Merseyrail Community Stadium, Haig Avenue, Southport, Merseyside PR8 6JZ
secretary@southportfc.net

Founded: 1881   **Nickname:** The Sandgrounders   **Manager:** Liam Watson
Previous Names: Southport Central 1888-1918, Southport Vulcan 1918-21.
Previous Leagues: Preston & District, Lancashire 1889-1903, Lancashire Combination 1903-11, Central 1911-21, Football League 1921-78, Northern Premier 1978-93, 2003-04, Conference 1993-2003.
Club Colours (change): All white

Ground Capacity: 6,008   **Seats:** 1,660   **Covered:** 2,760   **Clubhouse:** Yes   **Shop:** Yes
Previous Grounds: Sussex Road Sports Ground, Scarisbrick New Road 1886-1905, Ash Lane (later named Haig Avenue)
Record Attendance: 20,010 v Newcastle United - FA Cup 1932
Nearest Railway Station Meols Cop - 1mile away. Southport - 1.5miles away.   **Bus Route** 44 Arriva from the Southport Station.

RECORDS
Victory: 8-1 v Nelson - 01/01/31
Defeat: 0-11 v Oldham Athletic - 26/12/62
Goalscorer: Alan Spence - 98
Appearances: Arthur Peat - 401 (1962-72)
Additional: Paid £20,000 to Macclesfield Town for Martin McDonald

HONOURS
FA Comps: N/A
League: Football League Division Four 1972-73. Northern Premier League Premier Division 1992-93. Conference North 2004-05, 2009-10.
County FA: Lancashire Senior Cup 1904-05. Lancashire Junior Cup 1919-20, 92-93, 96-97, 97-98, 2001-01, 05-06, 07-08, 09-10. Liverpool Senior Cup 1930-31, 31-32, 43-44, 62-63, 74-75, 90-91, 92-93, 98-99, 2011-12.

08-09		09-10		10-11		11-12		12-13		13-14		14-15		15-16		16-17		17-18	
Conf N	5	Conf N	1	Conf	21	Conf	7	Conf	20	Conf	18	Conf	19	Nat	16	Nat	23	Nat N	15
FAC	3Q	FAC	1P	FAC	1P	FAC	1P	FAC	4Q	FAC	1P	FAC	3P	FAC	4Q	FAC	1Pr	FAC	2Q
FAT	QFr	FAT	1Pr	FAT	1Pr	FAT	1P	FAT	QF	FAT	1P	FAT	1Pr	FAT	2P	FAT	2P	FAT	3Qr

2017-18 STATS	**Goals Total** 62	**Games Without Scoring** 16 (5)	**Total No. of Scorers** 21	**Total Clean Sheets** 10
Most Consecutive Scoring Games 8	**Best Unbeaten Run** 6		**Most Consecutive Clean Sheets**	2

Best Att: 1,652 v Stockport County, National North   Number in brackets denotes consecutive runs.

SPENNYMOOR TOWN

Club Contact Details 01388 827 248
The Brewery Field, Durham Road, Spennymoor DL16 6JN
feedback@spennymoorunited.fsnet.co.uk

Founded: 2005   **Nickname:** The Moors   **Manager:** Jason Ainsley - 2007
Previous Names: Amalgamation of Evenwood Town & Spennymoor United in 2005-06.
Previous Leagues: Northern League 2005-14. Northern Premier 2014-17.

Club Colours (change): Black and white

Ground Capacity: 3,000   **Seats:** 224   **Covered:** 800   **Clubhouse:** Yes   **Shop:** Yes
Previous Grounds: None
Record Attendance: 2,670 v Darlington, Northern League 2012-13.

RECORDS
Victory: 10-0 v Billingham Town (H), Northern League Division One, 18/03/2014
Defeat: 2-8 v Clitheroe (A), FA Cup 2nd Qualifying Round, 29/09/2007
Goalscorer: Gavin Cogdon - 103
Appearances: Lewis Dodds - 227
Additional: Northern League record points tally of 109 during 2012-13.

HONOURS
FA Comps: FA Vase 2012-13.
League: Northern League Division One 2009-10, 2010-11, 2011-12, 2013-14, Division Two 2006-07.
County FA: Durham Challange Cup 2011-12.

08-09		09-10		10-11		11-12		12-13		13-14		14-15		15-16		16-17		17-18	
NL 1	4	NL 1	1	NL 1	1	NL 1	1	NL 1	2	NL 1	1	NP1N	5	NP1N	2	NP P	2	Nat N	8
FAC	EP	FAC	2Q	FAC	1Q	FAC	3Q	FAC	2Q	FAC	1Q	FAC	4Qr	FAC	2Q	FAC	1P	FAC	2Q
FAV	2Q	FAV	2Pr	FAV	5P	FAV	3P	FAV		FAV	5P	FAT	1P	FAT	3Q	FAT	1Q	FAT	4Pr

2017-18 STATS	**Goals Total** 87	**Games Without Scoring** 7	**Total No. of Scorers** 15	**Total Clean Sheets** 11
Most Consecutive Scoring Games 15	**Best Unbeaten Run** 10		**Most Consecutive Clean Sheets**	2

Best Att: 1,661 v Darlington, National North   Number in brackets denotes consecutive runs.

STOCKPORT COUNTY

Club Contact Details 0161 286 8888
Edgeley Park, Hardcastle Road, Stockport SK3 9DD
mark.lockyear@stockportcounty.com

Founded: 1883   **Nickname:** County or Hatters   **Manager:** Jim Gannon
Previous Names: Heaton Norris Rovers 1883-88, Heaton Norris 1888-90.
Previous Leagues: Lancashire 1863-1900. Football League 1900-2011.

Club Colours (change): Blue and white

Ground Capacity: 10,800   **Seats:** 10,800   **Covered:** Yes   **Clubhouse:** Yes   **Shop:** Yes
Previous Grounds: Heaton Norris Recreation Ground & other various locations 1883-89. Green Lane 1889-1902.
Record Attendance: 27,833 v Liverpool, FA Cup 5th Round 11/02/1950. 10,273 (all seated) v Leeds United, 28/12/2008.
Nearest Railway Station Stockport - Approx. half a mile from the ground.

RECORDS
Victory: 13-0 v Halifax Town, Division Three North 06/01/1934.
Defeat: 0-9 v Everton Reserves, Lancashire League, 09/12/1893.
Goalscorer: (League) Jack Connor - 132, 1951-56.
Appearances: (League) Andy Thorpe - 555, 1978-86, 88-92.
Additional: Paid, £800,000 for Ian Moore from Nottingham Forest, 07/1998.
HONOURS Received, £1,600,000 for Alun Armstrong from Middlesbrough, 02/1998.
FA Comps: None
League: Lancashire 1899-1900.
League Division Three North 1921-22, 36-37, Division Four 1966-67.
County FA: Manchester S.C. 1897-98,98-99, 1914-15,22-23. Cheshire Medal 1922-23,24-25,28-29,29-30,30-31. Ches' Bowl 1933-34,48-49, 52-53,55-56,56-57,58-59,60-61,62-63. Ches' S.C.1905-06,46-47,48-49,65-66,2015-16. Ches' Prem. Cup 1969-70,70-71, 2010-11.

	08-09		09-10		10-11		11-12		12-13		13-14		14-15		15-16		16-17		17-18	
	FL 1	18	FL 1	24	FL 2	24	Conf	16	Conf	21	Conf N	14	Conf N	11	Nat N	9	Nat N	8	Nat N	5
	FAC	Pr	FAC	2P	FAC	1Pr	FAC	4Q	FAC	1P	FAC	3Q	FAC	4Q	FAC	2Q	FAC	1P	FAC	3Qr
	FLC	1P	FLC	1P	FLC	1P	FAT	1Pr	FAT	2Pr	FAT	3Qr	FAT	2Pr	FAT	3Q	FAT	2Pr	FAT	4Pr

2017-18 STATS	Goals Total	98	Games Without Scoring	6	Total No. of Scorers	17	Total Clean Sheets	14
Most Consecutive Scoring Games	24	Best Unbeaten Run	8			Most Consecutive Clean Sheets		2

Best Att: 6,230 v Chorley, Play-off Qualifier   Number in brackets denotes consecutive runs.

YORK CITY

Club Contact Details 01904 624 447
Bootham Crescent, York YO30 7AQ
enquiries@yorkcityfootballclub.co.uk

Founded: 1922   **Nickname:** Minstermen   **Manager:** Martin Gray
Previous Names: None
Previous Leagues: Midland 1922-29. Football League 1929-2004, 2012-16. Conference 2004-12.

Club Colours (change): Red and navy blue

Ground Capacity: 9,496   **Seats:** 7,872   **Covered:** Yes   **Clubhouse:** Yes   **Shop:** Yes
Previous Grounds: Fulfordgate 1922-32
Record Attendance: 28,123 v Huddersfield Town - FA Cup Sixth Round Proper 1938
Nearest Railway Station York - 20 min walk away.

RECORDS
Victory: 9-1 v Southport - Division Three North 1957
Defeat: 0-12 v Chester City - Division Three North 1936
Goalscorer: Norman Wilkinson - 143 (1954-66)
Appearances: Barry Jackson - 539 (1958-70)
Additional: Paid £140,000 to Burnley for Adrian Randall December 1995
HONOURS Received £950,000 from Sheffield Wednesday for Richard Cresswell 25/03/1999
FA Comps: FA Trophy 2011-12, 16-17.
League: Football League Division Four 1983-84, Third Division Play-offs 1992-93.
Conference Premier Play-offs 2011-12.
County FA: North Riding Senior Cup 1949-50, 56-57, 69-70, 79-80, 87-88. 88-89, 95-96, 98-99, 99-00, 05-06, 09-10.

	08-09		09-10		10-11		11-12		12-13		13-14		14-15		15-16		16-17		17-18	
	Conf	17	Conf	5	Conf	8	Conf	4	FL 2	17	FL 2	7	FL 2	18	FL 2	24	Nat	21	Nat N	11
	FAC	4Qr	FAC	3P	FAC	3P	FAC	4Q	FAC	1Pr	FAC	1Pr	FAC	1Pr	FAC	1Pr	FAC	4Qr	FAC	3Q
	FAT	F	FAT	QF	FAT	1P	FAT	F	FLC	1P	FLC	1P	FLC	1P	FLC	2P	FAT	F	FAT	1P

2017-18 STATS	Goals Total	73	Games Without Scoring	11 (4)	Total No. of Scorers	18	Total Clean Sheets	7
Most Consecutive Scoring Games	18	Best Unbeaten Run	6			Most Consecutive Clean Sheets		3

Best Att: 3,944 v Darlington, National North   Number in brackets denotes consecutive runs.

NATIONAL SOUTH LEAGUE TABLE 2017-18

		P	W	D	L	F	A	GD	Pts
1	Havant & Waterlooville	42	25	11	6	70	30	40	86
2	Dartford	42	26	8	8	81	44	37	86
3	Chelmsford City	42	21	11	10	68	45	23	74
4	Hampton & Richmond Borough	42	18	18	6	58	37	21	72
5	Hemel Hempstead Town	42	19	13	10	71	51	20	70
6	Braintree Town	42	19	13	10	73	55	18	69*
7	Truro City	42	20	9	13	71	55	16	69
8	St Albans City	42	19	8	15	71	58	13	65
9	Bath City	42	17	12	13	64	48	16	63
10	Welling United	42	17	10	15	68	59	9	61
11	Wealdstone	42	16	11	15	64	62	2	59
12	Weston-super-Mare	42	16	7	19	66	73	-7	55
13	Chippenham Town	42	15	9	18	64	70	-6	54
14	Gloucester City	42	15	8	19	56	70	-14	53
15	East Thurrock United	42	13	11	18	68	84	-16	50
16	Oxford City	42	13	10	19	60	69	-9	49
17	Concord Rangers	42	12	10	20	46	62	-16	46
18	Eastbourne Borough	42	13	7	22	57	80	-23	46
19	Hungerford Town	42	12	7	23	45	68	-23	43
20	Poole Town	42	11	9	22	47	73	-26	42
21	Whitehawk	42	8	10	24	51	89	-38	34
22	Bognor Regis Town	42	5	12	25	41	78	-37	27

Play-Offs: Hemel Hempstead Town 0-0 2-3p Braintree Town. Hampton & Richmond 3-1 Truro City
Semi Finals: Dartford 0-1 Braintree Town. Chelmsford City 0-1 Hampton & Richmond Borough
Final: Hampton & Richmond Borough 1-1 3-4p Braintree Town

		1	2	3	4	5	6	7	8	9	10	11	12	13	14	15	16	17	18	19	20	21	22
1	Bath City		0-0	1-1	1-2	2-5	2-0	1-2	4-0	0-1	5-1	2-0	1-2	0-0	5-0	2-1	1-0	2-1	0-0	0-0	1-1	0-2	1-1
2	Bognor Regis Town	3-2		2-1	0-1	1-3	1-2	1-2	0-2	0-1	2-2	1-2	0-3	2-3	1-2	0-0	1-1	2-1	0-2	0-3	1-3	1-1	6-2
3	Braintree Town	0-2	3-0		2-2	2-0	2-1	2-2	4-0	3-2	3-0	2-1	1-3	1-2	5-0	0-0	1-0	1-0	1-1	2-2	1-1	0-1	4-3
4	Chelmsford City	1-1	0-0	2-2		2-0	1-0	1-0	1-2	5-2	2-0	1-2	0-2	3-3	1-1	1-2	2-1	0-2	2-0	3-0	4-1	1-1	4-2
5	Chippenham Town	0-3	1-0	1-1	3-2		1-2	2-2	2-2	4-0	2-0	3-3	0-0	5-1	1-2	3-2	0-1	3-3	2-0	0-0	1-0	2-0	2-1
6	Concord Rangers	0-1	2-1	0-1	0-2	4-2		1-1	1-4	2-1	1-1	1-0	1-1	1-0	1-0	2-1	0-1	1-2	2-2	3-1	0-2	2-2	1-0
7	Dartford	2-0	3-1	1-1	1-2	3-0	2-0		0-1	4-2	4-1	1-0	1-0	3-2	0-0	7-1	0-1	2-1	4-1	3-3	4-1	3-1	3-1
8	East Thurrock United	1-1	2-0	5-3	2-4	0-2	2-3	0-1		0-0	3-0	1-1	0-1	0-1	0-1	4-1	2-2	1-1	1-2	1-1	0-1	3-4	4-2
9	Eastbourne Borough	2-3	3-0	2-3	0-3	4-2	3-1	0-1	2-2		0-1	1-2	1-4	0-2	4-1	2-0	0-4	1-1	1-3	1-1	0-0	1-2	1-4
10	Gloucester City	2-1	3-2	1-3	0-2	1-0	1-0	0-1	3-1	1-2		1-1	0-1	1-0	4-0	0-1	2-2	1-4	0-3	2-2	0-1	1-3	3-1
11	Hampton & Richmond Borough	3-1	1-0	1-1	1-1	1-0	1-1	2-2	5-1	1-1	1-1		0-1	0-0	3-1	1-0	1-0	1-0	1-1	1-1	3-1	1-1	1-1
12	Havant & Waterlooville	1-2	0-0	0-0	1-1	4-0	3-2	0-0	6-1	3-2	2-1	0-0		1-1	2-0	3-2	2-2	2-1	1-2	1-0	2-3	2-0	4-0
13	Hemel Hempstead Town	1-1	3-1	4-3	3-1	3-1	1-1	0-3	2-0	3-0	3-1	1-0	0-0		1-2	2-0	0-1	2-0	1-2	1-0	2-2	1-1	3-0
14	Hungerford Town	1-2	1-1	0-1	1-1	2-1	2-0	1-0	2-2	0-1	2-3	2-2	0-1	0-2		1-2	4-0	3-1	0-1	1-3	1-4	2-0	0-1
15	Oxford City	1-1	4-0	1-2	2-0	0-1	1-1	0-2	3-3	2-1	0-3	0-0	0-1	4-1	2-0		2-3	2-3	3-1	3-2	1-1	3-3	0-1
16	Poole Town	0-4	2-2	0-3	0-0	2-0	1-1	0-1	2-3	0-4	0-3	0-1	1-3	2-4	1-2	2-0		0-1	0-3	2-1	2-3	3-1	1-1
17	St Albans City	2-0	1-2	2-1	2-1	2-0	2-1	4-0	7-2	2-2	2-3	1-3	2-1	2-2	0-0	1-1	2-1		0-1	2-1	1-2	3-1	0-3
18	Truro City	1-2	1-1	1-2	2-0	1-0	2-0	3-1	1-2	0-1	1-1	1-1	1-0	3-3	2-1	2-3	3-1	1-2		1-3	3-2	2-1	7-2
19	Wealdstone	2-1	3-0	3-1	0-2	4-4	2-1	1-2	3-0	2-3	1-2	0-3	0-1	1-1	1-0	1-1	4-1	1-3	2-1		1-0	2-1	2-1
20	Welling United	0-2	3-3	3-0	0-1	4-0	3-3	2-3	0-3	3-0	2-3	0-1	0-0	0-0	3-2	1-3	2-0	3-1	2-2	1-2		3-1	1-0
21	Weston-super-Mare	4-2	1-0	1-2	0-1	2-2	1-0	3-0	2-2	5-1	2-1	1-2	1-4	2-1	2-1	4-2	1-2	0-2	0-2	5-1	0-2		1-0
22	Whitehawk	1-1	2-2	1-1	0-2	1-3	2-0	0-4	2-3	0-1	1-1	1-3	0-0	0-5	0-3	0-3	2-2	1-1	3-2	0-1	2-1	5-1	

BATH CITY MATCH RESULTS 2017-18

Date	Comp	H/A	Opponents	Att:	Result	Goalscorers	Pos	No.
Aug 5	Nat South	A	Bognor Regis Town	726	L 2 - 3	Jarvis 60 Watkins 71	15	1
8	Nat South	H	Chippenham Town	1254	L 2 - 5	Watkins 10 Lemonheigh-Evans 81 (pen)	20	2
12	Nat South	H	Chelmsford City	493	L 1 - 2	Case 5	20	3
15	Nat South	A	Truro City	676	W 2 - 1	Lemonheigh-Evans 33 Straker 48	18	4
19	Nat South	A	Havant & Waterlooville	633	W 2 - 1	Morgan 47 Lemonheigh-Evans 56	12	5
26	Nat South	H	Poole Town	484	W 1 - 0	Morgan 42	12	6
28	Nat South	A	Gloucester City	516	L 1 - 2	Compton 87	13	7
Sept 2	Nat South	H	Welling United	542	D 1 - 1	Lucas 60	13	8
5	Nat South	H	Oxford City	416	W 2 - 1	Batten 58 Lucas 60	11	9
9	Nat South	A	Concord Rangers	283	W 1 - 0	Jarvis 72	10	10
11	Nat South	A	Hungerford Town	311	W 2 - 1	Compton 61 73	7	11
16	FAC 2Q	H	Knaphill	497	W 6 - 0	Compton 23 JARVIS 3 (25 62 88) Watkins 61 McCootie 56		12
23			Wealdstone	645	D 0 - 0		8	13
30	FAC 3Q	H	Hemel Hempstead T	510	W 3 - 0	Artus 45 Watkins 89 Lucas 90		14
Oct 7	Nat South	A	St Albans City	1510	L 0 - 2		10	15
14	FAC 4Q	H	Chelmsford City	878	D 0 - 0			16
16	FAC 4Qr	A	Chelmsford City	645	L 0 - 1			17
21	Nat South	H	Braintree Town	842	D 1 - 1	Rigg 79	11	18
24	Nat South	H	Dartford	449	L 1 - 2	Smith 45	11	19
28	Nat South	A	Hampton & Richmond B	562	L 1 - 3	Morgan 16	14	20
Nov 4	Nat South	A	Whitehawk	265	D 1 - 1	Lucas 42 (pen)	14	21
11	Nat South	H	East Thurrock United	927	W 4 - 0	Edwards 15 Welch-Hayes 45 Watkins 45 Smith 76	12	22
18	Nat South	A	Eastbourne Borough	520	W 3 - 2	Jarvis 37 68 Welch-Hayes 62	10	23
28	FAT 3Q	H	Margate	341	D 0 - 0			24
Dec 2	Nat South	H	Hemel Hempstead T	477	D 0 - 0		12	25
4	FAT 3Qr	A	Margate	275	W 2 - 2	Compton 2 (won 5-4 on pens)		26
9	Nat South	H	Bognor Regis Town	658	D 0 - 0		12	27
16	FAT 1	A	Hendon	256	L 1 - 2	Smith 47		28
22	Nat South	A	Chippenham Town	1502	W 3 - 0	Smith 7 67 Compton 28	10	29
26	Nat South	H	Weston-s-Mare	879	L 0 - 2		11	30
Jan 6	Nat South	H	Truro City	612	D 0 - 0		11	31
13	Nat South	A	Chelmsford City	755	D 1 - 1	Stearn 47	11	32
20	Nat South	H	Concord Rangers	569	W 2 - 0	Batten 42 Compton 80	10	33
27	Nat South	A	Oxford City	818	D 1 - 1	Stearn 45	10	34
30	Nat South	A	Weston-s-Mare	591	L 2 - 4	Smith 48 Case 90	11	35
Feb 3	Nat South	H	Hampton & Richmond	593	W 2 - 0	Artus 17 Compton 25 (pen)	9	36
10	Nat South	A	Braintree Town	430	W 2 - 0	Jarvis 23 Compton 33	8	37
17	Nat South	H	Whitehawk	731	D 1 - 1	Watkins 90	9	38
24	Nat South	A	East Thurerock United	946	D 1 - 1	Batten 34	9	39
Mar 10	Nat South	H	Eastbourne Borough	401	L 0 - 1		9	40
17	Nat South	H	Poole Town	363	W 4 - 0	Rigg 45 Watkins 48 Smith 68 Edwards 90	9	41
24	Nat South	H	Havant & Waterlooville	922	L 1 - 2	Smith 82	10	42
27	Nat South	A	Hemel Hempstead T	579	D 1 - 1	Rigg 14	10	43
Apr 2	Nat South	H	Gloucester City	739	W 5 - 1	Edwards 35 Welch-Hayes 43 Smith46 Semenyo 57 81	10	44
7	Nat South	A	Wealdstone	808	L 1 - 2	Richards 42	10	45
14	Nat South	A	Hungerford Town	847	W 5 - 0	Richards 9 Edwards 43 Watkins51 Batten 63 Jarvis 90	10	46
21	Nat South	A	Darrtford	1619	L 0 - 2		10	47
24	Nat South	A	Welling United	365	W 2 - 0	Semenyo 48 Smith 60	9	48
28	Nat South	H	St Albans City	1023	W 2 - 1	Smith 32 Richards 78	9	49

GOALSCORERS	SG	CSG	Pens	Hat tricks	Total		SG	CSG	Pens	Hat tricks	Total
2016-17 Watkins					14	Richards	3				3
Smith	8	2			11	Rigg	3				3
Compton	8	2	1		9	Semenyo	3				3
Jarvis	6			1	9	Welch-Hayes				3	3
Watkins	7	2			8	Artus	2				2
Batten	4				4	Case	2				2
Edwards	4				4	Stearn	2				2
Lucas	4	2	1		4	McCootie					1
Lemonheigh-Evans	3	2	1		3	Straker					1
Morgan	3	2			3	Walker					1

VANARAMA NATIONAL SOUTH - STEP 2

BOGNOR REGIS TOWN MATCH RESULTS 2017-18

Date	Comp	H/A	Opponents	Att:	Result	Goalscorers	Pos	No.
Aug 5	Nat South	H	Bath City	726	W 3 - 2	Parsons 23 81 Muitt 27	2	1
8	Nat South	A	Poole Town	487	D 2 - 2	Heath 9 Muitt 84	7	2
12	Nat South	A	Welling United	511	D 3 - 3	Muitt 9 Barnes 22 (og) Pearce 70	7	3
15	Nat South	H	Whitehawk	744	W 6 - 2	Pearce 5 59 Wild 42 Parsons 51 Suraci 8 89	5	4
19	Nat South	H	Weston-super-Mare	668	D 1 - 1	Beck 57	5	5
26	Nat South	A	East Thurrock United	265	L 0 - 2		6	6
28	Nat South	H	Eastbourne Borough	916	L 0 - 1		10	7
Sept 2	Nat South	A	Chelmsford City	898	D 0 - 0		10	8
5	Nat South	H	Hungerford Town	536	L 1 - 2	Wild 77	14	9
9	Nat South	A	Wealdstone	845	L 0 - 3		16	10
12	Nat South	A	Hemel Hempstead Town	341	L 1 - 3	Muitt 35	18	11
16	FAC 2Q	H	Weston-s-Mare	397	W 2 - 1	Baldwin 49 (og) Crane 90		12
23	Nat South	A	Gloucester City	609	D 2 - 2	Pearce 45 Muitt 77	18	13
30	FAC 3Q	A	Eastbourne Borough	762	W 2 - 0	Pearce 11 50		14
Oct 7	Nat South	A	Dartford	1126	L 1 - 3	Campbell 17	19	15
14	FAC 4Q	A	Oxford City	406	L 0 - 1			16
21	Nat South	H	Chippenham Town	495	L 1 - 3	Sekajja 85	19	17
28	Nat South	A	Truro City	604	D 1 - 1	Sekajja 36		18
Nov 4	Nat South	A	Braintree Town	497	L 0 - 3		20	19
11	Nat South	H	Hampton & Richmond B	749	L 1 - 2	Sekajja 13	21	20
18	Nat South	A	St Albans City	583	W 2 - 1	Campbell 12 Beck 44	21	21
21	Nat South	H	Oxford City	501	D 0 - 0		21	22
25	FAT 3Q	H	Hemel Hempstead Town	302	D 1 - 1	Sekajj 65		23
28	FAT3Qr	H	Hemel Hempstead Town	306	W 1 - 0	Sekajji 71		24
Dec 2	Nat South	H	Concord Rangers	549	L 1 - 2	Wood 76	21	25
9	Nat South	A	Bath City	658	D 0 - 0		21	26
16	FAT 1	A	Taunton Town	508	W 4 - 1	Swallow 56 86 Sekajia 81 Tuck 90		27
22	Nat South	H	Poole Town	602	D 1 - 1	Tuck 90	21	28
26	Nat South	A	Havant & Waterlooville	1010	D 0 - 0		21	29
Jan 1	Nat South	H	Havant & Waterlooville	1015	L 0 - 3		21	30
6	Nat South	A	Whitehawk	429	D 2 - 2	Muitt 65 72	21	31
13	FAT 2	H	Leyton Orient	1371	L 1 - 2	Muitt 89		32
20	Nat South	H	Wealdstone	706	L 0 - 3		21	33
27	Nat South	A	Hungerford Town	28	D 1 - 1	Muitt 53	21	34
Feb 3	Nat South	H	Truro City	517	L 0 - 2		21	35
10	Nat South	A	Chippenhsm Town	469	L 0 - 1		21	36
17	Nat South	H	Braintree Town	558	W 2 - 1	Gilot 3 Pearce 40	21	37
24	Nat South	A	Hampton & Richmond B	627	L 0 - 1		21	38
Mar 17	Nat South	H	East Thurrock United	402	L 0 - 2		21	39
20	Nat South	H	Welling United	327	L 1 - 3	Sekajia 85	21	40
24	Nat South	A	Weston-s-Mare	534	L 0 - 1		21	41
Apr 2	Nat South	A	Eastbourne Borough	626	L 0 - 3		21	42
7	Nat South	A	Gloucester City	275	L 2 - 3	Sekajia 68 (pen) Wood 90 (pen)	21	43
10	Nat South	H	St Albans City	330	W 2 - 1	Sekajia 8 Scutt 27	21	44
14	Nat South	H	Hemel Hempstead Town	403	L 2 - 3	Pearce 82 Amaluzor 89	22	45
17	Nat South	A	Concord Rangers	206	L 1 - 2	Sekajia 83	22	46
21	Nat South	A	Oxford City	352	L 0 - 4		22	47
24	Nat South	H	Chelmsford City	283	L 0 - 1		22	48
28	Nat South	H	Dartford	1017	L 1 - 2	Pearce 85	22	49

GOALSCORERS	SG	CSG	Pens	Hat tricks	Total		SG	CSG	Pens	Hat tricks	Total
2016-17 Sekajja					10	Swallow	1				2
Sekajja	9	2	1		10	Wild	2				2
Muitt	8	3			9	Wood	2		1		2
Pearce	7	2			9	Amaluzor					1
Parsons	2				3	Crane	1				1
Beck	2				2	Gilot	1				1
Campbell	2				2	Heath	1				1
Opponents					2	Scutt	1				1
Tuck	2				2						
Suraci	1				2						

CHELMSFORD CITY MATCH RESULTS 2017-18

Date	Comp	H/A	Opponents	Att:	Result	Goalscorers	Pos	No.
Aug 5	Nat South	H	Gloucester City	811	W 2 - 0	Oyenuga 2 87	2	1
8	Nat South	A	Welling United	611	W 1 - 0	Barnard 82 (pen)	2	2
12	Nat South	A	Bath City	493	W 2 - 1	Oyenuga 51 Barnard 73 (pen)	2	3
14	Nat South	H	St Albans City	1025	L 0 - 2		4	4
19	Nat South	A	Wealdstone	908	W 2 - 0	Dickson 57 Barnard 67	2	5
26	Nat South	`H	Truro City	730	W 2 - 0	Johnson 61 Dickson 79	2	6
28	Nat South	A	Concord Rangers	464	W 2 - 0	Davies 46 Barnard 78	1	7
Sept 2	Nat South	H	Bognor Regis Town	898	D 0 - 0		1	8
5	Nat South	A	Hampton & Richmond B	512	D 1 - 1	Dickson 3	1	9
9	Nat South	H	Weston-s- Mare	784	D 1 - 1	Barnard 8	1	10
11	Nat South	H	East Thurrock United	741	L 1 - 2	Green 7	2	11
16	FAC 2Q	H	Ramsgate	578	W 7 - 0	Spillane 40 Hitchcock 44 DICKSON (3) Stevenson Church		12
23	Nat South	A	Poole Town	503	D 0 - 0		6	13
30	FAC 3Q	H	Weymouth	664	W 2 - 1	Dickson 58 80		14
Oct 7	Nat South	H	Eastbourne Borough	785	W 5 - 2	Church 55 56 Spillane 81 Oyenuga 84 Dickson 90	5	15
14	FAC 4Q	A	Bath City	876	D 0 - 0			16
16	FAC 4Qr	H	Bath City	645	W 1 - 0	West 50		17
21	Nat South	A	Dartford	1027	W 1 - 0	West 15	2	18
28	Nat South	A	Chippenham Town	701	L 2 - 3	Spillane 57 Dickson 88	3	19
Nov 4	FAC 1	A	Gateshead	732	L 0 - 2			20
11	Nat South	H	Oxford City	977	L 1 - 2	Porter 65	9	21
18	Nat South	A	Whitehawk	273	W 2 - 0	Johnson 12 Dickson 15	6	22
21	Nat South	H	Havant & Waterlooville	577	D 1 - 1	Spillane 90	5	23
25	FAT 3Q	A	Wealdstone	520	D 1 - 1	Batt 80		24
29	FAT 3Qr	H	Wealdstone	367	L 1 - 2	West 24		25
Dec 2	Nat South	H	Hungerford Town	644	D 1 - 1	Spillane 6	6	26
9	Nat South	A	Gloucester City	294	W 2 - 0	Dickson 16 Oyenuga 82	5	27
22	Nat South	A	Welling United	787	W 4 - 1	Johnson 2 Daley 6 Oyenuga 38 Dickson 72		28
26	Nat South	A	Braintree Town	1465	D 2 - 2	Spillane 7 Oyenuga 54 (pen)	3	29
Jan 1	Nat South	H	Braintree Town	1662	D 2 - 2	Oyenuga 42 Batt 64	5	30
6	Nat South	A	St Albans City	774	L 1 - 2	Oyenuga 86	6	31
13	Nat South	A	Bath City	755	D 1 - 1	Hitchcock 88	6	32
23	Nat South	A	Hemel Hempstead Utd	530	L 1 - 3	Davies 90	7	33
27	Nat South	H	Hampton & Richmond B	708	L 1 - 2	Church 58	8	34
Feb 3	Nat South	H	Chippenham Town	727	W 2 - 0	Dickson 43 Omazusi 78	8	35
10	Nat South	A	Dartford	1102	W 2 - 1	Oyenuga 86 Miles 90	4	36
17	Nat South	H	Hemel Hempstead Town	973	D 3 - 3	Dickson 30 Church 38 Green 85	4	37
20	Nat South	A	Weston-s-Mare	423	W 1 - 0	Roberts 8	3	38
24	Nat South	A	Oxford City	451	L 0 - 2		4	39
Mar 10	Nat South	A	Hungerford Town	222	D 1 - 1	Dickson 90	4	40
17	Nat South	A	Truro City	402	L 0 2		5	41
Apr 2	Nat South	H	Concord Rangers	831	W 1 - 0	Fenwick 11	8	42
7	Nat South	H	Poole Town	745	W 2 - 1	Spillane 66 Fenwick 75	8	43
11	Nat South	H	Whitehawk	625	W 4 - 2	Spillane 4 FENWICK 3 (13pen 74 90)	6	44
14	Nat South	A	East Thurrock United	508	W 3 - 0	Graham 14 Dickson 28 68	4	45
16	Nat South	H	Wealdstone	695	W 4 - 2	FENWICK 4 (3 43 57 67)	4	46
21	Nat South	H	Havant & Waterlooville	1160	L 0 - 2		5	47
24	Nat South	A	Bognor Regis Town	283	W 1 - 0	Dickson 4	4	48
28	Nat South	A	Eastbourne Borough	613	W 3 - 0	Fenwick 52 68 Church 79	3	49
May 3	PO	H	Hampton & Richmond B	1651	L 0 - 1			50

GOALSCORERS	SG	CSG	Pens	Hat tricks	Total		SG	CSG	Pens	Hat tricks	Total
2016-17 Jeffers					22	Green					2
Dickson	15	2		1	19	Hitchcock					2
Fenwick	5	3		2	11	Daley					1
Oyenuga	9	5	2		10	Graham					1
Spillane	7				7	Miles					1
Church	5				6	Omazusi					1
Barnard	5		2		5	Porter					1
Johnson					3	Roberts					1
West	3				3	Stevenson					1
Batt					2	Tiryaki					1
Davies					2						

CHIPPENHAM TOWN MATCH RESULTS 2017-18

Date	Comp	H/A	Opponents	Att:	Result	Goalscorers	Pos	No.
Aug 5	Nat South	H	Havant & Waterlooville	668	D 0 - 0		11	1
8	Nat South	A	Bath City	1254	W 5 - 2	Smith 4 Pratt 16 Sandell 43 (p) 72 Richards 67	4	2
12	Nat South	A	Braintree Town	550	L 0 - 1		10	3
15	Nat South	H	Poole Town	565	L 0 - 2		13	4
19	Nat South	H	East Thurrock United	492	D 2 - 2	Pratt 9 Richards 35	14	5
26	Nat South	A	Weston-s-Mare	611	D 2 - 2	Pratt 27 Smith 74	15	6
28	Nat South	A	Oxford City	528	W 3 - 2	Richards 7 Guthrie 17 Sandell 55	14	7
Sept 2	Nat South	A	Eastbourne Borough	544	L 2 - 4	Pratt 1 Sandall 35	14	8
5	Nat South	H	Gloucester City	512	W 2 - 0	Hamilton (og) 2 Andrews 54	13	9
9	Nat South	A	Dartford	954	L 0 - 3		13	10
12	Nat South	A	Truro City	288	L 0 - 1		16	11
16	**FAC 2Q**	**A**	**Weymouth**	**609**	**L 0 - 2**			12
23	Nat South	H	Hemel Hempstead Town	546	W 5 - 1	Twine 41 47 Pratt 61 63 Smith 84	12	13
Oct 7	Nat South	A	Welling United	595	L 0 - 4		13	14
14	Nat South	H	Wealdstone	723	D 0 - 0		14	15
21	Nat South	A	Bognor Regis Town	495	W 3 - 1	Twine 39 Pratt 49 Jones 53	13	16
28	Nat South	A	Chelmsford City	701	W 3 - 2	Pratt 27 Twine 42 Richards 90	13	17
Nov 4	Nat South	A	Hampton & Richmond	459	L 0 - 1		13	18
11	Nat South	H	St Albans City	570	D 3 - 3	Richards 7 32 Ferguson 67	14	19
18	Nat South	A	Concord Rangers	249	L 2 - 4	Morton 15 Richards 28	14	20
25	**FAT 3Q**	**A**	**Whitehawk**	**138**	**L 1 - 2**	**Pratt 75**		21
Dec 2	Nat South	H	Whtehawk	488	W 2 - 1	Smith 68 Pratt 84	14	22
9	Nat South	A	Havant & Waterlooville	648	L 0 - 4		14	23
23	Nat South	H	Bath City	1602	L 0 - 3		10	24
26	Nat South	A	Hungerford Town	300	L 1 - 2	Mullings 33	16	25
Jan 1	Nat South	H	Hungerford Town	610	L 1 - 2	Smile 70	16	26
13	Nat South	H	Braintree Town	470	D 1 - 1	Jackson 1	17	27
20	Nat South	A	Dartford	543	D 2 - 2	Evans 51 McCootie 67	17	28
30	Nat South	A	Poole Town	343	L 0 - 2		17	29
Feb 3	Nat South	A	Chelmsford City	727	L 0 - 2		19	30
10	Nat South	H	Bognor Regis Town	469	W 1 - 0	Beck 50 (og)	18	31
17	Nat South	H	Hampton & Richmond	508	D 3 - 3	Guthrie 24 Ferguson 69 Sandell 79	19	32
24	Nat South	A	St Albans City	661	L 0 - 2		19	33
Mar 5	Nat South	A	Gloucester City	190	L 0 - 1		19	34
10	Nat South	H	Whitehawk	231	W 3 - 1	Riley-Lowe 15 (og) Ferguson 51 Chambers 86	17	35
17	Nat South	H	Weston-s-Mare	452	W 2 - 0	Sandell 9 Jones 12	17	36
20	Nat South	H	Concord Rangers	393	L 1 - 2	Smith 90	17	37
24	Nat South	A	East Thurrock United	265	W 2 - 0	Ferguson 24 Smith 64	16	38
30	Nat South	H	Eastbourne Borough	571	W 4 - 0	Ferguson 4 Sandell 32 Smile 36 Chambers 75	13	39
Apr 2	Nat South	A	Oxford City	392	W 1 - 0	Jackson 30	13	40
7	Nat South	A	Hemel Hempstead Town	441	L 1 - 3	Evans 90	16	41
14	Nat South	H	Truro City	667	W 2 - 0	Sandell 45 Jones 84	14	42
21	Nat South	A	Wealdstone	754	D 4 - 4	McCootie 2 SANDELL 3 (7 22 81)	14	43
28	Nat South	H	Welling United	531	W 1 - 0	Sandell 18	13	44

GOALSCORERS	SG	CSG	Pens	Hat tricks	Total		SG	CSG	Pens	Hat tricks	Total
2016-17 *Sandell*					*32*	Evans	2				2
Sandell	9	2	1	1	12	Guthrie	2				2
Pratt	9	2			10	Jackson	2				2
Richards	6				7	McCootie	2				2
Smith	6				6	Smile	2				2
Ferguson	5				5	Andrews					1
Twine	3				4	Morton					1
Jones	3				3	Mullings					1
Opponents					3						
Chambers	2				2						

CONCORD RANGERS MATCH RESULTS 2017-18

Date	Comp	H/A	Opponents	Att:	Result	Goalscorers	Pos	No.
Aug 5	Nat South	A	Wealdstone	752	L 1 - 2	Cox 47	19	1
8	Nat South	H	Hemel Hempstead Town	219	W 1 - 0	Cawley 50	14	2
12	Nat South	H	Truro City	257	D 2 - 2	Taaffe 52 90	13	3
15	Nat South	A	Dartford	750	L 0 - 2		15	4
19	Nat South	H	Whitehawk	240	W 1 - 0	Cox 43	11	5
26	Nat South	A	St Albans City	688	L 1 - 2	Cawley 48	11	6
28	Nat South	H	Chelmsford City	464	L 0 - 2		18	7
Sept 2	Nat South	A	Hungerford Town	209	L 0 - 2		20	8
5	Nat South	A	Eastbourne Borough	436	L 1 - 3	Cawley 53	21	9
9	Nat South	H	Bath City	283	L 0 - 1		21	10
12	Nat South	H	Braintree Town	275	L 0 - 1		21	11
16	FAC 2Q	H	Tunbridge Wells	191	W 4 - 0	Da Costa 3 Roast 9 Farrell 16 Knight 38		12
23	Nat South	A	Concord Rangers	498	D 1 - 1	Farrell 26	21	13
30	FAC 3Q	H	Dorking Wanderers	141	W 3 - 0	Nasha 17 Cawley 50 Cox 59		14
Oct 7	Nat South	A	Havant & Waterlooville	226	D 1 - 1	Cawley 8	21	15
14	FAC 4Q	A	Woking	1004	D 1 - 1	Cawley		16
17	FAC 4Qr	H	Woking	382	L 1 - 2	Akinwande 32 (aet)		17
25	Nat South	H	Weston-s-Mare	164	D 2 - 2	Cawley t6 15 (pen)	20	18
28	Nat South	A	Oxford City	243	D 1 - 1	Nasha 86	20	19
31	Nat South	A	Poole Town	193	D 1 - 1	Greenhalgh	20	20
Nov 4	Nat South	H	Gloucester City	243	D 1 - 1	Cawley 27 (pen)	19	21
11	Nat South	A	Welling United	636	D 3 - 3	Junior 9 Farrell 60 Da Costa 90	19	22
18	Nat South	H	Chippenham Town	249	W 4 - 2	Knight 23 61 Greenhalgh 55 Junior 82	18	23
25	FAT 3Q	A	Taunton Town	479	L 2 - 3	Cawley 32 Lee 60		24
Dec 2	Nat South	A	Bognor Regis Town	549	W 2 - 1	Taaffe 2 Da Costa 30	16	25
9	Nat South	H	Wealdstone	287	W 3 - 1	Da Costa 21 Greenhalgh 50 (pen) Lee 90	16	26
23	Nat South	A	Hemel Hempstead Town	416	D 1 - 1	Lee 67	16	27
Jan 1	Nat South	A	East Thurrock United	343	W 3 - 2	Akinwande 40 54 Cawley 72	16	28
6	Nat South	H	Dartford	485	D 1 - 1	Cawley 16	19	29
20	Nat South	A	Bath City	569	L 0 - 2		16	30
27	Nat South	H	Eastbourne Borough	213	W 2 - 1	Greenhalgh 11 21	15	31
Feb 3	Nat South	H	Oxford City	250	W 2 - 1	Akinwande 16 Cawley 89	14	32
10	Nat South	A	Weston-s-Mare	451	L 0 - 1		14	33
17	Nat South	A	Gloucester City	260	L 0 - 1		16	34
24	Nat South	H	Welling United	287	L 0 - 2		17	35
Mar 17	Nat South	H	St Albans City	185	L 1 - 2	Da Costa 88	19	36
20	Nat South	A	Chippenham Town	393	W 2 - 1	Taaffe 51 Freeman 72	18	37
24	Nat South	A	Whitehawk	225	L 0 - 2		18	38
27	Nat South	H	East Thurrock United	295	L 1 - 4	Da Costa 73 (pen)	18	39
Apr 2	Nat South	A	Chelmsford City	831	L 0 - 1		18	40
7	Nat South	H	Hampton & Richmond	254	W 1 - 0	Cawley 61	17	41
10	Nat South	A	Truro City	381	L 0 - 2		18	42
14	Nat South	A	Braintree Town	446	L 1 - 2	Topley	18	43
17	Nat South	H	Bognor Regis Town	206	W 2 - 1	Ighorae 3 Cawley 61	18	44
21	Nat South	H	Poole Town	222	L 0 - 1		18	45
24	Nat South	H	Hungerford Town	263	W 1 - 0	Taaffe 59	17	46
28	Nat South	A	Havant & Waterlooville	2270	L 2 - 3	Freeman 52 Cawley 80	17	47

GOALSCORERS	SG	CSG	Pens	Hat tricks	Total		SG	CSG	Pens	Hat tricks	Total
2016-17 Cawley					19	Freeman	3	2			2
Cawley	15	3	2		16	Junior	2	2			2
Da Costa	5		1		6	Nasha	2	2			2
Greenhalgh	4		1		5	Ighorae	1				1
Taaffe	3				5	Roast	1				1
Akinwande	3				4	Topley	1				1
Cox	3				3						
Farrell	3				3						
Knight	2				3						
Lee	3				3						

DARTFORD MATCH RESULTS 2017-18

Date	Comp	H/A	Opponents	Att:	Result		Goalscorers	Pos	No.
Aug 5	Nat South	H	Hungerford Town	917	D	0 - 0		12	1
8	Nat South	A	Braintree Town		D	2 - 2	Murphy 64 Bradbrook E 75	15	2
12	Nat South	A	Havant & Waterlooville	775	D	0 - 0		16	3
15	Nat South	H	Concord Rangers	750	W	2 - 0	Bradbrook E 37 Della-Verde 83	11	4
19	Nat South	H	Oxford City	812	W	7 - 1	Sho-Silva 9 Della-Verde 15 Pavey 24 Noble 39 MFULA 3 (50 51 69)	5	5
26	Nat South	A	Hemel Hempstead Town	411	W	3 0	Bradbrook E 53 86 Pavey 77	5	6
28	Nat South	H	East Thurrock United	934	L	0 - 1		6	7
Sept 2	Nat South	A	Havant & Waterlooville	574	D	2 - 2	Pugh 36 Bradbrook E 59	6	8
5	Nat South	A	Whitehawk	223	W	4 - 0	Pavey 8 Hayes 24 Bradbrook E 45 Della-Verde 90	6	9
9	Nat South	H	Chippenham Town	954	W	3 - 0	Pavey 26 Pugh 69 Hayes 77	3	10
12	Nat South	H	Eastbourne Borough	702	W	4 - 2	Brown 22 Pavey 60 Bradbrook E 64 Murphy 87	1	11
16	FAC 2Q	H	Barking	652	W	3 - 1	BRADBROOK E 3 (25 pen 33 65)		12
23	Nat South	A	Weston-s-Mare	559	L	0 - 3		4	13
30	FAC 3Q	A	Needham Market	379	W	6 - 1	PAVEY 3 (21 35 45) Murphy 49 Pugh 70 Hayes 85		14
Oct 7	Nat South	H	Bognor Regis Town	1126	W	3 - 1	Pavey 7 Bradbrook E 52 Pugh 65	4	15
14	FAC 4Q	A	Burgess Hill Town	873	W	1 - 0	Pavey 8		16
21	Nat South	A	Chelmsford City	1027	L	0 - 1		7	17
24	Nat South	A	Bath City	449	W	2 - 1	Pavey 27 79	7	18
28	Nat South	H	St Albans City	1070	W	2 - 1	Bradbrook E 6 Bender 60 (og)	1	19
Nov 5	FAC 1	H	Swindon Town	2705	L	1 - 5	Sho-Silva 83		20
11	Nat South	A	Truro City	541	L	1 - 3	Vint 24	2	21
18	Nat South	A	Gloucester City	820	W	4 - 1	Mfula 26 Della-Verde 34 53 Pavey 57	1	22
21	Nat South	H	Wealdstone	669	D	3 - 3	Pavey 7 69 Pugh 80	1	23
25	FAT 3Q	A	Brentwood	297	W	2 - 1	Bradbrook E 76 Noble 88		24
Dec 2	Nat South	A	Poole Town	411	W	1 - 0	Sho-Silva 8		25
9	Nat South	A	Hungerford Town	218	L	0 - 1		1	26
16	FAT 1	H	Boreham Wood	607	D	1 - 1	Murphy 67		27
19	FAT 1r	A	Boreham Wood	173	D	2 - 2	Hayes 52 Mills 77 (Lost 1-3 on pens)		28
23	Nat South	H	Braintree Town	936	D	1 - 1	Pugh 17	1	29
26	Nat South	A	Welling United	1401	W	3 - 2	Pugh 3 55 Pavey 90	1	30
Jan 1	Nat South	A	Welling United	1640	W	4 - 1	Hayes 19 Pugh 39 Pavey 73 78	1	31
6	Nat South	A	Concord Rangers	485	D	1 - 1	Hayes 56	1	32
13	Nat South	H	Havant & Waterlooville	1278	W	1 - 0	Murphy 2	1	33
20	Nat South	A	Chippenham Town	543	D	2 - 2	Pavey 33 59	1	34
27	Nat South	H	Whitehawk	1104	W	3 - 1	Vint 45 Pugh 64 72	1	35
Feb 3	Nat South	A	St Albans City	807	L	0 - 4		1	36
10	Nat South	H	Chelmsford City	1102	L	1 - 2	Hayes 33	1	37
17	Nat South	A	Wealdstone	1002	W	2 - 1	Mills 80 Pavey 82	1	38
24	Nat South	H	Truro City	946	W	4 - 1	Pugh 15 Brown 46 Mills 48 Gerring 85 (og)	1	39
Mar 10	Nat South	H	Poole Town	928	L	0 - 1		2	40
17	Nat South	H	Hemel Hempstead Town	737	W	3 - 2	Pugh 32 81 Pavey 90	2	41
24	Nat South	A	Oxford City	363	W	2 - 0	Bradbrook E 5 Murphy 77	2	42
30	Nat South	H	Hampton & Richmond B	1371	W	1 - 0	Pavey 90	2	43
Apr 7	Nat South	H	Weston-s-Mare	1025	W	3 - 1	Brown 3 Bradbrook E 29 Pavey 77	2	44
10	Nat South	A	Gloucester City	228	W	1 0	Pavey 39	1	45
14	Nat South	A	Eastbourne Borough	733	W	1 - 0	Mills 33	1	46
17	Nat South	A	East Thurrock United	497	W	1 - 0	Mills 78	1	47
21	Nat South	H	Bath City	1619	W	2 - 0	Mills 37 Pavey 69	1	48
28	Nat South	A	Bognor Regis Town	1017	W	2 - 1	Mills 59 Vint 77	2	49
May 6	PO	H	Braintree Town	1794	L	0 - 1			50

GOALSCORERS	SG	CSG	Pens	Hat tricks	Total		SG	CSG	Pens	Hat tricks	Total
2016-17 E.Bradbrook					24	Sho-Silva	3				3
Pavey	19	3		1	26	Vint	3				3
E.Bradbrook	12	2	1	1	15	Noble	2				2
Pugh	11	3			14	Opponents					2
Hayes	6	2			7	Junior					1
Mills	5				6						
Murphy	6				6						
Della-Verde	4	2			5						
Mfula	2			1	4						
Brown	3				3						

EAST THURROCK UNITED MATCH RESULTS 2017-18

Date	Comp	H/A	Opponents	Att:	Result	Goalscorers	Pos	No.
Aug 5	Nat South	H	Hampton & Richmond B	268	D 1 - 1	Agyemang 53		1
8	Nat South	A	Whitehawk	201	W 3 - 2	Smith 44 Higgins 55 (pen) Marlow 77		2
12	Nat South	A	Poole Town	350	W 3 - 2	Harris 41 Agyemang 45 50		3
15	Nat South	H	Braintree Town	442	W 5 - 3	Higgins 8 70 Smith 19 Akinwande 75 Agyemang 87		4
19	Nat South	A	Chippenham Town	492	D 2 - 2	Smith 47 54	3	5
26	Nat South	H	Bognor Regis Town	265	W 2 - 0	Agyemang 12 Higgins 47	3	6
28	Nat South	A	Dartford	934	W 1 - 0	Higgins 20	2	7
Sept 2	Nat South	H	Wealdstone	411	D 1 - 1	Higgins 89	2	8
9	Nat South	A	Oxford City	174	D 3 - 3	Higgins 14 Nawarro 64 (og) Burns 79	5	9
11	Nat South	A	Chelmsford City	741	W 2 - 1	Cornhill 24 33	3	10
16	FAC 2Q	A	**Biggleswade Town**	191	W 1 - 0	**Higgins 65**		11
23	Nat South	H	Truro City	362	L 1 - 2	Smith 17	4	12
26	Nat South	H	St Albans City	286	D 1 - 1	Higgins 36	5	13
30	FAC 3Q	H	**Harlow Town**	159	D 2 - 2	**Higgins 20 60 (pen)**		14
Oct 3	FAC 3Qr	A	**Harlow Town**	329	W 2 - 1	**Harris 38 Smith 62**		15
7	Nat South	A	Hungerford Town	221	D 2 - 2	Higgins 32 Cornhill 64	6	16
14	FAC 4Q	H	**Ebbsfleet United**	669	D 0 - 0			17
17	FAC 4Qr	A	**Ebbsfleet United**	866	L 0 - 3			18
21	Nat South	A	Eastbourne Borough	427	D 2 - 2	Belho 39 Cornhill 42	8	19
28	Nat South	H	Hemel Hempstaed Town	295	L 0 - 1		9	20
Nov 4	Nat South	H	Weston-s-Mare	221	L 3 - 4	Higgins 6 50 Burns 61		21
11	Nat South	A	Batgh City	927	L 0 - 4		11	22
18	Nat South	H	Havant & Waterlooville	203	L 0 - 1		13	23
21	Nat South	H	Gloucester City	174	W 3 - 0	Harris 58 Burns 76 Higgins 78	11	24
25	FAT 3Q	H	**Shortwood United**	128	W 3 - 1	**Higgins (pen) Harris Expiteta**		25
Dec 2	Nat South	A	Welling United	432	W 3 - 0	Harris 13 Higgins 71 82	9	26
9	Nat South	H	Hamnpton & Richmond	583	L 1 - 5	Richardson 76	10	27
16	FAT 1	H	**Aldershot Town**	252	W 4 - 0	**RICHARDSON 3 (49 63 70) Alexander 33 (og)**		28
23	Nat South	H	Whitehawk	202	W 4 - 2	Higgins 19 Sammons 43 55 Richardson 74	9	29
Jan 1	Nat South	A	Concord Rangers	343	L 2 - 3	Higgins 16 79	9	30
6	Nat South	A	Braintree Town	445	L 0 - 4		12	31
13	FAT2	H	**Chester**	347	W 1 - 0	**Ekpiteta 17**		32
20	Nat South	H	Oxford City	218	W 4 - 1	Ekpiteta 13 17 Higgins 85 Agyemang 88	9	33
27	Nat South	A	St Albans City	602	L 2 - 7	Smith 23 Snedker 30 (og)	12	34
Feb 2	FAT 3	A	**Spennymoor Town**	743	D 1 - 1	**Smith 29**		35
6	FAT 3r	H	**Spennymoor Town**	238	L 2 - 5	**Agyemang 4 Smith 51**		36
10	Nat South	H	Eastbourne Borough	215	D 0 - 0		13	37
17	Nat South	A	Weston-s-Mare	548	D 2 - 2	Higgins 7 Agyemang 20	13	38
24	Nat South	H	Bath City	217	D 1 - 1	Agyemang 52	13	39
Mar 4	Nat South	A	Hemel Hempstead Town	210	L 0 - 2		13	40
10	Nat South	H	Welling United	318	L 0 - 1		14	41
17	Nat South	A	Bognor Regis Town	402	W 2 - 0	Higgins 6 90	14	42
20	Nat South	H	Poole Town	165	D 2 - 2	Harris 6 Higgins 32	14	43
24	Nat South	H	Chippenham Town	265	L 0 - 2		14	44
27	Nat South	A	Concord Rangers	295	W 4 - 1	Cornhill 9 Scott 25 Smith 54 Higgins 57	12	45
Apr 7	Nat South	A	Truro City	409	W 2 - 1	Higgins 19 49	12	46
14	Nat South	H	Chelmsford City	508	L 2 - 4	Higgins 22 Smith 75	13	47
17	Nat South	H	Dartford	497	L 0 - 1		13	48
21	Nat South	A	Gloucester City	251	L 1 - 3	Knott 50	15	49
23	Nat South	A	Wealdstone	690	L 0 - 3		15	50
25	Nat South	A	Havant & Waterlooville	1153	L 1 - 6	Harris 33	15	51
28	Nat South	H	Hungerford Town	312	L 0 - 1		15	52

GOALSCORERS	SG	CSG	Pens	Hat tricks	Total		SG	CSG	Pens	Hat tricks	Total
2016-17 Wraight					20	Sammons					2
Higgins	23	4	3		30	Akinwande					1
Smith	10	3			11	Belho					1
Agyemang	8	2			9	Knott					1
Harris	7	3			7	Marlow					1
Cornhill	6				5	Scott					1
Richardson	3	3		1	5						
Ekpiteta	2				4						
Burns	3				3						
Opponents					3						

EASTBOURNE BOROUGH MATCH RESULTS 2017-18

Date	Comp	H/A	Opponents	Att:	Result	Goalscorers	Pos	No.
Aug 5	Nat South	H	Braintree Town	598	L 2 - 3	Odubade 18 Pinney 20	16	1
8	Nat South	A	Havant & Waterlooville	644	L 2 - 3	Worrall 90 Hendon 90	16	2
12	Nat South	A	Hampton & Richmond B	338	D 1 - 1	Pinney 52	17	3
15	Nat South	H	Welling United	521	D 0 - 0		20	4
19	Nat South	A	Truro City	412	W 1 - 0	Worrall 90	16	5
26	Nat South	H	Wealdstone	631	D 1 - 1	Taylor 35	16	6
28	Nat South	A	Bognor Regis Town	916	W 1 - 0	Wills 72	12	7
Sept 2	Nat South	H	Chippenham Town	544	W 4 - 2	Taylor 18 44 Harris 49 Torres 77	9	8
5	Nat South	H	Concord Rangers	436	W 3 - 1	Harris 24 Taylor 29 64	8	9
9	Nat South	A	St Albans City	543	D 2 - 2	Odubade 50 Torres 90	8	10
12	Nat South	A	Dartford	702	L 2 - 4	Taylor 83 Noble 89 (og)	10	11
16	FAC 2Q	H	Carshalton Athletic	438	W 4 - 3	Odubade (2) Torres Taylor		12
23	FAC 3Q	A	Oxford City	642	W 2 - 0	Odubade 1 Torres 50	9	13
30	FAC 3Q	H	Bognor Regis Town	762	L 0 - 2			14
Oct 7	Nat South	A	Chelmsford City	785	L 2 - 5	Taylor 18 Dawes 45	11	15
14	Nat South	H	Hemel Hempstead Town	507	L 0 - 2		11	16
21	Nat South	H	East Thurrock United	427	D 2 - 2	Torres 58 Dawes 74	12	17
28	Nat South	A	Hungerford Town	227	W 1 - 0	Drage 76	12	18
Nov 4	Nat South	H	Poole Town	487	L 0 - 4		13	19
11	Nat South	A	Weston-super-Mare	488	L 1 - 5	McCallum 43	15	20
18	Nat South	H	Bath City	520	L 2 - 3	Dawes 45 87	15	21
25	FAT 3Q	H	Royston	277	D 1 - 1	Drage 35 (pen)		22
28	FAT 3Qr	A	Royston	189	D 2 - 2	McCallum Ransom 82 (Won 4-3 on pens)		23
Dec 2	Nat South	A	Gloucester City	231	W 2 - 1	Simpemba 20 Taylor 24	15	24
9	Nat South	A	Braintree Town	389	L 2 - 3	Okojie 13 Khindo-John 75	15	25
16	FAT 1	A	Dover Athletic	424	L 0 - 3			26
23	Nat South	H	Havant & Waterlooville	487	L 1 - 4	Okojie 83	15	27
26	Nat South	A	Whitehawk	258	W 1 - 0	Odubade 20 (pen)	14	28
Jan 1	Nat South	H	Whitehawk	521	L 1 - 4	McCallum 19	15	29
6	Nat South	A	Welling United	404	L 0 - 3		15	30
13	Nat South	H	Hampton & Richmond B	492	L 1 - 2	Dawes 8	15	31
20	Nat South	A	St Albans City	420	D 1 - 1	Willls	15	32
27	Nat South	A	Concord Rangers	212	L 1 - 2	McCallum 87	16	33
Feb 3	Nat South	H	Hungerford Town	391	W 4 - 1	Odubade 11 McCallum 26 54 Dawes 42	15	34
10	Nat South	A	East Thurrock United	215	D 0 - 0		14	35
17	Nat South	A	Poole Town	479	W 4 - 0	Dawes 4 Harris 19 McCallum 37 90	14	36
24	Nat South	H	Weston-s-Mare	409	L 1 - 2	Odubade 33	16	37
Mar 10	Nat South	H	Gloucester City	493	L 0 1		16	38
13	Nat South	A	Bath City	401	W 1 - 0	Odubade 60	15	39
24	Nat South	H	Truro City	465	L 1 - 3	Odubade 13	17	40
26	Nat South	A	Wealdstone	751	W 3 - 2	Taylor 1 45 Dawes 87	17	41
30	Nat South	A	Chippenham Town	571	L 0 - 4		17	42
Apr 2	Nat South	H	Bognor Regis Town	626	W 3 - 0	Okojie 25 Taylor 49 McCallum 69	15	43
7	Nat South	A	Oxford City	221	L 1 - 2	Odubade 85	18	44
14	Nat South	H	Dartford	733	L 0 - 1		16	45
21	Nat South	A	Hemel Hempstead Town	583	L 0 - 3		17	46
28	Nat South	H	Chelmsford City	613	L 0 - 3		18	47

GOALSCORERS	SG	CSG	Pens	Hat tricks	Total		SG	CSG	Pens	Hat tricks	Total
2016-17 Romain					20	Wills					2
Taylor	8	2			12	Worrall		2			2
Odubade	9	2	1		11	Hendon					1
McCallum	7				9	Khindo-John					1
Dawes	8	2	1		8	Opponents					1
Torres	5	2			5	Orrall					1
Okojile	3				3	Ransome					1
Drage			1		2	Simpemba					1
Harris					2						
Pinney	2				2						

GLOUCESTER CITY MATCH RESULTS 2017-18

Date	Comp	H/A	Opponents	Att:	Result	Goalscorers	Pos	No.
Aug 5	Nat South	A	Chelmsford City	811	L 0 - 2		21	1
7	Nat South	H	Truro City	352	L 0 - 3		22	2
12	Nat South	H	Wealdstone	403	D 2 - 2	Thomas 54 Cundy 85	19	3
15	Nat South	A	Weston-s-Mare	553	L 1 - 3	Parselle 18	22	4
19	Nat South	H	Hemel Hempstead Town	295	W 1 - 0	Hanks 85	21	5
26	Nat South	A	Hungerford Town	332	W 3 - 2	E.Williams 16 Parker 33 62	13	6
28	Nat South	H	Bath City	516	W 2 - 1	Parker 45 Kotwica 54	9	7
Sept 2	Nat South	A	St Albans City	904	W 3 - 2	Avery 3 E. Williams 54 Cundy 84	8	8
5	Nat South	A	Chippenham Town	612	L 0 - 2		12	9
9	Nat South	H	Havant & Waterlooville	322	L 0 - 1		12	10
11	Nat South	H	Hampton & Richmond B	207	D 1 - 1	Parker 55	12	11
16	**FAC 2Q**	**H**	**Hungerford Town**	**275**	**L 0 - 3**			12
23	Nat South	A	Bognor Regis Town	609	D 2 - 2	E.Williams 73 90	13	13
Oct 7	Nat South	H	Braintree Town	346	L 1 - 3	Chambers 18	15	14
21	Nat South	H	Welling United	269	L 0 - 1		17	15
28	Nat South	A	Poole Town	421	W 3 - 0	Chambers 54 Parker 56 Storer 84	17	16
Nov 4	Nat South	A	Concord Rangers	243	D 1 - 1	Knowles 63	16	17
11	Nat South	H	Whitehawk	261	W 3 - 1	Parker 9 Chambers 32 Knowles 62	16	18
18	Nat South	A	Dartford	820	L 1 - 4	Edge 64	16	19
21	Nat South	A	East Thurrock United	174	L 0 - 3		16	20
25	**FAT 3Q**	**A**	**Chesham United**	**245**	**L 1 - 2**	**Chambers 32**		21
Dec 2	Nat South	H	Eastbourne United	231	L 1 - 2	Parker 52	16	22
9	Nat South	H	Chelmsford City	294	L 0 - 2		18	23
23	Nat South	A	Truro City	523	D 1 - 1	E.Williams 74 (pen)	18	24
26	Nat South	H	Oxford City	324	L 0 - 1		19	25
Jan 1	Nat South	A	Oxford City	332	W 3 - 0	Knowles 7 Chambers 42 Moore 73	18	26
6	Nat South	H	Weston-s-Mare	292	L 1 - 3	Avery 60	18	27
Feb 3	Nat South	H	Poole Town	259	D 2 - 2	Knowles 19 Alawape-Williams 50 (og)	20	28
10	Nat South	A	Welling United	434	W 3 - 2	Chambers 58 Nanetti 75 (og) E Williams 90	19	29
17	Nat South	H	Concord Rangers	260	W 1 - 0	E.Williams 90 (pen)	17	30
19	Nat South	A	Wealdstone	788	W 2 - 1	H.Williams 37 Hanks 59	15	31
24	Nat South	A	Whitehawk	284	D 1 - 1	Parker 16	15	32
27	Nat South	H	Havant & Waterlooville	572	L 1 - 2	Hanks 52	15	33
Mar 5	Nat South	H	Chippenham Town	190	W 1 - 0	Moore 78	14	34
10	Nat South	A	Eastbourne Borough	493	W 1 - 0	Parker 13	13	35
17	Nat South	H	Hungerford Town	200	W 4 - 0	E.Williams 48 Parker 63 H.Williams 75 85	12	36
24	Nat South	A	Hemel Hempstead Town	521	L 1 - 3	E.Williams 39	12	37
Apr 2	Nat South	A	Bath City	739	L 1 - 5	Hall 24	14	38
8	Nat South	H	Bognor Regis Town	275	W 3 - 2	Parker 38 57 M.Williams 77	13	39
11	Nat South	H	Dartford	228	L 0 - 1		13	40
14	Nat South	A	Hampton & Richmond B	822	D 1 - 1	Parker 39	15	41
17	Nat South	H	St Albans City	202	L 1 - 4	Cundy 45	15	42
21	Nat South	H	East Thurrock United	251	W 3 - 1	Lawrence 12 Smerdon 26 Turner 76	11	43
28	Nat South	A	Braintree Town	616	L 0 - 3		14	44

GOALSCORERS	SG	CSG	Pens	Hat tricks	Total		SG	CSG	Pens	Hat tricks	Total
2016-17 Hopper					20	Edge					1
Parker	10	2			13	Hall					1
Williams E	8				9	Kotwica					1
Chambers	5				6	Lawrence					1
Knowles	4	2			4	Parselle					1
Cundy	3				3	Smerton					1
Hanks	3				3	Storer					1
Williams H	1				3	Thomas					1
Avery	2				2	Turner					1
Moore	2				2	Williams M					1
Opposition					2						

HAMPTON & RICHMOND BOROUGH MATCH RESULTS 2017-18

Date	Comp	H/A	Opponents	Att:	Result		Goalscorers	Pos	No.
Aug 5	Nat South	A	East Thurrock United	268	D	1 - 1	Kamara 59 (pen)	10	1
8	Nat South	H	Oxford City	302	W	1 - 0	Cawley 50	8	2
12	Nat South	H	Eastbourne Borough	336	D	1 - 1	Kretzschmar 41	8	3
15	Nat South	A	Hemel Hempstead Town	451	L	0 - 1		12	4
19	Nat South	A	Braintree Town	472	L	1 - 2	Wassmer 90	17	5
26	Nat South	H	Havant & Waterlooville	426	L	0 - 1		17	6
28	Nat South	A	Welling United	529	W	1 - 0	Moss 5		7
Sept 2	Nat South	H	Dartford	574	D	2 - 2	Kretzschmar 2 28	15	8
5	Nat South	H	Chelmsford City	512	D	1 - 1	Kretzschmar 90	15	9
9	Nat South	A	Hungerford Town	228	D	2 - 2	Kretzschmar 22 Napa 52	15	10
11	Nat South	A	Gloucester City	207	D	1 - 1	Hudson-Oddi 57	13	11
16	FAC 2Q	H	Potters Bar Town	392	D	1 - 1	Culley (pen) 7		12
19	FAC 2Qr	A	Potters Bar Town	179	W	3 - 0	Cook 49 Napa 59 McAuley 85		13
23	Nat South	A	Concord Rangers	498	D	1 - 1	Hudson-Odie 90 (pen)	17	14
30	FAC 3Q	A	Cinderford Town	233	W	3 - 2	Roberts Kiernan (2)		15
Oct 7	Nat South	A	Truro City	531	D	1 - 1	Cook 61	17	16
14	FAC 4Q	H	Truro City	784	L	0 - 2			17
21	Nat South	A	Whitehawk	217	W	3 - 1	Jolley 1 Hudson-Oddi 22 33		18
24	Nat South	H	St Albans City	421	W	1 - 0	Wassmer 28	13	19
28	Nat South	H	Bath City	562	W	3 - 1	Napa 44 Kretzachmar 80 Crawford 90	11	20
Nov 4	Nat South	A	Chippenham Town	459	W	1 - 0	Hudson-Odoi 45	9	21
11	Nat South	A	Bognor Regis Town	749	W	2 - 1	Hudson-Odoi 39 Kretzschmar 81 (pen)	8	22
18	Nat South	H	Poole Town	474	W	1 - 0	Coombes 48	5	23
25	FAT 3Q	H	Harlow Town	289	W	5 - 1	Crawford Kretzschmar (2) (1Pen) Kiernan(2)		24
Dec 2	Nat South	A	Weston-s-Mare	529	W	2 - 1	Wassmer 11 Kretzschmar 79	3	25
5	Nat South	H	East Thurrock United	583	W	5 - 1	Wassmer 3 Coombes 30 42 Kiernan 45 84	3	26
16	FAT 1	H	Heybridge Swifts	294	D	1 - 1	Randall 90		27
19	FAT 1r	A	Heybridge Swifts	206	L	2 - 3	Kretzschmar 44 58 (pen)		28
23	Nat South	A	Oxford City	259	D	0 - 0		5	29
26	Nat South	H	Wealdstone	817	D	1 - 1	Wassmer 6	5	30
Jan 1	Nat South	A	Wealdstone	929	W	3 - 0	CHARLES 3 (16 22 29)	3	31
6	Nat South	H	Hemel Hempstead Town	619	D	0 - 0		3	32
13	Nat South	A	Eastbourne Borough	492	W	2 - 1	Wassmer 45	2	33
27	Nat South	A	Chelmsford City	708	W	2 - 1	Kretzschmar 3 Charles 69	2	34
Feb 3	Nat South	A	Bath City	593	L	0 - 2		2	35
10	Nat South	H	Whitehawk	523	D	1 - 1	Wilk 47 (og)	3	36
17	Nat South	A	Chippenham Town	508	D	3 - 3	Kretzschmar 60 67 Jeffers 90	3	37
24	Nat South	H	Bognor Regis Town	627	W	1 - 0	Jeffers 84	2	38
Mar 10	Nat South	H	Weston-s-Mere	439	W	3 - 1	Hudson-Odie 35 62 Jeffers 41	3	39
17	Nat South	A	Havant & Waterlooville	958	D	0 - 0		3	40
20	Nat South	H	Hungerford Town	385	W	3 - 1	Kretzschmar 25 (pen) Jeffers 37 64	3	41
24	Nat South	H	Braintree Town	874	D	1 - 1	Wynter 81	3	42
30	Nat South	A	Dartford	1371	L	0 - 1		3	43
Apr 2	Nat South	H	Welling United	627	D	1 - 1	Kiernan 90	3	44
7	Nat South	A	Concord Rangers	254	L	0 - 1		3	45
14	Nat South	H	Gloucester City	822	D	1 - 1	Kretzschmar 42	4	46
17	Nat South	A	Poole Town	314	W	1 - 0	Wassmer 5	3	47
21	Nat South	A	St Albans City	1021	W	3 - 1	Wassmer 10 Jeffers 45 Roberts 78	3	48
28	Nat South	H	Truro City	1014	D	1 - 1	Cook 64	4	49
May 2	PO	H	Truro City	922	W	3 - 1	Cook 34 Hudson-Odie 99 120 (aet)		50
6	PO SF	A	Chelmsford City	1851	W	1 - 0	Kretzschmar 54 (pen)		51
13	PO Final	H	Braintree Town		D	1 - 1	Kretzschmar 8 (Lost 3-4 on pens)		52

GOALSCORERS	SG	CSG	Pens	Hat tricks	Total		SG	CSG	Pens	Hat tricks	Total
2016-17 Kabamba					19	Roberts	2				2
Kretzachmar	16	3	5		20	Cawley					1
Hudson-Oddi	7		1		10	Culley			1		1
Kiernan	4				8	Jolley					1
Wassmer	8				8	Kamara			1		1
Jeffers	5	3			6	McCauley					1
Charles	2		1		4	Moss					1
Cook	4				4	Opponents					1
Coombes	2				3	Randall					1
Napa	3				3	Wynter					1
Crawford	2				2						

HEMEL HEMPSTEAD MATCH RESULTS 2017-18

Date	Comp	H/A	Opponents	Att:	Result	Goalscorers	Pos	No.
Aug 5	Nat South	H	Whitehawk	409	W 3 - 0	Greenhough 12 Osborne 79 Howe 89	1	1
8	Nat South	A	Concord Rangers	219	L 0 - 1		12	2
12	Nat South	A	Hungerford Town	235	W 2 - 0	Parkes 60 Sheringham 66	6	3
15	Nat South	H	Hampton & Richmond B	451	W 1 - 0	Kaloczi 44	3	4
19	Nat South	A	Gloucester City	295	L 0 - 1		7	5
26	Nat South	H	Dartford	411	L 0 - 3		7	6
28	Nat South	A	Wealdstone	966	D 1 - 1	Driver 72	9	7
Sept 2	Nat South	H	Truro City	466	L 1 - 2	Hamblin 40	11	8
5	Nat South	A	Poole Town	276	W 4 - 2	Spetch 6 (og) Liburd 20 23 Parkes 69	9	9
9	Nat South	H	Braintree Town	469	W 4 - 3	Sheringham 21 Liburd 59 Kaloczi 63 Parkes 66	9	10
12	Nat South	H	Bognor Regis Town	341	W 3 - 1	Parkes 25 LIburd 55 Sheringham 80		11
16	FAC 2Q	H	Wingate & Finchley	377	D 0 - 0			12
19	FAC 2Q	A	Wingate & Finchley	251	W 2 - 1	Parkes Osborne 109 (aet)		13
23	Nat South	A	Chippenham Town	546	L 1 - 5	Walsh 52	10	14
30	FAC 3Q	A	Bath City	510	L 0 - 3			15
Oct 7	Nat South	H	Weston-s-Mare	460	D 1 - 1	Amaluzor 30	9	16
14	Nat South	A	Eastbourne Borough	507	W 2 - 0	Sheringham 7 Shulton 45	7	17
21	Nat South	H	Gloucester City	449	W 2 - 0	Sheringham 21 McCall 50	6	18
28	Nat South	A	East Thurrock United	295	W 1 - 0	Sheringham 26	2	19
Nov 11	Nat South	H	Havant & Waterlooville	886	D 1 - 1	Parkes 83 (pen)	5	20
18	Nat South	H	Welling United	453	D 2 - 2	German 8 Parkes 39 (pen)	8	21
25	FAT 3Q	H	Bognor Regis Town	302	D 1 - 1	German 16		22
28	FAT 3Qr	A	Bognor Regis Town	306	L 0 - 1			23
Dec 2	Nat South	A	Bath City	477	D 0 - 0		8	24
9	Nat South	A	Whitehawk	218	W 5 - 0	Hoskins 1,50 Kaloczi 33 Campbell-Mhlope 69 Osborn 72	6	25
23	Nat South	A	Concorde	416	D 1 - 1	Hoskins 74	6	26
26	Nat South	H	St Albans City	1259	D 2 - 2	Howe 63 McCall 80	7	27
Jan 1	Nat South	H	St Albans City	1266	W 2 - 0	Moyo 32 83	7	28
6	Nat South	A	Hampton & Richmond B	619	D 0 - 0		7	29
13	Nat South	A	Hungerford Town	449	L 1 - 2	Parkes 48	7	30
20	Nat South	H	Braintree Town	432	W 2 - 1	McCall 40 Nelson-Addy 90		31
23	Nat South	H	Chelmsford City	530	W 3 - 1	Parkes 25 (pen) 35 McCall 84	3	32
27	Nat South	H	Poole Town	560	L 0 - 1		3	33
Feb 10	Nat South	A	Oxford City	358	L 1 - 4	Ware 73	6	34
17	Nat South	A	Chelmsford City	973	D 3 - 3	Moyo 26 McCall 34 Yakubu 53	5	35
24	Nat South	H	Havant & Waterlooville	508	D 0 - 0		7	36
Mar 4	Nat South	A	East Thurrock United	210	W 2 - 0	Parkes 33 Watt 42	4	37
17	Nat South	A	Dartford	737	L 2 - 3	Parkes 36 Watt 45	7	38
24	Nat South	H	Gloucester City	521	W 3 - 1	Moyo 57 Parkes 77 Oliyide 89	7	39
27	Nat South	H	Bath City	579	D 1 - 1	Watt 20	7	40
30	Nat South	A	Truro City	527	D 3 - 3	Oliyide 16 71 Moyo 37	6	41
Apr 2	Nat South	H	Chippenham Town	441	W 3 - 1	Moyo 2 63 Oliyide 41	4	42
10	Nat South	A	Welling IUnited	442	D 0 - 0		5	43
14	Nat South	A	Bognor Regis Town	403	W 3 - 2	Watt 2 14 Moyo 71	5	44
19	Nat South	H	Wealdstone	732	W 1 - 0	Parkes 61	4	45
21	Nat South	H	Eastbourne Borough	583	W 3 - 0	McCall 5 Parkes 31 Osborne 87	4	46
28	Nat South	A	Weston-s-Mare	549	L 1 - 2		5	47
May 2	PO	H	Braintree Town	1165	D 0 - 0	(Lost 2-3 on pens)		48

GOALSCORERS	SG	CSG	Pens	Hat tricks	Total		SG	CSG	Pens	Hat tricks	Total
2016-17 Robinson					26	Amaluzor					1
Parkes	14	3	3		15	Campbell-Mhlope					1
Moyo	6	3			8	Driver					1
McCall	6	2			6	Greenhough					1
Sheringham	6	3			6	Hamblin					1
Watt	4	2			5	Nelson-Addy					1
Liburd	3	3			4	Opponents					1
Oliyide	3				4	Shulton					1
Osborne	4				4	Walsh					1
Hoskins	2				3	Ware					1
Kaloczi	2				3	Yakubu					1
German	2				2						
Howe	2				2						

HUNGERFORD TOWN MATCH RESULTS 2017-18

Date	Comp	H/A	Opponents	Att:	Result	Goalscorers	Pos	No.
Aug 5	Nat South	A	Dartford	917	D 0 - 0		14	1
7	Nat South	H	Weston-s-Mare	370	W 2 - 0	Willmoth 46 Williams	2	2
12	Nat South	H	Hemel Hempstead	235	L 0 - 2		14	3
15	Nat South	A	Oxford City	251	L 0 - 2		17	4
19	Nat South	A	Welling United	472	L 2 - 3	Soares 29 Hopper 90	19	5
26	Nat South	H	Gloucester City	332	L 2 - 3	Parselle 35 (og) Ngamvoulou 68	21	6
28	Nat South	A	Poole Town	453	W 2 - 1	Hopper 15 Soares 63	16	7
Sept 2	Nat South	H	Concord Rangers	209	W 2 - 0	Soares 51 Bignall 81	12	8
5	Nat South	A	Bognor Regis Town	536	W 2 - 1	Soares 53 Brown 68	10	9
9	Nat South	H	Hampton & Richmond B	228	D 2 - 2	Clark 66 Bignall 85	11	10
11	Nat South	H	Bath City	311	L 1 - 2	Soares 83	11	11
16	FAC 2Q	A	Gloucester City	275	W 3 - 0	Bignall 23 Brown 43 (pen) 69		12
23	Nat South	A	Braintree Town	475	L 0 - 5		15	13
30	FAC 3Q	H	Billericay Town	507	D 1 - 1	Brown 35 (pen)		14
Oct 3	FAC3Qr	A	Billericay Town	1024	L 1 - 6	Brown 51		15
7	Nat South	H	East Thurrock United	221	D 2 - 2	Bignall 15 Herring 49	14	16
14	Nat South	A	Whitehawk	290	W 3 - 0	Brown 6 23 Elliott 9 (og)	13	17
21	Nat South	A	St Albans City	539	D 0 - 0		14	18
28	Nat South	H	Eastbourne Borough	227	L 0 - 1		15	19
Nov 4	Nat South	H	Havant & Waterlooville	345	L 0 - 1		17	20
11	Nat South	A	Wealdstone	1021	L 0 - 1		17	21
18	Nat South	H	Truro City	224	L 0 - 1		17	22
25	FAT 3Q	H	Billericay Town	267	L 0 - 2			23
Dec 2	Nat South	A	Chelmsford City	644	D 1 - 1	Rodgers 87	18	24
9	Nat South	H	Dartford	216	W 1 - 0	Soares 23 (pen)	17	25
23	Nat South	A	Weston-s-Mare	440	L 1 - 2	Bryant 38	17	26
26	Nat South	H	Chippenham Town	300	W 2 - 1	Richards 12 (og) Wall 78	15	27
Jan 1	Nat South	A	Chippenham Town	610	W 2 - 1	Brown 24 32	14	28
6	Nat South	H	Oxford City	282	L 1 - 2	Bignall 60	14	29
13	Nat South	H	Hemel Hempstaed Town	449	W 2 - 1	Bignall 58 Hopper 64	12	30
27	Nat South	H	Bognor Regis Town	280	D 1 - 1	Soares 28	14	31
Feb 3	Nat South	A	Eastbourne Borough	391	L 1 - 4	Fragata 76	15	32
17	Nat South	A	Havant & Waterlooville	967	L 0 - 2		18	33
Mar 10	Nat South	H	Chelmsford City	222	D 1 - 1	Bignall 35	19	34
13	Nat South	H	St Albans City	200	W 3 - 1	SOARES 3 (15 56 60 (pen))	17	35
17	Nat South	A	Gloucester City	200	L 0 - 4		18	36
20	Nat South	A	Hampton & Richmond B	385	L 1 - 3	Leigh-Gilchrist 59	19	37
24	Nat South	H	Welling United	258	L 1 - 4	Herring 6	19	38
Apr 2	Nat South	H	Poole Town	297	W 4 - 0	Leigh-Gilchrist 1 84 Soares 75 Bignall 90	18	39
7	Nat South	H	Braintree Town	233	L 0 1		19	40
9	Nat South	A	Wealdstone	356	L 1 - 3	Kilgour 51	19	41
14	Nat South	A	Bath City	847	L 0 - 5		19	42
17	Nat South	A	Truro City	326	L 1 - 2	Lynch 90	19	43
21	Nat South	H	Whitehawk	264	L 0 - 1		19	44
24	Nat South	A	Concord Rangers	263	L 0 1		19	45
28	Nat South	A	East Thurrock United	312	W 1 - 0	Bignall 37	19	46

GOALSCORERS	SG	CSG	Pens	Hat tricks	Total		SG	CSG	Pens	Hat tricks	Total
2016-17 Brown					12	Fragata					1
Soares	9	3	1	1	11	Kllgour					1
Bignall	9	2			9	Lynch					1
Brown	6	2	2		9	Ngamvoulou					1
Hopper	3				3	Rodgers					1
Leigh-Gilchrist	2				3	Wall					1
Opponents					3	Williams					1
Herring	2				2	Willmoth					1
Bryant					1						
Clark					1						

OXFORD CITY MATCH RESULTS 2017-18

Date	Comp	H/A	Opponents	Att:	Result	Goalscorers	Pos	No.
Aug 5	Nat South	H	St Albans City	283	L 2 - 3	Paterson 24 Pearce 90	17	1
8	Nat South	A	Hampton & Richmond B	302	L 0 - 1		18	2
12	Nat South	A	Whitehawk	208	W 3 - 0	Paterson 6 Hirst 20 Fleet 28	15	3
15	Nat South	H	Hungerford Town	251	W 2 - 0	McEachran 48 Paterson 66	10	4
19	Nat South	A	Dartford	812	L 1 - 2	Paterson 52	13	5
26	Nat South	H	Welling United	252	D 1 - 1	Sinclair 45	13	6
28	Nat South	A	Chippenham Town	528	L 2 - 3	McEachran 10 Paterson 65 (pen)	17	7
Sept 2	Nat South	H	Braintree Town	312	L 1 - 2	Paterson 7	18	8
5	Nat South	A	Bath City	416	L 1 - 2	Amankwaaw 28 (og)	19	9
9	Nat South	H	East Thurrrock United	174	D 3 - 3	Pearce 4 Paterson 35 Fleet 74	19	10
12	Nat South	H	Weston-s-Mare	125	D 3 - 3	Poku 14 Fleet 54 McEachran 77	19	11
16	FAC 2Q	A	Whitehawk	295	W 3 - 1	Fleet 31 McEachran 41 60		12
23	Nat South	A	Eastbourne United	642	L 0 - 2		19	13
30	FAC 3Q	H	Leiston	185	W 4 - 2	Oastler 15 Pearce 81 Forde 90 Sinclair 90		14
Oct 7	Nat South	H	Poole Town	252	L 2 - 3	Paterson 20 90	20	15
14	FAC 4Q	H	Bognor Regis Town	406	W 1 - 0	Paterson 32		16
21	Nat South	A	Hemel Hempstead Town	449	L 0 - 2		21	17
28	Nat South	H	Concord Rangers	245	D 1 - 1	Sinclair 60	21	18
Nov 4	FAC 1	A	Colchester United	1775	W 1 - 0	Paterson 46		19
11	Nat South	A	Chelmsford City	977	W 2 - 1	Pearce 13 Poku 54	20	20
18	Nat South	H	Wealdstone	349	W 3 - 2	Oxlaid-Chamberlain 5 McEachran 8 Fleet 87	20	21
21	Nat South	A	Bognor Regis Town	501	D 0 - 0		20	22
25	FAT 3Q	H	Hereford	480	L 1 - 2	Grant 11		23
Dec 2	FAC 2	A	Notts County	5092	L 2 - 3	Sinclair 53 Paterson 73		24
5	Nat South	H	Truro City	275	W 3 - 1	PATERSON 3 (18 62 93)	19	25
9	Nat South	A	St Albans City	606	D 1 - 1	Sinclair 20	19	26
23	Nat South	H	Hampton & Richmond B	259	D 0 - 0		19	27
26	Nat South	A	Gloucester City	324	W 1 - 0	Sinclair 16	17	28
Jan 1	Nat South	H	Gloucester City	332	L 0 - 3		19	29
6	Nat South	A	Hungerford Town	282	W 2 - 1	Paterson 31 Sinclair 47	16	30
9	Nat South	A	Havant & Waterlooville	601	L 2 - 3	Poku 51 Paterson 59 (pen)	16	31
13	Nat South	H	Whitehawk	232	L 0 - 1		18	32
20	Nat South	A	East Thurrock United	420	L 1 - 4	Paterson 64	18	33
27	Nat South	H	Bath City	818	D 1 - 1	Paterson 75 (pen)	17	34
Feb 3	Nat South	A	Concord Rangers	259	L 1 - 2	Grant 58	17	35
10	Nat South	H	Hemel Hempstead T	358	W 4 - 1	Grant 16 Oxlade-Chamberlain 24 Prior 78 Nombe 84	17	36
17	Nat South	H	Truro City	465	W 3 - 2	Paterson 53 (pen) Nombe 61 76	15	37
24	Nat South	H	Chelmsford City	451	W 2 - 0	Nombe 7 50	14	38
Mar 10	Nat South	H	Havant & Waterlooville	410	L 0 - 1		15	39
17	Nat South	A	Welling United	404	W 3 - 1	Sinclair 60 Nombe 76 Grant 90	15	40
24	Nat South	H	Dartford	363	L 0 - 2		15	41
Apr 2	Nat South	H	Chippenham Town	392	L 0 - 1		16	42
7	Nat South	H	Eastbourne Borough	221	W 2 1	Pickering 33 (og) Paterson 58	15	43
14	Nat South	A	Weston-s-Mare	524	L 2 - 4	Cotter 26 Sinclair 31	17	44
21	Nat South	H	Bognor Regis Town	352	W 4 - 0	Patterson 32 43 Musonda 76 Sinclair 89	16	45
24	Nat South	A	Braintree Town	466	D 0 - 0		16	46
26	Nat South	A	Wealdstone	727	D 1 - 1	Patterson 9	16	47
28	Nat South	A	Poole Town	716	L 0 - 2		16	48

GOALSCORERS	SG	CSG	Pens	Hat tricks	Total		SG	CSG	Pens	Hat tricks	Total
2016-17 Fondop					9	Ox-Chamb'n	2				2
Paterson	20	3	4	1	24	Cotter					1
Sinclair	10	2			10	Forde					1
McEachran	5				6	Hirst					1
Nombe	4	3			6	Musonda					1
Fleet	6	3			5	Oastler					1
Grant	4	2			4	Prior					1
Pearce	4				4						
Poku	3				3						
Opposition	2				2						

POOLE TOWN MATCH RESULTS 2017-18

Date	Comp	H/A	Opponents	Att:	Result	Goalscorers	Pos	No.
Aug 5	Nat South	A	Weston-super-Mare	558	W 2 - 1	Oxlade-Chamberlain 78 Smeethin 90	7	1
8	Nat South	H	Bognor Regis Town	487	D 2 - 2	Cooper 24 Lee 46	9	2
12	Nat South	H	East Thurrock United	350	L 2 - 3	Devlin 33 Bell-Baggle 47	11	3
15	Nat South	A	Chippenham Town	565	W 1 - 0	Devlin 90	9	4
19	Nat South	H	St Albans City	388	L 0 - 1		10	5
26	Nat South	A	Bath City	484	L 0 - 1		10	6
28	Nat South	H	Hungerford Town	453	L 1 - 2	Spetch 51	15	7
Sept 2	Nat South	A	Whitehawk	298	D 2 - 2	Bentley 24 Bedford 32	16	8
5	Nat South	H	Hemel Hempstead T	276	L 2 - 4	Bentley 4 38 (pen)	18	9
9	Nat South	A	Welling United	452	L 0 - 2		20	10
11	Nat South	A	Wealdstone	807	L 1 - 3	Bentley 62	20	11
16	**FAC 2Q**	**A**	**Salisbury**	**995**	**W 2 - 0**	**Whisken 62 Bedford 85**		**12**
23	Nat South	H	Chelmsford City	503	D 0 - 0		20	13
30	**FAC 3Q**	**A**	**Slough Town**	**680**	**L 1 - 2**	**Bentley 30**		**14**
Oct 7	Nat South	A	Oxford City	252	W 3 - 2	Bentley 43 68 Bedford 78	18	15
21	Nat South	A	Havant & Waterlooville	830	D 2 - 2	Neale 49 Bentley 77	18	16
28	Nat South	H	Gloucester City	421	L 0 - 3		18	17
31	Nat South	A	Concord Rangers	193	D 1 - 1	Spetch 60	18	18
Nov 4	Nat South	A	Eastbourne Borough	487	W 4 - 0	BENTLEY 3 (14 20 68 pen) Devlin 49	17	19
11	Nat South	H	Braintree Town	470	L 0 - 3		18	20
18	Nat South	A	Hampton & Richmond	474	L 0 - 1		19	21
25	**FAT 3Q**	**A**	**St Albans City**	**317**	**L 1 - 3**	**Devlin (pen) 40**		**22**
Dec 2	Nat South	H	Dartford	411	L 0 - 1		20	23
9	Nat South	H	Weston-s-Mare-21	324	W 3 - 1	Devlin 19 (pen) Bentley 45 Gyebi 86	20	24
22	Nat South	A	Bognor Regis Town	602	D 1 - 1	Bentley 65	20	25
26	Nat South	H	Truro City	381	L 0 - 3		20	26
Jan 1	Nat South	A	Truro City	573	L 1 - 3	Balmer 88	20	27
20	Nat South	H	Welling United	390	L 2 - 3	Brooks 12 13	20	28
27	Nat South	A	Hemel Hempstaed T	540	W 1 - 0	Gillespie 31	20	29
30	Nat South	H	Chippenham Town	343	W 2 - 0	Baghdadi 43 Bentley 71 (pen)	20	30
Feb 3	Nat South	A	Gloucester City	259	D 2 - 2	Bentley 15 Hall 50 (og)	18	31
10	Nat South	H	Havant & Waterlooville	454	L 1 - 3	Bentley 40	20	32
17	Nat South	H	Eastbourne Borough	479	L 0 - 4		20	33
24	Nat South	A	Braintree Town	368	L 0 - 1		20	34
Mar 10	Nat South	A	Dartford	928	W 1 - 0	Whisken 63	20	35
17	Nat South	H	Bath City	363	L 0 - 4		20	36
20	Nat South	A	East Thurrock United	165	D 2 - 2	Brooks 49 Constable 92	20	37
24	Nat South	A	St Albans City	909	L 1 - 2	Brooks 38	20	38
Apr 2	Nat South	A	Hungerford Town	297	L 0 - 4		20	39
7	Nat South	A	Chelmsford City	745	L 1 - 2	Gillespie 4	20	40
14	Nat South	H	Wealdstone	442	W 2 - 1	Devlin 57 (pen) Bentley 68	20	41
17	Nat South	H	Hampton & Richmond	314	L 0 - 1		20	42
21	Nat South	A	Concord Rangers	222	W 1 - 0	Devlin 90	20	43
24	Nat South	H	Whitehawk	408	D 1 - 1	Devlin 16	20	44
28	Nat South	H	Oxford City	718	W 2 - 0	Constable 64 Devlin 83	20	45

GOALSCORERS	SG	CSG	Pens	Hat tricks	Total		SG	CSG	Pens	Hat tricks	Total
2016-17 Devlin					17	Balmer					1
Bentley	11	3	2	1	17	Bell-Baggie					1
Devlin	8	2	3		9	Cooper					1
Brooks	3	2			4	Gyebi					1
Bedford	3				3	Lee					1
Constable	2				2	Neale					1
Gillespie	2				2	Opponents					1
Spetch					2	Oxlade-Chamberlain					1
Whisken					2	Smeethin					1
Baghdadi					1						

ST ALBANS CITY MATCH RESULTS 2017-18

Date	Comp	H/A	Opponents	Att	Result	Goalscorers	Pos	No.
Aug 5	Nat South	A	Oxford City	283	W 3 - 2	Sambou 45 46 Merson 84	5	1
8	Nat South	H	Wealdstone	654	W 2 - 1	Merson 41 Banton 65	3	2
12	Nat South	H	Weston-s-Mare	497	W 3 - 1	Merson 16 Murrell-Williamson 74 Walker 88	1	3
14	Nat South	A	Chelmsford City	1025	W 2 - 0	Gardiner 19 Murrell-Wilkinson 58	1	4
19	Nat South	A	Poole Town	388	W 1 - 0	Murrell-Williamson 40	1	5
26	Nat South	H	Concord Rangers	688	W 2 - 1	Noble 51 Walker 65	1	6
28	Nat South	A	Braintree Town	528	L 0 - 1		2	7
Sept 2	Nat South	H	Gloucester City	904	L 2 - 3	Lucien 35 Gardiner 37	3	8
5	Nat South	H	Eastbourne Borough	543	D 2 - 2	Gardiner 45 Banton 45	6	9
12	Nat South	H	Havant & Waterlooville	403	W 2 - 1	Lucien 16 Merson 90	4	10
16	FAC 2Q	H	Cambridge City	276	D 3 - 3	Murrell-Williamson 14 Merson 18 75		11
19	FAC 2Qr	A	Cambridge City	276	W 2 - 0	Banton 33 Walker 42		12
26	Nat South	A	East Thurrock United	286	D 1 - 1	Murrell-Williamson 12	4	13
30	Nat South	A	Whitehawk	309	D 1 - 1	Monlouis 43	3	14
Oct 7	Nat South	H	Bath City	1510	W 2 - 0	Murrell-Williamson 45 Walker 60	2	15
14	FAC 4Q	H	Boreham Wood	1418	L 1 - 3	Banton 66		16
21	Nat South	H	Hungerford Town	539	D 0 - 0		3	17
24	Nat South	A	Hampton & Richmond B	421	L 0 - 1		3	18
28	Nat South	A	Dartford	1070	L 1 - 2	Walker 40	5	19
Nov 4	Nat South	H	Welling United	715	L 1 - 2	Pinney 90	7	20
11	Nat South	A	Chippenham Town	570	D 3 - 3	Banton 17 Bender 66 Murrell-Williamson 78	7	21
18	Nat South	A	Bognor Regis Town	583	L 1 - 2	Merson 33	9	22
25	FAT 3Q	H	Poole Town	317	W 3 - 1	Noble 38 (pen) Murrell-Williamson 71 80		23
Dec 2	Nat South	A	Truro City	513	W 2 - 1	Merson 71 Walker 81	7	24
9	Nat South	H	Oxford City	506	D 1 - 1	Merson 87	8	25
16	FAT 1	A	Whitehawk	142	W 2 - 1	Banton 16 Monlouis 60	8	26
23	Nat South	A	Wealdstone	911	W 3 - 1	Murrell-Williamson 15 47 Banton 65	8	27
26	Nat South	H	Hemel Hempstead Town	1259	D 2 - 2	Merson 66 81	8	28
Jan 1	Nat South	A	Hemel Hempstead Town	1266	L 0 - 2		8	29
6	Nat South	H	Chelmsford City	774	W 2 - 1	Monlouis 17 Eadie 45	8	30
13	FAT 2	A	Harrogate Town	634	D 1 - 1	Bender 66		31
16	FAT 2r	A	Harrogate Town	362	L 0 - 5			32
20	Nat South	A	Eastbourne Borough	420	D 1 - 1	Murrell-Williamson 53	8	33
27	Nat South	H	East Thurrock United	602	W 7 - 2	MERSON 4 (16 42 46 pen 56) Kiangebent 45 Walker 78 Banton 87	6	34
Feb 3	Nat South	H	Dartford	807	W 4 - 0	Merson 39 42 Kiangebeni 59 M-Williamson 65	4	35
17	Nat South	A	Welling United	517	L 1 - 3	Noble 49 (pen)	6	36
24	Nat South	H	Chippenham Town	661	W 2 - 0	Banton 90 Murrell-Williamson 90	5	37
Mar 10	Nat South	H	Truro City	712	L 0 - 1		6	38
12	Nat South	A	Hungerford Town	200	L 1 3	Noble 6	6	39
17	Nat South	A	Concord Rangers	185	W 2 - 1	Bradbury 52 Banton 82	4	40
20	Nat South	A	Weston-s-Mare	418	W 2 - 0	Sendles-White 75 Kiangebeni 89	4	41
24	Nat South	H	Poole Town	909	W 2 - 1	Murrell-Williamson 69 Kiangebeni 90	4	42
Apr 2	Nat South	H	Braintreee Town	812	W 2 - 1	Merson 59 85	4	43
7	Nat South	H	Whitehawk	757	L 0 - 3		6	44
10	Nat South	A	Bognor Regis Town	330	L 1 - 2	Bradbury 90	7	45
14	Nat South	A	Havant & Waterlooville	1051	L 1 - 2	Sendles-White 10	7	46
17	Nat South	A	Gloucester City	202	W 4 - 1	Bender 42 MERSON 3 (74 81 84)	6	47
21	Nat South	H	Hampton & Richmond B	1021	L 1 - 3	Banton 39	7	48
28	Nat South	A	Bath City	1023	L 1 - 2	Banton 45	8	49

GOALSCORERS	SG	CSG	Pens	Hat tricks	Total		SG	CSG	Pens	Hat tricks	Total
2016-17 Theophanous					19	Bradbury	2				2
Merson	13	3	2		22	Lucien	2				2
M-Williamson	13	3			15	Sanbou	1				2
Banton	12				12	Sandles-White	2				2
Walker	6				7	Bender	1				1
Kiangebeni	4				4	Pinney	1				1
Noble	4		1		4						
Gardiner	2	2			3						
Bender	3				3						
Monlouis	3				3						

TRURO MATCH RESULTS 2017-18

Date	Comp	H/A	Opponents	Att:	Result	Goalscorers	Pos	No.
Aug 5	Nat South	H	Welling United	506	W 3 - 2	Lamont 19 Cooke 44 Allen 45	6	1
7	Nat South	A	Gloucester City	352	W 3 - 0	Palmer 7 Gerring 41 Copp 75	1	2
12	Nat South	A	Concord Rangers	257	D 2 - 2	Keats 84 Yetton 87	3	3
15	Nat South	H	Bath City	676	L 1 - 2	Cooke 26	7	4
19	Nat South	H	Eastbourne Borough	412	L 0 - 1		9	5
26	Nat South	A	Chelmsford City	730	L 0 - 2		9	6
28	Nat South	H	Weston-s-Mare	441	W 2 - 1	Harvey 33 (pen) Cooke 64	7	7
Sept 2	Nat South	A	Hemel Hempstaed Town	466	W 2 - 0	Cooke 56 Keats 82	6	8
5	Nat South	A	Havant & Waterlooville	698	W 2 - 1	Keats 69 Cooke 90	6	9
9	Nat South	H	Whitehawk	413	W 7 - 2	KEATS 3 (8 31 55) Harvey 16 Cooke 60 Odofin 72 (og) Hartridge 88	4	10
12	Nat South	H	Chippenham Town	288	W 1 - 0	Neal 52	2	11
16	FAC 2Q	H	AFC Portchester	302	W 2 - 0	Neal 73 86		12
23	Nat South	A	East Thurrock United	362	W 2 - 1	Keats 21 Riley-Lowe 89	1	13
30	FAC 3Q	H	AFC Sudbury	359	W 4 - 1	Todd 45 Lamont 56 Harvey 83 Yetton 87		14
Oct 7	Nat South	A	Hampton & Richmond B	531	D 1 - 1	Riley-Lowe 78	3	15
14	FAC 4Q	H	Hampton & Richmond B	784	W 2 - 0	Keats 60 89		16
21	Nat South	A	Wealdstone	817	L 1 - 2	Harvey 81	4	17
28	Nat South	H	Bognor Regis Town	604	D 1 - 1	Gerring 16	6	18
Nov 5	FAC 1	A	Charlton Athletic	4494	L 1 - 3	Harvey 59		19
11	Nat South	H	Dartford	541	W 3 - 1	Harvey 13 (pen) Cooke 16 19	3	20
18	Nat South	A	Hungerford Town	224	W 1 - 0	Tyler 38 (og)	3	21
21	Nat South	A	Braintree Town	466	D 1 - 1	Cooke 36		22
25	FAT 3Q	A	Lewes	619	W 3 - 1	Todd 28 Harvey 29 Neal 38		23
Dec 2	Nat South	H	St Albans City	513	L 1 - 2	Harvey 90	4	24
4	Nat South	A	Oxford City	275	L 1 - 3	Neal 64	4	25
9	Nat South	A	Welling United	383	D 2 - 2	Cooke 24 Harvey 49	7	26
16	FAT 1	A	Sutton United	576	L 0 - 1			27
23	Nat South	H	Gloucester City	523	D 1 - 1	Harding 80	7	28
26	Nat South	A	Poole Town	381	W 3 - 0	Cooke 60 Harvey 68 79	6	29
Jan 1	Nat South	H	Poole Town	573	W 3 - 1	Thompson 1 Gerring 20 88	4	30
6	Nat South	A	Bath City	612	D 0 - 0		5	31
20	Nat South	H	Whitehawk	251	L 2 - 3	Lamont 19 Harding 32	6	32
Feb 3	Nat South	A	Bognor Regis Town	517	W 2 - 0	Gerring 79 Neal 90		33
10	Nat South	H	Wealdstone	391	L 1 - 3	Lamont 8	7	34
17	Nat South	H	Oxford City	465	L 2 - 3	Gerring 10 Lamont 19	7	35
24	Nat South	A	Dartford	946	L 1 - 4	Thompson 87	10	36
Mar 10	Nat South	A	St Albans City	712	W 1 - 0	Riley-Lowe 26	9	37
17	Nat South	H	Chelmsford Ci9ty	402	W 2 - 0	Palmer 7 Riley-Lowe 72	6	38
20	Nat South	H	Havant & Waterlooville	413	W 1 - 0	Harvey 64	5	39
24	Nat South	A	Eastbourne Borough	465	W 3 - 1	Owen-Evans 31 Richards 38 Cooke 51	5	40
30	Nat South	H	Hemel Hempstead Town	527	D 3 - 3	Owen-Evans 20 Copp 44 Harvey 90	5	41
Apr 7	Nat South	A	East Thurrock United	409	L 1 2	Harvey 80 (pen)	8	42
10	Nat South	A	Concord Rangers	381	W 2 - 0	Cooke 1 Palmer 27	6	43
14	Nat South	A	Chippenham Town	667	L 0 2		6	44
17	Nat South	H	Hungerford Town	326	W 2 - 1	Riley-Lowe 56 Thompson 77	6	45
21	Nat South	H	Braintree Town	521	L 1 2	Richards 27	8	46
24	Nat South	A	Weston-super-Mare	365	W 2 - 0	Wollacott 32 Lamont 57	6	
28	Nat South	A	Hampton & Richmond B	1014	D 1 - 1	Owen-Evans 3	7	
May 2	PO	A	Hampton & Richmond B	922	L 1 - 3	Neal 6		

GOALSCORERS	SG	CSG	Pens	Hat tricks	Total		SG	CSG	Pens	Hat tricks	Total
2016-17 Neal					18	Thompson	3				3
Harvey	12	2	2		14	Copp	2				2
Cooke	12	4			13	Harding	2				2
Keats	6	3		1	9	Opponents					2
Neal	6	2			7	Richards	2				2
Gerring	5	4			6	Todd	2				2
Lamont	6	2			6	Yetton	2				2
Riley-Lowe	5	2			5	Allen					1
Owen-Evans	3				3	Hartridge					1
Palmer	3				3	Wollacott					1

WEALDSTONE MATCH RESULTS 2017-18

Date	Comp	H/A	Opponents	Att:	Result	Goalscorers	Pos	No.
Aug 5	Nat South	H	Concord Rangers	752	W 2 - 1	Benyon 25 Fitchett 57	8	1
8	Nat South	A	St Albans City	654	L 1 - 2	Green 34	13	2
12	Nat South	A	Gloucester City	403	D 2 - 2	Benyon 43 70	13	3
14	Nat South	H	Havant & Waterlooville	922	L 0 - 1		14	4
19	Nat South	H	Chelmsford City	908	L 0 - 2		18	5
26	Nat South	A	Eastbourne Borough	631	D 1 - 1	Oshodi 84	18	6
28	Nat South	H	Hemel Hempstead Town	966	D 1 - 1	Fitchett 90	20	7
Sept 2	Nat South	A	East Thurrock United	411	D 1 - 1	Whichelow 13	18	8
5	Nat South	A	Weston-s-Mare	416	L 1 - 5	Oshodi 43	20	9
9	Nat South	A	Bognor Regis Town	845	W 3 - 0	Green 38 Sellers 71 Brown 77	17	10
11	Nat South	H	Poole Town	807	W 4 - 1	Whichelow 38 40 Eisa 44 Fitchett 90	13	11
16	FAC 2Q	H	Faversham Town	414	W 4 - 0	Green 32 39 Whichelow 48 Fitchett 70		12
23	Nat South	A	Bath City	645	D 0 - 0		14	13
30	FAC 3Q	A	Burgess Hill Town	590	L 0 - 1			14
Oct 7	Nat South	H	Whitehawk	993	W 2 - 1	Green 63 Eisa 88	12	15
14	Nat South	A	Chippenham Town	723	D 0 - 0		12	16
21	Nat South	H	Truro City	817	W 2 - 1	Eisa 27 29	10	17
28	Nat South	A	Welling United	666	W 2 - 1	Sellers 39 Green 49 (pen)	10	18
Nov 11	Nat South	H	Hungerford Town	1,021	W 1 - 0	Eisa 90 (pen)	10	19
18	Nat South	A	Oxford City	349	L 2 - 3	Eisa 35 68	12	20
21	Nat South	A	Dartford	669	D 3 - 3	Eisa 5 Green 13 87	10	21
25	FAT 3Q	H	Chelmsford City	520	D 1 - 1	Tiryaki		22
29	FAT 3Qr	A	Chelmsford City	367	W 2 - 1	Green 31(pen) Eisa 54		23
Dec 2	Nat South	H	Braintree Town	861	W 3 - 1	Olomowewe 8 Fitchett 32 Green 46	10	24
9	Nat South	A	Concord Rangers	287	L 1 - 3	Oshodi 58	11	25
16	FAT 1	H	Wingate & Finchley	371	W 1 - 0	Eisa 51		26
23	Nat South	H	St Albans City	911	L 1 - 3	Eisa 25	12	27
26	Nat South	A	Hampton & Richmond B	817	D 1 - 1	Eisa 39	13	28
Jan 1	Nat South	H	Hampton & Richmond B	929	L 0 - 3		13	29
13	FAT 2	H	Hereford	909	W 1 - 0	Wellard 26		30
20	Nat South	A	Bognor Regis Town	706	W 3 - 0	Scott 42 (og) Gayle 64 Eisa 74	13	31
27	Nat South	H	Weston-s-Mare	760	W 2 - 0	Whichelow 8 Eisa 57	12	32
Feb 3	FAT 3	H	Warrington Town	601	W 2 - 1	Green 64 (pen) 88	12	33
10	Nat South	A	Truro City	391	W 3 - 1	Pratt 48 49 Green 66	12	34
17	Nat South	H	Dartford	1002	L 1 - 2	Fitchett 67	12	35
19	Nat South	H	Gloucester City	788	L 1 - 2	Fitchett 73	12	36
Feb 24	FAT 4	A	Billericay Town	1823	W 5 - 2	BUBB 3 Wellard Whichelow		37
Mar 5	Nat South	H	Welling United	783	W 1 - 0	Wellard 90	12	38
10	Nat South	A	Braintree Town	510	D 2 - 2	Whichelow 60 Green 88	12	39
13	Nat South	A	Havant & Waterlooville	806	L 0 - 1		12	40
17	FAT SF 1	A	Brackley Town	1250	L 0 - 1			41
24	FAT SF 2	H	Brackley Town	2008	L 0 - 2			42
26	Nat South	H	Eastbourne Borough	751	L 2 - 3	Green 23 Whichelow 57	13	43
Apr 7	Nat South	H	Bath City	808	W 2 - 1	Shephard Olomowewe	11	44
9	Nat South	A	Hungerford Town	356	W 3 - 1	Fitchett 3 Sellers 37 Pratt 70 (pen)	11	45
14	Nat South	A	Poole Town	442	L 1 - 2	Whichelow 15	12	46
16	Nat South	A	Chelmsford City	695	L 0 - 3		12	47
19	Nat South	A	Hemel Hempstead Town	733	L 0 - 1		12	48
21	Nat South	H	Chippenham Town	754	D 4 - 4	Wilson 13 Bubb 45 Pratt 62 66	12	49
23	Nat South	H	East Thurock United	690	W 3 - 0	Bubb 11 Wellard 16 Monakana 44	11	50
26	Nat South	H	Oxford City	727	D 1 - 1	Pratt 47	11	51
28	Nat South	A	Whitehawk	507	W 1 - 0	Wellard 71	11	52

GOALSCORERS	SG	CSG	Pens	Hat tricks	Total		SG	CSG	Pens	Hat tricks	Total
2016-17 Benyon					20	Sellers	3				3
Green	12		3		15	Olomowewe	2				2
Eisa	12	3	1		14	Brown					1
Whichelow	6	2			9	Gayle					1
Fitchett	7			1	8	Monakana					1
Pratt	3	1			6	Opponents					1
Bubb	3			1	5	Shephard					1
Wellard	3				5	Tiryaki					1
Benyon	2				3	Wilson					1
Oshodi	3				3						

WELLING UNITED MATCH RESULTS 2017-18

Date	Comp	H/A	Opponents	Att:	Result	Goalscorers	Pos	No.
Aug 5	Nat South	A	Truro City	506	L 2 - 3	Coyle 51 60	18	1
8	Nat South	H	Chelmsford City	611	L 0 - 1		19	2
12	Nat South	H	Bognor Regis Town	511	D 3 - 3	Coyle 11 Goldberg 13 Healy 72	18	3
15	Nat South	A	Eastbourne Borough	321	D 0 - 0		21	4
19	Nat South	H	Hungerford Town	472	W 3 - 2	Coyle 4 Goldberg 15 T.Bradbrook 19	15	5
26	Nat South	A	Oxford City	252	D 1 - 1	Goldberg 60	15	6
28	Nat South	H	Hampton & Richmond B	529	L 0 - 1		19	7
Sept 2	Nat South	A	Bath City	542	D 1 - 1	Phipps 19	17	8
5	Nat South	A	Braintree Town	504	D 1 - 1	Monakana 36	16	9
9	Nat South	H	Poole Town	452	W 2 - 0	Phipps 54 Healy 71	15	10
12	Nat South	H	Whitehawk	309	W 1 - 0	Phipps 36	11	11
16	FAC 2Q	H	Haringey Borough	329	L 1 - 2	Healy 56		12
23	Nat South	A	Havant & Waterlooville	826	W 3 - 2	Jebb 30 42 Healy 64	11	13
Oct 7	Nat South	H	Chippenham Town	595	W 4 - 0	Healy 38 T.Bradbrook 42 48 Goldberg 63	8	14
10	Nat South	A	Weston-s-Mare	536	W 2 - 0	Phipps 23 Healy 33	7	15
21	Nat South	A	Gloucester City	269	W 1 - 0	Healy 84	5	16
28	Nat South	H	Wealdstone	666	L 1 - 2	Parkinson 65	7	17
Nov 4	Nat South	A	St Albans City	715	W 2 - 1	Healy 44 Jebb 67	7	18
11	Nat South	H	Concord Rangers	636	D 3 - 3	Healy 65 Phipps 68 85	4	19
18	Nat South	A	Hemel Hempstead Town	453	D 2 - 2	T.Bradbrook 56 Healy 58	7	20
25	FAT 3Q	H	Weston-s-Mare	322	L 0 - 1			21
Dec 2	Nat South	H	East Thurrock United	432	L 0 - 3		10	22
9	Nat South	H	Truro City	506	D 2 - 2	Parkinson 19 Jebb 63		23
23	Nat South	H	Chelmsford City	787	L 1 - 4	Goldberg 76	11	24
26	Nat South	H	Dartford	1401	L 2 - 3	Driver 76 Monakana 87	12	25
Jan 1	Nat South	A	Dartford	1640	L 1 - 4	Romain 24		26
6	Nat South	H	Eastbourne Borough	404	W 3 - 0	Durojaiye 10 Romain 79 Jebb 90	10	27
20	Nat South	H	Poole Town	390	W 3 - 2	Monakana 4 Goldberg 57 (pen) 65	9	28
27	Nat South	A	Braintree Town	528	W 3 - 0	Driver 61 Acheampong 67 Jebb 77	9	29
Feb 10	Nat South	H	Gloucester City	434	L 2 - 3	Goldberg 60 62 (pen)	11	30
17	Nat South	H	St Albans City	517	W 3 - 1	Goldberg 50 Parkinson 54 Philpot 72	10	31
24	Nat South	A	Concord Rangers	287	W 2 - 0	Parkinson 45 Greenhalgh 63 (og)	8	32
Mar 5	Nat South	A	Wealdstone	783	L 0 - 1		8	33
10	Nat South	H	East Thurrock United	318	W 1 - 0	Coombes 55	8	34
17	Nat South	A	Oxford City	404	L 1 - 3	Philpot 73	10	35
20	Nat South	A	Bognor Regis Town	327	W 3 - 1	Coombes 56 64 Philpot 37	7	36
24	Nat South	A	Hungerford Town	258	W 4 - 1	Philpot 35 74 Coombes 48 Coyle 62	6	37
Apr 2	Nat South	A	Hampton & Richmond B	627	D 1 - 1	Philpot 60	7	38
7	Nat South	H	Havant & Waterlooville	603	L 0 - 1		8	39
10	Nat South	H	Hemel Hempstead Town	442	D 0 - 0		8	40
14	Nat South	A	Whitehawk	294	L 1 - 2	Durojaiye 49	9	41
21	Nat South	H	Weston-s-Mare	491	L 1 - 3	Welch 55	9	42
24	Nat South	H	Bath City	365	L 0 - 2		9	43
28	Nat South	A	Chippenham Town	531	L 0 - 1		10	44

GOALSCORERS	SG	CSG	Pens	Hat tricks	Total		SG	CSG	Pens	Hat tricks	Total
2016-17 Coombes					8	Monakana	3				3
Goldberg	8	2	2		10	Driver	2				2
Healy	10	5			10	Durojaiye	2				2
Jebb	5	2			6	Romain	2	2			2
Philpot	4	4			6	Acheampong					1
Phipps	5	2			6	Opponents					1
Coyle	4				5						
Bradbrook T	3				4						
Coombes	4	2			4						
Parkinson	4	2			4						

WESTON-SUPER-MARE MATCH RESULTS 2017-18

Date	Comp	H/A	Opponents	Att:	Result	Goalscorers	Pos	No.
Aug 5	Nat South	H	Poole Town	558	L 1 - 2	Reid 90	20	1
7	Nat South	A	Hungerford Town	370	L 0 - 2		20	2
12	Nat South	A	St Albans City	497	L 1 - 3	Grubb 23 (pen)	21	3
15	Nat South	H	Gloucester City	553	W 2 - 1	Lee 33 Grubb 77	19	4
19	Nat South	A	Bognor Regis Town	668	D 1 - 1	Grubb 11	19	5
26	Nat South	H	Chippenham Town	611	D 2 - 2	Reid 76 Grubb 81	17	6
28	Nat South	A	Truro City	441	L 1 - 2	Lee 79	21	7
Sept 2	Nat South	H	Havant & Waterlooville	467	L 1 - 4	Cane 46	21	8
5	Nat South	A	Wealdstone	416	W 5 - 1	Grubb 29 86 Reid 54 65 Lee 90	18	9
9	Nat South	A	Chelmsford City	784	D 1 - 1	Rapai 82	18	10
12	Nat South	A	Oxford City	125	D 3 - 3	Grubb 2 40 Rapai 79	17	11
16	FAC 2Q	A	**Bognor Regis Town**	397	L 1 - 2	**Reid 43**		12
23	Nat South	H	Dartford	559	W 3 - 0	Hill 18 21 Collins 46	16	13
Oct 7	Nat South	A	Hemel Hempstead Town	460	D 1 - 1	Grubb 22	16	14
14	Nat South	H	Welling United	536	L 0 - 2		17	15
21	Nat South	A	Concord Rangers	164	D 2 - 2	Hill 54 Rapai 90	16	16
28	Nat South	H	Whitehawk	460	W 1 - 0	Hill 45	16	17
Nov 4	Nat South	A	East Thurrock United	221	W 4 - 3	Grubb 13 56 Hill 54 Lee 76		18
11	Nat South	H	Eastbourne Borough	488	W 5 - 1	Greenslade 6 Hill 60 74 Grubb 65 66	13	19
18	Nat South	A	Braintree Town	452	W 1 - 0	Harper 51	11	20
25	FAT 3Q	A	**Welling United**	322	W 1 - 0	**Hill 46**		21
Dec 2	Nat South	H	Hampton & Richmond B	529	L 1 - 2	Grubb	13	22
9	Nat South	A	Poole Town	324	L 1 - 3	Hill 90	13	23
19	FAT 1	A	**Chesham United**	193	W 2 - 0	**Greenslade 31 Grubb 90**		24
23	Nat South	H	Hungerford Town	440	W 2 - 1	Grubb 17 78	13	25
26	Nat South	A	Bath City	879	W 2 - 0	Hill 75 McCootie 83 (og)	10	26
Jan 6	Nat South	A	Gloucester City	202	W 3 - 1	Hill 1 (pen) Lee 35 Plummer 51	9	27
13	FAT 2	H	**Workington**	361	D 1 - 1	**Welch 15**		28
16	FAT 2r	A	**Workington**	576	L 1 - 2	**Diallo 54**		29
27	Nat South	A	Wealdstone	760	L 1 - 2	Hill 86	13	30
30	Nat South	H	Bath City	592	W 4 - 2	Hunter 12 Lee 30 Hill 65 (pen) Batten 90 (og)	9	31
Feb 3	Nat South	A	Whitehawk	180	L 1 - 5	Hill 33	11	32
10	Nat South	H	Concorde Rangers	451	W 1 - 0	Cane 16	10	33
17	Nat South	H	East Thurrock United	546	D 2 - 2	Hill 22 Scott 45	11	34
20	Nat South	H	Chelmsford City	123	L 0 - 1		11	35
24	Nat South	A	Eastbourne Borough	409	W 2 - 1	Dunnwald 39 Hill 61 (pen)	11	36
Mar 10	Nat South	A	Hampton & Richmond B	439	L 1 - 3	Baghdadi 13	11	37
17	Nat South	A	Chippenham Town	452	L 0 - 2		11	38
20	Nat South	H	St Albans City	418	L 0 - 2		11	39
24	Nat South	H	Bognor Regis Town	534	W 1 - 0	Dunnwald 21	11	40
27	Nat South	H	Braintree Town	424	L 1 - 2	Hill 62	11	41
30	Nat South	A	Havant & Waterlooville	1063	L 0 - 2		11	42
Apr 7	Nat South	A	Dartford	1025	L 1 - 3	Llewellyn 90	12	43
14	Nat South	H	Oxford City	524	W 4 - 2	Hill 5 (pen) 79 Welch 40 Parsons 52	11	44
21	Nat South	A	Welling United	491	L 1 - 3	Welch 55	13	45
24	Nat South	A	Truro City	365	L 0 - 2		13	46
28	Nat South	H	Hemel Hempstead Town	549	W 2 - 1	Welch 41 Cane 56	12	47

GOALSCORERS	SG	CSG	Pens	Hat tricks	Total		SG	CSG	Pens	Hat tricks	Total
2016-17 Grubb					20	Baghdadi					1
Hill	16	4	4		19	Collins					1
Grubb	12	4	1		17	Diallo					1
Lane	5				5	Harper					1
Reid	3				5	Hunter					1
Welch	3	2			4	Lee					
Cane	3				3	Llewellyn					1
Rapai	3	2			3	Parsons					1
Dunnwald	2				2	Plummer					1
Greenslade	2				2	Scott					1
Opponents					2						

WHITEHAWK MATCH RESULTS 2017-18

Date	Comp	H/A	Opponents	Att:	Result	Goalscorers	Pos	No.
Aug.5	Nat South	A	Hemel Hempstead U	409	L 0 - 3		22	1
8	Nat South	H	East Thurrock United	201	L 2 - 3	Tighe 66 87	22	2
12	Nat South	H	Oxford City	208	L 0 - 3		22	3
15	Nat South	A	Bognor Regis Town	744	L 2 - 6	Rose 10 Mongoy 15	22	4
19	Nat South	A	Concord Rangers	217	L 0 - 1		22	5
26	Nat South	H	Braintree Town	237	D 1 - 1	Gueye 14	22	6
28	Nat South	A	Havant & Waterlooville	838	L 0 - 4		22	7
Sept 2	Nat South	H	Poole Town	298	D 2 - 2	Tighe 65 Gordon 86	22	8
5	Nat South	H	Dartford	223	L 0 - 4		22	9
9	Nat South	A	Truro City	413	L 2 - 7	Rose 23 Gordon 82	22	10
12	Nat South	A	Welling United	309	L 0 - 1		22	11
16	FAC 2Q	H	Oxford City	295	L 1 - 3	Andoh 28		12
23	Nat South	H	St Albans City	309	D 1 - 1	Gueye 18	22	13
Oct.7	Nat South	A	Wealdstone	993	L 1 - 2	Marsh-Brown 28	22	14
14	Nat South	H	Hungerford Town	290	L 0 - 3		22	15
21	Nat South	H	Hampton & Richmond B	217	L 1 - 3	Elliott 62	22	16
28	Nat South	A	Weston-s-Mare	480	L 0 - 1		22	17
Nov.4	Nat South	H	Bath City	265	D 1 - 1	Lyons-Foster 81	22	18
11	Nat South	A	Gloucester City	261	L 1 - 3	Andoh 43	22	19
18	Nat South	H	Chelmsford City	273	L 0 - 2		22	20
25	FAT 3Q	H	Chippenham Town	138	W 2 - 1	Gueye 39 Cain 47		21
Dec.2	Nat South	A	Chippenham Town	488	L 1 - 2	Dieng 90	22	22
9	Nat South	H	Hemel Hempstead T	218	L 0 - 5		22	23
16	FAT 1	H	St Albans City	142	L 1 - 2	Marsh-Brown 52	22	24
23	Nat South	A	East Thurrock United	202	L 2 - 4	Pinney 9 Omotayo 83	22	25
26	Nat South	H	Eastbourne Borough	258	L 0 - 1		22	26
Jan.1	Nat South	A	Eastbourne Borough	521	W 4 - 1	Omotayo 28 54 Benyon 82 Marsh-Brown 84	22	27
6	Nat South	H	Bognor Regis Town	429	D 2 - 2	Omotayo 45 (pen) Mensah 79	22	28
13	Nat South	H	Oxford City	232	W 1 - 0	Omotayo 58	22	29
20	Nat South	A	Truro City	251	W 3 - 2	Marsh-Brown 15 Harding 50 ,(og) Omotayo 63	22	30
27	Nat South	A	Dartford	1104	L 1 - 2	Ijaha 56		31
Feb.3	Nat South	H	Weston-s-Mare	180	W 5 - 1	MARSH-BROWN 3 (12 31 85) Benyon 48 90	22	32
10	Nat South	A	Hampton & Richmond	523	D 1 - 1	Benyon 24	22	33
17	Nat South	A	Bath City	731	D 1 - 1	Ambroisine 23	22	34
24	Nat South	H	Gloucester City	284	D 1 - 1	Omotayo 3	22	35
Mar.10	Nat South	H	Chippenham Town	231	L 1 - 3	Benyon 79	22	36
24	Nat South	H	Concord Rangers	225	W 2 - 0	Ijaha 48 Lyons-Foster 68	22	37
Apr.2	Nat South	H	Havant & Waterlooville	277	D 0 - 0		22	38
7	Nat South	A	St Albans City	757	W 3 - 0	L'Ghoul 43 Adeloye 52 Omotayo 76	21	39
9	Nat South	A	Chelmsford City	625	L 2 - 4	Pinney 25 Omotayo 30	21	40
14	Nat South	H	Welling United	294	W 2 - 1	Macklin 18 Benyon 78	21	41
17	Nat South	A	Braintree Town	389	L 3 - 4	Macklin 27 82 Ambroisine 36	21	42
21	Nat South	A	Hungerford Town	264	W 1 - 0	Chaney 85	21	43
24	Nat South	A	Poole Town	408	D 1 - 1	Pinney 74	21	44
28	Nat South	A	Wealdstone	507	L 0 - 1		21	45

GOALSCORERS	SG	CSG	Pens	Hat tricks	Total		SG	CSG	Pens	Hat tricks	Total
2016-17 Mills					18	Adeloye					1
Omotayo	7	4	1		9	Cain					1
Marsh-Brown	5		1		7	Chaney					1
Benyon	5				6	Dieng					1
Gueye	3				3	Elliott					1
Macklin	2				3	L'Ghoul					1
Pinney	3				3	Mensah					1
Tighe	2				3	Mongoy					1
Ambroisine	2				2	Omotayo					1
Andoh	2				2	Opponents					1
Gordon	2				2	Rose					1
Ijaha	2				2						
Lyons-Foster	2				2						

BATH CITY

Club Contact Details 01225 423 087
Twerton Park, Twerton, Bath, Somerset BA2 1DB
info@bathcityfootballclub.co.uk

Founded: 1889   **Nickname:** The Romans   **Manager:** Jerry Gill
Previous Names: Bath AFC 1889-92. Bath Railway FC 1902-05. Bath Amateurs 1913-23 (Reserve side)
Previous Leagues: Western 1908-21. Southern 1921-79, 88-90, 97-2007. Football League Division Two North 1939-45. Alliance/Conference 1979-88, 90-97.
Club Colours (change): Black & white stripes

Ground Capacity: 8,880   **Seats:** 1,006   **Covered:** 4,800   **Clubhouse:** Yes   **Shop:** Yes
Previous Grounds: The Belvoir Ground 1889-92 & 1902-15. Lambridge Show Ground 1919-32.
Record Attendance: 18,020 v Brighton & Hove Albion - FA Cup 1960
Nearest Railway Station Bath Spa - 2 miles from ground or Avon Street - 1 mile   **Bus Route** No.5 - every 12mins from Town Centre.

RECORDS
Victory: 8-0 v Boston United - 1998-99
Defeat: 0-9 v Yeovil Town - 1946-47
Goalscorer: Paul Randall - 106
Appearances: David Mogg - 530
Additional: Paid £15,000 to Bristol City for Micky Tanner.
HONOURS Received £80,000 from Southampton for Jason Dodd.
FA Comps: None
League: Western Division Two 1928-29, Premier 1933-34.
Southern Premier Division 1959-60, 77-78, 2006-07.
County FA: Somerset Premier Cup 1929-30, 33-34, 35-36, 51-52, 52-53, 57-58, 59-60, 65-66, 67-68, 69-70, 77-78, 80-81, 81-82, 83 -84, 84-85, 85-86, 88-89, 89-90, 93-94, 94-95, 2007-08.

08-09		09-10		10-11		11-12		12-13		13-14		14-15		15-16		16-17		17-18	
Conf S	8	Conf S	4	Conf	10	Conf	23	Conf S	11	Conf S	7	Conf S	14	Nat S	14	Nat S	9	Nat S	9
FAC	3Q	FAC	2P	FAC	4Qr	FAC	1Pr	FAC	3Qr	FAC	4Q	FAC	4Q	FAC	3Qr	FAC	4Q	FAC	4Qr
FAT	1P	FAT		FAT	3Q	FAT	2P	FAT	3P	FAT	3Q	FAT	SF	FAT	3Q	FAT	1P	FAT	1P

2017-18 STATS   **Goals Total** 76   **Games Without Scoring** 11   **Total No. of Scorers** 17   **Total Clean Sheets** 18
Most Consecutive Scoring Games 12   **Best Unbeaten Run** 7   **Most Consecutive Clean Sheets** 3
Best Att: 1,254 v Chippenham Town, National South   Number in brackets denotes consecutive runs.

BILLERICAY TOWN

Club Contact Details 01277 286 474
New Lodge, Blunts Wall Road, Billericay CM12 9SA
info@billericaytownfc.co.uk

Founded: 1880   **Nickname:** Town or Blues   **Manager:** Harry Wheeler
Previous Names: Billericay FC.
Previous Leagues: Romford & District 1890-1914, Mid Essex 1918-47, South Essex Combination 1947-66, Essex Olympian 1966-71, Essex Senior 1971-77, Athenian 1977-79. Isthmian 1979-2012. Conference 2012-13.
Club Colours (change): All blue

Ground Capacity: 3,500   **Seats:** 424   **Covered:** 2,000   **Clubhouse:** Yes   **Shop:** Yes
Previous Grounds: None
Record Attendance: 3,841 v West Ham United - Opening of Floodlights 1977
Nearest Railway Station Billericay - 1.4km   **Bus Route** London Road - stop 300m away

RECORDS
Victory: 11-0 v Stansted (A) - Essex Senior League 05/05/1976
Defeat: 3-10 v Chelmsford City (A) - Essex Senior Cup 04/01/1993
Goalscorer: Freddie Claydon - 273
Appearances: J Pullen - 418
Additional: Leon Gutzmore scored 51 goals during the 1997-98 season.
HONOURS Received £22,500+ from West Ham United for Steve Jones November 1992
FA Comps: FA Vase 1975-76, 76-77, 78-79.
League: Chelmsford & District Division Three 1932-33. Essex Olympian 1969-70, 70-71. Essex Senior 1972-73, 74-75, 75-76. Athenian 1977-78, 78-79. Isthmian Division Two 1979-80, Premier Division 2011-12.
County FA: Essex Senior Cup 1975-76, 2010-11, 17-18. Essex Senior Trophy 1977-78, 79-80, 2017-18.

08-09		09-10		10-11		11-12		12-13		13-14		14-15		15-16		16-17		17-18	
Isth P	11	Isth P	13	Isth P	11	Isth P	1	Conf S	21	Isth P	10	Isth P	8	Isth P	9	Isth P	8	Isth P	1
FAC		FAC	2Q	FAC	2Qr	FAC	3Q	FAC	3Qr	FAC	2Q	FAC	3Q	FAC	1Qr	FAC	4Q	FAC	1Pr
FAT	1Q	FAT		FAT	1P	FAT	3Q	FAT	1P	FAT	2Qr	FAT	1Q	FAT	1Q	FAT	2Q	FAT	4P

2017-18 STATS   **Goals Total** 159   **Games Without Scoring** 1   **Total No. of Scorers** 20   **Total Clean Sheets** 22
Most Consecutive Scoring Games 62   **Best Unbeaten Run** 21   **Most Consecutive Clean Sheets** 5
Best Att: 3,400 v Leatherhead, FA Cup 1P   Number in brackets denotes consecutive runs.

CHELMSFORD CITY

Club Contact Details 01245 290 959
Melbourne Community Stadium, Salerno Way, Chelmsford CM1 2EH

Founded: 1878   **Nickname:** City or Clarets   **Manager:** Rod Stringer
Previous Names: Chelmsford FC 1878-1938.
Previous Leagues: North Essex (FM) 1895-1900. South Essex 1900-13. Athenian (FM) 1912-22. Middlesex County 1922-38. Essex & Suffolk Border 1923-24. London 1924-35. Eastern Counties (FM) 1935-38. Southern League 1938-2004. Isthmian 2004-08
Club Colours (change): Claret and white

Ground Capacity: 3,000   **Seats:** 1,300   **Covered:** 1,300   **Clubhouse:** Yes   **Shop:** Yes
Previous Grounds: New Writtle Street 1938-97, Maldon Town 1997-98, Billericay Town 1998-2005
Record Attendance: 16,807 v Colchester United - Southern League 10/09/1949. Melbourne Park: 3,201 v AFC Wimbledon,
Nearest Railway Station Chelmsford - take bus or taxi to ground.   **Bus Route** No. 54 and 56 opposite the train station.

RECORDS
Victory: 10-1 v Bashley (H) - Southern League 26/04/2000
Defeat: 1-10 v Barking (A) - FA Trophy 11/11/1978
Goalscorer: Tony Butcher - 286 (1956-71)
Appearances: Tony Butcher - 560 (1956-71)
Additional: Paid £10,000 to Dover Athletic for Tony Rogers, 1992 and to Heybridge Swifts for Kris Lee ,2001
Received £50,000 from Peterborough United for David Morrison, 1994

HONOURS
FA Comps: None
League: Middlesex County 1923-24. London League 1930-31. Southern League 1930-40 (joint), 45-46, 67-68, 71-72, Division One South 88-89. Isthmian League Premier Division 2007-08.
County FA: Essex Senior Cup 1892-93, 1901-02, 85-86, 88-89, 92-93, 2002-03, 08-09 16-17. East Anglian Cup 1924-25, 26-27, 28-29. Essex Professional Cup 1957-58, 69-70, 70-71, 73-74, 74-75.

08-09		09-10		10-11		11-12		12-13		13-14		14-15		15-16		16-17		17-18	
Conf S	5	Conf S	3	Conf S	4	Conf S	6	Conf S	5	Conf S	17	Conf S	10	Nat S	15	Nat S	4	Nat S	3
FAC	2Q	FAC	4Q	FAC	2P	FAC	2Pr	FAC	2P	FAC	2Q	FAC	4Qr	FAC	3Q	FAC	2Q	FAC	1P
FAT	3Q	FAT	3P	FAT	3Q	FAT	1P	FAT	3P	FAT	3Q	FAT	3Q	FAT	1P	FAT	3Pr	FAT	3Qr

2017-18 STATS	**Goals Total**	80	**Games Without Scoring**	8	**Total No. of Scorers**	20	**Total Clean Sheets**	18
Most Consecutive Scoring Games	18	**Best Unbeaten Run**	6			**Most Consecutive Clean Sheets**	4	

Best Att: 1,662 v Braintree Town, National South   *Number in brackets denotes consecutive runs.*

CHIPPENHAM TOWN

Club Contact Details 01249 650 400
Hardenhuish Park, Bristol Road, Chippenham SN14 6LR

Founded: 1873   **Nickname:** The Bluebirds   **Manager:** Mark Collier
Previous Names: None
Previous Leagues: Hellenic, Wiltshire Senior, Wiltshire Premier, Western. Southern >2017.

Club Colours (change): All royal blue

Ground Capacity: 3,000   **Seats:** 300   **Covered:** 1,000   **Clubhouse:** Yes   **Shop:** Yes
Previous Grounds: Played at four different locations before moving in to Hardenhuish on 24/09/1919.
Record Attendance: 4,800 v Chippenham United - Western League 1951
Nearest Railway Station Chippenham - 1km   **Bus Route** Bus stops within 200m of the ground.

RECORDS
Victory: 9-0 v Dawlish Town (H) - Western League
Defeat: 0-10 v Tiverton Town (A) - Western League
Goalscorer: Dave Ferris
Appearances: Ian Monnery

HONOURS
FA Comps: None
League: Western League 1951-52. Southern League Premier Division 2016-17.
County FA: Wiltshire Senior Cup. Wiltshire Senior Shield x4.

08-09		09-10		10-11		11-12		12-13		13-14		14-15		15-16		16-17		17-18	
SthP	8	SthP	3	SthP	7	SthP	11	SthP	15	SthP	18	SthP	11	SthP	8	SthP	1	Nat S	13
FAC	3Q	FAC	4Q	FAC	2Q	FAC	1Q	FAC	4Q	FAC	1Q	FAC	3Q	FAC	4Q	FAC	3Q	FAC	2Q
FAT	2Qr	FAT	2P	FAT	2Qr	FAT	1P	FAT	2Q	FAT	2Q	FAT	2Q	FAT	1Q	FAT	2Q	FAT	3Q

2017-18 STATS	**Goals Total**	65	**Games Without Scoring**	15 (3)	**Total No. of Scorers**	16	**Total Clean Sheets**	10
Most Consecutive Scoring Games	10	**Best Unbeaten Run**	3			**Most Consecutive Clean Sheets**	3	

Best Att: 1,602 v Bath City, National South   *Number in brackets denotes consecutive runs.*

CONCORD RANGERS

Club Contact Details 01268 515 750
Aspect Arena, Thames Road, Canvey Island, Essex SS8 0HH
media@concordrangers.co.uk

Founded: 1967   **Nickname:** Beach Boys   **Manager:** Sammy Moore
Previous Names: None
Previous Leagues: Thundermite Boys League 1967-73. Vange & District 1973-79. Mid-Essex 1979-88. Essex Intermediate 1988-91. Essex Senior 1991-2008. Isthmian 2008-13.
Club Colours (change): Yellow and blue

Ground Capacity: 3,250   **Seats:** 375   **Covered:** Yes   **Clubhouse:** Yes   **Shop:**
Previous Grounds: Waterside 70s-85
Record Attendance: 1,537 v Mansfield Town, FA Cup First Round Replay, 25/11/2014.
Nearest Railway Station Benfleet - Approx. 3 miles from the ground.   **Bus Route** First Buses operate a regular service to Thorney Bay Road, 5-10min walk from there

RECORDS
Goalscorer: Tony Stokes - 120
Appearances: Steve King - 312 (2013-16)

HONOURS
FA Comps: None

League: Essex Intermediate League Division 2 1990-91.
Essex Senior League 1997-98, 2003-04, 07-08.
County FA: Essex Senior Cup 2013-14, 14-15, 15-16.

08-09		09-10		10-11		11-12		12-13		13-14		14-15		15-16		16-17		17-18	
Isth1N	5	Isth1N	2	Isth P	8	Isth P	14	Isth P	4	Conf S	9	Conf S	7	Nat S	10	Nat S	18	Nat S	17
FAC	1Q	FAC	1Q	FAC	3Q	FAC	2Qr	FAC	2Qr	FAC	4Q	FAC	1Pr	FAC	2Q	FAC	3Q	FAC	4Qr
FAT	2Q	FAT	3Q	FAT	1Q	FAT	1Q	FAT	2Q	FAT	1P	FAT	2P	FAT	3Q	FAT	3Q	FAT	3Q

2017-18 STATS   **Goals Total** 57   **Games Without Scoring** 13   **Total No. of Scorers** 15   **Total Clean Sheets** 6
Most Consecutive Scoring Games 18   **Best Unbeaten Run** 6   **Most Consecutive Clean Sheets** 1
Best Att: 485 v Dartford, National South   *Number in brackets denotes consecutive runs.*

DARTFORD

Club Contact Details 01322 299 991
Princes Park Stadium, Grassbanks, Darenth Road, Dartford DA1 1RT
info@dartfordfc.com

Founded: 1888   **Nickname:** The Darts   **Manager:** Adam Flanagan - 13/05/2018
Previous Names: None
Previous Leagues: Kent League (FM) 1894-96, 97-98, 99-1902, 09-14, 21-26, 93-96, Southern (FM) 1896-97, 1926-81, 82-84, 86-92, 96-2006. West Kent 1902-09. Alliance 1981-82, 84-86.
Club Colours (change): White and black

Ground Capacity: 4,097   **Seats:** 642   **Covered:** Yes   **Clubhouse:** Yes   **Shop:** Yes
Previous Grounds: The Brent/Westgate House, Potters Meadow, Engleys Meadow, Summers Meadow, Watling Street
Record Attendance: 4,097 v Horsham YMCA - Isthmian Division 1 South 11/11/2006 and v Crystal Palace - Friendly 20/07/2007
Nearest Railway Station Dartford - bus ride away from the ground.   **Bus Route** Fasttrack B towards Bluewater/Dartford.

RECORDS
Appearances: Steve Robinson - 692
Additional: Paid £6,000 to Chelmsford City for John Bartley
Received £25,000 from Redbridge Forest for Andy Hessenthaler

HONOURS
FA Comps: None

League: Southern League Division 2 1896-97, Eastern Section 1930-31, 31-32, Southern Championship 30-31, 31-32, 73-74, 83-84, Southern Division 1980-81. West Kent 1908-09. Isthmian League Div.1 North 2007-08, Premier Division 2009-10.
County FA: Kent Senior Cup 1930-31, 31-32, 32-33, 34-35, 46-47, 69-70, 72-73, 86-87, 87-88, 2010-11, 15-16.
Kent Senior Trophy 1995-96.

08-09		09-10		10-11		11-12		12-13		13-14		14-15		15-16		16-17		17-18	
Isth P	8	Isth P	1	Conf S	10	Conf S	2	Conf	8	Conf	22	Conf	23	Nat S	8	Nat S	3	Nat S	2
FAC	2Q	FAC	3Q	FAC	1Pr	FAC	4Q	FAC	4Qr	FAC	1P	FAC	2P	FAC	2Q	FAC	1P	FAC	1P
FAT	3Qr	FAT	3Q	FAT	3P	FAT	3Pr	FAT	SF	FAT	1Pr	FAT	3Pr	FAT	3Q	FAT	2P	FAT	1Pr

2017-18 STATS   **Goals Total** 97   **Games Without Scoring** 8   **Total No. of Scorers** 13   **Total Clean Sheets** 13
Most Consecutive Scoring Games 10   **Best Unbeaten Run** 9   **Most Consecutive Clean Sheets** 2
Best Att: 2,705 v Swindon Town, FA Cup 1P   *Number in brackets denotes consecutive runs.*

DULWICH HAMLET

Club Contact Details 020 7274 8707
Tooting & Mitcham FC, Imperial Fields, Bishopsford Road, Morden SM4 6BF

Founded: 1893   **Nickname:** Hamlet   **Manager:** Gavin Rose
Previous Names: None
Previous Leagues: Camberwell 1894-97. Southern Suburban 1897-1900, 01-07. Dulwich 1900-01. Spartan 1907-08. Isthmian 1907-2018.

Club Colours (change): Navy and pink

Ground Capacity: 3,500   **Seats:** 612   **Covered:** 1,200   **Clubhouse:** Yes   **Shop:** Yes
Previous Grounds: Woodwarde Rd 1893-95,College Farm 95-96,Sunray Ave 1896-02,Freeman's Gd,Champ Hill 02-12,Champ Hill (old grd)12-92.
Champion Hill Stadium 1992-2018.
Record Attendance: 3,000 v Maidstone United, 18/04/2015.
Nearest Railway Station Mitcham Tram stop - 0.5km away

RECORDS
Victory: 13-0 v Walton-on-Thames, Surrey Senior Cup, 1936-37
Defeat: 1-10 v Hendon, Isthmian league, 1963-64
Goalscorer: Edgar Kail - 427 (1919-33)
Appearances: Reg Merritt - 576 (1950-66)
Additional: Received £35,000 from Charlton Athletic for Chris Dickson 2007

HONOURS
FA Comps: FA Amateur Cup 1919-20, 31-32, 33-34, 36-37.
League: Isthmian League Premier Division x4, Division One 1977-78, Division One South 2012-13.

County FA: London Senior Cup x5. Surrey Senior Cup x16.
London Challenge Cup 1998-99.

08-09		09-10		10-11		11-12		12-13		13-14		14-15		15-16		16-17		17-18	
Isth1S	12	Isth1S	12	Isth1S	5	Isth1S	3	Isth1S	1	Isth P	6	Isth P	4	Isth P	5	Isth P	3	Isth P	2
FAC	2Qr	FAC	1Q	FAC	Pr	FAC	2Q	FAC	2Q	FAC	3Q	FAC	1Q	FAC	2Q	FAC	2Q	FAC	2Q
FAT	2Q	FAT	P	FAT	2Q	FAT	1Q	FAT	P	FAT	3Qr	FAT	2Q	FAT	2P	FAT	QFr	FAT	2Q

2017-18 STATS	**Goals Total**	100	**Games Without Scoring**	4	**Total No. of Scorers**	23	**Total Clean Sheets**	22
Most Consecutive Scoring Games	23	**Best Unbeaten Run**	10		**Most Consecutive Clean Sheets**			4
Best Att:	2,417 v Needham Market, Isthmian Premier				Number in brackets denotes consecutive runs.			

EAST THURROCK UNITED

Club Contact Details 01375 644 166
Rookery Hill, Corringham, Essex SS17 9LB
speight.n@sky.com

Founded: 1969   **Nickname:** The Rocks   **Manager:** John Coventry
Previous Names: Corringham Social > 1969 (Sunday side)
Previous Leagues: South Essex Combination 1969-70. Greater London 1970-72. Metropolitan London 1972-75. London Spartan 1975-79. Essex Senior 1979-92. Isthmian 1992-2004, 05-16. Southern 2004-05.
Club Colours (change): Amber & black

Ground Capacity: 3,500   **Seats:** 160   **Covered:** 1,000   **Clubhouse:** Yes   **Shop:** Yes
Previous Grounds: Billet, Stanford-le-Hope 1970-73, 74-76, Grays Athletic 1973-74, Tilbury FC 1977-82, New Thames Club 1982-84.
Record Attendance: 1,661 vs Dulwich Hamlet, Isthmian League Premier Division Play-off final, 2016
Nearest Railway Station Stanford-le-Hope or Basildon.   **Bus Route** 100 - Stops 100 metres from the ground.

RECORDS
Victory: 7-0 v Coggeshall (H) - Essex Senior League 1984
Defeat: 0-9 v Eton Manor (A) - Essex Senior League 1982
Goalscorer: Graham Stewart - 102
Appearances: Glen Case - 600+
Additional: £22,000 from Leyton Orient for Greg Berry 1990

HONOURS
FA Comps: None
League: Metropolitan London Division Two 1972-73.
Isthmian League Division Three 1999-2000, Division One North 2010-11.
County FA: East Anglian Cup 2002-03.

08-09		09-10		10-11		11-12		12-13		13-14		14-15		15-16		16-17		17-18	
Isth1N	2	Isth1N	5	Isth1N	1	Isth P	10	Isth P	5	Isth P	20	Isth P	13	Isth P	3	Nat S	13	Nat S	15
FAC	3Q	FAC	2Q	FAC	2Qr	FAC	1P	FAC	4Qr	FAC	1Qr	FAC	1P	FAC	3Q	FAC	2Q	FAC	4Qr
FAT	3Q	FAT	P	FAT	P	FAT	2Pr	FAT	2Qr	FAT	1Pr	FAT	3Q	FAT	1P	FAT	2P	FAT	3Pr

2017-18 STATS	**Goals Total**	84	**Games Without Scoring**	13	**Total No. of Scorers**	14	**Total Clean Sheets**	10
Most Consecutive Scoring Games	16	**Best Unbeaten Run**	11		**Most Consecutive Clean Sheets**			2
Best Att:	669 v Ebbsfleet United, FA Cup 4Q				Number in brackets denotes consecutive runs.			

EASTBOURNE BOROUGH

Club Contact Details 01323 766 265
Langney Sports Club, Priory Lane, Eastbourne BN23 7QH
info@ebfc.co.uk

Founded: 1964   **Nickname:** Borough   **Manager:** Jamie Howell
Previous Names: Langney FC 1964-68. Langney Sports 1968-2001.
Previous Leagues: Eastbourne & District 1964-73. Eastbourne & Hastings 1973-83. Sussex County 1983-2000. Southern 2000-2004.

Club Colours (change): All red (All blue)

Ground Capacity: 4,151   **Seats:** 542   **Covered:** 2,500   **Clubhouse:** Yes   **Shop:** Yes
Previous Grounds: Local Recreation Grounds. Princes Park >1983.
Record Attendance: 3,770 v Oxford United - FA Cup 1st Round 05/11/05
Nearest Railway Station Pevensey & Westham - 15-20 mins walk.   **Bus Route** The LOOP Bus from the town centre.

RECORDS
Victory: 11-1 v Crowborough, Sussex Senior Cup Quarter-final, 13/01/2009
Defeat: 0-8 v Sheppey United (A) - FA Vase 09/10/93 and v Peacehaven & Tels (A) - Sussex Co. Div.1 09/11/93
Goalscorer: Nigel Hole - 146
Appearances: Darren Baker - 952 (1992-2013)
Additional: Paid £1,800 to Yeovil Town for Yemi Odoubade.
HONOURS Received £25,000 from Oxford United for Yemi Odoubade.
FA Comps: None
League: Eastbourne & Hastings Premier Division 1981-82.
Sussex County League Division Three 1986-87, Division Two 1987-88, Division One 1999-2000, 02-03.
County FA: Sussex Senior Challenge Cup 2001-02, 08-09, 15-16.

	08-09		09-10		10-11		11-12		12-13		13-14		14-15		15-16		16-17		17-18	
Conf	13	Conf	19	Conf	23	Conf S	18	Conf S	12	Conf S	10	Conf S	11	Nat S	17	Nat S	11	Nat S	18
FAC	1Pr	FAC	4Qr	FAC	4Q	FAC	4Q	FAC	3Qr	FAC	3Q	FAC	4Qr	FAC	4Q	FAC	1P	FAC	3Q
FAT	1P	FAT	2Pr	FAT	3Pr	FAT	3Qr	FAT	3Q	FAT	3Q	FAT	3Q	FAT	2P	FAT	3Qr	FAT	1P

2017-18 STATS	**Goals Total**	64	**Games Without Scoring**	12 (3)	**Total No. of Scorers**	16	**Total Clean Sheets**	10
Most Consecutive Scoring Games	9	**Best Unbeaten Run**	8			**Most Consecutive Clean Sheets**		2
Best Att:	762 v Bognor Regis Town, FA Cup 3Q					Number in brackets denotes consecutive runs.		

GLOUCESTER CITY

Club Contact Details 01386 442 303
Evesham United FC, The Spiers & Hartwell Jubilee Stadium, Cheltenham Road WR11 2LZ
chris.gage@gloucestercityafc.com

Founded: 1883   **Nickname:** The Tigers   **Manager:** Marc Richards
Previous Names: Gloucester 1883-86,1889-1901, Gloucester Nomads 1888-89, Gloucester YMCA 1910-25, Gloucester City 1902-10,1925to date
Previous Leagues: Bristol & District (now Western) 1893-96, Gloucester & Dist. 1897-1907, North Gloucestershire 1907-10,
Gloucestershire Northern Senior (FM) 1920-34, Birmingham Combination 1934-39, Southern 1939-2000
Club Colours (change): Yellow & black

Ground Capacity: 3,000   **Seats:** 300   **Covered:** Yes   **Clubhouse:** Yes   **Shop:** Yes
Previous Grounds: Longlevens 1934-64. Horton Rd 1964-86. Meadow Pk 1986-2007. FGR 07-08. Cirencester T. 08-10. Cheltenham 10-17.
Record Attendance: Longlevens: 10,500 v Tottenham - Friendly 1952. Meadow Park: 4,500 v Dagenham & Red. - FAT 3rd Q Rnd
Nearest Railway Station Evesham - 30/40 mins walk from the ground.

RECORDS
Victory: 12-1 v Bristol Saint George, April 1934
Defeat: 0-14 v Brimscombe FC, January 1923
Goalscorer: Jerry Causon - 206 (1930-36)
Appearances: Tom Webb - 675+ (2001 to date)
Additional: Paid £25,000 to Worcester City for Steve Ferguson 1990-91
HONOURS Received £25,000 from AFC Bournemouth for Ian Hedges 1990
FA Comps: None
League: Gloucester & District Division One 1897-98, 99-1900, 03-04. North Gloucestershire Division One 1907-08, 08-09.
Gloucestershire Northern Senior 1933-34. Southern League Midland Division 1988-89, Premier Division Play-off 2008-09.
County FA: Glos Junior Cup 1902-03. Glos Senior Amateur Cup 1931-32. Glos Senior Cup 1937-38, 49-50, 50-51, 52-53, 54-55, 55-56, 57-58, 65
-66, 68-69, 70-71, 74-75, 78-79, 79-80, 81-82, 82-83, 83-84, 90-91, 92-93.

	08-09		09-10		10-11		11-12		12-13		13-14		14-15		15-16		16-17		17-18	
SthP	3	Conf N	18	Conf N	14	Conf N	14	Conf N	11	Conf N	17	Conf N	14	Nat N	15	Nat N	10	Nat S	14
FAC	1Q	FAC	4Qr	FAC	2Q	FAC	4Q	FAC	1P	FAC	1P	FAC	4Q	FAC	4Q	FAC	2Q	FAC	2Q
FAT	2Q	FAT	3Q	FAT	3P	FAT	3Qr	FAT	3Q	FAT	1P	FAT	3Qr	FAT	3Qr	FAT	3Q	FAT	3Q

2017-18 STATS	**Goals Total**	57	**Games Without Scoring**	11 (2)	**Total No. of Scorers**	19	**Total Clean Sheets**	7
Most Consecutive Scoring Games	14	**Best Unbeaten Run**	5			**Most Consecutive Clean Sheets**		3
Best Att:	516 v Bath City, National South					Number in brackets denotes consecutive runs.		

HAMPTON & RICHMOND BOROUGH

HRBFC

Club Contact Details 0208 979 2456
Beveree Stadium, Beaver Close, Station Road, Hampton TW12 2BX
secretary@hamptonfc.net

Founded: 1921 **Nickname:** Beavers or Borough **Manager:** Gary McCann
Previous Names: Hampton 1921-99
Previous Leagues: Kingston & District 1921-33. South West Middlesex 1933-59. Surrey Senior 1959-64. Spartan 1964-71. Athenian 1971-73. Isthmian 1973-2007, 12-16. Conference 2007-12.
Club Colours (change): Red & blue

Ground Capacity: 3,500 **Seats:** 750 **Covered:** 800 **Clubhouse:** Yes **Shop:** Yes
Previous Grounds: Moved to the Beveree Stadium in 1959
Record Attendance: 3,500 v Hayes & Yeading United, Conference South Play-off Final, 2008-09
Nearest Railway Station Hampton - less than half a mile from the ground.

RECORDS
Victory: 11-1 v Eastbourne United - Isthmian League Division 2 South 1990-91
Defeat: 0-13 v Hounslow Town - Middlesex Senior Cup 1962-63
Goalscorer: Peter Allen - 176 (1964-73)
Appearances: Tim Hollands - 750 (1977-95)
Additional: Paid £3,000 to Chesham United for Matt Flitter June 2000
Received £40,000 from Queens Park Rangers for Leroy Phillips

HONOURS
FA Comps: None
League: Surrey Senior 1963-64. Spartan 1964-65, 65-66, 66-67, 69-70.
Isthmian Premier Division 2006-07, 2015-16.
County FA: Middlesex Charity Cup 1969-70, 95-96, 97-98, 98-99. Middlesex Super Cup 1999-00, 06-07.
Middlesex Senior Cup 2005-06, 07-08, 11-12, 13-14, 16-17.

	08-09		09-10		10-11		11-12		12-13		13-14		14-15		15-16		16-17		17-18	
	Conf S	2	Conf S	14	Conf S	18	Conf S	21	Isth P	13	Isth P	12	Isth P	15	Isth P	1	Nat S	7	Nat S	4
	FAC	4Q	FAC	4Q	FAC	3Q	FAC	3Q	FAC	3Q	FAC	4Q	FAC	1Q	FAC	1Q	FAC	3Q	FAC	4Q
	FAT	3Q	FAT	1Pr	FAT	2P	FAT	3P	FAT	1Pr	FAT	3Q	FAT	1Q	FAT	3Q	FAT	3Qr	FAT	1Pr

2017-18 STATS **Goals Total** 73 **Games Without Scoring** 9 **Total No. of Scorers** 19 **Total Clean Sheets** 12
Most Consecutive Scoring Games 11 **Best Unbeaten Run** 10 **Most Consecutive Clean Sheets** 2
Best Att: 3,127 v Braintree Town, Play-off Final
Number in brackets denotes consecutive runs.

HEMEL HEMPSTEAD TOWN

Club Contact Details 01442 264 300
Vauxhall Road, Adeyfield Road, Hemel Hempstead HP2 4HW
dean.chance@ntlworld.com

Founded: 1885 **Nickname:** The Tudors **Manager:** Dean Brennan & Stuart Maynard
Previous Names: Apsley End 1885-99. Hemel Hempstead 1899-1955, 72-99. Hemel H'stead Town 1955-72. Merged with Hemel H'stead Utd '72.
Previous Leagues: West Herts 1885-99. Herts County 1899-1922. Spartan 1922-52. Delphian 1952-63. Athenian 1963-77. Isthmian 1977-2004. Southern 2004-14.
Club Colours (change): All red

Ground Capacity: 3,152 **Seats:** 300 **Covered:** 900 **Clubhouse:** Yes **Shop:** Yes
Previous Grounds: Salmon Meadow 1885-1928. Gees Meadow 1928-29. Crabtree Lane (Wood Lane Ground) 1929-72.
Record Attendance: 3,500 v Tooting & Mitcham - Amateur Cup 1962 (Crabtree Lane)
Nearest Railway Station Hemel Hempstead - Taxi ride away from the ground **Bus Route** 320 from Stop 'A' outside the station

RECORDS
Victory: 13-0 v RAF Uxbridge (A), Spartan Division One, 1933-34. and v Chipperfield Corinthians (H), St Mary's Cup QF, 2014-15.
Defeat: 1-13 v Luton Town, FA Cup First Qualifying Round, 05/10/1901.
Goalscorer: Dai Price
Appearances: John Wallace - 1012

HONOURS
FA Comps: None
League: West Herts 1894-95, 97-98, 1904-05. Herts County 1899-1900. Spartan Division One 1933-34.
Isthmian League Division Three 1997-98, Division Two 1999-2000. Southern Premier Division 2013-14.
County FA: Herts Senior Cup 1905-06, 07-08, 08-09, 25-26, 2012-13, 14-15.
Herts Charity Shield 1925-26, 35-36, 51-52,63-64, 76-77, 83-84. Herts Charity Cup 2004-05, 08-09, 09-10.

	08-09		09-10		10-11		11-12		12-13		13-14		14-15		15-16		16-17		17-18	
	SthP	5	SthP	20	SthP	15	SthP	19	SthP	4	SthP	1	Conf S	9	Nat S	6	Nat S	12	Nat S	5
	FAC	2Q	FAC	1Qr	FAC	1Q	FAC	2Q	FAC	1Q	FAC	4Qr	FAC	1P	FAC	3Qr	FAC	4Qr	FAC	3Q
	FAT	1P	FAT	1Q	FAT	1Q	FAT	2Q	FAT	1Qr	FAT	3Q	FAT	3P	FAT	1P	FAT	3Qr	FAT	3Qr

2017-18 STATS **Goals Total** 73 **Games Without Scoring** 11 (2) **Total No. of Scorers** 22 **Total Clean Sheets** 16
Most Consecutive Scoring Games 7 **Best Unbeaten Run** 7 **Most Consecutive Clean Sheets** 3
Best Att: 1,266 v St Albans City, National South
Number in brackets denotes consecutive runs.

HUNGERFORD TOWN

Club Contact Details 01488 682 939
Bulpitt Lane, Hungerford RG17 0AY
nmatthews@rhsystems.co.uk

Founded: 1886   **Nickname:** The Crusaders   **Manager:** Ian Herring 21/08/17
Previous Names: N/A
Previous Leagues: Hungerford League. Newbury League (FM) 1909-39. Newbury & District. Swindon & District. Hellenic 1958-78, 2003-09.
Isthmian 1978-2003. Southern 2009-16.
Club Colours (change): White & black

Ground Capacity: 2,500   **Seats:** 400   **Covered:** 400   **Clubhouse:** Yes   **Shop:** Yes
Previous Grounds: Hungerford Marsh Field.
Record Attendance: 1,684 v Sudbury Town - FA Vase Semi-final 1988-89
Nearest Railway Station Hungerford - Approx. one mile from the ground.   **Bus Route** Priory Close stop - 120m away

RECORDS
Goalscorer: Ian Farr - 268
Appearances: Dean Bailey and Tim North - 400+
Additional: Paid £4,000 to Yeovil Town for Joe Scott. Received £3,800 from Barnstaple Town for Joe Scott.
Isthmian representatives in Anglo Italian Cup 1981.

HONOURS
FA Comps: None
League: Newbury League 1912-13, 13-14, 19-20, 21-22.
Hellenic Division One 1970-71, Premier Division 2008-09.
County FA: Berks & Bucks Senior Cup 1981-82. Basingstoke Senior Cup 2012-13, 14-15.

	08-09		09-10		10-11		11-12		12-13		13-14		14-15		15-16		16-17		17-18	
	Hel P	1	Sthsw	17	Sthsw	7	Sthsw	5	Sthsw	2	SthP	6	SthP	4	SthP	5	Nat S	6	Nat S	19
FAC	EPr		FAC	2Q	FAC	3Q	FAC	2Qr	FAC	2Qr	FAC	3Q	FAC	1Q	FAC	1Qr	FAC	3Q	FAC	3Qr
FAV	5P		FAT	3Q	FAT	1Qr	FAT	P	FAT	P	FAT	3P	FAT	1Qr	FAT	2P	FAT	3Q	FAT	3Q

2017-18 STATS   **Goals Total** 50   **Games Without Scoring** 16 (6)   **Total No. of Scorers** 16   **Total Clean Sheets** 9
Most Consecutive Scoring Games 9   **Best Unbeaten Run** 4   **Most Consecutive Clean Sheets** 2
Best Att: 507 v Billericay, FA Cup 3Q   Number in brackets denotes consecutive runs.

OXFORD CITY

Club Contact Details 01865 744 493
Court Place Farm, Marsh Lane, Marston, Oxford OX3 0NQ
ctoxford@oxfordcityfc.com

Founded: 1882   **Nickname:** City   **Manager:** Mark Jones
Previous Names: The original club folded in 1988 when they were evicted from their White House Ground and did not reform until 1990.
Previous Leagues: Isthmian 1907-88, 94-2005, South Midlands 1990-93, Spartan South Midlands 2005-06

Club Colours (change): Blue & white

Ground Capacity: 3,000   **Seats:** 520   **Covered:** 400   **Clubhouse:** Yes   **Shop:** Yes
Previous Grounds: Grandpont 1884-1900, The White House 1900-1988, Cuttleslowe Park 1990-91, Pressed Steel 1991-93
Record Attendance: White House - 9,756 v Leytonstone, FA Amateur Cup, 05/02/1949
Nearest Railway Station Oxford - three miles from the ground.   **Bus Route** 14A from the Station to the ground.

RECORDS
Victory: 15-0 v Woodstock Town, Oxford Senior Cup, 29/01/1966
Defeat: 0-14 v Newbury, 21/12/1895
Goalscorer: John Woodley - 414. In the 1964-65 season Woodley scored 62 goals.
Appearances: John Woodley - 917 (1959-79)
Additional: Paid £3,000 to Woking for S Adams
Received £15,000 from Yeovil Town for Howard Forinton

HONOURS
FA Comps: FA Amateur Cup 1905-06.
League: Spartan South Midlands Premier Division 1992-93, 2005-06.
Isthmian Division One 1995-96.
County FA: Oxford Senior Cup 1899-00, 00-01, 11-12, 28-29 (Res), 30-31 (Res), 41-42, 43-44, 44-45, 45-46, 48-49, 50-51, 53-54, 56-57,59-60, 60
-61, 61-62, 62-63, 64-65, 66-67, 67-68, 68-69, 69-70, 70-71 (Sh), 71-72, 73-74, 82-83, 83-84, 85-86, 96-97, 98-99, 99-00, 02-03, 17-18.

	08-09		09-10		10-11		11-12		12-13		13-14		14-15		15-16		16-17		17-18	
	SthP	6	SthP	13	SthP	14	SthP	2	Conf N	10	Conf N	20	Conf N	6	Nat S	12	Nat S	14	Nat S	16
FAC	4Q		FAC	1P	FAC	4Q	FAC	1Pr	FAC	2Q	FAC	4Q	FAC	2Q	FAC	3Q	FAC	2Qr	FAC	2P
FAT	2Qr		FAT	2Q	FAT	1Q	FAT	1Q	FAT	2P	FAT	3Q	FAT	2Pr	FAT	3P	FAT	3Q	FAT	3Q

2017-18 STATS   **Goals Total** 72   **Games Without Scoring** 13   **Total No. of Scorers** 15   **Total Clean Sheets** 10
Most Consecutive Scoring Games 10   **Best Unbeaten Run** 5   **Most Consecutive Clean Sheets** 2
Best Att: 818 v Bath City, National South   Number in brackets denotes consecutive runs.

SLOUGH TOWN

Club Contact Details 07792 126 124
Arbour Park, Stoke Road, Slough SL2 5AY (do not send correspondence to the ground)
gensec@sloughtownfc.net

Founded: 1890 **Nickname:** The Rebels **Manager:** Neil Baker & Jon Underwood
Previous Names: Slough FC. Slough United.
Previous Leagues: Southern Alliance 1892-93, Berks & Bucks 1901-05, Gt Western Suburban 1909-19, Spartan 1920-39, Herts & Middx 1940-45, Corinthian 1946-63, Athenian 1963-73, Isthmian 1973-90, 94-95, 98-2007, Conference 1990-94, 95-98, Southern 2007-2018.

Club Colours (change): Yellow & blue

Ground Capacity: 2,000 **Seats:** 250 **Covered:** Yes **Clubhouse:** Yes **Shop:** Yes
Previous Grounds: Dolphin Stad 1890-1936. Wrexham Park >2003. Stag Meadow W & Eton 03-07. Holloways Park B'field SYCOB 07-16.
Record Attendance: 1,401 v Hayes & Yeading United, Southern Premier, 29/08/2016 - first fixture at the all new Arbour Park.
Nearest Railway Station Slough **Bus Route** First Group 1, 13, 12, 14, 353.

RECORDS
Victory: 17-0 v Railway Clearing House - 1921-22
Defeat: 1-11 v Chesham Town - 1909-10
Goalscorer: Ted Norris - 343 in 226 appearances. Scored 84 during the 1925-26 season.
Appearances: Terry Reardon - 475 (1964-81)
Additional: Paid £18,000 to Farnborough Town for Colin Fielder
Received £22,000 from Wycombe Wanderers for Steve Thompson

HONOURS
FA Comps: None
League: Isthmian League 1980-81, 89-90. Athenian League x3.
County FA: Berks & Bucks Senior Cup x10.

08-09		09-10		10-11		11-12		12-13		13-14		14-15		15-16		16-17		17-18	
Sthsw	16	SthM	5	SthC	5	SthC	2	SthC	6	SthC	5	SthP	16	SthP	17	SthP	5	SthP	3
FAC	1Q	FAC	3Q	FAC	1Q	FAC	3Qr	FAC	1Pr	FAC	Pr	FAC	1Q	FAC	2Q	FAC	3Q	FAC	2P
FAT	1Q	FAT	2Q	FAT	1Qr	FAT	P	FAT	1Qr	FAT	1Q	FAT	2Qr	FAT	2Q	FAT	3Q	FAT	3Qr

2017-18 STATS	**Goals Total** 141	**Games Without Scoring** 6	**Total No. of Scorers** 19	**Total Clean Sheets** 17
Most Consecutive Scoring Games 16	**Best Unbeaten Run** 13		**Most Consecutive Clean Sheets**	3
Best Att: 1,950 v Rochdale, FA Cup 1P			Number in brackets denotes consecutive runs.	

ST ALBANS CITY

Club Contact Details 01727 848 914
Clarence Park, York Road, St. Albans, Herts AL1 4PL

Founded: 1908 **Nickname:** The Saints **Manager:** Ian Allinson
Previous Names: N/A
Previous Leagues: Herts County 1908-10. Spartan 1908-20. Athenian 1920-23. Isthmian 1923-2004. Conference 2004-11. Southern 2011-14.

Club Colours (change): Yellow & blue

Ground Capacity: 5,007 **Seats:** 667 **Covered:** 1,900 **Clubhouse:** Yes **Shop:** Yes
Previous Grounds: N/A
Record Attendance: 9,757 v Ferryhill Athletic - FA Amateur Cup 1926
Nearest Railway Station St. Albans City - 5-10 minute walk from the ground.

RECORDS
Victory: 14-0 v Aylesbury United (H) - Spartan League 19/10/1912
Defeat: 0-11 v Wimbledon (H) - Isthmian League 1946
Goalscorer: Wilfred Minter - 356 in 362 apps. (Top scorer for 12 consecutive seasons from 1920-32)
Appearances: Phil Wood - 900 (1962-85)
Additional: Wilfred Minter scored seven goals in an 8-7 defeat by Dulwich Hamlet, the highest tally by a player on the losing side of an FAC tie.

HONOURS
Paid £6,000 to Yeovil Town for Paul Turner 1957. Received £92,759 from Southend United for Dean Austin 1990.
FA Comps: None
League: Herts County Western Division 1909-09, Western & Championship 09-10. Spartan B Division 1909-10, Spartan 11-12. Athenian League 1920-21, 21-22. Isthmian League 1923-24, 26-27, 27-28, Division One 1985-86.
County FA: London Senior Cup 1970-71.

08-09		09-10		10-11		11-12		12-13		13-14		14-15		15-16		16-17		17-18	
Conf S	12	Conf S	13	Conf S	22	SthP	8	SthP	11	SthP	4	Conf S	13	Nat S	18	Nat S	10	Nat S	8
FAC	2Qr	FAC	2Q	FAC	4Q	FAC	2Qr	FAC	3Q	FAC	1P	FAC	4Q	FAC	1P	FAC	1P	FAC	4Q
FAT	1P	FAT	3Q	FAT	1P	FAT	1Q	FAT	1Q	FAT	2P	FAT	3Qr	FAT	3Q	FAT	3Qr	FAT	2Pr

2017-18 STATS	**Goals Total** 83	**Games Without Scoring** 7	**Total No. of Scorers** 16	**Total Clean Sheets** 14
Most Consecutive Scoring Games 10	**Best Unbeaten Run** 7		**Most Consecutive Clean Sheets**	3
Best Att: 1,510 v Bath City, National South			Number in brackets denotes consecutive runs.	

TORQUAY UNITED

Club Contact Details 01803 328 666
Plainmoor, Torquay, Devon TQ1 3PS
reception@torquayunited.com

Founded: 1899   **Nickname:** The Gulls   **Manager:** Gary Owers - 13/09/2017
Previous Names: Torquay United & Ellacombe merged to form Torquay Town 1910, then merged with Babbacombe to form Torquay Utd in 1921
Previous Leagues: Western 1921-27. Football League 1927-2007, 09-14. Conference 2007-09.

Club Colours (change): Yellow

Ground Capacity: 6,500   **Seats:** 2,950   **Covered:** Yes   **Clubhouse:** Yes   **Shop:** Yes
Previous Grounds: Recreation Ground. Cricketfield Road > 1910.
Record Attendance: 21,908 v Huddersfield Town, FA Cup 4th Rnd, 29/01/1955.
Nearest Railway Station Torre, 25 mins away. Main Torquay 2+ miles away.

RECORDS
Victory: 9-0 v Swindon Town, Division Three South, 08/03/1952
Defeat: 2-10 v Fulham, Division Three South, 07/09/1931
Goalscorer: Sammy Collins - 219 in 379 games (1948-58) Scored 40 during the 1955-56 season.
Appearances: Dennis Lewis - 443 (1947-59)
Additional: Paid £75,000 for Leon Constantine from Peterborough United, December 2004.
HONOURS   Received £650,000 from Crewe for Rodney Jack, July 1998.
FA Comps: None
League: Torquay & District 1909-09. Plymouth & District 1911-12. Southern Western Section 1926-27.
     Football League Fourth Division Play-offs 1990-91. Conference Play-offs 2008-09.
County FA: Devon Senior Cup 1910-11, 21-22. Devon Bowl/Devon St Luke's Bowl 1933-34, 34-35, 36-37,45-46, 47-48, 48-49,
     54-55 (shared), 57-58, 60-61, 69-70, 70-71, 71-72, 95-96 (shared), 97-98, 2006-07.

08-09		09-10		10-11		11-12		12-13		13-14		14-15		15-16		16-17		17-18	
Conf	4	FL 2	17	FL 2	7	FL 2	5	FL 2	19	FL 2	24	Conf	13	Nat	18	Nat	17	Nat	22
FAC	4P	FAC	3P	FAC	4P	FAC	2P	FAC	1P	FAC	1P	FAC	4Q	FAC	4Q	FAC	4Qr	FAC	4Q
FAT	3P	FLC	1P	FLC	1P	FLC	1P	FLC	1P	FLC	1P	FAT	SF	FAT	QF	FAT	1P	FAT	1P

2017-18 STATS	**Goals Total** 45	**Games Without Scoring** 19 (3)	**Total No. of Scorers** 16	**Total Clean Sheets** 10
Most Consecutive Scoring Games 5	**Best Unbeaten Run** 10		**Most Consecutive Clean Sheets**	3
Best Att: 3,496 v Guiseley, National League			Number in brackets denotes consecutive runs.	

TRURO CITY

Club Contact Details 01872 225 400
Torquay United FC, Plainmoor, Torquay, Devon TQ1 3PS

Founded: 1889   **Nickname:** City, White Tigers, The Tinmen   **Manager:** Lee Hodges
Previous Names: N/A
Previous Leagues: Cornwall County. Plymouth & District >1951. South Western (FM) 1951-2006. Western 2006-08. Southern 2008-11, 13-15.
     Conference 2011-13.
Club Colours (change): All white

Ground Capacity: 6,500   **Seats:** 2,950   **Covered:** Yes   **Clubhouse:** Yes   **Shop:** Yes
Previous Grounds: Truro School. Tolgarrick > mid-1900s. 2018 - Tryew Road under development hence groundshare with Torquay
Record Attendance: 1,400 v Aldershot - FA Vase
Nearest Railway Station Truro - 10min walk from the ground.

RECORDS
Misc: 115 points & 185 goals, Western League Division One (42 games) 2006-07.
     Became first British club to achieve five promotions in six seasons.

HONOURS
FA Comps: FA Vase 2006-07.
League: Plymouth & District 1936-37. South Western League 1960-61, 69-70, 92-93, 95-96, 97-98. Western Div. One 2006-07,
     Premier Division 07-08. Southern Division One South & West 2008-09, Premier Division 2010-11.
County FA: Cornwall Senior Cup 1894-95, 1901-02, 02-03, 10-11, 23-24, 26-27, 27-28, 37-38, 58-59, 66-67, 69-70, 94-95, 97-98, 2005
     -06, 06-07, 07-08.

08-09		09-10		10-11		11-12		12-13		13-14		14-15		15-16		16-17		17-18	
Sthsw	1	SthP	11	SthP	1	Conf S	14	Conf S	22	SthP	17	SthP	3	Nat S	4	Nat S	19	Nat S	7
FAC	2Qr	FAC	3Qr	FAC	2Q	FAC	3Q	FAC	3Q	FAC	2Q	FAC	1Q	FAC	3Q	FAC	2Q	FAC	1P
FAT	1Qr	FAT	1Pr	FAT	3Q	FAT	1P	FAT	3Q	FAT	1Q	FAT	3Q	FAT	2Pr	FAT	1Pr	FAT	3Q

2017-18 STATS	**Goals Total** 83	**Games Without Scoring** 5 (2)	**Total No. of Scorers** 18	**Total Clean Sheets** 14
Most Consecutive Scoring Games 20	**Best Unbeaten Run** 10		**Most Consecutive Clean Sheets**	3
Best Att: 676 v Bath City, National South			Number in brackets denotes consecutive runs.	

WEALDSTONE

Club Contact Details 01895 637 487
Grosvenor Vale, Ruislip, Middlesex HA4 6JQ
office@wealdstonefc.co.uk

Founded: 1899   **Nickname:** The Stones   **Manager:** Bobby Wilkinson - 23/08/2017
Previous Names: N/A
Previous Leagues: Willesden & District 1899-1906, 08-13, London 1911-22, Middlesex 1913-22, Spartan 1922-28, Athenian 1928-64,
Isthmian 1964-71, 95-2006, 2007-14. Southern 1971-79, 81-82, 88-95, Conference 1979-81, 82-88

Club Colours (change): Blue & white

Ground Capacity: 3,607   **Seats:** 329   **Covered:** 1,166   **Clubhouse:** Yes   **Shop:** No
Previous Grounds: Locket Road, Belmont Road, Lower Mead Stadium 1922-91, Watford FC, Yeading FC, Edgware Town, Northwood FC
Record Attendance: 13,504 v Leytonstone - FA Amateur Cup 4th Round replay 05/03/1949 (at Lower Mead Stadium)
Nearest Railway Station Ruislip and Ruislip Gardens both walking distance.   **Bus Route** E7

RECORDS
Victory: 22-0 v The 12th London Regiment (The Rangers) - FA Amateur Cup 13/10/1923
Defeat: 0-14 v Edgware Town (A) - London Senior Cup 09/12/1944
Goalscorer: George Duck - 251
Appearances: Charlie Townsend - 514
Additional: Paid £15,000 to Barnet for David Gipp
           Received £70,000 from Leeds United for Jermaine Beckford

HONOURS
FA Comps: FA Amateur Cup 1965-66. FA Trophy 1984-85.
League: Athenian 1951-52. Southern Division One South 1973-74, Southern Division 1981-82. Conference 1984-85.
Isthmian Division Three 1996-97, Premier 2013-14.
County FA: Middlesex Junior Cup 1912-13. Senior 1929-30, 37-38, 40-41, 41-42, 42-43, 45-46, 58-59, 62-63, 63-64, 67-68, 84-85. Charity Cup 1929
-30, 30-31, 37-38, 38-39, 49-50, 63-64, 68-68, 03-04, 10-11 Prem Cup 2003-04, 07-08, 08-09, 10-11. London Senior 1961-62.

	08-09		09-10		10-11		11-12		12-13		13-14		14-15		15-16		16-17		17-18	
Isth P	7	Isth P	6	Isth P	12	Isth P	4	Isth P	3	Isth P	1	Conf S	12	Nat S	13	Nat S	8	Nat S	11
FAC	1Qr	FAC	1P	FAC	3Qr	FAC	1Q	FAC	2Q	FAC	3Q	FAC	2Qr	FAC	1P	FAC	4Q	FAC	3Q
FAT	2Q	FAT	3Q	FAT	1Pr	FAT	SF	FAT	3Qr	FAT	2Qr	FAT	2P	FAT	1P	FAT	3P	FAT	SF

2017-18 STATS	**Goals Total** 80	**Games Without Scoring** 11 (3)	**Total No. of Scorers** 17	**Total Clean Sheets** 12
	Most Consecutive Scoring Games 12	**Best Unbeaten Run** 5	**Most Consecutive Clean Sheets**	3

Best Att: 2,008 v Brackley Town, FA Trophy Semi Final 2nd Leg   Number in brackets denotes consecutive runs.

WELLING UNITED

Club Contact Details 0208 301 1196
Park View Road Ground, Welling, Kent DA16 1SY
info@wellingunited.com

Founded: 1963   **Nickname:** The Wings   **Manager:** Steve King
Previous Names: None
Previous Leagues: Eltham & District Sunday 1963-71, Metropolitan 1971-75, London Spartan 1975-78, Athenian 1978-81,
Southern 1981-86, 2000-04, Conference 1986-2000

Club Colours (change): Red & white

Ground Capacity: 4,000   **Seats:** 1,070   **Covered:** 1,500   **Clubhouse:** Yes   **Shop:** Yes
Previous Grounds: Butterfly Lane, Eltham 1963-77.
Record Attendance: 4,100 v Gillingham - FA Cup First Round Proper, 22nd November 1989
Nearest Railway Station Welling - 15-20 minute walk from the ground.   **Bus Route** Numbers 89, 486 and B16.

RECORDS
Victory: 7-1 v Dorking - 1985-86
Defeat: 0-7 v Welwyn Garden City - 1972-73
Additional: Paid £30,000 to Enfield for Gary Abbott
           Received £95,000 from Birmingham City for Steve Finnan 1995

HONOURS
FA Comps: None
League: Southern League Premier Division 1985-86. Conference South 2012-13.

County FA: Kent Senior Cup 1985-86, 98-99, 2008-09.
London Senior Cup 1989-90. London Challenge Cup 1991-92.

	08-09		09-10		10-11		11-12		12-13		13-14		14-15		15-16		16-17		17-18	
Conf S	7	Conf S	9	Conf S	6	Conf S	3	Conf S	1	Conf	16	Conf	20	Nat	24	Nat S	16	Nat S	10
FAC	2Qr	FAC	3Q	FAC	2Q	FAC	2Q	FAC	4Q	FAC	2P	FAC	4Q	FAC	2P	FAC	4Q	FAC	2Q
FAT	2P	FAT	1P	FAT	1Pr	FAT	1P	FAT	1P	FAT	1Pr	FAT	2P	FAT	2P	FAT	3P	FAT	3Q

2017-18 STATS	**Goals Total** 66	**Games Without Scoring** 10 (2)	**Total No. of Scorers** 14	**Total Clean Sheets** 11
	Most Consecutive Scoring Games 13	**Best Unbeaten Run** 4	**Most Consecutive Clean Sheets**	3

Best Att: 1,401 v Dartford, National South   Number in brackets denotes consecutive runs.

WESTON-SUPER-MARE

Club Contact Details 01934 621 618
Woodspring Stadium, Winterstoke Road, Weston-super-Mare BS24 9AA
enquiries@wsmafc.co.uk

Founded: 1887   **Nickname:** Seagulls   **Manager:** Marc McGregor - July 2017
Previous Names: Borough or Weston-super-Mare
Previous Leagues: Western League 1900-02, 10-18, 48-92. Bristol & District and Somerset County 1921-45. Southern 1992-04.

Club Colours (change): White & black

Ground Capacity: 3,500 **Seats:** 350   **Covered:** 2,000   **Clubhouse:** Yes   **Shop:** Yes
Previous Grounds: 'Great Ground' Locking Road >1955. Langford Road 1955-83. Woodspring Park 1983-2004.
Record Attendance: 2,949 v Doncaster Rovers, FA Cup First Round Proper, 18th November 2014.
Nearest Railway Station Weston-Super-Mare - 25-30 minute walk away.

RECORDS
Victory: 11-0 v Paulton Rovers
Defeat: 1-12 v Yeovil Town Reserves
Goalscorer: Matt Lazenby - 180
Appearances: Harry Thomas - 740
Additional: Received £20,000 from Sheffield Wednesday for Stuart Jones
HONOURS
FA Comps: None
League: Western League 1991-92.
County FA: Somerset Senior Cup 1926-67.
          Somerset Premier Cup 2010-11, 11-12, 17-18.

08-09		09-10		10-11		11-12		12-13		13-14		14-15		15-16		16-17		17-18	
Conf S	17	Conf S	21	Conf S	12	Conf S	13	Conf S	7	Conf S	11	Conf S	17	Nat S	16	Nat S	15	Nat S	12
FAC	2Q	FAC	2Q	FAC	3Q	FAC	4Q	FAC	3Qr	FAC	3Q	FAC	1P	FAC	4Q	FAC	2Q	FAC	2Q
FAT	3Q	FAT	3Qr	FAT	3Q	FAT	3Q	FAT	3Q	FAT	1Pr	FAT	1P	FAT	2P	FAT	3Q	FAT	2Pr

2017-18 STATS	**Goals Total**	72	**Games Without Scoring**	7 (3)	**Total No. of Scorers**	19	**Total Clean Sheets**	8
Most Consecutive Scoring Games	19	**Best Unbeaten Run**	6			**Most Consecutive Clean Sheets**		2
Best Att:	611 v Chippenham Town, National South					*Number in brackets denotes consecutive runs.*		

WOKING

Club Contact Details 01483 772 470
The Laithwaite Community Stadium, Kingfield Road, Woking, Surrey GU22 9AA
admin@wokingfc.co.uk

Founded: 1889   **Nickname:** The Cards   **Manager:** Alan Dowson - 16/05/2018
Previous Names: None
Previous Leagues: West Surrey 1895-1911. Isthmian 1911-92.

Club Colours (change): Red, white & black

Ground Capacity: 6,000 **Seats:** 2,500   **Covered:** 3,900   **Clubhouse:** Yes   **Shop:** Yes
Previous Grounds: Wheatsheaf, Ive Lane (pre 1923)
Record Attendance: 6,000 v Swansea City - FA Cup 1978-79 and v Coventry City - FA Cup 1996-97
Nearest Railway Station Woking - about 15 mins from the ground.

RECORDS
Victory: 17-4 v Farnham - 1912-13
Defeat: 0-16 v New Crusaders - 1905-06
Goalscorer: Charlie Mortimore - 331 (1953-65)
Appearances: Brian Finn - 564 (1962-74)
Additional: Paid £60,000 to Crystal Palace for Chris Sharpling
HONOURS   Received £150,000 from Bristol Rovers for Steve Foster
FA Comps: FA Amateur Cup 1957-58. FA Trophy 1993-94, 94-95, 96-97 (Joint record number of victories).
League: West Surrey 1895-96. Isthmian League Division Two South 1986-87, Premier Division 1991-92.
         Conference South 2011-12.
County FA: Surrey Senior Cup 1912-13, 26-27, 55-56, 56-57, 71-72, 90-91, 93-94, 95-96, 99-00, 03-04, 2011-12, 13-14, 16-17.

08-09		09-10		10-11		11-12		12-13		13-14		14-15		15-16		16-17		17-18	
Conf	21	Conf S	5	Conf S	5	Conf S	1	Conf	12	Conf	9	Conf	7	Nat	12	Nat	18	Nat	21
FAC	4Qr	FAC	1P	FAC	P	FAC	3Q	FAC	4Q	FAC	4Q	FAC	1P	FAC	4Q	FAC	2P	FAC	2Pr
FAT	1P	FAT	2P	FAT	1P	FAT	3Q	FAT	2P	FAT	2P	FAT	3Pr	FAT	QF	FAT	1P	FAT	1P

2017-18 STATS	**Goals Total**	67	**Games Without Scoring**	11 (2)	**Total No. of Scorers**	19	**Total Clean Sheets**	9
Most Consecutive Scoring Games	15	**Best Unbeaten Run**	9			**Most Consecutive Clean Sheets**		2
Best Att:	3,790 v Aldershot Town, National League					*Number in brackets denotes consecutive runs.*		

Action from Alfreton Town v Chorley in the National North - Chorley won 2-0. Photo: Bill Wheatcroft.

National North and South Action

Midfield action from the National South match between Weston-Super-Mare and Hemel Hempstead Town. Photo: Peter Barnes.

ISTHMIAN PREMIER LEAGUE TABLE 2017-18

		P	W	D	L	F	A	GD	Pts
1	Billericay Town	46	30	9	7	110	50	60	99
2	Dulwich Hamlet	46	28	11	7	91	41	50	95
3	Hendon	46	25	10	11	96	59	37	85
4	Folkestone Invicta	46	25	10	11	104	71	33	85
5	Leiston	46	23	10	13	82	53	29	79
6	Leatherhead	46	24	7	15	68	49	19	79
7	Margate	46	20	17	9	77	53	24	77
8	Staines Town	46	21	12	13	106	83	23	75
9	Wingate & Finchley	46	20	9	17	63	71	-8	69
10	Metropolitan Police	46	19	12	15	76	71	5	66*
11	Tonbridge Angels	46	19	7	20	58	63	-5	64
12	Harrow Borough	46	19	6	21	69	76	-7	63
13	Kingstonian	46	18	5	23	57	70	-13	59
14	Dorking Wanderers	46	16	10	20	77	80	-3	58
15	Thurrock	46	17	6	23	68	79	-11	57
16	Worthing	46	15	12	19	71	84	-13	57
17	Enfield Town	46	14	14	18	72	80	-8	56
18	Merstham	46	15	11	20	69	80	-11	56
19	Needham Market	46	13	10	23	65	84	-19	49
20	Brightlingsea Regent	46	13	9	24	67	89	-22	48
21	Harlow Town	46	13	8	25	55	88	-33	47
22	Lowestoft Town	46	12	7	27	52	92	-40	43
23	Burgess Hill Town	46	9	9	28	64	102	-38	36
24	Tooting & Mitcham United	46	9	9	28	52	101	-49	36

Play-Off Semi Finals: Dulwich Hamlet 1-0 | Hendon 4-0 Folkestone Invicta
Final: Dulwich Hamlet 1-1, 4-3p Hendon

PREMIER DIVISION	1	2	3	4	5	6	7	8	9	10	11	12	13	14	15	16	17	18	19	20	21	22	23	24
1 Billericay Town		4-0	6-1	1-0	1-3	2-1	2-2	2-0	2-0	4-3	0-1	1-0	4-0	5-0	1-1	2-2	3-0	5-0	5-3	1-0	2-1	1-0	2-2	4-0
2 Brightlingsea Regent	1-1		5-2	2-3	2-2	2-1	1-2	3-1	1-1	2-1	2-0	0-7	0-1	2-0	0-1	1-3	0-1	2-3	2-2	1-3	0-3	0-3	1-0	3-0
3 Burgess Hill Town	3-4	1-2		1-3	1-1	2-4	1-1	2-0	2-3	2-4	5-1	0-1	2-1	0-5	1-1	0-0	1-4	1-1	1-1	2-5	0-1	3-1	3-1	4-1
4 Dorking Wanderers	0-1	3-2	2-1		0-1	2-2	5-3	2-2	0-4	0-3	1-3	1-1	0-2	8-0	4-2	4-0	4-1	3-2	1-1	2-0	2-3	2-2	2-2	4-2
5 Dulwich Hamlet	1-3	2-1	3-2	4-0		1-1	4-3	4-0	2-0	0-1	4-0	4-0	3-0	1-0	1-1	1-2	0-0	2-0	1-1	2-1	1-2	2-1	1-2	3-0
6 Enfield Town	1-1	2-0	3-2	3-2	3-1		1-1	1-0	3-0	1-0	1-3	0-1	2-2	3-0	2-1	2-2	4-4	0-2	3-4	3-1	0-1	1-1	1-1	0-1
7 Folkestone Invicta	2-1	3-2	3-1	3-1	0-3	5-1		1-1	1-3	3-2	3-0	2-0	2-1	1-1	2-1	5-2	0-2	2-0	2-2	3-1	3-1	5-0	1-2	
8 Harlow Town	2-4	2-0	1-1	2-2	2-3	0-2	3-2		2-1	0-3	0-1	2-1	1-0	2-0	1-1	1-2	4-3	1-3	2-4	3-2	2-1	2-1	0-1	3-2
9 Harrow Borough	0-2	1-2	3-2	3-4	0-1	5-0	0-3	2-1		0-4	2-0	1-2	0-5	6-0	0-4	2-2	3-0	3-2	1-2	2-0	2-0	1-1	3-0	1-0
10 Hendon	4-1	4-2	2-2	0-0	3-3	3-0	3-3	6-0	6-0		1-3	1-4	2-1	1-1	1-1	3-0	2-0	1-0	3-0	4-1	2-1	4-0	0-1	4-3
11 Kingstonian	0-2	0-1	0-0	0-1	4-1	1-1	6-0	0-1	0-0	0-4		1-3	3-2	1-3	2-1	1-2	4-0	3-1	0-1	2-1	0-1	2-1	0-0	
12 Leatherhead	1-1	2-1	2-1	1-0	0-1	2-0	1-2	2-1	0-2	1-2	2-0		2-2	2-1	0-2	2-1	1-0	0-1	0-2	1-0	2-0	4-0	3-0	
13 Leiston	3-1	3-2	2-0	1-0	2-2	1-0	1-5	0-0	3-0	1-2	2-0	1-2		0-1	2-2	3-1	3-0	2-0	2-2	3-1	2-0	2-0	4-0	2-3
14 Lowestoft Town	1-2	1-2	1-2	0-0	1-3	3-0	0-2	0-3	1-1	2-1	2-1	0-2	0-2		1-0	1-3	2-4	2-4	1-0	1-2	0-0	1-1	1-0	
15 Margate	1-2	4-2	2-0	1-0	1-0	1-1	1-3	4-2	1-1	3-2	0-2	0-0	2-2	1-0		0-2	1-1	3-1	2-0	2-0	0-0	3-2	3-4	1-1
16 Merstham	0-3	3-3	4-2	1-2	0-4	1-1	2-0	2-0	1-1	1-1	1-1	1-0	6-2	1-2	0-0		2-1	1-5	2-1	0-1	2-2	4-1	0-4	
17 Metropolitan Police	2-2	1-1	2-0	4-1	1-4	1-1	3-1	2-1	1-0	1-2	3-2	1-2	1-1	0-1	2-2	0-3		3-2	4-2	3-1	2-0	2-0	2-0	3-1
18 Needham Market	1-1	0-3	3-1	2-0	0-3	2-2	2-2	5-1	0-1	3-3	1-2	0-0	2-5	0-2	3-2	1-3	1-1		1-2	2-1	4-2	1-0	0-1	0-2
19 Staines Town	0-2	2-1	3-1	0-2	1-1	3-2	4-4	4-1	2-1	4-0	5-0	3-0	1-4	3-1	2-2	4-2	1-5	1-1		5-2	3-1	6-0	0-5	3-3
20 Thurrock	0-5	3-3	4-2	3-2	0-1	3-1	1-2	1-0	2-0	0-1	1-0	2-0	0-0	3-0	0-1	1-1	0-0	1-0	0-2		2-2	4-1	2-4	3-2
21 Tonbridge Angels	2-1	2-0	0-1	2-4	2-3	0-0	2-1	1-4	0-4	2-0	2-0	1-0	2-1	0-0	5-4	2-1	2-1		1-2			1-2	1-0	1-2
22 Tooting & Mitcham Utd	2-6	1-1	1-2	1-2	1-3	0-4	0-1	0-1	5-2	0-2	3-2	1-4	0-2	2-5	1-3	3-1	0-2	1-0	1-7	4-1	0-0		2-0	4-3
23 Wingate & Finchley	1-3	2-1	2-0	2-0	0-0	2-1	2-1	2-0	1-3	2-2	0-1	3-1	0-1	4-3	1-0	3-2	1-0	1-1	0-0	2-4	2-1	1-1		1-0
24 Worthing	2-1	2-2	2-0	3-1	0-2	2-2	3-2	2-2	2-2	1-2	1-2	1-1	1-1	0-0	0-5	3-2	3-3	1-0	2-2	1-2	2-0	3-0	2-1	

ISTHMIAN NORTH LEAGUE TABLE 2017-18

		P	W	D	L	F	A	GD	Pts
1	AFC Hornchurch	46	32	7	7	97	35	62	103
2	Potters Bar Town	46	28	9	9	87	42	45	90*
3	Bowers & Pitsea	46	28	5	13	94	48	46	89
4	Haringey Borough	46	27	8	11	84	49	35	89
5	Heybridge Swifts	46	26	9	11	105	53	52	87
6	Canvey Island	46	24	8	14	100	65	35	80
7	Maldon & Tiptree	46	20	9	17	94	83	11	69
8	Dereham Town	46	20	11	15	75	63	12	68*
9	Bury Town	46	17	14	15	67	65	2	65
10	Barking	46	18	10	18	63	63	0	64
11	Witham Town	46	18	8	20	59	66	-7	62
12	AFC Sudbury	46	15	14	17	57	66	-9	59
13	Soham Town Rangers	46	16	10	20	67	73	-6	58
14	Aveley	46	15	12	19	61	67	-6	57
15	Hertford Town	46	16	9	21	55	85	-30	57
16	Grays Athletic	46	14	14	18	72	80	-8	56
17	Tilbury	46	16	8	22	73	95	-22	56
18	Waltham Abbey	46	13	10	23	73	87	-14	49
19	Cheshunt	46	14	8	24	72	103	-31	49*
20	Ware	46	13	9	24	49	81	-32	48
21	Brentwood Town	46	12	10	24	71	96	-25	46
22	Mildenhall Town	46	11	13	22	54	86	-32	46
23	Romford	46	10	11	25	51	97	-46	41
24	Norwich United	46	8	16	22	63	95	-32	40

Play-Off Semi Finals: Bowers & Pitsea 0-2 Canvey Island I Haringey Borough 2-0 Heybridge Swifts
Final: Haringey Borough 3-1 Canvey Island

NORTH DIVISION	1	2	3	4	5	6	7	8	9	10	11	12	13	14	15	16	17	18	19	20	21	22	23	24
1 AFC Hornchurch		1-0	2-1	0-1	1-0	3-4	3-0	1-0	3-1	0-1	2-2	2-1	2-0	1-0	1-0	2-0	1-0	1-0	4-1	3-0	1-1	5-4	1-5	0-1
2 AFC Sudbury	1-0		1-1	3-1	4-3	3-0	1-1	1-1	3-0	1-4	1-0	1-2	1-1	3-2	1-1	0-2	2-2	0-2	2-1	0-1	3-2	2-0	1-3	1-2
3 Aveley	0-2	1-1		0-1	1-3	1-0	1-0	3-0	4-1	2-2	1-1	1-3	3-1	0-1	0-5	3-1	1-1	2-2	5-1	2-2	0-2	1-3	0-1	2-1
4 Barking	1-1	1-0	2-1		2-0	3-3	3-1	1-0	2-3	1-0	3-1	1-2	1-2	0-1	2-1	1-3	3-1	0-3	2-0	0-2	0-1	2-3	1-0	0-2
5 Bowers & Pitsea	1-0	2-0	2-0	4-0		4-1	4-2	2-1	4-0	3-2	1-0	1-2	1-1	1-2	4-2	3-1	1-3	4-2	4-0	4-0	3-2	2-0	0-2	3-0
6 Brentwood Town	1-6	2-2	1-2	1-0	1-3		1-2	0-2	1-1	1-1	1-1	2-0	2-2	1-3	2-5	7-1	5-2	2-1	1-3	3-3	3-1	4-1	1-2	
7 Bury Town	1-4	1-1	0-0	0-0	0-0	2-0		2-1	1-2	0-1	1-1	1-2	4-2	2-1	1-2	2-2	2-1	1-1	2-1	6-1	0-0	4-2	1-0	
8 Canvey Island	2-0	3-2	3-0	1-1	3-0	5-0	1-0		7-1	4-1	3-0	1-0	2-1	3-0	2-1	1-2	1-4	0-3	1-0	0-3	2-3	3-0	2-2	4-1
9 Cheshunt	1-1	3-2	2-1	0-4	2-1	2-0	1-2	3-3		0-2	1-0	0-5	5-2	0-1	2-3	3-2	6-3	0-4	2-4	2-2	0-1	4-2	1-3	1-1
10 Dereham Town	0-0	2-0	2-2	3-3	0-3	2-2	2-0	2-2	1-0		0-1	0-2	3-2	2-1	2-3	3-1	0-0	3-1	2-2	0-2	3-0	2-0	1-2	1-1
11 Grays Athletic	0-2	3-1	4-2	1-0	1-0	3-1	3-6	2-2	1-6		3-3	1-1	1-4	2-2	2-2	2-1	1-3	1-2	1-0	3-1	0-4	2-2	4-1	
12 Haringey Borough	1-2	3-0	3-2	1-1	0-2	1-0	4-2	2-0	3-2	2-1	1-1		0-1	3-3	2-2	6-0	4-0	1-2	2-0	2-0	4-1	2-0	1-0	
13 Hertford Town	0-3	0-1	0-3	2-4	1-0	4-0	0-6	1-0	1-0	0-0	1-0	0-1		0-3	2-3	2-2	1-1	1-1	1-0	0-1	3-2	0-4	2-1	1-1
14 Heybridge Swifts	0-2	0-1	3-0	3-0	3-1	3-1	1-1	4-1	3-1	1-2	3-3	0-0	6-0		5-0	2-1	3-1	0-0	9-1	2-1	2-1	3-0	6-1	2-1
15 Maldon & Tiptree	1-2	1-2	3-1	3-1	2-2	4-1	0-2	2-0	0-2	5-1	2-0	3-1	2-3	4-2		1-2	4-1	2-4	1-2	3-1	4-2	1-1	1-1	0-2
16 Mildenhall Town	0-6	0-1	1-2	0-2	1-1	1-1	0-0	1-3	1-2	0-1	2-1	1-2	2-0	0-2	2-2		0-0	0-0	0-0	2-1	4-6	0-1	1-0	2-1
17 Norwich United	0-2	3-1	0-3	1-1	1-1	2-1	1-2	4-3	3-1	1-3	2-2	0-2	1-2	1-2	3-3	1-1		0-1	1-1	0-3	3-3	2-0	0-0	1-3
18 Potters Bar Town	1-2	0-0	0-1	2-0	1-0	2-1	3-0	1-1	2-2	1-0	1-3	2-1	1-0	3-2	3-0	2-0	4-1		2-1	3-1	4-0	3-0	1-0	1-1
19 Romford	0-6	1-1	1-1	2-1	0-5	3-2	1-2	0-2	1-3	0-2	3-2	1-1	1-4	1-5	4-2	1-1	3-0	0-0		0-1	4-1	1-2	0-2	1-1
20 Soham Town Rangers	1-2	0-2	1-1	1-1	0-2	1-3	2-2	2-2	2-2	1-4	0-0	3-0	5-0	0-3	1-3	2-2	4-1	1-3	1-1		2-1	3-1	2-3	0-1
21 Tilbury	2-2	0-0	0-2	1-3	0-3	2-1	1-1	2-6	1-0	2-0	1-2	0-1	1-0	3-1	2-5	4-4	3-2	3-0	2-0		1-2	2-1	3-3	
22 Waltham Abbey	2-2	2-2	0-1	2-2	0-1	1-1	4-1	1-2	3-2	3-4	2-1	2-3	1-2	3-3	0-1	5-1	1-1	0-3	3-1	1-2	2-2		3-1	2-2
23 Ware	0-4	1-1	0-0	0-1	2-4	0-2	0-1	1-5	3-1	2-1	0-5	0-0	1-0	0-0	0-1	1-1	1-3	1-4	0-2	2-3	0-2	2-1		3-2
24 Witham Town	1-6	4-0	1-0	1-0	0-2	2-1	2-2	1-3	3-2	2-0	1-4	2-0	2-3	1-1	1-2	0-1	1-0	1-2	1-0	1-2	0-2	2-0	0-1	

ISTHMIAN SOUTH LEAGUE TABLE 2017-18

		P	W	D	L	F	A	GD	Pts
1	Carshalton Athletic	46	31	9	6	99	54	45	102
2	Lewes	46	30	9	7	93	38	55	99
3	Cray Wanderers	46	25	14	7	112	46	66	89
4	Greenwich Borough	46	25	12	9	99	47	52	87
5	Corinthian-Casuals	46	26	9	11	86	47	39	87
6	Walton Casuals	46	25	11	10	98	52	46	86
7	Hythe Town	46	25	11	10	92	63	29	86
8	Whyteleafe	46	20	13	13	87	70	17	73
9	Hastings United	46	20	13	13	84	67	17	73
10	Thamesmead Town	46	20	12	14	103	81	22	72
11	Phoenix Sports	46	20	9	17	79	68	11	69
12	Herne Bay	46	21	5	20	81	89	-8	68
13	South Park	46	19	6	21	79	91	-12	63
14	Sittingbourne	46	18	8	20	68	72	-4	62
15	Horsham	46	16	8	22	71	90	-19	56
16	Ramsgate	46	15	9	22	79	85	-6	54
17	VCD Athletic	46	15	7	24	69	91	-22	52
18	Guernsey	46	13	10	23	65	98	-33	49
19	Faversham Town	46	13	9	24	61	73	-12	48
20	Chipstead	46	12	10	24	64	78	-14	46
21	Ashford United	46	10	8	28	60	111	-51	38
22	East Grinstead Town	46	9	9	28	63	128	-65	36
23	Molesey	46	7	12	27	55	103	-48	30*
24	Shoreham	46	3	5	38	33	138	-105	8*

Play-Off Semi Finals: Cray Wanderers 2-5 Walton Casuals | Greenwich Borough 0-3 Corinthian-Casuals
Final: Corinthian-Casuals 0-0, 2-4p Walton Casuals

SOUTH DIVISION		1	2	3	4	5	6	7	8	9	10	11	12	13	14	15	16	17	18	19	20	21	22	23	24
1	Ashford United		0-1	3-1	0-1	2-1	1-1	3-1	1-2	3-0	1-3	3-5	1-2	3-3	1-3	0-1	2-3	1-0	3-0	3-1	0-4	4-1	2-5	1-4	1-1
2	Carshalton Athletic	4-2		2-1	0-0	1-1	5-1	2-1	0-3	0-0	1-1	0-2	2-1	2-1	3-2	5-0	2-2	4-4	4-1	3-0	1-0	2-1	7-0	2-1	4-3
3	Chipstead	2-3	3-4		1-2	0-1	4-0	1-1	2-2	1-0	1-3	3-0	4-1	2-4	0-1	2-2	2-3	1-1	2-1	1-2	0-2	0-2	3-1	1-1	1-2
4	Corinthian-Casuals	3-0	2-4	2-3		0-1	3-2	1-0	1-0	5-0	3-2	1-3	2-0	0-0	1-3	4-1	0-2	4-2	2-0	3-1	5-0	2-1	0-1	1-0	0-0
5	Cray Wanderers	9-1	1-2	0-0	4-2		1-1	4-2	2-2	4-0	1-1	3-1	4-3	4-1	1-2	4-0	3-1	5-1	7-0	3-2	8-0	2-2	4-2	2-2	5-1
6	East Grinstead Town	3-2	2-0	2-1	0-5	0-7		1-1	2-2	0-2	1-7	3-5	2-2	0-3	0-4	1-1	1-2	1-0	7-2	1-3	0-2	3-3	0-3	0-2	1-8
7	Faversham Town	1-1	1-2	0-2	0-1	0-0	3-1		2-2	1-2	1-2	0-3	1-2	0-3	2-0	2-1	3-2	1-2	6-1	1-1	2-1	0-0	3-1	0-1	0-2
8	Greenwich Borough	5-0	1-2	1-0	2-0	0-0	4-1	1-0		4-0	2-2	1-0	0-2	1-2	1-1	4-1	3-0	3-0	4-0	5-1	2-1	1-2	1-3	3-3	1-1
9	Guernsey	1-1	2-1	2-0	0-1	0-1	4-2	3-1	1-2		1-1	2-4	1-3	1-1	0-3	3-2	1-1	1-4	5-2	3-0	1-3	2-2	4-2	1-3	4-4
10	Hastings United	2-1	2-0	0-0	2-1	1-1	3-1	1-0	2-5	3-1		2-4	3-3	2-3	1-2	3-0	1-1	4-2	1-0	1-2	2-0	1-2	2-1	1-0	2-1
11	Herne Bay	3-0	1-2	3-1	1-4	2-1	2-2	3-1	1-0	1-3	0-3		1-1	1-2	0-0	1-5	3-1	4-1	0-1	4-1	2-3	4-0	1-0	2-1	
12	Horsham	3-0	0-1	1-2	1-4	0-3	1-1	0-3	0-2	2-1	2-2	1-2		2-1	2-1	3-1	2-1	1-4	3-0	1-5	0-0	3-4	3-2	2-4	2-5
13	Hythe Town	1-0	0-4	5-3	1-1	2-1	3-2	3-0	0-0	5-1	2-2	1-1	1-1		2-0	2-1	1-3	4-1	6-0	3-2	3-2	2-1	2-1	1-2	1-0
14	Lewes	5-1	0-1	0-0	0-1	2-1	2-0	3-0	2-0	1-0	2-0	8-1	4-2	1-0		3-0	1-0	3-2	4-0	2-2	3-1	2-2	3-0	1-1	1-1
15	Molesey	1-3	0-0	3-0	1-2	1-1	4-2	2-1	1-6	2-4	4-3	0-0	2-1	1-2	0-4		3-4	1-1	1-2	2-3	3-1	3-3	1-1	1-2	0-4
16	Phoenix Sports	2-0	1-1	2-2	0-0	0-0	0-1	0-1	0-2	5-0	3-0	3-1	1-0	2-0	2-2		4-0	4-0	0-1	1-2	2-3	0-3	0-3	2-5
17	Ramsgate	3-0	0-2	3-0	2-2	1-2	4-0	3-2	1-2	0-0	1-2	2-1	1-0	2-2	2-0	2-1	1-3		3-3	1-1	1-3	2-3	0-1	2-2	4-1
18	Shoreham	4-2	1-3	0-3	0-3	0-3	2-4	1-1	1-0	0-3	1-1	0-1	1-2	0-3	2-2	1-1	0-2	1-5		0-4	0-4	0-3	0-1	0-2	1-4
19	Sittingbourne	0-0	3-1	1-1	2-2	0-0	1-2	1-2	1-2	4-0	2-0	3-0	1-3	1-0	0-1	1-0	0-1	2-3	1-0		0-3	2-2	3-2	0-2	2-1
20	South Park	5-0	2-3	1-3	1-6	0-1	3-1	1-1	1-8	2-1	1-1	1-1	3-2	2-2	0-2	4-1	2-2	2-1	4-2	1-2		2-1	2-0	2-1	3-0
21	Thamesmead Town	3-1	2-3	1-0	1-1	0-1	4-5	2-3	2-4	5-0	2-4	2-1	5-0	2-1	0-0	3-0	5-2	1-3	4-1	2-2	6-2		2-2	2-1	2-3
22	VCD Athletic	2-2	1-4	1-3	0-1	0-0	2-1	0-5	0-1	2-2	1-1	2-3	2-1	1-2	1-2	4-0	0-1	3-1	1-0	3-1	1-2	3-1		3-2	3-3
23	Walton Casuals	4-0	0-1	4-0	0-0	5-2	3-0	4-3	1-1	2-2	2-1	7-0	1-1	2-2	2-1	2-1	1-0	3-1	3-0	2-1	0-0	3-1		4-2
24	Whyteleafe	1-1	1-1	2-1	2-1	0-2	2-1	1-1	1-1	2-0	1-0	6-2	0-2	2-2	0-0	2-1	0-1	1-0	2-0	2-1	3-1	1-3	3-0	3-2	

THE VELOCITY TROPHY 2017-18

HOLDERS: BILLERICAY TOWN

FIRST ROUND

Harrow Borough	v	Metropolitan Police	1-3	122
Wingate & Finchley	v	Haringey Borough	3-0	78
Canvey Island	v	Brentwood Town	0-1	238
Tonbridge Angels	v	Herne Bay	10-1	180
South Park	v	Molesey	3-1	51
Thamesmead Town	v	Phoenix Sports	4-3	59
Carshalton Athletic	v	Dorking Wanderers	1-3	113
Ashford United	v	Greenwich Borough	0-2	142
Chipstead	v	Leatherhead	5-0	89
AFC Hornchurch	v	Aveley	5-1	98
Margate	v	East Grinstead Town	2-1	196
Cheshunt	v	Waltham Abbey	2-0	108
Soham Town Rangers	v	Witham Town	0-0, 9-8p	93
Harlow Town	v	Bury Town	1-1, 3-4p	113
Faversham Town	v	Hythe Town	2-5	97
AFC Sudbury	v	Brightlingsea Regent	5-1	113
Tooting & Mitcham United	v	Merstham	1-1, 3-4p	74
Whyteleafe	v	Corinthian-Casuals	1-2	77
Bowers & Pitsea	v	Grays Athletic	0-2	113
Maldon & Tiptree	v	Leiston	1-1, 5-4p	77
Walton Casuals	v	Kingstonian	2-1	157
Staines Town	v	Dulwich Hamlet	1-1, 2-4p	125
Shoreham	v	Worthing	4-1	142
Romford	v	Tilbury	1-1, 5-3p	84
VCD Athletic	v	Folkestone Invicta	0-3	70
Sittingbourne	v	Ramsgate	2-0	104
Enfield Town	v	Hertford Town	1-1, 9-8p	178
Billericay Town	v	Barking	5-1	518
Potters Bar Town	v	Ware	4-1	63
Horsham	v	Burgess Hill Town	4-2	83
Heybridge Swifts	v	Mildenhall Town	4-2	108

SECOND ROUND

Sittingbourne	v	Merstham	1-0	126
Wingate & Finchley	v	Potters Bar Town	2-1	60
Soham Town Rangers	v	Brentwood Town	2-3	88
South Park	v	Chipstead	2-5	68
Margate	v	Corinthian-Casuals	2-2, 3-5p	253
Bury Town	v	Heybridge Swifts	0-0, 4-5p	179
Romford	v	AFC Hornchurch	2-1	105
Dulwich Hamlet	v	Greenwich Borough	4-1	444
Tonbridge Angels	v	Hythe Town	0-0, 3-5p	173
Maldon & Tiptree	v	Billericay Town	0-3	336
Hendon	v	Grays Athletic	5-1	65
Cheshunt	v	Enfield Town	1-4	199
Shoreham	v	Dorking Wanderers	0-4	70
Folkestone Invicta	v	Metropolitan Police	1-2	141
Walton Casuals	v	Horsham	3-0	70
Thamesmead Town	v	AFC Sudbury	3-2	67

THIRD ROUND

Billericay Town	v	Heybridge Swifts	1-1, 5-3p	355
Wingate & Finchley	v	Sittingbourne	3-2	71
Hythe Town	v	Hendon	1-2	121
Metropolitan Police	v	Romford	4-2	28
Enfield Town	v	Chipstead	4-3	125
Dulwich Hamlet	v	Walton Casuals	HW	
Thamesmead Town	v	Corinthian-Casuals	1-1	56
Shoreham	v	Brentwood Town	2-3	52

QUARTER-FINALS

Hendon	v	Corinthian-Casuals	1-3	93
Wingate & Finchley	v	Billericay Town	0-1	172
Metropolitan Police	v	Enfield Town	2-1	66
Brentwood Town	v	Dulwich Hamlet	0-1	119

SEMI-FINALS

Billericay Town	v	Corinthian-Casuals	3-1	442

Liam Hughes 45,   *Gabriel Odunaike 22*
Billy Bricknell 55
Adam Cunnington 57

Dulwich Hamlet	v	Metropolitan Police	0-0, 1-4p	210

FINAL

Billericay Town	v	Metropolitan Police	5-3	626

Jake Robinson 11   *Tom Bird 25 (P)*
Billy Bricknell 86,86,96   *Jonathan Wright 57*
Daniel Waldren 99   *Thomas Hickey 59*

BILLERICAY MATCH RESULTS 2017-18

Date	Comp	H/A	Opponents	Att:	Result	Goalscorers	Pos	No.
Aug 12	Isthmian	H	Kingstonian	1141	L 0 - 1		19	1
15	Isthmian	A	Lowestoft Town	603	W 2 - 1	Robinson 10 Theophanous 84	14	2
19	Isthmian	A	Dulwich Hamlet	1688	W 3 - 1	Bricknell 43 72 (pen) Robinson 87	6	3
26	Isthmian	H	Burgess Hill Town	1110	W 6 - 0	Evans 5 CUNNINGTON 3 (50 63 68) Bricknell 78 (pen) Deering 90	2	4
28	Isthmian	A	Thurrock	523	W 5 - 0	Bricknell 3 65 Robinson 15 23 Cunnington 59	1	5
Sept 2	FAC 1Q	H	Didcot Town	1159	W 5 - 0	ROBINSON 3 (38 67 75) Modeste72 Cunnington (p) 90		6
9	Isthmian	H	Leatherhead	1651	W 1 - 0	Johnson 19	1	7
12	Isthmian	A	Brightlingsea R	898	W 4 - 0	Cunnington 25 Robinson 62 64 Pennant 90	1	8
17	FAC 2Q	A	Thamesmead Town	433	D 1 - 1	Robinson 4		9
19	FAC 2Qr	H	Thamesmead Town	774	W 5 - 0	ROBINSON 3 (6 24 29) Cunnington 33 Theophanous 52		10
23	Isthmian	A	Tooting & Mitcham United	1104	W 1 - 0	Modeste 90	1	11
30	FAC 3Q	H	Hungerford Town	507	D 1 - 1	Modeste 67		12
Oct 2	FAC 3Qr	H	Hungerford Town	1024	W 6 - 1	Theophanous 41BRICKNELL 3(43 60 62) Lynch 75 85(og)		13
7	Isthmian	H	Hendon	1988	W 4 - 3	Modeste 12 Cunnington 26 45 Bricknell 35 (pen)	2	14
14	FAC 4Q	A	Brackley Town	731	D 3 - 3	Cunnington 47 76 Theophanous 72		15
17	FAC 4Qr	H	Brackley Town	1464	W 2 - 1	Evans 27 Deering 31		16
20	Isthmian	H	Enfield	1559	W 2 - 1	Bricknell 74 (pen) Deering 86	3	17
28	FAT 1Q	H	Tooting & Mitcham United	864	W 3 - 1	Ellul 81 82 Modeste 89		18
31	Isthmian	A	Needham Market	607	D 1 - 1	Robinson 23	3	19
Nov 5	FAC 1	A	Leatherhead	1797	D 1 - 1	Bricknell 67 (pen)		20
11	FAT 2Q	H	Bury	1376	W 6 - 2	Cunnington Swaine ROBINSON 3 Deering		21
14	Isthmian	A	Merstham	247	W 3 - 0	Theophanous 45 48 Bricknell 53	4	22
16	FAC 1r	H	Leatherhead	3400	L 1 - 3	Cunnington 64		23
18	Isthmian	A	Harlow Town	501	W 4 - 2	Watt 29 Robinson 78 Cunningham 80 Theophanous 87	3	24
20	Isthmian	H	Kingstonian	285	W 2 0	Bricknell 49 (pen) Theophanous 69	2	25
25	FAT 3Q	H	Hungerford Town	267	W 2 - 0	Robinson 35 Watt 81		26
28	Isthmian	A	Harrow Borough	201	W 2 - 0	Robinson 60 Cunnington 86	2	27
Dec 2	Isthmian	H	Leiston	209	W 4 - 0	Cunnington 3 ROBINSON 3 (59 78 90)	2	28
5	Isthmian	H	Merstham	545	D 2 - 2	Cunnington 45 74	2	29
9	Isthmian	A	Staines Town	454	W 2 - 0	Robinson 33 53	2	30
16	FAT 1	H	Havant & Waterlooville	705	W 3 - 1	Robinson 4 49 Deering 90		31
Dec 19	Isthmian	A	Metropolitan Police	602	W 3 - 0	Robinson 2 Theophanous	1	32
23	Isthmian	A	Burgess Hill Town	513	W 4 - 3	Paine 17 Theophanous 45 Deering 53 Robinson 68	1	33
26	Isthmian	H	Thurrock	1653	W 1 - 0	Robinson 57	1	34
Jan 6	Isthmian	H	Margate	1570	D 1 - 1	Cunnington 67	2	35
13	FAT 2	H	Stourbridge	1081	W 3 - 2	Robinson 10 Modeste 65 Bricknell 90		36
27	Isthmian	A	Tooting & Mitcham United	466	W 6 - 2	Waldren 16 89 Swaine 18 ROBINSON 3 (21pen 38 64)	2	37
30	Isthmian	H	Worthing	594	W 4 - 0	Cunnington 48 83 Deering 55 87	1	38
Feb 3	FAT 3	A	Harrogate Town	846	D 2 - 2	Swaine 11 Cunnington 70		39
5	FAT 3r	H	Harrogate Town	820	W 3 - 2	Modeste 22 Robinson 34 Cunnington 54		40
10	Isthmian	A	Metropolitan Police	310	D 2 - 2	Robinson 10 Modeste 38	1	41
13	Isthmian	H	Lowestoft Town	643	W 5 - 0	Deering 3 69 Waldren 49 Bricknell 61 Robinson 73	1	42
17	Isthmian	A	Leiston	502	L 1 - 3	Cunnington 8	1	43
21	Isthmian	A	Folkestone Invicta	728	L 1 - 2	Bricknell 90 (pen)	1	44
24	FAT 4	H	Wealdstone	1823	L 2 - 5	Swaine 27 Modeste 66		45
Mar 3	Isthmian	A	Worthing	1163	L 1 - 2	Robinson 74	1	46
6	Isthmian	H	Dulwich Hamlet	988	L 1 - 3	Inman 8	2	47
15	Isthmian	H	Dorking Wanderers	279	W 1 - 0	Deering 80	2	48
22	Isthmian	A	Tonbridge Angels	526	L 1 - 2	Bricknell 36	3	49
24	Isthmian	A	Hendon	462	L 1 4	O'Hara 82	3	50
26	Isthmian	A	Wingate & Finchley	240	W 3 - 1	Waldren 35 Bricknell 48 (pen) Robinson 67	2	51
28	Isthmian	H	Harrow Borough	313	W 2 - 0	Robinson 65 Rooney 78	2	52
31	Isthmian	A	Leatherhead	623	D 1 - 1	Robinson 7	2	53
Apr 3	Isthmian	H	Tonbridge Angels	505	W 2 - 1	Deering 53 Hughes 68	1	54
5	Isthmian	A	Brightlingsea Regent	452	D 1 - 1	Bricknell 77 (pen)	1	55
7	Isthmian	A	Enfield Town	690	D 1 - 1	Cunnington 24	1	56
9	Isthmian	H	Staines Town	580	W 5 - 3	Paine 6 Bricknell 14 Modeste 35 Robinson 71 85	1	57
14	Isthmian	H	Wingate & Finchley	237	D 2 - 2	Paine 64 Deering 90	1	58
17	Isthmian	A	Dorking Wanderers	326	W 1 - 0	Modeste 39	1	59
19	Isthmian	H	Needham Market	741	W 5 - 0	ROBINSON 3 (3 34 (pen) 66) Deering 9 O'Hara 30	1	60
21	Isthmian	A	Margate	832	W 2 - 1	Deering 29 Robinson 62 (pen)	1	61
24	Isthmian	H	Harlow Town	1687	W 2 - 0	Kizzi 42 Cunnington 87	1	62
28	Isthmian	H	Folkestone Invicta	2206	D 2 - 2	Modeste 39 O'Hara 90	1	63

GOALSCORERS	SG	CSG	Pens	Hat tricks	Total		SG	CSG	Pens	Hat tricks	Total
2016-17 Bricknell					18	Elful	1				2
Robinson	28	5	3	5	48	Evans	2				2
Cunnington	20	3	1	1	26	Watt	2				2
Bricknell	16	2	9	1	20	Hughes					1
Deering	12	2			15	Inman					1
Modeste	12	2			12	Johnson					1
Theophanous	9	2			10	Kizzi					1
Swaine	3				4	Lynch					1
Waldren	4				4	Opponent					1
O'Hara	3				3	Pennant					1
Paine	3				3	Rooney					1

BRIGHTLINGSEA REGENT MATCH RESULTS 2017-18

Date	Comp	H/A	Opponents	Att:	Result	Goalscorers	Pos	No.
Aug 12	Isthmian	A	Tooting & Mitcham United	290	D 1 - 1	Richardson 26	9	1
15	Isthmian	H	Leiston	281	L 0 - 1		17	2
19	Isthmian	A	Tonbridge	484	L 0 - 2		21	3
26	Isthmian	H	Hendon	291	W 2 - 1	Hunt 74 Kelloy 90	17	4
28	Isthmian	A	Needham Market	347	W 3 - 0	Doyle 30 Condon 39 Hunt 90	13	5
Sept 2	FAC 1Q	A	Hanwell Topwn	142	L 1 - 4	Cripps 45		6
9	Isthmian	H	Enfield Town	263	W 2 - 1	Gould 12 Hunt 83	10	7
12	Isthmian	A	Billericay Town	898	L 0 - 4		11	8
16	Isthmian	H	Merstham	148	D 3 - 3	Cripps 27 Richardson 80 88	11	9
23	Isthmian	A	Dorking Wanderers	223	L 2 - 3	Hunt 32 (pen) Condon 75	13	10
26	Isthmian	H	Wingate & Finchley	161	W 1 - 0	Richardson 58	12	11
Oct 3	Isthmian	A	Leiston	249	L 2 - 3	Condon 20 Richardson 56	13	12
7	Isthmian	A	Thurrock	128	D 3 - 3	Hogan 18 Rees 47 Hunt 56	13	13
10	Isthmian	H	Kingstonian	195	W 2 - 0	Goode 26 (og) Condon 29	9	14
14	Isthmian	A	Tooting & Mitcham United	222	L 0 - 3		11	15
21	Isthmian	A	Harrow Borough	158	W 2 - 1	Gould 18 Richardson 51	11	16
29	FAT 1Q	A	Thamesmead Town	156	L 1 - 3	Condon 29		17
Nov 4	Isthmian	H	Harlow Town	181	W 3 - 1	Hunt 21 Condon 25 Turner 60	9	18
14	Isthmian	A	Wingate & Finchley	121	L 1 - 2	Gould 62	11	19
18	Isthmian	H	Folkestone Invicta	198	L 1 - 2	Cripps 52	12	20
21	Isthmian	H	Burgess Hill Town	140	W 5 - 2	Ashford 1 Cripps 40 Condon 47 Hunt 56 88	10	21
Dec 9	Isthmian	A	Dulwich Hamlet	1628	L 1 - 2	Griggs 45	13	22
16	Isthmian	H	Staines Town	178	D 2 - 2	Griggs 70 Condon 90	12	23
19	Isthmian	A	Margate	362	L 2 - 4	Hunt 16 Condon 61	12	24
23	Isthmian	A	Hendon	189	L 2 - 4	Hunt 27 90	12	25
26	Isthmian	H	Needham Market	219	L 2 - 3	Condon 28 Hunt 90	14	26
30	Isthmian	H	Tonbridge Angels	261	L 0 - 3		16	27
Jan 1	Isthmian	A	Lowestoft Town	341	W 2 - 1	Hunt 29 53	13	28
6	Isthmian	A	Metropolitan Police	110	D 1 - 1	Condon 14	14	29
13	Isthmian	H	Worthing	208	W 3 - 0	Gould 70 Hunt 73 (pen) 87	13	30
20	Isthmian	A	Kingstonian	221	W 1 - 0	Harvey 7	12	31
37	Isthmian	H	Dorking Wanderers	180	L 2 - 3	Hunt 12 Gould 90	12	32
Feb 3	Isthmian	A	Folkestone Invicta	357	L 2 - 3	Hunt 73 Turner 90	13	33
10	Isthmian	H	Margate	184	L 0 - 1		14	34
17	Isthmian	A	Leatherhead	351	L 1 - 2	Ashford 83	16	35
24	Isthmian	H	Merstham	151	L 1 - 3	Hunt 12	17	36
Mar 10	Isthmian	H	Dulwich Hamlet	346	D 2 2	Turner 41 Condon 82	19	37
17	Isthmian	A	Burgess Hill Town	211	W 2 - 1	Condon 8 Turner 71	19	38
24	Isthmian	H	Thurrock	183	L 1 - 3	Hunt 62 (pen)	19	39
27	Isthmian	A	Staines Town	153	L 1 - 2	Gould 15	19	40
31	Isthmian	A	Enfield Town	420	L 0 - 2		20	41
Apr 2	Isthmian	H	Lowestoft Town	252	W 2 - 0	Hunt 12 90 (pen)	18	42
4	Isthmian	H	Billericay Town	452	D 1 - 1	Hunt 48	17	43
7	Isthmian	H	Harrow Borough	192	D 1 - 1	Keys 22	19	44
14	Isthmian	A	Harlow Town	247	L 0 - 2		20	45
16	Isthmian	H	Leatherhead	150	L 0 - 7		20	46
21	Isthmian	H	Metropolitan Police	142	L 0 - 1		20	47
28	Isthmian	H	Worthing	1060	D 2 - 2	Condon 68 Hunt 90 (pen)	20	48

GOALSCORERS	SG	CSG	Pens	Hat tricks	Total		SG	CSG	Pens	Hat tricks	Total
Hunt	19	3	5		24	Hogan					1
Condon	14	2			14	Kelloy					1
Gould	5	2			6	Keys					1
Richardson	5				6	Opponents					1
Cripps	4	2			4	Rees					1
Turner	4				4						
Ashford	2				2						
Griggs	2	2			2						
Doyle					1						
Harvey					1						

BURGESS HILL MATCH RESULTS 2017-18

Date	Comp	H/A	Opponents	Att:	Result	Goalscorers	Pos	No.
Aug 12	Isthmian	H	Needham Market	323	D 1 - 1	Nezval 76	11	1
14	Isthmian	A	Kingstonian	252	D 0 - 0		9	2
19	Isthmian	H	Folkestone Invicta	335	D 1 - 1	Cook 76	16	3
26	Isthmian	A	Billericay Town	1110	L 1 - 6	Richmond 21	22	4
28	Isthmian	H	Worthing	525	W 4 - 1	Bolton 7 Garrod 9 Elphick 63 (og) L. Harding 88	17	5
Sept 2	FAC 1Q	A	Erith Town	105	W 3 - 0	Garrod 21 42 P.Harding 90		6
9	Isthmian	A	Wingate & Finchley	74	L 0 - 2		18	7
12	Isthmian	H	Tooting & Mitcham United	276	W 3 - 1	Diav 29 Brivio 59 Adelakun 65	14	8
16	FAC 2Q	A	Colney Heath	153	D 3 - 3	P.Harding 15 Diav 21 36		9
19	FAC 2Qr	H	Colney Heath	255	W 3 - 0	P.Harding 15 Garrod 37 (pen) 83		10
26	Isthmian	A	Tonbridge Angels	462	L 0 - 1		16	11
30	FAC 3Q	H	Wealdstone	590	W 1 - 0	Toure 90		12
Oct 3	Isthmian	H	Kingstonian	328	W 5 - 1	DIAU 3 (23 50 61) P.Harding 43 Smith-Joseph 75	13	13
7	Isthmian	H	Lowestoft Town	479	L 0 - 5		19	14
14	FAC 4Q	H	Dartford	873	L 0 - 1			15
21	Isthmian	A	Dulwich Hamlet	1971	L 2 - 3	Garrod 48 Taylor 59 (og)	19	16
24	Isthmian	A	Metropolitan Police	101	L 0 - 2		19	17
28	FAT 1Q	A	Aveley	197	W 2 - 0	L. Harding 32 P.Harding 40 (pen)	19	18
Nov 4	Isthmian	H	Leiston	312	W 2 - 1	Rodriguez 34 L. Harding 53	19	19
7	Isthmian	A	Tooting & Mitcham United	152	W 2 - 1	Rodriguez 14 Richmond 90	16	20
11	FAT 2Q	A	Hendon	165	L 0 - 3			21
14	Isthmian	H	Metropolitan Police	244	L 1 - 4	L. Harding 4	16	22
18	Isthmian	A	Hendon	192	D 2 - 2	L.Harding 89 P.Harding 90	17	23
21	Isthmian	A	Brightlingsea Regent	140	L 2 - 5	P.Harding 62 Bennett 89	20	24
25	Isthmian	A	Thurrock	88	L 2 - 4	Richmond 36 Garrod 45	21	25
Dec 2	Isthmian	H	Margate	280	D 1 - 1	Rodriguez 68		26
16	Isthmian	H	Merstham	315	D 0 - 0		20	27
23	Isthmian	H	Billericay Town	513	L 3 - 4	Taylor 9 O'Neill 16 P.Harding 31	23	28
26	Isthmian	H	Worthing	662	L 0 - 2		23	29
30	Isthmian	A	Folkestone Invicta	373	L 1 - 3	L..Harding 90	24	30
Jan 6	Isthmian	A	Staines Town	227	D 1 - 1	Tighe 86	24	31
13	Isthmian	H	Harrow Borough	287	L 2 - 3	Tighe 32 Ngamvoulou 68	24	32
23	Isthmian	H	Harlow Town	158	W 2 - 0	Tighe 19 34	23	33
27	Isthmian	A	Tonbridge Angels	432	W 1 - 0	Smith-Joseph 8	23	34
Feb 3	Isthmian	H	Hendon	278	L 2 - 4	Brivio 23 72	24	35
7	Isthmian	A	Leatherhead	247	L 1 - 2	Brivio 68	24	36
10	Isthmian	A	Harlow Town	164	D 1 - 1	Tighe 68	24	37
13	Isthmian	A	Enfield Town	251	L 2 - 3	Brivio 59 Sanusi 90	24	38
17	Isthmian	A	Margate	547	L 0 - 2		24	39
24	Isthmian	H	Thurrock	235	L 2 - 5	Tighe 54 Fofana 72	24	40
Mar 6	Isthmian	A	Needham Market	214	L 1 - 3	Rodrigues 83	24	41
17	Isthmian	H	Brightlingsea Regent	211	L 1 - 2	Richmond 77	24	42
20	Isthmian	H	Dorking Wanderers	223	L 1 - 3	Smith-Joseph 68	24	43
24	Isthmian	A	Lowestoft Town	524	W 2 - 1	Rodriguez 20 61	23	44
27	Isthmian	A	Merstham	163	L 2 - 4	Tighe 20 89	23	45
Apr 2	Isthmian	A	Dorking Wanderers	205	L 1 - 2	L. Harding 62 Bennett 89	23	46
5	Isthmian	H	Wingate & Finchley	240	W 3 - 1	Sanusi 12 L. Harding 52 Greenleaf 53	22	47
7	Isthmian	H	Dulwich Hamlet	480	D 1 - 1	Tighe 57	22	48
10	Isthmian	H	Enfield Town	287	L 2 - 4	L. Harding 34 Brivio 58	23	49
12	Isthmian	H	Leatherhead	324	L 0 - 1		23	50
14	Isthmian	A	Leiston	292	L 0 - 2		23	51
21	Isthmian	H	Staines Town	436	D 1 - 1	P. Harding 5	23	52
28	Isthmian	A	Harrow Borough	248	L 2 - 3	P. Harding 35 L. Harding 45	23	53

GOALSCORERS	SG	CSG	Pens	Hat tricks	Total		SG	CSG	Pens	Hat tricks	Total
2016-17 Richardson-Brown					13	Adelakun					1
L.Harding	10	2			10	Bennett					1
P.Harding	10	2	1		10	Bolton					1
Tighe	6				9	Cook					1
Garrod	4	2	1		7	Fofana					1
Brivio	6				6	Greenleaf					1
Diav	3	2		1	6	Nezval					1
Rodriguez	5	2			6	Ngamvoulou					1
Richmond	4				4	O'Neill					1
Smith-Joseph	3				3	Taylor					1
Opponents					2	Toure					1
Sanusi	2				2						

DORKING WANDERERS MATCH RESULTS 2017-18

Date	Comp	H/A	Opponents	Att:	Result	Goalscorers	Pos	No.
Aug 12	Isthmian	A	Leiston	405	L 0 - 1		20	1
15	Isthmian	H	Metropolitan Police	245	W 4 - 1	BRIGGS 3 (7 17 42) McShane 89	12	2
19	Isthmian	A	Thurrock	118	L 2 - 3	Tolfrey 36 (pen) Briggs 88	15	3
26	Isthmian	H	Staines Town	275	D 1 - 1	Hamlin 89	16	4
28	Isthmian	A	Margate	630	L 0 - 1		19	5
Sept 2	FAC 1Q	H	Worthing	281	W 3 - 2	Ray 6 Philpott 52 Briggs 65		6
9	Isthmian	H	Dul;wich Hamlet	331	L 0 - 1		20	7
12	Isthmian	H	Worthing	224	W 4 - 2	Briggs 32 55 Ray 65 McShane 88	18	8
16	FAC 2Q	A	Cheshunt	170	W 3 - 1	McShane 15 Tolfrey 33 Chandlk 85		9
23	Isthmian	H	Brightlingsea	223	W 3 - 2	Pearse 9 McShane 33 Tolfrey 44	15	10
26	Isthmian	A	Tonbridge Angels	332	L 0 - 2		16	11
30	FAC 3Q	A	Concord Rangers	141	L 0 - 3			12
Oct 3	Isthmian	A	Metropolitan Police	109	L 1 - 4	McShane 49	12	13
7	Isthmian	A	Merstham	271	W 2 - 1	Tolfrey 61 Boulter 82	18	14
10	Isthmian	A	Harlow Town	130	D 2 - 2	Sole 18 Pinnock 75	17	15
14	Isthmian	H	Leiston	227	L 0 - 2		18	16
21	Isthmian	H	Needham Market	176	W 3 - 2	Taylor 34 McShane 49 Chambers 85	15	17
28	FAT 1Q	H	Ware	175	W 5 - 0	Sole 11 39 Briggs 63 Chendlik 79 90		18
Nov 4	Isthmian	A	Folkestone Invicta	409	L 1 3	Sole 41	15	19
7	Isthmian	A	Worthing	498	L 1 - 3	Briggs 89	15	20
11	FAT 2Q	H	Leiston	188	W 4 - 1	Tolfrey 16 McShane 48 Ray 72 Sole 81		21
18	Isthmian	A	Harrow Borough	145	W 4 - 3	Tolfrey 17 Taylor 20 Briggs 23 Boulter 83	14	22
25	FAT 3Q	A	Havant & Waterloovile	233	L 1 - 3	Sole 16		23
Dec 2	Isthmian	A	Kingstonian	242	D 0 - 0		16	24
5	Isthmian	H	Tonbridge Angels	205	L 2 - 3	Taylor 10 Sole 12	16	25
16	Isthmian	A	Enfield Town	319	L 2 - 3	Tolfrey 21 Sole 44	19	26
19	Isthmian	H	Hendon		L 0 - 3		19	27
23	Isthmian	A	Staines Town	228	W 2 - 0	McShane 5 Briggs 87	19	28
26	Isthmian	H	Margate	263	W 4 - 2	McShane 1 Philpot 56 78 Taylor 83	17	29
30	Isthmian	H	Thurrock	265	W 2 - 0	McShane 34 59	13	30
Jan 13	Isthmian	A	Lowestoft Town	344	D 0 - 0		17	31
20	Isthmian	A	Harlow Town	212	D 2 - 2	McShane 1 Putman 12	16	32
27	Isthmian	A	Brightlingsea Regent	180	W 3 - 2	Chendlik 64 90 Putman 72	15	33
30	Isthmian	A	Tooting & Mitcham	195	D 2 - 2	McShane 56 Walker 61	15	34
Feb 10	Isthmian	A	Hendon	175	D 0 - 0		16	35
17	Isthmian	H	Kingstonian	308	L 1 - 2	Sole 20 (pen)	17	36
Mar 10	Isthmian	A	Tooting & Mitcham United	209	W 2 - 1	McShane 40 43	16	37
15	Isthmian	A	Billericay Town	279	L 0 - 1		17	38
17	Isthmian	A	Leatherhead	354	L 0 - 1		19	39
20	Isthmian	A	Burgess Hill Town	223	W 3 - 1	Moore 66 Taylor 74 Walker 81	19	40
24	Isthmian	H	Merstham	191	W 4 - 0	Moore 39 Walker 63 Taylor 81 Chendlik 84	14	41
27	Isthmian	H	Leatherhead	1014	D 1 - 1	Taylor 44	14	42
Apr 2	Isthmian	H	Burgess Hill Town	205	W 2 - 1	Sheridan 53 Taylor 82	14	43
5	Isthmian	H	Enfield	206	D 2 - 2	Moore 10 Putman 51	14	44
7	Isthmian	A	Needham Market	255	L 0 - 2		14	45
12	Isthmian	A	Dulwich Hamlet	551	W 0 - 4		15	46
14	Isthmian	H	Folkestone Invicta	237	W 5 - 3	McShane 6 38 Sole 29 Putman 76 Tolfrey 90	14	47
17	Isthmian	H	Billericay Town	326	L 0 - 1		14	48
19	Isthmian	H	Wingate & Finchley	153	D 2 - 2	Tolfrey 17 McShane 45	14	49
21	Isthmian	A	Wingate & Finchley	101	L 0 - 2		15	50
24	Isthmian	H	Harrow Borough	131	L 0 - 4		15	51
28	Isthmian	H	Lowestoft Town	343	W 8 - 0	Pearse 16 22 Tolfrey 45 Walker 46 Taylor 56 Sole 81 Chendlik 74 83	14	52

GOALSCORERS	SG	CSG	Pens	Hat tricks	Total		SG	CSG	Pens	Hat tricks	Total
McShane	134	3			17	Philpott	2				3
Briggs	8	2		1	11	Ray	3				3
Sole	10	2	1		11	Boulter	2				2
Tolfrey	9	2	1		10	Chambers					1
Taylor	8	4			9	Hamlin					1
Chandlik	4				8	Pinnock					1
Walker	3				5	Sheridan					1
Putman	4				3						
Moore	3				3						
Pearse	2				3						

DULWICH HAMLET MATCH RESULTS 2017-18

Date	Comp	H/A	Opponents	Att:	Result	Goalscorers	Pos	No.
Aug 12	Isthmian	H	Staines Town	1096	D 1 - 1	Green 4	11	1
15	Isthmian	A	Dulwich Hamlet	260	W 3 - 0	Kargbo 2 Faal 84 90	5	2
19	Isthmian	H	Billericay Town	1688	L 1 - 3	Carew 45	13	3
26	Isthmian	A	Leisteon	341	D 2 - 2	Clunis 18 Mlng 38	14	4
28	Isthmian	H	Tooting & Mitcham United	1866	W 2 - 1	Beaney 59 80	10	5
Sept 2	FAC 1Q	H	Hastings United	1288	W 3 - 1	BOAKYE-YIADOM 3 (79, 89 90)		6
9	Isthmian	A	Brightlingsea Regent	331	W 1 - 0	Hayles 2	9	7
12	Isthmian	H	Hendon	659	L 0 - 1		10	8
16	FAC 2Q	A	Slough Town	712	L 2 - 3	Weatherstone 45 Clunis 75		9
23	Isthmian	H	Leatherhead	1752	W 4 - 0	Faal 4 41 Beaney 23 Clunis 53	6	10
26	Isthmian	A	Harrow Borough	203	W 1 - 0	Carew 81	5	11
30	Isthmian	A	Worthing	297	W 2 - 0	Kargbo 28 Clunis 67	3	12
Oct 7	Isthmian	H	Needham Market	2417	W 2 - 0	Ferguson 52 Boakye-Yiadom 44	2	13
14	Isthmian	A	Staines Town	322	D 1 - 1	Clunis 47		14
17	Isthmian	H	Harlow Town	552	W 4 - 0	Clunis 16 90 Chambers 29 Allasani 55	2	15
21	Isthmian	H	Burgess Hill Town	1971	W 3 - 2	Ferguson 34 Clunis 49 Chambers 65	2	16
24	Isthmian	A	Merstham	336	W 4 - 0	Ferguson 14 55 Allassani 18 75	1	17
28	FAT 1Q	A	Waltham Abbey	203	W 3 - 0	Allassani 48 Ferguson 50 Chambers 57		18
Nov 4	Isthmian	A	Thurrock	196	W 1 - 0	Allassani 40	1	19
11	FAT 2Q	A	Harlow Town	363	L 1 - 2	Allaasani 33		20
14	Isthmian	H	Harrow Borough	1199	W 2 - 0	Carew 59 Weatherstone 73	1	21
18	Isthmian	A	Metropolitan Police	321	W 4 - 1	ALLASSANI 3 (15 19 39) Weatherstone 30	1	22
21	Isthmian	A	Hendon	306	D 3 - 3	Carew 14 80 (pen) Hayles 90	1	23
25	Isthmian	H	Lowestoft Town	1832	W 1 - 0	Hayles 76	1	24
Dec 2	Isthmian	A	Enfield Town	599	L 1 - 3	Allassani 53	1	25
9	Isthmian	H	Brightlingsea Regent	1828	W 2 - 1	Carew 30 (pen) Allassani 34	1	26
16	Isthmian	A	Tonbridge Angels	539	D 1 - 1	Clunis 48	1	27
23	Isthmian	H	Leiston	1079	W 3 - 0	Allassani 13 59 Green 78	2	28
26	Isthmian	A	Tooting & Mitcham United	636	W 3 - 1	Green 8 Allassani 18 Clunis 41	2	29
Jan 1	Isthmian	H	Kingstonian	1516	W 4 - 0	ALLASSANI 3 (29 50 85) Boakye-Yiadom 88	1	30
6	Isthmian	H	Folkestone Invicta	2004	W 4 - 3	Weatherstone 39 Green 45 Clunis 63 Boakye-Yiadom 85	1	31
13	Isthmian	A	Margate	860	L 0 - 1		1	32
20	Isthmian	H	Merstham	1692	L 1 - 2	Carew 15	1	33
23 Jan	Isthmian	H	Wingate & Finchley	158	L 1 - 2	Clunis 45	2	34
Feb 3	Isthmian	H	Metropolitan Police	1465	D 0 - 0		2	35
17	Isthmian	H	Enfield Town	2158	D 1 - 1	Carew 63	2	36
24	Isthmian	A	Wingate & Finchley	322	D 0 - 0		3	37
Mar 6	Isthmian	A	Billericay Town	988	W 3 - 1	Akinyemi 43 83 Clunis 90	1	38
10	Isthmian	A	Brightlingsea Regent	346	D 2 - 2	V-Guimaraes 27 Akinyemi 52	2	39
18	Isthmian	A	Worthing	840	W 3 - 0	Ming 40 Akinyemi 54 Clunis 63	1	40
20	Isthmian	A	Lowestoft Town	378	W 3 - 1	Ferguson 30 Marshall (og) 44 Clunis 46	1	41
24	Isthmian	A	Needham Market	495	W 3 - 0	Clunis 7 20 Ferguson 47	1	42
Apr 6	Isthmian	A	Burgess Hill Town	480	D 1 - 1	Clunis 15	1	43
10	Isthmian	H	Tonbridge Angels	581	L 1 - 2	Green 90	1	44
12	Isthmian	A	Dorking Wanderers	551	W 4 - 0	Allassani 32 Carew 49Green 53 Weatherstone 78	1	45
14	Isthmian	H	Thurrock	1003	W 2 - 1	Carew 27 Green 79	1	46
18	Isthmian	A	Leatherhead	644	W 1 - 0	Acheampong 90	2	47
21	Isthmian	A	Folkestone Invicta	921	W 2 - 0	Carew 31 Clunis 33 36	2	48
26	Isthmian	A	Kingstonian	316	W 1 - 0	Acheampong 50	2	49
28	Isthmian	H	Margate	1266	D 1 - 1	Chambers 80	2	50
May 3	PO SF	H	Leiston	1285	W 1 - 0	Carew 71		51
7	PO Final	H	Hendon	3321	D 1 - 1	Tomlin 54 (Won 4-3 on pens)		52

GOALSCORERS	SG	CSG	Pens	Hat tricks	Total		SG	CSG	Pens	Hat tricks	Total
2016-17 Tomlin					17	Beaney	2				3
Clunis	16	4			20	Chambers	4	2			4
Allassani	12	4		2	18	Hayles	3	2			3
Carew	9	2	2		11	Kargbo	2				2
Ferguson	6	3			7	Ming	2				2
B-Yiadom	4		1		6	Acheampong	2				2
Green	6	2			7	Opponents					1
Akinyemi	3				4	V-Guimaraes					1
Faal	2				4						
Weatherstone	4	2			5						

ENFIELD TOWN MATCH RESULTS 2017-18

Date	Comp	H/A	Opponents	Att:	Result	Goalscorers	Pos	No.
Aug 12	Isthmian	H	Folkestone Invicta	613	D 1 - 1	Roberts 48	12	1
15	Isthmian	A	Hendon	292	L 0 - 3		14	2
19	Isthmian	H	Metropolitan Police	378	D 4 - 4	Thomas 4 Youngs 73 Robinson 77 (og) Higgs 90	20	3
26	Isthmian	A	Tooting & Mitcham United	306	L 0 - 4		12	4
28	Isthmian	H	Harlow Town	514	W 1 - 0	Sherwood 13 (og)	8	5
Sept 2	FAC 1Q	H	Harrow Borough	421	W 2 - 1	Thomas 11 87		6
9	Isthmian	A	Brightlingsea Regent	263	L 1 - 2	Thomas 57	14	7
12	Isthmian	A	Wingate & Finchley	209	L 1 - 2	Higgs 70	15	8
16	FAC 2Q	A	Hanwell Town	210	D 0 - 0			9
18	FAC 2Qr	H	Hanwell Town	278	W 5 - 0	Roberts 45 Purse 49 (pen) Blake 88 Blackman 90 Moore 90		10
23	Isthmian	A	Needham Market	304	D 2 - 2	Coakley 52 (og) Higgs 81	16	11
30	FAC 3Q	H	Phoenix Sports	501	W 3 - 0	Noto 7 Thomas 12 Moore 87		12
Oct 3	Isthmian	H	Hendon	362	W 1 - 0	Youngs 11	13	13
7	Isthmian	A	Margate	509	W . 2 - 1	Parcell 1 McKenzie 64	12	14
14	FAC 4Q	A	Maidstone United	1495	D 2 - 2	Thomas 20 Purse 57 (pen)		15
17	FAC 4Qr	H	Maidstone United	820	L 1 - 3	Greene 75 (aet)		16
21	Isthmian	A	Billericay Town	1559	L 1 - 2	McKenzie 35	18	17
24	Isthmian	A	Leiston	333	D 2 - 2	Noto 55 McKenzie 90	16	18
28	FAT 1Q	A	Royston Town	303	L 0 - 2			19
31	Isthmian	A	Staines Town	199	L 2 - 3	Roberts 50 Greene 79	18	20
Nov 18	Isthmian	H	Thurrock	390	W 3 - 1	Thomas 6 50 Blake 90	16	21
21	Isthmian	H	Wingate & Finchley	292	D 1 - 1	Benyon 40	15	22
25	Isthmian	A	Leatherhead	397	L 0 - 2		15	23
28	Isthmian	A	Folkestone Invicta	335	L 1 - 5	Thomas 11	17	24
Dec 2	Isthmian	H	Dulwich Hamlet	599	W 3 1	Thomas 28 Blackman 68 Ward-Cochrane 90	16	25
5	Isthmian	A	Leiston	186	L 0 - 2		16	26
16	Isthmian	H	Dorking	319	W 3 - 2	Youngs 17 Blake 69 Blackman 78	14	27
23	Isthmian	H	Tooting & Mitcham United	391	D 1 - 1	Hope 85	14	28
26	Isthmian	A	Harlow Town	260	W 2 - 0	Hope 27 Purse 82 (pen)	11	29
30 Dec	Isthmian	A	Metropolitan Police	182	D 1 - 1	Purse 42 (pen)	11	30
Jan 1	Isthmian	H	Harrow Borough	382	W 3 - 0	Youngs 10 McKenzie 56 Longe-King 68 (og)	12	31
6	Isthmian	A	Worthing	813	D 2 - 2	Greene 45 Youngs 88	12	32
8 Jan	Isthmian	A	Kingstonian	205	L 1 - 4	Blackman 55 (pen)	12	33
13	Isthmian	H	Merstham	381	D 2 - 2	Hope 4 Blackman 38	12	34
16	Isthmian	H	Tonbridge Angels	281	L 0 - 1		12	35
27	Isthmian	H	Needham Market	389	L 0 - 2		14	36
Feb 3	Isthmian	A	Thurrock	162	L 1 - 3	Parcell 76	16	37
6	Isthmian	A	Lowestoft Town	222	L 0 - 3		16	38
10	Isthmian	H	Kingstonian	315	L 1 - 3	Campbell 11	18	39
13	Isthmian	H	Burgess Hill Town	251	W 3 - 2	Olomowewe 3 Blake 15 41	15	40
17	Isthmian	A	Dulwich Hamlet	2158	D 1 - 1	Youngs 78	14	41
24	Isthmian	A	Leatherhead	384	L 0 - 1		15	42
Mar 10	Isthmian	H	Lowestoft Town	442	W 3 - 0	Mitchell-King 40 Blackman 55 (pen) Hope 90	13	43
17	Isthmian	H	Staines Town	322	L 3 - 4	Hockney 18 Campbell 30 Wadkins 49	14	44
24	Isthmian	A	Margate	630	D 1 - 1	Wynter 88	16	45
31	Isthmian	H	Brightlingsea Regent	420	W 2 - 0	Blake 89 Greene 90	15	46
Apr 2	Isthmian	A	Harrow Borough	216	L 0 - 5		15	47
5	Isthmian	A	Dorking Wanderers	206	D 2 - 2	Wynter 77 Mubiayi 89	15	48
7	Isthmian	H	Billericay Town	690	D 1 - 1	Blake 90	18	49
10	Isthmian	A	Burgess Hill Town	287	W 4 - 2	Wynter 16 Thomas 42 64 Blake 53	16	50
14	Isthmian	A	Tonbridge Angels	474	W 4 - 1	Wadkins 6 79 Greene 53 Youngs 60	16	51
21	Isthmian	H	Worthing	458	L 0 - 1		16	52
28	Isthmian	A	Merstham	220	D 1 - 1	Rumens 90	17	53

GOALSCORERS	SG	CSG	Pens	Hat tricks	Total		SG	CSG	Pens	Hat tricks	Total
2016-17 Crook					17	Wynter	3				3
Thomas	7	2			12	Campbell					2
Blake					8	Moore					2
Youngs					7	Noto					2
Blackman		2			6	Parcell	2				2
Greene					5	Benyon					1
Hope					4	Hockney					1
McKenzie					4	Mitchell-King					1
Opponents					4	Mubiayi					1
Purse			4		4	Olomowewe					1
Higgs					3	Rumens					1
Roberts					3	Ward-Cochrane					1
Wadkins	2				3						

FOLKESTONE INVICTA MATCH RESULTS 2017-18

Date	Comp	H/A	Opponents	Att:	Result	Goalscorers	Pos	No.
Aug 12	Isthmian	A	Enfield	513	D 1 - 1	Yusuff 75	13	1
15	Isthmian	H	Merstham	322	W 2 - 1	Yusuff 9 Cooper 77 (og)	6	2
19	Isthmian	A	Burgess HIll Town	335	D 1 - 1	Yusuff 41 (pen)	8	3
26	Isthmian	H	Needham Market	374	L 0 - 2		15	4
28	Isthmian	A	Tonbridge Angels	534	W 3 - 2	Yusuff 21 (pen) Heard 53 Vincent 56	11	5
Sept 2	FAC 1Q	H	Greenwich Borough	351	W 3 - 2	Hasler 45 Everitt 75 McCann i90		6
9	Isthmian	H	Staines Town	401	W 2 - 0	Taylor 21 McCann 90	8	7
16	FAC 2Q	H	Tooting & Mitcham United	335	W 3 - 1	Dines (og) 6 O'Mara 47 Yusuff 60		8
23	Isthmian	A	Hendon	457	W 3 - 2	Yusuff 51 (pen) Vincent 70 Taylor 84	7	9
30	FAC 3Q	H	Aylesbury United	473	W 2 - 1	Taylor 25 Yusuff 56		10
Oct 3	Isthmian	A	Merstham	180	L 0 - 2		9	11
7	Isthmian	A	Metropolitan Police	165	L 1 - 3	Draycott 4	10	12
14	FAC 1Q	A	Slough Town	926	L 0 - 1			13
17	Isthmian	H	Leatherhead	317	W 3 - 0	McCann 25 Davies 66 Hasler 81	13	14
21	Isthmian	A	Leiston	321	W 5 - 1	Heard 8 Draycott 17 Hasler 26 Yusuff 45 (pen) 74 (pen)	13	15
24	Isthmian	A	Tooting & Mitcham United	222	W 1 - 0	Davies 64	7	16
29	FAT 1Q	A	Leiston	191	D 1 - 1	Draycott 5		17
31	FAT 1Qr	H	Leiston	301	D 1 - 1	Heard 101 (Lost 5-6 on pens)		18
Nov 4	Isthmian	H	Dorking	409	W 3 - 1	Draycott 36 Heard 86 Yusuff 90 (pen)	6	19
8	Isthmian	A	Leatherhead	294	W 2 - 1	Vincent 45 Hasler 58	4	20
11	Isthmian	H	Tooting & Mitcham United	439	W 3 - 1	Draycott 7 80 Yusuff 84	2	21
18	Iathmian	A	Brighlingsea	198	W 2 - 1	Hasler 28 Yuseff 90 (pen)	2	22
28	Isthmian	H	Enfield Town	335	W 5 - 1	Yusuff 23 73 Ter Horst 26 90 Hasler 45	2	23
Dec 2	Isthmian	A	Wingate & Finchley	156	L 1 - 2	Vilcu 82 (og)	4	24
9	Isthmian	H	Harrow Borough	349	L 1 - 3	Yusuff 87	4	25
12	Isthmian	H	Worthing	237	L 1 - 2	Vincent 63	4	26
16	Isthmian	A	Harlow Town	150	L 2 - 3	Yusuff 25 Ter Horst 90	5	27
23	Isthmian	A	Needham Market	261	D 2 - 2	Yusuff 65 Draycott 90	6	28
27	Isthmian	H	Tonbridge Angels	532	W 3 1	Heard 58 Yussuf 45 Draycott 67	5	29
30	Isthmian	H	Burgess Hill Town	373	W 3 - 1	Yusuff 62 McCann 69 Heard 76	4	30
Jan 1	Isthmian	A	Margate	653	W 3 - 1	Heard 34 McCann 40 Everitt 47	3	31
6	Isthmian	A	Dulwich Hamlet	2004	L 3 - 4	Yussuff 20 73 Draycott 88	3	32
8	Isthmian	H	Thurrock	306	D 2 - 2	Draycott 45 69	4	33
16	Isthmian	A	Lowestoft Town	226	W 2 - 0	Draycott 2 Taylor 35	3	34
27	Isthmian	A	Hendon	326	D 3 - 3	Draycott 26 Davies 65 70	4	35
Feb 3	Isthmian	H	Brightlingsea REgent	357	W 3 - 2	Dolan 45 Taylor 57 Draycott 88	4	36
10	Isthmian	A	Worthing	. 604	L 2 - 3	Ter Horst 42 88	5	37
17	Isthmian	H	Wingate & Finchley	446	W 5 - 0	Yusuff 24 (pen) Ter Horst 59 79 Taylor 85 Walmsley 90	5	38
20	Isthmian	H	Billericay	728	W 2 - 1	McCann 14 Ter Horst 45	4	39
24	Isthmian	A	Kingstonian	253	D 1 - 1	Yusuff 61	4	40
Mar 3	Isthmian	H	Harlow Town	475	D 1 - 1	Draycott 65	4	41
6	Isthmian	A	Kingstonian	321	W 3 - 0	Draycott 42 Taylor 78 90	3	42
10	Isthmian	A	Harrow Borough	168	W 3 - 0	Yusuff 35 (pen) 73 Taylor 90	1	43
24	Isthmian	H	Metropolitan Police	468	W 5 - 2	Yusuff 13 Hasler 37 Ter Horst 41 Taylor 81 Chendlik 84	2	44
27	Isthmian	H	Lowestoft Town	363	W 2 - 1	Taylor 81 Yusuff 90	2	45
26	Isthmian	H	Margate	946	D 1 - 1	Yusuff 79 (pen)	3	46
Apr 7	Isthmian	A	Leiston	465	W 2 0	Hasler 44 Yusuff 52	2	47
12	Isthmian	A	Staines Town	247	D 4 - 4	TER HORST 3 (10 22 90) Dolan 52	6	48
14	Isthmian	A	Dorking Wanderers	237	L 3 - 5	Hasler 21 Taylor 52 Dolan 86	3	49
17	Isthmian	A	Thurrock	173	W 2 - 1	McCann 25 Taylor 79	3	50
21	Isthmian	H	Dulwich Hamlet	921	L 0 - 3		3	51
28	Isthmian	A	Billericay Town	2206	D 2 - 2	Taylor 6 89	4	52
May 3	PO SF	A	Hendon	722	L 0 - 4			53

GOALSCORERS	SG	CSG	Pens	Hat tricks	Total		SG	CSG	Pens	Hat tricks	Total
2016-17 Draycott					22	Dolan	3				3
Yusuff	25	4	10		29	Opponents	3				3
Draycott	14	5			16	Everett	2				2
Taylor	13	2			15	Chendlik					1
Ter Horst	8	2		1	12	O'Mara					1
Hasler	8	2			9	Walmsley					1
Heard	6	3			7						
McCann	7	2			7						
Davies	3				4						
Vincent	4				4						

HARLOW TOWN MATCH RESULTS 2017-18

Date	Comp	H/A	Opponents	Att:	Result	Goalscorers	Pos	No.
Aug 12	Isthmian	A	Harrow Borough	236	L 1 - 2	Read 30	17	1
15	Isthmian	H	Dulwich Hamlet	260	L 2 - 3	Gordon 8 Read 30	20	2
19	Isthmian	A	Hendon	244	L 0 - 1		23	3
26	Isthmian	H	Lowestoft Town	203	W 2 - 0	Read 65 Dobson 69	21	4
28	Isthmian	A	Enfield Town	514	L 0 - 1		21	5
Sept 2	FAC 1Q	A	Thurrock	159	D 1 - 1	Fagg 44		6
5	FAC 1Qr	H	Thurrock	230	W 2 - 1	Dobson 18 Neita 63		7
9	Isthmian	H	Tonbridge Angels	234	W 2 - 1	Neita 2 Read 74	17	8
12	Isthmian	A	Leiston	244	D 0 - 0		19	9
16	FAC 2Q	A	Lowestoft Town	395	W 1 - 0	Fagg 62		10
23	Isthmian	A	Kingstonian	223	L 0 - 6		20	11
26	Isthmian	H	Needham Market	141	L 1 - 3	Nunn 51 (og)	22	12
30	FAC 3Q	A	East Thurrock United	159	D 2 - 2	Read 32 Vidal 35		13
Oct 2	FAC 3Qr	A	East Thurrock United	329	L 1 - 2	Neita 30		14
7	Isthmian	A	Leatherhead	406	L 1 - 2	Neita 32	22	15
10	Isthmian	H	Dorking Wanderers	130	D 2 - 2	Small 14 Dobson 69	17	16
14	Isthmian	H	Harrow Borough	184	W 2 - 1	Read 49 (pen) Dobson 68	22	17
17	Isthmian	A	Dulwich Hamlet	552	L 0 - 4		22	18
21	Isthmian	A	Margate	168	D 1 - 1	Read 90	22	19
28	FAT 1Q	A	Aylesbury	91	D 0 - 0			20
31	FAT 1Qr	A	Aylesbury	121	W 4 - 2	Small 6 Dobson 27 Read 38 Dadson 50		21
Nov 4	Isthmian	A	Brightlingsea Town	181	L 1 - 3	Dadson 12	23	22
7	Isthmian	A	Leiston	140	W 1 - 0	Dadson 66	20	23
11	FAT 2Q	A	Dulwich Hamlet	363	W 2 - 1	Read 27 Taylor 36 (og)		24
18	Isthmian	H	Billericay Town	501	L 2 - 4	Mayasi 19 Dadson 65	23	25
21	Isthmian	H	Needham Market	264	L 1 - 5	Maduako 4	23	26
25	FAT 3Q	A	Hampton & Richmond B	289	L 1 - 5	Hawes 85		27
Dec 2	Isthmian	H	Worthing	180	W 3 - 2	Sanko 15 Simms 45 Read 90	22	28
9	Isthmian	A	Metropolitan Police	90	L 1 - 2	Read 44	22	29
16	Isthmian	H	Folkeston Invicta	150	W 3 - 2	Davies 45 (og) Sanko 45 Newman 59 (og)	21	30
19	Isthmian	A	Staines Town	169	L 1 - 4	Martin (og) 30	23	31
23	Isthmian	A	Lowestoft Town	393	W 3 - 0	Dadson 36 Read 54 72	20	32
26	Isthmian	H	Enfield	260	L 0 - 2		21	33
30	Isthmian	H	Hendon	258	L 0 - 3		22	34
Jan 1	Isthmian	A	Thurrock	136	L 0 - 1		23	35
6	Isthmian	H	Tooting & Mitcham United	204	W 2 - 1	Read 76 Edwards 90	19	36
13	Isthmian	A	Wingate & Finchley	102	L 0 - 2		20	37
20	Isthmian	A	Dorking Wanderers	212	D 2 - 2	Small 45 Ajala 77	21	38
23	Isthmian	A	Burgess Hill Town	158	L 0 - 2		23	39
27	Isthmian	H	Kingstonian	190	L 0 - 1		22	40
30	Isthmian	H	Merstham	131	L 1 - 2	Edwards 77	23	41
Feb 10	Isthmian	H	Burgess Hill Town	164	D 1 - 1	Read 12	23	42
17	Isthmian	A	Worthing	685	D 2 - 2	Foy 41 53	23	43
24	Isthmian	H	Staines Town	167	L 2 - 4	Read 71 Udoji 71 (og)	23	44
Mar 3	Isthmian	A	Folkestone Invicta	475	D 1 - 1	Read 44	23	45
10	Isthmian	A	Metropolitan Police	101	W 4 - 3	Small 22 Clarke 63 (pen) Foy 75 84	22	46
17	Isthmian	A	Merstham	110	L 0 - 2		22	47
24	Isthmian	H	Leatherhead	219	W 2 - 1	Foy 2 March 18	22	48
Apr 2	Isthmian	H	Thurrock	215	W 3 - 2	Simms 10 Scales 58 Small 78	21	49
7	Isthmian	A	Margate	451	L 2 - 4	Foy 13 32	21	50
14	Isthmian	H	Brightlingsea Town	247	W 2 - 0	Read 11 (pen) Foy 27	21	51
17	Isthmian	H	Tonbridge Angels	235	D 0 - 0		21	52
21	Isthmian	A	Tooting & Mitcham United	248	W 1 - 0	Read 40	21	53
24	Isthmian	A	Billericay Town	1689	L 0 - 2		21	54
28	Isthmian	H	Wingate & Finchley	277	L 0 - 1		21	55

GOALSCORERS	SG	CSG	Pens	Hat tricks	Total		SG	CSG	Pens	Hat tricks	Total
2016-17 Read					27	Simms	2				2
Read	18	2	2		19	Ajala					1
Foy	5				8	Clarke					1
Opponents					6	Gordon					1
Dadson	5	3			5	Hawes					1
Dobson	5	2			5	Maduako					1
Small	4				5	March					1
Neita	4	2			4	Mayasi					1
Sonko	2	2			3	Scales					1
Edwards	2				2	Vidal					1
Fagg	2				2						

HARROW BOROUGH MATCH RESULTS 2017-18

Date	Comp	H/A	Opponents	Att:	Result	Goalscorers	Pos	No.
Aug 12	Isthmian	H	Harlow Town	239	W 2 - 1	O'Connor 35 83	3	1
15	Isthmian	A	Wingate & Finchley	134	W 3 - 1	Cumberbatch 10 Banya 52 O'Connor 62	1	2
19	Isthmian	A	Leatherhead	355	W 2 - 0	O'Connor 8 Preddie 27	1	3
26	Isthmian	H	Tonbridge	203	W 2 - 0	Bryan 9 Turl 58	1	4
28	Isthmian	A	Hendon	316	L 0 - 6		3	5
Sept 2	FAC 1Q	A	Enfield Town	421	L 1 - 2	Bryan 75		6
9	Isthmian	H	Merstham	140	D 2 - 2	Stanislaus 35 Richards 86	3	7
12	Isthmian	A	Staines Town	183	L 1 - 2	Preddie 79	5	8
23	Isthmian	H	Margate	552	D 1 - 1	Richards 90	8	9
26	Isthmian	H	Dulwich Hamlet	203	L 0 - 1		11	10
30	Isthmian	A	Lowestoft Town	378	D 1 - 1	Banya 23	9	11
Oct 3	Isthmian	H	Wingate & Finchley	162	W 3 - 0	Banya 12 Richards 45 McDonald-Roberts 64	6	12
7	Isthmian	H	Kingstonian	227	W 2 - 0	Stanislaus 33 (pen) 35	5	13
14	Isthmian	A	Harlow Town	184	L 1 - 2	Cumberbatch 38	5	14
21	Isthmian	H	Brightlingsea Regent	156	L 1 - 2	Ujah 61	7	15
28	FAT 1Q	H	Haringey Borough	103	D 1 - 1	Cumberbatch 90 (pen)		16
30	FAT 1Qr	A	Haringay Borough	170	L 0 - 1			17
Nov 2	Isthmian	A	Tooting & Mitcham United	266	L 2 - 5	Moore 58 74		18
11	Isthmian	A	Thurrock	118	L 0 - 2		13	19
14	Isthmian	A	Dulwich Hamlet	1199	L 0 - 2		13	20
18	Isthmian	H	Dorking Wanderers	145	L 3 - 4	Moss 30 Cumberbatch 37 Bryan 65	13	21
21	Isthmian	H	Staines Town	149	L 1 2	Preddie 58	14	22
25	Isthmian	A	Worthing	592	D 2 - 2	Preddie 51 Moss 90	14	23
28	Isthmian	A	Billericay Town	201	L 0 - 2		14	24
Dec 2	Isthmian	H	Metropolitan Police	114	W 3 - 0	Banya 5 Cumberbatch 17 Moss 90	12	25
9	Isthmian	A	Folkestone Invicta	349	W 3 1	Kabba 23 Banya 39 Bryan 90	11	26
16	Isthmian	H	Leiston	121	L 0 - 5		13	27
23	Isthmian	A	Tonbridge Angels	377	L 1 - 2	Cumberbatch 72 (pen)		28
26	Isthmian	H	Hendon	280	L 0 - 4		16	29
30	Isthmian	H	Leatherhead	180	L 1 - 2	Moss 75	17	30
Jan 1	Isthmian	A	Enfield Town	382	L 0 - 2		18	31
6	Isthmian	H	Needham Market	141	W 3 - 2	Moss 3 Kabba 8 Banya 82	15	32
13	Isthmian	A	Burgess Hill Town	287	W 3 - 2	Bryan 3 Moss 7 Moore 82	15	33
27	Isthmian	H	Margate	171	L 0 - 4		18	34
Feb 10	Isthmian	H	Thurrock	132	W 2 - 0	Cumberbatch 51 58	17	35
17	Isthmian	A	Metropolitan Police	116	L 0 - 1		18	36
24	Isthmian	H	Worthing	178	W 1 - 0	Moss 9	16	37
Mar 10	Isthmian	H	Folkestone Invicta	168	L 0 - 3		18	38
24	Isthmian	A	Kingstonian	224	W 1 - 0	Moore 17	18	39
28	Isthmian	H	Billericay Town	313	L 0 - 2		18	40
31	Isthmian	A	Merstham	148	W 1 - 0	Cumberbatch 73	18	41
Apr 2	Isthmian	H	Enfield Town	216	W 5 - 0	Cumberbatch 48 55 Preddie 57 Moss 79 90	16	42
6	Isthmian	A	Brightlingsea Regent	192	D 1 1	Moore 13	16	43
10	Isthmian	A	Leiston	170	L 0 - 3		16	44
12	Isthmian	H	Lowestoft Town	113	W 6 - 0	Moss19 MOORE 3(58 61 64) Cole 68(og) Banya 70	14	45
14	Isthmian	H	Tooting & Mitcham United	198	D 1 - 1	Cumberbatch 11	16	46
21	Isthmian	A	Needham Market	303	W 1 - 0	Moss 8	13	47
24	Isthmian	A	Dorking Wanderers	131	W 4 - 0	Richards 16 Moore 22 45 O'Connor 54	12	48
28	Isthmian	H	Burgess Hill Town	248	W 3 - 2	Moss 55 Moore 86 Cumberbatch 90	12	49

GOALSCORERS	SG	CSG	Pens	Hat tricks	Total		SG	CSG	Pens	Hat tricks	Total
2016-17 Driver					12	Kabba	2				2
Cumberbatch	11				13	M-Roberts					1
Moss	10	2			12	Opponents					1
Moore	7	2	1		11	Turl					1
Banya	7	2			7	Ujah					1
Bryan	5				5						
Preddie	5	2			5						
O'Connor	4	3			5						
Richards	4				4						
Stanislaus	1		1		3						

HENDON MATCH RESULTS 2017-18

Date	Comp	H/A	Opponents	Att:	Result		Goalscorers	Pos	No.
Aug 12	Isthmian	A	Tonbridge Angels	495	L	0 - 1		21	1
15	Isthmian	H	Enfield Town	292	W	3 - 0	MUIR 3 (7 19 52)	13	2
19	Isthmian	H	Harlow Town	244	W	1 - 0	Cole 65	5	3
26	Isthmian	A	Brightlingsea Regent	201	L	1 - 2	Cole 75	9	4
28	Isthmian	H	Harrow Borough	316	W	6 - 0	Ball 1 MUIR 3 (6 16 39) Joseph 69 Cole 73	5	5
Sept 2	FAC 1Q	H	Wingate & Finchley	298	D	1 - 1	Bray 87		6
5	FAC 1Qr	A	Wingate & Finchley	266	L	2 - 4	Muir 53 87		7
9	Isthmian	A	Metropolitan Police	110	W	2 - 1	Joseph 8 Cole 90	4	8
12	Isthmian	A	Dulwich Hamlet	659	W	1 - 0	Walker 90	2	9
23	Isthmian	H	Folkestone Invicta	457	L	2 - 3	Muir 47 49	4	10
26	Isthmian	H	Staines Town	147	W	3 0	Muir 31 90 Joseph 76	2	11
30	Isthmian	H	Tooting & Mitcham United	219	W	4 - 0	Lee 47 Ball 52 Joseph 62 Walker 67	2	12
Oct 3	Isthmian	A	Enfield	362	L	0 - 1		3	13
7	Isthmian	A	Billericay Town	1988	L	3 - 4	Nathaniel-George 3 90 Cole 17	3	14
14	Isthmian	H	Tonbridge Angels	265	W	2 - 1	Corcoron 55 Muir 90 (pen)	3	15
17	Isthmian	H	Needham Market	153	W	1 - 0	Joseph 25	1	16
21	Isthmian	A	Worthing	514	W	2 - 1	Muir 72 Walker 87	2	17
28	FAT 1Q	H	Kings Langley	171	W	3 - 1	Muir 18 Ball 28 Diedhiou 36		18
Nov 4	Isthmian	H	Kingstonian	297	L	1 - 3	Muir 28	2	19
11	FAT 2Q	H	Burgess Hill Town	165	W	3 - 0	Muir 15 (pen) 59 Joseph 25		20
18	Isthmian	H	Burgess Hill Town	192	D	2 - 2	Diedhou 45 Joseph 90	6	21
21	Isthmian	H	Dulwich Hamlet	306	D	3 - 3	Muir 6 43 (pen) Diedhiou 17	6	22
25	FAT 3Q	H	Slough Town	251	D	1 - 1	Ibe 90		23
28	FAC 3Qr	A	Slough Town	626	D	1 - 1	Uchechi 32 (Won 3-0 on pens)		24
Dec 2	Isthmian	H	Thurrock	178	W	4 - 1	Maclaren 18 Diedhiou 22 Muir 25 59 (pen)	5	25
9	Isthmian	A	Margate	425	L	2 - 3	Walker 31 Diedhiou 78	7	26
16	FAT 1	H	Bath City	256	W	2 - 1	Lee 30 Cole 74		27
19	Isthmian	A	Dorking Wanderers	184	W	3 - 0	Muir 4 Corcoron 10 Philpot 74 (og)	6	28
23	Isthmian	A	Brightlingsea Regent	189	W	4 - 2	Cole 10 Diedhiou 72 Muir 75 Walker 90	5	29
26	Isthmian	A	Harrow Borough	280	W	4 - 0	Walker 38 62 Diedhiou 48 Muir 83 (pen)	3	30
30	Isthmian	H	Harlow Town	256	W	3 - 0	MUIR 3 (51pen 54 89)	3	31
Jan 1	Isthmian	H	Wingate & Finchley	237	L	0 - 1		4	32
13	FAT 2	A	Sutton United	785	L	0 - 3			33
20	Isthmian	A	Needham Market	239	D	3 - 3	Walker 33 Nathaniel-George 50 53	5	34
27	Isthmian	H	Folkestone Invicta	326	D	3 - 3	White 73 Joseph 76 Maclaren 90	7	35
30	Isthmian	H	Leatherhead	181	L	1 - 4	Nathaniel-George 66	7	36
Feb 3	Isthmian	A	Burgess Hill Town	278	W	4 - 2	MUIR 3 (11 39 62) Walker 90	7	37
10	Isthmian	H	Dorking Wanderers	175	D	0 - 0		7	38
13	Isthmian	H	Leiston	147	W	2 - 1	Walker 3 Lee 69	4	39
17	Isthmian	A	Thurrock	139	W	1 - 0	Nathaniel-George 52	4	40
24	Isthmian	H	Lowestoft Town	192	D	1 - 1	Joseph 59	5	41
Mar 10	Isthmian	H	Margate	309	D	1 - 1	Walker 3	5	42
13	Isthmian	H	Merstham	137	D	1 - 1	Muir 35 (pen)	5	43
17	Isthmian	A	Tooting & Mitcham United	138	W	2 - 0	Nathaniel-George 25 Murray 82	5	44
20	Isthmian	A	Staines Town	194	L	0 4		7	45
24	Isthmian	H	Billericay Town	482	W	4 - 1	Muir 55 (pen) 60 Walker 63 90	5	46
31	Isthmian	H	Metropolitan Police	277	W	2 - 0	Sprague 71 Walker 82	4	47
Apr 2	Isthmian	A	Wingate & Finchley	207	D	2 - 2	Muir 37 (pen) 59 (pen)	4	48
7	Isthmian	H	Worthing	260	W	4 - 3	Muir 7 (p) Joseph 15 Walker 57 N-George 90	4	49
10	Isthmian	A	Lowestoft Town	205	L	1 - 2	Joseph 51	4	50
14	Isthmian	A	Kingstonian	240	D	0 - 0		5	51
21	Isthmian	A	Merstham	273	W	3 - 0	Corcoran 11 Nathaniel-George 64 Walker 66	4	52
25	Isthmian	A	Leatherhead	449	W	2 - 1	Murphy, Walker		53
28	Isthmian	A	Leiston	617	W	2 1	Nathaniel-George 62 Uchechi 63	3	54
May 3	PO SF	H	Folkestone Invicta	722	W	4 - 0	Walker 6, Nathaniel-George 16, Joseph 43, Muir 44		55
7	PO Final	A	Dulwich Hamlet	3321	D	1 - 1	Nathaniel-George 36 (Lost 3-4 on pens)		56

GOALSCORERS	SG	CSG	Pens	Hat tricks	Total		SG	CSG	Pens	Hat tricks	Total
2016-17 Muir					9	Maclaren	2				2
Muir	23	4	11	4	38	Uchechi	2				2
Walker	14	2			18	Bray					1
Joseph	12	2			12	Ibe					1
Nathaniel-George	9	4			12	Murphy					1
Cole	7	3			7	Murray					1
Diedhiou	7	2			7	Opponents					1
Ball	3				3	Sprague					1
Corcoran	3				3	White					1
Lee	3				3						

KINGSTONIAN MATCH RESULTS 2017-18

Date	Comp	H/A	Opponents	Att:	Result	Goalscorers	Pos	No.
Aug 12	Isthmian	A	Billericay Town	1141	W 1 - 0	Taylor 90	5	1
14	Isthmian	H	Burgess Hill Town	252	D 0 - 0		1	2
19	Isthmian	A	Staines Town	323	L 0 - 5		14	3
26	Isthmian	H	Leatherhead	416	L 0 - 4		19	4
28	Isthmian	A	Merstham	251	W 2 - 1	Derry 70 Taylor 77	16	5
Sept 2	FAC 1Q	H	Shoreham	220	W 3 - 2	Haysman 8 Taylor 45 (pen) 72 (pen)		6
9	Isthmian	H	Lowestoft Town	218	W 3 - 2	Haysman 37 Taylor 76 Sappleton 80	11	7
11	Isthmian	H	Metropolitan Police	182	L 1 - 2	James 77 (og)	11	8
16	FAC 2Q	H	Brackley	289	L 0 - 3			9
23	Isthmian	H	Harlow Town	223	W 6 - 0	Collins 21 62 Derry 32 Little 37 Taylor 45 Haysman 74	9	10
26	Isthmian	A	Worthing	151	W 2 - 1	Derry 64 Mbo 70	6	11
30	Isthmian	H	Tonbridge Angels	264	W 2 - 1	Haysman 43 59	4	12
Oct 3	Isthmian	A	Burgess Hill Town	328	L 1 - 5	Haysman 16	5	13
7	Isthmian	A	Harrow Borough	227	L 0 - 2		7	14
10	Isthmian	A	Brightingsea Regent	195	L 0 - 2		7	15
14	Isthmian	A	Lowestoft Town	391	L 1 - 2	Gough 27	8	16
21	Isthmian	A	Wingate & Finchley	215	W 2 - 1	Alderson 4 Fiddes 90	6	17
28	FAT 1Q	H	Thurrock	225	D 3 - 3	Mbo 25 31 Rodgers 79		18
31	FAT 1Qr	A	Thurrock	84	W 4 - 1	Goode 24 Oseyemi 28 Derry 31 (pen) Collins 49		19
Nov 4	Isthmian	A	Hendon	297	W 3 - 1	Derry 4 78 Miles 54	8	20
7	Isthmian	A	Metropolitan Police	235	L 2 - 3	Fiddes 10 Gnahore 55	8	21
11	FAT 2Q	A	Ashford Town	163	D 2 - 2	Collins 57 Derry 75		22
13	FAT 2Qr	H	Ashford Town	175	W 2 - 0	Grant 41 Derry 61		23
18	Isthmian	A	Tooting & Mitcham United	262	L 2 - 3	Elliott 58 Derry 83	9	24
20	Isthmian	H	Billericay Town	285	L 0 - 2		9	25
26	FAT 3Q	H	Heybridge Swifts	251	D 2 - 2	Grant 67 Miles 85		26
?	FAT 3Qr	A	Heybridge Swifts	187	L 1 - 5	Grant 87 (pen)		27
Dec 2	Isthmian	H	Dorking Wanderers	247	D 0 - 0		12	28
9	Isthmian	H	Leiston	242	L 0 - 2		14	29
23	Isthmian	A	Leatherhead	537	L 0 - 2		17	30
Jan 1	Isthmian	A	Dulwich Hamlet	1516	L 0 - 4		20	31
6	Isthmian	H	Thurrock	220	L 0 - 2		21	32
8 Jan	Isthmian	H	Enfield Town	205	W 4 - 1	Theophanous 5 Mbo 42 McCollin 53 Oli 64		33
13	Isthmian	A	Needham Market	244	W 2 - 1	Theophanous 2 48	16	34
20	Isthmian	H	Brightlingsea Regent	221	L 0 - 1		18	35
27	Isthmian	A	Harlow Town	190	W 1 - 0	McCollin 80	16	36
29 Jan	Isthmian	H	Margate	225	L 1 - 3	McCollin 39	17	37
Feb 3	Isthmian	H	Tooting & Mitcham United	249	L 0 - 1		17	38
10	Isthmian	A	Enfield	315	W 3 - 1	Hunte 23 McCollin 75 Amoo 86	15	39
17	Isthmian	A	Dorking Wanderers	308	W 3 - 1	West 58 Ciardini 71 76	13	40
24	Isthmian	H	Folkestone Invicta	253	D 1 - 1	Wiliams 53	14	41
Mar 6	Isthmian	A	Folkestone Invicta	321	L 0 - 3		15	42
10	Isthmian	H	Leiston	208	L 1 - 3	Ajyala 7	15	43
17	Isthmian	A	Tonbridge Angels	308	L 1 - 3	Hunte 4	17	44
24	Isthmian	H	Harrow Borough	224	L 0 - 1		20	45
26	Isthmian	H	Worthing	259	D 0 - 0		20	46
Apr 7	Isthmian	A	Wingate & Finchley	375	W 1 - 0	Faal 53	19	47
10	Isthmian	A	Margate	375	W 2 - 0	Faal 38 Williams 60	18	48
14	Isthmian	H	Hendon	240	D 0 - 0		18	49
16	Isthmian	H	Merstham	204	W 2 - 1	Cundle 28 Faal 90 (pen)	18	50
21	Isthmian	A	Thurrock	196	L 0 - 1		18	51
23	Isthmian	H	Staines Town	227	W 3 - 1	Faal 57 66 Ajakaiye 60		52
26	Isthmian	H	Dulwich Hamlet	316	L 0 - 1			53
28	Isthmian	H	Needham Market	234	W 4 - 0	Ajakaiye 57 Cundle 70 Faal 77 90		54

GOALSCORERS	SG	CSG	Pens	Hat tricks	Total
2016-17 Moss					26
Derry	8		1		9
Faal	4		1		7
Haysman	5	2			6
Taylor	5	3	2		6
Collins	3				4
Mbo	3				4
McCollin	4				4
Grant	3		1		3
Theophanous	2				3
Ciardini	1				2
Cundle	2				2
Fiddes	2				2
Hunte	2				2
Miles	2				2

	SG	CSG	Pens	Hat tricks	Total
Williams	2				2
Ajakaiye	2				2
Alderson					1
Amoo					1
Ayala					1
Elliott					1
Gnahore					1
Goode					1
Gough					1
Little					1
Oli					1
Opponents					1
Oseyemi					1
Rodgers					1
Sappleton					1
West					1

LEATHERHEAD MATCH RESULTS 2017-18

Date	Comp	H/A	Opponents	Att:	Result		Goalscorers	Pos	No.
Aug 12	Isthmian	H	Lowestoft Town	305	W	2 - 1	Midson 7 73	4	1
16	Isthmian	H	Worthing	423	W	3 - 0	Nnamani 44 Kandi 66 Blackman 87	1	2
19	Isthmian	H	Harrow Borough	355	L	0 - 2		7	3
26	Isthmian	A	Kingstonian	415	W	4 - 0	Minshull 27 Midson 56 Kandi 69 Ambrosine 72	3	4
28	Isthmian	H	Metropolitan Police	321	W	1 - 0	Kandi 77	2	5
Sept 2	FAC 1Q	H	Cray Valley PM	283	W	6 - 0	KANDI 3 (28 38 52) Midson 32 36 Blackmsn 79		6
9	Isthmian	A	Billericay Town	1651	L	0 - 1		5	7
16	FAC2Q	A	Ware	149	W	5 - 2	MIDSON 4 (2 pens) Gallagher		8
23	Isthmian	A	Dulwich Hamlet	1752	L	0 - 4		11	9
27	Isthmian	H	Margate	383	L	0 - 2		13	10
30	FAC3Q	A	Ashford Town	277	W	2 - 1	Minshull 13 Midson 56		11
Oct 4	Isthmian	A	Worthing	176	D	1 - 1	Midson 90	12	12
7	Isthmian	H	Harlow Town	406	W	2 - 1	Midson 42 Williams-Bowers 57	11	13
14	FAC 4Q	A	Margate	879	W	2 - 1	Moore 75 Midson 85		14
17	Isthmian	A	Folkestone Invicta	317	L	0 - 3		16	15
21	Isthmian	A	Staines Town	317	L	0 - 3		17	16
28	FAT 1Q	H	Hythe Town	201	W	1 - 0	Midson 83 (pen)		17
Nov 5	FAC 1	H	Billericay Town	1797	D	1 - 1	Midson 21		18
7	Isthmian	A	Folkestone Invicta	294	L	1 - 2	Nash 9 (pen)	20	19
11	FAT 2Q	A	Royston Town	219	L	2 - 3	Nash Theobalds		20
16	FAC 1r	A	Billericay Town	3400	W	3 - 1	Midson 68 84 (pen) Moore 90		21
19	Isthmian	H	Wingate & Finchley	371	W	4 - 0	Ambroisine 25 NASH 3 (32 35 77)	16	22
21	Isthmian	A	Lowestoft Town	231	L	1 - 3	Minshull 55	19	23
25	Isthmian	H	Enfield Town	397	W	2 - 0	McManus 54 71	13	24
Dec 3	FAC 2	A	Wycombe Wanderers	3835	L	1 - 3	Midson 3	13	25
6	Isthmian	H	Thurrock	219	L	0 - 2		13	26
19	Isthmian	H	Needham Market	270	D	0 - 0		14	27
23	Isthmian	H	Kingstonian	537	W	2 - 0	Nash 6 Arthur 39	16	28
27	Isthmian	A	Metropolitan Police	348	W	2 - 1	McManus 30 Gasson 72	12	29
30	Isthmian	A	Harrow Borough	180	W	2 - 1	McManus 53 Midson 57	11	30
Jan 1	Isthmian	A	Tooting & Mitcham United	422	W	2 - 0	Derry 15 Midson 35	11	31
6	Isthmian	A	Leiston	255	W	2 - 1	Derry 40 Moore 55	10	32
10	Isthmian	H	Merstham	316	W	2 - 1	Midson 82 Derry 85	9	33
13	Isthmian	A	Tonbridge Angels	492	W	1 - 0	Richards 31	9	34
16	Isthmian	A	Margate	398	D	0 - 0		9	35
20	Isthmian	A	Thurrock	162	L	0 - 1		10	36
30	Isthmian	A	Hendon	181	W	4 - 1	Satiriou 2 Gallagher 44 Derry 55 Midson 57	9	37
Feb 3	Isthmian	A	Wingate & Finchley	155	L	1 - 3	Midson 85	10	38
7	Isthmian	H	Burgess Hill Town	247	W	2 - 1	Clohessy 6 Minshull 87	9	39
17	Isthmian	H	Brightlingsea Regent	351	W	2 - 1	Midson 21 88 (pen)	9	40
24	Isthmian	H	Enfield Town	384	W	1 - 0	Richards 35	8	41
Mar 17	Isthmian	H	Dorking Wanderers	354	W	1 - 0	Derry 62	8	42
21	Isthmian	H	Needham Market	244	L	0 - 1		9	43
24	Isthmian	A	Harlow Town	219	L	1 - 2	Pollock 90	9	44
27	Isthmian	A	Dorking Wanderers	1014	D	1 - 1	Derry 17 (pen)	9	45
31	Isthmian	H	Billericay Town	623	D	1 - 1	Pollock 31	8	46
Apr 2	Isthmian	A	Tooting & Mitcham United	212	W	4 - 1	Derry 20 (p) 73 Theobalds 42 Williams-Bowers77	8	47
12	Isthmian	A	Burgess Hill Town	324	W	1 - 0	Richards 17	8	48
7	Isthmian	H	Staines Town	407	W	2 - 0	Boakye-Yiadom 44 Richards 78	8	49
14	Isthmian	A	Merstham	266	D	1 - 1	Midson 69	7	50
16	Isthmian	A	Brightlingsea Regent	150	W	7 - 0	Richards 32 Boakye-Yiadom 19 63 Davies 77 NNAMANI 3(50 60 88 pen)	7	51
18	Isthmian	H	Dulwich Hamlet	644	L	0 - 1		7	52
22	Isthmian	H	Leiston	407	D	2 - 2	Derry 45 90	7	53
25	Isthmian	H	Hendon	449	L	1 - 2	Midson	7	54
28	Isthmian	A	Tonbridge Angels	518	W	2 - 0	Derry 41 Gallagher 62	6	55

GOALSCORERS	SG	CSG	Pens	Hat tricks	Total		SG	CSG	Pens	Hat tricks	Total
2016-17 Carr					7	Moore	3				3
Midson	20	4	5	1	27	Ambrosine	2				2
Derry	9	3	2		11	Blackman	2				2
Kandi	4	3		1	6	Pollock	2				2
Nash	4	2	1	1	6	Theobalds	2				2
Richards	5				5	Williams-Bowers	2				2
Minshull	5				4	Arthur					1
McManus	3				4	Clohessy					1
Nnamani				1	4	Gasson					1
Boakye-Yiadom	2				3	Satiriou					1
Gallagher	3				3						

LEISTON MATCH RESULTS 2017-18

Date	Comp	H/A	Opponents	Att:	Result	Goalscorers	Pos	No.
Aug 12	Isthmian	H	Dorking Wanderers	405	W 1 - 0	Hammond 48	6	1
15	Isthmian	A	Brightlingsea Regent	285	W 1 - 0	Hammond 27	3	2
19	Isthmian	A	Margate	624	D 2 - 2	Lawrence 54 Marsden 90	4	3
26	Isthmian	H	Dulwich Hamlet	341	D 2 - 2	Finch 41 Jefford 90	5	4
28	Isthmian	A	Lowestoft Town	593	W 2 - 0	McAuley (og) 51 Marsden 55	4	5
Sept 2	FAC 1Q	A	Aylesbury	109	W 3 - 1	Lawrence 37 Docherty 54 Dunbar 56		6
9	Isthmian	H	Thurrock	253	W 3 - 1	Blake 28 51 Ainsley 37 (pen)	2	7
12	Isthmian	H	Harlow Town	244	D 0 - 0		3	8
16	FAC 2Q	H	Crowborough Athletic	234	W 4 - 2	Jefford 12 Finch 22 82 Henderson 30		9
23	Isthmian	H	Metropolitan Police	256	W 3 - 0	Blake 29 Marsden 42 Eagle 90	2	10
30	FAC 3Q	A	Oxford City	185	L 2 - 4	Poku 10 Blake 75		11
Oct 3	Isthmian	H	Brightlingsea Regent	249	W 3 - 2	Jefford 19 Ainsley 35 Lawrence 86	2	12
7	Isthmian	H	Staines Town	323	D 2 - 2	Jefford 14 Ainsley 79	3	13
14	Isthmian	A	Dorking Wanderers	227	W 2 - 0	Brothers 62 Marsden 80	3	14
17	Isthmian	A	Tonbridge Angels	279	L 0 - 1		3	15
21	Isthmian	H	Folkestone Invicta	321	L 1 - 5	Blake 61	4	16
24	Isthmian	A	Enfield Town	333	D 2 - 2	Pelling 2 Brothers 26	4	17
29	FAT 1Q	H	Folkeston Invicta	191	D 1 - 1	Blake 61		18
31	FAT 1Qr	A	Folkestone Invicta	301	D 1 - 1	Jefford 115 (Won 6-5 on pens)		19
Nov 4	Isthmian	A	Burgess Hill Town	312	L 1 - 2	Jefford 90	7	20
7	Isthmian	A	Harlow Town	140	L 0 - 1		7	21
11	FAT 2Q	A	Dorking Wanderers	188	L 1 - 4	Finch 79		22
18	Isthmian	A	Worthing	511	D 1 - 1	Blake 36	8	23
25	Isthmian	H	Tooting & Mitcham United	265	W 2 - 0	Ainsley 60 Finch 88	8	24
Dec 2	Isthmian	A	Billericay Town	894	L 0 - 4		8	25
5	Isthmian	H	Enfield Town	186	W 2 - 0	Finch 32 Marsden 54	7	26
9	Isthmian	H	Kingstonian	242	W 2 - 0	Brothers 19 Lawrence 43	6	27
16	Isthmian	A	Harrow Borough	121	W 5 - 0	Bullard 23 Finch 44 54 Ainsley 45 Trotter 89	4	28
19	Isthmian	H	Merstham	191	W 3 - 1	Finch 16 Ainsley 57 Lawrence 77	4	29
23	Isthmian	A	Dulwich Hamlet	1079	L 0 - 3		4	30
26	Isthmian	H	Lowestoft Town	511	L 0 - 1		6	31
Jan 1	Isthmian	A	Needham Market	513	W 5 - 2	Henderson 28 Blake 40 Brothers 53 Finch 63 Ainsley 79 (pen)	5	32
6	Isthmian	H	Leatherhead	255	L 1 - 2	Blake 33	6	33
9	Isthmian	A	Wingate & Finchley	103	W 1 - 0	Blake 13	6	34
27	Isthmian	A	Metropolitan Police	130	D 1 - 1	Ainsley 26	8	35
Feb 3	Isthmian	H	Worthing	258	L 2 - 3	Finch 6 Henderson 31	9	36
10	Isthmian	A	Merstham	161	L 0 - 1		10	37
13	Isthmian	A	Hendon	147	L 1 - 2	Marsden 19	10	38
17	Isthmian	H	Billericay Town	502	W 3 - 1	Jefford 45 Mills 64 Henderson 76	9	39
24	Isthmian	A	Tooting & Mitcham United	149	W 2 - 0	Bullard 45 Ainsley 82 (pen)	9	40
Mar 6	Isthmian	H	Margate	202	D 2 - 2	Docherty 62 Reed 88	8	41
10	Isthmian	A	Kingstonian	205	W 3 - 1	Finch 2 Bentley 75 (og) Reed 86	7	42
17	Isthmian	H	Wingate & Finchley	198	W 4 - 0	Mills 18 Finch 48 Ainsley 55 (pen) Reed 90	7	43
20	Isthmian	H	Tonbridge Angels	201	W 2 - 0	Lawrence 72 Docherty 83	6	44
24	Isthmian	A	Staines Town	274	W 4 - 1	Ainsley 2 (pen) Mills 16 Reed 66 Brothers 82	6	45
31	Isthmian	A	Thurrock	139	D 0 - 0		7	46
Apr 7	Isthmian	A	Folkestone Invicta	465	L 0 - 2		7	47
10	Isthmian	H	Harrow Borough	170	W 3 - 0	Jefford 33 Finch 48 Ainsley 59	7	48
14	Isthmian	H	Burgess Hill Town	292	W 2 - 0	Ainsley 59 90 (pen)	6	49
21	Isthmian	A	Leatherhead	407	D 2 - 2	Blake 80 90	5	50
24	Isthmian	H	Needham Market	402	W 2 - 0	Reed 4 Brothers 59	5	51
28	Isthmian	H	Hendon	617	L 1 - 2	Marsden 70	5	52
May 3	PO SF	A	Dulwich Hamlet	1285	L 0 - 1			53

GOALSCORERS	SG	CSG	Pens	Hat tricks	Total		SG	CSG	Pens	Hat tricks	Total
2016-17 Blake					38	Docherty	3				3
Finch	12				14	Mills	3				3
Ainsley	12	2	6		14	Bullard	2				2
Blake	10	3			12	Hammond	2	2			2
Jefford	8	2			8	Opponents	2				2
Marsden	6				7	Dunbar					1
Lawrence	6				6	Eagle					1
Brothers	5				6	Pelling					1
Henderson	4				4	Poku					1
Reed	5	3			5	Trotter					1

LOWESTOFT MATCH RESULTS 2017-18

Date	Comp	H/A	Opponents	Att:	Result	Goalscorers	Pos	No.
Aug 12	Isthmian	A	Leatherhead	308	L 1 - 2	Cole 90	18	1
15	Isthmian	H	Billericay Town	603	L 1 - 2	Reed 15	21	2
19	Isthmian	H	Worthing	438	W 1 - 0	Reed 41	18	3
26	Isthmian	A	Harlow	203	L 0 - 2		21	4
28	Isthmian	H	Leiston	593	L 0 - 2		22	5
Sept 2	FAC 1Q	A	Bedford Town	264	W 1 - 0	Cole 61		6
9	Isthmian	A	Kingstonian	218	L 2 - 3	Humphreys 35 Reed 47 (pen)	22	7
12	Isthmian	A	Needham Market	294	W 2 - 0	Greenleaf 76 78	22	8
16	FAC 2Q	H	Harlow Town	395	L 0 - 1			9
23	Isthmian	A	Staines Town	199	L 1 - 3	Zielonka 9	22	10
26	Isthmian	H	Thurrock	254	W 1 - 0	McAuley 82	19	11
30	Isthmian	H	Harrow Borough	378	D 1 - 1	McAuley 90	17	12
Oct 7	Isthmian	A	Burgess Hill Town	479	W 5 - 0	Nyadzayo 14 REED 3 (35 50 57) Greenleaf 73	17	13
14	Isthmian	H	Kingstonian	391	W 2 - 1	Reed 45 (pen) 68	13	14
21	Isthmian	A	Merstham	120	L 2 - 6	Nyadzayo 37 Cole 40	16	15
28	FAT 1Q	A	Worthing	512	L 0 - 3			16
Nov 4	Isthmian	H	Metropolitan Police	395	L 1 - 3	Reed 90	17	17
7	Isthmian	H	Needham Market	319	L 2 - 4	Zielonka 27 McAuley 68	18	18
11	Isthmian	H	Merstham	342	W 1 - 0	Zielonka 15	15	19
14	Isthmian	H	Thurrock	98	L 0 - 3		15	20
18	Isthmian	H	Margate	358	L 0 - 2		18	21
21	Isthmian	H	Leatherhead	231	W 3 - 1	Reed 23 50 Bammant 62	13	22
25	Isthmian	A	Dulwich Hamlet	1,832	L 0 - 1		15	23
Dec 2	Isthmian	A	Tooting & Mitcham	194	W 5 - 2	Borror 45 Foy 69 75 Bammant 70 81	14	24
23	Isthmian	H	Harlow Town	393	L 0 - 3		18	25
26	Isthmian	A	Leiston	511	W 1 - 0	Dunbar 7 (og)	15	26
30	isthmian	A	Worthing	706	D 0 - 0		14	27
Jan 1	Isthmian	H	Brightlingsea Regent	341	L 1 - 2	Hodd 19	16	28
6	Isthmian	A	Tonbridge Angels	438	D 2 - 2	Hodd 45 Cotton 73	17	29
13	Isthmian	H	Dorking	344	D 0 - 0		18	30
16	Isthmian	H	Folkestone Invicta	226	L 0 - 2		18	31
27	Isthmian	H	Staines Town	342	L 2 - 4	McAuley 50 Bammant 55	19	32
30	Isthmian	A	Wingate & Finchley	92	L `3 - 4	Hodd 5 Bammant 14 Reed 40	20	33
Feb 3	Isthmian	A	Margate	530	L 0 - 1		20	34
6	Isthmian	H	Enfield Town	222	W 3 - 0	Reed 24 73 Eagle 39	18	35
13	Isthmian	A	Billericay Town	643	L 0 - 5		20	36
17	Isthmian	H	Tooting & Mitcham United	423	D 0 - 0		20	37
24	Isthmian	A	Hendon	192	D 1 - 1	Reed 9	20	38
Mar 10	Isthmian	A	Enfield Town	443	L 0 - 3		20	39
21	Isthmian	H	Dulwich Hamlet	378	L 1 - 3	Cole 90	20	40
24	Isthmian	H	Burgess Hill Town	524	L 1 - 2	Cole 90 (pen)	22	41
27	Isthmian	A	Folkestone Invicta	363	L 1 - 2	McAuley 30	22	42
Apr 2	Isthmian	A	Brightlingsea Regent	252	L 0 - 2		22	43
10	Isthmian	H	Hendon	305	W 2 - 1	Hodd 45 Batlokwa 70	22	44
12	Isthmian	A	Harrow Borough	113	L 0 - 6		22	45
14	Isthmian	A	Met Police	80	W 1 - 0	Schaar 16	20	46
17	Isthmian	H	Wingate & Finchley	353	D 1 - 1	Cole 9 (pen)	19	47
21	Isthmian	H	Tonbridge Angels	512	L 1 - 2	Bammant 68	22	48
28	Isthmian	A	Dorking Wanderers	343	L 0 - 8		22	49

GOALSCORERS	SG	CSG	Pens	Hat tricks	Total		SG	CSG	Pens	Hat tricks	Total
2016-17 Reed					21	Batlokwa					1
Reed	10	2	2	1	15	Borror					1
Bammant	4				6	Cotton					1
Cole	4		2		6	Eagle					1
McAuley	5	2			5	Humphreys					1
Hodd	4				4	Opponents					1
Greenleaf	2				3	Schaar					1
Zielonka	3	2			3						
Foy					2						
Nyadzayo					2						

MARGATE MATCH RESULTS 2017-18

Date	Comp	H/A	Opponents	Att:	Result	Goalscorers	Pos	No.
Aug 12	Isthmian	A	Thurrock	178	W 1 - 0	Collin 47	7	1
15	Isthmian	H	Tonbridge Angels	632	D 0 - 0		9	2
19	Isthmian	H	Leiston	624	D 2 - 2	Evans 3 Bodkin 15	9	3
26	Isthmian	A	Wingate & Finchley	175	L 0 - 1		13	4
28	Isthmian	H	Dorking Wanderers	630	W 1 - 0	Chiedozie 73	9	5
Sept 2	FAC 1Q	H	East Grinstead Town	458	W 3 - 1	Stannard 18 Chiedozie 25 52		6
9	Isthmian	A	Worthing	256	W 5 - 0	Smith 4 Chiedozie 35 COLLIN 3 (46 52 74)	7	7
16	FAC 2Q	A	Kings Langley	258	W 1 - 0	Smith 60		8
23	Isthmian	H	Harrow Borough	552	D 1 - 1	Smith 59	10	9
27	Isthmian	A	Leatherhead	383	W 2 - 0	Mills 8 Chiedozie 73	6	10
30	FAC 3Q	H	Herne Bay	1009	W 2 - 0	Chiedozie 52 59		11
Oct 3	Isthmian	A	Tonbridge Angels	367	D 0 - 0		9	12
7	Isthmian	A	Enfield	509	L 1 - 2	Purse 52 (og)	10	13
14	FAC 4Q	H	Leatherhead	879	L 1 - 2	Stannard 89		14
17	Isthmian	H	Merstham	369	L 0 - 2		14	15
21	Isthmian	A	Harlow Town	168	D 1 - 1	May31	14	16
28	FAT 1Q	A	Staines Town	247	W 3 - 0	Evans 29 Sessegnon 50 Chiedozie 65 (pen)		17
31	Isthmian	H	Metropolitan Police	358	D 1 - 1	Chiedozie 16 (pen)	14	18
Nov 4	Isthmian	H	Staines Town	464	W 2 - 0	Chiedozie 59 Evans 75	10	19
7	Isthmian	A	Merstham	145	L 1 - 2	Chiedozie 41	9	20
18	Isthmian	A	Lowestoft Town	358	W 2 - 0	Haysman 39 Chiedozie 78 (pen)	7	21
21	Isthmian	A	Tooting & Mitcham United	160	W 3 - 1	Chiedozie 8 20 Haysman 64	7	22
25	FAT 2Q	H	Egham Town	370	W 2 - 0	Collin 65 70		23
28	FAT 3Q	A	Bath City	341	D 0 - 0			24
Dec 2	Isthmian	A	Burgess Hill Town	280	D 1 - 1	Haysman 78	7	25
9	Isthmian	H	Hendon	425	W 3 - 2	Collin 15 65 Martin 77	8	26
19	Isthmian	H	Brightlingsea Regent	363	W 4 - 2	Swift 50 Collin 54 May 75 Chiedozie 84	8	27
23	Isthmian	H	Wingate & Finchley	538	L 3 - 4	Vilcu 5 (og) Chiedozie 24 (pen) 90 (pen)		28
26	Isthmian	A	Dorking Wanderers	263	L 2 - 4	May 58 Collin 90 (pen)	8	29
Jan 1	Isthmian	H	Folkestone Invicta	653	L 1 - 3	Chiedozie 12	9	30
6	Isthmian	A	Billericay Town	1570	D 1 - 1	Martin 46	9	31
9	Isthmian	H	Needham Market	369	W 3 - 1	CHIEDOZIE 3 (5 85 90)	8	32
13	Isthmian	H	Dulwich Hamlet	860	W 1 - 0	Haysman 85	8	33
16	Isthmian	H	Leatherhead	398	D 0 - 0		8	34
20	Isthmian	H	Tooting & Mitcham United	542	W 3 - 2	Chiedozie 14 (pen) 18 Blackman 48	6	35
23	Isthmian	H	Thurrock	334	W 2 - 0	Chiedozie 42 68	4	36
27	Isthmian	A	Harrow Borough	171	W 4 - 0	Chiedozie 2 (pen) 58 Haysman 39 Collin 47	3	37
29	Isthmian	A	Kingstonian	225	W 3 - 1	Chiedozie 31 34 Haysman 64	3	38
Feb 3	Isthmian	H	Lowestoft Town	530	W 1 - 0	Chiedozie 61	3	39
10	Isthmian	A	Brightlingsea Regent	184	W 1 - 0	Haysman 79	2	40
17	Isthmian	H	Burgess Hill Town	547	W 2 - 0	Collin 16 Chiedozie 25	2	41
24	Isthmian	A	Needham Market	303	L 2 - 3	Chiedozie 45 May 89	2	42
Mar 6	Isthmian	A	Leiston	202	D 2 - 2	Evans 45 90	3	43
10	Isthmian	A	Hendon	309	D 1 - 1	May.42	3	44
17	Isthmian	A	Metropolitan Police	90	D 2 - 2	Collin 65 (pen) 71	4	45
24	Isthmian	H	Enfield	630	D 1 - 1	Martin 12	4	46
31	Isthmian	H	Worthing	545	D 1 - 1	Chiedozie 72	5	47
Apr 2	Isthmian	A	Folkestone Invicta	946	D 1 - 1	Collin 66	5	48
7	Isthmian	H	Harlow Town	375	W 4 - 2	May 51 67 Collin 62 Chiedozie 75	6	49
10	Isthmian	A	Kingstonian	375	L 0 - 2		6	50
14	Isthmian	A	Staines Town	316	D 2 - 2	Evans 42 Friend 53	5	51
21	Isthmian	H	Billericay Town	832	L 1 - 2	May27	6	52
28	Isthmian	A	Dulwich Hamlet	1266	D 1 - 1	Essuman 66	7	53

GOALSCORERS	SG	CSG	Pens	Hat tricks	Total		SG	CSG	Pens	Hat tricks	Total
2016-17 Buchanan					7	Blackman					1
Chiedozie	24	6	7	1	34	Bodkin					1
Collin	11	2	2	1	16	Essuman					1
May	7				8	Friend					1
Haysman	7	2			7	Mills					1
Evans	5				6	Sessegnon					1
Martin	3				3	Swift					1
Smith	3	3			3						
Opponents					2						
Stannard					2						

MERSTHAM MATCH RESULTS 2017-18

Date	Comp	H/A	Opponents	Att:	Result	Goalscorers	Pos	No.
Aug 12	Isthmian	H	Wingate & Finchley	190	W 4 - 1	Addai 37 44 Ryan Hall 62 (pen) Bamba 78	1	1
15	Isthmian	A	Folkestone Invicta	322	L 1 - 2	Reece Hall 45	11	2
19	Isthmian	H	Tooting & Mitcham	273	D 2 - 2	Ryan Hall 70 (pen) Bennett 83	10	3
26	Isthmian	A	Metropolitan Police	308	W 3 - 0	Reece Hall 6 Ryan Hall 32 (pen) Fofana 85	6	4
28	Isthmian	H	Kingstonian	251	L 1 - 2	Ryan Hall 62 (pen)	12	5
Sept 2	FAC 1Q	A	**Tooting & Mitcham Utd**	256	L 0 - 2			6
9	Isthmian	A	Harrow Borough	140	D 2 - 2	Ryan Hall 25 60	13	7
16	Isthmian	H	Brightlingsea Rovers	148	D 3 - 3	Hutchings 8 Addai 15 Cooper 43	13	8
23	Isthmian	A	Thurrock	116	D 1 - 1	Kabba 28	14	9
30	Isthmian	H	Metropolitan Police	112	D 0 - 0		15	10
Oct 3	Isthmian	H	Folkestone Invicta	180	W 2 - 0	Bamba 13 Addai 88	12	11
7	Isthmian	H	Dorking Wanderers	271	L 1 - 2	Ryan Hall 22	14	12
14	Isthmian	A	Wingate & Finchley	131	L 2 - 3	Bennett 4 (pen) Hamilton-Forbes 17	16	13
17	Isthmian	A	Margate	369	W 2 - 0	Pingling 17 Henriques 71	12	14
21	Isthmian	H	Lowestoft Town	120	W 6 - 2	Ryan HALL 3 (12 31 35) Bennett 25 Reece Hall 83 Bamba 90	13	15
24	Isthmian	H	Dulwich Hamlet	336	L 0 - 4		14	16
28	FAT 1Q	A	**Sittingbourne**	165	D 1 - 1	**Pingling 15**		17
31	FAT 1Qr	H	**Sittingbourne**	126	L 0 - 2			18
Nov 7	Isthmian	H	Margate	145	L 1 - 2	Ryan Hall 8	14	19
11	Isthmian	A	Lowestoft Town	342	L 0 - 1		14	20
14	Isthmian	H	Billericay Town	247	L 0 - 3		14	21
18	Isthmian	H	Staines Town	121	L 1 - 5	Cooper 30	14	22
Dec 2	Isthmian	A	Tonbridge	444	W 1 - 0	Addai 89	15	23
9	Isthmian	H	Needham Market	102	W 2 - 1	Ryan Hall 17 Bonnett-Johnson 70	13	24
5	Isthmian	A	Billericay Town	545	D 2 - 2	McCollin 44 67		25
16	Isthmian	A	Burgess Hill Town	315	D 0 - 0		11	26
19	Isthmian	A	Leiston	191	L 1 - 3	Addai 34	13	27
30	Isthmian	A	Tooting & Mitcham United	251	L 1 - 3	Maynard-Bennett 10	15	28
Jan 1	Isthmian	H	Worthing	230	L 0 4		17	29
10	Isthmian	A	Leatherhead	316	L 1 - 2	Ryan Hall 61	18	30
13	Isthmian	A	Enfield Town	381	D 2 - 2	Kavanagh 51 Harwood 87	19	31
20	Isthmian	A	Dulwich Hamlet	1692	W 2 - 1	Penny 17 81	17	32
27	Isthmian	H	Thurrock	141	W 2 - 1	Penny 38 Addai 54	16	33
30	Isthmian	A	Harlow Town	131	W 2 - 1	Reece Hall 73 Penny 90	15	34
Feb 3	Isthmian	A	Staines Town	230	L 2 - 4	Bonnett-Johnson 47 Collin 88	14	35
10	Isthmian	H	Leiston	151	W 1 - 0	Harwood 67	12	36
17	Isthmian	H	Tonbridge Angels	286	L 0 - 1		12	37
24	Isthmian	A	Brightlingsea Rovers	151	W 3 - 1	Penny 25 Addai 81 Bennett 90	12	38
Mar 10	Isthmian	A	Needham Market	383	W 3 - 1	Bennett 9 31 Penny 38	11	39
13	Isthmian	H	Hendon	137	D 1 1	Hayden-Smith 35	12	40
17	Isthmian	H	Harlow Town	198	W 2 - 0	Hayden-Smith 49 Addai 90	12	41
24	Isthmian	A	Dorking Wanderers	191	L 0 - 4		13	42
27	Isthmian	H	Burgess Hill Town	163	W 4 - 2	Kavanagh 39 (pen) Penny 40 Reece Hall 61 75	12	43
31	Isthmian	H	Harrow Borough	148	L 0 - 1		12	44
Apr 2	Isthmian	A	Worthing	716	L 2 - 3	Reece Hall 66 Henriques 89	12	45
14	Isthmian	H	Leatherhead	266	D 1 - 1	Henriques 35	13	46
16	Isthmian	A	Kingstonian	204	L 1 - 2	Kavanagh 56	13	47
21	Isthmian	A	Hendon	273	L 0 - 3		17	48
28	Isthmian	H	Enfield Town	220	D 1 - 1	Kavanagh 79	18	49

GOALSCORERS	SG	CSG	Pens	Hat tricks	Total		SG	CSG	Pens	Hat tricks	Total
2016-17 Bennett					19	Harwood	2				2
Ryan Hall	12	3	4	1	13	Hayden-Smith	2				2
Addai	7				9	McCollin	1				2
Reece Hall	4	3			7	Pingling	2				2
Penny	5	3	1		7	Collin					1
Bennett	4				6	Fofana					1
Kavanagh	3				4	Hamilton-Forbes					1
Bamba	3				3	Hutchings					1
Henriques	3				3	Kabba					1
Bonnett-Johnson	2				2	Maynard-Bennett					1
Cooper	2				2						

METROPOLITAN POLICE MATCH RESULTS 2017-18

Date	Comp	H/A	Opponents	Att:	Result	Goalscorers	Pos	No.
Aug 12	Isthmian	H	Worthing	115	W 3 - 1	Macklin 1 29 James 8	2	1
15	Isthmian	A	Dorking	245	L 1 - 4	Webb 31	15	2
19	Isthmian	A	Enfield Town	378	D 4 - 4	Putman 31 60 Collins 43 James 84	12	3
26	Isthmian	H	Merstham	308	L 0 - 3		18	4
28	Isthmian	A	Leatherhead	321	L 0 - 1		20	5
Sept 2	FAC 1Q	H	Staines Town	153	W 3 - 2	James 28 Collins 50 Bird 54		6
9	Isthmian	H	Hendon	110	L 1 - 2	Gasson 66	21	7
11	Isthmian	A	Kingstonian	182	W 2 - 1	Robertson 65 Macklin 72	17	8
16	FAC 2Q	H	Heybridge Swifts	84	D 2 - 2	Putman 55 Kealy 80		9
23	Isthmian	A	Leiston	256	L 0 - 3		21	10
30	Isthmian	A	Merstham	112	D 0 - 0		20	11
Oct 3	Isthmian	H	Dorking	109	W 4 - 1	Macklin 17 Wright 30 71 Kealy 90	18	12
7	Isthmian	H	Folkestone Invicta	165	W 3 - 1	Gasson 14 Macklin 70 76	14	13
10	Isthmian	H	Wingate & Finchley	130	W 2 - 0	Kealy 16 29	11	14
14	Isthmian	A	Worthing	855	D 3 - 3	MACKLIN 3 (7 86 pen 89)	10	15
21	Isthmian	H	Thurrock	106	W 3 - 1	James 20 48 Macklin 22	8	16
24	Isthmian	H	Burgess Hill Town	101	W 2 - 0	Wright 23 74	5	17
28	FAT 1Q	H	AFC Sudbury	90	W 3 - 0	Mummery 53 Macklin 55 (pen) Wright 89		18
31	Isthmian	A	Margate	358	D 1 - 1	Macklin 85	5	19
Nov 4	Isthmian	A	Lowestoft	395	W 3 - 1	Wright 12 Mummery 78 Macklin 89	4	20
7	Isthmian	H	Kingstonian	235	W 3 - 2	Robertson 78 Bird 86 90	2	21
11	FAT 2Q	A	Thamesmead	82	W 1 - 0	Macklin 48		22
14	Isthmian	A	Burgess Hill Town	244	W 4 - 1	Arthur 16 Gasson 43 Mummery 59 Macklin 63	2	23
18	Isthmian	H	Dulwich Hamlet	321	L 1 - 4	Newton 86	4	24
25	FAT 3Q	H	Wingate & Finchley	63	L 0 - 1			25
Dec 2	Isthmian	A	Harrow Borough	114	L 0 - 3			26
9	Isthmian	H	Harlow	90	W 2 - 1	Salmon 62 Bird 64	5	27
16	Isthmian	A	Needham Market	215	D 1 - 1	Macklin 28	6	28
19	Isthmian	A	Billericay Town	602	L 0 - 3			29
27	Isthmian	H	Leatherhead	348	L 1 - 2	Gasson 72		30
30	Isthmian	H	Enfield Town	182	D 1 - 1	Robertson 65	7	31
Jan 1	Isthmian	A	Staines Town	257	W 5 - 1	Mummery 45 Arthur 55 Wright 63 Brown 66 Haydon 86 (og)	7	32
6	Isthmian	H	Brightlingsea Regent	110	D 1 - 1	Robinson 11	7	33
13	Isthmian	A	Tooting & Mitcham United	237	W 2 - 0	Wright 77 Fiddes 90	6	34
20	Isthmian	A	Wingate & Finchley	90	L 0 - 1		7	35
23	Isthmian	H	Tonbridge Angels	126	W 2 - 0	Mummery 38 Wright 32	6	36
27	Isthmian	H	Leiston	130	D 1 - 1	James 26	6	37
Feb 3	Isthmian	A	Dulwich Hamlet	1485	D 0 - 0		8	38
10	Isthmian	H	Billericay Town	310	D 2 - 2	Gasson 9 Wright 77	8	39
17	Isthmian	H	Harrow Borough	116	W 1 - 0	Pepera 65 (og)	10	40
24	Isthmian	A	Tonbridge Angels	380	L 0 - 2		10	41
Mar 10	Isthmian	H	Harlow Town	101	L 3 - 4	Robertson 51 Bird 53 James 65	10	42
17	Isthmian	A	Margate	90	D 2 - 2	Hippolyte-Patrick 25 Bird 89	10	43
24	Isthmian	A	Folkestone Invicta	458	L 2 - 5	Gasson 18 Goode 49	11	44
27	Isthmian	H	Needham Market	86	W 3 - 2	Wright 45 Williams 52 Enver-Marum 66	11	45
31	Isthmian	A	Hendon	277	L 0 - 2		11	46
Apr 7	Isthmian	A	Thurrock	106	D 0 - 0		10	47
14	Isthmian	H	Lowestoft Town	80	L 0 - 1		11	48
19	Isthmian	H	Staines Town	146	W 4 - 2	Enver-Marum 24 Gasson 47 80 Hippolyte-Patrick 87	11	49
21	Isthmian	A	Brightlingsea Regent	142	W 1 - 0	Nurse 79	11	50
28	Isthmian	H	Tooting & Mitcham United	226	W 2 - 0	Enver-Marum 1 Hickey 20	10	51

GOALSCORERS	SG	CSG	Pens	Hat tricks	Total		SG	CSG	Pens	Hat tricks	Total
2016-17 Collins					11	Hippolyte-Patrick					2
Macklin	10	3	2	1	16	Opponents					2
Wright	10	2			12	Williams					2
James	6				7	Brown					1
Bird	5				6	Fiddes					1
Gasson	6				6	Goode					1
Mummery	5				5	Hickey					1
Kealy	3	2			4	Newton					1
Robertson	4				4	Nurse					1
Enver-Marum					3	Robinson					1
Putman	3				3	Salmon					1
Arthur	2				2	Webb					1
Collins	2				2						

NEEDHAM MARKET MATCH RESULTS 2017-18

Date	Comp	H/A	Opponents	Att:	Result	Goalscorers	Pos	No.
Aug 12	Isthmian	A	Burgess Hill Town	323	D 1 - 1	Harrison 45	14	1
15	Isthmian	H	Thurrock	262	W 2 - 1	Harrison 32 Gibbs 43	7	2
19	Isthmian	H	Wingate & Finchley	234	L 0 - 1		11	3
26	Isthmian	A	Folkestone Invicta	374	W 2 - 0	Gibbs 65 Harrison 90	7	4
28	Isthmian	H	Brightlingseas Regent	347	L 0 - 3		10	5
Sept 2	FAC 1Q	A	Clapton	167	W 3 - 0	Heath 65 Ingram 77 Harrison 83		6
9`	Isthmian	A	Tooting & Mitcham United	230	D 1 - 1	Nunn 2	15	7
12	Isthmian	H	Lowestoft	294	L 0 - 2		17	8
16	FAC 2Q	H	Chesham United	166	W 2 - 0	Harrison 30 Morphew 49		9
23	Isthmian	H	Enfield Town	304	D 2 - 2	Ingram 40 Morphew 90 (pen)	17	10
26	Isthmian	A	Harlow Town	141	W 3 - 1	Morphew 31 Heath 42 Nunn 45	14	11
30	FAC 3Q	H	Dartford	379	L 1 - 6	Nunn 55		12
Oct 3	Isthmian	A	Thurrock	84	L 0 - 1		16	13
7	Isthmian	A	Dulwich Hamlet	2417	L 0 - 2		20	14
17	Isthmian	A	Hendon	153	L 0 - 1		20	15
21	Isthmian	A	Dorking Wanderers	175	L 2 - 3	Griffiths 51 75	20	16
28	FAT 1Q	H	Arlesey Town	173	W 3 - 1	Heath 11 88 Mills 68		17
31	Isthmian	H	Billericay Town	607	D 1 - 1	Heath 66	19	18
Nov 4	Isthmian	H	Worthing	262	L 0 - 2		21	19
7	Isthmian	A	Lowestoft Town	319	W 4 - 2	Mills 36 Heath 52 Ingram 64 Harrison 79	19	20
11	FAT 2Q	A	Brentwood Town	166	L 1 - 3	Wright 66		21
18	Isthmian	A	Tonbridge Angels	383	L 4 - 5	Wright 17 Harrison 32 Morphew 71(p) Griffiths 85	22	22
21	Isthmian	H	Harlow Town	264	W 5 - 1	Morphew 1 Heath19 Ingram 37 Griffiths 63 Harrison 80	18	23
Dec 2	Isthmian	H	Staines Town	223	L 1 - 2	Gibbs 80	21	24
9`	Isthmian	A	Merstham	102	L 1 - 2	Simmons 39	21	25
16	Isthmian	H	Metropolitan Police	215	D 1 - 1	Sands 76	22	26
19	Isthmian	H	Leatherhead	270	D 0 - 0		21	27
23	Isthmian	H	Fokestone Invicta	261	D 2 - 2	Sands 84 85	21	28
26	Isthmian	A	Brightlingsea Regent	219	W 3 - 2	Ingram 9 Sands 17 Heath 56	20	29
30	Isthmian	A	Wingate & Finchley	151	D 1 - 1	Mills 35	19	30
Jan 1	Isthmian	H	Leiston	513	L 2 - 5	Ingram 4 Morphew 52 (pen)	19	31
6	Isthmian	A	Harrow Borough	141	L 2 - 3	Griffiths 63 68	20	32
9`	Isthmian	A	Margate	369	L 1 - 3	Morphew 70 (pen)	19	33
13	Isthmian	H	Kingstonian	244	L 1 - 2	Sands 90	21	34
20	Isthmian	H	Hendon	239	D 3 - 3	Kamanzi 12 Mills 60 88	21	35
27	Isthmian	A	Enfield Town	389	W 2 - 0	Mills 12 Morphew 19 (pen)	20	36
Feb 3	Isthmian	H	Tonbridge Angels	233	W 4 - 2	Ingram 7 Sands 22 Mills 72 81	19	37
17	Isthmian	A	Staines Town	240	D 1 - 1	Sands 48	21	38
24	Isthmian	H	Margate	303	W 3 - 2	Griffiths 35 71 Morphew 84 (pen)	17	39
Mar 6	Isthmian	H	Burgess Hill Town	214	W 3 - 1	Heath 34 Nunn 77 Ocran 81	17	40
10	Isthmian	A	Merstham	255	L 1 - 2	Ocran 24	17	41
21	Isthmian	A	Leatherhead	244	W 1 - 0	Nunn 88	14	42
24	Isthmian	H	Dulwich Hamlet	495	L 0 - 3		17	43
27	Isthmian	A	Metropolitan Police	86	L 2 - 3	Ingram 36 Ocran 66	17	44
31	Isthmian	H	Tooting & Mitcham United	265	W 1 - 0	Griffiths 90 (pen)	17	45
Apr 7	Isthmian	H	Dorking Wanderers	255	W 2 - 0	Griffiths 87 (pen)	17	46
14	Isthmian	A	Worthing	768	L 0 - 1		19	47
19	Isthmian	A	Billericay Town	741	L 0 - 5		19	48
21	Isthmian	H	Harrow Borough	303	L 0 - 1		19	49
24	Isthmian	A	Leiston	402	L 0 - 2		19	50
28	Isthmian	A	Kingstonian	234	L 0 - 4		19	51

GOALSCORERS	SG	CSG	Pens	Hat tricks	Total		SG	CSG	Pens	Hat tricks	Total
2016-17 Ingram					16	Gibbs	3				3
Griffiths	6	2	2		10	Wright	2	2			2
Heath	8	2			9	Kamanzi					1
Morphew	8	3	6		9	Simmons					1
Harrison	7	2			8						
Ingram	8				8						
Mills	6	3			8						
Sands	6	3			7						
Nunn	5	2			5						
Ocran	4				4						

STAINES TOWN MATCH RESULTS 2017-18

Date	Comp	H/A	Opponents	Att:	Result	Goalscorers	Pos	No.
Aug 12	Isthmian	A	Dulwich Hamlet	1086	D 1 - 1	Driver 63	15	1
15	Isthmian	H	Tooting & Mitcham United	269	W 6 - 0	Buchanan 8 12 Gough 40 Worsfold 50 Bettamer 66 90	4	2
19	Isthmian	H	Kingstonian	323	W 5 - 0	Bettamer 20 Worsfold 43 Buchanan 45 Hippolyte 89 Collins 90	2	3
26	Isthmian	A	Dorking Wanderers	275	D 1 - 1	Bettamer 15	4	4
28	Isthmian	H	Wingate & Finchley	175	L 0 - 5		7	5
Sept 2	FAC 1Q	A	Metropolitan Police	153	L 2 - 3	Worsfold 42 Buchanan 88		6
9	Isthmian	A	Folkestone Invicta	401	L 0 - 2		13	7
12	Isthmian	H	Harrow Borough	183	W 2 - 1	Richards (og) 43 Driver 47	9	8
17	Isthmian	A	Worthing	180	D 2 - 2	Bettamer 18 Buchanan 37	8	9
23	Isthmian	H	Lowestoft Town	199	W 3 - 1	Bettamer 12 Hippolyte 28 57	5	10
26	Isthmian	A	Hendon	147	L 0 - 3		8	11
Oct 3	Isthmian	A	Tooting & Mitcham United	152	W 7 - 0	BETTAMER 3 (32 64 81) Brown 51 BUCHANAN 3 (72,75 78)	6	12
7	Isthmian	A	Leiston	323	D 2 - 2	Buchanan 9 56	6	13
14	Isthmian	H	Dulwich Hamlet	322	D 1 - 1	Bettamer 63	7	14
21	Isthmian	H	Leatherhead	317	W 3 - 0	Buchanan 35 Bettamer 63 Worsfold	5	15
28	FAT 1Q	H	Margate	247	L 0 - 3			16
31	Isthmian	H	Enfield	199	W 3 - 2	Buchanan 43 Bettamer 70 Worsfold 50	5	17
Nov 4	Isthmian	A	Margate	462	L 0 - 2		5	18
11	Isthmian	H	Tonbridge Angels	311	W 3 - 1	Driver 50 Buchanan 74 Hippolyte 82	5	19
18	Isthmian	H	Merstham	121	W 5 - 1	Driver 5 Bettamer 26 Brown 38 Brewer 45 Buchanan 70 (pen)	5	20
21	Isthmian	A	Harrow Borough	149	W 2 - 1	Buchanan 80 90		21
Dec 2	Isthmian	H	Needham Market	223	W 2 - 1	Ahmidi 14 Buchanan 84	3	22
9	Isthmian	H	Billericay Town	454	L 0 - 2		3	23
16	Isthmian	A	Brightlingsea Regent	178	D 2 - 2	Miller-Rodney 35 Buchanan 46	3	24
Dec 19	Isthmian	H	Harlow Town	169	W 4 - 1	Buchanan Driver Bettamer Ahmidi	3	25
23	Isthmian	H	Dorking Wanderers	228	L 0 - 2		3	26
26	Isthmian	A	Wingate & Finchley	170	D 1 - 1	Clifton 11	4	27
Jan 1	Isthmian	H	Metropolitan Police	257	L 1 - 5	Bettamer 52	6	28
6	Isthmian	H	Burgess Hill Town	227	W 3 - 1	Buchanan 16 Bettamer 25 Taylor 79 (og)	5	29
13	Isthmian	A	Thurrock	136	W 2 - 0	Driver 55 Martin 73	3	30
27	Isthmian	H	Lowestoft Town	342	W 4 - 2	Worsfold 30 Buchanan 36 60 Bettamer 80	5	31
Feb 3	Isthmian	H	Merstham	230	W 4 - 2	BUCHANAN 3 (19 45 71p)Bettamer 27	5	32
10	Isthmian	A	Tonbridge Angels	340	L 1 - 2	Brown 9	6	33
17	Isthmian	H	Needham Market	240	D 1 - 1	Bettamer 19	6	34
24	Isthmian	A	Harlow Town	167	W 4 - 2	Worsfold 13 Driver 59 75 Bettamer 83	6	35
Mar 6	Isthmian	H	Worthing	160	D 3 - 3	Worsfold Buchanan Bettamer	6	36
17	Isthmian	H	Enfield Town	322	W 4 - 3	Driver 12 68 Bettamer 15 Buchanan 76	6	37
20	Isthmian	H	Hendon	194	W 4 - 0	Buchanan12 Miller-Rodney15 Worsfold 54 Ahmidi 67	5	38
24	Isthmian	H	Leiston	274	L 1 - 4	Driver 41	7	39
27	Isthmian	H	Brightlingsea Town	153	W 2 - 1	Ahmidi 39 Worsfold 54	7	40
Apr 9	Isthmian	A	Billericay	580	L 3 - 5	Buchanan 31 77 Worsfold 39	7	41
7	Isthmian	A	Leatherhead	407	L 0 - 2		7	42
12	Isthmian	H	Folkestone Invicta	247	D 4 - 4	BUCHANAN 3 (12 36 82) Bettamer 72	7	43
14	Isthmian	H	Margate	318	D 2 - 2	Buchanan 82 Bettamer 89	8	44
19	Isthmian	A	Metropolitan Police	146	L 2 - 4	Bettamer 52 Buchanan 70	8	45
21	Isthmian	A	Burgess Hill Town	436	D 1 - 1	Bettamer 73	8	46
23	Isthmian	A	Kingstonian	227	L 1 - 3	Buchanan 90	8	47
28	Isthmian	H	Thurrock	275	W 5 - 2	BUCHANAN 4 (24 27 82 88) Bettamer 29	8	48

GOALSCORERS	SG	CSG	Pens	Hat tricks	Total		SG	CSG	Pens	Hat tricks	Total
2016-17 Bettamer					16	Brewer					1
Buchanan	26	4	2	4	40	Clifton					1
Bettamer	24	4	1		27	Collins					1
Driver	7	2			11	Gough					1
Worsfold	11				11	Martin					1
Ahmidi	4				4						
Hippolyte	3				4						
Brown	3				3						
Miller-Rodney	2				2						
Opponents					2						

THURROCK MATCH RESULTS 2017-18

Date	Comp	H/A	Opponents	Att:	Result	Goalscorers	Pos	No.
Aug 12	Isthmian	H	Margate	178	L 0 - 1		22	1
15	Isthmian	A	Needham Market	262	L 1 - 2	Clark 83	24	2
19	Isthmian	H	Dorking	118	W 3 - 2	STIMSON 3 (17 55 90)	17	3
25	Isthmian	H	Worthing	147	W 3 - 2	Christou 2 25 Stimson 51	10	4
28	Isthmian	H	Billericay Town	523	L 0 - 5		18	5
Sept 2	FAC 1Q	H	Harlow Town	159	D 1 - 1	Spence 86		6
5	FAC 1Qr	A	Harlow Town	159	L 1 - 2	Spence 14		7
9	Isthmian	A	Leiston	253	L 1 - 3	Morgan 49	19	8
12	Isthmian	H	Tonbridge Angels	118	D 2 - 2	Nouble 31 Christou 76	21	9
23	Isthmian	H	Merstham	116	D 1 - 1	Oli 3	19	10
26	Isthmian	A	Lowestoft Town	254	L 0 - 1		20	11
Oct 3	Isthmian	H	Needham Market	84	W 1 - 0	Sutton 33	18	12
7	Isthmian	H	Brightlingsea Regent	128	D 3 - 3	Oli 28 Stimson 83 Spence 90	21	13
21	Isthmian	A	Metropolitan Police	106	L 1 - 3	Macklin 68 (og)	21	14
27	FAT Q1	A	Kingstonian	225	D 3 - 3	Christou 27 Clark 66 80		15
31	FAT 1Qr	H	Kingstonian	84	L 1 - 4	Osifuwa 90		16
Nov 4	Isthmian	H	Dulwich Hamlet	196	L 0 - 1		22	17
11	Isthmian	A	Harrow Borough	118	W 2 - 0	Nouble 23 Winn 90	21	18
14	Isthmian	H	Lowestoft Town	98	W 3 - 0	Sutton 7 Spence 28 Winn 51	17	19
18	Isthmian	A	Enfield Town	390	L 1 - 3	Nouble 16	19	20
21	Isthmian	A	Tonbridge Angels	251	L 1 - 2	Spence 90	21	21
25	Isthmian	H	Burgess Hill Town	88	W 4 - 2	Oli 1 Winn 62 Christou 67 Stimson 85	16	22
Dec 2	Isthmian	A	Hendon	178	L 1 - 4	Winn 45 (pen)	18	23
5	Isthmian	A	Leatherhead	219	W 2 - 0	Oli 44 Ujah 58	15	24
9	Isthmian	H	Wingate & Finchley	87	L 2 - 4	Stimson 28 Ujah 67	16	25
16	Isthmian	A	Tooting & Mitcham United	150	L 1 - 4	Ribiero-Goncalves 90	17	26
23	Isthmian	A	Worthing	470	W 2 - 1	Ogunrindle 78 Spence 81	15	27
26	Isthmian	A	Billericay Town	1653	L 0 - 1		16	28
30	Isthmian	A	Dorking	265	L 0 - 2		18	29
Jan 1	Isthmian	H	Harlow Town	136	W 1 - 0	Ujar 41	15	30
6	Isthmian	A	Kingstonian	220	W 1 - 0	Christou 30	13	31
8	Isthmian	A	Folkestone Invicts	306	D 2 - 2	Pindy 46 Spence 65	13	32
13	Isthmian	H	Staines Town	138	L 0 - 2		14	33
20	Isthmian	H	Leatherhead	162	W 2 - 0	Sutton 37 Pindy 41	13	34
Jan 23	Isthmian	A	Margate	334	L 0 - 2		13	35
27	Isthmian	A	Merstham	141	L 1 - 2	Sutton 30	13	36
Feb 3	Isthmian	H	Enfield Town	162	W 3 - 1	Clark 16 Dunn 40 Christou 44	12	37
10	Isthmian	A	Harrow Borough	132	L 0 - 2		13	38
17	Isthmian	H	Hendon	139	L 0 - 1		13	39
24	Isthmian	A	Burgess Hill Town	235	W 5 - 2	Morgan 30 Spence 45 Winn 65 Stimson 68 86	13	40
Mar 10	Isthmian	A	Wingate & Finchley	104	W 4 - 2	Spence 38 81 Clark 50 52 (pen)	13	41
13	Isthmian	H	Tooting & Mitcham United	108	W 4 - 1	Stimson 45 79 Nouble 70 Winn 85	12	42
24	Isthmian	A	Brightlingsea Regent	183	W 3 - 1	Winn 30 Sutton 82 Cave 87	12	43
31	Isthmian	H	Leiston	139	D 0 - 0			44
Apr 2	Isthmian	A	Harlow Town	215	L 2 - 3	Winn 33 Spence 43	13	45
7	Isthmian	H	Metropolitan Police	106	D 0 - 0		13	46
14	Isthmian	A	Dulwich Hamlet	1003	L 1 - 2	Clark 48	15	47
17	Isthmian	H	Folkestone Invicta	173	L 1 - 2	Winn 45	15	48
21	Isthmian	H	Kingstonian	196	W 1 - 0	Spence 25	12	49
28	Isthmian	A	Staines Town	275	L 2 - 5	Winn 1 Clark 8	15	50

GOALSCORERS	SG	CSG	Pens	Hat tricks	Total		SG	CSG	Pens	Hat tricks	Total
Spence	10	2			12	Morgan	2				2
Stimson	8	2		1	11	Cave					1
Winn	9	2	1		9	Dunn					1
Clark	6		1		8	Ogunrindle					1
Christou	6	2			7	Opponents					1
Sutton	5				5	Osifuwaa					1
Nouble	4				4	Ribiero-G					1
Oli	4				4	Sutton					1
Ujah	3				3						
Pindy	2				2						

TONBRIDGE ANGELS MATCH RESULTS 2017-18

Date	Comp	H/A	Opponents	Att:	Result	Goalscorers	Pos	No.
Aug 12	Isthmian	H	Hendon	495	W 1 - 0	Elder 77	8	1
15	Isthmian	A	Margate	632	D 0 - 0		10	2
19	Isthmian	H	Brightlingside Regent	484	W 2 - 0	Turner 64 McCollin 90	3	3
26	Isthmian	A	Harrow Borough	203	L 0 - 2		8	4
28	Isthmian	H	Folkestone Invicta	534	L 2 - 3	Turner 15 Elder 24	11	5
Sept 2	FAC 1Q	A	Faversgham Town	346	L 1 - 3	McCollin 37		6
9	Isthmian	A	Harlow Town	234	L 1 - 2	Akrofi 44	16	7
12	Isthmian	A	Thurrock	118	D 2 - 2	Akrofi 44 Kinnear 87	16	8
23	Isthmian	A	Burgess Hill Town	462	W 1 - 0	Akrofi 71	12	9
26	Isthmian	H	Dorking Wanderers	332	W 2 - 0	Turner 60 McCollin 90		10
30	Isthmian	A	Kingstonian	264	L 1 - 2	Adonis-Taylor 90	11	11
Oct 3	Isthmian	H	Margate	367	D 0 - 0		10	12
7	Isthmian	H	Wingate & Finchley	635	W 1 - 0	Akrofi 60	8	13
14	Isthmian	A	Hendon	265	L 1 - 2	Kinnear 52	9	14
17	Isthmian	H	Leiston	279	W 2 - 1	Akrofi 25 Elder 52	6	15
21	Isthmian	H	Tooting & Mitcham United	549	L 1 - 2	Turner 10	9	16
28	FAT 1Q	H	Hebridge Swifts	405	D 3 - 3	Thompson 11 Turner 17 Vidal 20		17
31	FAT 1Qr	A	Heybridge Swifts	224	L 1 - 2	Akrofi 80		18
Nov 11	Isthmian	A	Staines Town	311	L 1 - 3	Elder 40	11	19
18	Isthmian	H	Needham Market	383	W 5 - 4	Turner 9 (p) Elder 41 60 Akrofi 48 Kwayie 90	10	20
21	Isthmian	H	Thurrock	251	W 2 - 1	Elder 42 Akrofi 51	9	21
Dec 2	Isthmian	H	Merstham	444	L 0 - 1		11	22
5	Isthmian	A	Dorking Wanderers	205	W 3 - 2	Elder 23 Akrofi 43 62	9	23
9	Isthmian	A	Worthing	571	L 0 - 2		10	24
16	Isthmian	H	Dulwich Hamlet	539	D 1 - 1	Turner 65	9	25
23	Isthmian	H	Harrow Borough	377	W 2 - 0	Akrofi 51 Elder 75	9	26
26	Isthmian	A	Folkestone Invicta	532	L 1 - 3	Thompson 11	10	27
30	Isthmian	A	Brightlingsea Regent	261	W 3 - 0	Turner 25 Bennett 60 Bantick 67	9	28
Jan 6	Isthmian	H	Lowestoft Town	438	D 2 - 2	Vidal 3 (pen) Turner 12	11	29
13	Isthmian	A	Leatherhead	492	L 0 - 1		11	30
16	Isthmian	A	Enfield Town	281	W 1 - 0	Akrofi 44	11	31
23	Isthmian	A	Metropolitan Police	126	L 0 - 2		11	32
27	Isthmian	H	Burgess Hill Town	432	L 0 - 1		11	33
Feb 3	Isthmian	A	Needham Market	233	L 2 - 4	Bantick 86 Turner 88	11	34
10	Isthmian	H	Staines Town	340	W 2 - 1	Akrofi 13 Bantick 24	11	35
17	Isthmian	A	Merstham	286	W 1 - 0	Thompson 71	11	36
24	Isthmian	H	Metropolitan Police	380	W 2 - 0	Turner 28 Smith 52	10	37
Mar 10	Isthmian	H	Worthing	363	L 1 - 2	Turner 62	10	38
17	Isthmian	H	Kingstonian	308	W 3 - 1	Akrofi 9 Whitnall 52 Turner 72	11	39
20	Isthmian	H	Leiston	201	L 0 - 2		11	40
22	Isthmian	H	Billericay Town	526	W 2 - 1	Turner 78 Elder 85	10	41
24	Isthmian	A	Wingate & Finchley	131	L 1 - 2	Miles 61	10	42
Apr 3	Isthmian	A	Billericay Town	505	L 1 - 2	Elder 66	12	43
7	Isthmian	A	Tooting & Mitcham United	119	D 0 - 0		12	44
10	Isthmian	A	Dulwich Hamlet	581	W 2 - 1	Akroft 42 Bantick 45	12	45
14	Isthmian	H	Enfield Town	474	L 1 - 4	Akrofi 16	10	46
17	Isthmian	H	Harlow Town	235	D 0 - 0		10	47
21	Isthmian	A	Lowestoft Town	512	W 2 - 1	Akrofi 39 Kwayie 89	10	48
28	Isthmian	A	Leatherhead	518	L 0 - 2		11	49

GOALSCORERS	SG	CSG	Pens	Hat tricks	Total		SG	CSG	Pens	Hat tricks	Total
2016-17 Elder					*21*	A-Taylor					1
Akrofi	15	3			17	Bennett					1
Turner	14	3	1		14	Miles					1
Elder	10	3			11	Smith					1
Bantick	4				4	Whitnall					1
McCollin	3				3						
Kinnear	3				3						
Kwayie	2				2						
Thompson	2				2						
Vidal	2		2		2						

TOOTING & MITCHAM UNITED MATCH RESULTS 2017-18

Date	Comp	H/A	Opponents	Att:	Result		Goalscorers	Pos	No.
Aug 12	Isthmian	H	Brightlingsea Regent	290	D	1 - 1	Dunn 48	16	1
15	Isthmian	A	Staines Town	269	L	0 - 6		19	2
19	Isthmian	A	Merstham	273	D	2 - 2	Dixon 57 Cunningham 71	23	3
26	Isthmian	H	Enfield Town	308	L	0 - 4		23	4
28	Isthmian	A	Dulwich Hamlet	1866	L	1 - 2	Dunn 6	23	5
Sept 2	FAC 1Q	H	Merstham	256	W	2 - 0	O'Neil 42 Baxter 81		6
9	Isthmian	H	Needham Market	230	D	1 - 1	Dines 45	21	7
12	Isthmian	A	Burgess Hill Town	276	L	1 - 3	Folkes	23	8
16	FAC 2Q	A	Folkestone Invicta	335	L	1 - 3	Folkes 73		9
23	Isthmian	A	Billericay Town	1104	L	0 - 1		23	10
30	Isthmian	A	Hendon	219	L	0 - 4		23	11
Oct 3	Isthmian	H	Staines Town	152	L	0 - 7		23	12
7	Isthmian	H	Worthing	265	W	4 - 3	O'Neill 15 McNaughton 51 Folkes 78 Dunn 82	23	13
14	Isthmian	A	Brightlingsea Regent	222	W	3 - 0	Dixon 3 Folkes 53 Spencer 88	23	14
21	Isthmian	A	Tonbridge Angels	549	W	2 - 1	Folkes 14 Adonis-Taylor 59 (og)	23	15
24	Isthmian	H	Folkestone Invicta	222	L	0 - 1		23	16
28	FAT 1Q	A	Billericay Town	864	L	1 - 3	Dixon 38		17
Nov 4	Isthmian	H	Harrow Borough	266	W	5 - 2	Clements 9 Dixon 35 Folkes 36 Bennett 82 89	20	18
7	Isthmian	H	Burgess Hill Town	152	L	1 - 2	Dixon 63	22	19
11	Isthmian	H	Folkestone Invicta	439	L	1 - 3	Bassett 39	23	20
18	Isthmian	H	Kingstonian	262	W	3 - 2	Elliott 24 (og) Wedgeworth 28 Dixon 64	20	21
21	Isthmian	H	Margate	160	L	1 - 3	Jones 90	22	22
25	Isthmian	A	Leiston	285	L	0 - 2		22	23
Dec 2	Isthmian	H	Lowestoft Town	194	L	2 - 5	Baker 55 (og) Clements 90		24
16	Isthmian	H	Thurrock	150	W	4 - 1	Dixon 53 57 Clements 65 80	22	25
23	Isthmian	A	Enfield Town	391	D	1 - 1	Clements 40	22	26
26	Isthmian	A	Dulwich Hamlet	636	L	1 - 3	Dunn 6	22	27
30	Isthmian	H	Merstham	251	W	3 - 1	Dixon 6 Clements 67 Morgan-Griffiths 83	21	28
Jan 1	Isthmian	A	Leatherhead	422	L	0 - 2		21	29
6	Isthmian	A	Harlow	204	L	1 - 2	O'Neill 85	23	30
13	Isthmian	H	Metropolitan Police	227	L	0 - 2		23	31
20	Isthmian	A	Margate	542	L	2 - 3	Wedgeworth 2 O'Neill 65		32
30 Jan	Isthmian	A	Dorking Wanderers	195	D	2 - 2	Pierson 32 Bennett 90	23	33
27	Isthmian	H	Billericay Town	466	L	2 - 6	Morgan-Griffiths 6 Wedgeworth 83 (pen)	24	34
Feb 3	Isthmian	A	Kingstonian	249	W	1 - 0	Dines 37	22	35
6	Isthmian	A	Wingate & Finchley	111	D	1 - 1	Mavila 50 (og)	22	36
10	Isthmian	A	Wingate & Finchley	173	W	2 - 0	O'Neill 20 55	22	37
17	Isthmian	A	Lowestoft Town	423	D	0 - 0		22	38
24	Isthmian	H	Lieston	149	L	0 - 1		22	39
Mar 10	Isthmian	A	Dorking Wanderers	209	L	1 - 2	Folkes 1	22	40
13	Isthmian	A	Thurrock	108	L	1 - 4	Wedgeworth 55 (pen)	22	41
17	Isthmian	H	Hendon	138	L	0 - 2		23	42
24	Isthmian	A	Worthing	852	L	0 - 3		23	43
31	Isthmian	A	Needham Market	265	L	0 - 1		23	44
Apr 2	Isthmian	A	Leatherhead	212	L	1 - 4	Wilson 90	23	45
7	Isthmian	H	Tonbridge Angels	119	D	0 - 0		23	46
14	Isthmian	A	Harrow Borough	198	D	1 - 1	Morgan-Griffiths 69	23	47
21	Isthmian	H	Harlow Town	248	L	0 - 1		24	48
28	Isthmian	A	Metropolitan Police	226	L	0 - 2		24	49

GOALSCORERS	SG	CSG	Pens	Hat tricks	Total		SG	CSG	Pens	Hat tricks	Total
Dixon	9	3			9	Bassett					1
Folkes	7	3			7	Baxter					1
Clements	5	3			6	Cunningham					1
O'Neill	5				6	Jones					1
Dunn	4				4	Pierson					1
Opponents	4				4	Pierson					1
Wedgeworth	4		2		4	Spencer					1
Bennett	2				3	Wilson					1
M-Griffiths	3				3						
Dines	2				2						

WINGATE & FINCHLEY MATCH RESULTS 2017-18

Date	Comp	H/A	Opponents	Att:	Result	Goalscorers	Pos	No.
Aug 12	Isthmian	A	Merstham	190	L 1 - 4	Obafemi 73	24	1
15	Isthmian	H	Harrow Borough	134	L 1 - 3	Charles-Smith 35	24	2
19	Isthmian	A	Needham Market	234	W 1 - 0	Laney 53	19	3
26	Isthmian	H	Margate	175	W 1 - 0	Beccles-Richards 57	13	4
28	Isthmian	A	Staines Town	266	W 5 - 0	Cronin 12 90 McCall 47 Obafemi 80 Ifil 83	8	5
Sept 2	FAC 1Q	A	Hendon	298	D 1 - 1	McCall 47		6
9	Isthmian	H	Burgess Hill Town	74	W 2 - 0	Laney 63 90	6	7
12	Isthmian	H	Enfield Town	209	W 2 - 1	Beccles-Richards 18 Cronin 53	4	8
16	FAC 2Q	H	Hemel Hempstead Town	377	D 0 - 0			9
19	FAC 2Qr	A	Hemel Hempstead Town	251	L 1 - 2	Beccles-Richards 5 (aet)		10
23	Isthmian	H	Worthing	125	D 1 - 1	Laney 40	3	11
26	Isthmian	A	Brightlingsea Regent	161	L 0 - 1		4	12
Oct 3	Isthmian	A	Harrow Borough	162	L 0 - 3		6	13
7	Isthmian	A	Tonbridge Angels	635	L 0 - 1		9	14
10	Isthmian	A	Metropolitan Police	130	L 0 - 2		10	15
14	Isthmian	H	Merstham	131	W 3 - 2	Laney 67 74 Pattie 83	6	16
21	Isthmian	A	Kingstonian	215	L 1 - 2	Rifat 36	10	17
28	FAT 1Q	A	Biggleswade Town	144	W 5 - 0	Cronin Ifil Laney Beccles-Richards Rifat		18
Nov 11	FAT 2Q	A	Corinthian-Casuals	180	W 3 - 1	Pattie 41 Laney 64 Beccles-Richards 79		19
14	Isthmian	H	Brightlingsea Regent	121	W 2 - 1	Laney 24 Pattie 90	11	20
19	Isthmian	A	Leatherhead	371	L 0 - 4		11	21
21	Isthmian	A	Enfield Town	292	D 1 - 1	Obafemi 86	11	22
25	FAT 3Q	A	Metropolitan Police	63	W 1 - 0	Cronin		23
Dec 2	Isthmian	H	Folkestone Invicta	156	W 2 - 1	Obafemi 4 Charles-Smith 53	9	24
9	Isthmian	A	Thurrock	87	W 4 - 2	Charles-Smith 5 Obafemi 25 53 Laney 38	9	25
16	FAT 1	A	Wealdstone	371	L 0 - 1			26
23	Isthmian	A	Margate	536	W 4 - 3	Charles-Smith 45 Laney 62 67 Ifil 89	10	27
26	Isthmian	H	Staines Town	170	D 1 - 1	Abrahams 4	9	28
30	Isthmian	H	Needham Market	151	D 1 - 1	Charles-Smith 78	10	29
Jan 1	Isthmian	A	Hendon	237	W 1 - 0	Monville 40	8	30
9	Isthmian	H	Leiston	103	L 0 - 1		8	31
13	Isthmian	H	Harlow Town	102	W 2 - 0	Cronin 28 (pen) Laney 53	10	32
20	Isthmian	A	Metropolitan Police	90	W 1 - 0	Obafemi 50	9	33
23	Isthmian	A	Dulwich Hamlet	742	W 2 - 1	Obafemi 76 Hayles 90 (og)	8	34
27	Isthmian	A	Worthing	606	L 1 - 2	Cronin 53 (pen)	9	35
30	Isthmian	H	Lowestoft Town	97	W 4 - 3	Beccles-Richards 28 Charles-Smith 65 Rifat 84 Pattie 90	7	36
Feb 3	Isthmian	A	Leatherhead	155	W 3 - 1	Beccles-Richards 17 39 Mavila 34 (pen)	6	37
5	Isthmian	H	Tooting & Mitcham United	111	D 1 - 1	Charles-Smith 43	6	38
10	Isthmian	A	Tooting & Mitcham United	173	L 0 - 2		6	39
17	Isthmian	A	Folkeston Invicta	446	L 0 - 5		7	40
24	Isthmian	H	Dulwich Hamlet	311	D 0 - 0		8	41
Mar 10	Isthmian	H	Thurrock	104	L 2 - 4	Eadie 9 Beddles-Richards 45	9	42
17	Isthmian	A	Leiston	198	L 0 - 4		9	43
24	Isthmian	H	Tonbridge Angels	131	W 2 - 1	Beccles-Richards 10 Ifil 40		44
26	Isthmian	H	Billericay Town	249	L 1 - 3	Rapai 87	9	45
Apr 3	Isthmian	H	Hendon	207	D 2 - 2	Rapai 50 Charles-Smith 53	9	46
5	Isthmian	A	Burgess Hil Town	240	L 1 - 3	Rapai 82	9	47
7	Isthmian	H	Kingstonian	121	L 0 - 1		9	48
14	Isthmian	A	Billericay Town	237	D 2 - 2	Beccles-Richards 47 Cronin 55 (pen)	9	49
17	Isthmian	A	Lowestoft Town	353	D 1 - 1	Charles-Smith 6	9	50
19	Isthmian	A	Dorking Wanderers	153	D 2 - 2	Eadie 52 Clarke 78	9	51
21	Isthmian	H	Dorking Wanderers	101	W 2 - 0	Ebelebe 31 Beckles-Richards 58	9	52
28	Isthmian	A	Harlow Town	277	W 1 - 0	Cronin 88	9	53

GOALSCORERS	SG	CSG	Pens	Hat tricks	Total		SG	CSG	Pens	Hat tricks	Total
2016-17 Becklee-Richards					*18*	Eadie	2				2
Laney	11	3			13	McCall	2				2
Beccles-Richards	10	2			12	Abrahams					1
Charles-Smith	9				9	Clarke					1
Cronin	9		3		9	Ebelebe					1
Obafemi	6				8	Mavila			1		1
Ifil	4				4	Monville					1
Pattie	3				4	Opponents					1
Rapai	3	3			3						
Rifat	2				3						

WORTHING MATCH RESULTS 2017-18

Date	Comp	H/A	Opponents	Att:	Result	Goalscorers	Pos	No.
Aug 12	Isthmian	A	Metropolitan Police	116	L 1 - 3	Newton 58	23	1
16	Isthmian	A	Leatherhead	423	L 0 - 3		23	2
19	Isthmian	A	Lowestoft	438	L 0 - 1		24	3
25	Isthmian	A	Thurrock	147	L 2 - 3	Fraser 34 Elphick 55	24	4
28	Isthmian	A	Burgess Hiull Town	525	L 1 - 4	Pope 8	24	5
Sept 2	FAC 1Q	A	Dorking Wanderers	281	L 2 - 3	Newton 29 Fraser 48		6
9	Isthmian	H	Margate	256	L 0 - 5		24	7
12	Isthmian	A	Dorking Wanderers	224	L 2 - 4	Pope 12 Dawes 85	24	8
17	Isthmian	H	Staines Town	180	D 2 - 2	Dawes 74 O'Sullivan 82	17	9
23	Isthmian	A	Wingate & Finchley	125	L 0 - 1		24	10
26	Isthmian	H	Kingstonian	151	L 1 - 2	Parsons 33	24	11
30	Isthmian	H	Dulwich Hamlet	297	L 0 - 2		24	12
Oct 4	Isthmian	H	Leatherhead	176	D 1 - 1	Pope 71	24	13
7	Isthmian	A	Tooting & Mitcham United	265	L 3 - 4	Rance 28 Parsons 32 Newton 69	24	14
14	Isthmian	H	Metropolitan Police	855	D 3 - 3	Pamment 28 90 (pen) Newton 60	24	15
21	Isthmian	H	Hendon	614	L 1 - 2	Young 53	24	16
28	FAT 1Q	H	Lowestoft Town	512	W 3 - 0	Pope 16 90 Pamment 90		17
Nov 4	Isthmian	A	Needham Market	262	W 2 - 0	Pamment 59 Ovendon 90	24	18
7	Isthmian	A	Dorking Wanderers	498	W 3 - 1	Sparks 9 Hallard 37 Pammant 49	24	19
11	FAT 2Q	A	Thame United	136	L 0 - 1			20
18	Isthmian	H	Leiston	511	D 1 - 1	Hallard 16	24	21
25	Isthmian	H	Harrow Borough	592	D 2 - 2	Young 54 Wild 80	24	22
Dec 2	Isthmian	A	Harlow Town	180	L 2 - 3	Pamment 2 Myles-Meakurns 31	24	23
9	Isthmian	H	Tonbridge Angels	571	W 2 - 0	Pamment 63 (pen) Wild 65	24	24
12	Isthmian	A	Folkestone Invicta	237	W 2 1	Pamment 5 (pen) Rance 74 (pen)	24	25
23	Isthmian	H	Thurrock	470	L 1 - 2	Myles-Meekums 46	24	26
26	Isthmian	H	Burgess Hill Town	662	W 2 - 0	Young 22 Pamment 42	24	27
30	Isthmian	H	Lowestoft Town	706	D 0 - 0		24	28
Jan 1	Isthmian	A	Merstham	230	W 4 - 0	PAMMENT 3 (22 49 89) Clarke 68	22	29
6	Isthmian	H	Enfield Town	813	D 2 - 2	Pope 21 Wild 75	22	30
13	Isthmian	A	Brightlingsea Regent	208	L 0 - 2		22	31
27	Isthmian	H	Wingate & Finchley	606	W 2 - 1	Pamment 58 Newton 80	21	32
30	Isthmian	H	Billericay Town	593	L 0 - 4		21	33
Feb 3	Isthmian	A	Leiston	258	W 3 - 2	Sparks 19 Newton 22 Cook 59	21	34
10	Isthmian	H	Folkestone Invicta	604	W 3 - 2	Newton 17 Myles-Meekums 39 Starkey 66	20	35
17	Isthmian	H	Harlow Town	685	D 2 - 2	Newton 8 Myles-Meekums 27	20	36
24	Isthmian	A	Harrow Borough	178	L 0 - 1		21	37
Mar 2	Isthmian	H	Billericay Town	1163	W 2 - 1	Pamment 71 73	18	38
6	Isthmian	A	Staines Town	160	D 3 3	Pamment 38 Myles-Meekums 54 Newton 72	17	39
10	Isthmian	A	Tonbridge Angels	363	W 2 - 1	Newton 89 Pope 90	15	40
18	Isthmian	A	Dulwich Hamlet	840	L 0 - 3		15	41
24	Isthmian	H	Tooting & Mitcham United	852	W 3 - 0	Pamment 3 Sparks 56 Myles-Meekums	14	42
26	Isthmian	A	Kingstonian	259	D 0 - 0		14	43
31	Isthmian	A	Margate	545	D 1 - 1	Clarke 77	15	44
Apr 2	Isthmian	H	Merstham	716	W 3 - 2	Barker 30 Sparks 57 Pope 76	13	45
7	Isthmian	A	Hendon	266	L 3 - 4	Myles-Meekums 16 Pope 78 Barker 79	15	46
14	Isthmian	H	Needham Market	768	W 1 - 0	Colbran 14	17	47
21	Isthmian	A	Enfield	458	W 1 - 0	Newton 11	16	48
28	Isthmian	H	Brightlingsea Regent	1060	D 2 - 2	Barker 69 Rents 76	16	49

GOALSCORERS	SG	CSG	Pens	Hat tricks	Total		SG	CSG	Pens	Hat tricks	Total
2016-17 Dawes					24	Fraser	2				2
Pamment	13	3	2	1	17	Hallard	2				2
Newton	9	3			11	Parsons	2				2
Pope	7				9	Rance	2		1		2
Myles-Meakurns	7				7	Colbran					1
Sparks	4				4	Cook					1
Wild	3				3	Elphick					1
Young	3				3	O'Sullivan					1
Barker	3				3	Ovendon					1
Clarke	2				2	Rents					1
Dawes	2				2	Starkey					1

ISTHMIAN LEAGUE
CLUB DIRECTORY 2018-19

PREMIER DIVISION

1 AFC Hornchurch
2 Bishops Stortford
3 Bognor Regis Town
4 Brightlingsea Regent
5 Burgess Hill Town
6 Carshalton Athletic
7 Corinthian Casuals
8 Dorking Wanderers
9 Enfield Town
10 Folkestone Invicta
11 Haringey Borough
12 Harlow Town
13 Kingstonian
14 Leatherhead
15 Lewes
16 Margate
17 Merstham
18 Potters Bar Town
19 Tonbridge Angels
20 Whitehawk
21 Wingate & Finchley
22 Worthing

NORTH		SOUTH CENTRAL		SOUTH EAST	
1	AFC Sudbury	1	Ashford Town (Middx)	1	Ashford United
2	Aveley	2	Bedfont Sports	2	Cray Wanderers
3	Barking	3	Bracknell Town	3	East Grinstead Town
4	Basildon United	4	Chalfont St Peter	4	Faversham Town
5	Bowers & Pitsea	5	Cheshunt	5	Greenwich Borough
6	Brentwood Town	6	Chipstead	6	Guernsey
7	Bury Town	7	Egham Town	7	Hastings United
8	Canvey Island	8	FC Romania	8	Haywards Heath
9	Coggeshall Town	9	Hanwell Town	9	Herne Bay
10	Dereham Town	10	Hayes & Yeading United	10	Horsham
11	Felixstowe & Walton Utd	11	Hertford Town	11	Hythe Town
12	Grays Athletic	12	Marlow	12	Phoenix Sports
13	Great Wakering Rovers	13	Molesey	13	Ramsgate
14	Heybridge Swifts	14	Northwood	14	Sevenoaks Town
15	Maldon & Tiptree	15	South Park	15	Sittingbourne
16	Mildenhall Town	16	Tooting & Mitcham United	16	Thamesmead Town
17	Romford	17	Uxbridge	17	Three Bridges
18	Soham Town Rangers	18	Waltham Abbey	18	VCD Athletic
19	Tilbury	19	Ware	19	Whitstable Town
20	Witham Town	20	Westfield	20	Whyteleafe

AFC HORNCHURCH

Club Contact Details 01708 220 080
The Stadium, Bridge Avenue, Upminster, Essex RM14 2LX

Founded: 2005   **Nickname:** The Urchins   **Manager:** Jim McFarlane
Previous Names: Formed in 2005 after Hornchurch F.C. folded
Previous Leagues: Essex Senior 2005-06. Isthmian 2006-12. Conference 2012-13.

Club Colours (change): Red and white

Ground Capacity: 3,500   **Seats:** 800   **Covered:** 1,400   **Clubhouse:** Yes   **Shop:** Yes
Previous Grounds: None
Record Attendance: 3,500 v Tranmere Rovers - FA Cup 2nd Round 2003-04
Nearest Railway Station Upminster Bridge Underground - 0.4km

RECORDS
Misc: Won the Essex League with a record 64 points in 2005-06

HONOURS
FA Comps: None
League: Essex Senior 2005-06. Isthmian League Division One North 2006-07, 17-18.

County FA: Essex Senior Cup 2012-13.

08-09		09-10		10-11		11-12		12-13		13-14		14-15		15-16		16-17		17-18	
Isth P	6	Isth P	9	Isth P	10	Isth P	2	Conf S	20	Isth P	5	Isth P	23	Isth1N	5	Isth1N	4	Isth1N	1
FAC	1P	FAC	1Q	FAC	2Qr	FAC	1Q	FAC	2Q	FAC	4Q	FAC	1Qr	FAC	4Q	FAC	1Q	FAC	3Q
FAT	1Qr	FAT	3Qr	FAT	1P	FAT	2P	FAT	3Q	FAT	1Q	FAT	3Q	FAT	1Q	FAT	P	FAT	Pr

BISHOP'S STORTFORD

Club Contact Details 01279 306 456
ProKit Uk Stadium, Woodside Park, Dunmow Road, Bishop's Stortford CM23 5RG
fredplume@hotmail.co.uk

Founded: 1874   **Nickname:** Blues or Bishops   **Manager:** Adam Flint
Previous Names: None
Previous Leagues: East Herts 1896-97, 1902-06, 19-21. Stansted & Dist. 1906-19, Herts Co. 1921-25, 26-29, Herts & Essex Border 1925-26, Spartan 1929-51, Delphian (FM) 1951-63, Athenian 1963-71, Isthmian 1971-2004, Conference 2004-17, Southern 2017-18.
Club Colours (change): Blue and white

Ground Capacity: 4,000   **Seats:** 525   **Covered:** 700   **Clubhouse:** Yes   **Shop:** Yes
Previous Grounds: Silver Leys 1874-97. Hadham Rd 97-1900. Havers Lane 00-03. Laundry Field 03-19. Brazier's Field 1919-97.Shared>99
Record Attendance: 6,000 v Peterborough Town - FA Cup 2nd Round 1972-73 and v Middlesbrough - FA Cup 3rd Round replay
Nearest Railway Station Bishop's Stortford - 20 minute walk from ground.

RECORDS
Victory: 11-0 v Nettleswell & Buntwill - Herts Junior Cup 1911
Defeat: 0-13 v Cheshunt (H) - Herts Senior Cup 1926
Goalscorer: Post 1929 Jimmy Badcock - 123
Appearances: Phil Hopkins - 543

HONOURS
FA Comps: FA Amateur Cup 1973-74. FA Trophy 1980-81.
League: Stansted & District 1910-11, 12-13, 19-20. Spartan Division Two East 1931-32. Delphian 1954-55.
        Athenian Division One 1965-66, Premier 69-70. Isthmian Division One 1980-81, 93-94.
County FA: Herts Senior Cup 1932-33, 58-59, 59-60, 63-64, 70-71, 72-73, 73-74, 75-76, 86-87, 2005-06, 09-10, 11-12.
        London Senior Cup 1973-74.

08-09		09-10		10-11		11-12		12-13		13-14		14-15		15-16		16-17		17-18	
Conf S	9	Conf S	18	Conf S	16	Conf N	10	Conf N	17	Conf S	15	Conf S	16	Nat S	11	Nat S	21	SthP	18
FAC	4Q	FAC	2Q	FAC	2Qr	FAC	4Q	FAC	1P	FAC	1P	FAC	2Qr	FAC	2Q	FAC	3Q	FAC	1Q
FAT	3Qr	FAT	1P	FAT	3Q	FAT	1P	FAT	1P	FAT	3Q	FAT	1P	FAT	3Q	FAT	3Q	FAT	2Q

BOGNOR REGIS TOWN

Club Contact Details 01243 822 325
Nyewood Lane, Bognor Regis PO21 2TY
sajcook2@aol.com

Founded: 1883   **Nickname:** The Rocks   **Manager:** Jack Pearce - July 2017
Previous Names: None
Previous Leagues: West Sussex 1896-1926, Brighton & Hove District 1926-27, Sussex County 1927-72, Southern League 1972-81, Isthmian 1982-2004, 2009-17, Conference 2004-09, 17-18.

Club Colours (change): White & green

Ground Capacity: 4,100   **Seats:** 350   **Covered:** 2,600   **Clubhouse:** Yes   **Shop:** Yes
Previous Grounds: None
Record Attendance: 3,642 v Swnsea City - FA Cup 1st Round replay 1984
Nearest Railway Station Bognor is within walking distance to the ground.

RECORDS
Victory: 24-0 v Littlehampton - West Sussex League 1913-14
Defeat: 0-19 v Shoreham - West Sussex League 1906-07
Goalscorer: Kevin Clements - 206. On 16/12/14 Jason Prior scored his 100th goal for the club making it the fastest century of goals.
Appearances: Mick Pullen - 967 (20 seasons)
Additional: Paid £2,000 for Guy Rutherford 1995-96. Received £10,500 from Brighton & Hove for John Crumplin and Geoff Cooper, and from Crystal Palace for Simon Rodger.

HONOURS
FA Comps: None

League: Isthmian League Division 1 South Play-offs 2011-12. Isthmian Premier Division play-offs 2016-17.

County FA: Sussex Professional Cup 1973-74. Sussex Senior Cup x9.

08-09		09-10		10-11		11-12		12-13		13-14		14-15		15-16		16-17		17-18	
Conf S	21	Isth P	22	Isth1S	2	Isth1S	2	Isth P	14	Isth P	3	Isth P	14	Isth P	2	Isth P	2	Nat S	22
FAC	2Qr	FAC	1Q	FAC	2Q	FAC	3Q	FAC	2Q	FAC	2Qr	FAC	1Qr	FAC	4Q	FAC	2Q	FAC	4Q
FAT	1P	FAT	2Q	FAT	3Qr	FAT	P	FAT	3Q	FAT	3Q	FAT	1Qr	FAT	SF	FAT	1Q	FAT	2P

BRIGHTLINGSEA REGENT

Club Contact Details 01206 304 119
North Road, Brightlingsea, Essex CO7 0PL

Founded: 1928   **Nickname:** The Rs   **Manager:** Tom Rothery
Previous Names: Brightlingsea Athletic & Brightlingsea Town merged to form Brightlingsea United 1928-2005. Merged with Regent Park Rangers.
Previous Leagues: Essex Senior 1972-91. Eastern Counties 1990-02, 2011-14. Essex & Suffolk Border 2002-2011.

Club Colours (change): Red & black

Ground Capacity: 1,000   **Seats:** Yes   **Covered:** Yes   **Clubhouse:** Yes   **Shop:**
Previous Grounds: Bell Green (Bellfield Close). Recreation Ground (Regent Road) > 1920.
Record Attendance: 1,200 v Colchester United, friendly, 1988.
Nearest Railway Station Alresford - 4.8km   **Bus Route** Spring Chase - stop 300m away

RECORDS
Best FA Cup   First Qualifying Round 2014-15, 16-17, 17-18.
FA Trophy   Second Qualifying Round (replay) 2016-17.
FA Vase   Fifth Round Proper 2013-14.

HONOURS
FA Comps: None

League: Essex & Suffolk Border Division One 1946-47, 60-61, Premier 2010-11. Essex Senior 1988-89, 89-90. Isthmian Division One North 2016-17.
County FA: None

08-09		09-10		10-11		11-12		12-13		13-14		14-15		15-16		16-17		17-18	
EsSuP	9	EsSuP	4	EsSuP	1	EC1	5	EC1	3	ECP	2	Isth1N	6	Isth1N	8	Isth1N	1	Isth P	20
										FAC	EPr	FAC	1Q	FAC	Pr	FAC	1Q	FAC	1Q
						FAV	1Q	FAV	3P	FAV	5P	FAT	1Q	FAT	Pr	FAT	2Qr	FAT	1Q

BURGESS HILL TOWN

Club Contact Details 01444 254 832
Green Elephant Stadium, Leylands Park, Maple Drive, Burgess Hill, West Sussex RH15 8DL
timspencer57@hotmail.com

Founded: 1882   **Nickname:** Hillians   **Manager:** Ian Chapman
Previous Names: Burgess Hill 1882-1969.
Previous Leagues: Mid Sussex >1958, Sussex County 1958-2003, Southern 2003-04

Club Colours (change): Green & black

Ground Capacity: 2,500   **Seats:** 408   **Covered:** Yes   **Clubhouse:** Yes   **Shop:** Yes
Previous Grounds: Moved to Leylands Park in 1969.
Record Attendance: 2,005 v AFC Wimbledon - Isthmian League Division One 2004-05
Nearest Railway Station Wivelsfield - 0.4km

RECORDS
Goalscorer:	Ashley Carr - 208
Appearances:	Paul Williams - 499
Best FA Cup	Fourth Qualifying Round 1999-2000, 08-09, 14-15, 16-17(r), 17-18.
FA Trophy	Second Round Proper 2003-04, 04-05, 14-15.
FA Vase	Quarter Finals 2001-02.

HONOURS
FA Comps: None
League: Mid-Sussex 1900-01, 03-04, 39-40, 56-57. Sussex County Division Two 1974-75, Division One 75-76, 96-97, 98-99, 2001-02, 02-03. Isthmian Division One South 2014-15.
County FA: Sussex Senior Cup 1883-84, 84-85, 85-86.

	08-09		09-10		10-11		11-12		12-13		13-14		14-15		15-16		16-17		17-18	
Isth1S	19	Isth1S	7	Isth1S	7	Isth1S	20	Isth1S	8	Isth1S	6	Isth1S	1	Isth P	21	Isth P	20	Isth P	23
FAC	4Q	FAC	P	FAC	2Q	FAC	P	FAC	P	FAC	2Q	FAC	4Q	FAC	1Q	FAC	4Qr	FAC	4Q
FAT	1Q	FAT	2Q	FAT	1Q	FAT	1Q	FAT	Pr	FAT	Pr	FAT	2P	FAT	1Q	FAT	3Q	FAT	2Q

CARSHALTON ATHLETIC

Club Contact Details 020 8642 2551
War Memorial Sports Ground, Colston Avenue, Carshalton SM5 2PN
chrisblanchard@carshaltonathletic.co.uk

Founded: 1905   **Nickname:** Robins   **Manager:** Peter Adeniyi
Previous Names: Mill Lane Mission 1905-07.
Previous Leagues: Croydon & District 1905-10. Southern Suburban 1910-22. Surrey Senior (Founding Members) 1922-23. London 1923-46. Corinthian 1946-56. Athenian 1956-73. Isthmian 1973-2004. Conference 2004-06.

Club Colours (change): All red

Ground Capacity: 8,000   **Seats:** 240   **Covered:** 4,500   **Clubhouse:** Yes   **Shop:** Yes
Previous Grounds: Various before moving to Colston Avenue during the 1920-21 season.
Record Attendance: 7,800 v Wimbledon - London Senior Cup, Jan 1959.
Nearest Railway Station Carshalton - 0.3km

RECORDS
Victory:	13-0 v Worthing - Isthmian League Cup 28/01/1991
Defeat:	0-11 v Southall - Athenian League March 1963
Goalscorer:	Jimmy Bolton - 242 during seven seasons
Appearances:	Jon Warden - 504
Additional:	Paid £15,000 to Enfield for Curtis Warmington
	Received £30,000 from Crystal Palace for Ian Cox 1994

HONOURS
FA Comps: None
League: Corinthian 1952-53, 53-54. Isthmian Division One South 2002-03, 17-18.

County FA: Surrey Intermediate Cup 1921-22, 31-32. Surrey Senior Shield 1975-76. Surrey Senior Cup 1988-89, 89-90, 91-92. London Challenge Cup 1991-92.

	08-09		09-10		10-11		11-12		12-13		13-14		14-15		15-16		16-17		17-18	
Isth P	4	Isth P	17	Isth P	13	Isth P	16	Isth P	20	Isth P	23	Isth1S	20	Isth1S	10	Isth1S	6	Isth1S	1
FAC	2Q	FAC	1Q	FAC	4Qr	FAC	2Q	FAC	2Q	FAC	1Q	FAC	1Q	FAC	2Q	FAC	1Qr	FAC	2Q
FAT	1Q	FAT	2Pr	FAT	2Q	FAT	3P	FAT	2Q	FAT	3Q	FAT	P	FAT	P	FAT	Pr	FAT	P

CORINTHIAN-CASUALS

Club Contact Details 020 8397 3368
King George's Field, Queen Mary Close, Hook Rise South, KT6 7NA
hanna.newton@icloud.com

Founded: 1939	**Nickname:** Casuals	**Manager:** James Bracken

Previous Names: Casuals and Corinthians merged in 1939
Previous Leagues: Isthmian 1939-84, Spartan 1984-96, Combined Counties 1996-97

Club Colours (change): Chocolate and pink

Ground Capacity: 2,000 **Seats:** 161 **Covered:** 700 **Clubhouse:** Yes **Shop:** Yes
Previous Grounds: Kingstonian's Richmond Road 1939-46. Polytechnic Ground in Chiswick 46-50. Oval 50-63. Dulwich Hamlet's Champion Hill 63-68,
Record Attendance: Tooting & Mitcham United's Sandy Lane 68-83, Molesey's Walton Road 83-84, 86-88. Wimbledon Park Athletics Stadium 84-86.
Nearest Railway Station Tolworth - 0.6km

RECORDS
Goalscorer: Cliff West - 215
Appearances: Simon Shergold - 526
Best FA Cup First Round Proper 1965-66, 83-84.
FA Amateur C Finalists 1955-56. **FA Trophy:** Second Round Proper 2002-03.
FA Vase Fisth Round Proper 1983-84.

HONOURS
FA Comps: None
League: London Spartan Senior Division 1985-86.

County FA: Surrey Senior Cup 1953-54, 2010-11.

08-09	09-10	10-11	11-12	12-13	13-14	14-15	15-16	16-17	17-18
Isth1S 20	Isth1S 13	Isth1S 20	Isth1S 13	Isth1S 14	Isth1S 17	Isth1S 13	Isth1S 6	Isth1S 4	Isth1S 5
FAC P	FAC P	FAC 1Q	FAC P	FAC P	FAC F	FAC F	FAC F	FAC 1Q	FAC 1Q
FAT P	FAT 1Q	FAT P	FAT P	FAT P	FAT P	FAT Pr	FAT 1P	FAT 1Q	FAT 2Q

DORKING WANDERERS

Club Contact Details 07500 006 240
Meadowbank Stadium, Mill Lane, Dorking RH4 1DX
m-clarke@blueyonder.co.uk

Founded: 1999	**Nickname:** Wanderers	**Manager:** Marc White

Previous Names: None
Previous Leagues: Crawley & District 1999-2000. West Sussex 2000-2007. Sussex County 2007-2015.

Club Colours (change): Red & white stripes

Ground Capacity: 2,000 **Seats:** 200 **Covered:** Yes **Clubhouse:** Yes **Shop:**
Previous Grounds: Big Field Brockham >2007. West Humble Playing Fields 2007-18.
Record Attendance: N/A
Nearest Railway Station Dorking West and Dorking Deepdene

RECORDS
Best FA Cup Third Qualifying Round 2017-18.
FA Trophy Third Qualifying Round 2017-18.
FA Vase Second Qualifying Round 2012-13, 13-14(r), 14-15.

HONOURS
FA Comps: None
League: West Sussex Division Four North 2000-01, Division Two North 2003-04, Premier Division 2006-07.
Sussex County Division Three 2010-11.
County FA: None

08-09	09-10	10-11	11-12	12-13	13-14	14-15	15-16	16-17	17-18
		SxC3 1	SxC2 3	SxC1 20	SxC1 8	SxC1 2	Isth1S 2	Isth1S 2	Isth P 14
					FAC Pr	FAC 2Qr	FAC 1Q	FAC 1Q	FAC 3Q
				FAV 2Q	FAV 2Qr	FAV 2Q	FAT 1Qr	FAT P	FAT 3Q

ENFIELD TOWN

Club Contact Details 07787 875 650
Queen Elizabeth Stadium, Donkey Lane, Enfield EN1 3PL
nigel.howard71@gmail.com

Founded: 2001   **Nickname:** ET's or Towners   **Manager:** Andy Leese
Previous Names: Broke away from Enfield F.C. in 2001
Previous Leagues: Essex Senior 2001-2005. Southern 2005-2006.

Club Colours (change): White & blue

Ground Capacity: 2,500   **Seats:** Yes   **Covered:** Yes   **Clubhouse:** Yes   **Shop:** No
Previous Grounds: Brimsdown Rovers FC 2001-2010
Record Attendance: 969 v Tottenham Hotspur, friendly, November 2011.
Nearest Railway Station Southbury - 1.2km

RECORDS
Victory: 7-0 v Ilford (A) - 29/04/2003
Goalscorer: Liam Hope - 108 (2009-15)
Appearances: Rudi Hall

HONOURS
FA Comps: None
League: Essex Senior 2002-03, 04-05.

County FA: Middlesex Charity Cup 2001-02, 07-08.

08-09	09-10	10-11	11-12	12-13	13-14	14-15	15-16	16-17	17-18
Isth1N 12	Isth1N 4	Isth1N 6	Isth1N 2	Isth P 16	Isth P 19	Isth P 7	Isth P 6	Isth P 4	Isth P 17
FAC P	FAC 2Q	FAC 3Q	FAC P	FAC 2Q	FAC 2Qr	FAC 2Qr	FAC 4Q	FAC 1Q	FAC 4Qr
FAT 1Q	FAT 2Q	FAT 2Q	FAT 1Q	FAT 3Q	FAT 2Q	FAT 1Q	FAT 2Q	FAV 2Q	FAT 1Q

FOLKESTONE INVICTA

Club Contact Details 01303 257 461
The Fullicks Stadium, Cheriton Road CT19 5JU
richardmurrill@gmail.com

Founded: 1936   **Nickname:** The Seasiders   **Manager:** Neil Cugley
Previous Names: None
Previous Leagues: East Kent Amateur. Kent County Eastern Section. Kent 1990-98, Southern 1998-2004

Club Colours (change): Yellow & black

Ground Capacity: 4,000   **Seats:** 900   **Covered:** Yes   **Clubhouse:** Yes   **Shop:** Yes
Previous Grounds: South Road Hythe > 1991, County League matches on council pitches
Record Attendance: 2,332 v West Ham United, benefit match, 1996-97.
Nearest Railway Station Folkestone West - 0.4km

RECORDS
Victory: 13-0 v Faversham Town - Kent League Division One, May 1995.
Defeat: 1-7 v Crockenhill - Kent League Division One, February 1993 & v Welling United, Kent Senior Cup, February 2009.
Goalscorer: James Dryden - 141
Appearances: Michael Everitt - 631

HONOURS
FA Comps: None
League: Kent County Eastern Division One 1969-70, Premier 78-79. Kent Division Two 1991-92.
            Isthmian Division One South 2015-16.
County FA: Kent Intermediate Shield 1991-92.

08-09	09-10	10-11	11-12	12-13	13-14	14-15	15-16	16-17	17-18
Isth1S 11	Isth1S 2	Isth P 22	Isth1S 4	Isth1S 5	Isth1S 2	Isth1S 2	Isth1S 1	Isth P 16	Isth P 4
FAC 2Q	FAC 1Q	FAC 2Qr	FAC 1Q	FAC 1Q	FAC 2Q	FAC 1Qr	FAC 1Qr	FAC 3Q	FAC 4Q
FAT Pr	FAT P	FAT 3Q	FAT 3Q	FAT Pr	FAT 2Qr	FAT 2Qr	FAT Pr	FAT 2Q	FAT 1Qr

HARINGEY BOROUGH

Club Contact Details 0208 888 9933
Coles Park, White Hart Lane, Tottenham, London N17 7JP
baconjw@hotmail.com

Founded: 1973   **Nickname:** Borough   **Manager:** Tom Loizou
Previous Names: Edmonton & Haringey 1973-76. Haringey Borough 1976-95. Tufnell Park 1995-96.
Previous Leagues: Athenian 1973-84. Isthmian 1984-89. Spartan South Midlands 1989-2013. Essex Senior 2013-15.

Club Colours (change): Yellow & blue

Ground Capacity: 2,500   **Seats:** 280   **Covered:** yes   **Clubhouse:** Yes   **Shop:** No
Previous Grounds: None
Record Attendance: 1,133 v Leyton Orient, FA Trophy First Round Proper, 16/12/2017.
Nearest Railway Station White Hart Lane - 1.5km. Wood Green (UG) - 1.5km   **Bus Route** W3 stops outside the ground.

RECORDS
Best FA Cup   Fourth Qualifying Round 2017-18.
FA Trophy   First Round Proper 2017-18.
FA Vase   Quarter Finals 1977-78.

HONOURS
FA Comps: None
League: Essex Senior 2014-15.
County FA: London Senior Cup 1990-91

08-09		09-10		10-11		11-12		12-13		13-14		14-15		15-16		16-17		17-18	
SSM P	18	SSM P	15	SSM P	8	SSM P	5	SSM P	9	ESen	2	ESen	1	Isth1N	15	Isth1N	5	Isth1N	4
FAC		FAC	EP	FAC	EPr	FAC	P	FAC	P	FAC	2Q	FAC	EP	FAC	1Q	FAC	1Q	FAC	4Q
FAV	1Q	FAV	1Qr	FAV	1P	FAV	3P	FAV	2Q	FAV	3P	FAV	1Pr	FAT	2Qr	FAT	P	FAT	1P

HARLOW TOWN

Club Contact Details 01279 443 196
The Harlow Arena, off Elizabeth Way, The Pinnacles, Harlow CM19 5BE
harlowtownfc@aol.com

Founded: 1879   **Nickname:** Hawks   **Manager:** Danny Chapman
Previous Names: Harlow & Burnt Mill 1898-1902.
Previous Leagues: East Hertfordshire > 1932, Spartan 1932-39, 46-54, London 1954-61, Delphian 1961-63, Athenian 1963-73, Isthmian 1973-92, Inactive 1992-93, Southern 2004-06

Club Colours (change): Red & white

Ground Capacity: 3,500   **Seats:** 500   **Covered:** 500   **Clubhouse:** Yes   **Shop:** Yes
Previous Grounds: Green Man Field 1879-60. Harlow Sportcentre 1960-2006.
Record Attendance: 9,723 v Leicester City - FA Cup 3rd Round replay 08/01/1980

RECORDS
Victory: 14-0 v Bishop's Stortford - 11/04/1925
Defeat: 0-11 v Ware (A) - Spartan Division 1 East 06/03/1948
Goalscorer: Dick Marshall scored 64 during 1928-29, Alex Read scored 52 during 2013-14.
Appearances: Norman Gladwin - 639 (1951-70)

HONOURS
FA Comps: None
League: East Herts Division One 1911-12, 22-23, 28-29, 29-30. Athenian Division One 1971-72.
       Isthmian Division One 1978-79, Division Two North 1988-89.
County FA: Essex Senior cup 1978-79

08-09		09-10		10-11		11-12		12-13		13-14		14-15		15-16		16-17		17-18	
Isth P	20	Isth1N	22	Isth1N	4	Isth1N	7	Isth1N	21	Isth1N	4	Isth1N	2	Isth1N	3	Isth P	10	Isth P	21
FAC	1P	FAC	Pr	FAC	2Q	FAC	P	FAC	P	FAC	2Q	FAC	1Qr	FAC	4Q	FAC	2Q	FAC	3Qr
FAT	1Q	FAT	P	FAT	1P	FAT	3Q	FAT	Pr	FAT	P	FAT	1Q	FAT	2Q	FAT	2P	FAT	3Q

KINGSTONIAN

Club Contact Details 020 8330 6869
Corinthian-Casuals FC, King George's Field, Queen Mary Close, Hook Rise South, KT6 7NA
secretary@kingstonian.com

Founded: 1885 **Nickname:** The K's **Manager:** Leigh Dynan - 24/10/2017
Previous Names: Kingston & Suburban YMCA 1885-87, Saxons 1887-90, Kingston Wanderers 1893-1904, Old Kingstonians 1908-19
Previous Leagues: Kingston & District, West Surrey, Southern Suburban, Athenian 1919-29, Isthmian 1929-98, Conference 1998-2001

Club Colours (change): Red and white hoops

Ground Capacity: 3,400 **Seats:** 125 **Covered:** Yes **Clubhouse:** Yes **Shop:** Yes
Previous Grounds: Several > 1921, Richmond Road 1921-89. Kingsmeadow 1989-2017. Leatherhead FC 2017-18.
Record Attendance: 8,760 v Dulwich Hamlet at Richmond Road 1933.
Nearest Railway Station Tolworth - 0.6km

RECORDS
Victory: 15-1 v Delft - 1951
Defeat: 0-11 v Ilford - Isthmian League 13/02/1937
Goalscorer: Johnnie Wing - 295 (1948-62)
Appearances: Micky Preston - 555 (1967-85)
Additional: Paid £18,000 to Rushden & Diamonds for David Leworthy 1997
Received £150,000 from West Ham United for Gavin Holligan 1999

HONOURS
FA Comps: FA Amateur Cup 1932-33. FA Trophy 1998-99, 99-2000.
League: Isthmian 1933-34, 36-37, 97-98, Division One South 2008-09.
Athenian League x2.
County FA: Surrey Senior Cup 1910-11, 13-14, 25-26, 30-31, 31-32, 34-35, 38-39, 51-52, 62-63, 63-64, 66-67, 97-98, 2005-06..
London Senior Cup 1962-63, 64-65, 86-87.

	08-09		09-10		10-11		11-12		12-13		13-14		14-15		15-16		16-17		17-18
Isth1S	1	Isth P	5	Isth P	7	Isth P	11	Isth P	11	Isth P	2	Isth P	11	Isth P	7	Isth P	17	Isth P	13
FAC	3Q	FAC	2Q	FAC	3Qr	FAC	1Q	FAC	2Q	FAC	1Q	FAC	3Q	FAC	2Q	FAC	1Q	FAC	2Q
FAT	P	FAT	3Q	FAT	2Q	FAT	1Q	FAT	1P	FAT	1Q	FAT	1Q	FAT	3Q	FAT	3Q	FAT	3Qr

LEATHERHEAD

Club Contact Details 01372 360 151
Fetcham Grove, Guildford Road, Leatherhead, Surrey KT22 9AS

Founded: 1946 **Nickname:** The Tanners **Manager:** Nikki Bull
Previous Names: Club was formed when Leatherhead Rose and Leatherhead United merged in 1946.
Previous Leagues: Surrey Senior 1946-50, Metropolitan 1950-51, Delphian 1951-58, Corinthian 1958-63, Athenian 1963-72

Club Colours (change): Green & white

Ground Capacity: 3,400 **Seats:** 125 **Covered:** Yes **Clubhouse:** Yes **Shop:** Yes
Previous Grounds: None
Record Attendance: 5,500 v Wimbledon - 1976
Nearest Railway Station Leatherhead - half a mile away

RECORDS
Victory: 13-1 v Leyland Motors - Surrey Senior League 1946-47
Defeat: 1-11 v Sutton United
Goalscorer: Steve Lunn scored 46 goals during 1996-97
Appearances: P Caswell - 200
Additional: Paid £1,500 to Croydon for B Salkeld
Received £1,500 from Croydon for B Salkeld

HONOURS
FA Comps: None
League: Surrey Senior 1946-47, 47-48, 48-49, 49-50. Corinthian 1962-63. Athenian 1963-64.

County FA: Surrey Senior Cup 1968-69. Surrey Senior Shield 1968-69. Surrey Intermediate Cup 1968-69.

	08-09		09-10		10-11		11-12		12-13		13-14		14-15		15-16		16-17		17-18
Isth1S	15	Isth1S	5	Isth1S	4	Isth P	19	Isth1S	6	Isth1S	3	Isth P	10	Isth P	11	Isth P	13	Isth P	6
FAC	P	FAC	2Qr	FAC	P	FAC	4Qr	FAC	2Q	FAC	3Q	FAC	1Q	FAC	1Qr	FAC	1Q	FAC	2P
FAT	P	FAT	1Q	FAT	P	FAT	1Q	FAT	3Qr	FAT	2Q	FAT	3Q	FAT	1Q	FAT	1Q	FAT	2Q

LEWES

Club Contact Details 01273 470 820
The Dripping Pan, Mountfield Road, Lewes, East Sussex BN7 2XD
barry@lewesfc.com

Founded: 1885   **Nickname:** Rooks   **Manager:** Darren Freeman
Previous Names: None
Previous Leagues: Mid Sussex 1886-1920, Sussex County 1920-65, Athenian 1965-77, Isthmian 1977-2004, Conference 2004-11.

Club Colours (change): Red & black

Ground Capacity: 3,000   **Seats:** 600   **Covered:** 1,400   **Clubhouse:** Yes   **Shop:** Yes
Previous Grounds: Played at Convent Field for two seasons before WWI
Record Attendance: 2,500 v Newhaven - Sussex County League 26/12/1947
Nearest Railway Station Lewes - 0.3km   **Bus Route** Priory School - stop 100m away

RECORDS
Goalscorer: 'Pip' Parris - 350
Appearances: Terry Parris - 662
Additional: Paid £2,000 for Matt Allen
Received £2,500 from Brighton & Hove Albion for Grant Horscroft

HONOURS
FA Comps:
League: Mid Sussex 1910-11, 13-14. Sussex County 1964-65. Athenian Division Two 1967-68, Division One 1969-70.
Isthmian Division Two 2001-02, Division One South 2003-04. Conference South 2007-08.
County FA: Sussex Senior Cup 1964-65, 70-71, 84-85, 2000-01, 05-06.

	08-09		09-10		10-11		11-12		12-13		13-14		14-15		15-16		16-17		17-18	
	Conf	24	Conf S	19	Conf S	21	Isth P	6	Isth P	19	Isth P	16	Isth P	19	Isth P	23	Isth1S	9	Isth1S	2
FAC	4Qr		FAC	3Q	FAC	4Q	FAC	1Q	FAC	2Q	FAC	3Q	FAC	2Q	FAC	1Q	FAC	1Qr	FAC	1Q
FAT	2Pr		FAT	2P	FAT	3Q	FAT	2Q	FAT	2Qr	FAT	1Q	FAT	3Q	FAT	1Qr	FAT	1Q	FAT	3Q

MARGATE

Club Contact Details 01843 221 769
Hartsdown Park, Hartsdown Road, Margate, Kent CT9 5QZ
secretary@margate-fc.com

Founded: 1896   **Nickname:** The Gate   **Manager:** Steve Brown and Mike Sandman
Previous Names: Margate Town 1896-1929.
Previous Leagues: Kent 1911-23, 24-28, 29-33, 37-38, 46-59. Southern 1933-37, 59-2001, Conference 2001-05, 15-17. Isthmian 2005-15.

Club Colours (change): Blue & white

Ground Capacity: 3,000   **Seats:** 400   **Covered:** 1,750   **Clubhouse:** Yes   **Shop:** Yes
Previous Grounds: At least six before moving to Hartsdown in 1929. Shared with Dover Ath. 2002-03 and Ashford Town 04-05.
Record Attendance: 14,169 v Tottenham Hotspur - FA Cup 3rd Round 1973
Nearest Railway Station Margate - 0.7 miles from the ground.

RECORDS
Victory: 12-1 v Deal Cinque Ports, FA Cup 1Q, 1919-20 and v Erith & Belvedere, Kent League, 1927-28.
Defeat: 0-11 v AFC Bournemouth (A), FA Cup, 20/11/1971.
Goalscorer: Martin Buglione - 158
Appearances: Bob Harrop - 564
Additional: Paid £5,000 to Dover Athletic for Steve Cuggy

HONOURS
FA Comps: None
League: Kent 1932-33, 37-38, 46-47, 47-48. Southern League Eastern Section & Championship 1935-36, Division One 1962-63,
Division One South 1977-78, Premier Division 2000-01.
County FA: Kent Senior Cup 1935-36, 36-37, 73-74, 93-94, 97-98, 2002-03, 03-04, 04-05.

	08-09		09-10		10-11		11-12		12-13		13-14		14-15		15-16		16-17		17-18	
	Isth P	19	Isth P	19	Isth P	16	Isth P	15	Isth P	9	Isth P	11	Isth P	2	Nat S	19	Nat S	22	Isth P	7
FAC	1Q		FAC	1Qr	FAC	2Qr	FAC	3Q	FAC	3Q	FAC	2Q	FAC	2Q	FAC	4Q	FAC	4Qr	FAC	4Q
FAT	1Q		FAT	1Q	FAT	2Q	FAT	2Qr	FAT	1Q	FAT	3Q	FAT	1Q	FAT	3Q	FAT	3Qr	FAT	3Q

MERSTHAM

Club Contact Details 01737 644 046
Moatside Stadium, Weldon Way, Merstham, Surrey RH1 3QB
richardbaxter01@hotmail.com

Founded: 1892   **Nickname:** The Moatsiders   **Manager:** Hayden Bird
Previous Names: None
Previous Leagues: Redhill & District. Surrey Intermediate. Surrey Senior 1964-78. London Spartan 1978-84. Combined Counties 1984-2008.

Club Colours (change): Yellow & black

Ground Capacity: 2,500   **Seats:** 174   **Covered:** 100   **Clubhouse:** Yes   **Shop:** No
Previous Grounds: None
Record Attendance: 1,920 v Oxford United, FAC First Round Proper, 05/11/2016
Nearest Railway Station Merstham - 0.7km

RECORDS
Defeat:	1-8 v Aldershot Town, FA First Qualifying Round, 1996-97.
Best FA Cup	First Round Proper 2016-17.
FA Trophy	Second Qualifying Round 2009-10, 12-13, 16-17.
FA Vase	Quarter Finals 2007-08.

HONOURS
FA Comps: None
League: Redhill & District 1934-35, 35-36, 49-50, 50-51. Surrey Intermediate 1952-53. Surrey Senior 1971-72. Combined Counties
     Premier Division 2007-08.
County FA: East Surrey Junior Cup 1929-30. Surrey Senior Charity Cup 1976-77. East Surrey Charities Senior Cup 1979-80, 80-81.
     East Surrey Charity Cup 1998-99, 2004-05, 06-07. Surrey Senior Cup 2007-08, 15-16, 17-18.

08-09	09-10	10-11	11-12	12-13	13-14	14-15	15-16	16-17	17-18
Isth1S 8	Isth1S 16	Isth1S 19	Isth1S 9	Isth1S 12	Isth1S 7	Isth1S 4	Isth P 10	Isth P 20	Isth P 18
FAC 3Q	FAC Pr	FAC P	FAC 2Q	FAC P	FAC 2Q	FAC 2Q	FAC 1Q	FAC 1P	FAC 1Q
FAT 1Q	FAT 2Q	FAT P	FAT 1Q	FAT 2Q	FAT Pr	FAT 2Q	FAT 1Qr	FAT 2Q	FAT 1Qr

POTTERS BAR TOWN

Club Contact Details 01707 654 833
Pakex Stadium, Parkfield, Watkins Rise, Potters Bar EN6 1QB
jeff@jeffbarnes.co.uk

Founded: 1960   **Nickname:** Grace or Scholars   **Manager:** Steve Ringrose - 21/02/15
Previous Names: Mount Grace Old Scholars 1960-84. Mount Grace 1984-91.
Previous Leagues: Barnet & District 1960-65, North London Combination 1965-68, Herts Senior County 1968-91,
     Spartan South Midlands 1991-2005, Southern 2005-06, 13-17. Isthmian 2006-13.
Club Colours (change): Maroon & white

Ground Capacity: 2,000   **Seats:** 150   **Covered:** 250   **Clubhouse:** Yes   **Shop:** Yes
Previous Grounds: None
Record Attendance: 268 v Wealdstone - FA Cup 1998 (4,000 watched a charity match in 1997)
Nearest Railway Station Potters Bar - 0.9km

RECORDS
Goalscorer:	Micky Gray scored 51 during a single season. Richard Howard has come closest to that record having scored 49 goals during seasons 2004-05 and 2006-07 respectively.
Best FA Cup	Fourth Qualifying Round 2006-07, 16-17.
FA Trophy	Second Round Qualifying 2011-12, 17-18(r).
FA Vase	Sixth Round Proper 1997-98.

HONOURS
FA Comps: None
League: North London Combination Premier Division 1967-68. Herst Senior county Premier Division 1990-91.
     Spartan South Midlands Premier Division 1996-97, 2004-05.
County FA: None

08-09	09-10	10-11	11-12	12-13	13-14	14-15	15-16	16-17	17-18
Isth1N 19	Isth1N 14	Isth1N 13	Isth1N 12	Isth1N 10	SthC 15	SthC 14	SthC 12	SthC 9	Isth1N 2
FAC Pr	FAC 3Q	FAC P	FAC P	FAC 1Qr	FAC P	FAC P	FAC 2Q	FAC 4Q	FAC 2Qr
FAT P	FAT Pr	FAT 1Qr	FAT 2Q	FAT 1Q	FAT 1Qr	FAT Pr	FAT Pr	FAT P	FAT 2Qr

TONBRIDGE ANGELS

Club Contact Details 01732 352 417
Longmead Stadium, Darenth Avenue, Tonbridge, Kent TN10 3JF
chcole1063@aol.com

Founded: 1947   **Nickname:** Angels   **Manager:** Steve McKimm
Previous Names: Tonbridge FC 1947-94.
Previous Leagues: Southern 1948-80, 93-2004, Kent 1989-93, Isthmian 2004-11.

Club Colours (change): Blue and white

Ground Capacity: 3,000   **Seats:** 760+   **Covered:** 1,500   **Clubhouse:** Yes   **Shop:** Yes
Previous Grounds: The Angel 1948-80
Record Attendance: 8,236 v Aldershot - FA Cup 1951 at The Angel.
Nearest Railway Station Tonbridge - 3.1km   **Bus Route** Heather Walk - stop 250m away

RECORDS
Victory: 11-1 v Worthing - FA Cup 1951
Defeat: 2-11 v Folkstone - Kent Senior Cup 1949
Goalscorer: Jon Main scored 44 goals in one season including seven hat-tricks
Appearances: Mark Giham

HONOURS
FA Comps: None
League: Kent 1992-93.

County FA: Kent Senior Cup 1964-65, 74-75. Kent Senior Shield 1951-52, 55-56, 57-58, 58-59, 63-64.

	08-09		09-10		10-11		11-12		12-13		13-14		14-15		15-16		16-17		17-18	
	Isth P	3	Isth P	8	Isth P	2	Conf S	9	Conf S	16	Conf S	21	Isth P	20	Isth P	4	Isth P	6	Isth P	11
FAC	1Q	FAC	3Q	FAC	1Q	FAC	2Q	FAC	2Q	FAC	3Q	FAC	2Q	FAC	2Q	FAC	4Q	FAC	1Q
FAT	1Q	FAT	3Q	FAT	3Q	FAT	3Qr	FAT	2P	FAT	1Pr	FAT	3Qr	FAT	2Q	FAT	2Qr	FAT	1Qr

WHITEHAWK

Club Contact Details 01273 609 736
The TerraPura Ground, East Brighton Park, Wilson Avenue, Brighton BN2 5TS

Founded: 1945   **Nickname:** Hawks   **Manager:** Jude MacDonald
Previous Names: Whitehawk & Manor Farm Old Boys untill 1960.
Previous Leagues: Brighton & Hove District >1952. Sussex County 1952-2010. Isthmian 2010-13. Conference/National 2013-18.

Club Colours (change): Red and white

Ground Capacity: 3,000   **Seats:** 800   **Covered:** Yes   **Clubhouse:** Yes   **Shop:** No
Previous Grounds: N/A
Record Attendance: 2,174 v Dagenham & Redbridge, FA Cup Second Round Proper replay, 6th December 2015.
Nearest Railway Station Brighton Central - two & half miles from the ground.   **Bus Route** B&H Bus No.7 or 27

RECORDS
Goalscorer: Billy Ford
Appearances: Ken Powell - 1,103
Victory: 14-0 v Southdown (H), Sussex Junior Cup Second Round, 27/03/1948.
Defeat: 2-13 v St Luke's Terrace Old Boys (A), Brighton & Hove District Division Two, 02/11/1946.
Misc: Scored 127 goals in 32 matches during the 1961-62 season.

HONOURS
FA Comps: None
League: Sussex County League Division One 1961-62, 63-64, 83-84, 2009-10, Division Two 1967-68, 80-81.
     Isthmian League Division One South 2011-12, Premier Division 2012-13.
County FA: Sussex Senior Cup 1950-51, 61-62, 2011-12, 14-15. Sussex RUR Charity Cup 1954-55, 58-59, 90-91.

	08-09		09-10		10-11		11-12		12-13		13-14		14-15		15-16		16-17		17-18	
	SxC1	13	SxC1	1	Isth1S	3	Isth1S	1	Isth P	1	Conf S	19	Conf S	4	Nat S	5	Nat S	17	Nat S	21
FAC	EPr	FAC	EP	FAC	3Q	FAC	2Qr	FAC	2Qr	FAC	2Q	FAC	3Qr	FAC	2Pr	FAC	1Pr	FAC	2Q
FAV	2P	FAV	SF	FAT	1Q	FAT	1Q	FAT	3Q	FAT	2Pr	FAT	3Q	FAT	1P	FAT	2P	FAT	1P

THE NON-LEAGUE PAPER

ESSENTIAL READING FOR FOLLOWERS OF THE NATIONAL GAME

BE CLOSE TO THE PASSION

ONLY £1.50 EVERY SUNDAY IN RETAILERS

BUY FROM YOUR LOCAL NEWSAGENT OR SUPERMARKET OR SUBSCRIBE ONLINE AT:
WWW.THENONLEAGUEFOOTBALLPAPER.COM

WINGATE & FINCHLEY

Club Contact Details 0208 446 2217
Maurice Rebak Stadium, Summers Lane, Finchley N12 0PD
mark@wingatefinchley.com

Founded: 1991   **Nickname:** Blues   **Manager:** Keith Rowland
Previous Names: Wingate (founded 1946) and Finchley (founded late 1800s) merged in 1991
Previous Leagues: South Midlands 1991-95, Isthmian 1995-2004, Southern 2004-2006

Club Colours (change): Blue

Ground Capacity: 1,500   **Seats:** 500   **Covered:** 500   **Clubhouse:** Yes   **Shop:** No
Previous Grounds: None
Record Attendance: 528 v Brentwood Town (Division One North Play-Off) 2010/11

RECORDS
Victory: 9-1 v Winslow, South Midlands League, 23/11/1991
Defeat: 0-9 v Edgware, Isthmian Division Two, 15/01/2000
Goalscorer: Marc Morris 650 (including with Wingate FC)
Appearances: Marc Morris 720 (including with Wingate FC)

HONOURS
FA Comps: None
League: None

County FA: London Senior Cup 2010-11.

08-09		09-10		10-11		11-12		12-13		13-14		14-15		15-16		16-17		17-18	
Isth1N	7	Isth1N	3	Isth1N	3	Isth P	13	Isth P	18	Isth P	21	Isth P	12	Isth P	13	Isth P	5	Isth P	9
FAC	2Q	FAC	2Qr	FAC	Pr	FAC	1Q	FAC	2Q	FAC	1Qr	FAC	3Q	FAC	3Q	FAC	2Q	FAC	2Qr
FAT	1P	FAT	Pr	FAT	1Q	FAT	1Q	FAT	2Qr	FAT	2Qr	FAT	1Q	FAT	1Q	FAT	1Pr	FAT	1P

WORTHING

Club Contact Details 01903 233 444
Woodside Road, Worthing, West Sussex BN14 7HQ
secretary@worthingfc.com

Founded: 1886   **Nickname:** Rebels   **Manager:** Adam Hinshelwood
Previous Names: None
Previous Leagues: West Sussex 1896-1904, 1905-14, 19-20, Brighton Hove & District 1919-20, Sussex County 1920-40, Corinthian 1948-63, Athenian 1963-77

Club Colours (change): All red

Ground Capacity: 3,650   **Seats:** 500   **Covered:** 1,500   **Clubhouse:** Yes   **Shop:** No
Previous Grounds: None
Record Attendance: 3,600 v Wimbledon - FA Cup 14/11/1936
Nearest Railway Station Worthing - 0.6km

RECORDS
Victory: 25-0 v Littlehampton (H) - Sussex League 1911-12
Defeat: 0-14 v Southwick (A) - Sussex County League 1946-47
Goalscorer: Mick Edmonds - 276
Appearances: Mark Knee - 414
Additional: Received £7,500 from Woking for Tim Read 1990

HONOURS
FA Comps: None
League: Sussex League 1920-21, 21-22, 26-27, 28-29, 30-31, 33-34, 38-39. Sussex League West 1945-46.
Isthmian League Division Two 1981-82, 92-93, Division One 1982-83.
County FA: Sussex Senior Cup x21.

08-09		09-10		10-11		11-12		12-13		13-14		14-15		15-16		16-17		17-18	
Isth1S	5	Isth1S	3	Isth1S	14	Isth1S	7	Isth1S	10	Isth1S	15	Isth1S	6	Isth1S	3	Isth P	15	Isth P	16
FAC	3Q	FAC	2Q	FAC	2Q	FAC	3Q	FAC	1Q	FAC	P	FAC	2Q	FAC	3Q	FAC	3Q	FAC	1Q
FAT	2Q	FAT	Pr	FAT	1Q	FAT	2Q	FAT	P	FAT	P	FAT	2Q	FAT	1Q	FAT	2Pr	FAT	2Q

AFC SUDBURY

Club Contact Details 01787 376 213
King's Marsh Stadium, Brundon Lane, Sudbury CO10 7HN
afcsudbury@gmail.com

Founded: 1999 **Nickname:** Yellows or The Suds **Manager:** Mark Morsley
Previous Names: Sudbury Town (1874) and Sudbury Wanderers (1958) merged in 1999
Previous Leagues: Eastern Counties 1999-2006, Isthmian 2006-08, Southern 2008-10.

Club Colours (change): Yellow & blue

Ground Capacity: 2,500 **Seats:** 200 **Covered:** 1,500 **Clubhouse:** Yes **Shop:** Yes
Previous Grounds: The Priory Stadium
Record Attendance: 1,800
Nearest Railway Station Sudbury - 1.5km **Bus Route** Bulmer Road - stop 100m away

RECORDS
Goalscorer: Gary Bennett - 172
Appearances: Paul Betson - 376
Best FA Cup First Round Proper 2000-01.
FA Trophy First Round Proper 2006-07, 08-09, 10-11, 14-15.

HONOURS
FA Comps: None
League: Eastern Counties League 2000-01, 01-02, 02-03, 03-04, 04-05. Isthmian League Division One North 2015-16.

County FA: Suffolk Premier Cup 2001-02, 02-03, 03-04.

	08-09		09-10		10-11		11-12		12-13		13-14		14-15		15-16		16-17		17-18	
	SthM		SthM	14	Isth1N	7	Isth1N	8	Isth1N	17	Isth1N	10	Isth1N	3	Isth1N	1	Isth P	23	Isth1N	12
FAC		Pr	FAC	1Q	FAC	Pr	FAC	3Q	FAC	1Q	FAC	3Q	FAC	1Q	FAC	2Q	FAC	2Q	FAC	3Q
FAT		1P	FAT	1Qr	FAT	1P	FAT	1Q	FAT	P	FAT	3Qr	FAT	1P	FAT	2Q	FAT	2P	FAT	1Q

AVELEY

Club Contact Details 01708 934 890
Parkside, Park Lane, Aveley RM15 4PX
craigjohnson.aveleyfc@gmail.com

Founded: 1927 **Nickname:** The Millers **Manager:** James Webster
Previous Names: Lodge Meadow 1927-51.
Previous Leagues: Thurrock Combination 1946-49, London 1949-57, Delphian 1957-63, Athenian 1963-73,
Isthmian 1973-2004, Southern 2004-06

Club Colours (change): All blue

Ground Capacity: 3,500 **Seats:** 424 **Covered:** Yes **Clubhouse:** Yes **Shop:** No
Previous Grounds: Lodge Meadow 1927-52. Mill Field 1952-2018.
Record Attendance: 3,741 v Slough Town - FA Amateur Cup 27/02/1971
Nearest Railway Station Purfleet

RECORDS
Victory: 11-1 v Histon - 24/08/1963
Defeat: 0-8 v Orient, Essex Thameside Trophy
Goalscorer: Jotty Wilks - 214
Appearances: Ken Riley - 422

HONOURS
FA Comps: None
League: London Division One 1950-51, Premier Division 54-55. Athenian 1970-71. Isthmian Division One North 2008-09.

County FA: Essex Thameside Trophy 1979-80, 2004-05, 06-07.

	08-09		09-10		10-11		11-12		12-13		13-14		14-15		15-16		16-17		17-18	
	Isth1N	1	Isth P	3	Isth P	19	Isth P	20	Isth P	5	Isth1N	13	Isth1N	9	Isth1N	12	Isth1N	7	Isth1N	14
FAC		1Q	FAC	3Qr	FAC	1Q	FAC	2Q	FAC	2Q	FAC	1Q	FAC	3Q	FAC	3Q	FAC	P	FAC	P
FAT		1Q	FAT	1Q	FAT	1Q	FAT	1Q	FAT	P	FAT	P	FAT	P	FAT	P	FAT	P	FAT	1Q

BARKING

Club Contact Details 0203 244 0069
Mayesbrook Park, Lodge Avenue, Dagenham RM8 2JR
secretary@barking-fc.co.uk

Founded: 1880   **Nickname:** The Blues   **Manager:** Justin Gardner
Previous Names: Barking Rov. Barking Woodville. Barking Working Lads Institute, Barking Institute. Barking T. Barking & East Ham United.
Previous Leagues: South Essex, London, Athenian. Isthmian. Southern. Essex Senior >2017.

Club Colours (change): All blue

Ground Capacity: 2,500   **Seats:** 200   **Covered:** 600   **Clubhouse:** Yes   **Shop:** Yes
Previous Grounds: Barking Park Recreation Ground. Vicarage Field 1884-1973.
Record Attendance: 1,972 v Aldershot, FA Cup Second Round Proper, 1978.
Nearest Railway Station Upney (District Line), 2 miles   **Bus Route** 368 (50 yards) 5, 145, 364 (400 yards)

RECORDS
Goalscorer: Neville Fox - 242 (1965-73).
Appearances: Bob Makin - 569.
Victory: 14-0 v Sheppey United, Mithras Cup, 02/12/1969
Best FA Cup   Second Round Proper replay 1981-82.   **FA Amateur Cup:** Finalists 1926-27.
FA Trophy   Second Round Proper 1979-80.   **FA Vase:** Fifth Round Proper 1996-97.

HONOURS
FA Comps: None

League: South Essex Division One 1898-99, 1911-12, Division Two 1900-01. Division Two 1901-02. London Division One A 1909-10,
Premier 1920-21. Athenian 1934-35. Isthmian Premier 1978-79. Essex Senior 2016-17.
County FA: Essex Senior Cup 1893-94, 95-96, 1919-20, 45-46, 62-63, 69-70, 89-90.
London Senior Cup 1911-12, 20-21, 26-27, 78-79.

08-09		09-10		10-11		11-12		12-13		13-14		14-15		15-16		16-17		17-18	
ESen	12	ESen	8	ESen	6	ESen	7	ESen	6	ESen	12	ESen	3	ESen	4	ESen	1	Isth1N	10
FAC	EP	FAC	EP	FAC	P	FAC	EPr	FAC	EPr	FAC	Pr	FAC	EP	FAC	Pr	FAC	Pr	FAC	2Q
FAV	1Qr	FAV	2Qr	FAV	1P	FAV	1P	FAV	1P	FAV	2P	FAV	1Q	FAV	2P	FAV	1P	FAT	1Q

BASILDON UNITED

Club Contact Details 01268 521 278
The Ho Ho Stadium, Gardiners Close, Basildon SS14 3AW

Founded: 1963   **Nickname:** The Bees   **Manager:** Marc Harrison
Previous Names: Armada Sports.
Previous Leagues: Grays & Thurrock. Greater London. Essex Senior. Athenian. Isthmian. Essex Senior >2018.

Club Colours (change): Yellow & black

Ground Capacity: 2,000   **Seats:** 400   **Covered:** 1,000   **Clubhouse:** Yes   **Shop:** No
Previous Grounds: Gloucester Park Bowl 1963-70.
Record Attendance: 4,000 v West Ham, ground opening 11/08/1970 (4,999 watched a West Ham XI open Gloucester Park Bowl)
Nearest Railway Station Basildon (C2C), 2 miles   **Bus Route** 5 (First), 400 metres from ground

RECORDS
Best FA Cup   Third Qualifying Round 1983-84, 98-99.
FA Trophy   Second Qualifying Round 1985-86.
FA Vase   Quarter Finals 1980-81.

HONOURS
FA Comps: None

League: Essex Senior 1976-77, 77-78, 78-79, 79-80, 93-94.
Isthmian Division Two 1983-84.
County FA: Essex Senior Trophy 1978-79.

08-09		09-10		10-11		11-12		12-13		13-14		14-15		15-16		16-17		17-18	
ESen	8	ESen	12	ESen	12	ESen	18	ESen	13	ESen	8	ESen	12	ESen	2	ESen	9	ESen	2
		FAC	P	FAC	EP	FAC	EP	FAC	1Q	FAC	P	FAC	P	FAC	1Q	FAC	P	FAC	P
FAV	2P	FAV	1P	FAV	2Q	FAV	1P	FAV	1Q	FAV	1Q	FAV	1Q	FAV	3P	FAV	3P	FAV	1P

BOWERS & PITSEA

Club Contact Details 07910 626 727
Len Salmon Stadium, Crown Avenue, Pitsea, Basildon SS13 2BE
lee-stevens@sky.com

Founded: 1946 **Nickname:** **Manager:** Rob Small
Previous Names: Bowers United > 2004.
Previous Leagues: Thurrock & Thameside Combination. Olympian. Essex Senior >2016.

Club Colours (change): Red & white

Ground Capacity: 2,000 **Seats:** 200 **Covered:** 1,000 **Clubhouse:** Yes **Shop:** Yes
Previous Grounds: Pitsea Market. Gun Meadow.
Record Attendance: 1,800 v Billericay Town, FA Vase.
Nearest Railway Station Pitsea - 1.7km **Bus Route** Wilsner - stop 200m award

RECORDS
Victory: 14-1 v Stansted, 2006-07
Defeat: 0-8 v Ford United, 1996-97
Goalscorer: David Hope scored 50 during the 1998-99 season.

HONOURS
FA Comps: None
League: Thurrock & Thameside Combination 1958-59. Essex Senior 1980-81, 98-99, 2015-16.

County FA: None

08-09		09-10		10-11		11-12		12-13		13-14		14-15		15-16		16-17		17-18	
ESen	11	ESen	17	ESen	14	ESen	15	ESen	19	ESen	14	ESen	2	ESen	1	Isth1N	6	Isth1N	3
FAC	EP	FAC	P	FAC	P	FAC	EP	FAC	EP	FAC	EP	FAC	1Q	FAC	EP	FAC	Pr	FAC	P
FAV	1Pr	FAV	1Q	FAV	2Q	FAV	2Q	FAV	1Q	FAV	1P	FAV	1P	FAV	SF	FAT	1Q	FAT	1Qr

BRENTWOOD TOWN

Club Contact Details
The Arena, Brentwood Centre, Doddinghurst Road, Brentwood CM15 9NN
info@brentwoodtownfc.co.uk

Founded: 1954 **Nickname:** Blues **Manager:** Craig Shipman
Previous Names: Manor Athletic, Brentwood Athletic, Brentwood F.C.
Previous Leagues: Romford & District, South Essex Combination, London & Essex Border, Olympian, Essex Senior

Club Colours (change): Sky blue & white

Ground Capacity: 1,000 **Seats:** 150 **Covered:** 250 **Clubhouse:** Yes **Shop:** No
Previous Grounds: King George's Playing Fields (Hartswood), Larkins Playing Fields 1957-93
Record Attendance: 763 v Cheshunt, Isthmian Division One North, 23/04/2011.
Nearest Railway Station Shenfield - 2.1km **Bus Route** Leisure Centre - stop 150m away

RECORDS
Best FA Cup Third Round Proper 1969-70.
FA Trophy First Round Proper 1969-70.
FA Vase First Round 2004-05, 06-07.

HONOURS
FA Comps: None
League: Essex Senior 2000-01, 2006-07.

County FA: None

08-09		09-10		10-11		11-12		12-13		13-14		14-15		15-16		16-17		17-18	
Isth1N	3	Isth1N	12	Isth1N	5	Isth1N	9	Isth1N	9	Isth1N	19	Isth1N	4	Isth P	22	Isth1N	14	Isth1N	21
FAC	1Qr	FAC	P	FAC	3Qr	FAC	1Qr	FAC	3Q	FAC	1Qr	FAC	2Q	FAC	4Q	FAC	P	FAC	P
FAV	1Q	FAV	1Q	FAV	1Q	FAV	1Q	FAV	3Qr	FAV	P	FAV	1Qr	FAV	2Q	FAV	P	FAT	3Q

BURY TOWN

Club Contact Details 01284 754 721
The Denny Bros Stadium, Cotton Lane, Bury St Edmunds IP33 1XP
wendy@burytownfc.co.uk

Founded: 1872 **Nickname:** The Blues **Manager:** Ben Chenery
Previous Names: Bury St Edmunds 1872-1885, 1895-1908. Bury Town 1885-95. Bury United 1908-23.
Previous Leagues: Norfolk & Suffolk Border, Essex & Suffolk Border, Eastern Counties 1935-64, 76-87, 97-2006, Metropolitan 1964-71,
Southern 1971-76, 87-97

Club Colours (change): Blue & white

Ground Capacity: 3,500 **Seats:** 300 **Covered:** 1,500 **Clubhouse:** Yes **Shop:** Yes
Previous Grounds: Kings Road 1888-1978
Record Attendance: 2,500 v Enfield - FA Cup Fourth Qualifying Round 1986
Nearest Railway Station Bury St Edmunds - 0.7km

RECORDS
Goalscorer: Doug Tooley - 251 in nine seasons
Appearances: Dick Rayner - 610 over 12 seasons
Additional: Paid £1,500 to Chelmsford City for Mel Springett
Received £5,500 from Ipswich Town for Simon Milton

HONOURS
FA Comps: None
League: Metropolitan 1965-66, 68-69. Eastern Counties 1963-64. Southern Division One Central 2009-10
County FA: Suffolk Senior Cup 1936-37, 37-38, 38-39, 44-45, 84-85.
Suffolk Premier Cup x12 - Firstly in 1958-59 and most recently in 2013-14.

	08-09		09-10		10-11		11-12		12-13		13-14		14-15		15-16		16-17		17-18	
	SthC	7	SthC	1	Isth P	3	Isth P	5	Isth P	7	Isth P	15	Isth P	24	Isth1N	13	Isth1N	11	Isth1N	9
FAC	1P		4Q		3Qr		2Q		4Q		1Q		1Q		2Q		P		P	
FAT	1P		P		2Q		3Qr		1Qr		1P		1Q		1P		1Q		2Q	

CANVEY ISLAND

Club Contact Details 01268 682 991
The Frost Financial Stadium, Park Lane, Canvey Island, Essex SS8 7PX
g.sutton@sky.com

Founded: 1926 **Nickname:** The Gulls **Manager:** Danny Heale
Previous Names: None
Previous Leagues: Southend & District, Thurrock & Thames Combination, Parthenon, Metropolitan, Greater London 1964-71,
Essex Senior 1971-95, Isthmian 1995-2004, Conference 2004-06

Club Colours (change): Yellow & blue

Ground Capacity: 4,100 **Seats:** 500 **Covered:** 827 **Clubhouse:** Yes **Shop:** Yes
Previous Grounds: None
Record Attendance: 3,553 v Aldershot Town - Isthmian League 2002-03
Nearest Railway Station Leigh-on-Sea - 3.2km **Bus Route** Transport Museum - stop 100m away

RECORDS
Goalscorer: Andy Jones
Appearances: Steve Ward
Additional: Paid £5,000 to Northwich Victoria for Chris Duffy
Received £4,500 from Farnborough Town for Brian Horne

HONOURS
FA Comps: FA Trophy 2000-01.
League: Thurrock Combination 1955-56. Greater London Division One 1967-68, 68-69. Essex Senior 1986-87, 92-93. Isthmian Division
Two 1995-96, 97-98, Division One 1998-99, Premier Division 2003-04.
County FA: Essex Senior Cup 1998-99, 99-00, 01-02, 11-12.

	08-09		09-10		10-11		11-12		12-13		13-14		14-15		15-16		16-17		17-18	
	Isth P	12	Isth P	16	Isth P	6	Isth P	8	Isth P	8	Isth P	13	Isth P	17	Isth P	14	Isth P	22	Isth1N	6
FAC	1Q		2Q		3Qr		2Q		1Q		4Q		4Qr		1Q		2Qr		P	
FAT	1Qr		1Q		1Q		3Q		3Qr		2Q		1Qr		2Q		1Q		P	

COGGESHALL TOWN

Club Contact Details 01376 562 843
West Street, Coggeshall CO6 1NT
secretary@coggeshalltownfc.co.uk

Founded: 1878   **Nickname:** Seed Growers   **Manager:** Graeme Smith - June 2014
Previous Names: None
Previous Leagues: North Essex 1899-1909. Colchester & District/Essex & Suffolk Border 1909-39, 58-72, 90-96, 2000-2016. North Essex. Braintree & Dist. Colchester & E Essex 1950-58. Essex Senior 1972-90. Essex Inter. 1996-98, 99-00. Eastern Co 2016-18.

Club Colours (change): Red & black

Ground Capacity: -   **Seats:** Yes   **Covered:** Yes   **Clubhouse:** Yes   **Shop:**
Previous Grounds: Mynheer Park. Barnard Field 1880-81. Highfields Farm Park 1881-90, 95-1960. Fabians Field 1890-95.
Record Attendance: 1,124 v Tiptree United, Essex & Suffolk Border League, 1967-68.
Nearest Railway Station Kelvedon - 3.6km

RECORDS
Best FA Vase   Second Qualifying Round 2017-18.

HONOURS
FA Comps: None
League: North Essex x4. Essex & Suffolk Border Division II B 1909-10, 10-11, Division One 1962-63, Premier Division 1966-67, 67-68, 69-70, 2015-16. Eastern Counties Premier 2017-18.
County FA: Essex Intermediate Cup 1970-71.

08-09	09-10	10-11	11-12	12-13	13-14	14-15	15-16	16-17	17-18
EsSuP 16	EsSu1 4	EsSu1 5	EsSu1 5	EsSu1 2	EsSuP 7	EsSuP 6	EsSuP 1	EC1 2	ECP 1
									FAV 2Q

DEREHAM TOWN

Club Contact Details 01362 690 460
Aldiss Park, Norwich Road, Dereham, Norfolk NR20 3PX
enquiries@derehamtownfc.co.uk

Founded: 1884   **Nickname:** Magpies   **Manager:** Neal Simmons
Previous Names: Dereham and Dereham Hobbies.
Previous Leagues: Norwich District. Dereham & District. Norfolk & Suffolk. Anglian Comb. Eastern Counties > 2013.

Club Colours (change): Black & white

Ground Capacity: 2,500   **Seats:** 150   **Covered:** 500   **Clubhouse:** Yes   **Shop:** Yes
Previous Grounds: Bayfields Meadow. Recreation Ground >1996.
Record Attendance: 3000 v Norwich City, Friendly, 07/2001.

                      Bus Route Paget Adams Drive - stop 300m away

RECORDS
Best FA Cup   Third Qualifying Round replay 2012-13.
FA Trophy   Second Qualifying Round 2014-15.
FA Vase   Fifth Round Proper 2008-09.

HONOURS
FA Comps: None
League: Anglian Combination Division One 1989-90, Premier Division 97-98. Eastern Counties Premier Division 2012-13.

County FA: Norfolk Senior Cup 2005-06, 06-07, 15-16.

08-09	09-10	10-11	11-12	12-13	13-14	14-15	15-16	16-17	17-18
ECP 4	ECP 10	ECP 2	ECP 10	ECP 1	Isth1N 7	Isth1N 7	Isth1N 9	Isth1N 18	Isth1N 8
FAC Pr	FAC 1Q	FAC EP	FAC EP	FAC 3Qr	FAC 1Q	FAC 2Q	FAC P	FAC 2Q	FAC 2Q
FAV 5P	FAV 2P	FAV 1Q	FAV 1P	FAV 2P	FAT 1Q	FAT 2Q	FAT P	FAT P	FAT Pr

FELIXSTOWE & WALTON UNITED

Club Contact Details 01394 282 627
Dellwood Avenue, Felixstowe IP11 9HT
webmaster@felixstowefootball.co.uk

Founded: 2000   **Nickname:** Seasiders   **Manager:** Kevin O'Donnell - Oct 2012
Previous Names: Felixstowe Port & Town and Walton United merged in July 2000.
Previous Leagues: Eastern Counties 2000-18.

Club Colours (change): Red & white

Ground Capacity: 2,000   **Seats:** 200   **Covered:** 200   **Clubhouse:** Yes   **Shop:** Yes
Previous Grounds: None
Record Attendance:
Nearest Railway Station Felixstowe - 0.3km

RECORDS
Best FA Cup   Third Qualifying Round 2016-17.
FA Vase   Second Round Proper 2011-12, 16-17.

HONOURS
FA Comps: None
League: None

County FA: None

08-09		09-10		10-11		11-12		12-13		13-14		14-15		15-16		16-17		17-18	
ECP	12	ECP	7	ECP	18	ECP	18	ECP	14	ECP	3	ECP	5	ECP	4	ECP	2	ECP	2
FAC	EP	FAC	EP	FAC	2Qr	FAC	P	FAC	Pr	FAC	P	FAC	1Q	FAC	EPr	FAC	3Q	FAC	EP
FAV	1Pr	FAV	1Pr	FAV	1P	FAV	2P	FAV	2Q	FAV	1Q	FAV	1P	FAV	1Q	FAV	2P	FAV	1P

GRAYS ATHLETIC

Club Contact Details 07870 592 382
Aveley FC, Parkside, Park Lane, Aveley RM15 4PX
graysathleticfc@hotmail.co.uk

Founded: 1890   **Nickname:** The Blues   **Manager:** Jamie Stuart
Previous Names: Grays Juniors 1890.
Previous Leagues: Grays & District. South Essex. Athenian 1912-14, 58-83. London 1914-24, 26-39,.Kent 1924-26. Corinthian 1945-58. Isthmian 1958-2004. Conference 2004-10

Club Colours (change): All royal blue

Ground Capacity: 3,500   **Seats:** 424   **Covered:** Yes   **Clubhouse:** Yes   **Shop:** No
Previous Grounds: Recreation Ground Bridge Road. Rookery Hill (East Thurrock Utd). Rush Green Road. Mill Field (Aveley FC).
Record Attendance: 9,500 v Chelmsford City - FA Cup 4th Qualifying Round 1959
Nearest Railway Station Purfleet

RECORDS
Victory: 12-0 v Tooting & Mitcham United - London League 24/02/1923
Defeat: 0-12 v Enfield (A) - Athenian League 20/04/1963
Goalscorer: Harry Brand - 269 (1944-52)
Appearances: Phil Sammons - 673 (1982-97)
Additional: Paid £12,000 to Welling United for Danny Kedwell.
               Received £150,000 from Peterborough United for Aaron McLean.

HONOURS
FA Comps: FA Trophy 2004-05, 05-06.
League: South Essex Division Two B 1908-09. Corinthian 1945-46. London Prmier (Amateur) 1914-15, Premier 1921-22, 26-27, 29-30. Isthmian Division Two South 1984-85, Division One North 2012-13. Conference South 2004-05.
County FA: Essex Senior Cup 1914-15, 20-21, 22-23, 44-45, 56-57, 87-88, 93-94, 94-95. East Anglian Cup 1944-45.

08-09		09-10		10-11		11-12		12-13		13-14		14-15		15-16		16-17		17-18	
Conf	19	Conf	23	Isth1N	10	Isth1N	5	Isth1N	1	Isth P	14	Isth P	6	Isth P	15	Isth P	24	Isth1N	16
FAC	1Pr	FAC	4Q	FAC	2Qr	FAC	1Q	FAC	2Q	FAC	3Q	FAC	3Qr	FAC	4Qr	FAC	1Q	FAC	1Qr
FAT	1P	FAT	1P	FAT	3Qr	FAT	2Q	FAT	2Qr	FAT	3Q	FAT	2Q	FAT	3Qr	FAT	1Qr	FAT	1Qr

GREAT WAKERING ROVERS

Club Contact Details 01702 217 812
Burroughs Park, Little Wakering Hall Lane, Great Wakering SS3 0HH
secretary@gwrovers.com

Founded: 1919   **Nickname:** Rovers   **Manager:** Ian O'Connell
Previous Names: None
Previous Leagues: Southend & District 1919-81, Southend Alliance 1981-89, Essex Intermediate 1989-92, Essex Senior 1992-99, 2012-14, Isthmian 1999-2004, 14-17, Southern 2004-05.

Club Colours (change): Green & white

Ground Capacity: 3,000   **Seats:** 250   **Covered:** Yes   **Clubhouse:** Yes   **Shop:**
Previous Grounds: Great Wakering Rec
Record Attendance: 1,150 v Southend United - Friendly 19/07/2006
Nearest Railway Station Shoeburyness - 3.2km   **Bus Route** Barrow Hall Rd (Little Wakering Rd) - 631m

RECORDS
Victory: 9-0 v Eton Manor - 27/12/1931
Defeat: 1-7 v Bowers United - Essex Senior League 01/04/1998
Appearances: John Heffer - 511
Best FA Cup   Second Qualifying Round 1998-99, 2006-07.
FA Trophy   First Round Proper 2002-03, 04-05. **FA Vase:** Fifth Round 1997-98, 2001-02.

HONOURS
FA Comps: None
League: Essex Intermediate Division Three 1990-91, Division Two 91-92. Essex Senior 1994-95, 2013-14, 17-18.

County FA: None

08-09		09-10		10-11		11-12		12-13		13-14		14-15		15-16		16-17		17-18	
Isth1N	13	Isth1N	9	Isth1N	15	Isth1N	22	ESen	4	ESen	1	Isth1N	15	Isth1N	18	Isth1N	24	ESen	1
FAC	1Q	FAC	Pr	FAC	1Q	FAC	Pr	FAC	P	FAC	P	FAC	P	FAC	P	FAC	P	FAC	EP
FAT	2Qr	FAT	P	FAT	1Q	FAT	P	FAV	1P	FAV	3P	FAT	P	FAT	P	FAT	P	FAV	3P

HEYBRIDGE SWIFTS

Club Contact Details 01621 852 978
The Texo Stadium, Scraley Road, Heybridge, Maldon, Essex CM9 8JA
secretaryhsfc@btinternet.com

Founded: 1880   **Nickname:** Swifts   **Manager:** Jody Brown
Previous Names: Heybridge FC.
Previous Leagues: Essex & Suffolk Border, North Essex, South Essex, Essex Senior 1971-84

Club Colours (change): Black & white

Ground Capacity: 3,000   **Seats:** 550   **Covered:** 1,200   **Clubhouse:** Yes   **Shop:** Yes
Previous Grounds: Bentall's Sports Ground 1890-1964. Sadd's Athletic ground share 1964-66.
Record Attendance: 2,477 v Woking - FA Trophy Quarter-finals 1997.
Bus Route Scylla Close - stop 1km away

RECORDS
Goalscorer: Arthur 'Stumpy' Moss - 193 (1948-60)
Appearances: John Pollard - 543
Additional: Paid £1,000 for Dave Rainford and for Lee Kersey
                  Received £35,000 from Southend United for Simon Royce

HONOURS
FA Comps: None
League: Essex & Suffolk Border Division Two (West) 1920-21, Division One 30-31. Essex Senior 1981-82, 82-83, 83-84.
Isthmian Division Two North 1989-90.
County FA: Essex Junior Cup 1931-32. East Anglian Cup 1993-94, 94-95.

08-09		09-10		10-11		11-12		12-13		13-14		14-15		15-16		16-17		17-18	
Isth P	21	Isth1N	6	Isth1N	9	Isth1N	16	Isth1N	6	Isth1N	3	Isth1N	12	Isth1N	20	Isth1N	21	Isth1N	5
FAC	2Q	FAC	3Qr	FAC	Pr	FAC	1Q	FAC	2Q	FAC	4Q	FAC	P	FAC	1Q	FAC	1Qr	FAC	1P
FAT	3Q	FAT	P	FAT	Pr	FAT	P	FAT	P	FAT	1Q	FAT	1Q	FAT	2Qr	FAT	1Q	FAT	2P

MALDON & TIPTREE

Club Contact Details 01621 853 762
Park Drive, Maldon CM9 5JQ
club.secretary@maldontiptreefc.co.uk

Founded: 1946   **Nickname:** The Jammers   **Manager:** Wayne Brown
Previous Names: Maldon Town were rebranded in 2010.
Previous Leagues: Chelmsford & Mid-Essex. North Essex. Essex & Suffolk Border. Eastern Counties 1966-72. Essex Senior 1972-2004. Southern 2004-05.

Club Colours (change): Blue & red

Ground Capacity: 2,800   **Seats:** 155   **Covered:** 300   **Clubhouse:** Yes   **Shop:**
Previous Grounds: Sadd's Ground 1946-47. Promenade 1947-50. Farmbridge Road 1950-1994.
Record Attendance: 1,163 v AFC Sudbury, FA Vase semi-final 2003.

                                    Bus Route Jersey Road - stop 50m away

RECORDS
Best FA Cup   Third Qualifying Round 2000-01, 11-12.
FA Trophy   Third Qualifying Round 2011-12.
FA Vase   Semi Finals 2002-03.

HONOURS
FA Comps: None
League: Mid-Essex Premier Division 1949-50, 50-51. Essex & Suffolk Border Premier Division 1965-66. Essex Senior 1984-85.

County FA: Essex Intermediate Cup 1951-52.

08-09		09-10		10-11		11-12		12-13		13-14		14-15		15-16		16-17		17-18	
Isth1N	16	Isth1N	17	Isth1N	8	Isth1N	11	Isth1N	2	Isth1N	9	Isth1N	19	Isth1N	7	Isth1N	2	Isth1N	7
FAC	Pr	FAC	1Q	FAC	2Q	FAC	3Q	FAC	2Qr	FAC	1Q	FAC	P	FAC	P	FAC	1Q	FAC	1Qr
FAT	P	FAT	P	FAT	P	FAT	3Q	FAT	P	FAT	1Q	FAT	P	FAT	P	FAT	1Q	FAT	2Q

MILDENHALL TOWN

Club Contact Details 01638 713 449
Recreation Way, Mildenhall, Suffolk IP28 7HG
bhensby@talktalk.net

Founded: 1898   **Nickname:** The Hall   **Manager:** Dean Greygoose - Dec 2014
Previous Names: None
Previous Leagues: Bury & District. Cambridgeshire. Cambridgeshire Premier. Eastern Counties >2017.

Club Colours (change): Amber & black

Ground Capacity: 2,000   **Seats:** 100   **Covered:** 200   **Clubhouse:** Yes   **Shop:** Yes
Previous Grounds: Several pre World War II
Record Attendance: 450 v Derby County, Friendly, July 2001.

                                    Bus Route Maids Head - stop 250m away

RECORDS
Best FA Cup   Third Qualifying Round 2000-01
FA Trophy   Third Qualifying Round 2017-18
FA Vase   Fifth Round Proper 2005-06, 06-07

HONOURS
FA Comps: None
League: Eastern Counties Premier Division 2016-17.

County FA: Suffolk Junior Cup 1899-1900. Cambridgeshire Junior Cup 1992-93.
                 Cambridgeshire Invitation Cup 1995-96, 2009-10, 10-11.

08-09		09-10		10-11		11-12		12-13		13-14		14-15		15-16		16-17		17-18	
ECP	11	ECP	6	ECP	5	ECP	7	ECP	7	ECP	10	ECP	10	ECP	6	ECP	1	Isth1N	22
FAC	1Q	FAC	2Q	FAC	EP	FAC	EP	FAC	EP	FAC	1Qr	FAC	1Q	FAC	2Q	FAC	EP	FAC	1Qr
FAV	2P	FAV	1Q	FAV	1Q	FAV	2Q	FAV	1Q	FAT	1Pr	FAT	2Q	FAT	2P	FAT	2Q	FAT	3Q

ROMFORD

Club Contact Details 01375 6444 166 (MD only) or 07973 71707
East Thurrock FC, Rookery Hill, Stanford-le-Hope SS17 9LB
ewenson@aol.com

Founded: 1876	**Nickname:** Boro	**Manager:** Paul Martin

Previous Names: Original club founded in 1876 folded during WW1, Reformed in 1929 folded again in 1978 and reformed in 1992
Previous Leagues: Essex Senior 1992-96, 2002-09. Isthmian 1997-2002.

Club Colours (change): Yellow & blue

Ground Capacity: 3,500 **Seats:** 160 **Covered:** 1,000 **Clubhouse:** Yes **Shop:** Yes
Previous Grounds: Hornchurch Stadium 1992-95. Rush Green 1995-96. Sungate 1996-2001. The Mill Field (Aveley FC). Thurrock FC
Record Attendance: 820 v Leatherhead - Isthmian Division Two
Nearest Railway Station Stanford-le-Hope or Basildon. **Bus Route** 100 - Stops 100 metres from the ground.

RECORDS
Goalscorer: Danny Benstock. Vinny John scored 45 goals during season 1997-98.
Appearances: Paul Clayton - 396 (2006-15)
Victory: 9-0 v Hullbridge Sports, Essex Senior, 21/10/1995.
Misc: Mark Lord became the oldest player to play for the club aged 48yrs 90 days on 03/03/2015.

HONOURS
FA Comps: None
League: Essex Senior 1995-96, 2008-09. Isthmian Division Two 1996-97.
County FA: East Anglian Cup 1997-98.

08-09		09-10		10-11		11-12		12-13		13-14		14-15		15-16		16-17		17-18	
ESen	1	Isth1N	13	Isth1N	12	Isth1N	13	Isth1N	8	Isth1N	11	Isth1N	20	Isth1N	16	Isth1N	16	Isth1N	23
FAC	P	FAC	1Qr	FAC	2Q	FAC	1Q	FAC	P	FAC	1Q	FAC	2Qr	FAC	Pr	FAC	1Q	FAC	1Q
FAV	2P	FAT	P	FAT	3Q	FAT	P	FAT	1Q	FAT	P	FAT	Pr	FAT	1Q	FAT	2Q	FAT	P

SOHAM TOWN RANGERS

Club Contact Details 01353 720 732
Julius Martin Lane, Soham, Ely, Cambridgeshire CB7 5EQ

Founded: 1947	**Nickname:** Greens, Town or Rangers	**Manager:** Rob Mason

Previous Names: Soham Town and Soham Rangers merged in 1947
Previous Leagues: Peterborough & District, Eastern Counties 1963-2008, Southern 2008-11.

Club Colours (change): Green & white stripes

Ground Capacity: 2,000 **Seats:** 250 **Covered:** 1,000 **Clubhouse:** Yes **Shop:** Yes
Previous Grounds: None
Record Attendance: 3,000 v Pegasus - FA Amateur Cup 1963
Bus Route Julius Martin Lane - stop 200m away

RECORDS
Best FA Cup Third Qualifying Round 1970-71
FA Trophy Second Qualifying Round 2012-13, 13-14
FA Vase Fifth Round 2004-05

HONOURS
FA Comps: None
League: Peterborough & District 1959-60, 61-62. Eastern Counties Premier Division 2007-08.
County FA: Cambridgeshire Challenge Cup 1957-58. Cambridgeshire Invitation Cup 1990-91, 97-98, 98-99, 2005-06.

08-09		09-10		10-11		11-12		12-13		13-14		14-15		15-16		16-17		17-18	
SthC	15	SthC	11	SthC	17	Isth1N	19	Isth1N	7	Isth1N	8	Isth1N	11	Isth1N	17	Isth1N	19	Isth1N	13
FAC	P	FAC	Pr	FAC	P	FAC	P	FAC	1Q	FAC	P	FAC	P	FAC	P	FAC	1Qr	FAC	1Qr
FAT	2Q	FAT	1Qr	FAT	1Q	FAT	P	FAT	2Q	FAT	2Q	FAT	P	FAT	P	FAT	1Q	FAT	P

TILBURY

Club Contact Details 01375 843 093
Chadfields, St Chads Road, Tilbury, Essex RM18 8NL
amercer67@googlemail.com

Founded: 1895   **Nickname:** The Dockers   **Manager:** Joe Keith
Previous Names: None
Previous Leagues: Grays & District/South Essex, Kent 1927-31, London, South Essex Combination (Wartime), Corinthian 1950-57,
Delphian 1962-63, Athenian 1963-73, Isthmian 1973-2004, Essex Senior 2004-05

Club Colours (change): Black & white/black/black (All purple)

Ground Capacity: 4,000   **Seats:** 350   **Covered:** 1,000   **Clubhouse:** Yes   **Shop:** No
Previous Grounds: Orient Field 1895-46.
Record Attendance: 5,500 v Gorleston - FA Cup 1949
Nearest Railway Station Tilbury Town - 1.1km   **Bus Route** Raphael Avenue - stop 75m away

RECORDS
Goalscorer: Ross Livermore - 282 in 305 games
Appearances: Nicky Smith - 424 (1975-85)
Additional: Received £2,000 from Grays Athletic for Tony Macklin 1990 and from Dartford for Steve Connor 1985
Best FA Cup Third Round Proper 1977-78 **FA Amateur Cup:** Quarter Finals 1946-47
FA Trophy Third Round Proper 1982-83 **FA Vase:** Fourth Round Proper 1988-89, 99-00

HONOURS
FA Comps: None
League: Athenian 1968-69. Isthmian Division Two 1975-76.
County FA: Essex Senior Cup x4. East Anglian Cup 2008-09.

	08-09		09-10		10-11		11-12		12-13		13-14		14-15		15-16		16-17		17-18	
Isth1N	11	Isth1N	11	Isth1N	19	Isth1N	3	Isth1N	16	Isth1N	16	Isth1N	14	Isth1N	11	Isth1N	12	Isth1N	17
FAC	P	FAC	P	FAC	1Q	FAC	1Q	FAC	1Q	FAC	2Q	FAC	1Q	FAC	1Q	FAC	1Q	FAC	1Q
FAT	1Qr	FAT	P	FAT	P	FAT	P	FAT	P	FAT	1Q	FAT	Pr	FAT	1P	FAT	Pr	FAT	P

WITHAM TOWN

Club Contact Details 01376 511 198
Village Glass Stadium, Spa Road, Witham CM8 1UN
withamtownfcsecretary@gmail.com

Founded: 1947   **Nickname:** Town   **Manager:** Mark Ashford - 08/06/2018
Previous Names: Witham Town Football Clubs did exist before both World Wars with both folding due to the conflicts.
Previous Leagues: Mid-Essex 1947-52. South Essex 1952-58. Essex & Suffolk Border 1958-71. Essex Senior 1971-87, 2009-12.
Isthmian 1987-2009.

Club Colours (change): White & blue

Ground Capacity: 2,500   **Seats:** 157   **Covered:** 780   **Clubhouse:** Yes   **Shop:** No
Previous Grounds: Crittall Windows works ground 1949-75.
Record Attendance: Att: 800 v Billericay Town, Essex Senior Lge, May 1976.
Nearest Railway Station Witham - 1.1km   **Bus Route** Cuppers Close - stop 200m away

RECORDS
Goalscorer: Colin Mitchell.
Appearances: Keith Dent.

HONOURS
FA Comps: None
League: Braintree & District 1920-21, 24-25. Mid-Essex Division Three 1935-36, 47-48. Division Two 48-49. South Essex 1955-56.
Essex & Suffolk Border 1964-65, 70-71. Essex Senior 1970-71, 85-86, 2011-12.
County FA: Essex Senior Trophy 1985-86.

	08-09		09-10		10-11		11-12		12-13		13-14		14-15		15-16		16-17		17-18	
Isth1N	21	ESen	2	ESen	3	ESen	1	Isth1N	4	Isth1N	2	Isth P	22	Isth1N	19	Isth1N	13	Isth1N	11
FAC	1Q	FAC	P	FAC	Pr	FAC	P	FAC	1Q	FAC	2Qr	FAC	4Q	FAC	2Q	FAC	2Q	FAC	1Q
FAT	1Q	FAV	1P	FAV	3P	FAV	3P	FAT	P	FAT	1Q	FAT	2Q	FAT	P	FAT	1Q	FAT	1Q

ASHFORD TOWN (MIDDLESEX)

Club Contact Details 01784 245 908
Robert Parker Stadium, Stanwell, Staines TW19 7BH

Founded: 1958   **Nickname:** Ash Trees   **Manager:** Ben Murray
Previous Names: Ashford Albion 1958-64.
Previous Leagues: Hounslow & District 1964-68, Surrey Intermediate 1968-82, Surrey Premier 1982-90, Combind Counties 1990-2000, 14-16, Isthmian 20 00-04, 06-10, Southern 2004-06, 10-14, 16-18.

Club Colours (change): Tangerine, white & black

Ground Capacity: 2,550   **Seats:** 250   **Covered:** 250   **Clubhouse:** Yes   **Shop:** No
Previous Grounds: Clockhouse Lane Recreation 1958-85.
Record Attendance: 992 v AFC Wimbledon - Isthmian League Premier Division 26/09/2006
Nearest Railway Station Heathrow Terminal 4 Underground - 1.5km   **Bus Route** Genesis Close - stop 400m away

RECORDS
Goalscorer: Andy Smith
Appearances: Alan Constable - 650
Additional: Received £10,000 from Wycombe Wanderers for Dannie Bulman 1997

HONOURS
FA Comps: None
League: Surrey Intermediate (Western) Prmeier Division A 1974-75. Surrey Premier 1982-90.
         Combined Counties 1994-95, 95-96, 96-97, 97-98, 99-00.
County FA: Middlesex Senior Charity Cup 1999-00, 11-12, 16-17. Aldershot Senior Cup 2002-03, 11-12.
         Middlesex Premier Cup 2006-07. Surrey Senior Cup 2008-09.

08-09		09-10		10-11		11-12		12-13		13-14		14-15		15-16		16-17		17-18	
Isth P	10	Isth P	20	SthC	16	SthC	9	SthC	10	SthC	22	CCP	3	CCP	2	SthC	10	Sth1E	12
FAC	4Qr	FAC	3Qr	FAC	1Qr	FAC	P	FAC	2Q	FAC	1Q	FAC	Pr	FAC	1Q	FAC	1Q	FAC	3Q
FAT	1Qr	FAT	1Q	FAT	2P	FAT	2Q	FAT	1Qr	FAT	P	FAV	1P	FAV	1Pr	FAT	1Qr	FAT	2Qr

BEDFONT SPORTS

Club Contact Details 0208 831 9067 or 07967 370 109
Bedfont Sports Club, Hatton Road, Bedfont TW14 9JA

Founded: 2000   **Nickname:** The Eagles   **Manager:** Paul Johnson
Previous Names: Bedfont Sunday became Bedfont Sports in 2002 - Bedfont Eagles (1978) merged with the club shortly afterwards.
Previous Leagues: Hounslow & District 2003-04. Middlesex County 2004-09.

Club Colours (change): Red & black

Ground Capacity: 3,000   **Seats:** Yes   **Covered:** 200   **Clubhouse:** Yes   **Shop:**
Previous Grounds: N/A
Record Attendance:
Nearest Railway Station Hatton Cross or Feltham BR   **Bus Route** London Transport 203, H25, H26

RECORDS
Best FA Cup   Preliminary Round 2011-12(r), 13-14, 15-16, 16-17
FA Vase   Third Round Proper Replay 2016-17

HONOURS
FA Comps: None
League: Hounslow & District League Division One 2003-04.

County FA: Middlesex County Premier Cup 2009-10.

08-09		09-10		10-11		11-12		12-13		13-14		14-15		15-16		16-17		17-18	
		CC1	9	CC1	4	CC1	2	CCP	13	CCP	17	CCP	16	CCP	13	CCP	8	CCP	2
						FAC	Pr	FAC	EP	FAC	P	FAC	EP	FAC	P	FAC	P	FAC	EP
				FAV	1Q	FAV	1P	FAV	2Q	FAV	2Q	FAV	1P	FAV	1P	FAV	3Pr	FAV	1Q

BRACKNELL TOWN

Club Contact Details 01344 412 305
Larges Lane Bracknell RG12 9AN

Founded: 1896 **Nickname:** The Robins **Manager:** Carl Davies
Previous Names: Old Bracknell Wanderers 1896-1962.
Previous Leagues: Ascot & District. Reading & District 1949-58. Great Western Comb. 1958-63, Surrey Senior 1963-70, London Spartan 1970-75, Isthmian 1984-2004, Southern 2004-10, Hellenic 2010-18.

Club Colours (change): Red & white

Ground Capacity: 2,500 **Seats:** 150 **Covered:** 500 **Clubhouse:** Yes **Shop:** Yes
Previous Grounds: Field next to Downshire Arms. Station Field > 1933
Record Attendance: 2,500 v Newquay - FA Amateur Cup 1971
Nearest Railway Station Bracknell - 0.5km **Bus Route** Larges Bridge Drive stop - 282m away

RECORDS

Goalscorer:	Justin Day
Goalscorer:	James Woodcock
Best FA Cup	First Round Proper 2000-01
FA Trophy	First Round Proper 2002-03, 03-04, 04-05
FA Vase	Quarter Finals 2017-18

HONOURS
FA Comps: None
League: Ascot & District 1911-12, 32-33, Division Two 13-14. Surrey Senior 1969-70.
Spartan Senior Division 1980-81, Premier 1982-83. Isthmian Division Three 1993-94.
County FA: Berks & Bucks Senior Trophy 2016-17

08-09	09-10	10-11	11-12	12-13	13-14	14-15	15-16	16-17	17-18
Sthsw	Sthsw 22	Hel P 16	Hel P 21	Hel1E 5	Hel P 13	Hel P 9	Hel P 14	Hel P 2	Hel P 2
FAC 1Q	FAC P	FAC P	FAC EP	FAC 1Q	FAC P	FAC EP	FAC 1Q	FAC P	FAC P
FAT 1Q	FAT 1Q	FAV 2P	FAV 2Q	FAV 2Q	FAV 2Q	FAV 2Q	FAV 2Qr	FAV 1P	FAV QF

CHALFONT ST PETER

Club Contact Details 01753 886 477
Mill Meadow, Gravel Hill, Amersham Road, Chalfont St Peter SL9 9QX
colinfinch.cspfc1962@gmail.com

Founded: 1926 **Nickname:** Saints **Manager:** Danny Edwards
Previous Names: None
Previous Leagues: G W Comb. Parthernon. London. Spartan. L Spartan. Athenian. Isthmian, Spartan South Midlands 2006-11.

Club Colours (change): Red & green

Ground Capacity: 4,500 **Seats:** 220 **Covered:** 120 **Clubhouse:** Yes **Shop:** Yes
Previous Grounds: Gold Hill Common 1926-49.
Record Attendance: 2,550 v Watford benefit match 1985
Nearest Railway Station Gerrards Cross - 2.3km **Bus Route** The Waggon & Horses Pub - stop 250m away

RECORDS

Victory:	10-1 v Kentish Town (away) Spartan League Premier Division 23 Dec 2008
Defeat:	0-13 v Lewes (away) Isthmian Division 3, 7 Nov 2000
Appearances:	Colin Davies

HONOURS
FA Comps: None
League: Spartan Division Two 1975-76. Isthmian Division Two 1987-88. Spartan South Midlands Premier Division 2010-11.

County FA: Berks & Bucks Intermediate Cup 1952-53, 84-85.

08-09	09-10	10-11	11-12	12-13	13-14	14-15	15-16	16-17	17-18
SSM P 3	SSM P 2	SSM P 1	SthC 12	SthC 16	SthC 14	SthC 16	SthC 6	SthC 18	Sth1E 9
FAC 2Q	FAC P	FAC P	FAC 1Q	FAC 3Qr	FAC 2Q	FAC 3Q	FAC P	FAC 1Q	FAC Pr
FAV SF	FAV 2P	FAV 2Pr	FAT 1Q	FAT 1Q	FAT Pr	FAT 1Q	FAT 1Q	FAV 2Qr	FAT 1Qr

CHESHUNT

Club Contact Details 01992 625 793
Cheshunt Stadium, Theobalds Lane, Cheshunt, Herts EN8 8RU
info@cheshuntfc.com

Founded: 1946   **Nickname:** Ambers   **Manager:** Craig Edwards
Previous Names: None
Previous Leagues: London 1947-51, 56-59, Delphian 1952-55, Aetolian 1960-62, Spartan 1963-64, 88-93, Athenian 1965-76, Isthmian 1977-87, 94-2005, Southern 2006-08

Club Colours (change): Amber & black

Ground Capacity: 3,500   **Seats:** 424   **Covered:** 600   **Clubhouse:** Yes   **Shop:** No
Previous Grounds: Gothic Sports Ground 1946-47. College Road 1947-50. Brookfield Lane 1950-52, 53-58.
Record Attendance: 5,000 v Bromley - FA Amateur Cup 2nd Round 28/01/1950
Nearest Railway Station Theobalds Grove - 0.6km

RECORDS
Defeat: 0-10 v Etonn Manor - London League 17/04/1956
Goalscorer: Darrell Cox - 152 (1997-2005, 07-08, 2010)
Appearances: John Poole - 526 (1970-76, 79-83)
Additional: Received £10,000 from Peterborough United for Lloyd Opara

HONOURS
FA Comps: None
League: London Division One 1947-48, 48-49, Premier 49-50, Division One 1948, 49. Spartan 1962-63. Athenian 1967-68, 75-76. Isthmian Division Two 2002-03.
County FA: London Charity Cup 1974. East Anglian Cup 1975. Herts Charity Cup 2006, 2008.

08-09		09-10		10-11		11-12		12-13		13-14		14-15		15-16		16-17		17-18	
Isth1N	14	Isth1N	15	Isth1N	18	Isth1N	18	Isth1N	11	Isth1N	15	Isth1N	18	Isth1N	6	Isth1N	10	Isth1N	19
FAC	1Q	FAC	P	FAC	1Q	FAC	Pr	FAC	Pr	FAC	P	FAC	P	FAC	P	FAC	1Q	FAC	2Q
FAT	1Q	FAT	P	FAT	P	FAT	P	FAT	P	FAT	1Q	FAT	P	FAT	2Q	FAT	1Q	FAT	1Q

CHIPSTEAD

Club Contact Details 01737 553 250
High Road, Chipstead, Surrey CR5 3SF

Founded: 1906   **Nickname:** Chips   **Manager:** Anthony Williams
Previous Names: None
Previous Leagues: Surrey Intermediate 1962-82, Surrey Premier 1982-86, Combined Counties 1986-2007

Club Colours (change): Green, white & black

Ground Capacity: 2,000   **Seats:** 150   **Covered:** 200   **Clubhouse:** Yes   **Shop:** Yes
Previous Grounds: None
Record Attendance: 1,170
Nearest Railway Station Coulsdon South from where a Taxi can be taken to the ground. Chipstead a dangerous 1.25m walk away   **Bus Route** 405 to Star Lane, Hooley. Ground is a further 20min walk from there

RECORDS
Goalscorer: Mick Nolan - 124
Best FA Cup   Fourth Qualifying Round 2008-09
FA Trophy   Second Qualifying Round
FA Vase   Third Round Proper 1997-98, 98-99

HONOURS
FA Comps: None
League: Combined Counties Premier 1989-90, 2006-07.
County FA: East Surrey Charity Cup 1960-61.

08-09		09-10		10-11		11-12		12-13		13-14		14-15		15-16		16-17		17-18	
Isth1S	21	Isth1S	19	Isth1S	10	Isth1S	12	Isth1S	20	Isth1S	13	Isth1S	15	Isth1S	21	Isth1S	20	Isth1S	20
FAC	4Q	FAC	1Q	FAC	2Qr	FAC	2Q	FAC	1Q	FAC	3Q	FAC	1Qr	FAC	P	FAC	1Q	FAC	2Q
FAT	P	FAT	2Q	FAT	P	FAT	1Q	FAT	P	FAT	P	FAT	P	FAT	1Q	FAT	Pr	FAT	Pr

EGHAM TOWN

Club Contact Details 01784 437 055
Runnymead Stadium, Tempest Road, Egham TW20 8XD

Founded: 1877   **Nickname:** Sarnies   **Manager:** Simon Lane
Previous Names: Runnymead Rovers 1877-1905. Egham F.C. 05-63.
Previous Leagues: West Surrey. Surrey Senior. Spartan. Athenian. Isthmian. Southern. Combined Counties 2006-13. Southern 2013-18.

Club Colours (change): Red & white

Ground Capacity: 5500   **Seats:** 262   **Covered:** 3300   **Clubhouse:** Yes   **Shop:** No
Previous Grounds: Moved to Recreation Ground - now Runnymead Stadium - in 1963.
Record Attendance: 1400 v Wycombe Wanderers, FAC 2nd Qualifying Round 1972-73.
Nearest Railway Station Egham - 1km   **Bus Route** Charta Road - stop 200m away

RECORDS
Goalscorer: Mark Butler - 153.
Appearances: Dave Jones - 850+.
Best FA Cup Fourth Qualifying Round 1990-91, 2016-17
FA Vase Fourth Round Proper 1984-85

HONOURS
FA Comps: None
League: West Surrey 1921-22. Surrey Senior 1922-23. Spartan 1971-72. Athenian Division Two 1974-75.
     Combined Counties 2012-13.
County FA: None

08-09		09-10		10-11		11-12		12-13		13-14		14-15		15-16		16-17		17-18	
CCP	13	CCP	4	CCP	13	CCP	4	CCP	1	SthC	11	SthC	15	SthC	3	SthC	5	Sth1E	16
FAC	EP	FAC	EPr	FAC	EP	FAC	Pr	FAC	P	FAC	P	FAC	P	FAC	Pr	FAC	4Q	FAC	1Qr
FAV	2P	FAV	2Q	FAV	2P	FAV	2P	FAV	1P	FAT	2Q	FAT	1Q	FAT	1Q	FAT	P	FAT	2Q

FC ROMANIA

Club Contact Details 01992 625 793
Cheshunt FC, Theobalds Lane, Cheshunt, Herts EN8 8RU

Founded: 2006   **Nickname:** The Wolves   **Manager:** Ion Vintila
Previous Names: None
Previous Leagues: Sunday London Weekend 2006-07. Essex Business Houses 2007-10. Middlesex County 2010-13. Essex Senior 2013-18.

Club Colours (change): Yellow & red

Ground Capacity: 3,500   **Seats:** 424   **Covered:** 600   **Clubhouse:** Yes   **Shop:**
Previous Grounds: Hackey Marshes 2006-07. Low Hall Rec Walthamstow 2007-10. Leyton Sport Centre 2010-12.
Record Attendance:
Nearest Railway Station Theobalds Grove – 5 mins walk

RECORDS
Best FA Cup Second Qualifying Round 2014-15, 17-18(r)
FA Vase Fourth Round Proper 2015-16

HONOURS
FA Comps: None
League: None

County FA: None

08-09		09-10		10-11		11-12		12-13		13-14		14-15		15-16		16-17		17-18	
EsxBH2	6	EsxBH2	4	Midx1SE	2	MidxP	2	MidxP	2	ESen	5	ESen	6	ESen	3	ESen	3	ESen	3
												FAC	2Q	FAC	EP	FAC	EP	FAC	2Qr
								FAV	2Q	FAV	1Q	FAV	2Q	FAV	4P	FAV	3Pr	FAV	2Pr

HANWELL TOWN

Club Contact Details 020 8998 1701
Reynolds Field, Preivale Lane, Perivale, Greenford, UB6 8TL

Founded: 1920 **Nickname:** Magpies **Manager:** Ray Duffy
Previous Names: None
Previous Leagues: London. Dauntless. Wembley & District. Middlesex County 1970-83. London Spartan/Spartan 1983-97.
Spartan South Midlands (Founder Member) 1997-2006, 2007-14. Southern 2006-07, 14-18.

Club Colours (change): Black & white

Ground Capacity: 1,250 **Seats:** 175 **Covered:** 600 **Clubhouse:** Yes **Shop:** No
Previous Grounds: Moved to Reynolds Field in 1981.
Record Attendance: 600 v Spurs, floodlight switch on, 1989.
Nearest Railway Station Perivale Underground - 0.6km **Bus Route** Perivale Lane - stop 200m away

RECORDS
Goalscorer: Keith Rowlands
Appearances: Phil Player 617 (20 seasons)
Best FA Cup Third Qualifying Round 2015-16
FA Trophy Second Qualifying Round 2006-07, 16-17(r)
FA Vase Fifth Round Proper 2013-14

HONOURS
FA Comps: None
League: London Spartan Senior Division 1983-84. Spartan South Midlands Premier 2013-14.

County FA: London Senior Cup 1991-92, 92-93.

08-09		09-10		10-11		11-12		12-13		13-14		14-15		15-16		16-17		17-18	
SSM P	7	SSM P	13	SSM P	15	SSM P	21	SSM P	6	SSM P	1	SthC	7	SthC	20	SthC	11	Sth1E	18
FAC	P	FAC	P	FAC	EP	FAC	EP	FAC	EP	FAC	EPr	FAC	P	FAC	3Q	FAC	2Qr	FAC	1Q
FAV	2Q	FAV	2Q	FAV	1Q	FAV	1P	FAV	1Pr	FAV	5P	FAT	P	FAT	P	FAT	2Q	FAT	1Q

HAYES & YEADING UNITED

Club Contact Details 0208 573 2075
SKYex Community Stadium, Beaconsfield Road, Hayes UB4 0SL
info@hyufc.com

Founded: 2007 **Nickname:** United **Manager:** Paul Hughes
Previous Names: Hayes - Botwell Mission 1909-29. Hayes and Yeading merged to form today's club in 2007
Previous Leagues: Isthmian. Conference 2007-16. Southern 2016-18.

Club Colours (change): Red & white

Ground Capacity: 6,000 **Seats:** 2,500 **Covered:** 3,900 **Clubhouse:** Yes **Shop:** Yes
Previous Grounds: Kingfield Stadium (Woking FC) 2012-13.
Record Attendance: 1,881 v Luton Town - Conference Premier 06/03/2010
Nearest Railway Station Hayes & Harlington - 5-10min taxi ride from ground **Bus Route** From Uxbridge Underground take bus
towards Shep Bush, alight at Springfield Rd

RECORDS
Victory: 8-2 v Hillingdon Borough (A) - Middlesex Senior Cup 11/11/08
Defeat: 0-8 v Luton Town (A) - Conference Premier 27/03/10
Goalscorer: Josh Scott - 40 (2007-09)
Appearances: James Mulley - 137 (2007-10)

HONOURS
FA Comps: None
League: None

County FA: None

08-09		09-10		10-11		11-12		12-13		13-14		14-15		15-16		16-17		17-18	
Conf S	4	Conf	17	Conf	16	Conf	21	Conf S	17	Conf S	20	Conf S	19	Nat S	21	SthP	23	Sth1E	3
FAC	4Q	FAC	4Q	FAC	1P	FAC	4Q	FAC	4Q	FAC	2Qr	FAC	2Q	FAC	2Q	FAC	2Q	FAC	3Q
FAT	2P	FAT	1P	FAT	1P	FAT	1P	FAT	1P	FAT	1P	FAT	1P	FAT	3Qr	FAT	1Q	FAT	1Q

HERTFORD TOWN

Club Contact Details 01992 583 716
Hertingfordbury Park, West Street, Hertford, SG13 8EZ

Founded: 1901 **Nickname:** The Blues **Manager:** Gavin Kelsey
Previous Names: Port Vale Rovers 1901.
Previous Leagues: Herts Senior County 1908-20. Middlsex 1920-21. Spartan 1921-59. Delphian 1959-63. Athenian 1963-72. Eastern Counties 1972-73. Spartan South Midlands 1973-2017.

Club Colours (change): All blue

Ground Capacity: 6,500 **Seats:** 200 **Covered:** 1,500 **Clubhouse:** Yes **Shop:** Yes
Previous Grounds: Hartham Park 1901-08.
Record Attendance: 5,000 v Kingstonian FA Am Cup 2nd Round 1955-56.
Nearest Railway Station Hertford North - 0.8km

RECORDS
Appearances: Robbie Burns
Best FA Cup Fourth Qualifying Round 1973-74
FA Trophy Second Round Proper 1979-80
FA Vase Third Round Proper 1986-87, 2003-04, 12-13, 15-16

HONOURS
FA Comps: None
League: Spartan Division One Eastern Section 1949-50. Delphian 1960-61, 61-62.

County FA: Herts Senior Cup 1966-67. East Anglian Cup 1962-63, 69-70.

08-09		09-10		10-11		11-12		12-13		13-14		14-15		15-16		16-17		17-18	
SSM P	10	SSM P	16	SSM P	9	SSM P	16	SSM P	17	SSM P	16	SSM P	11	SSM P	8	SSM P	2	Isth1N	15
FAC	EP	FAC	EP	FAC	P	FAC	1Q	FAC	EP	FAC	1Q	FAC	1Q	FAC	EPr	FAC	P	FAC	2Q
FAV	1P	FAV	2Q	FAV	1P	FAV	1Q	FAV	3P	FAV	1Q	FAV	1P	FAV	3P	FAV	1P	FAT	1Q

MARLOW

Club Contact Details 01628 483 970
Alfred Davies Memorial Ground, Oak tree Road, Marlow SL7 3ED
terry.staines@ntlworld.com

Founded: 1870 **Nickname:** The Blues **Manager:** Mark Bartley
Previous Names: Great Marlow
Previous Leagues: Reading & District, Spartan 1908-10, 28-65, Gt Western Suburban, Athenian 1965-84, Isthmian 1984-2004. Southern 2004-12, 13-18. Hellenic 2012-13.

Club Colours (change): All royal blue

Ground Capacity: 3,000 **Seats:** 250 **Covered:** 600 **Clubhouse:** Yes **Shop:** No
Previous Grounds: Crown ground 1870-1919, Star Meadow 1919-24
Record Attendance: 3,000 v Oxford United - FA Cup 1st Round 1994
Nearest Railway Station Marlow - 1km **Bus Route** Oak Tree Road - stop 100m away

RECORDS
Goalscorer: Kevin Stone
Appearances: Mick McKeown - 500+
Additional: Paid £5,000 to Sutton United for Richard Evans
Received £8,000 from Slough Town for David Lay

HONOURS
FA Comps: None
League: Spartan 1937-38, Division Two West 1929-30. Isthmian Division One 1987-88. Hellenic Premier Division 2012-13.

County FA: Berks & Bucks Senior Cup x11

08-09		09-10		10-11		11-12		12-13		13-14		14-15		15-16		16-17		17-18	
SthM	9	SthM	15	SthC	11	SthC	22	Hel P	1	SthC	17	SthC	11	Sthsw	13	SthC	4	Sth1E	14
FAC	1Q	FAC	1Q	FAC	P	FAC	1Q	FAC	1Q	FAC	P	FAC	P	FAC	Pr	FAC	Pr	FAC	2Q
FAT	1Q	FAT	2Q	FAT	Pr	FAT	1Qr	FAV	2P	FAT	3Q	FAT	P	FAT	3Q	FAT	1Q	FAT	Pr

MOLESEY

Club Contact Details 020 8979 4823
412 Walton Road, West Molesey KT8 2JG

Founded: 1946   **Nickname:** The Moles   **Manager:** Peter Leilliott
Previous Names: None.
Previous Leagues: Surrey Intermediate 1946-53. Surrey Senior 1953-59. Spartan 1959-73. Athethian 1973-77. Isthmian 1977-2008.
Combined Counties 2008-15.

Club Colours (change): White/black/black.

Ground Capacity: 4,000   **Seats:** 160   **Covered:** Yes   **Clubhouse:** Yes   **Shop:** Yes
Previous Grounds: RecreatioN Ground 1946-53.
Record Attendance: 1,255 v Sutton United, Surrey Senior Cup sem-final 1966.
Nearest Railway Station Hampton - 1.5km   **Bus Route** Grange Road - stop 150m away

RECORDS
Goalscorer: Michael Rose (139).
Appearances: Frank Hanley (453).
Best FA Cup First Round Proper 1993-94
FA Trophy First Round Proper 1990-91, 94-95, 98-99, 2004-05
FA Vase Quarter Finals 1981-82

HONOURS
FA Comps: None
League: Surrey Intermediate 1946-47. Surrey Senior 1957-58. Combined Counties Premier Division 2014-15.

County FA: Surrey Senior Charity Cup 1956-57

	08-09		09-10		10-11		11-12		12-13		13-14		14-15		15-16		16-17		17-18	
CCP	11	CCP	8	CCP	3	CCP	5	CCP	10	CCP	11	CCP	1	Isth1S	9	Isth1S	19	Isth1S	23
FAC	P	FAC	1Q	FAC	EP	FAC	EP	FAC	EP	FAC	Pr	FAC	P	FAC	1Q	FAC	P	FAC	P
FAV	3P	FAV	1P	FAV	1P	FAV	1P	FAV	1Q	FAV	1Q	FAV	2Q	FAT	3Q	FAT	P	FAT	P

NORTHWOOD

Club Contact Details 01923 827 148
Northwood Park, Chestnut Avenue, Northwood, Middlesex HA6 1HR
enquiriesatnorthwoodfc.com

Founded: 1926   **Nickname:** Woods   **Manager:** Dean Barker
Previous Names: Northwood United 1926-1945.
Previous Leagues: Harrow & Wembley 1932-69, Middlesex 1969-78, Hellenic 1979-84, London Spartan 1984-93,
Isthmian 1993-2005, 2007-10, Southern 2005-07, 10-18.

Club Colours (change): All red

Ground Capacity: 3,075   **Seats:** 308   **Covered:** 932   **Clubhouse:** Yes   **Shop:** No
Previous Grounds: Northwood Recreation Ground 1926-1928. Northwood Playing Fields 1928-1971.
Record Attendance: 1,642 v Chlesea - Friendly July 1997
Nearest Railway Station Northwood Hills Underground - 0.7km

RECORDS
Victory: 15-0 v Dateline (H) - Middlesex Intermediate Cup 1973
Defeat: 0-8 v Bedfont - Middlesex League 1975
Goalscorer: Lawrence Yaku scored 61 goals during season 1999-2000
Appearances: Chris Gell - 493+

HONOURS
FA Comps: None
League: Harrow, Wembley & District Premier 1932-33, 33-34, 34-35, 35-36, 36-37, 47-48, 48-49. Middlesex Premier 1977-78.
Hellenic Division One 1978-79. Spartan Premier 1991-92. Isthmian Division One North 2002-03.
County FA: Middlesex Intermediate Cup 1978-79. Middlesex Senior Cup 2006-07, 15-16.

	08-09		09-10		10-11		11-12		12-13		13-14		14-15		15-16		16-17		17-18	
Isth1N	6	Isth1N	10	SthC	20	SthC	7	SthC	13	SthC	9	SthC	10	SthC	7	SthC	20	Sth1E	17
FAC	P	FAC	1Qr	FAC	1Q	FAC	P	FAC	3Q	FAC	P	FAC	1Qr	FAC	2Q	FAC	P	FAC	P
FAT	2Q	FAT	1Pr	FAT	Pr	FAT	Pr	FAT	P	FAT	P	FAT	2Q	FAT	1Q	FAT	1Qr	FAT	P

SOUTH PARK

Club Contact Details 01737 245 963
King George's Field, Whitehall Lane, South Park RH2 8LG
spfc1897@hotmail.com

Founded: 1897   **Nickname:** The Sparks   **Manager:** Mick Sullivan
Previous Names: South Park & Reigate Town 2001-03.
Previous Leagues: Redhill & District. Crawley & District > 2006. Combined Counties 2006-14.

Club Colours (change): All red

Ground Capacity: 2,000   **Seats:** 113   **Covered:** Yes   **Clubhouse:** Yes   **Shop:** Yes
Previous Grounds: Crescent Road. Church Road.
Record Attendance: 643 v Metropolitan Police, 20/10/2012
Nearest Railway Station Reigate - 2km   **Bus Route** Sandcross Lane - stop 200m away

RECORDS
Best FA Cup   Fourth Qualifying Round 2012-13
FA Vase   Fourth Round Proper 2011-12

HONOURS
FA Comps: None
League: Combined Counties Premier Division 2013-14.

County FA: Surrey Premier Cup 2010-11.

08-09		09-10		10-11		11-12		12-13		13-14		14-15		15-16		16-17		17-18	
CC1	14	CC1	6	CC1	3	CCP	8	CCP	4	CCP	1	Isth1S	14	Isth1S	11	Isth1S	8	Isth1S	13
				FAC	1Q	FAC	P	FAC	4Q	FAC	1Qr	FAC	1Qr	FAC	2Q	FAC	2Q	FAC	P
FAV	2Q	FAV	2Qr	FAV	2Q	FAV	4P	FAV	3P	FAV	3P	FAT	1Q	FAT	1Q	FAT	2P	FAT	Pr

TOOTING & MITCHAM UNITED

Club Contact Details 020 8685 6193
KNK Stadium, Imperial Fields, Bishopsford Road, Morden, Surrey SM4 6BF

Founded: 1932   **Nickname:** The Terrors   **Manager:** Frank Wilson
Previous Names: Tooting Town (Founded in 1887) and Mitcham Wanderers (1912) merged in 1932 to form Tooting & Mitcham FC.
Previous Leagues: London 1932-37, Athenian 1937-56

Club Colours (change): Black and white stripes/black/black (blue/white/blue)

Ground Capacity: 3,500   **Seats:** 612   **Covered:** 1,200   **Clubhouse:** Yes   **Shop:** Yes
Previous Grounds: Sandy Lane, Mitcham
Record Attendance: 17,500 v Queens Park Rangers - FA Cup 2nd Round 1956-57 (At Sandy Lane)
Nearest Railway Station Mitcham Tram Stop - 0.5km

RECORDS
Victory: 11-0 v Welton Rovers - FA Amateur Cup 1962-63
Defeat: 1-8 v Kingstonian - Surrey Senior Cup 1966-67
Goalscorer: Alan Ives - 92
Appearances: Danny Godwin - 470
Additional: Paid £9,000 to Enfield for David Flint
                    Received £10,000 from Luton Town for Herbie Smith

HONOURS
FA Comps: None
League: Athenian 1949-50, 54-55. Isthmian 1975-76, 59-60, Division Two 2000-01, Division One South 2016-17.

County FA: London Senior Cup 1942-43, 48-49, 58-59, 59-60, 2006-07, 07-08, 15-16. Surrey Senior cup 1937-38, 43-44, 44-45, 52-53, 59-60, 75-76, 76-77, 77-78, 2007-07. Surrey Senior Shield 1951-52, 60-61, 61-62, 65-66.

08-09		09-10		10-11		11-12		12-13		13-14		14-15		15-16		16-17		17-18	
Isth P	9	Isth P	12	Isth P	14	Isth P	21	Isth1S	16	Isth1S	11	Isth1S	11	Isth1S	17	Isth1S	1	Isth P	
FAC	1Q	FAC	1P	FAC	2Q	FAC	1Q	FAC	1Q	FAC	P	FAC	3Q	FAC	2Q	FAC	P	FAC	2Q
FAT	1Q	FAT	2Q	FAT	1Q	FAT	1Q	FAT	1Q	FAT	P	FAT	P	FAT	1Q	FAT	1Q	FAT	1Q

UXBRIDGE

Club Contact Details 01895 443 557
Honeycroft Road, West Drayton, Middlesex UB7 8HX
sec@uxbridgefc.co.uk

Founded: 1871   **Nickname:** The Reds   **Manager:** Tony Choules
Previous Names: Uxbridge Town 1923-45
Previous Leagues: Southern 1894-99, Greatt Western Suburban 1906-19, 20-23, Athenian 1919-20, 24-37, 63-82,
Spartan 1937-38, London 1938-46, Great Western Comb. 1939-45, Corinthian 1946-63, Athenian 1963-82.
Isthmian 1982-2004. Southern 2004-18.
Club Colours (change): Red & white

Ground Capacity: 3,770   **Seats:** 339   **Covered:** 760   **Clubhouse:** Yes   **Shop:**
Previous Grounds: RAF Stadium 1923-48, Cleveland Road 1948-78
Record Attendance: 1,000 v Arsenal - Opening of the floodlights 1981
Nearest Railway Station West Drayton - 1km

RECORDS
Goalscorer: Phil Duff - 153
Appearances: Roger Nicholls - 1,054
Best FA Cup Second Round Proper 1873-74 **FA Amateur Cup:** Finalists 1897-98
FA Trophy Second Round Proper 1998-99, 99-2000, 00-01, 08-09
FA Vase Fourth Round Proper 1983-84

HONOURS
FA Comps: None
League: Corinthian 1959-60.
County FA: Middlesex Senior Cup 1893-94, 95-96, 1950-51, 2000-01, Charity Cup 1907-08, 12-13, 35-36, 81-82, 2012-13, 13-14.
London Challenge Cup 1993-94, 96-97, 98-99.

08-09		09-10		10-11		11-12		12-13		13-14		14-15		15-16		16-17		17-18	
Sthsw	13	Sthsw	15	SthC	13	SthC	4	SthC	11	SthC	10	SthC	12	SthC	15	SthC	17	Sth1E	15
FAC	1Qr	FAC	2Q	FAC	P	FAC	P	FAC	1Q	FAC	1Q	FAC	2Q	FAC	3Q	FAC	2Q	FAC	P
FAT	2P	FAT	1Qr	FAT	2P	FAT	1P	FAT	2Qr	FAT	P	FAT	2Q	FAT	P	FAT	1Q	FAT	P

WALTHAM ABBEY

Club Contact Details 01992 711 287
Capershotts, Sewardstone Road, Waltham Abbey, Essex EN9 1NX
secretary@wafc.info

Founded: 1944   **Nickname:** Abbotts   **Manager:** Mark Stimson
Previous Names: Abbey Sports amalgamated with Beechfield Sports in 1974 to form Beechfields. Club then renamed to Waltham Abbey in 1976
Previous Leagues: London Spartan/Spartan. Essex & Herts Border. Essex Senior.

Club Colours (change): Green and white hoops

Ground Capacity: 3,500   **Seats:** 200   **Covered:** 500   **Clubhouse:** Yes   **Shop:** No
Previous Grounds: None
Record Attendance:
Nearest Railway Station Waltham Cross - 2km   **Bus Route** Catersfield - stop 100m away

RECORDS
Best FA Cup Third Qualifying Round 2014-15
FA Trophy First Qualifying Round 2006-07, 09-10, 12-13, 13-14
FA Vase Second Round Proper 1997-98

HONOURS
FA Comps: None
League: London Spartan Division One 1977-78, Senior Division 1978-79.
County FA: London Senior Cup 1998-99. Essex Senior Cup 2004-05.

08-09		09-10		10-11		11-12		12-13		13-14		14-15		15-16		16-17		17-18	
Isth1N	4	Isth1N	21	Isth1N	11	Isth1N	14	Isth1N	12	Isth1N	18	Isth1N	10	Isth1N	21	Isth1N	20	Isth1N	18
FAC	1Q	FAC	1Q	FAC	P	FAC	1Q	FAC	2Q	FAC	1Q	FAC	3Q	FAC	P	FAC	1Q	FAC	P
FAT	Pr	FAT	1Q	FAT	P	FAT	Pr	FAT	1Q	FAT	1Q	FAT	P	FAT	2Q	FAT	1Q	FAT	1Q

WARE

Club Contact Details 01920 462 064
Wodson Park, Wadesmill Road, Ware, Herts SG12 0UQ
spink405@btinternet.com

Founded: 1892 **Nickname:** Blues **Manager:** John Dreyer
Previous Names: Ware Town.
Previous Leagues: East Herts, North Middlesex 1907-08, Herts County 1908-25, Spartan 1925-55, Delphian 1955-63, Athenian 1963-75, Isthmian 1975-2015. Southern 2015-16.

Club Colours (change): Blue & white

Ground Capacity: 3,300 **Seats:** 500 **Covered:** 312 **Clubhouse:** Yes **Shop:** Yes
Previous Grounds: Highfields, Canons Park, London Road, Presdales Lower Park 1921-26
Record Attendance: 3,800 v Hendon - FA Amateur Cup, January 1957.
Nearest Railway Station Ware - 1.9km **Bus Route** Wodson Park - stop 100m away

RECORDS
Victory: 10-1 v Wood Green Town
Defeat: 0-11 v Barnet
Goalscorer: George Dearman scored 98 goals during 1926-27
Appearances: Gary Riddle - 654

HONOURS
FA Comps: None
League: East Herts 1897-88, 98-99, 99-1900, 02-03, 03-04, 05-06 (shared), 06-07. Herts County 1908-09, 21-22.
Spartan Division Two B 1926-27, Division One 51-52, Premier 52-53. Isthmian Division Two 2005-06.
County FA: Herts Senior Cup 1898-99, 1903-04, 06-07, 21-22, 53-54. Herts Charity Shield 1926-27, 52-53, 56-57, 58-59, 62-63, 85-86.
East Anglian Cup 1973-74.

08-09		09-10		10-11		11-12		12-13		13-14		14-15		15-16		16-17		17-18	
Isth1N	9	Isth1N	19	Isth1N	14	Isth1N	21	Isth1N	19	Isth1N	21	Isth1N	10	SthC	11	Isth1N	22	Isth1N	20
FAC	3Q	FAC	1Q	FAC	P	FAC	P	FAC	1Q	FAC	P	FAC	P	FAC	P	FAC	P	FAC	2Q
FAT	1Q	FAT	P	FAT	P	FAT	P	FAT	P	FAT	Pr	FAT	1Q	FAT	P	FAT	2Q	FAT	1Q

WESTFIELD

Club Contact Details 01483 771 106
Woking Park, off Elmbridge Lane, Kingfield, Woking GU22 9BA

Founded: 1953 **Nickname:** The Field **Manager:** Tony Reid
Previous Names: None
Previous Leagues: Woking & District. Surrey Intermediate > 1962. Parthenon 1962-63. Surrey Senior 1963-78.
Combined Counties (FM) 1978-2018

Club Colours (change): Amber & black

Ground Capacity: 1000 **Seats:** Yes **Covered:** Yes **Clubhouse:** Yes **Shop:**
Previous Grounds: Moved to Woking Park in 1960
Record Attendance: 325 v Guernsey, Combined Counties Division One, 2011-12
Nearest Railway Station Woking **Bus Route** Arriva 34, 35

RECORDS
Best FA Cup Second Qualifying Round 2017-18
FA Vase Fourth Round Proper 2000-01

HONOURS
FA Comps: None
League: Surrey Senior League 1972-73, 73-74. Combined Counties Premier 2017-18.

County FA: Surrey County Junior Charity Cup 1954-55

08-09		09-10		10-11		11-12		12-13		13-14		14-15		15-16		16-17		17-18	
CC1	13	CC1	16	CC1	13	CC1	8	CC1	3	CCP	4	CCP	14	CCP	9	CCP	2	CCP	1
FAC	EP	FAC	N/A	FAC	N/A	FAC	EP	FAC	EP	FAC	1Qr	FAC	P	FAC	EPr	FAC	EP	FAC	2Q
FAV	2Q	FAV	1Q	FAV	1Q	FAV	2Q	FAV	1Q	FAV	1P	FAV	2P	FAV	2Q	FAV	2Q	FAV	3P

ASHFORD UNITED

Club Contact Details 01233 611 838
The Homelands, Ashford Road TN26 1NJ
info@ashfordunitedfc.com

Founded: 1930   **Nickname:** The Nuts & Bolts   **Manager:** Gary Alexander
Previous Names: Ashford Town 1930-2010.
Previous Leagues: Kent 1930-59. Southern 1959-2004. Isthmian 2004-10. Kent Invicta 2011-2013. Southern Counties East 2013-17.

Club Colours (change): Green & white

Ground Capacity: 3,200   **Seats:** 500   **Covered:** Yes   **Clubhouse:** Yes   **Shop:**
Previous Grounds: Essella Park 1931-1987.
Record Attendance: At Essella Park - 6,525 v Crystal Palace, FAC 1st Rnd, 1959-60. At Homelands - 3,363 v Fulham, FAC 1st , 1994-95.
Nearest Railway Station Ham Street - 4.2km   **Bus Route** Smithfields Crossroads - stop 600m away

RECORDS
Victory: 15-0 v Erith & Belvedere, Kent League, 28/04/1937.
Defeat: 3-14 v Folkestone Reserves, Kent League, 1933-34.
Goalscorer: Dave Arter - 197. Shaun Welford scored 48 goals during the 2016-17 season.
Stuart Zanone scored 7 v Lingfield (A), Southern Counties East, 24/03/2015.
Appearances: Peter McRobert - 765

HONOURS
FA Comps: None
League: Kent 1948-49. Southern Counties East 2016-17.
County FA: Kent Senior Cup 1958-59, 62-63, 92-93, 95-96. Kent Senior Trophy 2016-17.

08-09		09-10		10-11	11-12		12-13		13-14		14-15		15-16		16-17		17-18	
Isth1S	7	Isth1S	20		K_lv	5	K_lv	3	SCEP	2	SCEP	2	SCEP	3	SCEP	1	Isth1S	21
FAC	1Q	FAC	1Q				FAC	P	FAC	P	FAC	P	FAC	EP	FAC	1Q	FAC	1Q
FAT	P	FAT	1Q		FAV	1Qr	FAV	2Q	FAV	4P	FAV	4P	FAV	QF	FAV	2P	FAT	P

CRAY WANDERERS

Club Contact Details 020 8460 5291
Bromley FC, Hayes Lane, Bromley, Kent BR2 9EF
marksimpson937@btinternet.com

Founded: 1860   **Nickname:** Wanderers or Wands   **Manager:** Tony Russell - 04/05/2015
Previous Names: Cray Old Boys (immediately after WW1); Sidcup & Footscray (start of WW2).
Previous Leagues: Kent 1894-1903, 1906-07, 1909-1914, 1934-38, 1978-2004; West Kent & South Suburban Leagues (before WW1); London 1920-1934, 1951-1959; Kent Amateur 1938-1939, 1946-1951; South London Alliance 1943-1946; Aetolian 1959-1964; Greater London 1964-1966; Metropolitan 1966-1971; Met. London 1971-1975; London Spartan 1975-1978.
Club Colours (change): Amber & black

Ground Capacity: 5,000   **Seats:** 1,300   **Covered:** 2,500   **Clubhouse:** Yes   **Shop:** Yes
Previous Grounds: Northfield Farm (1950-51), Tothills (aka Fordcroft, 1951-1955), Grassmeade (1955-1973), Oxford Road (1973-1998).
Record Attendance: (Grassmeade) 2,160vLeytonstone,FAAm.R3, 68-69; (Oxford R) 1,523vStamford,FAVQF 79-80; (Hayes L)1,082vAFC Wim, 04-05
Nearest Railway Station Bromley South - 1km   **Bus Route** Hayes Road - stop 160m away

RECORDS
Victory: 15-0 v Sevenoaks - 1894-95.
Defeat: 2-15 (H) and 0-14 (A) v Callenders Athletic - Kent Amateur League, 1947-48.
Goalscorer: Ken Collishaw 274 (1954-1965)
Appearances: John Dorey - 454 (1961-72).
Additional: Unbeaten for 28 Ryman League games in 2007-2008.

HONOURS
FA Comps: None
League: Kent 1901-02, 80-81, 2002-03, 03-04. London 1956-57, 57-58. Aetolian 1962-63. Greater London 1965-66.
Metropolitan London 1974-75; London Spartan 1976-77, 77-78.
County FA: Kent Amateur Cup 1930-31, 62-63, 63-64, 64-65. Kent Senior Trophy 1992-93, 2003-04.

08-09		09-10		10-11		11-12		12-13		13-14		14-15		15-16		16-17		17-18	
Isth1S	2	Isth P	15	Isth P	9	Isth P	9	Isth P	17	Isth P	24	Isth1N	16	Isth1N	4	Isth1S	11	Isth1S	3
FAC	1Q	FAC	1Q	FAC	2Qr	FAC	3Q	FAC	3Q	FAC	1Q	FAC	1Q	FAC	1Q	FAC	1Q	FAC	P
FAT	3Q	FAT	1Q	FAT	2Q	FAT	1Q	FAT	3Q	FAT	1Q	FAT	3Q	FAT	P	FAT	2Q	FAT	3Q

EAST GRINSTEAD TOWN

Club Contact Details 01342 325 885
The GAC Stadium, East Court, College Lane, East Grinstead RH19 3LS
richard.tramontin@egtfc.co.uk

Founded: 1890   **Nickname:** The Wasps   **Manager:** Matt Longhurst
Previous Names: East Grinstead 1890-1997.
Previous Leagues: Mid Sussex, Sussex County, Souhern Amateur. Sussex County >2014.

Club Colours (change): Amber & black stripes (Blue & yellow)

Ground Capacity: 3,000   **Seats:** Yes   **Covered:** Yes   **Clubhouse:** Yes   **Shop:** No
Previous Grounds: West Ground 1890-1962. King George's Field 1962-67.
Record Attendance: 2,006 v Lancing F A Am Cup, November 1947
Nearest Railway Station East Grinstead - 1.1km   **Bus Route** East Court - stop 100m away

RECORDS
Appearances: Guy Hill
Best FA Cup   Second Qualifying Round 1947-48, 50-51, 52-53, 7-72
FA Trophy   First Qualifying Round 2015-16, 16-17
FA Vase   Third Round Proper 1974-75

HONOURS
FA Comps: None
League: Mid-Sussex 1901-02, 36-37. Southern Amateur DivisioN Three 1931-32. Sussex County Division Two 2007-08.

County FA: Sussex RUR Cup 2003-04.

	08-09	09-10	10-11	11-12	12-13	13-14	14-15	15-16	16-17	17-18
	SxC1 17	SxC1 15	SxC1 7	SxC1 9	SxC1 8	SxC1 2	Isth1S 22	Isth1S 20	Isth1S 18	Isth1S 22
	FAC P	FAC 1Q	FAC 1Q			FAC EP	FAC Pr	FAC P	FAC P	FAC 1Q
	FAV 2P	FAV 1P	FAV 2Q		FAV 1Qr	FAV 2P	FAT Pr	FAT 1Q	FAT 1Q	FAT P

FAVERSHAM TOWN

Club Contact Details 01795 591 900
Shepherd Neame Stadium, Salters Lane, Faversham Kent ME13 8ND
wendy-walker@hotmail.co.uk

Founded: 1884   **Nickname:** Lillywhites   **Manager:** Ray Turner
Previous Names: Faversham Invicta, Faversham Services, Faversham Railway and Faversham Rangers pre War.
Previous Leagues: Kent 1884-1900, 1904-12, 24-34, 37-59, 66-71, 76-2003. Kent County 1934-37. Aetolian/Greater London 1959-66.
     Metropolitan 1971-73. Athenian 1973-76. Kent County 2005-10.
Club Colours (change): White & black

Ground Capacity: 2,000   **Seats:** 200   **Covered:** 1,800   **Clubhouse:** Yes   **Shop:** No
Previous Grounds: Moved in to Salters Lane in 1948.
Record Attendance:
Nearest Railway Station Faversham - 0.6km

RECORDS
Best FA Cup   Third Qualifying Round 2016-17
FA Trophy   Second Qualifying Round 201-12
FA Vase   Third Round Proper 1991-92

HONOURS
FA Comps: None
League: Kent 1969-70, 70-71, 77-78, 89-90, Division Two 1895-96. Kent County 2009-10.

County FA: Kent Amateur Cup 1956-57, 58-59, 71-72, 72-73, 73-74. Kent Senior Trophy 1976-77, 77-78.

	08-09	09-10	10-11	11-12	12-13	13-14	14-15	15-16	16-17	17-18
	Kent P 4	Kent P 1	Isth1S 8	Isth1S 17	Isth1S 3	Isth1S 10	Isth1S 3	Isth1S 5	Isth1S 10	Isth1S 19
	FAC EP	FAC 1Q	FAC 1Q	FAC 1Q	FAC 1Qr	FAC 2Q	FAC 2Q	FAC 1Qr	FAC 3Qr	FAC 2Q
	FAV 2Q	FAV 2P	FAT 1Q	FAT 2Q	FAT 1Q	FAT P	FAT 1Q	FAT P	FAT 1Q	FAT P

GREENWICH BOROUGH

Club Contact Details 07946 721 878
DGS Stadium, Middle Park Avenue, Eltham SE9 5HP
geoffgrant@ntlworld.com

Founded: 1928 **Nickname:** Boro **Manager:** Luke Medley
Previous Names: Woolwich Borough Council Athletic 1928-65. London Borough of Greenwich 1965-84.
Previous Leagues: Woolwich & District 1928-29. Kent Amateur 1929-39, 46-48. South London Alliance 1948-76. London Spartan 1976-84. Kent/Southern Counties East 1984-2016.

Club Colours (change): Red & black

Ground Capacity: 1,000 **Seats:** 100 **Covered:** Yes **Clubhouse:** Yes **Shop:**
Previous Grounds: Danson Park 1928-37. Harrow Meadow 1937-2009. Holmesdale FC 2009-13. Dartford FC 2013-16.
Record Attendance: 2,000 v Charlton Athletic, turning on of floodlights, 1978.
Nearest Railway Station Mottingham - 15min walk away **Bus Route** 160 stops at the ground

RECORDS
Best FA Cup	Fourth Qualifying Round 2014-15
FA Trophy	Preliminary Round 2016-17(r), 17-18
FA Vase	Fifth Round Proper 2007-08

HONOURS
FA Comps:
League: Woolwich & District 1928-29. South London Alliance Division Two 1954-55, Division One 1955-56, Premier Division 1960-61, 61-62, 62-63, 63-64, 64-65, 65-66, 73-74. London Spartan 1979-80. Kent 1986-87, 87-88. Southern Counties East 2015-16.
County FA: Kent Senior Trophy 1984-85.

08-09		09-10		10-11		11-12		12-13		13-14		14-15		15-16		16-17		17-18	
Kent P	3	Kent P	5	Kent P	4	Kent P	16	Kent P	15	SCE	9	SCE	4	SCE	1	Isth1S	3	Isth1S	4
				FAC	EP	FAC	EP	FAC	1Q	FAC	P	FAC	4Q	FAC	1Q	FAC	1Q	FAC	1Q
		FAV	1P	FAV	1P	FAV	1P	FAV	1Q	FAV	1P	FAV	4P	FAV	2P	FAT	Pr	FAT	P

GUERNSEY

Club Contact Details 01481 747 279
Footes Lane Stadium, St Peter Port, Guernsey GY1 2UL
mark.letissier@guernseyfc.com

Founded: 2011 **Nickname:** Green Lions **Manager:** Tony Vance
Previous Names: None
Previous Leagues: Combined Counties 2011-13.

Club Colours (change): Green & white

Ground Capacity: 5,000 **Seats:** 720 **Covered:** Yes **Clubhouse:** Yes **Shop:** No
Previous Grounds: None
Record Attendance: 4,290 v. Spennymoor Town, FA Vase semi-final first leg, 23/03/2013
Bus Route Bus stops outside the ground

RECORDS
Victory:	11-0 v Crawley Down Gatwick, Isthmian Division One South, 01/01/2014
Defeat:	0-8 v Merstham, Isthmian Division One South, 18/11/2014
Goalscorer:	Ross Allen - 239 in 226 appearances. (Scored 57 in all competitions during 2011-12)

HONOURS
FA Comps: None
League: Combined Counties Division One 2011-12.

County FA: None

08-09	09-10	10-11	11-12		12-13		13-14		14-15		15-16		16-17		17-18	
			CC1	1	CCP	2	Isth1S	4	Isth1S	10	Isth1S	13	Isth1S	21	Isth1S	18
							FAC	2Q	FAC	P	FAC	Pr	FAC	Pr	FAC	Pr
					FAV	SF	FAT	1Q	FAT	1Q	FAT	P	FAT	P	FAT	P

HASTINGS UNITED

Club Contact Details 01424 444 635
The Pilot Field, Elphinstone Road, Hastings TN34 2AX

Founded: 1894   **Nickname:** The U's or The Arrows   **Manager:** Chris Agutter
Previous Names: Rock-a-Nore 1894-1921. Hastings and St Leonards Amateurs 1921-79. Hastings Town 1979-2002.
Previous Leagues: South Eastern 1904-05, Southern 1905-10, Sussex County 1921-27, 52-85, Southern Amateur 1927-46, Corinthian 1946-48

Club Colours (change): All white

Ground Capacity: 4,050   **Seats:** 800   **Covered:** 1,750   **Clubhouse:** Yes   **Shop:** Yes
Previous Grounds: Bulverhythe Recreation > 1976
Record Attendance: 4,888 v Nottingham Forest - Friendly 23/06/1996
Nearest Railway Station Ore - 0.9km. Hastings - 1.9km.

RECORDS
Goalscorer: Terry White scored 33 during 1999-2000
Additional: Paid £8,000 to Ashford Town for Nicky Dent
Received £50,000 from Nottingham Forest for Paul Smith

HONOURS
FA Comps: None
League: Southern Division Two B 1909-10, Southern Division 1991-92, Eastern Division 2001-01.
Sussex County Division Two 1979-80.
County FA: Sussex Senior Cup 1935-36, 37-38, 95-96, 97-98.

08-09		09-10		10-11		11-12		12-13		13-14		14-15		15-16		16-17		17-18	
Isth P	17	Isth P	7	Isth P	18	Isth P	18	Isth P	22	Isth1S	5	Isth1S	19	Isth1S	7	Isth1S	5	Isth1S	9
FAC	1Q	FAC	1Q	FAC	1Q	FAC	1Q	FAC	3P	FAC	1Q	FAC	2Q	FAC	3Q	FAC	3Qr	FAC	1Q
FAT	3Q	FAT	1Q	FAT	1Qr	FAT	1Qr	FAT	1Q	FAT	2Q	FAT	P	FAT	2Q	FAT	2Qr	FAT	1Q

HAYWARDS HEATH TOWN

Club Contact Details 01444 412 837
Hanbury Park Stadium, Haywards Heath RH16 3PT

Founded: 1888   **Nickname:** The Blues   **Manager:** Shaun Saunders
Previous Names: Haywards Heath Juniors 1888-94. Haywards Heath Excelsior 1894-95. Haywards Heath 1895-1989.
Previous Leagues: Mid-Sussex 1888-1927. Sussex County/Southern Combination 1927-52, 61-2018. Metropolitan 1952-61.

Club Colours (change): Blue & white

Ground Capacity: **Seats:** Yes   **Covered:** Yes   **Clubhouse:** Yes   **Shop:**
Previous Grounds:
Record Attendance:
Nearest Railway Station Haywards HEath - 1.9km   **Bus Route** Market Square - stop 84m away

RECORDS
Best FA Cup Fourth Qualifying Round 1945-46
FA Vase Third Round Proper 1990-91

HONOURS
FA Comps: None
League: Sussex County/Southern Combination 1949-50, 69-70, 2017-18, Eastern Division 45-46/ Division One 2015-16.
County FA: Sussex Senior Cup 1941-42, 57-58. Sussex RUR Cup 1943-44, 66-67, 74-75, 75-76. Sussex Intermediate Cup 2012-13

08-09		09-10		10-11		11-12		12-13		13-14		14-15		15-16		16-17		17-18	
SxC3	3	SxC3	3	SxC3	8	SxC3	15	SxC3	2	SxC2	5	SxC2	9	SC1	1	SCP	2	SCP	1
												FAC	EP			FAC	P	FAC	1Qr
FAV	2Q	FAV	1Q			FAV	1Qr			FAV	2Q	FAV	1Q	FAV	2P	FAV	2P	FAV	2P

HERNE BAY

Club Contact Details 01227 374 156
Winch's Field, Stanley Gardens, Herne Bay CT6 5SG
johnbhbfc@aol.com

Founded: 1886 **Nickname:** The Bay	**Manager:** John Embery & Jermaine Darlington

Previous Names: None.
Previous Leagues: East Kent. Faversham & Dist. Cantebury & Dist. Kent Am. Athenian.

Club Colours (change): Blue & white

Ground Capacity: 3,000 **Seats:** 200 **Covered:** 1,500 **Clubhouse:** Yes **Shop:** Yes
Previous Grounds: Mitchell's Athletic Ground. Herne Bay Memorial Park.
Record Attendance: 2,303 v Margate, FA Cup 4th Qual. 1970-71.
Nearest Railway Station Herne Bay - 0.8km

RECORDS
Victory: 19-3 v Hythe Wanderers - Feb 1900.
Defeat: 0-11 v 7th Dragon Guards - Oct 1907.
Misc: Most League Victories in a Season: 34 - 1996-97.

HONOURS
FA Comps: None
League: East Kent 1902-03, 03-04, 04-05, 05-06. Athenian Division Two 1970-71. Kent 1991-92, 93-94, 96-97, 97-98, 2011-12, Division Two 1954-55.
County FA: Kent Amateur Cup 1957-58. Kent Senior Trophy 1978-79, 1996-97.

08-09		09-10		10-11		11-12		12-13		13-14		14-15		15-16		16-17		17-18	
Kent P	6	Kent P	2	Kent P	2	Kent P	1	Isth1S	19	Isth1S	18	Isth1S	9	Isth1S	8	Isth1S	17	Isth1S	12
FAC	Pr	FAC	EP	FAC	EP	FAC	1Q	FAC	P	FAC	Pr	FAC	1Q	FAC	2Qr	FAC	2Qr	FAC	3Q
FAV	1Q	FAV	2P	FAV	4P	FAV	SF	FAT	P	FAT	1Qr	FAT	P	FAT	2Qr	FAT	1Qr	FAT	P

HORSHAM

Club Contact Details 01403 252 689 / 07952 351 712 (MD)
Sussex FA Headquaters, Culver Road, Lancing West Sussex BN15 9AX
jeff.barrett@btinternet.com

Founded: 1881 **Nickname:** Hornets	**Manager:** Dominic Di Paola

Previous Names: None
Previous Leagues: West Sussex Senior, Sussex Co 1926-51, Metropolitan 1951-57, Corinthian 1957-63, Athenian 1963-73, Isthmian 1973-2015. Southern Combination 2015-16,

Club Colours (change): Yellow & green

Ground Capacity: **Seats:** Yes **Covered:** Yes **Clubhouse:** Yes **Shop:** Yes
Previous Grounds: Horsham Park, Hurst Park, Springfield Park, Gorings Mead
Record Attendance: 7,134 v Swindon - FA Cup First Round Proper, November 1966
Nearest Railway Station Lancing - 5min walk from the ground.

RECORDS
Victory: 16-1 v Southwick - Sussex County League 1945-46
Defeat: 1-11 v Worthing - Sussex Senior Cup 1913-14
Goalscorer: Mick Browning
Appearances: Mark Stepney
Additional: Paid £2,500 to Lewes for Lee Farrell, July 2007.
Received £10,000 from Tonbridge Angels for Carl Rook, December 2008.

HONOURS
FA Comps: None
League: West Sussex Senior 1899-00, 1900-01, 01-02, 25-26. Sussex County 1931-32, 32-33, 34-35, 36-37, 37-38, 46-47. Metropolitan 1951-52. Athenian Division Two 1969-70, Division One 72-73. Isthmian Division Three 1995-96. Southern Combination 2015-16.
County FA: Sussex Senior Cup 1933-34, 38-39, 49-50, 53-54, 71-72, 73-74, 75-76.

08-09		09-10		10-11		11-12		12-13		13-14		14-15		15-16		16-17		17-18	
Isth P	13	Isth P	11	Isth P	17	Isth P	22	Isth1S	15	Isth1S	16	Isth1S	24	SCom	1	Isth1S	16	Isth1S	15
FAC	4Qr	FAC	1Q	FAC	1Q	FAC	2Qr	FAC	2Q	FAC	3Q	FAC	1Q	FAC	Pr	FAC	P	FAC	2Q
FAT	2Q	FAT	1Qr	FAT	2Q	FAT	1Q	FAT	P	FAT	1Q	FAT	3Q	FAV	1P	FAT	1Q	FAT	P

HYTHE TOWN

Club Contact Details 01303 264 932 / 238 256
Reachfields Stadium, Fort Road, Hythe CT21 6JS

Founded: 1910 **Nickname:** The Cannons **Manager:** Sam Denly
Previous Names: Hythe Town 1910-1992, Hythe United 1992-2001
Previous Leagues: Kent Amateur League, Kent League, Southern League, Kent County League, Kent League.

Club Colours (change): Red & white

Ground Capacity: 3,000 **Seats:** 350 **Covered:** 2,400 **Clubhouse:** Yes **Shop:** Yes
Previous Grounds: South Road 1910-77.
Record Attendance: 2,147 v Yeading, FA Vase Semi-Final, 1990.
Nearest Railway Station Hythe - 0.5km

RECORDS
Victory: 10-1 v Sporting Bengal, 2008-09
Defeat: 1-10 v Swanley Furness, 1997-98
Goalscorer: Dave Cook - 130
Appearances: John Walker - 354, Jason Brazier - 349, Dave Cook - 346, Lee Winfield - 344

HONOURS
FA Comps: None
League: Kent County Eastern Division Two 1936-37, Division One 71-72, Premier Division 73-74, 74-75, 75-76.
Kent League 1988-89, 2010-11.
County FA: Kent Senior Cup 2011-12.
Kent Senior Trophy 1990-91.

08-09		09-10		10-11		11-12		12-13		13-14		14-15		15-16		16-17		17-18	
Kent P	2	Kent P	3	Kent P	1	Isth1S	8	Isth1S	4	Isth1S	8	Isth1S	16	Isth1S	4	Isth1S	7	Isth1S	7
FAC	1Qr	FAC	2Qr	FAC	1P	FAC	2Q	FAC	P	FAC	P	FAC	2Q	FAC	P	FAC	2Q	FAC	Pr
FAV	1P	FAV	1P	FAV	3P	FAT	2Q	FAT	1Qr	FAT	2Qr	FAT	1Q	FAT	P	FAT	1P	FAT	1Q

PHOENIX SPORTS

Club Contact Details 01322 526 159
Phoenix Sports Ground, Mayplace Road East, Barnehurst, Kent DA7 6JT
alf_levy@sky.com

Founded: 1935 **Nickname:** None **Manager:** Paul Bryon
Previous Names: St Johns Welling. Lakeside. Phoenix.
Previous Leagues: Spartan League. Kent County > 2011. Kent Invicta 2011-13.

Club Colours (change): Green & black

Ground Capacity: 2,000 **Seats:** 108 **Covered:** Yes **Clubhouse:** Yes **Shop:** No
Previous Grounds: Danson Park >1950.
Record Attendance:
Nearest Railway Station Barnehurst - 1.1km **Bus Route** Woodside Road - stop 50m away

RECORDS
Best FA Cup Third Qualifying Round 2017-18
FA Trophy Second Qualifying Round 2016-17
FA Vase Fifth Round Proper 2014-15

HONOURS
FA Comps: None
League: Kent County Division One West 1999-2000, 2007-08, Division Two West 2004-05. Kent Invicta 2012-13.
Southern Counties East 2014-15.
County FA: London Senior Trophy 2017-18

08-09		09-10		10-11		11-12		12-13		13-14		14-15		15-16		16-17		17-18	
KC P	8	KC P	4	KC P	5	K_lv	2	K_lv	1	SCE	6	SCE	1	Isth1N	14	Isth1N	8	Isth1N	11
												FAC	EPr	FAC	2Q	FAC	P	FAC	3Q
										FAV	1P	FAV	5P	FAT	1Qr	FAT	2Q	FAT	P

RAMSGATE

Club Contact Details 01843 591 662
Southwood Stadium, Prices Avenue, Ramsgate, Kent CT11 0AN
secretary@ramsgate-fc.co.uk

Founded: 1945   **Nickname:** The Rams   **Manager:** Lloyd Blackman
Previous Names: Ramsgate Athletic > 1972
Previous Leagues: Kent 1949-59, 1976-2005, Southern 1959-76

Club Colours (change): All red

Ground Capacity: 2,500   **Seats:** 400   **Covered:** 600   **Clubhouse:** Yes   **Shop:** Yes
Previous Grounds: None
Record Attendance: 5,038 v Margate - 1956-57
Nearest Railway Station Ramsgate - 1km

RECORDS
Victory: 11-0 & 12-1 v Canterbury City - Kent League 2000-01
Goalscorer: Mick Willimson
Best FA Cup   First Round Proper 1955-56, 2005-06
FA Trophy   Third Qualifying Round 1969-70, 75-76, 2008-09, 09-10, 12-13, 13-14
FA Vase   Quarter Finals 1999-2000

HONOURS
FA Comps: None
League: Kent Division One 1949-50, 55-56, 56-57, Premier 1998-99, 2004-05. Isthmian Division One 2005-06.

County FA: Kent Senior Shield 1960-61, 67-68, 68-69. Kent Senior Cup 1963-64. Kent Senior Trophy 1987-88, 88-89, 98-99.

08-09		09-10		10-11		11-12		12-13		13-14		14-15		15-16		16-17		17-18	
Isth P	22	Isth1S	14	Isth1S	9	Isth1S	10	Isth1S	7	Isth1S	12	Isth1S	21	Isth1S	12	Isth1S	12	Isth1S	16
FAC	1Q	FAC	P	FAC	Pr	FAC	Pr	FAC	P	FAC	P	FAC	1Q	FAC	P	FAC	1Q	FAC	2Q
FAT	3Q	FAT	3Q	FAT	1Qr	FAT	P	FAT	3Q	FAT	3Q	FAT	P	FAT	1Q	FAT	P	FAT	P

SEVENOAKS TOWN

Club Contact Details 07876 444 274
Greatness Park, Seal Road, Sevenoaks TN14 5BL
secretary@sevenoakstownfc.co.uk

Founded: 1883   **Nickname:** Town   **Manager:** Micky Collins
Previous Names: None.
Previous Leagues: Sevenoaks League. Kent Amateur/County. Kent/Southern Counties East >2018.

Club Colours (change): Blue & black

Ground Capacity: 2,000   **Seats:** 150   **Covered:** 200   **Clubhouse:** Yes   **Shop:**
Previous Grounds: None
Record Attendance:
Nearest Railway Station Bat & Ball - 0.4km

RECORDS
Best FA Cup   Second Qualifying Round 2016-17(r)
FA Vase   Third Round Proper 2017-18

HONOURS
FA Comps: None
League: Kent County 1984-85, 95-96, 2002-03. Southern Counties East Premier 2017-18.

County FA:

08-09		09-10		10-11		11-12		12-13		13-14		14-15		15-16		16-17		17-18	
Kent P	14	Kent P	6	Kent P	7	Kent P	14	Kent P	17	SCE	16	SCE	8	SCE	5	SCEP	3	SCEP	1
FAC	Pr	FAC	Pr	FAC	EP	FAC	P	FAC	EP	FAC	EP	FAC	EP	FAC	EPr	FAC	2Qr	FAC	1Q
FAV	2Q	FAV	1Q	FAV	1Q	FAV	2Q	FAV	1P	FAV	1P	FAV	1Q	FAV	2Q	FAV	2Q	FAV	3P

SITTINGBOURNE

Club Contact Details 01795 410 777
Woodstock Park, Broadoak Road, Sittingbourne ME9 8AG
john@sittingbournefc.com

Founded: 1886   **Nickname:** Brickies   **Manager:** Aslan Odev
Previous Names: Sittingbourne United 1881-86
Previous Leagues: Kent 1894-1905, 1909-27, 30-39, 45-59, 68-91, South Eastern 1905-09, Southern 1927-30, 59-67

Club Colours (change): Red & black

Ground Capacity: 3,000   **Seats:** 300   **Covered:** 600   **Clubhouse:** Yes   **Shop:** Yes
Previous Grounds: Sittingbourne Rec. 1881-90, Gore Court 1890-92, The Bull Ground 1892-1990. Central Park 1990-2001
Record Attendance: 5,951 v Tottenham Hotspur - Friendly 26/01/1993
Nearest Railway Station Sittingbourne - 3.1km   **Bus Route** Kent Science Park - stop 500m away

RECORDS
Victory: 15-0 v Orpington, Kent League 1922-23)
Defeat: 0-10 v Wimbledon, SL Cup 1965-66)
Additional: Paid £20,000 to Ashford Town for Lee McRobert 1993
                    Received £210,000 from Millwall for Neil Emblem and Michael Harle 1993

HONOURS
FA Comps: None
League: Kent 1902-03, 57-58, 58-59, 75-76, 83-84, 90-91. Southern Southern Division 1992-93, 95-96.

County FA: Kent Senior Cup 1901-02, 28-29, 29-30, 57-58.

08-09	09-10	10-11	11-12	12-13	13-14	14-15	15-16	16-17	17-18
Isth1S 6	Isth1S 9	Isth1S 11	Isth1S 19	Isth1S 9	Isth1S 14	Isth1S 12	Isth1S 18	Isth1S 15	Isth1S 14
FAC 1Q	FAC 2Q	FAC P	FAC 1Q	FAC 1Q	FAC 3Q	FAC P	FAC 2Q	FAC Pr	FAC Pr
FAT 1Q	FAT 1Q	FAT P	FAT 1Q	FAT 1Q	FAT P	FAT P	FAT P	FAT P	FAT 2Qr

THAMESMEAD TOWN

Club Contact Details 01322 299 991
Dartford FC, Princes Park, Grassbanks, Darenth Road, Dartford DA1 1RT
secretaryttfc@hotmail.com

Founded: 1969   **Nickname:** The Mead   **Manager:** Tommy Warrilow
Previous Names: Thamesmead FC 1969-85.
Previous Leagues: London Spartan 1980-91. Kent 1991-2008.

Club Colours (change): Green & white

Ground Capacity: 4,097   **Seats:** 640   **Covered:** Yes   **Clubhouse:** Yes   **Shop:** Yes
Previous Grounds: Crossways. Meridian Sports Ground > 1985. Bayliss Avenue 1985-2017.
Record Attendance: 400 v Wimbledon - Ground opening 1988
Nearest Railway Station Dartford - 1.4km   **Bus Route** Fasttrack B towards Bluewater/Dartford.

RECORDS
Victory: 9-0 v Kent Police - Kent League 19/04/1994
Goalscorer: Delroy D'Oyley
Best FA Cup   Third Qualifying Round 2016-17
FA Vase   Fifth Round Proper 1995-96

HONOURS
FA Comps: None
League: Kent Premier 2007-08

County FA: Kent Senior Trophy 2004-05.

08-09	09-10	10-11	11-12	12-13	13-14	14-15	15-16	16-17	17-18
Isth1N 18	Isth1N 7	Isth1N 17	Isth1N 10	Isth1N 3	Isth P 22	Isth1N 13	Isth1N 10	Isth1N 17	Isth1S 10
FAC 2Qr	FAC 1Q	FAC P	FAC 2Qr	FAC 2Q	FAC 2Q	FAC P	FAC 1Q	FAC 3Q	FAC 2Qr
FAT P	FAT Pr	FAT 2Qr	FAT 3Qr	FAT 1Q	FAT 1Q	FAT 2Q	FAT 3Q	FAT P	FAT 2Q

THREE BRIDGES

Club Contact Details 01293 442 000
Jubilee Walk, Three Bridges Road, Crawley, RH10 1LQ
lorraine.bonner@lw.com

Founded: 1901　**Nickname:** Bridges　　　　**Manager:** Martin Dynan
Previous Names: Three Bridges Worth 1936-52. Three Bridges United 1953-64.
Previous Leagues: Mid Sussex, E Grinstead, Redhill & Dist 36-52. Sussex County/Southern Combintion >2012, 2017-18. Isthmian 2012-17.

Club Colours (change): Yellow & black

Ground Capacity: 3,500　**Seats:** 120　　**Covered:** 600　　**Clubhouse:** Yes　**Shop:**
Previous Grounds: None
Record Attendance: 2,000 v Horsham 1948
　　　　　Nearest Railway Station: Three Bridges - 0.4km　　**Bus Route** Jubilee Walk - stop 71m away

RECORDS
Appearances: John Malthouse
Best FA Cup　Second Qualifying Round 1982-83, 83-84, 2002-03
FA Vase　　　Fifth Round Proper 1981-82

HONOURS
FA Comps: None
League: Sussex County Division One 1953-54, 2011-12.

County FA: Sussex RUR Charity Cup 1982-83, 87-88, 2007-08

	08-09		09-10		10-11		11-12		12-13		13-14		14-15		15-16		16-17		17-18	
	SxC1	5	SxC1	7	SxC1	5	SxC1	1	Isth1S	21	Isth1S	19	Isth1S	7	Isth1S	14	Isth1S	23	SCP	2
FAC	EP		FAC	EP	FAC	P	FAC	EP	FAC	P	FAC	1Q	FAC	Pr	FAC	P	FAC	P	FAC	P
FAV	1Q		FAV	2Q	FAV	3P	FAV	4Pr	FAT	2Q	FAT	2Q	FAT	1Q	FAT	P	FAT	P	FAV	1P

VCD ATHLETIC

Club Contact Details 01322 524 262
Oakwood, Old Road, Crayford DA1 4DN
davejoyo@yahoo.co.uk

Founded: 1916　**Nickname:** The Vickers　　　　**Manager:** Keith McMahon
Previous Names: Vickers (Erith). Vickers (Crayford) Now Vickers Crayford Dartford Athletic.
Previous Leagues: Dartford & District. Kent County. Isthmian

Club Colours (change): Green & white

Ground Capacity: 1,180　**Seats:** Yes　　**Covered:** Yes　　**Clubhouse:** Yes　**Shop:** No
Previous Grounds: Groundshared with Thamesmead (5 seasons), Lordswood (2) and Greenwich Boro' (1) whilst waiting for planning at Oakwood.
Record Attendance: 13,500 Away v Maidstone, 1919.
Nearest Railway Station Crayford - 0.9km

RECORDS
Best FA Cup　Second Qualifying Round 2002-03, 08-09, 11-12(r), 14-15, 16-17
FA Trophy　　Second Qualifying Round 2015-16
FA Vase　　　Fifth Round Proper 2005-06, 06-07

HONOURS
FA Comps: None
League: Kent County 1952-53, 63-64, 96-97. Kent 2008-09. Isthmian Division One North 2013-14.

County FA: Kent Junior Cup 1926-27. Kent Amateur Cup 1961-62, 63-64. Kent Intermediate Cup 1995-96.
　　　　　Kent Senior Trophy 2005-06, 08-09.

	08-09		09-10		10-11		11-12		12-13		13-14		14-15		15-16		16-17		17-18	
	Kent P	1	Isth1N	8	Kent P	3	Kent P	3	Kent P	2	Isth1N	1	Isth P	18	Isth P	24	Isth1N	15	Isth1S	17
FAC	2Q		FAC	1Q	FAC	Pr	FAC	2Qr	FAC	1Q	FAC	P	FAC	2Q	FAC	1Qr	FAC	2Q	FAC	P
FAV	4P		FAT	1Q	FAV	2P	FAV	3Pr	FAV	1Pr	FAT	Pr	FAT	1Q	FAT	2Q	FAT	1Q	FAT	P

WHITSTABLE TOWN

Club Contact Details 01227 266 012
The Belmont Ground, Belmont Road, Belmont, Whitstable CT5 1QP

Founded: 1886   **Nickname:** Oystermen or Natives   **Manager:** Scott Porter
Previous Names: None
Previous Leagues: East Kent 1897-1909, Kent 1909-59, 67-2007, Aetolian 1959-60, 63-64, Kent Amateur 1960-62, 64-67, South East Anglian 1962-63, Isthmian 2007-16. Southern Counties East 2016-18.

Club Colours (change): Red & white

Ground Capacity: 3,000 **Seats:** 500   **Covered:** 1,000   **Clubhouse:** Yes   **Shop:** Yes
Previous Grounds: None
Record Attendance: 2,500 v Gravesend & Northfleet - FA Cup 19/10/1987. **Previous Lges:** Greater London 1964-67, Kent 1967
Nearest Railway Station Whitstable 400 yards away

RECORDS
Goalscorer:	Barry Godfrey
Appearances:	Frank Cox - 429 (1950-60)
Best FA Cup	Third Qualifying Round 1957-58, 88-89, 89-90
FA Trophy	Second Round Proper 2013-14
FA Vase	Fifth Round Proper 1996-97

HONOURS
FA Comps: None
League: Kent Division Two (Mid Kent) 1927-28, Division Two 33-34, 49-50, Premier Division 2006-07.
Kent Amateur Eastern Division 1960-61
County FA:

08-09		09-10		10-11		11-12		12-13		13-14		14-15		15-16		16-17		17-18	
Isth1S	16	Isth1S	18	Isth1S	15	Isth1S	18	Isth1S	17	Isth1S	20	Isth1S	8	Isth1S	23	SCEP	5	SCEP	2
FAC	1Q	FAC	2Q	FAC	2Q	FAC	P	FAC	P	FAC	Pr	FAC	1Q	FAC	1Qr	FAC	Pr	FAC	EP
FAT	1Q	FAT	Pr	FAT	P	FAT	P	FAT	2Q	FAT	2P	FAT	P	FAT	P	FAV	1Qr	FAV	3P

WHYTELEAFE

Club Contact Details 0208 660 5491
15 Church Road, Whyteleafe, Surrey CR3 0AR

Founded: 1946   **Nickname:** The Leafe   **Manager:** John Scarborough & Paul Dale
Previous Names: None
Previous Leagues: Caterham & Ed, Croydon. Thornton Heath & District. Surrey Interm. (East) 1954-58. Surrey Senior 1958-75. Spartan 1975-81. Athenian 1981-84. Isthmian 1984-2012.

Club Colours (change): White with green

Ground Capacity: 2,000 **Seats:** 400   **Covered:** 600   **Clubhouse:** Yes   **Shop:** Yes
Previous Grounds: None
Record Attendance: 2,210 v Chester City - FA Cup 1999-2000
Nearest Railway Station Whyteleafe South - 0.4km

RECORDS
Misc:	Paid £1,000 to Carshalton Athletic for Gary Bowyer Received £25,000 for Steve Milton
Best FA Cup	First Round Proper 1999-2000
FA Trophy	Fourth Round Proper 1998-99
FA Vase	FiFth Round Proper 1980-81, 85-86

HONOURS
FA Comps: None
League: Surrey Senior Premier Division 1968-69. Southern Counties East 2013-14.

County FA: Surrey Senior Cup 1968-69.

08-09		09-10		10-11		11-12		12-13		13-14		14-15		15-16		16-17		17-18	
Isth1S	18	Isth1S	15	Isth1S	16	Isth1S	21	Kent P	6	SCE	1	Isth1S	5	Isth1S	15	Isth1S	14	Isth1S	8
FAC	3Q	FAC	P	FAC	P	FAC	Pr	FAC	EP	FAC	2Q	FAC	1Q	FAC	Pr	FAC	2Q	FAC	Pr
FAT	P	FAT	2Qr	FAT	Pr	FAT	1Q	FAV	1P	FAV	2P	FAT	2Q	FAT	P	FAT	P	FAT	P

N⚽N
LEAGUE DAY
13.10.18
Support your
LOCAL
FOOTBALL CLUB

nonleagueday.co.uk

NORTHERN PREMIER LEAGUE PREMIER DIVISION LEAGUE TABLE 2017-18

		P	W	D	L	F	A	GD	Pts
1	Altrincham	46	28	11	7	101	42	59	95
2	Ashton United	46	23	13	10	85	59	26	82
3	Warrington Town	46	23	13	10	72	49	23	82
4	Grantham Town	46	24	9	13	90	55	35	81
5	Farsley Celtic	46	23	11	12	87	69	18	80
6	Shaw Lane	46	25	7	14	79	62	17	79*
7	Witton Albion	46	19	13	14	83	63	20	70
8	Rushall Olympic	46	19	9	18	73	79	-6	66
9	Buxton	46	17	13	16	71	66	5	64
10	Barwell	46	17	13	16	65	67	-2	64
11	Stourbridge	46	16	14	16	67	56	11	62
12	Workington	46	18	8	20	72	69	3	62
13	Mickleover Sports	46	16	13	17	68	60	8	61
14	Stafford Rangers	46	16	13	17	54	58	-4	61
15	Matlock Town	46	18	6	22	69	75	-6	60
16	Nantwich Town	46	16	9	21	62	72	-10	57
17	Hednesford Town	46	15	12	19	60	79	-19	57
18	Lancaster City	46	14	13	19	66	72	-6	55
19	Marine	46	14	11	21	67	78	-11	53
20	Coalville Town	46	15	7	24	70	92	-22	52
21	Whitby Town	46	12	14	20	60	82	-22	50
22	Stalybridge Celtic	46	14	6	26	57	90	-33	48
23	Halesowen Town	46	13	10	23	48	76	-28	45*
24	Sutton Coldfield Town	46	10	6	30	52	108	-56	35*

Play-Off Semi Finals: Ashton United 2-1 Farsley Celtic | Warrington Town 0-3 Grantham Town
Final: Ashton United 2-0 Grantham Town

PREMIER DIVISION	1	2	3	4	5	6	7	8	9	10	11	12	13	14	15	16	17	18	19	20	21	22	23	24
1 Altrincham		3-2	4-0	1-1	4-2	6-0	1-0	3-0	3-0	4-0	1-1	3-0	1-1	5-1	4-0	5-1	0-3	1-2	4-1	2-1	1-1	1-0	3-4	2-3
2 Ashton United	3-3		1-1	1-4	1-2	1-1	2-1	3-0	1-2	2-1	3-0	3-0	1-1	2-1	2-1	3-3	1-0	1-2	1-0	2-0	2-0	4-0	2-1	0-1
3 Barwell	1-3	1-1		2-1	2-1	3-4	1-1	1-1	1-1	1-0	0-4	2-1	2-1	0-2	4-4	1-0	1-2	1-0	1-1	2-1	0-1	1-0	0-1	1-0
4 Buxton	0-0	1-0	1-1		2-2	3-3	0-3	2-1	2-2	1-2	2-1	2-3	0-2	3-0	1-2	0-2	1-1	2-2	1-1	0-1	2-1	0-2	2-0	4-2
5 Coalville Town	0-3	1-2	0-3	1-5		2-3	1-3	1-0	5-2	1-4	2-3	2-1	2-0	0-3	2-5	1-3	0-0	4-0	0-1	4-2	0-3	0-1	2-1	3-0
6 Farsley Celtic	0-1	3-3	1-2	3-0	3-1		3-0	3-1	1-3	0-0	3-0	1-2	2-3	1-0	4-2	1-0	5-4	1-4	0-1	0-2	4-0	1-1	3-3	2-0
7 Grantham Town	0-2	1-1	4-1	0-1	0-1	2-2		1-2	1-1	3-2	5-0	2-1	0-3	0-0	7-1	3-1	1-2	0-0	4-2	6-1	0-0	2-0	1-1	3-2
8 Halesowen Town	0-2	1-1	1-0	1-3	2-3	1-2	1-3		2-1	4-3	1-1	3-2	0-0	0-1	2-0	0-0	1-1	2-0	1-0	0-2	1-1	3-1	1-3	1-5
9 Hednesford Town	0-3	1-1	2-3	1-2	1-1	2-1	1-3	2-0		1-1	3-2	2-0	1-3	1-0	1-1	1-3	2-1	2-1	1-1	3-0	0-2	0-0	1-0	1-1
10 Lancaster City	1-2	0-3	1-1	1-1	4-2	1-1	3-1	2-0	0-1		3-0	1-2	1-1	1-2	0-2	2-0	1-1	1-0	0-0	2-1	2-2	4-1	4-0	2-2
11 Marine	0-3	3-4	0-1	2-3	0-1	1-2	1-1	1-0	2-0	3-0		1-2	1-3	1-1	2-2	1-2	1-1	3-1	0-4	5-0	0-4	0-3	2-2	2-0
12 Matlock Town	1-0	1-2	0-2	3-3	3-1	1-2	2-3	2-0	3-2	4-3	2-2		1-0	0-3	2-1	2-0	2-0	0-0	5-0	1-3	1-2	2-3	2-0	
13 Mickleover Sports	1-2	2-5	3-3	2-2	2-2	2-2	1-0	0-0	5-0	0-1	1-2	2-0		1-2	1-1	1-3	0-2	1-0	1-2	2-0	1-3	2-1	1-1	1-0
14 Nantwich Town	1-1	2-3	2-2	1-3	1-3	1-1	3-1	1-3	1-5	3-0	1-1	0-2	1-2		1-2	2-3	0-3	2-3	2-0	0-0	2-1	1-0	3-2	2-0
15 Rushall Olympic	2-0	4-2	1-1	2-0	1-1	1-1	0-2	3-1	1-2	3-0	0-2	1-0	1-4		1-3	1-2	1-0	1-2	5-1	1-2	3-3	0-0	1-0	
16 Shaw Lane	1-2	0-0	3-2	2-0	2-0	1-0	0-2	3-2	3-1	0-0	1-3	2-1	1-2	0-2	2-0		5-2	2-0	3-1	3-1	5-0	0-0	1-1	3-2
17 Stafford Rangers	0-2	1-0	1-0	1-4	4-1	0-2	1-2	0-0	0-1	2-2	1-4	2-0	1-1	3-0	0-4	1-2		2-0	1-0	4-1	0-0	2-2	0-4	1-2
18 Stalybridge Celtic	0-0	2-2	4-2	0-1	0-3	1-4	1-3	1-0	2-2	5-2	0-2	4-1	0-5	1-0	1-2	0-1	2-0		3-1	1-1	2-0	3-1	0-5	1-3
19 Stourbridge	1-1	2-3	2-1	2-1	2-1	1-2	0-2	1-2	2-0	0-0	0-2	1-1	1-1	1-1	5-0	1-1	0-0	4-1		2-1	2-1	1-1	0-0	2-3
20 Sutton Coldfield Town	0-4	0-2	0-6	2-1	1-1	0-1	1-2	4-1	0-2	3-1	3-3	2-1	1-3	3-4	3-1	2-3	2-0	0-4		0-2	1-1	2-6	4-1	
21 Warrington Town	0-0	0-1	2-0	1-0	1-3	4-2	2-1	1-1	4-1	5-1	0-0	2-0	3-1	0-0	2-0	0-1	1-5	2-1		2-1	2-2	1-1		
22 Whitby Town	1-1	3-2	1-0	1-1	2-2	0-2	1-5	5-0	2-2	0-5	3-2	0-3	3-2	2-1	2-3	0-3	0-0	4-1	1-3	2-2	2-2		1-2	1-1
23 Witton Albion	0-2	1-1	2-2	1-0	5-2	1-4	2-3	2-3	3-0	2-0	1-1	3-3	0-2	4-1	1-2	4-0	1-2	4-1	1-0	1-0	1-2	1-0		1-0
24 Workington	5-2	1-2	0-2	1-2	1-0	1-2	0-2	3-1	1-0	2-0	2-1	0-1	3-0	2-1	4-1	2-0	0-0	3-4	2-1	4-0	1-1	1-3	1-1	

NORTHERN PREMIER LEAGUE DIVISION ONE NORTH LEAGUE TABLE 2017-18

		P	W	D	L	F	A	GD	Pts
1	South Shields	42	32	7	3	112	37	75	103
2	Scarborough Athletic	42	30	5	7	101	42	59	95
3	Hyde United	42	27	11	4	90	35	55	92
4	Bamber Bridge	42	20	14	8	81	54	27	74
5	Prescot Cables	42	22	6	14	78	55	23	72
6	Trafford	42	17	15	10	61	50	11	66
7	Tadcaster Albion	42	17	11	14	67	46	21	62
8	Colne	42	18	8	16	68	61	7	62
9	Colwyn Bay	42	17	10	15	77	58	19	61
10	Atherton Collieries	42	15	13	14	50	55	-5	58
11	Glossop North End	42	15	8	19	66	72	-6	53
12	Clitheroe	42	15	6	21	69	79	-10	51
13	Droylsden	42	13	11	18	67	77	-10	50
14	Ramsbottom United	42	14	6	22	61	70	-9	48
15	Ossett Albion	42	12	11	19	56	76	-20	47
16	Ossett Town	42	14	5	23	55	77	-22	47
17	Brighouse Town	42	14	4	24	59	93	-34	46
18	Kendal Town	42	13	6	23	61	89	-28	45
19	Mossley	42	11	11	20	57	81	-24	44
20	Radcliffe Borough	42	12	8	22	51	89	-38	44
21	Skelmersdale United	42	8	13	21	53	84	-31	37
22	Goole AFC	42	8	7	27	49	109	-60	31

Play-Off Semi Finals: Bamber Bridge 2-1 Tadcaster Albion I Prescot Cables 3-0 Trafford
Final: Bamber Bridge 1-0 Prescot Cables

DIVISION ONE NORTH	1	2	3	4	5	6	7	8	9	10	11	12	13	14	15	16	17	18	19	20	21	22
1 Atherton Collieries		1-1	4-0	2-5	0-2	3-1	0-5	1-1	3-2	1-1	0-0	3-1	2-0	0-2	1-0	1-1	3-2	2-1	1-1	0-2	0-0	0-1
2 Bamber Bridge	1-1		3-2	2-1	1-1	2-2	2-2	1-1	6-1	1-1	4-0	2-2	1-0	3-2	1-0	3-0	2-3	0-0	0-0	3-2	3-1	5-0
3 Brighouse Town	0-3	3-3		2-0	2-1	2-2	2-3	0-2	2-3	1-1	2-3	1-0	4-2	1-3	2-1	0-1	3-2	0-1	1-0	1-5	2-3	0-2
4 Clitheroe	1-0	0-3	3-2		1-3	1-3	2-0	4-1	1-2	2-0	3-0	1-1	4-1	2-2	1-3	0-2	4-3	0-4	2-2	0-1	0-1	1-1
5 Colne	0-2	0-3	3-1	0-6		4-0	3-1	5-0	4-0	2-2	2-1	1-1	1-0	1-2	2-1	3-3	1-0	1-3	2-1	1-2	0-0	1-1
6 Colwyn Bay	1-2	2-2	4-0	5-1	0-0		1-2	5-1	5-0	0-3	2-1	5-0	1-1	1-0	3-0	3-0	2-2	1-2	1-1	4-2	1-1	1-1
7 Droylsden	1-1	1-1	0-3	0-3	1-2	3-1		2-3	1-1	1-3	0-1	2-0	2-0	2-1	1-3	3-1	1-0	1-3	2-0	1-2	2-2	1-1
8 Glossop North End	1-2	0-1	5-2	2-0	3-1	1-0	1-1		3-1	0-0	2-1	1-0	2-3	3-3	2-3	2-2	1-3	2-1	5-0	1-3	0-1	1-1
9 Goole AFC	1-1	1-4	0-3	1-2	2-3	0-1	2-2	0-3		1-4	0-4	5-1	2-2	0-3	1-4	1-1	1-0	1-3	3-3	1-3	2-0	1-0
10 Hyde United	4-0	0-1	5-1	4-0	1-0	4-3	2-1	2-0	5-0		3-1	5-1	1-0	1-1	2-1	4-1	1-1	3-1	0-0	1-1	4-1	6-1
11 Kendal Town	0-1	3-2	1-2	1-1	1-2	2-1	3-3	1-0	1-3	0-2		2-5	5-1	1-0	1-1	2-3	2-1	2-2	2-3	1-1	0-1	4-2
12 Mossley	2-0	1-3	2-1	1-3	1-1	2-0	0-0	0-0	4-2	1-2	5-4		1-4	3-2	2-0	0-0	2-0	1-3	4-4	2-3	0-0	1-1
13 Ossett Albion	3-1	4-0	0-0	3-0	2-1	0-3	3-3	1-2	1-1	2-0	2-2	1-0		1-2	0-0	2-1	0-2	2-5	3-1	2-2	2-2	1-4
14 Ossett Town	2-3	1-0	3-4	2-2	3-1	0-2	1-3	2-1	7-2	0-2	0-1	1-0	0-1		0-6	0-1	1-1	1-2	2-0	0-2	0-2	0-3
15 Prescot Cables	3-1	2-1	1-0	3-2	0-2	3-1	3-1	1-2	2-1	2-2	2-0	2-2	1-1	1-2		0-1	2-1	3-1	2-2	0-0	2-1	2-1
16 Radcliffe Borough	0-2	1-2	2-3	1-2	3-4	2-1	0-7	0-6	2-0	0-2	1-3	0-1	1-2	3-0	0-4		3-1	1-3	4-1	0-4	3-2	0-0
17 Ramsbottom United	1-0	0-1	2-1	1-0	0-4	1-2	3-1	4-2	3-0	1-2	3-1	2-4	0-0	0-2	1-0	3-0		1-3	1-1	2-3	2-1	3-1
18 Scarborough Athletic	1-0	2-3	4-0	4-1	2-0	0-2	2-0	4-1	0-0	7-0	4-1	2-0	3-1	3-0	5-1	2-1		2-1	1-3	3-0	1-1	
19 Skelmersdale United	0-0	1-3	0-1	1-4	2-0	0-2	2-3	2-0	1-2	0-2	0-2	2-1	3-1	3-0	1-6	3-3	3-2	1-4		0-1	1-3	1-1
20 South Shields	3-1	1-0	5-0	4-1	2-1	4-1	6-1	3-0	2-0	3-0	5-0	5-1	3-1	5-0	5-2	0-0	4-0	1-3	3-1		0-0	2-2
21 Tadcaster Albion	0-0	5-0	5-0	2-1	3-2	2-1	4-0	4-0	3-0	0-1	3-1	2-0	7-1	0-1	1-2	1-2	1-1	0-0	1-2	0-2		1-1
22 Trafford	1-1	1-1	0-2	3-1	1-0	0-0	3-0	3-2	2-1	1-0	4-0	1-0	1-0	4-0	0-2	3-0	2-1	1-2	2-2	1-2	1-0	

NORTHERN PREMIER LEAGUE DIVISION ONE SOUTH LEAGUE TABLE 2017-18

		P	W	D	L	F	A	GD	Pts
1	Basford United	42	31	7	4	101	42	59	100
2	Alvechurch	42	25	10	7	78	49	29	85
3	Frickley Athletic	42	26	7	9	117	61	56	82*
4	Bedworth United	42	22	8	12	73	58	15	74
5	Chasetown	42	22	7	13	83	64	19	73
6	Stamford	42	19	14	9	66	34	32	71
7	Leek Town	42	20	8	14	80	50	30	68
8	Lincoln United	42	21	5	16	85	81	4	68
9	Corby Town	42	18	6	18	74	75	-1	60
10	Cleethorpes Town	42	18	13	11	82	57	25	55*
11	Stocksbridge Park Steels	42	13	14	15	75	66	9	53
12	Peterborough Sports	42	15	6	21	70	78	-8	51
13	Spalding United	42	14	8	20	52	62	-10	50
14	Loughborough Dynamo	42	13	10	19	61	78	-17	49
15	Sheffield FC	42	10	15	17	66	85	-19	45
16	Belper Town	42	12	9	21	46	90	-44	45
17	Gresley FC	42	11	10	21	49	91	-42	43
18	Kidsgrove Athletic	42	11	9	22	70	90	-20	42
19	Carlton Town	42	10	11	21	66	76	-10	41
20	Newcastle Town	42	10	9	23	49	73	-24	39
21	Market Drayton Town	42	10	9	23	51	97	-46	39
22	Romulus	42	8	11	23	57	94	-37	35

Play-Off Semi Finals: Bedworth United 2-1 Chasetown I Frickley Athletic 1-2 Stamford
Final: Bedworth United 2-1 Stamford

DIVISION ONE SOUTH	1	2	3	4	5	6	7	8	9	10	11	12	13	14	15	16	17	18	19	20	21	22
1 Alvechurch		1-2	0-0	2-4	3-2	2-1	1-0	1-0	2-0	2-1	4-2	3-1	3-2	2-3	2-1	0-0	4-0	2-1	3-2	1-2	1-5	1-0
2 Basford United	1-1		2-0	1-0	6-2	1-1	2-2	4-0	3-2	1-1	5-0	3-2	3-2	1-0	4-1	5-1	3-0	3-0	4-0	2-1	2-1	3-1
3 Bedworth United	0-0	1-1		0-2	3-1	2-0	2-1	2-0	3-2	2-0	3-2	2-1	3-0	1-1	2-1	0-0	3-2	3-2	2-0	2-3	1-2	3-1
4 Belper Town	0-2	0-1	1-1		2-1	1-2	0-7	1-0	0-6	0-2	1-3	1-2	1-1	1-2	1-2	2-1	1-0	2-2	1-2	2-1	0-0	0-3
5 Carlton Town	1-3	2-3	2-1	4-1		2-4	1-1	1-1	2-2	1-2	0-1	0-1	1-2	0-2	3-0	3-1	1-1	3-1	3-0	0-0	1-1	1-1
6 Chasetown	0-1	5-0	3-1	5-1	3-0		1-1	2-1	3-4	4-0	4-0	1-0	1-3	0-0	3-1	1-1	5-4	2-0	4-3	2-0	0-2	3-1
7 Cleethorpes Town	1-0	2-3	3-1	4-4	2-2	1-1		1-4	0-1	4-1	2-1	1-1	1-3	3-1	2-0	5-1	1-2	6-0	0-4	2-1	1-0	1-1
8 Corby Town	3-1	1-4	0-1	5-0	2-1	2-1	1-1		1-2	0-2	3-1	2-1	2-3	2-0	4-4	0-1	2-2	5-1	1-1	3-1	1-1	2-1
9 Frickley Athletic	1-2	2-2	2-4	5-1	4-0	5-0	1-2	3-0		3-0	4-4	3-2	5-3	1-0	8-0	2-0	4-2	3-3	1-0	1-0	2-0	2-1
10 Gresley FC	1-1	1-0	1-2	1-2	3-2	0-4	2-2	1-4	1-6		0-3	1-3	3-4	2-0	2-1	1-1	1-0	2-2	0-1	1-8	1-2	3-3
11 Kidsgrove Athletic	1-2	0-2	1-2	0-3	3-3	1-1	0-1	1-2	3-2	2-2		1-1	2-2	3-2	4-0	2-3	2-5	1-1	2-2	0-1	0-1	2-1
12 Leek Town	3-3	0-1	3-0	0-0	4-3	1-2	0-0	6-1	2-2	0-1	0-1		3-1	1-0	2-1	4-2	0-3	3-1	3-0	0-0	1-0	2-0
13 Lincoln United	0-1	1-0	1-3	8-1	1-1	3-1	4-5	5-2	2-1	2-0	2-1	0-9		5-2	0-1	3-1	0-0	2-1	4-1	1-0	0-1	1-5
14 Loughborough Dynamo	0-3	1-3	3-2	1-3	0-3	1-2	0-2	4-3	2-2	2-2	3-3	0-3	0-2		3-1	0-0	2-1	4-1	1-1	2-0	3-1	1-2
15 Market Drayton Town	0-3	0-5	1-5	1-1	1-3	1-3	3-2	1-2	0-6	5-0	4-3	3-2	1-3	2-2		5-2	1-2	0-2	1-1	1-0	0-0	0-2
16 Newcastle Town	1-1	1-2	2-3	2-0	1-0	0-3	1-0	2-4	0-1	2-1	0-2	0-1	1-2	1-2	0-0		0-3	3-0	2-0	6-1	0-1	2-2
17 Peterborough Sports	1-3	1-2	2-0	4-0	1-4	2-3	1-4	2-0	3-2	1-1	3-0	1-2	2-3	1-2	0-1	1-0		5-1	3-1	0-2	2-0	1-9
18 Romulus	2-6	0-5	1-2	1-2	2-2	2-1	2-3	0-1	1-2	1-0	2-4	0-0	3-0	4-0	0-0	3-1	1-1		2-2	1-2	3-1	3-2
19 Sheffield FC	2-2	1-2	1-1	0-1	2-1	1-1	1-1	2-3	3-4	0-2	3-2	0-4	3-2	2-2	4-4	4-3	3-2	2-2		5-1	0-0	2-2
20 Spalding United	0-1	1-3	2-1	1-1	1-2	2-0	0-3	2-1	1-3	1-2	1-3	1-3	2-1	1-3	0-0	2-0	2-0	1-1	3-0		0-0	1-1
21 Stamford	0-0	3-1	1-1	3-0	1-0	6-0	1-0	2-0	2-4	6-0	4-1	1-0	3-0	1-1	4-0	1-1	1-1	3-0	2-2	1-1		1-1
22 Stocksbridge Park Steels	2-2	0-0	4-2	1-1	2-1	4-0	1-1	2-3	1-1	1-1	3-2	4-3	1-1	4-3	0-1	0-2	1-2	2-1	1-2	0-2	1-0	

LEAGUE CUP 2017-18

HOLDERS: BAMBER BRIDGE

PRELIMINARY ROUND

Chasetown	v	Market Drayton Town	0-3	141
Colne	v	Clitheroe	2-0	130
Scarborough Athletic	v	Sheffield FC	5-0	504
Lincoln United	v	Corby Town	4-4, 6-5p	104

ROUND ONE

Belper Town	v	Basford United	5-5, 4-5p	95
Altrincham	v	Ashton United	3-3, 4-3p	246
Bedworth United	v	Barwell	2-0	110
Colne	v	Workington	1-2	89
Colwyn Bay	v	Warrington Town	2-3	133
Frickley Athletic	v	Stocksbridge Park Steels	3-3, 6-7p	120
Glossop North End	v	Mossley	1-1, 3-4p	190
Grantham Town	v	Lincoln United	3-2	159
Halesowen Town	v	Romulus	1-1, 3-4p	131
Hednesford Town	v	Rushall Olympic	2-0	233
Hyde United	v	Trafford	0-0, 5-4p	167
Kendal Town	v	Lancaster City	0-2	168
Marine	v	Brighouse Town	4-1	169
Mickleover Sports	v	Loughborough Dynamo	3-1	101
Newcastle Town	v	Market Drayton Town	3-1	78
Prescot Cables	v	Bamber Bridge	1-4	165
Shaw Lane AFC	v	Cleethorpes Town	3-5	100
Skelmersdale United	v	Atherton Collieries	0-3	101
South Shields	v	Farsley Celtic	2-2, 5-3p	1056
Spalding United	v	Gresley FC	1-1, 4-3p	109
Stamford	v	Peterborough Sports	1-0	216
Sutton Coldfield Town	v	Stafford Rangers	1-1, 5-6p	77
Whitby Town	v	Scarborough Athletic	1-2	643
Witton Albion	v	Radcliffe Borough	3-0	114
Carlton Town	v	Matlock Town	1-1, 1-4p	125
Kidsgrove Athletic	v	Leek Town	2-1	169
Tadcaster Albion	v	Ossett Albion	2-1	175
Stourbridge	v	Alvechurch	2-4	431
Ramsbottom United	v	Stalybridge Celtic	3-0	182
Buxton	v	Coalville Town	3-5	87
Nantwich Town	v	Droylsden	3-1	135
Ossett Town	v	Goole AFC	2-0	96

ROUND TWO

Gresley FC	v	Basford United	2-4	79
Hednesford Town	v	Newcastle Town	1-0	192
Matlock Town	v	Grantham Town	3-2	132
Mickleover Sports	v	Bedworth United	3-0	71
Mossley	v	Altrincham	3-3, 5-4p	109
Nantwich Town	v	Witton Albion	2-3	138
Ramsbottom United	v	Hyde United	0-0, 4-3p	156
Romulus	v	Kidsgrove Athletic	0-1	26
Scarborough Athletic	v	Ossett Town	2-1	441
South Shields	v	Stocksbridge Park Steels	2-1	605
Stafford Rangers	v	Alvechurch	1-1, 4-2p	163
Coalville Town	v	Stamford	5-1	69
Cleethorpes Town	v	Tadcaster Albion	3-2	106
Warrington Town	v	Lancaster City	0-2	108
Workington	v	Marine	2-1	163
Atherton Collieries	v	Bamber Bridge	2-2, 4-2p	143

ROUND THREE

Basford United	v	Kidsgrove Athletic	3-0	114
Matlock Town	v	Hednesford Town	1-3	223
Mossley	v	Ramsbottom United	0-3	100
Mickleover Sports	v	Witton Albion	3-3, 4-3p	119
Lancaster City	v	Workington	0-0, 4-5p	114
Stafford Rangers	v	Coalville Town	2-3	145
Cleethorpes Town	v	South Shields	0-2	152
Atherton Collieries	v	Scarborough Athletic	2-0	141

QUARTER-FINALS

Coalville Town	v	Mickleover Sports	3-0	52
Hednesford Town	v	Basford United	5-0	188
Atherton Collieries	v	Ramsbottom United	2-0	162
Workington	v	South Shields	1-5	229

SEMI-FINALS

Hednesford Town	v	Atherton Collieries	1-4	211

Daniel Glover 72 (P)   *Jordan Cover 49, 70*
Bradley Cooke 53
Ben Harcastle 90

South Shields	v	Coalville Town	2-3	908

Michael Richardson 19, 74   *Daniel Creaney 2*
Natham Watson 49, 66

FINAL

Atherton Collieries	v	Coalville Town	2-1	374

Joshua Messer 8   *Nathan Watson 84*
Jordan Cover 65

ALTRINCHAM MATCH RESULTS 2017-18

Date	Comp	H/A	Opponents	Att:	Result		Goalscorers	Pos	No.
Aug 12	NPL	H	Stafford RangersW	611	L	0 - 3		23	1
15	NPL	A	Nantwich Town	670	D	1 - 1	Johnston 86 (pen)	20	2
19	NPL	A	Matlock Town	457	L	0 - 1		23	3
22	NPL	H	Whitby Town	579	W	1 - 0	Hancock 32	19	4
26	NPL	H	Coalville Town	592	W	4 - 2	Poole 10 Hancock 13 Jones 75 Hulme 90	14	5
28	NPL	A	Witton Albion	754	W	2 - 0	Poole 15 Mulholland 37	10	6
Sept 2	FAC 2Q	A	Abbey Hey	381	D	3 - 3	Johnston 5 Hancock 16 Hulme 23		7
9	NPL	A	Barwell	221	W	3 - 1	Poole 17 Hancock 40 Peers 90	8	8
12	NPL	A	Workington	339	L	2 - 5	Harrop 28 Hulme 66	9	9
16	FAC 3Q	A	Shildon	345	L	0 - 1			10
19	NPL	H	Farsley Celtic	497	W	6 - 0	Hancock 9 86 Peers 22 Johnston 48 Hulme 55 Hannigan 71	10	11
23	NPL	H	Grantham Town	736	W	1 - 0	Hulme 50	8	12
26	NPL	A	Hednesford Town	378	W	3 - 0	Hancock 33 Hulme 39 66	5	13
30	NPL	A	Stalybridge Celtic	528	D	0 - 0		5	14
Oct 3	NPL	H	Nantwich Town	636	W	5 - 1	Hannigan 37 Hulme 45 Johnston 45 Hancock 60 90	4	15
7	NPL	H	Rushall Olympic	984	W	4 - 0	Harrison 17 Hancock 38 Johnston 73 Hulme 89	3	16
10	NPL	A	Whitby Town	271	D	1 - 1	Poole 10	2	17
14	NPL	`H	Halesowen Town	808	W	3 - 0	Hancock 46 Johnston 53 (pen) Poole 81	1	18
21	NPL	H	Warrington Town	952	D	0 - 0		1	19
24	NPL	H	Lancaster City	618	W	4 - 0	Poole 36 Hulme 74 Richman 83 Johnston 86	1	20
28	FAT 1Q	H	Clitheroe	517	W	3 - 0	Johnston 54 Peers 81 90	1	21
Nov 4	NPL	H	Buxton	974	D	1 - 1	Hancock 8	1	22
11	FAT 2Q	H	Ramsbottom United	781	W	4 - 1	HULME 3 (17 34 49) Poole 85	1	23
18	NPL	A	Sutton Coldfield Town	269	W	4 - 0	Hulme 2 81 Jones 9 Moult 52	1	24
25	FAT 3Q	A	Alfreton Town	329	W	2 - 0	Marshall 7 (og) Johnston 17 (pen)	1	25
Dec 2	NPL	A	Mickleover Sports	250	W	2 - 0	Peers 20 Hulme 31		26
16	FAT 1	A	Warrington Town	545	D	0 - 0			27
19	FAT 1r	H	Warrington Town	453	L	1 - 2	Hulme 52		28
23	NPL	H	Matlock Town	807	W	3 - 0	Hulme 14 67 Hancock 89	1	29
26	NPL	A	Marine	619	W	3 - 0	Hannigan 30 Hulme 54 Hancock 83	1	30
30	NPL	A	Coalville Town	282	W	3 - 0	Poole 45 Hulme 71 Miller 87	1	31
Jan 1	NPL	H	Witton Albion	1013	L	3 - 4	Hulme 6 Poole 54 White 67	1	32
6	NPL	A	Farsley Celtic	380	W	1 - 0	Hulme 64	1	33
13	NPL	A	Stafford Rangers	599	W	2 - 0	Hulme 61 Harrison 77		34
27	NPL	H	Warrington Town	1419	D	1 - 1	Poole 90	1	35
Feb 6	NPL	H	Ashton United	610	W	3 - 2	Harrop 2 Poole 15 Hulme 73	1	36
17	NPL	H	Sutton Coldfield Town	905	W	2 - 1	Harrop 20 Johnston 79 (pen)	1	37
24	NPL	A	Ashton United	546	D	3 - 3	Johnston 32 (pen) 57 Jones 62	1	38
Mar 6	NPL	H	Stourbridge	542	W	4 - 1	Hampson 13 Poole 15 25 Johnston 38	1	39
13	NPL	H	Workington	510	L	2 - 3	Peers 61 69	1	40
17	NPL	H	Stalybridge Celtic	844	L	1 - 2	Johnston 90	1	41
20	NPL	H	Mickleover Sports	532	D	1 - 1	Moult 71	1	42
24	NPL	A	Halesowen Town	565	W	2 - 0	Hulme 11 Richman 39	1	43
27	NPL	H	Shaw Lane	805	W	5 - 1	Peers 10 Richman 48 Hulme 56 58 Moult 74	1	44
31	NPL	A	Rushall Olympic	382	L	0 - 2		1	45
Apr 7	NPL	A	Lancaster City	313	W	2 - 1	Hulme 10 Hannigan 17	1	46
9	NPL	A	Stourbridge	426	D	1 - 1	Hancock 75	1	47
14	NPL	H	Barwell	880	W	4 - 0	Densmore 38 Hancock 40 Johnston 47 Hulme 59	1	48
17	NPL	A	Buxton	434	D	0 - 0		1	49
19	NPL	A	Shaw Lane	292	W	2 - 1	Johnston 40 Hancock 85	1	50
21	NPL	A	Grantham Town	689	W	2 - 0	Merrie 50 Johnston 79	1	51
25	NPL	H	Marine	482	D	1 - 1	Hulme 10	1	52
28	NPL	H	Hednesford Town	1856	W	3 - 0	Hannigan 3 Moult 51 Hancock 90	1	53

GOALSCORERS	SG	CSG	Pens	Hat tricks	Total		SG	CSG	Pens	Hat tricks	Total
2016-17 Miller					10	Richman	3				3
Hulme	25	7		1	31	Harrison					2
Hancock	16	2			18	Densmore					1
Johnston	17	2	5		17	Hampson					1
Poole	12	2			13	Merrie					1
Peers	5	2			8	Miller					1
Hannigan	5				5	Mulholland					1
Moult	4				4	Opponents					1
Harrop	3				3	White					1
Jones	3				3						

ASHTON UNITED MATCH RESULTS 2017-18

Date	Comp	H/A	Opponents	Att:	Result	Goalscorers	Pos	No.
Aug 12	NPL	A	Hednesford Town	383	D 1 - 1	Chadwick 77	10	1
15	NPL	H	Farsley Celtic	175	D 1 - 1	Cartwright 68	17	2
19	NPL	H	Grantham Town	187	W 2 - 1	Tomsett 43 Lees 90	10	3
22	NPL	A	Warrington Town	245	W 1 - 0	Pritchard 29	5	4
26	NPL	A	Sutton Coldfield Town	193	W 2 - 0	Platt 23 Durnin 75	1	5
28	NPL	H	Buxton	254	L 1 - 4	Chadwick 60	6	6
Sept 2	FAC 1Q	A	Marine	324	W 3 - 1	Dyche 27 Tomsett 53 Chadwick 58 (pen)		7
5	NPL	A	Whitby Town	207	L 2 - 3	Tomsett 3 McGoldrick 87 (og)	10	8
12	NPL	H	Lancaster City	116	W 2 - 1	Dyche 32 Chadwick 70	9	9
16	FAC 2Q	A	Newcastle Benfield	149	L 1 - 2	Johnson 86	9	10
19	NPL	A	Marine	239	W 4 - 3	Chadwick 67 (pen) 73 (pen) Johnson 80 Lees 90	9	11
23	NPL	A	Nantwich Town	291	W 3 - 2	Chadwick 10 82 (pen) Lees 20	6	12
26	NPL	H	Workington	133	L 0 - 1		10	13
30	NPL	H	Hednesford Town	154	L 1 - 2	Tomsett 90	10	14
Oct 7	NPL	A	Mickleover Sports	345	W 5 - 2	Dyche 27 Evangelinos 55 Chadwick 83 90 Tomsett 84	9	15
10	NPL	H	Warrington Town	202	W 2 - 0	Platt 14 Dyche 77	6	16
14	NPL	A	Stafford Rangers	514	L 0 - 1		8	17
21	NPL	H	Shaw Lane	152	D 3 - 3	Johnson 16 Tomsett 20 Chadwick 89	8	18
24	NPL	A	Farsley Celtic	137	D 3 - 3	Chadwick 6 52 Dyche 9	7	19
28	FAT 1	H	Frickley Athletic	121	W 4 - 1	Chadwick 26 Tomsett 76 Johnson 82 Dyche 85		20
31	NPL	H	Matlock Town	133	W 3 - 0	Chsdwick 8 (pen) Dyche 45 Tomsett 52	5	21
Nov 4	NPL	A	Coalville United	165	W 2 - 1	Johnson 57 Fawns 78	5	22
11	FAT 2	A	Warrington Town	313	D 1 - 1	Chadwick 65		23
15	FAT 2r	H	Warrington Town	163	D 2 - 2	Dyche 61 90 (Lost 2-4 on pens)		24
18	NPL	H	Barwell	148	D 1 - 1	Pilkington 90	8	25
Dec 2	NPL	H	Rushall Olympic	143	W 2 - 1	Chadwick 25 (pen) 79 (pen)	6	26
23	NPL	H	Grantham Town	287	D 1 - 1	Evangelinos 81	6	27
30	NPL	H	Sutton Coldfield Town	168	W 2 - 0	Smith 9 Evangelinos 40	6	28
Jan 6	NPL	H	Marine	209	W 3 - 0	Evangelinos 20 23 Tomsett 87		29
13	NPL	A	Witton Albion	326	L 0 - 1		6	30
23	NPL	H	Stourbridge	158	W 1 - 0	Chalmers 25 (pen)		31
27	NPL	A	Shaw Lane	185	D 0 - 0		4	32
Feb 6	NPL	A	Altrincham	610	L 2 - 3	Chalmers 83 Pritchard 90	4	33
13	NPL	A	Lancasterr City	167	W 3 - 0	Pritchard 38 Tomsett 41 Mooney 69	5	34
17	NPL	A	Barwell	192	D 1 - 1	Mooney 42	5	35
24	NPL	H	Altrincham	546	D 3 - 3	Pritchard 33 68 Chadwick 89	5	36
Mar 10	NPL	H	Halesowen Town	188	W 3 - 0	Dean Smalley 21 Mooney 79 Pritchard 8 (pen)	3	37
13	NPL	H	Coalvillle Town	126	L 1 - 2	Sheridan 57	3	38
17	NPL	H	Stourbridge	367	W 3 - 2	Evangelinos 45 69 Granite 90	3	39
22	NPL	A	Buxton	347	L 0 - 1		3	40
24	NPL	H	Witton Albion	244	W 2 - 1	Dean Smalley 65 Dyche 81	3	41
27	NPL	A	Rushall Olympic	162	L 2 - 4	Tomsett 2 Pritchard 65	4	42
31	NPL	H	Mickleover Sports	204	D 1 - 1	Evangelinos 3	4	43
Apr 3	NPL	A	Stalybridge Celtic	360	D 2 - 2	Mooney 42 Dean Smalley 70	4	44
7	NPL	A	Whitby Town	172	W 4 - 0	Dean Smalley 3 Baines 7 Granite 27 Dom Smalley71(pen)	4	45
10	NPL	H	Stafford Rangers	138	W 1 - 0	Dean Smalley 8	4	46
14	NPL	H	Halesowen Town	375	D 1 - 1	Tomsett 90	4	47
17	NPL	H	Stalybridge Celtic	304	L 1 - 2	Baines 23	4	48
21	NPL	H	Nantwich Town	205	W 2 - 1	Tomsett 6 Sheridan 45	4	49
24	NPL	H	Matlock Town	248	W 2 - 1	Pritchard 22 Dyche 77	4	50
28	NPL	A	Workington	398	W 2 - 1	Pritchard 25 Tomsett 90	2	51
May 1	PO SF	H	Farsley Celtic	604	W 2 - 1	Tomsett 37 Chalmers 68 (pen)		52
5	PO Final	H	Grantham Town	931	W 2 - 0	Tomsett 57 Evangelinos 88		53

GOALSCORERS	SG	CSG	Pens	Hat tricks	Total		SG	CSG	Pens	Hat tricks	Total
2016-17 Chadwick					19	Baines	2				2
Chadwick	14	4	7		19	Granite	2				2
Tomsett	15	3			16	Platt	2				2
Dyche	9	3			10	Sheridan	2				2
Evangelinos	7	3			9	Cartwright					1
Pritchard	8	2	1		9	Durnin					1
Johnson	4				5	Fearns					1
Mooney	4	2			4	Opponents					1
Dean Smalley	3	3			4	Pilkington					1
Chalmers	3		2		3	Dom Smalley			1		1
Lees	3				3	Smith					1

BARWELL MATCH RESULTS 2017-18

Date	Comp	H/A	Opponents	Att:	Result	Goalscorers	Pos	No.
Aug 12	NPL	H	Whitby Town	152	W 1 - 0	Seal 79	8	1
15	NPL	A	Halesowen Town	345	L 0 - 1		12	2
19	NPL	A	Marine	301	W 1 - 0	Townsend 23	8	3
22	NPL	H	Rushall Olympic	144	D 4 - 4	Probert 53 (og) Seal 55 Robbins 61 Stenson 90	8	4
26	NPL	H	Witton Albion	162	L 0 - 1		13	5
28	NPL	A	Nantwich Town	352	D 2 - 2	Bates 45 McDonald (og) 74	14	6
Sept 2	FAC 2Q	A	Sutton Coldfield Town	186	W 2 - 9	Towers 79 90		7
5	NPL	A	Sutton Coldfield Town	103	W 6 - 0	Cleet (og) Perry 38 Nisevic 47 Seal 55 Towers 58 Robbins 79	13	8
9	NPL	H	Altrincham	221	L 1 - 3	Perry 64	12	9
11	NPL	A	Stourbridge	595	L 1 - 2	Perry 57 (pen)	12	10
16	FAC 3Q	A	AFC Telford United	541	L 0 - 2			11
19	NPL	H	Matlock Town	148	W 2 - 1	Stenson 37 Story 87	12	12
23	NPL	A	Farsley Celtic	179	W 2 - 1	Seal 46 (pen) Stenson 54	10	13
26	NPL	H	Mickleover SWports	138	W 2 - 1	Seal 9 49	8	14
28	NPL	A	Whitby Town	219	L 0 - 1		9	15
Oct 3	NPL	H	Halesowen Town	136	D 1 - 1	Perry 58	7	16
7	NPL	H	Shaw Lane	211	W 1 - 0	Stenson 58	7	17
10	NPL	A	Rushall Olympic	229	D 1 - 1	Perry 82 (pen)	8	18
14	NPL	H	Warrington Town	183	L 0 - 1		10	19
21	NPL	A	Stalybridge Celtic	345	L 2 - 4	Story 45 54	10	20
28	FAT Q1	H	Carlton Town	138	W 1 - 0	Bertram 10 (og)		21
31	NPL	A	Stafford Rangers	376	L 0 - 1		13	22
Nov 4	NPL	H	Hednesford Town	178	D 1 - 1	Stenson 81	13	23
11	FAT 2Q	H	Mildenhall Town	176	L 0 - 1			24
18	NPL	A	Ashton United	148	D 1 - 1	Stenson 90	15	25
Dec 2	NPL	A	Buxton	270	D 1 - 1	Nisevic 43	16	26
23	NPL	H	Marine	137	L 0 - 4		17	27
26	NPL	A	Coalville Town	198	W 3 - 0	Stenson 16 Nisevic 24 Hickey 33	17	28
30	NPL	A	Witton Albion	270	D 2 - 2	Stenson 22 Heath 71		29
Jan 1	NPL	H	Nantwich Town	163	L 0 - 2		16	30
6	NPL	A	Matlock Town	402	W 2 - 0	Stenson 33 Piggon 67	15	31
13	NPL	A	Lancaster City	237	D 1 - 1	Hickey 50	15	32
20	NPL	A	Workington	472	W 2 - 0	Hickey 43 Story 74	12	33
23	NPL	H	Grantham Town	202	D 1 - 1	Hildreth 79	12	34
27	NPL	H	Stalybridge Celtic	171	W 1 - 0	Stenson 11	10	35
Feb 3	NPL	H	Buxton	139	W 2 - 1	Hickey 21 Stenson 44	9	36
10	NPL	A	Hednesford Town	373	W 3 - 2	Stenson 47 51 Piggon 64	6	37
17	NPL	H	Ashton United	192	D 1 - 1	Reid 32	7	38
24	NPL	H	Workington	157	D 1 - 1	Hickey 37	7	39
Mar 10	NPL	A	Warrington Town	172	L 0 - 2		7	40
24	NPL	A	Grantham Town	319	L 1 - 4	Stenson 88	9	41
27	NPL	H	Stafford Rangers	1722	L 1 - 2	Morris 27 (og)	9	42
Apr 5	NPL	H	Coalville Town	237	W 2 - 1	Stenson 25 Piggon 35	7	43
7	NPL	H	Sutton Coldfield Town	145	W 2 - 1	Flint 35 (og) Stenson 60	7	44
14	NPL	A	Altrincham	880	L 0 - 4		8	45
17	NPL	H	Lancaster City	134	W 1 - 0	Stenson 33	8	46
21	NPL	H	Farsley Celtic	151	L 3 - 4	Stenson 34 Hickey 52 74	9	47
24	NPL	H	Stourbridge	126	D 1 - 1	Baldwin 90	9	48
26	NPL	A	Shaw Lane	127	L 2 - 3	Baldwin 76 Warmington 89	9	49
28	NPL	A	Mickleover Sports	166	D 3 - 3	Hickey 7 Piggon 12 34	10	50

GOALSCORERS	SG	CSG	Pens	Hat tricks	Total		SG	CSG	Pens	Hat tricks	Total
2016-17 Hickey					21	Baldwin	2				2
Stenson	17	3			18	Robbins	2				2
Hickey	7	2			8	Bates					1
Opponents					6	Heath					1
Seal	5	2	1		6	Hildreth					1
Perry	4		2		5	Reid					1
Piggon	4				5	Townsend					1
Story	3				4	Warmington					1
Nisevic	3				3						
Towers	3				3						

BUXTON MATCH RESULTS 2017-18

Date	Comp	H/A	Opponents	Att:	Result	Goalscorers	Pos	No.
Aug 12	NPL	H	Lancaster City	244	L 1 - 2	Dixon 4	16	1
15	NPL	A	Witton Albion	336	L 0 - 1		21	2
19	NPL	A	Stafford Rangers	592	W 4 - 1	Doran 33 Smith 49 Hardy 57 90	13	3
22	NPL	H	Shaw Lane	320	L 0 - 2		20	4
26	NPL	H	Halesowen Town	278	W 2 - 0	Morrison 4 Hardy 28	15	5
28	NPL	A	Ashton United	254	W 4 - 1	HARDY 3 (25 42 75) Young 44	11	6
Sept 2	FAC 1Q	H	Frickley Athletic	157	W 3 - 2	Morrison 36 Maguire 57 Hardy 79 (pen)	9	7
5	NPL	A	Nantwich Town	350	W 3 - 1	Stair 32 (og) Hardy 36 58	6	8
8	NPL	H	Mickleover Sports	359	L 0 - 2		7	9
12	NPL	A	Stalybridge Celtic	206	W 1 - 0	Hardy 34	7	10
16	FAC 2Q	H	Chasetown	314	W 4 - 1	Hardy 9 20 Doran 11 Young 90		11
23	NPL	A	Sutton Coldfield Town	177	L 1 - 2	Hardy 44 (pen)	12	12
26	NPL	H	Whitby Town	218	L 0 - 2		14	13
30	FAC 3Q	H	Alvechurch	309	W 2 - 1	Ravenhill 87 Smith 90		14
Oct 3	NPL	H	Witton Albion	238	W 2 - 0	Abbott 5 Smith 45	13	15
7	NPL	H	Marine	346	W 2 - 1	Hinsley 30 Hardy 50	13	16
9	NPL	A	Shaw Lane	241	L 0 - 2		13	17
14	FAC 4Q	A	Gateshead	653	L 1 - 2	Hardy 67		18
21	NPL	A	Coalville Town	166	W 5 - 1	McWilliams 18 Hardy 34 90 Wilson 69 81	13	19
24	NPL	H	Warrington	240	W 2 - 1	Hardy 21 Wilson 51	8	20
28	FAT 1Q	H	Cleethorps Town	261	L 1 - 2	Hinsley 2		21
31	NPL	H	Rushall Olympic	154	L 1 - 2	Abbott 35	8	22
Nov 4	NPL	A	Altrincham	974	D 1 - 1	Hinsley 2	10	23
11	NPL	H	Farsley Celtic	337	D 3 - 3	Hardy 4 37 (pen) Wilson 80	10	24
18	NPL	H	Grantham Town	331	L 0 - 3		11	25
Dec 2	NPL	H	Barwell	270	D 1 - 1	Hinsley 33	14	26
16	NPL	H	Grantham Town	297	W 1 - 0	Hardy 10	8	27
23	NPL	H	Stafford Rangers	300	D 1 - 1	McGee 52 (pen)	9	28
26	NPL	A	Matlock Town	930	D 3 - 3	HARDY 3 (12 26 79 pen)	9	29
30	NPL	A	Halesowen Town	424	W 3 - 1	HARDY 3 (1 29 31)	8	30
6	NPL	A	Warrington Town	271	L 0 - 1		11	31
13	NPL	H	Stalybridge Celtic	375	D 2 - 2	Broadbent 65 McDermott 75	12	32
20	NPL	A	Farsley Celtic	231	L 0 - 3		13	33
27	NPL	H	Coalville Town	271	D 2 - 2	Hardy 21 (pen) McGee 89	13	34
Feb 3	NPL	A	Barwell	139	L 1 - 2	Hardy 34 (pen)	15	35
17	NPL	A	Stourbridge	476	L 1 - 2	Grayson 30	15	36
Mar 13	NPL	H	Stourbridge	172	D 1 - 1	Hardy 54 (pen)	14	37
17	NPL	A	Workington	299	W 2 - 1	Maguire 36 Wilson 72	16	38
22	NPL	H	Ashton United	347	W 1 - 0			39
24	NPL	H	Hednesford Town	366	D 2 - 2	Hardy 59 72	13	40
31	NPL	A	Marine	396	L 2 - 3	Hardy 34 Grayson 56 Maguire 88		41
Apr 3	NPL	H	Matlock Town	330	L 2 - 3	Taylor 59 Amos 70	13	42
5	NPL	A	Hednesford Town	277	W 2 - 1	Broadbent 22 Wilson 54	13	43
7	NPL	A	Workington	305	W 4 - 2	Hardy 27 (pen) 90 Wilson 37 Grayson 76	9	44
10	NPL	A	Rushall Olympic	171	L 0 - 2			45
14	NPL	A	Mickleover Sports	232	D 2 - 2	Degirolamo 50 Wilson 81	9	46
17	NPL	H	Altrincham	434	D 0 - 0		9	47
19	NPL	H	Nantwich Town	239	W 3 - 0	Hardy 38 86 (pen) Meade 49	8	48
21	NPL	H	Sutton Coldfield Town	341	L 0 - 1		8	49
24	NPL	H	Lancaster City	125	D 1 - 1	Kilifin	8	50
28	NPL	A	Whitby Town	272	D 1 - 1	Chippendale 45	9	51

GOALSCORERS	SG	CSG	Pens	Hat tricks	Total		SG	CSG	Pens	Hat tricks	Total
2016-17 Grayson					20	Young	2				2
Hardy	23	4	10	3	37	Amos					1
Wilson	7				8	Chippendale					1
Hinsley	4				4	Degirolamo					1
Grayson	3				3	Dixon					1
Maguire	3				3	Kilifin					1
Abbott	2				2	McDermott					1
Broadbent	2				2	McWilliams					1
Doran	2				2	Meade					1
McGee	2		1		2	Opponents					1
Morrison	2				2	Ravenhill					1
Smith	2				2	Smith					1
						Taylor					1

COALVILLE TOWN MATCH RESULTS 2017-18

Date	Comp	H/A	Opponents	Att:	Result	Goalscorers	Pos	No.
Aug 12	NPL	A	Farsley Celtic	244	L 1 - 3	Cox 11	19	1
15	NPL	H	Stourbridge	173	L 0 - 1		23	2
19	NPL	H	Warrington Town	128	L 0 - 3		24	3
22	NPL	A	Grantham Town	242	W 1 - 0	McDonald 88	24	4
26	NPL	A	Altrincham	592	L 2 - 4	Towers 32 Anderson 53	24	5
28	NPL	H	Mickleover Sports	227	W 2 - 0	Anderson 24 74	19	6
Sept 2	FAC 2Q	A	St Ives Town	203	L 0 - 1			7
5	NPL	H	Matlock Town	137	W 2 - 1	Anderson 10 Yates 33 (og)	15	8
9	NPL	A	Marine	237	W 1 - 0	Watson 35	11	9
12	NPL	H	Hednesford Town	217	W 5 - 2	Towers 8 Watson 23 Oji 37(og) Creaney 49 52	8	10
16	NPL	H	Witton Albion	159	W 2 - 1	McGlinchey 6 Towers 54	5	11
19	NPL	A	Sutton Coldfield Town	126	D 1 - 1	Watson 41	4	12
23	NPL	H	Stalybridge Celtic	155	W 4 - 0	Creaney 29 56 Watson 65 67	2	13
26	NPL	A	Rushall Olympic	211	D 1 - 1	Freeman 35	3	14
30	NPL	H	Farsley Celtic	158	L 2 - 3	Watson 31 Baldwin 56 (og)	6	15
Oct 2	NPL	A	Stourbridge	640	L 1 - 2	McGlinchey 53	6	16
7	NPL	A	Workington Town	401	L 0 - 1		10	17
10	NPL	H	Grantham Town	224	L 1 - 3	Creaney 76 (pen)	12	18
14	NPL	A	Witton Albion	259	L 2 - 5	Cox 41 Freeman 69	13	19
21	NPL	H	Buxton	166	L 1 - 5	Creaney 7	16	20
28	FAT 1Q	A	Redditch United	208	W 1 - 0	Watson 76		21
31	NPL	A	Halesowen Town	278	W 3 - 2	Towers 13 Creaney 33 (pen) Watson 78	15	22
Nov 4	NPL	H	Ashton United	165	L 1 - 2	Watson 13	14	23
11	FAT 2Q	A	Alvechurch	213	W 5 - 1	McGlinchey 8 90 CREANEY 3 (23 63 80)		24
18	NPL	A	Lancaster City	259	L 2 - 4	Watson 16 Jenno 86	16	25
25	FAT 3Q	A	York City	1001	L 1 - 3	Creaney 78		26
Dec 2	NPL	A	Nantwich Town	209	W 3 - 1	Taylor 26 Hollis 44 Creaney 52	15	27
9	NPL	A	Whitby Town	239	D 2 - 2	Watson 24 Creaney 59	15	28
23	NPL	A	Warrington Town	228	W 3 - 1	McGlinchey 32 49 Creaney 84	11	29
26	NPL	H	Barwell	198	L 0 - 3		12	30
30	NPL	H	Altrincham	282	L 0 - 3		14	31
Jan 1	NPL	A	Mickleover Sports	149	D 2 - 2	Watson 13 Anderson 78	14	32
6	NPL	H	Sutton Coldfield Town	128	W 4 - 2	CREANEY 3 (11 30 45) Watson 35	14	33
13	NPL	A	Hednesford Town	398	D 1 - 1	Watson 73	14	34
23	NPL	H	Stafford Rangers	118	D 0 - 0		14	35
27	NPL	A	Buxton	271	D 2 - 2	Watson 49 (pen) 63	14	36
Feb 3	NPL	H	Nantwich Town	110	L 0 - 3		16	37
6	NPL	H	Shaw Lane	103	L 1 - 3	Jenno 68	16	38
17	NPL	H	Lancaster City	131	L 1 - 4	Dixon 38	17	39
24	NPL	A	Shaw Lane	193	L 0 - 2		18	40
Mar 13	NPL	A	Ashton United	126	W 2 - 1	McGlinchley 30 Watson70	17	41
17	NPL	A	Stafford Rangers	145	L 1 - 4	Watson 20	18	42
24	NPL	H	Whitby Town	132	L 0 - 1		18	43
Apr 5	NPL	A	Barwell	237	L 1 - 2	Crane 54	18	44
7	NPL	A	Matlock Town	356	L 1 - 2	Creaney 6	21	45
14	NPL	H	Marine	109	L 2 - 3	Bryant 6 Howes 90	22	46
17	NPL	H	Halesowen Town	103	W 1 - 0	Watson 90 (pen)	21	47
21	NPL	A	Stalybridge Celtic	285	W 3 - 0	Towers 20 Taylor 59 Woolley 85	21	48
25	NPL	H	Workington Town	120	W 3 - 0	Creaney 16 29 Watson 51	19	49
28	NPL	H	Rushall Olympic	116	L 2 - 5	Creaney 8 Woolley 78	20	50

GOALSCORERS	SG	CSG	Pens	Hat tricks	Total		SG	CSG	Pens	Hat tricks	Total
2016-17 Watson					15	Taylor	2				2
Creaney	15	4	3	2	21	Woolley	2				2
Watson	19	3	2		20	Bryant					1
McGlinchey	4				7	Crane					1
Anderson	4	2			5	Dixon					1
Towers	5	2			5	Hollis					1
Opponents					3	Howes					1
Cox					2	McDonald					1
Freeman					2						
Jenno					2						

FARSLEY CELTIC MATCH RESULTS 2017-18

Date	Comp	H/A	Opponents	Att:	Result	Goalscorers	Pos	No.
Aug 12	NPL	H	Coalville Town	244	W 3 - 1	Cartman 32 Walshaw 50 (pen) 78	3	1
15	NPL	A	Ashton United	175	D 1 - 1	Walshaw 77	3	2
19	NPL	A	Halesowen Town	357	W 2 - 1	Cartman 29 Walshaw 31	2	3
22	NPL	H	Lancaster City	283	D 0 - 0		2	4
26	NPL	H	Rushall Olympic	176	W 1 - 0	Walshaw 32 (pen)	2	5
28	NPL	A	Shaw Lane	287	L 0 - 1		4	6
Sept 2	FAC 1Q	A	Stalybridge Celtic	289	L 1 - 2	Walshaw 35		7
5	NPL	A	Stalybridge Celtic	215	W 5 - 4	Atkinson 24 Walshaw 36 66 Baldwin 61 Harris 73	3	8
9	NPL	A	Warrington Town	251	L 2 - 4	Walshaw 33 (pen) Walker 68	5	9
12	NPL	H	Grantham Town	172	W 3 - 0	Walshaw 41 Atkinson 45 Walker 86	4	10
16	NPL	H	Halesowen Town	218	W 3 - 1	Watson 27 Marshall 30 Walshaw 90	2	11
19	NPL	A	Altrincham	497	L 0 - 6		4	12
23	NPL	H	Barwell	179	L 1 - 2	Walshaw 87 (pen)	7	13
26	NPL	A	Marine	255	W 2 - 1	Baldwin 30 Walshaw 51 (pen)	4	14
30	NPL	A	Coalville Town	158	W 3 - 2	Walshaw 25 (pen) Priestley 63 Atkinson 78	2	15
Oct 7	NPL	H	Nantwich Town	260	W 2 - 0	Walshaw 67 82	4	16
14	NPL	A	Lancaster City	271	D 1 - 1	Clayton 71		17
21	NPL	H	Mickleover Sports	188	L 0 - 3		4	18
24	NPL	H	Ashton United	137	D 3 - 3	Atkinson 19 Preistley 78 Walshaw 90	4	19
28	FAT 1Q	H	South Shields	382	D 1 - 1	Walshaw 62		20
31	FAT 1Qr	A	South Shields	1012	L 3 - 4	Watson 90 Ellis 113 Parkin 114 (aet)		21
Nov 4	NPL	H	Workington	278	D 3 - 3	WALSHAW 3 (10 28 74)	6	22
11	NPL	A	Buxton	337	D 3 - 3	Watson 15 (pen) Walshaw 70 Preistley 90	6	23
18	NPL	A	Stafford Rangers	490	W 2 - 0	Cartman 10 Priestley 79	5	24
25	NPL	H	Sutton Coldfield Town	217	L 0 - 1		5	25
Dec 2	NPL	A	Hednesford Town	304	L 1 - 2	Cartman 54	7	26
26	NPL	A	Whitby Town	369	W 2 - 0	Walker 57 Cockerline 62	7	27
30	NPL	A	Rushall Olympic	179	D 1 - 1	Ellis 89	7	28
Jan 1	NPL	H	Shaw Lane	226	W 4 - 2	Ellis 21 Cartman 56 90 Cockerline 70	6	29
6	NPL	H	Altrincham	380	L 0 - 1		8	30
13	NPL	A	Grantham Town	287	D 2 - 2	Ellis 26 Clayton 34	8	31
20	NPL	A	Buxton	231	W 3 - 0	Cartman 11 Parkin 80 82	6	32
Jan 23	NPL	H	Matlock Town	141	L 1 - 2	Turner 45	6	33
27	NPL	A	Mickleover Sports	236	D 2 - 2	Cartman 49 Murray 87	6	34
Feb 3	NPL	H	Hednesford Town	204	L 1 - 3	Atkinson 5	7	35
12	NPL	A	Stourbridge	402	W 2 - 1	Atkinson 18 Baldwin 46	5	36
17	NPL	H	Stafford Rangers	246	W 1 - 0	Watson 52	6	37
24	NPL	A	Sutton Coldfield Town	144	W 1 - 0	Watson 84	4	38
Mar 17	NPL	H	Matlock Town	189	W 2 - 1	Ellis 62 79	4	39
24	NPL	H	Stourbridge	262	L 1 - 4	Watson 5 (pen)	5	40
31	NPL	A	Nantwich Town	298	D 1 - 1	Clayton 9	5	41
Apr 5	NPL	H	Whitby Town	146	W 4 - 0	Turner 39 Cartman 59 61 Parkin 82	4	42
7	NPL	A	Stalybridge Celtic	325	W 4 - 1	CARTMAN 3 (31 35 80) Turner 48	5	43
10	NPL	A	Workington	189	W 2 - 1	Turner 9 76	5	44
12	NPL	H	Witton Albion	198	D 1 - 1	Cartman 42	5	45
14	NPL	H	Warrington Town	252	L 0 - 2		5	46
21	NPL	A	Barwell	151	W 4 - 3	Turner 27 90 Clayton 62 Walker 88	5	47
22	NPL	A	Witton Albion	163	W 4 - 1	Parkin 28 BALDWIN 3 (50 56 66)	5	48
28	NPL	H	Marine	354	W 3 - 0	Cartman 10 Parkin 44 Baldwin 77	5	49
May 1	PO SF	A	Ashton United	604	L 1 - 2	Turner 71		50

GOALSCORERS	SG	CSG	Pens	Hat tricks	Total		SG	CSG	Pens	Hat tricks	Total
Walshaw	17	5	6	1	22	Walker	4	2			4
Cartman	11	2		1	15	Cockerline	2				2
Turner	6	3			8	Harris					1
Baldwin	4			1	7	Marshall					1
Atkinson	6				6	Murray					1
Ellis	5	2			6						
Parkin	5				6						
Watson	6		2		6						
Clayton	4				4						
Priestley	4	2			4						

GRANTHAM TOWN MATCH RESULTS 2017-18

Date	Comp	H/A	Opponents	Att:	Result	Goalscorers	Pos	No.
Aug 12	NPL	H	Marine	265	W 5 - 0	Wright 44 77 Lee Shaw 60 68 McMenemy 86	1	1
15	NPL	A	Rushall Olympic	242	W 2 - 0	Lee Shaw 45 71	1	2
19	NPL	A	Ashton United	187	L 1 - 2	Luke Shaw 73	6	3
22	NPL	H	Coalville Town	242	L 0 - 1		9	4
26	NPL	H	Whitby Town	244	W 2 - 0	Luke Shaw 70 Meadows 86	6	5
28	NPL	H	Matlock Town	529	W 3 - 2	Hempenstall 15 Burrows 24 Lee Shaw 34	2	6
Sept 2	FAC 1Q	H	Holbeach United	302	W 2 - 1	Luke Shaw 24 Wright 45 (pen)		7
5	NPL	A	Mickleover Sports	235	L 0 - 1		5	8
9	NPL	H	Workington	236	W 3 - 2	Hempenstall 56 86 Lee Shaw 90	2	9
12	NPL	A	Farsley Celtic	172	L 0 - 3		6	10
16	FAC 2Q	H	Alvechurch	332	L 3 - 4	Galinski 43 Lewis 74 Dasaolu 90		11
19	NPL	H	Haleasowen Town	175	L 1 - 2	Wright 39	9	12
23	NPL	A	Altrincham	736	L 0 - 1		11	13
26	NPL	H	Sutton Coldfield Town	164	W 6 - 1	Lee SHAW 4 (18 29 78 81) Luke Shaw 81 Wright 90	11	14
30	NPL	A	Marine	389	D 1 - 1	Wright 37	12	15
Oct 3	NPL	H	Rushall Olympic	186	W 7 - 1	Hempenstall 9 WRIGHT 3 (15 (pen) 39 49) Luto 31 39 Hollingsworth 45	7	16
7	NPL	H	Stafford Rangers	320	L 1 - 2	Lee Shaw 86 (pen)	12	17
10	NPL	A	Coalville Town	224	W 3 - 1	Meadows 30 Lee Shaw 51 Luke Shaw 63	7	18
13	NPL	H	Stalybridge Celtic	272	D 0 - 0		7	19
21	NPL	A	Stourbridge	600	W 2 - 0	Story 45 54		20
28	FAT 1Q	H	Halesowen Town	226	W 1 - 0	Hempenstall 51		21
31	NPL	A	Hednesford Town	299	W 3 - 1	King 25 (og) Lee Shaw 30 79	4	22
Nov 4	NPL	H	Lancaster City	274	W 3 - 2	Hempenstall 3 Burrows 61 77	3	23
11	FAT Q2	A	Kidsgrove Athletic	242	W 2 - 0	Galinski 82 Lee Shaw 90 (pen)		24
18	NPL	A	Buxton	331	W 3 - 0	LEE SHAW 3 (28 78 pen 88)	3	25
25	FAT Q3	H	Chorley	361	L 3 - 4	Meadows 9 Lee Shaw 27 45		26
Dec 2	NPL	A	Witton Albion	237	W 3 - 2	Hempenstall 21 56 Galinski 75	2	27
16	NPL	H	Buxton	297	L 0 - 1		3	28
23	NPL	H	Ashton United	287	D 1 - 1	Lee Shaw 73	3	29
Jan 1	NPL	A	Matlock Town	270	W 2 - 1	Lee Shaw 29 45	3	30
6	NPL	A	Halesowen Town	336	W 3 - 1	Burrows 30 Lee Shaw 37 Wright 64	2	31
13	NPL	H	Farsley Celtic	287	D 2 - 2	Burrows 5 Hempenstall 15	2	32
23	NPL	A	Barwell	202	D 1 - 1	Hempenstall 53	2	33
27	NPL	A	Stourbridge	256	W 4 - 2	Wright 22 Meadows 37 Lee Shaw 45 Hollingsworth 45	2	34
Feb 3	NPL	H	Witton Albiuon	239	D 1 - 1	Lewis 90	3	35
24	NPL	A	Nantwich Town	327	L 1 - 3	Lee Shaw 89	6	36
Mar 13	NPL	H	Nantwich Town	183	D 0 - 0		6	37
17	NPL	A	Warrington Town	241	L 1 - 2	Meadows 90	6	38
22	NPL	A	Shaw Lane	193	W 2 - 0	Burrows 47 69	5	39
24	NPL	H	Barwell	319	W 4 - 1	Hakeem 37 Meadows 53 90 Osbourne 84	4	40
27	NPL	A	Stalybridge Celtic	276	W 3 - 1	Hakeem 17 Lee Shaw 24 Osborne 88	3	41
31	NPL	A	Stafford Rangers	563	W 2 - 1	Meadows 35 Hempenstall 60	3	42
Apr 2	NPL	H	Shaw Lane	484	W 3 - 1	Lee Shaw 58 73 Hemperstall 84	3	43
7	NPL	H	Mickleover Sports	377	L 0 - 3		3	44
10	NPL	A	Lancaster City	123	L 1 - 3	Burrows 64	3	45
14	NPL	A	Workington	228	W 2 - 0	Osbourne 34 Lee Shaw 90	3	46
17	NPL	H	Hednesford Town	271	D 1 - 1	Galinski 90	3	47
19	NPL	A	Whitby Town	223	W 5 - 1	Meadows12 Hempenstall 50 85Osbourne 73 Wright90	3	48
21	NPL	H	Altrincham	689	L 0 - 2		3	49
24	NPL	A	Warrington Town	301	D 0 - 0		4	50
28	NPL	A	Sutton Coldfield Town	207	W 2 - 0	Hempenstall 20 50	4	51
May 1	PO SF	A	Warrington Town	737	W 3 - 0	Galinski 62 Meadows 71 Hempenstall 85		52
5	PO Final	A	Ashton United	931	L 0 - 2			53

GOALSCORERS	SG	CSG	Pens	Hat tricks	Total		SG	CSG	Pens	Hat tricks	Total
2016-17 *Lee Shaw*					23	Hollingsworth	2				2
Lee Shaw	18	4x2	3	2	30	Lewis	2				2
Hempenstall	13	3			17	Luto	2				2
Wright	8	3	2	1	12	Story	1				2
Meadows	9				10	Dasaolu					1
Burrows	5				8	McMenemy					1
Galinski	5				5	Opponents					1
Luke Shaw	5				5						
Osbourne	3	2			4						
Hakeem					2						

HALESOWEN TOWN MATCH RESULTS 2017-18

Date	Comp	H/A	Opponents	Att:	Result	Goalscorers	Pos	No.
Aug 12	NPL	A	Workington	638	L 1 - 3	Taylor 62 (og)	20	1
15	NPL	H	Barwell	345	W 1 - 0	Shearer 90	14	2
19	NPL	H	Farsley Celtic	357	L 1 - 2	Agbor 87	17	3
22	NPL	H	Hednesford Town	404	L 0 - 2		22	4
26	NPL	A	Buxton	278	L 1 - 2	Maguire 45 (og)	22	5
28	NPL	H	Sutton Coldfield Town	372	L 0 - 2		23	6
Sept 2	FAC 2Q	H	Basford United	359	L 0 - 3			7
5	NPL	H	Stafford Rangers	261	D 1 - 1	Finney 62	23	8
12	NPL	H	Witton Albion	208	L 1 - 3	Kelly 59	24	9
16	NPL	H	Farsley Celtic	218	L 1 - 3	Chilton 68	23	10
19	NPL	A	Grantham Town	175	W 2 - 1	Smith 37 Udah 80	23	11
23	NPL	H	Warrington Town	280	D 1 - 1	Spray 69	23	12
26	NPL	A	Stalybridge Celtic	191	L 0 - 1		24	13
30	NPL	H	Workington	259	L 1 - 5	Udah 5	24	14
Oct 3	NPL	A	Barwell	136	D 1 - 1	Kelly 71	22	15
7	NPL	A	Stourbridge	2306	W 2 - 1	Udah 6 44	22	16
10	NPL	H	Hednesford Town	352	W 2 - 1	Mutton 31 (og) Udah 36	21	17
14	NPL	A	Altrincham	808	L 0 - 3		21	18
21	NPL	H	Lancaster City	612	W 4 - 3	Charlton 37 McAtee 48 57 Diop 90	21	19
28	FAT 1Q	A	Grantham Town	226	L 0 - 1			20
31	NPL	H	Coalville Town	278	L 2 - 3	Jones 24 Udah 38	21	21
Nov 4	NPL	A	Rushall Olympic	391	L 1 - 3	Udah 87	22	22
11	NPL	H	Shaw Lane	308	D 0 - 0		23	23
18	NPL	H	Marine	276	D 1 - 1	Lawton 83	23	24
25	NPL	A	Matlock Town	342	L 0 - 2		23	25
Dec 2	NPL	H	Whitby Town	225	W 3 - 1	McAtee 36 81 Kelly 61	21	26
26	NPL	H	Mickleover Sports	402	D 0 - 0		22	27
30	NPL	H	Buxton	424	L 1 - 3	Ekongo 36	22	28
Jan 1	NPL	A	Sutton Coldfield Town	287	W 1 - 0	Goddard 55	22	29
6	NPL	H	Grantham Town	338	L 1 - 3	Agbor 87	22	30
13	NPL	H	Nantwich Town	308	L 0 - 1		22	31
20	NPL	A	Shaw City	175	L 2 - 3	Ekongo 37 Goddard 42	22	32
27	NPL	A	Lancaster City	259	L 0 - 2		22	33
Feb 3	NPL	A	Whitby Town	202	L 0 - 5		22	34
10	NPL	H	Rushall Olympic	420	W 2 - 0	Knight 46 Kelly 65	21	35
17	NPL	A	Marine	462	L 0 - 1		23	36
24	NPL	H	Matlock Town	362	W 3 - 2	Weir-Daley 3 Agbor 88 Knight 90	23	37
Mar 10	NPL	A	Ashton United	183	L 0 - 3		23	38
17	NPL	A	Nantwich Town	193	W 3 - 1	Bragoli 11 Hughes 21 61	23	39
24	NPL	H	Altrincham	565	L 0 - 2		23	40
27	NPL	A	Witton Albion	247	W 3 - 2	Ryan 27 (og) Ali 76 Hughes 90	23	41
31	NPL	H	Stourbridge	1763	W 1 - 0	Ali 36	23	42
Apr 7	NPL	A	Stafford Rangers	475	D 0 - 0		23	43
14	NPL	H	Ashton United	375	D 1 - 1	Agbor 70	23	44
17	NPL	A	Coalville Town	103	L 0 - 1		23	45
21	NPL	A	Warrington Town	300	D 1 - 1	Agbor 71	23	46
25	NPL	A	Mickleover Sports	175	D 0 - 0		23	47
28	NPL	H	Stalybridge Celtic	446	W 2 - 0	Agbor 57 Ali 67	23	48

GOALSCORERS	SG	CSG	Pens	Hat tricks	Total		SG	CSG	Pens	Hat tricks	Total
2016-17 *Anderson*					*18*	Bragoli					1
Udah	5	2			7	Charlton					1
Agbor	6				6	Chilton					1
Kelly	4				4	Diop					1
McAtee	2				4	Finney					1
Opponents					4	Jones					1
Ali	3				3	Lawton					1
Hughes	2				3	Shearer					1
Ekongo	2				2	Smith					1
Goddard	2				2	Spray					1
Knight	2				2	Weir-Daley					1

HEDNESFORD TOWN MATCH RESULTS 2017-18

Date	Comp	H/A	Opponents	Att:	Result	Goalscorers	Pos	No.
Aug 12	NPL	H	Ashton United	383	D 1 - 1	Glover 34 (pen)	11	1
15	NPL	A	Matlock Town	347	L 2 - 3	Doyle-Charles 10 (og) Lawrie 42	15	2
19	NPL	A	Shaw Lane	152	L 1 - 3	Dodd 30	22	3
22	NPL	H	Halesowen Town	404	W 2 - 0	Green 1 Rodgers 10	18	4
26	NPL	H	Lancaster City	412	D 1 - 1	Glover 87	16	5
28	NPL	A	Stafford Ranagers	1226	W 1 - 0	Dodd 61	15	6
Sept 2	FAC 2Q	A	Boston Town	157	L 0 - 2			7
4	NPL	A	Stourbridge	683	L 0 - 2		15	8
9	NPL	H	Sutton Coldfield Town	410	W 3 - 0	Rodgers 14 Glover 23 Thorley 86	13	9
12	NPL	A	Coalville Town	217	L 2 - 5	Glover 32 90 (pen)	15	10
16	NPL	A	Workington	379	L 0 - 1		19	11
19	NPL	H	Nantwich Town	319	W 1 - 0	Stair 19 (og)	13	12
23	NPL	A	Mickleover Sports	200	L 0 - 5		13	13
26	NPL	H	Altrincham	378	L 0 - 3		15	14
30	NPL	A	Ashton United	154	W 2 - 1	Lawrie 15 Oji 56	14	15
Oct 3	NPL	H	Matlock Town	333	W 2 - 0	Mbunga 51 68	13	16
7	NPL	H	Witton Albion	467	W 1 - 0	Weir 78	11	17
10	NPL	A	Halesowen Town	352	L 1 - 2	Graham 63	13	18
14	NPL	H	Workington	403	D 1 - 1	Steele 90	12	19
21	NPL	A	Whitby Town	274	D 2 - 2	Graham 47 67	11	20
28	FAT 1Q	H	Mickleover Sports	226	W 1 - 0	Glover 85	11	21
31	NPL	H	Grantham Town	299	L 1 - 3	Steele 56	14	22
Nov 4	NPL	A	Barwell	178	D 1 - 1	Fitzpatrick 86	15	23
11	FAT 2Q	H	Cleethorpes Town	369	D 1 - 1	Butlin 34		24
15	FAT 2Qr	A	Cleethorpes Town	225	L 1 - 2	Graham 22		25
18	NPL	H	Stalybridge Celtic	346	W 2 - 1	Fitzgibbon 11 Glover 88	12	26
Dec 2	NPL	H	Farsley Celtic	304	W 2 1	Glover 3 (pen) Bailey 80	9	27
23	NPL	H	Shaw Lane	302	L 1 - 3	Gatter 5	13	28
26	NPL	A	Rushall Olympic	578	W 2 - 1	Walsh 31 Gatter 49	10	29
30	NPL	A	Lancaster City	345	W 1 - 0	Oji 75	9	30
Jan 1	NPL	H	Stafford Rangers	892	W 2 - 1	Butlin 29 Gatter 45	8	31
6	NPL	A	Nantwich Town	404	W 5 - 1	Lawrie 55 74 Mendez-Jones 58 Thorley 80 Glover 86	7	32
13	NPL	A	Coalville Town	396	D 1 - 1	Lawrie 90	7	33
27	NPL	H	Whitby Town	393	D 0 - 0		8	34
Feb 3	NPL	A	Farsley Cekltic	204	W 3 - 1	Fitzpatrick 45 Glover 78 Lawrie 90	5	35
10	NPL	H	Barwell	373	L 2 - 3	Graham 45 Thorley 89	7	36
17	NPL	A	Stalybridge Celtic	389	D 2 - 2	Fitzgibbon 39 Thorley 90	8	37
24	NPL	H	Warrington Town	346	L 0 - 2		9	38
Mar 10	NPL	A	Marine	305	L 0 - 2		9	39
17	NPL	H	Marine	246	W 3 - 2	Lawrie 52 Glover 63 72	9	40
20	NPL	A	Warrington Town	223	L 1 - 4	Glover 9	9	41
24	NPL	A	Buxton	366	D 2 - 2	Glover 52 87	8	42
31	NPL	A	Witton Albion	294	L 0 - 3		9	43
April 5	NPL	H	Buxton	325	L 1 - 2	Bailey 6	10	44
7	NPL	H	Stourbridge	347	D 1 - 1	Glover 90	12	45
14	NPL	A	Sutton Coldfield Town	185	L 1 - 4	Dwyer 59 (pen)	15	46
17	NPL	A	Grantham Town	271	D 1 - 1	Glover 90	15	47
19	NPL	H	Rushall Olympic	229	D 1 - 1	King 57	15	48
21	NPL	H	Mickleover Sports	216	L 1 - 3	Glover 80	16	49
28	NPL	A	Altrinc ham	1856	L 0 - 3		17	50

GOALSCORERS	SG	CSG	Pens	Hat tricks	Total		SG	CSG	Pens	Hat tricks	Total
2016-17 *Glover*					13	Mbunga	1				2
Glover	14	3	3		18	Oji	2				2
Lawrie	7				7	Opponents					2
Graham	4				5	Rodgers	2				2
Thorley	3				4	Steele	2				2
Gatter	3	2			3	Dwyer			1		1
Bailey	2				2	Green					1
Butlin	2				2	King					1
Dodd	2				2	Mendez-Jones					1
Fitzgibbon	2				2	Walsh					1
Fitzpatrick	2				2	Weir					1

LANCASTER CITY MATCH RESULTS 2017-18

Date	Comp	H/A	Opponents	Att:	Result	Goalscorers	Pos	No.
Aug 12	NPL	A	Buxton	244	W 2 - 1	S.Bailey 37 Wood 68	7	1
15	NPL	H	Warrington	260	D 2 - 2	Clark 66 90	5	2
19	NPL	H	Mickleover Sports	269	D 1 - 1	Winder 84	9	3
22	NPL	A	Farsley Celtic	233	D 0 - 0		11	4
26	NPL	A	Hednesford Town	412	D 1 - 1	Steele 61	12	5
28	NPL	H	Stalybridge Celtic	354	W 1 - 0	Kilifin 21	9	6
Sept 2	FAC 1Q	A	Colne	301	W 1 - 0	Wills 24		7
9	NPL	H	Shaw Lane	221	W 2 - 0	Carney 49 Tam 87	7	8
12	NPL	A	Ashton United	116	L 1 - 2	Carney 68	11	9
16	FAC 2Q	H	Droylsden	303	W 4 - 0	Meulensteen 2 Carney 5 Winder 60 89		10
19	NPL	A	Whitby Town	240	W 4 - 1	Wood 17 Carney 25 Tam 69 S. Bailey 77	9	11
23	NPL	A	Stourbridge	899	D 0 - 0		9	12
26	NPL	H	Witton Albion	206	W 4 - 0	Dugdale 26 KILIFIN 3 (29 35 86)	8	13
30	FAC 3Q	A	Shaw Lane	304	L 1 - 2	Kilifin 22	8	14
Oct 3	NPL	A	Warrington Town	202	L 1 - 5	Wood 79	11	15
7	NPL	A	Sutton Coldfield Town	238	W 2 - 0	Wood 60 Mayers 90	8	16
14	NPL	H	Farsley Celtic	271	D 1 - 1	Mercer 39	11	17
21	NPL	A	Halesowen Town	612	L 3 - 4	Williams 76 Meolensteen 80 90	12	18
24	NPL	A	Altrincham	618	L 0 - 4		12	19
28	FAT 1Q	A	Mossley	174	W 1 - 0	Williams 20		20
31	NPL	H	Marine	253	W 3 - 0	Carney 7 S.Bailey 66 (pen) 68	10	21
Nov 4	NPL	A	Grantham Town	274	L 2 - 3	Williams 7 Maulensteen 11	13	22
11	FAT 2Q	A	Stratford Town	252	W 3 - 0	Francis (og) 8 Winder 23 42		23
18	NPL	H	Coalville Town	259	W 4 - 2	Carney 25 45 Winder 75 C. Bailey 81	10	24
25	FAT 3Q	H	Mildenhall	242	W 1 - 0	Kilifin 90		25
Dec 2	NPL	H	Matlock Town	258	L 1 - 2	Kilifin 21	13	26
16	FAT 1	H	Stockport County	578	L 1 - 3	Windsor 54 (pen)		27
23	NPL	A	Mickleover Sports	166	W 1 - 0	Williams 87	10	28
26	NPL	H	Workington	405	D 2 - 2	Akrigg 75 C.Bailey 90	11	29
30	NPL	H	Hednesford Town	345	L 0 - 1		13	30
Jan 1	NPL	A	Stalybridge Celtic	281	L 2 - 5	Mercer 12 S. Bailey 45	13	31
6	NPL	A	Whitby Town	247	W 5 - 0	S.Bailey11 74 C.Bailey 28 Djabi 47Jones48	12	32
13	NPL	H	Barwell	237	D 1 - 1	C.Bailey 22	13	33
20	NPL	A	Nantwich Town	255	L 0 - 3		14	34
Jan 23	NPL	A	Nantwich Town	214	L 1 - 2	Djabi 38	14	35
27	NPL	H	Halesowen Town	259	W 2 - 0	Djabi 15 Akrigg 72	11	36
Feb 3	NPL	A	Matlock Town	311	L 3 - 4	S.Bailey 34 Jarvis 82 Carney 87	11	37
6	NPL	A	Rushall Olympic	131	L 0 - 3		11	38
13	NPL	A	Ashton United	167	L 0 - 3		11	39
17	NPL	A	Coalville Town	131	W 4 - 1	Kilifin 20 Tam 47 Mercer 55 79	11	40
24	NPL	H	Rushall Olympic	209	L 0 - 2		12	41
Mar 10	NPL	A	Stafford Rangers	406	D 2 - 2	C. Bailey 89 Gregory 90	12	42
13	NPL	A	Marine	286	L 0 - 3		15	43
24	NPL	H	Stafford Rangers	299	D 1 - 1	Carney 52	16	44
31	NPL	H	Sutton Coldfield Town	217	W 2 - 1	Carney 33 S.Bailey 45	16	45
Apr 2	NPL	A	Workington	258	L 0 - 2		16	46
7	NPL	A	Altrincham	313	L 1 - 2	Simpson 23	17	47
10	NPL	H	Grantham Town	123	W 3 - 1	S.Bailey 21 Carney 56 Kilifin 85	17	48
14	NPL	A	Shaw Lane	160	D 0 - 0		17	49
17	NPL	A	Barwell	134	L 1 - 2		17	50
21	NPL	H	Stourbridge	238	D 0 - 0		18	51
24	NPL	H	Buxton	125	D 1 - 1	Kilifin 90	18	52
28	NPL	A	Witton Albion	323	L 0 - 2		18	53

GOALSCORERS	SG	CSG	Pens	Hat tricks	Total		SG	CSG	Pens	Hat tricks	Total
2016-17 *Udah*					7	Agrigg					2
Carney	10	4			11	Clark					2
S.Bailey	6		1		10	Dugdale					1
Kilifin	8	2		1	10	Gregory					1
Winder	4				6	Jarvis					1
C.Bailey	5				5	Jones					1
Meolensteen	3				4	Mayers					1
Mercer	3				4	Opponents					1
Wood	4				4	Simpson					1
Williams	4				4	Steele					1
Djabi	3				3	Willis					1
Tam	3				3	Windsor					1

MARINE MATCH RESULTS 2017-18

Date	Comp	H/A	Opponents	Att.	Result	Goalscorers	Pos	No.
Aug 12	NPL	A	Grantham Town	265	L 0 - 3		24	1
15	NPL	H	Workington	254	W 2 - 0	Smart 49 Hughes 63	16	2
19	NPL	H	Barwell	301	L 0 - 1		21	3
22	NPL	A	Stalybridge Celtic	319	W 2 - 0	Bailey 47 Strickland 81	12	4
26	NPL	A	Stourbridge	639	W 2 - 0	Murray 2 39	8	5
28	NPL	H	Warrington Town	444	L 0 - 4		13	6
Sept 2	FAC 2Q	H	**Ashton United**	324	L 1 - 3	**Strickland 90**		7
5	NPL	A	Witton Albion	267	D 1 - 1	Edgar 12	13	8
9	NPL	H	Coalville Town	237	L 0 - 1		18	9
12	NPL	A	Nantwich Town	204	D 1 - 1	Mitchley 67	18	10
16	NPL	A	Matlock Town	305	D 2 - 2	Mitchley 10 Hughes 84	15	11
19	NPL	H	Ashton United	239	L 3 - 4	Mitchley 20 Smart 59 Murray 85	17	12
23	NPL	A	Whitby Town	253	L 2 - 3	Bakker 69 Murray 88	19	13
26	NPL	H	Farsley Celtic	255	L 1 - 2	Lomax 78	20	14
30	NPL	H	Grantham Town	389	D 1 - 1	Hughes 90	20	15
Oct 3	NPL	A	Workington	341	L 1 - 2	Mitchley 78	21	16
7	NPL	A	Buxton	346	L 1 - 2	Lomax 5	21	17
10	NPL	H	Stalybridge Celtic	385	W 3 - 1	Edgar 24 Mitchley 44 Marie 84	19	18
14	NPL	H	Matlock Town	372	L 1 - 2	Lomax 16	20	19
21	NPL	A	Rushall Olympic	202	W 2 - 0	Mitchley 7 (pen) Tongue 57	20	20
28	FAT 1Q	A	**Whitby Town**	279	W 3 - 1	**Mitchley 3 62 Wylie 74**	20	21
31	NPL	A	Lancaster City	253	L 0 - 3		20	22
Nov 11	FAT 2Q	A	**Atherton Collieries**	462	W 5 - 1	**Mitchley 8 61 Murray 48 90 Bailey 84**		23
18	NPL	A	Halesowen Town	278	D 1 - 1	Murray 69	21	24
25	FAT 3Q	H	**FC United**	778	W 1 - 0	**Mlitchley 19 (pen)_**		25
Dec 2	NPL	A	Stafford Rangers	415	W 4 - 1	Da Silva 4 Smart 16 Calveley (og) Tongue 88	21	26
16	FAT 1	A	**Chorley**	704	W 3 - 1	**Hughes 17 O'Keefe 74 (og) Mitchley 90**		27
23	NPL	A	Barwell	137	W 4 - 0	Da Silver 26 Murray 28 Hughes 44 Mitchley 60	17	28
26	NPL	H	Altrincham	619	L 0 - 3		20	29
30	NPL	H	Stourbridge	410	L 0 - 4		20	30
Jan 1	NPL	A	Warrington Town	255	D 0 - 0		21	31
6	NPL	A	Ashton United	208	L 0 - 3		21	32
13	FAT 2	A	**Dover Athletic**	565	L 3 - 4	**Michley 8 (pen) 78 (pen) Brewster 86**		33
23	NPL	H	Shaw Lane	284	L 1 - 2	McGrath 69	21	34
27	NPL	H	Rushall Olympic	259	D 2 - 2	Mitchley 70 (pen) Strickland 83	21	35
Feb 3	NPL	H	Stafford Rangers	446	D 1 - 1	Mitchley 75	21	36
6	NPL	A	Sutton Coldfield Town	102	L 1 - 3	Mitchley 74	21	37
17	NPL	H	Halesowen Town	462	W 1 - 0	Tongue 10	22	38
24	NPI	H	Mickleover Sports	323	L 1 - 3	McGrath 80	22	39
Mar 10	NPL	A	Hednesford Town	305	W 2 - 0	Short 41 Brewster 59	22	40
13	NPL	H	Lancaster City	286	W 3 - 0	Hughes 15 Mitchley 47 Murray 81	20	41
17	NPL	A	Hednesford Town	246	L 2 - 3	Amis 31 Mitchley 85	22	42
24	NPL	H	Sutton Coldfield Town	402	W 5 - 0	MITCHLEY 3 (13 45 65 pen) Amis 31 40	21	43
27	NPL	H	Nantwich Town	362	D 1 - 1	Amis 62		44
31	NPL	H	Buxton	398	L 2 - 3	Amis 22 Tongue 27	21	45
Apr 9	NPL	A	Shaw Lane	172	W 3 - 1	Hughes 23 Field 34 Tongue 65	20	46
14	NPL	A	Coalville Town	109	W 3 - 1	Tongue 34 63 Brewster 70	19	47
17	NPL	H	Mickleover Sports	155	W 2 - 1	Smart 64 Brewster 68	19	48
19	NPL	H	Witton Albion	316	D 2 - 2	Murray 65 Short 90	19	49
21	NPL	H	Whitby Town	507	L 0 - 3		19	50
25	NPL	A	Altrincham	482	D 1 - 1	Murray 53	19	51
28	NPL	A	Farsley Celtic	354	L 0 - 3		19	52

GOALSCORERS	SG	CSG	Pens	Hat tricks	Total		SG	CSG	Pens	Hat tricks	Total
2016-17 *Mitchley*					25	Bailey					2
Mitchley	17	4	6	1	23	Da Silva					2
Murray	9	2			11	Edgar					2
Hughes	7	2			7	McGrath	2				2
Tongue	4	3			7	Opponents					2
Amis	3	3			5	Short	2				2
Brewster	4				4	Bakker					1
Smart	4				4	Field					1
Lomax	3				3	Marie					1
Strickland	3				3	Wylie					1

MATLOCK TOWN MATCH RESULTS 2017-18

Date	Comp	H/A	Opponents	Att:	Result	Goalscorers	Pos	No.
Aug 13	NPL	A	Stourbridge	1050	D 1 - 1	Newsham 5	12	1
15	NPL	H	Hednesford Town	347	W 3 - 2	Harrad 5 78 Sharpe 23 (pen)	6	2
19	NPL	H	Altrincham	457	W 1 - 0	Wiley 48	4	3
22	NPL	H	Sutton Coldfield Town	165	D 3 - 3	Harrad 37 Wiley 45 Cribley 55	4	4
26	NPL	A	Warrington Town	243	L 0 - 2		11	5
28	NPL	H	Grantham Town	529	L 2 - 3	Newsham 45 Harrad 90	16	6
Sept 1	**FAC 2Q**	**A**	**Haughmond**	**236**	**L 2 - 3**	**Rose 45 Yates 62**		**7**
4	NPL	A	Coalville Town	137	L 1 - 2	Harrad 49 (pen)	16	8
9	NPL	H	Whitby Town	372	L 1 - 2	Rose 73	19	9
12	NPL	H	Mickleover Sports	315	W 1 - 0	Harrad 73	16	10
16	NPL	H	Marine	305	D 2 - 2	Harrad 51 68 (pen)	14	11
19	NPL	A	Barwell	148	L 1 - 2	Harrad 64	16	12
23	NPL	A	Workington	429	W 1 - 0	Harrad 58 (pen)	13	13
26	NPL	H	Shaw Lane	320	L 0 - 1		15	14
30	NPL	H	Sutton Coldfield Town	334	W 5 - 0	Blake 17 Rose 47 Wlliams 77 (pen) 88 Etches 90	14	15
Oct 3	NPL	A	Hednesford Town	333	L 0 - 2		15	16
7	NPL	A	Stalybridge Celtic	529	L 1 - 4	Etches 90	16	17
14	NPL	A	Marine	372	W 2 - 1	Waite 31 Yates 74	15	18
21	NPL	H	Stafford Rangers	439	W 2 - 0	Waite 13 Harrad 56	14	19
28	**FAT 1Q**	**A**	**Glossop North End**	**310**	**L 2 - 3**	**Harrad 50 59**		**20**
31	NPL	A	Ashton United	133	L 0 - 3		17	21
Nov 11	NPL	A	Nantwich Town	444	L 0 - 3		17	22
18	NPL	A	Witton Albion	320	D 3 - 3	Harrad 20 German 48 Yates 52	17	23
25	NPL	H	Halesowen Town	342	W 2 - 0	Williams 40 Green 42	14	24
Dec 2	NPL	A	Lancaster City	256	W 2 - 1	Green 21 German 69	12	25
23	NPL	A	Altrincham	807	L 0 - 3		15	26
26	NPL	A	Buxton	930	D 3 - 3	Harrad 70 (pen) 80 Yates 90	15	27
Jan 1	NPL	A	Grantham Town	270	L 1 - 2	Jackson 61	17	28
6	NPL	H	Barwell	402	L 0 - 2		16	29
13	NPL	A	Mickleover Sports	412	L 0 - 2		17	30
23	NPL	A	Farsl;ey Celtic	141	W 2 - 1	Limb 22 52	17	31
27	NPL	A	Stafford Rangers	468	L 1 - 2		18	32
Feb 3	NPL	H	Lancaster City	311	W 4 - 3	Bennett 13 Harrad 28 80 Vince 90	17	33
6	NPL	H	Warrington Town	191	L 1 - 3	Bennett 3	18	34
15	NPL	H	Witton Albion	421	L 2 - 3	Bennett 63 Harrad 67	20	35
24	NPL	A	Halesowen Town	363	L 2 - 3	Harrad 9 Cribley 62	20	36
Mar 6	NPL	A	Nantwich Town	186	W 2 - 0	Williams 9 German 39	17	37
17	NPL	A	Farsley Celtic	189	L 1 - 2	Harrad 33	19	38
24	NPL	A	Rushall Olympic	221	L 0 - 1		22	39
28	NPL	H	Stourbridge	242	D 0 - 0		21	40
Apr 3	NPL	A	Buxton	330	W 3 - 2	German 73 Wallace 79 Doyle-Charles 90	20	41
7	NPL	H	Coalville Town	356	W 3 - 1	Limb 33 45 Williams 70	18	42
14	NPL	A	Whitby Town	314	W 3 - 0	Limb 11 61 Williams 90	16	43
17	NPL	H	Rushall Olympic	242	W 2 - 1	Smart 64 Brewster 68	16	44
19	NPL	H	Stalybridge Celtic	261	W 2 - 0	Ondong-Mba 64 Wood 70	13	45
21	NPL	H	Workington	320	W 2 - 0	Yates 25 German 61	10	46
24	NPL	H	Ashton United	248	L 1 - 2	Cribley 17		47
28	NPL	A	Shaw Lane	219	L 1 - 2	Cribley 67	15	48

GOALSCORERS	SG	CSG	Pens	Hat tricks	Total		SG	CSG	Pens	Hat tricks	Total
2016-17 _Dinanga_					**29**	Wiley					2
Harrad	16	4	4		21	Blake					1
Limb	4				6	Brewster					1
Williams	5		1		6	Doyle-Charles					1
German	5				5	Jackson					1
Yates	5				5	Ondong-Mba					1
Bennett	3	3			3	Rose					1
Cribley	3				3	Sharpe		1			1
Rose	3				3	Smart					1
Etches					2	Vince					1
Green					2	Wallace					1
Newsham					2	Wood					1
Waite					2						

MICKLEOVER SPORTS MATCH RESULTS 2017-18

Date	Comp	H/A	Opponents	Att:	Result	Goalscorers	Pos	No.
Aug 12	NPL	H	Witton Albion	225	D 1 - 1	Gordon 57	12	1
14	NPL	A	Shaw Lane	187	W 2 - 1	Garnett 31 Grayson 37	9	2
19	NPL	A	Lancaster City	269	D 1 - 1	Dales 69	11	3
22	NPL	H	Stafford Rangers	303	L 0 - 2		14	4
26	NPL	H	Nantwich Town	183	L 1 - 2	Grayson 6	17	5
28	NPL	A	Coalville Town	227	L 0 - 2		19	6
Sept 2	FAC 2Q	H	Hinckley AFC	305	W 2 - 1	Thomas 23 McGrath 71		7
5	NPL	H	Grantham Town	235	W 1 - 0	Grayson 28	18	8
8	NPL	A	Buxton	359	W 2 - 0	Mills 24 Dales 43	16	9
12	NPL	A	Matlock Town	315	L 0 - 1		17	10
16	FAC 3Q	A	Basford United	217	L 0 - 1			11
19	NPL	H	Stourbridge	188	L 1 - 2	Grayson 24	18	12
23	NPL	H	Hednesford Town	200	W 5 - 0	Turner 7 Garnett 28 38 Belgrave 48 Dales 54	13	13
26	NPL	A	Barwell	138	L 1 - 2	Morrison 71	16	14
30	NPL	A	Witton Albion	247	W 2 - 0	Mills 57 Brown 58 (og)	15	15
Oct 3	NPL	H	Shaw Lane	186	L 1 - 3	Mills 42	16	16
7	NPL	H	Ashton United	345	L 2 - 5	Dales 75 Garnett 77	18	17
10	NPL	A	Stafford Rangers	417	D 1 - 1	Morris 22	17	18
14	NPL	H	Rushall Olympic	211	D 1 - 1	Tyrell 73	18	19
21	NPL	A	Farsley Celtic	188	W 3 - 0	Mills 2 Garnett 75 Dales 79	17	20
28	FAT 1Q	A	Hednesford Town	308	L 0 - 1			21
31	NPL	H	Whitby Town	154	W 2 - 1	Garnett 19 Dales 44	14	22
Nov 4	NPL	A	Stalybridge Celtic	258	W 5 - 0	McGrath 5 (pen) Dales 40 69 Scott 52 Garnett 86	9	23
11	NPL	H	Sutton Coldfield Town	230	W 2 - 0	Dales 13 Mills 55	8	24
18	NPL	H	Warrington Town	214	L 1 - 3	Garnett 35	9	25
25	NPL	A	Rushall Olympic	226	L 0 - 1		10	26
Dec 2	NPL	H	Altrincham	260	L 1 - 2	Garnett 85	11	27
9	NPL	A	Workington	387	L 0 - 2		11	28
23	NPL	H	Lancaster City	166	L 0 - 1		11	29
26	NPL	A	Halesowen Town	402	D 0 - 0		14	30
30	NPL	A	Nantwich Town	272	W 2 - 1	Mills 47 Dales 52	12	31
Jan 1	NPL	H	Coalville Town	149	D 2 - 2	McGrath 70 Dales 75	12	32
6	NPL	A	Stourbridge	529	D 1 - 1	Dales 90	13	33
13	NPL	H	Matlock Town	412	W 2 - 0	Garnett 15 Mills 63	10	34
27	NPL	H	Farsley Celtic	236	D 2 - 2	Mills 51 Dales 65	12	35
Feb 17	NPL	A	Warrington Town	283	L 1 - 3	Mills 35	13	36
24	NPL	A	Marine	323	W 3 - 1	Dales 27 75 Garnett 33	11	37
Mar 17	NPL	A	Sutton Coldfield Town	172	L 1 - 2	Dales 28	15	38
20	NPL	A	Altrincham	532	D 1 - 1	Walsh 38	15	39
24	NPL	H	Workington	252	W 1 - 0	Burgin 51	15	40
27	NPL	A	Whitby Town	192	L 2 - 3	Dales 47 78	15	41
30	NPL	A	Ashton United	204	D 1 - 1	Mills 25	15	42
Apr 7	NPL	A	Grantham Town	377	W 3 - 0	Phillips 5 Hickman 19 Garnett 44	15	43
14	NPL	H	Buxton	232	D 2 - 2	Dales 14 McGrath 56	15	44
17	NPL	H	Marine	155	L 1 - 2	Hickman 52	17	45
21	NPL	A	Hednesford Town	216	W 3 - 1	Mills 18 Barnes-Homer 53 Norcross 74	17	46
23	NPL	H	Stalybridge Celtic	90	W 1 - 0	Garnett 90	15	47
25	NPL	H	Halesowen Town	175	D 0 - 0		14	48
28	NPL	H	Barwell	166	D 3 - 3	Norcross 5 50 McGrath 57	13	49

GOALSCORERS	SG	CSG	Pens	Hat tricks	Total		SG	CSG	Pens	Hat tricks	Total
2016-17 *Baskerville*					18	Gordon					1
Dales	16	3			19	Morris					1
Garnett	12	2			13	Morrison					1
Mills	11	3			11	Opponents					1
McGrath	4		1		5	Phillips					1
Grayson	2				4	Scott					1
Norcross					3	Thomas					1
Hickman	2				2	Turner					1
Barnes-Homer					1	Tyrell					1
Belgrave					1	Walsh					1
Burgin					1						

NANTWICH TOWN MATCH RESULTS 2017-18

Date	Comp	H/A	Opponents	Att:	Result	Goalscorers	Pos	No.
Aug 12	NPL	A	Stalybridge Celtic	468	L 0 - 1		17	1
15	NPL	H	Altrincham	670	D 1 - 1	Forbes 31	19	2
19	NPL	H	Workington	307	W 2 - 0	Clayton 38 Davies 48	12	3
21	NPL	A	Stourbridge	681	D 1 - 1	Bell 50	12	4
26	NPL	A	Mickleover Sports	183	W 2 - 1	Cooke 53 (pen) Anderson 59	9	5
28	NPL	H	Barwell	352	D 2 - 2	Bell 25 Clayton 90	12	6
Sept 1	FAC 1Q	A	City of Liverpool	1024	W 2 - 1	Stair 38 Cooke 90		7
5	NPL	H	Buxton	350	L 1 - 3	Maguire 3 (og)	14	8
9	NPL	A	Rushall Olympic	181	W 4 - 1	Stair 27 Cooke 30 Anderson 46 Jones 85	10	9
12	NPL	A	Marine	204	D 1 - 1	Davies 40	10	10
16	FAC 2Q	A	Shepshed Dynamo	318	W 1 - 0	Jones 76		11
19	NPL	A	Hednesford Town	319	L 0 - 1		15	12
23	NPL	H	Ashton United	291	L 2 - 3	Clayton 90 Stair 90	17	13
26	NPL	A	Stafford Rangers	412	L 0 - 3		19	14
30	FAC 3Q	H	Nuneaton Town	479	W 3 - 1	Forbes 30 Stair 60 Cooke 63		15
Oct 3	NPL	A	Altrincham	636	L 1 - 5	Mullarkey 90	19	16
7	NPL	A	Farsley Celtic	260	L 0 - 2		20	17
14	FAC 4Q	H	Kettering Town	760	D 1 - 1	Cooke 73		18
17	FAC 4Qr	A	Kettering Town	903	W 1 - 0	Clayton 19		19
21	NPL	H	Witton Albion	315	W 3 - 2	Hopley 2 (og) Cooke 11 Bell 63	22	20
28	FAT 1Q	A	Rushall Olympic	136	L 0 - 2			21
Nov 4	FAC 1	A	Stevenage	1436	L 0 - 5			22
11	NPL	A	Matlock Town	444	W 3 - 0	Clayton 1 Forbes 50 82	20	23
18	NPL	H	Whitby Town	305	W 1 - 0	McDonald 4	19	24
Dec 2	NPL	H	Coalville Town	209	L 1 - 3	Stair 13	22	25
5	NPL	H	Stourbridge	208	W 2 - 0	Clayton 20 Cole 67	18	26
23	NPL	A	Workington	452	L 1 - 2	Bell 36	21	27
26	NPL	H	Sutton Coldfield Town	366	D 0 - 0		19	28
30	NPL	H	Mickleover Sports	272	L 1 - 2	Wildin 11	19	29
Jan 1	NPL	A	Barwell	163	W 2 - 1	Clayton 1 Cooke 70	19	30
6	NPL	A	Hednesford Town	404	L 1 - 5	Clayton 42 (pen)	18	31
13	NPL	A	Halesowen Town	318	W 1 - 0	Mwasile 15	16	32
20	NPL	H	Lancaster City	255	W 3 - 0	Clayton 41 Cooke 70 72	16	33
23	NPL	A	Lancaster City	314	W 2 - 1	Cooke 12 50	16	34
27	NPL	A	Witton Albion	394	L 1 - 4	Cooke 70	16	35
Feb 3	NPL	A	Coalville Town	110	W 3 - 0	Cooke 7 Forbes 40 Mwasile 68	13	36
17	NPL	A	Whitby Town	301	L 1 - 2	Cotterell 32	14	37
24	NPL	H	Grantham Town	327	W 3 - 1	Cooke 15 Clayton 36 Bell 72	13	38
Mar 6	NPL	A	Matlock Town	186	L 0 - 2		13	39
13	NPL	A	Grantham Town	183	D 0 - 0		12	40
17	NPL	H	Halesowen Town	193	L 1 - 3	Bell 17	13	41
20	NPL	H	Stalybridge Celtic	205	L 2 - 3	Cooke 25 Bell 52	14	42
24	NPL	H	Shaw Lane	173	W 2 - 0	Cooke 12 Mwasile 65	14	43
27	NPL	A	Marine	362	D 1 - 1	Clayton 20		44
31	NPL	H	Farsley Celtic	298	D 1 - 1	Clayton 9	15	45
Apr 2	NPL	A	Sutton Coldfield Town	221	W 3 - 1	Cole 5 Wakefield 32 Jones 39	15	46
7	NPL	H	Warrington	269	W 2 - 1	Mullarkey 40 Clayton 45 (pen)	11	47
10	NPL	A	Warrington	201	D 0 - 0		11	48
14	NPL	H	Rushall Olympic	264	L 1 - 2	Clayton 51	12	49
19	NPL	A	Buxton	239	L 0 - 3		13	50
21	NPL	A	Ashton United	205	L 1 - 2	Tomsett 35 (og)	13	51
24	NPL	H	Shaw Lane	121	L 2 - 3	Cole 19 Bell 44	14	52
28	NPL	H	Stafford Rangers	448	L 0 - 3		16	53

GOALSCORERS	SG	CSG	Pens	Hat tricks	Total		SG	CSG	Pens	Hat tricks	Total
2016-17 Cooke					20	Davies					2
Cooke	14	4	1		16	Cole					2
Clayton	13	2	2		14	Mullarkey	2				2
Bell	7				8	Cotterell					1
Forbes	5				5	McDonald					1
Stair	5				5	Wakefield					1
Jones					3	Wildin					1
Mwasile					3						
Opponents					3						
Anderson					2						

RUSHALL OLYMPIC MATCH RESULTS 2017-18

Date	Comp	H/A	Opponents	Att:	Result	Goalscorers	Pos	No.
Aug 12	NPL	A	Warrington	239	L 0 - 2		22	1
15	NPL	H	Grantham Town	242	L 0 - 2		24	2
19	NPL	H	Stalybridge Celtic	231	W 1 - 0	Dell 76 (pen)	20	3
22	NPL	A	Barwell	144	D 4 - 4	Dell 2 Waldron 31 Mugisha 67 Probert 90	18	4
26	NPL	A	Farsley Celtic	178	L 0 - 1		20	5
28	NPL	H	Stourbridge	522	L 1 - 2	Waldron 43	22	6
Sept 2	FAC 2Q	H	**Potton United**	139	W 1 - 0	**Mugisha 84**		7
4	NPL	A	Shaw Lane	132	L 0 - 2		22	8
9	NPL	H	Nantwich Town	181	L 1 - 4	Hull 6	22	9
12	NPL	H	Sutton Coldfield T	192	W 5 - 1	Hull 13 Mugisha 16 Adelekan 45 Landell 58 O'Neill-Martin 88	21	10
16	FAC 3Q	A	**AFC Mansfield**	110	D 0 - 0			11
19	FAC 3Qr	H	**AFC Mansfield**	114	L 1 - 2	**Landell 1**		12
23	NPL	A	Witton Albion	286	W 2 - 1	Landell 33 Mugisha 82	22	13
26	NPL	H	Coalville Town	211	D 1 - 1	Landell 78	22	14
30	NPL	H	Warrington Town	187	L 1 - 2	Adelekan 18	22	15
Oct 3	NPL	A	Grantham Town	186	L 1 - 7	Gould 18	23	16
7	NPL	A	Altrincham	984	L 0 - 4		24	17
10	NPL	H	Barwell	229	D 1 - 1	Landell 28	23	18
14	NPL	A	Mickleover Sports	211	D 1 - 1	Tyrell 73 ?	23	19
21	NPL	H	Marine	202	L 0 - 2		23	20
28	FAT 1Q	H	**Nantwich Town**	136	W 2 - 0	**Hull 45 Brodie 76 (pen)**		21
31	NPL	A	Buxton	154	W 2 - 1	Waldron 47 Brodie 62	22	22
Nov 4	NPL	H	Halesowen Town	391	W 3 - 1	Brodie 39 (pen) Atkinson 44 Fanovich 61	21	23
11	FAT 2Q	H	**Rushall Olympic**	240	L 2 - 3	**Hakeem 20 Sangha 71**		24
14	NPL	A	Stafford Rangers	406	W 4 - 0	Waldren 34 Fonovitch 52 Brodie 62 (pen) Sangha 75	21	25
18	NPL	A	Workington	430	L 1 - 4	Butterfield 62	20	26
25	NPL	H	Mickleover Sports	228	W 1 - 0	Sangha 5	18	27
Dec 2	NPL	A	Ashton United	143	L 1 - 2	Brodie 43	18	28
23	NPL	A	Stalybridge Celtic	303	W 2 - 1	Landell 8 Waldron 50	18	29
26	NPL	H	Hednesford Town	578	L 1 - 2	Brodie 19	18	30
30	NPL	H	Farsley Celtic	179	D 1 - 1	Waldren 13	18	31
Jan 1	NPL	A	Stourbridge	767	L 0 - 5		20	32
13	NPL	H	Sutton Coldfield T	205	W 4 - 3	Hull 6 Dubidat 51 65 Brodie 90 (pen)	19	33
20	NPL	H	Whitby Town	163	D 3 - 3	Waldron 4 (pen) 11 Dubidat 5	17	34
27	NPL	A	Marine	400	D 2 - 2	Landell 10 Whitall 20	19	35
Feb 6	NPL	H	Lancaster City	131	W 3 - 0	Brodie 15 32 Archer 80	18	36
10	NPL	A	Halesowen Town	420	L 0 - 2		19	37
17	NPL	H	Workington	162	W 1 - 0	Waldron 44	16	38
20	NPL	H	Stafford Rangers	266	L 1 - 2	Maye 76	17	39
24	NPL	A	Hednesford Town	346	W 2 - 0	Waldron 17 25	16	40
Mar 24	NPL	H	Matlock Town	221	W 1 - 0	Brodie 5	16	41
27	NPL	H	Ashton United	1945	W 4 - 2	Waldron 5 Dubidat 54 Fonovich 63 Paisley 90	16	42
31	NPL	H	Altrincham	382	W 2 - 0	Whittall 45 Waldron 88	16	43
Apr 7	NPL	H	Shaw Lane	186	L 1 - 3	Brodie 77	16	44
10	NPL	H	Buxton	171	W 2 - 0	Whittall 8 Archer 90	16	45
14	NPL	H	Nantwich Town	264	W 2 - 1	Singh 16 Waldron 39	14	46
17	NPL	A	Matlock Town	242	L 1 - 2	Fonovich 1	13	47
19	NPL	A	Hednesford Town	229	D 1 - 1	Waldron 80	12	48
21	NPL	H	Witton Albion	221	D 0 - 0		11	49
24	NPL	A	Whitby Town	164	W 3 - 2	Singh 55 Hull 64 Waldron 65	10	50
28	NPL	A	Coalville Town	116	W 5 - 2	Hull 29 Singh 49 Waldron 52 (pen) Dubidat 63 Maye 66	8	51

GOALSCORERS	SG	CSG	Pens	Hat tricks	Total		SG	CSG	Pens	Hat tricks	Total
2016-17 *Alex Reid*					15	Adelekan	2				2
Waldron	15	3	2		17	Dell	2		1		2
Brodie	10		4		12	Maye	2				2
Landell	7	3			7	Atkinson					1
Hull	6	2			6	Butterfield					1
Dubidat	2				5	Gould					1
Mugisha	4				4	Hakeem					1
Fanovich	2				3	O'Neill-Martin					1
Sangha	3				3	Paisley					1
Singh	3				3	Probert					1
Whitall	3				3	Tyrell					1
Archer	2				2						

SHAW LANE AFC MATCH RESULTS 2017-18

Date	Comp	H/A	Opponents	Att:	Result	Goalscorers	Pos	No.
Aug 12	NPL	A	Sutton Coldfield Town	187	L 1 - 3	Rothery 82	21	1
14	NPL	H	Mickleover Sports	187	L 1 - 2	Clayton 45	21	2
19	NPL	H	Hednesford Town	152	W 3 - 1	Bailey 2 (og) Quaiter 44 Clayton 75	15	3
22	NPL	A	Buxton	320	W 2 - 0	Walker 34 Harris 55	10	4
26	NPL	A	Stalybridge Celtic	285	W 1 - 0	Norris 71	7	5
28	NPL	H	Farsley Celtic	287	W 1 - 0	Reeves 69	3	6
Sept 2	FAC 1Q	H	Radcliffe Borough	187	W 3 - 1	Chilaka 10 25 Norris 36		7
4	NPL	H	Rushall Oyumpic	132	W 2 - 0	Abadaki 22 Walker 90	1	8
9	NPL	A	Lancaster City	221	L 0 - 2		4	9
12	NPL	A	Whitby Town	241	W 3 - 0	Walker 15 85 Clayton 81	3	10
16	FAC2Q	A	Blyth Spartans	543	W 2 - 1	Clayton 6 Reeves 90		11
18	NPL	H	Workington	164	W 3 - 2	Clayton 22 Reeves 61 Byrne 72	1	12
23	NPL	H	Stafford Rangers	261	W 5 - 2	Clayton 20 45 Reeves 10 Hough 41 Byrne 71	1	13
26	NPL	A	Matlock Town	320	W 1 - 0	Harris 51	1	14
30	FAC 3Q	A	Lancaster City	304	W 2 - 1	Reeves 14 54		15
Oct 3	NPL	A	Mickleover Sports	186	W 3 - 1	Reeves 26 28 Chilaka 86	1	16
7	NPL	A	Barwell	211	L 0 - 1		2	17
9	NPL	A	Buxton	241	W 2 - 0	Clayton 32 Byrne 47	1	18
14	FAC 4Q	A	Barrow	864	W 2 - 1	Harris 9 Reeves 76		19
21	NPL	A	Ashton United	152	D 3 - 3	Clayton 21 Woodford 32 (og) Harris 43	2	20
28	FAT 1Q	H	Ramsbottom United	183	D 2 - 2	Young 14 Harris 90 (pen)		21
31	FAT 1Qr	A	Ramsbottom United	174	L 1 - 4	Clayton 15		22
Nov 4	FAC 1	H	Mansfield Town	1700	L 1 - 3	Bennett 41		23
11	NPL	A	Halesowen Town	308	D 0 - 0		4	24
18	NPL	H	Stourbridge	253	W 3 - 1	Harris 20 (pen) 25 Chilaka 59		25
Dec 2	NPL	A	Warrington Town	221	W 5 - 0	Chilaka 4 Norris 16 Clayton 37 Harris 47 Byrne 64(p)	3	26
16	NPL	H	Witton Albion	184	D 1 - 1	Clayton 80	2	27
23	NPL	A	Hednesford Town	302	W 3 - 1	Walker 70 90 Reeves 80	2	28
Jan 1	NPL	A	Farsley Celtic	226	L 2 - 4	Reeves 1 Clayton 12	4	29
13	NPL	H	Whitby Town	185	D 0 - 0		4	30
20	NPL	H	Halesowen Town	175	W 3 - 2	Harris 4 Walker 73 Platt 80 (og)	3	31
23	NPL	A	Marine	284	W 2 - 1	Reeves 25 Norris 61	3	32
27	NPL	H	Ashton United	185	D 0 - 0		3	33
Feb 3	NPL	A	Stourbridge	514	D 1 - 1	Pierpoint 3 (og)	3	34
6	NPL	A	Coalville Town	102	W 3 - 1	Pollard 47 Reeves 66 Harris 90 (pen)	2	35
24	NPL	H	Coalville Town	193	W 2 - 0	Clayton 45 Reeves 50	2	36
Mar 17	NPL	A	Witton Albion	201	L 0 - 4		5	37
20	NPL	A	Workington	269	L 0 - 2		6	38
22	NPL	H	Grantham Town	193	L 0 - 2		6	39
24	NPL	H	Nantwich Town	172	L 0 - 2		6	40
27	NPL	A	Altrincham	805	L 1 - 5	Harris 37 (pen)	6	41
29	NPL	A	Sutton Coldfield Town	100	W 3 - 1	Reeves 4 Byrne 28 Norris 36	5	42
Apr 2	NPL	A	Grantham Town	484	L 1 - 3	Lugsden 12	6	43
7	NPL	A	Rushall Olympic	186	W 3 - 1	Clayton 84 Dyson 88 90	6	44
9	NPL	H	Marine	172	L 1 - 3	Lugsden 12	6	45
12	NPL	H	Stalybridge Celtic	136	W 2 - 0	Dyson 15 Reeves 50	6	46
14	NPL	H	Lancaster City	160	D 0 - 0		6	47
17	NPL	A	Warrington Town	241	L 1 - 2	Chilaka 27	6	48
19	NPL	H.	Altrincham	292	L 1 - 2	Reeves 43	6	49
21	NPL	A	Stafford Rangers	560	W 2 - 1	Reeves 6 (pen) 69	6	50
24	NPL	A	Nantwich Town	121	W 3 - 2	Chilaka 59 Abadaki 68 Lugsden 70	6	51
26	NPL	H	Barwell	127	W 3 - 2	Byrne 59 Abadaki 83 Chilaka 86	6	52
28	NPL	H	Matlock Town	219	W 2 - 1	Harris 85 90	6	53

GOALSCORERS	SG	CSG	Pens	Hat tricks	Total		SG	CSG	Pens	Hat tricks	Total
Reeves	15	3	1		19	Abadaki	3				3
Clayton	14	4			15	Bennett					1
Harris	13	3	3		13	Hough					1
Chilaka	7	2			8	Quaiter					1
Walker	5				7	Pollard					1
Byrne	6	2	1		6	Rothery					1
Norris	5				5	Young					1
Opponents	4				4						
Dyson	2				3						
Lugsden	3				3						

STAFFORD RANGERS MATCH RESULTS 2017-18

Date	Comp	H/A	Opponents	Att:	Result	Goalscorers	Pos	No.
Aug 12	NPL	A	Altrincham	611	W 3 - 0	Westwood 10 Thomas 44 Bachelor 52	2	1
15	NPL	H	Sutton Coldfield Town	614	W 4 - 1	Langston 42 61 Westwood 55 Bailey 88	2	2
19	NPL	H	Buxton	592	L 1 - 4	Westwood 70	7	3
22	NPL	A	Mickleover Sports	303	W 2 - 0	Westwood 52 90	1	4
26	NPL	A	Workington	418	D 0 - 0		5	5
28	NPL	H	Hednesford Town	1226	L 0 - 1		8	6
Sept 2	FAC 2Q	A	Peterborough Sports	284	W 4 - 3	Gregory 47 Batchelor 68 90 Langston 83		7
5	NPL	A	Halesowen Town	261	D 1 - 1	Sherratt 82	9	8
9	NPL	H	Witton Albion	445	L 0 - 4		14	9
12	NPL	A	Warrington Town	201	L 0 - 1		14	10
16	FAC 3Q	H	Tamworth	782	W 1 - 0	Reid 63		11
23	NPL	A	Shaw Lane	261	L 2 - 5	Abadaki 55 Westwood 63	21	12
26	NPL	H	Nantwich Town	412	W 3 - 0	Bailey 2 Abadaki 20 Gregory 62	18	13
30	FAC 4Q	H	AFC Telford United	1137	D 1 - 1	Batchelor 9		14
Oct 3	FAC 4Qr	A	AFC Telford United	869	L 1 - 4	Gregory 15		15
7	NPL	A	Grantham Town	320	W 2 - 1	Sherratt 20 Reid 31	17	16
10	NPL	H	Mickleover Sports	417	D 1 - 1	Gregory 11	16	17
17	NPL	H	Ashton United	514	W 1 - 0	Gregory 81	16	18
21	NPL	A	Matlock Town	439	L 0 - 2		18	19
28	FAT 1Q	H	St Ives Town	495	W 6 - 0	Morris 17 McDonald 22 42 Briscoe 51 Gregory 59 Westwood 90		20
31	NPL	H	Barwell	376	W 1 - 0	Morris 57	16	21
Nov 4	NPL	A	Whitby Town	303	D 0 - 0		16	22
7	NPL	A	Sutton Coldfield Town	211	W 3 - 2	Westwood 1 90 Morris 48	12	23
11	FAT 2Q	H	South Shields	955	W 3 - 1	McDONALD 3 (8 78 83)		24
14	NPL	H	Rushall Olympic	406	L 0 - 4		13	25
18	NPL	H	Farsley Celtic	490	L 0 - 2		14	26
25	FAT 3Q	A	Gainsborough Trinity	299	L 0 - 2			27
Dec 2	NPL	H	Marine	415	L 1 - 4	Fletcher 90	17	28
23	NPL	A	Buxton	300	D 1 - 1	Westwood 14	16	29
26	NPL	H	Stourbridge	944	W 1 - 0	McDonald 77	16	30
30	NPL	H	Workington	497	L 1 - 2	Thompson-Brown 69	17	31
Jan 1	NPL	A	Hednesford Town	892	L 1 - 2	Mendez-Jones 74 (og)	18	32
13	NPL	H	Altrincham	599	L 0 - 2		18	33
23	NPL	A	Coalville Town	118	D 0 - 0		18	34
27	NPL	H	Matlock Town	468	W 2 - 0	Hawley 15 49	17	35
Feb 3	NPL	A	Marine	445	D 1 - 1	McDonald 44	18	36
6	NPL	A	Stalybridge Celtic	173	L 0 - 2		18	37
10	NPL	H	Whitby Town	413	D 2 - 2	Thompson-Brown 23 Thomas 44	17	38
17	NPL	A	Farsley Celtic	246	L 0 - 1		19	39
20	NPL	A	Rushall Olympic	266	W 2 - 1	Reid 45 Perry 71	15	40
24	NPL	H	Stalybridge Celtic	426	W 2 - 0	Reid 1 Westwood 50	14	41
Mar 10	NPL	H	Lancaster Cirty	406	D 2 - 2	Thompson-Brown 31 Morris 62	12	42
13	NPL	A	Warrington Town	301	D 0 - 0		12	43
17	NPL	H	Coalville Town	145	W 4 - 1	Perry 13 80 Thompson-Brown 26 Morris 64	11	44
24	NPL	A	Lancaster City	299	D 1 - 1	Thompson-Brown 89	11	45
27	NPL	A	Barwell	172	W 2 - 1	Thompson-Brown 33 (pen) 45 (pen)	13	46
31	NPL	H	Grantham Town	563	L 1 - 2	Abadaki 12	13	47
Apr 7	NPL	H	Halesowen Town	475	D 0 - 0		13	48
10	NPL	A	Ashton United	138	L 0 - 1		13	49
14	NPL	A	Witton Albion	318	W 2 - 1	Thompson-Brown 2 Sherratt 40	13	50
21	NPL	H	Shaw Lane	560	L 1 - 2	Thompson-Brown 64 (pen)	15	51
26	NPL	A	Stourbridge	368	D 0 - 0		15	52
28	NPL	A	Nantwich Town	448	W 3 - 0	Thompson-Brown16 (pen) 51 (pen) White 55	14	53

GOALSCORERS	SG	CSG	Pens	Hat tricks	Total		SG	CSG	Pens	Hat tricks	Total
2016-17 Perry					12	Perry	2				3
Westwood	9	4			11	Sherratt					3
Thompson-Brown	9	3	5		11	Bailey					2
McDonald	7			1	7	Hawley					2
Gregory	6				6	Thomas					2
Morris	4				5	Briscoe					1
Bachelor	3				4	Fletcher					1
Reid	4	2			4	Opponents					1
Abadaki	3				3	White					1
Langston	2				3						

STALYBRIDGE CELTIC MATCH RESULTS 2017-18

Date	Comp	H/A	Opponents	Att:	Result	Goalscorers	Pos	No.
Aug 12	NPL	H	Nantwich Town	458	W 1 - 0	Honeyball 45	9	1
15	NPL	A	Whitby Town	256	L 1 - 4	Burns 21	15	2
19	NPL	A	Rushall Olympic	231	L 0 - 1		19	3
22	NPL	H	Marine	319	L 0 - 2		24	4
26	NPL	H	Shaw Lane	285	L 0 - 1		24	5
28	NPL	A	Lancaster City	354	L 0 - 1		24	6
Sept 2	FAC 2Q	H	Farsley Celtic	289	W 2 - 1	Dickinson 13 Bailey-Jones 90		7
5	NPL	A	Farsley Celtic	215	L 4 - 5	Bailey-Jones 4 19 Honeyball 11 Dickinson 52	24	8
9	NPL	H	Stourbridge	306	W 3 - 1	Dickinson 41 (pen) 69 Forde 74 (og)	22	9
12	NPL	H	Buxton	206	L 0 - 1		24	10
16	FAC 3Q	H	Chorley	551	L 1 - 3	Dickinson 88 (pen)		11
19	NPL	A	Witton Albion	244	L 1 - 4	Roberts 52	24	12
23	NPL	A	Coalville Town	159	L 0 - 4		24	13
26	NPL	H	Halesowen Town	191	W 1 - 0	Dickinson 9	23	14
30	NPL	H	Altrincham	528	D 0 - 0		23	15
Oct 3	NPL	H	Whitby Town	228	W 3 - 1	Cofie 11 Killock 50 Dickinson 90	21	16
7	NPL	H	Matlock Town	529	W 4 - 1	Dickinson 24 Bailey-Jones 62 81 Charles 90	19	17
10	NPL	A	Marine	385	L 1 - 3	Dickinson 53	20	18
14	NPL	A	Grantham Town	272	D 0 - 0		19	19
21	NPL	H	Barwell	345	W 4 - 2	Bailey-Jones 19 Roberts 50 Wolfenden 70 Charles90		20
28	FAT 1Q	H	Prescott Cables	285	D 0 - 0			21
31	FAT 1Qr	H	Prescott Cables	171	W 5 - 1	Dickinson 4 33 Bailey-Jones 64 Charles 73 Cofie 83		22
Nov 4	NPL	H	Mickleover Sports	258	L 0 - 5		19	23
11	FAT 2Q	H	Rushall Olympic	240	W 3 - 2	Hughes 36 83 Bailey-Jones 76		24
18	NPL	A	Hednesford Town	346	L 1 - 2	Roberts 69	22	25
25	FAT 3Q	A	Blyth Spartans	482	L 1 - 2	Hughes 69		26
Dec 2	NPL	A	Sutton Coldfield T	131	L 0 - 2		23	27
23	NPL	H	Rushall Olympic	303	L 1 - 2	Hall (og) 6	23	28
Jan 1	NPL	A	Lancaster City	281	W 5 - 2	CHAPELL 3 (43 65 71) Ashworth 57 Bailey-Jones 79	23	29
13	NPL	A	Buxton	275	D 2 - 2	Dickinson 25 Chapell 36	23	30
27	NPL	A	Barwell	171	L 0 - 1		23	31
Feb 3	NPL	H	Sutton Coldfield T	310	D 1 - 1	Hughes 32	23	32
6	NPL	H	Stafford Rangers	173	W 2 - 0	Hughes 58 63	22	33
13	NPL	A	Warrington	227	W 1 - 0	Wolfenden 74	22	34
17	NPL	H	Hednesford Town	389	D 2 - 2	Benbow 37 Broadhurst 90	21	35
24	NPL	A	Stafford Rangers	426	L 0 - 2		21	36
Mar 10	NPL	A	Workington	324	W 4 - 3	Dickinson 6 Hughes 26 71 Wilkinson 49	21	37
17	NPL	A	Altrincham	844	W 2 - 1	Wolfenden 16 Dickinson 87	21	38
20	NPL	A	Nantwich Town	205	W 3 - 2	Wolfenden 8 90 Hughes 42	21	39
24	NPL	H	Warrington Town	615	W 2 - 0	Dickinson 42 (pen) Wilkinson 45	18	40
27	NPL	H	Grantham Town	275	L 1 - 3	Honeyball 90	18	41
Apr 3	NPL	H	Ashton United	360	D 2 - 2	Wolfenden 16 Dickinson 87	18	42
7	NPL	H	Farsley Celtic	325	L 1 - 4	Pouamount 90	19	43
12	NPL	A	Shaw Lane	136	L 0 - 2		22	44
14	NPL	A	Stourbridge	520	L 1 - 4	Holgate 90	22	45
17	NPL	A	Ashton United	304	W 2 - 1	Wolfenden 69 Charles 84	22	46
19	NPL	A	Matlock Town	261	L 0 - 2		22	47
21	NPL	H	Coalville Town	285	L 0 - 3		22	48
23	NPL	A	Mickleover Sports	90	L 0 - 1		22	49
25	NPL	H	Workington	93	L 1 - 3	Roberts 66	22	50
26	NPL	H	Witton Albion	187	L 0 - 5		22	51
28	NPL	A	Halesowen Town	446	L 0 - 2		22	52

GOALSCORERS	SG	CSG	Pens	Hat tricks	Total		SG	CSG	Pens	Hat tricks	Total
2016-17 Owens					7	Opponents					2
Dickinson	14	2x3	3		16	Wilkinson					2
Bailey-Jones	7	2			9	Ashworth					1
Hughes	6				9	Benbow					1
Wolfenden	6				7	Broadhurst					1
Chapell	2			1	4	Burns					1
Charles	4				4	Holgate					1
Roberts	4				4	Killock					1
Honeyball	3				3	Pouamount					1
Cofie	2				2						

STOURBRIDGE MATCH RESULTS 2017-18

Date	Comp	H/A	Opponents	Att:	Result	Goalscorers	Pos	No.
Aug 13	NPL	H	Matlock Town	1050	D 1 - 1	Archer 45	13	1
15	NPL	A	Coalville Town	173	W 1 - 0	Archer 15	8	2
19	NPL	A	Whitby Town	231	W 3 - 1	McCone 9 Archer 30 82	3	3
21	NPL	H	Nantwich Town	681	D 1 - 1	Archer 18	7	4
26	NPL	H	Marine	839	L 0 - 2		10	5
28	NPL	A	Rushall Olympic	522	W 2 - 1	Broadhurst 6 10	5	6
Sept 2	FAC 1Q	A	Loughborough Dynamo	262	W 3 - 1	Broadhurst 51 61 Cooke 77		7
4	NPL	H	Hednesford Town	683	W 2 - 0	Archer 33 Rowe 63	4	8
9	NPL	A	Stalybridge Celtic	306	L 1 - 3	Broadhurst 85	6	9
11	NPL	H	Barwell	595	W 2 - 1	Rowe 5 (pen) Cooke 73	2	10
17	FAC 2Q	H	St Ives Town	765	W 2 - 0	Broadhurst 35 67		11
19	NPL	A	Mickleover Sports	188	W 2 - 1	Forde 56 Duggan 57	6	12
23	NPL	H	Lancaster City	899	D 0 - 0		5	13
26	NPL	A	Warrington Town	200	W 5 - 1	Pierpoint 15 Archer 19 53 Broadhurst 58 McCone 63	2	14
30	FAC 3Q	H	Alfreton Town	646	W 3 - 1	Tonks 26 Green 58 Broadhurst 88		15
Oct 2	NPL	H	Coalville Town	640	W 2 - 1	Dodd 34 Archer 90	2	16
7	NPL	H	Halesowen Town	2306	L 1 - 2	Broadhurst 63	5	17
14	FAC 4Q	H	Macclesfield Town	1152	L 0 - 5			18
21	NPL	H	Grantham Town	600	L 0 - 2		7	19
28	FAT 1Q	H	Basford United	404	W 1 - 0	Forde 61		20
31	NPL	A	Sutton Coldfield Town	209	W 4 - 0	Shearer 2 Perry 37 Forde 73 Cooke 90	7	21
Nov 4	NPL	H	Witton Albion	737	D 0 - 0		7	22
11	FAT 2Q	A	St Neots Town	323	W 3 - 2	Broadhurst 48 Benbow 52 (pen) Green 76		23
18	NPL	A	Shaw Lane	253	L 1 - 3	Benbow 62	8	24
25	FAT 3Q	A	Bradford PA	256	D 1 - 1	Perry 33		25
27	FAT 3Qr	H	Bradford PA	385	W 2 - 1	Killock (og) 50 Shearer 58		26
Dec 2	NPL	A	Workington	363	L 1 - 2	Shearer 87	10	27
5	NPL	A	Nantwich Town	209	L 0 - 2		10	28
16	FAT 1	H	Leamington	404	W 1 - 0	Dodd 48		29
23	NPL	H	Whitby Town	557	D 1 - 1	Broadhurst 50 (pen)	12	30
26	NPL	A	Stafford Rangers	944	L 0 - 1		13	31
30	NPL	A	Marine	410	W 4 - 0	Westlake 23 Broadhurst 29 (p) Benbow 34 Cooke 90	11	32
Jan 1	NPL	H	Rushall Olympic	767	W 5 - 0	Anderson 30 Broadhurst 38 (pen) Tonks 53 Dodd 78 Shearer 81	10	33
6	NPL	H	Mickleover Sports	529	D 1 - 1	Tonks 35	10	34
13	FAT 2	A	Billericay Town	1081	L 2 - 3	Broadhurst 47 Pierpoint 49		35
17	NPL	A	Grantham Town	256	L 2 - 4	Potts 33 (og) Perry 90	15	36
23	NPL	A	Ashton United	148	L 0 - 1		14	37
Feb 3	NPL	H	Shaw Lane	310	D 1 - 1	Benbow 47	14	38
12	NPL	H	Farsley Celtic	402	L 1 - 2	Benbow 20	14	39
17	NPL	H	Buxton	476	W 2 - 1	Benbow 37 Broadhurst 90	14	40
Mar 6	NPL	A	Altrincham	542	L 1 - 4	Shearer 47	15	41
13	NPL	A	Buxton	172	D 1 - 1	Broadhurst 50	14	42
17	NPL	H	Ashton United	367	L 2 - 3	Anderson 54 Broadhurst 72 (pen)	14	43
20	NPL	A	Witton Albion	223	L 0 - 1		15	44
24	NPL	A	Farsley Celtic	262	W 4 - 1	Benbow 11 55 McCone 52 Cooke 90	15	45
26	NPL	H	Sutton Coldfield Town	476	W 2 - 1	Hayden 29 Smith 90 (og)	14	46
28	NPL	A	Matlock Town	242	D 0 - 0		14	47
31	NPL	A	Halesowen Town	1753	L 0 - 1		14	48
Apr 7	NPL	A	Hednesford Town	347	D 1 - 1	Benbow 63	14	49
9	NPL	H	Altrincham	426	D 1 - 1	Benbow 11	14	50
14	NPL	H	Stalybridge Celtic	420	W 4 - 1	McCone 4 Carnat 7 62 Benbow 59	10	51
16	NPL	H	Workington	379	L 2 - 3	Birch 26 Benbow 47		52
21	NPL	A	Lancaster City	238	D 0 - 0			53
24	NPL	A	Barwell	126	D 1 - 1	Birch 68	11	54
26	NPL	H	Stafford Rangers	368	D 0 - 0		13	55
28	NPL	H	Warrington Town	473	W 2 - 1	Broadhurst 43 Benbow 45	11	56

GOALSCORERS	SG	CSG	Pens	Hat tricks	Total		SG	CSG	Pens	Hat tricks	Total
2016-17 Benbow					36	Tonks	3				3
Broadhurst	16	2	4		19	Anderson	2				2
Benbow	11	3	1		13	Birch	2				2
Archer	7	4			9	Carnet	1				2
Cooke	4				5	Green	2				2
Shearer	4				5	Pierpoint	2				2
McCone	4				4	Rowe	2		1		2
Dodd	3				3	Duggan					1
Forde	3	2			3	Hayden					1
Opponents					3	Westlake					1
Perry	3				3						

SUTTON COLDFIELD TOWN MATCH RESULTS 2017-18

Date	Comp	H/A	Opponents	Att:	Result	Goalscorers	Pos	No.
Aug 12	NPL	H	Shaw Lane	187	W 3 - 1	Flint 7 McMillan 78 Vincent 86	4	1
15	NPL	A	Staffordf Rangers	614	L 1 - 4	Birch 77	13	2
19	NPL	A	Witton Albion	298	L 0 - 1		16	3
22	NPL	H	Matlock Town	165	D 3 - 3	SINGH 3 (1 42 87)	16	4
26	NPL	H	Ashton United	193	L 0 - 2		19	5
28	NPL	A	Halesowen Town	372	W 2 - 0	Birch 2 Lavell-Moore 53	17	6
Sept 2	FAC 1Q	H	Barwell	186	L 0 - 2			7
5	NPL	H	Barwell	103	L 0 - 6		21	8
9	NPL	A	Hednesford Town	410	L 0 - 3		21	9
12	NPL	A	Rushall Olympic	192	L 1 - 5	Martin 47	22	10
16	NPL	A	Whitby Town	197	D 2 - 2	Carson 20 57	21	11
19	NPL	H	Coalville Town	126	D 1 - 1	Smith 58	21	12
23	NPL	H	Buxton Town	177	W 2 - 1	Singh 75 90	20	13
26	NPL	A	Grantham Town	164	L 1 - 6	Singh 50	21	14
30	NPL	A	Matlock Town	334	L 0 - 5		22	15
Oct 7	NPL	H	Lancaster City	235	L 0 - 2		23	16
14	NPL	H	Whitby Town	186	D 1 - 1	Singh 14	24	17
21	NPL	A	Workington	359	L 0 - 4		24	18
28	FAT 1Q	A	Stamford	229	L 0 - 3			19
31	NPL	H	Stourbridge	209	L 0 - 4		24	20
Nov 4	NPL	A	Warrington	232	L 1 - 2	Singh 66	24	21
7	NPL	H	Stafford Rangers	211	L 2 - 3	O'Callaghan 17 Singh 90	24	22
11	NPL	A	Mickleover Sports	230	L 0 - 2		24	23
18	NPL	H	Altrincham	269	L 0 - 4		24	24
25	NPL	A	Farsley Celtic	217	W 1 - 0	Singh 14	24	25
Dec 2	NPL	A	Stalybridge Celtic	131	W 2 - 0	Singh 52 Waters 61	24	26
23	NPL	H	Witton Albion	168	L 2 - 6	O'Callaghan 63 Lyttle 87	24	27
26	NPL	A	Nantwich Town	366	D 0 - 0		24	28
30	NPL	A	Ashton United	168	L 0 - 2		24	29
Jan 1	NPL	H	Halesowen Town	287	L 0 - 1		24	30
6	NPL	A	Coalville Town	128	L 2 - 4	Richards 72 (pen) 76	24	31
13	NPL	H	Rushall Olympic	205	L 3 - 4	Richards 14 (pen) 47 Howarth 72	24	32
27	NPL	H	Workington	234	W 4 - 1	Richards 3 72 Lyttle 79 Flint 84	24	33
Feb 3	NPL	A	Stalybridge Celtic	310	D 1 - 1	Richards 76 (pen)	24	34
6	NPL	H	Marine	102	W 3 - 1	O'Callaghan 9 Flint 24 Beresford 78	24	35
10	NPL	H	Warrington Town	235	L 0 - 2		24	36
17	NPL	A	Altrincham	905	L 1 - 2	Lyttle 13	24	37
24	NPL	H	Farsley Celtic	144	L 0 - 1		24	38
Mar 17	NPL	H	Mickleover Sports	172	W 2 - 1	Richards 7 (pen) King 50 (og)	24	39
24	NPL	A	Marine	402	L 0 - 5		24	40
26	NPL	A	Stourbridge	476	L 1 - 2	Hawley 60	24	41
29	NPL	A	Shaw Lane	100	L 1 - 3	Dell 90	24	42
31	NPL	A	Lancaster City	100	L 1 - 2	Smith 85		43
Apr 2	NPL	H	Nantwich Town	221	L 1 - 3	Mullarkey 51 (og)	24	44
7	NPL	A	Barwell	145	L 1 - 2	Hawley 42	24	45
14	NPL	H	Hednesford Town	185	W 4 - 1	Hawley 4 90 Richards 19 Smith 68	24	46
21	NPL	A	Buxton Town	341	W 1 - 0	Hawley 67	24	47
28	NPL	H	Grantham Town	207	L 1 - 2	Smith 67	24	48

GOALSCORERS	SG	CSG	Pens	Hat tricks	Total		SG	CSG	Pens	Hat tricks	Total
2016-17 *Rodgers*					7	Opponents					2
Singh	8	2		1	11	Bereford					1
Richards	6	4	4		9	Dell					1
Hawley	4	3			5	Howarth					1
Smith	4				4	L-Moore					1
Flint	3				3	Martin					1
Lyttle	3				3	McMillan					1
O'Callaghan	3				3	Vincent					1
Birch	2				2	Waters					1
Carson	1				2						

WARRINGTON TOWN MATCH RESULTS 2017-18

Date	Comp	H/A	Opponents	Att:	Result	Goalscorers	Pos	No.
Aug 12	NPL	H	Rushall Olympic	239	W 2 - 0	Hughes 17 Mwasile 90	6	1
15	NPL	A	Lancaster City	260	D 2 - 2	Jerome 12 Hine 80	4	2
19	NPL	A	Coalville Town	128	W 3 - 0	Williams 46 (pen) Gray 57 Hine 73	1	3
22	NPL	H	Ashton United	245	L 0 - 1		7	4
26	NPL	H	Matlock Town	243	W 2 - 0	Hughes 43 Gray 45	4	5
28	NPL	A	Marine	444	W 4 - 0	Hine 33 Williams 63 (pen) 82 (pen) Hughes 68	1	6
Sept 2	FAC 2Q	H	Grimsby Borough	297	W 1 - 0	Sanogo 80		7
5	NPL	A	Workington	351	D 1 - 1	Gray 33	2	8
9	NPL	H	Farsley Celtic	251	W 4 - 2	Gray 27 55 Hughes 45 Williams 90 (pen)	1	9
12	NPL	H	Stafford Rangers	201	W 1 - 0	Barnes 51	1	10
16	FAC 3Q	H	Hyde United	429	D 1 - 1	Kinsella 68		11
19	FAC 3Qr	A	Hyde United	433	L 0 - 2			12
23	NPL	A	Halesowen Town	280	D 1 - 1	Richards 17	3	13
26	NPL	H	Stourbridge	200	L 1 - 5	Williams 50	3	14
30	NPL	A	Rushall Olympic	187	W 2 - 1	Williams 33 (pen) Beeley 78	3	15
Oct 3	NPL	H	Lancaster City	202	W 5 - 1	Barrington 4 Goulding 35 Williams 64 Richards 80 McDonald 90	1	16
7	NPL	H	Whitby Town	341	W 2 - 1	McCarten 59 Hine 80	3	17
10	NPL	A	Ashton United	202	L 0 - 2		3	18
14	NPL	A	Barwell	183	W 1 - 0	Sanogo 75	2	19
21	NPL	H	Altrincham	952	D 0 - 0		3	20
24	NPL	A	Buxton	240	L 1 - 2	McDonald 31	3	21
28	FAT 1Q	H	Bamber Bridge	239	W 2 - 1	McDonald 51 80		22
Nov 4	NPL	H	Sutton Coldfield Town	232	W 2 - 1	Jennings 1 McKeown 60		23
11	FAT 2Q	H	Ashton United	313	D 1 - 1	Sanogo 68		24
15	FAT 2Qr	A	Ashton United	163	D 2 - 2	McDonald 18 26 (Won 4-2 on pens)		25
18	NPL	A	Mickleover Sports	214	W 3 - 1	Barnes 40 Williams 66 (pen) Gray 76	2	26
25	FAT 3Q	A	Tamworth	468	D 2 - 2	Vassallo 21 McDonald 76		27
28	FAT 3Qr	H	Tamworth	223	W 3 - 0	McDonald 11 33 Gray 89		28
Dec 2	NPL	A	Shaw Lane	221	L 0 - 5		4	29
16	FAT 1	H	Altrincham	545	D 0 - 0			30
19	FAT 1r	H	Altrincham	452	W 2 - 1	Goulding 87 McDonald 90		31
23	NPL	H	Coalville Town	228	L 1 - 3	McDonald 89	5	32
26	NPL	H	Witton Albion	503	W 2 - 1	Gray 79 90	4	33
Jan 1	NPL	H	Marine	255	D 0 - 0		5	34
6	NPL	H	Buxton	271	W 1 - 0	Jennings 55 (pen)	3	35
13	FAT 2	A	Ebbsfleet United	911	D 1 - 1	Kinsella 64		36
16 Jan	FAT 2r	H	Ebbsfleet United	334	W 2 - 0	Gray 61 McDonald 67		37
27	NPL	A	Altrincham	1419	D 1 - 1	Vasallo 19	5	38
Feb 3	FAT 3	A	Wealdstone	601	L 1 - 2	Piggott 82		39
6	NPL	A	Matlock Town	191	W 3 - 1	Piggott 6 , 7 Barnes 50	5	40
10	NPL	A	Sutton Coldfield Town	235	W 2 - 0	Gray 45 Higgins 81	4	41
13	NPL	H	Stalybridge Celtic	227	L 0 - 1		4	42
17	NPL	H	Mickleover Sports	283	W 3 - 1	Goulding 3 Williams 24 McDonald 75	2	43
24	NPL	A	Hednrsford Town	346	W 2 - 0	Gray 20 Williams 56	2	44
Mar 10	NPL	H	Barwell	172	W 2 - 0	McDonald 60 70	2	45
13	NPL	A	Stafford Rangers	301	D 0 - 0		2	46
17	NPL	H	Grantham Town	241	W 2 - 1	Green 13 McDonald 53	2	47
20	NPL	H	Hednesford Town	223	W 4 - 1	Williams 37 81 Green 42 Gray 54	2	48
24	NPL	A	Stalybridge Celtic	615	L 0 - 2		2	49
27	NPL	H	Workington	210	D 1 - 1	McLeod	2	50
Apr 2	NPL	H	Witton Albion	479	D 2 - 2	Green 33 Jennings 56 (pen)	2	51
7	NPL	A	Nantwich Town	269	L 1 - 2	Williams 28 (pen)	2	52
10	NPL	H	Nantwich Town	201	D 0 - 0		2	53
12	NPL	A	Whitby Town	198	D 2 - 2	Higgins 7 90	2	54
14	NPL	A	Farsley Celtic	252	W 2 - 0	Hayhurst 22 Williams 54	2	55
17	NPL	H	Shaw Lane	241	W 2 - 1	Williams 7 (pen) McKeown 48	2	56
21	NPL	H	Halesowen Town	300	D 1 - 1	McDonald 57	2	57
24	NPL	A	Grantham Town	301	D 0 - 0		2	58
28	NPL	A	Stourbridge	473	L 1 - 2	Piggott 14	3	59
May 1	PO SF	H	Grantham Town	737	L 0 - 3			60

GOALSCORERS	SG	CSG	Pens	Hat tricks	Total		SG	CSG	Pens	Hat tricks	Total
2016-17 Kilheeney					7	Richards	2				2
McDonald	13	2			17	Kinsella	2				2
Williams	13	3	8		15	McKeown					2
Gray	11	2			13	Vassallo	2				2
Hine	4	2			4	Barrington					1
Hughes	4	2			4	Beeley					1
Piggott	3				3	Hayhurst					1
Barnes	3				3	Jerome					1
Goulding	3				3	McCarten					1
Green	3				3	McLeod					1
Higgins	2				3	Mwasile					1
Jennings	3		2		3						
Sanogo	3				3						

WHITBY TOWN MATCH RESULTS 2017-18

Date	Comp	H/A	Opponents	Att:	Result	Goalscorers	Pos	No.
Aug 12	NPL	A	Barwell	152	L 0 - 1		18	1
15	NPL	H	Stalybridge Celtic	256	W 4 - 1	Weledji 10 Carson 48 90 Honeyball 83 (og)	10	2
19	NPL	H	Stourbridge	231	L 1 - 3	Bythway 24	14	3
22	NPL	A	Altrincham	579	L 0 - 1		21	4
26	NPL	A	Grantham Town	244	L 0 - 2		21	5
28	NPL	H	Workington	288	D 1 - 1	Weledji 56	21	6
Sept 2	FAC 2Q	A	Penistone Church	496	L 2 - 3	Bythway 6 Brennan 25 (og)		7
5	NPL	H	Ashton United	207	W 3 - 2	Weledji 36 Tymon 70 Carson 90 (pen)	17	8
9	NPL	H	Matlock Town	372	W 2 - 1	Weledji 10 Roberts 86	17	9
12	NPL	H	Shaw Lane	241	L 0 - 3		20	10
16	NPL	H	Sutton Coldfield Town	197	D 2 - 2	Carson 20 57	20	11
19	NPL	A	Lancaster City	240	L 1 - 4	Campbell 58	20	12
23	NPL	H	Marine	253	W 3 - 2	Hume 5 68 Carson 30	14	13
26	NPL	A	Buxton	218	W 2 - 0	Tymon 17 Risborough 90	12	14
30	NPL	H	Barwell	219	W 1 - 0	Carson 40 (pen)	11	15
Oct 3	NPL	A	Stalybridge Celtic	228	L 1 - 3	Walton 85 (og)	13	16
7	NPL	A	Warrington Town	341	L 1 - 2	Tymon 90	15	17
10	NPL	H	Altrincham	226	D 1 - 1	Carson 58 (pen)	15	18
14	NPL	A	Sutton Coldfield Town	186	D 1 - 1	Risborough 84	14	19
21	NPL	H	Hednesford Town	274	D 2 - 2	Campbell 29 53	15	20
28	FAT 1Q	H	Marine	279	L 1 - 3	McWilliams 29		21
31	NPL	A	Mickleover Sports	154	L 1 - 2	Weledji 7	18	22
Nov 4	NPL	H	Stafford Rangers	303	D 0 - 0		18	23
18	NPL	A	Nantwich Town	305	L 0 - 1		18	24
25	NPL	H	Witton Albion	248	L 1 - 2	Fryatt 2	19	25
Dec 2	NPL	A	Halesowen Town	225	L 1 3	Fryatt 5	19	26
8	NPL	H	Coalville Town	239	D 2 - 2	Tymon 22 Campbell 79 (pen)	19	27
23	NPL	A	Stourbridge	557	D 1 - 1	Weledji 80	20	28
26	NPL	H	Farsley Celtic	369	L 0 - 2		21	29
Jan 1	NPL	A	Workington	520	W 3 - 1	Fairley 60 Mondal 79 Maloney 90	19	30
6	NPL	H	Lancaster City	247	L 0 - 5		19	31
13	NPL	A	Shaw Lane	185	D 0 - 0		20	32
20	NPL	A	Rushall Olympic	162	D 3 - 3	Gay 44 87 Mondal 61	20	33
27	NPL	A	Hednesford Town	393	D 0 - 0		20	34
Feb 3	NPL	H	Halesowen Town	202	W 5 - 0	Snaith 51 80 Mondal 58 63 Fairley 67	19	35
10	NPL	A	Stafford Rangers	413	D 2 - 2	Maloney 61 (pen) Patton 90	20	36
17	NPL	H	Nantwich Town	301	W 2 - 1	Tymon 44 Hume 66	18	37
24	NPL	A	Witton Albion	229	L 0 - 1		19	38
Mar 24	NPL	H	Coalville Town	132	W 1 - 0	Mondal 86	17	39
27	NPL	H	Mickleover Sports	192	W 3 - 2	Mondal 1 Patton 55 Maloney 66 (pen)	17	40
Apr 5	NPL	A	Farsley Celtic	146	L 0 - 4		18	41
7	NPL	A	Ashton United	172	L 0 - 4		20	42
12	NPL	H	Warrington Town	198	D 2 - 2	Maloney 2 Tymon 44	20	43
14	NPL	H	Matlock Town	314	L 0 - 3		20	44
19	NPL	H	Grantham Town	223	L 1 - 5	Mondal 25	20	45
21	NPL	A	Marine	507	W 3 - 0	Patton 43 79 Hume 90	20	46
24	NPL	H	Rushall Olympic	164	L 2 - 3	Maloney 34 Fryatt 48	21	47
28	NPL	H	Buxton	272	D 1 - 1	Tymon 60	21	48

GOALSCORERS	SG	CSG	Pens	Hat tricks	Total		SG	CSG	Pens	Hat tricks	Total
2016-17 *Hopson*					27	Opponents					3
Carson	6		3		8	Bythway	2				2
Tymon	7				7	Fairley	2				2
Weledji	6				6	Gay	1				2
Mondal	5				6	Patton					2
Maloney	5		2		5	Risborough	2				2
Campbell	3		1		4	Snaith	1				2
Patton	3				4	McWilliams					1
Fryatt	3				3	Roberts					1
Hume	3				3						

WITTON ALBION MATCH RESULTS 2017-18

Date	Comp	H/A	Opponents	Att:	Result	Goalscorers	Pos	No.
Aug 12	NPL	A	Mickleover Sports	225	D 1 - 1	Tames 2 (pen)	13	1
15	NPL	H	Buxton	336	W 1 - 0	Jones 88	9	2
19	NPL	H	Sutton Coldfield Town	298	W 1 - 0	Tames 6	5	3
22	NPL	A	Workington	391	D 1 - 1	Hopley 51	6	4
26	NPL	A	Barwell	162	W 1 - 0	Jones 59	4	5
28	NPL	H	Altrincham	752	L 0 - 2		7	6
Sept 2	FAC 1Q	H	South Shields	534	L 0 - 2			7
5	NPL	H	Marine	267	D 1 - 1	Jones 49	7	8
9	NPL	A	Stafford Rangers	445	W 4 - 0	Tames 10 84 Jones 35 Hopley 44	3	9
12	NPL	A	Halesowen Town	208	W 3 - 1	Jones 16 Tames 19 (pen) Haywood 89	2	10
16	NPL	A	Coalville Town	159	L 1 - 2	Hopley 10	4	11
19	NPL	H	Stalybridge Celtic	244	W 4 - 1	Ryan 14 Jones 20 Tames 66 (pen) 74 (pen)	1	12
23	NPL	H	Rushall Olympic	286	L 1 - 2	Tames 70 (pen)	4	13
26	NPL	A	Lancaster City	206	L 0 - 4		7	14
30	NPL	H	Mickleover Sports	247	L 0 - 2		7	15
Oct 3	NPL	A	Buxton	238	L 0 - 2		8	16
7	NPL	A	Hednesford Town	467	L 0 - 1		14	17
10	NPL	H	Workington	226	W 1 - 0	Haywood 9	10	18
14	NPL	H	Coalville Town	259	W 5 - 2	Owens 3 Foley 23 Hopley 52 72 Hedley 67	6	19
21	NPL	A	Nantwich Town	315	L 2 - 3	Hopley 29 Williams 82 (pen)	9	20
28	FAT 1Q	A	Workington	401	L 0 - 4			21
Nov 4	NPL	A	Stourbridge	737	D 0 - 0		11	22
18	NPL	H	Matlock Town	320	D 3 - 3	Hopley 12 Williams 42 Owens 55	12	23
25	NPL	A	Whitby Town	248	W 2 - 1	Owens 60 Hopley 76	8	24
Dec 2`	NPL	H	Grantham Town	237	L 2 - 3	Hopley 85 90	8	25
16	NPL	A	Shaw Lane	184	D 1 - 1	Dale 88	9	26
23	NPL	A	Sutton Coldfield Town	168	W 6 - 2	Hopley 10 Tames 36 (pen) Jones 39 40 Dale 50 62	7	27
26	NPL	H	Warrington Town	503	L 1 - 2	Jones 33	8	28
30	NPL	H	Barwell	270	D 2 - 2	Tames 61 (pen) Hopley 90	10	29
Jan 1	NPL	A	Altrincham	1013	W 4 - 3	Owens 8 81 Foley 24 Jones 88	9	30
13	NPL	H	Ashton United	326	D 1 - 1	Tames 5	9	31
27	NPL	A	Nantwich Town	394	W 4 - 1	Hopley 3 75 Foley 28 Tames 79	9	32
Feb 3	NPL	A	Grantham Town	239	D 1 - 1	Tames 76	10	33
17	NPL	A	Matlock Town	421	W 3 - 2	Dale 14 Jones 57 Tames 90	9	34
24	NPL	H	Whitby Town	229	W 1 - 0	Wilson 14	8	35
Mar 10	NPL	H	Shaw Lane	201	W 4 - 0	Devine 19 Dale 32 Tames 43 Hopley 49	7	36
20	NPL	H	Stourbridge	223	W 1 - 0	Owens 88	5	37
24	NPL	H	Ashton United	244	L 1 - 2	Tames 60	7	38
27	NPL	H	Halesowen Town	247	L 2 - 3	Hopley 17 Tames 56 (pen)	7	39
31	NPL	H	Hednesford Town	294	W 3 - 0	Hopley 7 83 Tames 20 (pen)	6	40
Apr 2	NPL	H	Warrington Town	479	D 2 - 2	Tames 3 Owens 86	6	41
12	NPL	A	Farsley Celtic	198	D 1 - 1	Hopley 56	6	42
14	NPL	A	Stafford Rangers	316	L 1 - 2	Tames 87 (pen)	7	43
19	NPL	A	Marine	316	D 2 - 2	Hopley 56 Tames 90	7	44
24	NPL	H	Farsley Celtic	164	L 1 - 4	Williams 15		45
21	NPL	A	Rushall Olympic	221	D 0 - 0			46
26	NPL	H	Stalybridge Celtic	187	W 5 - 0	Tames 35 40 Jones 52 Haywood 65 Hopley 68	7	47
28	NPL	H	Lancaster Cityy	323	W 2 - 0	Tames 48 81	7	48

GOALSCORERS	SG	CSG	Pens	Hat tricks	Total		SG	CSG	Pens	Hat tricks	Total
Tames	21	4	10		25	Hedley					1
Hopley	17	3			20	Hopley					1
Jones	10	3			12	Wilson					1
Owens	6				7						
Dale	4				5						
Foley	3				3						
Haywood	3				3						
Williams	3		1		3						
Devine	1										
Headley	1										

WORKINGTON MATCH RESULTS 2017-18

Date	Comp	H/A	Opponents	Att:	Result		Goalscorers	Pos	No.
Aug 12	NPL	H	Halesowen Town	638	W	3 - 1	Ryan 2 Alison 8 Smith 20	5	1
15	NPL	A	Marine	264	L	0 - 2		12	2
19	NPL	A	Nantwich Town	307	L	0 - 2		18	3
22	NPL	H	Witton Albion	391	D	1 - 1	Tinnion 82	17	4
26	NPL	H	Stafford Rangers	418	D	0 - 0			5
28	NPL	A	Whitby Town	288	D	1 - 1	Douglas 59	18	6
Sept 2	FAC 2Q	A	**Scarborough Athletic**	794	L	0 - 1			7
5	NPL	H	Warrington	351	D	1 - 1	Earl 53	20	8
9	NPL	A	Grantham Town	236	L	2 - 3	Earl 14 Alison 70	20	9
12	NPL	H	Altrincham	339	W	5 - 2	ALLISON 3 (23 68 86) Tinnion 39 (pen) Joel 76	15	10
16	NPL	H	Hednesford Town	379	W	1 - 0	Tinnion 38	12	11
18	NPL	A	Shaw Lane	164	L	2 - 3	Smith 45 Tinnion 69		12
23	NPL	H	Matlock Town	429	L	0 - 1		18	13
26	NPL	A	Ashton United	133	W	1 - 0	Allison 66	13	14
30	NPL	A	Rushall Olympic	187	W	5 - 1	Allison 35 Egan 38 48 Symington 49 Hall 90	13	15
Oct 3	NPL	H	Marine	341	W	2 - 1	Wylie 3 (og) Waterston 59	9	16
7	NPL	H	Coalville Town	401	W	1 - 0	Tinnion 34 (pen)	6	17
10	NPL	A	Witton Albion	226	L	0 - 1		9	18
14	NPL	A	Hednesford Town	403	D	1 - 1	Allison 24 (pen)	9	19
21	NPL	H	Sutton Coldfield Town	359	W	4 - 0	Joel 46 77 Hall 83 Waterston 89	6	20
28	FAT 1Q	H	`Witton Albion`	401	W	4 - 0	**Douglas 29 Allison 30 48 Joel 32**		21
Nov 4	NPL	A	Farsley Celtic	278	D	3 - 3	Tinnion 8 Allison 89 Douglas 90	8	22
11	FAT 2Q	A	**Chasetown**	257	W	3 - 1	**Wordsworth 50 Joel 59 78**		23
18	NPL	A	Rushall Olympic	430	W	4 - 1	Douglas 38 Allison 76 90 Waterston 88	7	24
25	FAT 3Q	A	**Glossop North End**	368	D	0 - 0			25
Dec 2	NPL	H	Stourbridge	383	W	2 - 1	Joel 41 McLuckie 90	4	26
9	NPL	A	Mickleover Sports	387	W	3 - 0	Wordswoth 13 44 McLuckie 84	4	27
16	FAT 1	H	**Hartlepool United**	771	W	1 - 0	**Allison 52**		28
23	NPL	H	Nantwich Town	452	W	2 - 1	Symington 6 Douglas 72	4	29
26	NPL	A	Lancaster City	405	D	2 - 2	McLuckie 12 Tinnion 75	3	30
30	NPL	A	Stafford Rangers	497	W	2 - 1	Tinnion 64 McLuckie 77		31
Jan 1	NPL	H	Whitby Town	520	L	1 - 3	Waterston 26	5	32
13	FAT 2	A	**Weston-s-Mare**	361	D	1 - 1	**Allison 66**	5	33
16	FAT 2r	H	**Weston--s-Mare**	576	W	2 - 1	**Calvert 32 McLuckie 70**		34
20	NPL	H	Barwell	472	L	0 - 2		7	35
27	NPL	A	Sutton Coldfield Town	234	L	1 - 4	Calvert 27	7	36
Feb 3	FAT 3	H	**Bromley**	897	D	1 - 1	**McLuckie 48**		37
6	FAT 3r	A	**Bromley**	604	L	1 - 7	**Waterson 6**		38
17	NPL	A	Rushall Olympic	162	L	0 - 1		10	39
24	NPL	A	Barwell	157	L	0 - 1		10	40
Mar 10	NPL	H	Stalybridge Celtic	324	L	3 - 4	Smith 8 Allsion 63 (pen) Joel 79	10	41
13	NPL	A	Altrincham	510	W	3 - 2	Allison 23 28 Rigg 80	10	42
17	NPL	H	Buxton	299	L	1 - 2	Symington 18	10	43
20	NPL	H	Shaw Lane	269	W	2 - 0	Douglas 30 69	10	44
24	NPL	A	Mickleover Sports	252	L	0 - 1		10	45
27	NPL	A	Warrington Town	210	D	1 - 1	Symington 48	10	46
Apr 2	NPL	H	Lancaster City	358	W	2 - 0	Douglas 69 Wilson 89	9	47
7	NPL	A	Buxton	205	L	2 - 4	Allison 68 (pen) Symington 89	10	48
10	NPL	H	Farsley Celtic	189	L	1 - 2	Symington 82		49
14	NPL	H	Grantham Town	228	L	0 - 2		14	50
16	NPL	A	Stourbridge	379	W	3 - 2	Rigg 3 82 (pen) Holliday 49	10	51
21	NPL	H	Matlock Town	320	L	0 - 2		12	52
25	NPL	A	Stalybridge Celtic	93	W	3 - 1	Allison 31 Rigg 61 Mossop 70	12	53
26	NPL	A	Coalville Town	120	L	0 - 3		12	54
28	NPL	H	Ashton United	394	L	1 - 2	Allison 24 (pen)	12	55

GOALSCORERS	SG	CSG	Pens	Hat tricks	Total		SG	CSG	Pens	Hat tricks	Total
2016-17 *Symington*					14	Wordsworth	2				3
Allison	16	2	3	1	21	Calvert	2				2
Douglas	6	2			8	Earl	2	2			2
Joel	6	2			8	Egan	1				2
Tinnion	8	3	2		8	Hall	2				2
McLuckie	6	2			6	Holliday					1
Symington	6				6	Mossop					1
Waterstone	4				5	Opponents					1
Rigg	3		1		4	Ryan					1
Smith	3				3	Wilson					1

NORTHERN PREMIER LEAGUE
CLUB DIRECTORY 2018-19

PREMIER DIVISION

1 Bamber Bridge
2 Basford United
3 Buxton
4 Farsley Celtic
5 Gainsborough Trinity
6 Grantham Town
7 Hednesford Town
8 Hyde United
9 Lancaster City
10 Marine
11 Matlock Town
12 Mickleover Sports
13 Nantwich Town
14 North Ferriby United
15 Scarborough Athletic
16 South Shields
17 Stafford Rangers
18 Stalybridge Celtic
19 Warrington Town
20 Whitby Town
21 Witton Albion
22 Workington

EAST

1 AFC Mansfield
2 Belper Town
3 Brighouse Town
4 Carlton Town
5 Cleethorpes Town
6 Frickley Athletic
7 Gresley FC
8 Lincoln United
9 Loughborough Dynamo
10 Marske United
11 Morpeth Town
12 Ossett United
13 Pickering Town
14 Pontefract Collieries
15 Sheffield FC
16 Spalding United
17 Stamford
18 Stocksbridge Park Steels
19 Tadcaster Albion
20 Wisbech Town

WEST

1 Atherton Collieries
2 Chasetown
3 Clitheroe
4 Colne
5 Colwyn Bay
6 Droylsden
7 Glossop North End
8 Kendal Town
9 Kidsgrove Athletic
10 Leek Town
11 Market Drayton Town
12 Mossley
13 Newcastle Town
14 Prescot Cables
15 Radcliffe FC
16 Ramsbottom United
17 Runcorn Linnets
18 Skelmersdale United
19 Trafford
20 Widnes

BAMBER BRIDGE

Club Contact Details 01772 909 690
Sir Tom Finney Stadium, Brownedge Road, Bamber Bridge PR5 6UX
admin@bamberbridgefc.com

Founded: 1952	**Nickname:** Brig		**Manager:** Neil Reynolds

Previous Names: None
Previous Leagues: Preston & District 1952-90, North West Counties 1990-93

Club Colours (change): White & black

Ground Capacity: 3,000 **Seats:** 554 **Covered:** 800 **Clubhouse:** Yes **Shop:** Yes
Previous Grounds: King George V, Higher Wallton 1952-86
Record Attendance: 2,300 v Czech Republic - Pre Euro '96 friendly
Nearest Railway Station Lostock Hall - 0.9km. Bamber Bridge - 0.9km   **Bus Route** Irongate - stop 100m away

RECORDS
Victory: 8-0 v Curzon Ashton - North West Counties 1994-95
Additional: Paid £10,000 to Horwich RMI for Mark Edwards
                   Received £15,000 from Wigan Athletic for Tony Black 1995

HONOURS
FA Comps: None
League: Preston & District Premier Division 1980-81, 85-86, 86-87, 89-90. North West Counties Division Two 1991-92.
        Northern Premier Premier Division 1995-96.
County FA: Lancashire FA Amateur Shield 1981-82, Trophy 1994-95.

08-09	09-10	10-11	11-12	12-13	13-14	14-15	15-16	16-17	17-18
NP1N 11	NP1N 14	NP1N 7	NP1N 10	NP1N 9	NP1N 4	NP1N 3	NP1N 12	NP1N 11	NP1N 4
FAC 1Q	FAC 2Q	FAC 2Qr	FAC 1Q	FAC 2Q	FAC 1Qr	FAC 3Q	FAC 4Q	FAC P	FAC 1Q
FAT P	FAT 1Q	FAT 2Q	FAT 1Q	FAT P	FAT P	FAT 1Q	FAT P	FAT 1Q	FAT 1Q

BASFORD UNITED

Club Contact Details 0115 924 4491
Greenwich Avenue, off Bagnall Road, Basford, Nottingham NG6 0LD

Founded: 1900	**Nickname:** Community		**Manager:** Martin Carruthers

Previous Names: None
Previous Leagues: Notts Alliance 1905-39, 1946-2004. Notts Amateur League 1939-46. Notts Amateur Alliance 2004-06. Notts Senior 2006-11.
        Central Midlands 2011-12. East Midlands Counties 2012-13. Northern Counties East 2013-14. Midland League 2014-15.
Club Colours (change): All amber

Ground Capacity: **Seats:**   **Covered:** Yes **Clubhouse:** Yes **Shop:**
Previous Grounds: Old Peer Tree Inn, Dolly Tub > 1903, Catchems Corner 1903-30, Vernon Avenue 1930-34, Mill Street 1934-91.
Record Attendance: 3,500 v Grantham United, FACup 1937.
Nearest Railway Station Highbury Vale Tram Stop - 400m   **Bus Route** Christina Avenue - stop 150m away

RECORDS
Misc: Former club secretary, Wallace Brownlow, who took up the post when 19 in 1907, remained in the position until his
                 death in 1970 - a world record of 63 years.

HONOURS
FA Comps: None
League: Notts Alliance 1905-06, 07-08, 19-20, Division One 1997-98. Central Midlands Southern 2011-12.
        East Midland Counties 2012-13. Midland Football Premier Division 2014-15. Northern Premier Division One South 2017-18.
County FA: Notts Senior Cup 1946-47, 87-88, 2014-15, 15-16, 17-18, Intermediate Cup 2005-06.

08-09	09-10	10-11	11-12	12-13	13-14	14-15	15-16	16-17	17-18
NottS 3	NottS 2	NottS 2	CMSth 1	EMC 1	NCEP 5	MFLP 1	NP1S 4	NP1S 6	NP1S 1
					FAC 1Q	FAC Pr	FAC 2Q	FAC P	FAC 3Q
				FAV 2P	FAV 2Q	FAV 2Q	FAT 2Q	FAT P	FAT 1Q

BUXTON

Club Contact Details 01298 23197
The Silverlands, Buxton, Derbyshire SK17 6QH

Founded: 1877 **Nickname:** The Bucks **Manager:** Steve Halford and Paul Phillips
Previous Names: None
Previous Leagues: Combination 1891-99. Manchester 1899-1932. Cheshire County 1932-40, 46-73.
Northern Premier 1973-98, 2006- Northern Counties East 1998-2006.

Club Colours (change): Blue & white

Ground Capacity: 5,200 **Seats:** 490 **Covered:** 2,500 **Clubhouse:** Yes **Shop:** Yes
Previous Grounds: The Park (Cricket Club) 1877-78. Fields at Cote Heath and Green Lane 1878-84.
Record Attendance: 6,000 v Barrow - FA Cup 1st Round 1962-63
Nearest Railway Station Higher Buxton - walking distance from the gorund.

RECORDS
Goalscorer: Mark Reed - 251 (469 appearances)
Appearances: David Bainbridge - 642
Additional: Paid £5,000 to Hyde United for Gary Walker 1989
Received £16,500 from Rotherham for Ally Pickering 1989

HONOURS
FA Comps: None
League: Manchester 1931-32. Cheshire County 1972-73.
Northern Counties East 2005-06. Northern Premier Division One 2006-07.
County FA: Derbyshire Senior Cup 1938-39, 45-46, 56-57, 59-60, 71-72, 80-81, 85-86, 86-87, 2008-09, 11-12.

08-09	09-10	10-11	11-12	12-13	13-14	14-15	15-16	16-17	17-18
NP P 14	NP P 8	NP P 6	NP P 13	NP P 7	NP P 13	NP P 10	NP P 11	NP P 7	NP P 8
FAC 3Q	FAC 4Q	FAC 4Q	FAC 2Q	FAC 4Q	FAC 2Q	FAC 3Q	FAC 3Qr	FAC 1Q	FAC 4Q
FAT 2Q	FAT 2Q	FAT 1Q	FAT 2Q	FAT 1Pr	FAT 2Q	FAT 2Q	FAT 3Q	FAT 2Q	FAT 1Q

FARSLEY CELTIC

Club Contact Details 0113 255 7292
Throstle Nest, Newlands, Pudsey, Leeds, LS28 5BE
jgreaves@farsleyceltic.com

Founded: 2010 **Nickname:** The Villagers **Manager:** Adam Lakeland
Previous Names: Farsley AFC 2010-15.
Previous Leagues: Northern Counties East 2010-11.

Club Colours (change): All blue

Ground Capacity: 4,000 **Seats:** 300 **Covered:** 1,500 **Clubhouse:** Yes **Shop:** Yes
Previous Grounds: None
Record Attendance: 11,000 v Tranmere Rovers, FA Cup First Round Proepr, 1974-75 (at Elland Road)
Nearest Railway Station New Pudsey - 1km **Bus Route** Town Street - stop 500m away

RECORDS
Victory: 8-0 v Arnold Town (H) Northern Counties East Premier 2010-11.
Defeat: 5-1 v Tadcaster Albion, President's Cup Final 27/04/11.

HONOURS
FA Comps: None
League: Northern Counties East Premier Division 2010-11.

County FA: West Riding County Cup 2016-17.

08-09	09-10	10-11	11-12	12-13	13-14	14-15	15-16	16-17	17-18
		NCEP 1	NP1N 4	NP1N 14	NP1N 7	NP1N 12	NP1N 9	NP1N 2	NP P 5
				FAC 1Qr	FAC P	FAC 2Q	FAC 1Q	FAC 3Q	FAC 1Q
			FAT 1Qr	FAT Pr	FAT P	FAT 1Q	FAT 1Q	FAT 1P	FAT 1Qr

GAINSBOROUGH TRINITY

Club Contact Details 01427 613 295
The Martin & Co Arena, Gainsborough, Lincolnshire DN21 2QW

Founded: 1873   **Nickname:** The Blues   **Manager:** Lee Sinnott
Previous Names: Trinity Recreationists
Previous Leagues: Midland (FM) 1889-96, 1912-60, 61-68. Football League 1896-1912. Yorkshire 1960-61.
Northern Premier (FM) 1968-2004.
Club Colours (change): All blue

Ground Capacity: 4,340 **Seats:** 504   **Covered:** 2,500   **Clubhouse:** Yes   **Shop:** Yes
Previous Grounds: Played at Bowling Green Ground and Sincil Bank when Northolme was being used for cricket.
Record Attendance: 9,760 v Scunthorpe United - Midland League 1948
Nearest Railway Station Gainsborough Central - less than half a mile away.

RECORDS
Victory: 7-0 v Fleetwood Town and v Great Harwood Town
Defeat: 1-7 v Stalybridge Celtic - Northern Premier 2000-01 and v Brentford - FA Cup 03-04.
Additional: Paid £3,000 to Buxton for Stuart Lowe
               Received £30,000 from Lincoln City for Tony James

HONOURS
FA Comps: None
League: Midland 1890-91, 1927-28, 48-49, 66-67.

County FA: Lincolnshire County Senior Cup 1889-90, 92-93, 94-95, 97-98, 1903-04, 04-05, 06-07, 10-11, 46-47, 47-48, 48-49,
50-51, 51-52, 57-58, 58-59, 63-64, 70-71, 2002-03, 15-16, 17-18. Lincolnshire Shield 2007-08.

08-09		09-10		10-11		11-12		12-13		13-14		14-15		15-16		16-17		17-18	
Conf N	13	Conf N	14	Conf N	18	Conf N	4	Conf N	8	Conf N	16	Conf N	17	Nat N	18	Nat N	19	Nat N	20
FAC	2Q	FAC	3Q	FAC	2Q	FAC	4Q	FAC	2Qr	FAC	2Q	FAC	4Q	FAC	1P	FAC	2Q	FAC	1P
FAT	3Q	FAT	2Pr	FAT	3Q	FAT	3Q	FAT	SF	FAT	3Q	FAT	1P	FAT	3Qr	FAT	3Qr	FAT	1P

GRANTHAM TOWN

Club Contact Details 01476 402 224
South Kesteven Sports Stadium, Trent Road, Gratham NG31 7XQ
psnixon@hotmail.com

Founded: 1874   **Nickname:** Gingerbreads   **Manager:** Ian Culverhouse
Previous Names: Grantham FC 1874-1987.
Previous Leagues: Midland Amateur Alliance, Central Alliance 1911-25, 59-61, Midland Counties 1925-59, 61-72,
Southern 1972-79, 85-2006, Northern Premier 1979-85
Club Colours (change): Black & white stripes

Ground Capacity: 7,500 **Seats:** 750   **Covered:** 1,950   **Clubhouse:** Yes   **Shop:** Yes
Previous Grounds: London Road >1990-91. Spalding United FC 1990-91.
Record Attendance: 6,578 v Middlesbrough, FA Cup Third Round Proper, 1973-74.
Nearest Railway Station Grantham - 1.5km   **Bus Route** Meres Leisure Centre - stop 100m away

RECORDS
Victory: 13-0 v Rufford Colliery (H) - FA Cup 15/09/1934
Defeat: 0-16 v Notts County Rovers (A) - Midland Amateur Alliance 22/10/1892
Goalscorer: Jack McCartney - 416
Appearances: Chris Gardner - 664
Additional: Received £20,000 from Nottingham Forest for Gary Crosby

HONOURS
FA Comps: None
League: Midland Amateur 1910-11. Central Alliance 1924-25. Midland 1963-64, 70-71, 71-72.
Southern Division One North 1972-73, 78-79, Midland Division 97-98. Northern Premier Division One South 2011-12.
County FA: Lincolnshire Senior Cup 1884-85, 1971-72, 82-83, County Senior Cup 1936-37, Senior Cup 'A' 1953-54, 60-61, 61-62,
County Shield 2003-04, 04-05.

08-09		09-10		10-11		11-12		12-13		13-14		14-15		15-16		16-17		17-18	
NP1S	13	NP1S	11	NP1S	5	NP1S	1	NP P	19	NP P	15	NP P	12	NP P	18	NP P	8	NP P	4
FAC	1Q	FAC	Pr	FAC	Pr	FAC	3Q	FAC	2Q	FAC	1Qr	FAC	3Q	FAC	1Q	FAC	1Qr	FAC	2Q
FAT	P	FAT	Pr	FAT	P	FAT	1Q	FAT	1Q	FAT	1Qr	FAT	1Qr	FAT	1Q	FAT	2Q	FAT	3Q

HEDNESFORD TOWN

Club Contact Details 01543 422 870
Keys Park, Park Road, Hednesford, Cannock WS12 2DZ

Founded: 1880 **Nickname:** The Pitmen **Manager:** Rob Smith
Previous Names: Hednesford 1938-74
Previous Leagues: Walsall & District, Birmingham Comb. 1906-15, 45-53, West Mids 1919-39, 53-72, 74-84, Midland Counties 1972-74, Southern 1984-95, 2001-2005, 2009-11, Conference 1995-2001, 05-06, 13-16. Northern Premier 2006-09, 11-13.

Club Colours (change): White and black

Ground Capacity: 6,500 **Seats:** 1,011 **Covered:** 5,335 **Clubhouse:** Yes **Shop:** Yes
Previous Grounds: The Tins 1880-1903. The Cross Keys 1903-95.
Record Attendance: 4,412 v FC United of Manchester, Northern Premier League Premier Division play-off final, 11/05/13.
Nearest Railway Station Hednesford - 1.6km **Bus Route** Brickworks Road - stop 200m away

RECORDS
Victory: 12-1 v Redditch United - Birmingham Combination 1952-53
Defeat: 0-15 v Burton - Birmingham Combination 1952-53
Goalscorer: Joe O'Connor - 220 in 430 games
Appearances: Kevin Foster - 470
Additional: Paid £12,000 to Macclesfield Town for Steve Burr
Received £40,000 from Blackpool for Kevin Russell

HONOURS
FA Comps: FA Trophy 2003-04.
League: Birmingham Combination 1909-10, 50-51. West Midlands (Reg) 1940-41, 77-78.
Southern League Premier Division 1994-95.
County FA: Staffordshire Senior Cup 1897-98, 1969-70, 73-74, 2012-13.
Birmingham Senior Cup 1935-36, 2008-09, 12-13.

	08-09	09-10	10-11	11-12	12-13	13-14	14-15	15-16	16-17	17-18
	NP P 8	SthP 4	SthP 2	NP P 5	NP P 2	Conf N 4	Conf N 8	Nat N 21	NP P 15	NP P 16
FAC	1Q	1Q	1Q	3Q	3Qr	1P	2Q	3Q	1Q	2Q
FAT	3P	1Q	1Q	2Qr	1P	1P	3Q	3Q	2Qr	2Qr

HYDE UNITED

Club Contact Details 0161 367 7273
Ewen Fields, Walker Lane, Hyde SK14 5PL
gmbranchpcs@gmail.com

Founded: 1919 **Nickname:** The Tigers **Manager:** Darren Kelly
Previous Names: Hyde United 1919-2010, Hyde F.C. 2010-15.
Previous Leagues: Lancashire & Cheshire 1919-21, Manchester 1921-30, Cheshire County 1930-68, 1970-82, Northern Premier 1968-70, 1983-2004. Football Conference 2004-15.

Club Colours (change): Red & navy

Ground Capacity: 4,250 **Seats:** 530 **Covered:** 4,073 **Clubhouse:** Yes **Shop:** Yes
Previous Grounds: None
Record Attendance: 7,600 v Nelson - FA Cup 1952
Nearest Railway Station Newton for Hyde - 0.8km **Bus Route** Walker Lane - stop 110m away

RECORDS
Victory: 13-1 v Eccles United, 1921-22.
Goalscorer: Pete O'Brien - 247. Ernest Gillibrand 86 goals during the 1929-30 season, including 7 against New Mills.
Appearances: Steve Johnson - 623 (1975-1988)
Additional: Paid £8,000 to Mossley for Jim McCluskie 1989
Received £50,000 from Crewe Alexandra for Colin Little 1995

HONOURS
FA Comps: None
League: Manchester 1920-21, 21-22, 22-23, 28-29, 29-30. Cheshire 1954-55, 55-56, 81-82.
Northern Premier Division One North 2003-04, Premier Division 2004-05. Conference North 2011-12.
County FA: Cheshire Senior Cup 1945-46, 62-63, 69-70, 80-81, 89-90, 96-97. Manchester Senior Cup 1974-75, Premier Cup 1993-94, 94-95, 95-96, 98-99.

	08-09	09-10	10-11	11-12	12-13	13-14	14-15	15-16	16-17	17-18
	Conf N 20	Conf N 15	Conf N 19	Conf N 1	Conf 18	Conf 24	Conf N 22	NP P 22	NP1N 10	NP1N 3
FAC	2Q	2Qr	2Qr	3Q	4Qr	4Q	2Q	2Qr	2Q	1P
FAT	3Qr	3Qr	1P	1P	1Pr	1P	2P	1Qr	P	P

LANCASTER CITY

Club Contact Details 01524 382 238
Giant Axe, West Road, Lancaster LA1 5PE
secretary@lancastercityfc.com

Founded: 1911   **Nickname:** Dolly Blues   **Manager:** Phil Brown
Previous Names: Lancaster Town 1911-37
Previous Leagues: Lancashire Combination 1911-70, Northern Premier League 1970-82, 87-2004,
North West Counties 1982-87, Conference 2004-07

Club Colours (change): Blue & white

Ground Capacity: 3,500   **Seats:** 513   **Covered:** 900   **Clubhouse:** Yes   **Shop:** Yes
Previous Grounds: None
Record Attendance: 7,506 v Carlisle United - FA Cup Fourth Qualifying Round, 17/11/1927

RECORDS
Victory: 17-2 v Appleby, FA Cup, 1915.
Defeat: 0-10 v Matlock Town - Northern Premier League Division 1 1973-74
Goalscorer: David Barnes - 130, 1979-84, 88-91. Jordan Connerton scored 38 during the 2009-10 season.
Appearances: Edgar J Parkinson - 591, 1949-64.
Additional: Paid £6,000 to Droylsden for Jamie Tandy
Received £25,000 from Birmingham City for Chris Ward

HONOURS
FA Comps: None
League: Northern Premier Division One 1995-96, Division One North 2016-17.

County FA: Lancashire Junior Cup (ATS Challenge Trophy) 1927-28, 28-29, 30-31, 33-34, 51-52, 74-75.

08-09		09-10		10-11		11-12		12-13		13-14		14-15		15-16		16-17		17-18	
NP1N	7	NP1N	2	NP1N	8	NP1N	6	NP1N	13	NP1N	6	NP1N	11	NP1N	6	NP1N	1	NP P	17
FAC	P	FAC	1Q	FAC	P	FAC	3Q	FAC	1Q	FAC	2Qr	FAC	3Q	FAC	2Q	FAC	3Q	FAC	3Q
FAT	1Qr	FAT	2Qr	FAT	2Q	FAT	P	FAT	P	FAT	1Q	FAT	Pr	FAT	Pr	FAT	1Q	FAT	1P

MARINE

Club Contact Details 0151 924 1743
The Marine Travel Arena, College Road, Crosby, Liverpool L23 3AS
richard@marinefc.com

Founded: 1894   **Nickname:** Mariners   **Manager:** Tommy Lawson
Previous Names: None
Previous Leagues: Liverpool Zingari, Liverpool County Combination, Lancashire Combination 1935-39, 46-69,
Cheshire County 1969-79

Club Colours (change): White & black

Ground Capacity: 3,185   **Seats:** 400   **Covered:** 1,400   **Clubhouse:** Yes   **Shop:** Yes
Previous Grounds: Waterloo Park 1894-1903
Record Attendance: 4,000 v Nigeria - Friendly 1949
Nearest Railway Station Blundellsands & Crosby - 0.5km   **Bus Route** Brompton Avenue - stop 175m away

RECORDS
Victory: 14-0 v Sandhurst - FA Cup 1st Qualifying Round 01/10/1938
Defeat: 2-11 v Shrewsbury Town - FA Cup 1st Round 1995
Goalscorer: Paul Meachin - 200
Appearances: Peter Smith 952
Additional: Paid £6,000 to Southport for Jon Penman October 1985
Received £20,000 from Crewe Alexandra for Richard Norris 1996

HONOURS
FA Comps: None
League: I Zingari Division Two 1901-02, Division One 02-03, 03-04, 09-10, 19-20, 20-21, 22-23. Liverpool Combination Division One 1927-28, 30-31,
33-34, 34-35, 43-44. Cheshire County 1973-74, 75-76, 76-77. Northern Premier Premier Division 1993-94, 84-95.
County FA: Lancashire Amateur Cup 1921-22, 25-26, 30-31, Junior Cup /Trophy 78-79, 87-88, 90-91, 99-00. Liverpool Challenge Cup 42-43, 44-45,
71-72, Non-League Cup 1968-69, 75-76, 76-77, Senior Cup 78-79, 84-85, 87-88, 89-90, 93-94, 99-00, 07-08.

08-09		09-10		10-11		11-12		12-13		13-14		14-15		15-16		16-17		17-18	
NP P	13	NP P	9	NP P	9	NP P	7	NP P	11	NP P	20	NP P	21	NP P	15	NP P	18	NP P	19
FAC	1Q	FAC	1Q	FAC	1Qr	FAC	1Q	FAC	4Q	FAC	1Q	FAC	3Q	FAC	3Q	FAC	2Qr	FAC	2Q
FAT	2Q	FAT	1Q	FAT	2Q	FAT	3Q	FAT	1Q	FAT	2Q	FAT	2Q	FAT	3Q	FAT	1P	FAT	2P

MATLOCK TOWN

Club Contact Details 01629 583 866
Proctors Cars Stadium, Causeway Lane, Matlock, Derbyshire DE4 3AR
keith61brown@yahoo.co.uk

Founded: 1885   **Nickname:** The Gladiators   **Manager:** Dave Hoole
Previous Names: None
Previous Leagues: Midland Combination 1894-96, Matlock and District, Derbyshire Senior, Central Alliance 1924-25, 47-61,
Central Combination 1934-35, Chesterfield & District 1946-47, Midland Counties 1961-69

Club Colours (change): Blue & white

Ground Capacity: 2,257   **Seats:** 560   **Covered:** 1,200   **Clubhouse:** Yes   **Shop:** Yes
Previous Grounds: None
Record Attendance: 5,123 v Burton Albion - FA Trophy Semi-final, 1975
Nearest Railway Station Matlock - 0.3km   **Bus Route** Causeway Lane - stop 100m away

RECORDS
Victory:	10-0 v Lancaster City (A) - 1974
Defeat:	0-8 v Chorley (A) - 1971
Goalscorer:	Peter Scott
Appearances:	Mick Fenoughty
Additional:	Paid £2,000 for Kenny Clark 1996
	Received £10,000 from York City for Ian Helliwell

HONOURS
FA Comps: FA Trophy 1974-75. Anglo Italian Non-League Cup 1979.
League: Central Alliance North Division 1959-60, 60-61. Midland Counties 1961-62, 68-69.
County FA: Derbyshire Senior Cup 1974-75, 76-77, 77-78, 83-84, 84-85, 91-92, 2003-04, 09-10, 14-15, 16-17.

08-09		09-10		10-11		11-12		12-13		13-14		14-15		15-16		16-17		17-18	
NP P	15	NP P	7	NP P	11	NP P	14	NP P	17	NP P	12	NP P	14	NP P	17	NP P	9	NP P	14
FAC	1Q	FAC	2Qr	FAC	3Q	FAC	2Q	FAC	1Qr	FAC	2Q	FAC	1Q	FAC	1Qr	FAC	4Q	FAC	2Q
FAT	1Q	FAT	1P	FAT	2Qr	FAT	3Q	FAT	2P	FAT	3Q	FAT	1Q	FAT	1P	FAT	2P	FAT	1Q

MICKLEOVER SPORTS

Club Contact Details 01332 512 826
Mickleover Sports Club, Station Road, Mickleover Derby DE3 9FB
tonyshawmickleoversports@gmail.com

Founded: 1948   **Nickname:** Sports   **Manager:** John McGrath
Previous Names: Mickleover Old Boys 1948-93
Previous Leagues: Derby & District Senior 1948-93. Central Midlands 1993-99, Northern Counties East 1999-2009

Club Colours (change): Red & black

Ground Capacity: 1,500   **Seats:** 280   **Covered:** 500   **Clubhouse:** Yes   **Shop:** Yes
Previous Grounds: None
Record Attendance: 1,074 v FC United of Manchester, Northern Premier League Premier Division, 02/10/10.
Nearest Railway Station Peartree - 5.1km   **Bus Route** Buxton Drive - stop 100m away

RECORDS
Misc:	Won 16 consecutive League matches in 2009-10 - a Northern Premier League record
Best FA Cup	Third Qualifying Round 2010-11, 14-15, 17-18
FA Trophy	Third Qualifying Round 2014-15, 16-17(r)
FA Vase	Fourth Round Proper 2000-01

HONOURS
FA Comps: None
League: Central Midlands Supreme Division 1998-99. Northern Counties East Division One 2002-03, Premier Division 2008-09.
Northern Premier League Division One South 2009-10, 14-15.
County FA: None

08-09		09-10		10-11		11-12		12-13		13-14		14-15		15-16		16-17		17-18	
NCEP	1	NP1S	1	NP P	15	NP P	21	NP1S	21	NP1S	5	NP1S	1	NP P	20	NP P	16	NP P	12
FAC	P	FAC	2Q	FAC	3Q	FAC	2Q	FAC	Pr	FAC	2Qr	FAC	3Q	FAC	1Q	FAC	2Q	FAC	3Q
FAV	2Q	FAT	P	FAT	2Q	FAT	1Q	FAT	P	FAT	2Q	FAT	3Q	FAT	1Q	FAT	3Qr	FAT	1Q

NANTWICH TOWN

Club Contact Details 01270 621 771
Weaver Stadium, Waterlode, Kingsley Fields, Nantwich, CW5 5BS
secretary@nantwichtownfc.com

Founded: 1884   **Nickname:** The Dabbers   **Manager:** Dave Cooke
Previous Names: Nantwich
Previous Leagues: Shropshire & Dist. 1891-92, Combination 1892-94, 1901-10, Cheshire Junior 1894-95, Crewe & Dist. 1895-97, North Staffs & Dist. 1897-1900, Cheshire 1900-01, Manchester 1910-12, 65-68, Lancs. Com. 1912-14, Cheshire Co. 1919-38, 68-82, Crewe & Dist. 1938-39, 47-48, Crewe Am. Comb. 1946-47, Mid-Cheshire 1948-65, North West Co. 1982-2007
Club Colours (change): All green

Ground Capacity: 3,500   **Seats:** 350   **Covered:** 495   **Clubhouse:** Yes   **Shop:** Yes
Previous Grounds: London Road/Jackson Avenue (1884-2007)
Record Attendance: 5,121 v Winsford United - Cheshire Senior Cup 2nd Round 1920-21
Nearest Railway Station Nantwich - 1.1km   **Bus Route** Malbank School - stop 150m away

RECORDS
Victory: 20-0 v Whitchurch Alexandra (home) 1900/01 Cheshire League Division 1, 5 April 1901
Defeat: 2-16 v Stalybridge Celtic (away) 1932/33 Cheshire County League, 22 Oct 1932
Goalscorer: John Scarlett 161 goals (1992/3 to 2005/6).
Bobby Jones scored 60 goals during season 1946-47, Gerry Duffy scored 42 during season 1961-62
Additional: Received £20,000 from Crewe Alexandra for Kelvin Mellor - Feb 2008

HONOURS
FA Comps: FA Vase 2005-06.
League: Mid-Cheshire 1963-64. Cheshire County 1980-81.
County FA: Crew Amateur Combination 1946-47. Cheshire Amateur Cup 1895-96, 1963-64.
Cheshire Senior Cup 1932-33, 75-76, 2007-08, 11-12, 17-18.

08-09		09-10		10-11		11-12		12-13		13-14		14-15		15-16		16-17		17-18	
NP P	3	NP P	10	NP P	17	NP P	10	NP P	14	NP P	19	NP P	15	NP P	8	NP P	5	NP P	15
FAC	4Q	FAC	1Q	FAC	2Q	FAC	1P	FAC	1Q	FAC	1Q	FAC	1Q	FAC	1Q	FAC	4Q	FAC	1P
FAT	1P	FAT	1P	FAT	1P	FAT	1Q	FAT	2Qr	FAT	3Q	FAT	2Q	FAT	SF	FAT	1P	FAT	1Q

NORTH FERRIBY UNITED

Club Contact Details 01482 634 601
The Chadwick Stadium, Grange Lane, Church Road, North Ferriby HU14 3AB
info@northferribyunitedfc.co.uk

Founded: 1934   **Nickname:** United   **Manager:** Chris Bolder
Previous Names: None
Previous Leagues: East Riding Church, East Riding Amateur 1946-69, Yorkshire 1969-82, Northern Counties East 1982-2000. Northern Premier 2000-13. Conference/National 2013-18.
Club Colours (change): Green & white

Ground Capacity: 3,000   **Seats:** 501   **Covered:** 1,000   **Clubhouse:** Yes   **Shop:** Yes
Previous Grounds: None
Record Attendance: 1,927 v Hull City - Charity game 2005
Nearest Railway Station Ferriby - 5 min walk from the ground.

RECORDS
Victory: 9-0 v Hatfield Main - Northern Counties East 1997-98
Defeat: 1-7 v North Shields - Northern Counties East 1991
Goalscorer: Mark Tennison - 161. Andy Flounders scored 50 during season 1998-99.
Appearances: Paul Sharp - 497 (1996-2006)
Additional: Received £60,000 from Hull City for Dean Windass

HONOURS
FA Comps: FA Trophy 2014-15.
League: East Riding Church 1937-38. Yorkshire Div. Two 1970-71. Northern Counties East Div. One 1985-86, Premier 1999-00. Northern Premier League Division One 2004-05, Premier Division 2012-13. National North Play-offs 2015-16.
County FA: East Riding Senior Cup 1970-71, 76-77, 77-78, 78-79, 90-91, 96-97, 97-98, 98-99, 99-2000, 00-01, 01-02, 02-03, 06-07, 07-08, 08-09, 09-10, 10-11, 12-13.

08-09		09-10		10-11		11-12		12-13		13-14		14-15		15-16		16-17		17-18	
NP P	10	NP P	4	NP P	5	NP P	9	NP P	1	Conf N	2	Conf N	10	Nat N	2	Nat	24	Nat N	22
FAC	2Q	FAC	2Q	FAC	3Qr	FAC	2Q	FAC	2Q	FAC	4Q	FAC	4Q	FAC	4Qr	FAC	4Q	FAC	2Q
FAT	2Qr	FAT	3Qr	FAT	1Q	FAT	1P	FAT	2Q	FAT	QF	FAT	F	FAT	3Q	FAT	1P	FAT	3Q

SCARBOROUGH ATHLETIC

Club Contact Details 07538 903 723
Flamingo Land Stadium, Scarborough Leisure Village, Ashburn Rd YO11 2JW
club.secretary@scarboroughathletic.com

Founded: 2007   **Nickname:** The Seadogs   **Manager:** Steve Kittrick - Jan 2016
Previous Names: Formed after Scarborough F.C. folded in 2007.
Previous Leagues: Northern Counties East 2007-13.

Club Colours (change): Red & white

Ground Capacity: 2,000   **Seats:** 250   **Covered:** Yes   **Clubhouse:** Yes   **Shop:** No
Previous Grounds: Queensgate - Bridlington FC >2017.
Record Attendance: 2,038 v Sheffield United, Opening of the new ground friendly, 15/07/2017.
Nearest Railway Station Scarborough - 1km

RECORDS
Victory: 13-0 v Brodsworth, Northern Counties East, 2009-10.
Defeat: 0-6 v Thackley 16/04/2013 and AFC Telford United 16/11/2013.
Goalscorer: Ryan Blott - 231, including 42 scored during the 2008-09 season and 5 each against Yorkshire Amateur's (08/11/08) and Armthorpe Welfare (14/04/12).
Appearances: Ryan Blott - 376 (20/10/07 - 29/04/16).

HONOURS
FA Comps: None
League: Northern Counties East Division One 2008-09, Premier 2012-13.
County FA: None

08-09		09-10		10-11		11-12		12-13		13-14		14-15		15-16		16-17		17-18	
NCE1	1	NCEP	5	NCEP	10	NCEP	3	NCEP	1	NP1S	7	NP1N	6	NP1N	20	NP1N	3	NP1N	2
		FAC	EP	FAC	P	FAC	1Q	FAC	EP	FAC	2Q	FAC	2Q	FAC	P	FAC	P	FAC	4Q
FAV	4P	FAV	2P	FAV	3P	FAV	1P	FAV	1P	FAT	3Q	FAT	1Q	FAT	P	FAT	P	FAT	P

SOUTH SHIELDS

Club Contact Details 0191 454 7800
Mariners Park, Shaftesbury Avenue, Jarrow, Tyne & Wear NE32 3UP
philip.reay@southshieldsfc.co.uk

Founded: 1974   **Nickname:** Mariners   **Manager:** Graham Fenton & Lee Picton
Previous Names: South Shields Mariners.
Previous Leagues: Northern Alliance 1974-76, Wearside 1976-95.

Club Colours (change): Claret & white

Ground Capacity: 3,500   **Seats:** Yes   **Covered:** Yes   **Clubhouse:** Yes   **Shop:** No
Previous Grounds: Filtrona Park (renamed Mariners Park in 2015) 1992-2013. Eden Lane 2013-15.
Record Attendance: 3,464 v Coleshill Town, FA Vase semi-final, 2016-17.
Nearest Railway Station Bede - 0.2km   **Bus Route** Taunton Avenue - stop 200m away

RECORDS
Best FA Cup   Fourth Qualifying Round 2017-18
FA Trophy   Second Qualifying Round 2014-15, 17-18

HONOURS
FA Comps: FA Vase 2016-17.
League: Northern Alliance 1975-76. Wearside 1976-77, 92-93, 94-95. Northern Division Two 2015-16, Division One 2016-17.
County FA: Monkwearmouth Charity Cup 1986-87. Durham Senior Challenge Cup 2016-17.

08-09		09-10		10-11		11-12		12-13		13-14		14-15		15-16		16-17		17-18	
NL 1	19	NL 1	11	NL 1	11	NL 1	13	NL 1	23	NL 2	17	NL 2	15	NL 2	1	NL 1	1	NP1N	1
FAC	P	FAC	EP	FAC	Pr	FAC	Pr	FAC	1Q	FAC	Pr					FAC	EP	FAC	4Q
FAV	1Q	FAV	1P	FAV	1P	FAV	1P	FAV	1P	FAV	1P	FAV	2Q	FAV	3P	FAV	F	FAT	2Q

STAFFORD RANGERS

Club Contact Details 01785 602 430
Marston Road, Stafford ST16 3BX
secretary@staffordrangersfc.co.uk

Founded: 1876 **Nickname:** Rangers   **Manager:** Steve Burr
Previous Names: None
Previous Leagues: Shropshire 1891-93, Birmingham 1893-96, N. Staffs. 1896-1900, Cheshire 1900-01, Birmingham Combination 1900-12, 46-52, Cheshire County 1952-69, N.P.L. 1969-79, 83-85, Alliance 1979-83, Conf. 1985-95, 2005-11. Southern >2005.

Club Colours (change): Black & white

Ground Capacity: 4,000 **Seats:** 530 **Covered:** Yes **Clubhouse:** Yes **Shop:** Yes
Previous Grounds: None
Record Attendance: 8,536 v Rotherham United - FA Cup 3rd Round 1975
Nearest Railway Station Stafford - 1.8km   **Bus Route** Co-operative Strret - stop 200m away

RECORDS
Victory: 15-0 v Kidsgrove Athletic - Staffordshire Senior Cup 2003
Defeat: 0-12 v Burton Town - Birmingham League 1930
Goalscorer: M. Cullerton - 176. Les Box scored seven against Dudley Town, FA Cup, 06/09/1958.
Appearances: Jim Sargent
Additional: Paid £13,000 to VS rugby for S. Butterworth
Received £100,000 from Crystal Palace for Stan Collymore

HONOURS
FA Comps: FA Trophy 1971-72.
League: Birmingham Combination 1912-13. Cheshire County 1968-69. Northern Premier 1971-72, 84-85, Division One South 2015-16. Southern Premier Division 2002-03. Coference North 2005-06.
County FA: Staffordshire Senior Cup 1954-55, 56-57, 62-63, 71-72, 77-78, 86-87, 91-92, 2002-03, 04-05, 14-15, 17-18.

08-09		09-10		10-11		11-12		12-13		13-14		14-15		15-16		16-17		17-18	
Conf N	18	Conf N	16	Conf N	20	NP P	16	NP P	15	NP P	22	NP1S	6	NP1S	1	NP P	13	NP P	13
FAC	2Q	FAC	2Qr	FAC	2Qr	FAC	2Q	FAC	2Q	FAC	2Q	FAC	1Qr	FAC	P	FAC	1Q	FAC	4Q
FAT	3Q	FAT	3Q	FAT	3Q	FAT	2Q	FAT	1P	FAT	1Q	FAT	1Q	FAT	1Qr	FAV	3Q	FAT	3Q

STALYBRIDGE CELTIC

Club Contact Details 0161 338 2828
Bower Fold, Mottram Road, Stalybridge, Cheshire SK15 2RT
secretary@stalybridgeceltic.co.uk

Founded: 1909 **Nickname:** Celtic   **Manager:** Steve Burr
Previous Names: None
Previous Leagues: Lancs & Cheshire Am. 1909-11. Lancashire Comb 1911-12, Central 1912-14, 15-21, Southern 1914-15, Football Lge 1921-23, Cheshire Co. 1923-82, North West Co. 1982-87, N.P.L. 1987-92, 98-2001, 02-04, Conference 1992-98, 01-02, 04-17.

Club Colours (change): Royal blue & white

Ground Capacity: 6,500 **Seats:** 1,500 **Covered:** 2,400 **Clubhouse:** Yes **Shop:** Yes
Previous Grounds: None
Record Attendance: 9,753 v West Bromwich Albion - FA Cup replay 1922-23
Nearest Railway Station Stalybridge - 1.5 miles from the ground.

RECORDS
Victory: 16-2 v Manchester NE - 01/05/1926 and v Nantwich - 22/10/1932
Defeat: 1-10 v Wellington Town - 09/03/1946
Goalscorer: Harry Dennison - 215
Appearances: Kevan Keelan - 395
Additional: Cecil Smith scored 77 goals during the 1931-32 season
Paid £15,000 to Kettering Town for Ian Arnold 1995. Received £16,000 from Southport for Lee Trundle.

HONOURS
FA Comps: None
League: Lancashire Combination Division Two 1911-12. Cheshire County 1979-80. North West Counties 1983-84, 86-87. Northern Premier League Premier Division 1991-92, 2000-01.
County FA: Manchester Senior Cup 1922-23. Cheshire Senior Cup 1952-53, 2000-01.

08-09		09-10		10-11		11-12		12-13		13-14		14-15		15-16		16-17		17-18	
Conf N	6	Conf N	9	Conf N	10	Conf N	6	Conf N	13	Conf N	19	Conf N	19	Nat N	12	Nat N	21	NP P	22
FAC	3Q	FAC	3Qr	FAC	4Q	FAC	2Q	FAC	4Q	FAC	2Q	FAC	2Q	FAC	1P	FAC	3Q	FAC	3Q
FAT	2P	FAT	2P	FAT	2P	FAT	2P	FAT	3Q	FAT	1P	FAT	3Qr	FAT	3Q	FAT	3Qr	FAT	3Q

WARRINGTON TOWN

Club Contact Details 01925 653 044
Cantilever Park, Loushers Lane, Warrington WA4 2RS
info@warringtontownfc.co.uk

Founded: 1949   **Nickname:** The Wire   **Manager:** Paul Carden
Previous Names: Stockton Heath Albion 1949-61
Previous Leagues: Warrington & District 1949-52, Mid Cheshire 1952-78, Cheshire County 1978-82,
North West Counties 1982-90 Northern Premier 1990-97

Club Colours (change): Yellow & blue

Ground Capacity: 2,500   **Seats:** 350   **Covered:** 650   **Clubhouse:** Yes   **Shop:** Yes
Previous Grounds: Stockton Lane 1949-50, 55-56. London Road 1950-53. Loushers Lane 1953-55.
Record Attendance: 2,600 v Halesowen Town - FA Vase Semi-final 1st leg 1985-86
Nearest Railway Station Warrington Central - 2.3km   **Bus Route** Fairfield Gardens - stop 200m away

RECORDS
Goalscorer: Steve Hughes - 167
Appearances: Neil Whalley
Additional: Paid £50,000 to Preston North End for Liam Watson Received £60,000 from P.N.E. for Liam Watson
Players to progress - Roger Hunt, Liverpool legend and 1966 World Cup winner.

HONOURS
FA Comps: None
League: Mid-Cheshire 1960-61. North West Counties 1989-90, Division Two 2000-01.
Northern Premier Division One North 2015-16.
County FA: None

08-09	09-10	10-11	11-12	12-13	13-14	14-15	15-16	16-17	17-18
NP1N 19	NP1N 9	NP1N 9	NP1N 11	NP1N 10	NP1N 3	NP1N 9	NP1N 1	NP P 10	NP P 3
FAC 1Q	FAC 2Qr	FAC 3Q	FAC 2Q	FAC 2Q	FAC 2Qr	FAC 2P	FAC P	FAC 1Q	FAC 3Qr
FAT 3Q	FAT 1Q	FAT P	FAT Pr	FAT P	FAT P	FAT P	FAT 3Q	FAT 1Q	FAT 3P

WHITBY TOWN

Club Contact Details Office: 01947 604847 CH: 01947 605 153
Turnbull Ground, Upgang Lane, Whitby, North Yorks YO21 3HZ
peterjohnt17@hotmail.com

Founded: 1926   **Nickname:** Seasiders   **Manager:** Chris Hardy
Previous Names: Whitby United was formed after Whitby Whitehall Swifts and Whitby Town merged 1926-49.
Previous Leagues: Northern 1926-97

Club Colours (change): All royal blue

Ground Capacity: 3,500   **Seats:** 622   **Covered:** 1,372   **Clubhouse:** Yes   **Shop:** Yes
Previous Grounds: None
Record Attendance: 4,000 v Scarborough - North Riding Cup 18/04/1965
Nearest Railway Station Whitby - 1km   **Bus Route** Argyle Road - 120m away

RECORDS
Victory: 11-2 v Cargo Fleet Works - 1950
Defeat: 3-13 v Willington - 24/03/1928
Goalscorer: Paul Pitman - 382
Appearances: Paul Pitman - 468
Additional: Paid £2,500 to Newcastle Blue Star for John Grady 1990
Received £5,000 from Gateshead for Graham Robinson 1997

HONOURS
FA Comps: FA Vase 1996-97.
League: Northern 1992-93, 96-97.
Northern Premier Division One 1997-98.
County FA: North Riding Senior Cup 1964-65, 67-68, 82-83, 89-90, 2004-05, 16-17.

08-09	09-10	10-11	11-12	12-13	13-14	14-15	15-16	16-17	17-18
NP P 19	NP P 14	NP P 16	NP P 17	NP P 13	NP P 9	NP P 13	NP P 19	NP P 6	NP P 21
FAC 2Qr	FAC 2Q	FAC 1Q	FAC 3Q	FAC 3Q	FAC 1Qr	FAC 1Q	FAC 1Qr	FAC 2Q	FAC 2Q
FAT 3Q	FAT 2Q	FAT 3Qr	FAT 1Q	FAT 3Q	FAT 1Q	FAT 1Q	FAT 2Q	FAT 2Q	FAT 1Q

Coalville Town's Taylor and Coton combine to make sure Witton Albion's Evans does not get his head to the ball...

Northern Premier League Premier Division Action

...Coton again denies Witton, this time it's Hopley who sees his shot saved. Photos: Keith Clayton.

WITTON ALBION

Club Contact Details 01606 430 08
Wincham Park, Chapel Street, Wincham, CW9 6DA
mike.harper@sky.com

Founded: 1887 **Nickname:** The Albion **Manager:** Carl Macauley - 19/10/15
Previous Names: None
Previous Leagues: Lancashire Combination, Cheshire County > 1979, Northern Premier 1979-91, Conference 1991-94

Club Colours (change): Red & white stripes

Ground Capacity: 4,813 **Seats:** 650 **Covered:** 2,300 **Clubhouse:** Yes **Shop:** Yes
Previous Grounds: Central Ground (1910-1989)
Record Attendance: 3,940 v Kidderminster Harries - FA Trophy Semi-final 13/04/1991

RECORDS
Victory: 13-0 v Middlewich (H)
Defeat: 0-9 v Macclesfield Town (A) - 18/09/1965
Goalscorer: Frank Fidler - 175 (1947-50)
Appearances: Brian Pritchard - 729
Additional: Paid £12,500 to Hyde United for Jim McCluskie 1991
Received £11,500 from Chester City for Peter Henderson

HONOURS
FA Comps: None
League: Cheshire County 1948-49, 49-50, 53-54. Northern Premier Premier Division 1990-91.

County FA: Cheshire Senior Cup x7.

08-09	09-10	10-11	11-12	12-13	13-14	14-15	15-16	16-17	17-18
NP P 20	NP1S 7	NP1N 10	NP1N 3	NP P 4	NP P 16	NP P 22	NP1N 11	NP1S 2	NP P 7
FAC 2Qr	FAC P	FAC P	FAC 4Q	FAC 2Q	FAC 1Q	FAC 1Q	FAC 2Q	FAC 2Qr	FAC 1Q
FAT 1Q	FAT 3Qr	FAT 3Qr	FAT 3Q	FAT 2Q	FAT 2Q	FAT 2Qr	FAT 1Q	FAT 1Pr	FAT 1Q

WORKINGTON

Club Contact Details 01900 602 871
Borough Park, Workington, Cumbria CA14 2DT
olenacum@gmail.com

Founded: 1921 **Nickname:** Reds **Manager:** Lee Andrews & David Hewson
Previous Names: Workington AFC 1921-
Previous Leagues: North Eastern 1921-51, Football League 1951-77, Northern Premier 1977-2005. Conference 2005-14.

Club Colours (change): Red and white

Ground Capacity: 3,101 **Seats:** 500 **Covered:** 1,000 **Clubhouse:** Yes **Shop:** Yes
Previous Grounds: Lonsdale Park 1921-37.
Record Attendance: 21,000 v Manchester United - FA Cup 3rd round 04/01/1958
Nearest Railway Station Workington - 0.6km **Bus Route** Tesco - stop 100m away

RECORDS
Victory: 17-1 v Cockermouth Crusaders - Cumberland Senior League 19/01/1901
Defeat: 0-9 v Chorley (A) - Northern Premier League 10/11/1987
Goalscorer: Billy Charlton - 193
Appearances: Bobby Brown - 469
Additional: Paid £6,000 to Sunderland for Ken Chisolm 1956
Received £33,000 from Liverpool for Ian McDonald 1974

HONOURS
FA Comps: None
League: North West Counties 1998-99

County FA: Cumberland County Cup x25 (Most recently 2016-17).

08-09	09-10	10-11	11-12	12-13	13-14	14-15	15-16	16-17	17-18
Conf N 12	Conf N 4	Conf N 11	Conf N 13	Conf N 14	Conf N 22	NP P 2	NP P 5	NP P 4	NP P 11
FAC 2Qr	FAC 4Q	FAC 4Qr	FAC 2Q	FAC 4Q	FAC 4Q	FAC 2Q	FAC 2Q	FAC 3Qr	FAC 2Q
FAT 3P	FAT QF	FAT 3Qr	FAT 3Q	FAT 3Q	FAT 3Q	FAT 3Q	FAT 1Q	FAT 1Q	FAT 3Pr

ATHERTON COLLIERIES

Club Contact Details 07968 548 056
The Kensite Stadium, Alder Street, Atherton, Greater Manchester M46 9EY
secretaryacfc1916@yahoo.co.uk

Founded: 1916   **Nickname:** Colls   **Manager:** Michael Clegg
Previous Names: None
Previous Leagues: Bolton Combination 1918-21, 52-71. Lancashire Alliance 1921. Manchester 1945-48. West Lancashire 1948-50. Lancashire
Combination 1950-52, 71-78. Cheshire County 1978-82.

Club Colours (change): Black & white

Ground Capacity: 2,500   **Seats:** Yes   **Covered:** Yes   **Clubhouse:** Yes   **Shop:** No
Previous Grounds: None
Record Attendance: 3,300 in the Bolton Combination 1920's.
Nearest Railway Station Atherton - 0.7km   **Bus Route** High Street - stop 100m away

RECORDS
Best FA Cup   Third Qualifying Round 1994-95
FA Vase   Fifth Round 2016-17
FA Trophy   Second Qualifying Round 2017-18

HONOURS
FA Comps: None
League: Bolton Combination 1919-20, 36-37, 37-38, 38-39, 40-41, 44-45, 56-57, 58-59, 60-61, 64-65.
North West Counties Division Three 1986-87, Division One 2014-15, Premier 2016-17.
County FA: Lancashire County FA Shield 1919-20, 22-23, 41-42, 45-46, 56-57, 64-65.

	08-09		09-10		10-11		11-12		12-13		13-14		14-15		15-16		16-17		17-18	
	NWCP	22	NWC1	6	NWC1	5	NWC1	4	NWC1	4	NWC1	5	NWC1	1	NWCP	3	NWCP	1	NP1N	10
FAC	EP		FAC	P	FAC	Pr	FAC	P	FAC	1Q	FAC	Pr	FAC	Pr	FAC	Pr	FAC	P	FAC	2Q
FAV	2Q		FAV	2Q	FAV	2Q	FAV	2Q	FAV	1Q	FAV	1Q	FAV	2P	FAV	3P	FAV	5P	FAT	2Q

CHASETOWN

Club Contact Details 01543 682 222
The Scholars, Church Street, Chasetown, Walsall WS7 3QL

Founded: 1954   **Nickname:** The Scholars   **Manager:** Scott Dundas
Previous Names: Chase Terrace Old Scholars 1954-72
Previous Leagues: Cannock Youth 1954-58, Lichfield & District 1958-61, Staffordshire County 1961-72,
West Midlands 1972-94, Midland Alliance 1994-2006, Southern 2006-09

Club Colours (change): Royal blue & white

Ground Capacity: 2,000   **Seats:** 151   **Covered:** 220   **Clubhouse:** Yes   **Shop:** Yes
Previous Grounds: Burntwood Recreation
Record Attendance: 2,420 v Cardiff City - FA Cup 3rd Round January 2008
Nearest Railway Station Hednesford - 6.4km   **Bus Route** Queen Street - stop 160m away

RECORDS
Victory: 14-1 v Hanford - Walsall Senior Cup 1991-92
Defeat: 1-8 v Telford United Reserves - West Midlands League
Goalscorer: Tony Dixon - 197. Mick Ward scored 39 goals during the 1987-88 season, whilst a player by the name of Keith Birch
scored 11 in a 21-1 win over Lichfield Laundry.
Misc: The club became the first from the eighth tier of English football to reach the Third Round Proper of the FA Cup during
the 2007-08 season.

HONOURS
FA Comps: None
League: West Midlands 1978. Midland Alliance 2004-05.

County FA: Walsall Senior Cup 1990-91, 92-93, 2004-05.

	08-09		09-10		10-11		11-12		12-13		13-14		14-15		15-16		16-17		17-18	
	SthM	4	NP1S	2	NP P	10	NP P	20	NP1S	5	NP1S	12	NP1S	13	NP1S	7	NP1S	17	NP1S	5
FAC	3Q		FAC	Pr	FAC	1Q	FAC	2Q	FAC	2Q	FAC	1Qr	FAC	1Qr	FAC	3Qr	FAC	2Q	FAC	2Q
FAT	3Q		FAT	1Qr	FAT	QF	FAT	2Q	FAT	2Q	FAT	1Q	FAT	3Q	FAT	Pr	FAT	P	FAT	2Q

CLITHEROE

Club Contact Details
Shawbridge, off Pendle Road, Clitheroe, Lancashire BB7 1LZ
secretary@clitheroefc.co.uk

Founded: 1877   **Nickname:** The Blues   **Manager:** Stuart Mellish
Previous Names: Clitheroe Central 1877-1903.
Previous Leagues: Blackburn & District, Lancashire Combination 1903-04, 05-10, 25-82, North West Counties 1982-85

Club Colours (change): All blue

Ground Capacity: 2,000   **Seats:** 250   **Covered:** 1,400   **Clubhouse:** Yes   **Shop:** No
Previous Grounds: None
Record Attendance: 2,050 v Mangotsfield - FA Vase Semi-final 1995-96
Nearest Railway Station Clitheroe - 0.6km   **Bus Route** Hayhurst Street - 50m away

RECORDS
Goalscorer: Don Francis
Appearances: Lindsey Wallace - 670
Additional: Received £45,000 from Crystal Palace for Carlo Nash.

HONOURS
FA Comps: None
League: Lancashire Combination Division Two 1959-60, Division One 1979-80.
     North West Counties Division Three 1983-84, Division Two 1984-85, Division One 1985-86, 2003-04.
County FA: Lancashire Challenge Trophy 1892-93, 1984-85.

08-09	09-10	10-11	11-12	12-13	13-14	14-15	15-16	16-17	17-18
NP1N 12	NP1N 8	NP1N 6	NP1N 19	NP1N 8	NP1N 17	NP1N 13	NP1N 7	NP1N 7	NP1N 12
FAC 2Q	FAC 1Q	FAC P	FAC 2Q	FAC 1Q	FAC P	FAC 1Q	FAC 1Q	FAC P	FAC 1Q
FAT 2Q	FAT 2Q	FAT 2Q	FAT Pr	FAT Pr	FAT Pr	FAT 1Q	FAT P	FAT P	FAT 1Q

COLNE

Club Contact Details 01282 862 545
The XLCR Stadium, Harrison Drive, Colne, Lancashire BB8 9SL
secretary@colnefootballclub.com

Founded: 1996   **Nickname:** The Reds   **Manager:** Steve Cunningham
Previous Names: None
Previous Leagues: North West Counties 1996-2016.

Club Colours (change): Red & white

Ground Capacity: 1,800   **Seats:** 160   **Covered:** 1,000   **Clubhouse:** Yes   **Shop:** Yes
Previous Grounds: None
Record Attendance: 1,742 v AFC Sudbury F.A. Vase SF 2004. 2,762 (at Accrington Stanley) v FC United, NWC Challenge Cup,
Nearest Railway Station Colne - 0.6km   **Bus Route** Tennyson Road - stop 100m away

RECORDS
Goalscorer: Geoff Payton
Appearances: Richard Walton

HONOURS
FA Comps: None
League: North West Counties League Division Two 2003-04, Premier Division 2015-16.

County FA: None

08-09	09-10	10-11	11-12	12-13	13-14	14-15	15-16	16-17	17-18
NWCP 18	NWCP 8	NWCP 5	NWCP 8	NWCP 8	NWCP 9	NWCP 4	NWCP 1	NP1N 5	NP1N 8
FAC 1Q	FAC EP	FAC P	FAC EP	FAC EPr	FAC EPr	FAC EP	FAC 1Q	FAC 1Q	FAC 1Q
FAV 1P	FAV 1P	FAV 1P	FAV 1P	FAV 2Q	FAV 2Q	FAV 1P	FAV 2P	FAT P	FAT P

COLWYN BAY

Club Contact Details 01492 514 680
Llanelian Road, Old Colwyn, North Wales LL29 8UN
pauledwardscbfc@gmail.com

Founded: 1881 **Nickname:** The Bay / Seagulls **Manager:** Alan Morgan
Previous Names: Colwyn Bay United 1907
Previous Leagues: North Wales Coast 1898-1900. 1901-21, 33-35, Welsh National 1921-30, North Wales Combination 1930-31,
Welsh League (North) 1945-84, North West Counties 1984-91. Northern Premier 1991-2011. Football Conference 2011-15.

Club Colours (change): Claret and sky blue

Ground Capacity: 2,500 **Seats:** 500 **Covered:** 700 **Clubhouse:** Yes **Shop:** Yes
Previous Grounds: Eirias Park >1984.
Record Attendance: 5,000 v Borough United at Eirias Park 1964
Nearest Railway Station Colwyn Bay - 2.4km **Bus Route** Bus stops outside the ground

RECORDS
Goalscorer: Peter Donnelly
Appearances: Bryn A Jones

HONOURS
FA Comps: None
League: North Wales Football Combination 1930-31. Welsh League (North) 1964-65, 80-81, 82-83, 83-84.
Northern Division One 1991-92.
County FA: None

08-09		09-10		10-11		11-12		12-13		13-14		14-15		15-16		16-17		17-18	
NP1N	4	NP1N	4	NP P	2	Conf N	12	Conf N	18	Conf N	12	Conf N	20	NP P	23	NP1N	15	NP1N	9
FAC	P	FAC	P	FAC	2Qr	FAC	2Q	FAC	3Qr	FAC	4Q	FAC	3Qr	FAC	1Q	FAC	1Q	FAC	1Q
FAT	1Qr	FAT	P	FAT	2Q	FAT	1P	FAT	3Q	FAT	3Q	FAT	3Q	FAT	1Q	FAT	1Qr	FAT	P

DROYLSDEN

Club Contact Details 0161 370 1426
Market Street, Droylsden, M43 7AY
windowsindenton@gmail.com

Founded: 1892 **Nickname:** The Bloods **Manager:** David Pace
Previous Names: None
Previous Leagues: Manchester, Lancashire Combination 1936-39, 50-68, Cheshire County 1939-50, 68-82,
North West Counties 1982-87, Northern Premier 1986-2004

Club Colours (change): All red

Ground Capacity: 3,000 **Seats:** 500 **Covered:** 2,000 **Clubhouse:** Yes **Shop:** Yes
Previous Grounds: None
Record Attendance: 15,000 v Hyde United, Manchester League, 1921.
Nearest Railway Station Droylsden - 240m away **Bus Route** Bus stops outside the ground

RECORDS
Victory: 13-2 v Lucas Sports Club
Goalscorer: E. Gillibrand - 275 (1931-35)
Appearances: Paul Phillips - 326
Additional: Received £11,000 from Crewe Alexandra for Tony Naylor 1990
Defeat: 1-13 v Chorley, Northern Prmeier Premier Division, 05/04/2014.

HONOURS
FA Comps: None
League: Manchester 1930-31, 32-33. North West Counties Division Two 1986-87. Northern Premier Division One 1998-99.
Conference North 2006-07.
County FA: Manchester Junior Cup 1922-23, Manchester Premier Cup x12 - Firstly in 1946-47 and most recently in 2009-10,
Manchester Senior Cup 1972-73, 75-76, 78-79.

08-09		09-10		10-11		11-12		12-13		13-14		14-15		15-16		16-17		17-18	
Conf N	7	Conf N	5	Conf N	8	Conf N	9	Conf N	21	NP P	24	NP1N	10	NP1N	19	NP1N	13	NP1N	13
FAC	2Pr	FAC	2Q	FAC	2Pr	FAC	4Qr	FAC	2Q	FAC	1Q	FAC	2Q	FAC	3Q	FAC	Pr	FAC	2Q
FAT	3Q	FAT	3Q	FAT	3Pr	FAT	2P	FAT	3Q	FAT	1Q	FAT	P	FAT	P	FAT	Pr	FAT	3Q

GLOSSOP NORTH END

Club Contact Details 01457 855 469
Surrey Street, Glossop, Derbys SK13 7AJ
lesleyodonnell1971@sky.com

Founded: 1886   **Nickname:** Peakites / The Hillmen   **Manager:** Mark Canning & Andy Bishop
Previous Names: Glossop North End1886-1896 and Glossop FC 1898-1992. Reformed in 1992.
Previous Leagues: North Cheshire 1890-94. Combination 1894-96. Midland 1896-98. The Football League 1898-1918. Lancashire Comb. 1919 -20, 57-66. Manchester 1920-57, 66-78. Cheshire County (Founder member) 1978-82. North West Counties (FM)1982-2015.

Club Colours (change): All royal blue

Ground Capacity: 2,374   **Seats:** 209   **Covered:** 509   **Clubhouse:** Yes   **Shop:** Yes
Previous Grounds: Pyegrove. Silk Street. Water Lane. Cemetery Road. North Road 1890-1955.
Record Attendance: 10,736 v Preston North End F.A. Cup 1913-1914
Nearest Railway Station Glossop - 0.4km   **Bus Route** St Mary's Road - stop 300m away

RECORDS
Best FA Cup   First Round Proper 1896-97
FA Trophy   Third Qualifying Round 2017-18
FA Vase   Finalists 2014-15

HONOURS
FA Comps: None
League: Manchester 1927-28. North West Counties Premier Division 2014-15.
County FA: Manchester FA Premier Cup 1996-97, 97-98. Derbyshire Senior Cup 2000-01.

08-09		09-10		10-11		11-12		12-13		13-14		14-15		15-16		16-17		17-18	
NWCP	5	NWCP	7	NWCP	14	NWCP	6	NWCP	13	NWCP	3	NWCP	1	NP1N	4	NP1N	8	NP1N	11
FAC	P	FAC	1Q	FAC	1Q	FAC	EP	FAC	P	FAC	1Q	FAC	2Q	FAC	1Qr	FAC	Pr	FAC	P
FAV	F	FAV	3P	FAV	1P	FAV	3P	FAV	2Qr	FAV	2P	FAV	F	FAT	Pr	FAT	1Q	FAT	3Qr

KENDAL TOWN

Club Contact Details 01539 727 472
ST&B Accountants Stadium, Parkside Road, Kendal, Cumbria LA9 7BL
gudge1@talk21.com

Founded: 1919   **Nickname:** The Mintcakes / The Field / The Town   **Manager:** David Foster
Previous Names: Netherfield AFC 1919-2000
Previous Leagues: Westmorland, North Lancashire Combination 1945-68, Northern Premier 1968-83, North West Counties 1983-87

Club Colours (change): Black and white stripes

Ground Capacity: 2,490   **Seats:** 450   **Covered:** 1000   **Clubhouse:** Yes   **Shop:** Yes
Previous Grounds: None
Record Attendance: 5,184 v Grimsby Town - FA Cup 1st Round 1955
Nearest Railway Station Kendal - 1.3km   **Bus Route** Castle Circle - stop 200m away

RECORDS
Victory: 11-0 v Great Harwood - 22/03/1947
Defeat: 0-10 v Stalybridge Celtic - 01/09/1984
Goalscorer: Tom Brownlee
Additional: Received £10,250 from Manchester City for Andy Milner 1995

HONOURS
FA Comps: None
League: Lancashire Combination 1948-49, 64-65.
County FA: Westmorlands Senior Cup x12. Lancashire Senior Cup 2002-03.

08-09		09-10		10-11		11-12		12-13		13-14		14-15		15-16		16-17		17-18	
NP P	5	NP P	5	NP P	8	NP P	11	NP P	21	NP1N	10	NP1N	16	NP1N	15	NP1N	12	NP1N	18
FAC	2Q	FAC	4Q	FAC	1Q	FAC	3Q	FAC	3Q	FAC	P	FAC	Pr	FAC	2Q	FAC	P	FAC	1Q
FAT	1Q	FAT	1Q	FAT	3Q	FAT	2Qr	FAT	1Qr	FAT	1Qr	FAT	P	FAT	1Q	FAT	2Q	FAT	1Q

KIDSGROVE ATHLETIC

Club Contact Details 01782 782 412
The Novus Stadium, Hollinwood Road, Kidsgrove, Staffs ST7 1DH

Founded: 1952   **Nickname:** The Grove   **Manager:** Ryan Austin
Previous Names: None
Previous Leagues: Buslem and Tunstall 1953-63, Staffordshire County 1963-66, Mid Cheshire 1966-90,
North West Counties 1990-2002

Club Colours (change): All blue

Ground Capacity: 2,000   **Seats:** 1,000   **Covered:** 800   **Clubhouse:** Yes   **Shop:** Yes
Previous Grounds: Vickers and Goodwin 1953-60
Record Attendance: 1,903 v Tiverton Town - FA Vase Semi-final 1998
Nearest Railway Station Kidsgrove - 0.8km   **Bus Route** Grove Avenue - stop 200m away

RECORDS
Victory: 23-0 v Cross Heath W.M.C. - Staffordshire Cup 1965
Defeat: 0-15 v Stafford Rangers - Staffordshire Senior Cup 20/11/2001
Goalscorer: Scott Dundas - 53 (1997-98)
Additional: Paid £10,000 to Stevenage Borough for Steve Walters
           Received £3,000 for Ryan Baker 2003-04

HONOURS
FA Comps: None
League: Staffordshire County Division Two 1963-64, Premier 65-66. Mid-Cheshire 1970-71, 77-78, 86-87, 87-88.
North West Counties Premier Division 1997-98, 2001-02.
County FA: Staffordshire Senior Cup 2003-04, 06-07, 08-09, 10-11, 11-12.

08-09		09-10		10-11		11-12		12-13		13-14		14-15		15-16		16-17		17-18	
NP1S	15	NP1S	4	NP1S	7	NP1S	13	NP1S	18	NP1S	21	NP1S	20	NP1S	15	NP1S	12	NP1S	18
FAC	1Q	FAC	1Q	FAC	2Q	FAC	4Q	FAC	P	FAC	1Q	FAC	P	FAC	Pr	FAC	2Q	FAC	2Q
FAT	1Q	FAT	P	FAT	Pr	FAT	1Q	FAT	1Q	FAT	2Q	FAT	P	FAT	2Qr	FAT	2Q	FAT	2Q

LEEK TOWN

Club Contact Details 01538 399 278
Harrison Park, Macclesfield Road, Leek, Cheshire ST13 8LD

Founded: 1946   **Nickname:** The Blues   **Manager:** Neil Baker
Previous Names: None
Previous Leagues: Staffordshire Co., Manchester 1951-54, 57-73, West Midlands (B'ham) 1954-56, Cheshire Co. 1973-82, North West Counties
1982-87, Northern Premier 1987-94, 95-97, Southern 1994-95, Conference 1997-99

Club Colours (change): All blue

Ground Capacity: 3,600   **Seats:** 650   **Covered:** 3,000   **Clubhouse:** Yes   **Shop:** Yes
Previous Grounds: None
Record Attendance: 3,512 v Macclesfield Town - FA Cup 1973-74

RECORDS
Goalscorer: Dave Sutton - 144
Appearances: Gary Pearce - 447
Additional: Paid £2,000 to Sutton Town for Simon Snow
           Received £30,000 from Barnsley for Tony Bullock

HONOURS
FA Comps: None
League: Staffordshire County 1949-50, 50-51. Manchester 1951-52, 71-72, 72-73. Cheshire County 1974-75.
Northern Premier Division One 1989-90, Premier Division 1996-97.
County FA: Staffordshire Senior Cup 1995-96.

08-09		09-10		10-11		11-12		12-13		13-14		14-15		15-16		16-17		17-18	
NP1S	9	NP1S	8	NP1S	16	NP1S	5	NP1S	10	NP1S	3	NP1S	2	NP1S	8	NP1S	9	NP1S	7
FAC	1Qr	FAC	P	FAC	P	FAC	3Qr	FAC	3Q	FAC	Pr	FAC	4Q	FAC	1Qr	FAC	1Q	FAC	1Q
FAT	P	FAT	2Q	FAT	P	FAT	2Qr	FAT	2Qr	FAT	2P	FAT	2Qr	FAT	P	FAT	2Q	FAT	2Q

MARKET DRAYTON TOWN

Club Contact Details 01630 661 780
Greenfields Sports Ground, Greenfields Lane, Market Drayton TF9 3SL
rpope2nt@gmail.com

Founded: 1969 **Nickname:** None	**Manager:** Carl Abbott

Previous Names: Little Drayton Rangers > 2003
Previous Leagues: West Midlands (Regional) 1969-2006, Midland Alliance 2006-09

Club Colours (change): All red (All blue)

Ground Capacity: 1,000   **Seats:** Yes   **Covered:** Yes   **Clubhouse:** Yes   **Shop:** No
Previous Grounds: Not known
Record Attendance: 440 vs. AFC Telford, Friendly 11/07/09. 229 vs. Witton Albion, Unibond South 25/08/09
                    Bus Route Cmetery Road Jct - stop 400m away

RECORDS

Victory:	(League) 9-0 Home vs. Racing Club Warwick 10/03/09
Best FA Cup	Second Qualifying Round 2007-08, 10-11
FA Trophy	First Qualifying Round 2010-11, 14-15, 15-16
FA Vase	Fifth Round Proper 2008-09

HONOURS
FA Comps: None
League: West Midlands (Regional) 2005-06. Midland Alliance 2008-09.

County FA: None

08-09	09-10	10-11	11-12	12-13	13-14	14-15	15-16	16-17	17-18
MidAl 1	NP1S 13	NP1S 18	NP1S 16	NP1S 15	NP1S 19	NP1S 19	NP1S 11	NP1S 14	NP1S 21
FAC P	FAC 2Q	FAC 2Q	FAC P	FAC 1Qr	FAC P	FAC 1Q	FAC 1Q	FAC P	FAC 1Q
FAV 5P	FAT Pr	FAT 1Qr	FAT P	FAT P	FAT P	FAT 1Qr	FAT P	FAT 1Q	FAT P

MOSSLEY

Club Contact Details 01457 832 369
Seel Park, Market Street, Mossley, Lancashire OL5 0ES
john.wharmby@mossleyfc.com

Founded: 1903 **Nickname:** Lilywhites	**Manager:** Dave Wild & Terry Hincks

Previous Names: Park Villa 1903-04, Mossley Juniors
Previous Leagues: Ashton, South East Lancashire, Lancashire Combination 1918-19, Cheshire County 1919-72,
                  Northern Premier 1972-95, North West Counties 1995-2004

Club Colours (change): White & black

Ground Capacity: 4,000   **Seats:** 220   **Covered:** 1,500   **Clubhouse:** Yes   **Shop:** Yes
Previous Grounds: Moved to Seel Park in 1911.
Record Attendance: 7,000 v Stalybridge Celtic 1950
Nearest Railway Station Mossley - 0.3km   **Bus Route** Stamford Street - 200m away

RECORDS

Victory:	9-0 v Urmston, Manchester Shield, 1947
Defeat:	2-13 v Witton Albion, Cheshire League, 1926
Goalscorer:	David Moore - 235 (1974-84). Jackie Roscoe scored 58 during the 1930-31 season.
Appearances:	Jimmy O'Connor - 613 (1972-87)
Additional:	Paid £2,300 to Altrincham for Phil Wilson
	Received £25,000 from Everton for Eamonn O'Keefe

HONOURS
FA Comps: None
League: Ashton & District 1911-12, 14-15. Northern Premier 1978-79, 79-80, Division One 2005-06.

County FA: Manchester Premier Cup 1937-38, 48-49, 60-61, 66-67, 67-68, 88-89, 90-91, 2011-12, 12-13, 14-15, 15-16.
               Manchester Challenge Trophy 2011-12.

08-09	09-10	10-11	11-12	12-13	13-14	14-15	15-16	16-17	17-18
NP1N 10	NP1N 7	NP1N 15	NP1N 14	NP1N 5	NP1N 15	NP1N 7	NP1N 13	NP1N 17	NP1N 19
FAC 3Q	FAC P	FAC 4Q	FAC Pr	FAC P	FAC Pr	FAC Pr	FAC Pr	FAC 1Q	FAC 1Qr
FAT P	FAT 3Qr	FAT 2Q	FAT P	FAT 1Qr	FAT 2Q	FAT 1Q	FAT 1Q	FAT 1Q	FAT 1Q

NEWCASTLE TOWN

Club Contact Details 01782 662 350
Lyme Valley Stadium, Buckmaster Avenue, Clayton, ST5 3BX
secretary@newcastletownfc.co.uk

Founded: 1964	**Nickname:** The Castle	**Manager:** Robin Van Der Laan

Previous Names: Parkway Hanley, Clayton Park & Parkway Clayton. Merged as NTFC in 1986.

Previous Leagues: Newcatle & District, Staffs Co & Mid Cheshire, North West Counties

Club Colours (change): Blue & white

Ground Capacity: 4,000 **Seats:** 300 **Covered:** 1,000 **Clubhouse:** Yes **Shop:** Yes

Previous Grounds: None

Record Attendance: 3,948 v Notts County - FA Cup 1996

RECORDS
Goalscorer: Andy Bott - 149

Appearances: Dean Gillick - 632

HONOURS
FA Comps: None

League: Mid Cheshire Division Two 1982-83, 90-91, Division One 85-86. North West Counties Premier Division 2009-10.

County FA: Walsall Senior Cup 1993-94, 94-95. Staffordshire Senior Cup 2009-10.

08-09		09-10		10-11		11-12		12-13		13-14		14-15		15-16		16-17		17-18	
NWCP	3	NWCP	1	NP1S	2	NP1S	15	NP1S	17	NP1S	8	NP1S	3	NP1S	14	NP1S	7	NP1S	20
FAC	P	FAC	P	FAC	4Q	FAC	1Qr	FAC	P	FAC	1Qr	FAC	Pr	FAC	1Qr	FAC	P	FAC	1Q
FAV	2P	FAV	2P	FAT	1Q	FAT	1Qr	FAT	1Q	FAT	P	FAT	1Q	FAT	1Qr	FAT	P	FAT	1Qr

PRESCOT CABLES

Club Contact Details 0151 430 0507
Valerie Park, Eaton Street, Prescot L34 6ND

Founded: 1884	**Nickname:** Tigers	**Manager:** Brian Richardson

Previous Names: Prescot > 1995

Previous Leagues: Liverpool County Combination, Lancashire Combination 1897-98, 1918-20, 27-33, 36-76,
Mid Cheshire 1976-78, Cheshire County 1978-82, North West Counties 1982-2003

Club Colours (change): Amber & black

Ground Capacity: 3,200 **Seats:** 500 **Covered:** 600 **Clubhouse:** Yes **Shop:** Yes

Previous Grounds: None

Record Attendance: 8,122 v Ashton National - 1932

RECORDS
Victory: 18-3 v Great Harwood - 1954-55

Defeat: 1-12 v Morecambe - 1936-37

Goalscorer: Freddie Crampton

Appearances: Harry Grisedale

HONOURS
FA Comps: None

League: Lancashire Combination Division Two 1951-52, Premier 1956-57. Mid-Cheshire 1976-77.
Cheshire County Division Two 1979-80. North West Counties 2002-03.
County FA: Liverpool Challenge Cup 1927-28, 28-29, 29-30, 48-49, 61-62, 77-78. Liverpool Non-League Cup 1952-53, 58-59, 60-61.
Liverpool Senior Cup 2016-17, 17-18.

08-09		09-10		10-11		11-12		12-13		13-14		14-15		15-16		16-17		17-18	
NP P	22	NP1N	15	NP1N	21	NP1N	16	NP1N	17	NP1N	20	NP1N	20	NP1N	16	NP1N	16	NP1N	5
FAC	3Q	FAC	P	FAC	1Qr	FAC	P	FAC	1Q	FAC	P	FAC	1Q	FAC	P	FAC	P	FAC	Pr
FAT	1Q	FAT	P	FAT	1Q	FAT	P	FAT	1Q	FAT	P	FAT	1Q	FAT	P	FAT	1Q	FAT	1Qr

RADCLIFFE

Club Contact Details 0161 724 8346
Stainton Park, Pilkington Road, Radcliffe, Lancashire M26 3PE
secretary@radcliffefc.com

Founded: 1949   **Nickname:** The Boro   **Manager:** Jonathan Macken
Previous Names: Radcliffe Borough >2018
Previous Leagues: South East Lancashire, Manchester 1953-63, Lancashire Combination 1963-71,
Cheshire County 1971-82, North West Counties 1982-97

Club Colours (change): All blue

Ground Capacity: 4,000   **Seats:** 350   **Covered:** 1,000   **Clubhouse:** Yes   **Shop:** Yes
Previous Grounds: Ashworth Street. Bright Street > 1970.
Record Attendance: 2,495 v York City - FA Cup 1st Round 2000-01
Nearest Railway Station Radcliffe - 1.3km   **Bus Route** Lowe Street - 100m away

RECORDS
Goalscorer: Ian Lunt - 147. Jody Banim scored 46 during a single season.
Appearances: Simon Kelly - 502
Additional: Paid £5,000 to Buxton for Gary Walker 1991
Received £20,000 from Shrewsbury Town for Jody Banim 2003

HONOURS
FA Comps: None
League: South Lancashire Division Two 1950-51, Division One 51-52, Premier 80-81. North West Counties Division Two 1982-83,
Division One 84-85. Northern Premier Division One 1996-97.
County FA: Manchester Premier Cup 2007-08.

08-09		09-10		10-11		11-12		12-13		13-14		14-15		15-16		16-17		17-18	
NP1N	16	NP1N	10	NP1N	18	NP1N	15	NP1N	15	NP1N	18	NP1N	19	NP1N	18	NP1N	20	NP1N	20
FAC	P	FAC	3Q	FAC	1Q	FAC	3Q	FAC	Pr	FAC	1Q	FAC	1Q	FAC	P	FAC	1Q	FAC	1Q
FAT	1Q	FAT	1Qr	FAT	2Qr	FAT	2Qr	FAT	1Q	FAT	1Q	FAT	P	FAT	2Q	FAT	P	FAT	P

RAMSBOTTOM UNITED

Club Contact Details 01706 822 799
The Harry Williams Stadium, Acrebottom (off Bridge Street) BL0 0BS.
secretary@rammyunited.co.uk

Founded: 1966   **Nickname:** The Rams   **Manager:** Mark fell
Previous Names: None
Previous Leagues: Bury Amateur 1966-69. Bolton Combination 1969-89. Manchester 1989-95. North West Counties 1995-2012.

Club Colours (change): Blue & white

Ground Capacity: 2,000   **Seats:** Yes   **Covered:** Yes   **Clubhouse:** Yes   **Shop:** No
Previous Grounds: None
Record Attendance: 2,104 v FC United of Manchester, Northern Premier League Premier Division, 04/04/15.

RECORDS
Victory: 9-0 v Stantondale (H), NWCFL Division Two, 9th November 1996.
Defeat: 0-7 v Salford City (A), NWCFL Division One, 16th November 2002.
Goalscorer: Russell Brierley - 176 (1996-2003). Russell Brierley scored 38 during the 1999-2000 season.

HONOURS
FA Comps: None
League: Bolton Combination Division One 1972-73, Premier Division 76-77. Manchester Division One 1990-91.
North West Counties Division Two 1996-97, Premier Division 2011-12.
County FA: None

08-09		09-10		10-11		11-12		12-13		13-14		14-15		15-16		16-17		17-18	
NWCP	14	NWCP	4	NWCP	2	NWCP	1	NP1N	6	NP1N	5	NP P	17	NP P	24	NP1N	14	NP1N	14
FAC	P	FAC	P	FAC	1Q	FAC	1Q	FAC	2Q	FAC	2Q	FAC	1Q	FAC	1Q	FAC	P	FAC	P
FAV	1P	FAV	1P	FAV	1P	FAV	2P	FAT	2Q	FAT	3Q	FAT	1P	FAT	1Qr	FAT	3Q	FAT	2Q

RUNCORN LINNETS

Club Contact Details 07973 416 580
Millbank Linnets Stadium, Murdishaw Ave, Runcorn, Cheshire WA7 6HP
secretary@RuncornLinnetsFC.co.uk

Founded: 2006   **Nickname:** Linnets   **Manager:** Michael Ellison
Previous Names: None
Previous Leagues: North West Counties 2006-18.

Club Colours (change): Yellow & green

Ground Capacity: 1,600   **Seats:** Yes   **Covered:** Yes   **Clubhouse:** Yes   **Shop:**
Previous Grounds:
Record Attendance: 1,037 v Witton Albion, pre season friendly July 2010
Nearest Railway Station Runcorn East - 1.2km   **Bus Route** Halton Arms stop - 62m away

RECORDS
Best FA Cup   Third Qualifying Round 2013-14
FA Vase   Third Round Proper 2008-09, 17-18

HONOURS
FA Comps: None
League: North West Counties Premier 2017-18.

County FA: None

	08-09	09-10	10-11	11-12	12-13	13-14	14-15	15-16	16-17	17-18
NWCP	11	11	12	5	6	2	2	2	4	1
FAC	P	P	P	2Q	EPr	3Q	P	1Q	EP	P
FAV	3P	2Q	1P	1P	1P	1P	1P	2P	1P	3P

SKELMERSDALE UNITED

Club Contact Details 07930 823 388
Prescot Cables FC, Valerie Park, Eaton Street, Prescot L34 6HD
alangreenhalgh@live.co.uk

Founded: 1882   **Nickname:** Skem / Blueboys   **Manager:** David Powell
Previous Names: Skelmsdale Young Rovers. Skelmersdale Wesleyans.
Previous Leagues: Liverpool County Combination, Lancashire Combination 1891-93, 1903-07, 21-24, 55-56, 76-78,
    Cheshire County 1968-71, 78-82, Northern Premier 1971-76, North West Counties 1983-2006
Club Colours (change): All blue

Ground Capacity: 3,200   **Seats:** 500   **Covered:** 600   **Clubhouse:** Yes   **Shop:** Yes
Previous Grounds: White Moss Park >2002. Westgate Interactive Stadium 2002-04. West Lancashire College Stadium 2004-17.
Record Attendance: 7,000 v Slough Town - FA Amateur Cup Semi-final 1967

RECORDS
Goalscorer: Stuart Rudd - 230
Appearances: Robbie Holcroft - 422 including 398 consecutively
Additional: Paid £2,000 for Stuart Rudd
                   Received £4,000 for Stuart Rudd

HONOURS
FA Comps: FA Amateur Cup 1970-71. Barassi Anglo-Italian Cup 1970-71.
League: Northern Premier Division One North 2013-14.

County FA: Lancashire Junior Cup x2. Lancashire Non-League Cup x2. Liverpool Senior Cup 2014-15.

	08-09	09-10	10-11	11-12	12-13	13-14	14-15	15-16	16-17	17-18
NP1N	2	5	2	7	1					21
NP P						6	7	16	24	
FAC	1Q	P	2Q	2Q	2Q	2Q	2Q	2Q	1Qr	1Q
FAT	1P	2Q	1Q	P	3P	1Q	1Q	1Pr	1Q	P

TRAFFORD

Club Contact Details 0161 747 1727
First Point, Shawe View, Pennybridge Lane, Flixton Urmston M41 5DL

Founded: 1990   **Nickname:** The North   **Manager:** Tom Baker
Previous Names: North Trafford 1990-94
Previous Leagues: Mid Cheshire 1990-92, North West Counties 1992-97, 2003-08, Northern Premier 1997-2003

Club Colours (change): All white

Ground Capacity: 2,500 **Seats:** 292   **Covered:** 740   **Clubhouse:** Yes   **Shop:** Yes
Previous Grounds: None
Record Attendance: 803 v Flixton - Northern Premier League Division 1 1997-98. 2,238 (at Altrincham FC) FAC P v FC United
Nearest Railway Station Urmston - 0.3km

RECORDS
Victory: 10-0 v Haslingden St.Mary's (Lancs Amt Shield 1991)
Goalscorer: Scott Barlow - 100
Appearances: Lee Southwood - 311
Additional: NWC League Record: 18 consecutive league wins in 2007-08
                       Most Points In One Season: 95 points from 38 games 2007-08

HONOURS
FA Comps: None
League: North West Counties Division One 1996-97, 2007-08.

County FA: Manchester Challenge Trophy 2004-05.

08-09		09-10		10-11		11-12		12-13		13-14		14-15		15-16		16-17		17-18	
NP1N	15	NP1N	12	NP1N	14	NP1N	12	NP1N	4	NP P	10	NP P	23	NP1N	8	NP1N	6	NP1N	6
FAC	P	FAC	Pr	FAC	1Q	FAC	1Q	FAC	3Q	FAC	3Q	FAC	1Q	FAC	P	FAC	2Q	FAC	Pr
FAT	1Q	FAT	P	FAT	P	FAT	P	FAT	2Q	FAT	2Q	FAT	2Q	FAT	P	FAT	2Q	FAT	P

WIDNES

Club Contact Details 0151 510 6000
Select Security Stadium, Lower House Lane, Widnes, Cheshire WA8 7DZ

Founded: 2003   **Nickname:** Vikings   **Manager:** Steve Akrigg & Kevin Towey
Previous Names: Formed as Dragons AFC in 2003. Widnes Dragons > 2012. Widnes Vikings 2012-14.
Previous Leagues: Junior Leagues 2003-12.

Club Colours (change): White & black

Ground Capacity: 13,350 **Seats:** Yes   **Covered:** Yes   **Clubhouse:** Yes   **Shop:**
Previous Grounds: The club moved to Halton Stadium in 2012.
Record Attendance: 462 v Charnock Richard, North West Counties Division One, 22/04/2017
Nearest Railway Station Widnes - 1.5km   **Bus Route** Cricketers Arms stop - 121m away

RECORDS
Victory: (League) 8-0 v St Helens Town, 08/04/2017
Defeat: (League) 1-10 v Northwich Manchester Villa, 13/12/2014

HONOURS
FA Comps: None
League: North West Counties Division One 2016-17.

County FA: None

08-09	09-10	10-11	11-12	12-13		13-14		14-15		15-16		16-17		17-18	
				WCh3	4	NWC1	14	NWC1	16	NWC1	13	NWC1	1	NWCP	2
														FAC	EP
								FAV	2Q			FAV	2Q	FAV	1Q

ATHERTON COLLIERIES

Club Contact Details 07968 548 056
The Kensite Stadium, Alder Street, Atherton, Greater Manchester M46 9EY
secretaryacfc1916@yahoo.co.uk

Founded: 1916   **Nickname:** Colls   **Manager:** Michael Clegg
Previous Names: None
Previous Leagues: Bolton Combination 1918-21, 52-71. Lancashire Alliance 1921. Manchester 1945-48. West Lancashire 1948-50. Lancashire
               Combination 1950-52, 71-78. Cheshire County 1978-82.

Club Colours (change): Black & white

Ground Capacity: 2,500   **Seats:** Yes   **Covered:** Yes   **Clubhouse:** Yes   **Shop:** No
Previous Grounds: None
Record Attendance: 3,300 in the Bolton Combination 1920's.
Nearest Railway Station Atherton - 0.7km   **Bus Route** High Street - stop 100m away

RECORDS
Best FA Cup   Third Qualifying Round 1994-95
FA Vase   Fifth Round 2016-17
FA Trophy   Second Qualifying Round 2017-18

HONOURS
FA Comps: None
League: Bolton Combination 1919-20, 36-37, 37-38, 38-39, 40-41, 44-45, 56-57, 58-59, 60-61, 64-65.
           North West Counties Division Three 1986-87, Division One 2014-15, Premier 2016-17.
County FA: Lancashire County FA Shield 1919-20, 22-23, 41-42, 45-46, 56-57, 64-65.

08-09		09-10		10-11		11-12		12-13		13-14		14-15		15-16		16-17		17-18	
NWCP	22	NWC1	6	NWC1	5	NWC1	4	NWC1	4	NWC1	5	NWC1	1	NWCP	3	NWCP	1	NP1N	10
FAC	EP	FAC	P	FAC	Pr	FAC	P	FAC	1Q	FAC	Pr	FAC	Pr	FAC	Pr	FAC	P	FAC	2Q
FAV	2Q	FAV	2Q	FAV	2Q	FAV	2Q	FAV	1Q	FAV	1Q	FAV	2P	FAV	3P	FAV	5P	FAT	2Q

CHASETOWN

Club Contact Details 01543 682 222
The Scholars, Church Street, Chasetown, Walsall WS7 3QL

Founded: 1954   **Nickname:** The Scholars   **Manager:** Scott Dundas
Previous Names: Chase Terrace Old Scholars 1954-72
Previous Leagues: Cannock Youth 1954-58, Lichfield & District 1958-61, Staffordshire County 1961-72,
               West Midlands 1972-94, Midland Alliance 1994-2006, Southern 2006-09

Club Colours (change): Royal blue & white

Ground Capacity: 2,000   **Seats:** 151   **Covered:** 220   **Clubhouse:** Yes   **Shop:** Yes
Previous Grounds: Burntwood Recreation
Record Attendance: 2,420 v Cardiff City - FA Cup 3rd Round January 2008
Nearest Railway Station Hednesford - 6.4km   **Bus Route** Queen Street - stop 160m away

RECORDS
Victory: 14-1 v Hanford - Walsall Senior Cup 1991-92
Defeat: 1-8 v Telford United Reserves - West Midlands League
Goalscorer: Tony Dixon - 197. Mick Ward scored 39 goals during the 1987-88 season, whilst a player by the name of Keith Birch
              scored 11 in a 21-1 win over Lichfield Laundry.
Misc: The club became the first from the eighth tier of English football to reach the Third Round Proper of the FA Cup during
              the 2007-08 season.

HONOURS
FA Comps: None
League: West Midlands 1978. Midland Alliance 2004-05.

County FA: Walsall Senior Cup 1990-91, 92-93, 2004-05.

08-09		09-10		10-11		11-12		12-13		13-14		14-15		15-16		16-17		17-18	
SthM	4	NP1S	2	NP P	10	NP P	20	NP1S	5	NP1S	12	NP1S	13	NP1S	7	NP1S	17	NP1S	5
FAC	3Q	FAC	Pr	FAC	1Q	FAC	2Q	FAC	2Q	FAC	1Qr	FAC	1Qr	FAC	3Qr	FAC	2Q	FAC	2Q
FAT	3Q	FAT	1Qr	FAT	QF	FAT	2Q	FAT	2Q	FAT	1Q	FAT	3Q	FAT	Pr	FAT	P	FAT	2Q

CLITHEROE

Club Contact Details
Shawbridge, off Pendle Road, Clitheroe, Lancashire BB7 1LZ
secretary@clitheroefc.co.uk

Founded: 1877   **Nickname:** The Blues   **Manager:** Stuart Mellish
Previous Names: Clitheroe Central 1877-1903.
Previous Leagues: Blackburn & District, Lancashire Combination 1903-04, 05-10, 25-82, North West Counties 1982-85

Club Colours (change): All blue

Ground Capacity: 2,000   **Seats:** 250   **Covered:** 1,400   **Clubhouse:** Yes   **Shop:** No
Previous Grounds: None
Record Attendance: 2,050 v Mangotsfield - FA Vase Semi-final 1995-96
Nearest Railway Station Clitheroe - 0.6km   **Bus Route** Hayhurst Street - 50m away

RECORDS
Goalscorer: Don Francis
Appearances: Lindsey Wallace - 670
Additional: Received £45,000 from Crystal Palace for Carlo Nash.

HONOURS
FA Comps: None
League: Lancashire Combination Division Two 1959-60, Division One 1979-80.
         North West Counties Division Three 1983-84, Division Two 1984-85, Division One 1985-86, 2003-04.
County FA: Lancashire Challenge Trophy 1892-93, 1984-85.

08-09		09-10		10-11		11-12		12-13		13-14		14-15		15-16		16-17		17-18	
NP1N	12	NP1N	8	NP1N	6	NP1N	19	NP1N	8	NP1N	17	NP1N	13	NP1N	7	NP1N	7	NP1N	12
FAC	2Q	FAC	1Q	FAC	P	FAC	2Q	FAC	1Q	FAC	P	FAC	1Q	FAC	1Q	FAC	P	FAC	1Q
FAT	2Q	FAT	2Q	FAT	2Q	FAT	Pr	FAT	Pr	FAT	Pr	FAT	1Q	FAT	P	FAT	P	FAT	1Q

COLNE

Club Contact Details 01282 862 545
The XLCR Stadium, Harrison Drive, Colne, Lancashire BB8 9SL
secretary@colnefootballclub.com

Founded: 1996   **Nickname:** The Reds   **Manager:** Steve Cunningham
Previous Names: None
Previous Leagues: North West Counties 1996-2016.

Club Colours (change): Red & white

Ground Capacity: 1,800   **Seats:** 160   **Covered:** 1,000   **Clubhouse:** Yes   **Shop:** Yes
Previous Grounds: None
Record Attendance: 1,742 v AFC Sudbury F.A. Vase SF 2004. 2,762 (at Accrington Stanley) v FC United, NWC Challenge Cup,
Nearest Railway Station Colne - 0.6km   **Bus Route** Tennyson Road - stop 100m away

RECORDS
Goalscorer: Geoff Payton
Appearances: Richard Walton

HONOURS
FA Comps: None
League: North West Counties League Division Two 2003-04, Premier Division 2015-16.

County FA: None

08-09		09-10		10-11		11-12		12-13		13-14		14-15		15-16		16-17		17-18	
NWCP	18	NWCP	8	NWCP	5	NWCP	8	NWCP	8	NWCP	9	NWCP	4	NWCP	1	NP1N	5	NP1N	8
FAC	1Q	FAC	EP	FAC	P	FAC	EP	FAC	EPr	FAC	EPr	FAC	EP	FAC	1Q	FAC	1Q	FAC	1Q
FAV	1P	FAV	1P	FAV	1P	FAV	1P	FAV	2Q	FAV	2Q	FAV	1P	FAV	2P	FAT	P	FAT	P

COLWYN BAY

Club Contact Details 01492 514 680
Llanelian Road, Old Colwyn, North Wales LL29 8UN
pauledwardscbfc@gmail.com

Founded: 1881	**Nickname:** The Bay / Seagulls	**Manager:** Alan Morgan

Previous Names: Colwyn Bay United 1907
Previous Leagues: North Wales Coast 1898-1900. 1901-21, 33-35, Welsh National 1921-30, North Wales Combination 1930-31, Welsh League (North) 1945-84, North West Counties 1984-91. Northern Premier 1991-2011. Football Conference 2011-15.

Club Colours (change): Claret and sky blue

Ground Capacity: 2,500 **Seats:** 500 **Covered:** 700 **Clubhouse:** Yes **Shop:** Yes
Previous Grounds: Eirias Park >1984.
Record Attendance: 5,000 v Borough United at Eirias Park 1964
Nearest Railway Station Colwyn Bay - 2.4km **Bus Route** Bus stops outside the ground

RECORDS
Goalscorer: Peter Donnelly
Appearances: Bryn A Jones

HONOURS
FA Comps: None
League: North Wales Football Combination 1930-31. Welsh League (North) 1964-65, 80-81, 82-83, 83-84. Northern Division One 1991-92.
County FA: None

08-09	09-10	10-11	11-12	12-13	13-14	14-15	15-16	16-17	17-18
NP1N 4	NP1N 4	NP P 2	Conf N 12	Conf N 18	Conf N 12	Conf N 20	NP P 23	NP1N 15	NP1N 9
FAC P	FAC P	FAC 2Qr	FAC 2Q	FAC 3Qr	FAC 4Q	FAC 3Qr	FAC 1Q	FAC 1Q	FAC 1Q
FAT 1Qr	FAT P	FAT 2Q	FAT 1P	FAT 3Q	FAT 3Q	FAT 3Q	FAT 1Q	FAT 1Qr	FAT P

DROYLSDEN

Club Contact Details 0161 370 1426
Market Street, Droylsden, M43 7AY
windowsindenton@gmail.com

Founded: 1892	**Nickname:** The Bloods	**Manager:** David Pace

Previous Names: None
Previous Leagues: Manchester, Lancashire Combination 1936-39, 50-68, Cheshire County 1939-50, 68-82, North West Counties 1982-87, Northern Premier 1986-2004

Club Colours (change): All red

Ground Capacity: 3,000 **Seats:** 500 **Covered:** 2,000 **Clubhouse:** Yes **Shop:** Yes
Previous Grounds: None
Record Attendance: 15,000 v Hyde United, Manchester League, 1921.
Nearest Railway Station Droylsden - 240m away **Bus Route** Bus stops outside the ground

RECORDS
Victory: 13-2 v Lucas Sports Club
Goalscorer: E. Gillibrand - 275 (1931-35)
Appearances: Paul Phillips - 326
Additional: Received £11,000 from Crewe Alexandra for Tony Naylor 1990
Defeat: 1-13 v Chorley, Northern Prmeier Premier Division, 05/04/2014.

HONOURS
FA Comps: None
League: Manchester 1930-31, 32-33. North West Counties Division Two 1986-87. Northern Premier Division One 1998-99. Conference North 2006-07.
County FA: Manchester Junior Cup 1922-23, Manchester Premier Cup x12 - Firstly in 1946-47 and most recently in 2009-10, Manchester Senior Cup 1972-73, 75-76, 78-79.

08-09	09-10	10-11	11-12	12-13	13-14	14-15	15-16	16-17	17-18
Conf N 7	Conf N 5	Conf N 8	Conf N 9	Conf N 21	NP P 24	NP1N 10	NP1N 19	NP1N 13	NP1N 13
FAC 2Pr	FAC 2Q	FAC 2Pr	FAC 4Qr	FAC 2Q	FAC 1Q	FAC 2Q	FAC 3Q	FAC Pr	FAC 2Q
FAT 3Q	FAT 3Q	FAT 3Pr	FAT 2P	FAT 3Q	FAT 1Q	FAT P	FAT P	FAT Pr	FAT 3Q

GLOSSOP NORTH END

Club Contact Details 01457 855 469
Surrey Street, Glossop, Derbys SK13 7AJ
lesleyodonnell1971@sky.com

Founded: 1886   **Nickname:** Peakites / The Hillmen   **Manager:** Mark Canning & Andy Bishop
Previous Names: Glossop North End 1886-1896 and Glossop FC 1898-1992. Reformed in 1992.
Previous Leagues: North Cheshire 1890-94. Combination 1894-96. Midland 1896-98. The Football League 1898-1918. Lancashire Comb. 1919-20, 57-66. Manchester 1920-57, 66-78. Cheshire County (Founder member) 1978-82. North West Counties (FM)1982-2015.

Club Colours (change): All royal blue

Ground Capacity: 2,374   **Seats:** 209   **Covered:** 509   **Clubhouse:** Yes   **Shop:** Yes
Previous Grounds: Pyegrove. Silk Street. Water Lane. Cemetery Road. North Road 1890-1955.
Record Attendance: 10,736 v Preston North End F.A. Cup 1913-1914
Nearest Railway Station Glossop - 0.4km   **Bus Route** St Mary's Road - stop 300m away

RECORDS
Best FA Cup   First Round Proper 1896-97
FA Trophy   Third Qualifying Round 2017-18
FA Vase   Finalists 2014-15

HONOURS
FA Comps: None

League: Manchester 1927-28. North West Counties Premier Division 2014-15.

County FA: Manchester FA Premier Cup 1996-97, 97-98. Derbyshire Senior Cup 2000-01.

	08-09		09-10		10-11		11-12		12-13		13-14		14-15		15-16		16-17		17-18	
NWCP	5	NWCP	7	NWCP	14	NWCP	6	NWCP	13	NWCP	3	NWCP	1	NP1N	4	NP1N	8	NP1N	11
FAC	P	FAC	1Q	FAC	1Q	FAC	EP	FAC	P	FAC	1Q	FAC	2Q	FAC	1Qr	FAC	Pr	FAC	P
FAV	F	FAV	3P	FAV	1P	FAV	3P	FAV	2Qr	FAV	2P	FAV	F	FAT	Pr	FAT	1Q	FAT	3Qr

KENDAL TOWN

Club Contact Details 01539 727 472
ST&B Accountants Stadium, Parkside Road, Kendal, Cumbria LA9 7BL
gudge1@talk21.com

Founded: 1919   **Nickname:** The Mintcakes / The Field / The Town   **Manager:** David Foster
Previous Names: Netherfield AFC 1919-2000
Previous Leagues: Westmorland, North Lancashire Combination 1945-68, Northern Premier 1968-83, North West Counties 1983-87

Club Colours (change): Black and white stripes

Ground Capacity: 2,490   **Seats:** 450   **Covered:** 1000   **Clubhouse:** Yes   **Shop:** Yes
Previous Grounds: None
Record Attendance: 5,184 v Grimsby Town - FA Cup 1st Round 1955
Nearest Railway Station Kendal - 1.3km   **Bus Route** Castle Circle - stop 200m away

RECORDS
Victory: 11-0 v Great Harwood - 22/03/1947
Defeat: 0-10 v Stalybridge Celtic - 01/09/1984
Goalscorer: Tom Brownlee
Additional: Received £10,250 from Manchester City for Andy Milner 1995

HONOURS
FA Comps: None

League: Lancashire Combination 1948-49, 64-65.

County FA: Westmorlands Senior Cup x12. Lancashire Senior Cup 2002-03.

	08-09		09-10		10-11		11-12		12-13		13-14		14-15		15-16		16-17		17-18	
NP P	5	NP P	8	NP P	8	NP P	11	NP P	21	NP1N	10	NP1N	16	NP1N	15	NP1N	12	NP1N	18
FAC	2Q	FAC	4Q	FAC	1Q	FAC	3Q	FAC	3Q	FAC	P	FAC	P	FAC	2Q	FAC	P	FAC	1Q
FAT	1Q	FAT	1Q	FAT	3Q	FAT	2Qr	FAT	1Q	FAT	1Qr	FAT	P	FAT	1Q	FAT	2Q	FAT	1Q

KIDSGROVE ATHLETIC

Club Contact Details 01782 782 412

The Novus Stadium, Hollinwood Road, Kidsgrove, Staffs ST7 1DH

Founded: 1952   **Nickname:** The Grove   **Manager:** Ryan Austin

Previous Names: None

Previous Leagues: Buslem and Tunstall 1953-63, Staffordshire County 1963-66, Mid Cheshire 1966-90, North West Counties 1990-2002

Club Colours (change): All blue

Ground Capacity: 2,000   **Seats:** 1,000   **Covered:** 800   **Clubhouse:** Yes   **Shop:** Yes

Previous Grounds: Vickers and Goodwin 1953-60

Record Attendance: 1,903 v Tiverton Town - FA Vase Semi-final 1998

Nearest Railway Station Kidsgrove - 0.8km   **Bus Route** Grove Avenue - stop 200m away

RECORDS

Victory:	23-0 v Cross Heath W.M.C. - Staffordshire Cup 1965
Defeat:	0-15 v Stafford Rangers - Staffordshire Senior Cup 20/11/2001
Goalscorer:	Scott Dundas - 53 (1997-98)
Additional:	Paid £10,000 to Stevenage Borough for Steve Walters
	Received £3,000 for Ryan Baker 2003-04

HONOURS

FA Comps: None

League: Staffordshire County Division Two 1963-64, Premier 65-66. Mid-Cheshire 1970-71, 77-78, 86-87, 87-88. North West Counties Premier Division 1997-98, 2001-02.

County FA: Staffordshire Senior Cup 2003-04, 06-07, 08-09, 10-11, 11-12.

	08-09		09-10		10-11		11-12		12-13		13-14		14-15		15-16		16-17		17-18	
NP1S	15	NP1S	4	NP1S	7	NP1S	13	NP1S	18	NP1S	21	NP1S	20	NP1S	15	NP1S	12	NP1S	18
FAC	1Q	FAC	1Q	FAC	2Q	FAC	4Q	FAC	P	FAC	1Q	FAC	P	FAC	Pr	FAC	2Q	FAC	2Q
FAT	1Q	FAT	P	FAT	Pr	FAT	1Q	FAT	1Q	FAT	2Q	FAT	P	FAT	2Qr	FAT	2Q	FAT	2Q

LEEK TOWN

Club Contact Details 01538 399 278

Harrison Park, Macclesfield Road, Leek, Cheshire ST13 8LD

Founded: 1946   **Nickname:** The Blues   **Manager:** Neil Baker

Previous Names: None

Previous Leagues: Staffordshire Co., Manchester 1951-54, 57-73, West Midlands (B'ham) 1954-56, Cheshire Co. 1973-82, North West Counties 1982-87, Northern Premier 1987-94, 95-97, Southern 1994-95, Conference 1997-99

Club Colours (change): All blue

Ground Capacity: 3,600   **Seats:** 650   **Covered:** 3,000   **Clubhouse:** Yes   **Shop:** Yes

Previous Grounds: None

Record Attendance: 3,512 v Macclesfield Town - FA Cup 1973-74

RECORDS

Goalscorer:	Dave Sutton - 144
Appearances:	Gary Pearce - 447
Additional:	Paid £2,000 to Sutton Town for Simon Snow
	Received £30,000 from Barnsley for Tony Bullock

HONOURS

FA Comps: None

League: Staffordshire County 1949-50, 50-51. Manchester 1951-52, 71-72, 72-73. Cheshire County 1974-75. Northern Premier Division One 1989-90, Premier Division 1996-97.

County FA: Staffordshire Senior Cup 1995-96.

	08-09		09-10		10-11		11-12		12-13		13-14		14-15		15-16		16-17		17-18	
NP1S	9	NP1S	8	NP1S	16	NP1S	5	NP1S	10	NP1S	3	NP1S	2	NP1S	8	NP1S	9	NP1S	7
FAC	1Qr	FAC	P	FAC	P	FAC	3Qr	FAC	3Q	FAC	Pr	FAC	4Q	FAC	1Qr	FAC	1Q	FAC	1Q
FAT	P	FAT	2Q	FAT	P	FAT	2Qr	FAT	2Qr	FAT	2P	FAT	2Qr	FAT	P	FAT	2Q	FAT	2Q

MARKET DRAYTON TOWN

Club Contact Details 01630 661 780
Greenfields Sports Ground, Greenfields Lane, Market Drayton TF9 3SL
rpope2nt@gmail.com

Founded: 1969 **Nickname:** None **Manager:** Carl Abbott
Previous Names: Little Drayton Rangers > 2003
Previous Leagues: West Midlands (Regional) 1969-2006, Midland Alliance 2006-09

Club Colours (change): All red (All blue)

Ground Capacity: 1,000 **Seats:** Yes **Covered:** Yes **Clubhouse:** Yes **Shop:** No
Previous Grounds: Not known
Record Attendance: 440 vs. AFC Telford, Friendly 11/07/09. 229 vs. Witton Albion, Unibond South 25/08/09
Bus Route Cmetery Road Jct - stop 400m away

RECORDS
Victory: (League) 9-0 Home vs. Racing Club Warwick 10/03/09
Best FA Cup Second Qualifying Round 2007-08, 10-11
FA Trophy   First Qualifying Round 2010-11, 14-15, 15-16
FA Vase   Fifth Round Proper 2008-09

HONOURS
FA Comps: None
League: West Midlands (Regional) 2005-06. Midland Alliance 2008-09.
County FA: None

	08-09	09-10	10-11	11-12	12-13	13-14	14-15	15-16	16-17	17-18
	MidAl 1	NP1S 13	NP1S 18	NP1S 16	NP1S 15	NP1S 19	NP1S 19	NP1S 11	NP1S 14	NP1S 21
FAC	P	2Q	2Q	P	1Qr	P	1Q	1Q	P	1Q
FAV/FAT	5P	Pr	1Qr	P	P	P	1Qr	P	1Q	P

MOSSLEY

Club Contact Details 01457 832 369
Seel Park, Market Street, Mossley, Lancashire OL5 0ES
john.wharmby@mossleyfc.com

Founded: 1903 **Nickname:** Lilywhites **Manager:** Dave Wild & Terry Hincks
Previous Names: Park Villa 1903-04, Mossley Juniors
Previous Leagues: Ashton, South East Lancashire, Lancashire Combination 1918-19, Cheshire County 1919-72,
Northern Premier 1972-95, North West Counties 1995-2004

Club Colours (change): White & black

Ground Capacity: 4,000 **Seats:** 220 **Covered:** 1,500 **Clubhouse:** Yes **Shop:** Yes
Previous Grounds: Moved to Seel Park in 1911.
Record Attendance: 7,000 v Stalybridge Celtic 1950
Nearest Railway Station Mossley - 0.3km **Bus Route** Stamford Street - 200m away

RECORDS
Victory: 9-0 v Urmston, Manchester Shield, 1947
Defeat: 2-13 v Witton Albion, Cheshire League, 1926
Goalscorer: David Moore - 235 (1974-84). Jackie Roscoe scored 58 during the 1930-31 season.
Appearances: Jimmy O'Connor - 613 (1972-87)
Additional: Paid £2,300 to Altrincham for Phil Wilson
                 Received £25,000 from Everton for Eamonn O'Keefe

HONOURS
FA Comps: None
League: Ashton & District 1911-12, 14-15. Northern Premier 1978-79, 79-80, Division One 2005-06.
County FA: Manchester Premier Cup 1937-38, 48-49, 60-61, 66-67, 67-68, 88-89, 90-91, 2011-12, 12-13, 14-15, 15-16.
Manchester Challenge Trophy 2011-12.

	08-09	09-10	10-11	11-12	12-13	13-14	14-15	15-16	16-17	17-18
	NP1N 10	NP1N 7	NP1N 15	NP1N 14	NP1N 5	NP1N 15	NP1N 7	NP1N 13	NP1N 17	NP1N 19
FAC	3Q	P	4Q	Pr	P	Pr	Pr	Pr	1Q	1Qr
FAT	P	3Qr	2Q	P	1Qr	2Q	1Q	1Q	1Q	1Q

NEWCASTLE TOWN

Club Contact Details 01782 662 350
Lyme Valley Stadium, Buckmaster Avenue, Clayton, ST5 3BX
secretary@newcastletownfc.co.uk

Founded: 1964   **Nickname:** The Castle   **Manager:** Robin Van Der Laan
Previous Names: Parkway Hanley, Clayton Park & Parkway Clayton. Merged as NTFC in 1986.
Previous Leagues: Newcatle & District, Staffs Co & Mid Cheshire, North West Counties

Club Colours (change): Blue & white

Ground Capacity: 4,000   **Seats:** 300   **Covered:** 1,000   **Clubhouse:** Yes   **Shop:** Yes
Previous Grounds: None
Record Attendance: 3,948 v Notts County - FA Cup 1996

RECORDS
Goalscorer: Andy Bott - 149
Appearances: Dean Gillick - 632

HONOURS
FA Comps: None
League: Mid Cheshire Division Two 1982-83, 90-91, Division One 85-86. North West Counties Premier Division 2009-10.
County FA: Walsall Senior Cup 1993-94, 94-95. Staffordshire Senior Cup 2009-10.

	08-09		09-10		10-11		11-12		12-13		13-14		14-15		15-16		16-17		17-18	
	NWCP	3	NWCP	1	NP1S	2	NP1S	15	NP1S	17	NP1S	8	NP1S	3	NP1S	14	NP1S	7	NP1S	20
	FAC	P	FAC	P	FAC	4Q	FAC	1Qr	FAC	P	FAC	1Qr	FAC	Pr	FAC	1Qr	FAC	P	FAC	1Q
	FAV	2P	FAV	2P	FAT	1Q	FAT	1Qr	FAT	1Q	FAT	P	FAT	1Q	FAT	1Qr	FAT	P	FAT	1Qr

PRESCOT CABLES

Club Contact Details 0151 430 0507
Valerie Park, Eaton Street, Prescot L34 6ND

Founded: 1884   **Nickname:** Tigers   **Manager:** Brian Richardson
Previous Names: Prescot > 1995
Previous Leagues: Liverpool County Combination, Lancashire Combination 1897-98, 1918-20, 27-33, 36-76,
                        Mid Cheshire 1976-78, Cheshire County 1978-82, North West Counties 1982-2003
Club Colours (change): Amber & black

Ground Capacity: 3,200   **Seats:** 500   **Covered:** 600   **Clubhouse:** Yes   **Shop:** Yes
Previous Grounds: None
Record Attendance: 8,122 v Ashton National - 1932

RECORDS
Victory: 18-3 v Great Harwood - 1954-55
Defeat: 1-12 v Morecambe - 1936-37
Goalscorer: Freddie Crampton
Appearances: Harry Grisedale

HONOURS
FA Comps: None
League: Lancashire Combination Division Two 1951-52, Premier 1956-57. Mid-Cheshire 1976-77.
             Cheshire County Division Two 1979-80. North West Counties 2002-03.
County FA: Liverpool Challenge Cup 1927-28, 28-29, 29-30, 48-49, 61-62, 77-78. Liverpool Non-League Cup 1952-53, 58-59, 60-61.
              Liverpool Senior Cup 2016-17.

	08-09		09-10		10-11		11-12		12-13		13-14		14-15		15-16		16-17		17-18	
	NP P	22	NP1N	15	NP1N	21	NP1N	16	NP1N	17	NP1N	20	NP1N	20	NP1N	16	NP1N	16	NP1N	5
	FAC	3Q	FAC	P	FAC	1Qr	FAC	P	FAC	1Q	FAC	1Q	FAC	1Q	FAC	P	FAC	P	FAC	Pr
	FAT	1Q	FAT	P	FAT	1Q	FAT	P	FAT	P	FAT	P	FAT	1Q	FAT	P	FAT	1Q	FAT	1Qr

RADCLIFFE

Club Contact Details 0161 724 8346
Stainton Park, Pilkington Road, Radcliffe, Lancashire M26 3PE
secretary@radcliffefc.com

Founded: 1949   **Nickname:** The Boro   **Manager:** Jonathan Macken
Previous Names: Radcliffe Borough >2018
Previous Leagues: South East Lancashire, Manchester 1953-63, Lancashire Combination 1963-71,
Cheshire County 1971-82, North West Counties 1982-97

Club Colours (change): All blue

Ground Capacity: 4,000   **Seats:** 350   **Covered:** 1,000   **Clubhouse:** Yes   **Shop:** Yes
Previous Grounds: Ashworth Street. Bright Street > 1970.
Record Attendance: 2,495 v York City - FA Cup 1st Round 2000-01
Nearest Railway Station Radcliffe - 1.3km   **Bus Route** Lowe Street - 100m away

RECORDS
Goalscorer: Ian Lunt - 147. Jody Banim scored 46 during a single season.
Appearances: Simon Kelly - 502
Additional: Paid £5,000 to Buxton for Gary Walker 1991
Received £20,000 from Shrewsbury Town for Jody Banim 2003

HONOURS
FA Comps: None
League: South Lancashire Division Two 1950-51, Division One 51-52, Premier 80-81. North West Counties Division Two 1982-83,
Division One 84-85. Northern Premier Division One 1996-97.
County FA: Manchester Premier Cup 2007-08.

08-09		09-10		10-11		11-12		12-13		13-14		14-15		15-16		16-17		17-18	
NP1N	16	NP1N	10	NP1N	18	NP1N	15	NP1N	15	NP1N	18	NP1N	19	NP1N	18	NP1N	20	NP1N	20
FAC	P	FAC	3Q	FAC	1Q	FAC	3Q	FAC	Pr	FAC	1Q	FAC	1Q	FAC	P	FAC	1Q	FAC	1Q
FAT	1Q	FAT	1Qr	FAT	2Qr	FAT	2Qr	FAT	1Q	FAT	1Q	FAT	P	FAT	2Q	FAT	P	FAT	P

RAMSBOTTOM UNITED

Club Contact Details 01706 822 799
The Harry Williams Stadium, Acrebottom (off Bridge Street) BL0 0BS.
secretary@rammyunited.co.uk

Founded: 1966   **Nickname:** The Rams   **Manager:** Mark fell
Previous Names: None
Previous Leagues: Bury Amateur 1966-69. Bolton Combination 1969-89. Manchester 1989-95. North West Counties 1995-2012.

Club Colours (change): Blue & white

Ground Capacity: 2,000   **Seats:** Yes   **Covered:** Yes   **Clubhouse:** Yes   **Shop:** No
Previous Grounds: None
Record Attendance: 2,104 v FC United of Manchester, Northern Premier League Premier Division, 04/04/15.

RECORDS
Victory: 9-0 v Stantondale (H), NWCFL Division Two, 9th November 1996.
Defeat: 0-7 v Salford City (A), NWCFL Division One, 16th November 2002.
Goalscorer: Russell Brierley - 176 (1996-2003). Russell Brierley scored 38 during the 1999-2000 season.

HONOURS
FA Comps: None
League: Bolton Combination Division One 1972-73, Premier Division 76-77. Manchester Division One 1990-91.
North West Counties Division Two 1996-97, Premier Division 2011-12.
County FA: None

08-09		09-10		10-11		11-12		12-13		13-14		14-15		15-16		16-17		17-18	
NWCP	14	NWCP	4	NWCP	2	NWCP	1	NP1N	6	NP1N	5	NP P	17	NP P	24	NP1N	14	NP1N	14
FAC	P	FAC	P	FAC	1Q	FAC	1Q	FAC	1Q	FAC	2Q	FAC	1Q	FAC	1Q	FAC	P	FAC	P
FAV	1P	FAV	1P	FAV	1P	FAV	2P	FAT	2Q	FAT	3Q	FAT	1P	FAT	1Qr	FAT	3Q	FAT	2Q

RUNCORN LINNETS

Club Contact Details 07973 416 580
Millbank Linnets Stadium, Murdishaw Ave, Runcorn, Cheshire WA7 6HP
secretary@RuncornLinnetsFC.co.uk

Founded: 2006	Nickname: Linnets	Manager: Michael Ellison

Previous Names: None
Previous Leagues: North West Counties 2006-18.

Club Colours (change): Yellow & green

Ground Capacity: 1,600 **Seats:** Yes **Covered:** Yes **Clubhouse:** Yes **Shop:**
Previous Grounds:
Record Attendance: 1,037 v Witton Albion, pre season friendly July 2010
Nearest Railway Station Runcorn East - 1.2km   **Bus Route** Halton Arms stop - 62m away

RECORDS
Best FA Cup   Third Qualifying Round 2013-14
FA Vase   Third Round Proper 2008-09, 17-18

HONOURS
FA Comps: None
League: North West Counties Premier 2017-18.

County FA: None

08-09	09-10	10-11	11-12	12-13	13-14	14-15	15-16	16-17	17-18
NWCP 11	NWCP 11	NWCP 12	NWCP 5	NWCP 6	NWCP 2	NWCP 2	NWCP 2	NWCP 4	NWCP 1
FAC P	FAC P	FAC P	FAC 2Q	FAC EPr	FAC 3Q	FAC P	FAC 1Q	FAC EP	FAC P
FAV 3P	FAV 2Q	FAV 1P	FAV 1P	FAV 1P	FAV 1P	FAV 1P	FAV 2P	FAV 1P	FAV 3P

SKELMERSDALE UNITED

Club Contact Details 07930 823 388
Prescot Cables FC, Valerie Park, Eaton Street, Prescot L34 6HD
alangreenhalgh@live.co.uk

Founded: 1882	Nickname: Skem / Blueboys	Manager: David Powell

Previous Names: Skelmsdale Young Rovers. Skelmsdale Wesleyans.
Previous Leagues: Liverpool County Combination, Lancashire Combination 1891-93, 1903-07, 21-24, 55-56, 76-78,
Cheshire County 1968-71, 78-82, Northern Premier 1971-76, North West Counties 1983-2006

Club Colours (change): All blue

Ground Capacity: 3,200 **Seats:** 500 **Covered:** 600 **Clubhouse:** Yes **Shop:** Yes
Previous Grounds: White Moss Park >2002. Westgate Interactive Stadium 2002-04. West Lancashire College Stadium 2004-17.
Record Attendance: 7,000 v Slough Town - FA Amateur Cup Semi-final 1967

RECORDS
Goalscorer: Stuart Rudd - 230
Appearances: Robbie Holcroft - 422 including 398 consecutively
Additional: Paid £2,000 for Stuart Rudd
Received £4,000 for Stuart Rudd

HONOURS
FA Comps: FA Amateur Cup 1970-71. Barassi Anglo-Italian Cup 1970-71.
League: Northern Premier Division One North 2013-14.

County FA: Lancashire Junior Cup x2. Lancashire Non-League Cup x2. Liverpool Senior Cup 2014-15.

08-09	09-10	10-11	11-12	12-13	13-14	14-15	15-16	16-17	17-18
NP1N 2	NP1N 5	NP1N 2	NP1N 7	NP1N 1	NP P 6	NP P 7	NP P 16	NP P 24	NP1N 21
FAC 1Q	FAC P	FAC 2Q	FAC P	FAC 2Q	FAC 2Q	FAC 2Q	FAC 2Q	FAC 1Qr	FAC 1Q
FAT 1P	FAT 2Q	FAT 1Q	FAT P	FAT 3P	FAT 1Q	FAT 1Q	FAT 1Pr	FAT 1Q	FAT P

TRAFFORD

Club Contact Details 0161 747 1727
First Point, Shawe View, Pennybridge Lane, Flixton Urmston M41 5DL

Founded: 1990   **Nickname:** The North   **Manager:** Tom Baker
Previous Names: North Trafford 1990-94
Previous Leagues: Mid Cheshire 1990-92, North West Counties 1992-97, 2003-08, Northern Premier 1997-2003

Club Colours (change): All white

Ground Capacity: 2,500   **Seats:** 292   **Covered:** 740   **Clubhouse:** Yes   **Shop:** Yes
Previous Grounds: None
Record Attendance: 803 v Flixton - Northern Premier League Division 1 1997-98. 2,238 (at Altrincham FC) FAC P v FC United
Nearest Railway Station Urmston - 0.3km

RECORDS
Victory: 10-0 v Haslingden St.Mary's (Lancs Amt Shield 1991)
Goalscorer: Scott Barlow - 100
Appearances: Lee Southwood - 311
Additional: NWC League Record: 18 consecutive league wins in 2007-08
                Most Points In One Season: 95 points from 38 games 2007-08

HONOURS
FA Comps: None
League: North West Counties Division One 1996-97, 2007-08.

County FA: Manchester Challenge Trophy 2004-05.

08-09		09-10		10-11		11-12		12-13		13-14		14-15		15-16		16-17		17-18	
NP1N	15	NP1N	12	NP1N	14	NP1N	12	NP1N	4	NP P	10	NP P	23	NP1N	8	NP1N	6	NP1N	6
FAC	P	FAC	Pr	FAC	1Q	FAC	1Q	FAC	3Q	FAC	3Q	FAC	1Q	FAC	P	FAC	2Q	FAC	Pr
FAT	1Q	FAT	P	FAT	P	FAT	P	FAT	2Q	FAT	2Q	FAT	2Q	FAT	P	FAT	2Q	FAT	P

WIDNES

Club Contact Details 0151 510 6000
Select Security Stadium, Lower House Lane, Widnes, Cheshire WA8 7DZ

Founded: 2003   **Nickname:** Vikings   **Manager:** Steve Akrigg & Kevin Towey
Previous Names: Formed as Dragons AFC in 2003. Widnes Dragons > 2012. Widnes Vikings 2012-14.
Previous Leagues: Junior Leagues 2003-12.

Club Colours (change): White & black

Ground Capacity: 13,350   **Seats:** Yes   **Covered:** Yes   **Clubhouse:** Yes   **Shop:**
Previous Grounds: The club moved to Halton Stadium in 2012.
Record Attendance: 462 v Charnock Richard, North West Counties Division One, 22/04/2017
Nearest Railway Station Widnes - 1.5km   **Bus Route** Cricketers Arms stop - 121m away

RECORDS
Victory: (League) 8-0 v St Helens Town, 08/04/2017
Defeat: (League) 1-10 v Northwich Manchester Villa, 13/12/2014

HONOURS
FA Comps: None
League: North West Counties Division One 2016-17.

County FA: None

08-09	09-10	10-11	11-12	12-13		13-14		14-15		15-16		16-17		17-18	
				WCh3	4	NWC1	14	NWC1	16	NWC1	13	NWC1	1	NWCP	2
														FAC	EP
						FAV	2Q			FAV	2Q	FAV	1Q		

Goalmouth action from Hereford's last Southern Premier league match of the 2017-18 season against Kettering Town...

Southern League Premier Division Action

...after which, they were presented with the impressive Southern League Premier Division winners trophy.
Photos: Peter Barnes

SOUTHERN LEAGUE PREMIER DIVISION LEAGUE TABLE 2017-18

		P	W	D	L	F	A	GD	Pts
1	Hereford	46	36	5	5	111	33	78	113
2	King's Lynn Town	46	30	10	6	99	39	60	100
3	Slough Town	46	30	9	7	111	49	62	99
4	Kettering Town	46	30	7	9	122	56	66	97
5	Weymouth	46	30	7	9	103	48	55	97
6	Tiverton Town	46	24	6	16	78	69	9	78
7	Royston Town	46	24	5	17	84	65	19	77
8	Chesham United	46	21	11	14	85	61	24	74
9	Banbury United	46	19	15	12	90	59	31	72
10	Basingstoke Town	46	21	8	17	92	72	20	71
11	Hitchin Town	46	19	9	18	67	66	1	66
12	St Neots Town	46	17	13	16	79	79	0	64
13	Frome Town	46	18	7	21	78	96	-18	61
14	Redditch United	46	15	10	21	73	73	0	55
15	Stratford Town	46	15	10	21	68	81	-13	55
16	Biggleswade Town	46	14	11	21	52	63	-11	53
17	Merthyr Town	46	13	14	19	76	98	-22	53
18	Bishop's Stortford	46	14	10	22	74	79	-5	52
19	Dorchester Town	46	13	12	21	62	83	-21	51
20	Farnborough	46	15	6	25	82	120	-38	51
21	Kings Langley	46	8	14	24	63	98	-35	38
22	St Ives Town	46	8	9	29	54	105	-51	33
23	Gosport Borough	46	5	5	36	41	142	-101	19*
24	Dunstable Town	46	4	5	37	27	137	-110	17

Play-Off Semi Finals: King's Lynn Town 3-0 Weymouth | Slough Town 3-1 Kettering Town
Final: King's Lynn Town 1-2 Slough Town

PREMIER DIVISION	1	2	3	4	5	6	7	8	9	10	11	12	13	14	15	16	17	18	19	20	21	22	23	24
1 Banbury United		1-1	1-1	2-1	1-1	5-1	1-2	4-1	3-4	5-0	0-1	1-0	1-1	1-2	1-1	3-3	1-3	3-0	2-2	3-1	1-1	4-0	1-2	1-2
2 Basingstoke Town	3-1		2-0	3-2	5-0	1-1	2-0	4-3	1-3	3-0	3-1	1-0	3-2	1-2	4-3	2-0	3-0	0-0	1-4	3-2	1-0	2-1	6-2	3-3
3 Biggleswade Town	1-1	1-2		2-2	0-3	1-1	0-2	3-0	1-2	2-0	0-1	2-1	0-0	2-2	2-0	2-1	1-0	1-1	3-5	0-2	3-1	4-0	1-2	
4 Bishop's Stortford	0-5	2-0	0-0		1-1	1-0	4-1	2-2	4-0	2-1	0-1	0-3	0-2	2-3	2-0	4-0	3-0	0-3	2-2	4-3	1-2	1-1	1-2	2-3
5 Chesham United	1-3	4-1	2-0	2-1		2-2	2-0	0-0	5-1	3-0	1-3	0-0	2-0	1-3	1-0	13-1	2-0	1-2	1-1	4-0	2-2	1-3	1-1	0-6
6 Dorchester Town	0-2	1-0	2-1	1-0	1-1		1-1	4-0	1-4	7-2	0-1	1-4	4-1	0-2	1-0	1-2	1-0	0-1	0-1	6-0	0-4	1-2	3-0	0-3
7 Dunstable Town	0-5	0-6	0-2	0-5	1-4	0-1		1-0	1-2	0-2	0-4	0-4	1-2	0-0	1-4	0-6	1-1	0-5	0-3	0-0	2-3	2-3	1-2	2-1
8 Farnborough	1-0	4-3	2-1	0-5	2-0	3-3	4-0		5-3	1-2	2-4	4-1	3-4	5-2	0-4	2-2	1-3	0-1	1-2	2-1	2-4	1-4	2-3	2-6
9 Frome Town	0-2	1-0	2-3	2-1	1-3	3-1	3-0	1-1		2-0	0-3	3-4	2-2	0-0	2-1	1-2	1-0	1-4	0-4	0-1	2-2	3-0	0-1	1-4
10 Gosport Borough	0-4	0-8	1-1	1-3	1-5	3-3	1-0	2-4	7-0		0-4	0-3	0-7	1-7	1-2	1-1	2-5	2-3	1-5	0-0	0-1	0-1	0-5	0-4
11 Hereford	3-0	4-1	1-0	2-0	3-0	4-1	2-0	0-1	1-0	5-1		5-0	4-1	0-2	3-0	1-1	5-2	2-0	0-1	4-0	1-0	5-2	1-0	2-0
12 Hitchin Town	0-3	2-1	1-0	0-0	0-0	1-0	1-3	5-1	2-1	0-3		0-0	0-4	6-0	2-0	1-0	1-0	0-1	2-2	2-2	4-0	1-2	3-1	
13 Kettering Town	3-0	3-0	3-1	6-0	3-1	4-3	6-0	6-2	3-0	2-0	1-3	4-1		1-0	1-1	5-0	1-0	4-1	0-0	4-1	3-0	2-0	2-3	2-0
14 King's Lynn Town	1-1	2-1	3-0	2-1	0-1	3-0	5-0	3-1	0-0	2-0	3-2	2-0	2-1		3-2	0-0	3-1	4-0	1-0	1-1	1-1	4-1	2-0	1-1
15 Kings Langley	3-4	1-1	1-1	4-1	0-0	2-2	1-0	0-3	2-7	1-1	3-3	1-2	2-5	0-0		2-2	1-2	1-0	0-2	0-3	4-3	2-0	2-2	2-3
16 Merthyr Town	1-3	1-1	0-2	0-0	1-2	1-1	3-1	3-0	3-4	5-0	0-0	0-0	2-4	0-1	4-1		2-2	2-1	4-5	3-2	1-0	3-1	2-1	0-3
17 Redditch United	2-2	3-0	1-0	2-2	3-1	4-0	5-0	7-1	4-1	4-2	0-2	2-2	0-0	0-1	2-2	1-1		1-0	1-4	4-0	2-2	0-2	3-2	1-2
18 Royston Town	1-1	1-0	4-0	4-2	0-2	3-1	1-1	4-3	3-0	5-0	1-4	2-1	4-3	2-0	4-0	5-1	2-1		0-4	2-1	2-1	1-2	3-0	1-2
19 Slough Town	0-1	1-1	2-1	2-4	2-1	2-0	8-1	5-1	2-1	5-1	2-2	4-0	1-2	2-2	1-1	3-2	4-0	2-1		3-0	2-1	1-1	2-0	3-0
20 St Ives Town	2-2	2-2	1-2	0-1	0-2	1-2	2-1	2-4	2-2	1-0	0-2	1-3	3-4	1-3	1-1	2-3	1-0	1-3	1-4		1-1	2-6	1-2	1-2
21 St Neots Town	3-0	2-1	0-0	2-2	3-1	5-0	2-2	0-1	1-6	0-4	1-3	1-1	2-4	0-5	3-2	5-2	2-1	3-1	3-1	3-1		2-2	1-0	1-2
22 Stratford Town	2-3	0-1	1-0	3-1	1-3	2-0	5-1	2-2	1-2	2-0	1-2	1-2	0-4	1-5	3-1	2-2	0-0	1-1	0-1	3-0	1-1		1-2	0-2
23 Tiverton Town	0-0	3-2	3-1	2-1	1-2	0-0	7-1	2-0	2-2	2-0	2-2	3-1	0-3	1-0	3-2	3-1	1-0	1-2	3-0	2-3	1-2	2-1		2-1
24 Weymouth	1-1	3-2	2-0	1-1	1-0	2-2	2-0	6-0	0-2	5-0	0-2	3-0	3-1	3-1	2-0	3-2	5-0	3-0	1-0	0-1	3-1	1-1	2-0	

SOUTHERN LEAGUE DIVISION EAST LEAGUE TABLE 2017-18

		P	W	D	L	F	A	GD	Pts
1	Beaconsfield Town	42	29	5	8	99	46	53	92
2	AFC Rushden & Diamonds	42	27	10	5	92	25	67	91
3	Hayes & Yeading United	42	26	5	11	103	49	54	83
4	Hartley Wintney	42	26	4	12	96	53	43	82
5	AFC Dunstable	42	23	10	9	80	37	43	79
6	Cambridge City	42	23	8	11	99	53	46	77
7	Kempston Rovers	42	21	10	11	80	68	12	73
8	Bedford Town	42	22	6	14	70	48	22	72
9	Chalfont St Peter	42	20	12	10	56	39	17	72
10	Moneyfields	42	19	12	11	79	63	16	69
11	Thame United	42	20	4	18	84	78	6	64
12	Ashford Town (Middx)	42	16	8	18	81	68	13	56
13	Aylesbury United	42	17	4	21	52	73	-21	52*
14	Marlow	42	13	10	19	54	75	-21	49
15	Uxbridge	42	14	7	21	58	87	-29	49
16	Egham Town	42	13	9	20	54	88	-34	48
17	Northwood	42	10	11	21	54	71	-17	41
18	Hanwell Town	42	9	7	26	48	88	-40	34
19	Fleet Town	42	8	10	24	38	86	-48	34
20	Barton Rovers	42	8	9	25	39	86	-47	33
21	Aylesbury	42	9	6	27	40	88	-48	33
22	Arlesey Town	42	3	5	34	36	123	-87	14

Play-Off Semi Finals: Hartley Wintney 2-0 AFC Dunstable I Hayes & Yeading United 0-1 Cambridge City
Final: Hartley Wintney 1-0 Cambridge City

DIVISION EAST	1	2	3	4	5	6	7	8	9	10	11	12	13	14	15	16	17	18	19	20	21	22
1 AFC Dunstable		0-3	5-0	2-2	2-0	3-0	1-0	2-2	1-0	2-2	0-2	6-1	4-0	6-1	0-1	3-3	2-1	2-1	0-0	2-0	1-0	2-1
2 AFC Rushden & Diamonds	1-0		0-0	1-0	7-1	4-1	5-0	1-2	0-0	2-0	1-0	0-0	7-1	2-0	2-0	0-1	3-1	0-0	2-2	4-0	6-0	1-1
3 Arlesey Town	0-7	1-2		1-3	0-2	0-2	0-0	1-2	0-2	1-6	1-1	2-3	0-0	2-3	1-6	1-9	0-4	0-1	0-4	1-3	2-3	0-2
4 Ashford Town (Middx)	1-3	0-2	3-2		2-0	0-1	1-0	0-2	2-2	1-2	1-1	2-3	10-0	1-4	0-1	4-0	7-1	4-2	2-1	2-2	1-1	4-1
5 Aylesbury	1-2	0-4	1-5	2-2		0-1	0-1	1-3	0-4	1-2	0-2	0-0	1-1	0-3	2-0	0-2	2-2	3-1	0-2	2-3	1-1	3-2
6 Aylesbury United	1-1	0-2	1-0	2-1	1-2		2-3	1-4	0-3	1-6	1-2	4-0	1-1	1-0	0-2	1-0	0-2	1-0	2-2	2-0	7-2	2-2
7 Barton Rovers	0-2	0-2	1-1	1-2	3-1	0-2		2-3	0-1	0-1	0-1	0-1	1-0	1-1	1-3	1-2	2-2	4-0	1-2	1-1	1-1	0-1
8 Beaconsfield Town	4-0	1-1	7-0	5-0	0-3	3-2	0-0		0-0	3-2	1-2	3-1	2-0	2-0	1-2	0-1	2-4	4-0	1-0	2-2	0-1	4-0
9 Bedford Town	0-2	0-1	2-0	1-0	4-1	3-1	6-0	0-1		1-4	2-0	2-1	2-0	1-0	1-1	0-3	5-1	3-2	3-1	0-0	1-0	0-2
10 Cambridge City	0-2	0-1	7-3	1-2	0-1	1-0	0-1	1-2	5-1		0-0	6-1	4-1	3-0	4-1	0-2	1-1	7-1	1-1	1-0	4-2	5-1
11 Chalfont St Peter	1-0	2-2	2-0	2-0	1-0	0-1	1-2	4-2	0-4	1-1		3-0	0-0	0-1	3-1	1-1	1-1	1-1	1-2	2-0	1-2	3-0
12 Egham Town	0-0	2-1	1-2	1-1	4-1	2-0	0-3	1-5	2-1	1-2	0-1		3-0	1-0	1-2	2-0	1-3	2-2	1-2	2-2	1-2	3-3
13 Fleet Town	2-2	0-4	0-2	1-2	2-0	0-1	1-0	0-2	0-1	1-2	1-1	3-0		0-0	0-3	0-4	2-2	2-0	1-4	1-0	4-2	6-0
14 Hanwell Town	0-2	0-1	2-1	2-1	2-3	1-3	4-1	1-5	0-5	2-2	2-3	0-1	2-0		2-4	1-4	1-2	0-0	3-3	1-3	0-2	0-2
15 Hartley Wintney	1-0	2-1	4-1	2-1	4-0	3-4	7-0	0-1	2-0	1-2	1-1	7-1	2-0	5-1		1-6	2-1	3-0	5-1	2-0	2-0	4-0
16 Hayes & Yeading United	0-2	1-0	2-1	1-2	1-1	4-0	5-0	0-2	4-0	3-1	1-2	6-1	3-0	2-2	3-1		3-0	3-0	2-2	4-2	4-2	4-0
17 Kempston Rovers	1-0	1-1	5-0	3-2	2-0	4-0	4-1	4-3	2-1	0-4	0-1	2-2	1-1	1-1	1-0	3-2		2-1	3-1	1-1	0-4	4-1
18 Marlow	1-0	2-4	1-0	1-1	1-0	0-1	2-2	0-1	2-2	3-3	1-1	4-2	1-2	3-1	3-0	3-1	1-2		3-0	1-0	3-1	1-1
19 Moneyfields	1-1	1-3	1-0	2-0	5-2	3-0	5-1	2-4	0-2	1-1	1-0	2-0	1-1	3-1	2-2	2-5	2-1	3-1		2-0	4-1	2-3
20 Northwood	2-2	1-1	3-1	1-7	0-1	3-0	1-1	2-3	1-2	2-3	0-2	0-1	2-1	2-0	3-1	2-0	3-0	1-2	1-1		1-3	0-1
21 Thame United	0-5	0-3	7-1	3-0	2-0	1-5	5-2	1-2	3-1	1-0	4-1	2-3	4-0	3-1	0-3	0-1	1-3	4-0	2-3	3-3		1-0
22 Uxbridge	0-1	1-4	3-2	2-4	2-1	1-0	6-1	1-3	3-1	1-2	0-2	1-2	3-2	1-2	2-2	3-0	0-2	1-2	0-0	2-1	1-5	

SOUTHERN LEAGUE DIVISION WEST LEAGUE TABLE 2017-18

		P	W	D	L	F	A	GD	Pts
1	Taunton Town	42	31	10	1	107	41	66	103
2	Salisbury	42	25	9	8	108	55	53	84
3	Wimborne Town	42	23	8	11	104	57	47	77
4	Evesham United	42	23	7	12	73	53	20	76
5	Swindon Supermarine	42	21	11	10	86	54	32	74
6	Didcot Town	42	21	10	11	89	63	26	73
7	Cirencester Town	42	22	7	13	93	74	19	73
8	Bideford	42	21	9	12	79	58	21	72
9	Bristol Manor Farm	42	20	9	13	83	61	22	69
10	AFC Totton	42	19	9	14	65	49	16	66
11	Winchester City	42	17	10	15	73	66	7	61
12	Kidlington	42	15	12	15	80	64	16	57
13	Cinderford Town	42	14	12	16	81	71	10	54
14	Yate Town	42	14	14	14	72	74	-2	53*
15	Larkhall Athletic	42	13	6	23	66	78	-12	45
16	Mangotsfield United	42	10	11	21	53	86	-33	41
17	Shortwood United	42	10	10	22	63	124	-61	40
18	North Leigh	42	10	8	24	53	84	-31	38
19	Paulton Rovers	42	10	7	25	57	81	-24	37
20	Slimbridge	42	9	8	25	54	130	-76	35
21	Barnstaple Town	42	7	8	27	53	105	-52	29
22	Bishops Cleeve	42	8	3	31	43	107	-64	24*

Play-Off Semi Finals: Evesham United 1-1, 4-5p Swindon Supermarine | Wimborne Town 2-0 Didcot Town
Final: Wimborne Town 0-0, 3-4p Swindon Supermarine

DIVISION WEST		1	2	3	4	5	6	7	8	9	10	11	12	13	14	15	16	17	18	19	20	21	22
1	AFC Totton		3-1	2-3	6-0	3-1	1-1	2-1	2-1	1-1	1-3	2-0	4-0	2-1	0-3	1-3	1-2	1-2	3-1	0-4	1-1	1-0	5-0
2	Barnstaple Town	0-3		1-2	3-2	0-2	1-2	0-2	0-4	0-2	3-3	0-3	1-1	1-5	4-0	0-2	1-3	0-3	1-3	0-2	1-1	1-4	2-3
3	Bideford	2-1	1-1		1-0	3-1	2-2	3-0	1-0	1-3	0-4	4-1	3-3	2-0	2-1	2-2	2-2	3-1	0-1	0-1	1-2	2-0	1-2
4	Bishops Cleeve	1-3	1-5	1-2		0-2	0-3	0-1	1-5	2-3	1-0	0-3	4-0	1-1	3-2	1-3	4-0	1-1	0-5	1-3	1-7	4-2	0-2
5	Bristol Manor Farm	2-3	5-1	1-0	6-0		4-2	2-2	3-3	1-5	1-0	2-1	3-1	1-0	3-1	2-3	3-3	3-0	1-1	1-1	4-1	4-1	1-1
6	Cinderford Town	1-0	1-3	3-4	4-0	2-0		2-3	7-1	1-3	0-2	3-1	4-3	1-1	3-4	1-1	3-4	9-0	1-1	2-3	1-1	2-2	0-0
7	Cirencester Town	3-0	3-1	2-1	3-1	1-1	5-4		1-2	0-1	3-2	1-2	5-1	3-1	2-1	2-3	6-1	4-0	4-2	0-2	1-2	1-0	4-4
8	Didcot Town	0-0	4-2	0-0	1-0	2-0	1-1	4-0		3-0	1-0	4-2	3-4	3-0	3-0	3-1	1-1	4-0	0-0	0-4	4-2	2-4	4-2
9	Evesham United	1-0	2-0	3-0	2-1	1-0	1-0	2-5	0-2		1-3	2-0	1-1	3-2	1-0	1-2	2-2	3-0	3-3	0-3	1-2	1-1	0-1
10	Kidlington	0-0	5-2	1-2	2-0	2-3	4-1	1-1	3-3	0-3		1-2	2-2	2-1	3-0	0-1	3-0	2-2	1-1	2-2	1-3	1-1	2-2
11	Larkhall Athletic	0-1	2-0	0-1	0-2	2-0	0-1	3-3	2-3	2-2	1-1		0-2	5-0	2-1	1-2	3-0	2-2	3-3	2-3	1-3	1-2	1-0
12	Mangotsfield United	1-1	0-3	1-1	2-0	2-1	1-1	1-1	2-0	0-2	2-5	3-1		1-3	1-0	0-5	3-2	1-2	0-3	0-1	1-2	1-1	1-3
13	North Leigh	0-1	5-0	4-3	3-1	2-5	0-3	1-2	0-2	0-2	0-5	1-1	1-0		5-3	2-1	1-2	1-1	0-3	1-1	1-1	1-2	1-4
14	Paulton Rovers	1-1	1-2	1-3	3-0	0-1	1-1	0-3	2-2	2-0	0-1	1-3	2-4	0-1		0-2	3-2	1-2	0-2	2-2	1-0	2-2	2-0
15	Salisbury	2-0	0-1	4-0	0-0	1-1	2-3	8-2	2-1	0-0	6-1	1-2	3-0	2-0	2-2		6-1	5-1	0-2	2-0	2-0	2-2	6-2
16	Shortwood United	1-3	3-3	0-6	2-3	2-2	2-1	0-3	3-3	0-4	0-5	1-0	1-0	2-1	2-3	0-8		2-2	3-1	1-2	0-5	2-4	1-1
17	Slimbridge	0-2	2-2	4-3	1-2	2-1	0-1	1-3	3-6	3-5	3-1	4-2	0-2	0-2	1-4	2-5	1-3		1-3	2-2	1-8	2-0	1-5
18	Swindon Supermarine	1-0	3-0	0-5	4-2	1-0	4-0	2-1	1-0	2-0	2-2	4-2	2-2	1-1	2-1	2-2	5-1	8-0		2-3	0-1	1-1	2-0
19	Taunton Town	2-1	3-0	1-1	4-0	2-1	1-0	2-1	3-1	1-0	3-2	5-2	2-1	1-0	3-0	4-1	3-3	9-0	1-0		3-3	4-1	1-4
20	Wimborne Town	1-1	5-2	2-2	3-1	1-3	0-1	5-1	0-1	3-4	1-0	1-3	3-1	5-0	4-1	4-2	5-2	5-0	3-0	1-1		3-0	4-2
21	Winchester City	1-1	1-1	2-3	2-1	1-2	2-0	1-2	2-0	2-0	0-1	3-1	3-0	2-0	1-1	4-5	5-1	3-0	3-2	0-5	1-0		4-1
22	Yate Town	0-1	3-3	0-1	2-0	1-3	2-2	2-2	2-2	2-1	3-1	3-1	1-1	3-3	0-4	0-1	3-0	1-1	2-0	0-2	2-0	1-1	

LEAGUE CHALLENGE CUP 2017-18

HOLDERS: HAYES & YEADING UNITED

PRELIMINARY ROUND

Northwood	v	Egham Town	1-3	52

ROUND ONE

Kempston Rovers	v	King's Lynn Town	3-1	101
Beaconsfield Town	v	Slough Town	2-2, 5-3p	186
Cambridge City	v	St Ives Town	6-2	193
Dorchester Town	v	Salisbury	1-2	249
Hitchin Town	v	Bishop's Stortford	4-2	138
AFC Dunstable	v	Dunstable Town	1-1, 3-1p	84
AFC Rushden & Diamonds	v	St Neots Town	1-0	225
Arlesey Town	v	Biggleswade Town	0-1	91
Barnstaple Town	v	Tiverton Town	0-0, 3-2p	102
Barton Rovers	v	Royston Town	0-3	58
Bedford Town	v	Kettering Town	2-4	152
Bideford	v	Taunton Town	2-2, 4-5p	137
Chalfont St Peter	v	Egham Town	1-1, 7-6p	56
Chesham United	v	Aylesbury	3-0	108
Cinderford Town	v	Slimbridge	3-2	69
Cirencester Town	v	Larkhall Athletic	1-2	55
Didcot Town	v	Banbury United	2-2, 5-4p	124
Fleet Town	v	Basingstoke Town	2-6	139
Gosport Borough	v	Moneyfields	2-2, 3-4p	199
Hanwell Town	v	Uxbridge	2-1	87
Hayes & Yeading United	v	Ashford Town (Middx)	3-0	103
Marlow	v	Aylesbury United	4-2	70
Paulton Rovers	v	Frome Town	1-2	168
Redditch United	v	Bishops Cleeve	9-1	98
Shortwood United	v	Merthyr Town	7-2	48
Thame United	v	Kings Langley	0-4	44
Weymouth	v	Wimborne Town	3-0	205
Winchester City	v	AFC Totton	1-4	107
Yate Town	v	Bristol Manor Farm	1-3	119
Farnborough	v	Hartley Wintney	1-6	152
Kidlington	v	Swindon Supermarine	3-0	52
Evesham United	v	Stratford Town	4-7	159

ROUND TWO

Barnstaple Town	v	Taunton Town	2-4	105
Biggleswade Town	v	Cambridge City	2-1	97
Chesham United	v	AFC Dunstable	4-2	84
Kings Langley	v	Hitchin Town	2-4	126
Moneyfields	v	Basingstoke Town	1-4	94
Redditch United	v	Stratford Town	3-0	111
Royston Town	v	Kempston Rovers	6-1	64
Frome Town	v	Bristol Manor Farm	2-1	103
Kidlington	v	Didcot Town	1-1, 2-3p	78
AFC Rushden & Diamonds	v	Kettering Town	3-2	615
Hanwell Town	v	Egham Town	3-5	48
Hartley Wintney	v	Marlow	1-2	94
Hayes & Yeading United	v	Slough Town	3-1	131
Shortwood United	v	Cinderford Town	1-3	41
AFC Totton	v	Weymouth	0-1	146
Larkhall Athletic	v	Salisbury	4-3	95

ROUND THREE

AFC Rushden & Diamonds	v	Hitchin Town	0-0, 3-4p	222
Basingstoke Town	v	Marlow	1-3	110
Biggleswade Town	v	Kempston Rovers	0-2	65
Cinderford Town	v	Redditch United	1-4	66
Egham Town	v	Hayes & Yeading United	1-1, 2-4p	83
Weymouth	v	Larkhall Athletic	0-1	174
Frome Town	v	Taunton Town	HW	
Didcot Town	v	Chesham United	0-0, 5-4p	82

QUARTER-FINALS

Didcot Town	v	Redditch United	3-0	85
Hitchin Town	v	Kempston Rovers	2-0	105
Hayes & Yeading United	v	Marlow	6-5	94
Frome Town	v	Larkhall Athletic	0-1	86

SEMI-FINALS

Hitchin Town	v	Hayes & Yeading United	1-1, 4-2p	186
Daniel Webb 68		*Immanuelson Duku 58*		
Didcot Town	v	Larkhall Athletic	0-0, 4-2p	108

FINAL

Hitchin Town	v	Didcot Town	1-0	401
Connor Vincent 9				

BANBURY UNITED MATCH RESULTS 2017-18

Date	Comp	H/A	Opponents	Att:	Result	Goalscorers	Pos	No.
Aug 12	SPL	H	Dorchester Town	369	W 5 - 1	Winters 8 McDonagh 10 Nash 22 Carnell 52 Louis 62	2	1
15	SPL	A	Chesham United	335	W 3 - 1	Winters 24 McDonagh 59 Louis 90	1	2
19	SPL	A	Hltchin Town	391	W 3 - 0	Nash 10 Louis 62 Carnell 70	1	3
26	SPL	H	Bishops Stortford	453	W 2 - 1	Louis 38 Shamsi 70	1	4
28	SPL	A	Dunstable Town	197	W 5 - 0	Louis 37 Winters 54 Pond 71 82 McDonagh 74	1	5
Sept 2	FAC 1Q	H	Tiverton Town	436	W 4 - 2	Louis 63 Bond 65 Sharmei 72 McDonagh 85	1	6
9	SPL	H	Frome Town	453	L 3 - 4	Bradbury 17 Louis 87 Howards 90	3	7
12	SPL	H	Redditch United	337	L 1 - 3	Louis 90	7	8
16	FAC 2Q	H	Thatcham Town	450	W 2 - 0	Parnell 42 Pond 47		9
23	SPL	A	Kings Langley	252	W 4 - 3	McDonagh 55 Camell 58 Louis 62 Self 65	6	10
26	SPL	A	Kettering Town	653	L 0 - 3		6	11
30	FAC 3Q	H	Shildon	700	L 2 - 3	Winters 29 Johnson 82		12
Oct 7	SPL	A	Basingstoke Town	486	L 1 - 3	Winters 45	11	13
10	SPL	H	Hereford	1011	L 0 - 1		11	14
17	SPL	A	Gosport Borough	230	L 4 - 4	Louis 3 Shsmsi 7 Bradbury 16 McDonagh 81	9	15
21	SPL	A	Dorchester Town	396	W 2 - 0	Louis 4 Shamsi 65	8	16
24	SPL	H	Chesham United	384	D 1 - 1	Louis 9	9	17
28	FAT 1Q	H	Tiverton Town	248	D 2 - 2	Shamsi 15 Louis 45		18
31	FAT 1Qr	H	Tiverton Town	230	W 3 - 2	Hawtin 10 85 McDonagh 101 (aet)		19
Nov 4	SPL	H	Tiverton Town	413	L 1 - 2	Peake-Pijnen 55	10	20
7	SPL	H	Kings Lynn Town	277	L 1 - 2	Pond 66	10	21
11	FAT 2Q	A	Farnborough	269	D 3 - 3	Carnell 56 McDonagh 59 67		22
18	SPL	A	St Neots Town	336	D 1 - 1	McDonagh 31	10	23
21	SPL	H	Slough Town	325	D 2 - 2	Sandy 24 Howards 87	10	24
25	FAT 2Qr	H	Farnborough	380	L 2 - 3	Louis (2)		25
28	SPL	H	Kettering Town	301	D 1 - 1	Louis 71 (pen)	12	26
Dec 2	SPL	A	St Ives Town	201	D 2 - 2	Self 35 McDonagh 89	13	27
5	SPL	A	Merthyr Town	379	W 3 - 1	McDonagh 23 Carnell 27 Howards 88	10	28
9	SPL	H	Royston Town	265	W 3 - 0	McDonagh 54 Howards 63 Louis 88	8	29
16	SPL	H	Weymouth	377	L 1 - 2	Baggie 45 (og)	9	30
22	SPL	A	Biggleswade Town	162	D 1 - 1	Carnell 88	9	31
26	SPL	H	Dunstable Town391	391	L 1 - 2	Self 14	11	32
Jan 1	SPL	A	Stratford Town	376	W 3 - 2	Winters 32 Johnson 51 Howards 82	9	33
6	SPL	H	Hitchin Town	369	W 1 - 0	Self 47	9	34
9	SPL	A	Farnborough	216	L 0 - 1		9	35
13	SPL	A	Bishop's Stortford	301	W 5 - 0	Sandy 6 30 McDonagh 32 Carnell 50 Winters 76	7	36
16	SPL	A	Redditch United	270	D 2 - 2	Johnson 50 Bradbury 71	7	37
27	SPL	A	Hereford	2932	L 0 - 3		10	38
Feb 3	SPL	H	Gosport Borough	342	W 5 - 0	Sandy 45 (pen) JOHNSON 3 (48 58 74) Self 62	10	39
6	SPL	H	Basingstoke Town	255	D 1 - 1	Carnell 88	10	40
10	SPL	A	Slough Town	514	W 1 - 0	Johnson 66	8	41
17	SPL	A	Kings Lynn Town	1042	D 1 - 1	Self 71	8	42
24	SPL	H	Bedford Town	315	D 1 - 1	Sandy 79 (pen)	8	43
Mar 10	SPL	H	Farnborough	373	W 4 - 1	SANDY 4 (32 46 75 (pen) 89)	8	44
24	SPL	H	St Ives Town	366	W 3 - 1	Self 9 Johnson 72 Winters 81	8	45
April 7	SPL	A	Biggleswade Town	348	D 1 - 1	Carnell 64	9	46
10	SPL	A	Royston Town	173	D 1 - 1	Wright 60	9	47
12	SPL	H	Stratford Town	302	W 4 - 0	Sandy 16 (pen) Johnson 45 Howards 47 Awadh 75	9	48
14	SOL	A	Weymouth	895	D 1 - 1	Johnson 42	9	49
17	SPL	A	St Neots Town	166	L 0 - 3		9	50
21	SPL	H	Merthyr Town	512	D 3 - 3	Howards 50 69 Sandy 75	9	51
25	SPL	A	Frome Town	152	W 2 - 0	Wise 83 Camell 86	8	52
28	SPL	A	Tiverton Town	283	D 0 - 0		9	53

GOALSCORERS	SG	CSG	Pens	Hat tricks	Total		SG	CSG	Pens	Hat tricks	Total
2016-17 Johnson					15	Bradbury	3				3
Louis	16	8	1		17	Hawtin	1				2
McDonagh	13	2			14	Nash	2				2
Sandy	7	2	3	1	11	Awadh					1
Carnell	10				10	Bond					1
Johnson	8	2		1	10	Opponents					1
Howards	7	2			8	Parnell					1
Winters	8	2			8	Peake-Pijnell					1
Self	7				7	Wise					1
Shamsi	5				5	Wright					1
Pond	3				4						

BASINGSTOKE TOWN MATCH RESULTS 2017-18

Date	Comp	H/A	Opponents	Att:	Result	Goalscorers	Pos	No.
Aug 12	SPL	H	Frome Town	296	L 1 - 3	Wright 49 (pen)	20	1
14	SPL	A	Dorchester Town	469	L 0 - 1		20	2
19	SPL	A	Kettering Town	557	L 0 - 3		22	3
26	SPL	H	Chesham United	218	W 5 0	Wright 5 35 (pen) Jarvis 59 62 Smart 75	17	4
28	SPL	A	Gosport Borough	271	W 8 - 0	Wright 2 40 (pen) Smart 16 48 McKnight 70 91 Sanders 75 (og) Collier 78	14	5
Sept 2	FAC 1Q	H	Hartley Wintney	554	D 2 - 2	Wright 11 Johnson-Schuster 67		6
5	FAC 1Qr	A	Hartley Wintney	620	L 0 - 1			7
9	SPL	H	St Ives Town	248	W 3 - 2	Smart 9 Wright 35 Deadfield 80	11	8
12	SPL	H	Merthyr Town	203	W 2 - 0	Smart 67 77	10	9
16	SPL	A	Tiverton Town	220	L 2 - 3	Smart 46 Kennedy 94	10	10
23	SPL	A	Hitchin Town	403	L 1 - 2	Collier 83	12	11
26	SPL	A	Weymouth	487	L 2 - 3	Wright 4 Smart 63	13	12
30	SPL	H	Redditch United	286	W 3 - 0	Wright 75 (pen) Johnson-Schuster 78 Bunting 82	11	13
Oct 7	SPL	H	Banbury United	486	W 3 - 1	Argent 5 Artwell 76 90	10	14
14	SPL	A	Bishop's Stortford	353	L 0 - 2		11	15
21	SPL	A	Frome Town	218	L 0 - 1		16	16
24	SPL	A	Dorchester Town	257	D 1 - 1	Carmichael 23 (og)	15	17
28	FAT 1Q	A	Dorchester Town	290	L 1 - 2	Argent 90		18
Nov 4	SPL	A	Kings Langley	264	D 1 - 1	Wright 90 (pen)	15	19
11	SPL	H	Biggleswade Town	317	W 2 - 0	Smart 11 Bunting 52	14	20
18	SPL	H	Kings Lynn Town	303	L 1 - 2	Wright 49 (pen)	15	21
25	SPL	A	St Neots Town	233	L 1 - 2	Argent 24 (pen)	16	22
28	SPL	H	Weymouth	308	D 3 - 3	Argent 30 Smart 40 Wright 56	17	23
Dec 9	SPL	A	Hereford	2794	L 1 - 4	Bayliss 4	19	24
16	SPL	A	Dunstable Town	111	W 6 - 0	ARGENT 5 (8 (pen) 21 63 85 90) Bennett 52	18	25
19	SPL	A	Merthyr Tydfil	302	D 1 - 1	Bunting 67	18	26
22	SPL	A	Royston Town	293	D 0 - 0		17	27
26	SPL	H	Gosport Borough	325	W 3 - 0	Bunting 33 76 Smart 63	16	28
Jan 1	SPL	A	Farnborough	395	L 3 - 4	Smart 2 Demuria 52 Wright 60	17	29
6	SPL	H	Kettering Town	422	W 3 - 2	Smart 29 Bunting 65 90	16	30
13	SPL	A	Chesham United	2892	L 1 - 4	Bunting 68	16	31
27	SPL	A	Tiverton Town	318	W 6 - 2	ARGENT 5 (9 pen 49 pen 54 72 74) Bennett 81	15	32
Feb 3	SPL	A	Biggleswade Town	135	W 2 - 1	Bunting 38 70	15	33
6	SPL	A	Banbury United	255	D 1 - 1	Wright 84	15	34
17	SPL	A	Redditch United	312	L 0 - 3		15	35
20	SPL	H	Stratford Town	194	W 2 - 1	Smart 42 Wright 79	15	36
24	SPL	H	Hitchin Town	312	W 1 - 0	Demuria 5	13	37
Mar 5	SPL	A	Slough Town	471	D 1 - 1	McKnight 70	12	38
10	SPL	H	St Neots Town	284	W 1 - 0	Smart 53	10	39
17	SPL	H	Hereford	704	W 3 - 1	Argent 2 90 Hollamby 76	10	40
24	SPL	A	Slough Town	503	L 1 - 4	Smart 11	10	41
27	SPL	A	Kings Lynn Town	581	L 1 - 2	Deadfield 35	10	42
Apr 2	SPL	H	Farnborough	358	W 4 - 3	Bunting 7 26 Smart 29 Deadfield 60	10	43
7	SPL	A	Royston Town	314	L 0 - 1		11	44
14	SPL	H	Dunstable Town	310	W 2 - 0	Bayliss 54 Bunting 59	11	45
17	SPL	H	Biushop's Stortford	211	W 3 - 2	Bunting 21 Smart 37 Deadfield 73	11	46
21	SPL	H	Stafford Rangers	266	W 1 - 0	Macauley 90	10	47
26	SPL	A	St Ives Town	76	D 2 - 2	Bunting 22 47	10	48
28	SPL	H	Kings Langley	357	W 4 - 3	McKnight 8 83 Bunting 44 Deadfield 81	10	49

GOALSCORERS	SG	CSG	Pens	Hat tricks	Total		SG	CSG	Pens	Hat tricks	Total
2016-17 *Jarvis*					13	Demuria	2				2
Smart	17	3			18	Jarvis	1				2
Bunting	12	2			17	Johnson-Schuster	2				2
Argent	7	2	2	2	16	Bayliss	2				2
Wright	13	4	6		15	Opponents					2
Deadfield	5				5	Hollamby					1
McKnight	1				5	Kennedy					1
Artwell	2				2	Macauley					1
Bennett	2				2						
Collier	2				2						

BIGGLESWADE TOWN MATCH RESULTS 2017-18

Date	Comp	H/A	Opponents	Att:	Result	Goalscorers	Pos	No.
Aug 12	SPL	H	Chesham United	202	L 0 - 3		20	1
15	SPL	A	St Ives Town	184	W 2 - 1	Hill 7 Montgomery 85 (og)	12	2
19	SPL	A	Frome Town	197	W 3 - 2	Miller 11 (og) Bowen 28 Hill 57	8	3
26	SPL	H	Hitchin Town	379	W 2 - 1	Bowen 31 Penfold 61	6	4
28	SPL	H	Bishop's Stortford	312	D 0 - 0		8	5
Sept 2	FAC 2Q	A	North Leigh	92	D 2 - 2	Bowen 20 Parker 30		6
5	FAC 2Qr	H	North Leigh	113	W 3 - 2	Bowen 23 Perry 53 Daniel 58		7
9	SPL	A	Gosport Borough	162	W 2 - 0	Daniel 44 Perry 89	8	8
12	SPL	H	St Neots Town	201	W 2 - 0	Bowen 4 44	6	9
16	FAC 3Q	H	East Thurrock Town	191	L 0 - 1			10
23	SPL	A	Redditch Town	244	L 0 - 1		8	11
26	SPL	A	Kings Lynn Town	589	L 0 - 3		8	12
30	SPL	A	Farnborough	201	W 3 - 0	BAILEY 3 (42 66 76)	9	13
Oct 7	SPL	H	Slough Town	760	L 1 - 2	Hill 24	9	14
10	SPL	A	Kettering Town	352	D 0 - 0		7	15
17	SPL	H	Chesham United	210	L 0 - 2		13	16
21	SPL	A	St Ives Town	172	L 0 - 2		13	17
28	FAT 1Q	H	Wingate & Finchley	144	L 0 - 5			18
Nov.4.	SPL	A	Dorchester Town	401	L 1 - 2	Burnett 78	16	19
11	SPL	A	Basingstoke Town	317	L 0 - 2		16	20
14	SPL	A	St Neots Town	138	D 0 - 0		16	21
18	SPL	H	Kings Langley	186	W 2 - 0	Brooks 60 76	15	22
21	SPL	H	Royston Town	143	D 1 - 1	Hall 6	14	23
25	SPL	A	Weymouth	530	L 0 - 2		15	24
28	SPL	H	Kings Lynn Town	155	D 2 - 2	Bailey 4 Brooks 42	16	25
Dec 2	SPL	A	Merthyr Town	488	W 2 - 0	Brooks 72 77	14	26
9	SPL	H	Tiverton Town	115	W 4 - 0	BROOKS 3 (13 17 65 pen) Hoyle 67	13	27
16	SPL	A	Stratford Town	183	L 0 - 1		14	28
22	SPL	H	Banbury United	162	D 1 - 1	Parker 52	13	29
26	SPL	H	Bishops Stortford	250	D 2 - 2	Fielding 5 Hall 53	13	30
Jan 1	SPL	A	Dunstable Town	141	W 2 - 0	Bowen 32 Burnett 80		31
6	SPL	A	Frome Town	175	L 1 - 2	Burnett 75	14	32
13	SPL	A	Hitchin Town	658	W 1 - 0	Hicks 25	13	33
27	SPL	A	Kettering Town	597	L 1 - 3	Daniel 74	13	34
Feb 3	SPL	H	Basingstoke Town	135	L 1 - 2	Parker 4	15	35
10	SPL	A	Hereford	2376	L 0 - 1		16	36
17	SPL	A	Farnborough	261	L 1 - 2	Hicks 22	18	37
24	SPL	H	Redditch Town	151	W 1 - 0	Bowen 37	17	38
Mar 10	SPL	H	Weymouth	205	L 1 - 2	Dennis 78 (og)	18	39
24	SPL	H	Merthyr Town	202	W 2 - 1	Hicks 8 60	18	40
30	SPL	A	Gosport Borough	289	D 1 - 1	Hall 80	17	41
Apr 7	SPL	A	Banbury United	348	D 1 - 1	Parker 84	16	42
10	SPL	A	Slough Town	159	L 3 - 5	Hicks 54 Hall 58 Kaziboni 74	16	43
12	SPL	A	Kings Langley	130	D 1 - 1	Bailey 65	15	44
14	SPL	H	Stratford Town	125	W 3 - 1	Bowen 42 Bailey 62 Griffith 74	14	45
17	SPL	H	Hereford	740	L 0 - 1		14	46
19	SPL	A	Tiverton Town	126	L 1 - 3	Bowen 86 (pen)	14	47
21	SPL	A	Royston Town	256	L 0 - 4		16	48
24	SPL	A	Dunstable Town	121	L 0 - 2		16	49
28	SPL	H	Dorchester Town	159	D 1 - 1	Hall 23	16	50

GOALSCORERS	SG	CSG	Pens	Hat tricks	Total		SG	CSG	Pens	Hat tricks	Total
2016-17 Effiong					23	Parker	3				3
Bowen	8	2	1		10	Perry	2				2
Brooks	4	3	1	1	8	Fielding					1
Bailey	4		1		6	Griffith					1
Hall	5				5	Hicks					1
Hicks	3				5	Hoyle					1
Burnett	3				3	Kaziboni					1
Daniel	3	2			3	Penfold					1
Hill	3				3						
Opponents	3				3						

BISHOP'S STORTFORD MATCH RESULTS 2017-18

Date	Comp	H/A	Opponents	Att:	Result	Goalscorers	Pos	No.
Aug 12	SPL	A	Tiverton Town	253	L 1 - 2	Williams 52	15	1
15	SPL	H	Kings Lynn Town	356	L 2 - 3	Williams 43 Foxley 90	21	2
19	SPL	H	Weymouth	288	L 2 - 3	Williams 1 Foxley 74	21	3
26	SPL	A	Banbury United	453	L 1 - 2	Williams 29	23	4
28	SPL	H	Biggleswade	312	D 0 - 0		22	5
Sept 2	FAC 1Q	A	Potters Bar Town	181	L 0 - 1			6
9	SPL	A	Merthyr Town	438	D 0 - 0		22	7
12	SPL	H	Kings Langley	238	W 2 - 0	Foxley 26 Williams 64	17	8
23	SPL	A	Frome Town	225	L 1 - 2	Foxley 18	20	9
26	SPL	A	Dunstable Town	105	W 5 - 0	Akinyemi 2 WILLIAMS 3 (11 16 69) Hughes 42	19	10
Oct 7	SPL	A	Gosport Borough	262	W 3 - 1	Hyde-Skerritt 21 71 Hughes 35	18	11
10	SPL	H	Chesham United	234	D 1 - 1	Hughes 71	18	12
14	SPL	H	Basingstoke Town	353	W 2 - 0	Moncur 24 Akinyemi 67	15	13
17	SPL	A	St Ives Town	162	W 1 - 0	Foxley 53	14	14
21	SPL	H	Tiverton Town	322	L 1 - 2	Robinson 86	17	15
24	SPL	A	Kings Lynn Town	856	L 1 - 2	Moncur 26	18	16
28	FAT 1Q	H	Hanwell Town	205	W 4 - 0	Duffey (og) 44 Akinyemi 78 Richefonde 88 Williams 90		17
31	SPL	H	Kettering Town	355	L 0 - 2		18	18
Nov 4	SPL	A	Stratford Town	184	L ! - 3	Taylor 86	18	19
11	FAT 2Q	A	Lewes	568	L 0 - 2			20
14	SPL	A	Kings Langley	181	L 1 - 4	Akinyemi 3	18	21
18	SPL	H	Farnborough	252	D 2 - 2	Williams 67 Westcott 94	18	22
25	SPL	A	Redditch United	258	D 2 - 2	Akinyemi 40 Apostolopoulos 72 (og)	19	23
28	SPL	H	Dunstable Town	205	W 4 - 1	Moncur 31 Ager 48 Williams 58 Robinson 84	18	24
Dec 2	SPL	H	St Neots Town	307	L 1 - 2	Westcott 31	18	25
9	SPL	A	Slough Town	551	W 4 - 2	Fraser 6 (og) Williams 47 90 Clifford 63	17	26
19	SPL	H	Hitchin Town	232	L 0 - 3		17	27
22	SPL	H	Dorchester Town	228	W 1 - 0	Foxley 83	16	28
26	SP	A	Biggleswade Town	250	D 2 - 2	Williams 34 (pen) Ekpiteta 72	17	29
Jan 1	SPL	H	Royston Town	377	L 0 - 3		19	30
6	SPL	H	Weymouth	730	D 1 1	Foxley 73	15	31
13	SPL	H	Banbury United	301	L 0 - 5		20	32
27	SPL	H	Chesham United	282	L 1 - 2	Cureton 39	20	33
Feb 3	SPL	H	St Ives Town	307	W 4 - 3	Akinyemi 18 54 Cureton 56 Ekpiteta 74	19	34
6	SPL	A	Hereford	1772	L 0 - 2		19	35
17	SPL	A	Kettering Town	558	L 0 - 6		20	36
24	SPL	H	Frome Town	231	W 4 - 0	Akinyemi 16 82 Cureton 70 79	20	37
Mar 10	SPL	H	Redditch United	242	W 3 - 0	Expiteta 60 Cureton 68 Hughes 70	19	38
13	SPL	H	Gosport Borough	211	W 2 - 1	Westcott 56 Foxley 70	19	39
17	SPL	H	Slough Town	289	D 2 - 2	Mason 53 Foxley 81	19	40
24	SPL	H	St Neots Town	280	D 2 - 2	Foxley 44 Casey 86	19	41
Apr 2	SPL	A	Royston Town	387	L 2 - 4	Hughes 20 Cureton 84	19	42
7	SPL	A	Dorchester Town	368	L 0 - 1		19	43
11	SPL	A	Farnborough	169	W 5 - 0	Robinson 45 Foxley 49 59 Cureton 52 90	18	44
14	SPL	H	Hereford	738	L 0 - 1		18	45
17	SPL	A	Basingstoke Town	211	L 2 - 3	Hughes 67 Ekpiteta 85	18	46
21	SPL	A	Hitchin Town	431	L 0 - 1		20	47
24	SPL	H	Merthyr Town	177	W 4 - 0	Mason 12 Foxley 41 88 Cureton 61	18	48
28	SPL	H	Stratford Town	307	D 1 - 1	Robinson 90	18	49

GOALSCORERS	SG	CSG	Pens	Hat tricks	Total		SG	CSG	Pens	Hat tricks	Total
2016-17 Akinwande, Callander & Greene					3	Westcott	3				3
Foxley	11	3			14	Mason					2
Williams	11	4	1	1	14	Hyde-Skerrit	1				2
Akinyemi	7				9	Ager					1
Cureton	5				9	Casey					1
Hughes	5	3			6	Clifford					1
Ekpiteta	4				4						
Robinson	3				4						
Moncur	3				3						
Opponents					3						

CHESHAM UNITED MATCH RESULTS 2017-18

Date	Comp	H/A	Opponents	Att:	Result	Goalscorers	Pos	No.
Aug 12	SPL	A	Biggleswade Town	202	W 3-0	Osobu 29 72 Cathline 90	3	1
15	SPL	H	Banbury United	335	L 1-3	Bush 61	10	2
19	SPL	H	Tiverton Town	269	D 1-1	Short 69		3
26	SPL	A	Basingstoke Town	218	L 0-5		16	4
28	SPL	H	Kings Langley	343	W 1-0	Bunting 88	13	5
Sept 2	FAC 1Q	A	Great Yarmouth Town	277	W 2-0	Hutton 55 Bush 85		6
9	SPL	A	Redditch United	221	L 1-3	Bevans 25	15	7
12	SPL	H	Dunstable Town	193	W 2-0	Swales 5 McGleish 81	14	8
16	FAC 2Q	A	Needham Market	166	L 0-2			9
23	SPL	A	Kettering Town	598	L 1-3	Bevans 54	16	10
26	SPL	A	Stratford Town	178	W 3-1	Iaciofano 52 Toomey 60 65		11
Oct 7	SPL	H	Royston Town	412	L 1-2	Iaciofano 72	17	12
10	SPL	A	Bishops Stortford	234	D 1-1	Iaciofano 31	16	13
14	SPL	A	Dorchester Town	380	D 1-1	Toomey 16	16	14
17	SPL	H	St Neots Town	192	D 2-2	Parr 12 (og) Bush 81	17	15
21	SPL	H	Biggleswade Town	210	W 2-0	Crilley 14 Toomey 80	14	16
24	SPL	A	Banbury United	384	D 1-1	Toomey 34	14	17
28	FAT 1Q	A	Hayes & Yeading United	182	W 3-0	IACIOFENO 3 (20 26 55)		18
Nov 4	SPL	A	Kings Lynn Town	648	W 1-0	Iaciofano 60	14	19
11	FAT 2Q	H	Hitchin Town	297	W 3-1	Toomey 42 55 Crilley 90		20
Nov 14	SPL	A	Dunstable Town	93	W 4-1	Murphy 18 Faciofano 41 86 Toomey 87	11	21
18	SPL	H	Merthyr Town	230	W 13-1	Bevans 2(p) Murphy 6 33 IACIOFANO 4 (13 34 60 67) Crilley 28 TOOMEY 3 (15 36 40) Bush 50 Hutton 64	8	22
21	SPL	H	Farnborough	187	D 0-0		5	23
25	FAT 3Q	H	Gloucester City	245	W 2-1	Hutton 64 Swales 85		24
28	SPL	H	Stratford Town	151	L 1-3	Crilley 37	9	25
Dec 2	SPL	A	Weymouth	602	L 0-1		11	26
4	SPL	H	Frome Town	174	W 5-1	Bush 3 11 Crilley 18 Iaciofano 79 McGleish 86	8	27
19	FAT 1	H	Weston-s-Mare	193	L 0-2			28
22	SPL	H	Hereford	554	L 1-3	Bevans 79	11	29
26	SPL	A	Kings Langley	317	D 0-0		12	30
Jan 1	SPL	H	Slough Town	520	D 1-1	Shamsi 90	14	31
6	SPL	A	Tiverton Town	201	W 2-1	Watkins 45 Bush 66	12	32
13	SPL	H	Basingstoke Town	292	W 4-1	Swales 23 Bush 31 39 Murphy 72	10	33
20	SPL	A	Royston United	246	W 2-0	Louis 33 77 (pen)	9	34
23	SPL	A	Gosport Borough	211	W 5-1	Hutton 21 Toomey 25 69 Louis 59 (pen) Dhillon 85	7	35
27	SPL	H	Bishops Stortford	282	W 2-1	Toomey 57 Hutton 66	6	36
30	SPL	H	St Ives Town	211	W 4-0	Louis 22 37 Crilley 33 Swales 73	5	37
Feb 3	SPL	A	St Neots Town	239	L 1-3	McDermott 47 (og)	7	38
10	SPL	H	Dorchester Town	234	D 2-2	Crilley 40 Shamsi 82	7	39
12	SPL	A	Hitchin Town	281	D 0-0		6	40
17	SPL	A	Frome Town	211	W 3-1	Green 40 58 Toomey 83	5	41
24	SPL	H	Kettering Town	409	W 2 0	Toomey 68 Bush 79	5	42
Mar 10	SPL	H	Hitchin Town	305	D 0-0		6	43
24	SPL	H	Weymouth	402	L 0-6		7	44
31	SPL	H	Redditch United	231	W 2-0	Louis 18 Bush 90	7	45
Apr 2	SPL	A	Slough Town	784	L 1-2	Swales 10	7	46
7	SPL	A	Hereford	2704	L 0-3		8	47
10	SPL	A	Merthyr Town	305	W 2-1	Louis 9 Swales 70	7	48
14	SPL	H	Gosport Borough	352	W 3-0	Louis 8 Harper 77 (og) Bevans 90 (pen)	7	49
21	SPL	A	Farnborough	252	L 0-2		8	50
24	SPL	A	St Ives Town	70	W 2-0	Bates 28 Bevans 73	8	51
28	SPL	H	Kings Lynn Town	341	D 1-1	Bush 55	8	52

GOALSCORERS	SG	CSG	Pens	Hat tricks	Total		SG	CSG	Pens	Hat tricks	Total
2016-17 *Pearce*					16	Dhillon	2				2
Toomey	11	2		1	16	Green		1			2
Iaciofano	8	3	2		14	McGleish	2				2
Bush	10	2			12	Osobu	1				2
Louis	6	2	2		8	Shamsi	2				2
Crilley	7				7	Bates					1
Bevans	6		1		6	Bunting					1
Hutton	5				5	Cathline					1
Swales	5		1		5	Short					1
Murphy	3				4	Watkins					1
Opponents					3						

DORCHESTER TOWN MATCH RESULTS 2017-18

Date	Comp	H/A	Opponents	Att:	Result	Goalscorers	Pos	No.
Aug 12	SPL	A	Banbury United	369	L 1 - 5	Jerrard 75 (pen)	23	1
14	SPL	H	Basingstoke Town	469	W 1 - 0	Griggs 61	4	2
19	SPL	H	Kings Lynn Town	371	L 0 - 2		18	3
26	SPL	A	Redditch United	241	L 0 - 4		19	4
28	SPL	H	Weymoutth	1505	L 0 - 3		20	5
Sept 2	FAC 2Q	A	AFC Portchester	391	L 0 - 1			6
9	SPL	A	St Neots Town	178	L 0 - 5		23	7
11	SPL	H	Frome Town	349	L 1 - 4	Lowes 39		8
23	SPL	A	Dunstable Town	91	W 1 - 0	Lanahan 46	19	9
27	SPL	A	Farnborough	222	D 3 - 3	Lanahan 3 16 Lowes 45	21	10
Oct 7	SPL	A	Hereford	2596	L 1 - 4	Oates 9 (og)	20	11
Oct 9	SPL	H	Gosport Borough	325	W 7 - 2	RODRIGUEZ 3 (19 4171) Carmichael 23 Jerrard 43 Panesar-Dower 72 Bowles 89	20	12
14	SPL	H	Chesham United	380	D 1 - 1	Egan 90	20	13
17	SPL	A	Kings Langley	176	D 2 - 2	Lowes 49 64	20	14
21	SPL	H	Banbury United	396	L 0 - 2		20	15
24	SPL	A	Basingstoke Town	257	D 1 - 1	Rodriguez 72	19	16
28	FAT 1Q	H	Basingstoke Town	290	W 2 - 1	Ormrod 52 69 (pen)		17
Nov 4	SPL	A	Biggleswade Town	401	W 2 - 1	Rose 43 Lanahan 90	20	18
11	FAT 2Q	H	Heybridge Swifts	319	L 1 - 2	Ormorod 3		19
15	SPL	A	Frome Town	234	L 1 - 3	Baghdadi 38	20	20
18	SPL	H	Kettering Town	410	W 4 - 1	Lowes 7 Lanahan 15 Jerrard 68 Baghdadi 78	19	21
25	SPL	A	Merthyr Town	923	D 1 - 1	Davies 38	20	22
Dec 2	SPL	A	Royston Town	198	L 1 - 3	Blair 20	20	23
4	SPL	H	Stratford Town	276	L 1 - 2	Lowes 61	20	24
9	SPL	H	Hitchin Town	318	L 1 - 4	Baghdadi 38	20	25
16	SPL	H	St Ives Town	360	W 6 - 0	BAGHDADI 4(37 59 64 75) Lowes 51Jerrard 90	20	26
18	SPL	H	Farnborough	333	W 4 - 0	Bastick 53 58 Lanahan 84 Baghdadi 90	20	27
23	SPL	A	Bishops Stortford	228	L 0 - 1		20	28
26	SPL	A	Weymouth	1885	D 2 - 2	Egan 70 Lanahan 78	20	29
Jan 1	SPL	H	Tiverton Town	489	W 3 - 0	Lanahan 23 Blair 47 65	20	30
6	SPL	A	Kings Lynn Town	646	L 0 - 3		20	31
13	SPL	A	Redditch United	443	W 1 - 0	Collins 30	19	32
16	SPL	A	Slough Town	436	L 0 - 2			33
20	SPL	H	Hereford	909	L 0 - 1		19	34
27	SPL	A	Gosport Borough	244	D 3 - 3	Collins 18 Bastick 40 Rowels 90	19	35
Feb 3	SPL	H	Kings Lamgley	373	W 1 - 0	Blair 24	18	36
10	SPL	A	Chesham United	234	D 2 - 2	Pope 50 Lanahan 79	18	37
17	SPL	A	Stratford Town	214	L 0 - 2		19	38
24	SPL	H	Dunstable Town	383	D 1 - 1	Pope 33	19	39
Mar 10	SPL	H	Merthyr Town	409	L 1 - 2	Winsper 61	20	40
24	SPL	H	Royston Town	397	W 1 - 0	Rodriguez 79	20	41
27	SPL	A	Kettering Town	502	L 3 - 4	Pope 2 Egan 57 Lowes 62	20	42
Apr 7	SPL	H	Bishop's Stortford	368	W 1 - 0	Blair 45	19	43
9	SPL	H	St Neots Town	257	L 0 - 4		20	44
14	SPL	A	St Ives Town	192	W 2 - 1	Pope 3 20	19	45
17	SPL	A	Tiverton Town	176	D 0 - 0		19	46
21	SPL	H	Slough Town	487	L 0 - 1		19	47
23	SPL	A	Hitchin Town	207	D 0 - 0		19	48
28	SPL	A	Biggleswade Town	159	D 1 - 1	Pope 39	19	49

GOALSCORERS	SG	CSG	Pens	Hat tricks	Total		SG	CSG	Pens	Hat tricks	Total
2016-17 Walker					11	Collins					2
Lanahan	9	2			9	Bowles					1
Baghdadi	5			1	8	Carmichael					1
Lowes	6				8	Davies					1
Pope	4				6	Griggs		1			1
Blair	4				5	Opponents					1
Rodriguez	3		1		5	Panesar-Dower					1
Jarrard	4				4	Rose					1
Bastick	3				3	Rowells					1
Egan	2				3	Winsper					1
Omorod	2		1		3						

DUNSTABLE TOWN MATCH RESULTS 2017-18

Date	Comp	H/A	Opponents	Att:	Result	Goalscorers	Pos	No.
Aug 12	SPL	A	Redditch United	215	L 0 - 5		24	1
15	SPL	H	Kings Langley	145	L 1 - 4	Trif 56	24	2
18	SPL	H	Merthyr Town	93	L 0 - 6		24	3
26	SPL	A	Royston Town	185	D 1 - 1	Okito 60	24	4
28	SPL	H	Banbury United	197	L 0 - 5		24	5
Sept 2	FAC 1Q	A	**Royston Town**	234	L 0 - 2			6
9	SPL	A	Slough Town	786	L 1 - 8	Hudson 44	24	7
12	SPL	A	Chesham United	193	L 0 - 2		24	8
23	SPL	H	Dorchester Town	91	L 0 - 1		23	9
26	SPL	H	Bishop's Stortford	105	L 0 - 5		24	10
Oct 7	SPL	H	Farnborough	254	W 1 - 0	Osie-Bonsu 71	23	11
10	SPL	A	St Neots Town	180	D 2 - 2	Parr 10 (og) Amu 76 (pen)	23	12
14	SPL	A	Stratford Town	194	L 1 - 5	Osie-Bonsu 59	23	13
17	SPL	H	Kings Lynn Town	129	L 0 - 4		23	14
21	SPL	H	Redditch United	193	D 1 - 1	Amu 22	23	15
24	SPL	A	Kings Langley	245	L 0 - 1		23	16
28	FAT 1Q	H	**Lewes**	102	L 1 - 4	**Osie-Bonsu 59**		17
31	SPL	A	Hereford	1686	L 0 - 2		23	18
Nov 4	SPL	H	Frome Town	86	L 1 - 2	Osie-Bonsu 90	23	19
11	SPL	A	St Ives Town	185	L 1 - 2	Sonuga 47	23	20
14	SPL	H	Chesham United	93	L 1 - 4	Amu 9	23	21
18	SPL	A	Gosport Borough	188	L 0 - 1		23	22
25	SPL	H	Tiverton Town	106	L 1 - 2	Amu 36 (pen)	23	23
28	SPL	A	Bishop's Stortford	205	L 1 - 4	Black 14	23	24
Dec 2	SPL	A	Hitchin Town	457	L 0 - 1		23	25
16	SPL	H	Basingstoke Town	111	L 0 - 6		23	26
22	SPL	A	Kettering Town	540	L 0 - 6		23	27
26	SPL	A	Banbury United	391	W 2 - 1	Ogden 19 Kioso 72	23	28
Jan 1	SPL	H	Biggleswade Town	141	L 0 - 2		23	29
13	SPL	H	Royston Town	107	L 0 - 5		23	30
20	SPL	A	Farnborough	227	L 0 - 4		23	31
Jan 23	SPL	H	Weymouth	121	W 2 - 1	Young 25 Amu 65	23	32
27	SPl	H	St Neots Town	105	L 2 - 3	Young 45 Trif 65	23	33
Feb 3	SPL	A	Kings Lynn Town	699	L 0 - 5		23	34
10	SPL	H	Stratford Town	75	L 2 - 3	Ogden 60 Amu 90	23	35
13	SPL	A	Merthyr Town	256	L 1 - 3	Lamptey 19	23	36
17	SPL	H	Hereford	509	L 0 - 4		23	37
24	SPL	A	Dorchester Town	383	D 1 - 1	Black 51	23	38
Mar 10	SPL	A	Tiverton Town	288	L 1 - 7	Amu 64 (pen)	23	39
17	SPL	A	Weymouth	481	L 0 - 2		23	40
24	SPL	H	Hitchin Town	273	L 0 - 4		23	41
30	SPL	H	Slough Town	282	L 0 - 3		23	42
Apr7	SPL	H	Kettering Town	259	L 1 - 2	Amu 52 (pen)	23	43
14	SPL	A	Basingstoke Town	310	L 0 - 2		23	44
21	SPL	H	St Ives Town	164	D 0 - 0		24	45
24	SPL	A	Biggleswade Town	121	W 2 - 0	Lamptey 13 Trif 67	24	46
26	SPL	H	Gosport Borough	352	L 0 - 2		24	47
28	SPL	A	Frome Town	261	L 0 - 3		24	48

GOALSCORERS	SG	CSG	Pens	Hat tricks	Total		SG	CSG	Pens	Hat tricks	Total
2016-17 *Cathline*					9	Okito					1
Amu	7		4		8	Opponents					1
Osie-Bonsu					4	Sonuga					1
Trif					3						
Black					2						
Lamptey					2						
Ogden	2				2						
Young	2				2						
Hudson					1						
Kioso					1						

FARNBOROUGH MATCH RESULTS 2017-18

Date	Comp	H/A	Opponents	Att:	Result		Goalscorers	Pos	No.
Aug 12	SPL	A	St Neots Town	225	W	1 - 0	Ciardini 17	9	1
16	SPL	H	Royston Town	324	L	0 - 1		14	2
19	SPL	H	Redditch United	328	L	1 - 3	Coles 89	17	3
26	SPL	A	Merthyr Town	451	L	0 - 3		18	4
28	SPL	H	Slough Town	483	L	1 - 2	Coles 80	19	5
Sept 2	FAC 1Q	H	Salisbury	396	L	2 - 3	Walker 43 Coles 48		6
9	SPL	A	Kings Langley	186	W	3 - 0	Southam 77 Walker 88 Calcutt 91	20	7
12	SPL	A	Gosport Borough	167	W	4 - 2	Walker 8 Cureton 12 16 Calcutt 24	15	8
23	SPL	H	St Ives Town	274	W	2 - 1	Walker 11 86	13	9
27	SPL	H	Dorchester Town	222	D	3 - 3	Coles 48 Ciardini 66 Calcutt 90	14	10
30	SPL	A	Biggleswade Town	201	L	0 - 3		14	11
Oct 7	SPL	A	Dunstable Town	254	L	0 - 1		16	12
11	SPL	H	Weymouth	299	L	2 - 6	Huggins 11 Travers 27 (og)	17	13
14	SPL	H	Hitchin Town	230	W	4 - 1	Coles 32 Cureton 38 Emmerson 63 Southam 66	14	14
17	SPL	A	Hereford	2014	W	1 - 0	Coles 47	11	15
21	SPL	H	St Neots Town	285	L	2 - 4	Cureton 31 (pen) Fearn 77	15	16
24	SPL	A	Royston Town	174	L	3 - 4	Evans 33 Cureton 45 90	16	17
28	FAT 1Q	A	Larkhall Athletic	130	W	3 - 1	Barton 60 Cureton 85 Calcutt 90		18
Nov 4	FAT	A	Kettering Town	403	L	3 - 4	Calcutt 54 Barton 63 Cureton 90		19
11	FAT 2Q	H	Banbury United	269	D	3 - 3	Coles 21 77 Ciardini 58		20
18	SPL	H	Bishop's Stortford	252	D	2 - 2	Coles 8 Dormer 90	17	21
21	SPL	A	Chesham United	187	D	0 - 0		17	22
25	FAT 2Qr	A	Banbury United	380	W	3 - 2	Higgins Coles 30 (pen) Ciardini 90		23
28	FAT 3Q	H	Hartley Wintney	255	L	1 - 2	Calcutt 75		24
Dec 2	SPL	A	Stratford Town	184	D	2 - 2	Ciardini 20 Cureton 90	19	25
6	SPL	H	Gosport Borough	177	L	1 - 2	Roberts 90	19	26
10	SPL	H	Kings Lynn Town	194	W	5 - 2	CIARDINI 4 (6 35 47 73) Cureton 45	18	27
16	SPL	H	Frome Town	187	W	5 - 3	Walker 37 Coles 65 Cureton 72 75 Bellamy 82	16	28
18	SPL	A	Dorchester Town	333	L	0 - 4		16	29
22	SPL	A	Tiverton Town	283	L	0 - 2		16	30
26	SPL	H	Slough Town	668	L	1 - 5	Walker 69	19	31
Jan 1	SPL	H	Basingstoke Town	395	W	4 - 3	Evans 30 Calcutt 33 (pen) 76 Ellington 82	18	32
6	SPL	A	Redditch United	284	L	1 - 7	Huggins 9	18	33
10	SPL	H	Banbury United	216	W	1 - 0	Emmerson 56	16	34
13	SPL	H	Merthyr Town	286	D	2 - 2	Calcutt 68 Walker 87	17	35
20	SPL	H	Dunstable Town	227	W	4 - 0	Walker 8 (pen) Coles 11 Barton 56 Ormrod 78	16	36
27	SPL	A	Weymouth	608	L	0 - 6		17	37
Feb 3	SPL	H	Hereford	812	L	2 - 4	Harris-Sealey 70 Coles 90	15	38
10	SPL	A	Hitchin Town	280	W	3 - 0	Coles 15 Elias-Fernandes 24 47	15	39
17	SPL	H	Biggleswade Town	261	W	2 - 1	Antwi- Nyame 2 Elias-Fernandes 18	14	40
24	SPL	A	St Ives Town	239	W	4 - 2	Calcutt 24 Harris-Sealey 28 51 Elias-Fernandes 72	14	41
Mar 10	SPL	A	Banbury United	373	L	1 - 4	Antwi-Nyama 56	15	42
17	SPL	A	Kings Lynn Town	490	L	1 - 3	Elias-Fernandes 35	17	43
24	SPL	H	Stratford Town	224	L	1 - 4	Harris-Sealey 5	17	44
30	SPL	H	Kings Langley Town	229	L	0 - 4		18	45
Apr 2	SPL	A	Basingstoke Town	358	L	3 - 4	King 18 24 Calcutt 50	18	46
7	SPL	H	Tiverton Town	205	L	2 - 3	Calcutt 40 Harris-Sealey 78	18	47
11	SPL	H	Bishops Stortford	169	L	0 - 5		20	48
14	SPL	A	Frome Town	211	D	1 - 1	Calcutt 67	20	49
21	SPL	H	Chesham United	252	W	2 - 0	Elias-Fernandes 42 Campbell 90	18	50
28	SPL	A	Kettering Town	712	L	2 - 6	Elias-Fernandes 7 Toseland 72 (og)	20	51

GOALSCORERS	SG	CSG	Pens	Hat tricks	Total		SG	CSG	Pens	Hat tricks	Total
Coles	13	2	1		14	Opponents					2
Calcutt	11	2	1		12	Southam	2				2
Cureton	9	4	1		12	Bellamy					1
Ciardini	6			1	9	Campbell					1
Walker	8	4	1		9	Dormer					1
E-Fernandes	6	3			7	Ellington					1
Harris-Sealey	4				5	Fearn					1
Barton	3	2			3	Higgins					1
Antwi-Nyame					2	Ormorod					1
Emmerson	2				2	Roberts					1
Evans	2				2	Tumelty					1
Huggins	2				2						
King	1				2						

FROME TOWN MATCH RESULTS 2017-18

Date	Comp	H/A	Opponents	Att:	Result	Goalscorers	Pos	No.
Aug 12	SPL	A	Basingstoke Town	295	W 3 - 1	Johnson-Schuster 8 (og) Jackson 21 Davies 65	4	1
16	SPL	H	Weymouth	408	L 1 - 4	Mapstone 37	15	2
19	SPL	H	Biggleswade Town	197	L 2 - 3	Davies 54 (pen) Jefferies 80	16	3
26	SPL	A	Kings Lynn	948	D 0 - 0		14	4
28	SPL	H	Tiverton Town	258	L 0 - 1		11	5
Sept 2	FAC 1Q	H	AFC Totton	191	W 2 - 1	Jefferies 57 Davies 71		6
9	SPL	A	Banbury United	453	W 4 - 3	Jefferies 25 Miller 40 Davies 49 72	12	7
11	SPL	H	Dorchester Town	349	W 4 - 1	Jackson 15 75 Raynes 52 Davies 56	12	8
16	FAC 2Q	A	Tavistock	410	W 2 - 1	Jackson 23 Jefferies 43		9
23	SPL	H	Bishops Stortford	225	W 2 - 1	Teale 16 Miller 70	11	10
27	SPL	H	Hereford	531	L 0 - 3		11	11
Oct 7	SPL	H	St Neots Town	251	D 2 - 2	Knight 42 Raynes 53	13	12
14	SPL	A	Royston Town	198	L 0 - 3		18	13
21	SPL	H	Basingstoke Town	218	W 1 - 0	Page 6	18	14
24	SPL	A	Weymouth	805	W 2 - 0	Raynes 18 Jefferies 90	14	15
28	FAT 1Q	A	Shortwood United	96	L 0 - 2			16
Nov 1	SPL	H	Stratford Town	197	W 3 - 0	Miller 25 Bath 58 Knight 74	10	17
4	SPL	A	Dunstable Town	86	W 2 - 1	Morgan 9 Knight 74	9	18
15	SPL	H	Dorchester Town	234	W 3 - 1	Jackson 11 79 Davies 85	7	19
18	SPL	A	St Ives Town	145	D 2 - 2	Jackson 64 Mapstone 78	7	20
21	SPL	A	Redditch United	206	L 1 - 4	Page 65	8	21
25	SPL	H	Hitchin Town	277	L 3 - 4	Davies 45 (pen) Hemmings 77 Miller 79	9	22
Dec 2	SPL	H	Kettering Town	267	D 2 - 2	Miller 14 Jackson 78	10	23
4	SPL	A	Chesham United	1784	L 1 - 5	Davies 76	11	24
9	SPL	A	Kings Langley	135	W 7 - 2	Knight 37 Davies 40 Hemmings 45 Raynes 71 Jefferies 72 Mapstone 82 Jackson 90 (pen)	10	25
16	SPL	A	Farnborough	187	L 3 - 5	Jackson 9 63 Mapstone 75	10	26
20	SPL	H	Gosport Borough	192	W 2 - 0	Jackson 27 Davies 83	9	27
Jan 1	SPL	H	Merthyr Town	367	L 1 - 2	Davies 35	12	28
6	SPL	A	Biggleswade Town	175	W 2 - 1	Mapstone 44 Knight 47	11	29
13	SPL	H	Kings Lynn Town	229	D 0 - 0		12	30
20	SPL	A	St Neots Town	277	W 6 - 1	Jefferies 8 Raynes 32 Hemmings 53 Page 59 Bath 76 88 10		31
27	SPL	H	Redditch Town	256	W 1 - 0	Miller 90	9	32
Feb 3	SPL	A	Stratford Town	172	W 2 - 1	Raynes 4 Mapstone 66	9	33
10	SPL	H	Royston Town	164	L 1 - 4	Raynes 5	10	34
17	SPL	A	Chesham United	211	L 1 - 3	Davies 21	10	35
26	SPL	A	Bishop's Stortford	231	L 0 - 4		10	36
Mar 10	SPL	A	Slough Town	581	L 1 - 2	Miller 11	12	37
15	SPL	H	St Ives Town	120	L 0 - 1		13	38
17	SPL	H	Kings Langley	117	W 2 - 1	Miller 65 (pen) Raynes 72	11	39
21	SPL	A	Hereford	1685	L 0 - 1		11	40
24	SPL	A	Kettering Town	610	L 0 - 0		12	41
27	SPL	A	Tiverton Town	215	D 2 - 2	Miller 41 Davies 87	12	42
Apr 2	SPL	A	Merthyr Town	402	W 4 - 3	Raynes 14 Brace 24 Mapstone 77 Davies 84	12	43
4	SPL	H	Slough Town	161	L 0 - 4		12	44
7	SPL	A	Hitchin Town	317	L 1 - 5	Brace 90	12	45
14	SPL	H	Farnborough	211	D 1 - 1	Bath 24	13	46
21	SPL	A	Gosport Borough	238	L 0 - 7		13	47
25	SPL	H	Banbury United	152	L 0 - 2		13	48
28	SPL	H	Dunstable Town	261	W 3 0	Raynes 14 34 Bath 85	13	49

GOALSCORERS	SG	CSG	Pens	Hat tricks	Total		SG	CSG	Pens	Hat tricks	Total
2016-17 *Jackson*					22	Page	3				3
Davies	14	3	2		15	Brace	2				2
Jackson	9	2	1		12	Morgan					1
Raynes	10	2			11	Opponents					1
Miller	9		1		9	Teale					1
Jefferies	6	2			7						
Mapstone	7				7						
Bath	4				5						
Knight	5				5						
Hemmings	3				3						

GOSPORT BOROUGH MATCH RESULTS 2017-18

Date	Comp	H/A	Opponents	Att:	Result	Goalscorers	Pos	No.
Aug 12	SPL	A	Kings Lynn Town	827	L 0 - 2		21	1
15	SPL	H	Slough Town	382	L 1 - 5	Przespolewskli-Scott 49	23	2
19	SPL	H	Royston Town	287	L 2 - 3	Saidy 13 Kimber 72	23	3
26	SPL	A	Tiverton Town	265	L 0 - 2		24	4
28	SPL	H	Basingstoke Town	271	L 0 - 8		24	5
Sept 2	FAC 1Q	H	Bridgwater Town	257	W 1 - 0	Vine 18		6
9	SPL	A	Biggleswade Town	162	L 0 - 2		24	7
12	SPL	H	Farnborough	167	L 2 - 4	Dawson 28 King 80	24	8
16	FAC 2Q	H	Swindon Supermarine	176	L 1 - 2	Mitford 53		9
23	SPL	A	Stratford Town	150	L 0 - 2		24	10
26	SPL	A	Kings Langley	403	D 1 - 1	Buse 78	23	11
30	SPL	A	Hitchin Town	255	L 0 - 3		23	12
Oct 7	SPL	H	Bishop's Stortford	262	L 1 - 3	Onwuachu 27		13
9	SPL	A	Dorchester Town	241	L 2 - 7	Onwuachu 75 Smith 80		14
14	SPL	A	Merthyr Town	443	L 0 - 5		24	15
17	SPL	H	Banbury United	230	L 0 - 4		24	16
24	SPL	A	Slough Town	678	L 1 - 5	Onwuacho 36	24	17
28	FAT 1Q	H	Bristol Manor Farm	160	W 1 - 0	Lis 35		18
Nov 4	SPL	H	St Neots Town	236	L 0 - 1		24	19
11	FAT 2Q	A	Hartley Wintney	216	L 0 - 3			20
18	SPL	H	Dunstable Town	188	W 1 - 0	Thomson 45	24	21
25	SPL	A	Kettering Town	565	L 0 - 2		24	22
28	SPL	H	Kings Langley	151	L 1 - 2	Sanders 81 (pen)	24	23
Dec 6	SPL	A	Farnborough	177	W 2 - 1	Davis 32 Thomson 45	23	24
20	SPL	A	Frome Town	192	L 0 - 2			25
23	SPL	A	St Ives Town	231	L 0 - 1			26
26	SPL	A	Basingstoke Town	325	L 0 - 3		23	27
Jan 1	SPL	H	Weymouth	418	L 0 - 4		23	28
6	SPL	A	Royston Town	245	L 0 - 5		23	29
13	SPL	H	Tiverton Town	218	L 0 - 5		23	30
23	SPL	A	Chesham United	211	L 1 - 5	McAllister 45	24	31
27	SPL	H	Dorchester Town	244	D 3 - 3	McAllister 20 Bombelenga 45 Smith 85	24	32
Feb 3	SPL	A	Banbury United	342	L 0 - 5		24	33
6	SPL	H	Kings Lynn Town	241	L 1 - 7	Lea 35	24	34
10	SPL	H	Merthyr Town	269	D 1 - 1	Bombelenca 81	24	35
17	SPL	H	Hitchin Town	457	L 1 - 2	McAllister 14	24	36
20	SPL	A	Redditch United	211	L 2 - 4	McAllister 3 Pennery 33	24	37
24	SPL	H	Stratford Town	238	L 0 - 1		24	38
Mar 6	SPL	H	Hereford	539	L 0 - 4		24	39
13	SPL	A	Bishop's Stortford	211	L 1 - 2	Vine 23	24	40
17	SPL	H	Redditch United	223	L 2 - 5	Sanders 58 Wright 60	24	41
24	SPL	A	Hereford	2710	L 1 - 5	Vine 49	24	42
31	SPL	H	Biggleswade Town	289	D 1 - 1	Vine 77	24	43
Apr 2	SPL	A	Weymouth	1007	L 0 - 5		24	44
7	SPL	H	St Ives Town	241	D 0 - 0		24	45
14	SPL	A	Chesham United	352	L 0 - 3		24	46
17	SPL	H	Kettering Town	241	L 0 - 7		24	47
21	SPL	H	Frome Town	238	W 7 - 0	WRIGHT 4 (8 69 72 89) PENNERY 3 (18 30 32)	23	48
26	SPL	A	Dunstable Town	352	W 2 - 0	Wright 73 McAllister 87	23	49
28	SPL	A	St Neots Town	280	W 4 - 0	Wright 45 Sanders 54 Wrightson-David 85 Lea 86	23	50

GOALSCORERS	SG	CSG	Pens	Hat tricks	Total		SG	CSG	Pens	Hat tricks	Total
2016-17 Wright					10	Buse					1
Wright	4		1		7	Davis					1
McAllister	5	2			5	Dawson					1
Pennery	2		1		4	Kimber					1
Vine	4	3			4	King					1
Onwuachu	3	3			3	Lis					1
Sanders	3	2	1		3	Mitford					1
Bombelenga	2	2			2	Przespolewski-Scott					1
Lea	2				2	Saidy					1
Smith	2	2			2	Wrightson-David					1
Thomson	2	2			2						

HEREFORD MATCH RESULTS 2017-18

Date	Comp	H/A	Opponents	Att:	Result		Goalscorers	Pos	No.
Aug 12	SPL	A	Kings Langley	661	D	3 - 3	Molyneux 77 Preece 79 Mills 88	11	1
15	SPL	H	Tiverton Town	2424	W	1 - 0	Mills 80 (pen)	5	2
19	SPL	H	Slough Town	2684	L	0 - 1		13	3
26	SPL	A	St Neots Town	516	W	3 - 1	Haysham 21 Mills 45 Molyneux 60	9	4
28	SPL	H	Merthyr Town	3366	D	1 - 1	Hill 84	10	5
Sept 2	FAC 1Q	H	Godalming Town	1737	W	8 - 0	MILLS 3 (4 29 53) Preece 20 Haysham 58 85 Reffell 74 Preen 68		6
9	SPL	A	Royston Town	512	W	4 - 1	MILLS 3 (16 55 (pen) 60) Haysham 87	9	7
12	SPL	H	Stratford Town	2005	W	5 - 2	Preen 28 34 McGrath 32 Hill 39 Symons 85	8	8
16	FAC 2Q	A	Kempston Rovers	429	W	4 - 0	Preen 40 Mills 47 (pen) 62 (pen) Smith 90		9
23	SPL	A	Weymouth	1518	W	2 - 0	Mills 22 Bowen 63	7	10
26	SPL	A	Frome Town	531	W	3 - 0	Preen 24 Mills 37 Reffell 41	4	11
30	FAC 3Q	H	AFC Hornchurch	2440	W	2 - 0	Reffell 61 Mills 64 (pen)		12
Oct 7	SPL	A	Dorchester Town	2596	W	4 - 1	Mills 51(pen) 73 Smith 55 Reffell 65	3	13
10	SPL	A	Banbury United	1011	W	1 - 0	Reffell 33	3	14
14	FAC 4Q	A	Eastleigh	1345	W	2 - 1	McGrath 14 Preen 43		15
17	SPL	H	Farnborough	2014	L	0 - 1		5	16
21	SPL	H	Kings Langley	2319	W	3 - 0	Mills 39 47 Symons 86	5	17
24	SPL	A	Tiverton Town	620	D	2 - 2	Haysham 19 Smith 40	5	18
28	FAT 1Q	H	Weymouth	1552	W	4 - 1	MILLS 3 (35 38 79) Smith 73		19
31	SPL	H	Dunstable Town	1686	W	2 - 0	Smith 47 (pen) Reffell 81	4	20
Nov 4	FAC 1	H	AFC Telford United	4712	W	1 - 0	Mills 68		21
11	FAT 2Q	H	Potters Bar Town	1368	D	0 - 0			22
14	FAT 2Qr	A	Potters Bar Town	230	W	2 - 1	Smith 13 Doyle (og) 31		23
18	SPL	H	Hitchin Town	2104	W	5 - 0	Duffus 17 35 SMITH 3 (45 62 73)	4	24
21	SPL	H	St Ives Town	1705	W	4 - 0	Duffus 21 Mills 35 40 Symons 79	2	25
25	FAT 3Q	H	Oxford City	480	W	2 - 1	Mills 20 O'Shea 61		26
Dec 9	SPL	H	Basingstoke Town	2794	W	4 - 1	Dearman 17 Refell 31 Mills 43 73	5	27
14	FAC 2	H	Fleetwood Town	4235	L	0 - 2			28
17	FAT 1	H	Dagenham & Redbridge	1518	W	3 - 2	Murphy 18 Smith 27 Symons 76 (pen)		29
19	SPL	A	Kettering Town	909	W	3 - 1	Richards 7 Mills 36 Symons 89	4	30
22	SPL	A	Chesham United	554	W	3 - 1	Bird 40 92 Smith 92	5	31
26	SPL	A	Merthyr Town	2612	D	0 - 0		4	32
Jan 1	SPL	H	Redditch United	3083	W	5 - 0	Mills 16 (pen) 84 Haysham 19 37 Smith 32	4	33
6	SPL	A	Slough Town	1561	D	2 - 2	Oates 89 Reffell 90	4	34
9	SPL	A	Stratford Town	707	W	2 - 1	Mills 57 (pen) 58	3	35
20	SPL	H	Dorchester Town	909	W	1 - 0	Smith 61	3	36
27	SPL	H	Banbury United	2932	W	3 0	Bird 14 Mills 67 (pen) Reffell 73	3	37
30	SPL	A	Kings Lynn Town	1181	L	2 - 3	Cullinane-Liburd 8 Mills 45	4	38
Feb 3	SPL	A	Farnborough	812	W	4 - 2	MILLS 3 (45 62 77) Richards 90	3	39
6	SPL	H	Bishop's Stortford	1772	W	2 - 0	Bird 48 Smith 58	2	40
10	SPL	H	Biggleswade Town	2376	W	1 - 0	Reffell 90	2	41
17	SPL	H	Dunstable Town	509	W	4 - 0	Purdie 25 Smith 32 Green 77 Richards 90	1	42
20	SPL	H	St Neots Town	2402	W	1 - 0	O'Shea 55	1	43
24	SPL	H	Weymouth	2766	W	2 - 0	Mytie-Williams 55 Refell 69	1	44
Mar 6	SPL	A	Gosport Borough	539	W	4 - 0	Symons 13 72 Myrie-Williams 64 O'Shea 71	1	45
10	SPL	H	Kings Lynn Town	3,424	L	0 - 2		1	46
17	SPL	A	Basingstoke Town	704	L	1 - 3	Cullinane-Liburd 64	1	47
20	SPL	H	Frome Town	1685	W	1 - 0	Mills 36	1	48
24	SPL	H	Gosport Borough	2710	W	5 - 1	MYRIE-WILLIAMS 3 (32 51 59) Oates 41 Smith 64	1	49
30	SPL	H	Royston Town	2657	W	2 - 0	Smith 39 Purdie 83	1	50
Apr 2	SPL	A	Redditch United	1651	W	2 - 0	Oates 21 Smith 61	1	51
7	SPL	H	Chesham United	2704	W	3 - 0	Reffell 8 Smith 12 Myrie-Williams 67	1	52
14	SPL	A	Bishop's Stortford	738	W	1 - 0	McGrath 90	1	53
17	SPL	A	Biggleswade Town	740	W	1 - 0	Purdie 71 (pen)	1	54
21	SPL	H	Kettering Town	4556	W	4 - 1	O'Shea 12 Purdie 13 Smith 16 68	1	55
25	SPL	H	Hitchin Town	346	W	3 - 0	Haysham 36 Smith 50 Myrie-Williams 88	1	56
28	SPL	A	St Ives Town	702	W	2 - 0	O'Shea 33 Mills 68 (pen)	1	57

GOALSCORERS	SG	CSG	Pens	Hat tricks	Total			SG	CSG	Pens	Hat tricks	Total
Mills	24	5	10	4	39		Richards	3				3
Smith	19	4	1	1	22		Cullinane-Liburd	2				2
Reffell	10	4			12		Hill	2				2
Haysham	6	2			8		Molyneux	2				2
Myrie-Williams	5		1		7		Preece	2				2
Symons	5		1		7		Bowen	1				1
Preen	4	2			6		Dearman	1				1
O'Shea	5				5		Green	1				1
Bird	3				4		Murphy	1				1
Purdie	4		1		4		Opponents					1
Duffus	2				3							
McGrath	3				3							
Oates	3				3							

HITCHIN TOWN MATCH RESULTS 2017-18

Date	Comp	H/A	Opponents	Att:	Result	Goalscorers	Pos	No.
Aug 12	SPL	A	Merthyr Town	439	D 0 - 0		13	1
14	SPL	H	St Neots Town	520	D 2 - 2	Brooks 45 59	11	2
19	SPL	H	Banbury United	391	L 0 - 3		20	3
26	SPL	A	Biggleswade Town	379	L 1 - 2	Bailey 44	21	4
28	SPL	H	Royston Town	513	W 1 - 0	Donnelly 35	16	5
Sept 2	FAC 1Q	A	**Haringey Borough**	171	D 1 - 1	**Gordon 12 (og)**		6
4	FAC 1Qr	H	**Haringey Borough**	201	D 1 - 1	**Donnelly 34 (Lost 2-3 on pens)**		7
9	SPL	A	Tiverton Town	247	L 1 - 3	Rolfe 79	19	8
12	SPL	A	Slough Town	442	L 0 - 4		20	9
23	SPL	A	Basingstoke Town	403	W 2 - 1	McNamara 25 Donnelly 65	18	10
25	SPL	H	St Ives Town	325	D 2 - 2	McNamara 52 Dowie 69	17	11
30	SPL	A	Gosport Borough	255	W 3 - 0	Donnelly 5 Charles 55 90	16	12
Oct 7	SPL	H	Stratford Town	755	W 4 - 0	Donnelly 18 33 Charles 79 87	12	13
14	SPL	A	Farnborough	230	L 1 - 4	Donnelly 22	17	14
16	SPL	H	Redditch United	318	W 1 - 0	McNamara 48	13	15
21	SPL	H	Merthyr Town	433	W 2 - 0	Bailey 61 90	10	16
24	SPL	A	St Neots Town	333	D 1 - 1	Donnelly 70	10	17
28	FAT 1Q	H	**Cheshunt**	265	W 5 - 0	**Webb 39 Green 43 Bailey 45 Donnelly 61 Charles 73**		18
Nov 4	SPL	H	Weymouth	453	W 3 - 1	Donnelly 6 Bailey 49 51	11	19
11	SPL	A	Chesham United	297	L 1 - 3	Bailey 53		20
18	SPL	A	Hereford	2104	L 0 - 5		14	21
25	SPL	A	Frome Town	277	W 4 - 3	Bailey 13 Bickerstaff 33 Vincent 36 80	11	22
28	SPL	A	St Ives Town	175	W 3 - 1	Kirkpatrick 54 (pen) Bickerstaff 89 Bailey 90	8	23
Dec 2	SPL	H	Dunstable Town	457	W 1 - 0	Charles 47	7	24
9	SPL	A	Dorchester Town	316	W 4 - 1	Bickerstaff 4 Kirkpatrick 16 (p) Bailey 36 McNamara 55	7	25
16	SPL	H	Kettering Town	489	D 0 - 0		7	26
19	SPL	A	Bishop's Stortford	232	W 3 - 0	Webb 3 Charles 17 Kirkpatrick 90 (pen)	6	27
26	SPL	A	Royston Town	493	L 1 - 2	Charles 32	7	28
30	SPL	H	Kings Langley	540	W 6 - 0	Smith 9 Bailey 40 69 Charles 50 55 Kirkpatrick 62 (p)	6	29
Jan 6	SPL	A	Banbury United	369	L 0 - 1		7	30
13	SPL	A	Biggleswade Town	658	L 0 - 1		9	31
27	SPL	H	Kings Lynn Town	500	L 0 - 4		11	32
Feb 3	SPL	A	Redditch United	274	D 2 - 2	Kirkpatrick 46 (pen) Rolfe 85	11	33
10	SPL	H	Farnborough	280	L 1 - 3	Donnelly 63	12	34
12	SPL	H	Chesham United	281	D 0 - 0		12	35
17	SPL	H	Gosport Borough	457	W 2 - 1	Burns 9 Kirkpatrick 80	12	36
24	SPL	A	Basingstoke Town	312	L 0 - 1		12	37
Mar 10	SPL	A	Chesham United	305	D 0 - 0		11	38
24	SPL	A	Dunstable Town	273	W 4 - 0	Bickerstaff 22 McNamara 24 33 Kirkpatrick 40 (pen)	11	39
27	SPL	A	Stratford Town	186	W 2 - 1	Donnelly 8 Logan 25	11	40
30	SPL	H	Tiverton Town	606	L 1 - 2	Webb 90	11	41
Apr 2	SPL	A	Kings Langley	242	W 2 - 1	Syme 48 Tshikala 90	10	42
7	SPL	H	Frome Town	317	W 5 - 1	Charles 36 51 Roberts 46 (og) Vincent 58 Logan 75	10	43
14	SPL	A	Kettering Town	611	L 1 - 4	Bickerstaff 81 (pen)	10	44
16	SPL	H	Slough Town	321	L 0 - 1		11	45
21	SPL	H	Bishops Stortford	431	W 1 - 0	Burns 90	11	46
23	SPL	H	Dorchester Town	207	D 0 - 0		11	47
25	SPL	H	Hereford	346	L 0 - 3		11	48
28	SPL	A	Weymouth	1102	L 0 - 3		11	49
								50
								51
								52
								53
								54
								55
								56

GOALSCORERS	SG	CSG	Pens	Hat tricks	Total		SG	CSG	Pens	Hat tricks	Total
2016-17 *Burns*					20	Burns	2				2
Bailey	9	3			12	Logan	2				2
Donnelly	10	3			12	Opponents					2
Charles	8	3			12	Rolfe	2				2
Kirkpatrick	7		6		7	Dowie					1
McNamara	5	2			6	Green					1
Bickerstaff	4	2	1		5	Smith					1
Vincent	2				3	Syme					1
Webb	3				3	Tshikala					1
Brooks	1				2						

KETTERING TOWN MATCH RESULTS 2017-18

Date	Comp	H/A	Opponents	Att:	Result		Goalscorers	Pos	No.
Aug 12	SPL	A	Slough Town	760	W	2 - 1	Solkhon 28 Milnes 89	6	1
15	SPL	H	Redditch United	606	W	1 - 0	Meikle 90	3	2
19	SPL	H	Basingstoke Town	557	W	3 - 0	Solkhon 25 Howe 77 Baker 90	3	3
26	SPL	A	Kings Langley	261	W	5 2	Hoenes 25 O'Connor 37 Rowe 81 Stevens 86 90	2	4
28	SPL	H	St Neots Town	727	W	3 - 0	Milnes 16 Hoenes 19 (pen) Howe 33	2	5
Sept 3	FAC 1Q	A	Romulus	249	W	3 - 0	Hoenes 5 61 O'Connor 48		6
9	SPL	A	Weymouth	684	L	1 - 3	Buckley 20 (og)	4	7
12	SPL	A	St Ives Town	354	W	4 - 3	Milnes 2 Solkhon 9 69 Richens 61	2	8
16	FAC 2Q	H	Kidsgrove Athletic	543	W	2 - 0	Meikle 80 O'Connor 85		9
23	SPL	H	Chesham United	598	W	3 - 1	O'Connor 14 90 Stevens 79	1	10
26	SPL	H	Banbury United	653	W	3 - 0	Solkhorn 16 Milnes 67 Howe 90 (pen)	1	11
30	FAC 3Q	A	Basford United	525	W	3 - 2	Hoenes 16 O'Connor 18 86		12
Oct 7	SPL	H	Merthyr Town	857	W	5 - 0	Stevens 24 44 O'Connor 63 Stohrer 79 Toseland 82	1	13
10	SPL	A	Biggleswade Town	352	D	0 - 0		1	14
14	FAC 4Q	A	Nantwich Town	760	D	1 - 1	Richens 44		15
17	FAC 4Qr	H	Nantwich Town	903	L	0 - 1			16
21	SPL	H	Slough Town	824	D	0 - 0		4	17
24	SPL	A	Redditch United	467	D	0 - 0		4	18
28	FAT 1Q	A	Leek Town	390	L	2 - 3	Toseland 57 O'Connor 68		19
31	SPL	A	Bishop's Stortford	355	W	2 - 0	O'Connor 24 Hoenes 51	3	20
Nov 4	SPL	A	Farnborough	403	W	4 - 3	Hoenes 2 Mulligan 13 Toseland 37 Stevens 90		21
18	SPL	A	Dorchester Town	410	L	1 - 4	Howe 67	5	22
25	SPL	H	Gosport Borough	565	W	2 - 0	O'Connor 6 Solkhon 68	4	23
28	SPL	A	Banbury United	301	D	1 - 1	Meikle 21	4	
Dec 2	SPL	A	Frome Town	267	D	2 - 2	O'Connor 35 79	4	24
4	SPL	H	St Ives Town	499	W	4 - 1	O'Connor 17 Howe 54 Milnes 73 Hoenes 82	2	25
9	SPL	H	Stratford Town	608	W	2 - 0	Stevens 4 Howe 88	2	26
11	SPL	A	Hitchin Town	469	D	0 - 0		2	27
19	SPL	H	Hereford	909	L	1 - 3	O'Connor 81	2	28
23	SPL	H	Dunstable Town	540	W	6 - 0	Howe10 54 Marshall 35 Stohrer 70 Stevens 85 88(p)	2	29
26	SPL	A	St Neots Town	509	W	4 - 2	Howe 8 63 O'Connor 67 Stevens 78	2	30
Jan 1	SPL	H	Kings Lynn Town	1019	W	1 - 0	O'Connor 20	1	31
6	SPL	H	Basingstoke Town	422	L	2 - 3	O'Connor 82 Stevens 84	2	32
13	SPL	H	Kings Langley	612	D	1 - 1	O'Connor 7	2	33
20	SPL	A	Merthyr Town	556	W	4 - 2	O'Connor 9 Howe 28 Stevens 53 Solkhon 56	1	34
27	SPL	H	Biggleswade Town	597	W	3 - 1	Stevens 37 O'Connor 45 Pendley 49	1	35
Feb 3	SPL	A	Royston Town	410	L	3 - 4	Meikle 3 Stevens 42 Solkhon 66 (pen)	4	36
17	SPL	H	Bishop's Stortford	558	W	6 - 0	Stevens 17 24 O'Connor 23 42 Solkhon 37(p) Pendley 66	4	37
20	SPL	H	Tiverton Town	181	W	3 - 0	Solkhon 25 (pen) 62 Stevens 90	4	38
24	SPL	A	Chesham United	409	L	0 - 2		4	39
Mar 17	SPL	A	Stratford Town	248	W	4 - 0	Solkhon 14 (pen) Richens 58 Stevens 61 O'Connor 88	4	40
20	SPL	H	Royston Town	500	W	4 - 1	Solkhon 52 Stevens 58 O'Connor 61 Meikle 90	4	41
24	SPL	H	Frome Town	610	W	3 - 0	Hoenes 8 Solkhon 25 (pen) O'Connor 50	4	42
27	SPL	H	Dorchester Town	502	W	4 - 3	Solkhon 44 O.CONNOR 3 (45 75 87)	4	43
Apr 7	SPL	A	Dunstable Town	259	W	2 - 1	Stevens 45 71	4	44
12	SPL	A	Kings Lynn Town	1147	L	1 - 2	Solkhon 52 (pen)	4	45
14	SPL	H	Hitchin Town	611	W	4 - 1	O'CONNOR 4 (8 37 47 54)	4	46
17	SPL	A	Gosport Borough	241	W	7 - 0	Stevens 12 73 Solkhon 19 26 (p) Howe 54 84 O'Connor 864	4	47
19	SPL	H	Weymouth	745	W	2 - 0	Solkhon 11 (pen) 25	4	48
21	SPL	A	Hereford	4556	L	1 - 4	Stevens 49	3	49
24	SPL	H	Tiverton Town	519	L	2 - 3	Stevens 33 Solkhon 87 (pen)	4	50
28	SPL	H	Farnborough	712	W	6 - 2	Solkhon 27 (pen) O'Connor 46 55 STEVENS 3(52 64 84pen) 4		51
May 2	PO SF	A	Slough Town	1246	L	1 - 3	O'Connor 36		52

GOALSCORERS	SG	CSG	Pens	Hat tricks	Total		SG	CSG	Pens	Hat tricks	Total
2016-17 O'Connor					19	Pendley	2				2
O'Connor	27	5		1	37	Stohrer	2				2
Stevens	21	5	1	1	28	Baker					1
Solkhon	13		11		21	Marshall					1
Howe	10	2	1		13	Mulligan					1
Hoenes	8	3	1		9	Opponents					1
Meikle	4				5	Rowe					1
Milnes	4				5						
Richens	3				3						
Toseland	3				3						

KING'S LYNN MATCH RESULTS 2017-18

Date	Comp	H/A	Opponents	Att:	Result	Goalscorers	Pos	No.
Aug 12	SPL	H	Gosport Borough	827	W 2 - 0	Clunan 2 (pen) Parker 39	5	1
15	SPL	A	Bishops Stortford	355	W 3 - 2	Parker 7 Mettam 12 Gash 47	2	2
19	SPL	A	Dorchester Town	3712	W 2 - 0	Clunan 43 (pen) Parker 53	2	3
26	SPL	H	Frome Town	948	D 0 - 0		3	4
28	SPL	A	St Ives Town	470	W 3 - 1	Siddons 77 84 Whayman 90	3	5
Sept 2	FAC 1Q	H	Coleshill Town	817	W 4 - 1	Mettam 7 18 Hawkins 9 Norman 24		6
9	SPL	H	Stratford Town	659	W 4 - 1	Gash 25 Clunan 36 (pen) Mettam 45 78	1	7
12	SPL	A	Royston Town	273	L 0 - 2		4	8
16	FAC 2Q	A	Nuneaton Town	627	L 1 - 3	Norman 90		9
23	SPL	H	Tiverton Town	686	W 2 - 0	Parker 16 Hawkins 38	3	10
26	SPL	H	Biggleswade Town	589	W 3 - 0	Parker 60 Hawkins 66 Jarvis 90	2	11
Oct 7	SPL	A	Weymouth	662	L 1 - 3	Gash 69	4	12
10	SPL	A	Hitchin Town	1067	W 2 - 0	Parker 56 Gash 75	4	13
14	SPL	H	Kings Langley	903	W 3 - 2	Clunan 4 50 Siddons 20	2	14
17	SPL	A	Dunstable Town	129	W 4 - 0	Hawkins 27 Clunan 50 (pen) Gaughran 76 Fryatt 90		15
24	SPL	H	Bishop Stortford	856	W 2 - 1	Holt 9 Hawkins 17	2	16
28	FAT 1Q	H	Mildenhall Town	534	L 0 - 1			17
Nov 4	SPL	H	Chesham United	648	L 0 - 1		3	18
7	SPL	A	Banbury United	277	W 2 - 1	Clunan 25 (pen) Norman 34	1	19
14	SPL	H	Royston Town	514	W 4 - 0	Gash 62 Hawkins 65 90 Clunan 72 (pen)	1	20
18	SPL	A	Basingstoke Town	303	W 2 - 1	Clunan 25 (pen) Gaughran 52	1	21
25	SPL	A	Kings Langley	201	D 0 - 0		1	22
28	SPL	A	Biggleswade Town	155	D 2 - 2	Clunan 20 (pen) Parker 75	1	23
Dec 2	SPL	H	Redditch United	621	W 3 - 1	Clunan 63 (pen) 68 (pen) Norman 85	1	24
5	SPL	A	St Neots Town	282	W 5 - 0	Lappin 10 Parker 48 Gash 69 Ward 74 Mettam 76	1	25
9	SPL	A	Farnborough Town	194	L 2 - 5	Hawkins 1 Siddons 87	1	26
22	SPL	H	Merthyr Town	502	W 1 - 0	Gash 69	1	27
26	SPL	H	St Ives Town	801	D 1 - 1	Lappin 30 (pen)	1	28
Jan 1	SPL	A	Kettering Town	1019	L 0 - 1		2	29
6	SPL	H	Dorchester Town	646	W 3 - 0	Clunan 28 44 (pen) Mettam 44	1	30
13	SPL	A	Frome Town	229	D 0 - 0		1	31
20	SPL	H	Weymouth	684	D 1 - 1	Lappin 75	2	32
27	SPL	H	Hitchin Town	500	W 4 - 0	Gash 17 King 45 57 Hawkins 60	2	33
30	SPL	H	Hereford	1181	W 3 - 2	Gash 49 Hawkins 54 Hilliard 90	2	34
Feb 3	SPL	H	Dunstable Town	699	W 5 - 0	Parker 36 Hawkins 39 Fryatt 51 Siddons 73 McQuaid 77	1	35
6	SPL	H	Gosport Borough	241	W 7 - 1	Frary 5 HAWKINS 3 (14 46 52) Fryatt 57 Gash 81 Siddons 90	1	36
17	SPL	H	Banbury United	1942	D 1 - 1	Hilliard 90	2	37
24	SPL	H	Tiverton Town	211	L 0 1		2	38
Mar 10	SPL	A	Hereford	3424	W 2 - 0	Fryatt 58 Hilliard 63	2	39
13	SPL	A	Slough Town	752	W 1 - 0	Ward 64	2	40
17	SPL	H	Farnborough Town	490	W 3 - 1	Hilliard 13 Gash 68 Siddons 82	2	41
24	SPL	H	Redditch United	381	W 1 - 0	Gash 62	2	42
27	SPL	H	Basingstoke Town	581	W 2 - 1	Demuria (og) King	2	43
31	SPL	A	Stratford Town	282	W 5 - 1	Ward 3 12 Mettam 36 Fry 50 (og) Siddons 81	2	44
Apr 7	SPL	H	Merthyr Town	721	D 0 - 0		2	45
12	SPL	H	Kettering Town	1147	W 2 - 1	Gash 59 Fryatt 70	2	46
14	SPL	A	Slough Town	822	D 2 - 2	King 15 45	2	47
21	SPL	A	St Neots Town	884	D 1 - 1	Gash 76	2	48
28	SPL	A	Chesham United	341	W 3 - 1	Parker 7 23 Norman 51	2	49
Mar 2	PO SF	H	Weymouth	1223	W 3 - 0	Norman 13 Parker 15 King 39		50
7	PO Final	H	Slough Town	2842	L 1 - 2	Hilliard 26		51

GOALSCORERS	SG	CSG	Pens	Hat tricks	Total		SG	CSG	Pens	Hat tricks	Total
2016-17 *Clunan*					11	Hilliard	5				5
Clunan	11	3	11		14	Ward	3				4
Gash	14	2			14	Lappin	3		1		3
Hawkins	11	4		1	14	Gaughran	2				2
Parker	11	3			12	Opponents					2
Mettam	6	2			8	Frary					1
Siddons	6	2			8	Holt					1
King	4				6	Jarvis					1
Norman	6	2			6	McQuaid					1
Fryatt	5	2			5	Whayman					1

KINGS LANGLEY MATCH RESULTS 2017-18

Date	Comp	H/A	Opponents	Att:	Result	Goalscorers	Pos	No.
Aug 12	SPL	H	Hereford	561	D 3 - 3	Ward 3 Weiss 55 Price 90	12	1
15	SPL	A	Dunstable Town	145	W 4 - 1	Price 2 70 Weiss 12 Turner 27	4	2
19	SPL	A	St Ives Town	224	W 1 - 0	Price 31	10	3
26	SPL	H	Kettering Town	261	L 2 - 5	Weiss 7 Price 80	12	4
28	SPL	A	Chesham United	343	L 0 - 1		15	5
Sept 2	FAC 1Q	A	Haverhill Borough	126	W 8 - 0	Turner (2) Price (2) Mitchell Weiss (2) Ward		6
9	SPL	H	Farnborugh	186	L 0 - 3		18	7
12	SPL	A	Bishop's Stortford	238	L 0 2		19	8
16	FAC 2Q	H	Margate	258	L 0 - 1			9
23	SPL	H	Banbury United	252	L 3 - 4	Weiss 12 Johnson 60 Hitchcock 69 (pen)	21	10
26	SPL	H	Gosport Borough	211	D 1 - 1	Price 47	20	11
Oct 7	SPL	H	Redditch United	305	L 1 - 2	Hitchcock 9 (pen)	21	12
14	SPL	A	Kings Lynn Town	903	L 2 - 3	Adebiyi 43 Ward 58	21	13
17	SPL	H	Dorchester Town	176	D 2 - 2	Turner 16 Weiss 45	21	14
21	SPL	A	Hereford	2319	L 0 - 3		21	15
24	SPL	H	Dunstable Town	245	W 1 - 0	Hitchcock 34 (pen)	21	16
28	FAT 1Q	A	Hendon	171	L 1 - 3	Adebiyi 32		17
Nov 4	SPL	H	Basingstoke Town	264	D 1 - 1	Ocran 39	21	18
11	SPL	A	Weymouth	634	L 0 - 2		21	19
14	SPL	H	Bishops Stortford	181	W 4 - 1	Tring 11 30 Johnson 55 Turner 76	21	20
18	SPL	A	Biggleswade Town	186	L 0 - 2		21	21
21	SPL	A	Stratford Town	130	L 1 - 3	Recci (og) 53	14	22
25	SPL	H	Kings Lynn Town	201	D 0 - 0		21	23
28	SPL	A	Gosport Borough	151	D 1 - 1	Ward 19	21	24
Dec 2	SPL	A	Tiverton Town	182	L 2 - 3	Turner 25 Ward 58		25
9	SPL	H	Frome Town	135	L 2 - 7	Weiss 12 55	21	26
16	SPL	H	Merthyr Town	157	D 2 - 2	King 60 Weiss 82	21	27
23	SPL	A	St Neots Town	318	L 2 - 3	Tring 2 Herd 29 (og)	21	28
26	SPL	H	Chesham United	317	D 0 - 0		21	29
30	SPL	A	Hitchin Town	540	L 0 - 6		21	30
Jan 6	SPL	H	St Ives Town	173	L 0 - 3		22	31
13	SPL	A	Kettering Town	612	D 1 - 1	Adebiyi 90	22	32
20	SPL	A	Redditch United	290	D 2 - 2	Weiss 65 90	22	33
27	SPL	H	Stratford Town	135	W 2 - 0	Ball 35 90	21	34
30	SPL	A	Slough Town	450	D 1 - 1	Ball 73	21	35
Feb 3	SPL	A	Dorchester Town	373	L 0 - 1		21	36
17	SPL	H	Slough Town	419	L 0 - 2		21	37
20	SPL	H	Royston Town	118	W 1 - 0	Turner 79	21	38
24	SPL	A	Banbury United	315	D 1 - 1	Johnson 90	21	39
Mar 10	SPL	A	Royston Town	240	L 0 - 2		21	40
17	SPL	A	Frome Town	117	L 1 - 2	Godfrey 45	21	41
24	SPL	H	Tiverton Town	160	D 2 - 2	Ward 47 (pen) Williams 62	21	42
31	SPL	A	Farnborough	229	W 4 - 0	Johnson 7 Weiss 12 Jung 22 Ward 81 (pen)	21	43
Apr 2	SPL	H	Hitchin Town	242	L 1 - 2	Weiss 90	21	44
7	SPL	H	St Neots Town	136	W 4 - 3	Weiss 17 22 Parr 25 (og) Johnson 40	21	45
12	SPL	H	Biggleswade Town	130	D 1 - 1	Weiss 19	21	46
14	SPL	A	Merthyr Town	402	L 1 - 4	Weiss 73	21	47
21	SPL	H	Weymouth	318	L 2 - 3	Johnson 77 Ward 90	21	48
28	SPL	A	Basingstoke Town	357	L 3 - 4	Johnson 55 Weiss 58 Turner 78	21	49

GOALSCORERS	SG	CSG	Pens	Hat tricks	Total		SG	CSG	Pens	Hat tricks	Total
2016-17 L Toomey					11	Tring	2				3
Weiss	15	4			19	Godfrey					1
Price	5	4			8	Jung					1
Turner	7				8	King					1
Ward	8	2	2		8	Mitchell					1
Johnson	8				7	Ocran					1
Adebiyi	3				3	Williams					1
Ball	2				3						
Hitchcock	3		3		3						
Opponents					3						

MERTHYR TOWN MATCH RESULTS 2017-18

Date	Comp	H/A	Opponents	Att:	Result	Goalscorers	Pos	No.
Aug 12	SPL	H	Hitchin Town	439	D 0 - 0		14	1
15	SPL	A	Stratford Town	258	D 2 - 2	Wright 27 Hancock 38	19	2
19	SPL	A	Dunstable Town	93	W 6 - 0	Jenkins 6 46 Fleetwood 22 (p) 67 Copp 60 Evans 79	9	3
26	SPL	H	Farnborough	451	W 3 - 0	Davies 39 Morgan 43 Fleetwood 67	7	4
28	SPL	A	Hereford	3366	D 1 - 1	Copp 66	9	5
Sept 2	FAC 1Q	H	Willand Rovers	303	W 6 - 1	Bowen 23 Patten 39 Touray 53 78 Morgan 86 89		6
9	SPL	H	Bishop's Stortford	438	D 0 - 0		10	7
12	SPL	H	Basingstoke Town	203	L 0 - 2		11	8
16	FAC 2Q	A	Havant & Waterlooville	296	L 1 - 2	Traylor 10		9
23	SPL	H	Royston Town	412	W 2 - 1	Evans 38 84	9	10
26	SPL	H	Tiverton Town	403	W 2 - 1	Richards 26 Traylor 45	8	11
30	SPL	A	St Ives Town	272	W 3 - 2	Bowen 10 Traylor 55 90	5	12
Oct 7	SPL	A	Kettering Town	857	L 0 - 5		8	13
10	SPL	H	Slough Town	355	L 4 - 5	Traylor 5 21 Touray 10 Nisbet 19 (og)	9	14
14	SPL	H	Gosport Borough	443	W 5 - 0	Richards 1 Traylor 5 73 Evans 18 Jenkins 63	7	15
17	SPL	A	Weymouth	527	L 2 - 3	Traylor 25 Richards 64	7	16
21	SPL	A	Hitchin Town	433	L 0 - 2		9	17
24	SPL	A	Stratford Town	351	W 3 - 1	Traylor 22 Morgan 80 Richards 90	9	18
28	FAT 1Q	A	Taunton Town	456	L 1 - 2	Richards 64		19
Nov 4	SPL	A	Redditch United	305	D 1 - 1	Copp 89	8	20
18	SPL	A	Chesham United	230	L 1 - 3	Flower 83	13	21
25	SPL	H	Dorchester Town	923	D 1 - 1	Davies 52	14	22
28	SPL	A	Tiverton Town	230	L 1 - 3	Mammonla (og) 90	14	23
Dec 2	SPL	H	Biggleswade Town	488	L 0 - 2		16	24
5	SPL	H	Banbury United	379	L 1 - 3	Prosser 81	16	25
9	SPL	A	St Neots Town	237	L 2 - 5	Morgan 10 Harris 24	16	26
16	SPL	A	Kings Langley	157	D 2 - 2	Bowen 31 Evans 77	17	27
19	SPL	H	Basingstoke Town	302	D 1 - 1	John 81	16	28
22	SPL	H	Kings Lynn Town	502	L 0 - 1		18	29
26	SPL	H	Hereford	2612	D 0 - 0		18	30
Jan 1	SPL	A	Frome Town	367	W 2 - 1	Traylor 65 79	16	31
13	SPL	A	Farnborough	286	D 2 - 2	Traylor 78 81	18	32
20	SPL	H	Kettering Town	556	L 2 - 4	Morgan 61 Traylor 85	18	33
27	SPL	A	Slough Town	663	L 2 - 3	Jenkins 30 Traylor 54	18	34
Feb 3	SPL	H	Weymouth	357	L 0 - 3		19	35
10	SPL	A	Bosport Borough	208	D 1 - 1	Jenkins 22	19	36
13	SPL	H	Dunstable Town	256	W 3 - 1	Wright 54 Traylor 59 83	18	37
17	SPL	H	St Ives Town	437	W 3 - 2	Jones 16 Morgan 62 Traylor 90 (pen)	17	38
Mar 10	SPL	A	Dorchester Town	409	W 2 - 1	Traylor 16 47	17	39
13	SPL	A	Royston Town	181	L 1 - 5	Jones 25 (pen)	17	40
17	SPL	H	St Neots Town	316	W 1 - 0	Wright 2	16	41
24	SPL	A	Biggleswade Town	202	L 1 - 2	Jenkins 31	16	42
Apr 2	SPL	H	Frome Town	402	L 3 - 4	Jones 11 Prosser 29 Wright 55	17	43
7	SPL	A	Kings Lynn Town	720	D 0 - 0		17	44
10	SPL	H	Chesham United	305	L 1 - 2	Prosser 78	17	45
14	SPL	H	Kings Langley	402	W 4 - 1	Evans 1 Prosser 40 44 Wright 79	17	46
21	SPL	A	Banbury United	512	D 3 - 3	Traylor 39 (pen) Jones 74 90	17	47
24	SPL	A	Bishop's Stortford	177	L 0 - 4		17	48
28	SPL	H	Redditch United	477	D 2 - 2	Prosser 47 51 (pen)	17	49

GOALSCORERS	SG	CSG	Pens	Hat tricks	Total		SG	CSG	Pens	Hat tricks	Total
2016-17 Traylor					25	Copp	3				3
Traylor	15	4	2		22	Fleetwood	2		1		3
Morgan	6				7	Touray	2				3
Prosser	7		2		7	Davies	2				2
Evans	4				6	Opponents					2
Jenkins	5				6	Flower					1
Jones	4		1		5	Hancock					1
Richards	5	2			5	Harris					1
Wright	3				5	John					1
Bowen	3				3	Patten					1

REDDITCH UNITED MATCH RESULTS 2017-18

Date	Comp	H/A	Opponents	Att:	Result	Goalscorers	Pos	No.
Aug 12	SPL	H	Dunstable Town	215	W 5 - 0	ANGUS 3 (9 11 45) Weir-Daley 38 Mukendi 85	1	1
15	SPL	A	Kettering Town	606	L 0 - 1		7	2
19	SPL	A	Farnborough Town	328	W' 3 - 1	Thanoj 45 Angus 60 Weir-Daley 90	4	3
26	SPL	H	Dorchester Town	241	W 4 - 0	Angus 30 Mukendi 34 Weir-Daley 46 70	4	4
28	SPL	A	Stratford Town	312	D 0 - 0		5	5
Sept 2	FAC 1Q	A	Lincoln United	114	W 1 - 0	Weir-Daley 43		6
9	SPL	H	Chesham United	221	W 3 - 1	Pendley 16 Weir-Daley 22 Angus 77	5	7
12	SPL	A	Banbury Town	337	W 3 - 1	Angus 24 Weir-Daley 31 Johnson 75	3	8
16	FAC 2Q	A	Stratford Town	326	L 1 - 4	Weir-Daley 68		9
23	SPL	H	Biggleswade Town	244	W 1 - 0	Angus 31	2	10
26	SPL	H	Slough Town	449	L 1 - 4	Angus 17	4	11
30	SPL	A	Basingstoke Town	286	L 0 - 3		6	12
Oct 7	SPL	A	Kings Langley	306	W 2 - 1	Angus 71 76 (pen)	5	13
14	SPL	H	St Ives Town	318	W 4 - 0	Thanoj 3 Angus 40 79 (pen) Weir-Daley 76	5	14
16	SPL	A	Hitchin Town	318	L 0 - 1		5	15
21	SPL	A	Dunstable Town	193	D 1 - 1	Wright 37	6	16
24	SPL	A	Kettering Town	467	D 0 - 0		6	17
28	FAT 1Q	H	Coalville Town	208	L 0 - 1			18
Nov 4	SPL	H	Merthyr Town	305	D 1 - 1	Da Veiga Monteiro 83	7	19
11	SPL	A	Tiverton Town	223	L 0 - 1		7	20
18	SPL	A	Royston Town	217	L 1 - 2	Weir-Daley 44	9	21
21	SPL	H	Frome Town	206	W 4 - 1	Sammons 21 Angus 23 Pendley 49 Da V.M.	7	22
25	SPL	H	Bishops Stortford	258	D 2 - 2	Angus 3 Pendley 59	7	23
Dec 2	SPL	A	Kings Lynn Town	621	L 1 - 3	Sammons 36	8	24
16	SPL	H	St Neots Town	234	D 2 - 2	Sammons 82 Weir-Daley 90	8	25
22	SPL	A	Weymouth	629	L 0 - 5		12	26
Dec 26	SPL	H	Stratford Town	345	L 0 - 2		14	27
Jan 1	SPL	A	Hereford	3083	L 2 - 5	Sammons 8 (Pen) Fleetwood 29	15	28
6	SPL	A	Farnborough Town	284	W 7 - 1	Page 12 FLEETWOOD 4 (43 50 52 60) Simpson 29 Wright 80	15	29
13	SPL	A	Dorchester Town	443	L 0 - 1		15	30
16	SPL	H	Banbury United	270	D 2 - 2	Page 9 Fleetwood 90	15	31
20	SPL	A	Kings Langley	290	D 2 - 2	Dunkley 6 Sammons 42	15	32
27	SPL	A	Frome Town	256	L 0 - 1		15	33
Feb 3	SPL	H	Hitchin Town	274	D 2 - 2	Davie 14 Fleetwood 74	15	34
6	SPL	A	Slough Town	375	L 0 - 4		16	35
17	SPL	H	Basingstoke Town	312	W 3 - 0	Fleetwood 45 Page 46 Sammons 78 (pen)	16	36
20	SPL	H	Gosport Borough	211	W 4 - 2	Davie 7 61 Sammons 23 Morrell 84	13	37
24	SPL	A	Biggleswade Town	151	L 0 - 1		16	38
Mar 10	SPL	A	Bishop's Stortford	242	L 0 - 3		16	39
17	SPL	A	Gosport Borough	223	W 5 - 1	Mutton 9 Fleetwood 25 41 Wright 47 Mills 63	14	40
24	SPL	H	Kings Lynn Town	381	L 0 - 1		15	41
30	SPL	A	Chesham United	231	L 0 - 2		15	42
Apr 2	SPL	H	Hereford	1651	L 0 - 2		15	43
4	SPL	H	Royston Town	156	W 1 - 0	Fleetwood 52	15	44
7	SPL	H	Weymouth	332	L 1 - 2	Dunkley 11	14	45
14	SPL	A	St Neots Town	228	L 1 - 2	Sammons 42 (pen)	14	46
19	SPL	A	St Ives Town	74	L 0 - 1		15	47
21	SPL	H	Tiverton Town	302	W 3 - 2	Fleetwood 2 Page 19 73	14	48
28	SPL	A	Merthyr Town	471	D 2 - 2	Page 21 Fleetwood 90	14	49

GOALSCORERS	SG	CSG	Pens	Hat tricks	Total		SG	CSG	Pens	Hat tricks	Total
2016-17 Johnson					9	Dunckley	2				2
Angus	11	2	2	1	15	Mukendi	2				2
Fleetwood	10	2		1	13	Thanoj	2				2
Weir-Daley	9	4			11	Johnson					1
Sammons	8		2		8	Mills					1
Page	5				6	Morrell					1
Davie	2				3	Mutton					1
Pendley	3	2			3	Simpson					1
Wright	3				3						
Da Veiga Monteiro	2				2						

ROYSTON TOWN MATCH RESULTS 2017-18

Date	Comp	H/A	Opponents	Att:	Result	Goalscorers	Pos	No.
Aug 12	SPL	H	Stratford Town	224	L 1 - 2	Frendo 21		1
16	SPL	A	Farnborough	324	W 1 - 0	Potton 16		2
19	SPL	A	Gosport Borough	287	W 3 - 2	Castiglione 18 Braithwaite 47 Ingrey 85	7	3
26	SPL	H	Dunstable Town	195	D 1 - 1	Ives 12	11	4
28	SPL	A	Hitchin Town	513	L 0 - 1		12	5
Sept 2	FAC 1Q	A	Dunstable Town	234	W 2 - 0	Marriott 25 Vasey 83	12	6
9	SPL	A	Hereford	512	L 1 - 4	Marriott 6	15	7
12	SPL	H	Kings Lynn Town	273	W 2 - 0	Scott Bridges 72 Marriott 81	14	8
16	FAC 2Q	A	Braintree Town	256	D 2 - 2	Scott Bridges 23 Marriott 67		9
19	FAC 2Qr	H	Braintree Town	251	L 1 - 2	Murray 63		10
23	SPL	A	Merthyr Town	413	L 1 - 2	Scott Bridges 31	17	11
26	SPL	H	St Neots Town	207	L 1 - 3	Oyinsane 5	17	12
Oct 7	SPL	A	Chesham United	412	W 2 - 1	Frendo 22 Marriott 48	15	13
10	SPL	A	St Ives Town	200	W 2 - 1	Marriott 8 73	13	14
14	SPL	H	Frome Town	198	W 3 - 0	Frendo 20 47 Scott Bridges 78	12	15
21	SPL	A	Stratford Town	236	D 1 - 1	Corcoran 62		16
24	SPL	A	Farnborough	174	W 4 - 3	Scott Bridges 63 Vasey 82 86 Murray 90	13	17
28	FAT 1Q	H	Enfield Town	303	W 2 - 0	Marriott 41 Potton 66		18
Nov 11	FAT 2Q	H	Leatherhead	219	W 3 - 2	Darling 42 Castiglione 53 Murray 90		19
14	SPL	A	Kings Lynn Town	514	L 0 - 4		14	20
18	SPL	H	Redditch United	217	W 2 - 1	Powell 46 Scott Bridges 59	12	21
21	SPL	A	Biggleswade Town	143	D 1 - 1	Frendo 32	12	22
25	FAT 3Qr	A	Eastbourne Borough	277	D 1 - 1	Potton 80		23
28	FAT 3	H	Eastbourne Borough	189	L 2 - 2	Castiglione 16 Asafu-Adaye 47 (Lost 2-3 on pens)		24
Dec 2	SPL	H	Dorchester Town	198	W 3 - 1	Potton 45 Oyinsani 70 85	13	25
9	SPL	A	Banbury United	265	L 0 - 3		15	26
23	SPL	A	Basingstoke Town	293	D 0 - 0		15	27
26	SPL	A	Hitchin Town	493	W 2 - 1	Marriott 6 Scott Bridges 10	12	28
30	SPL	H	Tiverton Town	239	W 3 - 0	Frendo 57 65 Marriott 76	10	29
Jan 1	SPL	A	Bishops Stortford	377	W 3 - 0	MARRIOTT 3 (17 37 63)	8	30
6	SPL	H	Gosport Borough	245	W 5 - 0	Corcoran 32 Marriott 33 90 (pen) Frendo 40 54	8	31
13	SPL	A	Dunstable Town	107	W 5 - 0	MARRIOTT 3 (19 75 (pen) 79) Scott Bridges 24 67	6	32
20	SPL	H	Chesham United	246	L 0 - 2		8	33
23	SPL	H	St Neots Town	225	W 2 - 1	Frendo 6 Chappell 16	7	34
30	SPL	H	Weymouth	218	L 1 - 2	Frendo 19	8	35
Feb 3	SPL	H	Kettering Tiown	410	W 4 - 3	Marriott 32 (pen) Scott Bridges 35 Castiglione 63 Gordon 86	6	36
10	SPL	A	Frome Town	164	W 4 - 1	Scott Bridges 70 Gordon 30 78 Hankins 87	5	37
17	SPL	A	Weymouth	811	L 0 - 3		7	38
20	SPL	A	Kings Langley	118	L 0 - 1		9	39
Mar 10	SPL	H	Kings Langley	240	W 4 - 0	Marriott 17 65 Braithwaite 54 Gordon 88	9	40
13	SPL	H	Merthyr Town	181	W 5 - 1	MARRIOTT 4 (22 79 83 85) Murray 30	7	41
20	SPL	A	Kettering Town	500	L 1 - 4	Murray 2	8	42
24	SPL	A	Dorchester Town	397	L 0 - 1		9	43
27	SPL	A	St Ives Town	178	W 3 - 1	MARRIOTT 3 (24 50 76)	8	44
31	SPL	A	Hereford	2657	L 0 - 2		8	45
Apr 2	SPL	H	Bishop's Stortford	387	W 4 - 2	Hankins 60 Scott Bridges 70 (pen) Castiglione 75 Powell 808	6	46
4	SPL	A	Redditch United	156	L 0 - 1		8	47
7	SPL	H	Basingstoke Town	251	W 1 - 0	Murray 48	6	48
10	SPL	A	Banbury United	173	D 1 - 1	Powell 9	6	49
14	SPL	A	Tiverton Town	229	W 2 - 1	Corcoran 20 Scott Bridges 79	6	50
21	SPL	H	Biggleswade Town	256	W 4 - 0	Fielding 17 (og) Marriott 18 63 (pen) Baulk 78	6	51
24	SPL	H	Slough Town	255	L 0 - 4		6	52
28	SPL	A	Slough Town	759	L 1 - 2	Murray 51	7	53

GOALSCORERS	SG	CSG	Pens	Hat tricks	Total		SG	CSG	Pens	Hat tricks	Total
Marriott	19	4	4	4	30	Powell	3				3
Scott Bridges	11	2	1		13	Braithwaite	1				2
Frendo	8				11	Hankins	2				2
Murray	7	2			7	Asafu-Adaye					1
Castiglone	4				5	Baulk					1
Gordon	4				4	Chappell					1
Potton	5	2			4	Darling					1
Oyinsane	2				3	Ingrey					1
Vasey	2				3	Ives					1
Corcoran	3				3	Opponents					1

SLOUGH TOWN MATCH RESULTS 2017-18

Date	Comp	H/A	Opponents	Att:	Result	Goalscorers	Pos	No.
Aug 12	SPL	H	Kettering Town	760	L 1 - 2	Dobson 90	17	1
15	SPL	A	Gosport Borough	382	W 5 - 1	Lench 5 Flood 27 53 (p) Jackman 77 Dobson 93	8	2
19	SPL	A	Hereford	2684	W 1 - 0	Togwell 45	5	3
26	SPL	H	St Ives Town	618	W 3 - 0	Flood 38 Dobson 46 78	5	4
28	SPL	A	Farnborough	483	W 2 - 1	Lench 11 Flood 90	4	5
Sept 2	FAC 1Q	A	Berkhampstead	366	W 3 - 1	Williams 15 Togwell 35 Lench 55		6
9	SPL	H	Dunstable Town	786	W 8 - 1	WADKINS 3 (14 54 64) Nisbet 55 Williams 71 91 Flood 82 Dobson 88	2	7
12	SPL	H	Hitchin Town	442	W 4 - 0	DOBSON 3 (24 71 75) Dunn 86	1	8
16	FAC 2Q	H	Dulwich Hamlet	712	W 3 - 2	Wadkins 53 Togwell 78 Williams 84		9
23	SPL	A	St Neots Town	310	L 1 - 3	Flood 5	5	10
26	SPL	A	Redditch United	449	W 4 - 1	Flood 24 54 Williams 41 Harris 69	3	11
30	FAC 3Q	H	Poole Town	680	W 2 - 1	Flood 57 Wells 83		12
Oct 7	SPL	H	Biggleswade Town	760	W 2 - 1	Harris 41 Wadkins 80	2	13
10	SPL	A	Merthyr Town	355	W 5 - 4	Smart 50 Flood 62 Harris 72 Dobson 89 90	2	14
14	FAC 4Q	H	Folkestone Invicta	926	W 1 - 0	Harris 4		15
17	SPL	H	Tiverton Town	514	W 2 - 0	Dobson 22 Flood 34	2	16
21	SPL	A	Kettering Town	824	D 0 - 0		1	17
24	SPL	A	Gosport Borough	678	W 5 - 1	WADKINS 3 (14 34 72) Williams 40 81	1	18
28	FAT 1Q	A	Kidlington	201	W 4 - 1	LENCH 3 (7 45 85) Williams 90		19
Nov 4	FAC 1	A	Gainsborough Trinity	1630	W 6 - 0	LENCH 3 (35 46 64) Flood 52 Williams 71 Fraser 75		20
11	FAT 2Q	A	Malden & Tiptree	179	W 4 - 1	Lench 41 Dobson 61 72 Togwell 90		21
18	SPL	H	Weymouth	923	W 3 - 0	Wells 24 Dobson 40 Jackman 86	2	22
21	SPL	A	Banbury United	325	D 2 - 2	Dobson 7 Flood 77	2	23
25	FAT 3Q	H	Hendon	251	D 1 - 1	Dobson 90		24
28	FAT 3Qr	H	Hendon	626	D 1 - 1	Williams 89 (Lost 0-3 on pens)		25
Dec 4	FAC 2	H	Rochdale	1950	L 0 - 4			26
9	SPL	H	Bishop's Stortford	551	L 2 - 4	Dobson 40 Clifford 77 (og)	6	27
22	SPL	H	Stratford Town	598	D 1 - 1	Inns 90	6	28
26	SPL	A	Farnborough	668	W 5 - 1	Dobson 2 Nisbet 49 Webb 55 Flood 65 James 80	6	29
Jan 1	SPL	A	Chesham United	520	D 1 - 1	Harris 76	7	30
6	SPL	H	Hereford	1561	D 2 - 2	Flood 45 Harris 50	6	31
16	SPL	H	Dorchester Town	436	W 2 - 0	Lench 8 Williams 45	6	32
27	SPL	H	Merthyr Town	663	W 3 - 2	Lench 6 90 Dobson 63	5	33
30	SPL	H	Kings Langley	450	D 1 - 1	Inns 30	5	34
Feb 3	SPL	A	Tiverton Town	286	L 0 - 3		8	35
6	SPL	H	Redditch United	375	W 4 - 0	Harris 8 51 Dobson 25 Mutton 85 (og)	5	36
10	SPL	A	Banbury United	614	L 0 - 1		6	37
17	SPL	A	Kings Langley	419	W 2 - 0	Nesbit 26 Flood 32	6	38
24	SPL	H	St Neots Town	615	W 2 - 1	Coles 1 44	6	39
Mar 6	SPL	H	Basingstoke Town	471	D 1 - 1	Flood 79	5	40
10	SPL	H	Frome Town	551	W 2 - 1	Flood 48 Dunn 68	5	41
13	SPL	A	Kings Lynn Town	752	L 0 - 1		5	42
17	SPL	A	Bishop's Stortford	289	D 2 - 2	Harris 75 Coles 88	5	43
20	SPL	A	St Ives Town	179	W 4 - 1	Dunn 42 (pen) Harris 45 50 Williams 90	5	44
24	SPL	A	Basingstoke Town	503	W 4 - 1	Harris 6 Wells 45 Williams 54 Dunn 90	5	45
27	SPL	A	Weymouth	822	L 0 - 1		5	46
30	SPL	A	Dunstable Town	282	W 3 - 0	Togwell 25 90 Williams 40	5	47
Apr 2	SPL	H	Chesham United	784	W 2 - 1	Dobson 22 Harris 86	5	48
4	SPL	A	Frome Town	161	W 4 - 0	Harris 35 Coles 38 Gilkes 83 Dobson 87	5	49
7	SPL	A	Stratford Town	314	W 1 - 0	Coles 35	5	50
10	SPL	A	Biggleswade Town	159	W 5 - 3	FLOOD 3 (7 18 64) Williams 37 Coles 90	4	51
14	SPL	H	Kings Lynn Town	822	D 2 - 2	Coles 1 87	5	52
16	SPL	A	Hitchin Town	321	W 1 - 0	Lench 70	4	53
21	SPL	A	Dorchester Town	487	W 1 - 0	Coles 84	4	54
24	SPL	A	Royston Town	255	W 4 - 0	Harris 3 11 Coles 20 Dobson 85	4	55
28	SPL	A	Royston Town	759	W 2 - 1	Dobson 6 48	3	56
May 2	PO SF	H	Kettring Town	1246	W 3 - 1	Coles 13 Dobson 52 71 (pens)		57
7	PO Final	A	King's Lynn Town	2842	W 2 - 1	Flood 43 Williams 89		58

GOALSCORERS	SG	CSG	Pens	Hat tricks	Total		SG	CSG	Pens	Hat tricks	Total
2016-17 Dobson					17	Wells	3				3
Dobson	20	4	2	1	27	Inns	2				3
Flood	18	3	1	1	21	Jackman	2				2
Harris	13	3			16	Opponents					2
Williams	13	3			16	Dunn					1
Lench	8	3		2	13	Fraser					1
Coles	9	4			11	Gilkes					1
Wadkins	4			2	8	James					1
Togwell	5				6	Smart					1
Dunn	4		1		4	Webb					1
Nisbet	3				3						

ST. IVES TOWN MATCH RESULTS 2017-18

Date	Comp	H/A	Opponents	Att:	Result	Goalscorers	Pos	No.
Aug 12	SPL	A	Weymouth	665	W 1 - 0	Hilliard 83	10	1
15	SPL	H	Biggleswade Town	184	L 1 - 2	Clark 70	12	2
19	SPL	H	Kings Langley	224	D 1 - 1	Seymore-Shove 69	14	3
26	SPL	A	Slough Town	616	L 0 - 3		15	4
28	SPL	H	Kings Lynn Town	470	L 1 - 3	Hartley 58	18	5
Sept 2	FAC 1Q	H	Coalville Town	203	W 1 - 0	Draycott 72		6
9	SPL	A	Basingstoke Town	248	L 2 - 3	Hartley 44 Seymore-Shove 61	20	7
12	SPL	H	Kettering Town	354	L 3 - 4	KELLY 3 (1 62 72)	21	8
16	FAC 2Q	A	Stourbridge	765	L 0 - 2			9
23	SPL	A	Farnborough	274	L 1 - 2	Ogbonna 17	22	10
25	SPL	A	Hitchin Town	325	D 2 - 2	Hartley 12 Clark 65	22	11
30	SPL	H	Merthyr Town	272	L 2 - 3	Draycott 14 Hall 84	22	12
Oct 7	SPL	H	Tiverton Town	251	L 1 - 2	Seymore-Shove 26	22	13
10	SPL	A	Royston Town	200	L 1 - 2	Hall 19	22	14
14	SPL	A	Redditch United	316	L 0 - 4		22	15
17	SPL	H	Bishops Stortford	162	L 0 - 1		22	16
21	SPL	H	Weymouth	226	L 1 - 2	Seymore-Shove 69	23	17
24	SPL	A	Biggleswade Town	172	W 2 - 0	Clark 21 Seymour-Shove 87	22	18
28	FAT 1Q	A	Stafford Rangers	495	L 0 - 6			19
Nov 11	SPL	H	Dunstable Town	185	W 2 - 1	Hall 19 Clark 24	22	20
18	SPL	H	Frome Town	145	D 2 - 2	McGowan 7 Hall 18	22	21
21	SPL	A	Hereford	1705	L 0 - 4		22	22
25	SPL	A	Stratford Town	201	L 0 - 3		22	23
28	SPL	H	Hitchin Town	175	L 1 - 3	Hall 29 (pen)	22	24
Dec 2	SPL	H	Banbury United	201	D 2 - 2	McGeorge 2 Snaith 25	22	25
5	SPL	A	Kettering Town	499	L 1 - 4	Draycott 88	22	26
16	SPL	A	Dorchester Town	360	L 0 - 6		22	27
23	SPL	H	Gosport Borough	231	W 1 - 0	Moyes 59	22	28
26	SPL	A	Kings Lynn Town	801	D 1 - 1	Watson 48	22	29
Jan 6	SPL	A	Kings Langley	173	W 3 - 0	Snaith 54 Knowles 65 Clark 67	21	30
9	SPL	H	St Neots Town	236	D 1 - 1	Rogers 49	21	31
20	SPL	A	Tiverton Town	312	W 3 - 2	Snaith 56 (pen) 75 Rogers 90	21	32
30	SPL	A	Chesham United	211	L 0 - 4		22	33
Feb 3	SPL	A	Bishop's Stortford	307	L 3 - 4	Baker 10 Snaith 28 Knowles 66	22	34
17	SPL	A	Merthyr Town	427	L 2 - 3	Watson 28 (pen) Baker 63	22	35
24	SPL	H	Farnborough	239	L 2 - 4	Knowles 19 Ogbonna 65	22	36
Mar 14	SPL	A	Frome Town	91	L 0 - 1		22	37
20	SPL	H	Slough Town	179	L 1 - 4	Clark 27	22	38
24	SPL	A	Banbury United	366	L 1 - 3	Baker 15	22	39
27	SPL	H	Royston Town	178	L 1 - 3	Baker 41	22	40
Apr 5	SPL	A	St Neots Town	238	L 1 - 3	Kelly 88	22	41
7	SPL	A	Gosport Borough	241	D 0 - 0		22	42
14	SPL	H	Dorchester Town	192	L 1 - 2	Kelly 23	22	43
17	SPL	H	Stratford Town	67	L 2 - 6	Clark 3 Knowles 38 (pen)	22	44
19	SPL	H	Redditch United	74	W 1 - 0	Snaith 52	22	45
21	SPL	A	Dunstable Town	164	D 0 - 0		22	46
24	SPL	H	Chesham United	70	L 0 - 2		22	47
26	SPL	H	Basingstoke Town	76	D 2 - 2	Ogbonna 54 61 (pen)	22	48
28	SPL	H	Hereford	702	L 0 - 2		22	49

GOALSCORERS	SG	CSG	Pens	Hat tricks	Total		SG	CSG	Pens	Hat tricks	Total
2016-17 Seymore-Shove					13	Hartley	3				3
Clark	7	2			7	Rogers	2	2			2
Snaith	5		1		6	Watson	2		1		2
Hall	5		1		5	Hilliard					1
Kelly	3		1	1	5	McGeorge					1
Seymore-Shove	5	2			5	McGowan					1
Baker	4				4	Moyes					1
Knowles	3		1		4						
Ogbonna	3		1		4						
Draycott	3				3						

ST. NEOTS TOWN MATCH RESULTS 2017-18

Date	Comp	H/A	Opponents	Att:	Result		Goalscorers	Pos	No.
Aug 12	SPL	H	Farnborough	275	L	0 - 1		18	1
14	SPL	A	Hitchin Town	520	D	2 - 2	Wiltshire 45 Watson 90	15	2
19	SPL	A	Stratford Town	209	D	1 - 1	Semble-Ferris 21	19	3
26	SPL	H	Hereford	516	W	3 - 1	Haysham 21 Mills 46 Molyneux 60	20	4
28	SPL	A	Kettering Town	727	L	0 - 3		21	5
Sept 1	FAC 1Q	A	Cambridge City	312	L	1 - 3	Watson 75		6
9	SPL	H	Dorchester Town	178	W	5 - 0	Herd 9 Sinclair 65 Sembie-ferris 67 Williams 72 79 (pen)	17	7
12	SPL	A	Biggleswade Town	201	L	0 - 2		18	8
23	SPL	H	Slough Town	310	W	3 - 1	Meechan 6 78 Semble-Ferris 90	17	9
26	SPL	H	Royston Town	207	W	3 - 1	Horne 14 Meechan 64 Thomas 76 (og)	15	10
30	SPL	A	Tiverton Town	229	W	2 - 1	Home 25 41	12	11
Oct 7	SPL	A	Frome Town	251	D	2 - 2	Williams 59 Semble-Ferris 73	12	12
10	SPL	H	Dunstable Town	180	D	2 - 2	Meechan 25 Williams 65	12	13
14	SPL	H	Weymouth	348	L	1 - 2	Herd 64	13	14
17	SPL	A	Chesham United	192	D	2 - 2	Parr 16 Sinclair 76	12	15
21	SPL	A	Farnborough	285	W	4 - 2	Knight 8 Wood 42 Meechan 84 Williams 90	11	16
24	SPL	H	Hitchin Town	333	D	1 - 1	Williams 49	11	17
28	FAT 1Q	H	Corby Town	275	W	3 - 2	Sembie-Ferris 52 McDevitt 60 Meechan 64		18
Nov 4	SPL	A	Gosport Borough	236	W	1 - 0	Williams 12 (pen)	12	19
11	FAT 2Q	H	Stourbridge	323	L	2 - 3	Semble-Ferris 46 Bradshaw 84		20
14	SPL	H	Biggleswade Town	138	D	0 - 0		12	21
18	SPL	A	Banbury United	336	D	1 - 1	Williams 54	11	22
25	SPL	H	Basingstoke Town	233	W	2 - 1	Bridges 26 Herd 90 (pen)	10	23
Dec 2	SPL	A	Bishop's Stortford	307	W	2 - 1	Bridges 8 Shariff 65	9	24
5	SPL	H	Kings Lynn Town	209	L	0 - 5		10	25
9	SPL	H	Merthyr Town	237	W	5 - 2	Irwin 14 56 Semble-Ferris 30 Knight 31 49	9	26
16	SPL	A	Redditch United	234	D	2 - 2	Broccoli 3 Wood 18	8	27
23	SPL	H	Kings Langley	318	W	3 - 2	Semble-Ferris 24 Irwin 27 Williams 82	7	28
26	SPL	H	Kettering Town	509	L	2 - 4	Irwin 58 Williams 68	8	29
Jan 6	SPL	H	Stratford Town	233	D	2 - 2	Williams 27 Shariff 86	10	30
9	SPL	A	St Ives Town	236	D	1 - 1	Shariff 82	10	31
20	SPL	A	Frome Town	277	L	1 - 6	Semble-Ferris 90	12	32
23	SPL	A	Royston Town	275	L	1 - 2	Irwin74	12	33
27	SPL	A	Dunstable Town	105	W	3 - 2	Williams 14 (pen) 90 Parr 70	12	34
Feb 3	SPL	H	Chesham United	239	W	3 - 1	Herd 13 (pen) Irwin 28 39	11	35
10	SPL	A	Weymouth	653	L	1 - 3	Bradshaw 73	11	36
17	SPL	H	Tiverton Town	184	W	1 - 0	Wood 26	11	37
20	SPL	A	Hereford	2402	L	0 - 1		11	38
24	SPL	A	Slough Town	615	L	1 - 2	Shariff 45	11	39
Mar 10	SPL	A	Basingstoke Town	264	L	0 - 1		13	40
17	SPL	A	Merthyr Town	316	L	0 - 1		13	41
24	SPL	H	Bishop's Stortford	280	D	2 - 2	Shariff 47 Williams 62	14	42
Apr 5	SPL	H	St Ives Town	238	W	3 - 1	Bridges 4 Shariff 40 Norville-Williams 54	14	43
7	SPL	A	Kings Langley	136	L	3 - 4	Knight 4 81 Shariff 81	14	44
9	SPL	A	Dorchester Town	257	W	4 - 0	Meecham 6 Semble -Ferris 17 Shariff 47 58	13	45
14	SPL	H	Redditch United	228	W	2 - 1	McDevitt 5 Meechan 37	12	46
17	SPL	H	Banbury United	166	W	3 - 0	Norville -Williams 30 Williams 49 Shariff 86	11	47
21	SPL	A	Kings Lynn Town	884	D	1 - 1	Shariff 86	11	48
28	SPL	H	Gosport Borough	280	L	0 - 4		12	49

GOALSCORERS	SG	CSG	Pens	Hat tricks	Total		SG	CSG	Pens	Hat tricks	Total
2016-17 Brown					19	Bradshaw	2				2
Williams (Dylan)	14	2	3		15	McDevitt	2				2
Shariff	10	4			11	Norville-Williams	2				2
Semble -Ferris	9				10	Parr	2				2
Meechan	7	2			8	Sinclair	2				2
Irwin	5	2			7	Watson	2				2
Knight	3				5	Broccoli	1				1
Herd	4		2		4	Haysham					1
Bridges	3	2			3	Mills					1
Horne	2				3	Molyneux					1
Wood	3				3	Opponents					1
						Wiltshire					1

STRATFORD TOWN MATCH RESULTS 2017-18

Date	Comp	H/A	Opponents	Att:	Result	Goalscorers	Pos	No.
Aug 12	SPL	A	Royston Town	224	W 2 - 1	Stephens 5 Thomas 27	7	1
15	SPL	H	Merthyyr Town	258	D 2 - 2	Luckie 40 Ahenkorah 50	6	2
19	SPL	H	St Neots Town	324	D 1 - 1	Fry 8	11	3
26	SPL	A	Weymouth	676	D 1 - 1	Evans 30	14	4
28	SPL	H	Redditch United	312	D 0 - 0		11	5
Sept 2	FAC 1Q	H	Newcastle Town	187	W 4 - 0	Luckie 42 Grocott 54 Ahenkorah 65 (pen) 90		6
9	SPL	A	Kings Lynn Town	659	L 1 - 5	Stephens 68 (pen)	13	7
12	SPL	A	Hereford	2005	L 2 - 5	Stephens 79 Luckie 81	16	8
16	FAC 2Q	H	Redditch United	326	W 4 - 1	Fry 33 Francis 64 Grocott 82 85 (pen)		9
23	SPL	H	Gosport Borough	150	W 2 - 0	Francis 5 Grocott 11	15	10
26	SPL	H	Chesham United	178	L 1 - 3	Luckie 90	15	11
30	FAC 3Q	A	Scarborough Athletic	1180	D 2 - 2	Stephens 7 Summerfield 23		12
Oct 3	FAC 3Qr	H	Scarborough Athletic	498	L 1 - 4	Luckie 26		13
7	SPL	A	Hitchin Town	755	L 0 - 4		19	14
14	SPL	H	Dunstable Town	194	W 5 - 1	Akenkorah 7 TAYLOR 3 (28 41 44) Marsden 73	19	15
21	SPL	H	Royston Town	236	D 1 - 1	Stephens 2	19	16
24	SPL	A	Merthyr Town	351	L 1 - 3	Summerfield 40	19	17
28	FAT 1Q	H	Bedworth United	176	W 2 - 1	Taylor 26 Grocott 48		18
Nov 1	SPL	A	Frome Town	197	L 0 - 3		19	19
4	SPL	H	Bishop's Stortford	184	W 3 - 1	Grocott 34 (pen) Bako 70 Stephens 75	19	20
11	FAT 2Q	A	Lancaster City	252	L 0 - 3			21
18	SPL	A	Tiverton Town	227	L 1 - 2	Stephens 5	20	22
21	SPL	H	Kings Langley	130	W 3 - 1	Grocott 30 Summerfield 33 Stephens 63	18	23
25	SPL	H	St Ives Town	201	W 3 - 0	Stephens 25 Luckie 29 Ahenkorah 80 (pen)		24
28	SPL	A	Chesham United	151	W 3 - 1	Evans 6 Grocott 62 Locke 89 (og)	15	25
Dec 2	SPL	H	Farnborough	184	D 2 - 2	Taylor 2 Stephens 66	15	26
4	SPL	A	Dorchester Town	276	W 2 - 1	Stephens 68 Recci 85	13	27
9	SPL	A	Kettering Town	508	L 0 - 2		15	28
16	SPL	H	Biggleswade Town	183	W 1 - 0	Taylor 58	13	29
22	SPL	A	Slough Town	598	D 1 - 1	Taylor 54	13	30
26	SPL	A	Redditch United	345	W 2 - 0	Stephens 34 45	10	31
Jan 1	SPL	H	Banbury United	376	L 2 - 3	Stephens 18 Taylor 61	13	32
6	SPL	A	St Neots Town	233	D 2 - 2	Ahenkorah 15 Stephens 33	13	33
9	SPL	H	Hereford	707	L 1 - 2	Taylor 88	13	34
13	SPL	H	Weymouth	274	D 0 - 0		14	35
27	SPL	A	KIngs Langley	135	L 0 - 2		14	36
Feb 3	SPL	H	Frome Town	172	L 1 - 2	Stephens 84	14	37
10	SPL	A	Dunstable Town	78	W 3 - 0	Taylor 9 50 Francis 76	14	38
17	SPL	H	Dorchester Town	214	W 2 - 0	Ahenkorah 44 Grocott 45	13	39
20	SPL	A	Basingstoke Town	194	L 1 - 2	Taylor 52	14	40
24	SPL	A	Gosport Borough	238	W 1 - 0	Thomas 49	14	41
Mar 17	SPL	H	Kettering Town	248	L 0 - 4		15	42
20	SPL	H	Tiverton Town	146	L 1 - 2	Stephens 51	15	43
24	SPL	A	Farnborough	224	W 4 - 1	Stephens 19 40 Grocott 25 30	13	44
27	SPL	H	Hitchin Town	186	L 1 - 2	Francis 12	15	45
31	SPL	H	Kings Lynn Town	282	L 1 - 5	Recci 16	15	46
Apr 7	SPL	H	Slough Town	314	L 0 - 1		15	47
12	SPL	A	Banbury United	302	L 0 - 4		15	48
14	SPL	A	Biggleswade Town	125	L 1 - 3	Stephens 52 (pen)	16	49
17	SPL	A	St Ives Town	67	W 6 - 2	Evans 2 Ahenkorah 17 Fry 24 Stephens 32 56 Taylor 35	15	50
21	SPL	H	Basingstoke Town	266	L 0 - 1		15	51
28	SPL	A	Bishop's Stortford	307	D 1 - 1	Stephens 26	15	52

GOALSCORERS	SG	CSG	Pens	Hat tricks	Total		SG	CSG	Pens	Hat tricks	Total
2016-17 Akenkorah					13	Recci	2				2
Stephens	20	3	2		23	Thomas					2
Taylor	10	2		1	13	Bako					1
Grocott	10	2	2		11	Marsden					1
Akenkorah	7		2		8	Opponents					1
Luckie	4				6						
Francis	4	2			4						
Evans	3				3						
Fry	3				3						
Summerfield	3				3						

TIVERTON TOWN MATCH RESULTS 2017-18

Date	Comp	H/A	Opponents	Att:	Result		Goalscorers	Pos	No.
Aug 12	SPL	H	Bishop's Stortford	253	W	2 - 1	Gardner 55 Bath 78	8	1
15	SPL	A	Hereford United	2424	L	0 - 1		13	2
19	SPL	A	Chesham United	269	D	1 - 1	Short 89	15	3
26	SPL	H	Gosport Borough	265	W	2 - 0	Price 83 Bath 84	10	4
28	SPL	A	Frome Town	258	W	1 - 0	Price 10	7	5
Sept 2	FAC 1Q	A	Banbury United	436	L	2 - 4	Landricombe 39 81		6
9	SPL	H	Hitchin Town	247	W	3 - 1	Landricombe 19 45 Howe 62	7	7
12	SPL	H	Weymouth	249	W	2 - 1	Landricombe 48 Short 66	5	8
16	SPL	H	Basingstoke Town	220	W	3 - 2	Landricombe 17 19 Mammola 45	1	9
23	SPL	A	Kings Lynn Town	686	L	0 - 2		4	10
26	SPL	A	Merthyr Town	403	L	1 - 2	Landricombe 70	5	11
30	SPL	H	St Neots Town	229	L	1 - 2	Landricombe 68	7	12
Oct 7	SPL	A	St Ives Town	251	W	2 - 1	Howe 45 81	6	13
17	SPL	A	Slough Town	514	L	0 - 2		7	14
21	SPL	A	Bishops Stortford	322	W	2 - 1	Howe 56 62	7	15
24	SPL	H	Hereford	620	D	2 - 2	Howe 26 (pen) Bath 84	7	16
28	FAT 2Q	H	Banbury United	248	D	2 - 2	Howe 60 (pen) Hall 64		17
31	FAT 2Qr	A	Banbury United	230	L	2 - 3	Landricombe 58 77		18
Nov 4	SPL	A	Banbury United	413	W	2 - 1	Landricombe 72 Howe 82	6	19
11	SPL	H	Redditch United	223	W	1 - 0	Landricombe 25	6	20
14	SPL	A	Weymouth	517	L	0 - 2		6	21
18	SPL	H	Stratford Town	227	W	2 - 1	Bath 72 Landricombe 81	6	22
25	SPL	H	Dunstable Town	106	W	2 - 1	Landricombe 5 62		23
28	SPL	H	Merthyr Town	230	W	3 - 1	Landricombe 5 Price 55 Hurst 82	3	24
Dec 2	SPL	H	Kings Langley	182	W	3 - 2	LANDRICOMBE 3 (30 48 pen 79 4pen)	3	25
9	SPL	A	Biggleswade Town	115	L	0 - 4		4	26
23	SPL	H	Farnborough	283	W	2 - 0	Landricombe 23 Price 76	4	27
30	SPL	A	Royston Town	239	L	0 - 3		4	28
Jan 1	SPL	A	Dorchester Town	489	L	0 - 3		5	29
6	SPL	H	Chesham United	201	L	1 - 2	Bath 61	5	30
13	SPL	A	Gosport Borough	218	W	5 - 0	Landricombe 26 34 Short 37 Lewington 70 J.Rogers 85	5	31
20	SPL	H	St Ives Town	312	L	2 - 3	Landricombe 21 Price 46	5	32
27	SPL	A	Basingstoke Town	213	L	2 - 6	Lewington 76 Landricombe 90	7	33
Feb 3	SPL	H	Slough Town	286	W	3 - 0	Hall 49 77 Bath 63	7	34
17	SPL	A	St Neots Town	184	L	0 - 1		9	35
20	SPL	H	Kettering Town	181	L	0 3		9	36
24	SPL	H	Kings Lynn Town	211	W	1 - 0	Bath 87	7	37
Mar 10	SPL	H	Dunstable Town	288	W	7 - 1	J.Rogers 21 47 BATH 3 (33 43 49) Landricombe 76 Lewington 90		38
20	SPL	A	Stratford Town	146	W	2 - 1	Short 1 Landricombe 80	7	39
24	SPL	A	Kings Langley	160	D	2 - 2	Landricombe 53 Bath 77	6	40
27	SPL	H	Frome Town	215	D	2 - 2	Landricombe 4 Bath 89	6	41
31	SPL	A	Hitchin Town	606	W	2 - 1	J.Rogers 43 Landricombe 45	6	42
Apr 7	SPL	A	Farnborough	205	L	2 - 3	J.Rogers Bath	6	43
14	SPL	H	Royston Town	229	L	1 - 2	Hurst 1	7	44
17	SPL	H	Dorchester Town	176	D	0 - 0			45
19	SPL	H	Biggleswade Town	126	W	3 - 1	Bath 12 27 Short 70	8	46
21	SPIL	A	Redditch United	302	L	2 - 3	Lewington 6 Bath 67	7	47
24	SPL	A	Kettering Town	519	W	3 - 2	Landricombe 72 82 J.Rogers 83	7	48
28	SPL	H	Banbury United	283	D	0 - 0		6	52

GOALSCORERS	SG	CSG	Pens	Hat tricks	Total		SG	CSG	Pens	Hat tricks	Total
Landricombe	24	7	2	1	32	Mammola	1				1
Bath	11	2		1	16						
Howe	8	3	2		8						
Rogers	5				6						
Price	5	2			5						
Short	5				5						
Lewington	4				4						
Hall	2				3						
Hurst	2				2						
Gardner	1				1						

WEYMOUTH MATCH RESULTS 2017-18

Date	Comp	H/A	Opponents	Att:	Result	Goalscorers	Pos	No.
Aug 12	SPL	H	St Ives Town	665	L 0 - 1		19	1
16	SPL	A	Frome Town	408	W 4 - 1	Wakefield 1 Goodship 43 Rose 51 Thomson 70	9	2
19	SPL	A	Bishops Stortford	288	W 3 - 2	Thomson 14 18 Travers 77	6	3
26	SPL	H	Stratford Town	676	D 1 - 1	Rose 90	8	4
28	SPL	H	Dorchester Town	1505	W 3 - 0	Goodship 26 McCarthy 45 55	6	5
Sept 2	FAC 1Q	A	Odd Down	190	W 5 - 0	Thomson BAKER 3 McCarthy		6
9	SPL	H	Kettering Town	684	W 3 - 1	Thomson 28 Rose 33 Baker 83	6	7
12	SPL	A	Tiverton Town	249	L 1 - 2	Rose 82	9	8
16	FAC 2Q	H	Chippenham Town	609	W 2 - 0	Cooper 26 Davis 40		9
23	SPL	H	Hereford	1518	L 0 - 2		10	10
26	SPL	A	Basingstoke Town	487	W 3 - 2	Thomson 51 Brooks 81 Goodship 90 (pen)	10	11
30	FAC 3Q	A	Chelmsford City	664	L 1 - 2	Baker 89		12
Oct 7	SPL	H	Kings Lynn Town	662	W 3 - 1	Goodship 28 75 Davis 84	7	13
11	SPL	A	Farnborough	299	W 6 - 2	Baker 4 27 Tubbs 10 Carmichael 59 Goodship 82 Thomson 90		14
14	SPL	A	St Neots Town	348	W 2 - 1	Goodship 5 Baker 49	5	15
17	SPL	H	Merthyr Town	527	W 3 - 2	GOODSHIP 3 (40 54 87)	4	16
21	SPL	A	St Ives Town	226	W 2 - 1	Goodship 70 Baker 89	3	17
24	SPL	H	Frome Town	805	L 0 - 2		3	18
28	FAT 1Q	A	Hereford	1552	L 1 - 4	McCarthy 54		19
Nov 4	SPL	A	Hitchin Town	453	L 1 - 3	Davis 45	5	20
11	SPL	H	Kings Langley	634	W 2 - 0	Tring 85 (og) Seaman 90	2	21
14	SPL	H	Tiverton Town	517	W 2 - 0	Carmichael 73 Down 83	2	22
18	SPL	A	Slough Town	923	L 0 - 3		3	23
25	SPL	H	Biggleswade Town	530	W 2 - 0	Wakefield 33 Baker 69	2	24
28	SPL	A	Basingstoke Town	308	D 3 - 3	Goodship 44 90 Carmichael 57	2	25
Dec 2	SPL	H	Chesham United	602	W 1 - 0	Baggie 19	2	26
16	SPL	A	Banbury United	377	W 2 - 1	Baker 3 56	3	27
22	SPL	H	Redditch United	629	W 5 - 0	GOODSHIP 3 (15 21 82) Baker 60 Thomson 72	3	28
26	SPL	H	Dorchester Town	1885	D 2 - 2	Davis 39 Goodship 69	3	29
Jan 1	SPL	A	Gosport Borough	418	W 4 - 0	Goodship 45 56 Thomson 67 Baggie 85	3	30
6	SPL	H	Bishop's Stortford	730	D 1 - 1	Brooks 59	3	31
13	SPL	A	Startford Town	274	D 0 - 0		4	32
20	SPL	A	Kings Lynn Town	684	D 1 - 1	Goodship 86	4	33
23	SPL	A	Dunstable Town	121	L 1 - 2	Brooks 72	4	34
27	SPL	H	Farnborough	608	W 6 - 0	McCarthy 10 Baker 21 Goodship 30 62 Thomson 60 Baggie 90	4	35
30	SPL	A	Royston Town	218	W 2 - 1	Goodship 53 69 (pen)	3	36
Feb 3	SPL	A	Merthyr Town	367	W 3 - 0	Baker 34 Carmichael 65 Goodship 83	3	37
10	SPL	H	St Neots Town	653	W 3 - 1	Goodship 34 (pen) Zubar 84 Ngalo 90	3	38
17	SPL	H	Royston Town	811	W 3 - 0	Brooks 19 Thomson 44 Goodship 72	3	39
24	SPL	A	Hereford	2766	L 0 - 2		3	40
Mar 10	SPL	A	Biggleswade Town	205	W 2 - 1	Da Silva 3 Goodship 45	3	41
17	SPL	H	Dunstable Town	481	W 2 - 0	Brooks 42 Goodship 45	3	42
24	SPL	A	Chesham United	402	W 6 - 0	Thomson 16 Baggie 32 Goodship 75 Baker 77 Brooks 85 86	3	43
27	SPL	H	Slough Town	822	W 1 - 0	Brooks 60	3	44
Apr 2	SPL	H	Gosport Borough	1007	W 5 - 0	Baker 2 GOODSHIP 3 (25 44 73) Sanders 88(og)	3	45
7	SPL	A	Redditch United	332	W 2 - 1	Thomson 7 Goodship 25	3	46
14	SPL	H	Banbury United	895	D 1 - 1	Goodship 24	3	47
19	SPL	A	Kettering Town	745	L 0 - 2		3	48
21	SPL	A	Kings Langley	318	W 3 - 2	Goodship 45 86 Baker 90	4	49
28	SPL	H	Hitchin Town	1102	W 3 - 0	Brooks 59 Baggie 81 Goodship 86	5	50
May 1	PO SF	A	King's Lynn Town	1223	L 0 - 3			51

GOALSCORERS	SG	CSG	Pens	Hat tricks	Total		SG	CSG	Pens	Hat tricks	Total
2016-17 Fleetwood					18	Opponents	2				2
Goodship	26	5	3	3	38	Wakefield	2				2
Baker	13	2		1	18	Cooper					1
Thomson	10	2			13	Da Silver					1
Brooks	8	2			9	Down					1
Baggie	5				5	Ngalo					1
McCarthy	4	2			5	Seaman					1
Carmichael	4				4	Travers					1
Davis	4				4	Tubbs					1
Rose	4	2			4	Zubar					1

SOUTHERN LEAGUE
CLUB DIRECTORY 2018-19

PREMIER CENTRAL

1 AFC Rushden & Diamonds
2 Alvechurch
3 Banbury United
4 Barwell
5 Bedworth United
6 Biggleswade Town
7 Coalville Town
8 Halesowen Town
9 Hitchin Town
10 Kettering Town
11 King's Lynn Town
12 Leiston
13 Lowestoft Town
14 Needham Market
15 Redditch United
16 Royston Town
17 Rushall Olympic
18 St Ives Town
19 St Neots Town
20 Stourbridge
21 Stratford Town
22 Tamworth

PREMIER SOUTH

1 Basingstoke Town
2 Beaconsfield Town
3 Chesham United
4 Dorchester Town
5 Farnborough
6 Frome Town
7 Gosport Borough
8 Harrow Borough
9 Hartley Wintney
10 Hendon
11 Kings Langley
12 Merthyr Town
13 Metropolitan Police
14 Poole Town
15 Salisbury
16 Staines Town
17 Swindon Supermarine
18 Taunton Town
19 Tiverton Town
20 Walton Casuals
21 Weymouth
22 Wimborne Town

EAST

1 AFC Dunstable
2 Aylesbury
3 Aylesbury United
4 Barton Rovers
5 Bedford Town
6 Berkhamsted
7 Bromsgrove Sporting
8 Cambridge City
9 Coleshill Town
10 Corby Town
11 Didcot Town
12 Dunstable Town
13 Kempston Rovers
14 Kidlington
15 North Leigh
16 Peterborough Sports
17 Sutton Coldfield Town
18 Thame United
19 Welwyn Garden City
20 Yaxley

WEST

1 AFC Totton
2 Barnstaple Town
3 Bideford
4 Blackfield & Langley
5 Bristol Manor Farm
6 Cinderford Town
7 Cirencester Town
8 Evesham United
9 Fleet Town
10 Highworth Town
11 Larkhall Athletic
12 Mangotsfield United
13 Melksham Town
14 Moneyfields
15 Paulton Rovers
16 Slimbridge
17 Street
18 Thatcham Town
19 Winchester City
20 Yate Town

AFC RUSHDEN & DIAMONDS

Club Contact Details 01933 359 206
Rushden & Higham United FC, Hayden Road, Rushden NN10 0HX
secretary@afcdiamonds.com

Founded: 2011   **Nickname:** The Diamonds   **Manager:** Andy Peaks
Previous Names: None
Previous Leagues: United Counties 2012-15. Southern 2015-16. Northern Premier 2016-17.

Club Colours (change): White & blue

Ground Capacity: 2,000   **Seats:** 100   **Covered:** 250   **Clubhouse:** Yes   **Shop:** Yes
Previous Grounds: The Dog & Duck Wellingborough Town FC 2011-17.
Record Attendance: 1,162 v Barwell, 27/10/2015.
Nearest Railway Station Wellingborough and Bedford   **Bus Route** X46/X47, 49, 50, 26 to Rushden town
centre a 10 min walk from the ground

RECORDS
Victory: 9-0 v Buckingham Town (A) 15/12/12 and v Desborough Town (A) 21/02/15
Goalscorer: Tom Lorraine - 54 in 150 appearances, 2014- present.
Appearances: Brad Harris - 213, 2013 - present
Additional: 28 matches unbeaten, 13/01/2015 - 31/10/2015.

HONOURS
FA Comps: None
League: United Counties Premier Division 2014-15.

County FA: Northamptonshire Senior Cup 2015-16.

08-09	09-10	10-11	11-12	12-13	13-14	14-15	15-16	16-17	17-18
				UCL 1 2	UCL P 3	UCL P 1	SthC 5	NP1S 5	Sth1E 2
					FAC 3Q	FAC 1Q	FAC 4Qr	FAC 3Q	FAC 2Qr
				FAV 3P	FAV 4P	FAV 2P	FAT P	FAT 2Q	FAT P

ALVECHURCH

Club Contact Details 0121 445 2929
Lye Meadow, Redditch Road, Alvechurch B48 7RS
alvechurchfc@btinternet.com

Founded: 1929   **Nickname:** The Church   **Manager:** Ian Long
Previous Names: Alvechurch FC >1993. Re-formed in 1994 as Alvechurch Villa > 1996.
Previous Leagues: Worcestershire Combination/Midland Combination 1961-73, 94-2003. West Midlands (Reg) 1973-78. Southern 1978-93.
Midland Alliance 2003-14. Midland Football League 2014-17. Northern Premier 2017-18.

Club Colours (change): Amber & black.

Ground Capacity: 3,000   **Seats:** 100   **Covered:** 300   **Clubhouse:** Yes   **Shop:**
Previous Grounds: Played in the local park until moving to Lye Meadow.
Record Attendance: 13,500 v Enfield, FA Amateur Cup Quarter-final, 1964-65.
Nearest Railway Station Alvechurch - 0.7km   **Bus Route** Bus stops at the ground.

RECORDS
Victory: 13-0 v (A) Alcester Town.
Defeat: 0-9 v (H) Coalville Town.
Goalscorer: Graham Allner. Keith Rostill scored 53 goals during the 2002-03 season.
Appearances: Kevin Palmer.
Additional: Paid £3,000 to Worcester City for Peter Gocan, 1989. Received £34,000 from Aston Villa for Andy Comyn, 1989.
In 1971, the club played out the longest FA Cup tie in history when it took six games to beat Oxford City in the 4Q Round.

HONOURS
FA Comps: None
League: Worcestershire Combination Division 1962-63, 64-65, 66-67. Midland Combination Division One 1971-72, Premier 2002-03.
West Midlands (Reg) Premier 1973-74, 74-75, 75-76, 76-77. Southern Midland Division 1980-81. Midland Football Premier 2016-17.
County FA: Worcestershire Senior Cup 1972-73, 73-74, 76-77, Senior Urn 2003-04, 04-05, 07-08, 12-13.

08-09	09-10	10-11	11-12	12-13	13-14	14-15	15-16	16-17	17-18
MidAl 10	MidAl 7	MidAl 20	MidAl 13	MidAl 11	MidAl 13	MFLP 15	MFLP 2	MFLP 1	NP1S 2
FAC P	FAC P	FAC EP	FAC 1Q	FAC EPr	FAC EP	FAC EP	FAC P	FAC P	FAC 3Q
FAV 1P	FAV 2Q	FAV 2Q	FAV 2Q	FAV 2Q	FAV 3P	FAV 1Q	FAV 4P	FAV 2P	FAT 2Q

BANBURY UNITED

Club Contact Details 01295 263 354
The Banbury Plant Hire Community Stadium, off Station Road, Banbury OX16 5AD
bworsley@btinternet.com

Founded: 1931   **Nickname:** Puritans   **Manager:** Mike Ford
Previous Names: Spencer Villa 1931-34. Banbury Spencer. Club reformed in 1965 as Banbury United
Previous Leagues: Banbury Junior 1933-34, Oxon Senior 1934-35, Birmingham Combination 1935-54,
West Midlands 1954-66, Southern 1966-90, Hellenic 1991-2000

Club Colours (change): Red & gold

Ground Capacity: 6,500   **Seats:** 250   **Covered:** 250   **Clubhouse:** Yes   **Shop:** Yes
Previous Grounds: Middleton Road 1931-34.
Record Attendance: 7,160 v Oxford City - FA Cup 3rd Qualifying Round 30/10/1948
Nearest Railway Station Banbury - 0.2km

RECORDS
Victory: 12-0 v RNAS Culham - Oxon Senior Cup 1945-46
Defeat: 2-11 v West Bromwich Albion 'A' - Birmingham Combination 1938-39
Goalscorer: Dick Pike and Tony Jacques - 222 (1935-48 and 1965-76 respectively). Jacues also scored 62 in a single season, 1967-68.
Appearances: Jody McKay - 576
Additional: Paid £2,000 to Oxford United for Phil Emsden
                 Received £20,000 from Derby County for Kevin Wilson 1979

HONOURS
FA Comps: None

League: Oxfordshire Junior Banbury Division 1933-34. Oxfordshire Senior 1934-35. Hellenic Premier 1999-2000.

County FA: Oxford Senior Cup 1978-79, 87-88, 2003-04, 05-06, 06-07, 14-15.

08-09		09-10		10-11		11-12		12-13		13-14		14-15		15-16		16-17		17-18	
SthP	19	SthP	12	SthP	16	SthP	16	SthP	16	SthP	19	SthP	21	Sthsw	2	SthP	6	SthP	9
FAC	1Q	FAC	1Qr	FAC	1Q	FAC	1Q	FAC	1Q	FAC	1Qr	FAC	1Q	FAC	2Q	FAC	P	FAC	3Q	FAC	3Q
FAT	1Q	FAT	2Qr	FAT	2Qr	FAT	3Qr	FAT	1Qr	FAT	1Q	FAT	3Q	FAT	1Qr	FAT	1Q	FAT	2Qr

BARWELL

Club Contact Details 01455 843 067
Kirkby Road Sports Ground, Kirkby Road, Barwell LE9 8FQ
shirley.brown16@ntlworld.com

Founded: 1992   **Nickname:** Canaries   **Manager:** Jimmy Ginnelly
Previous Names: Barwell Athletic FC and Hinckley FC amalgamated in 1992.
Previous Leagues: Midland Alliance 1992-2010, Northern Premier League 2010-11, 13-18. Southern 2011-13.

Club Colours (change): Light green & yellow

Ground Capacity: 2,500   **Seats:** 256   **Covered:** 750   **Clubhouse:** Yes   **Shop:** Yes
Previous Grounds: None
Record Attendance: 1,279 v Whitley Bay, FA Vase Semi-Final 2009-10.

RECORDS
Goalscorer: Andy Lucas
Appearances: Adrian Baker

HONOURS
FA Comps: None
League: Midland Alliance 2009-10.
           Northern Premier Division One South 2010-11.
County FA: Leicestershire Challenge Cup 2014-15, 16-17.

08-09		09-10		10-11		11-12		12-13		13-14		14-15		15-16		16-17		17-18	
MidAl	2	MidAl	1	NP1S	1	SthP	9	SthP	7	NP P	14	NP P	8	NP P	9	NP P	14	NP P	10
FAC	1Q	FAC	EP	FAC	4Q	FAC	2Q	FAC	3Qr	FAC	1Q	FAC	4Q	FAC	1P	FAC	2Q	FAC	3Q
FAV	3P	FAV	SF	FAT	P	FAT	2Q	FAT	1Q	FAT	1Q	FAT	3Qr	FAT	1Q	FAT	2Q	FAT	2Q

BEDWORTH UNITED

Club Contact Details 02476 314 752
The Oval, Coventry Road, Bedworth CV12 8NN
andrew.stickley@live.co.uk

Founded: 1895   **Nickname:** Greenbacks   **Manager:** Stuart Storer
Previous Names: Bedworth Town 1947-68
Previous Leagues: Birmingham Combination 1947-54, Birmingham/West Midlands 1954-72. Southern 1972-2013, 14-16.
Northern Premier 2013-14, 16-18.

Club Colours (change): All green

Ground Capacity: 3,000 **Seats:** 300   **Covered:** 300   **Clubhouse:** Yes   **Shop:** Yes
Previous Grounds: British Queen Ground 1911-39
Record Attendance: 5,172 v Nuneaton Borough - Southern League Midland Division 23/02/1982
Nearest Railway Station Bedworth - 0.5km   **Bus Route** Bus stops at the Leisure Centre

RECORDS
Goalscorer: Peter Spacey - 1949-69
Appearances: Peter Spacey - 1949-69
Additional: Paid £1,750 to Hinckley Town for Colin Taylor 1991-92
Received £30,000 from Plymouth Argyle for Richard Landon

HONOURS
FA Comps: None
League: Birmingham Combination 1948-49, 49-50.

County FA: Birmingham Senior Cup 1978-79, 80-81, 81-82.

08-09		09-10		10-11		11-12		12-13		13-14		14-15		15-16		16-17		17-18	
SthM	14	SthM	16	SthC	15	SthC	3	SthP	21	NP1S	20	SthC	4	SthP	21	NP1S	11	NP1S	4
FAC	Pr	FAC	4Q	FAC	2Q	FAC	1Q	FAC	2Q	FAC	P	FAC	2Qr	FAC	2Q	FAC	3Q	FAC	P
FAT	2Q	FAT	P	FAT	1Q	FAT	1Q	FAT	1Q	FAT	P	FAT	P	FAT	1Q	FAT	1Q	FAT	1Q

BIGGLESWADE TOWN

Club Contact Details 01767 318 202 (Matchdays)
The Carlsberg Stadium, Langford Road, Biggleswade SG18 9JT
michaeldraxler@hotmail.com

Founded: 1874   **Nickname:** The Waders   **Manager:** Lee Allinson
Previous Names: Biggleswade FC. Biggleswade & District.
Previous Leagues: Biggleswade & District 1902-20. Bedford & District. Northamptonshire/United Counties 1920-39 / 1951-55, 1963-80. Spartan
1945-51. Eastern Counties 1955-63. South Midlands/SSM 1980-2009.

Club Colours (change): White with green trim/green/green (Blue & black stripes/black/blue & black)

Ground Capacity: 3,000 **Seats:** 300   **Covered:** 400   **Clubhouse:** Yes   **Shop:**
Previous Grounds: Fairfield
Record Attendance: 2,000
Nearest Railway Station Biggleswade - 1km

RECORDS
Victory: 12-0 v Newmarket Town (A), Eastern Counties.
Best FA Cup   First Round Proper 2013-14
FA Trophy   Second Qualifying Round 1974-75, 2014-15, 16-17(r)
FA Vase   Quarter Finals 2008-09

HONOURS
FA Comps: None
League: Biggleswade & District 1902-03. Spartan South Midlands Premier Division 2008-09.

County FA: Bedfordshire Senior Cup 1902-03, 07-08, 46-47, 50-51, 61-62, 62-63, 66-67, 73-74.
Bedfordshire Premier Cup 2009. Bedfordshire Senior Challenge Cup 2012-13.

08-09		09-10		10-11		11-12		12-13		13-14		14-15		15-16		16-17		17-18	
SSM P	1	SthM	12	SthC	4	SthC	8	SthC	4	SthP	9	SthP	19	SthP	14	SthP	7	SthP	16
FAC	EP	FAC	P	FAC	1Q	FAC	2Qr	FAC	1Q	FAC	1P	FAC	3Q	FAC	2Q	FAC	2Q	FAC	3Q
FAV	QF	FAT	1Q	FAT	1Q	FAT	1Q	FAT	P	FAT	1Q	FAT	2Q	FAT	1Q	FAT	2Qr	FAT	1Q

COALVILLE TOWN

The Ravens

Club Contact Details 01530 833 365
Owen Street Sports Ground, Owen St, Coalville LE67 3DA
coalville.secretary@gmail.com

Founded: 1926   **Nickname:** The Ravens   **Manager:** Adam Stevens
Previous Names: Ravenstoke Miners Ath. 1926-58. Ravenstoke FC 1958-95. Coalville 1995-98.
Previous Leagues: Coalville & Dist. Amateur. North Leicester. Leicestershire Senior. Midland Alliance > 2011. Northern Premier 2011-18.

Club Colours (change): Black & white stripes/black/white (Red & yellow stripes/red/red)

Ground Capacity: 2,000   **Seats:** 240   **Covered:** 240   **Clubhouse:** Yes   **Shop:** Yes
Previous Grounds: None
Record Attendance: 1,500.

RECORDS
Appearances: Nigel Simms.
Additional: 153 goals scored during 2010-11 season.

HONOURS
FA Comps: None
League: Coalville & District Amateur 1952-53. North Leicestershire 1988-89, 89-90. Leicestershire Senior 2001-02, 02-03.
     Midland Football Alliance 2010-11.
County FA: Leicestershire Senior Cup 1999-00. Leicestershire Challenge Cup 2012-13.

08-09		09-10		10-11		11-12		12-13		13-14		14-15		15-16		16-17		17-18	
MidAl	3	MidAl	2	MidAl	1	NP1S	14	NP1S	2	NP1S	2	NP1S	10	NP1S	3	NP P	17	NP P	20
FAC	3Q	FAC	P	FAC	2Q	FAC	P	FAC	1Q	FAC	2Q	FAC	2Qr	FAC	2Q	FAC	2Q	FAC	2Q
FAV	4Pr	FAV	3P	FAV	F	FAT	P	FAT	2Q	FAT	1Pr	FAT	P	FAT	1Q	FAT	1Q	FAT	3Q

HALESOWEN TOWN

1873

Club Contact Details 0121 629 0727
The Grove, Old Hawne Lane, Halesowen B63 3TB
secretary@halesowentown.com

Founded: 1873   **Nickname:** Yeltz   **Manager:** John Hill
Previous Names: None
Previous Leagues: Birmingham & District/West Midlands 1892-1905, 06-11, 46-86, Birmingham Combination 1911-39. Southern 1986-12.
     Northern Premier 2012-18.

Club Colours (change): All blue

Ground Capacity: 5,000   **Seats:** 525   **Covered:** 930   **Clubhouse:** Yes   **Shop:** Yes
Previous Grounds: None
Record Attendance: 5,000 v Hendon - FA Cup 1st Round Proper 1954
Nearest Railway Station Old Hill - 1.8km   **Bus Route** Cranmoor Crescent - stop 50m away

RECORDS
Victory: 13-1 v Coventry Amateurs - Birmingham Senior cup 1956
Defeat: 0-8 v Bilston - West Midlands League 07/04/1962
Goalscorer: Paul Joinson - 369
Appearances: Paul Joinson - 608
Additional: Paid £7,250 to Gresley Rovers for Stuart Evans
     Received £40,000 from Rushden & Diamonds for Jim Rodwell
HONOURS
FA Comps: FA Vase 1984-85, 85-86
League: West Midlands (Reg) 1946-47, 82-83, 83-84, 84-85, 85-86. Southern League Midland Division 1989-90, Western Division
     2001-02. Northern Premier Division One South 2013-14.
County FA: Worcestershire Senior Cup 1951-52, 61-62, 2002-03, 04-05. Birmingham Senior Cup 1983-84, 97-98.
     Staffordshire Senior Cup 1988-89.

08-09		09-10		10-11		11-12		12-13		13-14		14-15		15-16		16-17		17-18	
SthP	10	SthP	8	SthP	21	Sthsw	12	NP1S	7	NP1S	1	NP P	11	NP P	13	NP P	19	NP P	23
FAC	3Q					FAC	P	FAC	P	FAC	3Q	FAC	3Q	FAC	2Q	FAC	3Qr	FAC	2Q
FAT	1Qr			FAT	1Q	FAT	P	FAT	2Q	FAT	1Q	FAT	1P	FAT	1Q	FAT	2Q	FAT	1Q

HITCHIN TOWN

Club Contact Details 01462 459 028 (match days only)
Top Field, Fishponds Road, Hitchin SG5 1NU
roy.izzard@outlook.com

Founded: 1865   **Nickname:** Canaries   **Manager:** Mark Burke
Previous Names: Hitchin FC 1865-1911. Re-formed in 1928
Previous Leagues: Spartan 1928-39, Herts & Middlesex 1939-45, Athenian 1945-63, Isthmian 1964-2004

Club Colours (change): Yellow & green

Ground Capacity: 5,000   **Seats:** 500   **Covered:** 1,250   **Clubhouse:** Yes   **Shop:** Yes
Previous Grounds: None
Record Attendance: 7,878 v Wycombe Wanderers - FA Amateur Cup 3rd Round 08/02/1956
Nearest Railway Station Hitchin - 1.3km   **Bus Route** Buss stops outside the ground

RECORDS
Victory: 13-0 v Cowley and v RAF Uxbridge - both Spartan League 1929-30
Defeat: 0-10 v Kingstonian (A) and v Slough Town (A) - 1965-66 and 1979-80 respectively
Goalscorer: Paul Giggle - 214 (1968-86)
Appearances: Paul Giggle - 769 (1968-86)
Additional: Paid £2,000 to Potton United for Ray Seeking
                   Received £30,000 from Cambridge United for Zema Abbey, January 2000

HONOURS
FA Comps: None
League: Spartan 1934-35. Isthmian League Division One 1992-93.

County FA: AFA Senior Cup 1931-32. London Senior Cup 1969-70. East Anglian Cup 1972-73.
Herts Senior Cup x14 Most recently 2016-17.

08-09		09-10		10-11		11-12		12-13		13-14		14-15		15-16		16-17		17-18	
SthP	20	SthC	2	SthC	2	SthP	14	SthP	13	SthP	13	SthP	9	SthP	3	SthP	4	SthP	11
FAC	3Q	FAC	1Qr	FAC	2Qr	FAC	1Q	FAC	3Qr	FAC	1Qr	FAC	2Q	FAC	3Qr	FAC	2Qr	FAC	1Qr
FAT	2Q	FAT	3Qr	FAT	P	FAT	2Q	FAT	3Q	FAT	1Qr	FAT	1Qr	FAT	3Q	FAT	1P	FAT	1Q

KETTERING TOWN

Club Contact Details 01536 217 006
Latimer Park, Burton Latimer, Kettering NN15 5PS
info@ketteringtownfc.com

Founded: 1872   **Nickname:** The Poppies   **Manager:** Marcus Law
Previous Names: Kettering > 1924
Previous Leagues: Midland 1892-1900, also had a team in United Counties 1896-99, Southern 1900-30, 1950-79, 2001-02,
Birmingham 1930-50, Alliance/Conference 1979-2001, 02-03, Isthmian 2003-04

Club Colours (change): Red & black

Ground Capacity: **Seats:** Yes   **Covered:** Yes   **Clubhouse:** Yes   **Shop:**
Previous Grounds: North Park, Green Lane, Rockingham Road > 2011. Nene Park 2011-13.
Record Attendance: 11,536 v Peterborough - FA Cup 1st Round replay 1958-59
Nearest Railway Station Kettering - 4.1km   **Bus Route** Station Road - stop 150m away

RECORDS
Victory: 16-0 v Higham YMCI - FA Cup 1909
Defeat: 0-13 v Mardy - Southern League Division Two 1911-12
Goalscorer: Roy Clayton - 171 (1972-81)
Appearances   Roger Ashby
Additional: Paid £25,000 to Macclesfield for Carl Alford 1994.
                   Recieved £150,000 from Newcastle United for Andy Hunt

HONOURS
FA Comps: None
League: Midland 1895-96, 99-1900. United Counties 1904-05, 38-39. Southern 1927-28, 56-57, 72-73, 2001-02, Division One Central
2014-15. Conference North 2007-08.
County FA: Northamptonshire Senior Cup 2016-17.

08-09		09-10		10-11		11-12		12-13		13-14		14-15		15-16		16-17		17-18	
Conf	8	Conf	6	Conf	14	Conf	24	SthP	22	SthC	3	SthC	1	SthP	6	SthP	9	SthP	4
FAC	4P	FAC	2Pr	FAC	4Q	FAC	1P	FAC	2Q	FAC	P	FAC	2Q	FAC	3Qr	FAC	4Q	FAC	4Qr
FAT	3P	FAT	1P	FAT	1Pr	FAT	1P	FAT	1Q	FAT	1Q	FAT	1Q	FAT	2Q	FAT	2Q	FAT	1Q

KING'S LYNN TOWN

Club Contact Details 01553 760 060
The Walks Stadium, Tennyson Road, King's Lynn PE30 5PB

Founded: 1879 **Nickname:** Linnets **Manager:** Simon Clark - May 2018
Previous Names: King's Lynn Town formed in 2010 after King's Lynn FC folded.
Previous Leagues: United Counties 2010-12. Northern Premier 2012-15.

Club Colours (change): Yellow & blue

Ground Capacity: 8,200 **Seats:** 1,400 **Covered:** 5,000 **Clubhouse:** Yes **Shop:** Yes
Previous Grounds: None
Record Attendance: 12,937 v Exeter City FAC 1st Rnd 1950-51.
Nearest Railway Station King's Lynn - 5min walk away. **Bus Route** Serviced by Eastern Counties & Norfolk Green

RECORDS
Victory: 7-1 v Gosport Borough (A), Southern Premier, 06/02/2018

HONOURS
FA Comps: None
League: Northern Premier Division One South 2012-13.

County FA: Norfolk Senior Cup 2016-17.

08-09	09-10	10-11	11-12	12-13	13-14	14-15	15-16	16-17	17-18
		UCL P 2	UCL P 2	NP1S 1	NP P 11	NP P 18	SthP 9	SthP 13	SthP 2
			FAC 4Q	FAC 1Qr	FAC 1Q	FAC 4Q	FAC 3Q	FAC 3Q	FAC 2Q
		FAV SF	FAV 2P	FAT 3P	FAT 1Q	FAT 3Q	FAT 2Q	FAV 1P	FAT 1Q

LEISTON

Club Contact Details 01728 830 308
LTAA, Victory Road, Leiston IP16 4DQ
trevorelmy@btinternet.com

Founded: 1880 **Nickname:** The Blues **Manager:** Glenn Driver
Previous Names: Leiston Works Athletic 1919-35.
Previous Leagues: North Suffolk. Suffolk & Ipswich. South East Anglian/East Anglian. Essex & Suffolk Border. Norfolk & Suffolk.
Ipswich & District 1953-2001. Eastern Counties 2001-2011. Isthmian 2011-18.

Club Colours (change): All blue

Ground Capacity: 2,250 **Seats:** 250 **Covered:** 500 **Clubhouse:** Yes **Shop:**
Previous Grounds: Leiston Recreation Ground 1880-1921.
Record Attendance: 1,250 v Fleetwood Town, FA Cup First round Proper, 2008-09.
Bus Route Alde Valley Sixth Form - stop 300m away

RECORDS
Goalscorer: Lee McGlone - 60 (League).
Appearances: Gareth Heath - 201 (League).

HONOURS
FA Comps: None
League: Suffolk & Ipswich/Ipswich & District 1900-01, 01-02, 02-03, Division 2B 1937-38 / Division One 83-84.
Eastern Counties Premier Division 2010-11. Isthmian Division One North 2011-12.
County FA: Suffolk Junior Cup 1894-95, 82-83, 83-84.
East Anglian Cup 2007-08.

08-09	09-10	10-11	11-12	12-13	13-14	14-15	15-16	16-17	17-18
ECP 7	ECP 3	ECP 1	Isth1N 1	Isth P 12	Isth P 9	Isth P 9	Isth P 8	Isth P 7	Isth P 5
FAC 1Pr	FAC EP	FAC 4Qr	FAC 1Q	FAC 2Q	FAC 1Q	FAC 2Q	FAC 3Q	FAC 4Q	FAC 3Q
FAV 4P	FAV 3P	FAV QF	FAT P	FAT 3Qr	FAT 1Q	FAT 1P	FAT 2Q	FAT 1Pr	FAT 2Q

LOWESTOFT TOWN

Club Contact Details 01502 573 818
Crown Meadow, Love Road, Lowestoft NR32 2PA
terrylynes@yahoo.com

Founded: 1880   **Nickname:** The Trawler Boys or Blues   **Manager:** Jamie Godbold
Previous Names: Original club merged with Kirkley in 1887 to form Lowestoft and became Lowestoft Town in 1890
Previous Leagues: North Suffolk 1897-35, Eastern Counties 1935-2009. Isthmian 2009-2014, 16-18. Conference 2014-16.

Club Colours (change): All blue

Ground Capacity: 3,000 **Seats:** 466   **Covered:** 500   **Clubhouse:** Yes   **Shop:** Yes
Previous Grounds: Crown Meadow Athletic Ground 1880-1889. North Denes 1889-94.
Record Attendance: 5,000 v Watford - FA Cup 1st Round 1967
Nearest Railway Station Lowestoft - 0.7km

RECORDS
Best FA Cup	First Round Proper 1926-27, 38-39, 66-67, 67-68, 77-78, 2009-10
FA Trophy	Second Round Proper 1971-72
FA Vase	Finalists 2007-08

HONOURS
FA Comps: None
League: Eastern Counties League 1935-36 (shared), 37-38, 62-63, 64-65, 65-66, 66-67, 67-68, 69-70, 70-71, 77-78, 2005-06, 08-09. Isthmian League Division One North 2009-10.
County FA: Suffolk Senior Cup 1902-03, 22-23, 25-26, 31-32, 35-36, 46-47, 47-48, 48-49, 55-56, Premier Cup 1966-67, 71-72, 74-75, 78-79, 79-80, 99-00, 00-01, 04-05, 05-06, 08-09, 11-12, 14-15, 15-16. East Anglian Cup 1929-30, 70-71, 77-78.

08-09		09-10		10-11		11-12		12-13		13-14		14-15		15-16		16-17		17-18	
ECP	1	Isth1N	1	Isth P	4	Isth P	3	Isth P	2	Isth P	4	Conf N	16	Nat N	20	Isth P	11	Isth P	22
FAC	1Q	FAC	1P	FAC	2Q	FAC	3Q	FAC	4Q	FAC	1Q	FAC	3Q	FAC	2Q	FAC	1Q	FAC	2Q
FAV	SF	FAT	1Q	FAT	1P	FAT	1P	FAT	1Q	FAT	1Q	FAT	1P	FAT	1P	FAT	1Q	FAT	1Q

NEEDHAM MARKET

Club Contact Details 01449 721 000
Bloomfields, Quinton Road, Needham Market IP6 8DA
m.easlea@sky.com

Founded: 1919   **Nickname:** The Marketmen   **Manager:** Richard Wilkins
Previous Names: None
Previous Leagues: Suffolk & Ipswich Senior, Eastern Counties. Isthmian >2018.

Club Colours (change): All red

Ground Capacity: 4,000 **Seats:** 250   **Covered:** 250   **Clubhouse:** Yes   **Shop:** Yes
Previous Grounds: Young's Meadow 1919. Crowley Park >1996.
Record Attendance: 1,784 v Cambridge United, FAC Fourth Qualifying Round, 26/10/2013.
Nearest Railway Station Needham Market - 0.6km   **Bus Route** Quinton Road stop - 38m away

RECORDS
Victory:	10-1 v I[swich Wanderers (A) , FA Cup Preliminary Round, 01/09/2007
Defeat:	2-6 v Lowestoft Town (A), FA Trophy First round Qualifier, 19/10/2010
Goalscorer:	Craig Parker - 111 (2007-2011) Most goals in a season - Craig Parker 40 (2011-11).
Appearances:	Rhys Barber - 334 (2006-2012)
Additional:	Most goals scored in a season - 196 in 70 games (2007-08)

HONOURS
FA Comps: None
League: Eastern Counties Premier Division 2009-10. Isthmian Division One North 2014-15.
County FA: Suffolk Senior Cup 1989-90, 2004-05. Suffolk & Ipswich Senior League 1995-96. East Anglian Cup 2006-07. Suffolk Premier Cup 2016-17.

08-09		09-10		10-11		11-12		12-13		13-14		14-15		15-16		16-17		17-18	
ECP	3	ECP	1	Isth1N	2	Isth1N	4	Isth1N	16	Isth1N	5	Isth1N	1	Isth P	20	Isth P	9	Isth P	
FAC	2Q	FAC	2Q	FAC	3Q	FAC	2Q	FAC	1Q	FAC	4Q	FAC	3Q	FAC	1Qr	FAC	1Q	FAC	3Q
FAV	QF	FAV	QF	FAT	1Qr	FAT	1Q	FAT	P	FAT	P	FAT	P	FAT	1Q	FAT	2Q	FAT	2Q

REDDITCH UNITED

Club Contact Details 01527 67450
The TRICO Stadium, Bromsgrove Road, Redditch B97 4RN

Founded: 1891   **Nickname:** The Reds   **Manager:** Paul Davis
Previous Names: Redditch Town
Previous Leagues: Birmingham Combination 1905-21, 29-39, 46-53, West Midlands 1921-29, 53-72,
Southern 1972-79, 81-2004, Alliance 1979-80. Conference 2004-11.

Club Colours (change): Red & black

Ground Capacity: 5,000   **Seats:** 400   **Covered:** 2,000   **Clubhouse:** Yes   **Shop:** Yes
Previous Grounds: HDA Sports Ground, Millsborough Road
Record Attendance: 5,500 v Bromsgrove Rovers - Wets Midlands League 1954-55
Nearest Railway Station Redditch - 0.4km   **Bus Route** Bus stops outside the ground

RECORDS
Misc: Paid £3,000 to Halesowen Town for Paul Joinson. Received £40,000 from Aston Villa for David Farrell.
Played nine games in nine days at the end of the 1997-98 season.

Victory: 7-1 v Farnborough (H), Southern Premier, 06/01/2018

HONOURS
FA Comps: None
League: Birmingham Combination 1913-14, 32-33, 52-53. Birmingham & District Southern Division 1954-55.
Southern Division One North 1975-76, Western Division 2003-04.
County FA: Worcestershire Senior Cup 1893-94, 29-30, 74-75, 76-76, 2007-08, 13-14.
Birmingham Senior Cup 1924-25, 31-32, 38-39, 76-77, 2004-05. Staffordshire Senior Cup 1990-91.

08-09		09-10		10-11		11-12		12-13		13-14		14-15		15-16		16-17		17-18	
Conf N	14	Conf N	19	Conf N	21	SthP	15	SthP	19	SthP	10	SthP	6	SthP	2	SthP	17	SthP	14
FAC	2Q	FAC	4Qr	FAC	4Q	FAC	1Q	FAC	1Q	FAC	1Qr	FAC	1Qr	FAC	1Q	FAC	1Q	FAC	2Q
FAT	2P	FAT	1P	FAT	1P	FAT	1Q	FAT	1Q	FAT	3Q	FAT	3Q	FAT	1Q	FAV	2Q	FAT	1Q

ROYSTON TOWN

Club Contact Details 01763 241 204
Garden Walk, Royston, Herts, SG8 7HP
terry.mckinnell@talktalk.net

Founded: 1872   **Nickname:** The Crows   **Manager:** Steve Castle
Previous Names: None
Previous Leagues: Buntingford & District 1919-29. Cambridgeshire 1929-48. Herts County 1948-60, 63-77. South Midlands 1960-63, 77-84.
Isthmian 1984-94. Spartan South Midlands 1994-2012.

Club Colours (change): White & black

Ground Capacity: 5,000   **Seats:** 300   **Covered:** Yes   **Clubhouse:** Yes   **Shop:** No
Previous Grounds: Newmarket Road, Baldock Road and Mackerell Hall before acquiring Garden Walk in 1932.
Record Attendance: 876 v Aldershot Town, 1993-94.
Nearest Railway Station Royston - 0.7km   **Bus Route** St Mary's School - stop 150m away

RECORDS
Best FA Cup Third Qualifying Round 1998-99
FA Trophy First Round Proper Reply 2016-17
FA Vase Fifth Round Proper 2009-10

HONOURS
FA Comps: None
League: Cambridgeshire Division Two 1929-30. Herts County Division One 1969-70, 72-73, Premier 1976-77.
South Midlands Division One 1977-78, 2008-09, Premier Division 2011-12. Southern Division One Central 2016-17.
County FA: Herts Charity Shield 1981-82, 96-97. Herts Intermediate Cup 1988-89.

08-09		09-10		10-11		11-12		12-13		13-14		14-15		15-16		16-17		17-18	
SSM1	1	SSM P	4	SSM P	3	SSM P	1	SthC	7	SthC	7	SthC	2	SthC	2	SthC	1	SthP	7
FAC	1Q	FAC	1Q	FAC	EP	FAC	P	FAC	1Qr	FAC	2Q	FAC	P	FAC	Pr	FAC	P	FAC	2Qr
FAV	1P	FAV	5P	FAV	2Pr	FAV	4P	FAT	1Qr	FAT	P	FAT	1Q	FAT	2Q	FAT	1Pr	FAT	3P

RUSHALL OLYMPIC

Club Contact Details 01922 641 021
Dales Lane off Daw End Lane, Rushall, Nr Walsall WS4 1LJ
rofc.secretary@hotmail.com

Founded: 1951	**Nickname:** The Pics	**Manager:** Liam McDonald

Previous Names: None
Previous Leagues: Walsall Amateur 1952-55, Staffordshire County (South) 1956-78, West Midlands 1978-94,
Midland Alliance 1994-2005, Southern 2005-08. Northern Premier 2008-18.

Club Colours (change): Gold and black

Ground Capacity: 1,400 **Seats:** 200 **Covered:** 200 **Clubhouse:** Yes **Shop:** Yes
Previous Grounds: Rowley Place 1951-75, Aston University 1976-79
Record Attendance: 2,000 v Leeds United Ex players

RECORDS
Goalscorer: Graham Wiggin
Appearances: Alan Dawson - 400+

HONOURS
FA Comps: None
League: West Midlands (Reg) Division One 1979-80. Midland Alliance 2004-05.
County FA: Staffordshire Senior Cup 2015-16. Walsall Senior Cup 2015-16.

	08-09	09-10	10-11	11-12	12-13	13-14	14-15	15-16	16-17	17-18
	NP1S 5	NP1S 12	NP1S 3	NP P 8	NP P 6	NP P 7	NP P 9	NP P 10	NP P 12	NP P 8
FAC	P	1Q	Pr	4Q	1Q	4Q	2Q	3Q	2Q	3Qr
FAT	1Qr	1Q	2Q	1Q	1P	2Q	3Qr	2Qr	1Q	2Q

ST. IVES TOWN

Club Contact Details 01480 463 207
Pro-Edge Stadium, Westwood Road, St. Ives PE27 6DT
sitfcsecretary@aol.com

Founded: 1887	**Nickname:** Saints	**Manager:** Ricky Marheineke

Previous Names: None
Previous Leagues: Cambridgeshire, Central Amateur, Hunts, Peterborough & District. United Counties > 2013.

Club Colours (change): Black & white

Ground Capacity: 2,000 **Seats:** Yes **Covered:** Yes **Clubhouse:** Yes **Shop:** No
Previous Grounds: Meadow Lane.
Record Attendance: 1,523 v AFC Rushden & Diamonds, Southern Division One Central Play-off Final, 02/05/2016.

RECORDS
Victory: 0-6 v Stafford Rangers (A), FAT 1Q, 28/10/2017 & v Dorchester Town (A), Southern Premier, 16/12/2017
Best FA Cup Second Qualifying Round 2013-14, 15-16, 17-18
FA Vase Quarter Finals 2011-12

HONOURS
FA Comps: None
League: Southern Division One Central Play-offs 2015-16.
County FA: Hunts Senior Cup 1900/01, 11-12, 22-23, 25-26, 29-30, 81-82, 86-87, 87-88, 2006-07, 08-09, 11-12, 15-16.
Hunts Premier Cup 2006-07, 08-09.

	08-09	09-10	10-11	11-12	12-13	13-14	14-15	15-16	16-17	17-18
	UCL P 6	UCL P 10	UCL P 11	UCL P 3	UCL P 2	SthC 13	SthC 9	SthC 4	SthP 15	SthP 22
FAC	EP	1Q	EP	Pr	P	2Q	Pr	2Q	1Q	2Q
FAV	5P	5P	4P	QF	2Pr	FAT 2Q	FAT P	FAT 1Q	FAV 3Q	FAT 1Q

ST. NEOTS TOWN

Club Contact Details 01480 470 012
Rowley Park, Kester Way, Cambridge Road, St Neots, PE19 6SN
enquiries@stneotstownfc.co.uk

Founded: 1879 **Nickname:** Saints **Manager:** Matt Clements
Previous Names: St Neots 1879-1924. St. Neots & District 1924-1957.
Previous Leagues: Biggleswade & Dist. Bedfordshire & Dist/South Midlands 1927-36, 46-49. United Co. 1936-39, 51-56, 66-69, 73-88, 94-2011. Metropolitan (Founder Members) 1949-51, 60-66. Central Alliance 1956-60. Eastern Co. 1969-73. Hunts Junior 1990-94.

Club Colours (change): Dark blue & light blue

Ground Capacity: 3,000 **Seats:** 250 **Covered:** 850 **Clubhouse:** Yes **Shop:** No
Previous Grounds: Town Common 1879-1899. Shortsands 1899-1988. Priory Park 1990-93. Old Rowley Park 1993-2008.
Record Attendance: 2,000 v Wisbech 1966
Nearest Railway Station St Neots - 06.km

RECORDS
Misc: 105 points obtained in the 2010-11 season - a United Counties record.

In 1968-69 the club won the Huntingdonshire Senior Cup for the 12th consecutive time - an English record for Senior cups.

HONOURS
FA Comps: None
League: South Midlands 1932-33. Metropolitan 1949-50. United Counties 1967-68, 2010-11, Division One 1994-95.
Huntingdonshire 1990-91, 91-92, 92-93, 93-94. Southern Division One Central 2011-12.
County FA: Huntingdonshire Senior Cup x37 - Firstly in 1888-89 and most recently in 2013-14.
Huntingdonshire Premier Cup 2001-02.

08-09		09-10		10-11		11-12		12-13		13-14		14-15		15-16		16-17		17-18	
UCL P	17	UCL P	2	UCL P	1	SthC	1	SthP	12	SthP	16	SthP	5	SthP	20	SthP	19	SthP	12
FAC	P	FAC	P	FAC	1Q	FAC	P	FAC	2Q	FAC	2Qr	FAC	1Qr	FAC	2Qr	FAC	1Qr	FAC	1Q
FAV	3P	FAV	2Q	FAV	5P	FAT	2Q	FAT	1Q	FAT	2Q	FAT	3Qr	FAT	2Q	FAT	2Qr	FAT	2Q

STOURBRIDGE

Club Contact Details 01384 394 040
War Memorial Athletic Ground, High Street, Amblecote DY8 4HN
clive1974eades@gmail.com

Founded: 1876 **Nickname:** The Glassboys **Manager:** Gary Hackett
Previous Names: Stourbridge Standard 1876-87
Previous Leagues: West Midlands (Birmingham League) 1892-1939, 54-71, Birmingham Combination 1945-53,
Southern 1971-2000. Midland Alliance 2000-06. Southern 2006-14. Northern Premier 2014-18.

Club Colours (change): Red and white stripes

Ground Capacity: 2,089 **Seats:** 250 **Covered:** 750 **Clubhouse:** Yes **Shop:** Yes
Previous Grounds: None
Record Attendance: 5,726 v Cardiff City - Welsh Cup Final 1st Leg 1974

RECORDS
Goalscorer: Ron Page - 269
Appearances: Ron Page - 427
Additional: Received £20,000 from Lincoln City for Tony Cunningham 1979

HONOURS
FA Comps: None
League: Birmingham 1923-24. Birmingham Combination 1951-52. Southern Division One North 1973-74, Midland Division 1990-91.
Midland Alliance 2001-02, 02-03.
County FA: Worcestershire Junior Cup 1927-28. Hereford Senior Cup 1954-55. Birmingham Senior Cup 1949-50, 58-59, 67-68.
Worcestershire Senior Cup x11 - Firstly in 1904-05 and most recently in 2012-13.

08-09		09-10		10-11		11-12		12-13		13-14		14-15		15-16		16-17		17-18	
SthP	16	SthP	9	SthP	8	SthP	6	SthP	2	SthP	5	NP P	16	NP P	6	NP P	3	NP P	11
FAC	2Qr	FAC	1P	FAC	2Q	FAC	2P	FAC	1Qr	FAC	2P	FAC	3Qr	FAC	2P	FAC	3P	FAC	4Q
FAT	1P	FAT	3Qr	FAT	3Q	FAT	3Q	FAT	1Q	FAT	3Qr	FAT	2Q	FAT	3P	FAT	1Q	FAT	2P

STRATFORD TOWN

Club Contact Details 01789 269 336
The DCS Stadium, Knights Lane, Tiddington, Stratford Upon Avon CV37 7BZ
stratfordtownfcsecretary@outlook.com

Founded: 1941   **Nickname:** The Town   **Manager:** Darren Byfield - May 2018
Previous Names: Straford Rangers 1941-49. Stratford Town Amateurs 1964-70.
Previous Leagues: Local leagues > 1954. Worcestershire/Midland Combination 1954-57, 70-75, 77-94. Birmingham & District/West Midlands (Reg) 1957-70. Hellenic 1975-77. Midland Alliance (Founder Members) 1994-2013.

Club Colours (change): All blue

Ground Capacity: 1,400   **Seats:** Yes   **Covered:** Yes   **Clubhouse:** Yes   **Shop:** Yes
Previous Grounds: A number of pitches before Alcester Road by the late 1940s where they stayed until 2007.
Record Attendance: 1,078 v Aston Villa, Birmingham Senior Cup, Oct. 1996.
Nearest Railway Station Stratford-upon-Avon - 2.8km   **Bus Route** Alveston Primary School - stop 50m away

RECORDS

Best FA Cup	Third Qualifying Round 2004-05, 06-07, 11-12, 17-18(r)
Amateur Cup	Third Round 1962-63
FA Trophy	Second Qualifying Round 2014-15, 15-16, 17-18
FA Vase	Fifth Round Proper 2008-09

HONOURS
FA Comps: None
League: Worcestershire/Midland Combination 1956-57, 86-87.
Midland Alliance 2012-13.
County FA: Birmingham Senior Cup 1962-63.

08-09		09-10		10-11		11-12		12-13		13-14		14-15		15-16		16-17		17-18	
MidAl	6	MidAl	3	MidAl	5	MidAl	8	MidAl	1	Sthsw	10	Sthsw	3	SthP	19	SthP	14	SthP	15
FAC	1Q	FAC	2Qr	FAC	P	FAC	3Q	FAC	EP	FAC	P	FAC	P	FAC	1Q	FAC	1Q	FAC	3Qr
FAV	5P	FAV	2P	FAV	1P	FAV	1P	FAV	2Q	FAT	Pr	FAT	2Q	FAT	2Q	FAT	1Qr	FAT	2Q

TAMWORTH

Club Contact Details 01827 657 98
The Lamb Ground, Kettlebrook, Tamworth, Staffordshire B77 1AA
clubsec@thelambs.co.uk

Founded: 1933   **Nickname:** The Lambs   **Manager:** Mike Fowler
Previous Names: None
Previous Leagues: Birmingham Combination 1933-54. West Midlands (originally Birmingham & District League) 1954-72, 84-88. Southern 1972-79, 83-84, 89-2003. Northern Premier 1979-83. Conference/National 2003-18.

Club Colours (change): All red (All yellow)

Ground Capacity: 4,100   **Seats:** 518   **Covered:** 1,191   **Clubhouse:** Yes   **Shop:** Yes
Previous Grounds: Jolly Sailor Ground 1933-34
Record Attendance: 5,500 v Torquay United - FA Cup 1st Round 15/11/69
Nearest Railway Station Tamworth - within walking distance of the ground.

RECORDS

Victory:	14-4 v Holbrook Institue (H) - Bass Vase 1934
Defeat:	0-11 v Solihull (A) - Birmingham Combination 1940
Goalscorer:	Graham Jessop - 195
Appearances:	Dave Seedhouse - 869
Additional:	Paid £7,500 to Ilkeston Town for David Hemmings, December 2000
	Received £12,000 from Kidderminster Harriers for Scott Rickards, 2003

HONOURS
FA Comps: FA Vase 1988-89.
League: West Midlands League 1963-64, 65-66, 71-72, 87-88.
Southern League Divison One Midland 1996-97, Premier Division 2002-03. Conference North 2008-09.
County FA: Staffordshire Senior Cup 1958-59, 63-64, 65-66, 2001-02.
Birmingham Senior Cup 1960-61, 65-66, 68-69.

08-09		09-10		10-11		11-12		12-13		13-14		14-15		15-16		16-17		17-18	
Conf N	1	Conf	16	Conf	19	Conf	18	Conf	19	Conf	23	Conf N	7	Nat N	7	Nat N	9	Nat N	21
FAC	4Q	FAC	4Q	FAC	2P	FAC	3P	FAC	4Q	FAC	2P	FAC	4Qr	FAC	2Q	FAC	2Q	FAC	2Q
FAT	3Q	FAT	QF	FAT	1P	FAT	1P	FAT	3P	FAT	QF	FAT	3Q	FAT	1P	FAT	3Qr	FAT	3Pr

BASINGSTOKE TOWN

Club Contact Details 01256 327 575
The Ark Cancer Charity Stadium, Western Way, Basingstoke RG22 6EZ
admin@btfc.co.uk

Founded: 1896   **Nickname:** Dragons   **Manager:** Jason Bristow
Previous Names: The club was formed by the merger of Aldworth United and Basingstoke Albion in 1896.
Previous Leagues: Hampshire 1900-40, 45-71, Southern 1971-87, Isthmian 1987-2004. Conference 2004-16.

Club Colours (change): All blue (All white)

Ground Capacity: 6,000   **Seats:** 651   **Covered:** 2,000   **Clubhouse:** Yes   **Shop:** Yes
Previous Grounds: Castle Field 1896-1947
Record Attendance: 5,085 v Wycombe Wanderers - FA Cup 1st Round replay 1997-98
Nearest Railway Station Basingstoke - 2.6km   **Bus Route** Mansfield Road - 50m away

RECORDS
Victory: 10-1 v Chichester City (H) - FA Cup 1st Qualifying Round 1976
Defeat: 0-8 v Aylesbury United - Southern League April 1979
Goalscorer: Paul Coombs - 159 (1991-99)
Appearances: Billy Coomb
Additional: Paid £4,750 to Gosport Borough for Steve Ingham

HONOURS
FA Comps: None
League: Hampshire North Division 1911-12, 19-20, Division One 1967-68, 69-70, 70-71.
          Southern Southern Division 1984-85.
County FA: Hampshire Senior Cup 1970-71, 89-90, 95-96, 96-97, 2007-08, 13-14, 16-17.

	08-09	09-10	10-11	11-12	12-13	13-14	14-15	15-16	16-17	17-18
	Conf S	18	Conf S	15	Conf S	13	Conf S	5	Conf S	14	Conf S	14	Conf S	3	Nat S	22	SthP	12	SthP	10
	FAC	4Q	FAC	3Q	FAC	4Q	FAC	1P	FAC	3Q	FAC	2Q	FAC	1Pr	FAC	1P	FAC	2Q	FAC	1Qr
	FAT	2P	FAT	3Q	FAT	1P	FAT	2P	FAT	3Q	FAT	1Pr	FAT	1Pr	FAT	3Q	FAT	3Q	FAT	1Q

BEACONSFIELD TOWN

Club Contact Details 01494 676 868
Holloways Park, Windsor Road, Beaconsfield, Bucks HP9 2SE
info@beaconsfieldtownnfc.co.uk

Founded: 1994   **Nickname:** The Rams   **Manager:** Gary Meakin - June 2017
Previous Names: Slough YCOB and Beaconsfield United merged in 1994. Beaconsfield SYCOB 1994-2017.
Previous Leagues: Spartan South Midlands 1004-2004, 07-08, Southern 2004-07.

Club Colours (change): Red, white & blue

Ground Capacity: 3,500   **Seats:** Yes   **Covered:** Yes   **Clubhouse:** Yes   **Shop:** No
Previous Grounds: None
Record Attendance: Not known
Nearest Railway Station Beaconsfield - 2.8km

RECORDS
Goalscorer: Allan Arthur
Appearances: Allan Arthur
Best FA Cup   Fourth Qualifying Round 2016-17
FA Trophy   Second Qualifying Round 2017-18(r)
FA Vase   Second Round Proper 2003-04

HONOURS
FA Comps: None
League: Spartan South Midlands 2000-01, 03-04, 07-08. Southern Division One East 2017-18.

County FA: Berks and Bucks Senior Trophy 2003-04, Senior Cup 2012-13.

	08-09	09-10	10-11	11-12	12-13	13-14	14-15	15-16	16-17	17-18
	Sthsw	4	SthM	19	SthC	22	SthC	5	SthC	5	SthC	8	SthC	20	SthC	9	SthC	16	Sth1E	1
	FAC	1Q	FAC	P	FAC	P	FAC	2Qr	FAC	P	FAC	1Q	FAC	2Q	FAC	1Q	FAC	4Q	FAC	1Q
	FAT	P	FAT	1Q	FAT	1Q	FAT	P	FAT	Pr	FAT	P	FAT	P	FAT	P	FAT	1Q	FAT	2Qr

CHESHAM UNITED

Club Contact Details 01494 783 964
The Meadow, Amy Lane, Amersham Road, Chesham HP5 1NE

Founded: 1917   **Nickname:** The Generals   **Manager:** Jon Meakes
Previous Names: Chesham Town and Chesham Generals merged in 1917 to form Chesham United.
Previous Leagues: Spartan 1917-47, Corinthian 1947-63, Athenian 1963-73, Isthmian 1973-2004

Club Colours (change): Claret & blue

Ground Capacity: 5,000   **Seats:** 284   **Covered:** 2,500   **Clubhouse:** Yes   **Shop:** Yes
Previous Grounds: None
Record Attendance: 5,000 v Cambridge United - FA Cup 3rd Round 05/12/1979
Nearest Railway Station Chesham underground - 0.7km   **Bus Route** The Wild Rover Pub - stop 250m away

RECORDS
Goalscorer: John Willis
Appearances: Martin Baguley - 600+
Additional: Received £22,000 from Oldham Athletic for Fitz Hall
Victory: 13-1 v Merthyr Town (H), Southern Premier, 18/11/2017

HONOURS
FA Comps: None
League: Spartan 1921-22, 22-23, 24-25, 32-33. Isthmian Division Two North 1986-87, Division One 1986-87, 97-97, Premier Division 1992-93.
County FA: Berks & Bucks Senior Cup x13. Most recently 2017-18

08-09		09-10		10-11		11-12		12-13		13-14		14-15		15-16		16-17		17-18	
SthM	5	SthM	4	SthP	6	SthP	4	SthP	3	SthP	2	SthP	12	SthP	13	SthP	11	SthP	8
FAC	3Q	FAC	3Q	FAC	2Qr	FAC	2Q	FAC	1Q	FAC	1Q	FAC	1Qr	FAC	2P	FAC	1P	FAC	2Q
FAT	1P	FAT	1Qr	FAT	1Qr	FAT	2Qr	FAT	2P	FAT	1P	FAT	1Q	FAT	1Pr	FAT	2Q	FAT	1P

DORCHESTER TOWN

Club Contact Details 01305 262 451
The Avenue Stadium, Weymouth Avenue, Dorchester DT1 2RY

Founded: 1880   **Nickname:** The Magpies   **Manager:** Steve Thompson
Previous Names: None
Previous Leagues: Dorset, Western 1947-72

Club Colours (change): Black & white

Ground Capacity: 5,229   **Seats:** 710   **Covered:** 2,846   **Clubhouse:** Yes   **Shop:** Yes
Previous Grounds: Council Recreation Ground, Weymouth Avenue 1908-1929, 1929-90, The Avenue Ground 1929
Record Attendance: 4,159 v Weymouth - Southern Premier 1999
Nearest Railway Station Dorchester South & West - 0.9km

RECORDS
Victory: 7-0 v Canterbury (A) - Southern League Southern Division 1986-87
Defeat: 0-13 v Welton Rovers (A) - Western League 1966
Appearances: Mark Jermyn - 600+ over 14 seasons
Additional: Denis Cheney scored 61 goals in one season. Paid £12,000 to Gloucester City for Chris Townsend 1990. Received £35,000 from Portsmouth for Trevor Sinclair.

HONOURS
FA Comps: None
League: Western Division One 1954-55. Southern Southern Division 1979-80, 86-87, Division One East 2002-03.
County FA: Dorset Senior Cup x12 - Firstly in 1950-51 and most recently in 2011-12.

08-09		09-10		10-11		11-12		12-13		13-14		14-15		15-16		16-17		17-18	
Conf S	19	Conf S	17	Conf S	17	Conf S	11	Conf S	8	Conf S	22	SthP	17	SthP	12	SthP	18	SthP	19
FAC	1Pr	FAC	3Q	FAC	3Q	FAC	2Q	FAC	2P	FAC	2Q	FAC	4Q	FAC	1Qr	FAC	1Q	FAC	2Q
FAT	3Q	FAT	3Q	FAT	2Pr	FAT	3Q	FAT	1Pr	FAT	3Q	FAT	1Q	FAT	2Qr	FAT	2Q	FAT	2Q

FARBOROUGH

Club Contact Details 07957 936 436
Rushmoor Community Stadium, Cherrywood Road, Farnborough, Hants GU14 8DU
info@farnboroughfc.co.uk

Founded: 1967   **Nickname:** Boro   **Manager:** Spencer Day
Previous Names: Farnborough Town 1967-2007
Previous Leagues: Surrey Senior 1968-72, Spartan 1972-76, Athenian 1976-77, Isthmian 1977-89, 99-2001, 15-16.
Alliance/Conference 1989-90, 91-93, 94-99, 2010-15. Southern 1990-91, 93-94, 2007-10.

Club Colours (change): Yellow and blue

Ground Capacity: 7,000   **Seats:** 627   **Covered:** 1,350   **Clubhouse:** Yes   **Shop:** Yes
Previous Grounds: Queens Road Recreation ground.
Record Attendance: 2,230 v Corby Town - Southern Premier 21/03/2009
Nearest Railway Station Frimley - 0.7km

RECORDS
Victory: 7-0 v Newport (I.O.W.) (A) - Southern League Division 1 South & West 01/12/2007
Defeat: 0-4 v Hednesford Town (A) - Southern League Premier Division 04/03/2010
Goalscorer: Dean McDonald - 35 (in 53+3 Appearances 2009-10)
Appearances: Nic Ciardini - 147 (2007-10)

HONOURS
FA Comps: None

League: Spartan 1972-73, 73-74, 74-75. London Spartan 1975-76. Athenian Division Two 1976-77. Isthmian Division Two 1978-79, Division One 84
-85, Premier 2000-01. Southern Premier 1990-91, 93-94, 2009-10, Division One South & West 2007-08.
County FA: Hampshire Senior Cup 1974-75, 81-82, 83-84, 85-86, 90-91, 2003-04, 05-06.

08-09		09-10		10-11		11-12		12-13		13-14		14-15		15-16		16-17		17-18	
SthP	2	SthP	1	Conf S	2	Conf S	16	Conf S	13	Conf S	16	Conf S	20	Isth P	18	SthC	2	SthP	20
FAC	2Q	FAC	4Qr	FAC	4Qr	FAC	2Qr	FAC	2Q	FAC	2Qr	FAC	2Qr	FAC	2Qr	FAC	2Q	FAC	1Q
FAT	2P	FAT	1P	FAT	3Q	FAT	1Pr	FAT	1P	FAT	3Qr	FAT	3P	FAT	1Qr	FAT	P	FAT	3Q

FROME TOWN

Club Contact Details 01373 464 087
The Special Effect Stadium, Badgers Hill, Berkley Road, Frome BA11 2EH

Founded: 1904   **Nickname:** The Robins   **Manager:** Danny Greaves - May 2018
Previous Names: None
Previous Leagues: Wiltshire Premier 1904, Somerset Senior 1906-19, Western 1919, 63-2009

Club Colours (change): Red and white

Ground Capacity: 2,200   **Seats:** 250   **Covered:** Yes   **Clubhouse:** Yes   **Shop:** Yes
Previous Grounds: None
Record Attendance: 8,000 v Leyton Orient - FA Cup 1st Round 1958
Nearest Railway Station Frome - 0.9km   **Bus Route** Bus stops outside the ground

RECORDS
Victory: 7-2 v kings Langley (A), Southern Premier, 09/12/2017
Defeat: 0-7 v Gosport Borough (A), Southern Premier, 21/04/2018

HONOURS
FA Comps: None
League: Somerset County 1906-07, 08-09, 10-11.
Western Division Two 1919-20, Division One 2001-02, Premier Division 1978-79.
County FA: Somerset Senior Cup 1932-33, 33-34, 50-51 Somerset Premier Cup 1966-67, 68-69 (shared), 82-83, 2008-09.

08-09		09-10		10-11		11-12		12-13		13-14		14-15		15-16		16-17		17-18	
WestP	2	Sthsw	6	Sthsw	4	SthP	12	SthP	18	SthP	14	SthP	20	SthP	16	SthP	8	SthP	13
FAC	3Qr	FAC	P	FAC	2Q	FAC	2Qr	FAC	2Q	FAC	1Qr	FAC	3Qr	FAC	1Qr	FAC	1Q	FAC	2Q
FAV	3P	FAT	1Q	FAT	1Q	FAT	1Q	FAT	1Q	FAT	1Qr	FAT	1Q	FAT	3Qr	FAT	3Q	FAT	1Q

GOSPORT BOROUGH

Club Contact Details 023 9252 5797
Aerial Direct Stadium, Privett Park, Privett Road, Gosport, Hampshire PO12 0SX

Founded: 1944   **Nickname:** The 'Boro'   **Manager:** Craig McAllister - June 2018
Previous Names: Gosport Borough Athletic
Previous Leagues: Portsmouth & District 1944-45, Hampshire 1945-78. Southern 1978-92, 2007-13. Wessex 1992-2007. Conference 2013-17.

Club Colours (change): Yellow & blue

Ground Capacity: 4,500   **Seats:** 1,000   **Covered:** Yes   **Clubhouse:** Yes   **Shop:** Yes
Previous Grounds: None
Record Attendance: 4,770 v Pegasus - FA Amateur Cup 1953
Nearest Railway Station Portsmouth Harbour   **Bus Route** X5 (to Southampton) & 9/9A (to Fareham)

RECORDS
Victory: 19-1 v Widbrook United, Portsmouth Senior Cup, 2016-17.
Defeat: 0-9 v Gloucester City - Southern Premier Division 1989-90 and v Lymington & N.M. - Wessex Lge 99-2000
Goalscorer: Justin Bennett- 257
Appearances: Tony Mahoney - 765

HONOURS
FA Comps: None
League: Portsmouth & District 1944-45. Hampshire 1945-46, 76-77, 77-78.
      Wessex 2006-07.
County FA: Hampshire Senior Cup 1987-88, 2014-15.

08-09		09-10		10-11		11-12		12-13		13-14		14-15		15-16		16-17		17-18	
Sthsw	12	Sthsw	8	Sthsw	13	Sthsw	3	SthP	5	Conf S	12	Conf S	6	Nat S	9	Nat S	20	SthP	23
FAC	3Q	FAC	P	FAC	Pr	FAC	P	FAC	4Qr	FAC	2Q	FAC	1P	FAC	3Qr	FAC	2Q	FAC	2Q
FAT	1Q	FAT	2Q	FAT	P	FAT	1P	FAT	2Q	FAT	F	FAT	2P	FAT	3Q	FAT	1P	FAT	2Q

HARROW BOROUGH

Club Contact Details 0844 561 1347
Earlsmead, Carlyon Avenue, South Harrow HA2 8SS

Founded: 1933   **Nickname:** Boro   **Manager:** Steve Baker - 25/01/15
Previous Names: Roxonian 1933-38, Harrow Town 1938-66
Previous Leagues: Harrow & District 1933-34, Spartan 1934-40, 45-58, West Middlesex Combination 1940-41, Middlesex Senior 1941-45,
      Delphian 1956-63, Athenian 1963-75. Isthmian 1975-2018.

Club Colours (change): All red

Ground Capacity: 3,070   **Seats:** 350   **Covered:** 1,000   **Clubhouse:** Yes   **Shop:** Yes
Previous Grounds: Northcult Road 1933-34.
Record Attendance: 3,000 v Wealdstone - FA Cup 1st Qualifying Road 1946
Nearest Railway Station Northolt Underground - 1.1km

RECORDS
Victory: 13-0 v Handley Page (A) - 18/10/1941
Defeat: 0-8 on five occasions
Goalscorer: Dave Pearce - 153
Appearances: Les Currell - 582, Colin Payne - 557, Steve Emmanuel - 522

HONOURS
FA Comps: None
League: Isthmian League 1983-84.

County FA: Middlesex Senior Cup 1982-83, 92-93, 2014-15. Middlesex Premier Cup 1981-82.
      Middlesex Senior Charity Cup 1979-80, 92-93, 2005-06, 6-07, 14-15.

08-09		09-10		10-11		11-12		12-13		13-14		14-15		15-16		16-17		17-18	
Isth P	14	Isth P	14	Isth P	5	Isth P	17	Isth P	15	Isth P	18	Isth P	16	Isth P	17	Isth P	21	Isth P	12
FAC	1Qr	FAC	1Qr	FAC	1P	FAC	2Q	FAC	1Q	FAC	1Q	FAC	1Qr	FAC	4Qr	FAC	1P	FAC	1Q
FAT	2Q	FAT	2Qr	FAT	1Q	FAT	2Qr	FAT	1Q	FAT	1Q	FAT	1Q	FAT	1Q	FAV	3Q	FAT	1Qr

HARTLEY WINTNEY

Club Contact Details 01252 843 586 (Clubhouse)
Memorial Playing Fields, Green Lane, Hartley Wintney RG27 8DL

Founded: 1897   **Nickname:** The Row   **Manager:** Dan Brownlie & Anthony Millerick
Previous Names: None
Previous Leagues: Basingstoke & District. Aldershot & District >1978. Founder members of the Home Counties League (renamed Combined Counties League) 1978- 2017.

Club Colours (change): All orange

Ground Capacity: 2,000   **Seats:** 113   **Covered:** Yes   **Clubhouse:** Yes   **Shop:** Yes
Previous Grounds: Causeway Farm 1897-1953.
Record Attendance: 1,392 v AFC Wimbledon , Combined Counties League Premier, 25/01/03.
Nearest Railway Station Winchfield - 1.9km   **Bus Route** Green Lane - stop 100m away

RECORDS
Best FA Cup   Fourth Qualifying Round 2013-14
FA Vase   Fifth Round 2015-16

HONOURS
FA Comps: None
League: Combined Counties League 1982-83, 2015-16, 16-17.

County FA: None

08-09		09-10		10-11		11-12		12-13		13-14		14-15		15-16		16-17		17-18	
CCP	21	CC1	5	CC1	7	CC1	3	CCP	19	CCP	7	CCP	9	CCP	1	CCP	1	Sth1E	4
FAC	P	FAC	EP	FAC	Pr	FAC	3Q	FAC	P	FAC	4Q	FAC	Pr	FAC	3Q	FAC	EP	FAC	2Q
FAV	1Q	FAV	2Q	FAV	1Q	FAV	1P	FAV	1Q	FAV	2P	FAV	2Q	FAV	5P	FAV	2P	FAT	1P

HENDON

Club Contact Details 020 8205 1645
Silver Jubilee Park, Townsend Lane, Kingsbury, London NW9 7NE
hendonfc@freenetname.co.uk

Founded: 1908   **Nickname:** Dons or Greens   **Manager:** James Gray
Previous Names: Christ Church Hampstead > 1908, Hampstead Town > 1933, Golders Green > 1946
Previous Leagues: Finchley & District 1908-11, Middlesex 1910-11, London 1911-14, Athenian 1914-63. Isthmian 1963-2018.

Club Colours (change): Green and white

Ground Capacity: 3,070   **Seats:** 350   **Covered:** 1,000   **Clubhouse:** Yes   **Shop:**
Previous Grounds: Claremont Road. Vale Farm (Wembley FC). Earlsmead (Harrow Borough FC).
Record Attendance: 9,000 v Northampton Town - FA Cup 1st Round 1952
Nearest Railway Station Hendon - 1.1km   **Bus Route** Queensbury Road - 700m away

RECORDS
Victory: 13-1 v Wingate - Middlesex County Cup 02/02/1957
Defeat: 2-11 v Walthamstowe Avenue, Athenian League 09/11/1935
Goalscorer: Freddie Evans - 176 (1929-35)
Appearances: Bill Fisher - 787 - (1940-64)
Additional: Received £30,000 from Luton Town for Iain Dowie

HONOURS
FA Comps: FA Amateur Cup 1959-60, 64-65, 71-72. European Amateur Champions 1972-73.
League: Finchley & District Division Three 1908-09, DivisioN Two 09-10, Division One 10-11. Middlesex 1912-13, 13-14.
    Athenian 1952-53, 55-56, 60-61. Isthmian 1964-65, 72-73.
County FA: London Senior Cup 1963-64, 68-69, 2008-09, 11-12 14-15. Middlesex Senior Cup x15 - Firstly in 1933-34 / Most recently 2003-04.
    Middlesex Intermediate Cup 1964-65, 66-67, 72-73. London Intermediate Cup 1962-63, 64-65, 72-73, 75-76, 79-80.

08-09		09-10		10-11		11-12		12-13		13-14		14-15		15-16		16-17		17-18	
Isth P	16	Isth P	10	Isth P	15	Isth P	7	Isth P	10	Isth P	8	Isth P	2	Isth P	19	Isth P	19	Isth P	3
FAC	3Q	FAC	4Q	FAC	1P	FAC	4Q	FAC	1P	FAC	2P	FAC	3Q	FAC	1Q	FAC	4Q	FAC	1Qr
FAT	2Q	FAT	2Q	FAT	2Q	FAT	1Q	FAT	1Q	FAT	1P	FAT	3Q	FAT	1Q	FAT	1Q	FAT	2P

KINGS LANGLEY

Club Contact Details 07730 410 330
Gaywood Park, Hempstead Road, Kings Langley Herts WD4 8BS

Founded: 1886	**Nickname:** Kings		**Manager:** Steve Conroy

Previous Names: None
Previous Leagues: West Herts (Founder Member) 1891-1920, 22-34. Southern Olympian 1934-39.
Hertfordshire County 1920-22, 46-52, 55-2001. Parthenon 1952-55. Spartan South Midlands 1955-2015.

Club Colours (change): White & black

Ground Capacity: 1,963 **Seats:** Yes **Covered:** Yes **Clubhouse:** Yes **Shop:**
Previous Grounds: Groomes Meadow. Blackwell Meadow. Kings Langley Common. Home Park 1913-80.
Record Attendance: Not known Oxhey, Rolls Royce & Buncefield Lane and Leavesden Hospital Ground between 1980-97.
Nearest Railway Station Kings Langley - 1.6km

RECORDS
Misc: 47 consecutive matches unbeaten in all competitions between 15-09-07 and 15-10-08.

HONOURS
FA Comps: None
League: West Herts Div.3 1911-12, Div.2 1919-20, 30-31, 34-35. Southern Olympian Div.1 1936-37. Herts County 1949-50, 51-52, 65-66, 66-67, Div.1 1975-76. Spartan South Midlands Div.2 2007-08, Premier 2014-15. Southern Div.1 Central 2015-16.
County FA: Herts Charity Shield 1966-67. Herts Intermediate Cup 2006-07, 07-08. Herts Senior Centenary Trophy 2011-12.

08-09		09-10		10-11		11-12		12-13		13-14		14-15		15-16		16-17		17-18	
SSM1	2	SSM1	7	SSM1	3	SSM1	4	SSM1	6	SSM1	2	SSM P	1	SthC	1	SthP	20	SthP	21
						FAC	EP	FAC	EPr	FAC	1Q	FAC	Pr	FAC	P	FAC	2Q	FAC	2Q
				FAV	1Q	FAV	2Q	FAV	1Q	FAV	1Q	FAV	2P	FAT	1Q	FAT	3Q	FAT	1Q

MERTHYR TOWN

Club Contact Details 01685 359 074
Loadlok Community Stadium, Penydarren Park, Park Terrace CF47 8RF
footballsecretary@merthyrtownfc.co.uk

Founded: 2010	**Nickname:** Martyrs		**Manager:** Gavin Williams

Previous Names: None
Previous Leagues: Western League 2010-12.

Club Colours (change): White & black

Ground Capacity: **Seats:** Yes **Covered:** Yes **Clubhouse:** Yes **Shop:**
Previous Grounds: Rhiw Dda'r (Taff's Well AFC) 2010-11.
Record Attendance: Not known
Nearest Railway Station Merthyr Tydfil - 0.6km **Bus Route** St Mary's Church - stop 100m away

RECORDS
Victory: 9-0 v Bishops Cleeve, Southern Division One South & West, 06/04/2015.
Defeat: 1-13 v Chesham United (A), Southern Premier, 18/11/2017.

HONOURS
FA Comps: None
League: Western League Division One 2010-11, Premier Division 2011-12.
Southern Division One South & West 2014-15.
County FA: None

08-09	09-10	10-11		11-12		12-13		13-14		14-15		15-16		16-17		17-18	
		West1	1	WestP	1	Sthsw	3	Sthsw	2	Sthsw	1	SthP	10	SthP	3	SthP	17
		FAC	EP	FAC	1Qr	FAC	3Q	FAC	1Q	FAC	P	FAC	2Q	FAC	3Q	FAC	2Q
		FAV	2Q	FAV	2Q	FAT	1P	FAT	3Q	FAT	3Qr	FAT	3Qr	FAT	2Qr	FAT	1Q

METROPOLITAN POLICE

Club Contact Details 020 8398 7358
Imber Court, Ember Lane, East Molesey, Surrey KT8 0BT
ph.allen@btinternet.com

Founded: 1919   **Nickname:** The Met   **Manager:** Gavin MacPherson
Previous Names: None
Previous Leagues: Spartan 1928-60, Metropolitan 1960-71, Southern 1971-78. Isthmian 1978-2018.

Club Colours (change): All blue

Ground Capacity: 3,000   **Seats:** 297   **Covered:** 1,800   **Clubhouse:** Yes   **Shop:** No
Previous Grounds: None
Record Attendance: 4,500 v Kingstonian - FA Cup 1934
Nearest Railway Station Thames Ditton - 0.8km

RECORDS
Victory: 10-1 v Tilbury - 1995
Defeat: 1-11 v Wimbledon - 1956
Goalscorer: Mario Russo
Appearances: Pat Robert

HONOURS
FA Comps: None
League: Spartan League x7.
      Isthmian League Division One South 2010-11.
County FA: Middlesex Senior Cup 1927-28, Surrey Senior Cup 1932-33, 2014-15. London Senior Cup 2009-10.

08-09		09-10		10-11		11-12		12-13		13-14		14-15		15-16		16-17		17-18	
Isth1S	4	Isth1S	10	Isth1S	1	Isth P	12	Isth P	6	Isth P	17	Isth P	5	Isth P	12	Isth P	18	Isth P	
FAC	1Q	FAC	1Q	FAC	4Qr	FAC	1Q	FAC	1P	FAC	1Qr	FAC	2Q	FAC	1Qr	FAC	2Q	FAC	2Q
FAT	1Q	FAT	1Q	FAT	Pr	FAT	1Q	FAT	2Qr	FAT	2Q	FAT	3Q	FAT	3Q	FAV	1Q	FAT	3Q

POOLE TOWN

Club Contact Details 01794 517 991
Tatnam Ground, Oakdale School, School Lane, Poole BH15 3JR
secretary@pooletownfc.co.uk

Founded: 1890   **Nickname:** The Dolphins   **Manager:** Tom Killick
Previous Names: Poole Rovers and Poole Hornets merged in 1890 to form Poole FC > 1934 (Known as Poole & St. Mary's 1919-20).
Previous Leagues: Dorset 1896-1903, 04-05, 10-11. Hampshire 1903-04, 05-10, 11-23, 34-35, 96-2004. Western 1923-26, 30-34, 35-57.
      Southern 1926-30, 57-96, 2011-16. Wessex 2004-11. National 2016-18.

Club Colours (change): Red & white

Ground Capacity: 2,000   **Seats:** 268   **Covered:** Yes   **Clubhouse:** Yes   **Shop:** Yes
Previous Grounds: Ye Old Farm Ground. Wimborne Road Rec > 1933. Poole Stadium 1933-94. Hamworthy Utd 1994-96. Holt Utd 1996.
Record Attendance: 6,575 v Watford, FAC 1Pr, 1962-63 (at Poole Stadium). 2,203 v Corby, Southern Premier, 2014-15 (at
Nearest Railway Station Poole - 3/4 mile from the ground.

RECORDS
Victory: 12-0 v Welton Rovers (H) Western League 26/04/1939.
Defeat: 1-12 v Boscombe (A) Hampshire League (West) 20/12/1913.
Additional: Transfer fee paid £5,000 for Nicky Dent 1990.
            Transfer fee received reported as £180,000 for Charlie Austin from Swindon Town 2009.

HONOURS
FA Comps: None
League: Western 1956-57. Hampshire Division One 1999-00. Wessex Premier Division 2008-09, 09-10, 10-11.
      Southern Division One South & West 2012-13, Premier 2015-16.
County FA: Dorset Senior Cup 1894-95, 96-97, 98-99, 1901-02, 03-04, 06-07, 25-26, 26-27, 37-38, 46-47, 74-75, 88-89, 97-98, 2008
      -09, 12-13, 13-14.

08-09		09-10		10-11		11-12		12-13		13-14		14-15		15-16		16-17		17-18	
WexP	1	WexP	1	WexP	1	Sthsw	2	Sthsw	1	SthP	7	SthP	2	SthP	1	Nat S	5	Nat S	20
FAC	2Q	FAC	1Q	FAC	4Q	FAC	3Q	FAC	P	FAC	4Qr	FAC	2Qr	FAC	4Q	FAC	2Q	FAC	3Q
FAV	2P	FAV	4P	FAV	SF	FAT	1Qr	FAT	2Qr	FAT	2Q	FAT	1P	FAT	1Q	FAT	3Qr	FAT	3Q

SALISBURY

Club Contact Details 01722 776 655
Raymond McEnhill Stadium, Partridge Way, Old Sarum SP4 6PU
info@salisburyfc.co.uk

Founded: 2015 **Nickname:** The Whites **Manager:** Steve Claridge
Previous Names: None
Previous Leagues: Wessex 2015-16.

Club Colours (change): White and black

Ground Capacity: 4,000 **Seats:** 500 **Covered:** 2,247 **Clubhouse:** Yes **Shop:**
Previous Grounds: None
Record Attendance: 3,450 v Hereford FC, FA Vase Semi-final 2nd leg, 2015-16.
Nearest Railway Station Salisbury - 4km **Bus Route** Bus stops outside the ground

RECORDS
Victory: 9-1 v Bournemouth - Wessex Premier 25/08/15.
Defeat: 4-1 v AFC Porchester - Wessex Premier 30/04/16.
Goalscorer: Sam Wilson - 40 - 2015-16.
Appearances: Thomas Whelan - 54 - 2015-16.

HONOURS
FA Comps: None
League: Wessex Premier Division 2015-16.

County FA: None

08-09	09-10	10-11	11-12	12-13	13-14	14-15	15-16	16-17	17-18
							WexP 1	Sthsw 2	Sth1W 2
								FAC 2Q	FAC 2Q
							FAV SF	FAT 1Q	FAT P

STAINES TOWN

Club Contact Details 01784 469 240
Wheatsheaf Park, Wheatsheaf Lane, Staines TW18 2PD

Founded: 1892 **Nickname:** The Swans **Manager:** Cristian Colas - May 2018
Previous Names: Staines Albany & St Peters Institute merged in 1895. Staines 1905-18, Staines Lagonda 1918-25, Staines Vale (WWII)
Previous Leagues: Great Western Suburban, Hounslow & District 1919-20, Spartan 1924-35, 58-71, Middlesex Senior 1943-52, Parthenon 1952-53, Hellenic 1953-58, Athenian 1971-73, Isthmian 1973-2009, 15-18. Conference 2009-15.

Club Colours (change): Yellow and blue

Ground Capacity: 3,000 **Seats:** 300 **Covered:** 850 **Clubhouse:** Yes **Shop:** Yes
Previous Grounds: Groundshared with Walton & Hersham and Egham Town whilst new Wheatsheaf stadium was built 2001-03.
Record Attendance: 2,860 v Stokcport County, FAC, 2007
Nearest Railway Station Staines - 1.3km **Bus Route** Penton Hook Road - stop 100m away

RECORDS
Victory: 14-0 v Croydon (A) - Isthmian Division 1 19/03/1994
Defeat: 1-18 - Wycombe Wanderers (A) - Great Western Suburban League 27/12/1909
Goalscorer: Alan Gregory - 122
Appearances: Dickie Watmore - 840

HONOURS
FA Comps: None
League: Spartan League 1959-60. Athenian League Division Two 1971-72, Division One 1974-75, 88-89.

County FA: Middlesex Senior cup 1975-76, 76-77, 77-78, 88-89, 90-91, 94-95, 97-98, 2009-10, 12-13. Barassi Cup 1975-76.

08-09	09-10	10-11	11-12	12-13	13-14	14-15	15-16	16-17	17-18
Isth P 2	Conf S 8	Conf S 15	Conf S 15	Conf S 18	Conf S 8	Conf S 21	Isth P 16	Isth P 12	Isth P 8
FAC 2Qr	FAC 2Pr	FAC 4Q	FAC 4Q	FAC 2Q	FAC 1P	FAC 3Qr	FAC 1P	FAC 3Q	FAC 1Q
FAT 1Q	FAT 3Q	FAT 3Q	FAT 2P	FAT 3Qr	FAT 1Pr	FAT 3Qr	FAT 1Q	FAT 1Q	FAT 1Q

SWINDON SUPERMARINE

Club Contact Details 01793 828 778
The Webbswood Stadium, South Marston, Swindon SN3 4BZ
supermarinefc@aol.com

Founded: 1992   **Nickname:** Marine   **Manager:** Lee Spalding
Previous Names: Club formed after the amalgamation of Swindon Athletic and Supermarine
Previous Leagues: Wiltshire, Hellenic1992-2001.

Club Colours (change): All blue (All red)

Ground Capacity: 2,600   **Seats:** 325   **Covered:** Yes   **Clubhouse:** Yes   **Shop:** Yes
Previous Grounds: Supermarine: Vickers Airfield > Mid 1960s
Record Attendance: 1,550 v Aston Villa
Nearest Railway Station Swindon - 5.8km   **Bus Route** Stanton Fitzwarren Turn - stop 300m away

RECORDS
Goalscorer: Damon York - 136 (1990-98)
Appearances: Damon York - 314 (1990-98)
Additional: Paid £1,000 to Hungerford Town for Lee Hartson

HONOURS
FA Comps: None
League: Hellenic League Premier Division 1997-98, 2000-01.

County FA: Wiltshire Premier Shield 1996-97, 2006-07. Senior Cup 2016-17.

08-09		09-10		10-11		11-12		12-13		13-14		14-15		15-16		16-17		17-18	
SthP	13	SthP	14	SthP	10	SthP	21	Sthsw	4	Sthsw	5	Sthsw	14	Sthsw	4	Sthsw	7	Sth1W	5
FAC	1Q	FAC	1Q	FAC	2P	FAC	2Q	FAC	1Q	FAC	P	FAC	2Q	FAC	1Q	FAC	3Q	FAC	3Q
FAT	3P	FAT	1Q	FAT	3Q	FAT	1P	FAT	1Q	FAT	1Q	FAT	P	FAT	2Q	FAT	1Q	FAT	1Q

TAUNTON TOWN

Club Contact Details 01823 254 909
The Viridor Stadium, Wordsworth Drive, Taunton, Somerset TA1 2HG
admin@tauntontown.com

Founded: 1947   **Nickname:** The Peacocks   **Manager:** Leigh Robinson
Previous Names: None
Previous Leagues: Western 1954-77, 83-2002, Southern 1977-83

Club Colours (change): Claret and sky blue

Ground Capacity: 2,500   **Seats:** 300   **Covered:** 1,000   **Clubhouse:** Yes   **Shop:** Yes
Previous Grounds: Mountfields. French Weir. Victoria Park. Huish Old Boys. Denman's Park > 1953.
Record Attendance: 3,284 v Tiverton Town - FA Vase Semi-final 1999
Nearest Railway Station Taunton - 1.4km   **Bus Route** Milford Road - stop 20m away

RECORDS
Victory: 12-0 v Dawlish Town (A) - FA Cup Preliminary Round 28/08/1993
Defeat: 0-8 v Cheltenham Town (A) - FA Cup 2nd Qualifying Round 28/09/1991
Goalscorer: Tony Payne. Reg Oram scored 67 in one season
Appearances: Tony Payne

HONOURS
FA Comps: FA Vase 2000-01.
League: Western League 1968-69, 89-90, 95-96, 98-99, 99-2000, 2000-01.
           Southern Division One 2017-18.
County FA: Somerset Senior Cup 1969-70, Premier Cup 2002-03, 05-06, 13-14, 14-15, 16-17.

08-09		09-10		10-11		11-12		12-13		13-14		14-15		15-16		16-17		17-18	
Sthsw	20	Sthsw	19	Sthsw	9	Sthsw	17	Sthsw	18	Sthsw	8	Sthsw	4	Sthsw	3	Sthsw	4	Sth1W	1
FAC	1Q	FAC	1Q	FAC	1Q	FAC	1Qr	FAC	1Qr	FAC	Pr	FAC	1Q	FAC	2Qr	FAC	1Pr	FAC	1Qr
FAT	P	FAT	1Q	FAT	Pr	FAT	1Q	FAT	2Q	FAT	P	FAT	Pr	FAT	2Q	FAT	3Q	FAT	1P

TIVERTON TOWN

Club Contact Details 01884 252 397
Ladysmead, Bolham Road, Tiverton, Devon EX16 6SG
ramsayfindlay@hotmail.co.uk

Founded: 1913   **Nickname:** Tivvy   **Manager:** Martyn Rogers
Previous Names: Tiverton Athletic.
Previous Leagues: East Devon 1913-28. North Devon 1928-32. Exeter & District 1932-73. Western 1973-99.

Club Colours (change): All yellow

Ground Capacity: 3,500   **Seats:** 520   **Covered:** 2,300   **Clubhouse:** Yes   **Shop:** Yes
Previous Grounds: Athletic Ground (Amory Park) 1913-21. Elm Field (The Elms) 1921-46.
Record Attendance: 3,000 v Leyton Orient - FA Cup 1st Round Proper 12/11/1994.
Nearest Railway Station Tiverton Parkway - 2km   **Bus Route** Park Road - stop 300m away

RECORDS
Victory: 14-1 v University College SW, 11/02/1933.
Defeat: 0-10 v Dawlish Town, 27/12/1969.
Goalscorer: Phil Everett - 378.
Appearances: Tom Gardner - 510.

HONOURS
FA Comps: FA Vase 1997-98, 98-99.
League: East Devon Senior Division 1924-25, 25-26, 26-27, 27-28. North Devon 1931-32.
        Exeter & District 1933-34, 64-65, 65-66. Western 1993-94, 94-95, 96-97, 97-98.
County FA: Devon Senior Cup 1955-56, 65-66.
        Devon St Luke's Cup 1990-91, 91-92, 92-93, 93-94, 94-95, 96-97, 1999-2000, 02-03, 05-06, 16-17.

08-09		09-10		10-11		11-12		12-13		13-14		14-15		15-16		16-17		17-18	
SthP	12	SthP	19	SthP	20	Sthsw	9	Sthsw	16	Sthsw	3	Sthsw	16	Sthsw	8	Sthsw	3	SthP	6
FAC	2Q	FAC	1Q	FAC	1Qr	FAC	P	FAC	P	FAC	P	FAC	1Qr	FAC	P	FAC	Pr	FAC	1Q
FAT	2Pr	FAT	1Q	FAT	1Q	FAT	3Q	FAT	1Q	FAT	3Qr	FAT	1Q	FAT	2Q	FAT	1Q	FAT	2Qr

WALTON CASUALS

Club Contact Details
Elmbridge Sports Hub, Waterside Drive, Walton-on-Thames, Surrey KT12 2JP
waltoncasualsjuniors@hotmail

Founded: 1948   **Nickname:** The Stags   **Manager:** Anthony Gale
Previous Names: None
Previous Leagues: Surrey Intermediate 1948-69. Surrey Senior 1969-71. Suburban 1971-92. Surrey County 1992-95.
        Combined Counties 1995-2005.

Club Colours (change): Orange and black

Ground Capacity: 2,000   **Seats:** 153   **Covered:** 403   **Clubhouse:** Yes   **Shop:** Yes
Previous Grounds: Elm Grove Rec. 1948-69. Franklyn Road 69-71. Stompond Lane 71-72. Liberty Lane 72-80. Waterside Stadium 80-2015.
Record Attendance: 1,748 v AFC Wimbledon - Combined Counties League 12/04/2004   Moatside 2015-16. Church Road 2016-17.
Nearest Railway Station Both Walton and Hersham stations about 43min walk.   **Bus Route** Nos. 461 & 459 stop nearest the hub.

RECORDS
Goalscorer: Paul Mills - 111 in 123 appearances (1993-99).
Appearances: Lawrence Ennis - 288
Victory: 10-0 v Chessington United, Combined Counties Premier, 28/12/2004.
Defeat: 0-7 v Redhill, Surrey Senior Cup 1st Rnd, 08/12/98. v Chipstead, Combined Counties Premier, 09/11/2002.
        v Faversham Town, Isthmian Division One, 08/12/2012. v Faversham Town, Isthmian Division One, 09/04/2016.

HONOURS
FA Comps: None
League: Surban Southern Section 1982-83, Premier B 2012-13. Combined Counties Premier Division 2004-05.

County FA: None

08-09		09-10		10-11		11-12		12-13		13-14		14-15		15-16		16-17		17-18	
Isth1S	17	Isth1S	21	Isth1S	12	Isth1S	15	Isth1S	22	Isth1S	9	Isth1S	18	Isth1S	16	Isth1S	13	Isth1S	6
FAC	1Q	FAC	3Q	FAC	1Q	FAC	P	FAC	P	FAC	P	FAC	Pr	FAC	P	FAC	3Q	FAC	1Q
FAT	1Qr	FAT	Pr	FAT	1Q	FAT	Pr	FAT	P	FAT	Pr	FAT	1Q	FAT	1Qr	FAT	1P	FAT	1Q

WEYMOUTH

Club Contact Details 01305 785 558
Bob Lucas Stadium, Radipole Lane, Weymouth DT4 9XJ
secretary@theterras.co.uk

Founded: 1890   **Nickname:** The Terras   **Manager:** Mark Molesley
Previous Names: None
Previous Leagues: Dorset, Western 1907-23, 28-49, Southern 1923-28, 49-79, 89-2005, Alliance/Conference 1979-89, 2005-10.

Club Colours (change): Claret & blue

Ground Capacity: 6,600   **Seats:** 900   **Covered:** Yes   **Clubhouse:** Yes   **Shop:** Yes
Previous Grounds: Recreation Ground > 1987.
Record Attendance: 4,995 v Manchester United - Ground opening 21/10/97
Nearest Railway Station Weymouth - 2.2km   **Bus Route** Bus stops outside the ground

RECORDS
Goalscorer: W 'Farmer' Haynes - 275
Appearances: Tony Hobsons - 1,076
Additional: Paid £15,000 to Northwich Victoria for Shaun Teale
           Received £100,000 from Tottenham Hotspur for Peter Guthrie 1988
Defeat: 0-9 v Rushden & Diamonds, Conference South, 21/02/2009 - this was a game which, due to an administration issue, the club had to field their U18 team.

HONOURS
FA Comps: None

League: Dorset 1897-98, 1913-14, Division One 1921-22. Western Division One 1922-23, 36-37, 37-38, Division Two 33-34. Southern 1964-65, 65-66, Southern Division 1997-98. Conference South 2005-06.
County FA: Dorset Senior Cup x12 - Firstly in 1985-86 and most recently in 2016-17.

08-09		09-10		10-11		11-12		12-13		13-14		14-15		15-16		16-17		17-18	
Conf	23	Conf S	22	SthP	18	SthP	17	SthP	9	SthP	12	SthP	7	SthP	7	SthP	10	SthP	5
FAC	4Q	FAC	2Q	FAC	2Q	FAC	3Q	FAC	2Q	FAC	4Q	FAC	4Qr	FAC	1Q	FAC	4Q	FAC	3Q
FAT	1P	FAT	1P	FAT	2Q	FAT	2P	FAT	2Q	FAT	2Q	FAT	1Pr	FAT	3Q	FAT	1Pr	FAT	1Q

WIMBORNE TOWN

Club Contact Details 01202 884 821
The W+S Stadium, Cowgrove Road, Wimborne, Dorset BH21 4EL
barhamp@hotmail.co.uk

Founded: 1878   **Nickname:** Magpies   **Manager:** Matty Holmes
Previous Names: None
Previous Leagues: Dorset, Dorset Combination, Western 1981-86, Wessex 1986-2010

Club Colours (change): Black and white

Ground Capacity: 3,250   **Seats:** 275   **Covered:** 425   **Clubhouse:** Yes   **Shop:** Yes
Previous Grounds: None
Record Attendance: 3,250 v Bamber Bridge
                                       Bus Route First School - stop 400m away

RECORDS
Goalscorer: Jason Lovell
Appearances: James Sturgess

HONOURS
FA Comps: FA Vase 1991-92.
League: Dorset Division One 1980-81. Wessex 1991-92, 93-94, 99-2000.
County FA: Dorset Minor Cup 1912-13, Senior Amateur Cup 1936-37, 63-64, Senior Cup 91-92, 96-97.

08-09		09-10		10-11		11-12		12-13		13-14		14-15		15-16		16-17		17-18	
WexP	4	WexP	2	Sthsw	19	Sthsw	19	Sthsw	12	Sthsw	13	Sthsw	13	Sthsw	17	Sthsw	11	Sth1W	3
FAC	1Q	FAC	1Q	FAC	1Q	FAC	P	FAC	P	FAC	P	FAC	1Q	FAC	2Q	FAC	Pr	FAC	Pr
FAV	3P	FAV	2P	FAT	1Qr	FAT	P	FAT	2Q	FAT	P	FAT	1P	FAT	P	FAT	2Q	FAT	1Q

AFC DUNSTABLE

Club Contact Details 01582 891 433
Creasey Park, Creasey Park Drive, Brewers Hill Road LU6 1BB
afcdunstable2016@gmail.com

Founded: 1981   **Nickname:** Od's   **Manager:** Steve Heath
Previous Names: Old Dunstablians 1981- 2004.
Previous Leagues: Dunstable Alliance 1981-83. Luton District & South Bedfordshire 1983-95. South Midlands/Spartan South Midlands 1995-2016.

Club Colours (change): All royal blue

Ground Capacity: 3,200   **Seats:** 350   **Covered:** 1,000   **Clubhouse:** Yes   **Shop:** Yes
Previous Grounds: Manshead School 1981-94. Dunstable Cricket Club (Totternhoe) 1994-2009.
Record Attendance: Not known.

RECORDS
Best FA Cup   Second Qualifying Round 2012-13(r), 16-17
FA Trophy   Preliminary Round 2016-17, 17-18
FA Vase   Fourth Round Proper 2015-16

HONOURS
FA Comps: None

League: Spartan South Midlands Division Two 2003-04, 06-07, Premier Division 2015-16.

County FA: Bedfordshire Junior Cup 1989-90. Bedfordshire Senior Trophy 2006-07, 07-08. Bedfordshire Senior Cup 2016-17.

08-09		09-10		10-11		11-12		12-13		13-14		14-15		15-16		16-17		17-18	
SSM2	3	SSM1	5	SSM1	2	SSM P	3	SSM P	8	SSM P	9	SSM P	3	SSM P	1	SthC	7	Sth1E	5
						FAC	P	FAC	2Qr	FAC	EP	FAC	P	FAC	1Q	FAC	2Q	FAC	P
				FAV	2P	FAV	2Q	FAV	1P	FAV	1Qr	FAV	3P	FAV	4P	FAT	P	FAT	P

AYLESBURY

Club Contact Details 01296 431 655
SRD Stadium, Haywood Way, Aylesbury, Bucks. HP19 9WZ
infoaylesburyfc@gmail.com

Founded: 1930   **Nickname:** The Moles   **Manager:** Scott Reynolds
Previous Names: Negretti & Zambra FC 1930-54, Stocklake 1954-2000, Haywood United > 2000, Haywood FC 2000-06, Aylesbury Vale 2006-09.
Previous Leagues: Aylesbury District. Wycombe & District. Chiltern, Spartan South Midlands

Club Colours (change): Red & black

Ground Capacity: **Seats:** Yes   **Covered:** Yes   **Clubhouse:** Yes   **Shop:** No
Previous Grounds: Negretti & Zambra King's Cross 1930-49. Stocklake Industrial Estate 1949-87.
Record Attendance: Not known - if you know please email tw.publications@btinternet.com
Nearest Railway Station Aylesbury Vale Parkway - 1.2km   **Bus Route** O'grady Way - stop 200m away

RECORDS
Best FA Cup   Fourth Qualifying Round 2009-10
FA Trophy   First Qualifying Round 2010-11(r), 11-12(r), 13-14, 14-15, 15-16(r), 17-18(r)

HONOURS
FA Comps: None

League: Spartan South Midlands Division One 2003-04, Premier Division 2009-10.

County FA: Buckingham Charity Cup 2005-06. Berks & Bucks Senior Cup 2015-16.

08-09		09-10		10-11		11-12		12-13		13-14		14-15		15-16		16-17		17-18	
SSM P	15	SSM P	1	SthC	8	SthC	20	SthC	12	SthC	16	SthC	3	SthC	8	SthC	19	Sth1E	21
		FAC	4Q	FAC	Pr	FAC	P	FAC	P	FAC	1Q	FAC	1Q	FAC	1Qr	FAC	P	FAC	1Q
		FAV	1Q	FAT	1Qr	FAT	1Qr	FAT	P	FAT	1Q	FAT	1Q	FAT	1Qr	FAT	P	FAT	1Qr

AYLESBURY UNITED

Club Contact Details 01296 487 367 (Office)
Chesham United FC, The Meadow, Amy Lane, Chesham HP5 1NE
info@aylesburyunitedfc.co.uk

Founded: 1897   **Nickname:** The Ducks   **Manager:** Ben Williams
Previous Names: None
Previous Leagues: Post War: Spartan >1951, Delphian 51-63, Athenian 63-76, Southern 76-88, 2004-10, Conf. 88-89, Isthmian 89-2004.
Spartan South Midlands 2010-13.

Club Colours (change): Green & white

Ground Capacity: 5,000   **Seats:** 284   **Covered:** Yes   **Clubhouse:** Yes   **Shop:** No
Previous Grounds: Turnfurlong Lane. Buckingham Road >2006. Meadow View Park (Thame Utd) 2006-17.
Record Attendance: Turnfurlong Lane - 7,440 v Watford FAC 1st Rnd 1951-52. Buckingham Road - 6,031 v England 04/06/1988.
Nearest Railway Station Chesham underground - 0.7km   **Bus Route** The Wild Rover Pub - stop 250m away

RECORDS
Victory: 10-0 v Hornchurch & Upminster (H), Delphain League 17/04/1954
Defeat: 0-9 v Bishop's Stortford (A), Delphain League 08/10/1955
Goalscorer: Cliff Hercules - 301 (1984-2002)
Appearances: Cliff Hercules - 651+18 (1984-2002)

HONOURS
FA Comps: None

League: Spartan Western Division 1908-09, 28-29. Delphian 1953-54. Southern 1987-88.

County FA: Berks & Bucks Senior Cup 1913-14, 85-86, 96-97, 99-00. Berks & Bucks Senior Shield 2012-13.

08-09		09-10		10-11		11-12		12-13		13-14		14-15		15-16		16-17		17-18	
SthM	10	SthM	22	SSM P	6	SSM P	4	SSM P	2	SthC	12	SthC	13	SthC	19	SthC	13	Sth1E	13
FAC	4Q	FAC	1Qr	FAC	1Q	FAC	Pr	FAC	P	FAC	2Q	FAC	P	FAC	P	FAC	P	FAC	3Q
FAT	1Q	FAT	P	FAV	2P	FAV	2Q	FAV	1P	FAT	1Q	FAV	P	FAT	P	FAT	1Q	FAT	Pr

BARTON ROVERS

Club Contact Details 01582 707 772
Luton Road, Barton-le-Clay, Bedford MK45 4SD
bartonrovers@talktalk.net

Founded: 1898   **Nickname:** Rovers   **Manager:** Tony Fontenelle
Previous Names: None
Previous Leagues: Local village football leagues >1939. Luton & District 1947-54, South Midlands 1954-79, Isthmian 1979-2004

Club Colours (change): All royal blue

Ground Capacity: 4,000   **Seats:** 160   **Covered:** 1,120   **Clubhouse:** Yes   **Shop:** Yes
Previous Grounds: None
Record Attendance: 1,900 v Nuneaton Borough - FA Cup 4th Qualifying Round 1976
Nearest Railway Station Harlington - 4.6km   **Bus Route** The Memorial - stop 200m away

RECORDS
Goalscorer: Richard Camp - 152 (1989-98)
Appearances: Tony McNally - 598 (1988-2005)
Additional: Paid £1,000 to Hitchin Town for Bill Baldry 1980
Received £2,000 from AFC Wimbledon for Paul Barnes

HONOURS
FA Comps: None

League: South Midlands Division Two 1954-55, Division One 64-65, Premier 70-71, 71-72, 72-73, 74-75, 75-76, 76-77, 77-78, 78-79.

County FA: Bedfordshire Senior Cup 1971-72, 72-73, 80-81, 81-82, 89-90, 97-98, 98-99, 2014-15, Premier Cup 1995-96, Senior
Challenge Cup 2015-16.

08-09		09-10		10-11		11-12		12-13		13-14		14-15		15-16		16-17		17-18	
SthM	17	SthM	21	SthC	12	SthC	11	SthC	14	SthC	6	SthC	5	SthC	18	SthC	3	Sth1E	20
FAC	1Qr	FAC	P	FAC	P	FAC	1Qr	FAC	1Q	FAC	2Qr	FAC	3Q	FAC	1Q	FAC	2Q	FAC	P
FAT	P	FAT	2Qr	FAT	1Q	FAT	1Q	FAT	1Q	FAT	P	FAT	P	FAT	Pr	FAT	P	FAT	P

BEDFORD TOWN

Club Contact Details 01234 831 558
The Eyrie, Meadow Lane, Cardington, Bedford MK44 3LW
james.smiles@bedfordeagles.net

Founded: 1989   **Nickname:** The Eagles   **Manager:** Jon Taylor
Previous Names: Original Bedford Town founded in 1908 folded in 1982
Previous Leagues: South Midlands 1989-94, Isthmian 1994-2004, Southern 2004-06, Conference 2006-07

Club Colours (change): All blue

Ground Capacity: 3,000   **Seats:** 300   **Covered:** 1,000   **Clubhouse:** Yes   **Shop:** Yes
Previous Grounds: Allen Park, Queens Park, Bedford Park Pitch 1991-93
Record Attendance: 3,000 v Peterborough United - Ground opening 06/08/1993. At Queens Park - 18,407 v Everton, FAC, 1965-66
Nearest Railway Station Bedford St Johns - 3.8km   **Bus Route** Meadow Lane - stop 150m away

RECORDS
Defeat: 0-10 v Merthyr Tydfil, 1950-51, v Yeovil Town 1960-61
Goalscorer: Jason Reed. Joe Chamberlain scored 9 v Rushden Fosse, December 1911
Appearances: David Skinn
Victory: 9-0 v Weymouth, Southern League, 1954-55, v Poole 1958-59, v Ickleford, v Cardington

HONOURS
FA Comps: None
League: South Midlands Division One 1992-93, Premier Division 93-94. Isthmian Division Two 1998-99.

County FA: Bedfordshire Senior Cup 1994-95.

08-09		09-10		10-11		11-12		12-13		13-14		14-15		15-16		16-17		17-18	
SthP	15	SthP	18	SthP	17	SthP	10	SthP	10	SthP	22	SthC	17	SthC	14	SthC	8	Sth1E	8
FAC	2Qr	FAC	3Qr	FAC	2Q	FAC	1Q	FAC	1Q	FAC	2Q	FAC	Pr	FAC	1Q	FAC	P	FAC	1Q
FAT	1Q	FAT	1Q	FAT	1Q	FAT	1Q	FAT	2Q	FAT	1Qr	FAT	3Qr	FAT	2Q	FAT	P	FAT	1Qr

BERKHAMSTED

Club Contact Details 07525 872 914
Broadwater, Lower Kings Road, Berkhamsted HP4 2AL
keith55hicks@gmail.com

Founded: 2009   **Nickname:** Comrades   **Manager:** Steve Bateman
Previous Names: None
Previous Leagues: Spartan South Midlands 2009-18.

Club Colours (change): Yellow and blue

Ground Capacity: 2,500   **Seats:** 170   **Covered:** 350   **Clubhouse:** Yes   **Shop:** Yes
Previous Grounds: None
Record Attendance: 366 v Slough Town, FA Cup First Qualifying Round, 02/09/2017
Nearest Railway Station Berkhamsted - 0.3km   **Bus Route** Castel Hill Avenue - stop 190m away

RECORDS
Victory: 12-1 v Stotfold, FA Cup Extra Preliminary Round, 05/08/2017
Defeat: 1-7 v Hanwell Town, Spartan South Midlands Premier Division, 2011-12

HONOURS
FA Comps: None
League: Spartan South Midlands Division Two 2009-10, Division One 10-11.

County FA: Hertfordshire Charity Shield 2016-17

08-09	09-10		10-11		11-12		12-13		13-14		14-15		15-16		16-17		17-18	
	SSM2	1	SSM1	1	SSM P	7	SSM P	11	SSM P	5	SSM P	6	SSM P	5	SSM P	8	SSM P	2
					FAC	1Qr	FAC	2Q	FAC	1Q	FAC	EP	FAC	P	FAC	EP	FAC	1Q
			FAV	2Q	FAV	2Q	FAV	2P	FAV	2P	FAV	1P	FAV	5P	FAV	4P	FAV	3P

BROMSGROVE SPORTING

Club Contact Details 01527 876 949
The Victoria Ground, Birmingham Road, Bromsgrove, Worcs, B61 0DR
info@bromsgrovesporting.co.uk

Founded: 2009 **Nickname:** The Rouslers **Manager:** Brendan Kelly
Previous Names: None
Previous Leagues: Midland Combination 2010-14.

Club Colours (change): Red & white

Ground Capacity: 3,500 **Seats:** Yes **Covered:** Yes **Clubhouse:** Yes **Shop:** Yes
Previous Grounds: None
Record Attendance: 3,349 v Cleethorpes Town, FA Vase Semi Final First Leg, 11/03/2017
Nearest Railway Station Bromsgrove - 2km   **Bus Route** All Saints Road stop - 214m away

RECORDS
Best FA Cup   Preliminary Round 2014-15(r), 15-16, 16-17, 17-18
FA Vase   Semi Final 2016-17

HONOURS
FA Comps: None
League: Midland Football League Division One 2016-17, Premier 2017-18.

County FA: Worcestershire Senior Urn 2017-18

08-09	09-10	10-11	11-12	12-13	13-14	14-15	15-16	16-17	17-18
		MCm2 3	MCm1 3	MCmP 6	MCmP 2	MFL1 2	MFL1 2	MFL1 1	MFLP 1
						FAC Pr	FAC P	FAC P	FAC P
					FAV 1P	FAV 3P	FAV 1P	FAV SF	FAV 5P

CAMBRIDGE CITY

Club Contact Details 01223 233 226
St Ives Town FC, Westwood Road, St Ives, Cambridgeshire PE27 6DT
andy@cambridgecityfc.com

Founded: 1908 **Nickname:** Lilywhites **Manager:** Robbie Nightingale
Previous Names: Cambridge Town 1908-51
Previous Leagues: Bury & District 1908-13, 19-20, Anglian 1908-10, Southern Olympian 1911-14,
Southern Amateur 1913-35, Spartan 1935-50, Athenian 1950-58, Southern 1958-2004

Club Colours (change): Black and white

Ground Capacity: 2,722 **Seats:** 526 **Covered:** 220 **Clubhouse:** Yes **Shop:** Yes
Previous Grounds: City Ground.
Record Attendance: 12,058 v Leytonstone - FA Amateur Cup 1st Round 1949-50
                                                    Bus Route Langley Close - stop 300m away

RECORDS
Goalscorer: Gary Grogan
Appearances: Mal Keenan
Additional: Paid £8,000 to Rushden & Diamonds for Paul Coe
                   Received £100,000 from Millwall for Neil Harris 1998

HONOURS
FA Comps: None
League: Southern 1962-63, Southern Division 1985-86.

County FA: Suffolk Senior Cup 1909-10. East Anglian x9. Cambridgeshire Professional Cup 2012-13, 14-15, Invitational Cup 2014-15.

08-09	09-10	10-11	11-12	12-13	13-14	14-15	15-16	16-17	17-18
SthP 4	SthP 6	SthP 4	SthP 5	SthP 8	SthP 3	SthP 13	SthP 18	SthP 21	Sth1E 6
FAC 2Qr	FAC 3Q	FAC 3Q	FAC 1Qr	FAC 1Pr	FAC 2Q	FAC 1Q	FAC 1Q	FAC 2Q	FAC 2Qr
FAT 1P	FAT 2Q	FAT 3Q	FAT 2Q	FAT 1Q	FAT 2Qr	FAT 1Q	FAT 1Q	FAT 1Q	FAT 1Q

COLESHILL TOWN

Club Contact Details 01675 464 905
Pack Meadow, Packington Lane, Coleshill B46 3JQ
dave.brown@skanska.co.uk

Founded: 1894   **Nickname:** The Coleman   **Manager:** Cameron Stuart
Previous Names: Coleshill & District. Coleshill FC. Coleshill United 1919.
Previous Leagues: Birmingham Youth & Old Boys 1906-07, 56-67. Sutton & Erdington 1907-08. Trent Valley 1912. Sutton & District 1919-56. Worcestershire Combination/Midland Combination 1967-2008. Midland Alliance 2008-2014.

Club Colours (change): White & blue

Ground Capacity: 2,070   **Seats:** 570   **Covered:**   **Clubhouse:** Yes   **Shop:**
Previous Grounds: Memorial Ground >1974
Record Attendance:
Nearest Railway Station Coleshill Parkway - 3.6km   **Bus Route** St Edmunds Primary School - 258m away

RECORDS
Best FA Cup   Third Qualifying Round 2015-16
FA Vase   Semi Finals 2016-17

HONOURS
FA Comps: None
League: Sutton & District Division One 1952-53, 54-5. Birmingham Youth & Old Boys Suburban Division 1958-59.
Midland Combination Division Two 1969-70, Premier 07-08.
County FA: Walsall Senior Cup 1982-83

08-09		09-10		10-11		11-12		12-13		13-14		14-15		15-16		16-17		17-18	
MidAl	11	MidAl	8	MidAl	12	MidAl	16	MidAl	15	MidAl	4	MFLP	2	MFLP	5	MFLP	2	MFLP	2
FAC	P	FAC	P	FAC	3Q	FAC	Pr	FAC	EPr	FAC	EP	FAC	1Q	FAC	3Q	FAC	1Q	FAC	1Q
FAV	1P	FAV	1P	FAV	1Q	FAV	1Q	FAV	1Q	FAV	4P	FAV	2P	FAV	4P	FAV	SF	FAV	5P

CORBY TOWN

Club Contact Details 01536 406 640
Steel Park, Jimmy Kane Way, Rockingham Road, Corby NN17 2AE
gerry21@gmail.com

Founded: 1948   **Nickname:** The Steelmen   **Manager:** Steve Kinniburgh
Previous Names: Stewart & Lloyds (Corby) > 1947
Previous Leagues: United Counties 1935-52. Midland 1952-58. Southern 1958-2009, 13-15. Football Conference 2009-13, 15-16. Northern Premier 2016-18.

Club Colours (change): White and black

Ground Capacity: 3,893   **Seats:** 577   **Covered:** 1,575   **Clubhouse:** Yes   **Shop:** Yes
Previous Grounds: Occupation Road 1948-85.
Record Attendance: 2,240 v Watford - Friendly 1986-87
Nearest Railway Station Corby - 2.2km   **Bus Route** Dalton Road - stop 500m away

RECORDS
Goalscorer: David Holbauer - 159 (1984-95)
Appearances: Derek Walker - 601
Additional: Paid £2,700 to Barnet for Elwun Edwards 1981
Received £20,000 from Oxford United for Matt Murphy 1993

HONOURS
FA Comps: None
League: United Counties League 1950-51, 51-52. Southern League Premier Division 2008-09, 2014-15.

County FA: Northants Senior Cup 1950-51, 62-63, 75-76, 82-83, 2009-10, 12-13.

08-09		09-10		10-11		11-12		12-13		13-14		14-15		15-16		16-17		17-18	
SthP	1	Conf N	6	Conf N	13	Conf N	17	Conf N	20	SthP	11	SthP	1	Nat N	22	NP P	21	NP1S	9
FAC	2Q	FAC	2Q	FAC	1Pr	FAC	1P	FAC	4Q	FAC	1P	FAC	1Qr	FAC	2Qr	FAC	1Q	FAC	P
FAT	2Q	FAT	3P	FAT	3Q	FAT	3Qr	FAT	2Pr	FAT	1Q	FAT	1Q	FAT	3Q	FAT	1Q	FAT	1Q

DIDCOT TOWN

Club Contact Details 01235 813 138
GWR Loop Meadow Stadium, Bowmont Water, Didcot OX11 7GA
info@didcottownfc.co.uk

Founded: 1907   **Nickname:** Railwaymen   **Manager:** Andy Ballard
Previous Names: Didcot Village and Northbourne Wanderers amalgamated to form Didcot Town in 1907.
Previous Leagues: Metropolitan 1957-63, Hellenic 1963-2006

Club Colours (change): Red & white

Ground Capacity: 3,000   **Seats:** 350   **Covered:** 200   **Clubhouse:** Yes   **Shop:** Yes
Previous Grounds: Fleet Meadow. Edmonds Park. Cow Lane. Haydon Road. Station Road 1923-99.
Record Attendance: 2,707 - v Exeter City, FA Cup 1st Round, 08/11/2015
Nearest Railway Station Didcot Parkway - 0.4km

RECORDS
Goalscorer: Ian Concanon
Best FA Cup   First Round Proper 2015-16
FA Trophy   First Round Proper 2011-12, 14-15(r)

HONOURS
FA Comps: FA Vase 2004-05.
League: Hellenic Premier Division 1953-54, 2005-06, Division One 1976-77, 87-88.
County FA: Berks & Bucks Senior Trophy 2001-02, 02-03, 05-06.

	08-09		09-10		10-11		11-12		12-13		13-14		14-15		15-16		16-17		17-18	
Sthsw	5	SthP	15	SthP	19	Sthsw	16	Sthsw	17	Sthsw	12	Sthsw	7	Sthsw	10	Sthsw	12	Sth1W	6
FAC	1Q	FAC	2Q	FAC	3Q	FAC	1Qr	FAC	4Q	FAC	3Q	FAC	P	FAC	1P	FAC	P	FAC	1Q
FAT	P	FAT	1Q	FAT	1Q	FAT	1P	FAT	3Q	FAT	Pr	FAT	1Pr	FAT	1Q	FAT	P	FAT	P

DUNSTABLE TOWN

Club Contact Details 01582 891 433
Creasey Park Stadium, Brewers Hill Rd, Dunstable LU6 1BB

Founded: 1883   **Nickname:** The Duns / The Blues   **Manager:** Tony McCool - June 2017
Previous Names: Dunstable Town 1883-1976. Dunstable FC 1976-98.
Previous Leagues: Metropolitan & District 1950-61, 64-65. United Counties 1961-63. Southern 1965-76, 2004-09.
                     Spartan South Midlands 1998-2003, 09-13. Isthmian 2003-04.
Club Colours (change): Blue & white

Ground Capacity: 3,500   **Seats:** 350   **Covered:** 1000   **Clubhouse:** Yes   **Shop:** Yes
Previous Grounds: Kingsway 1950-58.
Record Attendance: 10,000 (approx) v Manchester United, friendly, July 1974
                                            Bus Route Langridge Court - stop 100m away

RECORDS
Victory: 12-0 v Welwyn Garden City, Spartan South Midlands League 2009-10.
Defeat: 0-13 v Arsenal 'A', Metropolitan League
Additional: Received £25,000 from Reading for Kerry Dixon 1980.

HONOURS
FA Comps: None
League: Spartan South Midlands Division One 1999-00, Premier 2002-03, 12-13. Southern Division One Central 2013-14.
County FA: Bedfordshire Senior Cup x12 - Firstly in 1895-96 and most recently in 2008-09. Bedforshire Premier Cup 1980-81, 82-83, 90-91, 2006-07, 11-12. Bedfordshire Intermediate Cup 1999-2000, 08-09.

	08-09		09-10		10-11		11-12		12-13		13-14		14-15		15-16		16-17		17-18	
SthM	21	SSM P	7	SSM P	7	SSM P	2	SSM P	1	SthC	1	SthP	14	SthP	11	SthP	16	SthP	24
FAC	2Q	FAC	P	FAC	EP	FAC	3Q	FAC	1Qr	FAC	2Q	FAC	2Q	FAC	3Q	FAC	1Q	FAC	1Q
FAT	P	FAV	1P	FAV	5P	FAV	2P	FAV	3P	FAT	2Q	FAT	1Q	FAT	1Q	FAT	2Q	FAT	1Q

KEMPSTON ROVERS

Club Contact Details 01234 852 346
Hillgrounds Leisure, Hillgrounds Road, Kempston, Bedford MK42 8SZ
howlett.home@btinternet.com

Founded: 1884 **Nickname:** Walnut Boys **Manager:** Jimmy Stoyles & Gary Flinn
Previous Names: Kempston Rovers 1884-2004. AFC Kempston Rovers 2004-16.
Previous Leagues: Bedford & District. Biggleswade & District. Bedfordshire & District County/South Midlands 1927-53.
United Counties 1957-2016.

Club Colours (change): Red, white & black

Ground Capacity: 2,000 **Seats:** 100 **Covered:** 250 **Clubhouse:** Yes **Shop:** Yes
Previous Grounds: None
Record Attendance: Not known
Nearest Railway Station Bedford - 1.3km **Bus Route** Prentice Gardens - stop 100m away

RECORDS
Best FA Cup Fourth Qualifying Round 1978-79
FA Trophy First Qualifying Round 2016-17
FA Vase Fifth Round Proper 1974-75, 80-81

HONOURS
FA Comps: None
League: Bedford & District Division One 1907-08, 08-09, Division Two South 22-23, 33-34. Biggleswade & District 1910-11.
United Counties Premier Division 1957-58, 73-74, 2015-16, Division One 85-86, 2010-11, Division Two 1955-56,
County FA: Bedfordshire Senior Cup 1908-09, 37-38, 76-77, 91-92. Huntingdonshire Premier Cup 1999-2000, 00-01.

08-09		09-10		10-11		11-12		12-13		13-14		14-15		15-16		16-17		17-18	
UCL 1	5	UCL 1	5	UCL 1	1	UCL P	10	UCL P	17	UCL P	12	UCL P	8	UCL P	1	SthC	6	Sth1E	7
FAC	EP			FAC	1Q	FAC	EP	FAC	1Q	FAC	EP	FAC	P	FAC	P	FAC	2Qr	FAC	2Q
FAV	2Q	FAV	2Q	FAV	1Q	FAV	1Q	FAV	2Q	FAV	1Q	FAV	2P	FAV	2P	FAT	1Q	FAT	P

KIDLINGTON

Club Contact Details 01865 849 777
Yarnton Road, Kidlington, Oxford OX5 1AT
dplatt45@hotmail.co.uk

Founded: 1909 **Nickname:** Greens **Manager:** Ady Fuller
Previous Names: None.
Previous Leagues: Villages Leagues > 1945. Oxford City Junior 1945-51. Oxfordshire Senior 1951-54. Hellenic 1954-2016.

Club Colours (change): Green

Ground Capacity: 1,500 **Seats:** Yes **Covered:** Yes **Clubhouse:** Yes **Shop:** No
Previous Grounds: None
Record Attendance: 2,000 v Showbiz XI, 1973.
Nearest Railway Station Oxford Parkway - 1.9km **Bus Route** Treeground Place - stop 100m away

RECORDS
Best FA Cup Second Qualifying Round 2015-16, 17-18
FA Trophy First Qualifying Round 2017-18
FA Vase Fifth Round 1976-77

HONOURS
FA Comps: None
League: Oxfordshire Senior 1952-53. Hellenic Premier Division 2015-16.

County FA: Oxfordshire Intermediate Cup 1952-53, 69-70, 84-85.

08-09		09-10		10-11		11-12		12-13		13-14		14-15		15-16		16-17		17-18	
Hel P	9	Hel P	11	Hel P	7	Hel P	18	Hel P	13	Hel P	6	Hel P	4	Hel P	1	SthC	12	Sth1W	12
FAC	P	FAC	1Q	FAC	EP	FAC	P	FAC	EPr	FAC	EPr	FAC	P	FAC	2Q	FAC	P	FAC	2Q
FAV	1P	FAV	1P	FAV	1P	FAV	2Q	FAV	3P	FAV	3P	FAV	1Q	FAV	QFr	FAT	P	FAT	1Q

NORTH LEIGH

Club Contact Details 01993 880 157
Eynsham Hall Park, North Leigh, Witney, Oxon OX29 6SL

Founded: 1908   **Nickname:** The Millers   **Manager:** Craig Dore and Darren James
Previous Names: None
Previous Leagues: Witney & District, Hellenic 1990-2008

Club Colours (change): Yellow and black

Ground Capacity: 2,000   **Seats:** 175   **Covered:** 200   **Clubhouse:** Yes   **Shop:** No
Previous Grounds: None
Record Attendance: 426 v Newport County - FA Cup 3rd Qualifying Round 16/10/2004
Nearest Railway Station Combe - 3.3km

RECORDS
Goalscorer:	P Coles
Appearances:	P King
Best FA Cup	Fourth Qualifying Round 2016-17
FA Trophy	First Round Proper 2016-17
FA Vase	Fourth Round Proper 2003-04

HONOURS
FA Comps: None

League: Witney & District Premier 1985-86, 86-87, 87-88, 88-89, 89-90. Hellenic Premier Division 2002-03, 07-08.

County FA: Oxfordshire Senior Cup 2011-12, 16-17.

08-09		09-10		10-11		11-12		12-13		13-14		14-15		15-16		16-17		17-18	
Sthsw	8	Sthsw	10	Sthsw	6	Sthsw	6	Sthsw	9	Sthsw	7	Sthsw	8	Sthsw	9	Sthsw	6	Sth1W	18
FAC	1Q	FAC	1Q	FAC	P	FAC	1Q	FAC	3Q	FAC	1Q	FAC	P	FAC	3Q	FAC	4Q	FAC	1Qr
FAT	1Q	FAT	P	FAT	1Qr	FAT	P	FAT	1Qr	FAT	1Q	FAT	1Q	FAT	1Q	FAT	1Pr	FAT	P

PETERBOROUGH SPORTS

Club Contact Details 01733 308 993
Lincoln Road, Peterborough PE1 3HA
jrobo1510@gmail.com

Founded: 1919   **Nickname:** The Turbines   **Manager:** James Dean
Previous Names: Brotherhoods Engineering Works 1919-99. Bearings Direct during 1999-2001.
Previous Leagues: Northants League (former UCL) 1919-23. Peterborough & District 1923-2013. United Counties 2013-17.
Northern Premier 2017-18.

Club Colours (change): All blue

Ground Capacity: **Seats:** Yes   **Covered:** Yes   **Clubhouse:** Yes   **Shop:** No
Previous Grounds: None
Record Attendance: Not known

RECORDS

HONOURS
FA Comps: None

League: Northants 1919-20, United Counties 1919-20, Division One 2015-16, Premier 2016-17.
Peterborough & District Division Three 1925-26, Division Three South 1980-81, Premier 2006-07.
County FA: Northants Junior Cup 2006-07, 15-16,

08-09	09-10	10-11	11-12		12-13		13-14		14-15		15-16		16-17		17-18	
			P&D P	3	P&D P	3	UCL 1	16	UCL 1	5	UCL 1	1	UCL P	1	NP1S	12
											FAC	1Qr	FAC	1Q	FAC	1Q
									FAV	2P	FAV	1Q	FAV	4P	FAT	P

SUTTON COLDFIELD TOWN

Club Contact Details 0121 354 2997
Central Ground, Coles Lane, Sutton Coldfield B72 1NL
murralln@gmail.com

Founded: 1879   **Nickname:** Royals   **Manager:** Neil Tooth
Previous Names: Sutton Coldfield F.C. 1879-1921
Previous Leagues: Central Birmingham, Walsall Senior, Staffordshire County, Birmingham Combination 1950-54,
West Midlands (Regional) 1954-65, 79-82, Midlands Combination 1965-79. Northern Premier 2010-18.

Club Colours (change): All blue

Ground Capacity: 4,500   **Seats:** 200   **Covered:** 500   **Clubhouse:** Yes   **Shop:** Yes
Previous Grounds: Meadow Plat 1879-89, Coles Lane 1890-1919
Record Attendance: 2,029 v Doncaster Rovers - FA Cup 1980-81
Nearest Railway Station Sutton Coldfield - 1.1km   **Bus Route** Douglas Road - stop 100m away

RECORDS
Goalscorer: Eddie Hewitt - 288
Appearances: Andy Ling - 550
Additional: Paid £1,500 to Gloucester for Lance Morrison, to Burton Albion for Micky Clarke and to Atherstone United for Steve
Farmer 1991. Received £25,000 from West Bromwich Albion for Barry Cowdrill 1979

HONOURS
FA Comps: None
League: West Midlands League 1979-80. Midland Combination x2.
NPL Division One South Play-off 2014-15.
County FA: Birmingham Senior Cup 2010-11.

08-09		09-10		10-11		11-12		12-13		13-14		14-15		15-16		16-17		17-18	
SthM	6	SthM	6	NP1S	6	NP1S	12	NP1S	6	NP1S	6	NP1S	4	NP P	12	NP P	20	NP P	24
FAC	P	FAC	3Qr	FAC	1Q	FAC	P	FAC	1Q	FAC	2Q	FAC	1Q	FAC	1Q	FAC	2Q	FAC	1Q
FAT	2Q	FAT	1Qr	FAT	P	FAT	1Q	FAT	P	FAT	P	FAT	P	FAT	1P	FAT	1Q	FAT	1Q

THAME UNITED

Club Contact Details 01844 214 401
The ASM Stadium, Meadow View Park, Tythrop Way, Thame, Oxon OX9 3RN
jake@jcpc.org.uk

Founded: 1883   **Nickname:** Red Kites   **Manager:** Mark West
Previous Names: Thame F.C.
Previous Leagues: Oxon Senior. Hellenic 1959-88, 2006-17. South Midlands 1988-91. Isthmian 1991-2004. Southern 2004-06.

Club Colours (change): Red & black

Ground Capacity: 2,500   **Seats:** Yes   **Covered:** Yes   **Clubhouse:** Yes   **Shop:**
Previous Grounds: Windmill Road 1883-2005. Aylesbury United FC 2005-06. AFC Wallingford 2006-11.
Record Attendance: 1,382 v Oxford United Jan 2011.
Nearest Railway Station Haddenham & Thame Parkway - 2.9km   **Bus Route** Queens Close - stop 350m away

RECORDS
Appearances: Steve Mayhew
Best FA Cup   Fourth Qualifying Round 2003-04, 04-05
FA Trophy   Third Round Proper 2002-03
FA Vase   Semi Finals 1998-99

HONOURS
FA Comps: None
League: Hellenic 1961-62, 69-70, 2016-17, Division One East 2009-10. South Midlands League 1990-91.
Isthmian Division Two 1994-95.
County FA: None

08-09		09-10		10-11		11-12		12-13		13-14		14-15		15-16		16-17		17-18	
Hel1E	9	Hel1E	1	Hel P	10	Hel P	9	Hel P	9	Hel P	10	Hel P	5	Hel P	6	Hel P	1	Sth1E	11
FAC	EPr	FAC	1Q	FAC	2Qr	FAC	2Q	FAC	P	FAC	EP	FAC	1Q	FAC	EPr	FAC	P	FAC	1Q
FAV	1Q	FAV	2Qr	FAV	2Q	FAV	2Q	FAV	2P	FAV	2Q	FAV	2P	FAV	3P	FAV	1P	FAT	3Q

WELWYN GARDEN CITY

Club Contact Details 01707 329 358
Herns Lane, Welwyn Garden City, Herts AL7 1TA
welwyngardencityfc@gmail.com

Founded: 1921 **Nickname:** Citizens **Manager:** Adam Fisher
Previous Names: Original club folded in 1935 and was reformed in 1937.
Previous Leagues: Mid-Herts 1922-26, 44-45. Beds & Dist 26-27. Spartan 27-35, 37-39, 45-51, 55-59. East, North & Mid-Herts Comb. 1939. Beds
& Herts Comb 1940. London 51-55. Herts Senior Co 59-70. Greater London 70-71. Met London (FM) 71-73.
Club Colours (change): Claret & sky blue South Mids 73-97. Spartan SM (FM) 1997-2018.

Ground Capacity: **Seats:** Yes **Covered:** Yes **Clubhouse:** Yes **Shop:**
Previous Grounds: Several before moving to Herns Lane in 1968
Record Attendance: Unknown
Nearest Railway Station Welwyn Garden City - 1.9km **Bus Route** Hernes Way - stop 160m away

RECORDS
Best FA Cup Third Qualifying Round 1998-99(r), 2005-06
FA Vase Fourth Round Proper Replay 2005-06
Goalscorer: Jason Caswell scored 51 goals during the 2014-15 season

HONOURS
FA Comps: None
League: South Midlands 1973-74, Division One 1981-82. Spartan South Midlands Division One 2014-15, Premier 17-18.
County FA: Hertfordshire FA Charity Shield 1927-28, 86-87, 87-88. Herts FA Senior Centenary Trophy 1984-85.

08-09	09-10	10-11	11-12	12-13	13-14	14-15	15-16	16-17	17-18
SSM P 9	SSM P 22	SSM1 17	SSM1 17	SSM1 13	SSM1 4	SSM1 1	SSM P 4	SSM P 6	SSM P 1
FAC EP	FAC EP	FAC EP				FAC 1Q	FAC 1Q	FAC P	FAC EP
FAV 1Q	FAV 1Q	FAV 2Q	FAV 1Q	FAV 1Q	FAV 3P	FAV 1P	FAV 1P	FAV 3P	FAV 3P

YAXLEY

Club Contact Details 01733 244 928
In2itive Park, Leading Drove, Holme Road, Yaxley, Peterborough PE7 3NA
yfc.sec@virginmedia.com

Founded: 1962 **Nickname:** The Cuckoos **Manager:** Andy Furnell
Previous Names: Yaxley British Legion 1963-86. Coalite Yaxley 1986-90. Clarksteel Yaxley 1990.
Previous Leagues: Peterborough & District 1962-88. Eastern Counties (Founder Member) 1988-92. Huntingdonshire 1992-94.
West Anglia 1994-95. United Counties 1995-2018.
Club Colours (change): All blue

Ground Capacity: 1,500 **Seats:** 150 **Covered:** yes **Clubhouse:** Yes **Shop:** Yes
Previous Grounds:
Record Attendance: 300v Wisbech Town, FA Vase Preliminary Round 1982-83
Bus Route Churhc Street stop 300m away

RECORDS
Best FA Cup Second Qualifying Round 2002-03, 06-07
FA Vase Fourth Round Proper 2014-15

HONOURS
FA Comps: None
League: Peterborough & District Division Three South 1968-69, Division Two 70-71, Premier 76-77, 83-84.
West Anglia 1994-95. United Counties Division One 1996-97, Premier 2017-18.
County FA: Hunts Senior Cup 1974-75, 75-76, 82-83, 83-84, 98-99, 2003-04, 04-05, 07-08. Hunts Premier Cup 2004-05

08-09	09-10	10-11	11-12	12-13	13-14	14-15	15-16	16-17	17-18
UCL P 14	UCL P 19	UCL P 16	UCL P 18	UCL P 12	UCL P 6	UCL P 4	UCL P 12	UCL P 3	UCL P 1
FAC 1Qr	FAC EP	FAC EP	FAC EP	FAC P	FAC EP	FAC EP	FAC 1Q	FAC Pr	FAC 1Q
FAV 1Pr	FAV 2Q	FAV 1Q	FAV 1P	FAV 1P	FAV 1Q	FAV 4P	FAV 3P	FAV 1P	FAV 3P

AFC TOTTON

Club Contact Details 02380 868 981
Testwood Stadium, Salisbury Road, Calmore, Totton SO40 2RW
enquiries@afctotton.com

Founded: 1886   **Nickname:** Stags   **Manager:** Louis Langdown - Nov 2016
Previous Names: Totton FC until merger with Totton Athletic in 1975
Previous Leagues: New Forest (Founder Members) 1904. Southampton Senior. Hampshire 1920-86, Wessex 1986-2008.

Club Colours (change): All blue

Ground Capacity: 3,000   **Seats:** 500   **Covered:** 500   **Clubhouse:** Yes   **Shop:** Yes
Previous Grounds: South Testwood Park 1886-1933.
Record Attendance: 2,315 v Bradford Park Avenue, 12/11/2011.
Nearest Railway Station Totton - 2.9km   **Bus Route** Cooks Lane - stop 300m away

RECORDS
Appearances:	Michael Gosney - 427
Best FA Cup	Second Round Proper 2011-12
FA Trophy	Third Qualifying Round 2006-07, 08-09(r)
FA Vase	Finalists 2008-09

HONOURS
FA Comps: None
League: New Forest 1905-06, 10-11, 13-14, 19-20, 25-26, 26-27, 47-48, 60-61, 61-62. Hampshire West 1924-25. Hampshire Division Two 1930-31,
66-67, Division One 81-82, 84-85. Wessex Premier Division 2007-08. Southern Division South & West 2010-11.
County FA: Hampshire Junior Cup 1913-14, Intermediate Cup 1946-47, 66-67, 81-82, 82-83, Senior Cup 2009-10, 10-11.

08-09	09-10	10-11	11-12	12-13	13-14	14-15	15-16	16-17	17-18
Sthsw 3	Sthsw 2	Sthsw 1	SthP 3	SthP 14	SthP 21	Sthsw 15	Sthsw 15	Sthsw 19	Sth1W 10
FAC 4Q	FAC 4Q	FAC P	FAC 2P	FAC 4Q	FAC 1Q	FAC 1Q	FAC P	FAC P	FAC 1Q
FAT 3Qr	FAT 2Q	FAT 2Q	FAT 1Q	FAT 1P	FAT 1Q	FAT 1Q	FAT P	FAT Pr	FAT Pr

BARNSTAPLE TOWN

Club Contact Details 01271 343 469
Mill Road, Barnstaple, North Devon EX31 1JQ

Founded: 1906   **Nickname:** Barum   **Manager:** Kevin Darch and Dave Griffiths
Previous Names: Pilton Yeo Vale
Previous Leagues: North Devon, Devon & Exeter, South Western. Western >2016.

Club Colours (change): Red and white

Ground Capacity: 5,000   **Seats:** 250   **Covered:** 1,000   **Clubhouse:** Yes   **Shop:** Yes
Previous Grounds: None
Record Attendance: 6,200 v Bournemouth & Boscombe Athletic, FA Cup 1st Round, 1951-52.
Nearest Railway Station Barnstaple - 1km

RECORDS
Victory:	12-1 v Tavistock, F.A. Cup 3rd Qualifying Round 1954.
Defeat:	0-11 v Odd Down, Western, 25/04/2013.
Appearances:	Ian Pope
Additional:	Paid £4,000 to Hungerford Town for Joe Scott.
	Received £6,000 from Bristol City for Ian Doyle.

HONOURS
FA Comps: None
League: North Devon 1904-05, 08-09. Exeter & District 1946-47. Western 1952-53, 79-80, Division One 1993-94, 2014-15.

County FA: Devon Pro Cup 1952-53, 62-63, 64-65, 67-68, 69-70, 71-72, 72-73, 74-75, 76-77, 77-78, 78-79, 79-80. 80-81.
Devon St Lukes Cup 1987-88. Devon Senior Cup 1992-93.

08-09	09-10	10-11	11-12	12-13	13-14	14-15	15-16	16-17	17-18
WestP 18	WestP 15	WestP 11	WestP 15	WestP 20	West1 3	West1 1	WestP 2	Sthsw 17	Sth1W 21
FAC EP	FAC P	FAC EP	FAC P	FAC EP	FAC EP	FAC EP	FAC 1Q	FAC 1Q	FAC 1Q
FAV 1P	FAV 1P	FAV 2Q	FAV 3P	FAV 1P	FAV 2P	FAV 2Q	FAV 2P	FAT 1Q	FAT P

BIDEFORD

Club Contact Details 01237 474 974
The Sports Ground, Kingsley Road, Bideford EX39 2LH
enquiries@bidefordafc.com

Founded: 1946   **Nickname:** The Robins   **Manager:** Sean Joyce
Previous Names: Bideford Town
Previous Leagues: Devon & Exeter 1947-49, Western 1949-72, 75-2010, Southern 1972-75

Club Colours (change): All red

Ground Capacity: 6,000   **Seats:** 375   **Covered:** 1,000   **Clubhouse:** Yes   **Shop:**
Previous Grounds: None
Record Attendance: 5,975 v Gloucester City - FA Cup 4th Qualifying Round 1949
                         Bus Route The Dairy - stop 100m away

RECORDS
Victory: 16-1 v Soundwell, 1950-51
Defeat: 1-10 v Taunton Town, 1998-99
Goalscorer: Tommy Robinson - 259
Appearances: Derek May - 647

HONOURS
FA Comps: None
League: Western 1963-64, 70-71, 71-72, 81-82, 82-83, 2001-02, 03-04, 04-05, 05-06, 09-10, Division Two 1951-52, Division Three
         1949-50. Southern Division One South & West 2011-12.
County FA: Devon Pro Cup 1960-61, 61-62, 63-64, 65-66, 66-67, 68-69, 70-71. Devon Senior Cup 1979-80.
         Devon St Lukes Bowl 1981-82, 83-84, 85-86, 95-96, 2009-10.

08-09		09-10		10-11		11-12		12-13		13-14		14-15		15-16		16-17		17-18	
WestP	6	WestP	1	Sthsw	10	Sthsw	1	SthP	20	SthP	8	SthP	15	SthP	23	Sthsw	10	Sth1W	8
FAC	1Qr	FAC	P	FAC	P	FAC	2Q	FAC	2Q	FAC	2Q	FAC	2Q	FAC	2Q	FAC	1Q	FAC	3Q
FAV	QF	FAV	2P	FAT	3Q	FAT	1Q	FAT	1Q	FAT	2Q	FAT	1Qr	FAT	3Q	FAT	P	FAT	P

BLACKFIELD & LANGLEY

Club Contact Details 02380 893 603
Gang Warily Rec., Newlands Rd, Southampton SO45 1GA

Founded: 1935   **Nickname:** Watersiders   **Manager:** Glenn Howes
Previous Names: None
Previous Leagues: Southampton Junior. Southampton Senior. Hampshire 1950-2000. Wessex 2000-18.

Club Colours (change): Green & white

Ground Capacity: 2,500   **Seats:** 180   **Covered:** Yes   **Clubhouse:** Yes   **Shop:**
Previous Grounds: Yes
Record Attendance: 240
                         Bus Route Gang Warily Leisure Centre - stop 50m away

RECORDS
Best FA Cup   Fourth Qualifying Round 2012-13
FA Vase   Fourth Round Proper 2012-13, 13-14

HONOURS
FA Comps: None
League: Southampton Junior Division One 1945-46. Southampton West Division 1946-47. Hampshire Division Three West 1951-52,
         Division Two 1984-85, Premier Division 97-98. Wessex Premier Division 2012-13, 17-18.
County FA: None

08-09		09-10		10-11		11-12		12-13		13-14		14-15		15-16		16-17		17-18	
Wex1	2	WexP	8	WexP	14	WexP	16	WexP	1	WexP	6	WexP	5	WexP	3	WexP	4	WexP	1
		FAC	EP	FAC	P	FAC	1Q	FAC	4Q	FAC	EP	FAC	2Qr	FAC	3Q	FAC	P	FAC	EPr
FAV	2Q	FAV	2Q	FAV	1P	FAV	2P	FAV	4P	FAV	4P	FAV	3P	FAV	1P	FAV	3P	FAV	4Pr

BRISTOL MANOR FARM

Club Contact Details 0117 968 3571
The Creek, Portway, Sea Mills, Bristol BS9 2HS
secretary@bristolmanorfarm.com

Founded: 1960   **Nickname:** The Farm   **Manager:** Lee Lashenko
Previous Names:
Previous Leagues: Bristol Suburban 1964-69. Somerset Senior 1969-77. Western 1977-2017.

Club Colours (change): Red & black

Ground Capacity: 2,000   **Seats:** 200   **Covered:** 350   **Clubhouse:** Yes   **Shop:** No
Previous Grounds: None
Record Attendance: 1,417 v Bristol City, pre-season friendly, 09/07/2017.
Nearest Railway Station Sea Mills - 0.3km   **Bus Route** Riverleaze - stop 50m away

RECORDS
Appearances: M. Baird
Victory: 10-0 v Devizes Town, Les Phillips Cup, 19/11/2016.
Defeat: 0-11 v Bristol City, Community Match, 09/07/2017

HONOURS
FA Comps: None
League: Western Division One 1982-83, Premier 2016-17.
County FA: Gloucestershire Challenge Trophy 1987-88, 2015-16. Gloucestershire Amateur Cup 1989-90.

	08-09	09-10	10-11	11-12	12-13	13-14	14-15	15-16	16-17	17-18
	WestP 5	WestP 7	WestP 7	WestP 8	WestP 18	WestP 2	WestP 4	WestP 3	WestP 1	Sth1W 9
FAC	EP	1Q	2Qr	EPr	EP	2Qr	P	1Q	EPr	P
FAV	1Q	4P	2P	2Q	2Q	1P	2P	QF	5P	FAT 1Q

CINDERFORD TOWN

Club Contact Details 01594 824 080
The Causeway, Edge Hills Road, Cinderford, Gloucestershire GL14 2QH

Founded: 1922   **Nickname:** The Foresters   **Manager:** Paul Michael
Previous Names: None
Previous Leagues: Gloucestershire Northern Senior 1922-39, 60-62, Western 1946-59, Warwickshire Combination 1963-64,
West Midlands 1965-69, Gloucestershire Co. 1970-73, 85-89, Midland Comb. 1974-84, Hellenic 1990-95

Club Colours (change): White & black

Ground Capacity: 3,500   **Seats:** 250   **Covered:** 1,000   **Clubhouse:** Yes   **Shop:** Yes
Previous Grounds: Mousel Lane, Royal Oak
Record Attendance: 4,850 v Minehead - Western League 1955-56
   Bus Route Forest High School - stop 200m away

RECORDS
Victory: 13-0 v Cam Mills - 1938-39
Defeat: 0-10 v Sutton Coldfield - 1978-79
Appearances: Russel Bowles - 528

HONOURS
FA Comps: None
League: Western Division Two 1956-57. Warwickshire Combination Western Division 1964-65. Hellenic Premier Division 1994-95.
Southern Division One South & West 2015-16.
County FA: Gloucestershire Senior Amateur Cup North x6. Gloucestershire Junior Cup North 1980-81. Gloucestershire Senior Cup
2000-01.

	08-09	09-10	10-11	11-12	12-13	13-14	14-15	15-16	16-17	17-18
	SthM 11	Sthsw 16	Sthsw 12	Sthsw 10	Sthsw 10	Sthsw 15	Sthsw 9	Sthsw 1	SthP 24	Sth1W 13
FAC	P	P	3Q	2Q	1Qr	P	P	1Q	1Q	3Q
FAT	P	1Q	2Q	P	1Q	P	Pr	P	1Q	P

CIRENCESTER TOWN

Club Contact Details 01285 654 543
The Corinium Stadium, Kingshill Lane, Cirencester GL7 1HS
scott.griffin@cirentownfc.plus.com

Founded: 1889   **Nickname:** Centurions   **Manager:** Charlie Griffin
Previous Names: None
Previous Leagues: Cheltenham 1889-1935. Gloucestershire Northern Senior 1935-68. Gloucestershire County (Founder Members) 1968-69.
Hellenic 1969-96.

Club Colours (change): Red & black stripes/black/red

Ground Capacity: 4,500   **Seats:** 550   **Covered:** 1,250   **Clubhouse:** Yes   **Shop:** Yes
Previous Grounds: Smithfield Stadium >2002.
Record Attendance: 2,600 v Fareham Town - 1969

                                     Bus Route Kingshill School - stop 150m away

RECORDS
Misc: Paid £4,000 to Gloucester City for Lee Smith
Best FA Cup   Fourth Qualifying Round 2001-02, 03-04
FA Trophy   Third Round Proper 2002-03
FA Vase   Third Round Proper 1975-76, 76-77

HONOURS
FA Comps: None
League: Cheltenham Division One 1927-28, 29-30, 48-49, 54-55, 55-56. Gloucestershire Northern Senior 1966-67, 67-68.
Hellenic Division One 1973-74, Premier Division 95-96. Southern Division One South & West 2013-14.
County FA: Gloucestershire Senior Amateur Cup 1989-90. Gloucestershire Senior Challenge Cup 1995-96, 2015-16.

08-09	09-10	10-11	11-12	12-13	13-14	14-15	15-16	16-17	17-18
Sthsw 14	Sthsw 5	SthP 13	SthP 22	Sthsw 11	Sthsw 1	SthP 8	SthP 15	SthP 22	Sth1W 7
FAC P	FAC 3Q	FAC 1Qr	FAC 1Q	FAC P	FAC 3Q	FAC 1Qr	FAC 2Q	FAC 2Q	FAC P
FAT P	FAT 1Q	FAT 1Pr	FAT 2Q	FAT P	FAT 1Q	FAT 1Q	FAT 1Pr	FAT 1Q	FAT 1Qr

EVESHAM UNITED

Club Contact Details 01386 442 303
Jubilee Stadium, Cheltenham Road, Evesham WR11 2LZ
eveshamunitedsecretary@hotmail.com

Founded: 1945   **Nickname:** The Robins   **Manager:** Paul Collicut
Previous Names: None
Previous Leagues: Worcester, Birmingham Combination, Midland Combination 1951-55, 65-92,
West Midlands (Regional) 1955-62

Club Colours (change): Red and white stripes/black/black

Ground Capacity: 3,000   **Seats:** Yes   **Covered:** Yes   **Clubhouse:** Yes   **Shop:** Yes
Previous Grounds: The Crown Meadow > 1968, Common Reed 1968-2006. Ground shared with Worcester City 2006-12.
Record Attendance: 2,338 v West Bromwich Albion - Friendly 18/07/1992

RECORDS
Victory: 11-3 v West Heath United
Defeat: 1-8 v Ilkeston Town
Goalscorer: Sid Brain
Appearances: Rob Candy
Additional: Paid £1,500 to Hayes for Colin Day 1992
                Received £5,000 from Cheltenham Town for Simon Brain

HONOURS
FA Comps: None
League: Midland Combination Premier Division 1991-92, Division One 1965-66, 67-68, 68-69.
Southern Division One Midlands 2007-08.
County FA: Worcestershire Senior Urn 1976-77, 77-78, Senior Cup 2008-09, 17-18.

08-09	09-10	10-11	11-12	12-13	13-14	14-15	15-16	16-17	17-18
SthP 9	SthP 16	SthP 12	SthP 20	Sthsw 14	Sthsw 16	Sthsw 2	Sthsw 6	Sthsw 5	Sth1W 4
FAC 1P	FAC 2Q	FAC 1Q	FAC 3Q	FAC P	FAC 1Q	FAC 4Q	FAC P	FAC 1Qr	FAC Pr
FAT 2Q	FAT 2Qr	FAT 2Q	FAT 1Qr	FAT P	FAT 1Q	FAT 1Qr	FAT 2Q	FAT 1Qr	FAT P

FLEET TOWN

Club Contact Details 01252 623 804 Match day only
Calthorpe Park, Crookham Road, Fleet, Hants GU51 5FA
info@fleettownfc.co.uk

Founded: 1890 **Nickname:** The Blues   **Manager:** Koo Dumbuya
Previous Names: Fleet FC 1890-1963
Previous Leagues: Hampshire 1961-77, Athenian, Combined Counties, Chiltonian, Wessex 1989-95, 2000-02, Southern 1995-2000, 02-04, 07-08, Isthmian 2004-07, 2008-11.

Club Colours (change): Blue & white

Ground Capacity: 2,000 **Seats:** 250 **Covered:** 250 **Clubhouse:** Yes **Shop:** Yes
Previous Grounds: Watsons Meadow > 1923.
Record Attendance: 1,336 v AFC Wimbledon, Isthmian League 08/01/2005
Nearest Railway Station Fllet - 2.1km   **Bus Route** Leawood Road - stop 150m away

RECORDS
Victory: 15-0 v Petersfield , Wessex League 26/12/1994
Defeat: 0-7 v Bashley, Southern League 12/04/2004
Goalscorer: Mark Frampton - 428
Appearances: Mark Frampton - 250
Additional: Paid £3,000 to Aldershot for Mark Russell

HONOURS
FA Comps: None
League: Wessex 1994-95.

County FA: Hampshire Senior Cup 2008-09. North Hants FA Cup 2008-09, 09-10.

08-09		09-10		10-11		11-12		12-13		13-14		14-15		15-16		16-17		17-18	
Isth1S	3	Isth1S	6	Isth1S	13	SthC	21	SthC	18	Sthsw	21	Sthsw	19	SthC	17	SthC	14	Sth1E	19
FAC	3Q	FAC	Pr	FAC	2Qr	FAC	1Q	FAC	P	FAC	P	FAC	2Q	FAC	1Qr	FAC	1Qr	FAC	Pr
FAT	1Q	FAT	2Q	FAT	1Q	FAT	1Q	FAT	Pr	FAT	P	FAT	1Q	FAT	P	FAT	1Q	FAT	Pr

HIGHWORTH TOWN

Club Contact Details 01793 766 263
Elms Recreation Ground, Highworth SN6 7DD

Founded: 1893 **Nickname:** Worthians   **Manager:** Jeff Roberts
Previous Names: None.
Previous Leagues: Cirencester & District. Swindon & District. Wiltshire Combination. Hellenic >2018.

Club Colours (change): All red

Ground Capacity: 2,000 **Seats:** 150 **Covered:** 250 **Clubhouse:** Yes **Shop:** No
Previous Grounds: Unknown
Record Attendance: 2,000 v QPR, opening of floodlights.
                                                       Bus Route Swindon Street stop - 90m away

RECORDS
Defeat: Kevin Higgs
Appearances: Rod Haines

HONOURS
FA Comps: None
League: Cirencester & District Division Two 1931-32. Swindon & District Division Three 1933-34, 54-55, Two 1955-56, One 1956-57, Premier 57-58, 58-59, 60-61, 61-62, 62-63, 63-64, 65-66, 66-67, 67-68. Hellenic Premier 2004-05.
County FA: Wiltshire Senior Cup 1963-64, 72-73, 95-96, 97-98.

08-09		09-10		10-11		11-12		12-13		13-14		14-15		15-16		16-17		17-18	
Hel P	6	Hel P	9	Hel P	4	Hel P	6	Hel P	16	Hel P	11	Hel P	7	Hel P	7	Hel P	6	Hel P	3
FAC	EP	FAC	1Q	FAC	1Qr	FAC	EP	FAC	EP	FAC	EP	FAC	P	FAC	P	FAC	2Q	FAC	P
FAV	2Q	FAV	2Q	FAV	1Q	FAV	2Pr	FAV	1Qr	FAV	1Q	FAV	SF	FAV	3P	FAV	2P	FAV	1P

LARKHALL ATHLETIC

Club Contact Details 01225 334 952
Plain Ham, Charlcombe Lane, Larkhall, Bath BA1 8DJ
larkhallathletic@gmail.com

Founded: 1914   **Nickname:** Larks   **Manager:** Phil Bater
Previous Names: None
Previous Leagues: Somerset Senior. Western 1976-2014.

Club Colours (change): All royal blue

Ground Capacity: 1,000   **Seats:** Yes   **Covered:** 50   **Clubhouse:** Yes   **Shop:** No
Previous Grounds: None
Record Attendance: 280 v Tunbridge Wells, FA Vase, Feb 2013
Nearest Railway Station Bath Spa - 2.8km   **Bus Route** Charlcombe Lane - stop 200m away

RECORDS
Victory: 8-0 v Oldland Abbotonians, 2007
Defeat: 1-6 v Exmouth Town, 2001
Goalscorer: Ben Highmore scored 52 goals during the 2008-09 season.
Appearances: Luke Scott - 600+ (as at July 2014)

HONOURS
FA Comps: None
League: Western Division One 1988-89, 08-09, Premier Division 2010-11, 13-14.
County FA: Somerset Junior Cup 1962-63, Senior Cup 1975-76, 2003-04.

08-09		09-10		10-11		11-12		12-13		13-14		14-15		15-16		16-17		17-18	
West1	1	WestP	14	WestP	1	WestP	3	WestP	5	WestP	1	Sthsw	5	Sthsw	11	Sthsw	13	Sth1W	15
FAC	1Q	FAC	P	FAC	P	FAC	1Q	FAC	1Qr	FAC	1Q	FAC	2Qr	FAC	2Qr	FAC	P	FAC	P
FAV	4P	FAV	3P	FAV	1Q	FAV	5P	FAV	5P	FAV	5P	FAT	P	FAT	1Q	FAT	P	FAT	1Q

MANGOTSFIELD UNITED

Club Contact Details 0117 956 0119
Cossham Street, Mangotsfield, Bristol BS16 9EN
davidj693@hotmail.co.uk

Founded: 1950   **Nickname:** The Field   **Manager:** Ollie Price
Previous Names: None
Previous Leagues: Bristol & District 1950-67. Avon Premier Combination 1967-72. Western 1972-2000.

Club Colours (change): Maroon & sky blue/sky blue/sky blue (White/black/black)

Ground Capacity: 2,500   **Seats:** 300   **Covered:** 800   **Clubhouse:** Yes   **Shop:** Yes
Previous Grounds: None
Record Attendance: 1,253 v Bath City - F.A. Cup 1974
                                                             Bus Route Cossham Street - stop 50m away

RECORDS
Victory: 17-0 v Hanham Sports (H) - 1953 Bristol & District League
Defeat: 3-13 v Bristol City United - Bristol & District League Division One
Goalscorer: John Hill
Appearances: John Hill - 600+
Misc: In the last 10 matches of the 2003/04 season, the club went 738 minutes (just over 8 games) without scoring and then
                   finished the campaign with 13 goals in the last two, which included a 9-0 away win.

HONOURS
FA Comps: None
League: Bristol & District Div.7 1951-52, Div.6 52-53, Div.4 53-54, Div.3 54-55, Div.2 55-56, Premier Comb Div.1 68-69. Somerset
      Senior Div.3 74-75, Div.2 75-76, 97-98, Prem 2004-05. Western 1990-91. Southern Division One West 2004-05.
County FA: Gloucestershire Senior Cup 1968-69, 75-76, 2002-03, 12-13. Gloucestershire F.A. Trophy x6.
      Somerset Premier Cup 1987-88.

08-09		09-10		10-11		11-12		12-13		13-14		14-15		15-16		16-17		17-18	
SthP	22	Sthsw	9	Sthsw	3	Sthsw	14	Sthsw	13	Sthsw	11	Sthsw	10	Sthsw	14	Sthsw	8	Sth1W	16
FAC	2Q	FAC	4Q	FAC	2Q	FAC	P	FAC	1Q	FAC	2Q	FAC	1Q	FAC	1Q	FAC	P	FAC	P
FAT	1Q	FAT	Pr	FAT	Pr	FAT	2Qr	FAT	Pr	FAT	2Q	FAT	2Q	FAT	2Q	FAT	P	FAT	P

MELKSHAM TOWN

Club Contact Details 01225 302 977
Oakfield Stadium, Eastern Way, Melksham SN12 7GU
markmtfc@virginmedia.com

Founded: 1876   **Nickname:** Town   **Manager:** Kieran Baggs
Previous Names: Melksham FC 1876-1951.
Previous Leagues: Wiltshire (Founder Members) 1894-1974. Western 1974-2018.

Club Colours (change): Yellow and black

Ground Capacity: **Seats:** Yes   **Covered:** Yes   **Clubhouse:** Yes   **Shop:**
Previous Grounds: Challymead Common 1876-83. Old Bear Field 1883-1920. Conigre 1920-2017.
Record Attendance: 2,821 v Trowbridge Town, FA Cup 1957-58.
Nearest Railway Station Melksham - 2.7km   **Bus Route** New Road - stop 300m away

RECORDS
Best FA Cup   Third Qualifying Round 1954-55, 57-58
FA Trophy   Second Qualifying Round 1982-83, 84085, 85-86, 87-87, 87-88
FA Vase   Quarter Finals 2017-18
Goalscorer: Gareth Lewis scored 72 goals during the 1968-69 season

HONOURS
FA Comps: None
League: Wiltshire 1903-04, Premier 1993-94.
         Western Division One 1979-80, 96-97, Premier Division 2014-15.
County FA: Wiltshire Senior Cup 1904-05, 69-70, 77-78, 2002-03, 07-08, 12-13, 13-14, 15-16.

08-09		09-10		10-11		11-12		12-13		13-14		14-15		15-16		16-17		17-18	
WestP	11	WestP	19	WestP	8	West1	2	WestP	13	WestP	7	WestP	1	WestP	5	WestP	3	WestP	2
FAC	EP	FAC	EP	FAC	EP	FAC	P	FAC	1Q	FAC	EPr	FAC	EPr	FAC	EPr	FAC	EP	FAC	EP
FAV	1P	FAV	1P	FAV	2P	FAV	2P	FAV	2Q	FAV	2Q	FAV	4P	FAV	2P	FAV	4Pr	FAV	QF

MONEYFIELDS

Club Contact Details 02392 665 260
Moneyfields Sports Ground, Moneyfield Ave, Copnor, Portsmouth PO3 6LA

Founded: 1987   **Nickname:** Moneys   **Manager:** David Carter
Previous Names: Portsmouth Civil Service 1987-94.
Previous Leagues: Portsmouth 1987-91. Hampshire 1991-98. Wessex 1998-2017.

Club Colours (change): Yellow and navy

Ground Capacity: 2,000   **Seats:** 150   **Covered:** 150   **Clubhouse:** Yes   **Shop:** Yes
Previous Grounds: Copnor Road 1987-94.
Record Attendance: 250 v Fareham, Wessex Division One 2005-06
Nearest Railway Station Hilsea - 1.6km   **Bus Route** Chichester Road - stop 400m away

RECORDS
Victory: 9-0v Blackfield & Langley 01-02.
Goalscorer: Lee Mould - 86
Appearances: Matt Lafferty - 229

HONOURS
FA Comps: None
League: Portsmouth Premier 1990-91.
         Hampshire Division Three 1991-92, Division Two 1992-93, Division One 1996-97.
County FA: Hampshire Intermediate 1991-92, 92-93.

08-09		09-10		10-11		11-12		12-13		13-14		14-15		15-16		16-17		17-18	
WexP	3	WexP	12	WexP	7	WexP	4	WexP	4	WexP	9	WexP	4	WexP	8	WexP	2	Sth1E	10
FAC	P	FAC	P	FAC	P	FAC	1Qr	FAC	P	FAC	1Q	FAC	EP	FAC	P	FAC	1Q	FAC	1Q
FAV	1Q	FAV	2P	FAV	3P	FAV	2Q	FAV	2P	FAV	3P	FAV	2Q	FAV	4P	FAV	2P	FAT	2Qr

PAULTON ROVERS

Club Contact Details 01761 412 907
Athletic Ground, Winterfield Road, Paulton, Bristol BS39 7RF
footballsecretary.prfc@gmail.com

Founded: 1881   **Nickname:** The Robins or Rovers   **Manager:** John Rendell - June 2017
Previous Names: None
Previous Leagues: Wiltshire Premier, Somerset Senior, Western

Club Colours (change): All maroon

Ground Capacity: 2,500   **Seats:** 253   **Covered:** 2,500   **Clubhouse:** Yes   **Shop:** Yes
Previous Grounds: Chapel Field, Cricket Ground, Recreation Ground
Record Attendance: 2,000 v Crewe Alexandra - FA Cup 1906-07

Bus Route Alexandra Park - stop 150m away

RECORDS
Goalscorer: Graham Colbourne
Appearances: Steve Tovey
Best FA Cup First Round Proper 2009-10
FA Trophy First Round Proper 2004-05
FA Vase Fifth Round Proper 1989-90

HONOURS
FA Comps: None
League: None
County FA: Somerset Junior Cup 1898-99, Senior Cup x12 - Firstly in 1900-01 and most recently in 1974-75, Premier Cup 2012-13.

	08-09		09-10		10-11		11-12		12-13		13-14		14-15		15-16		16-17		17-18	
	Sthsw	10	Sthsw	7	Sthsw	11	Sthsw	7	Sthsw	5	Sthsw	4	SthP	10	SthP	24	Sthsw	15	Sth1W	19
FAC		3Q	FAC	1P	FAC	2Q	FAC	P	FAC	Pr	FAC	P	FAC	2Qr	FAC	2Q	FAC	1Q	FAC	4Q
FAT		Pr	FAT	P	FAT	2Q	FAT	2Q	FAT	Pr	FAT	1Q	FAT	2Q	FAT	1Q	FAT	P	FAT	2Q

SLIMBRIDGE

Club Contact Details 07702 070 229
Thornhill Park, Cambridge, Glos GL2 7AF
info@slimbridgeafc.co.uk

Founded: 1899   **Nickname:** The Swans   **Manager:** Lee Driver-Dickerson - July 2018
Previous Names: None
Previous Leagues: Stroud & District. Gloucester Northern. Gloucestershire County >2009. Hellenic 2009-2013. Western 2013-15.

Club Colours (change): All blue (Green/black/black)

Ground Capacity: 1,500   **Seats:** Yes   **Covered:** Yes   **Clubhouse:** Yes   **Shop:** Yes
Previous Grounds: Various venues around Slimbridge before moving to Wisloe Road (now Thornhill Park) in 1951.
Record Attendance: 525 v Shortwood United, Hellenic Premier, 24/08/2003.
Nearest Railway Station Cam & Dursley - 0.8km   **Bus Route** Wisloe Road - stop 300m away

RECORDS
Victory: 12-1 v Cheltenham Civil Service, Reg Davis Cup, 18/08/2007
Defeat: 0-9 v Cinderford Town (A), 19/04/2018 and v Taunton Town (A), 24/04/2018
Goalscorer: Marvyn Roberts - 104 (in 221 appearances)
Appearances: Fred Ward - 505

HONOURS
FA Comps: None
League: Stroud & District Division Three 1951-52, Division Two 1952-53, Division one 1953-54, 98-99, Division Four 1989-90.
Hellenic Division 1 West 2003-04, 09-10, Premier 06-07. Gloucester Northern 2007-08. Gloucestershire County 2008-09.
County FA: Gloucester Challenge Trophy 2003-04, 05-06, 06-07. Gloucester Northern Senior Cup 2000-01.

	08-09		09-10		10-11		11-12		12-13		13-14		14-15		15-16		16-17		17-18	
	GlCo	1	Hel1W	1	Hel P	5	Hel P	5	Hel P	6	WestP	16	WestP	3	Sthsw	18	Sthsw	20	Sth1W	20
							FAC	P	FAC	EP	FAC	EPr	FAC	P	FAC	2Q	FAC	2Q	FAC	P
					FAV	1Q	FAV	1P	FAV	1Q	FAV	2Q	FAV	2Pr	FAT	P	FAT	P	FAT	P

STREET

Club Contact Details 01458 445 987
The Tannery Ground, Middlebrooks, Street BA16 0TA

Founded: 1880   **Nickname:** The Cobblers   **Manager:** Richard Fey
Previous Names: None
Previous Leagues: Somerset Senior 1880-1911, 22-30, 60-98. Western 1911-22, 30-39, 46-60, 98-2018.

Club Colours (change): All green

Ground Capacity: 1,000 **Seats:** 150   **Covered:** 25   **Clubhouse:** Yes   **Shop:**
Previous Grounds: Unknown
Record Attendance: 4,300 v Yeovil Town FA Cup 47

Bus Route Green Lane Ave - stop 220m away

RECORDS
Best FA Cup	First Round Proper 1938-39, 47-48
FA Trophy	First Qualifying Round 1969-70
FA Vase	Fifth Round Proper 2006-07

HONOURS
FA Comps: None
League: Somerset Senior 1892-93, 95-96, 97-98, 98-99, 1909-10, 63-64, 65-66, 1996-97, Division Three 93-94.
  Western Premier 2017-18.
County FA: Somerset Senior Cup 1897-98, 99-1900, 10-11

08-09		09-10		10-11		11-12		12-13		13-14		14-15		15-16		16-17		17-18	
WestP	13	WestP	6	WestP	13	WestP	10	WestP	6	WestP	5	WestP	13	WestP	7	WestP	2	WestP	1
FAC	Pr	FAC	EPr	FAC	P	FAC	EP	FAC	EP	FAC	1Q	FAC	EPr	FAC	P	FAC	1Q	FAC	P
FAV	3Pr	FAV	2Q	FAV	2Q	FAV	1Q	FAV	1P	FAV	2Q	FAV	2Q	FAV	1Q	FAV	1P	FAV	1P

THATCHAM TOWN

Club Contact Details 01635 862 016
Waterside Park, Crookham Hill, Thatcham, Berks RG18 4QR

Founded: 1895   **Nickname:** Kingfishers   **Manager:** Danny Robinson
Previous Names: Thatcham 1895-1974.
Previous Leagues: Reading Temperance 1896-1953. Hellenic (founder member) 1953-82, Athenian 1982-84, London Spartan 1984-86,
  Wessex 1986-2006. Southern 2006-14.

Club Colours (change): Blue and white

Ground Capacity: 1,500 **Seats:** 300   **Covered:** 300   **Clubhouse:** Yes   **Shop:** Yes
Previous Grounds: Station Road 1946-52, Lancaster Close 1952-92
Record Attendance: 1,400 v Aldershot - FA Vase
Nearest Railway Station Thatcham - 1.6km   **Bus Route** Vincent Road stop - 287m away

RECORDS
Best FA Cup	Fourth Qualifying Round 1996-97
FA Trophy	Second Qualifying Round 2008-09, 09-10, 11-12(r)

HONOURS
FA Comps: FA Vase 2017-18.
League: Reading Temperance Division Two 1905-06. Hellenic Division One 1958-59, 64-65, 72-73, Premier 1974-75, 2017-18.
  Wessex 1995-96.
County FA: Berks & Bucks Junior Cup 1935-36, Senior Cup 74-75, Senior Trophy 2004-05.
  Basingstoke Senior Cup 2008-09, 10-11, 11-12.

08-09		09-10		10-11		11-12		12-13		13-14		14-15		15-16		16-17		17-18	
Sthsw	6	Sthsw	12	Sthsw	5	Sthsw	8	SthC	17	Sthsw	19	Hel P	12	Hel P	2	Hel P	4	Hel P	1
FAC	2Q	FAC	P	FAC	1Q	FAC	P	FAC	2Q	FAC	P	FAC	EPr	FAC	1Q	FAC	EP	FAC	2Q
FAT	2Q	FAT	2Q	FAT	P	FAT	2Qr	FAT	P	FAT	P	FAV	1P	FAV	2Q	FAV	3P	FAV	F

WINCHESTER CITY

Club Contact Details 07768 848 905
The Simplyhealth City Ground, Hillier Way, Winchester SO23 7SR
commercial@winchestercityfc.co.uk

Founded: 1884   **Nickname:** The Capitals   **Manager:** Ousmane Dembele - June 2018
Previous Names: None
Previous Leagues: Hampshire 1898-71, 73-03. Southern 1971-73, 2006-09, 2012-13. Wessex 2003-06. 2009-12, 13-15.

Club Colours (change): Red & black

Ground Capacity: 4,500   **Seats:** 180   **Covered:** 275   **Clubhouse:** Yes   **Shop:** Yes
Previous Grounds: None
Record Attendance: 1,818 v Bideford, FA Vase Semi-final.
Nearest Railway Station Winchester - 0.9km   **Bus Route** Simonds Court - stop 250m away

RECORDS
Goalscorer: Andy Forbes.
Appearances: Ian Mancey.

HONOURS
FA Comps: FA Vase 2004.
League: Hampshire Division Two 1973-74, 91-92, Division One 2000-01, Premier Division 2002-03.
              Wessex Division One 2003-04, 05-06, Premier Division 2011-12.
County FA: Hants Senior Cup 1930-31, 2004-05.

08-09		09-10		10-11		11-12		12-13		13-14		14-15		15-16		16-17		17-18	
SthW	22	WexP	11	WexP	3	WexP	1	SthC	22	WexP	5	WexP	2	Sthsw	5	Sthsw	14	Sth1W	11
FAC	1Q	FAC	EP	FAC	EP	FAC	P	FAC	1Q	FAC	1Q	FAC	3Q	FAC	2Qr	FAC	3Q	FAC	1Q
FAV	1Q	FAV	1P	FAV	2Q	FAV	2P	FAT	P	FAV	1P	FAV	1P	FAT	1Q	FAT	3Q	FAT	P

YATE TOWN

Club Contact Details 01454 228 103
The Universal Components Stadium, Lodge Road, Yate, Bristol BS37 7LE
admin@yatetownfc.com

Founded: 1906   **Nickname:** The Bluebells   **Manager:** Paul Britton
Previous Names: Yate Rovers 1906-1930s. Yate YMCA 1933-58.
Previous Leagues: Bristol Premier Combination > 1968, Gloucestershire County 1968-83, Hellenic 1983-89, 2000-03, Southern 1989-2000

Club Colours (change): White & navy blue

Ground Capacity: 2,000   **Seats:** 236   **Covered:** 400   **Clubhouse:** Yes   **Shop:** Yes
Previous Grounds: Yate Aerodrome 1954-60. Sunnyside Lane 1960-84.
Record Attendance: 2,000 v Bristol Rovers v Bristol Rovers Past XI - Vaughan Jones testimonial 1990
Nearest Railway Station Yate - 1km   **Bus Route** North Road - stop 100m away

RECORDS
Victory: 13-3 v Clevedon - Bristol Premier Combination 1967-68
Goalscorer: Kevin Thaws
Appearances: Gary Hewlett
Additional: Paid £2,000 to Chippenham Town for Matt Rawlings 2003
                  Received £15,000 from Bristol Rovers for Mike Davis

HONOURS
FA Comps: None
League: Hellenic 1987-88, 88-89.

County FA: Gloucestershire Senior Cup 2004-05, 05-06.

08-09		09-10		10-11		11-12		12-13		13-14		14-15		15-16		16-17		17-18	
SthP	21	Sthsw	13	Sthsw	14	Sthsw	13	Sthsw	6	Sthsw	9	Sthsw	6	Sthsw	16	Sthsw	18	Sth1W	14
FAC	1Q	FAC	1Qr	FAC	P	FAC	2Qr	FAC	1P	FAC	3Qr	FAC	1Q	FAC	P	FAC	P	FAC	P
FAT	2Q	FAT	2Qr	FAT	P	FAT	2Q	FAT	Pr	FAT	Pr	FAT	P	FAT	P	FAT	1Q	FAT	1Q

COMBINED COUNTIES - STEP 5/6

COMBINED COUNTIES LEAGUE

Founded: 1978 **Sponsored by:** Cherry Red Records
Recent Champions - 2015: Molesey **2016:** Hartley Wintney **2017:** Hartley Wintney

PREMIER DIVISION

		P	W	D	L	F	A	GD	Pts
1	Westfield	42	34	4	4	145	43	102	106
2	Bedfont Sports	42	29	6	7	104	58	46	93
3	Sutton Common Rovers	42	27	6	9	92	48	44	87
4	Walton & Hersham	42	26	6	10	89	52	37	84
5	Balham	42	23	6	13	84	63	21	75
6	Redhill	42	20	5	17	84	66	18	65
7	Camberley Town	42	15	20	7	56	43	13	65
8	Knaphill	42	17	12	13	76	64	12	63
9	CB Hounslow United	42	18	6	18	77	66	11	60
10	Spelthorne Sports	42	17	8	17	68	65	3	59
11	Hanworth Villa	42	16	10	16	70	77	-7	58
12	Guildford City	42	16	8	18	74	88	-14	56
13	North Greenford United	42	15	10	17	75	76	-1	55
14	Horley Town	42	15	8	19	58	87	-29	53
15	Chertsey Town	42	14	7	21	66	83	-17	49
16	Colliers Wood United	42	14	5	23	69	74	-5	47
17	Abbey Rangers	42	12	11	19	58	69	-11	47
18	AFC Hayes	42	13	7	22	57	84	-27	46
19	Banstead Athletic	42	11	9	22	54	94	-40	42
20	Godalming Town	42	8	8	26	55	102	-47	32
21	Epsom & Ewell	42	5	12	25	45	105	-60	27
22	Farnham Town	42	5	10	27	49	98	-49	25

DIVISION ONE

		P	W	D	L	F	A	GD	Pts
1	Worcester Park	36	29	4	3	142	50	92	91
2	Cobham	36	24	7	5	108	44	64	79
3	Badshot Lea	36	25	4	7	120	64	56	79
4	Sheerwater	36	23	8	5	110	61	49	77
5	Raynes Park Vale	36	24	3	9	94	48	46	75
6	Staines Lammas	35	21	5	9	88	57	31	71*
7	Frimley Green	36	19	7	10	92	54	38	64
8	AC London	34	19	1	14	75	58	17	58
9	Eversley & California	36	17	5	14	95	84	11	53*
10	Ash United	35	15	5	15	64	78	-14	53*
11	Farleigh Rovers	35	13	6	16	72	87	-15	47*
12	FC Deportivo Galicia	34	10	5	19	60	79	-19	41*
13	Chessington & Hook United	35	11	4	20	82	105	-23	37
14	South Park Reserves	34	7	8	19	49	97	-48	32*
15	Kensington Borough	35	9	3	23	54	99	-45	30
16	Fleet Spurs	36	7	5	24	59	104	-45	26
17	Bedfont & Feltham	36	7	4	25	52	97	-45	25
18	Cove	36	6	4	26	42	98	-56	22
19	Bagshot	35	5	2	28	40	134	-94	17

PREMIER CHALLENGE CUP

HOLDERS: WESTFIELD

ROUND 1
Staines Lammas	v	Chertsey Town	2-2, 4-5p
South Park Reserves	v	Horley Town	3-4
Raynes Park Vale	v	Hanworth Villa	3-2 aet
CB Hounslow United	v	Eversley & California	5-2
Worcester Park	v	Epsom & Ewell	4-2
FC Deprtivo Galicia	v	AC London	1-0
Sutton Common Rovers	v	Westfield	3-1
Camberley Town	v	Redhill	0-3
Frimley Green	v	Cobham	1-4

ROUND 2
Spelthorne Sports	v	Ash United	5-1
Chertsey Town	v	Horley Town	1-0
Bedfont Sports	v	Farleigh Rovers	6-1
Walton & Hersham	v	Badshot Lea	6-1
Bedfont & Feltham	v	Godalming Town	0-1
Chessington & Hook Utd	v	Sheerwater	5-2
Knaphill	v	Guildford City	3-1
Kensington Borough	v	Raynes Park Vale	4-3
CB Hounslow United	v	Worcester Park	1-2
Abbey Rangers	v	FC Deportivo Galicia	1-3
Bagshot	v	North Greenford United	1-4
Colliers Wood United	v	Balham	4-1
Cove	v	Sutton Common Rovers	0-1
Redhill	v	Fleet Spurs	9-0
AFC Hayes	v	Cobham	0-1
Banstead Athletic	v	Farnham Town	0-3

ROUND 3
Spelthorne Sports	v	Chertsey Town	1-0
Bedfont Sports	v	Walton & Hersham	0-1
Godalming Town	v	Chessington & Hook United	3-2
Knaphill	v	Kensington Borough	2-0
Worcester Park	v	FC Deportivo Galicia	6-1
North Greenford United	v	Colliers Wood United	0-4
Sutton Common Rovers	v	Redhill	5-0
Cobham	v	Farnham Town	5-0

QUARTER FINALS
Spelthorne Sports	v	Walton & Hersham	1-3
Godalming Town	v	Knaphill	0-2
Worcester Park	v	Colliers Wood United	5-2
Sutton Common Rovers	v	Cobham	2-1

SEMI FINALS
Walton & Hersham	v	Knaphill	1-2
Worcester Park	v	Sutton Common Rovers	3-2

FINAL
Knaphill	v	Worcester Park	3-2 aet

DIVISION ONE CHALLENGE CUP

HOLDERS: AC LONDON
SEMI FINALS
Everseley & California	v	FC Deportivo Galicia	2-0
Worcester Park	v	Staines Lammas	0-1

FINAL
Eversley & California	v	Staines Lammas	0-2

CLUB MOVEMENTS
Premier Division - In: Badshot Lea (P), Cobham (P), Raynes Park Vale (P), Southall (P - SSM1).
Out: Epsom & Ewell (R), Farnham Town (R), Godalming Town (R), Westfield (P - IsthSC).
Division One - In: British Airways (P - MCL), Dorking W Res (N), Epsom & Ewell (R), Farnham Town (R), Godalming Town (R), Sandhurst (LM - Hel), Tooting Bec (P - SEI). **Out:** Farleigh Rovers, Staines Lammas and Worcester Park (D - Surrey Elite, due to ground grading). South Park Res (W).

352   www.nonleagueclubdirectory.co.uk

PREMIER DIVISION	1	2	3	4	5	6	7	8	9	10	11	12	13	14	15	16	17	18	19	20	21	22
1 AAbbey Rangers		2-1	2-2	6-3	0-4	1-1	0-1	1-0	4-2	0-0	1-1	1-1	5-0	2-3	2-1	0-3	1-3	0-3	1-1	1-1	0-4	3-2
2 AFC Hayes	2-1		2-1	1-2	0-2	2-2	0-3	1-3	1-0	2-0	1-0	4-1	3-2	1-2	2-0	1-3	1-2	1-3	3-2	1-1	2-3	2-3
3 Balham	2-1	3-0		2-0	2-4	0-2	1-0	2-1	3-1	4-0	3-0	3-1	1-1	0-1	3-2	3-2	4-0	2-0	1-3	3-1	0-1	1-2
4 Banstead Athletic	2-3	2-0	1-2		1-2	1-2	1-0	3-2	0-3	1-1	3-1	2-2	1-0	1-3	4-5	1-1	2-0	3-1	1-3	1-1	1-0	3-5
5 Bedfont Sports	1-0	2-1	4-8	5-0		0-0	2-1	6-1	5-3	7-0	1-0	3-2	4-2	5-2	1-4	2-2	1-0	3-0	3-0	3-2	2-1	0-5
6 Camberley Town	0-2	0-1	2-1	0-1	2-3		2-0	2-1	3-0	1-1	1-1	0-0	3-3	2-0	1-1	3-1	0-0	3-2	3-1	0-1	1-1	1-4
7 CB Hounslow United	3-2	4-3	5-0	0-1	3-1	0-1		5-1	1-4	4-2	3-1	3-0	1-2	3-0	0-1	1-1	2-2	1-0	1-0	1-0	0-2	2-4
8 Chertsey Town	1-1	1-1	3-0	7-1	2-4	0-0	1-1		1-1	1-0	3-2	1-0	0-1	1-2	2-0	1-3	1-4	4-2	1-4	1-2	1-2	0-3
9 Colliers Wood United	3-1	4-2	1-2	0-0	0-2	0-2	1-2	1-0		5-2	0-1	4-1	1-0	2-1	1-2	1-2	0-1	5-1	1-2	1-2	1-2	1-3
10 Epsom & Ewell	1-1	0-0	0-2	2-2	2-4	0-0	5-2	2-7	0-1		3-0	0-3	1-3	1-1	2-3	0-0	1-2	0-5	1-5	0-2	0-2	2-2
11 Farnham Town	1-0	0-2	2-3	3-3	0-0	0-3	1-2	2-3	2-3	0-0		1-2	1-2	1-2	3-3	1-1	2-5	0-4	5-1	0-1	0-2	1-2
12 Godalming Town	1-2	1-2	1-1	3-0	0-4	2-2	0-0	1-2	1-3	1-2	1-3		0-2	0-0	2-0	1-4	2-1	1-0	2-4	3-6	1-3	1-4
13 Guildford City	2-0	3-1	0-6	1-1	3-2	1-1	4-3	1-1	3-3	4-3	2-3	4-4		4-1	2-1	1-3	2-1	1-2	1-2	0-1	0-2	2-4
14 Hanworth Villa	2-1	5-0	1-1	2-1	1-3	1-2	3-3	1-5	1-1	2-3	1-1	2-0	5-4		2-2	1-1	3-0	0-3	1-1	2-1	0-2	1-5
15 Horley Town	0-5	2-2	5-1	2-1	1-2	0-0	2-4	2-0	3-1	3-2	1-1	2-1	0-1	2-1		1-1	3-2	1-0	0-4	0-0	0-2	0-4
16 Knaphill	0-0	0-2	1-2	3-0	2-1	1-1	1-1	4-1	3-2	6-2	3-1	3-0	1-2	2-0	4-0		2-2	5-0	1-0	0-2	1-5	0-6
17 North Greenford United	0-0	1-1	2-2	1-0	2-3	1-1	3-2	0-1	1-1	0-4	2-1	8-4	3-1	1-3	7-1	4-1		2-1	1-1	3-4	0-1	1-2
18 Redhill	1-3	4-1	3-1	1-1	1-1	1-1	4-3	4-0	5-2	3-0	3-0	1-2	2-0	1-4	3-0	1-0	7-2		1-0	1-1	0-3	0-2
19 Spelthorne Sports	1-0	3-1	1-0	1-0	0-0	1-1	1-0	2-3	0-4	0-0	2-2	2-3	3-3	1-4	0-1	2-0	3-0	2-4		4-1	2-0	1-3
20 Sutton Common Rovers	3-0	4-1	0-1	1-0	0-1	1-3	2-1	2-1	2-0	5-0	11-1	3-0	3-1	3-1	3-1	4-2	1-0	1-1	3-1		5-0	2-1
21 Walton & Hersham	3-2	1-1	3-3	9-1	1-0	0-0	2-4	7-0	1-0	4-0	4-3	3-1	0-3	1-1	3-0	1-1	1-3	3-2	2-0	1-3		1-3
22 Westfield	3-0	6-1	1-2	7-1	1-1	5-1	2-1	0-0	3-1	5-0	5-0	7-2	5-0	3-1	5-0	4-1	2-2	1-3	2-1	5-0	4-0	

DIVISION ONE	1	2	3	4	5	6	7	8	9	10	11	12	13	14	15	16	17	18	19
1 AC London		4-0	3-2	6-0	3-1	3-1	2-3	3-0	2-1	3-0	P-P	4-0	3-2	1-0	2-1	0-1	-	2-1	3-4
2 Ash United	0-3		1-4	3-1	5-4	4-1	0-5	1-0	1-4	0-0	1-0	3-1	3-1	3-2	1-4	1-3	1-1	2-2	1-1
3 Badshot Lea	3-2	5-2		2-1	5-0	3-2	2-0	6-2	2-1	4-1	5-1	0-2	2-1	3-0	2-2	3-3	2-1	0-2	4-4
4 Bagshot	2-4	1-5	2-4		0-5	4-2	0-2	2-1	0-2	3-5	2-0	2-7	0-2	1-3	0-4	1-5	1-3	1-6	0-9
5 Bedfont & Feltham	4-2	2-1	1-3	1-1		1-2	1-5	0-1	1-5	1-2	4-5	1-1	0-3	4-2	0-2	2-2	2-2	0-4	0-2
6 Chessington & Hook United	1-2	3-6	1-6	3-1	3-1		3-5	3-2	5-0	3-6	0-3	1-2	0-5	5-0	2-4	4-4	2-1	1-4	1-6
7 Cobham	3-2	5-0	2-2	5-0	1-0	5-2		3-3	2-1	1-1	5-0	6-2	3-0	5-2	2-1	2-1	1-1	1-3	0-1
8 Cove	0-1	0-3	1-6	1-2	0-3	1-3	0-2		1-3	2-5	1-0	1-1	1-2	0-2	0-3	1-3	4-1	0-1	1-11
9 Eversley & California	2-0	1-2	1-6	6-2	2-4	3-3	1-3	3-0		2-4	3-2	5-0	2-1	3-2	3-2	3-0	5-2	0-2	2-6
10 Farleigh Rovers	3-0	0-3	1-3	-	1-0	1-6	0-5	3-4	1-1		1-2	2-2	3-3	5-3	0-4	1-4	3-0	3-1	1-3
11 FC Deportivo Galicia	1-2	3-1	5-6	6-1	2-1	1-1	1-5	5-1	2-2	3-3		2-1	0-6	4-1	1-4	1-3	3-0	1-3	0-3
12 Fleet Spurs	3-4	0-2	1-4	4-0	2-0	3-3	0-6	2-5	3-7	0-5	3-1		1-1	0-2	3-2	2-3	0-2	1-4	3-4
13 Frimley Green	3-1	1-2	4-1	7-0	4-0	5-1	2-2	1-1	4-1	3-2	3-2	3-2		2-1	0-1	1-4	4-0	5-2	0-2
14 Kensington Borough	1-0	P-P	1-5	0-3	2-1	1-4	1-1	2-1	2-3	2-3	2-0	4-2	1-1		4-0	0-2	2-2	2-5	0-5
15 Raynes Park Vale	2-1	4-1	2-0	7-1	5-2	4-3	0-1	5-1	1-1	2-1	1-0	2-1	2-4	5-2		0-0	4-0	0-2	3-1
16 Sheerwater	5-1	1-0	4-2	4-1	9-0	2-0	1-2	4-3	4-7	4-3	2-1	4-1	1-1	8-1	0-2		7-4	4-1	2-5
17 South Park Reserves	2-1	3-3	0-10	3-1	0-2	0-5	0-5	0-0	4-4	1-2	P-P	4-1	1-2	4-2	2-3	2-2		1-3	2-1
18 Staines Lammas	3-2	3-1	0-2	3-3	4-1	-	2-1	0-1	3-1	5-0	1-1	3-2	2-2	6-1	0-4	2-2	3-0		2-3
19 Worcester Park	3-3	5-1	7-1	4-0	4-2	6-2	5-3	3-1	5-4	4-0	1-1	2-0	4-3	2-1	4-2	0-1	6-0	6-0	

PREMIER DIVISION

ABBEY RANGERS
Founded: 1976   Nickname:

Club Contact Details   (T) 01932 422 962
(E) graham.keable@ntlworld.com
Ground: Addlestone Moor, Addlestone, KT15 2QH
Nearest Railway Station Addlestone
Capacity: **Seats:** Yes   **Covered:** Yes   **Bus Route** No.461

Colours(change):   Black & whites
Previous Names: None
Previous Leagues: Surrey Elite 2011-2015

HONOURS: FA Comps: None
League: Surrey & Hants Border League 2004-05.
10 YEAR RECORD | Surrey Intermediate League (Western) Division One 2008-09.

08-09	09-10	10-11	11-12	12-13	13-14	14-15	15-16	16-17	17-18
Sul1 1	SulP	SulP	SuEI 10	SuEI 7	SuEI 3	SuEI 4	CC1 3	CCP 10	CCP 17
								FAC EP	FAC EP
							FAV 2P	FAV 3P	FAV 2Q

AFC HAYES
Founded: 1976   Nickname: The Brooks

Club Contact Details   (T) 020 8845 0110
(E) afchayesfootballsec@hotmail.co.uk
Ground: Farm Park, Kingshill Avenue, Hayes UB4 8DD
Nearest Railway Station Northholt or Haye & Harlington
Capacity: 2,000 **Seats:** 150   **Covered:** 200   **Bus Route** No.90

Colours(change):   Blue and white stripes
Previous Names: Brook House > 2007.
Previous Leagues: Spartan South Midlands 1988-2004. Isthmian 2004-06.
Southern 2006-15.
HONOURS: FA Comps: None
League: Spartan South Midlands Premier South 1997-98.
10 YEAR RECORD

08-09	09-10	10-11	11-12	12-13	13-14	14-15	15-16	16-17	17-18
Sthsw 9	Sthsw 21	SthC 19	SthC 10	SthC 15	SthC 18	SthC 22	CCP 16	CCP 17	CCP 18
FAC P	FAC P	FAC P	FAC 1Q	FAC P	FAC P	FAC 1Q	FAC Pr	FAC P	FAC EP
FAT 1Q	FAT P	FAT 1Q	FAT P	FAT 1Q	FAT P	FAT Pr	FAV 2Q	FAV 1Q	FAV 2Q

BADSHOT LEA
Founded: 1907   Nickname: Baggies

Club Contact Details   (T) 01252 320 385
(E)
Ground: Ash United, Shawfields Stadium, Youngs Drive off Shawfield Rd, Ash, GU12 6RE.
Nearest Railway Station Ash or Ash Vale
Capacity: 2500 **Seats:** 152   **Covered:** 160   **Bus Route** Stagecoach 20A, 550

Colours(change):   All claret & sky blue
Previous Names:
Previous Leagues: Surrey Intermediate. Hellenic > 2008.

HONOURS: FA Comps: None
League: Surrey Intermediate Division One 1936-37, 37-38, 85-86, Division Two 92-93
10 YEAR RECORD

08-09	09-10	10-11	11-12	12-13	13-14	14-15	15-16	16-17	17-18
CCP 7	CCP 10	CCP 6	CCP 17	CCP 7	CCP 15	CCP 8	CCP 17	CCP 21	CC1 3
	FAC 2Q	FAC EP	FAC P	FAC 3Q	FAC P	FAC P	FAC P	FAC P	FAC P
FAV 1P	FAV 3P	FAV 1Q	FAV 2Q	FAV 1Q	FAV 1Q	FAV 1Q	FAV 2Q	FAV 2Q	FAV 2Q

BALHAM
Founded: 2011   Nickname:

Club Contact Details   (T) 020 8942 8062
(E) g.cruttwell@btinternet.com
Ground: Colliers Wood Utd, Wibbandune Stadium, Lincoln Green, Wimbledon SW20 0AA
Nearest Railway Station Raynes Park
Capacity: 2000 **Seats:** 120   **Covered:** 420   **Bus Route** London Transport 265

Colours(change):   White & black/black/black (Maroon/white/maroon)
Previous Names:
Previous Leagues: Surrey South Eastern Combination 2011-15. Surrey Elite Intermediate 2015-2016

HONOURS: FA Comps: None
League: Surrey South Eastern Combination Intermediate Division One 2013-14.
10 YEAR RECORD

08-09	09-10	10-11	11-12	12-13	13-14	14-15	15-16	16-17	17-18
			SSECJ1 4	SSECI2 3	SSECI1 1	SuEI 3	SuEI 2	CC1 3	CCP 5
									FAV 1P

BANSTEAD ATHLETIC

Founded: 1944   Nickname: The A's

Club Contact Details (T) 01737 350 982   **(E)** terrymolloy@leyfield.eclipse.co.uk
Ground: Merland Rise, Tadworth, Surrey KT20 5JG
Nearest Railway Station Tattenham Corner
Capacity: 4000   **Seats:** 250   **Covered:** 800   **Shop:** Yes   **Bus Route** Metro 420 & 460

Colours(change): Amber & black
Previous Names: Banstead Juniors 1944-46.
Previous Leagues: Surrey Senior 1949-79. Athenian 1979-85. Isthmian 1985-2006.

HONOURS: FA Comps: None
      League: Surrey Senior League 1950-51, 51-52, 52-53, 53-54, 56-57, 64-65.
10 YEAR RECORD Combined Counties League Division One 2016-17.

08-09		09-10		10-11		11-12		12-13		13-14		14-15		15-16		16-17		17-18	
CCP	10	CCP	20	CCP	17	CCP	22	CC1	17	CC1	12	CC1	6	CC1	6	CC1	1	CCP	19
FAC	EP	FAC	EPr	FAC	P	FAC	1Q	FAC	EP					FAC	EPr	FAC	Pr	FAC	1Q
FAT	2P	FAV	2Q	FAV	2Q	FAV	2Q	FAV	2Q	FAV	2Q	FAV	1P	FAV	2Q	FAV	1P	FAV	1Q

CAMBERLEY TOWN

Founded: 1895   Nickname: Reds or Town

Club Contact Details (T) 01276 65 392   **(E)**
Ground: Krooner Park, Wilton Road, Camberley, Surrey GU15 2QW
Nearest Railway Station Camberley
Capacity: 1,976   **Seats:** 196   **Covered:** 300   **Shop:** Yes   **Bus Route** Stagecoach 1

Colours(change): Red and white stripes
Previous Names: St Michael's FC (St Michael's Camberley) 1895-1901. Camberley & Yorktown 1901-46. Camberley 1946-67.
Previous Leagues: East & West Surrey (West Surrey) 1898-99, 1910-22. Aldershot Comb 1902-03. Ascot & Dist 1903-10. Surrey Senior 1922-73.
      Spartan 1973-75. Athenian 1975-77, 82-84. Isthmian 1977-82, 84-2006.
HONOURS: FA Comps: None
      League: Ascot & Dist. 1904-05, 07-08, 08-09, 09-10. Aldershot Sen. Civilian 1912-13. West Surrey 1913-14. Surrey
10 YEAR RECORD Senior 1930-31, 31-32, 32-33.

08-09		09-10		10-11		11-12		12-13		13-14		14-15		15-16		16-17		17-18	
CCP	5	CCP	3	CCP	4	CCP	6	CCP	16	CCP	2	CCP	2	CCP	3	CCP	6	CCP	7
FAC	P	FAC	EP	FAC	P	FAC	P	FAC	P	FAC	1Qr	FAC	EP	FAC	EP	FAC	1Q	FAC	P
FAV	3P	FAV	1P	FAV	2P	FAV	1P	FAV	2Q	FAV	2Q	FAV	1P	FAT	QF	FAV	2P	FAV	1P

CB HOUNSLOW UNITED

Founded: 1989   Nickname: None

Club Contact Details (T) 0208 574 7055   **(E)**
Ground: Green Lane, Hounslow TW4 6DH
Nearest Railway Station Hatton Cross (Underground) Piccadilly Line
Capacity: 1200   **Seats:** 100   **Covered:** Yes   **Bus Route** London Transport 203, H25, H26

Colours(change): Green and black
Previous Names: CB United 1989-94.
Previous Leagues: Hounslow & District 1989-94. Middlesex County 1994-2006.

HONOURS: FA Comps: None
      League: Combined Counties League Division One 2015-16.
10 YEAR RECORD

08-09		09-10		10-11		11-12		12-13		13-14		14-15		15-16		16-17		17-18	
CC1	10	CC1	15	CC1	14	CC1	15	CC1	8	CC1	14	CC1	7	CC1	1	CCP	20	CCP	9
																FAC	1Q	FAC	P
												FAV	1Q	FAV	2Q	FAV	2Q	FAV	2Q

CHERTSEY TOWN

Founded: 1890   Nickname: Curfews

Club Contact Details (T) 01932 561 774   **(E)** chrisegay@googlemail.com
Ground: Alwyns Lane, Chertsey, Surrey KT16 9DW
Nearest Railway Station Chertsey
Capacity: 3,000   **Seats:** 240   **Covered:** 760   **Shop:** Yes   **Bus Route** Abellio 446, 451, 461, 557

Colours(change): Royal blue & white stripes
Previous Names: Chertsey 1890-1950.
Previous Leagues: Metropolitan. Spartan. Athenian. Isthmian, Combined Counties 2006-11. Southern 2011-14.

HONOURS: FA Comps: None
      League: None
10 YEAR RECORD

08-09		09-10		10-11		11-12		12-13		13-14		14-15		15-16		16-17		17-18	
CCP	3	CCP	2	CCP	2	SthC	17	SthC	20	SthC	21	CCP	20	CCP	18	CCP	19	CCP	15
FAC	P	FAC	P	FAC	2Q	FAC	2Q	FAC	P	FAC	2Q	FAC	EPr	FAC	P	FAC	1Q	FAC	P
FAV	1P	FAV	5Pr	FAV	2P	FAT	3Q	FAT	1Q	FAT	1Q	FAV	1P	FAV	2Q	FAV	1Q	FAV	1Q

COBHAM
Founded: 1892   Nickname: Hammers

Club Contact Details (T) 01932 866 386   (E) cobhamfootballclub@hotmail.com
Ground: Leg O'Mutton Field, Anvil Lane, Cobham KT11 1AA
Nearest Railway Station Cobham
Capacity: 2000 **Seats:** 112 **Covered:** 200   **Bus Route** Green Line 715

Colours(change): Red & black
Previous Names: None
Previous Leagues: Surrey Senior.

HONOURS: FA Comps: None
League: Kingston & District Division One 1928-29, 29-30.

10 YEAR RECORD																			
08-09		09-10		10-11		11-12		12-13		13-14		14-15		15-16		16-17		17-18	
CCP	22	CC1	7	CC1	8	CC1	11	CC1	11	CC1	16	CC1	11	CC1	7	CC1	11	CC1	2
FAC	P	FAC	P	FAC	1Q	FAC	EPr	FAC	EPr										
FAV	1P	FAV	1Q	FAV	1Q	FAV	1Q	FAV	2Q	FAV	2Q	FAV	2Q	FAV	2Q	FAV	2Q	FAV	1P

COLLIERS WOOD UNITED
Founded: 1874   Nickname: The Woods

Club Contact Details (T) 0208 942 8062   (E) collierswoodunited@yahoo.co.uk
Ground: Wibbandune Sports Ground, Lincoln Green, Wimbledon SW20 0AA
Nearest Railway Station Raynes Park
Capacity: 2000 **Seats:** 102 **Covered:** 100   **Shop:** Yes **Bus Route** London Transport 265

Colours(change): Royal blue & black
Previous Names: Vandyke 1874-1997. Vandyke Colliers United 1997-99.
Previous Leagues: Wimbledon & Sutton. Surrey Intermediate. Surrey County Senior

HONOURS: FA Comps: None
League: Surrey County Premier League 1997-98.

10 YEAR RECORD																			
08-09		09-10		10-11		11-12		12-13		13-14		14-15		15-16		16-17		17-18	
CCP	14	CCP	19	CCP	11	CCP	19	CCP	18	CCP	16	CCP	11	CCP	8	CCP	15	CCP	16
FAC	1Q	FAC	P	FAC	EP	FAC	EPr	FAC	P	FAC	P	FAC	EP	FAC	EP	FAC	2Qr	FAC	Pr
FAV	1Q	FAV	1Q	FAV	3P	FAV	1P	FAV	3P	FAV	1Q	FAV	4P	FAV	3P	FAV	1Q	FAV	1Q

GUILDFORD CITY
Founded: 1996   Nickname: The Sweeney

Club Contact Details (T) 01483 443 322   (E) barry.underwood@guildfordcityfc.co.uk
Ground: Spectrum Leisure Centre, Parkway, Guildford GU1 1UP
Nearest Railway Station Guildford Main Line (2 miles) & Guildford (London Rd) (1 mile)
Capacity: 1100 **Seats:** 269 **Covered:** Yes **Shop:** Yes **Bus Route** Arriva 100

Colours(change): Red & white stripes
Previous Names: AFC Guildford 1996-2005. Guildford United 2005-06.
Previous Leagues: Surrey Senior. Combined Counties > 2012. Southern 2012-14.

HONOURS: FA Comps: None
League: Southern League 1937-38, 55-56, League cup 1962-63, 66-67.
Combined Counties Division One 2003-04, Premier Division 2010-11, 11-12

10 YEAR RECORD																			
08-09		09-10		10-11		11-12		12-13		13-14		14-15		15-16		16-17		17-18	
CCP	20	CCP	7	CCP	1	CCP	1	SthC	9	Sthsw	22	CCP	17	CCP	14	CCP	16	CCP	12
FAC	EP	FAC	1Qr	FAC	2Q	FAC	EP	FAC	1Q	FAC	P	FAC	EP	FAC	P	FAC	1Q	FAC	1Q
FAV	1P	FAV	2Q	FAV	4P	FAV	2P	FAT	1Q	FAT	P	FAV	1P	FAV	1Q	FAV	1Q	FAV	1Q

HANWORTH VILLA
Founded: 1976   Nickname: The Vilans

Club Contact Details (T) 020 8831 9391   (E) db1959@btinternet.com
Ground: Rectory Meadows, Park Road, Hanworth TW13 6PN
Nearest Railway Station Feltham or Hampton
Capacity: 600 **Seats:** 100 **Covered:** Yes   **Bus Route** London United 111 or H25

Colours(change): Red & white
Previous Names: None
Previous Leagues: Hounslow & District Lge. West Middlesex Lge. Middlesex County League.

HONOURS: FA Comps: None
League: Hounslow & District Div.1 & Prem. West Middlesex Division One & Division Two.
Middlesex County 2002-03, 04-05.

10 YEAR RECORD																			
08-09		09-10		10-11		11-12		12-13		13-14		14-15		15-16		16-17		17-18	
CC1	2	CCP	17	CCP	5	CCP	3	CCP	9	CCP	8	CCP	19	CCP	7	CCP	3	CCP	11
						FAC	4Q	FAC	P	FAC	P	FAC	Pr	FAC	EP	FAC	P	FAC	P
				FAV	2Q	FAV	3Pr	FAV	4P	FAV	4P	FAV	3P	FAV	1P	FAV	1Q	FAV	2P

HORLEY TOWN
Founded: 1896   Nickname: The Clarets

Club Contact Details (T) 01293 822 000   (E)
Ground: The New Defence, Court Lodge Road, Horley RH6 8SP
Nearest Railway Station Horley
Capacity: 1800 **Seats:** 150 **Covered:** 100 **Shop:** Yes **Bus Route** Metrobus 100, 526

Colours(change): Claret & blue
Previous Names: Horley >1975
Previous Leagues: Surrey Intermediate 1925-51, 55- Surrey Senior 1951-55, 71-78, London Spartan 1978-81, Athenian 1981-84, Combined Counties 1984-96, Surrey County Senior 2002-03.
HONOURS: FA Comps: None
League: Surrey Intermediate 1926-27, Eastern Section 1950-51. Surrey Senior 1976-77.

10 YEAR RECORD

	08-09	09-10	10-11	11-12	12-13	13-14	14-15	15-16	16-17	17-18
CCP	12	14	16	7	12	19	12	6	7	14
FAC	EPr	Pr	P	1Q	Pr	1Q	EP	Pr	EP	P
FAV	1P	2Q	1P	2Q	1P	1Q	3P	1Q	1P	4P

KNAPHILL
Founded: 1924   Nickname: The Knappers

Club Contact Details (T) 01483 475 150   (E) knaphillfc.seniorsecretary@gmail.com
Ground: Brookwood Country Park, Redding Way, Knaphill GU21 2AY
Nearest Railway Station Brookwood or Woking
Capacity: 750 **Seats:** 50 **Covered:** Yes   **Bus Route** Arriva 34, 35

Colours(change): Red and black
Previous Names: None
Previous Leagues: Woking & District. Surrey Intermediate (Western) > 2007

HONOURS: FA Comps: None
League: Woking & District League 1978-79.
10 YEAR RECORD Surrey Intermediate League Division Three 1980-81, Division One 2005-06, Premier 06-07.

	08-09	09-10	10-11	11-12	12-13	13-14	14-15	15-16	16-17	17-18
CC1	5	3	9	12	12	3				
CCP							13	5	14	8
FAC							1Q	EP	EPr	2Q
FAV				1Q	1Q	2P	2P	4P	3P	2Q

RAYNES PARK VALE
Founded: 1995   Nickname: The Vale

Club Contact Details (T) 0208 540 8843   (E)
Ground: Prince George's Playing Field, Raynes Park SW20 9NB
Nearest Railway Station Raynes Park
Capacity: 1500 **Seats:** 120 **Covered:** 100   **Bus Route** London Buses 152 & 163

Colours(change): Blue and yellow
Previous Names: Raynes Park > 1995 until merger with Malden Vale.
Previous Leagues: Surrey County Premier Lge. Isthmian.

HONOURS: FA Comps: None
League: Combined Counties Division One 2002-03.
10 YEAR RECORD

	08-09	09-10	10-11	11-12	12-13	13-14	14-15	15-16	16-17	17-18
CCP	8	18	15	9	11	10	15	15	23	
CC1										5
FAC	P	P	P	P	Pr	Pr	Pr	EP	EP	EP
FAV	2Q	1Q	1P	1P	2Q	1Q	1P	1Q	1Q	1Q

REDHILL
Founded: 1894   Nickname: Reds/Lobsters

Club Contact Details (T) 01737 762 129   (E)
Ground: Kiln Brow, Three Arch Road, Redhill, Surrey RH1 5AE
Nearest Railway Station Redhill (mainline) Earlswood
Capacity: 2,000 **Seats:** 150 **Covered:** 150 **Shop:** Yes **Bus Route** 100, 400, 420, 430, 435, 460

Colours(change): Red & white
Previous Names: None
Previous Leagues: E & W Surrey. Spartan. Southern Sub. London. Athenian. Sussex County > 2013. Isthmian 2013-15.

HONOURS: FA Comps: None
League: London League 1922-23. Athenian League 1924-25, 83-84.
10 YEAR RECORD

	08-09	09-10	10-11	11-12	12-13	13-14	14-15	15-16	16-17	17-18
SxC1	7	5	8	10	2					
Isth1S						22	23			
CCP								20		6
CC1									2	
FAC	EP	EP	EP	1Q	1Q	1Q	3Q	EP	P	P
FAV/FAT	1P	2P	2Q	2Q	1Q	P(FAT)	Pr(FAT)	2Q	1Q	1Q

SOUTHALL

Founded: 1871   Nickname:

Club Contact Details (T)
(E) enquiries@southallfc.com
Ground: Robert Parker Stadium, Short Lane, Stanwell TW19 7BH

Capacity: 3,000 **Seats:** **Covered:**
Colours(change): Red and white
Previous Names:
Previous Leagues:

HONOURS: FA Comps: None
League: Great Western Suburban 1912-13. Athenian 1926-27.

10 YEAR RECORD | Spartan South Midlands Division One 2017-18.

08-09	09-10	10-11	11-12	12-13	13-14	14-15	15-16	16-17	17-18
MidxP 5	MidxP 10	MidxP 8	MidxP 3	SSM1 9	SSM1 11	SSM1 12	SSM1 12	SSM1 5	SSM1 1
									FAC P
					FAV 1Q	FAV 2Q	FAV 1P	FAV QF	FAV 2P

SPELTHORNE SPORTS

Founded: 1922   Nickname: Spelly

Club Contact Details (T) 01932 961 055
(E) flatty1@tiscali.co.uk
Ground: Spelthorne Sports Club, 296 Staines Rd West, Ashford Common, TW15 1RY
Nearest Railway Station Sunbury
Capacity: **Seats:** 50 **Covered:** Yes **Bus Route** 290 to outside the club.
Colours(change): Navy & sky blue
Previous Names: None
Previous Leagues: Surrey Intermediate (West) > 2009. Surrey Elite Intermediate 2009-11.

HONOURS: FA Comps: None
League: Surrey Elite Intermediate League 2010-11. Combined Counties Division One 2013-14.

08-09	09-10	10-11	11-12	12-13	13-14	14-15	15-16	16-17	17-18
	SuEI 5	SuEI 1	CC1 7	CC1 6	CCP 1	CCP 6	CCP 11	CCP 9	CCP 10
							FAC P	FAC P	FAC EP
						FAV 1P	FAV 1Q	FAV 1Qr	FAV 1P

SUTTON COMMON ROVERS

Founded: 1978   Nickname: Commoners

Club Contact Details (T) 020 8644 4440
(E) scrfcsecretary@outlook.com
Ground: Sutton United FC, Gander Green Lane, Sutton. Surrey SM1 2EY
Nearest Railway Station West Sutton
Capacity: 7,032 **Seats:** 765 **Covered:** 1,250 **Shop:** Yes **Bus Route** 413
Colours(change): All yellow
Previous Names: Inrad FC. Centre 21 FC . SCR Plough, SCR Grapes, SRC Litten Tree, SCR Kingfisher, Mole Valley SCR >2015.
Previous Leagues: South Eastern Combination.

HONOURS: FA Comps: None
League: Combined Counties League Division One 2009-10.

08-09	09-10	10-11	11-12	12-13	13-14	14-15	15-16	16-17	17-18
CC1 4	CC1 1	CCP 8	CCP 21	CC1 2	CCP 18	CCP 18	CCP 19	CCP 12	CCP 3
		FAC EP	FAC EP	FAC EPr	FAC EP	FAC P	FAC EP	FAC EPr	FAC P
FAV 1P	FAV 1Q	FAV 1Q	FAV 2Q	FAV 2Q	FAV 2Q	FAV 1Q	FAV 4P	FAV 3P	FAV 1Q

WALTON & HERSHAM

Founded: 1945   Nickname: Swans

Club Contact Details (T) 01932 245 263
(E) langley.grant@sky.com
Ground: Elmbridge Xcel Sports Hub, Waterside Drive, Walton-on-Thames, Surrey KT12 2JP
Nearest Railway Station Walton-on-Thames less a mile from the ground.
Capacity: 5,000 **Seats:** 400 **Covered:** 2,500 **Shop:** Yes
Colours(change): Red and white
Previous Names: Walton FC (Founded in 1895) amalgamated with Hersham FC in 1945.
Previous Leagues: Surrey Senior, Corinthian 1945-50, Athenian 1950-71. Isthmian 1971-2016.

HONOURS: FA Comps: Amateur Cup 1972-73
League: Corinthian 1946-47, 47-48, 48-49. Athenian League 1968-69.

08-09	09-10	10-11	11-12	12-13	13-14	14-15	15-16	16-17	17-18
Isth1S 14	Isth1S 8	Isth1S 6	Isth1S 11	Isth1S 18	Isth1S 21	Isth1S 17	Isth1S 22	CCP 5	CCP 4
FAC P	FAC 3Q	FAC 1Q	FAC 1Q	FAC 1Qr	FAC P	FAC P	FAC P	FAC Pr	FAC Pr
FAT 1Q	FAT 1Q	FAT P	FAT P	FAT 1Q	FAT P	FAT 1Q	FAT P	FAV 2P	FAV 3P

Bedfont & Feltham 2017-18

CB Hounslow 2017-18

Walton & Hersham 2017-18

AC LONDON

Founded: 2012   Nickname:

Club Contact Details (T) 0757 959 9999   **(E)** info@aclondon.co.uk
Ground: Whyteleafe FC, 15 Church Road, Whyteleafe CR3 0AR   **Capacity:** 2,000
Nearest Railway Station Whyteleafe South - 0.4km
HONOURS   **League:** None
FA Comps: None
Colours(change): Red & white

10 YEAR RECORD

08-09	09-10	10-11	11-12	12-13	13-14	14-15	15-16	16-17	17-18
							K_lv 10	CC1 7	CC1 8
									FAC P
								FAV 1Pr	FAV 2Q

ASH UNITED

Founded: 1911   Nickname: Green Army

Club Contact Details (T) 01252 320 385 / 345 757   **(E)** sec@ashunited.co.uk
Ground: Shawfield Stadium, Youngs Drive off Shawfield Road, Ash, GU12 6RE.   **Capacity:** 2500
Nearest Railway Station Ash or Ash Vale   **Bus Route** Stagecoach 20A, 550
HONOURS   **League:** Combined Counties 1981-82, 86-87, 98-99.
FA Comps: None
Colours(change): Green & red.

10 YEAR RECORD

08-09	09-10	10-11	11-12	12-13	13-14	14-15	15-16	16-17	17-18
CCP 9	CCP 11	CCP 18	CCP 13	CCP 20	CCP 1	CC1 10	CC1 10	CC1 12	CC1 10
FAC EP	FAC 1Q	FAC EP	FAC EP	FAC EP	FAC EP	FAC EP			
FAV 1P	FAV 1P	FAV 2Q	FAV 1Q	FAV 2P	FAV 1Q	FAV 1Q	FAV 1Q	FAV 1P	FAV 1Q

BAGSHOT

Founded: 1906   Nickname:

Club Contact Details (T)   **(E)**
Ground: Fleet Spurs FC, Kennels Lane, Southwood, Farnborough, Hants GU14 0ST

HONOURS   **League:** Aldershot & District Division Two 2005-06, Division One 2008-09, Senior Division 2011-12, 12-13,
FA Comps: None   13-14, 15-16.
Colours(change): Yellow & blue

10 YEAR RECORD

08-09	09-10	10-11	11-12	12-13	13-14	14-15	15-16	16-17	17-18
A&D1 1	A&DS 2	A&DS 3	A&DS 1	A&DS 1	A&DS 1	A&DS 1	A&DS 1	CC1 8	CC1 19
									FAV 1Q

BEDFONT & FELTHAM

Founded: 2012   Nickname: The Yellows

Club Contact Details (T) 020 8890 7264   **(E)** ssavoyffc@msn.com
Ground: The Orchard, Hatton Road, Bedfont TW14 9QT   **Capacity:** 1200
Nearest Railway Station Hatton Cross (Piccadilly Line)   **Bus Route** London Transport 203, H25, H26
HONOURS   **League:** None
FA Comps: None
Colours(change): Yellow & blue

10 YEAR RECORD

08-09	09-10	10-11	11-12	12-13	13-14	14-15	15-16	16-17	17-18
				CC1 13	CC1 5	CC1 5	CC1 2	CCP 22	CC1 17
						FAC 1Q	FAC 1Q	FAC EP	FAC EP
				FAV 2Q	FAV 1P	FAV 1Q	FAV 1Q	FAV 2Q	FAV 1Q

BRITISH AIRWAYS

Founded: 1974   Nickname:

Club Contact Details (T)   **(E)**
Ground: Bedfont & Feltham FC, The Orchard, Hatton Road, Bedfont TW14 9QT
Nearest Railway Station Hatton Cross (Piccadilly Line)   **Bus Route** London Transport 203, H25, H26
HONOURS   **League:** London Commercial Division One 2000-01, 01-02, 02-03, 03-04, 04-05, 05-06, 07-08, 08-09, 11-12.
FA Comps: None   Middlesex County Premier Division 2012-13, 17-18.
Colours(change): Navy and sky blue

10 YEAR RECORD

08-09	09-10	10-11	11-12	12-13	13-14	14-15	15-16	16-17	17-18
LonCom 1	LonCom 2	LonCom 2	LonCom 1	MidxP 1	MidxP 7	MidxP 11	MidxP 6	MidxP 2	MidxP 1

CHESSINGTON & HOOK UNITED
Founded: 1921   Nickname: Chessey

Club Contact Details (T) 01372 602 263   **(E)**
Ground: Chalky Lane, Chessington, Surrey KT9 2NF   **Capacity:** 3000
Nearest Railway Station Chessington South   **Bus Route** London United 71, 465
HONOURS   **League:** Kingston & District Division Four 1922-23, Division Two 1955-56, Division One 1957-58.
FA Comps: None
Colours(change): Blue and white

10 YEAR RECORD

08-09		09-10		10-11		11-12		12-13		13-14		14-15		15-16		16-17		17-18	
CCP	19	CCP	6	CCP	12	CCP	20	CCP	17	CCP	22	CC1	3	CCP	21	CC1	5	CC1	13
FAC	EP	FAC	EP	FAC	EP	FAC	P	FAC	P	FAC	P	FAC	1Q	FAC	1Q	FAC	Pr	FAC	P
FAV	1P	FAV	1Q	FAV	1Q	FAV	1Q	FAV	2Q	FAV	2P	FAV	2P	FAV	1Q	FAV	1Qr	FAV	2Q

COVE
Founded: 1897   Nickname: None

Club Contact Details (T) 01252 543 615   **(E)**
Ground: Oak Farm Fields, 7 Squirrels Lane, Farnborough GU14 8PF   **Capacity:** 2500
Nearest Railway Station Farnborough Main
HONOURS   **League:** Combined Counties League 2000-01.
FA Comps:
Colours(change): Yellow and black

10 YEAR RECORD

08-09		09-10		10-11		11-12		12-13		13-14		14-15		15-16		16-17		17-18	
CCP	6	CCP	12	CCP	9	CCP	11	CCP	3	CCP	5	CCP	4	CCP	22	CC1	17	CC1	18
FAC	EP	FAC	P	FAC	EPr	FAC	EP	FAC	P	FAC	1Q	FAC	EP	FAC	P	FAC	EP		
FAV	1P	FAV	2Q	FAV	1P	FAV	2Q	FAV	2Q	FAV	2P	FAV	1Q	FAV	1P	FAV	1Q	FAV	1Q

DORKING WANDERERS RES.
Founded: 1999   Nickname: Wanderers

Club Contact Details (T)   **(E)** customerservices@dorkingwanderers.com
Ground: West Humble Playing Fields, London Road, Dorking, RH5 6AD

HONOURS   **League:** None
FA Comps: None
Colours(change): Red & white

10 YEAR RECORD

08-09	09-10	10-11	11-12	12-13	13-14	14-15	15-16		16-17	17-18
							CC1	15		

EPSOM & EWELL
Founded: 1918   Nickname: E's or Salts

Club Contact Details (T) 01737 553 250   **(E)** p.beddoe1@ntlworld.com
Ground: Chipstead FC, High Road, Chipstead, Surrey CR5 3SF   **Capacity:** 2,000
Nearest Railway Station Kingswood
HONOURS   **League:** Sutton & Dist. Prem. 1922-23. Southern Suburban 1923-24.
FA Comps: None   Surrey Senior 1925-26, 26-27, 74-75. London 1927-28. Isthmian Division Two 1977-78.
Colours(change): Royal blue & white

10 YEAR RECORD

08-09		09-10		10-11		11-12		12-13		13-14		14-15		15-16		16-17		17-18	
CCP	4	CCP	5	CCP	10	CCP	14	CCP	5	CCP	3	CCP	7	CCP	4	CCP	4	CCP	21
FAC	1Q	FAC	P	FAC	1Q	FAC	P	FAC	1Q	FAC	EPr	FAC	Pr	FAC	EP	FAC	P	FAC	EP
FAV	1P	FAT	3P	FAV	2Q	FAV	2Q	FAV	1Q	FAV	2Q	FAV	1P	FAV	1Q	FAV	2P	FAV	2P

EVERSLEY & CALIFORNIA
Founded: 1910   Nickname: The Boars

Club Contact Details (T) 0118 973 2400   **(E)** secretary@eversley-californiafc.co.uk
Ground: ESA Sports Complex, Fox Lane, Eversley RG27 0NS   **Capacity:** 300+
Nearest Railway Station Fleet, Sandhurst
HONOURS   **League:** Surrey Elite Intermediate 2008-09.
FA Comps: None
Colours(change): Yellow and blue

10 YEAR RECORD

08-09		09-10		10-11		11-12		12-13		13-14		14-15		15-16		16-17		17-18	
SuEI	1	CC1	8	CC1	11	CC1	5	CC1	4	CC1	2	CC1	9	CC1	5	CC1	6	CC1	9
																		FAC	EP
												FAV	2Q			FAV	2Q	FAV	1Q

FARNHAM TOWN
Founded: 1906   Nickname: The Town

Club Contact Details (T) 01252 715 305   **(E)**
Ground: Memorial Ground, West Street, Farnham GU9 7DY   1,500
Nearest Railway Station Farnham   **Bus Route** Stagecoach 5, 14, 18, 19, 46, 64, 71, 536
HONOURS   **League:** Surrey Intermediate 1929-30, 30-31. Surrey Senior 1965-66, 66-67, 67-68.
FA Comps: None   Combined Counties 1990-91, 91-92, Division One 2006-07.
Colours(change): Claret & sky blue

10 YEAR RECORD

	08-09	09-10	10-11	11-12	12-13	13-14	14-15	15-16	16-17	17-18
	CC1 8	CC1 11	CC1 2	CCP 12	CCP 8	CCP 15	CCP 10	CCP 10	CCP 18	CCP 22
	FAC EP	FAC EPr	FAC P	FAC P	FAC EP	FAC P	FAC EP	FAC 1Q	FAC P	FAC P
	FAV 2Q	FAV 2Q	FAV 2Q	FAV 1P	FAV 2Q	FAV 1P	FAV 1Pr	FAV 1P	FAV 1Q	FAV 2P

FC DEPORTIVO GALICIA
Founded: 1968   Nickname:

Club Contact Details (T) 020 8831 9067   **(E)** rogelioloureda@hotmail.com
Ground: Bedfont Sports, Hatton Road, Bedfont, Middlesex TW14 8JA
Nearest Railway Station Hatton Cross or Feltham BR   **Bus Route** London Transport 203, H25, H26
HONOURS   **League:** Middlesex County Premier Division 2016-17.
FA Comps: None
Colours(change): Blue and white

10 YEAR RECORD

	08-09	09-10	10-11	11-12	12-13	13-14	14-15	15-16	16-17	17-18
	MidxP 12	MidxP 14	MidxP 7	MidxP 12	MidxP 13	MidxP 6	MidxP 12	MidxP 13	MidxP 1	CC1 12
									FAV 1Q	FAV 2Q

FLEET SPURS
Founded: 1948   Nickname: Spurs

Club Contact Details (T) 07833 985 703   **(E)** richardw@fleetspurs.co.uk
Ground: Southwood Sports Pavilion, Kenneis Lane, Farnborough Hampshire, GU14 0ST
HONOURS   **League:** Surrey Premier A Division 1968-69. Aldershot Senior 1990-91.
FA Comps: None   Hampshire Division Two 1997-98.
Colours(change): Red and blue

10 YEAR RECORD

	08-09	09-10	10-11	11-12	12-13	13-14	14-15	15-16	16-17	17-18
	Wex1 21	Wex1 3	Wex1 10	Wex1 7	Wex1 10	Wex1 12	Wex1 9	Wex1 12	Wex1 16	CC1 16
				FAC EP	FAC EP					
			FAV 2Q	FAV 1Q	FAV 2Q	FAV 1Q	FAV 1Qr	FAV 1Q	FAV 2Q	FAV 1Q

FRIMLEY GREEN
Founded: 1919   Nickname: The Green

Club Contact Details (T) 01252 835 089   **(E)** mogradyuk@yahoo.co.uk
Ground: Frimley Green Rec. Ground, Frimley Green, Camberley GU16 6JY   **Capacity:** 2000
Nearest Railway Station Frimley   **Bus Route** Stagecoach 3, Arriva 49
HONOURS   **League:** Combined Counties Division One 2012-13.
FA Comps: None
Colours(change): All blue

10 YEAR RECORD

	08-09	09-10	10-11	11-12	12-13	13-14	14-15	15-16	16-17	17-18
	CC1 16	CC1 13	CC1 15	CC1 10	CC1 1	CCP 12	CCP 21	CC1 12	CC1 13	CC1 7
	FAC P	FAC EP	FAC EP			FAC P	FAC EP	FAC EP		
	FAV 3Pr	FAV 2Q	FAV 2Q	FAV 1Q	FAV 2P	FAV 1Q	FAV 2Q	FAV 2Q	FAV 2Q	FAV 1P

GODALMING TOWN
Founded: 1950   Nickname: The G's

Club Contact Details (T) 01483 417 520   **(E)** godalmingtownfootballclub@gmail.com
Ground: Wey Court, Meadrow, Guildford, Surrey GU7 3JF   **Capacity:** 3,000
Nearest Railway Station Farncombe - 1/2 a mile from the ground.
HONOURS   **League:** Combined Counties Premier Division 1983-84, 2005-06.
FA Comps: None
Colours(change): Yellow & green

10 YEAR RECORD

	08-09	09-10	10-11	11-12	12-13	13-14	14-15	15-16	16-17	17-18
	Isth1S 9	Isth1S 4	Isth1S 17	Isth1S 5	SthC 3	Sthsw 18	SthC 8	SthC 10	Isth1S 24	CCP 20
	FAC 3Q	FAC P	FAC 1Q	FAC 4Q	FAC 1Qr	FAC P	FAC 1Qr	FAC 1Q	FAC 1Q	FAC 1Q
	FAT P	FAT 3Q	FAT 2Qr	FAT 2Q	FAT P	FAT P	FAT P	FAT P	FAT P	FAV 2Q

KENSINGTON BOROUGH

Founded: 2012   Nickname:

Club Contact Details (T)   **(E)**

Ground: Leatherhead FC, Fetcham Grove, Guildford Road, Leatherhead, Surrey KT22 9AS   **Capacity:** 3,400

Nearest Railway Station Leatherhead half a mile away

HONOURS   **League:** None

FA Comps: None

Colours(change): White and green

10 YEAR RECORD

08-09	09-10	10-11	11-12	12-13	13-14	14-15	15-16	16-17	17-18
					Midx2 3	Midx1SE 6	SSM2 5	SSM1 12	CC1 15
									FAV 1P

SANDHURST TOWN

Founded: 1910   Nickname: Fizzers

Club Contact Details (T) 01252 878 768   **(E)** secretarystfc@hotmail.co.uk

Ground: Bottom Meadow, Memorial Ground, Yorktown Rd, GU47 9BJ   **Capacity:** 1000

Nearest Railway Station Sandhurst - 0.9km   **Bus Route** Wellington Arms stop - 194m away

HONOURS   **League:** Reading & Disttrict Division One 1932-33, Premier 33-34.

FA Comps: None   Aldershot & District Division One 1980-81.

Colours(change): Red and black

10 YEAR RECORD

08-09	09-10	10-11	11-12	12-13	13-14	14-15	15-16	16-17	17-18
CCP 16	CCP 9	CCP 7	CCP 15	CCP 21	CC1 13	CC1 16	CC1 11	Hel1E 8	Hel1E 4
FAC EP	FAC EPr	FAC EP	FAC EP	FAC EP	FAC EPr				
FAV 2P	FAV 1Q	FAV 2Q	FAV 1Q	FAV 1P	FAV 1Q			FAV 1Q	FAV 1P

SHEERWATER

Founded: 1958   Nickname: Sheers

Club Contact Details (T) 07791 612 008   **(E)** trevor.wenden2@ntlworld.com

Ground: Sheerwater Recreation Ground, Blackmore Crescent, Woking GU21 5NS   **Capacity:** 1,000

Nearest Railway Station Woking or West Byfleet   **Bus Route** Arriva 436 and Abellio 446

HONOURS   **League:** None

FA Comps: None

Colours(change): All royal blue

10 YEAR RECORD

08-09	09-10	10-11	11-12	12-13	13-14	14-15	15-16	16-17	17-18
CC1 9	CC1 17	CC1 17	CC1 18	CC1 15	CC1 11	CC1 14	CC1 13	CC1 9	CC1 4

TOOTING BEC

Founded: 2004   Nickname:

Club Contact Details (T)   **(E)**

Ground: Imperial Fields, Bishopsford Road, Morden SM4 6BF

HONOURS   **League:** Surrey Elite Intermediate Division One 2009-10, Premier 2017-18.

FA Comps: None

Colours(change): Black & white

10 YEAR RECORD

08-09	09-10	10-11	11-12	12-13	13-14	14-15	15-16	16-17	17-18
Sul1 6	Sul1 1	SuEl 15	SuEl 13	SuEl 9	SuEl 7	SuEl 10	SuEl 7	SuEl 2	SuEl 1
									FAV 2Q

EAST MIDLANDS COUNTIES LEAGUE

Founded: 2008 **Sponsored by:** No sponsor
Recent Champions - 2015: Bardon Hill **2016:** St Andrews **2017:** West Bridgford

		P	W	D	L	F	A	GD	Pts
1	Dunkirk	40	28	5	7	133	49	84	89
2	Anstey Nomads	40	29	2	9	116	56	60	89
3	Teversal	40	28	3	9	93	51	42	87
4	Selston	40	25	6	9	97	59	38	81
5	Belper United	40	21	11	8	76	44	32	74
6	Kimberley Miners Welfare	40	21	8	11	75	56	19	71
7	Radford	40	21	7	12	104	57	47	70
8	Birstall United	40	21	6	13	98	67	31	69
9	Aylestone Park	40	21	3	16	90	67	23	66
10	Gedling Miners Welfare	40	20	2	18	71	65	6	62
11	Barrow Town	40	18	7	15	76	72	4	61
12	Clifton All Whites	40	17	8	15	102	73	29	59
13	Stapenhill	40	14	8	18	87	86	1	50
14	Holbrook Sports	40	14	2	24	60	82	-22	44
15	West Bridgford FC	40	14	2	24	56	96	-40	44
16	Graham Street Prims	40	11	10	19	56	86	-30	43
17	Ashby Ivanhoe	40	12	3	25	55	81	-26	39
18	Holwell Sports	40	10	8	22	61	98	-37	38
19	Borrowash Victoria	40	10	4	26	58	120	-62	34
20	Arnold Town	40	7	1	32	48	131	-83	19*
21	Radcliffe Olympic	40	4	2	34	27	143	-116	14

Blaby & Whetstone Athletic withdrew - record expunged.

LEAGUE CUP

HOLDERS: DUNKIRK

ROUND 1

Aylestone Park	v	Stapenhill	2-2, 3-5p
Barrow Town	v	Dunkirk	0-2
Gedling Miners Welfare	v	Kimberley Miners Welfare	3-0
Blaby & Whetstone Athletic	v	Belper United	2-1
Graham Street Prims	v	Clifton All Whites	2-6
Radcliffe Olympic	v	Borrowash Victoria	1-2

ROUND 2

Gedling Miners Welfare	v	Dunkirk	2-0
Stapenhill	v	Teversal	4-2
Selston	v	Birstall United	0-1
West Bridgford	v	Radford	0-3
Holwell Sports	v	Holbrook Sports	2-1
Anstey Nomads	v	Ashby Ivanhoe	3-1
Blaby & Whetstone Ath.	v	Clifton All Whites	AW
Borrowash Victoria	v	Arnold Town	AW

QUARTER FINALS

Holwell Sports	v	Gedling Miners Welfare	2-0
Clifton All Whites	v	Radford	0-1
Bistall United	v	Arnold Town	6-2
Anstey Nomads	v	Stapenhill	3-2

SEMI FINALS

Holwell Sports	v	Radford	0-2
Bistall United	v	Anstey Nomads	1-5

FINAL

Anstey Nomads	v	Radford	0-6

CLUB MOVEMENTS - In: Clipstone (R - NCEP), Eastwood Com (P - CMLS), Heanor Town (VR - MFLP), Ingles (P - LSL), Newark Flowserve (P - NSL), Rainworth MW (VR - NCEP), Sherwood Coll (P - CMLS). **Out:** Anstey Nomads, Aylestone Park, Birstall Utd & Holwell Sports (LM - UCL1), Dunkirk (P - MLP), Holbrook Sports (W - CMLS), Stapenhill (LM - ML1).

		1	2	3	4	5	6	7	8	9	10	11	12	13	14	15	16	17	18	19	20	21
1	Anstey Nomads		5-1	3-2	2-6	0-0	0-1	4-2	7-1	6-2	1-2	4-0	5-0	3-1	4-1	5-1	4-0	3-0	1-1	3-2	3-2	5-0
2	Arnold Town	1-2		3-1	0-9	1-4	1-1	1-4	2-5	1-10	0-4	0-3	3-1	0-2	8-3	1-2	4-0	2-0	0-5	0-5	0-2	1-4
3	Ashby Ivanhoe	0-1	3-0		5-3	1-4	1-2	0-3	1-4	3-4	1-0	0-1	0-1	3-2	5-1	0-2	0-1	1-3	0-2	1-1	0-0	0-1
4	Aylestone Park	1-2	4-0	3-1		0-2	1-6	2-2	1-3	0-0	1-2	3-1	5-1	5-0	2-0	3-1	3-0	3-2	0-1	0-3	2-4	2-0
5	Barrow Town	1-6	2-1	0-1	3-0		2-2	2-5	4-0	2-0	2-1	3-1	2-1	2-1	3-0	3-0	2-2	1-1	1-3	1-6	1-1	1-1
6	Belper United	4-2	6-0	2-0	1-0	3-0		0-2	5-0	1-1	2-1	0-2	0-0	3-0	2-2	0-2	2-0	1-1	2-1	3-1	1-1	3-0
7	Birstall United	4-0	5-0	2-1	1-4	3-0	3-1		3-1	1-1	1-1	0-2	2-2	1-2	2-1	1-2	8-1	3-2	4-0	4-2	4-0	2-3
8	Borrowash Victoria	4-2	0-2	0-2	0-3	2-2	0-2	3-2		1-7	2-4	3-0	1-1	0-2	1-1	0-2	1-6	4-1	1-4	2-1		
9	Clifton All Whites	1-2	5-1	4-1	1-0	1-2	2-2	3-2	6-1		2-3	2-3	3-2	4-3	1-2	0-1	8-0	0-0	2-4	2-2	2-1	2-4
10	Dunkirk	3-2	3-2	5-0	3-0	2-1	5-1	7-0	4-0	1-1		2-5	7-0	2-3	6-0	2-1	8-0	2-1	3-3	4-2	2-1	4-1
11	Gedling Miners Welfare	1-3	5-2	0-1	3-5	2-0	0-2	1-1	2-0	2-0	0-2		2-3	2-0	3-2	1-3	2-3	0-2	2-3	1-2	1-0	
12	Graham Street Prims	0-3	2-0	1-1	0-2	2-1	0-0	2-0	6-0	1-4	1-1	0-2		2-3	2-1	3-3	5-0	0-4	1-3	1-1	2-1	4-3
13	Holbrook Sports	0-4	2-0	3-0	2-3	0-3	2-4	0-4	2-5	0-6	1-2	4-1		2-1	0-1	6-0	1-0	0-2	1-4	0-1	2-2	
14	Holwell Sports	2-3	3-1	2-5	2-2	2-1	1-0	1-6	2-1	2-2	1-4	2-2	3-1	2-0		1-2	3-0	1-1	0-2	1-1	1-4	3-1
15	Kimberley Miners Welfare	1-2	3-1	3-0	5-1	1-4	5-1	0-0	5-0	0-3	2-1	3-1	1-1	1-1	1-1		5-0	0-4	1-1	2-2	3-0	4-0
16	Radcliffe Olympic	1-4	1-3	1-3	0-3	2-3	1-2	1-2	3-1	0-7	2-8	2-4	1-1	0-1	0-2	1-0		1-3	2-3	0-5	1-3	0-1
17	Radford	1-2	3-0	3-2	5-0	3-2	0-0	5-0	3-6	2-1	0-4	3-0	4-0	3-0	4-3	1-1	10-0		3-4	1-1	3-5	3-0
18	Selston	1-4	4-1	3-1	1-2	4-2	2-1	1-3	3-3	7-0	1-1	0-2	3-1	4-2	2-0	2-0	4-3		1-2	2-3	3-0	
19	Stapenhill	0-2	5-3	3-4	1-0	3-0	2-2	2-3	4-3	0-2	2-4	1-5	2-4	1-0	2-3	1-3	5-1	0-5	2-2		2-3	4-1
20	Teversal	3-1	1-0	4-2	0-3	3-1	0-1	3-1	4-0	2-0	4-3	2-0	1-0	1-0	3-1	6-0	4-1	1-2	4-0	2-1		3-1
21	West Bridgford FC	2-1	2-1	0-2	1-3	4-3	0-4	3-2	0-4	3-1	0-6	1-2	4-0	0-5	3-1	1-3	2-0	0-3	1-2	3-0	2-4	

ARNOLD TOWN

Founded: 1989   Nickname: Eagles

Club Contact Details (T) 0115 965 6000   **(E)**
Ground: Eagle Valley, Oxton Road, Arnold, Nottingham NG5 8PS

HONOURS   **League:** Northern Counties East 1985-86. Central Midlands 1992-93. Northern Counties Division One 1993
FA Comps: None   -94.
Colours(change): All maroon

10 YEAR RECORD

08-09	09-10	10-11	11-12	12-13	13-14	14-15	15-16	16-17	17-18
NCEP 6	NCEP 8	NCEP 18	NCEP 9	NCEP 19	EMC 6	EMC 10	EMC 18	EMC 15	EMC 20
FAC EP	FAC EP	FAC EP	FAC 1Q	FAC EP	FAC Pr	FAC EP			
FAV 3Pr	FAV 1P	FAV 1Pr	FAV 1P	FAV 2Q	FAV 1Q	FAV 1Q	FAV 2Q	FAV 1Q	FAV 1Q

ASHBY IVANHOE

Founded: 1948   Nickname: The Knights

Club Contact Details (T) 01530 413 140   **(E)** info@ashbyivanhoefc.com
Ground: NFU Sports Ground, Lower Packington Road, Ashby de la Zouch LE65 1TS

HONOURS   **League:** North Leicestershire 1994-95, 96-97, 98-99, 2002-03.
FA Comps: None   Leicestershire Senior Premier Division 2010-11.
Colours(change): Blue and red

10 YEAR RECORD

08-09	09-10	10-11	11-12	12-13	13-14	14-15	15-16	16-17	17-18
LeicSP 3	LeicSP 5	LeicSP 1	LeicSP 8	LeicSP 4	LeicSP 3	EMC 6	EMC 3	EMC 10	EMC 17
								FAC 1Q	
	FAV 1Q	FAV 2Q	FAV 2Q				FAV 1Q	FAV 1P	FAV 2Q

BARROW TOWN

Founded: Late 1800s   Nickname: The Riversiders

Club Contact Details (T) 01509 620 650   **(E)** newton-chris@sky.com
Ground: Riverside Park, Bridge Street, Quorn, Leicestershire LE12 8EN
Nearest Railway Station Barrow upon Soar - 1.7km
HONOURS   **League:** Leicester Senior Division One 1992-93.
FA Comps: None
Colours(change): Red & black

10 YEAR RECORD

08-09	09-10	10-11	11-12	12-13	13-14	14-15	15-16	16-17	17-18
EMC 6	EMC 12	EMC 5	EMC 5	EMC 2	EMC 19	EMC 9	EMC 13	EMC 14	EMC 11
FAC P	FAC EP	FAC P	FAC 3Q	FAC EP	FAC EP	FAC EP	FAC EP		
FAV 2Q	FAV 1Q	FAV 1Q	FAV 2Q	FAV 1Q	FAV 2Q	FAV 2Q	FAV 2Q	FAV 1Q	FAV 1Q

BELPER UNITED

Founded: 1920   Nickname:

Club Contact Details (T) 01773 825 549   **(E)**
Ground: Christchurch Meadow, Bridge Street, Belper DE56 1BA
Nearest Railway Station Belper
HONOURS   **League:** Midlands Regional Alliance Premier Division 1985-86, 94-95,
FA Comps: None   Division One 2004-05.
Colours(change): Green and black

10 YEAR RECORD

08-09	09-10	10-11	11-12	12-13	13-14	14-15	15-16	16-17	17-18
MidRAP 20	MidRAP 13	MidRAP 10	CMSth 9	CMSth 3	CMSth 10	CMSth 5	CMSth 2	EMC 13	EMC 5
									FAC P
					FAV 1Q	FAV 1P	FAV 1Q	FAV 1Q	FAV 2Q

BORROWASH VICTORIA

Founded: 1911   Nickname: The Vics

Club Contact Details (T) 01332 669 688   **(E)**
Ground: Anderson Electrical Arena, Borrowash Road, Spondon, Derby DE21 7PH
Nearest Railway Station Spondon - 1.2km
HONOURS   **League:** Derby & District 1952-53. East Midlands regional Premier 1977-78.
FA Comps: None   Midland Division One 1980-81. Northern Counties East Div.1 South 1983-84.
Colours(change): Red & white stripes

10 YEAR RECORD

08-09	09-10	10-11	11-12	12-13	13-14	14-15	15-16	16-17	17-18
EMC 2	EMC 11	EMC 2	EMC 2	EMC 4	EMC 5	EMC 16	EMC 9	EMC 12	EMC 19
FAC EP	FAC Pr	FAC P	FAC P	FAC P	FAC P	FAC EP			
FAV 1P	FAV 1P	FAV 2Q	FAV 2Q	FAV 4P	FAV 2P	FAV 2P	FAV 1P	FAV 1Q	

CLIFTON ALL WHITES
Founded: 1963   Nickname: All Whites

Club Contact Details (T)   (E) d.wigley@ntlworld.com
Ground: Green Lane, Clifton, Nottingham NG11 9AZ
Nearest Railway Station Beeston - 3.2km   Clifton Centre Tram Stop 426m from ground.
HONOURS   **League:** Notts Alliance Division One 1998-99. Central Midlands 2013-14.
FA Comps: None   Notts Senior Premier Division 2016-17.
Colours(change): All white

10 YEAR RECORD

08-09	09-10	10-11	11-12	12-13	13-14	14-15	15-16	16-17	17-18
			NottS1 2	CMSth 4	CMSth 1	CMSth 8	NottSP 6	NottSP 1	EMC 12
							FAV 2Q	FAV 2Q	FAV 1Qr

CLIPSTONE
Founded: 1928   Nickname: The Cobras

Club Contact Details (T)   (E) enquiries@clipstonefc.co.uk
Ground: The Lido Ground, Clipstone Road East, Clipstone Village NG21 9AB   **Capacity:** 500
Nearest Railway Station Mansfield Woodhouse - 4.9km   **Bus Route** Station Road - stop 27m away
HONOURS   **League:** Central Midlands 1993-94, 96-97. Northern Counties East Division One 2014-15.
FA Comps: None
Colours(change): Black & white

10 YEAR RECORD

08-09	09-10	10-11	11-12	12-13	13-14	14-15	15-16	16-17	17-18
CM Su 9	CM Su 10	CM Su 9	CMN 4	NCE1 11	NCE1 7	NCE1 1	NCEP 13	NCEP 16	NCEP 22
						FAC 1Q	FAC 1Q	FAC EP	FAC P
					FAV 2Q	FAV 2Q	FAV 1P	FAV 2Q	FAV 1P

EASTWOOD COMMUNITY
Founded: 2014   Nickname: Red Badgers

Club Contact Details (T) 01773 432 414   (E)
Ground: Play Soccer USA 3G Arena, Chewton Street, Eastwood, Notts NG5 3HB

HONOURS   **League:** Central Midlands South 2017-18.
FA Comps: None
Colours(change): Red and black

10 YEAR RECORD

08-09	09-10	10-11	11-12	12-13	13-14	14-15	15-16	16-17	17-18
						CMSth 13	CMSth 10	CMSth 2	CMSth 1
							FAV 1Q	FAV 2Q	FAV 2Q

GEDLING MINERS WELFARE
Founded: 1919   Nickname: Miners

Club Contact Details (T) 0115 926 6300   (E) norman.hay@virginmedia.com
Ground: Plains Social Club, Plains Road, Mapperley, Nottingham NG3 5RH
Nearest Railway Station Carlton - 3.5km
HONOURS   **League:** Notts Alliance 1945-46, 49-50, 50-51, 51–52, 53-54, 55-56, 57-58, 58-59,
FA Comps: None   59-60, 60-61, Division Two 2000-01.
Colours(change): Yellow and royal blue

10 YEAR RECORD

08-09	09-10	10-11	11-12	12-13	13-14	14-15	15-16	16-17	17-18
EMC 8	EMC 8	EMC 4	EMC 13	EMC 13	EMC 12	EMC 12	EMC 14	EMC 20	EMC 10
FAC EP	FAC EPr	FAC P	FAC EPr						
FAV 1Q	FAV 1Q	FAV 2Q	FAV 1Q	FAV 2Q	FAV 1Q	FAV 1P	FAV 1Q	FAV 1Q	FAV 1Q

GRAHAM STREET PRIMS
Founded: 1904   Nickname: Prims

Club Contact Details (T) 01332 332 092   (E)
Ground: Baytree Cars Arena, Borrowash Road, Spondon DE21 7PH
Nearest Railway Station Spondon - 1.2km
HONOURS   **League:** Central Alliance Premier Division 1970-71.
FA Comps: None   East Midlands Regional 1978-79.
Colours(change): Red & white

10 YEAR RECORD

08-09	09-10	10-11	11-12	12-13	13-14	14-15	15-16	16-17	17-18
EMC 13	EMC 18	EMC 14	EMC 14	EMC 8	EMC 10	EMC 18	EMC 11	EMC 19	EMC 16
					FAC EP	FAC EP			
FAV 1Q	FAV 2Q	FAV 2Q	FAV 1Q	FAV 1P	FAV 3P	FAV 1P	FAV 2Q	FAV 1Q	FAV 1Q

HEANOR TOWN
Founded: 1883   Nickname: The Lions

Club Contact Details (T)   **(E)** heanortownfc@hotmail.co.uk
Ground: The Town Ground, Mayfield Avenue, Heanor DE75 7EN   **Capacity:** 2,700
Nearest Railway Station Langley Mill - 2km   **Bus Route** Sports Ground stop - 132m away
HONOURS   **League:** Central Midlands Supreme Division 1994-95, 96-97.
FA Comps: None   East Midlands Counties 2011-12.
Colours(change): White & black

10 YEAR RECORD

08-09	09-10	10-11	11-12	12-13	13-14	14-15	15-16	16-17	17-18
EMC 12	EMC 7	EMC 3	EMC 1	NCEP 11	NCEP 8	NCEP 6	MFLP 6	MFLP 6	MFLP 13
	FAC EP	FAC EPr	FAC 1Q	FAC P	FAC EP	FAC P	FAC EP	FAC 1Q	FAC EP
FAV 2P	FAV 2Qr	FAV 2P	FAV 1Q	FAT 1Pr	FAV 1P	FAV 4P	FAV 2P	FAV 1P	FAV 1Q

INGLES
Founded: 1972   Nickname:

Club Contact Details (T) 01509 650 992   **(E)**
Ground: The Dovecote, Little Haw Lane, Shepshed, Leicestershire. LE12 9BN
HONOURS   **League:** North Leicestershire Division Three 1973-74, Division Two 74-75, Premier 92-93, 95-96, 2013-14.
FA Comps: None   Leicestershire Senior Premier Division 2017-18.
Colours(change): Red and white

10 YEAR RECORD

08-09	09-10	10-11	11-12	12-13	13-14	14-15	15-16	16-17	17-18
					NLeiP 1	LeicSP 3	LeicSP 5	LeicSP 7	LeicSP 1

KIMBERLEY MINERS WELFARE
Founded: 1926   Nickname: Miners

Club Contact Details (T) 07572 863 155   **(E)**
Ground: Kimberley MWFC, The Stag Ground, Kimberley, Nottingham NG16 2NB
Nearest Railway Station Ilkeston - 3.4km and Bulwell - 3.8km.
HONOURS   **League:** Spartan League 1947-48, 64-65, 65-66. Notts Amateur League 1985-86. Notts Alliance Division
FA Comps: None   Two 1994-95, Division One 95-96.
Colours(change): Red & black

10 YEAR RECORD

08-09	09-10	10-11	11-12	12-13	13-14	14-15	15-16	16-17	17-18
			NottSP 13	NottSP 5	NottSP 2	EMC 13	EMC 15	EMC 8	EMC 6
									FAC P
							FAV 1Q	FAV 2Qr	FAV 2P

NEWARK FLOWSERVE
Founded: Nickname:

Club Contact Details (T) 07885 364 425   **(E)**
Ground: Hawton Lane, Newark, Nottinghamshire NG24 3BU
HONOURS   **League:** Nottinghamshire Senior Premier Division 2017-18.
FA Comps: None
Colours(change): Amber and black

10 YEAR RECORD

08-09	09-10	10-11	11-12	12-13	13-14	14-15	15-16	16-17	17-18
CM P 6									NottSP 1

RADFORD
Founded: 1964   Nickname: The Pheasants

Club Contact Details (T) 0115 942 3250   **(E)**
Ground: Selhurst Street, Off Radford Road, Nottingham NG7 5EH
Nearest Railway Station Nottingham - 2.8km
HONOURS   **League:** East Midlands Regional League 1982-83.
FA Comps: None
Colours(change): Claret and sky blue

10 YEAR RECORD

08-09	09-10	10-11	11-12	12-13	13-14	14-15	15-16	16-17	17-18
EMC 14	EMC 19	EMC 19	EMC 17	EMC 19	EMC 15	EMC 3	EMC 2	EMC 7	EMC 7
	FAC EP						FAC P	FAC EP	FAC EPr
FAV 2Q	FAV 2Q	FAV 1Q	FAV 2Q	FAV 2Q	FAV 1Q	FAV 1Q	FAV 1P	FAV 2P	FAV 2Q

RAINWORTH M.W.

Founded: 1922   Nickname: The Wrens

Club Contact Details (T) 01623 792 495   (E) leslielee7@ntlworld.com

Ground: Welfare Ground, Kirklington Road, Rainworth, Mansfield NG21 0JY   **Capacity:** 2,201

Nearest Railway Station Mansfield - 4¼ miles   **Bus Route** Garden Avenue - stop 24m away

HONOURS   **League:** Notts Alliance 1971-72, 77-78, 78-79, 79-80, 80-81, 81-82, 82-83, 90-91, 95-96, 96-97.

FA Comps: None

Colours(change): All white

10 YEAR RECORD

08-09		09-10		10-11		11-12		12-13		13-14		14-15		15-16		16-17		17-18	
NCE1	2	NCEP	2	NP1S	20	NP1S	19	NP1N	14	NP1S	15	NP1S	21	NCEP	9	NCEP	18	NCEP	10
FAC	1Qr	FAC	2Q	FAC	P	FAC	P	FAC	1Qr	FAC	Pr	FAC	P	FAC	EPr	FAC	EP	FAC	EP
FAV	1P	FAV	3P	FAT	Pr	FAT	P	FAT	1Q	FAT	P	FAT	Pr	FAV	1Q	FAV	1Q	FAV	1Q

SELSTON

Founded: 1968   Nickname: The Parishioners

Club Contact Details (T) 01773 812 540   (E) nicolajohnson80@ntlworld.com

Ground: Parish Hall, Mansfield Road, Selston, Nottinghamshire NG16 6EE

Nearest Railway Station Kirkby in Ashfield - 4.5km

HONOURS   **League:** Midland Regional Alliance Division Two 2007-08. Notts Senior 2013-14.
   Central Midlands South Division 2015-16, 16-17.

FA Comps: None

Colours(change): Blue & black

10 YEAR RECORD

08-09		09-10		10-11		11-12		12-13		13-14		14-15		15-16		16-17		17-18	
MidRA1	4	MidRA1	3	MidRA1	5	NottSP	11	NottSP	11	NottSP	1	NottSP	4	CMSth	1	CMSth	1	EMC	4

SHERWOOD COLLIERY

Founded: 2008   Nickname:

Club Contact Details (T) 01623 631 747   (E)

Ground: Debdale Lane, Mansfield Woodhouse, Mansfield, Nottinghamshire NG19 7N

HONOURS   **League:** None

FA Comps: None

Colours(change): Black and blue

10 YEAR RECORD

08-09	09-10	10-11	11-12	12-13		13-14		14-15		15-16		16-17		17-18	
				CMN	15	CMN	11	CMN	17	CMN	5	CMN	3	CMN	2
												FAV	2P	FAV	2Q

TEVERSAL

Founded: 1918   Nickname: Tevie Boys

Club Contact Details (T) 01623 554 924   (E) Kev1.Newton@ntlworld.com

Ground: Teversal Grange Sports and Social Centre, Carnarvon Street, Teversal, NG17 3HJ   **Capacity:** 2,000

Nearest Railway Station Sutton Parkway - 4.5km

HONOURS   **League:** Central Midlands Division Two 1987-88.

FA Comps: None

Colours(change): Black and red

10 YEAR RECORD

08-09		09-10		10-11		11-12		12-13		13-14		14-15		15-16		16-17		17-18	
NCE1	14	NCE1	11	NCE1	18	NCE1	15	NCE1	10	NCE1	15	NCE1	20	NCE1	14	NCE1	16	EMC	3
FAC	EP	FAC	EPr	FAC	EPr			FAC	EP	FAC	EP								
FAV	1P	FAV	1Q			FAV	2Q	FAV	2Q	FAV	2Q	FAV	1Q	FAV	2Q	FAV	1Q	FAV	2Q

WEST BRIDGFORD

Founded: 1990   Nickname:

Club Contact Details (T) 07791 633 221   (E) adrianmclark@btinternet.com

Ground: Regatta Way, Gamston, West Bridgford, Nottingham NG2 5AT

HONOURS   **League:** East Midlands Counties 2016-17.

FA Comps: None

Colours(change): Black & red

10 YEAR RECORD

08-09	09-10	10-11	11-12		12-13		13-14		14-15		15-16		16-17		17-18	
			NottS2	2	NottS1	5	NottS1	2	NottSP	2	NottSP	3	EMC	1	EMC	15
														FAC	EP
												FAV	2Q	FAV	1Q

EASTERN COUNTIES LEAGUE

Founded: 1935 **Sponsored by:** Thurlow Nunn

Recent Champions: 2015: Norwich United **2016:** Norwich United **2017:** Mildenhall Town

PREMIER DIVISION	P	W	D	L	F	A	GD	Pts
1 Coggeshall Town	46	37	4	5	145	26	119	115
2 Felixstowe & Walton United	46	35	4	7	129	41	88	109
3 Stowmarket Town	46	33	4	9	126	51	75	103
4 Godmanchester Rovers	45	31	2	12	103	50	53	95
5 Brantham Athletic	46	26	9	11	93	62	31	87
6 Histon	46	25	8	13	100	62	38	83
7 Gorleston	46	21	11	14	99	77	22	74
8 Stanway Rovers	46	22	8	16	80	58	22	74
9 Newmarket Town	46	22	7	17	107	74	33	73
10 Kirkley & Pakefield	45	19	11	15	80	69	11	68
11 Saffron Walden Town	46	20	7	19	82	80	2	67
12 Thetford Town	46	19	9	18	84	78	6	66
13 Wroxham	46	18	12	16	74	70	4	66
14 Ely City	46	18	10	18	71	79	-8	63*
15 Great Yarmouth Town	46	15	14	17	64	69	-5	59
16 Long Melford	46	17	8	21	54	79	-25	59
17 Walsham le Willows	46	16	7	23	82	100	-18	55
18 FC Clacton	46	14	9	23	52	96	-44	51
19 Haverhill Rovers	46	12	13	21	59	79	-20	49
20 Haverhill Borough	46	12	4	30	66	120	-54	40
21 Hadleigh United	46	10	4	32	50	106	-56	34
22 Fakenham Town	44	7	4	33	28	124	-96	25
23 Ipswich Wanderers	45	4	9	32	33	108	-75	21
24 Wivenhoe Town	45	4	6	35	35	138	-103	17*

DIVISION ONE	P	W	D	L	F	A	GD	Pts
1 Woodbridge Town	40	32	5	3	136	41	95	101
2 Framlingham Town	40	29	7	4	115	36	79	94
3 Whitton United	40	29	2	9	132	46	86	89
4 Swaffham Town	40	26	7	7	138	53	85	85
5 Braintree Town Res	40	24	6	10	99	61	38	78
6 Kings Lynn Town Res	40	22	6	12	99	64	35	72
7 Debenham LC	39	20	7	12	69	53	16	67
8 Norwich CBS	39	20	5	14	93	60	33	65
9 Downham Town	40	15	10	15	67	63	4	55
10 Halstead Town	40	14	13	13	77	75	2	55
11 AFC Sudbury Res	40	14	7	19	69	78	-9	49
12 Diss Town	40	13	6	21	62	96	-34	45
13 Leiston Res	38	13	7	18	70	96	-26	43*
14 Little Oakley	39	11	10	18	69	97	-28	43
15 Cornard United	40	12	5	23	58	96	-38	41
16 Holland FC	40	13	4	23	68	82	-14	40*
17 March Town United	40	9	12	19	54	77	-23	39
18 Wisbech St Mary	38	11	5	22	61	105	-44	38
19 Norwich United Res	39	10	7	22	46	106	-60	37
20 Needham Market Res	40	6	3	31	52	149	-97	21
21 Team Bury	40	5	2	33	39	139	-100	17

RESERVE DIVISION	P	W	D	L	F	A	GD	Pts
1 Halstead Town Res	21	15	3	3	73	28	45	48
2 Witham Town Res	21	16	0	5	74	34	40	48
3 Haverhill Rovers Res	21	12	4	5	64	36	28	40
4 Hadleigh United Res	21	9	5	7	38	39	-1	32
5 Wivenhoe Town Res	19	9	1	9	50	51	-1	28
6 Whitton United Res	21	8	3	10	57	49	8	27
7 Felixstowe & Walton United Res	21	8	3	10	38	43	-5	27
8 Saffron Walden Town Res	19	6	8	5	44	32	12	26
9 Walsham le Willows Res	21	6	7	8	43	49	-6	25
10 Woodbridge Town Res	17	5	1	11	21	58	-37	16
11 Long Melford Res	22	5	1	16	27	72	-45	16
12 Stowmarket Town Res	20	2	6	12	17	55	-38	12

LEAGUE CUP

HOLDERS: MILDENHALL TOWN

ROUND 1

Brantham Athletic	v	Halstead Town	6-2
Kirkley & Pakefield	v	Norwich United Res	1-1, 4-3p
Saffron Walden Town	v	Haverhill Borough	3-1
Hadleigh United	v	Little Oakley	0-1
Felixstowe & Walton United	v	Whitton United	5-3
Framlington Town	v	Needham Market Res	1-2

ROUND 2

Swaffham Town	v	Downham Town	0-2
Wisbech St Mary	v	Ely City	HW
Diss Town	v	Wroxham	0-3
Fakenham Town	v	King's Lynn Town Res	2-2, 2-4p
Cornard United	v	Brantham Athletic	0-0, 4-5p
Wivenhoe Town	v	Holland	1-1, 5-3p
FC Clacton	v	Coggeshall Town	0-5
Haverhill Rovers	v	Newmarket Town	0-2
Kirkley & Pakefield	v	Gorleston	3-2
Thetford Town	v	Norwich CBS	3-0
Histon	v	Saffron Walden Town	3-0
Godmanchester Rovers	v	Braintree Town Res	5-0
Ipswich Wanderers	v	Woodbridge Town	2-1
Stanway Rovers	v	Little Oakley	4-0
Long Melford	v	Walsham le Willows	1-1, 5-6p
Felixstowe & Walton United	v	Needham Market Res	3-0

ROUND 3

Downham Town	v	Wisbech St Mary	1-3
Wroxham	v	King's Lynn Town Res	2-1
Brantham Athletic	v	Wivenhoe Town	3-0
Coggeshall Town	v	Newmarket Town	3-1
Kirkley & Pakefield	v	Thetford Town	1-2
Histon	v	Godmanchester Rovers	0-1
Ipswich Wanderers	v	Stanway Rovers	0-1
Walsham le Willows	v	Felixstowe & Walton Utd	2-2, 4-3p

QUARTER FINALS

Wisbech St Mary	v	Wroxham	3-7
Brantham Athletic	v	Coggeshall Town	0-0, 3-2
Thetford Town	v	Godmanchester Rovers	5-1
Stanway Rovers	v	Walsham le Willows	1-0

SEMI FINALS

Wroxham	v	Brantham Athletic	1-3
Thetford Town	v	Stanway Rovers	2-0

FINAL

Brantham Athletic	v	Thetford Town	4-2

DIVISION ONE CUP

HOLDERS: KING'S LYNN TOWN RESERVES

SEMI FINALS

Whitton United	v	Norwich United Res	3-0
Braintree Town Res	v	Wisbech St Mary	1-1, 2-3p

FINAL

Whitton United	v	Wisbech St Mary	2-2, 3-2p

EASTERN COUNTIES - STEP 5/6

PREMIER DIVISION	1	2	3	4	5	6	7	8	9	10	11	12	13	14	15	16	17	18	19	20	21	22	23	24
1 Brantham Athletic		0-3	2-1	5-0	2-2	1-1	5-2	3-1	0-0	2-1	4-1	4-1	2-3	1-0	3-0	0-1	2-1	2-1	3-1	2-4	3-1	6-1	1-0	0-0
2 Coggeshall Town	1-2		4-1	6-1	3-0	1-2	2-0	4-1	2-0	3-1	4-0	6-0	4-0	6-0	0-0	3-0	2-0	2-0	5-1	3-2	6-0	8-0	5-0	4-0
3 Ely City	2-1	0-6		3-0	1-0	0-3	0-2	3-3	2-2	4-1	5-1	1-1	0-6	3-0	3-1	1-1	1-1	0-0	1-1	2-1	2-0	0-0	3-1	2-1
4 Fakenham Town	0-1	0-3	2-1		2-0	0-4	1-5	2-6	1-2	2-1	0-2	2-0	0-2	-	2-2	0-0	0-4	0-3	0-3	0-4	2-2	0-1	1-2	1-1
5 FC Clacton	0-1	0-2	2-0	1-0		0-3	0-5	0-2	0-0	2-1	2-1	1-3	0-1	2-2	1-2	1-0	2-1	3-1	0-2	1-1	0-2	0-6	4-3	1-1
6 Felixstowe & Walton Utd	5-1	2-4	5-1	2-0	4-2		2-1	3-2	1-2	1-0	4-0	1-1	3-0	2-0	2-1	3-0	1-2	4-0	3-0	4-3	2-1	6-0	2-0	0-1
7 Godmanchester Rovers	4-0	1-1	2-1	2-0	1-1	0-4		2-0	4-1	6-0	3-1	1-4	0-1	2-0	-	5-0	1-2	2-0	0-3	1-0	2-0	5-0	6-1	2-0
8 Gorleston	1-1	0-7	2-1	2-0	4-0	1-4	0-2		1-1	6-2	4-3	4-1	1-1	6-0	3-2	2-1	3-4	5-1	2-1	0-2	2-1	5-2	4-1	0-0
9 Great Yarmouth Town	3-3	0-2	0-1	4-0	2-0	0-2	1-0	0-1		1-1	2-2	1-2	1-6	2-0	2-2	2-2	0-1	2-3	0-0	0-1	0-0	3-1	4-0	3-2
10 Hadleigh United	0-2	0-1	2-3	3-0	2-2	1-5	1-2	1-3	1-2		3-2	2-0	2-5	1-0	1-2	0-2	1-3	1-0	2-2	1-5	3-0	4-3	3-1	1-2
11 Haverhill Borough	1-1	0-1	1-2	2-0	3-4	0-3	3-5	1-3	1-3	1-0		3-2	0-2	2-2	1-2	3-1	0-6	2-1	0-3	0-6	3-2	1-3	2-1	0-4
12 Haverhill Rovers	3-2	1-1	2-0	1-2	0-2	1-1	0-2	1-1	3-3	2-0	1-0		0-2	4-0	1-2	3-1	0-1	4-4	1-1	0-1	0-5	1-4	2-1	1-1
13 Histon	0-2	2-1	3-2	8-0	2-0	1-1	4-2	2-0	5-1	1-0	2-3	3-1		6-1	2-2	3-1	1-5	4-0	0-1	0-2	0-1	2-3	3-1	1-0
14 Ipswich Wanderers	0-4	0-3	2-3	0-1	0-0	1-0	0-1	2-1	1-2	0-2	2-3	1-1	2-4		2-1	1-2	2-6	0-1	1-1	1-4	0-4	1-1	2-1	0-2
15 Kirkley & Pakefield	1-3	1-1	3-0	3-0	4-0	1-4	1-4	0-4	1-0	0-1	1-3	1-4	0-0	4-0		4-0	4-4	2-0	0-1	2-0	2-1	2-0	1-1	2-0
16 Long Melford	0-0	1-3	1-5	3-0	0-1	1-3	1-2	2-2	2-1	1-1	0-2	2-1	2-1	2-2	2-1		0-4	3-1	1-2	0-2	2-1	3-1	0-1	
17 Newmarket Town	2-4	2-1	4-3	6-0	2-2	1-4	1-2	1-1	0-1	3-1	5-2	0-0	4-0	4-3	6-2	2-3		0-2	1-4	0-2	2-2	5-0	2-0	5-1
18 Saffron Walden Town	2-1	0-3	0-0	7-0	3-4	4-0	2-1	2-1	2-2	2-0	1-0	2-2	3-1	2-2	2-0	3-2			0-3	1-5	5-0	1-4	2-1	5-1
19 Stanway Rovers	1-0	1-3	0-1	2-0	2-0	1-5	0-1	1-2	2-0	2-0	3-2	2-0	3-2	4-1	2-1	0-1	1-2	4-1		0-4	1-3	3-0	1-0	0-0
20 Stowmarket Town	4-0	1-2	4-2	7-1	6-0	4-2	3-2	1-0	0-1	2-1	2-2	2-1	2-1	3-0	1-2	5-1	0-0	2-3	2-1		5-1	4-3	2-0	2-2
21 Thetford Town	2-2	3-2	2-1	1-0	6-2	0-5	0-1	2-2	4-2	9-0	2-1	1-0	2-2	1-1	0-0	1-1	1-0	3-2	0-2	1-7		1-2	6-0	0-1
22 Walsham le Willows	2-3	0-2	1-2	4-1	5-0	0-1	1-2	2-2	1-1	2-0	3-1	2-2	1-3	2-0	0-3	0-1	1-0	2-1	3-3	2-3	0-1		4-0	2-2
23 Wivenhoe Town	0-3	0-7	1-1	-	2-5	0-8	2-4	1-1	1-2	1-0	2-1	1-2	1-1	0-0	1-5	1-4	3-2	0-0	0-9	0-1	0-6	1-5		0-4
24 Wroxham	2-3	0-2	1-0	3-4	2-0	0-4	0-3	3-2	1-3	6-0	7-2	0-0	0-0	1-1	1-4	0-1	3-1	2-1	2-2	2-1	2-1	5-2	4-1	

CLUB MOVEMENTS
PREMIER DIVISION
In: Framlington Town (P), Norwich United (R - Isth N), Whitton United (P), Woodbridge Town (P).
Out: Coggeshall Town (P - Isth N), Fakenham Town (R), Felixstowe & Walton United (P - Isth N),
Haverhill Borough (R), Ipswich Wanderers (R), Saffron Walden Town and Stanway Rovers (LM - ESL), Wivenhoe Town (R).

DIVISION ONE NORTH
In: Fakenham Town (R), Felixstowe & Walton Res (N), Harleston (P - AnC), Haverhill Borough (R),
Ipswich Wanderers (R), Lakenheath (P - CambCo), Mulbarton Wanderers (N).
Out: Framlington Town (P), Team Bury (F), Whitton United (P), Woodbridge Town (P).

DIVISION ONE SOUTH
In: Burnham Ramblers, Hackney Wick (R - ESL), Coggeshall United and Harwich & Parkeston (P - E&SB),
Wivenhoe Town (R).

DIVISION ONE	1	2	3	4	5	6	7	8	9	10	11	12	13	14	15	16	17	18	19	20	21
1 AFC Sudbury Res		1-2	0-4	0-2	6-1	1-1	2-2	1-2	2-1	2-5	2-0	4-0	3-2	5-0	2-1	2-0	1-2	4-0	1-5	1-2	2-1
2 Braintree Town Res	1-0		3-3	2-1	3-0	0-0	0-1	3-2	2-1	3-0	4-2	7-1	5-1	4-1	1-1	6-0	0-4	5-0	1-1	3-3	0-1
3 Cornard United	1-3	0-1		3-3	1-0	1-3	0-6	1-4	0-2	0-3	1-4	2-1	5-2	2-0	0-6	2-2	3-3	2-0	0-7	3-2	1-2
4 Debenham LC	0-0	2-1	2-0		2-2	3-0	0-5	2-1	4-0	1-1	0-2	5-0	3-1	1-1	3-2	1-0	1-3	2-1	0-4	2-2	0-3
5 Diss Town	2-0	0-3	0-3	0-4		4-3	0-2	1-1	2-3	2-1	3-0	2-1	2-2	2-0	2-3	2-1	0-4	0-2	0-8	0-2	0-4
6 Downham Town	3-0	2-1	4-1	1-4	2-2		0-1	1-3	1-1	1-1	0-1	3-0	1-2	3-0	0-2	1-3	2-1	3-0	3-2	4-0	0-4
7 Framlingham Town	3-0	2-0	2-0	2-0	7-0	0-1		5-1	3-1	2-0	3-2	2-2	3-1	7-2	4-0	2-0	3-0	2-1	2-1	4-0	1-1
8 Halstead Town	2-2	2-4	0-1	0-1	2-2	0-0	2-2		1-0	2-4	4-4	3-2	1-1	1-2	2-2	1-2	2-1	1-2	2-0	5-2	0-3
9 Holland FC	0-0	3-2	1-0	0-3	2-3	2-3	1-5	2-3		1-3	4-1	2-1	0-2	10-0	0-0	0-1	4-4	3-2	1-3	4-2	1-3
10 King's Lynn Town Res	2-2	3-4	2-1	2-0	3-2	2-2	2-0	1-1	4-0		8-1	7-0	3-1	4-3	2-1	4-0	1-1	4-0	2-3	1-2	2-1
11 Leiston Res	0-2	0-4	5-0	1-2	1-0	3-2	1-4	4-4	0-4	2-1		3-3	0-1	2-1	-	5-0	2-6	5-1	0-3	3-0	2-6
12 Little Oakley	3-2	2-2	1-1	0-1	1-1	1-1	3-3	0-3	3-2	4-2	0-0		2-1	3-0	1-1	3-2	1-6	10-1	1-6	1-3	0-2
13 March Town United	0-2	3-2	1-2	1-1	1-3	3-0	0-0	2-2	0-3	4-2	1-1	1-3		1-1	1-1	2-3	1-1	2-0	0-3	2-1	0-0
14 Needham Market Res	1-7	3-4	1-5	0-3	2-4	1-1	1-6	4-0	0-6	1-6	0-3	1-4	3-2		0-4	1-2	0-8	6-1	0-2	1-4	1-2
15 Norwich CBS	6-0	0-2	4-0	5-3	1-0	1-4	3-0	1-3	4-0	0-2	8-0	4-0	2-0	7-4		2-0	0-2	3-1	0-3	3-1	1-2
16 Norwich United Res	1-1	0-2	1-0	2-1	0-4	3-2	0-4	2-2	1-2	1-3	-	1-5	1-2	2-3	0-1		1-8	4-0	0-3	3-1	0-6
17 Swaffham Town FC	7-0	7-0	7-2	2-0	4-2	2-2	1-2	2-1	4-0	5-0	1-3	2-2	2-1	6-1	6-1	2-2		4-1	3-2	6-0	1-3
18 Team Bury	6-3	1-2	1-4	0-3	0-4	0-4	0-3	1-0	1-2	3-3	1-3	1-4	3-1	0-6	2-2	2-4			1-6	1-2	0-6
19 Whitton United	2-1	2-5	2-0	0-2	3-1	3-2	4-3	1-2	2-0	2-1	5-1	3-0	2-0	5-2	3-0	11-2	0-2	10-0		5-3	1-1
20 Wisbech St Mary	3-1	1-2	2-1	-	0-4	0-3	1-4	1-2	2-1	2-3	2-2	-	2-2	1-2	2-4	1-1	3-2	3-1	0-4		3-7
21 Woodbridge Town	2-1	4-3	3-2	3-1	8-3	4-0	2-2	2-2	5-0	3-0	3-1	4-1	5-1	6-1	4-2	7-0	1-2	2-1	1-0	7-0	

BRANTHAM ATHLETIC
Founded: 1887   Nickname: Blue Imps

Club Contact Details (T) 01206 392 506   (E)   secretary@branthamathletic.com
Ground: Brantham Leisure Centre, New Village, Brantham CO11 1RZ
Nearest Railway Station Manningtree - 1.5km
Capacity: 1,200 **Seats:** 200   **Covered:** 200   **Bus Route** Temple Pattle (Brooklands Close) - 120m
Colours(change): All blue (Pink/black/black)
Previous Names: Brantham & Stutton United 1996-98.
Previous Leagues: Eastern Counties. Suffolk & Ipswich.

HONOURS: FA Comps: None
League: Essex & Suffolk Border 1972-73, 73-74, 75-76, 76-77. Suffolk & Ipswich Senior League 2007-08.

10 YEAR RECORD

08-09	09-10	10-11	11-12	12-13	13-14	14-15	15-16	16-17	17-18
EC1 8	EC1 3	ECP 13	ECP 3	ECP 4	ECP 11	ECP 8	ECP 11	ECP 8	ECP 5
		FAC P	FAC P	FAC P	FAC 1Q	FAC EPr	FAC 1Q	FAC EP	FAC P
	FAV 2Q	FAV 1Q	FAV 1P	FAV 5P	FAV 4P	FAV 3P	FAV 1P	FAV 2Q	FAV 1Q

ELY CITY
Founded: 1885   Nickname: Robins

Club Contact Details (T) 01353 662 035   (E) derek.oakey11@gmail.com
Ground: The Ellgia Stadium, Downham Road, Ely CB6 2SH
Nearest Railway Station Ely - 2.5km
Capacity: 1,500 **Seats:** 200   **Covered:** 350   **Shop:** Yes
Colours(change): All red with white trim. (All green with red trim).
Previous Names: None.
Previous Leagues: Cambridgeshire 1901-02, 03-51. Peterborough & District 1951-58. Central Alliance 1958-60.

HONOURS: FA Comps: None
League: Peterborough & District 1955-56.
10 YEAR RECORD | Eastern Counties Division One 1996-97.

08-09	09-10	10-11	11-12	12-13	13-14	14-15	15-16	16-17	17-18
ECP 14	ECP 9	ECP 15	ECP 2	ECP 11	ECP 17	ECP 20	EC1 2	ECP 13	ECP 14
FAC EP	FAC EP	FAC EP	FAC 1Qr	FAC Pr	FAC EP	FAC EP	FAC EPr	FAC EP	FAC EP
FAV 1Q	FAV 3P	FAV 1Qr	FAV 1Q	FAV 4P	FAV 2Pr	FAV 1Q	FAV 2Q	FAV 5P	FAV 2P

FC CLACTON
Founded: 1892   Nickname: The Seasiders

Club Contact Details (T) 07581 056 174   (E) fcclactonsecretary@gmail.com
Ground: Rush Green Bowl, Rush Green Rd, Clacton-on-Sea CO16 7BQ
Nearest Railway Station Clacton-on-Sea - 1.8km
Capacity: 3,000 **Seats:** 200   **Covered:** Yes   **Shop:** Yes
Colours(change): White & royal blue /royal blue/royal blue (Claret & sky blue/sky blue/claret)
Previous Names: Clacton Town > 2007
Previous Leagues: Eastern Counties 1935-37, 38-58. Essex County 1937-38. Southern League 1958-64.

HONOURS: FA Comps: None
League: North Essex D2 1898-99, 99-1900. Clacton & District 1905-06. South East Anglian D2 1907-08. Colchester & District D2 1909-10. East Anglian 1910-11. Southern D1 1959-60. Eastern Counties D1 1994-95, 98-99.
10 YEAR RECORD

08-09	09-10	10-11	11-12	12-13	13-14	14-15	15-16	16-17	17-18
EC1 7	EC1 2	ECP 16	ECP 15	ECP 20	ECP 15	ECP 16	ECP 10	ECP 20	ECP 18
FAC 1Q	FAC P	FAC Pr	FAC P	FAC EP	FAC 2Qr	FAC P	FAC P	FAC EP	FAC EP
FAV 4P	FAV 2P	FAV 1P	FAV 1P	FAV 2Q	FAV 1Q	FAV 2Q	FAV 1P	FAV 1Q	FAV 1Q

FRAMLINGHAM TOWN
Founded: 1887   Nickname: The Castlemen

Club Contact Details (T)   (E) fionawhatling@tiscali.co.uk
Ground: Framingham Sports Club, Badingham Road, Framlingham IP13 9HS

Capacity: **Seats:**   **Covered:**
Colours(change): Green & white stripes/white/white (Red & white/red/red)
Previous Names: None
Previous Leagues: Ipswich & District 1887. Framlingham. Leiston. Woodbridge. Suffolk & Ipswich >2016.

HONOURS: FA Comps: None
League: Suffolk & Ipswich Division Two 1980-81, Senior Division 91-92.
10 YEAR RECORD

08-09	09-10	10-11	11-12	12-13	13-14	14-15	15-16	16-17	17-18
S&I S 7	S&I S 11	S&I S 10	S&I 1 16	S&I 1 10	S&I 1 5	S&I 1 2	S&I S 5	EC1 7	EC1 2
									FAC P
		FAV 1P	FAV 2Q					FAV 1Q	FAV 2P

GODMANCHESTER ROVERS
Founded: 1911   Nickname: Goody/Rovers

Club Contact Details (T) 07734 136 419 (Ground)   (E) secretary@godmanchesterroversfc.co.uk
Ground: The David Wilson Homes Ground, Godmanchester, Huntingdon PE29 2LQ
Nearest Railway Station Huntingdon - 3.1km
Capacity: **Seats:** Yes   **Covered:** Yes

Colours(change): Sky blue/navy/navy (All red)
Previous Names: None
Previous Leagues: Huntingdonshire County. Cambridgeshire >2002.

HONOURS: FA Comps: None
League: Eastern Counties League Division One 2011-12.

10 YEAR RECORD

08-09		09-10		10-11		11-12		12-13		13-14		14-15		15-16		16-17		17-18	
EC1	10	EC1	12	EC1	9	EC1	1	ECP	5	ECP	5	ECP	2	ECP	2	ECP	12	ECP	4
		FAC	1Q	FAC	EPr	FAC	P	FAC	P	FAC	P	FAC	P	FAC	P	FAC	Pr	FAC	EP
FAV	1Q	FAV	1Qr	FAV	2P	FAV	3P	FAV	1P	FAV	1P	FAV	1Pr	FAV	1Pr	FAV	1P	FAV	2Q

GORLESTON
Founded: 1887   Nickname: The Greens

Club Contact Details (T) 01493 602 802 (Ground)   (E) colin-bray@sky.com
Ground: Emerald Park, Woodfarm Lane, Gorleston, Norfolk NR31 9AQ
Capacity: **Seats:** Yes   **Covered:** Yes

Colours(change): All green (All blue)
Previous Names: None
Previous Leagues: Aldred/Yarmouth & District 1900-08. Norfolk & Suffolk/Anglian Combination 1908-35, 60-69. Eastern Counties 1935-60.

HONOURS: FA Comps: None
League: Yarmouth & District 1905-06, 07-08. Norfolk & Suffolk/Anglian Comb. 1920-21, 25-26, 29-30, 31-32, 32-33, 33-34, 34-35, 68-69. Eastern Counties 1952-53, 72-73, 79-80, 80-81, Division One 1995-96, 2010-11.

10 YEAR RECORD

08-09		09-10		10-11		11-12		12-13		13-14		14-15		15-16		16-17		17-18	
EC1	6	EC1	4	EC1	1	ECP	12	ECP	3	ECP	4	ECP	12	ECP	16	ECP	4	ECP	7
FAC	EP	FAC	Pr	FAC	EP	FAC	1Q	FAC	P	FAC	1Q	FAC	EP	FAC	EP	FAC	EP	FAC	1Q
FAV	2Q	FAV	2Qr	FAV	2P	FAV	2Q	FAV	1P	FAV	1P	FAV	1P	FAV	2P	FAV	4P	FAV	3P

GREAT YARMOUTH TOWN
Founded: 1897   Nickname: The Bloaters

Club Contact Details (T)   (E) jglewsley@btinternet.com
Ground: The Wellesley, Sandown Road, Great Yarmouth NR30 1EY
Nearest Railway Station Great Yarmouth - 1/2 mile away.
Capacity: 3,600   **Seats:** 500   **Covered:** 2,100   **Shop:** Yes

Colours(change): Yellow & black/black/black (All blue)
Previous Names: None
Previous Leagues: Norfolk & Suffolk 1897-1935.

HONOURS: FA Comps: None
League: Norfolk & Suffolk 1913-14, 26-27, 27-28. Eastern Counties 1968-69, Division One 2009-10.

10 YEAR RECORD

08-09		09-10		10-11		11-12		12-13		13-14		14-15		15-16		16-17		17-18	
EC1	5	EC1	1	ECP	14	ECP	21	EC1	10	EC1	8	EC1	4	EC1	3	ECP	5	ECP	15
FAC	Pr	FAC	P	FAC	EP	FAC	EP	FAC	P	FAC	EP	FAC	P	FAC	EP	FAC	EP	FAC	1Q
FAV	2Q	FAV	1Q	FAV	2Q	FAV	2Q	FAV	2Q	FAV	2P	FAV	3P	FAV	1P	FAV	1P	FAV	2Q

HADLEIGH UNITED
Founded: 1892   Nickname: Brettsiders

Club Contact Details (T) 01473 822 165 (Ground)   (E) waffhenderson@aol.com
Ground: The Millfield, Tinkers Lane, Duke St, Hadleigh IP7 5NF
Capacity: 3,000   **Seats:** 250   **Covered:** 500

Colours(change): All navy blue (All red)
Previous Names: None
Previous Leagues: Ipswich & District/Suffolk & Ipswich 1929-91.

HONOURS: FA Comps: None
League: Suffolk & Ipswich 1953-54, 56-57, 73-74, 76-77, 78-79, Division Two 1958-59. Eastern Counties 1993-94, 2013-14.

10 YEAR RECORD

08-09		09-10		10-11		11-12		12-13		13-14		14-15		15-16		16-17		17-18	
EC1	2	ECP	18	ECP	9	ECP	11	ECP	8	ECP	1	ECP	7	ECP	7	ECP	18	ECP	21
FAC	EP	FAC	EP	FAC	EP	FAC	P	FAC	1Q	FAC	P	FAC	1Q	FAC	EP	FAC	EP	FAC	P
FAV	1P	FAV	2Q	FAV	1P	FAV	1Q	FAV	QF	FAV	5P	FAV	2P	FAV	2Q	FAV	2Q	FAV	2Q

HAVERHILL ROVERS
Founded: 1886   Nickname: Rovers

Club Contact Details   **(T)** 01440 702 137 (Ground)   **(E)** barbarajoneshrfc@outlook.com
Ground: The New Croft, Chalkstone Way, Haverhill, Suffolk CB9 0BW

Capacity: 3,000   **Seats:** 200   **Covered:** 200
Colours(change): All red (All navy).
Previous Names: None.
Previous Leagues: East Anglian. Essex & Suffolk Border.

HONOURS: FA Comps: None
    League: Essex & Suffolk Border 1947-48, 62-63, 63-64.
10 YEAR RECORD | Eastern Counties 1978-79.

08-09		09-10		10-11		11-12		12-13		13-14		14-15		15-16		16-17		17-18	
ECP	21	ECP	12	ECP	8	ECP	14	ECP	10	ECP	7	ECP	17	ECP	12	ECP	16	ECP	19
FAC	EPr	FAC	EPr	FAC	Pr	FAC	1Q	FAC	P	FAC	P	FAC	EPr	FAC	EP	FAC	EP	FAC	Pr
FAV	2Q	FAV	1P	FAV	1P	FAV	1P	FAV	1P	FAV	1Q	FAV	2Q	FAV	1Q	FAV	2Q	FAV	1Q

HISTON
Founded: 1904   Nickname: The Stutes

Club Contact Details   **(T)** 01223 237 373 (Ground)   **(E)**
Ground: The Glassworld Stadium, Bridge Road, Impington, Cambridge CB24 9PH
Nearest Railway Station Cambridge - the following buses run every 20 minutes,
Capacity: 3,250   **Seats:** 450   **Covered:** 1,800   **Shop:** Yes   **Bus Route** Citi 8 and Guided Busway routes A, B and C
Colours(change): Red and black/black/black (Navy yellow/navy/yellow)
Previous Names: Histon Institute
Previous Leagues: Cambridgeshire 1904-48, Spartan 1948-60, Delphian 1960-63, Eastern Counties 1966-2000,
    Southern 2000-05, 14-17. Conference 2005-14.
HONOURS: FA Comps: None
    League: Eastern Counties 1999-2000. Southern League Premier 2004-05. Conference South 2006-07.
10 YEAR RECORD

08-09		09-10		10-11		11-12		12-13		13-14		14-15		15-16		16-17		17-18	
Conf	3	Conf	18	Conf	24	Conf N	16	Conf N	19	Conf N	21	SthP	18	SthP	22	SthC	21	ECP	6
FAC	3P	FAC	4Q	FAC	4Q	FAC	2Qr	FAC	3Qr	FAC	3Q	FAC	2Qr	FAC	1Q	FAC	2Q	FAC	EP
FAT	1P	FAT	1P	FAT	1P	FAT	3Q	FAT	3Q	FAT	3Q	FAT	2Q	FAT	1Qr	FAT	Pr	FAV	2Q

KIRKLEY & PAKEFIELD
Founded: 1886   Nickname: The Kirks

Club Contact Details   **(T)** 01502 513 549 (Ground)   **(E)** secretarykpfc@outlook.com
Ground: The Bungalow, Walmer Road, Lowestoft NR33 7LE
Nearest Railway Station Oulton Broad South - 1.8km
Capacity: 2,000   **Seats:** 150   **Covered:** 150   **Shop:** Yes
Colours(change): All royal blue (All maroon).
Previous Names: Kirkley. Kirkley & Waveney 1929-33. Merged with Pakefield in 2007.
Previous Leagues: North Suffolk. Norfolk & Suffolk. Anglian Combination.

HONOURS: FA Comps: None
    League: North Suffolk 1894-95, 96-97, 1901-02, 05-06, 07-08, 08-09.
10 YEAR RECORD | Anglian Combination Premier Division 2001-02, 02-03.

08-09		09-10		10-11		11-12		12-13		13-14		14-15		15-16		16-17		17-18	
ECP	6	ECP	4	ECP	12	ECP	13	ECP	12	ECP	12	ECP	4	ECP	5	ECP	11	ECP	10
FAC	EP	FAC	2Q	FAC	EP	FAC	EP	FAC	P	FAC	P	FAC	P	FAC	2Q	FAC	P	FAC	EP
FAV	2P	FAV	4P	FAV	2P	FAV	1Q	FAV	1Q	FAV	2Q	FAV	2P	FAV	2P	FAV	1Q	FAV	2Q

LONG MELFORD
Founded: 1868   Nickname: The Villagers

Club Contact Details   **(T)** 01787 312 187 (Ground)   **(E)** richard.j.powell@hotmail.co.uk
Ground: Stoneylands Stadium, New Road, Long Melford, Suffolk CO10 9JY
Nearest Railway Station Sudbury - 4.6km
Capacity: **Seats:** Yes   **Covered:** Yes
Colours(change): Black & white stripes/black/black (All purple)
Previous Names: N/A
Previous Leagues: Essex & Suffolk Border > 2003

HONOURS: FA Comps: None
    League: Essex & Suffolk Border Champions x5.
10 YEAR RECORD | Eastern Counties Division One 2014-15.

08-09		09-10		10-11		11-12		12-13		13-14		14-15		15-16		16-17		17-18	
EC1	19	EC1	16	EC1	12	EC1	9	EC1	13	EC1	11	EC1	1	ECP	9	ECP	17	ECP	16
FAC	EP					FAC	P	FAC	EP					FAC	P	FAC	P	FAC	P
FAV	1P	FAV	2Qr	FAV	2Q	FAV	1Q	FAV	1P	FAV	2Q	FAV	2Q	FAV	2Q	FAV	2Q	FAV	1Q

NEWMARKET TOWN
Founded: 1877   Nickname: The Jockeys

Club Contact Details (T) 07951 463 104 (Ground)   (E) newmarkettfc@gmail.com
Ground: Ridgeons Stadium, Cricket Field Road, Off Cheveley Rd, Newmarket CB8 8BT
Nearest Railway Station Newmarket - 0.4km
Capacity: 2,750 **Seats:** 144 **Covered:** 250 **Shop:** Yes

Colours(change): Yellow/blue/yellow & blue (Green/green/yellow)
Previous Names: None
Previous Leagues: Cambridgeshire Senior. Bury & District. Suffolk & Ipswich >1937. Eastern Counties 1937-52. Peterborough & District 1952-59.

HONOURS: FA Comps: None
League: Cambridgeshire Senior 1919-20. Bury & District 1926-27. Suffolk & Ipswich 1931-32, 32-33, 33-34. Peterborough & District 1957-58. Eastern Counties Division One 2008-09.

10 YEAR RECORD	08-09	09-10	10-11	11-12	12-13	13-14	14-15	15-16	16-17	17-18
	EC1 1	ECP 16	ECP 19	ECP 20	EC1 2	ECP 9	ECP 6	ECP 13	ECP 3	ECP 9
	FAC EP	FAC EP	FAC P	FAC EP	FAC EP	FAC Pr	FAC 1Q	FAC P	FAC EP	FAC P
	FAV 1P	FAV 1P	FAV 2Q	FAV 2Q	FAV 2Q	FAV 2P	FAV 2Q	FAV 1P	FAV 2Q	FAV 1P

NORWICH UNITED
Founded: 1903   Nickname: Planters

Club Contact Details (T) 01603 716 963 (Ground)   (E)
Ground: Plantation Park, Blofield, Norwich NR13 4PL
Nearest Railway Station Brundall - 2.1km
Capacity: 3,000 **Seats:** 100 **Covered:** 1,000 **Shop:** Yes **Bus Route** Surgery (Plantation Rd) stop - 48m away.

Colours(change): Yellow/blue/blue (All red)
Previous Names: Poringland & District > 1987
Previous Leagues: Norwich & District. Anglian Combination. Eastern Counties >2016. Isthmian 2016-18.

HONOURS: FA Comps: None
League: Anglian Combination Premier Division 1988-99. Eastern Counties Division One 1990-91, 01-02, Premier Division 2014-15, 15-16.

10 YEAR RECORD	08-09	09-10	10-11	11-12	12-13	13-14	14-15	15-16	16-17	17-18
	ECP 19	ECP 15	ECP 6	ECP 9	ECP 13	ECP 6	ECP 1	ECP 1	Isth1N 9	Isth1N 24
	FAC EPr	FAC P	FAC Pr	FAC EP	FAC 1Q	FAC EP	FAC 2Qr	FAC Pr	FAC P	FAC P
	FAV 2Q	FAV 2Q	FAV 1P	FAV 2Q	FAV 2Q	FAV 4P	FAV 5P	FAV 2P	FAT P	FAT P

STOWMARKET TOWN
Founded: 1883   Nickname: Gold and

Club Contact Details (T) 01449 612 533   (E)
Ground: Greens Meadow, Bury Road, Stowmarket, Suffolk IP14 1JQ
Nearest Railway Station Stowmarket - 1km
Capacity: **Seats:** Yes **Covered:** Yes

Colours(change): Old Gold & black/black/black (Red & white/red/red)
Previous Names: Stowuplands Corinthians. Stowmarket Corinthians. Stowmarket FC
Previous Leagues: Ipswich & District 1896-1925. Essex & Suffolk Border 1925-52.

HONOURS: FA Comps: None
League: Ipswich & District/Suffolk & Ipwich 1896-97, 97-98, 99-1900, 21-22. Essex & Suffolk Border 1950-51. Eastern Counties Division One 2016-17.

10 YEAR RECORD	08-09	09-10	10-11	11-12	12-13	13-14	14-15	15-16	16-17	17-18
	EC1 12	EC1 15	EC1 7	EC1 15	EC1 17	EC1 14	EC1 11	EC1 14	EC1 1	ECP 3
	FAC EP	FAC EP		FAC EP						FAC Pr
	FAV 2Q	FAV 2Q	FAV 2Q	FAV 2Q	FAV 1Q	FAV 2Q	FAV 2Q	FAV 2Q	FAV 1Q	FAV 2Q

THETFORD TOWN
Founded: 1883   Nickname: Brecklanders

Club Contact Details (T) 01842 766 120 (Ground)   (E) jackieskipp@live.co.uk
Ground: Recreation Ground, Mundford Road, Thetford, Norfolk IP24 1NB
Nearest Railway Station Thetford - 0.5km
Capacity: **Seats:** Yes **Covered:** Yes

Colours(change): Claret & blue/claret/claret (Sky blue/white/white)
Previous Names: None
Previous Leagues: Norwich & District. Norfolk & Suffolk. Founder member of Eastern Counties League

HONOURS: FA Comps: None
League: Norfolk & Suffolk League 1954-55.

10 YEAR RECORD	08-09	09-10	10-11	11-12	12-13	13-14	14-15	15-16	16-17	17-18
	EC1 16	EC1 11	EC1 5	EC1 2	ECP 19	ECP 16	ECP 14	ECP 19	ECP 7	ECP 12
	FAC EP		FAC EPr	FAC EP	FAC EP	FAC P	FAC P	FAC P	FAC EP	FAC EP
	FAV 2Q	FAV 2Q	FAV 2Q	FAV 2P	FAV 2Q	FAV 1P	FAV 2Q	FAV 1Q	FAV 2P	FAV 2P

WALSHAM-LE-WILLOWS

Founded: 1888   **Nickname:** The Willows

Club Contact Details (T) 01359 259 298 (Ground)   (E) gordonaross2@gmail.com
Ground: The Meadow, Summer Road, Walsham-le-Willows IP31 3AH

Capacity: **Seats:** 100   **Covered:** 100

Colours(change): Yellow/red/yellow (All maroon)
Previous Names: None
Previous Leagues: St Edmundsbury/Bury & District 1907-89. Suffolk & Ipswich 1989-2004.

HONOURS: FA Comps: None
League: Suffolk & Ipswich Senior Division 2001-02, 02-03. Eastern Counties Division One 2006-07.

10 YEAR RECORD

08-09		09-10		10-11		11-12		12-13		13-14		14-15		15-16		16-17		17-18	
ECP	10	ECP	13	ECP	17	ECP	17	ECP	6	ECP	8	ECP	15	ECP	14	ECP	14	ECP	17
FAC	P	FAC	EPr	FAC	EP	FAC	Pr	FAC	EP	FAC	EP	FAC	EPr	FAC	EP	FAC	EPr	FAC	EPr
FAV	2Q	FAV	2Q	FAV	2P	FAV	1P	FAV	1Pr	FAV	EP	FAV	2P	FAV	2Q	FAV	2Q	FAV	2Q

WHITTON UNITED

Founded: 1926   **Nickname:** The Boyos

Club Contact Details (T) 01473 464 030 (Ground)   (E) secretary@whittonunited.co.uk
Ground: King George V Playing Fields, Old Norwich Road, Ipswich IP1 6LE
Nearest Railway Station Westerfield - 2.9km
Capacity: **Seats:** Yes   **Covered:** Yes   **Bus Route** Maypole (Old Norwich Rd) - 52m away

Colours(change): Green and white stripes/green/green (All red)
Previous Names:
Previous Leagues: Essex & Border. Ispswich District. Suffolk & Ipswich.

HONOURS: FA Comps: None
League: Suffolk & Ipswich Senior 1946-47, 47-48, 65-66, 67-68, 91-92, 92-93.
10 YEAR RECORD Eastern Counties Division One 2013-14.

08-09		09-10		10-11		11-12		12-13		13-14		14-15		15-16		16-17		17-18	
ECP	dnf	EC1	10	EC1	2	EC1	3	EC1	7	EC1	1	ECP	11	ECP	20	EC1	11	EC1	3
FAC	EPr	FAC	EP	FAC	P	FAC	EP	FAC	P	FAC	Pr	FAC	P	FAC	P	FAC	EPr		
FAV	2Q	FAV	1P	FAV	2P	FAV	2P	FAV	1P	FAV	2Q	FAV	1P	FAV	1P	FAV	1Q	FAV	1P

WOODBRIDGE TOWN

Founded: 1885   **Nickname:** The Woodpeckers

Club Contact Details (T) 01394 385 308 (Ground)   (E) tfryatt6@btinternet.com
Ground: Notcutts Park, Fynn Road, Woodbridge IP12 4LS
Nearest Railway Station Woodbridge - 1.7km
Capacity: 3,000   **Seats:** 50   **Covered:** 200   **Shop:** No   **Bus Route** Ashton House (California) - 201m away

Colours(change): Black & white stripes/black/black. (All red).
Previous Names: None.
Previous Leagues: Ipswich & District. Suffolk & Ipswich.

HONOURS: FA Comps: None
League: Ipswich & District/Suffolk & Ipswich Senior 1912-13, 88-89, Division One 1986-87, 70-71.
10 YEAR RECORD Eastern Counties Division One 2017-18.

08-09		09-10		10-11		11-12		12-13		13-14		14-15		15-16		16-17		17-18	
ECP	18	ECP	19	ECP	10	ECP	6	ECP	15	ECP	20	EC1	17	EC1	9	EC1	4	EC1	1
FAC	P	FAC	EP	FAC	EP	FAC	EPr	FAC	EP	FAC	EP	FAC	EP					FAC	EP
FAV	2Q	FAV	2P	FAV	2Q	FAV	1Pr	FAV	2Q	FAV	2Q	FAV	1P	FAV	2Q	FAV	2Q	FAV	2Q

WROXHAM

Founded: 1892   **Nickname:** Yachtsmen

Club Contact Details (T) 01603 783 536 (Ground)   (E) secretary@wroxhamfc.com
Ground: Trafford Park, Skinners Lane, Wroxham NR12 8SJ
Nearest Railway Station Hoveton & Wroxham - 1.6km
Capacity: 2,500   **Seats:** 50   **Covered:** 250   **Bus Route** 722, 724 and 717.

Colours(change): All royal blue (All red)
Previous Names: None
Previous Leagues: East Norfolk. Norwich City. East Anglian. Norwich & Dist. Anglian Comb.

HONOURS: FA Comps: None
League: Anglian County League 1981-82, 82-83, 83-84, 84-85, 86-87.
10 YEAR RECORD Eastern Counties Division One 1988-89, Prem 91-92, 92-93, 93-94, 96-97, 97-98, 98-99, 2006-07, 11-12.

08-09		09-10		10-11		11-12		12-13		13-14		14-15		15-16		16-17		17-18	
ECP	5	ECP	8	ECP	3	ECP	1	Isth1N	14	Isth1N	22	Isth1N	8	Isth1N	22	Isth1N	23	ECP	13
FAC	3Q	FAC	P	FAC	Pr	FAC	3Q	FAC	1Q	FAC	1Q	FAC	2Q	FAC	1Q	FAC	P	FAC	EP
FAV	1P	FAV	F	FAV	3P	FAV	1P	FAT	1Qr	FAT	1Q	FAT	P	FAT	P	FAT	1Q	FAV	2Q

DIVISION ONE NORTH

AFC SUDBURY RESERVES
Founded: 1999 Nickname: AFC

Club Contact Details (T) 01787 376 213 (E) dave-afc@supanet.com
Ground: The Wardale Williams Stadium, Brundon Lane, Sudbury CO10 7HN
Nearest Railway Station Sudbury - 1.5km
HONOURS League: None
FA Comps: None
Colours(change): Yellow & blue

08-09	09-10	10-11	11-12	12-13	13-14	14-15	15-16	16-17	17-18
					EC1 16	EC1 14	EC1 10	EC1 18	EC1 11

CORNARD UNITED
Founded: 1964 Nickname: Ards

Club Contact Details (T) 07834 773 416 (E) paulw_66@outlook.com
Ground: Backhouse Lane, Great Cornard, Sudbury, Suffolk CO10 0NL
Nearest Railway Station Sudbury - 2.2km
HONOURS League: Colchester & East Essex Div.6 1971-72, Div.5 72-73, Div.4 73-74, Div.3 74-75
Essex & Suffolk Border 1988-89. Eastern Counties Division One 1989-90.
FA Comps: None
Colours(change): All blue

08-09	09-10	10-11	11-12	12-13	13-14	14-15	15-16	16-17	17-18
EC1 11	EC1 13	EC1 17	EC1 16	EC1 18	EC1 18	EC1 18	EC1 15	EC1 15	EC1 15
FAC 1Q	FAC EP								
FAV 2P	FAV 1Q	FAV 1Q	FAV 2Q	FAV 1Q	FAV 2Q	FAV 1Q	FAV 1Q	FAV 1Q	FAV 1Q

DEBENHAM LC
Founded: 1991 Nickname: The Hornets

Club Contact Details (T) 01728 861 101 (E) snelly1992@hotmail.co.uk
Ground: Debenham Leisure Centre, Gracechurch Street, Debenham IP14 6BL **Capacity:** 1,000
HONOURS League: Suffolk & Ipswich Division Seven 1991-92, Four 96-97, Three 99-2000,
One 03-04.
FA Comps: None
Colours(change): Yellow & black

08-09	09-10	10-11	11-12	12-13	13-14	14-15	15-16	16-17	17-18
EC1 3	ECP 14	ECP 22	EC1 7	EC1 15	EC1 12	EC1 7	EC1 13	EC1 12	EC1 7
FAC EP			FAC EP	FAC EP			FAC EP		
FAV 2P		FAV 2Q	FAV 2Q	FAV 1Qr	FAV 1P	FAV 2Q	FAV 2Q	FAV 1Q	FAV 1Pr

DISS TOWN
Founded: 1888 Nickname: Tangerines

Club Contact Details (T) 01379 651 223 (E) parndisstownfc@gmail.com
Ground: Brewers Green Lane, Diss, Norfolk IP22 4QP
Nearest Railway Station Diss - 0.5 miles
HONOURS League: Anglian Combination Division One 1967-68, 73-74, Premier 76-77, 78-79.
FA Comps: FA Vase 1993-94. Eastern Counties Division One 1991-92.
Colours(change): Tangerine & navy

08-09	09-10	10-11	11-12	12-13	13-14	14-15	15-16	16-17	17-18
EC1 9	EC1 5	EC1 3	ECP 16	ECP 17	ECP 18	ECP 19	EC1 7	EC1 6	EC1 12
FAC EP	FAC EP	FAC EP	FAC EP	FAC EP	FAC EP	FAC EP	FAC EP		FAC EP
FAV 1P	FAV 2Qr	FAV 1Q	FAV 3P	FAV 2P	FAV 1P	FAV 1Q	FAV 1P	FAV 2Q	FAV 2Q

DOWNHAM TOWN
Founded: 1881 Nickname: Town

Club Contact Details (T) (E) george.dickson@me.com
Ground: Memorial Field, Lynn Road, Downham Market PE38 9AU
Nearest Railway Station Downham Market - 1.25 miles
HONOURS League: Peterborough & District 1962-63, 73-74, 78-79, 86-87, 87-88.
FA Comps: None
Colours(change): All red

08-09	09-10	10-11	11-12	12-13	13-14	14-15	15-16	16-17	17-18
EC1 15	EC1 18	EC1 16	EC1 14	EC1 16	EC1 17	EC1 9	EC1 16	EC1 14	EC1 9
			FAV 2Q	FAV 2Q	FAV 1Q		FAV 2Q	FAV 2Q	FAV 1Q

FAKENHAM TOWN

Founded: 1884   Nickname: Ghosts

Club Contact Details (T) 01328 851 735 (Ground)   (E)

Ground: Clipbush Park, Clipbush Lane, Fakenham, Norfolk NR21 8SW

Bus Route Sanders Coaches No.9

HONOURS   **League:** Anglian Combination Division One 1971-72.

FA Comps: None

Colours(change): Amber & black

10 YEAR RECORD

08-09		09-10		10-11		11-12		12-13		13-14		14-15		15-16		16-17		17-18	
EC1	20	EC1	19	EC1	14	EC1	11	EC1	5	EC1	2	ECP	13	ECP	17	ECP	15	ECP	22
FAC	P							FAC	EP	FAC	EP	FAC	EPr	FAC	P	FAC	EP	FAC	EP
FAV	1Q	FAV	2Q	FAV	1Qr	FAV	1Q	FAV	2Q	FAV	2Q	FAV	2P	FAV	2Q	FAV	2Q	FAV	1Q

FELIXSTOWE & WALTON UNITED RES

Founded: 2000   Nickname: Seasiders

Club Contact Details (T) 01394 282 917   (E) tgbarnes@live.co.uk

Ground: Goldstar Ground, Dellwood Avenue, Felixstowe IP11 9HT

HONOURS   **League:** None

FA Comps: None

Colours(change):

10 YEAR RECORD

08-09	09-10	10-11	11-12	12-13	13-14	14-15	15-16	16-17	17-18

HARLESTON TOWN

Founded: 1885   Nickname:

Club Contact Details (T) 07887 781 603   (E)

Ground: Harleston Recreation Ground, Wilderness Lane, Harleston IP20 9DD

HONOURS   **League:** Anglian Combination Division Three 1980-81, 2010-11,

FA Comps: None   Division Two 1981-82, 2011-12, Premier 2017-18

Colours(change): Black & white

10 YEAR RECORD

08-09		09-10		10-11		11-12		12-13		13-14		14-15		15-16		16-17		17-18	
AnC4	4	AnC3	4	AnC3	1	AnC2	1	AnC1		AnC1	2	AnCP	3	AnCP	3	AnCP	2	AnCP	1

HAVERHILL BOROUGH

Founded: 2011   Nickname: Borough

Club Contact Details (T) 01440 702 137 (Ground)   (E) gabrown306@hotmail.com

Ground: The New Croft, Chalkestone Way, Haverhill, Suffolk CB9 0BW   **Capacity:** 3,000

HONOURS   **League:** Essex & Suffolk Border Division One 2011-12.

FA Comps: None

Colours(change): All navy

10 YEAR RECORD

08-09	09-10	10-11	11-12		12-13		13-14		14-15		15-16		16-17		17-18	
			EsSu1	1	EsSuP	2	EC1	4	EC1	6	EC1	8	EC1	3	ECP	20
									FAC	1Q	FAC	EP			FAC	1Q
							FAV	1Q	FAV	1P	FAV	1Q	FAV	1P	FAV	1Q

IPSWICH WANDERERS

Founded: 1980   Nickname: Wanderers

Club Contact Details (T) 01473 720 691 (Ground)   (E)

Ground: SEH Sports Centre, Humber Doucy Lane, Ipswich IP4 3NR

HONOURS   **League:** Eastern Counties Division One 1997-98, 04-05.

FA Comps: None

Colours(change): All blue

10 YEAR RECORD

08-09		09-10		10-11		11-12		12-13		13-14		14-15		15-16		16-17		17-18	
EC1	17	EC1	17	EC1	10	EC1	12	EC1	4	EC1	3	ECP	9	ECP	15	ECP	10	ECP	23
FAC	Pr					FAC	Pr	FAC	EP	FAC	P	FAC	1Q	FAC	2Q	FAC	EPr	FAC	EP
FAV	2Q	FAV	2Q	FAV	1P	FAV	2Q	FAV	1P	FAV	1P	FAV	2P	FAV	5Pr	FAV	2P	FAV	1Q

KING'S LYNN TOWN RESERVES

Founded: 1879   Nickname: The Linnets

Club Contact Details (T) 01553 760 060 (Ground)   **(E)** ncesar1947@yahoo.co.uk

Ground: The Walks Stadium, Tennyson Road, King's Lynn PE30 5PB.   **Capacity:** 8,200

Nearest Railway Station King's Lynn - 5min walk away.   **Bus Route** Serviced by Eastern Counties & Norfolk Green

HONOURS   **League:** None

FA Comps: None

Colours(change): Yellow & blue

10 YEAR RECORD

08-09	09-10	10-11	11-12	12-13	13-14	14-15	15-16	16-17	17-18
ECP 15	ECP Exp					EC1 5	EC1 5	EC1 10	EC1 6

LAKENHEATH

Founded: Nickname:

Club Contact Details (T) 07767 733 925   **(E)**

Ground: The Nest, Wings Road, Lakenheath IP27 9HN

HONOURS   **League:** Cambridgeshire County Senior Division A 2007-08, Premier 10-11.

FA Comps: None

Colours(change): Green & white

10 YEAR RECORD

08-09	09-10	10-11	11-12	12-13	13-14	14-15	15-16	16-17	17-18
CamP 2	CamP 3	CamP 1	CamP 2	CamP 9	CamP 5	CamP 2	CamP 6	CamP 3	CamP 8

LEISTON RESERVES

Founded: 1880   Nickname: Blues

Club Contact Details (T) 01728 830 308 (Ground)   **(E)**

Ground: The LTAA, Victory Road, Leiston, Suffolk IP16 4DQ

HONOURS   **League:** None

FA Comps: None

Colours(change): All blue

10 YEAR RECORD

08-09	09-10	10-11	11-12	12-13	13-14	14-15	15-16	16-17	17-18
						EC1 19	EC1 6	EC1 21	EC1 13

MARCH TOWN UNITED

Founded: 1885   Nickname: Hares

Club Contact Details (T) 01354 653 073 (Ground)   **(E)** r.bennett639@btinternet.com

Ground: GER Sports Ground, Robin Goodfellow Lane, March, Cambs PE15 8HS

Nearest Railway Station March - 0.7km   **Bus Route** Darthill Road stop - 290m away

HONOURS   **League:** United Counties Division One 1953-54. Eastern Counties 1987-88.

FA Comps: None

Colours(change): Amber & black

10 YEAR RECORD

08-09	09-10	10-11	11-12	12-13	13-14	14-15	15-16	16-17	17-18
EC1 13	EC1 7	EC1 8	EC1 4	EC1 14	EC1 19	EC1 8	EC1 11	EC1 16	EC1 17
FAC P	FAC EP	FAC P	FAC Pr	FAC EP				FAV 2Q	FAV 1Q
FAV 2Q	FAV 1P	FAV 1Q	FAV 1Q	FAV 1Q	FAV 2Q				

MULBARTON WANDERERS

Founded: 2002   Nickname:

Club Contact Details (T) 07738 716 925 (Secretary)   **(E)**

Ground: The Common, Mulbarton, Norfolk NR14 8AE

HONOURS   **League:** Anglian Combination Division Five 2010-11, Division Four 11-12, Division One 14-15.

FA Comps: None

Colours(change): Blue & black

10 YEAR RECORD

08-09	09-10	10-11	11-12	12-13	13-14	14-15	15-16	16-17	17-18
	AnC6 2	AnC5 1	AnC4 1	AnC3 2	AnC3 2	AnC1 1	AnCP 8	AnCP 3	AnCP 2

NEEDHAM MARKET RESERVES

Founded: 1919   Nickname: The Marketmen

Club Contact Details (T) 01449 721 000 (Ground)   **(E)** m.easlea@sky.com

Ground: Bloomfields, Quinton Road, Needham Market IP6 8DA.   **Capacity:** 1,000

Nearest Railway Station Needham Market - 0.6km   **Bus Route** Quinton Road stop - 38m away

HONOURS   **League:** None

FA Comps: None

Colours(change): Red

10 YEAR RECORD

08-09	09-10	10-11	11-12	12-13	13-14	14-15	15-16	16-17	17-18
					EC1 15	EC1 16	EC1 19	EC1 19	EC1 20

NORWICH CBS

Founded: 1888   Nickname:

Club Contact Details (T) 01603 569 835   **(E)**

Ground: Football Development Centre, Bowthorpe Park, Clover Hill Road, Norwich NR5 9ED

Bus Route Breckland Road stop - 176m away

HONOURS   **League:** Anglian Combination Premier Division 2016-17.

FA Comps: None

Colours(change): Sky blue

10 YEAR RECORD

08-09	09-10	10-11	11-12	12-13	13-14	14-15	15-16	16-17	17-18
AnCP 12	AnCP 12	AnCP 11	AnCP 4	AnCP 2	AnCP 2	AnCP 5	AnCP 2	AnCP 1	EC1 8
									FAV 4P

SWAFFHAM TOWN

Founded: 1892   Nickname: Pedlars

Club Contact Details (T) 01760 722 700 (Ground)   **(E)** rayewart@aol.com

Ground: The Pavillion, Shoemakers Lane, Swaffham, Norfolk PE37 7NT

Bus Route Greenhoe Place (Haspalls Rd) stop - 212m away

HONOURS   **League:** Anglian Combination Division Two 1973-74.

FA Comps: None   Eastern Counties Division One 2000-01.

Colours(change): Black & white

10 YEAR RECORD

08-09	09-10	10-11	11-12	12-13	13-14	14-15	15-16	16-17	17-18
EC1 18	EC1 14	EC1 15	EC1 13	EC1 9	EC1 7	EC1 2	ECP 18	ECP 21	EC1 4
					FAC P	FAC EP	FAC EP	FAC EP	FAC P
FAV 1Q	FAV 1Q	FAV 2Q	FAV 1Q	FAV 1P	FAV 1Pr	FAV 1Q	FAV 1P	FAV 1P	FAV 2Q

WISBECH ST MARY

Founded: 1993   Nickname: The Saints

Club Contact Details (T) 01945 411 777 (Ground, match days only)   **(E)** martin@jsholmes.com

Ground: Wisbech St Mary Playing Fields, Beechings Close, Wisbech St Mary PE13 4SS

Bus Route St Mary's Close (High Rd) stop - 362m away

HONOURS   **League:** Cambridgeshire County Division 1B 2008-09, Senior B 10-11,

FA Comps: None

Colours(change): All purple

10 YEAR RECORD

08-09	09-10	10-11	11-12	12-13	13-14	14-15	15-16	16-17	17-18
Cam1B 1	CamSB 3	CamSB 1	CamSA 3	CamP 7	CamP 8	CamP 15	CamP 5	EC1 13	EC1 18
							FAV 2Q	FAV 1Q	FAV 2P

DIVISION ONE SOUTH

BENFLEET

Founded: Nickname:

Club Contact Details (T) 01268 682 991 (Canvey Island FC)   (E)
Ground: Canvey Island FC, Frost Financial Stadium, 1 Park Lane, Canvey Island SS8 7PX

HONOURS   **League:** Essex Olympian Division One 1988-89, Division Two 2006-07, Division Three 15-16.
FA Comps: None

Colours(change): Sky and navy blue

10 YEAR RECORD

08-09	09-10	10-11	11-12	12-13	13-14	14-15	15-16	16-17	17-18
EsxOP 6	EsxOP 13	EsxO1 5	EsxO1 11	EsxO1 9	EsxO1 11	EsxO2 Exp	EsxO3 1	EsxO2 3	EsxO2 4

BRAINTREE TOWN RESERVES

Founded: 1898   Nickname: The Iron

Club Contact Details (T) 01376 330 976 & 01376 345 617 (Ground)   (E)
Ground: The Cressing Road Stadium, off Clockhouse Way, Cressing Road, Braintree CM7 3DE

HONOURS   **League:** None
FA Comps: None

Colours(change): Orange and blue

10 YEAR RECORD

08-09	09-10	10-11	11-12	12-13	13-14	14-15	15-16	16-17	17-18
				EC1 8	EC1 9	EC1 13	EC1 12	EC1 8	EC1 5

BRIGHTLINGSEA REGENT RES

Founded: 1928   Nickname: The Rs

Club Contact Details (T) 01206 304 199   (E) gridders43@pobox.com
Ground: North Road, Brightlingsea, Essex CO7 0PL

HONOURS   **League:** None
FA Comps: None

Colours(change):

10 YEAR RECORD

08-09	09-10	10-11	11-12	12-13	13-14	14-15	15-16	16-17	17-18

BURNHAM RAMBLERS

Founded: 1900   Nickname: Ramblers

Club Contact Details (T) 01621 784 383 (Ground)   (E) martin.leno@btopenworld.com
Ground: Leslie Fields Stadium, Springfield Road CM0 8TE   **Capacity:** 2,000
Nearest Railway Station Burnham on Crouch (Greater Anglia).   **Bus Route** 31X (Eastern National)
HONOURS   **League:** Mid-Essex 1927-28, 54-55, 62-63. Essex Olympian 1966-67. Essex Senior League 2012-13.
FA Comps: None

Colours(change): Blue & black

10 YEAR RECORD

08-09	09-10	10-11	11-12	12-13	13-14	14-15	15-16	16-17	17-18
ESen 7	ESen 3	ESen 7	ESen 4	ESen 1	Isth1N 17	Isth1N 24	ESen 14	ESen 21	ESen 20
FAC P	FAC EP	FAC 1Q	FAC Pr	FAC P	FAC 1Q	FAC P	FAC EP	FAC EP	FAC EP
FAV 2Q	FAV 1P	FAV 2P	FAV 1P	FAV 2P	FAT 1Q	FAT P	FAV 1Qr	FAV 2Q	FAV 1P

COGGESHALL UNITED

Founded: 2017   Nickname: Weavers

Club Contact Details (T) 01376 562 962 (Ground)   (E) secretary@coggeshallunitedfc.co.uk
Ground: West Street, Coggeshall, Essex CO6 1NT

HONOURS   **League:** None
FA Comps: None

Colours(change): Blue & black

10 YEAR RECORD

08-09	09-10	10-11	11-12	12-13	13-14	14-15	15-16	16-17	17-18
									EsSuP 2

FIRE UNITED CHRISTIANS
Founded: 2012   Nickname:

Club Contact Details (T) 02075 114 477 & 07472 525 666 (Ground)   **(E)** fireunitedcfc@hotmail.com
Ground: Terence MacMillan Stadium, Plaistow E13 8SD

HONOURS   **League:** None
FA Comps: None

Colours(change): Red & blue

10 YEAR RECORD

08-09	09-10	10-11	11-12	12-13	13-14	14-15	15-16	16-17	17-18
				Midx1SE 9	Midx1SE 7	Midx1SE 12		Midx1SE 9	Midx1SE 4

FRENFORD
Founded: 1945   Nickname:

Club Contact Details (T) 020 8518 0992 (Ground)   **(E)**
Ground: Jack Carter Centre, The Drive, Ilford, Essex, IG1 3PS

HONOURS   **League:** Ilford & District Premier 1975-76. Essex Olympian Division Two 1995-96, Premier 2011-12, 12-13.
FA Comps: None

Colours(change): Red & white

10 YEAR RECORD

08-09	09-10	10-11	11-12	12-13	13-14	14-15	15-16	16-17	17-18
EsxOP 2	EsxOP 4	EsxOP 3	EsxOP 1	EsxOP 1	EsxOP 3	EsxOP 7	EsxOP 7	EsxOP 5	EsxOP 2

HACKNEY WICK
Founded: 1995   Nickname: The Wickers

Club Contact Details (T)   **(E)**
Ground: The Old Spotted Dog, Upton Lane, Forest Gate E7 9NP   **Capacity:** 2,000
Nearest Railway Station Wanstead Park, 10 min walk or Stratford, 25 min walk   **Bus Route** 25, 6 min walk from Woodgrange Pk bus stop
HONOURS   **League:** Essex Sunday Corinthian 2011-12.
FA Comps: None

Colours(change): Yellow & black

10 YEAR RECORD

08-09	09-10	10-11	11-12	12-13	13-14	14-15	15-16	16-17	17-18
			EsxSC 1	ESen 10	ESen 20	ESen 15	ESen 8	ESen 17	ESen 21
							FAC EP	FAC EP	FAC EP
						FAV 2Q	FAV 1Q	FAV 1P	FAV 1Q

HALSTEAD TOWN
Founded: 1879   Nickname: Humbugs

Club Contact Details (T) 01787 472 082 (Ground)   **(E)** halsteadtownfc@aol.com
Ground: Rosemary Lane, Broton Industrial Estate, Halstead, Essex CO9 1HR

HONOURS   **League:** Essex & Suffolk Border Premier Division 1957-58, 68-69, 77-78.
FA Comps: None   Eastern Counties 1994-95, 95-96, Division One 2002-03.

Colours(change): Black & white

10 YEAR RECORD

08-09	09-10	10-11	11-12	12-13	13-14	14-15	15-16	16-17	17-18
EC1 4	EC1 6	EC1 11	EC1 6	EC1 11	EC1 6	EC1 10	EC1 4	EC1 9	EC1 10
FAC P	FAC 1Qr	FAC P	FAC EP	FAC P	FAC EP	FAC EPr		FAC 1Q	
FAV 1P	FAV 2Pr	FAV 2Q	FAV 1P	FAV 2Q	FAV 2Q	FAV 1Q	FAV 2Q	FAV 2Q	FAV 2Q

HARWICH & PARKESTON
Founded: 1875   Nickname: Shrimpers

Club Contact Details (T) 01255 503 643   **(E)**
Ground: Royal Oak, Main Road, Dovercourt, Harwich CO12 4AA   **Capacity:** 5,000

HONOURS   **League:** Essex & Suffolk Border Senior Division 1908-09, 13-14, 20-21, 21-22, 22-23, 28-29, 31-32, 32-33,
FA Comps: None   33-34. Eastern Counties 1935-36 (joint). Essex County 1937-38. Athenian Division Two 1964-65

Colours(change): Black & white stripes

10 YEAR RECORD

08-09	09-10	10-11	11-12	12-13	13-14	14-15	15-16	16-17	17-18
ECP 20	ECP Exp		EsSuP 2	EsSuP 5	EsSuP 3	EsSu1 5	EsSuP 9	EsSuP 6	EsSuP 10

HASHTAG UNITED

Founded: 2016 Nickname:

Club Contact Details (T) 0208 889 1415 (Matchday) **(E)** jay@hashtagunited.co.uk

Ground: Haringey Borough FC, Coles Park, White Hart Lane, Tottenham, London N17 7JP **Capacity:** 2,500

Nearest Railway Station White Hart Lane - 1.5km. Wood Green (UG) - 1.5km **Bus Route** W3 stops outside the ground.

HONOURS **League:** None

FA Comps: None

Colours(change): Blue & yellow (Purple & black)

10 YEAR RECORD									
08-09	09-10	10-11	11-12	12-13	13-14	14-15	15-16	16-17	17-18

HOLLAND

Founded: 2006 Nickname:

Club Contact Details (T) 07778 142 118 (Ground) **(E)** mark.sorrell@btinternet.com

Ground: Eastcliff Sports Ground, Dulwich Road, Holland-on-Sea CO15 5HP

Nearest Railway Station Clacton-on-Sea - 1.7km

HONOURS **League:** Essex & Suffolk Border Division One 2008-09.

FA Comps: None

Colours(change): Orange & white

10 YEAR RECORD																			
08-09		09-10		10-11		11-12		12-13		13-14		14-15		15-16		16-17		17-18	
EsSu1	1	EsSuP	7	EsSuP	5	EsSuP	12	EsSuP	4	EsSuP	10	EsSuP	4	EsSuP	4	EC1	5	EC1	16
																		FAV	2Q

LITTLE OAKLEY

Founded: 1947 Nickname: The Acorns

Club Contact Details (T) 01255 880 370 (Ground) **(E)**

Ground: War Memorial Club Ground, Harwich Road, Little Oakley, Harwich CO12 5ED

Nearest Railway Station Harwich International - 3.3km **Bus Route** Mayes Lane stop - 173m away

HONOURS **League:** Essex & Suffolk Border Division One 1985-86, Premier Division 1986-87, 87-88, 92-93, 2003-04, 15-16, 16-17.

FA Comps: None

Colours(change): Blue & black

10 YEAR RECORD																			
08-09		09-10		10-11		11-12		12-13		13-14		14-15		15-16		16-17		17-18	
EsSuP	4	EsSuP	6	EsSuP	13	EsSuP	6	EsSuP	7	EsSuP	6	EsSuP	2	EsSuP	4	EsSuP	1	EC1	14
																		FAV	2Q

LOPES TAVARES

Founded: 2015 Nickname:

Club Contact Details (T) 02037 704450 (Ground) **(E)** ktavares0906@gmail.com

Ground: 281 Prince Regent Lane, London E13 8SD

HONOURS **League:** None

FA Comps: None

Colours(change): All red

10 YEAR RECORD									
08-09	09-10	10-11	11-12	12-13	13-14	14-15	15-16	16-17	17-18
								EsxAIP 8	EsxAIP 5

MAY & BAKER E.C.

Founded: Nickname:

Club Contact Details (T) 0208 919 2156 / 3156 **(E)** mwright@cvc.com

Ground: M & B Sports and Social Club, Romford, Greater London RM7 0QX

HONOURS **League:** Essex Olympian Division One 2009/10.

FA Comps: None

Colours(change): Red & black

10 YEAR RECORD																			
08-09		09-10		10-11		11-12		12-13		13-14		14-15		15-16		16-17		17-18	
EsxOP	5	EsxO1	1	EsxOP	6	EsxOP	11	EsxOP	8	EsxOP	10	EsxOP	9	EsxOP	11	EsxOP	3	EsxOP	7

NEWBURY FOREST
Founded: 2003   Nickname:

Club Contact Details (T) 0208 550 3611   **(E)**
Ground: Redbridge FC, Oakside Stadium, Station Road, Barkingside, IG6 1NB

HONOURS
FA Comps: None   **League:** Romford & District Senior 2009-10.

Colours(change): All navy (All red)

10 YEAR RECORD

08-09	09-10	10-11	11-12	12-13	13-14	14-15	15-16	16-17	17-18
	RomS 1			EsxO1 3	EsxOP 7	EsxOP 10	EsxOP 14	EsxO1 6	EsxO1 8
							FAV 2Q	FAV 1Q	

WHITE ENSIGN
Founded: 1951   Nickname:

Club Contact Details (T) 01268 722 455 (Ground)   **(E)** alanday34@yahoo.com
Ground: Basildon Sporting Village, Cranes Farm Road, Basildon SS14 3GR

HONOURS
FA Comps: None   **League:** Essex Intermediate/Olympian Division Two 2002-03, Division One 03-04, 04-05, 06-07, 07-08.

Colours(change):

10 YEAR RECORD

08-09	09-10	10-11	11-12	12-13	13-14	14-15	15-16	16-17	17-18
EsxOP 12	EsxOP 10	EsxOP 12	EsxOP 8	EsxOP 7	EsxOP 13	EsxO1 2	EsxOP 5	EsxOP 12	EsxOP 4

WIVENHOE TOWN
Founded: 1925   Nickname: The Dragons

Club Contact Details (T)   **(E)** lorraineosman1969@yahoo.com
Ground: GMP Plant Hire Stadium, Broad Lane, Elmstead Road, Wivenhoe CO7 7HA   **Capacity:** 2876
Nearest Railway Station Wivenhoe - 2.4km.   **Bus Route** No.62.

HONOURS
FA Comps: None   **League:** Brightlingsea & Dist 1932-33, 36-37, 47-48. Colchester & East Essex Prem 1952-53, 55-56, D1 59-60, 69-70. Essex & Suffolk D2 1971-72, D1 72-73, Prem 78-79. Isth D2N 1987-88, D1 1989-90. Eastern C. D1 2015-16.

Colours(change): All blue

10 YEAR RECORD

08-09	09-10	10-11	11-12	12-13	13-14	14-15	15-16	16-17	17-18
ECP 17	ECP 20	ECP 20	ECP 19	ECP 18	ECP 19	ECP 18	EC1 1	ECP 19	ECP 24
FAC EP	FAC EPr			FAC EPr	FAC EPr	FAC P	FAC EP	FAC EP	FAC EP
FAV 3P	FAV 1P		FAV 1Q	FAV 2Qr	FAV 1Q	FAV 1P	FAV 2Q	FAV 1Q	FAV 1Q

WORMLEY ROVERS
Founded: 1921   Nickname:

Club Contact Details (T) 01992 460 650 (Ground)   **(E)**
Ground: Wormley Sports Club, Church Lane, Wormley EN10 7QF

HONOURS
FA Comps: None   **League:** Herts Senior County Division Three 1976-77, Division One 86-87.

Colours(change): Red & black

10 YEAR RECORD

08-09	09-10	10-11	11-12	12-13	13-14	14-15	15-16	16-17	17-18
HertP 13	HertP 2	HertP 7	HertP 8	HertP 7	HertP 8	HertP 5	HertP 15	HertP 8	HertP 5

ESSEX SENIOR LEAGUE

Founded: 1971 **Sponsored by:** No sponsor
Recent Champions: 2015: Haringey Borough **2016:** Bowers & Pitsea **2017:** Barking

Premier Division	P	W	D	L	F	A	GD	Pts
1 Great Wakering Rovers	40	30	4	6	107	29	78	94
2 Basildon United	40	29	5	6	83	29	54	92
3 FC Romania	40	28	7	5	98	37	61	91
4 Redbridge	40	28	4	8	97	56	41	88
5 Takeley	40	26	4	10	104	36	68	82
6 Clapton	40	19	6	15	64	62	2	63
7 West Essex	40	19	5	16	73	73	0	62
8 Sawbridgeworth Town	40	15	10	15	76	75	1	55
9 Enfield 1893	40	15	6	19	64	75	-11	51
10 Sporting Bengal United	40	15	5	20	69	87	-18	50
11 Tower Hamlets	40	14	7	19	63	78	-15	49
12 Woodford Town (2017)	40	13	9	18	66	86	-20	48
13 Ilford	40	14	5	21	53	66	-13	47
14 Southend Manor	40	12	10	18	65	81	-16	46
15 Hullbridge Sports	40	12	9	19	69	97	-28	45
16 Barkingside	40	12	7	21	64	74	-10	43
17 Waltham Forest	40	11	9	20	62	87	-25	42
18 Stansted	40	12	4	24	54	70	-16	40
19 Wadham Lodge	40	10	10	20	66	102	-36	40
20 Burnham Ramblers	40	10	4	26	64	120	-56	34
21 Hackney Wick	40	10	2	28	48	89	-41	26*

CLUB MOVEMENTS: In: Hoddesdon Town (LM - SSM), Leyton Athletic (NC from Wadham Lodge), Saffron Walden Town (LM - ECL), St Margaretsbury (LM - SSM), Stanway Rovers (LM - ECL).
Out: Basildon United (P - Isth N), Burnham Ramblers, Hackney Wick (R - EC1S) Great Wakering Rovers (P - Isth N), Wadham Lodge (NC to Leyton Athletic).

LEAGUE CHALLENGE CUP

HOLDERS: TAKELEY
ROUND 1

Redbridge	v	Ilford	1-3
Southend Manor	v	Clapton	2-2, 4-1p
Woodford Town	v	Waltham Forest	1-5
Barkingside	v	Enfield 1893	2-2, 4-3p
West Essex	v	Basildon United	0-5

ROUND 2

Sawbridgeworth Town	v	Burnham Ramblers	6-0
Ilford	v	Wadham Lodge	1-0
Southend Manor	v	Hackney Wick	3-3, 2-4p
Stansted	v	Sporting Bengal United	1-2
Great Wakering Rovers	v	Tower Hamlets	3-2
FC Romania	v	Waltham Forest	2-1
Barkingside	v	Basildon United	1-1, 3-4p
Takeley	v	Hullbridge Sports	4-1

QUARTER FINALS

Sawbridgeworth Town	v	Ilford	3-1
Hackney Wick	v	Sporting Bengal United	1-2
Great Wakering Rovers	v	FC Romania	2-0
Basildon United	v	Takeley	1-1, 3-2p

SEMI FINALS

Sawbridgeworth Town	v	Sporting Bengal United	3-1
Great Wakering Rovers	v	Basildon United	3-1

FINAL

Sawbridgeworth Town	v	Great Wakering Rovers	0-1

GORDON BRASTED MEMORIAL CUP

HOLDERS: TAKELEY
SEMI FINALS

Takeley	v	Clapton	2-1
Ilford	v	FC Romania	0-4

FINAL

Takeley	v	FC Romania	0-1

PREMIER DIVISION	1	2	3	4	5	6	7	8	9	10	11	12	13	14	15	16	17	18	19	20	21
1 Barkingside		0-2	2-1	2-3	0-1	0-1	0-2	3-0	1-1	0-1	1-2	1-1	1-1	1-2	1-0	0-4	3-1	2-3	1-2	0-3	2-2
2 Basildon United	3-1		4-0	2-0	1-2	2-0	2-1	7-0	1-0	1-0	1-0	1-3	1-2	5-1	3-0	1-0	3-0	2-1	0-3	1-1	3-0
3 Burnham Ramblers	1-5	1-2		0-3	2-3	2-2	0-4	1-3	2-4	3-2	4-3	1-2	1-4	4-1	0-1	0-4	1-1	3-2	0-1	2-5	3-1
4 Clapton	3-2	0-1	1-0		3-2	3-2	2-0	0-2	2-1	1-1	3-2	0-3	2-0	1-2	1-5	0-1	1-0	3-1	2-2	3-4	0-0
5 Enfield 1893	3-1	1-4	3-4	1-2		0-5	1-7	2-0	4-0	0-3	1-0	0-2	5-2	2-2	2-0	0-2	1-3	2-2	3-0	0-2	5-1
6 FC Romania	2-0	0-0	8-2	3-2	3-0		2-1	2-0	5-0	2-1	5-1	2-1	4-1	0-0	1-0	3-2	2-1	2-1	3-1	5-0	
7 Great Wakering Rovers	1-2	0-2	7-0	3-2	1-0	4-0		2-0	7-1	2-0	1-1	0-1	1-1	2-0	2-0	1-0	6-1	4-1	3-1	5-0	3-0
8 Hackney Wick	1-7	2-3	4-0	1-2	0-1	1-6	0-2		3-1	2-1	1-2	0-4	3-2	0-2	1-2	1-2	1-1	1-3	1-1	1-2	0-1
9 Hullbridge Sports	2-6	4-3	3-3	0-2	1-1	1-4	2-3	3-0		4-0	2-3	3-1	0-1	4-0	2-1	2-2	2-1	2-2	2-2	2-5	3-3
10 Ilford	1-3	0-1	1-1	1-4	1-3	0-2	0-1	2-1	3-1		1-2	3-1	0-0	1-2	2-0	0-1	1-1	0-3	3-1	2-0	1-0
11 Redbridge	2-1	0-2	3-1	2-1	1-1	3-2	2-1	6-1	5-1		1-1	2-0	3-2	3-2	3-0	2-1	3-1	4-4	3-1	2-0	
12 Sawbridgeworth Town	3-0	0-0	3-1	4-0	1-3	0-2	0-4	4-1	5-0	1-1	1-4		1-3	4-1	1-2	0-4	1-3	3-3	2-0	1-3	3-3
13 Southend Manor	1-1	1-2	1-2	3-3	2-2	0-2	1-1	0-3	2-4	0-3	0-3	4-3		0-2	0-1	1-1	3-2	2-0	3-2	3-4	3-3
14 Sporting Bengal United	2-3	0-0	6-1	1-3	3-1	2-6	0-2	3-1	2-3	1-2	2-1	4-2	2-3		2-1	2-2	2-3	3-2	4-1	2-0	1-4
15 Stansted	1-3	0-1	1-4	2-3	1-0	0-0	1-2	1-0	2-0	3-1	0-2	1-3	0-4	4-0		0-3	2-5	8-0	3-1	2-2	1-3
16 Takeley	7-0	1-1	9-0	2-0	5-4	0-1	2-2	4-1	2-0	5-1	2-0	1-2	6-0	2-0	4-1		3-0	1-2	4-1	3-1	4-1
17 Tower Hamlets	1-3	0-4	1-0	0-0	3-0	2-2	0-2	3-2	1-3	2-3	0-5	2-2	1-0	1-0	2-1	0-5		3-1	5-0	3-0	0-2
18 Wadham Lodge	1-1	1-4	1-5	1-1	1-3	0-2	0-5	1-3	2-0	2-0	1-3	1-1	2-3	2-2	3-2	0-3	2-2		4-2	3-3	2-6
19 Waltham Forest	2-2	0-2	2-6	1-0	1-2	1-1	0-2	2-1	1-1	3-1	1-4	3-3	2-2	2-3	2-1	2-0	4-1	3-1		0-2	1-3
20 West Essex	2-1	0-3	2-0	0-1	2-1	0-1	1-3	1-3	2-3	2-1	2-4	2-2	2-4	2-2	1-2	1-0	2-0	1-0	5-1	2-0	3-2
21 Woodford Town (2017)	2-1	3-2	5-2	2-1	0-0	0-2	0-1	1-2	1-1	0-5	1-2	4-0	3-3	2-0	1-1	1-4	1-6	2-4	1-4	2-0	

BARKINGSIDE

Founded: 1898 Nickname: The Side / Sky

Club Contact Details (T) 020 8552 3995 (E)
Ground: Cricketfield Stadium, 3 Cricklefield Place, Ilford IG1 1FY
Nearest Railway Station Ilford (underground) / Seven Kings (BR) ½ mile
Capacity: 3,500 **Seats:** 216 **Covered:** Yes **Bus Route** 86 outside ground

Colours(change): Sky blue & navy
Previous Names: None
Previous Leagues: London. Greater London. Met London. Spartan, South Midlands. Essex Senior > 2013. Isthmian 2013-16.

HONOURS: FA Comps: None
League: Spartan Premier Division 1996-97. Spartan South Midlands 1998-99.

10 YEAR RECORD	08-09		09-10		10-11		11-12		12-13		13-14		14-15		15-16		16-17		17-18	
	ESen	5	ESen	9	ESen	15	ESen	8	ESen	2	Isth1N	20	Isth1N	22	Isth1N	23	ESen	10	ESen	16
	FAC	P	FAC	EP	FAC	EP	FAC	EP	FAC	EP	FAC	P	FAC	1Q	FAC	P	FAC	P	FAC	EP
	FAV	2P	FAV	2Q	FAV	2Q	FAV	2Qr	FAV	1Q	FAT	P	FAT	2Q	FAT	P	FAV	2Q	FAV	2Q

CLAPTON

Founded: 1878 Nickname: Tons

Club Contact Details (T) 07983 588 883 (E) secretary@claptonfc.com
Ground: The Old Spotted Dog, Upton Lane, Forest Gate E7 9NP
Nearest Railway Station Forest Gate, 8-10 min walk or Plaistow (District Line), 5-7 min
Capacity: 2,000 **Seats:** 100 **Covered:** 180 **Shop:** No **Bus Route** 325, stops outside ground

Colours(change): Red & white
Previous Names: None
Previous Leagues: Southern (founder member). London. Isthmian (founder member).

HONOURS: FA Comps: FA Amateur Cup 1906-07, 08-09, 14-15, 23-24, 24-25.
League: Isthmian 1910-11, 22-23, Division Two 1982-83.

10 YEAR RECORD	08-09		09-10		10-11		11-12		12-13		13-14		14-15		15-16		16-17		17-18	
	ESen	16	ESen	16	ESen	17	ESen	17	ESen	18	ESen	10	ESen	8	ESen	7	ESen	2	ESen	6
	FAC	EP	FAC	EP	FAC	EP	FAC	EP	FAC	EP	FAC	P	FAC	EPr	FAC	P	FAC	P	FAC	1Q
	FAV	1Q	FAV	1Q	FAV	2Q	FAV	2Q	FAV	1P	FAV	1P	FAV	2Q	FAV	2Q	FAV	1Q	FAV	2Q

ENFIELD 1893 FC

Founded: 1893 Nickname: The E's

Club Contact Details (T) 07957 647 820 (E) enfieldfc@ntlworld.com
Ground: The Harlow Arena, Elizabeth Way, Harlow, Essex CM19 5BE
Nearest Railway Station Harlow Town, 1 mile
Capacity: 3,500 **Seats:** 500 **Covered:** Yes

Colours(change): White & royal blue
Previous Names: Enfield Spartans > 1900. Enfield > 2007.
Previous Leagues: Tottenham & District, North Middlesex, London, Athenian, Isthmian, Alliance, Southern

HONOURS: FA Comps: FA Amateur Cup 1966-67, 69-70. FA Trophy 1981-82, 87-88.
League: Alliance 1982-83, 85-86. Essex Senior 2010-11.

10 YEAR RECORD	08-09		09-10		10-11		11-12		12-13		13-14		14-15		15-16		16-17		17-18	
	ESen	2	ESen	4	ESen	1	ESen	7	ESen	9	ESen	3	ESen	16	ESen	20	ESen	18	ESen	9
			FAC	2Q	FAC	EP	FAC	Pr	FAC	EP	FAC	EPr	FAC	EP	FAC	EP	FAC	EP	FAC	EP
	FAV	2Q	FAV	2P	FAV	1P	FAV	4P	FAV	4P	FAV	4P	FAV	1P	FAV	1Q	FAV	2Q	FAV	3P

HODDESDON TOWN

Founded: 1879 Nickname: Lilywhites

Club Contact Details (T) 01920 462 064 (E) janedsinden@fsmail.net
Ground: Wodson Park, Wadesmill Road, Ware, Herts SG12 0UQ
Nearest Railway Station Ware - 1.9km
Capacity: 3,000 **Seats:** 100 **Covered:** Yes **Bus Route** Wodson Park - stop 90m away

Colours(change): White & black
Previous Names: None
Previous Leagues: Hertfordshire County 1920-25. Spartan 1963-75. London Spartan 1975-77. Athenian 1977-84. Spartan SM 1984-2018.

HONOURS: FA Comps: FA Vase 1974-75 (1st Winners).
League: Spartan 1970-71, Division One 1935-36, Division Two 'B' 1927-28.

10 YEAR RECORD	08-09		09-10		10-11		11-12		12-13		13-14		14-15		15-16		16-17		17-18	
	SSM1	5	SSM1	4	SSM1	9	SSM1	3	SSM1	3	SSM P	6	SSM P	19	SSM P	3	SSM P	7	SSM P	12
	FAC	EP	FAC	P	FAC	EP	FAC	EP	FAC	EPr	FAC	EPr	FAC	P	FAC	3Qr	FAC	P	FAC	EP
	FAV	1Q	FAV	3P	FAV	1Q	FAV	1P	FAV	1P	FAV	2Q	FAV	2Q	FAV	1P	FAV	3P	FAV	1Q

HULLBRIDGE SPORTS

Founded: 1945 Nickname:

Club Contact Details (T) 01702 230 420   (E) beryl@petre1942.fsnet.co.uk
Ground: Lower Road, Hullbridge, Hockley Essex SS5 6BJ
Nearest Railway Station Rayleigh, approx. 3 miles
Capacity: 1,500 **Seats:** 60 **Covered:** 60 **Shop:** No **Bus Route** 20, bottom of the hill

Colours(change): Blue & white
Previous Names: None
Previous Leagues: Southend & District. Southend Alliance.

HONOURS: FA Comps: None
League: Southend & District Division Two 1951-52, Division Three 1956-57, Division One 1965-66.

10 YEAR RECORD

	08-09	09-10	10-11	11-12	12-13	13-14	14-15	15-16	16-17	17-18
ESen	9	11	9	11	15	9	4	11	11	15
FAC	P	EPr	EP	EP	EP	P	EP	2Q	P	Pr
FAV	2Q	1Q	2P	1P	1P	4P	4P	4P	2P	4P

ILFORD

Founded: 1987 Nickname: The Foxes

Club Contact Details (T) 020 8514 8352   (E)
Ground: Cricklefield Stadium, 486 High Road, Ilford, Essex IG1 1FY
Nearest Railway Station Seven Kings (BR), approx. ½ mile
Capacity: 3,500 **Seats:** 216 **Covered:** Yes **Shop:** No **Bus Route** 86, outside ground

Colours(change): Blue and white hoops
Previous Names: Reformed as Ilford in 1987 after the original club merged with Leytonstone in 1980.
Previous Leagues: Spartan 1987-94, Essex Senior 1996-2004, Isthmian 2004-05, 2006-13, Southern 2005-06.

HONOURS: FA Comps: FA Amateur Cup 1928-29, 29-30.
League: Isthmian 1906-07, 20-21, 21-22, Division Two 2004-05.

10 YEAR RECORD

	08-09	09-10	10-11	11-12	12-13	13-14	14-15	15-16	16-17	17-18
	Isth1N 17	Isth1N 20	Isth1N 20	Isth1N 20	Isth1N 22	ESen 16	ESen 10	ESen 5	ESen 6	ESen 13
FAC	P	P	1Q	Pr	P	EP	EP	P	P	P
FAT/FAV	FAT P	FAT Pr	FAT 1Q	FAT P	FAT 1Q	FAV 1P	FAV 2Q	FAV 1P	FAV 1P	FAV 2Q

LEYTON ATHLETIC

Founded: 2008 Nickname: Wad Army

Club Contact Details (T) 07903 061 692   (E) wadamlodge.fc@hotmail.com
Ground: Wadham Lodge Sports Ground, Kitchener Road, Walthamstow E17 4JP
Nearest Railway Station Walthamstow Central - Victoria Line/London Overground, 1.4 miles
Capacity: 3,000 **Seats:** 216 **Covered:** Yes **Bus Route** 34,97, 215, 357, approx. ¼ mile

Colours(change): All white
Previous Names: Wadham Lodge >2018
Previous Leagues: Essex Business House League 2008-09. Essex Olympian League 2009-15. Essex Senior 2015-18.

HONOURS: FA Comps: None
League: Essex Olympian Division Three 2009-10, Division Two 2010-11.

10 YEAR RECORD

	08-09	09-10	10-11	11-12	12-13	13-14	14-15	15-16	16-17	17-18
		EsxO3 1	EsxO2 1	EsxO1 4	EsxO1 2	EsxOP 9	EsxOP 4	ESen 6	ESen 15	ESen 19
FAC										EPr
FAV									2P	1Q

REDBRIDGE

Founded: 1958 Nickname: Motormen

Club Contact Details (T)   (E) r.holloway338@btinternet.com
Ground: Oakside Stadium, Station Road, Barkingside, Essex IG6 1NB
Nearest Railway Station Barkingside Underground - 186m
Capacity: 3,000 **Seats:** **Covered:** **Bus Route** Barkingside - 395m away

Colours(change): Blue & white
Previous Names: Ford United 1958-2004
Previous Leagues: Aetolian 1959-64, Greater London 1964-71, Metropolitan 1971-74, Essex Senior 1974-97, Isthmian 1997-2004, 05-16.

HONOURS: FA Comps: None
League: Aetolian 1959-60, 61-62. Greater London 1970-71. Essex Senior 1991-92, 96-97.
Isthmian Division Three 1998-99, Division One 2001-02.

10 YEAR RECORD

	08-09	09-10	10-11	11-12	12-13	13-14	14-15	15-16	16-17	17-18
	Isth1N 8	Isth1N 18	Isth1N 16	Isth1N 6	Isth1N 20	Isth1N 14	Isth1N 23	Isth1N 24	ESen 14	ESen 4
FAC	P	P	2Q	2P	P	P	Pr	P	EP	P
FAT/FAV	FAT P	FAT P	FAT 1Q	FAT 3Q	FAT 1Q	FAT P	FAT P	FAT 1Q	FAV 2Q	FAV 2Qr

SAFFRON WALDEN TOWN

Founded: 1872   Nickname: The Bloods

Club Contact Details (T) 01799 520 980   (E)
Ground: The Meadow, 1 Catons Lane, Saffron Walden, Essex CB10 2DU
Nearest Railway Station Audley End - 3.5km
Capacity: **Seats:** Yes   **Covered:** Yes

Colours(change): Red & black stripes
Previous Names: Saffron Walden > 1967 Folded in 2011 reformed for 2012-13 season.
Previous Leagues: Essex Senior >2003. Eastern Counties 2004-11, 12-18.

HONOURS: FA Comps: None
League: Essex Senior 1973-74, 99-00. Eastern Counties 1982-83.

10 YEAR RECORD

	08-09	09-10	10-11	11-12	12-13	13-14	14-15	15-16	16-17	17-18
	EC1 7	EC1 14	EC1 6		EC1 6	ECP 5	EC1 3	ECP 8	ECP 9	ECP 11
	FAC 1Q	FAC EP	FAC Pr			FAC EP	FAC Pr	FAC 1Q	FAC 1Q	FAC Pr
	FAV 2Q	FAV 1Q	FAV 2Q		FAV 2Q	FAV 2Q	FAT 4P	FAV 3P	FAV 1P	FAV 1Q

SAWBRIDGEWORTH TOWN

Founded: 1890   Nickname: Robins

Club Contact Details (T) 01279 722 039   (E)
Ground: Crofters End, West Road, Sawbridgeworth CM21 0DE
Nearest Railway Station Sawbridgeworth, approx. ½ mile
Capacity: 2,500 **Seats:** 175 **Covered:** 300   **Bus Route** 510 & 511, approx. ½ mile

Colours(change): Red & black
Previous Names: Sawbridgeworth > 1976.
Previous Leagues: Stortford. Spartan. Herts County. Essex Olympian.

HONOURS: FA Comps: None
League: Essex Olympian 1971-72.

10 YEAR RECORD

	08-09	09-10	10-11	11-12	12-13	13-14	14-15	15-16	16-17	17-18
	ESen 13	ESen 10	ESen 16	ESen 6	ESen 14	ESen 6	ESen 5	ESen 10	ESen 5	ESen 8
				FAC EP	FAC EP	FAC EP	FAC EP	FAC EP	FAC 1Q	FAC EP
			FAV 2Q	FAV 2Q	FAV 2Q	FAV 2Q	FAV 1Q	FAV 1Q	FAV 2Q	FAV 1P

SOUTHEND MANOR

Founded: 1955   Nickname: The Manor

Club Contact Details (T) 07788 580 360   (E) southendmanor@btinternet.com
Ground: The Arena, Southchurch Park, Northumberland Crescent, Southend SS1 2XB
Nearest Railway Station Southend East (C2C), ½ mile to ground
Capacity: 2,000 **Seats:** 500 **Covered:** 700 **Shop:** No   **Bus Route** 7 & 8 (Arriva) to Woodgrange Drive, ¼ mile

Colours(change): Yellow & black
Previous Names: None
Previous Leagues: Southend Borough Combination. Southend & District Alliance.

HONOURS: FA Comps: None
League: Southend Borough Combination 1971-72, 73-74, 78-79, 79-80, 80-81, 81-82.
10 YEAR RECORD Southend & District Alliance 1983-84, 84-85. Essex Senior 1990-91.

	08-09	09-10	10-11	11-12	12-13	13-14	14-15	15-16	16-17	17-18
	ESen 4	ESen 7	ESen 5	ESen 2	ESen 7	ESen 19	ESen 18	ESen 16	ESen 7	ESen 14
	FAC P	FAC EPr	FAC P	FAC 4Q	FAC 1Q	FAC EPr	FAC EP	FAC P	FAC EPr	FAC P
	FAV 2Q	FAV 1P	FAV 2Q	FAV 3Pr	FAV 3P	FAV 2Q	FAV 2Q	FAV 2Qr	FAV 2Q	FAV 1Q

SPORTING BENGAL UNITED

Founded: 1996   Nickname: Bengal Tigers

Club Contact Details (T) 020 8980 1885   (E)
Ground: Mile End Stadium, Rhodeswell Rd, Off Burdett Rd E14 7TW
Nearest Railway Station Mile End – approx. 5 mins walk
Capacity: 2,000 **Seats:** Yes **Covered:** Yes   **Bus Route** 277, 309, D6, D7 – outside ground

Colours(change): All royal blue
Previous Names: None.
Previous Leagues: Asian League. London Intermediate, Kent 2003-11.

HONOURS: FA Comps: None
League: None

10 YEAR RECORD

	08-09	09-10	10-11	11-12	12-13	13-14	14-15	15-16	16-17	17-18
	Kent P 17	Kent P 15	Kent P 15	ESen 10	ESen 11	ESen 13	ESen 20	ESen 12	ESen 19	ESen 10
	FAC P	FAC EP			FAC EPr	FAC EPr	FAC EP	FAC EP	FAC 1Q	FAC EP
	FAV 1Q	FAV 1Q		FAV 3P	FAV 1P	FAV 1P	FAV 1Q	FAV 2P	FAV 1P	FAV 1Q

ST MARGARETSBURY
Founded: 1894 Nickname: The Bury

Club Contact Details (T) 01920 870 473   (E) smfc@niche-direct.com
Ground: Recreation Ground, Station Road, St Margarets SG12 8EH
Nearest Railway Station St Margarets - 0.3km
Capacity: 1,000 **Seats:** 60 **Covered:** 60   **Bus Route** St Mary's Church - stop 170m away

Colours(change): Red & black
Previous Names: Stanstead Abbots > 1962
Previous Leagues: East Herts, Hertford & District, Waltham & District 1947-48, Herts Senior County 1948-92. Spartan SM 1992-2018.

HONOURS: FA Comps: None
           League: Spartan 1995-96.

10 YEAR RECORD

08-09		09-10		10-11		11-12		12-13		13-14		14-15		15-16		16-17		17-18	
SSM P	14	SSM P	14	SSM P	18	SSM P	12	SSM P	4	SSM P	4	SSM P	8	SSM P	19	SSM P	20	SSM P	16
FAC	EP	FAC	P	FAC	P	FAC	EP	FAC	1Q	FAC	1Q	FAC	P	FAC	P	FAC	EP	FAC	1Q
FAV	1P	FAV	2Q	FAV	1Q	FAV	2Q	FAV	2Q	FAV	1P	FAV	3P	FAV	1Q	FAV	3P	FAV	1Qr

STANSTED
Founded: 1902 Nickname: Blues

Club Contact Details (T) 07921 403 842   (E)
Ground: Hargrave Park, Cambridge Road, Stansted CM24 8BX
Nearest Railway Station Stansted Mountfitchet - ¼ mile
Capacity: 2,000 **Seats:** 200 **Covered:** 400 **Shop:** No **Bus Route** 301 100 yards from ground

Colours(change): White & blue
Previous Names: None.
Previous Leagues: East Herts. Herts Senior County 1946-71.

HONOURS: FA Comps: FA Vase 1983-84.
           League: East Herts 1934-35. Essex Senior 2009-10.

10 YEAR RECORD

08-09		09-10		10-11		11-12		12-13		13-14		14-15		15-16		16-17		17-18	
ESen	10	ESen	1	ESen	2	ESen	16	ESen	17	ESen	17	ESen	7	ESen	9	ESen	8	ESen	18
FAC	P	FAC	EP	FAC	EP	FAC	1Q	FAC	EP	FAC	EPr	FAC	EP	FAC	Pr	FAC	EP	FAC	EP
FAV	1Q	FAV	2P	FAV	5P	FAV	2P	FAV	2Q	FAV	2Q	FAV	2Q	FAV	1Q	FAV	1Q	FAV	1Q

STANWAY ROVERS
Founded: 1956 Nickname: Rovers

Club Contact Details (T) 01206 578 187   (E)
Ground: Hawthorns, New Farm Road, Stanway, Colchester CO3 0PG
Nearest Railway Station Colchester - 3.7km
Capacity: 1,500 **Seats:** 100 **Covered:** 250 **Shop:** Yes

Colours(change): Amber & black
Previous Names: None.
Previous Leagues: Colchester & East Essex. Essex & Suffolk Border. Eastern Counties >2018.

HONOURS: FA Comps: None
           League: Colchester & East Essex Premier Division 1973-74. Essex & Suffolk Border Division Two 1981-82, 85-86.
10 YEAR RECORD   Eastern Counties Division One 2005-06.

08-09		09-10		10-11		11-12		12-13		13-14		14-15		15-16		16-17		17-18	
ECP	9	ECP	5	ECP	7	ECP	5	ECP	9	ECP	13	ECP	3	ECP	3	ECP	6	ECP	8
FAC	2Qr	FAC	1Qr	FAC	1Qr	FAC	EP	FAC	EP	FAC	EPr	FAC	EP	FAC	2Q	FAC	1Q	FAC	EP
FAV	4Pr	FAV	3P	FAV	3P	FAV	2Q	FAV	2Q	FAV	2Q	FAV	5P	FAV	3P	FAV	2P	FAV	2Q

TAKELEY
Founded: 1903 Nickname:

Club Contact Details (T) 01279 870 404   (E) Takeleyfc@mail.com
Ground: Station Road, Takeley, Bishop's Stortford CM22 6SQ
Nearest Railway Station Stansted Airport (overground) Epping (underground)
Capacity: 2,000 **Seats:** Yes **Covered:** Yes   **Bus Route** from Stansted Airport to Four Ashes Pub.

Colours(change): All royal blue
Previous Names: None.
Previous Leagues: Essex Intermediate/Olympian.

HONOURS: FA Comps: None
           League: Essex Olympian/Intermediate 1987-88, 2001-02, Division Two 1993-94.

10 YEAR RECORD

08-09		09-10		10-11		11-12		12-13		13-14		14-15		15-16		16-17		17-18	
ESen	3	ESen	6	ESen	13	ESen	3	ESen	3	ESen	7	ESen	11	ESen	18	ESen	4	ESen	5
				FAC	EP	FAC	EPr	FAC	P	FAC	EP	FAC	EPr	FAC	EP	FAC	EP	FAC	1Q
		FAV	2Q	FAV	1P	FAV	2Q	FAV	2P	FAV	2P	FAV	1Q	FAV	2Qr	FAV	2Q	FAV	1P

TOWER HAMLETS

Founded: 2000   Nickname: Green Army

Club Contact Details (T) 020 8980 1885   **(E)** thfcsecretary@hotmail.com
Ground: Mile End Stadium, Rhodeswell Rd, Poplar E14 7TW
Nearest Railway Station Mile End (Central, Dist, Hammersmith & City Lines), 5mins walk.
Capacity: 2,000 **Seats:** Yes   **Covered:** Yes   **Bus Route** 309, D6, D7, 277

Colours(change): Orange & black
Previous Names: Bethnal Green United 2000-2013.
Previous Leagues: Canery Wharf Summer League. Inner London. London Intermediate. Middlesex County >2009.

HONOURS: FA Comps: None
League: Middlesex County Premier Division 2008-09.

10 YEAR RECORD

08-09	09-10	10-11	11-12	12-13	13-14	14-15	15-16	16-17	17-18
MidxP 1	ESen 5	ESen 4	ESen 9	ESen 12	ESen 4	ESen 17	ESen 17	ESen 20	ESen 11
					FAC P	FAC EP	FAC Pr	FAC P	FAC P
					FAV 1P	FAV 1P	FAV 1Q	FAV 1Q	FAV 2P

WALTHAM FOREST

Founded: 1964   Nickname: The Stags

Club Contact Details (T)   **(E)**
Ground: Wadham Lodge, Kitchener Road, Walthamstow E17 4JP
Nearest Railway Station Walthamstow Central - Victoria Line/London Overground.
Capacity: 3,500 **Seats:** 216   **Covered:** Yes   **Bus Route** 34,97, 215, 357 – approx. ¼ mile

Colours(change): White & blue
Previous Names: Pennant 1964-88. Walthamstow Pennant 1988-95. Merged with Leyton to form Leyton Pennant 1995-2003.
Previous Leagues: Isthmian 2003-04, 06-14. Southern 2004-06.

HONOURS: FA Comps: None
League: None

10 YEAR RECORD

08-09	09-10	10-11	11-12	12-13	13-14	14-15	15-16	16-17	17-18
Isth1N 20	Isth1N 16	Isth1N 21	Isth1N 17	Isth1N 18	Isth1N 23	ESen 9	ESen 19	ESen 12	ESen 17
FAC P	FAC 1Q	FAC P	FAC 2Q	FAC 2Q	FAC P	FAC EP	FAC EP	FAC 2Q	FAC EPr
FAT P	FAT 1Qr	FAT 1Q	FAT 1Q	FAT 1Q	FAT P	FAV 1P	FAV 2Q	FAV 1P	FAV 1Q

WEST ESSEX

Founded: 1989   Nickname:

Club Contact Details (T) 07956 557 438   **(E)**
Ground: Barking FC, Mayesbrook Park, Lodge Avenue, Dagenham RM8 2JR
Nearest Railway Station Upney (District Line) 2 miles
Capacity: 2,500 **Seats:** 200   **Covered:** 600   **Bus Route** 368 (50 yards) 5, 145, 364 (400 yards)

Colours(change): Red & black
Previous Names: None
Previous Leagues: Ilford & District 1989-94. Essex Business Houses 1994-2010. Middlesex County 2010-2016.

HONOURS: FA Comps: None
League: Essex Business Houses Division One 2008-09.
10 YEAR RECORD Middlesex County Division One (Central & East) 2010-11, Premier Division 2015-16.

08-09	09-10	10-11	11-12	12-13	13-14	14-15	15-16	16-17	17-18
EsxBH1 1	EsxBHP 8	Midx1SE 1	MidxP 11	MidxP 10	MidxP 9	MidxP 7	MidxP 1	ESen 13	ESen 7
									FAC P
								FAV 1Q	FAV 2Q

WOODFORD TOWN 2017

Founded: 2000   Nickname:

Club Contact Details (T)   **(E)**
Ground: The Harlow Arena, Elizabeth Way, Harlow Essex CM19 5BE
Nearest Railway Station Harlow Town, 1 mile
Capacity: 3,500 **Seats:** Yes   **Covered:** Yes

Colours(change): All blue (All red)
Previous Names: Mauritius Sports merged with Walthamstow Ave & Pennant 2007. Mauritius Sports Ass. 09-11. Haringey & Waltham Dev. 11-13. Grhouse London 13-15
Previous Leagues: London Intermediate 2001-03.   **Previous Names Cont:** Greenhouse Sports 15-16. Haringey & Waltham 16-17.
Middlesex County 2003-2007.
HONOURS: FA Comps: None
League: None
10 YEAR RECORD

08-09	09-10	10-11	11-12	12-13	13-14	14-15	15-16	16-17	17-18
ESen 15	ESen 18	ESen 11	ESen 12	ESen 8	ESen 18	ESen 19	ESen 15	ESen 22	ESen 12
		FAC EP	FAC Pr	FAC P	FAC 1Q				
	FAV 1Q	FAV 1Q	FAV 2P	FAV 1Qr	FAV 2Q		FAV 2P		

HELLENIC LEAGUE

Founded: 1953 **Sponsored by:** Uhlsport
Recent Champions: 2015: Flackwell Heath **2016:** Kidlington **2017:** Thame United

PREMIER DIVISION

		P	W	D	L	F	A	GD	Pts
1	Thatcham Town	38	31	5	2	129	25	104	98
2	Bracknell Town	38	32	2	4	129	27	102	98
3	Highworth Town	38	28	4	6	113	50	63	88
4	Wantage Town	38	27	5	6	90	40	50	86
5	Flackwell Heath	38	22	8	8	88	55	33	74
6	Brimscombe & Thrupp	38	22	4	12	74	57	17	70
7	Binfield	38	19	7	12	82	76	6	64
8	Windsor	38	15	7	16	75	74	1	52
9	Longlevens	38	14	8	16	63	77	-14	50
10	Tuffley Rovers	38	14	7	17	50	72	-22	49
11	Oxford City Nomads	38	14	2	22	73	83	-10	44
12	Brackley Town Saints	38	12	7	19	71	63	8	43
13	Abingdon United	38	11	10	17	62	77	-15	43
14	Ascot United	38	12	4	22	54	82	-28	40
15	Royal Wootton Bassett	38	11	6	21	44	85	-41	39
16	Lydney Town	38	9	6	23	45	87	-42	33
17	Highmoor Ibis	38	7	8	23	52	100	-48	29
18	Fairford Town	38	6	10	22	59	98	-39	28
19	Woodley United	38	6	8	24	32	80	-48	26
20	Burnham	38	6	6	26	34	111	-77	21*

DIVISION ONE EAST

		P	W	D	L	F	A	GD	Pts
1	Virginia Water	24	18	4	2	65	26	39	58
2	Bicester Town	24	17	3	4	61	31	30	54
3	Penn & Tylers Green	24	15	3	6	59	34	25	48
4	Sandhurst Town	24	14	3	7	66	37	29	45
5	Holyport	24	13	3	8	61	46	15	42
6	Wokingham & Emmbrook	24	13	2	9	61	38	23	41
7	Wallingford Town	24	10	6	8	39	38	1	36
8	Thame Rangers	24	9	2	13	43	69	-26	29
9	Chalfont Wasps	24	6	3	15	30	54	-24	21
10	Didcot Town Reserves	24	3	11	10	36	42	-6	20
11	AFC Aldermaston	24	5	5	14	32	63	-31	20
12	Chinnor	24	5	4	15	26	57	-31	19
13	Milton United	24	2	3	19	22	66	-44	9

Henley Town withdrew - record expunged.

DIVISION ONE WEST

		P	W	D	L	F	A	GD	Pts
1	Ardley United	26	19	2	5	102	33	69	59
2	Shrivenham	26	17	3	6	74	38	36	54
3	Easington Sports	26	16	3	7	77	36	41	51
4	Pewsey Vale	26	15	4	7	71	38	33	49
5	Cirencester Town Dev'	26	14	4	8	64	41	23	46
6	North Leigh United	26	13	5	8	48	31	17	44
7	Letcombe	26	13	4	9	60	54	6	43
8	Clanfield 85	26	12	4	10	62	38	24	40
9	Headington Amateurs	26	13	1	12	55	44	11	40
10	Cheltenham Saracens	26	10	5	11	51	60	-9	32*
11	Kidlington Reserves	26	8	6	12	47	45	2	30
12	Woodstock Town	26	6	4	16	41	83	-42	22
13	New College	26	3	1	22	26	104	-78	10
14	Tytherington Rocks	26	0	0	26	18	151	-133	0

Shortwood United Res withdrew - record expunged.

LEAGUE CHALLENGE CUP

HOLDERS: BRACKNELL TOWN

ROUND 1

Cirencester Town Dev	v	Bishops Cleeve Dev	0-3
Wallingford Town	v	Ascot United	0-2
Virginia Water	v	Aston Clinton Res	8-1
Henley Town	v	AFC Aldermaston	2-3
North Leigh United	v	Ardley United	2-5
Sandhurst Town	v	Bicester Town	2-0
Bracknell Town	Bye		
Cheltenham Saracens	v	Woodstock Town	2-1
Milton United	v	Long Crendon	1-0
Chalvey Sports	v	Headington Amateurs	3-0
Flackwell Heath	Bye		
Highmoor Ibis	v	Windsor	0-2
New College Swindon	v	Moreton Rangers	1-4
Chalfont Wasps	v	Oxford City Nomads	1-7
Penn & Tylers Green	v	Abingdon Town	2-1
Easington Sports	v	Newest Town	3-0
Fairford Town	v	Kidlington Res	2-1
Clanfield (85)	v	Royal Wootton Bassett Town	0-1
Wantage Town	Bye		
Pewsey Vale	v	Carterton	1-0
Burham	v	Thame Rangers	0-1
Lydney Town	v	Faringdon Town	4-0
Abingdon United	Bye		
Shortwood United Res	v	Brimscombe & Thrupp	3-5 aet
Didcot Town Res	v	Wokingham & Emmbrook	4-2
Letcombe	v	Bourton Rovers	1-2
Thatcham Town	Bye		
Longlevens	v	Tuffley Rovers	2-1
Shrivenham	v	Brackley Town Saints	2-1
Highworth Town	v	Tytherington Rocks	4-1
Holyport	v	Chinnor	1-2
Binfield	v	Woodley United	1-0 aet

ROUND 2

Bishops Cleeve Res	v	Ascot United	1-0
Virginia Water	v	AFC Aldermaston	3-0
Ardley United	v	Sandhurst Town	5-2
Bracknell Town	v	Cheltenham Saracens	9-2
Milton United	v	Chalvey Sports	0-6
Flackwell Heath	v	Windsor	2-3
Moreton Rangers	v	Oxford City Nomads	5-1
Penn & Tylers Green	v	Easington Sports	2-4
Fairford Town	v	Royal Wootton Bassett Town	1-2 aet
Wantage Town	v	Pewsey Vale	1-0
Thame Rangers	v	Lydney Town	1-2
Abingdon United	v	Brimscombe & Thrupp	3-2
Didcot Town Res	v	Bourton Rovers	5-2
Thatcham Town	v	Longlevens	2-1
Shrivenham	v	Highworth Town	1-1, 3-2p
Chinnor	v	Binfield	1-2

ROUND 3

Bishops Cleeve Dev	v	Virginia Water	0-6
Ardley United	v	Bracknell Town	0-1
Chalvey Sports	v	Windsor	0-2
Moreton Rangers	v	Easington Sports	0-1
Royal Wootton Bassett Town	v	Wantage Town	1-5
Lydney Town	v	Abingdon United	0-2
Didcot Town Res	v	Thatcham Town	5-8
Shrivenham	v	Binfield	1-6

QUARTER FINALS

Virginia Water	v	Bracknell Town	0-1
Windsor	v	Easington Sports	4-1
Wantage Town	v	Abingdon United	1-1, 2-4p
Thatcham Town	v	Binfield	3-1

SEMI FINALS

Bracknell Town	v	Windsor	2-1
Abingdon United	v	Thatcham Town	2-4

FINAL

Bracknell Town	v	Thatcham Town	3-1

CLUB MOVEMENTS- Premier Division - In: Ardley United (P), Bishop's Cleeve (R - Sth1W), Bracknell Town (P - IsthSC), Holmer Green (LM - SSMP), Reading City (NC - from Highmoor Ibis), Shrivenham (P), Virginia Water (P). **Out:** Burnham (R), Highmoor Ibis (NC to Reading City), Highworth Town (P - SthW), Oxford City Nomads (F), Thatcham Town (P - SthW), Woodley United (R). **Division One East - In:** Abingdon Town (P), Burnham (R), Chalvey Sports (P), Woodley United (R). **Out:** Chalfont Wasps (D - GG). Virginia Water (P). **Division One West - In:** Almondsbury (LM - WL1), Carterton, Malmesbury Victoria (LM - WL1), Newent Town, Thornbury Town (P - GCL). **Out:** Ardley United (P), Headington Amateurs (D), Lecombe (D), Shrivenham (P), Woodstock Town (D).

PREMIER DIVISION

	Team	1	2	3	4	5	6	7	8	9	10	11	12	13	14	15	16	17	18	19	20
1	Abingdon United		4-0	0-3	1-1	0-5	0-2	2-3	1-0	0-1	3-0	2-2	3-1	4-2	0-2	6-1	1-8	1-1	1-2	0-4	3-0
2	Ascot United	1-1		2-6	1-2	2-0	4-0	2-0	4-2	2-2	2-3	2-6	1-0	4-3	0-4	0-1	1-2	1-1	1-3	4-2	1-3
3	Binfield	3-2	3-1		1-4	0-1	2-3	3-1	3-2	1-1	2-2	3-2	3-2	2-2	1-0	3-1	0-5	2-2	1-1	2-3	3-0
4	Brackley Town Saints	2-2	0-1	1-2		0-2	4-0	8-0	1-1	2-1	2-0	0-1	0-1	1-1	0-1	2-2	0-2	4-0	1-3	3-1	2-0
5	Bracknell Town	3-2	2-0	6-1	4-0		2-0	2-0	10-3	3-2	7-0	2-0	4-0	4-1	5-0	3-1	1-1	8-0	3-0	5-0	6-0
6	Brimscombe & Thrupp	4-1	3-0	1-2	4-1	0-2		4-1	3-1	4-4	1-3	0-2	1-0	1-0	2-0	3-0	0-1	1-0	1-0	4-4	2-0
7	Burnham	2-2	0-2	1-4	0-8	0-7	0-6		1-3	1-3	3-3	2-6	1-5	1-0	1-0	2-0	0-6	0-2	2-2	0-2	1-1
8	Fairford Town	2-2	4-4	1-2	1-2	0-2	2-7	1-1		2-6	3-1	1-5	2-6	1-2	1-3	4-0	1-3	2-1	1-3	6-2	0-1
9	Flackwell Heath	1-1	1-0	1-3	4-2	1-3	1-1	2-1	2-2		6-0	1-3	6-2	4-0	2-0	4-0	1-5	3-1	4-0	3-1	0-0
10	Highmoor Ibis	0-3	2-5	3-2	3-2	2-2	1-2	0-1	3-1	2-3		1-3	0-0	1-1	4-5	0-3	0-6	1-1	1-3	0-4	2-2
11	Highworth Town	2-4	3-0	1-1	1-0	1-0	4-0	1-1	3-1	2-3	5-3		3-3	5-1	7-0	3-2	0-2	3-0	2-4	3-2	6-0
12	Longlevens	3-2	2-0	2-1	4-3	0-3	1-1	2-1	1-1	0-2	2-0	1-6		4-1	3-5	1-1	0-2	1-1	0-2	3-0	1-4
13	Lydney Town	1-2	3-0	2-3	1-3	1-7	1-2	2-1	0-1	1-2	2-4	1-1			3-2	1-1	1-3	1-0	0-4	0-2	1-0
14	Oxford City Nomads	3-1	1-3	2-3	2-2	1-5	0-1	3-1	1-1	2-3	4-3	2-3	5-1	1-2		5-0	1-2	0-2	0-2	2-5	4-0
15	Royal Wootton Bassett Town	1-1	1-0	7-3	1-0	1-3	1-3	3-1	1-1	0-2	1-3	0-1	2-1	1-0	0-5		0-3	3-4	0-3	1-1	2-1
16	Thatcham Town	1-0	3-1	0-0	2-0	3-0	3-0	4-0	5-1	3-3	2-1	1-2	8-1	8-0	5-1	6-0		4-1	3-1	2-2	3-0
17	Tuffley Rovers	2-0	2-1	2-3	3-3	1-2	3-1	3-1	1-1	1-2	2-1	0-4	0-1	2-1	2-1	0-2	0-7		1-2	1-0	1-0
18	Wantage Town	5-0	4-0	2-0	3-2	3-2	5-0	2-0	2-0	2-0	1-3	1-1	1-2	4-1	3-0	2-1	3-1	3-1		0-0	4-0
19	Windsor	2-3	3-0	4-3	4-2	0-1	2-3	2-0	1-1	3-1	1-2	0-3	2-1	3-0	0-1	1-3	1-3	2-2			2-1
20	Woodley United	1-1	0-1	3-2	2-1	0-2	1-2	0-2	0-1	0-1	1-0	0-0	1-3	0-3	1-1	0-4	3-2	1-1	0-2	2-3	

DIVISION ONE EAST

	Team	1	2	3	4	5	6	7	8	9	10	11	12	13
1	AFC Aldermaston		0-1	2-1	4-0	1-1	0-4	4-3	1-4	3-5	2-0	1-1	1-1	2-4
2	Bicester Town	6-2		5-1	3-2	0-0	3-2	2-0	2-0	2-0	2-0	2-0	5-2	2-3
3	Chalfont Wasps	0-1	2-3		0-2	H-W	0-1	2-1	0-4	1-2	1-0	1-2	2-1	0-2
4	Chinnor	3-0	0-2	1-1		0-0	2-3	0-0	1-2	0-6	1-1	0-2	0-1	2-0
5	Didcot Town Reserves	2-2	1-1	2-2	1-3		1-2	2-0	0-1	3-2	3-4	1-3	0-0	1-4
6	Holyport	3-2	2-2	8-1	3-0	2-2		4-0	0-2	2-0	8-1	1-1	0-5	3-0
7	Milton United	2-1	1-5	1-2	2-3	1-1	3-2		0-2	0-0	0-1	1-3	2-3	0-5
8	Penn & Tylers Green	5-2	1-0	0-4	8-3	2-2	3-0	8-1		1-4	4-2	1-1	2-3	1-0
9	Sandhurst Town	3-0	1-4	5-1	4-1	4-1	6-1	2-1	3-2		5-1	1-2	2-2	3-4
10	Thame Rangers	4-0	2-3	3-2	5-1	0-7	3-4	5-2	1-3	3-2		1-1	0-2	1-0
11	Virginia Water	4-0	4-2	4-3	3-0	2-1	4-1	6-0	2-0	0-3	5-1		7-1	3-1
12	Wallingford Town AFC	1-1	1-2	2-1	3-0	2-2	2-1	1-0	1-1	0-1	3-4	1-2		0-2
13	Wokingham & Emmbrook	5-0	4-2	2-2	3-1	4-2	3-4	2-1	1-2	2-2	8-0	2-3	0-1	

DIVISION ONE WEST

	Team	1	2	3	4	5	6	7	8	9	10	11	12	13	14
1	Ardley United		6-1	3-1	0-3	2-1	1-2	3-0	9-2	3-0	2-0	3-2	2-0	10-0	10-1
2	Cheltenham Saracens	0-2		2-4	3-1	2-5	2-1	3-3	0-2	4-0	4-0	0-1	3-0	6-2	1-1
3	Cirencester Town Dev'	1-3	6-0		1-1	1-3	3-1	4-2	5-1	4-3	2-2	2-0	0-1	2-0	5-1
4	Clanfield (85)	4-1	2-2	3-1		0-1	0-1	0-0	3-1	4-0	1-3	1-2	2-0	3-0	5-0
5	Easington Sports	4-2	1-2	0-0	4-3		2-1	2-1	3-5	1-2	4-0	2-1	1-1	9-1	8-2
6	Headington Amateurs	0-4	4-0	1-4	2-1	1-2		1-1	3-2	3-2	1-2	0-3	0-1	4-3	5-1
7	Kidlington Reserves	0-1	4-1	1-1	1-2	1-6	2-3		3-4	3-1	1-0	1-4	1-0	9-0	1-1
8	Letcombe	1-1	1-0	2-1	3-2	1-2	0-2	1-1		1-0	0-0	0-2	1-6	5-0	5-2
9	New College Swindon	2-8	2-4	1-4	0-5	0-4	1-5	0-2	2-9		0-4	0-6	0-5	4-1	1-1
10	North Leigh United	1-0	1-2	3-0	3-1	2-1	3-0	1-1	2-3	3-0		2-3	0-1	2-0	2-0
11	Pewsey Vale	0-4	3-3	2-3	1-1	2-1	1-0	3-2	1-1	10-1	1-1		0-3	6-1	6-0
12	Shrivenham	6-6	5-0	3-2	6-3	1-1	3-1	2-0	2-0	6-1	0-4	4-2		9-2	2-1
13	Tytherington Rocks	0-11	1-4	2-6	1-7	0-8	0-8	0-5	0-4	0-3	1-5	0-6	0-7		3-4
14	Woodstock Town	1-5	2-2	0-1	1-4	2-1	0-5	2-1	2-5	4-0	2-2	2-3	5-0	4-0	

PREMIER DIVISION

ABINGDON UNITED
Founded: 1946   Nickname: The Yellows

Club Contact Details   (T) 01235 203 203   (E) secretaryaufc@virginmedia.com
Ground: The Northcourt, Northcourt Road, Abingdon OX14 1PL
Nearest Railway Station Radley - 2.5km
Capacity: 2,000 **Seats:** 158   **Covered:** 258   **Bus Route** Boundary House (Oxford Rd) stop - 215m

Colours(change): Yellow/blue/blue
Previous Names: None
Previous Leagues: North Berkshire 1949-58, Hellenic 1958-2006. Southern 2006-13.

HONOURS: FA Comps: None
     League: North Berks 1952-53.

10 YEAR RECORD

	08-09	09-10	10-11	11-12	12-13	13-14	14-15	15-16	16-17	17-18
	Sthsw 15	Sthsw 14	Sthsw 16	Sthsw 18	Sthsw 20	Hel P 17	Hel P 15	Hel P 19	Hel1W 2	Hel P 13
	FAC Pr	FAC 2Qr	FAC P	FAC 1Q	FAC P	FAC EPr	FAC 2Q	FAC EP	FAC EPr	
	FAT 1Q	FAT 1Q	FAT 1Q	FAT P	FAT P	FAV 1P	FAV 2Pr	FAV 1Q	FAV 1P	FAV 2Q

ARDLEY UNITED
Founded: 1945   Nickname: None

Club Contact Details   (T) 07961 488 800   (E) sharon.smith23@talk21.com
Ground: The Playing Fields, Fritwell Road, Ardley OX27 7PA
Nearest Railway Station Bicester North - 6.3km
Capacity: 1,000 **Seats:** 100   **Covered:** 200   **Shop:** No   **Bus Route** Water Lane stop - 121m away

Colours(change): All sky blue
Previous Names: None
Previous Leagues: Oxford Senior. Volunteered for relegation after 2016-17 season.

HONOURS: FA Comps: None
     League: Banbury District & Lord Jersey FA Divion One 1984-85. Oxfordshire Senior Division One 1988-89, Premier 1990-91. Hellenic Division One 1996-97, 97-98, Division One West 2017-18.

10 YEAR RECORD

	08-09	09-10	10-11	11-12	12-13	13-14	14-15	15-16	16-17	17-18
	Hel P 5	Hel P 7	Hel P 3	Hel P 3	Hel P 5	Hel P 2	Hel P 8	Hel P 13	Hel P 5	Hel1W 1
	FAC EP	FAC EPr	FAC EP	FAC Pr	FAC P	FAC 1Qr	FAC 2Q	FAC EP	FAC P	FAC EP
	FAV 2Q	FAV 1P	FAV 2Q	FAV 1P	FAV 3P	FAV 1Q	FAV 1P	FAV 1Q	FAV 2Q	FAV 1Q

ASCOT UNITED
Founded: 1965   Nickname: Yellaman

Club Contact Details   (T) 01344 291 107 (Ground)   (E) secascotutdfc@yahoo.com
Ground: Ascot Racecourse, Car Park 10, Winkfield Rd, Ascot SL5 7RA
Nearest Railway Station Ascot - 1.3km
Capacity: 1,150 **Seats:**   **Covered:**   **Shop:** Yes   **Bus Route** Hilltop Close (Cheapside Rd) stop - 934m

Colours(change): Yellow/blue/yellow
Previous Names: None.
Previous Leagues: Reading Senior.

HONOURS: FA Comps: None
     League: Reading Senior Division 2006-07.

10 YEAR RECORD

	08-09	09-10	10-11	11-12	12-13	13-14	14-15	15-16	16-17	17-18
	Hel1E 2	Hel P 15	Hel P 12	Hel P 14	Hel P 7	Hel P 3	Hel P 3	Hel P 4	Hel P 15	Hel P 14
				FAC EP	FAC P	FAC EP	FAC P	FAC EP	FAC 1Qr	FAC P
			FAV 2Q	FAV 2Q	FAV QFr	FAV 2P	FAV QF	FAV 3Pr	FAV 2P	FAV 1Q

BINFIELD
Founded: 1892   Nickname: Moles

Club Contact Details   (T) 01344 860 822 (Ground)   (E) robchallis@binfieldfc.com
Ground: Stubbs Lane off Hill Farm Lane, Binfield RG42 5NR
Nearest Railway Station Bracknell - 3.9km
Capacity: **Seats:** yes   **Covered:** yes   **Bus Route** Church Lane North stop - 628m

Colours(change): All red
Previous Names: None.
Previous Leagues: Ascot & District. Great Western Combination. Reading & Dist. Chiltonian.

HONOURS: FA Comps: None
     League: Great Western Combination 1946-47. Reading & District Division One 1975-76, 87-88, Division Two 86-87. Hellenic Division One East 2008-09.

10 YEAR RECORD

	08-09	09-10	10-11	11-12	12-13	13-14	14-15	15-16	16-17	17-18
	Hel1E 1	Hel P 8	Hel P 2	Hel P 8	Hel P 3	Hel P 5	Hel P 6	Hel P 8	Hel P 8	Hel P 7
		FAC EP	FAC 1Q	FAC P	FAC EP	FAC 2Q	FAC EP	FAC P	FAC EP	FAC P
	FAV 2P	FAV 1Q	FAV 2P	FAV 4P	FAV 3P	FAV 3P	FAV 2Q	FAV 1Qr	FAV 2Q	FAV 2Q

BISHOP'S CLEEVE
Founded: 1905   Nickname: The Mitres

Club Contact Details (T) 01242 676 166 (Ground)   (E) themitres@outlook.com
Ground: Kayte Lane, Bishop's Cleeve, Cheltenham GL52 3PD
Nearest Railway Station Cheltenham Spa - 4.9km
Capacity: 1,500 **Seats:** 50   **Covered:** 50   Yes   **Bus Route** Bus stops outside the ground

Colours(change): All Green
Previous Names: None
Previous Leagues: Cheltenham. North Gloucestershire. Hellenic 1983-2006. Southern 2006-18.

HONOURS: FA Comps: None
League: Cheltenham Division Two 1924-25, 30-31, 58-59, Division One 31-32, 34-35, 61-62, 63-64, 65-66, 66-67.
Gloucestershire Northern Senior Division Two 1967-68, Division One 68-69, 69-70, 72-73. Hellenic Division One

10 YEAR RECORD	08-09	09-10	10-11	11-12	12-13	13-14	14-15	15-16	16-17	17-18
	Sthsw 18	Sthsw 11	Sthsw 15	Sthsw 11	Sthsw 21	Sthsw 20	Sthsw 21	Sthsw 12	Sthsw 16	Sth1W 22
FAC	P	3Q	2Q	P	2Q	Pr	1Q	P	Pr	1Q
FAT	1Q	P	1Q	P	1Q	P	1Q	P	2Q	P

BRACKLEY TOWN SAINTS
Founded: 1890   Nickname: The Saints

Club Contact Details (T) 01280 704 077 (Ground)   (E) matthewwise@banburylitho.co.uk
Ground: St James Park, Churchill Way, Brackley, Northamptonshire, NN13 7EF
Capacity: 3,500 **Seats:** 300   **Covered:** 1,500   **Bus Route** Tesco (Oxford Rd) stop - 38m away

Colours(change): Red & white/white/red
Previous Names: Brackley Town Development > 2015
Previous Leagues: None

HONOURS: FA Comps: None
League: None

10 YEAR RECORD	08-09	09-10	10-11	11-12	12-13	13-14	14-15	15-16	16-17	17-18
							Hel1E 2	Hel P 16	Hel P 13	Hel P 12
FAC										EP
FAV									1Qr	1Q

BRIMSCOMBE & THRUPP
Founded: 1886   Nickname: Lilywhites

Club Contact Details (T) 07833 231 464   (E) allanboulton1@sky.com
Ground: 'The Meadow', London Road, Brimscombe Stroud, Gloucestershire GL5 2SH
Nearest Railway Station Stroud - 2.9km
Capacity: **Seats:** Yes   **Covered:** Yes   **Bus Route** Brewery Lane stop - 261m away

Colours(change): All blue
Previous Names: Brimscombe AFC 1886- late 1970s. Brimscombe and Thrupp merged.
Previous Leagues: Stroud & District. Gloucestershire Northern Senior. Gloucestershire County

HONOURS: FA Comps: None
League: Stroud & Dist. 1902-03, 06-07, 07-08, 12-13. Gloucestershire Northern Senior 1922-23, 30-31, 47-48, Division
Two 2004-05. Gloucestershire County 2010-11. Hellenic Division One West 2012-13.

10 YEAR RECORD	08-09	09-10	10-11	11-12	12-13	13-14	14-15	15-16	16-17	17-18
		GlCo 5	GlCo 1	Hel1W 4	Hel1W 1	Hel P 12	Hel P 10	Hel P 5	Hel P 7	Hel P 6
FAC							EP	Pr	3Q	P
FAV						2P	1P	3Pr	2Pr	1Q

FAIRFORD TOWN
Founded: 1891   Nickname: Town

Club Contact Details (T) 01285 712 071 (Ground)   (E) andyfiddler1706@gmail.com
Ground: Cinder Lane, London Road, Fairford GL7 4AX
Capacity: 2,000 **Seats:** 100   **Covered:** 250   **Shop:** Yes   **Bus Route** Hatherop Lane stop - 124m

Colours(change): All red.
Previous Names: None.
Previous Leagues: Cirencester & District. Swindon & District.

HONOURS: FA Comps: None
League: Swindon & District Prmeier Division 1964-65, 68-69.

10 YEAR RECORD	08-09	09-10	10-11	11-12	12-13	13-14	14-15	15-16	16-17	17-18
Hellenic Division One A 1971-72, Division One West 2016-17.	Hel P 14	Hel P 20	Hel P 21	Hel P 20	Hel1W 4	Hel1W 4	Hel1W 14	Hel1W 4	Hel1W 1	Hel P 18
FAC	1Q	EP	EP	EPr	P	EP	EP		EP	EPr
FAV	2Qr	2Q	1P	1P	1P	1P	2Q	1Q	1P	1Q

FLACKWELL HEATH
Founded: 1907   Nickname: Heathens

Club Contact Details (T) 01628 523 892 / 07932 952 538   (E) joparsons19@sky.com
Ground: Wilks Park, Magpie Lane, Heath End Rd, Flackwell Hth HP10 9EA
Nearest Railway Station Bourne End - 3km
Capacity: 2,000 **Seats:** 150   **Covered:** Yes   **Bus Route** Fernlea Close stop - 106m

Colours(change): All red.
Previous Names: None.
Previous Leagues: High Wycombe & District 1907-50. Great Western Combination 1950-76. Hellenic 1976-82. Athenian 1982-84. Isthmian 1984-2007.
HONOURS: FA Comps: None
League: Great Western Combination Division Two 1950-51, Premier 1957-58, 62-63.

10 YEAR RECORD	Hellenic Premier Division 2014-15.								
08-09	09-10	10-11	11-12	12-13	13-14	14-15	15-16	16-17	17-18
Hel P 16	Hel P 4	Hel P 8	Hel P 4	Hel P 10	Hel P 8	Hel P 1	Hel P 3	Hel P 3	Hel P 5
FAC P	FAC 2Q	FAC P	FAC EP	FAC EP	FAC EPr	FAC 3Q	FAC EP	FAC 1Q	FAC P
FAV 1P	FAV 3P	FAV 2P	FAV 3P	FAV 1P	FAV 1Q	FAV 5P	FAV 2P	FAV 1P	FAV 1P

HOLMER GREEN
Founded: 1908   Nickname: The Greens

Club Contact Details (T) 01494 711 485 (Ground)   (E) j.ostinelli@sky.com
Ground: Airedale Park, Watchet Lane, Holmer Green, Bucks HP15 6UF
Nearest Railway Station Great Missenden - 4.3km
Capacity: 1,000 **Seats:** 25   **Covered:** yes   **Bus Route** Copners Drive - stop 350m away

Colours(change): Green & white
Previous Names: None
Previous Leagues: Chesham & District 1908-38, Wycombe Combination 1984-95, Chiltonian 1995-98. Spartan South Midlands 1998-2018.
HONOURS: FA Comps: None
League: Wycombe Combination 1971-72, 73-74, 76-77, 80-81. Chiltonian Prmeier 1984-85, 85-86, 93-94.

10 YEAR RECORD	South Midlands Senior 1995-96. Spartan South Midlands 1998-99, Division One 2009-10.								
08-09	09-10	10-11	11-12	12-13	13-14	14-15	15-16	16-17	17-18
SSM P 20	SSM1 1	SSM P 17	SSM P 20	SSM P 22	SSM P 12	SSM P 20	SSM P 7	SSM P 14	SSM P 14
			FAC EP	FAC EP	FAC EP	FAC Pr	FAC EP	FAC EP	FAC P
		FAV 1Q	FAV 1Q	FAV 2Q	FAV 2Q	FAV 1Pr	FAV 1Q	FAV 2P	FAV 1Q

LONGLEVENS AFC
Founded: 1954   Nickname: Levens

Club Contact Details (T) 01452 530 388 (Clubhouse)   (E) bill1853@outlook.com
Ground: Saw Mills End, Corinium Avenue, Gloucester GL4 3DG
Nearest Railway Station Gloucester - 1.9km
Capacity: 500   **Seats:** Yes   **Covered:** Yes   **Bus Route** Budgen's Garage stop - 146m away

Colours(change): Red & black
Previous Names: None
Previous Leagues: Gloucestershire Northern Senior > 2011. Gloucestershire County 2011-14.
HONOURS: FA Comps: None
League: Gloucestershire Northern Division One 2008-09. Gloucestershire County 2012-13, 13-14.

10 YEAR RECORD	Hellenic Division One West 2014-15.								
08-09	09-10	10-11	11-12	12-13	13-14	14-15	15-16	16-17	17-18
GlN1 1	GlN1 5	GlN1 4	GlCo 9	GlCo 1	GlCo 1	Hel1W 1	Hel P 10	Hel P 12	Hel P 9
								FAC P	FAC P
							FAV 1Q	FAV 2Q	FAV 1P

LYDNEY TOWN
Founded: 1911   Nickname: The Town

Club Contact Details (T) 01594 844 523 (Ground)   (E) rogersansom@outlook.com
Ground: Lydney Recreation Ground, Swan Road, Lydney GL15 5RU
Nearest Railway Station Lydney Town - 144m
Capacity: 1,000 **Seats:** Yes   **Covered:** Yes   **Bus Route** Forest Parade - 156m away

Colours(change): Black & white
Previous Names: None
Previous Leagues: Local leagues 1911-52. Gloucestershire Northern Senior 1952-80, 84-. Hellenic 1980-84. Gloucestershire County 2005-06.
HONOURS: FA Comps: None
League: Gloucesteshire Northern Senior 1979-80. Gloucestershire County 2005-06. Hellenic League Division One West

10 YEAR RECORD	2006-07.								
08-09	09-10	10-11	11-12	12-13	13-14	14-15	15-16	16-17	17-18
Hel1W 8	Hel1W 8	Hel1W 5	Hel1W 13	Hel1W 10	Hel1W 2	Hel1W 3	Hel P 12	Hel P 9	Hel P 16
	FAC EP	FAC P	FAC EP					FAC EP	FAC EP
FAV 1Q	FAV 1Q	FAV 1P	FAV 1P	FAV 2Q	FAV 2Q		FAV 2Q	FAV 1P	FAV 2Q

READING CITY

Founded: 2001 **Nickname:** Mighty Moor

Club Contact Details (T) 07918 880 777 (E) chris.gallimore@sjpp.co.uk
Ground: Scours Lane, Tilehurst, Reading RG30 6AY
Nearest Railway Station Tilehurst - 1.2km
Capacity: **Seats:** Yes **Covered:** Yes **Bus Route** Cold Store stop - 277m away
Colours(change): Blue and white
Previous Names: Highmoor and Ibis merged to form today's club in 2001. Highmoor Ibis 2001-18.
Previous Leagues: Reading 2001-2011.

HONOURS: FA Comps: None
League: Reading Senior Division 2003-04, 10-11.

10 YEAR RECORD

08-09	09-10	10-11	11-12	12-13	13-14	14-15	15-16	16-17	17-18
ReadS 2	ReadS 4	ReadS 1	Hel1E 2	Hel P 12	Hel P 4	Hel P 2	Hel P 11	Hel P 14	Hel P 17
					FAC 1Q	FAC P	FAC EP	FAC P	FAC P
				FAV 2Q	FAV 1P	FAV 1P	FAV 1P	FAV 1P	FAV 1Q

ROYAL WOOTTON BASSETT

Founded: 1882 **Nickname:** Bassett

Club Contact Details (T) 01793 853 880 (Ground) (E) ian.thomas@wbtfc.co.uk
Ground: Gerrard Buxton Sports Ground Malmesbury Rd Royal Wootton Bassett SN4 8DS

Capacity: 4,500 **Seats:** 550 **Covered:** 1,250 **Shop:** No **Bus Route** The Farm stop - 69m
Colours(change): All blue
Previous Names: Wootton Bassett Town > 2015.
Previous Leagues: Vale of White 1898-99. Swindon & District 1899-1903. Wiltshire County 1903-08, 35-69, 76-88. Calne & District 1930. Wiltshire Combination 1969-76.
HONOURS: FA Comps: None
League: Calne & District 1931-32, 34-35, 35-36.

10 YEAR RECORD Wiltshire Division One 1958-59, Division Two 1984-85, Division One 1987-88.

08-09	09-10	10-11	11-12	12-13	13-14	14-15	15-16	16-17	17-18
Hel1W 4	Hel1W 2	Hel P 15	Hel1W 5	Hel1W 2	Hel P 14	Hel P 11	Hel P 15	Hel P 11	Hel P 15
FAC EPr	FAC P	FAC 1Qr	FAC EP	FAC 2Q	FAC EP	FAC P	FAC EP	FAC EP	FAC EP
FAV 2P	FAV 1Q	FAV 1P	FAV 1Q	FAV 1Q	FAV 2Q	FAV 2Q	FAV 2Q	FAV 2Q	FAV 2P

SHRIVENHAM

Founded: 1900 **Nickname:** Shrivy

Club Contact Details (T) 07711 263 113 (E) m.hirst@shrivenhamfc.co.uk
Ground: The Recreation Ground, Barrington Park, Shrivenham SN6 8BJ

Capacity: **Seats:** **Covered:** **Bus Route** Green (Townsend Rd) stop - 268m away
Colours(change): Blue & white
Previous Names: None.
Previous Leagues: North Berkshire.

HONOURS: FA Comps: None
League: North Berks Division Two 1994-95, Division One 1997-98, 2000-01.

10 YEAR RECORD Hellenic Division One West 2004-05.

08-09	09-10	10-11	11-12	12-13	13-14	14-15	15-16	16-17	17-18
Hel P 18	Hel P 16	Hel P 20	Hel P 16	Hel P 19	Hel P 15	Hel P 19	Hel1W 8	Hel1W 7	Hel1W 2
FAC EP	FAC 1Q	FAC 1Q	FAC EP	FAC P	FAC EP	FAC P	FAC EP		
FAT 2Pr	FAT 1P	FAT 1P	FAV 2Q	FAV 2Q	FAV 2Q	FAV 1Q	FAV 2Q	FAV 1Q	

TUFFLEY ROVERS

Founded: 1929 **Nickname:** Rovers

Club Contact Details (T) 07545 492 261 (E) admin@tuffleyroversfc.co.uk
Ground: Glevum Park Lower Tuffley Lane, Tuffley, Gloucester GL2 5DT
Nearest Railway Station Gloucester - 3.5km
Capacity: 1,000 **Seats:** 100 **Covered:** yes **Bus Route** Pearce Way stop - 197m away
Colours(change): Claret & blue
Previous Names: None
Previous Leagues: Gloucestershire County 1988-91, 2007-13. Hellenic 1991-06. Gloucestershire Northern 2006-07.

HONOURS: FA Comps: None
League: Gloucester County 1990-91. Gloucestershire Northern Division One 2006-07.

10 YEAR RECORD

08-09	09-10	10-11	11-12	12-13	13-14	14-15	15-16	16-17	17-18
GlCo 11	GlCo 3	GlCo 6	GlCo 3	GlCo 2	Hel1W 6	Hel1W 2	Hel P 17	Hel P 10	Hel P 10
							FAC 1Q	FAC EP	FAC 1Q
						FAV 1P	FAV 1Q	FAV 2P	FAV 1Q

VIRGINIA WATER
Founded: 1920   Nickname: The Waters

Club Contact Details **(T)** 01753 860 656 (Ground)   **(E)** gp738@hotmail.com
Ground: Windsor FC, Stag Meadow, St Leonards Road Windsor SL4 3DR
Nearest Railway Station Windsor & Eton Central - 1.5km
Capacity: **Seats:**   **Covered:**   **Bus Route** Stag Meadow stop - 131m away

Colours(change):   Maroon
Previous Names:
Previous Leagues: Surrey Elite Intermediate >2017

HONOURS: FA Comps: None
      League: Surrey County Premier Division 1992-93, 96-97. Surrey Elite Intermediate 2016-17.

10 YEAR RECORD	Hellenic Division One East 2017-18.								
08-09	09-10	10-11	11-12	12-13	13-14	14-15	15-16	16-17	17-18
		SuEI 6	SuEI 14	SuEI 11	SuEI 8	SuEI 7	SuEI 5	SuEI 1	Hel1E 1

WANTAGE TOWN
Founded: 1892   Nickname: Alfredians

Club Contact Details **(T)** 01235 764 781 (Ground)   **(E)** wantagetownfc-secretary@outlook.com
Ground: Alfredian Park, Manor Road, Wantage OX12 8DW

Capacity: 1,500 **Seats:** 50   **Covered:** 300   **Bus Route** King Alfreds School stop - 423m away

Colours(change):   Green & white/white/green with white hoops
Previous Names: None.
Previous Leagues: Swindon & District. North Berkshire. Reading & District. Hellenic > 2014. Southern 2014-17.

HONOURS: FA Comps: None
      League: Swindon & District 1907-08, 33-34, 52-53, 55-56. North Berks Division One 1919-20, 21-22.

10 YEAR RECORD	Hellenic Division 1 East 1980-81, 03-04, Premier Division 2010-11, 13-14.								
08-09	09-10	10-11	11-12	12-13	13-14	14-15	15-16	16-17	17-18
Hel P 11	Hel P 5	Hel P 1	Hel P 12	Hel P 2	Hel P 1	Sthsw 20	Sthsw 20	Sthsw 21	Hel P 4
FAC EP	FAC 1Q	FAC EP	FAC P	FAC 1Q	FAC P	FAC 1Qr	FAC P	FAC 1Qr	FAC P
FAV 2Q	FAV 1P	FAV 3P	FAV 3P	FAV 2P	FAV 2P	FAT P	FAT P	FAT 1Qr	FAV 2P

WINDSOR
Founded: 1892   Nickname: The Royalists

Club Contact Details **(T)** 01753 860 656 (Ground)   **(E)** gp738@hotmail.com
Ground: Stag Meadow, St Leonards Road, Windsor, Berks SL4 3DR
Nearest Railway Station Windsor & Eton - 1.5km
Capacity: 4,500 **Seats:** 450   **Covered:** 650   **Shop:** Yes **Bus Route** Stag Meadow stop - 131m away

Colours(change):   Red, white & green
Previous Names: Formed when Windsor Phoenix and Windsor St. Albans merged in 1892. Windsor & Eton 1892-2011.
Previous Leagues: W.Berks, Gt Western, Suburban, Athenian 22-29,63-81, Spartan 29-32, Gt W.Comb. Corinthian 45-50, Met 50-60,
      Delphian 60-63, Isthmian 1963-2006, Stouthern 2006-11. Combined Counties 2011-17.

HONOURS: FA Comps: None
      League: Athenian League 1979-80, 80-81. Isthmian League Division 1 1983-84.

10 YEAR RECORD	Southern League Division 1 South & West 2009-10.								
08-09	09-10	10-11	11-12	12-13	13-14	14-15	15-16	16-17	17-18
Sthsw 2	Sthsw 1	SthP Exp	CCP 2	CCP 6	CCP 6	CCP 5	CCP 12	CCP 11	Hel P 8
FAC P	FAC 2Q	FAC 1Q		FAC 1Q	FAC P	FAC P	FAC EP	FAC EP	FAC EP
FAT 3Q	FAT 1Qr	FAT 2Q	FAV 2Q	FAV 1P	FAV 1P	FAV 1P	FAV 1P	FAV 1Q	FAV QF

ABINGDON TOWN
Founded: 1870   Nickname: The Abbots

Club Contact Details (T) 07585 443 656
(E) secretary@abingdonfc.co.uk
Ground: Culham Road, Abingdon OX14 3HP
Capacity: 3,000

HONOURS
FA Comps: None
League: Oxford & District 1899-00, 1900-01. North Berks 1919-20, 22-23. Reading & District 1947-48. Spartan Premier 1988-89. Hellenic Premier 1956-57, 58-59, 59-60, 86-87, Division One 75-76.
Colours(change): Yellow and green

10 YEAR RECORD

08-09	09-10	10-11	11-12	12-13	13-14	14-15	15-16	16-17	17-18
Hel P 19	Hel P 12	Hel P 14	Hel P 11	Hel P 18	Hel P 20	NBk 1 3	NBk 1 5		Hel2E 7
FAC EP	FAC EP	FAC EP	FAC Pr	FAC P	FAC EP				
FAV 2Q	FAV 2Q	FAV 2Q	FAV 1P	FAV 1Q	FAV 1P				

AFC ALDERMASTON
Founded: 1952   Nickname: The Atomics

Club Contact Details (T) 01189 824 454 (Ground)
(E) martin.desay@gmail.com
Ground: AWE, Aldermaston, Reading RG7 8UA
Nearest Railway Station Midgham - 4km
Bus Route Calleva Park stop - 48m away
HONOURS
FA Comps: None
League: None
Colours(change): Red & black

10 YEAR RECORD

08-09	09-10	10-11	11-12	12-13	13-14	14-15	15-16	16-17	17-18
Wex1 14	Wex1 21	HantP 15	HantP 9	HantP 8	HantP 10	ReadP 5	ReadP 7	Hel1E 7	Hel1E 11
									FAV 1Q

BICESTER TOWN
Founded: 1876   Nickname: Foxhunters

Club Contact Details (T) 07184 676 319
(E) david_powell_128@msn.com
Ground: Ardley United FC, The Playing Fields Fritwell Road Ardley OX27 7PA
Nearest Railway Station Bicester North - 6.3km
Bus Route Water Lane stop - 121m away
HONOURS
FA Comps: None
League: Hellenic 1960-61, 79-80, Division One 1977-78.
Colours(change): Red & black

10 YEAR RECORD

08-09	09-10	10-11	11-12	12-13	13-14	14-15	15-16	16-17	17-18
Hel P 20	Hel P 21	Hel1W 2					Hel1E 2	Hel1E 5	Hel1E 2
	FAC EP	FAC EP							
FAV 1Q	FAV 2Q	FAV 1Q						FAV 2Q	

BURNHAM
Founded: 1878   Nickname: The Blues

Club Contact Details (T) 01628 668 654 (Ground)
(E) burnhamfcsec@aol.com
Ground: The Gore, Wymers Wood Road, Burnham, Slough SL1 8JG
2,500
Nearest Railway Station Taplow - 1.9km
Bus Route Pink Lane stop - 239m away
HONOURS
FA Comps: None
League: Hellenic 1975-76, 98-99. London Spartan 1984-85. Southern Division One Central 2012-13.
Colours(change): Blue & white

10 YEAR RECORD

08-09	09-10	10-11	11-12	12-13	13-14	14-15	15-16	16-17	17-18
Sthsw 17	SthM 3	SthC 14	SthC 15	SthC 1	SthP 20	SthP 23	Sthsw 21	Hel P 17	Hel P 20
FAC Pr	FAC 2Qr	FAC 2Q	FAC 3Q	FAC P	FAC 2Q	FAC 2Q	FAC Pr	FAC EP	FAC EP
FAT 2Q	FAT 3Q	FAT 1Qr	FAT Pr	FAT 2Q	FAT 2Q	FAT 2Qr	FAT P	FAV 2Q	FAV 2Q

CHALVEY SPORTS
Founded: 1885   Nickname: The Stab Monks

Club Contact Details (T) 07768 010760
(E) chalveysportsfc@gmail.com
Ground: Stoke Road, Slough SL2 5AY

HONOURS
FA Comps:
League: Great Western Combination 1954-55. East Berkshire Division One 1992-93, Premier 96-97. Hellenic Division Two East 2016-17, 17-18.
Colours(change): All navy

10 YEAR RECORD

08-09	09-10	10-11	11-12	12-13	13-14	14-15	15-16	16-17	17-18
	EBkP 8	EBkP 10	EBkP 8	EBkP 7	EBkP 2	EBkP 2	EBkP 2	Hel2E 1	Hel2E 1

CHINNOR

Founded: 1971   Nickname: The Biz

Club Contact Details (T) 01844 350 049   (E) daryl.ridgley@btopenworld.com
Ground: Station Road, Chinnor, Oxon OX39 4PX
Nearest Railway Station Princes Risborough - 4.9km   **Bus Route** Duck Square stop - 56m away
HONOURS   League: None
FA Comps: None

Colours(change): All blue

10 YEAR RECORD

08-09	09-10	10-11	11-12	12-13	13-14	14-15	15-16	16-17	17-18
Hel1E 8	Hel1E 10	Hel1E 13	Hel1E 10	Hel1E 6	Hel1E 8	Hel1E 5	Hel1E 6	Hel1E 10	Hel1E 12
					FAC EP		FAC EP		
				FAV 2Q	FAV 2Q	FAV 1P	FAV 1Q		

DIDCOT TOWN RESERVES

Founded: 1907   Nickname: Railwaymen

Club Contact Details (T) 01235 813 138   (E) jacquelyn.dtfc@btinternet.com
Ground: Loop Meadow Stadium, Bowmont Water, Didcot OX11 7GA   **Capacity:** 5,000
Nearest Railway Station Didcot Parkway - 0.4km   **Bus Route** Ladygrove Park Primary School stop - 171m
HONOURS   League: None
FA Comps: None

Colours(change): All red

10 YEAR RECORD

08-09	09-10	10-11	11-12	12-13	13-14	14-15	15-16	16-17	17-18
	Hel1E 15	Hel1E 14	Hel1E 16	Hel1E 3	Hel1E 12	Hel1E 12	Hel1E 11	Hel1E 9	Hel1E 10

HOLYPORT

Founded: 1934   Nickname: The Villagers

Club Contact Details (T) 07515 789 415   (E) richardtyrell@googlemail.com
Ground: Summerleaze Village, 7 Summerleaze Road SL6 8SP
Nearest Railway Station Furze Platt - 1km   **Bus Route** Veterinary Hospital stop - 133m away
HONOURS   League: Hayes & Giles Premier Division 1998-99, 99-2000, 01-02.
FA Comps: None   Hellenic Division One East 2010-11.

Colours(change): Claret & green

10 YEAR RECORD

08-09	09-10	10-11	11-12	12-13	13-14	14-15	15-16	16-17	17-18
Hel1E 5	Hel1E 3	Hel1E 1	Hel P 13	Hel P 14	Hel P 18	Hel P 16	Hel1E 7	Hel1E 13	Hel1E 5
		FAC EP	FAC EP	FAC EP	FAC EP	FAC EPr	FAC EP		
FAV 2Q	FAV 2Q	FAV 2P	FAV 1Q	FAV 1P	FAV 2Q	FAV 1Q	FAV 1Qr	FAV 1Q	FAV 2Q

MILTON UNITED

Founded: 1909   Nickname: Miltonians

Club Contact Details (T) 01235 832 999   (E) milton.united.fc@hotmail.co.uk
Ground: Potash Lane, Milton Heights, OX13 6AG
Nearest Railway Station Didcot Parkway - 4.7km. Appleford - 5.9km   **Bus Route** The Pack Horse stop - 69m away
HONOURS   League: Hellenic 1990-91, Division One East 2013-14.
FA Comps: None

Colours(change): Claret & sky blue

10 YEAR RECORD

08-09	09-10	10-11	11-12	12-13	13-14	14-15	15-16	16-17	17-18
Hel P 21	Hel1E 7	Hel1E 4	Hel1E 14	Hel1E 14	Hel1E 1	Hel P 14	Hel P 18	Hel1W 12	Hel1E 13
FAC EP	FAC P	FAC EP	FAC EP			FAC 1Q	FAC P	FAC EP	
FAV 2Qr	FAV 2Q	FAV 1Q	FAV 2Q	FAV 2Q	FAV 1P	FAV 2Q	FAV 2Q	FAV 2Q	FAV 1Q

PENN & TYLERS GREEN

Founded: 1905   Nickname: Penn

Club Contact Details (T) 01494 815 346   (E) hsvlatta1955@yahoo.co.uk
Ground: French School Meadows, Elm Road, Penn, Bucks HP10 8LF
Nearest Railway Station High Wycombe - 3.9km   **Bus Route** The Red Lion stop - 85m away
HONOURS   League: Wycombe Comb. Div.A 1911-12, Div.2 35-36, 56,57, 60-61, North 39-40, Div.1 46-47, Div.3 55-56, Prem 62
FA Comps: None   -63. Wycombe & Dist Sen 83-84. Hellenic D1E 2015-16, 16-17

Colours(change): Blue & white

10 YEAR RECORD

08-09	09-10	10-11	11-12	12-13	13-14	14-15	15-16	16-17	17-18
Hel1E 12	Hel1E 17	Hel1E 10	Hel1E 12	Hel1E 4	Hel1E 5	Hel1E 9	Hel1E 1	Hel1E 1	Hel1E 3

THAME RANGERS

Founded: Nickname: None

Club Contact Details (T) 01844 214 401   **(E)** rjcarr5@btinternet.com
Ground: Meadow View Park, Tythrop Way, Thame OX9 3RN
Nearest Railway Station Haddenham & Thame Parkway - 2.9km   **Bus Route** Queens Close stop - 309m away
HONOURS   **League:** Wycombe & District Senior Division 2015-16.
FA Comps: None   Spartan South Midlands Division Two 2016-17.
Colours(change): Red & black

10 YEAR RECORD

08-09	09-10	10-11	11-12	12-13	13-14	14-15	15-16	16-17	17-18
							WyDS 1	SSM2 1	Hel1E 8

WALLINGFORD TOWN

Founded: 1995   Nickname: Wally

Club Contact Details (T) 01491 835 044   **(E)** wallingfordtown@gmail.com
Ground: Wallingford Sports Park, Hithercroft Road, Wallingford OX10 9RB   **Capacity:** 1,500
Nearest Railway Station Wallingford - 366m   **Bus Route** Moses Winter Way stop - 58m away
HONOURS   **League:** None
FA Comps: None
Colours(change): Red & white

10 YEAR RECORD

08-09	09-10	10-11	11-12	12-13	13-14	14-15	15-16	16-17	17-18
NBk1 10	NBk1 5	NBk1 4	NBk1 11	NBk1 9	NBk1 9	NBk1 4	NBk1 6	NBk1 3	Hel1E 7
FAV 2Q	FAV 1Q	FAV 1P	FAV 1Q						FAV 2Q

WOKINGHAM & EMMBROOK

Founded: 2004   Nickname: Satsumas

Club Contact Details (T) 01189 780 209   **(E)**
Ground: Lowther Road Wokingham RG41 1JB
Nearest Railway Station Winnersh - 1.6km   **Bus Route** Toutley Close stop - 154m away
HONOURS   **League:** Hellenic Division One East 2014-15.
FA Comps: None
Colours(change): Orange/black/black.

10 YEAR RECORD

08-09	09-10	10-11	11-12	12-13	13-14	14-15	15-16	16-17	17-18
Hel1E 4	Hel1E 2	Hel P 11	Hel P 10	Hel P 8	Hel1E 2	Hel1E 1	Hel P 20	Hel1E 12	Hel1E 6
			FAC 1Q	FAC EP					
		FAV 2Q	FAV 2Q	FAV 1P			FAV 1P		

WOODLEY UNITED

Founded: 1904   Nickname: Woods or United

Club Contact Details (T) 0118 9453 555   **(E)** info@woodleyunitedfc.co.uk
Ground: Rivermoor Stadium, Scours Lane, Reading, Berkshire, RG30 6AY   **Capacity:** 2,000
Nearest Railway Station Tilehurst - 1.2km   **Bus Route** Cold Store stop - 277m away
HONOURS   **League:** Wargrave & District 1909-10, 26-27. Reading & District Division Three 28-29, Division One 32-33, Division
FA Comps: None   Two 50-51, Premier 57-58, 58-59, 85-86. Reading Division Four Kennet 91-92, Division Three Kennet 92-93,
Colours(change): Sky blue

10 YEAR RECORD

08-09	09-10	10-11	11-12	12-13	13-14	14-15	15-16	16-17	17-18
ReadS 1	Hel1E 4	Hel1E 5	Hel1E 5	Hel1E 3	Hel1E 14	Hel1E 8	Hel1E 13	Hel1E 2	Hel P 19
									FAC EP
						FAV 2Q	FAV 1Q	FAV 1Q	FAV 1Q

ALMONDSBURY

Founded: 1969   Nickname: The Almonds

Club Contact Details (T) 07711 009 198   **(E)** doug2004.coles@blueyonder.co.uk
Ground: The Field, Gloucester Road, Almondsbury, Bristol BS32 4AA   **Capacity:** 1,000
Nearest Railway Station Patchway - 2.9km   **Bus Route** Over Lane - stop 70m away
HONOURS   **League:** Bristol Suburban Premier Division 1990-91. Gloucestershire County 2003-04.
FA Comps: None
Colours(change): Green & white

10 YEAR RECORD

08-09	09-10	10-11	11-12	12-13	13-14	14-15	15-16	16-17	17-18
West1 18	West1 13	West1 12	West1 9	West1 10	West1 9	West1 5	West1 11	West1 22	West1 13
		FAC P	FAC EP	FAC 1Q		FAC EP	FAC 1Q		
	FAV 1Q	FAV 2Q	FAV 1Q	FAV 1Q	FAV 1P	FAV 1Q	FAV 2Q	FAV 2Q	FAV 1Q

DIVISION ONE WEST

CARTERTON

Founded: 1922   Nickname:

Club Contact Details (T) 07713 611 340   **(E)** dave@cartertonfc.com
Ground: Kilkenny Lane, Carterton, Oxfordshire OX18 1DY.   **Capacity:** 1,500

HONOURS   **League:** Witney & District Premier 1960-61, 65-66, Division One 1976-77, 84-85.
FA Comps: None   Hellenic Division One 1989-90, 93-94, Division One West 2015-16.
Colours(change): Yellow & blue

10 YEAR RECORD

08-09	09-10	10-11	11-12	12-13	13-14	14-15	15-16	16-17	17-18
Hel P 12	Hel P 17	Hel P 19	Hel1W 15	Hel1W 5	Hel1W 13	Hel1W 10	Hel1W 1	Hel P Exp	Hel2W 4
FAC P	FAC EPr				FAC EP			FAC EP	
FAV 2Q	FAV 2P		FAV 1P	FAV 2Q	FAV 1Q	FAV 2Q	FAV 2P	FAV 2Q	

CHELTENHAM SARACENS

Founded: 1964   Nickname: Sara's

Club Contact Details (T) 07468 515 471   **(E)** saracenschairman@outlook.com
Ground: Petersfield Park, Tewkesbury Road GL51 9DY
Nearest Railway Station Cheltenham Spa - 1.4km   **Bus Route** Moors Avenue stop - 171m away
HONOURS   **League:** Hellenic Division One 1999-2000.
FA Comps: None
Colours(change): All blue

10 YEAR RECORD

08-09	09-10	10-11	11-12	12-13	13-14	14-15	15-16	16-17	17-18
Hel1W 12	Hel1W 4	Hel1W 3	Hel P 15	Hel P 11	Hel P 16	Hel P 20	Hel1W 2	Hel1W 14	Hel1W 10
					FAC Pr	FAC P	FAC 1Q		
FAV 1Q	FAV 2Q	FAV 1Q	FAV 1Q	FAV 1P	FAV 1Q	FAV 1Q	FAV 1Q		

CIRENCESTER TOWN DEV.

Founded: 2011   Nickname: Centurions

Club Contact Details (T) 01285 654 543   **(E)** scott.griffin@cirentownfc.plus.com
Ground: Corinium Stadium, Kingshill Lane, Cirencester Glos GL7 1HS
Bus Route Kingshill School Grounds stop - 55m away

HONOURS   **League:** None
FA Comps: None
Colours(change): Red & black

10 YEAR RECORD

08-09	09-10	10-11	11-12	12-13	13-14	14-15	15-16	16-17	17-18
				Hel2W 3	Hel2W 3	Hel1W 4	Hel1W 11	Hel1W 5	Hel1W 5

CLANFIELD 85

Founded: 1890   Nickname: Robins

Club Contact Details (T) 07951 060 577   **(E)** peter.osborne@joma-sport.com
Ground: Radcot Road, Clanfield OX18 2ST
Bus Route Carter Institute stop - 399m away

HONOURS   **League:** North Berks Division Two 1924-25.
FA Comps: None   Hellenic Division One 1969-70.
Colours(change): All red

10 YEAR RECORD

08-09	09-10	10-11	11-12	12-13	13-14	14-15	15-16	16-17	17-18
Hel1W 11	Hel1W 10	Hel1W 4	Hel1W 8	Hel1W 11	Hel1W 5	Hel1W 9	Hel1W 12	Hel1W 10	Hel1W 8
		FAC EP	FAC EP						
FAV 2P	FAV 1Qr	FAV 2P	FAT 1P	FAV 1Q					FAV 2Q

EASINGTON SPORTS

Founded: 1946   Nickname: The Clan

Club Contact Details (T) 07748 152 785   **(E)** easingtonsports@hotmail.com
Ground: Addison Road, Banbury OX16 9DH
Nearest Railway Station Banbury - 1.6km   **Bus Route** Springfield Avenu stop - 117m away
HONOURS   **League:** Oxfordshire Senior Premier Division 1957-58, 58-59, Division One 1965-66.
FA Comps: None
Colours(change): Red & white

10 YEAR RECORD

08-09	09-10	10-11	11-12	12-13	13-14	14-15	15-16	16-17	17-18
Hel1W 13	Hel1W 6	Hel1W 11	Hel1W 6	Hel1W 8	Hel1W 9	Hel1W 4	Hel1W 5	Hel1W 4	Hel1W 3

KIDLINGTON RESERVES

Founded: 1909 Nickname: Greens

Club Contact Details (T) 01865 849 777 (Ground)
(E) barry.hiles@btinternet.com
Ground: Yarnton Road, Kidlington, Oxford OX5 1AT
Capacity: 1,500
Nearest Railway Station Oxford Parkway - 1.9km
Bus Route Treeground Place stop - 63m away
HONOURS **League:** None
FA Comps: None

Colours(change): All green

10 YEAR RECORD	09-10	10-11	11-12	12-13	13-14	14-15	15-16	16-17	17-18
08-09									Hel1W 11

MALMESBURY VICTORIA

Founded: 1896 Nickname: The Vics

Club Contact Details (T) 07825 172 500
(E) brendon@innov.co.uk
Ground: Flying Monk Ground, Gloucester Road, SN16 0AJ

Bus Route Bus stops outside the Supermarket
HONOURS **League:** Wiltshire Premier 1999-00, 2014-15.
FA Comps: None

Colours(change): Black & white stripes/black/red (Red & black stripes/red/black)

10 YEAR RECORD									
08-09	09-10	10-11	11-12	12-13	13-14	14-15	15-16	16-17	17-18
Hel1W 2	Hel P 19	Hel1W 13	Hel1W 16	Hel1W 15	Hel1W 12	Wilt 1	Wilt 3	West1 9	West1 15
FAV 1P	FAV 2Q	FAV 1Q			FAV 1Q	FAV 1P	FAV 2Q	FAV 1Q	FAV 2Q

NEW COLLEGE ACADEMY

Founded: 1984 Nickname: Blue College

Club Contact Details (T) 01793 824 828 (Ground)
(E) newcollegeswinfcsec@yahoo.co.uk
Ground: Supermarine S&S Club, Supermarine Drive, Swindon SN3 4BZ
Nearest Railway Station Swindon - 5.8km
Bus Route Stanton Fitzwarren Turn stop - 284m away
HONOURS **League:** Wiltshire Premier Division 2008-09, 09-10.
FA Comps: None

Colours(change): All royal blue

10 YEAR RECORD									
08-09	09-10	10-11	11-12	12-13	13-14	14-15	15-16	16-17	17-18
Wilt 1	Wilt 1	Wilt 3	Hel1W 11	Hel1W 14	Hel1W 11	Hel1W 12	Hel1W 13	Hel1W 13	Hel1W 13
					FAV 2Q	FAV 2Q	FAV 1Q	FAV 2Q	FAV 1Q

NEWENT TOWN AFC

Founded: Nickname:

Club Contact Details (T) 01531 821 509 (Ground)
(E) phil@calendarlady.co.uk
Ground: Wildsmith Meadow, Malswick, Newent GL18 1HE

HONOURS **League:** North Gloucestershire Premier 2012-13. Hellenic Division Two West 2017-18
FA Comps: None

Colours(change): Yellow & blue

10 YEAR RECORD									
08-09	09-10	10-11	11-12	12-13	13-14	14-15	15-16	16-17	17-18
NGIP 4	NGIP 3	NGIP 6	NGIP 3	NGIP 1	GIN2 3	GIN1 14	GIN1 3	GIN1 7	Hel2W 1

NORTH LEIGH DEVELOPMENT

Founded: 1908 Nickname: The Millers

Club Contact Details (T) 01993 880 157 (Ground)
(E) smj40@hotmail.co.uk
Ground: Eynsham Hall Park Sports Ground OX29 6SL.
Capacity: 2,000
Nearest Railway Station Combe (Oxon) - 3.3km
Bus Route Park Road Garden Centre - 67m away
HONOURS **League:** None
FA Comps: None

Colours(change): Yellow & black

10 YEAR RECORD									
08-09	09-10	10-11	11-12	12-13	13-14	14-15	15-16	16-17	17-18
HelR1 1	Hel1W 12			Hel1W 12	Hel1W 8	Hel1W 7	Hel1W 6	Hel1W 8	Hel1W 6

PEWSEY VALE
Founded: 1948   Nickname: Vale

Club Contact Details (T) 01672 562 990 (Ground)   (E) pewseyvalefc@hotmail.co.uk
Ground: Recreation Ground, Kings Corner Ball Road, Pewsey SN9 5BS

Nearest Railway Station Pewsey - 0.9km   **Bus Route** Co-op stop - 316m away

HONORS   **League:** Wiltshire Division One 1989-90, 92-93.
FA Comps: None

Colours(change): Black & white

10 YEAR RECORD

08-09		09-10		10-11		11-12		12-13		13-14		14-15		15-16		16-17		17-18	
Hel1W	17	Wilt	3	Wex1	4	Wex1	11	Wex1	5	Wex1	8	Wex1	10	Wex1	17	Wex1	21	Hel1W	4
						FAC	EP	FAC	P	FAC	EP	FAC	EP						
FAV	1Q	FAV	2Q	FAV	1Q	FAV	2Qr	FAV	1Q	FAV	1Q	FAV	1Q	FAV	1Q			FAV	1Q

THORNBURY TOWN
Founded: 1898   Nickname:

Club Contact Details (T) 01454 413 645 (Ground)   (E) pengelly.mike@gmail.com
Ground: Mundy Playing Fields, Kington Lane, Thornbury BS35 1NA

HONORS   **League:** Bristol Premier Combination x2. Gloucestershire County 2009-10, 17-18.
FA Comps: None

Colours(change): Red & black

10 YEAR RECORD

08-09		09-10		10-11		11-12		12-13		13-14		14-15		15-16		16-17		17-18	
GlCo	9	GlCo	1	GlCo	13	GlCo	16	GlCo	14	GlCo	6	GlCo	4	GlCo	4	GlCo	4	GlCo	1

TYTHERINGTON ROCKS
Founded: 1896   Nickname: The Rocks

Club Contact Details (T) 07837 555 776 (Ground)   (E) tramar1618@btinternet.com
Ground: Hardwicke Playing Field, Woodlands Road, Tytherington Glos GL12 8UJ

Bus Route Stowell Hill Road stop - 102m away

HONORS   **League:** Iron Acton & District 1944-45. Bristol & Suburban Div.3 1949-50, Prem Div.2 93-94, Prem Div.1 96-97, Prem
FA Comps: None   Div.1 97-98. Hellenic Div.1W 2011-12, 13-14.

Colours(change): Amber & black

10 YEAR RECORD

08-09		09-10		10-11		11-12		12-13		13-14		14-15		15-16		16-17		17-18	
Hel1W	9	Hel1W	11	Hel1W	8	Hel1W	1	Hel1W	3	Hel1W	1	Hel1W	15	Hel1W	14	Hel1W	15	Hel1W	14
														FAV	2Qr	FAV	1Q	FAV	2Q

#	DIVISION TWO EAST	P	W	D	L	F	A	GD	Pts
1	Chalvey Sports	22	17	4	1	89	14	75	55
2	Abingdon United Dev	22	17	2	3	75	26	49	53
3	Long Crendon	22	13	4	5	57	26	31	43
4	Virginia Water Res	22	10	3	9	52	45	7	33
5	Penn & Tylers Green Res	22	10	3	9	42	35	7	33
6	Aston Clinton	22	10	2	10	35	53	-18	32
7	Abingdon Town	22	9	3	10	55	65	-10	30
8	Stokenchurch	22	7	5	10	49	51	-2	26
9	Thame Rangers Dev	22	7	2	13	35	58	-23	23
10	Chalfont Wasps Res	22	5	5	12	37	48	-11	20
11	Chinnor Res	22	5	5	12	31	51	-20	20
12	London Rangers	22	3	0	19	39	124	-85	9.

#	DIVISION TWO WEST	P	W	D	L	F	A	GD	Pts
1	Newent Town	20	14	4	2	72	21	51	46
2	Bourton Rovers	20	13	4	3	78	22	56	43
3	Moreton Rangers	20	11	8	1	58	19	39	41
4	Carterton	20	12	3	5	66	36	30	39
5	Bishops Cleeve Dev	20	11	3	6	54	34	20	36
6	Brimscombe & Thrupp Res	20	8	3	9	46	42	4	27
7	Highworth Town Res	20	7	3	10	41	54	-13	24
8	Faringdon Town	20	5	5	10	28	35	-7	20
9	Clanfield 85 Dev	20	6	2	12	18	46	-28	20
10	Shrivenham Res	20	3	3	14	21	63	-42	12
11	Cheltenham Saracens Res	20	0	2	18	9	119	-110	2

MIDLAND FOOTBALL LEAGUE

Founded: 2014 After the merger of the Midland Football Alliance (1994) and the Midland Football Combination (1927)

Sponsor: Total Motion   **Recent Champions: 2015:** Basford United **2016:** Hereford **2017:** Alvechurch

PREMIER DIVISION	P	W	D	L	F	A	GD	Pts
1 Bromsgrove Sporting	42	31	5	6	110	50	60	98
2 Coleshill Town	42	28	8	6	106	47	59	92
3 Highgate United	42	28	6	8	92	47	45	90
4 Worcester City	42	24	11	7	94	41	53	83
5 Sporting Khalsa	42	20	11	11	83	58	25	71
6 Rugby Town	42	19	7	16	76	60	16	64
7 Shepshed Dynamo	42	18	9	15	95	76	19	63
8 Coventry United	42	18	7	17	80	77	3	61
9 Long Eaton United	42	18	7	17	65	86	-21	61
10 Coventry Sphinx	42	16	12	14	73	65	8	60
11 Quorn	42	18	6	18	77	89	-12	60
12 Westfields	42	17	8	17	86	83	3	59
13 Heanor Town	42	17	7	18	67	79	-12	58
14 Boldmere St Michaels	42	15	8	19	59	75	-16	53
15 Stourport Swifts	42	13	10	19	65	88	-23	49
16 Lye Town	42	13	8	21	62	79	-17	47
17 AFC Wulfrunians	42	14	5	23	52	88	-36	47
18 Loughborough University	42	12	7	23	57	82	-25	43
19 South Normanton Athletic	42	12	7	23	59	91	-32	43
20 Haughmond	42	9	11	22	58	80	-22	38
21 Shawbury United	42	10	7	25	59	80	-21	34*
22 Rocester	42	5	7	30	65	119	-54	22

DIVISION ONE	P	W	D	L	F	A	GD	Pts
1 Walsall Wood	42	36	2	4	173	36	137	110
2 Ilkeston Town	42	30	5	7	107	46	61	95
3 Atherstone Town	42	29	5	8	128	50	78	92
4 Leicester Road	42	28	6	8	99	52	47	90
5 Racing Club Warwick	42	25	6	11	112	69	43	81
6 Hinckley AFC	42	25	5	12	136	76	60	80
7 Heather St Johns	42	25	5	12	136	81	55	80
8 Littleton	42	24	1	17	88	53	35	73
9 Studley	42	21	8	13	84	77	7	71
10 Lichfield City	42	17	7	18	81	89	-8	58
11 Uttoxeter Town	42	16	8	18	87	101	-14	56
12 Paget Rangers	42	16	7	19	80	85	-5	55
13 Coventry Copsewood	42	16	4	22	65	91	-26	52
14 Heath Hayes	42	11	11	20	90	99	-9	44
15 Cadbury Athletic	42	11	11	20	66	82	-16	44
16 Chelmsley Town	42	12	8	22	55	89	-34	44
17 Brocton	42	11	10	21	69	87	-18	43
18 Pershore Town	42	11	8	23	64	95	-31	41
19 Nuneaton Griff	42	10	8	24	52	102	-50	38
20 Stafford Town	42	9	3	30	52	107	-55	30
21 Bolehall Swifts	42	7	4	31	34	143	-109	25
22 Coventry Alvis	42	4	4	34	34	182	-148	16

DIVISION TWO	P	W	D	L	F	A	GD	Pts
1 NKF Burbage	29	25	3	1	71	17	54	78
2 Smithswood Firs	27	22	2	3	74	32	42	68
3 Droitwich Spa	29	18	2	9	74	45	29	56
4 Feckenham	29	15	4	10	64	54	10	49
5 Hampton	30	15	4	11	57	63	-6	49
6 Montpellier	30	12	5	13	59	69	-10	41
7 Fairfield Villa	30	11	7	12	52	57	-5	40
8 Moors Academy	30	11	6	13	60	52	8	39
9 Barnt Green Spartak	30	11	6	13	48	57	-9	39
10 Northfield Town	29	11	5	13	41	51	-10	38
11 Knowle	29	11	4	14	59	59	0	37
12 Coton Green	29	8	8	13	49	51	-2	32
13 Earlswood Town	29	7	6	16	43	66	-23	27
14 Redditch Borough	29	7	4	18	51	62	-11	25
15 Bloxwich Town	30	7	4	19	39	70	-31	25*
16 Pelsall Villa	23	1	6	16	21	57	-36	9*

DIVISION THREE	P	W	D	L	F	A	GD	Pts
1 GNP Sports	30	26	2	2	144	23	121	80
2 Boldmere S&S Falcons	30	21	1	8	76	46	30	64
3 FC Stratford	30	18	5	7	98	36	62	59
4 Alcester Town	30	18	5	7	84	41	43	59
5 Bartestree	30	18	1	11	88	53	35	55
6 AFC Solihull	30	14	6	10	64	56	8	48
7 Coventrians	30	15	3	12	67	62	5	48
8 Central Ajax	30	13	7	10	74	78	-4	46
9 Inkberrow	30	13	6	11	74	50	24	45
10 Shipston Excelsior	30	13	4	13	63	69	-6	43
11 Birmingham Tigers	30	10	5	15	58	84	-26	35
12 CT Shush	30	7	9	14	42	60	-18	30
13 Continental Star	30	9	2	19	49	94	-45	28*
14 Enville Athletic	30	6	6	18	32	59	-27	24
15 Castle Vale Town	30	4	3	23	33	117	-84	15
16 Leamington Hibernian	30	1	3	26	26	144	-118	6

LEAGUE CUP

HOLDERS: ALVECHURCH

ROUND 1

Heanor Town	v Ilkeston Town	2-0
Stafford Town	v Nuneaton Griff	1-3
Rugby Town	v Coventry Sphinx	2-1
Brocton	v South Normanton Athletic	1-4
Coventry Alvis	v Loughborough University	2-1
AFC Wulfrunians	v Droitwich Spa	1-1, 4-2p
Pershore Town	v Bromsgrove Sporting	2-3
Stourport Swifts	v Cadbury Athletic	4-2
Walsall Wood	v Chelmsley Town	3-0
Bolehall Swifts	v Highgate United	0-6
Lye Town	v Paget Rangers	0-1
Coton Green	v Leicester Road	0-3
Shepshed Dynamo	v Coventry United	0-2
Lichfield City	v Long Eaton United	2-0
Barnt Green Spartak	v Heather St Johns	0-4

ROUND 2

Heanor Town	v Nuneaton Griff	7-0
Uttoxeter Town	v Heath Hayes	1-3
Rugby Town	v Coventry Copsewood	HW
South Normanton Athletic	v Coventry Alvis	7-0
AFC Wulfrunians	v Bromsgrove Sporting	0-1
Littleton	v Worcester City	2-0
Haughmond	v Coleshill Town	0-1
Shawbury United	v Sporting Khalsa	0-4
Stourport Swifts	v Westfields	2-1
Walsall Wood	v Highgate United	2-2, 5-4p
Racing Club Warwick	v Studley	2-1
Boldmere St Michaels	v Paget Rangers	5-3
Leicester Road	v Coventry United	1-3
Quorn	v Atherstone Town	2-2, 5-4p
Lichfield City	v Rocester	2-1
Hinckley AFC	v Heather St Johns	1-3

ROUND 3

Heanor Town	v Heath Hayes	3-0
Rugby Town	v South Normanton Athletic	AW
Bromsgrove Sporting	v Littleton	1-1, 3-4p
Coleshill Town	v Sporting Khalsa	2-2, 4-3p
Stourport Swifts	v Walsall Wood	0-4
Racing Club Warwick	v Boldmere St Michael	2-1
Coventry United	v Quorn	1-2
Lichfield City	v Heather St Johns	1-3

QUARTER FINALS

Heanor Town	v South Normanton Athletic	0-1
Littleton	v Coleshill Town	0-0, 1-3p
Walsall Wood	v Racing Club Warwick	3-0
Quorn	v Heather St Johns	4-6

SEMI FINALS

South Normanton Athletic	v Coleshill Town	0-4
Walsall Wood	v Heather St Johns	3-1

FINAL

Coleshill Town	v Walsall Wood	1-2

PREMIER DIVISION

		1	2	3	4	5	6	7	8	9	10	11	12	13	14	15	16	17	18	19	20	21	22
1	AFC Wulfrunians		0-1	0-2	0-2	0-5	1-0	2-1	2-1	1-2	1-3	0-2	2-1	0-1	1-0	1-4	0-3	2-1	0-3	2-4	3-3	1-3	2-2
2	Boldmere St Michaels	3-1		1-4	1-1	2-2	2-4	1-2	3-2	0-2	3-2	3-2	1-2	1-1	3-3	0-3	0-3	2-5	2-1	2-1	3-1	3-1	1-1
3	Bromsgrove Sporting	1-0	4-0		0-4	5-1	3-2	3-1	2-2	2-1	2-0	6-0	2-0	4-1	4-2	4-0	3-1	3-0	5-0	1-1	3-1	2-1	2-0
4	Coleshill Town	4-0	1-0	2-4		2-2	4-0	2-1	2-1	3-2	7-1	3-0	3-1	2-1	7-0	4-0	2-1	2-2	2-0	2-3	4-5	2-1	0-1
5	Coventry Sphinx	2-2	1-0	2-0	0-1		4-3	1-1	3-3	1-2	1-3	2-1	4-1	5-0	2-1	1-3	3-2	0-1	2-1	3-1	1-3	1-1	0-1
6	Coventry United	2-4	1-0	1-0	2-3	0-0		1-5	1-1	1-3	5-0	2-3	2-1	2-0	2-2	0-1	3-3	2-1	1-3	1-2	3-0	2-2	3-0
7	Haughmond	3-1	2-4	3-2	1-3	1-1	1-1		5-0	2-2	2-3	0-1	2-2	1-1	2-1	3-5	0-1	1-1	1-1	1-1	0-2	1-2	0-4
8	Heanor Town	1-2	1-1	0-1	1-3	2-0	0-2	2-0		3-2	1-2	2-1	2-1	1-4	4-1	3-2	1-1	1-5	3-2	1-1	5-1	1-1	1-1
9	Highgate United	1-2	1-0	3-1	2-0	3-1	5-0	4-1	2-0		1-2	2-0	1-1	1-0	3-2	2-1	8-0	2-2	2-1	1-1	3-2	6-0	1-1
10	Long Eaton United	1-0	0-1	2-2	0-5	1-1	1-3	2-0	1-2	0-4		2-2	1-4	0-2	3-2	1-0	2-0	3-1	2-2	4-2	1-2	2-1	2-2
11	Loughborough University	2-1	0-1	1-3	1-1	0-1	2-7	3-2	3-1	0-1	4-1		4-1	0-1	5-1	1-3	0-1	2-2	4-3	0-1	1-1	1-1	1-1
12	Lye Town	4-1	1-1	5-0	1-1	1-5	2-4	2-0	0-2	1-1	0-1	1-0		2-1	5-3	1-0	2-7	1-0	5-2	0-3	1-1	2-1	1-1
13	Quorn	5-1	0-3	0-4	3-4	4-3	7-1	1-0	2-2	1-2	2-3	3-1	3-0		4-3	3-2	2-1	2-0	2-0	0-1	2-2	3-3	2-1
14	Rocester	0-2	1-2	1-7	0-4	1-2	2-3	0-1	6-1	2-4	1-2	2-2	2-2	5-3		0-4	2-2	1-2	2-3	2-3	2-1	2-4	0-2
15	Rugby Town	1-2	2-1	1-2	1-0	0-0	0-0	0-1	4-1	2-2	1-1	5-2	0-0	2-0	2-3		2-0	3-2	6-1	3-1	3-2	1-2	0-1
16	Shawbury United	1-3	0-1	0-3	1-2	0-0	1-2	2-2	0-1	1-1	3-0	2-3	5-2	1-2	1-0			3-4	3-1	2-3	1-2	2-3	2-1
17	Shepshed Dynamo	5-5	3-2	3-0	0-1	2-5	0-2	1-1	2-3	2-0	2-1	3-1	1-3	1-1	3-1	4-1			0-3	0-0	6-1	6-2	0-2
18	South Normanton Athletic	1-2	2-1	0-3	1-3	2-3	0-3	2-0	0-1	0-3	0-1	3-2	1-1	2-1	1-0	2-1	1-4			4-2	1-4	1-1	2-1
19	Sporting Khalsa	0-0	5-0	0-1	1-3	0-0	3-0	3-0	3-2	3-1	1-2	4-0	2-1	2-3	4-0	1-2	2-0	2-2	2-2		2-2	4-2	1-1
20	Stourport Swifts	1-0	3-2	1-3	1-1	2-1	0-3	3-4	2-1	0-1	2-3	0-1	1-1	3-2	1-1	0-0	0-6	2-2	1-2			2-0	1-1
21	Westfields	1-2	3-1	3-3	1-1	1-0	1-4	4-3	0-3	2-3	4-0	2-1	3-1	6-0	1-1	4-3	3-0	4-5	6-1	2-0	2-1		2-4
22	Worcester City	5-0	0-0	3-3	3-3	5-1	3-0	2-0	3-0	3-0	5-0	2-1	1-0	8-0	4-0	1-1	2-0	3-2	1-1	3-5	4-1	1-0	

DIVISION ONE

		1	2	3	4	5	6	7	8	9	10	11	12	13	14	15	16	17	18	19	20	21	22
1	Atherstone Town		5-0	6-1	2-0	6-1	8-0	2-0	1-0	2-4	2-1	0-0	1-4	4-1	1-0	3-1	1-1	3-1	1-4	4-0	3-1	13-1	3-2
2	Bolehall Swifts	0-4		0-4	1-1	0-1	4-2	0-6	0-5	0-11	0-5	0-3	0-2	3-0	0-4	2-0	3-2	3-2	2-2	3-1	0-8	0-1	0-5
3	Brocton	0-2	1-1		3-0	1-2	7-3	2-2	3-3	1-3	1-2	1-3	0-1	1-4	2-1	1-1	2-2	1-1	0-4	2-1	1-2	2-1	0-6
4	Cadbury Athletic	1-4	3-1	0-2		0-1	2-4	1-1	3-3	1-3	3-3	1-1	1-2	3-3	1-3	4-0	3-1	1-2	2-0	0-1	1-1	0-1	
5	Chelmsley Town	1-1	3-0	1-2	1-1		4-0	2-0	2-2	1-2	0-5	1-2	0-3	3-0	1-0	4-1	0-2	1-3	0-3	1-1	0-3	2-2	0-7
6	Coventry Alvis	0-7	1-1	0-5	0-1	0-2		1-3	3-2	2-9	0-5	0-4	0-4	0-3	0-4	0-0	3-3	0-6	2-3	2-2	2-5	0-7	
7	Coventry Copsewood	2-0	2-1	2-0	1-7	3-2	3-0		2-2	1-4	0-5	1-3	1-2	0-2	1-4	0-4	1-1	1-0	1-2	2-1	1-3	4-3	0-1
8	Heath Hayes	2-6	1-0	3-2	1-2	1-1	4-0	3-1		2-5	1-4	2-3	2-4	5-5	2-4	1-2	2-3	1-2	2-0	2-2	2-3	1-1	2-5
9	Heather St Johns	2-2	8-0	1-0	5-2	3-1	4-0	7-2	5-3		1-6	2-4	1-4	3-0	2-2	2-2	1-3	0-0	3-1	5-0	2-3	5-3	1-3
10	Hinckley AFC	1-4	9-2	6-4	3-0	3-2	11-1	3-2	4-4	3-4		4-2	3-1	1-0	0-2	6-0	3-1	3-2	4-4	4-0	1-1	2-3	1-4
11	Ilkeston Town	1-2	0-2	4-1	4-0	4-2	3-0	2-0	0-2	3-1	4-1		1-3	2-0	2-0	4-1	6-0	2-1	3-2	2-0	1-0	3-0	3-2
12	Leicester Road	2-1	2-0	2-1	2-1	2-1	5-0	2-1	3-3	2-1	2-1	0-1		5-1	3-1	0-2	2-2	2-3	1-2	2-0	1-0	3-3	2-0
13	Lichfield City	2-4	1-3	2-4	1-0	1-0	4-0	1-2	4-3	2-0	2-2	2-2	2-5		1-0	3-1	1-2	3-1	1-2	0-1	5-1	3-2	1-3
14	Littleton	2-1	4-0	0-1	1-3	2-0	6-0	1-0	0-2	3-1	3-2	1-5	3-2	2-0		1-3	3-1	2-0	5-1	2-1	4-1	5-1	0-1
15	Nuneaton Griff	1-3	3-1	2-2	1-4	3-1	1-3	0-4	0-6	0-3	1-2	1-1	1-6	0-1	0-5		0-3	1-1	6-4	2-0	1-3	0-2	0-0
16	Paget Rangers	0-2	3-0	3-2	4-0	1-2	5-0	1-2	2-6	2-6	1-4	2-3	3-3	0-1	1-0			2-2	0-4	3-0	2-1	2-0	2-3
17	Pershore Town	0-3	3-0	1-1	1-3	4-0	1-2	4-1	2-3	4-2	2-3	0-4	0-0	1-4	1-0	0-0	2-7		0-5	1-2	3-4	3-0	1-7
18	Racing Club Warwick	1-0	3-0	3-2	4-1	2-2	11-2	1-0	3-1	0-3	2-0	4-2	1-5	3-3	1-0	5-0	1-0	0-1		0-2	5-1	3-0	0-4
19	Stafford Town	2-4	4-2	1-0	2-2	2-4	3-0	2-3	1-2	3-5	2-4	2-1	1-2	1-3	0-3	1-4	1-4	3-1	1-3		0-2	2-3	0-5
20	Studley	2-2	3-1	0-0	1-0	1-1	6-1	0-2	1-0	2-2	3-1	3-1	3-0	2-3	0-2	1-3	1-0	4-3	1-1	3-2		3-3	0-6
21	Uttoxeter Town	1-4	1-0	3-3	1-3	4-1	4-0	4-3	2-0	2-3	0-2	1-1	2-0	1-1	4-2	2-1	6-2	4-1	2-5	2-1	2-4		2-3
22	Walsall Wood	4-1	12-0	2-0	5-2	6-0	8-0	6-0	3-0	4-1	2-1	1-4	6-2	4-1	6-2	3-0	4-0	4-3	6-0	7-0	2-0		

RESERVE DIVISION

		P	W	D	L	F	A	GD	Pts
1	Gresley Res	15	11	2	2	54	17	37	35
2	Alvechurch Res	15	11	1	3	45	14	31	34
3	Coton Green Res	16	10	1	5	33	25	8	31
4	Knowle Res	16	7	0	9	26	24	2	21
5	Nuneaton Griff Res	16	6	3	7	21	37	-16	21
6	Bromsgrove Sporting Res	15	5	1	9	20	29	-9	16
7	Cadbury Athletic Res	15	5	5	10	23	31	-8	15
8	Bolehall Swifts Res	12	4	2	6	26	45	-19	14
9	Lichfield City Res	16	3	2	11	19	45	-26	11

CLUB MOVEMENTS

Premier Division - In: Dunkirk (P - EMCP), Ilkeston Town (P), Romulus (R - NPLS), Walsall Wood (P), Wolverhampton SC (P - WMP).

Out: Bromsgrove Sporting (P - SthE), Coleshill Town P - SthE), Haughmond (R - WMP), Rugby Town (LM - UCP), Shawbury United (R - WMP).

Division One - In: NKF Burbage (P), Rocester (R), Stapenhill (LM EMCP).

Out: Bolehall Swifts (R), Covnetry Alvis (R), Pershore Town (LM - WMP), Smithswood Firs (F), Stafford Town (R - SCSP).

AFC WULFRUNIANS

Founded: 2005   Nickname: The Wulfs

Club Contact Details **(T)** 07765 141 410   **(E)** birchkeith@yahoo.co.uk
Ground: Castlecroft Stadium, Castlecroft Road, Wolverhampton WV3 8NA
Nearest Railway Station Wolverhampton - 5km
Capacity: 2,000 **Seats:** Yes **Covered:** Yes   **Bus Route** Castlecroft Hotel stop - 218m away

Colours(change): Red/black/red
Previous Names: None
Previous Leagues: West Midlands (Regional). Midland Alliance 2013-14.

HONOURS: FA Comps: None
    League: West Midlands (Regional) League Division Two 2005-06, Premier Division 2008-09, 12-13.

10 YEAR RECORD

08-09		09-10		10-11		11-12		12-13		13-14		14-15		15-16		16-17		17-18	
WMP	1	WMP	3	WMP	3	WMP	5	WMP	1	MidAl	8	MFLP	7	MFLP	13	MFLP	17	MFLP	17
FAC	EPr	FAC	2Q	FAC	EP	FAC	1Q	FAC	1Q	FAC	2Q	FAC	P	FAC	1Q	FAC	EP	FAC	Pr
FAV	2Q	FAV	1P	FAV	2Q	FAV	2Q	FAV	3P	FAV	2P	FAV	1Pr	FAV	4P	FAV	2P	FAV	1Pr

BOLDMERE ST. MICHAELS

Founded: 1883   Nickname: The Mikes

Club Contact Details **(T)** 07866 122 254   **(E)** faulkner-c1@sky.com
Ground: Trevor Brown Memorial Ground, Church Road, Boldmere B73 5RY
Nearest Railway Station Chester Road - 0.9km
Capacity: 2,500 **Seats:** 230 **Covered:** 400   **Bus Route** Church Road stop - 106m away

Colours(change): White & black
Previous Names: None.
Previous Leagues: West Midlands (Regional). Midland Combination. Midland Alliance > 2014.

HONOURS: FA Comps: None
    League: Midland Combination Premier 1985-86, 88-89, 89-90.

10 YEAR RECORD

08-09		09-10		10-11		11-12		12-13		13-14		14-15		15-16		16-17		17-18	
MidAl	4	MidAl	6	MidAl	3	MidAl	12	MidAl	9	MidAl	2	MFLP	9	MFLP	11	MFLP	12	MFLP	14
FAC	EP	FAC	EP	FAC	EP	FAC	1Q	FAC	EP	FAC	EP	FAC	1Q	FAC	EPr	FAC	P	FAC	1Q
FAV	2P	FAV	3P	FAV	2P	FAV	2P	FAV	2P	FAV	2Q	FAV	1P	FAV	1P	FAV	2Q	FAV	2Q

COVENTRY SPHINX

Founded: 1946   Nickname: Sphinx

Club Contact Details **(T)** 07979 233 845   **(E)** sharon@coventrysphinx.co.uk
Ground: Sphinx Sports & Social Club, Sphinx Drive, Coventry CV3 1WA
Nearest Railway Station Coventry - 2.6km
Capacity: 1,000 **Seats:** Yes **Covered:** Yes   **Bus Route** Bulls Head Lane stop - 363m away

Colours(change): Sky blue & white/navy/navy
Previous Names: Armstrong Siddeley Motors. Sphinx > 1995.
Previous Leagues: Midland Combination. Midland Alliance 2007-14.

HONOURS: FA Comps: None
    League: Midland Combination Premier 2006-07.

10 YEAR RECORD

08-09		09-10		10-11		11-12		12-13		13-14		14-15		15-16		16-17		17-18	
MidAl	7	MidAl	9	MidAl	16	MidAl	3	MidAl	14	MidAl	7	MFLP	18	MFLP	19	MFLP	10	MFLP	10
FAC	EP	FAC	3Q	FAC	2Q	FAC	P	FAC	P	FAC	2Q	FAC	Pr	FAC	P	FAC	EP	FAC	EP
FAV	2P	FAV	2Q	FAV	2P	FAV	2P	FAV	2Q	FAV	2P	FAV	2Q	FAV	2P	FAV	2Q	FAV	1Q

COVENTRY UNITED

Founded: 2013   Nickname: Cov United

Club Contact Details **(T)** 07863 563 943   **(E)** graham.wood@coventryunited.co.uk
Ground: Coventry RFC, Butts Park Arena, The Butts, Coventry CV1 3GE
Nearest Railway Station Coventry - 1km
Capacity: 3,000 **Seats:** Yes **Covered:** Yes   **Bus Route** Albany Road stop - 156m away

Colours(change): Red/green/green
Previous Names: None
Previous Leagues: Midland Combination 2013-14.

HONOURS: FA Comps: None
    League: Midland Football League Division Two 2014-15, Division One 2015-16.

10 YEAR RECORD

08-09		09-10		10-11		11-12		12-13		13-14		14-15		15-16		16-17		17-18	
										MCm2	2	MFL2	1	MFL1	1	MFLP	8	MFLP	8
																FAC	1Q	FAC	EP
														FAV	2P	FAV	1P	FAV	3Pr

DUNKIRK
Founded: 1946   **Nickname:** The Boatmen

Club Contact Details (T) 07748 478 966   (E) philipallen1982@hotmail.co.uk
Ground: Ron Steel Spts Ground, Lenton Lane, Clifton Bridge, Nottingham NG7 2SA
Nearest Railway Station Beeston - 2.3km
Capacity: 1,500 **Seats:** 150   **Covered:** 150

Colours(change): All red
Previous Names: None
Previous Leagues: Notts Amateur 1946-75, Notts All. 1975-95, Central Midlands 1995-2008, East Midlands Counties 2008-10, 16-18. Mid All. 2010-14. Midland Football League 2014-16.
HONOURS: FA Comps: None
League: Notts Alliance Division Two 1981-82, Division One 1984-85.
10 YEAR RECORD Central Midlands Supreme Division 2004-05. East Midlands 2009-10, 17-18.

08-09		09-10		10-11		11-12		12-13		13-14		14-15		15-16		16-17		17-18	
EMC	5	EMC	1	MidAl	8	MidAl	18	MidAl	10	MidAl	19	MFLP	19	MFLP	20	EMC	5	EMC	1
FAC	EP	FAC	EP	FAC	1Q	FAC	EP	FAC	P	FAC	1Q	FAC	EP	FAC	3Q	FAC	1Q	FAC	1Q
FAV	2P	FAV	3P	FAV	3P	FAV	2Q	FAV	1P	FAV	2Q	FAV	2Q	FAV	2P	FAV	2Q	FAV	1P

HIGHGATE UNITED
Founded: 1948   **Nickname:** Red or Gate

Club Contact Details (T) 07527 941 993   (E) jimmymerry777@gmail.com
Ground: The Coppice, Tythe Barn Lane, Shirley Solihull B90 1PH
Nearest Railway Station Whitlocks End - 0.4km
Capacity: 2,000 **Seats:**   **Covered:**   **Bus Route** Whitlocks End stop - 302m away

Colours(change): All red
Previous Names: None.
Previous Leagues: Worcestershire/Midland Combination. Midland Alliance 2008-14.
HONOURS: FA Comps: None
League: Midland Combination Premier 1972-73, 73-74, 74-75.

08-09		09-10		10-11		11-12		12-13		13-14		14-15		15-16		16-17		17-18	
MidAl	13	MidAl	18	MidAl	18	MidAl	20	MidAl	19	MidAl	3	MFL1	1	MFLP	9	MFLP	7	MFLP	3
FAC	P	FAC	EPr	FAC	EP	FAC	P	FAC	EPr							FAC	2Q	FAC	EPr
FAV	1P	FAV	2Qr	FAV	2Q	FAV	1P	FAV	2Q					FAV	2P	FAV	2Q	FAV	3P

ILKESTON TOWN
Founded: 1945   **Nickname:** The Robins

Club Contact Details (T) 07876 492 902   (E) anthony.redwood@ilkestontownfc.co.uk
Ground: New Manor Ground, Awsworth Road, Ilkeston, Derbyshire DE7 8JF
Capacity: 3,029 **Seats:** 550   **Covered:** 2,000   **Shop:** Yes

Colours(change): All red
Previous Names: Ilkeston Town 1945-2010. Ilkeston 2010-17.
Previous Leagues: Notts & Derbyshire 1945-47, Central Alliance 1947-61, Midlands Counties 1961-71, 73-82, Southern 1971-73, 95-2004, N.C.E. 1982-86, Central Midlands 1986-90, West Midlands Reg. 1990-94, N.P.L. 2004-09, 11-17.
HONOURS: FA Comps: None
League: Midland Counties 1967-68. West Midlands Division One 1991-92, Premier Division 1993-94.

08-09		09-10		10-11		11-12		12-13		13-14		14-15		15-16		16-17		17-18	
NP P	2	Conf N	8	Conf N Exp		NP1S	3	NP P	12	NP P	17	NP P	5	NP P	14	NP P	23	MFL1	2
FAC	3Qr	FAC	1P	FAC	2Q			FAC	4Qr	FAC	1Q	FAC	3Q	FAC	1Q	FAC	3Q		
FAT	2P	FAT	1P			FAT	3Qr	FAT	2Q	FAT	1Q	FAT	1Q	FAT	2Qr	FAT	1Q		

LONG EATON UNITED
Founded: 1956   **Nickname:** Blues

Club Contact Details (T) 07971 416 444   (E) jim@longeatonutd.co.uk
Ground: Grange Park, Station Road, Long Eaton, Derbys NG10 2EG
Nearest Railway Station Attenborough - 1.9km
Capacity: 1,500 **Seats:** 450   **Covered:** 500   **Shop:** No   **Bus Route** School stop - 158m away

Colours(change): Blue and black
Previous Names: None
Previous Leagues: Central Alliance 1956-61, Mid Co Football Lge 1961-82, NCE 1982-89, 2002-14. Central Midlands 1989-2002
HONOURS: FA Comps: None
League: Northern Counties East Division One South 1984-85.

08-09		09-10		10-11		11-12		12-13		13-14		14-15		15-16		16-17		17-18	
NCEP	2	NCEP	10	NCEP	12	NCEP	15	NCEP	12	NCEP	11	MFLP	3	MFLP	18	MFLP	14	MFLP	9
FAC	2Q	FAC	P	FAC	EPr	FAC	EP			FAC	1Q	FAC	EP	FAC	1Q	FAC	P	FAC	EP
FAV	3P	FAV	2P	FAV	1Q	FAV	2P	FAV	3P	FAV	2P	FAV	1P	FAV	2P	FAV	3P	FAV	2Q

LOUGHBOROUGH UNIVERSITY
Founded: 1920   Nickname: The Scholars

Club Contact Details (T) 07561 468 745   (E) footballsecretary@lboro.ac.uk
Ground: Loughborough Uni Stadium, Holywell Sports Complex, Holywell Park LE11 3TU
Nearest Railway Station Loughborough - 4km
Capacity: 3,300 **Seats:** Yes   **Covered:** Yes   **Bus Route** Wheatsheaf stop - 172m away

Colours(change): Purple/purple/grey
Previous Names: Loughborough College
Previous Leagues: Leicestershire Senior. Midland Combination. Midland Alliance 2009-14.

HONOURS: FA Comps: None
         League: Midland Combination 2008-09.

10 YEAR RECORD

08-09		09-10		10-11		11-12		12-13		13-14		14-15		15-16		16-17		17-18	
MCmP	1	MidAl	13	MidAl	4	MidAl	5	MidAl	4	MidAl	14	MFLP	20	MFLP	14	MFLP	18	MFLP	18
		FAC	EP	FAC	EP	FAC	1Q	FAC	P	FAC	1Q	FAC	P	FAC	P	FAC	P	FAC	1Q
FAV	1P	FAV	1Pr	FAV	2Q	FAV	1P	FAV	1Q	FAV	2P	FAV	1Q	FAV	1Pr	FAV	2Q	FAV	2Q

LYE TOWN
Founded: 1930   Nickname: The Flyers

Club Contact Details (T) 07429 887 570   (E) dprobbo@gmail.com
Ground: Sports Ground, Stourbridge Road, Lye, Stourbridge, West Mids DY9 7DH
Nearest Railway Station Lye - 0.5km
Capacity: 1,000 **Seats:**   **Covered:**   **Bus Route** Cemetery Road stop - 93m away

Colours(change): Blue & white
Previous Names: Lye & Wollescote 1930-31.
Previous Leagues: Worcestershire Combination 1931-39. Birmingham & Dist/West Midlands (Regional) 1947-62/1962-2014.

HONOURS: FA Comps: None
         League: West Midlands (Regional) 2013-14.

10 YEAR RECORD

08-09		09-10		10-11		11-12		12-13		13-14		14-15		15-16		16-17		17-18	
WMP	11	WMP	19	WMP	11	WMP	15	WMP	2	WMP	1	MFLP	6	MFLP	8	MFLP	4	MFLP	16
FAC	P	FAC	EP			FAC	EP	FAC	P	FAC	P	FAC	EP	FAC	EPr	FAC	P		
FAV	1P	FAV	1Q	FAV	2Q	FAV	1Q	FAV	1P	FAV	1Q	FAV	2Q	FAV	2Q	FAV	1Q		

QUORN
Founded: 1924   Nickname: Reds

Club Contact Details (T) 07729 173 333   (E) k.molloy@ntlworld.com
Ground: Farley Way Stadium, Farley Way, Quorn, Leicestershire LE12 8RB
Nearest Railway Station Quorn & Woodhouse - 1.5km
Capacity: 1,550 **Seats:** 350   **Covered:** 250   **Bus Route** Alexander Road stop - 189m away

Colours(change): All red
Previous Names: Quorn Methodists
Previous Leagues: Leicestershire Senior, Midland Alliance > 2007. NPL 2007-2012. United Counties 2012-13. Midland Alliance 2013-14.

HONOURS: FA Comps: None
         League: Leicestershire Senior 2000-01

10 YEAR RECORD

08-09		09-10		10-11		11-12		12-13		13-14		14-15		15-16		16-17		17-18	
NP1S	12	NP1S	20	NP1S	15	NP1S	21	UCL P	7	MidAl	5	MFLP	11	MFLP	17	MFLP	11	MFLP	11
FAC	P	FAC	1Q	FAC	P	FAC	2Q	FAC	1Q	FAC	Pr	FAC	P	FAC	EP	FAC	EP	FAC	P
FAT	1Q	FAT	3Q	FAT	1Q	FAT	P	FAV	1P	FAV	1Q	FAV	2Q	FAV	2P	FAV	3P	FAV	2P

ROMULUS
Founded: 1979   Nickname: The Roms

Club Contact Details (T) 07738 829 549   (E) moz-football@hotmail.co.uk
Ground: Vale Stadium, Farnborough Road, Castle Vale, Birmingham B35 7LQ

Capacity: **Seats:**   **Covered:**

Colours(change): Red and white stripes/red/red
Previous Names: None
Previous Leagues: Midland Combination 1999-2004, Midland Alliance 2004-07, Southern 2007-2010. Northern Premier 2010-18.

HONOURS: FA Comps: None
         League: Midland Combination Division One 1999-00, Premier Division 2003-04.

10 YEAR RECORD

08-09		09-10		10-11		11-12		12-13		13-14		14-15		15-16		16-17		17-18	
SthM	11	SthM	8	NP1S	10	NP1S	20	NP1S	19	NP1S	11	NP1S	12	NP1S	10	NP1S	13	NP1S	22
FAC	2Q	FAC	2Q	FAC	1Q	FAC	1Q	FAC	P	FAC	P	FAC	1Q	FAC	P	FAC	1Qr	FAC	1Q
FAT	2Qr	FAT	1Q	FAT	2Q	FAT	2Q	FAT	3Q	FAT	Pr	FAT	1Q	FAT	Pr	FAT	Pr	FAT	P

SHEPSHED DYNAMO
Founded: 1994   Nickname: Dynamo

Club Contact Details (T) 07866 500 187   (E) dannypole@aol.com
Ground: The Dovecote, Butt Hole Lane, Shepshed, Leicestershire LE12 9BN

Capacity: 2,050 **Seats:** 570   **Covered:** 400   **Shop:** Yes   **Bus Route** Market Place stop - 229m away

Colours(change): Black & white
Previous Names: Shepshed Albion/Charterhouse > 1994
Previous Leagues: Leics Sen 1907-16,19-27, 46-50, 51-81, Mid Co 81-82,N.C.E. 82-83, Sth 83-88, 96-04, N.P.L.88-93, 04-12, Mid Com 93-94, Mid All 94-95,13-14. UCL 12-13.
HONOURS: FA Comps: Leicestershire Senior Cup x7
League: Midland Counties 1981-82. Northern Counties East 1982-83.

10 YEAR RECORD Midland Alliance 1995-96.

08-09		09-10		10-11		11-12		12-13		13-14		14-15		15-16		16-17		17-18	
NP1S	8	NP1S	17	NP1S	21	NP1S	22	UCL P	9	MidAl	16	MFLP	16	MFLP	4	MFLP	15	MFLP	7
FAC	2Q	FAC	P	FAC	Pr	FAC	Pr	FAC	EP	FAC	P	FAC	1Q	FAC	1Qr	FAC	EP	FAC	2Q
FAT	P	FAT	2Q	FAT	2Q	FAT	1Q	FAV	2P	FAV	2Q	FAV	2P	FAV	1Q	FAV	4P	FAV	3P

SOUTH NORMANTON ATHLETIC
Founded: 1926   Nickname: The Shiners

Club Contact Details (T) 07724 910 271   (E) ahopkin9@gmail.com
Ground: M J Robinson Structures Arena, Lees Lane South Normanton, Derby DE55 2AD
Nearest Railway Station Alfreton - 1.8km
Capacity: **Seats:** 150   **Covered:** 300   **Bus Route** Market Street stop - 105m away

Colours(change): Blue & white
Previous Names: South Normanton Miners Welfare 1926-90. Folded in 2008, reformed in 2009.
Previous Leagues: Alfreton &District Sunday Lge 1980-87, Mansfield Sunday Lge 1987-90, Central Midlands League 1990-2003, East Midlands Counties 2002-17.
HONOURS: FA Comps: None
League: None

10 YEAR RECORD

08-09	09-10		10-11		11-12		12-13		13-14		14-15		15-16		16-17		17-18	
	CM P	11	CM P	3	CMSth	3	CMSth	9	CMSth	2	EMC	7	EMC	4	EMC	2	MFLP	19
													FAC	Pr	FAC	P	FAC	EP
					FAV	1Q	FAV	2Q			FAV	2Q	FAV	2Q	FAV	1Q	FAV	1Q

SPORTING KHALSA
Founded: 1991   Nickname: Sporting

Club Contact Details (T) 07976 220 444   (E) manjit.gill@globeproperty.co.uk
Ground: Aspray Arena, Noose Lane, Willenhall WV13 3BB
Nearest Railway Station Wolverhampton - 3.9km
Capacity: 5,000 **Seats:** Yes   **Covered:** Yes   **Bus Route** Fibbersley Bridge stop - 125m away

Colours(change): Yellow & blue
Previous Names: None
Previous Leagues: Walsall & District Sunday 1991-96. West Midlands (Regional) 1996-97, 2005-15.
HONOURS: FA Comps: None
League: West Midlands (Regional) Premier Division 2014-15.

10 YEAR RECORD

08-09		09-10		10-11		11-12		12-13		13-14		14-15		15-16		16-17		17-18	
WM1	17	WM1	17	WM1	3	WMP	14	WMP	11	WMP	6	WMP	1	MFLP	3	MFLP	3	MFLP	5
								FAC	Pr			FAC	P	FAC	4Q	FAC	P	FAC	Pr
FAV	1Q	FAV	1Q	FAV	1Q	FAV	1Q	FAV	1Q	FAV	2Q	FAV	2Qr	FAV	1P	FAV	QF	FAV	2P

STOURPORT SWIFTS
Founded: 1882   Nickname: Swifts

Club Contact Details (T) 07780 997 758   (E) ghaighway@hotmail.co.uk
Ground: Walshes Meadow, Harold Davis Drive, Stourport on Severn DY13 0AA
Nearest Railway Station Hartlebury - 4.2km
Capacity: 2,000 **Seats:** 250   **Covered:** 150   **Shop:** Yes   **Bus Route** Swimming Pool stop - 104m away

Colours(change): Gold & black
Previous Names: None
Previous Leagues: Kidderminster/Worcestershire/West Midlands (Regional) > 1998, Midland Alliance 1998-2001, 12-14, Southern 2001-12.
HONOURS: FA Comps: None
League: Midland Alliance 2000-01.

10 YEAR RECORD

08-09		09-10		10-11		11-12		12-13		13-14		14-15		15-16		16-17		17-18	
SthM	16	SthM	17	Sthsw	17	Sthsw	21	MidAl	5	MidAl	10	MFLP	10	MFLP	10	MFLP	13	MFLP	15
																		FAC	EPr
																		FAV	5P

WALSALL WOOD
Founded: 1915   **Nickname:** Wood or Prims

Club Contact Details (T) 07775 512 373   (E) gevangelou67@gmail.com
Ground: Oak Park, Lichfield Road, Walsall Wood, Walsall WS9 9NP

Capacity: **Seats:** Yes   **Covered:** Yes

Colours(change): All Red
Previous Names: Walsall Borough (formed when Walsall Wood & Walsall Sportsco merged) 1982-96.
Previous Leagues: Midland Combinataion 1986-92, 2006-13. Staffordshire Senior 1992-93. West Midlands 1993-2006. Mid Alliance 2013-14.

HONOURS: FA Comps: None
League: Worcestershire/Midland Combination 1951-52, 2012-13. Midland Football Division One 2017-18.

10 YEAR RECORD

08-09		09-10		10-11		11-12		12-13		13-14		14-15		15-16		16-17		17-18	
MidCo	7	MidCo	6	MidCo	9	MidCo	14	MidCo	1	MidAl	6	WMP	4	MFLP	7	MFLP	20	MFL1	1
FAC	EP	FAC	EP	FAC	EP	FAC	EP			FAC	1Qr	FAC	P	FAC	EPr	FAC	EP	FAC	P
FAV	2Q	FAV	1P	FAV	2Q	FAV	2Q	FAV	QFr	FAV	2P	FAV	4Pr	FAV	3P	FAV	1P	FAV	3P

WESTFIELDS
Founded: 1966   **Nickname:** The Fields

Club Contact Details (T) 07860 410 548   (E) andrewmorris@westfieldsfc.com
Ground: Allpay Park, Widemarsh Common, Hereford HR4 9NA
Nearest Railway Station Hereford - 1km
Capacity: 2,250 **Seats:** 220   **Covered:** 400   **Shop:** Yes   **Bus Route** Priory Place stop - 165m away

Colours(change): All Maroon & sky blue
Previous Names: None.
Previous Leagues: Herefordshire Sunday 1966-73. Worcester & Dist. 1973-78. West Midlands (Regional) 1978-04. Midland Alliance 2004-14.

HONOURS: FA Comps: None
League: West Midlands (Regional) Division One 1986-87, Premier 2002-03.

10 YEAR RECORD

08-09		09-10		10-11		11-12		12-13		13-14		14-15		15-16		16-17		17-18	
MidAl	17	MidAl	5	MidAl	6	MidAl	2	MidAl	2	MidAl	12	WMP	8	MFLP	16	MFLP	5	MFLP	12
FAC	P	FAC	1Q	FAC	P	FAC	EP	FAC	2Qr	FAC	EP	FAC	P	FAC	1Q	FAC	1P	FAC	2Q
FAV	3Pr	FAV	2P	FAV	3P	FAV	1P	FAV	1P	FAV	4P	FAV	3P	FAV	1P	FAV	3P	FAV	4P

WOLVERHAMPTON SPORTING CFC
Founded: 2001   **Nickname:** Wolves

Club Contact Details (T) 07966 505 425   (E) wolvessporting@yahoo.co.uk
Ground: Pride Park, Hazel Lane, Great Wyrley, Staffs WS6 6AA
Nearest Railway Station Ladywood - 1km
Capacity: **Seats:**   **Covered:**   **Bus Route** Hazel Lane - stop 270m away

Colours(change): Black & orange
Previous Names:
Previous Leagues: West Midlands (Reg) > 2018.

HONOURS: FA Comps: None
League: West Midlands (Reg) Division Two 2006-07, Premier 2017-18.

10 YEAR RECORD

08-09		09-10		10-11		11-12		12-13		13-14		14-15		15-16		16-17		17-18	
WMP	8	WMP	20	WMP	18	WMP	19	WMP	10	WMP	18	WMP	16	WMP	4	WMP	3	WMP	1
																FAC	EP	FAC	EP
				FAV	1P	FAV	2Q	FAV	2Q	FAV	1Q	FAV	1Q	FAV	1Q	FAV	1P	FAV	5P

WORCESTER CITY
Founded: 1902   **Nickname:** City

Club Contact Details (T) 07811 076 933   (E) kevinpreece1987@gmail.com
Ground: The Victoria Ground, Birmingham Road, Bromsgrove B61 0DR
Nearest Railway Station Bromsgrove - two miles from the ground.
Capacity: 4,893 **Seats:** 400   **Covered:** Yes   **Shop:** Yes   **Bus Route** 144/144a from Crowngate Bus Station

Colours(change): Blue & white stripes/blue/blue
Previous Names: Formed when Berwick Rangers and Worcester Rovers amalgamated
Previous Leagues: Birmingham & District 1902-38. Southern 1938-79, 85-2004. Alliance 1979-85. Conference 2004-17.

HONOURS: FA Comps: None
League: Birmingham League 1913-14, 24-25, 28-29, 29-30. Southern League Division One North 1967-68, 76-77, Premier 1978-79.

10 YEAR RECORD

08-09		09-10		10-11		11-12		12-13		13-14		14-15		15-16		16-17		17-18	
Conf S	16	Conf S	20	Conf N	16	Conf N	7	Conf N	15	Conf N	15	Conf N	9	Nat N	17	Nat N	20	MFLP	4
FAC	2Q	FAC	3Qr	FAC	3Q	FAC	2Q	FAC	4Q	FAC	4Qr	FAC	2Pr	FAC	1P	FAC	3Q	FAC	Pr
FAT	3Q	FAT	3P	FAT	2Pr	FAT	3Q	FAT	3Q	FAT	2P	FAT	1P	FAT	1Pr	FAT	1P	FAV	2P

ATHERSTONE TOWN

Founded: 2004   Nickname: The Adders

Club Contact Details (T) 07980 037 883
(E) trn700@aol.com
Ground: Sheepy Road, Atherston, Warwickshire CV9 3AD

Nearest Railway Station Atherstone - 0.6km
Bus Route Lister Road stop - 118m away

HONOURS   **League:** Midland Combination Division 1 2004-05, Premier Division 2005-06. Midland Alliance 2007-08.
FA Comps: None

Colours(change): Red & white

10 YEAR RECORD

08-09		09-10		10-11		11-12		12-13		13-14		14-15		15-16		16-17		17-18	
SthM	3	SthM	13	SthC	21	MidAl	21	MCmP	9	MCmP	9	MFL1	13	MFL1	13	MFL1	4	MFL1	3
FAC	3Qr	FAC	P	FAC	Pr	FAC	P	FAC	EP	FAC	3Q	FAC	EPr					FAC	EP
FAT	P	FAT	1Q	FAT	P	FAV	1P	FAV	1Q	FAV	1P	FAV	2Q	FAV	1Q	FAV	2Q	FAV	1P

BROCTON

Founded: 1937   Nickname: The Badgers

Club Contact Details (T) 07791 841 774
(E) terryhomer@yahoo.co.uk
Ground: Silkmore Lane Sports Grd, Silkmore Lane, Stafford, Staffordshire ST17 4JH

Nearest Railway Station Stafford - 2km
Bus Route Silkmore Crescent stop - 30m away

HONOURS   **League:** Midland Combination Premier 2013-14.
FA Comps: None

Colours(change): Green & white/white/green

10 YEAR RECORD

08-09		09-10		10-11		11-12		12-13		13-14		14-15		15-16		16-17		17-18	
MCmP	16	MCmP	7	MCmP	8	MCmP	6	MCmP	5	MCmP	1	MFLP	13	MFLP	15	MFLP	21	MFL1	17
FAC	EPr	FAC	P	FAC	EPr	FAC	EP	FAC	EPr	FAC	1Q	FAC	Pr	FAC	EP	FAC	P	FAC	1Q
FAV	1Qr	FAV	2Q	FAV	2Q	FAV	3Pr	FAV	1Q	FAV	4P	FAV	4P	FAV	3P	FAV	2Q	FAV	2P

CADBURY ATHLETIC

Founded: 1994   Nickname:

Club Contact Details (T) 07899 912 171
(E) cadburyathleticfc@hotmail.co.uk
Ground: TSA Sports Ground, Eckersall Road, Kings Norton, Birmingham, B38 8SR
Capacity: 1,500

Nearest Railway Station Kings Norton - 0.5km
Bus Route Meadow Hill Road stop - 266m away

HONOURS   **League:** Midland Combination Division One 2013-14.
FA Comps: None

Colours(change): Purple & white quarters/purple/white

10 YEAR RECORD

08-09		09-10		10-11		11-12		12-13		13-14		14-15		15-16		16-17		17-18	
MCmP	11	MCmP	19	MCmP	6	MCmP	12	MCm1	3	MCm1	1	MFL1	6	MFL1	15	MFL1	5	MFL1	15
FAC	EP	FAC	EP			FAC	EP							FAC	P			FAC	EP
FAV	2Q	FAV	1Q	FAV	1Q	FAV	1Q	FAV	1Q	FAV	1Q	FAV	1Q	FAV	1Q	FAV	1P	FAV	1Q

CHELMSLEY TOWN

Founded: 1927   Nickname:

Club Contact Details (T) 07837 509 752
(E) louisehelenhughes@gmail.com
Ground: Coleshill FC Pack Meadow, Packington Lane, Coleshill, B46 3JQ
Capacity: 2,070

Nearest Railway Station Coleshill Parkway - 3.6km
Bus Route St Edwards Primary School stop - 258m away

HONOURS   **League:** Midland Combination Division One 1987-88.
FA Comps: None

Colours(change): Sky blue, white & black

10 YEAR RECORD

08-09		09-10		10-11		11-12		12-13		13-14		14-15		15-16		16-17		17-18	
MCm2	8	MCm2	13	MCm2	11	MCm2	3	MCm1	13	MCm1	6	MCm2	6	MCm2	2	MCm1	17	MFL1	16
																		FAV	2Q

COVENTRY COPSEWOOD

Founded: 1923   Nickname: The G's

Club Contact Details (T) 07884 585 440
(E) davide.wilson@hotmail.co.uk
Ground: Copsewood Sports & Social Club, Allard Way, Binley, Coventry CV3 1JP
Capacity: 2,000

HONOURS   **League:** Midland Combination Division One 1996-97.
FA Comps: None

Colours(change): All blue

10 YEAR RECORD

08-09		09-10		10-11		11-12		12-13		13-14		14-15		15-16		16-17		17-18	
MCmP	9	MCmP	5	MCmP	4	MCmP	3	MCmP	12	MCmP	16	MFL1	8	MFL1	11	MFL1	12	MFL1	13
FAV	1Q	FAV	2Qr	FAV	2P	FAV	1P	FAV	1Q	FAV	1Q	FAV	1Q	FAV	1Q	FAV	1P	FAV	2Q

HEATH HAYES

Founded: 1965   Nickname: The Hayes

Club Contact Details (T) 07974 851 604   **(E)** tonygough123@aol.com

Ground: Coppice Colliery Grd, Newlands Lane, Heath Hayes, Cannock, WS12 3HH   **Capacity:** 1,000

Nearest Railway Station Cannock - 2.7km   **Bus Route** Five Ways Inn stop - 253m away

HONOURS   **League:** Staffordshire County Division One 1977-78. West Midlands (Regional) Division One North 1998-99.

FA Comps: None   Midland Combination Premier Division 2009-10.

Colours(change): Blue & white/blue/blue

10 YEAR RECORD

08-09		09-10		10-11		11-12		12-13		13-14		14-15		15-16		16-17		17-18	
MCmP	10	MCmP	1	MidAl	11	MidAl	14	MidAl	18	MidAl	8	MFLP	22	MFL1	8	MFL1	14	MFL1	14
FAC	EP	FAC	P	FAC	P	FAC	EP	FAC	P	FAC	EP	FAC	EP	FAC	EP	FAC	EP		
FAV	2Q	FAV	1Q	FAV	3P	FAV	1P	FAV	1Q	FAV	1Q	FAV	1Q	FAV	1Q	FAV	1Q	FAV	2Q

HEATHER ST. JOHN'S

Founded: 1949   Nickname:

Club Contact Details (T) 07952 633 331   **(E)** adrianrock@hotmail.co.uk

Ground: St John's Park, Ravenstone Rd, Heather LE67 2QJ

Bus Route Holyoake Drive stop - 160m away

HONOURS   **League:** Leicester & District Division One 1965-66., 69-70, 71-72.

FA Comps: None   Midland Combination Division One 2006-07, Premier 10-11.

Colours(change): All royal blue

10 YEAR RECORD

08-09		09-10		10-11		11-12		12-13		13-14		14-15		15-16		16-17		17-18	
MCmP	5	MCmP	2	MCmP	1	MidAl	19	MidAl	20	MidAl	22	MFL1	16	MFL1	16	MFL1	8	MFL1	7
FAC	EP	FAC	P	FAC	P					FAC	EP	FAC	EP						
FAV	1Q	FAV	2Q	FAV	3P			FAV	1P	FAV	2Q	FAV	2Q	FAV	1Q	FAV	1Q	FAV	1P

HINCKLEY AFC

Founded: 2014   Nickname:

Club Contact Details (T) 07720 299 313   **(E)** secretary@hinckleyafc.org.uk

Ground: Ibstock Miner's Welfare Stadium, Leicester Road, Ibstock, LE67 6HN

HONOURS   **League:** None

FA Comps: None

Colours(change): Red & blue

10 YEAR RECORD

08-09	09-10	10-11	11-12	12-13	13-14	14-15		15-16		16-17		17-18	
						MFL1	3	MFL1	5	MFL1	2	MFL1	6
								FAC	2Q	FAC	EPr	FAC	1Q
						FAV	1Q	FAV	1P	FAV	5P	FAV	4P

LEICESTER ROAD

Founded: 2013   Nickname: The Knitters

Club Contact Details (T) 07814 414 726   **(E)** stuart.millidge43@hotmail.com

Ground: Leicester Road Stadium, Leicester Road, Hinckley, LE10 3DR

Nearest Railway Station Hinckley - 2.7km   **Bus Route** Leicester Road stop - 262m away

HONOURS   **League:** None

FA Comps: None

Colours(change): Blue & red/blue/blue

10 YEAR RECORD

08-09	09-10	10-11	11-12	12-13	13-14	14-15		15-16		16-17		17-18	
						MFL2	2	MFL1	4	MFL1	3	MFL1	4
										FAC	1Qr	FAC	P
								FAV	2Q	FAV	1P	FAV	1Q

LICHFIELD CITY

Founded: 1970   Nickname:

Club Contact Details (T) 07779 295 033   **(E)** darrenleaver@outlook.com

Ground: The McDonalds Community Stadium, Brownsfield Road, Lichfield, Staffs, WS13 6AY   **Capacity:** 1,500

Nearest Railway Station Lichfield Trent Valley High Level/Lichfield Trent Valley -   **Bus Route** Netherstowe Lane stop - 78m away

HONOURS   **League:** None

FA Comps: None

Colours(change): All royal blue

10 YEAR RECORD

08-09		09-10		10-11		11-12		12-13		13-14		14-15		15-16		16-17		17-18	
MCm3	5	MCm2	3	MCm2	4	MCm1	4	MCmP	10	MCmP	7	MFL1	12	MFL1	7	MFL1	7	MFL1	10
												FAC	P			FAC	P		
										FAV	1Q	FAV	2Q	FAV	1Q	FAV	2P	FAV	1Q

LITTLETON
Founded: 1890 Nickname: The Ton
Club Contact Details (T) 01905 909 125 (E) littletonfc@outlook.com
Ground: 5 Acres, Pebworth Road, North Littleton, Evesham, Worcs, WR11 8QL **Capacity:** 1,000
Nearest Railway Station Honeybourne - 3.1km **Bus Route** The Ivy Inn stop - 1.2km away
HONOURS **League:** Midland Combination Division Three 2001-02.
FA Comps: None
Colours(change): Red/red/white

10 YEAR RECORD

08-09	09-10	10-11	11-12	12-13	13-14	14-15	15-16	16-17	17-18
MCm1 5	MCm1 8	MCm1 5	MCm1 2	MCmP 2	MCmP 11	MFL1 9	MFL1 9	MFL1 9	MFL1 8
							FAV 2Q	FAV 2Q	FAV 2Q

NKF BURBAGE
Founded: 2009 Nickname: Panthers
Club Contact Details (T) 07875 669 591 (E) josephbroadbent19@gmail.com
Ground: Kirkby Road Sports Ground, Kirkby Road, Barwell LE9 8FQ
HONOURS **League:** Midland Football League Division Two 2016-17, 17-18.
FA Comps: None
Colours(change): Orange and black

10 YEAR RECORD

08-09	09-10	10-11	11-12	12-13	13-14	14-15	15-16	16-17	17-18
							LeicS1 2	MFL2 1	MFL2 1

NUNEATON GRIFF
Founded: 1972 Nickname: The Heartlanders
Club Contact Details (T) 07944 457 250 (E) nuneatongriff@sky.com
Ground: The Pingles Stadium, Avenue Road, Nuneaton, Warwickshire CV11 4LX **Capacity:** 1,500
HONOURS **League:** Coventry Alliance Premier 1996-97, 97-98.
FA Comps: None Midland Combination Premier Division 1999-2000, 00-01.
Colours(change): Blue & white

10 YEAR RECORD

08-09	09-10	10-11	11-12	12-13	13-14	14-15	15-16	16-17	17-18
MCmP 6	MCmP 12	MCmP 2	MCmP 11	MCmP 4	MCmP 3	MFL1 17	MFL1 3	MFL1 10	MFL1 19
FAC P	FAC P	FAC P	FAC EP	FAC 2Q	FAC EP	FAC EP		FAC EPr	
FAV 1Q	FAV 1Q	FAV 1Q	FAV 1Q	FAV 2Q	FAV 2Q	FAV 1P	FAV 5P	FAV 3P	FAV 1Q

PAGET RANGERS
Founded: 2011 Nickname: Bears or The Wee Gers
Club Contact Details (T) 07528 177 046 (E) paterson_r3@sky.com
Ground: Central Ground, Coles Lane, Sutton Coldfield, B72 1NL
HONOURS **League:** None
FA Comps: None
Colours(change): Gold and black

10 YEAR RECORD

08-09	09-10	10-11	11-12	12-13	13-14	14-15	15-16	16-17	17-18
					MCm2 3	MFL2 11	MFL2 4	MFL2 2	MFL1 12
							FAV 1Q	FAV 2P	FAV 2Q

RACING CLUB WARWICK
Founded: 1919 Nickname: Racers
Club Contact Details (T) 07926 188 553 (E) pja.murphy@hotmail.co.uk
Ground: Townsend Meadow, Hampton Road, Warwick, Warwickshire CV34 6JP **Capacity:** 1,300
Nearest Railway Station Warwick Parkway - 1.4km **Bus Route** Shakespeare Avenue stop - 131m away
HONOURS **League:** Warwick 1933-34, 34-35, 35-36. Leamington & District 37-38, 45-46, 46-47, 47-48. Midland
FA Comps: None Combination Premier Division 1987-88.
Colours(change): Gold/black/black

10 YEAR RECORD

08-09	09-10	10-11	11-12	12-13	13-14	14-15	15-16	16-17	17-18
MidAl 21	MCmP 22	MCmP 19	MCmP 13	MCmP 17	MCmP 12	MFL1 18	MFL1 10	MFL1 6	MFL1 5
FAC P									
FAV 1P		FAV 1Q	FAV 2P	FAV 2Q	FAV 1P	FAV 1Q	FAV 2P	FAV 1Q	FAV 3P

ROCESTER

Founded: 1876   Nickname: Romans

Club Contact Details (T) 07770 762 825   **(E)** secretary@rocesterfc.net

Ground: Hillsfield, Mill Street, Rocester, Uttoxeter ST14 5JX   **Capacity:** 4,000

Bus Route Ashbourne Road Garage stop - 152m away

HONOURS   **League:** Staffordshire Senior 1985-86, 86-87. West Mids (Regional) Division One 1987-88.
FA Comps: None   Midland Alliance 1998-99, 2003-04.

Colours(change): Amber & black

10 YEAR RECORD

	08-09	09-10	10-11	11-12	12-13	13-14	14-15	15-16	16-17	17-18
	MidAl 20	MidAl 16	MidAl 14	MidAl 6	MidAl 13	MidAl 20	MFLP 12	MFLP 12	MFLP 16	MFLP 22
FAC	EP	P	EP	1Q	P	EPr	EPr	Pr	P	EPr
FAV	2Q	1Q	1Q	1Q	4P	2P	1P	1P	2P	2Q

STAPENHILL

Founded: 1947   Nickname: The Swans

Club Contact Details (T) 07411 832 333   **(E)** stapenhillsecretary@yahoo.com

Ground: Edge Hill, Maple Grove, Stapenhill DE15 9NN.

Nearest Railway Station Burton-on-Trent - 3km

HONOURS   **League:** Leicestershire Senior 1958-59, 59-60, 86-87, 88-89, 2006-07.
FA Comps: None

Colours(change): All red

10 YEAR RECORD

	08-09	09-10	10-11	11-12	12-13	13-14	14-15	15-16	16-17	17-18
		LeicSP 12	LeicSP 4	LeicSP 5	LeicS1 5	EMC 2	EMC 15	EMC 12	EMC 11	EMC 13
FAC	EP						EPr			
FAV	1Q				1Q	1Q	1Q	1Q	2Q	1Q

STUDLEY

Founded: 1971   Nickname: Bees

Club Contact Details (T) 07745 310 077   **(E)** bobtheat@hotmail.co.uk

Ground: The Beehive, Abbeyfields Drive, Studley B80 7BF   **Capacity:** 1,500

Nearest Railway Station Redditch - 4.6km   **Bus Route** Red Hill Close stop - 49m away

HONOURS   **League:** Midland Combination Division One 1991-92.
FA Comps: None

Colours(change): Sky blue and navy

10 YEAR RECORD

	08-09	09-10	10-11	11-12	12-13	13-14	14-15	15-16	16-17	17-18
	MidAl 14	MidAl 11	MidAl 7	MidAl 17	MidAl 21	MCmP 6	MFL1 10	MFLP 12	MFLP 15	MFL1 9
FAC	1Q	P	EP	P	P	P	EP			
FAV	2Pr	1P	1P	2Q	1Q	2Q	1P	2Q	1Q	2Q

UTTOXETER TOWN

Founded: 1983   Nickname: Town

Club Contact Details (T) 07791 250 667   **(E)** uttoxetertfc@gmail.com

Ground: Oldfields Sports Ground, Springfield Road, Uttoxeter, ST14 7JX   **Capacity:** 1,000

Nearest Railway Station Uttoxeter - 1.1km   **Bus Route** Smithfield Road stop - 178m away

HONOURS   **League:** None
FA Comps: None

Colours(change): Yellow & blue

10 YEAR RECORD

	08-09	09-10	10-11	11-12	12-13	13-14	14-15	15-16	16-17	17-18
						StfSP 2	MFL1 5	StfSP 6	MFL1 11	MFL1 11
FAV								3P	2P	2Q

Division Two 2018-19

1 Barnt Green Spartak	9 Feckenham
2 Boldmere Sports & Social Falcons (P)	10 GNP Sports (P)
3 Bolehall Swifts (R)	11 Haughmond
4 Coton Green	12 Knowle
5 Coventry Alvis (R)	13 Lane Head
6 Earlswood Town	14 Moors Academy
7 FC Stratford (P)	15 Northfield Town
8 Fairfield Villa	16 Redditch Borough

NORTH WEST COUNTIES LEAGUE

Founded: 1982 **Sponsored by:** Hallmark Security

Recent Champions: 2015: Glossop North End **2016:** Colne **2017:** Atherton Collieries

PREMIER DIVISION	P	W	D	L	F	A	GD	Pts
1 Runcorn Linnets (C)	44	31	7	6	122	36	86	100
2 Widnes (P)	44	30	6	8	102	52	50	96
3 Runcorn Town	44	29	6	9	107	65	42	93
4 City of Liverpool FC	44	25	9	10	115	58	57	84
5 Bootle	44	25	8	11	122	61	61	83
6 Charnock Richard	44	24	7	13	103	72	31	79
7 1874 Northwich	44	24	7	13	85	56	29	79
8 Hanley Town	44	23	7	14	94	59	35	76
9 Barnoldswick Town	44	22	5	17	102	78	24	71
10 West Didsbury & Chorlton	44	21	4	19	99	120	-21	67
11 Squires Gate	44	19	7	18	79	94	-15	64
12 Ashton Athletic	44	19	5	20	86	69	17	62
13 Irlam	44	18	5	21	66	80	-14	59
14 Winsford United	44	16	10	18	77	87	-10	58
15 Congleton Town	44	16	8	20	83	85	-2	56
16 Northwich Victoria	44	17	5	22	77	93	-16	56
17 Padiham	44	16	5	23	85	96	-11	53
18 Burscough	44	15	5	24	82	103	-21	50
19 Abbey Hey	44	13	6	25	65	84	-19	45
20 AFC Liverpool	44	12	6	26	77	94	-17	42
21 Maine Road	44	11	4	29	59	117	-58	37
22 Barnton	44	4	7	33	61	171	-110	19
23 AFC Darwen	44	3	7	34	42	160	-118	16

DIVISION ONE	P	W	D	L	F	A	GD	Pts
1 Silsden AFC (C)	42	33	4	5	110	38	72	103
2 Litherland REMYCA (P)	42	31	6	5	117	39	78	99
3 Prestwich Heys	42	29	4	9	124	50	74	91
4 Whitchurch Alport	42	28	4	10	91	38	53	88
5 Sandbach United	42	27	3	12	90	57	33	84
6 Cammell Laird 1907	42	22	6	14	84	58	26	72
7 AFC Blackpool	42	21	5	16	92	78	14	68
8 Alsager Town	42	19	10	13	84	71	13	67
9 Holker Old Boys	42	19	8	15	72	89	-17	65
10 Stockport Town	42	15	8	19	81	87	-6	53
11 Carlisle City	42	16	5	21	71	80	-9	53
12 Cheadle Town	42	14	11	17	72	83	-11	53
13 Abbey Hulton United	42	14	8	20	56	66	-10	50
14 New Mills	42	14	7	21	68	95	-27	49
15 Eccleshall	42	13	8	21	66	105	-39	47
16 Chadderton	42	12	10	20	83	93	-10	46
17 Bacup Borough	42	14	4	24	65	95	-30	46
18 Atherton LR	42	13	5	24	61	81	-20	44
19 FC Oswestry Town	42	11	7	24	60	101	-41	39*
20 St Helens Town	42	8	8	26	55	98	-43	32
21 Daisy Hill	42	8	7	27	49	108	-59	31
22 Nelson	42	7	10	25	50	91	-41	27*

CLUB MOVEMENTS - Premier Division - In: Litherland REMYCA (P), Silsden (P), Whitchurch Alport (P).
Out: AFC Darwen (R - D1N), AFC Liverpool (R - D1N), Barnton (R - D1S), Maine Road (R - D1S), Runcorn Linnets (P - NPLW), Widnes (P - NPLW).
Division One - Out: Litherland REMYCA (P), Silsden (P), Whitchurch Alport (P).
Division One North: In: AFC Darwen (R), AFC Liverpool (R), Ashton Town (P - Ches), Avro (P - Manc), Cleator Moor Celtic (P - Wear), Garstang (P - WLancs), Longridge Town (P - WLancs), Lower Breck (P - Liv), Shelley Community (P - WYork), Steeton (P - WRA).
Division One South: In: Barton (R), Cheadle Heath Nomads (P - Ches), Ellesmere Rangers (LM - WMP), Maine Road (R), Rylands (P - Ches), St Martins (P - WM1), Stone Dominoes (P - Staf), Stone Old Alleyians (LM - WMP), Vauxhall Motors (P - WChes), Wythenshaw Amateurs (P - Manc), Wythenshawe Town (P - Ches).

PREMIER DIVISION	1	2	3	4	5	6	7	8	9	10	11	12	13	14	15	16	17	18	19	20	21	22	23
1 1874 Northwich		1-1	5-0	4-1	1-2	3-3	1-2	3-0	2-1	1-1	2-2	2-1	2-0	1-2	5-0	2-1	2-0	2-4	2-1	1-0	0-1	1-0
2 Abbey Hey	4-2		1-1	3-3	0-2	7-1	0-1	0-2	4-2	0-0	2-3	1-2	2-3	1-2	0-4	1-2	3-0	0-4	1-3	1-3	1-2	0-3	1-2
3 AFC Darwen	0-3	1-3		2-0	0-4	1-3	4-4	0-4	0-0	0-6	3-3	1-4	2-5	0-4	1-3	0-5	0-1	0-1	2-2	0-1	3-3	2-3	0-0
4 AFC Liverpool	3-0	3-1	4-2		1-3	5-0	2-1	3-4	1-2	0-5	0-2	1-2	2-0	0-1	1-2	2-4	1-3	1-2	1-2	0-0	3-2	2-4	4-0
5 Ashton Athletic	0-2	3-0	6-0	1-0		3-3	0-1	3-2	2-4	1-2	4-2	5-0	0-5	0-2	0-1	5-1	2-0	0-3	3-1	0-2	7-1	0-1	0-2
6 Barnoldswick Town	2-3	0-4	2-0	1-0	2-2		1-9	2-3	1-2	0-8	1-1	3-5	1-5	1-3	3-3	0-4	2-3	1-3	1-4	0-7	2-4	2-2	0-4
7 Barnton	0-1	2-0	10-0	3-3	4-3	5-0		2-3	1-2	0-4	5-1	0-0	3-4	3-3	4-1	5-0	4-1	0-0	3-3	1-0	3-3	5-2	3-0
8 Bootle	4-0	3-1	0-1	3-2	1-3	5-0	1-2		5-2	1-3	4-2	0-4	1-3	3-0	2-4	1-1	5-1	1-4	0-1	5-0	4-1	6-1	3-2
9 Burscough	0-1	3-2	1-0	2-3	1-4	4-2	1-1	4-1		1-2	2-2	1-1	2-1	1-4	2-1	2-1	1-2	2-5	3-2	4-5	0-1	1-6	
10 Charnock Richard	2-0	2-0	8-0	1-1	2-1	4-2	0-2	4-4	3-2		2-4	2-0	3-0	5-0	4-0	2-1	4-3	1-5	0-0	0-1	6-1	1-4	3-1
11 City of Liverpool FC	1-4	3-1	6-2	3-3	0-2	5-1	3-4	1-0	4-2	1-2		1-1	3-1	3-0	2-1	1-1	2-0	0-2	0-0	0-1	0-3	0-1	4-1
12 Congleton Town	4-2	0-1	9-1	2-2	1-0	4-1	3-1	3-4	5-2	1-4	2-0		3-0	1-0	4-1	3-2	4-1	0-2	1-1	5-2	1-2	1-4	1-1
13 Hanley Town	1-1	4-0	1-0	1-0	1-0	5-1	1-2	2-2	2-0	2-0	0-2	1-3		5-0	3-0	3-0	3-2	1-1	1-2	4-0	6-2	1-1	1-1
14 Irlam	0-3	1-2	3-5	0-2	3-1	4-0	0-3	1-1	1-2	0-2	0-0		2-1	0-2	0-4	1-0	2-3	4-0	3-0	1-3	1-5	
15 Maine Road	2-3	1-3	3-2	0-1	0-3	3-1	0-4	0-3	0-3	0-5	2-1	1-3	2-8	2-0		2-1	1-3	0-5	2-5	1-1	2-1	0-2	0-1
16 Northwich Victoria	0-2	0-2	5-0	3-1	0-2	5-2	2-3	3-1	1-1	3-2	3-2	0-2	3-2	1-4	1-0		1-2	3-0	1-3	1-1	1-2	2-2	0-3
17 Padiham	0-3	1-2	5-1	5-4	0-0	5-3	0-2	1-2	3-2	2-0	3-4	2-1	1-2	0-1	1-1	2-4		1-1	4-0	4-2	6-1	3-3	1-2
18 Runcorn Linnets	2-1	2-2	5-1	5-2	2-0	4-0	2-0	1-1	3-0	1-1	3-1	6-2	2-0	1-1	3-0	4-2	6-1		0-1	5-0	7-0	0-2	5-0
19 Runcorn Town	2-1	1-0	10-3	1-0	3-1	5-0	2-0	3-2	2-2	2-2	5-2	0-2	1-0	4-0	6-1	4-0	0-5		1-2	3-2	1-2	1-2	
20 Squires Gate	0-3	3-2	4-0	5-4	3-1	6-4	0-5	1-3	0-6	3-2	3-1	1-0	2-1	2-2	5-0	2-2	0-5	1-2		1-2	1-2	2-2	
21 West Didsbury & Chorlton	2-1	2-2	4-1	1-2	4-2	1-4	0-4	4-3	4-3	2-1	5-3	3-3	3-5	4-3	1-2	3-1	4-0	2-4	4-2		3-1	2-2
22 Widnes	2-2	0-1	4-0	2-0	2-2	7-1	3-2	2-0	3-0	0-1	2-1	3-0	5-1	4-0	3-1	2-1	0-1	1-2	0-1	4-0		3-1
23 Winsford United	1-1	1-2	2-0	4-3	3-3	1-1	0-4	1-0	1-5	2-2	2-1	3-3	0-2	1-3	5-1	2-3	2-1	0-4	2-4	2-2	1-3	2-1

NORTH WEST COUNTIES LEAGUE - STEP 5/6

THE MACRON CUP

HOLDERS: CITY OF LIVERPOOL

ROUND 1

Stockport Town	v	Maine Road	7-1
Whitchurch Alport	v	Northwich Victoria	1-1, 4-5p
Winsford United	v	Barnton	4-3
AFC Blackpool	v	Nelson	0-0, 2-3p
Ashton Athletic	v	Daisy Hill	6-3
Atherton LR	v	Carlisle City	0-4
Prestwich Heys	v	St Helens Town	4-0
Silsden AFC	v	Burscough	0-3
Cammell Laird 1907	v	Congleton Town	2-1
FC Oswestry Town	v	Chadderton	2-1
AFC Darwen	v	City of Liverpool	1-0
Runcorn Town	v	Alsager Town	3-3, 3-4p
Sandbach United	v	Irlam	2-3

ROUND 2

Stockport Town	v	Runcorn Linnets	2-1
Widnes	v	Carlisle City	1-1, 3-1p
Winsford United	v	West Didsbury & Chorlton	5-1
Bootle	v	Litherland REMYCA	4-2
Cheadle Town	v	Alsager Town	2-1
Eccleshall	v	FC Oswestry Town	0-3
Hanley Town	v	Northwich Victoria	3-5
Squires Gate	v	Burscough	1-2
Prestwich Heys	v	Nelson	1-1, 0-3p
Cammell Laird 1907	v	Irlam	1-1, 4-5p
Barnoldswick Town	v	Charnock Richard	0-4
Padiham	v	AFC Darwen	2-1
Abbey Hey	v	New Mills	5-3
Abbey Hulton United	v	1874 Northwich	1-4
Ashton Athletic	v	Backup Borough	6-1
AFC Liverpool	v	Holker Old Boys	7-2

ROUND 3

Stockport Town	v	Abbey Hey	2-1
Widnes	v	AFC Darwen	2-1
Burscough	v	Prestwich Heys	1-1, 8-7p
Winsford United	v	1874 Northwich	3-1
AFC Liverpool	v	Ashton Athletic	1-4
Cheadle Town	v	Northwich Victoria	1-1, AWp
Bootle	v	Charnock Richard	1-3
Irlam	v	FC Oswestry Town	3-1

QUARTER FINALS

Ashton Athletic	v	Widnes	0-2
Stockport Town	v	Irlam	0-4
Winsford United	v	Charnock Richard	1-1, 4-2p
Burscough	v	Northwich Victoria	2-1

SEMI FINALS

Irlam	v	Burscough	0-0 / 0-3
Widnes	v	Winsford United	5-0 / 2-2

FINAL

Widnes	v	Burscough	2-1

THE REUSCH FIRST DIVISION CUP

HOLDERS: CITY OF LIVERPOOL

SEMI FINALS (over two legs)

Cammell Laird 1907	v	Daisy Hill	3-1
Sanbach United	v	Prestwich Heys	1-2
Daisy Hill	v	Cammell Laird 1907	1-2
Prestwich Heys	v	Sanbach United	3-2

FINAL

Cammell Laird	v	Prestwich Heys	1-2

DIVISION ONE	1	2	3	4	5	6	7	8	9	10	11	12	13	14	15	16	17	18	19	20	21	22
1 Abbey Hulton United		4-2	1-1	2-4	4-1	0-2	1-1	1-0	3-0	2-0	2-3	3-0	0-3	0-1	3-2	0-3	1-3	1-3	3-1	1-2	3-3	0-1
2 AFC Blackpool	3-1		1-6	5-1	1-2	3-2	1-3	1-3	4-2	3-2	5-0	9-2	1-2	4-2	1-0	3-2	0-1	1-1	1-2	1-3	2-1	1-4
3 Alsager Town	2-0	4-1		1-0	3-0	3-2	0-1	2-2	1-4	1-2	2-1	2-1	5-2	2-1	2-3	2-3	0-1	1-1	1-1	0-2	2-2	-
4 Atherton LR	2-1	4-3	1-2		1-3	2-1	1-4	2-3	1-2	1-3	3-4	0-1	0-2	3-2	2-5	1-3	0-3	1-4	2-0	0-0	2-0	0-3
5 Bacup Borough	2-0	1-2	1-2	2-5		0-1	4-1	4-3	1-5	1-1	3-0	3-0	2-5	0-3	2-1	2-0	0-3	0-3	2-3	1-6	5-2	2-1
6 Cammell Laird 1907	2-1	1-1	3-1	3-1	1-0		3-1	3-0	1-2	5-0	5-1	3-2	5-1	2-0	0-0	3-0	1-4	0-1	4-0	4-1	2-1	2-2
7 Carlisle City	1-2	2-3	0-1	2-3	1-1	2-3		0-4	2-2	2-1	1-0	2-1	4-1	5-0	1-2	0-3	2-1	0-1	3-0	0-1	1-4	3-1
8 Chadderton	2-1	1-3	1-3	3-3	5-4	0-1	5-0		2-0	4-3	1-2	0-1	2-2	4-2	1-1	2-3	4-4	1-2	4-0	0-2	2-4	1-3
9 Cheadle Town	1-0	2-2	2-1	1-2	4-1	3-0	1-1	2-2		0-0	3-3	1-2	1-1	0-2	2-4	0-5	3-4	0-0	2-2	1-2	1-4	1-4
10 Daisy Hill	1-2	1-3	1-0	1-7	1-1	3-4	1-3	2-0	1-0		1-1	1-1	0-3	2-2	2-2	2-6	0-2	1-2	3-4	0-3	0-2	0-2
11 Eccleshall	0-0	2-2	1-1	0-4	3-2	4-2	2-1	2-2	3-4	1-3		3-0	2-4	1-1	2-0	3-5	0-2	2-1	3-2	0-5	4-1	0-2
12 FC Oswestry Town	2-2	1-3	0-2	1-2	2-0	3-2	3-3	1-4	2-3	5-0	4-0		4-0	2-2	2-0	0-2	1-4	0-2	0-3	0-0	1-5	0-1
13 Holker Old Boys	2-3	0-3	0-0	0-0	2-1	0-3	2-1	0-2	2-2	1-0	3-5	6-1		2-0	2-2	1-1	3-2	1-2	1-0	1-0	-	4-3
14 Litherland REMYCA	0-1	2-1	1-3	3-1	0-1	1-2	0-4	0-0	1-2	2-0	2-2	0-0	1-1		1-2	0-4	0-6	2-4	1-2	1-2	0-4	2-3
15 Nelson *	0-1	4-1	1-4	0-3	0-3	2-2	2-3	2-2	2-3	1-5	3-1	0-4	7-2	2-2		2-1	0-2	1-5	2-0	2-4	4-2	4-1
16 New Mills	2-2	0-1	2-1	4-0	3-1	3-0	7-2	4-2	3-1	8-0	3-0	5-2	5-0	4-1	4-0		1-1	2-1	4-0	0-4	8-1	1-3
17 Prestwich Heys	2-0	2-3	3-3	2-2	3-1	2-1	3-0	3-3	2-0	4-0	6-0	4-3	6-0	1-1	1-2	2-0		3-2	1-0	3-0	4-0	1-0
18 Sandbach United	1-2	1-4	4-2	2-2	7-1	1-0	2-1	4-2	1-3	4-0	2-1	4-0	0-1	3-0	0-6	0-2		1-0	3-1	1-0	2-1	
19 Silsden AFC (C)	0-0	2-3	3-0	3-3	1-2	1-1	2-3	3-1	2-3	1-3	1-2	2-3	1-3	2-2	0-2	0-2	1-4	3-2		1-4	3-3	1-5
20 St Helens Town	2-1	1-0	2-0	2-1	2-1	2-1	3-2	6-0	5-2	5-1	6-0	5-1	5-0	1-0	4-0	2-2	2-1	1-0	5-2		2-0	1-2
21 Stockport Town	3-1	0-0	2-1	0-1	1-1	1-1	0-1	4-2	2-2	2-1	3-2	7-0	1-3	2-4	6-1	2-1	2-6	3-2	1-1	1-3		0-1
22 Whitchurch Alport	0-0	1-0	2-0	1-1	3-0	2-0	2-1	3-1	2-0	5-0	2-0	1-1	5-1	5-1	5-0	0-1	0-2	0-2	5-1	0-1	3-0	

1874 NORTHWICH

Founded: 2012   Nickname:

Club Contact Details   (T) 07975 679 624   (E)
Ground: Winsford United FC, Wharton Road, Winsford, Cheshire CW7 3AE
Nearest Railway Station Winsford - 1.2km
Capacity: 6,000   **Seats:** Seats   **Covered:** Yes   **Bus Route** 37 & 37A from Winsford Railway Station

Colours(change): Green and black
Previous Names: None
Previous Leagues: None

HONOURS: FA Comps: None
League: None

10 YEAR RECORD

08-09	09-10	10-11	11-12	12-13	13-14	14-15	15-16	16-17	17-18
					NWC1 3	NWCP 3	NWCP 4	NWCP 5	NWCP 7
						FAC Pr	FAC P	FAC Pr	FAC 3Qr
					FAV 1Q	FAV 3P	FAV 2P	FAV 2P	FAV SF

ABBEY HEY

Founded: 1902   Nickname: Red Rebels

Club Contact Details   (T) 0161 231 7147   (E)
Ground: The Abbey Stadium, Goredale Avenue, Gorton, Manchester M18 7HD
Nearest Railway Station Ryder Brow - 0.5km
Capacity: 1,000   **Seats:** Yes   **Covered:** Yes   **Bus Route** Ryder Brow Road stop - 124m away

Colours(change): Red and black
Previous Names: Abbey Hey W.M.C.
Previous Leagues: Manchester Amateur, South East Lancashire, Manchester.

HONOURS: FA Comps: None
League: Manchester Amateur League 1964-65. South East Lancashire 1966-67, 68-69.
Manchester League Division One 1970-71, Premier 1981-82, 88-89, 88-89, 91-92, 93-94, 94-95.

10 YEAR RECORD

08-09	09-10	10-11	11-12	12-13	13-14	14-15	15-16	16-17	17-18
NWCP 21	NWCP 22	NWC1 15	NWC1 3	NWC1 2	NWCP 20	NWCP 14	NWCP 10	NWCP 14	NWCP 19
FAC EP	FAC EP	FAC EPr			FAC 2Q	FAC EP	FAC 2Q	FAC EP	FAC 1Qr
FAV 2P	FAV 2Q	FAV 2Qr	FAV 2Q	FAV 1Q	FAV 1Q	FAV 2Q	FAV 1P	FAV 2Q	FAV 1Q

ASHTON ATHLETIC

Founded: 1968   Nickname: Yellows

Club Contact Details   (T) 01942 716 360   (E)
Ground: Brocstedes Park, Downall Green, Ashton in Markerfield WN4 0NR
Nearest Railway Station Bryn - 1.6km.
Capacity: 600   **Seats:** 100   **Covered:** 300   **Bus Route** 156/157 St Helens/Bryn route

Colours(change): Yellow and blue
Previous Names: None.
Previous Leagues: Lancashire Combination, Manchester Amateur League

HONOURS: FA Comps: None
League: None

10 YEAR RECORD

08-09	09-10	10-11	11-12	12-13	13-14	14-15	15-16	16-17	17-18
NWCP 6	NWCP 21	NWCP 22	NWCP 14	NWCP 20	NWCP 6	NWCP 5	NWCP 7	NWCP 9	NWCP 12
FAC EP	FAC EP	FAC EP	FAC Pr	FAC Pr	FAC P	FAC EP	FAC EPr	FAC 2Q	FAC 3Q
FAV 1Pr	FAV 1Q	FAV 2Q	FAV 2Q	FAV 1Q	FAV 2Q	FAV 2Q	FAV 1Qr	FAV 2Q	FAV 3P

BARNOLDSWICK TOWN

Founded: 1972   Nickname: Town or Barlick

Club Contact Details   (T) 07528 410 204   (E)
Ground: Silentnight Stadium, West Close Road, Barnoldswick, Colne, BB18 5LJ
Nearest Railway Station Colne or Skipton
Capacity: **Seats:** Yes   **Covered:** Yes   **Bus Route** Greenberfield Road stop - 97m away

Colours(change): All blue
Previous Names: Today's club formed after the merger of Barnoldswick United and Barnoldswick Park Rovers in 2003
Previous Leagues: Craven, East Lancashire, West Lancashire.

HONOURS: FA Comps: None
League: West Lancashire Division One 1998-99.

10 YEAR RECORD

08-09	09-10	10-11	11-12	12-13	13-14	14-15	15-16	16-17	17-18
WLaP 6	NWC1 2	NWCP 7	NWCP 4	NWCP 9	NWCP 16	NWCP 19	NWCP 9	NWCP 11	NWCP 9
			FAC EP	FAC EP	FAC EPr	FAC EP	FAC EP	FAC EPr	FAC 1Q
		FAV 2Q	FAV 2P	FAV 3P	FAV 2Q	FAV 2Q	FAV 2Q	FAV 1P	FAV 1Q

BOOTLE
Founded: 1953   Nickname: Bucks

Club Contact Details   (T) 0151 525 4796   **(E)**
Ground: TDP Solicitors Stadium, Vestey Rd, Off Bridle Road, Bootle L30 1NY
Nearest Railway Station Aintree - 0.5km
Capacity: 1,750 **Seats:**   **Covered:** Yes   **Bus Route** Hereford Drive stop - 251m away

Colours(change):   All blue
Previous Names: Langton Dock 1953 - 1973.
Previous Leagues: Liverpool Shipping. Lancashire Combination. Cheshire. Liverpool County Combination >2006.

HONOURS: FA Comps: None
          League: Liverpool County Combination 1964-65, 65-66, 67-68, 68-69, 69-70, 70-71, 71-72, 72-73, 73-74.

10 YEAR RECORD   Lancashire Comb. 1975-76, 76-77. Cheshire County Div.2 1978-79. North West Counties Div.1 2008-09.

08-09		09-10		10-11		11-12		12-13		13-14		14-15		15-16		16-17		17-18	
NWC1	1	NWCP	3	NWCP	6	NWCP	3	NWCP	3	NWCP	8	NWCP	7	NWCP	8	NWCP	2	NWCP	5
FAC	1Q	FAC	P	FAC	P	FAC	P	FAC	1Q	FAC	1Qr	FAC	EP	FAC	EP	FAC	P	FAC	EP
FAV	4P	FAV	4P	FAV	2P	FAV	2Q	FAV	2P	FAV	1P	FAV	1P	FAV	2Q	FAV	3P	FAV	2P

BURSCOUGH
Founded: 1946   Nickname: Linnets

Club Contact Details   (T) 01704 896 776   **(E)**
Ground: Victoria Park, Bobby Langton Way, Mart Lane, Burscough L40 0SD
Nearest Railway Station Burscough Bridge - 0.2km
Capacity: 2,500 **Seats:** 270   **Covered:** 1,000   **Shop:** Yes   **Bus Route** Tesco stop - 105m away

Colours(change):   All green
Previous Names: None
Previous Leagues: Liverpool County Combination 1946-53, Lancashire Combination 1953-70, Cheshire County 1970-82, North West Counties 1982-98, Northern Premier League 1998-2007, 09-17, Conference 2007-09.
HONOURS: FA Comps: FA Trophy 2002-03.
          League: North West Counties Division One 1982-83. Northern Premier Premier Division 2006-07.

10 YEAR RECORD

08-09		09-10		10-11		11-12		12-13		13-14		14-15		15-16		16-17		17-18	
Conf N	21	NP P	16	NP P	19	NP P	22	NP1N	11	NP1N	14	NP1N	15	NP1N	5	NP1N	22	NWCP	18
FAC	2Q	FAC	3Q	FAC	1Q	FAC	1Qr	FAC	1Q	FAC	2Q	FAC	1Q	FAC	3Q	FAC	2Q	FAC	Pr
FAT	1P	FAT	1Q	FAT	1Q	FAT	1Q	FAT	2Q	FAT	1Qr	FAT	P	FAT	1Pr	FAT	P	FAV	1P

CHARNOCK RICHARD
Founded: 1933   Nickname:

Club Contact Details   (T) 01257 792 558   **(E)**
Ground: Mossie Park, Charter Lane, Charnock Richard, Chorley PR7 5LZ
Nearest Railway Station Euxton Balshaw Lane - 3km
Capacity: **Seats:** Yes   **Covered:** Yes   **Bus Route** Leeson Avenue stop - 299m away

Colours(change):   Green & white
Previous Names: None
Previous Leagues: Chorley Alliance (Sunday). Preston & District. West Lancashire >2016

HONOURS: FA Comps: None
          League: Chorley Alliance 1947-48, 56-57. Preston & District 1960-61, 66-67, 67-68, 68-69, 89-90.

10 YEAR RECORD   West Lancashire Division One 1997-98, Premier 2002-03, 08-09, 11-12, 12-13, 13-14, 14-15.

08-09		09-10		10-11		11-12		12-13		13-14		14-15		15-16		16-17		17-18	
WLaP	1	WLaP	4	WLaP	2	WLaP	1	WLaP	1	WLaP	1	WLaP	1	WLaP	2	NWC1	2	NWCP	6
																		FAC	EP
																FAV	2P	FAV	1P

CITY OF LIVERPOOL
Founded: 2015   Nickname: The Purps

Club Contact Details   (T) 0151 525 4796   **(E)** contact@colfc.co.uk
Ground: TDP Solicitors Stadium, Vesty Road, off Bridle Road, Bootle, Liverpool L30 1NY
Nearest Railway Station Aintree - 0.5km
Capacity: 1,750 **Seats:** Yes   **Covered:** Yes   **Bus Route** Arriva 15, 135 & 157

Colours(change):   All purple
Previous Names: None
Previous Leagues: None

HONOURS: FA Comps: None
          League: None

10 YEAR RECORD

08-09	09-10	10-11	11-12	12-13	13-14	14-15	15-16	16-17		17-18	
								NWC1	4	NWCP	4
										FAC	1Q
										FAV	3P

CONGLETON TOWN
Founded: 1901   Nickname: Bears

Club Contact Details (T) 01260 274 460   (E)
Ground: Ivy Gardens, Booth Street, Crescent Road, Congleton, Cheshire CW12 4DG
Nearest Railway Station Congleton - 1.9km
Capacity: 1,450 **Seats:** 250   **Covered:** 1,200   **Shop:** Yes   **Bus Route** Booth Street stop - 75m away
Colours(change): Black & white/black/red.
Previous Names: Congleton Hornets
Previous Leagues: Crew & District, North Staffs, Macclesfield, Cheshire, Mid Cheshire, NW Co, NPL

HONOURS: FA Comps: None
League: Crewe & District 1901-02, 02-03, 03-04. North Staffs & District 1919-20. Macclesfield & District 1939-40.
10 YEAR RECORD Mid Cheshire 1973-74, 75-76, 77-78.

	08-09	09-10	10-11	11-12	12-13	13-14	14-15	15-16	16-17	17-18
NWCP	4	NWCP 5	NWCP 11	NWCP 7	NWCP 10	NWCP 8	NWCP 6	NWCP 16	NWCP 15	
FAC	1Q	FAC 2Q	FAC Pr	FAC P	FAC Pr	FAC Pr	FAC 2Q	FAC P	FAC P	
FAV	1P	FAV 2P	FAV 1Q	FAV 1Q	FAV 1P	FAV 4P	FAV 2P	FAV 1P	FAV 1P	FAV 2Qr

HANLEY TOWN
Founded: 1966   Nickname:

Club Contact Details (T) 07977 519 498   (E)
Ground: Abbey Lane, Bucknall, Stoke-on-Trent, Staffordshire ST2 8AJ
Nearest Railway Station Stoke-on-Trent - 3.2km
Capacity: **Seats:** Yes **Covered:** Yes   **Bus Route** Abbey Lane stop - 229m away
Colours(change): All royal blue
Previous Names: None
Previous Leagues: London 1966-67. Staffordshire County Senior 1967-76. Mid-Cheshire 1976-88, 96-98. Midland/Staffordshire County 1998-2013.
HONOURS: FA Comps: None
League: London 1966-67. Staffordshire County Div.2 67-68, Div.1 68-69, Premier 72-73, 75-76. Mid-Cheshire Div.1 81-82.
10 YEAR RECORD Midland/Staffordshire County Senior 2004-05, 2006-07, 11-12, 12-13. North West Counties Div.1 2015-16.

	08-09	09-10	10-11	11-12	12-13	13-14	14-15	15-16	16-17	17-18
			StfSP 2	StfSP 1	StfSP 1	NWC1 4	NWC1 4	NWC1 1	NWCP 10	NWCP 8
								FAC P	FAC EPr	FAC P
							FAV 1P	FAV 1Q	FAV 1P	FAV 1P

IRLAM
Founded: 1969   Nickname: Mitchells/Shack

Club Contact Details (T) 07969 946 277   (E)
Ground: Silver Street, Irlam, Manchester M44 6HR
Nearest Railway Station Flixton - 2.3km
Capacity: **Seats:** 150 **Covered:** Yes   **Bus Route** Silver Street stop - 23m away
Colours(change): All blue
Previous Names: Mitchell Shackleton.
Previous Leagues: Manchester Amateur. Manchester.

HONOURS: FA Comps: None
League: Manchester Amateur Division Three 1973-74, Division Two 74-75. Manchester Premier Division 2002-03.
10 YEAR RECORD

	08-09	09-10	10-11	11-12	12-13	13-14	14-15	15-16	16-17	17-18
NWC1	8	NWC1 10	NWC1 9	NWC1 10	NWC1 14	NWC1 10	NWC1 14	NWC1 2	NWCP 8	NWCP 13
			FAC EP	FAC EP	FAC P				FAC EP	FAC EP
		FAV 2Q	FAV 2P	FAV 1Q	FAV 1Q	FAV 1Q	FAV 1Q	FAV 1Qr	FAV 1P	FAV 1P

LITHERLAND REMYCA
Founded: 1959   Nickname: The REMY

Club Contact Details (T) 0151 288 6288   (E)
Ground: Litherland Sports Park, Boundary Road, Litherland, Liverpool L21 7LA
Nearest Railway Station Aintree - 1.7km
Capacity: **Seats:** **Covered:**   **Bus Route** Moss Lane stop - 98m away
Colours(change): Red and black
Previous Names:
Previous Leagues: Liverpool County >2015.

HONOURS: FA Comps: None
League: Zingari Premier Division 1987-88, 93-94, 94-95, 95-96,
10 YEAR RECORD Division Two 2005-06. Liverpool County Division Two 2006-07.

	08-09	09-10	10-11	11-12	12-13	13-14	14-15	15-16	16-17	17-18
LivCP	4	LivCP 3	LivCP 13	LivCP 15	LivCP 9	LivCP 5	NWC1 9	NWC1 9	NWC1 3	NWC1 2
										FAC P
								FAV 1Q	FAV 1P	FAV 1P

NORTHWICH VICTORIA

Founded: 1874   Nickname: Vics, Greens

Club Contact Details (T) 01606 43008   (E) dave.thomas@northwichvics.co.uk
Ground: Wincham Park, Chapel Street, Northwich CW9 6DA
Nearest Railway Station Northwich (1.3 miles)
Capacity: **Seats:** Yes   **Covered:** Yes

Colours(change): Green and white
Previous Names: None
Previous Leagues: The Combination 1890-92, 1894-98, Football League 1892-94, Cheshire 1898-1900, Manchester 1900-12
Lancashire 1912-19, Cheshire County 1919-68, Northern Premier 1968-79, Conference 1979-2010
HONOURS: FA Comps: FA Trophy 1983-84.
League: Manchester 1902-03. Cheshire County 1956-57. Conference North 2005-06.

10 YEAR RECORD									
08-09	09-10	10-11	11-12	12-13	13-14	14-15	15-16	16-17	17-18
Conf 22	Conf N 12	NP P 12	NP P 2	NP1S 8	NP1N 9	NP1N 4	NP1N 3	NP1S 22	NWCP 16
FAC 4Q	FAC 2P	FAC 2Qr	FAC 2Q	FAC Pr	FAC 1Q	FAC 1Qr	FAC 2P	FAC P	FAC EPr
FAT 1P	FAT 3P	FAT 1P	FAT 3P	FAT 1Q	FAT 1Pr	FAT 1Qr	FAT 1Q	FAT Pr	FAV 1Q

PADIHAM

Founded: 1878   Nickname: Caldersiders

Club Contact Details (T) 01282 773 742   (E)
Ground: Arbories Memorial Sports Ground, Well Street, Padiham BB12 8LE
Nearest Railway Station Hapton - 2.2km
Capacity: 1,688 **Seats:** 159 **Covered:** Yes   **Bus Route** Memorial Park stop - 110m away

Colours(change): All blue.
Previous Names: None
Previous Leagues: Lancashire Comb. East Lancs Am. North East Lancs. West Lancs. North West Counties > 2013. NPL 2013-15.

HONOURS: FA Comps: None
League: West Lancashire Division Two 1971-72, 76-77, Division One 1999-00.
North West Counties 2012-13.

10 YEAR RECORD									
08-09	09-10	10-11	11-12	12-13	13-14	14-15	15-16	16-17	17-18
NWC1 2	NWCP 10	NWCP 4	NWCP 15	NWCP 1	NP1N 19	NP1N 22	NWCP 11	NWCP 7	NWCP 17
FAC P	FAC P	FAC EP	FAC EP	FAC P	FAC 1Q	FAC P	FAC 1Q	FAC P	FAC EP
FAV 1Q	FAV 2P	FAV 2Qr	FAV 2Qr	FAV 2P	FAV 1Q	FAT P	FAT 1Q	FAV 1Q	FAV 2P	FAV 1Q

RUNCORN TOWN

Founded: 1967   Nickname: Town

Club Contact Details (T) 07808 737 773   (E)
Ground: Pavilions Sports Complex, Sandy Lane, Weston Point, Runcorn WA7 4EX
Nearest Railway Station Runcorn - 1.6km
Capacity: 1,530 **Seats:** Yes **Covered:** Yes   **Bus Route** South Parade stop - 69m away

Colours(change): Sky and navy blue
Previous Names: Mond Rangers 1967-2005 (Amalgamated with ICI Weston 1974-75).
Previous Leagues: Runcorn Sunday 1967-73, Warrington & District 1973-84, West Cheshire 1984-10.

HONOURS: FA Comps: None
League: West Cheshire League Division Two 2006-07.

10 YEAR RECORD									
08-09	09-10	10-11	11-12	12-13	13-14	14-15	15-16	16-17	17-18
WCh1 4	WCh1 3	NWC1 2	NWCP 2	NWCP 4	NWCP 5	NWCP 13	NWCP 13	NWCP 3	NWCP 3
			FAC 1Q	FAC 1Q	FAC P	FAC 3Q	FAC P	FAC EP	FAC P
		FAV 4P	FAV 4Pr	FAV 5P	FAV 2P	FAV 2P	FAV 3Pr	FAV 1P	FAV 1P

SILSDEN

Founded: 1904   Nickname: The

Club Contact Details (T) 01535 958 850   (E)
Ground: Keighley Road, Keighley Road, Silsden BD20 0EH
Nearest Railway Station Steeton & Silsden - 1.1km
Capacity: **Seats:** Yes   **Covered:** Yes   **Bus Route** Keighley Road stop - 55m away

Colours(change): Red/black/red
Previous Names: Reformed in 1980.
Previous Leagues: Craven & District. West Riding County Amateur.

HONOURS: FA Comps: None
League: Craven Premier Division 1998-99. West Riding County Am. Division Two 99-2000, Division One 2000-01,
Premier Division 2002-03. North West Counties Division One 2017-18.

10 YEAR RECORD									
08-09	09-10	10-11	11-12	12-13	13-14	14-15	15-16	16-17	17-18
NWCP 9	NWCP 14	NWCP 16	NWCP 12	NWCP 18	NWCP 15	NWCP 10	NWCP 21	NWC1 11	NWC1 1
FAC P	FAC P	FAC EPr	FAC Pr	FAC EP	FAC EP	FAC EP	FAC P	FAC EPr	
FAV 2Q	FAV 2Q	FAV 1Q	FAV 1Q		FAV 2Q	FAV 1P	FAV 1P	FAV 2Q	FAV 2Q

SQUIRES GATE

Founded: 1948   Nickname: Gate

Club Contact Details (T) 01253 348 512   **(E)**
Ground: Brian Addison Stadium, School Road, Marton, Blackpool, Lancs FY4 5DS
Nearest Railway Station Squires Gate - 2.4km
Capacity: 1,000 **Seats:** 100 **Covered:** Yes
Bus Route St Nicholas School stop - 75m away

Colours(change): All blue.
Previous Names: Squires Gate British Legion FC >1953.
Previous Leagues: Blackpool & District Amateur 1958-61. West Lancashire 1961-91.

HONOURS: FA Comps: None
League: Blackpool & District Amateur League Division One 1955-56, 56-57.
10 YEAR RECORD | West Lancashire League Division Two 1980-81.

08-09	09-10	10-11	11-12	12-13	13-14	14-15	15-16	16-17	17-18
NWCP 10	NWCP 13	NWCP 9	NWCP 16	NWCP 21	NWCP 19	NWCP 6	NWCP 19	NWCP 19	NWCP 11
FAC Pr	FAC EPr	FAC EP	FAC 1Qr	FAC EP	FAC EP	FAC 1Qr	FAC EPr	FAC 1Q	FAC EP
FAV 1P	FAV 2Q	FAV 2Q	FAV 3P	FAV 2Q	FAV 2Q	FAV 1Q	FAV 2Q	FAV 1Q	FAV 1Q

WEST DIDSBURY & CHORLTON

Founded: 1908   Nickname: West

Club Contact Details (T)   **(E)**
Ground: The Recreation Ground, End of Brookburn Road, Chorlton, Manchester M21 8FF
Capacity: 1,000 **Seats:** Yes **Covered:** Yes

Colours(change): White and black
Previous Names: Christ Church AFC 1908-1920. West Didsbury AFC 1920-2003.
Previous Leagues: Manchester Alliance pre 1920. Lancashire & Cheshire Amateur 1920-2006. Manchester 2006-2012.

HONOURS: FA Comps: None
League: Lancashire & Cheshire Amateur Division Two 1987-88, Division One 88-89
10 YEAR RECORD | Manchester League Division One 2010-11.

08-09	09-10	10-11	11-12	12-13	13-14	14-15	15-16	16-17	17-18
Manc1 5	Manc1 2	Manc1 1	MancP 7	NCE1 3	NWCP 12	NWCP 16	NWCP 5	NWCP 6	NWCP 10
					FAC Pr	FAC P	FAC EP	FAC P	FAC Pr
			FAV 2Q	FAV 1Q	FAV 1P	FAV 1P	FAV 1P	FAV 2Q	FAV 1P

WHITCHURCH ALPORT

Founded: 1946   Nickname:

Club Contact Details (T)   **(E)**
Ground: Yockings Park, Black Park Road, Whitchurch SY13 1PG
Nearest Railway Station Whitchurch - 0.4km
Capacity: **Seats:** **Covered:**
Bus Route Railway Station stop - 501m away

Colours(change): All red
Previous Names:
Previous Leagues: Cheshire. Mercian Regional League.

HONOURS: FA Comps: WFA Am Cup 1973-74
League: Shrewsbury & District 1947-48. Mid Cheshire 1969-70.
10 YEAR RECORD

08-09	09-10	10-11	11-12	12-13	13-14	14-15	15-16	16-17	17-18
Ches2 7	Ches2 9	Ches2 3	Ches2 7	MerRP 11	MerRP 5	MerRP 4	NWC1 18	NWC1 5	NWC1 4
									FAC EP
								FAV 1Q	FAV 1Q

WINSFORD UNITED

Founded: 1883   Nickname: Blues

Club Contact Details (T) 01606 558 447   **(E)**
Ground: The Barton Stadium, Kingsway, Winsford, Cheshire CW7 3AE
Nearest Railway Station Winsford - 1.2km
Capacity: 3,000 **Seats:** 200 **Covered:** 5,000 **Shop:** Yes **Bus Route** Wesley Court stop - 34m away

Colours(change): All royal blue
Previous Names: Over Wanderers 1883-1887
Previous Leagues: The Combination 1902-04. Cheshire County 1919-40, 47-82. Northern Premier League 1987-2001.

HONOURS: FA Comps: None
League: Cheshire League 1920-21, 76-77.
10 YEAR RECORD | North West Counties League Division Two 2006-07.

08-09	09-10	10-11	11-12	12-13	13-14	14-15	15-16	16-17	17-18
NWCP 19	NWCP 19	NWCP 3	NWCP 7	NWCP 5	NWCP 14	NWCP 12	NWCP 14	NWCP 13	NWCP 14
FAC EPr	FAC EPr	FAC EP	FAC EPr	FAC P	FAC P	FAC EP	FAC EPr	FAC 1Qr	FAC EP
FAV 2Q	FAV 2P	FAV 2Q	FAV 2P	FAV 3P	FAV 2Pr	FAV 1P	FAV 1P	FAV 1Q	FAV 2Q

DIVISION ONE NORTH

AFC BLACKPOOL

Founded: 1947   **Nickname:** Mechanics

Club Contact Details (T) 01253 761 721   **(E)**

Ground: Mechanics Ground, Jepson Way, Common Edge Road, Blackpool, FY4 5DY   **Capacity:** 2,000

Nearest Railway Station Squires Gate - 2.2km   **Bus Route** Borough Boundary stop - 109m away

HONOURS   **League:** West Lancashire League 1960-61, 61-62.

FA Comps: None   North West Counties League Division Three 1985/86, Division One 2010-11.

Colours(change): Tangerine/Tangerine/white

10 YEAR RECORD

08-09		09-10		10-11		11-12		12-13		13-14		14-15		15-16		16-17		17-18	
NWC1	15	NWC1	15	NWC1	1	NWCP	9	NWCP	10	NWCP	13	NWCP	18	NWCP	22	NWC1	19	NWC1	7
FAC	EPr					FAC	Pr	FAC	EP	FAC	EP	FAC	EP	FAC	1Q	FAC	EP		
FAV	2Q	FAV	2Q	FAV	2P	FAV	1Q	FAV	2Q	FAV	1P	FAV	1Q	FAV	1Q	FAV	2Q	FAV	1Q

AFC DARWEN

Founded: 2009 (reformed)   **Nickname:** Salmoners

Club Contact Details (T) 01254 776 193   **(E)**

Ground: WEC Group Anchor Ground, Anchor Road, Darwen, Lancs BB3 0BB   **Capacity:** 4,000

Nearest Railway Station Darwen - 1.7km   **Bus Route** Birch Hall Avenue stop - 256m away

HONOURS   **League:** None

FA Comps: None

Colours(change): All red

10 YEAR RECORD

08-09	09-10		10-11		11-12		12-13		13-14		14-15		15-16		16-17		17-18	
	WLaP	8	NWC1	13	NWC1	13	NWC1	5	NWC1	9	NWC1	3	NWCP	18	NWCP	18	NWCP	23
													FAC	EP	FAC	EPr	FAC	EP
					FAV	1P			FAV	2Q	FAV	2P	FAV	2Q	FAV	1Q	FAV	1P

AFC LIVERPOOL

Founded: 2008   **Nickname:** Little Reds

Club Contact Details (T) 0151 9241743 or 0151 286 9101   **(E)**

Ground: Marine FC, College Road, Crosby, Liverpool L23 3AS   **Capacity:** 3,185

Nearest Railway Station Blundellsands & Crosby - 0.5km   **Bus Route** Brompton Avenue stop - 175m away

HONOURS   **League:** None

FA Comps: None

Colours(change): All red

10 YEAR RECORD

08-09		09-10		10-11		11-12		12-13		13-14		14-15		15-16		16-17		17-18	
NWC1	4	NWC1	5	NWC1	4	NWCP	19	NWCP	11	NWCP	7	NWCP	9	NWCP	17	NWCP	12	NWCP	20
				FAC	EP	FAC	EPr	FAC	P	FAC	P	FAC	EP	FAC	1Q	FAC	EPr	FAC	EP
		FAV	2Q	FAV	3P	FAV	2Qr	FAV	1P	FAV	1Q	FAV	2Q	FAV	1Q	FAV	1P	FAV	2Q

ASHTON TOWN

Founded: 1953   **Nickname:** The Town

Club Contact Details (T) 01942 724 448   **(E)**

Ground: The Ashton Town Stadium, Edge Green St, Ashton-in-Makerfield, Wigan, WN4 8SL.

HONOURS   **League:** St Helens Combination Division Two 1957-58.

FA Comps: None   Warrington & District League Division One 1959-60, 60-61, 62-63, 63-64, 64-65, 69-70.

Colours(change): All red

10 YEAR RECORD

08-09		09-10		10-11		11-12		12-13		13-14		14-15		15-16		16-17		17-18	
NWC1	18	NWC1	13	NWC1	16	NWC1	18	NWC1	6	NWC1	12	NWC1	17	NWC1	11	NWC1	22	ChesP	6
FAC	EP			FAC	EP					FAC	EP								
FAV	2Q	FAV	2Q	FAV	2Q	FAV	1Q	FAV	2Q	FAV	1Q	FAV	1P	FAV	2Q	FAV	1P	FAV	1Q

ATHERTON L.R.

Founded: 1956   **Nickname:** The Panthers

Club Contact Details (T) 01942 575 173   **(E)**

Ground: Crilly Park, Spa Road, Atherton, Manchester M46 9JX   **Capacity:** 3,000

Nearest Railway Station Atherton - 0.3km   **Bus Route** Devonshire Rad stop - 97m away

HONOURS   **League:** Bolton Combination Division Two A 1965-66.

FA Comps: None   North West Counties 1992-93, 93-94.

Colours(change): Yellow and navy

10 YEAR RECORD

08-09		09-10		10-11		11-12		12-13		13-14		14-15		15-16		16-17		17-18	
NWCP	12	NWCP	20	NWCP	10	NWCP	22	NWC1	13	NWC1	3	NWC1	12	NWC1	17	NWC1	20	NWC1	18
FAC	1Q	FAC	1Qr	FAC	Pr	FAC	P	FAC	P										
FAV	1Q	FAV	1Q	FAV	1P	FAV	1P	FAV	1Q	FAV	1P			FAV	2Q	FAV	1P	FAV	1Q

AVRO

Founded: 1936   Nickname:

Club Contact Details (T) 07920 779 382   **(E)**
Ground: Vestacare Stadium, White Bank Road, Oldham OL8 3JH

HONOURS   **League:** Manchester Division One 1988-89, 2003-04, Premier 09-10, 10-11, 17-18.
FA Comps: None

Colours(change): Blue, black and white

10 YEAR RECORD									
08-09	09-10	10-11	11-12	12-13	13-14	14-15	15-16	16-17	17-18
MancP 6	MancP 1	MancP 1	MancP 6	MancP 5	MancP 9	MancP 3	MancP 9	MancP 11	MancP 1

BACUP BOROUGH

Founded: 1875   Nickname: The Boro

Club Contact Details (T) 01706 878 655   **(E)**
Ground: Brian Boys Stadium, Cowtoot Lane, Blackthorn, Bacup, OL13 8EE   **Capacity:** 3,000
   Bus Route Thorn Cp School stop - 119m away

HONOURS   **League:** Lancashire Combination 1946-47.
FA Comps: None   North West Counties Division Two 2002-03

Colours(change): White and black

10 YEAR RECORD									
08-09	09-10	10-11	11-12	12-13	13-14	14-15	15-16	16-17	17-18
NWCP 8	NWCP 12	NWCP 11	NWCP 17	NWCP 17	NWCP 21	NWCP 21	NWC1 5	NWC1 18	NWC1 17
FAC 2Q	FAC EPr	FAC 1Q	FAC EP	FAC P			FAC EP	FAC EP	
FAV 2Q	FAV 2P	FAV 2P	FAV 2P	FAV 1Qr			FAV 2Q	FAV 2Q	FAV 2Q

CARLISLE CITY

Founded: 1975   Nickname: Sky Blues

Club Contact Details (T) 01228 523 777   **(E)**
Ground: Petteril Bank Road, Carlisle CA1 3AF
Nearest Railway Station Carlisle - 1.9km   **Bus Route** Ridgemount Road stop - 321m away
HONOURS   **League:** Northern Alliance Division One 1991-92.
FA Comps: None

Colours(change): All sky blue

10 YEAR RECORD									
08-09	09-10	10-11	11-12	12-13	13-14	14-15	15-16	16-17	17-18
NAI P 6	NAI P 10	NAI P 6	NAI P 5	NAI P 3	NAI P 2	NAI P 2	NAI P 3	NWC1 14	NWC1 11
								FAV 1Q	FAV 2Q

CHADDERTON

Founded: 1946   Nickname: Chaddy

Club Contact Details (T) 07506 104 005 (MD)   **(E)**
Ground: Andrew Street, Chadderton, Oldham, Greater Manchester OL9 0JT
Nearest Railway Station Freehold (Manc. Metrolink) - 1.1km   **Bus Route** Middleton Road stop - 133m away
HONOURS   **League:** Manchester Amateur League 1955-56, Division One 1962-63.
FA Comps: None   Manchester League Division Two 1964-65, Division One 1966-67.

Colours(change): All red

10 YEAR RECORD									
08-09	09-10	10-11	11-12	12-13	13-14	14-15	15-16	16-17	17-18
NWC1 10	NWC1 4	NWC1 6	NWC1 6	NWC1 12	NWC1 13	NWC1 6	NWC1 14	NWC1 9	NWC1 16
FAC EP	FAC EPr	FAC P	FAC EP	FAC P			FAC EP		
FAV 1Q	FAV 2Qr	FAV 1Q	FAV 2Q	FAV 2Q	FAV 1P	FAV 4P	FAV 2P	FAV 1P	FAV 2Q

CLEATOR MOOR CELTIC

Founded: 1909   Nickname:

Club Contact Details (T)   **(E)**
Ground: McGrath Park, Birks Road, Cleator Moor, Cumbria CA25 5HR
Nearest Railway Station Whitehaven
HONOURS   **League:** None
FA Comps: None

Colours(change): Green and white

10 YEAR RECORD									
08-09	09-10	10-11	11-12	12-13	13-14	14-15	15-16	16-17	17-18
Wear 11	Wear 5	Wear 15	Wear 7	Wear 4	Wear 4	Wear 3	Wear 4	Wear 3	Wear 2
			FAV 1Q						

DAISY HILL

Founded: 1894   Nickname: The Daisies

Club Contact Details (T) 01942 818 544   (E)
Ground: New Sirs, St James Street, Westhoughton, Bolton BL5 2EB
Nearest Railway Station Daisy Hill - 0.7km   **Bus Route** Hindley Road stop - 173m away
HONOURS   League: Wigan & District 1896-97.
FA Comps: None   Bolton Combination Premier Division 1962-63, 72-73, 75-76, 77-78.
          Colours(change): All royal blue

10 YEAR RECORD	09-10	10-11	11-12	12-13	13-14	14-15	15-16	16-17	17-18
08-09									
NWC1 17	NWC1 11	NWC1 14	NWC1 12	NWC1 16	NWC1 18	NWC1 8	NWC1 12	NWC1 16	NWC1 21
FAC EP		FAC EP		FAC EP					
FAV 2Q	FAV 2P	FAV 1Q	FAV 1Q	FAV 2Q	FAV 1Q	FAV 1P	FAV 2P	FAV 2Q	FAV 1Q

GARSTANG

Founded: 1895   Nickname:

Club Contact Details (T) 07501 119 458   (E)
Ground: The Riverside, Lancaster Road, Garstang PR3 1EB
Nearest Railway Station Lancaster (12 miles) or Preston (14.5)   **Bus Route** From Preston/Lancaster/Blackpool stop High St.
HONOURS   League: West Lancashire Premier 2007-08, 17-18.
FA Comps: None
          Colours(change): Red and black

10 YEAR RECORD	09-10	10-11	11-12	12-13	13-14	14-15	15-16	16-17	17-18
08-09									
WLaP 3	WLaP 6	WLaP 13	WLaP 16	WLa1 2	WLaP 10	WLaP 5	WLaP 9	WLaP 4	WLaP 1

HOLKER OLD BOYS

Founded: 1936   Nickname: Cobs

Club Contact Details (T) 01229 828 176   (E)
Ground: Rakesmoor, Rakesmoor Lane, Hawcoat, Barrow-in-Furness LA14 4QB
Nearest Railway Station Barrow-in-Furness - 2.6km   **Bus Route** Dunmail Raise stop - 151m away
HONOURS   League: West Lancashire 1986-87.
FA Comps: None
          Colours(change): Green/white/green

10 YEAR RECORD	09-10	10-11	11-12	12-13	13-14	14-15	15-16	16-17	17-18
08-09									
NWC1 9	NWC1 7	NWC1 3	NWC1 9	NWC1 7	NWC1 6	NWC1 5	NWC1 8	NWC1 17	NWC1 9
FAC EPr	FAC EP	FAC P	FAC P	FAC 1Q			FAC EPr	FAC P	
FAV 2Qr	FAV 2Q	FAV 2Q	FAV 2Q	FAV 1Q	FAV 1P	FAV 1P	FAV 2Q	FAV 1P	FAV 1Q

LONGRIDGE TOWN

Founded: 1996   Nickname:

Club Contact Details (T) 01772 786365 / 07710 514767   (E)
Ground: The Mike Riding Ground, Inglewhite Road, Longridge, Preston PR3 2NA
Nearest Railway Station Preston (7.7 miles)   **Bus Route** No.1 bus Preston to Berry Lane Longridge
HONOURS   League: Preston & District Division Three 2003-04. West Lancashire Division One 2011-12, Premier 16-17.
FA Comps: None
          Colours(change): All red

10 YEAR RECORD	09-10	10-11	11-12	12-13	13-14	14-15	15-16	16-17	17-18
08-09									
P&D P 3	WLa2 2	WLa1 4	WLa1 1	WLaP 3	WLaP 12	WLaP 6	WLaP 4	WLaP 1	WLaP 3

LOWER BRECK

Founded: 2010   Nickname:

Club Contact Details (T) 0151 263 6186   (E)
Ground: Anfield Sports & Community Centre, Lower Breck Road, Liverpool L6 0AG
Nearest Railway Station Liverpool Lime Street   **Bus Route** Arriva Bus 68 stops at the ground
HONOURS   League: Liverpool County Division Two 2012-13, Premier 17-18.
FA Comps: None
          Colours(change): Red and black

10 YEAR RECORD	09-10	10-11	11-12	12-13	13-14	14-15	15-16	16-17	17-18
08-09									
				LivC2 1	LivC1 4	LivCP 11	LivCP 3	LivCP 2	LivCP 1

NELSON
Founded: 1883   Nickname: Admirals

Club Contact Details (T) 01772 794 103   **(E)**
Ground: Little Wembley, Lomeshaye Way, Nelson, Lancs BB9 7BN.
    Capacity: 1500
Nearest Railway Station Nelson - 1km   **Bus Route** Business Village stop - 83m away
HONOURS   **League:** Lancashire 1895-96. Lancashire Combination 1949-50, 51-52. Football League Division Three North 1922-23.
FA Comps: None   North West Counties Division One 2013-14.
Colours(change): All blue

10 YEAR RECORD

08-09	09-10	10-11	11-12	12-13	13-14	14-15	15-16	16-17	17-18
NWCP 17	NWCP 17		NWC1 15	NWC1 10	NWC1 1	NWCP 11	NWCP 16	NWCP 21	NWC1 22
						FAC EP	FAC EP	FAC P	FAC EP
	FAV 3P			FAV 2Q	FAV 1P	FAV 2Qr	FAV 2Q	FAV 1Q	FAV 2Q

PRESTWICH HEYS
Founded: 1938   Nickname: The Heys

Club Contact Details (T) 0161 7773 8888 (MD)   **(E)**
Ground: Adie Moran Park, Sandgate Road, Whitefield M45 6WG
Nearest Railway Station Clifton - 3.5km   **Bus Route** Sandgate Road stop - 73m away
HONOURS   **League:** Lancashire Combination 1970-71. Manchester Division One 1996-97, Premier Division 2004-05, 04
FA Comps: None   -05, 05-06, 06-07, 15-16.
Colours(change): Red and white

10 YEAR RECORD

08-09	09-10	10-11	11-12	12-13	13-14	14-15	15-16	16-17	17-18
MancP 12	MancP 11	MancP 12	MancP 13	MancP 8	MancP 4	MancP 6	MancP 1	NWC1 8	NWC1 3
									FAV 1Q

SHELLEY
Founded: 1903   Nickname:

Club Contact Details (T) 07931 853 881   **(E)**
Ground: Storthes Hall, Huddersfield HD8 0WA
Nearest Railway Station Brockholes (2.5 miles), Stockmoor (2.3) Huddersfield (5.2)   **Bus Route** 398 Huddersfield Uni to Storthes Hall Park
HONOURS   **League:** Huddersfield & District Division Two A 1904-05, Division Two 28-29, 2000-01, Division Three 60-61,
FA Comps: None   86-87, 2010-11, Division Four 2009-10. West Yorkshire Division Two 2011-12.
Colours(change): Red and black

10 YEAR RECORD

08-09	09-10	10-11	11-12	12-13	13-14	14-15	15-16	16-17	17-18
		HudD3 3	WYk2 1	WYk1 2	WYkP 12	WYkP 10	WYkP 11	WYkP 8	WYkP 10

ST HELENS TOWN
Founded: 1946   Nickname: Town or Saints

Club Contact Details (T)   **(E)**
Ground: Ruskin Drive Sportsground, Ruskin Drive, Dentons Green, St Helens WA10 6RP
Nearest Railway Station St Helens Central - 1.9km   **Bus Route** Ruskin Drive stop - 153m away
HONOURS   **League:** Lancashire Combination Division Two 1950-51, Premier 1971-72 .
FA Comps: FA Vase 1986-87.
Colours(change): All blue

10 YEAR RECORD

08-09	09-10	10-11	11-12	12-13	13-14	14-15	15-16	16-17	17-18
NWCP 16	NWCP 9	NWCP 17	NWCP 21	NWCP 19	NWCP 17	NWCP 20	NWC1 7	NWC1 13	NWC1 20
FAC P	FAC 1Q	FAC Pr	FAC EP	FAC EP	FAC EPr	FAC EP	FAC EP		
FAV 2Q	FAV 1Q	FAV 3P	FAV 2Q	FAV 1P	FAV 1Q	FAV 3P	FAV 2Q	FAV 1Q	FAV 1Q

STEETON
Founded: 1905   Nickname:

Club Contact Details (T) 01535 606 044   **(E)**
Ground: Cougar Park, Royd Ings Avenue, Keighley BD21 3RF
Nearest Railway Station Keighly (0.8 miles)   **Bus Route** 662 (Bradford) & 760 (Leeds)
HONOURS   **League:** Keighley & District 1937-38, 38-39, 54-55. Craven & District 1959-60.
FA Comps: None   West Riding County Amateur Division Two 1988-89, 2000-01, Division One 2009-10.
Colours(change): All green

10 YEAR RECORD

08-09	09-10	10-11	11-12	12-13	13-14	14-15	15-16	16-17	17-18
	WRC1 1	WRCP 8	WRCP 6	WRCP 2	WRCP 5	WRCP 7	WRCP 10	WRCP 3	WRCP 3

ABBEY HULTON UNITED

Founded: 1947   Nickname:

Club Contact Details (T) 01782 570 302   **(E)**
Ground: Birches Head Road, Abbey Hulton, Stoke-on-Trent ST2 8DD
Nearest Railway Station Stoke-on-Trent - 4.2km   **Bus Route** Woodhead Road stop - 262m away
HONOURS   **League:** Staffordshire County Senior Premier Division 2016-17.
FA Comps: None
Colours(change): Orange/black/black

10 YEAR RECORD

08-09	09-10	10-11	11-12	12-13	13-14	14-15	15-16	16-17	17-18
			StfSP 5	StfSP 4	StfSP 7	StfSP 3	StfSP 8	StfSP 1	NWC1 13

ALSAGER TOWN

Founded: 1968   Nickname: The Bullets

Club Contact Details (T) 07888 750 532   **(E)**
Ground: Woodpark Stadium, Woodland Court, Alsager ST7 2DP   **Capacity:** 3,000
Nearest Railway Station Alsager - 0.9km   **Bus Route** Curzon Avenue stop - 374m away
HONOURS   **League:** None
FA Comps: None
Colours(change): White & black

10 YEAR RECORD

	08-09	09-10	10-11	11-12	12-13	13-14	14-15	15-16	16-17	17-18
NWCP	7	NWCP 18	NWCP 20	NWCP 13	NWCP 15	NWCP 18	NWCP 17	NWCP 20	NWC1 7	NWC1 8
FAC	EP	FAC EP	FAC EP	FAC EP	FAC EP	FAC EP	FAC EP	FAC 1Q	FAC P	FAC EP
FAV	2Pr	FAV 2P	FAV 2Q	FAV 1Q	FAV 2Q	FAV 2Q	FAV 1Q	FAV 3P	FAV 2Q	FAV 2P

BARNTON

Founded: 1946   Nickname: Villagers

Club Contact Details (T) 07484 793 822   **(E)**
Ground: Townfield, Townfield Lane, Barnton, Cheshire CW8 4LH
Nearest Railway Station Greenbank - 2.6km   **Bus Route** Crocus Street stop - 128m away
HONOURS   **League:** Mid-Cheshire/Cheshire 1979-80, 82-83, 88-89, 96-97, 97-98, 98-99, 99-2000, 2000-01, 01-02, 02 -03, 04-05, Division Two 2012-13.
FA Comps: None
Colours(change): Black and white

10 YEAR RECORD

08-09	09-10	10-11	11-12	12-13	13-14	14-15	15-16	16-17	17-18
Ches1 16	Ches2 10	Ches2 13	Ches2 13	Ches2 1	Ches1 5	NWC1 7	NWC1 3	NWCP 17	NWCP 22
								FAC EP	FAC EP
							FAV 2Q	FAV 2Q	FAV 2Q

CAMMELL LAIRD

Founded: 1907   Nickname: Lairds

Club Contact Details (T) 0151 645 3121   **(E)** toddywood@hotmail.com
Ground: Kirklands, St Peter's Road, Rock Ferry, Birkenhead CH42 1PY   **Capacity:** 2,000
Nearest Railway Station Rock Ferry - 0.7km   **Bus Route** St Peters Road stop - 58m away
HONOURS   **League:** West Cheshire x19 (Firstly in 1954-55 and most recently 2000-01). North West Counties Division Two 2004-05, Division One 2005-06.
FA Comps: None
Colours(change): All royal blue

10 YEAR RECORD

08-09	09-10	10-11	11-12	12-13	13-14	14-15	15-16	16-17	17-18
NP P	NP1S 16	NP1N 19	NP1N 22	NP1N 2	NP1N 11	NWC1 2	NWCP 15	NWCP 22	NWC1 6
FAC 1Q	FAC 2Q	FAC P	FAC 1Q	FAC 1Q	FAC 2Q	FAC EP			FAC P
FAT 3Qr	FAT 1Q	FAT 1Q	FAT P	FAT 3Q	FAT 1Q	FAV 1Q			FAV 1Q

CHEADLE HEATH NOMADS

Founded: 2004   Nickname:

Club Contact Details (T)   **(E)**
Ground: The Heath, Norbreck Avenue, Cheadle, Stockport SK8 2ET
Nearest Railway Station Stockport   **Bus Route** 11, 11a and 309
HONOURS   **League:** Cheshire Premier 2014-15.
FA Comps: None
Colours(change): Maroon and blue

10 YEAR RECORD

08-09	09-10	10-11	11-12	12-13	13-14	14-15	15-16	16-17	17-18
Ches1 13	Ches1 7	Ches1 16	Ches1 6	Ches1 12	Ches1 10	ChesP 1	ChesP 2	ChesP 5	ChesP 4

CHEADLE TOWN
Founded: 1961 **Nickname:**

Club Contact Details (T) 0161 428 2510 **(E)**
Ground: Park Road Stadium, Cheadle, Cheshire SK8 2AN
Nearest Railway Station Gatley - 1.8km **Bus Route** Stockport Road stop - 161m away
HONOURS **League:** Manchester Division One 1979-80.
FA Comps: None
Colours(change): Red and white

10 YEAR RECORD

08-09		09-10		10-11		11-12		12-13		13-14		14-15		15-16		16-17		17-18	
NWC1	7	NWC1	14	NWC1	10	NWC1	8	NWC1	7	NWC1	11	NWC1	10	NWC1	6	NWC1	12	NWC1	12
FAC	EP	FAC	EP	FAC	P	FAC	P	FAC	EPr	FAC	EP	FAC		FAC		FAC	1Q		
FAV	1Q	FAV	1Pr	FAV	1Q	FAV	1P	FAV	1P	FAV	2P	FAV	1Q	FAV	2Q	FAV	1Q	FAV	1Q

ECCLESHALL
Founded: 1971 **Nickname:** The Eagles

Club Contact Details (T) 01785 851 351 (MD) **(E)**
Ground: Pershall Park, Chester Road, Eccleshall ST21 6NE
Bus Route Pershall Farm stop - 228m away
HONOURS **League:** Staffordshire County Premier 1982-83. Staffordshire Senior 1989-90.
FA Comps: None Midland 2001-02, 02-03.
Colours(change): All royal blue

10 YEAR RECORD

08-09		09-10		10-11		11-12		12-13		13-14		14-15		15-16		16-17		17-18	
NWC1	11	NWC1	9	NWC1	11	NWC1	7	NWC1	15	NWC1	17	NWC1	15	NWC1	16	NWC1	21		
FAC	EP	FAC	EP	FAC	1Q	FAC	Pr	FAC	EP										
FAV	1P	FAV	1Qr	FAV	1P	FAV	1Q	FAV	1P	FAV	2Q	FAV	1P	FAV	2Q	FAV	1Q	FAV	1Q

ELLESMERE RANGERS
Founded: 1969 **Nickname:** The Rangers

Club Contact Details (T) 07947 864 357 **(E)** john.edge2@homecall.co.uk
Ground: Beech Grove, Ellesmere, Shropshire SY12 0BT **Capacity:** 1,250
Nearest Railway Station Gobowen (7 miles) **Bus Route** Lakelands School - stop 50m away
HONOURS **League:** West Midlands (Reg) Division One 2005-06, Premier 2009-10.
FA Comps: None
Colours(change): Sky blue & navy blue

10 YEAR RECORD

08-09		09-10		10-11		11-12		12-13		13-14		14-15		15-16		16-17		17-18	
WMP	4	WMP	1	MidAl	13	MidAl	15	MidAl	22	WMP	11	WMP	4	WMP	10	WMP	7	WMP	6
FAC	1Qr	FAC	EP	FAC	EP	FAC	EP	FAC	EP	FAC	P	FAC	EP	FAC	EP				
FAV	2Q	FAV	1Q	FAV	2Q	FAV	2P	FAV	1Qr	FAV	2Q	FAV	EP	FAV	1P	FAV	1Q	FAV	1Q

FC OSWESTRY TOWN
Founded: 2013 **Nickname:** Town

Club Contact Details (T) 01691 684 840 **(E)**
Ground: The Venue, Burma Road, Oswestry, Shropshire SY11 4AS
Nearest Railway Station Gobowen - 2.1km **Bus Route** Park Crescent Jct stop - 325m away
HONOURS **League:** Mercain Regional Premier Division 2015-16.
FA Comps: None
Colours(change): All blue

10 YEAR RECORD

08-09	09-10	10-11	11-12	12-13		13-14		14-15		15-16		16-17		17-18	
				MerR1	7	MerR1	3	MerRP	5	MerRP	1	NWC1	15	NWC1	19
												FAV	1Q	FAV	1Q

MAINE ROAD
Founded: 1955 **Nickname:** Blues

Club Contact Details (T) 0161 861 0344 **(E)**
Ground: Brantingham Road, Chorlton-cum-Hardy M21 0TT **Capacity:** 2,000
Nearest Railway Station Chorlton (Manc. Metrolink) - 768m **Bus Route** Manley Road stop - 170m away
HONOURS **League:** Manchester Amateur Sunday 1971-72. Manchester Premier 1982-83, 83-84, 84-85, 85-86.
FA Comps: None North West Counties Division Two 1989-90.
Colours(change): All sky blue.

10 YEAR RECORD

08-09		09-10		10-11		11-12		12-13		13-14		14-15		15-16		16-17		17-18	
NWCP	13	NWCP	6	NWCP	13	NWCP	18	NWCP	2	NWCP	4	NWCP	15	NWCP	12	NWCP	15	NWCP	21
FAC	Pr	FAC	1Q	FAC	EPr	FAC	1Q	FAC	1Q	FAC	EP	FAC	EP	FAC	P	FAC	1Q	FAC	Pr
FAV	1Pr	FAV	1Q	FAV	1Pr	FAV	2Q	FAV	1P	FAV	2P	FAV	1P	FAV	2Q	FAV	1Q	FAV	1Q

NEW MILLS

Founded: pre1890 **Nickname:** The Millers

Club Contact Details (T) 01663 747 435 (E)

Ground: Church Lane, New Mills SK22 4NP **Capacity:** 1,650

Nearest Railway Station New Mills Central - 0.7km **Bus Route** School (Bus Park) stop - 72m away

HONOURS **League:** Manchester Premier Division 1924, 26, 56, 63, 65, 66, 67, 68, 70, 71.

FA Comps: None North West Counties Division Two 2007-08, Premier Division 2010-11.

Colours(change): Amber & black

10 YEAR RECORD

08-09		09-10		10-11		11-12		12-13		13-14		14-15		15-16		16-17		17-18	
NWCP	2	NWCP	2	NWCP	1	NP1S	9	NP1N	3	NP1N	16	NP1N	21	NP1N	22	NWCP	20	NWC1	14
FAC	EP	FAC	P	FAC	2Q	FAC	1Q	FAC	2Q	FAC	1Qr	FAC	P	FAC	P	FAC	EP	FAC	EP
FAV	1P	FAV	5P	FAV	2P	FAT	P	FAT	3Q	FAT	P	FAT	2Q	FAT	P	FAV	2Q	FAV	1Q

RYLANDS

Founded: 1911 **Nickname:**

Club Contact Details (T) 01925 635 880 (E)

Ground: Rylands Recreation Club, Gorsey Lane, Warrington WA2 7RZ **Capacity:** 1345

Nearest Railway Station Warrington Central (1.4 miles) **Bus Route** No.3 from Warrington to Beresford Street

HONOURS **League:** Mid-Cheshire 1980-81, 83-84.

FA Comps: None

Colours(change): All blue

10 YEAR RECORD

08-09		09-10		10-11		11-12		12-13		13-14		14-15		15-16		16-17		17-18	
Ches1	4	Ches1	10	Ches1	7	Ches1	12	Ches1	6	Ches1	8	ChesP	9	ChesP	14	ChesP	10	ChesP	11

SANDBACH UNITED

Founded: 2004 **Nickname:**

Club Contact Details (T) 01270 768 389 (E)

Ground: Sandbach Community Football Centre, Hind Heath Road, Sandbach CW11 3LZ

Nearest Railway Station Sandbach - 1.4km **Bus Route** Salt Line Way stop - 260m away

HONOURS **League:** None

FA Comps: None

Colours(change): Blue and white

10 YEAR RECORD

08-09	09-10	10-11		11-12		12-13		13-14		14-15		15-16		16-17		17-18	
		StfSP		Ches2	5	Ches2	6	Ches2	2	ChesP	11	ChesP	4	NWC1	6	NWC1	5
																FAV	2Q

ST MARTINS

Founded: 1897 **Nickname:** Saints

Club Contact Details (T) 01691 684 840 (E)

Ground: The Venue, Burma Road, Parkhall, Oswestry, Shrops. SY11 4AS **Capacity:** 5,000

HONOURS **League:** Oswestry & District 1919-20, 52-53, 54-55. West Shropshire Alliance Division Three 1973-74,

FA Comps: None Premier 89-90, 2000-01. Shropshire County Division One 1997-98, 2007-08, Premier 2009-10.

Colours(change): Yellow and black

10 YEAR RECORD

08-09		09-10		10-11		11-12		12-13		13-14		14-15		15-16		16-17		17-18	
ShrCP	6	ShrCP	1	WM2	2	WM2	5	WM1	16	WM1	14	WM1	3	WM1	6	WM1	8	WM1	4
																		FAV	1Q

STOCKPORT TOWN

Founded: 2014 **Nickname:** The Lions

Club Contact Details (T) 0161 494 3140 (E)

Ground: Lambeth Grove, Woodley, Stockport SK6 1QX

Nearest Railway Station Woodley - 0.7km. Bredbury - 0.8km **Bus Route** Hyde Road stop - 414m away

HONOURS **League:** None

FA Comps: None

Colours(change): Red & white stripes

10 YEAR RECORD

08-09	09-10	10-11	11-12	12-13	13-14	14-15	15-16		16-17		17-18	
							NWC1	4	NWC1	10	NWC1	10
									FAV	1P	FAV	2Q

STONE DOMINOES

Founded: 1987   Nickname: The Doms

Club Contact Details (T) 01785 761 891   **(E)**

Ground: Wellbeing Centre, Stone Dominoes, Staffordshire ST15 0NF

Nearest Railway Station Stafford (8.5 miles)   **Bus Route** D&G Bus No.14 stops at Labour In Vain

HONOURS   **League:** Midland 1999-2000. North West Counties Division One 2009-10.

FA Comps: None

Colours(change): Red & black

10 YEAR RECORD

08-09		09-10		10-11		11-12		12-13		13-14	14-15	15-16		16-17		17-18	
NWC1	3	NWC1	1	NWCP	19	NWCP	20	NWCP	22			StfS1	4	StfS1	2	StfSP	11
FAC	P	FAC	P	FAC	EPr	FAC	1Q	FAC	EP								
FAV	4P	FAV	2P	FAV	1P	FAV	1Q	FAV	1Q								

STONE OLD ALLEYNIANS

Founded: 1962   Nickname:

Club Contact Details (T) 01785 761 891   **(E)** phil.johnson2016@hotmail.com

Ground: Wellbeing Park, Yarnfield Lane, Yarnfield ST15 0NF   **Capacity:** 2,000

Nearest Railway Station Norton Bridge - 2.8km   **Bus Route** Labour-in-Vain Pub - stop 650m away

HONOURS   **League:** Mid Staffordshire Division Two 1965-66, 80-81, Division One 71-72, 74-75, 78-79.

FA Comps: None

Colours(change): White & black

10 YEAR RECORD

08-09		09-10		10-11		11-12		12-13		13-14		14-15		15-16		16-17		17-18	
WM2	3	WM2	4	WM1	6	WM1	5	WM1	10	WM1	8	WM1	2	WMP	14	WMP	12	WMP	13
												FAV	2Q	FAV	2Q	FAV	2Qr	FAV	2Q

VAUXHALL MOTORS

Founded: 1963   Nickname: The Motormen

Club Contact Details (T) 0151 328 1114 (Club) 327 2294 (Social)   **(E)**

Ground: Rivacre Park, Rivacre Road, Ellesmere Port, South Wirrall CH66 1NJ   **Capacity:** 3,500

Nearest Railway Station Overpool (1.4 miles) or Hooton (1.7)

HONOURS   **League:** North West Counties Division Two 1988-89, 95-96, Division One 99-2000.

FA Comps: None

Colours(change): White/blue/blue

10 YEAR RECORD

08-09		09-10		10-11		11-12		12-13		13-14		14-15		15-16		16-17		17-18	
Conf N	11	Conf N	20	Conf N	17	Conf N	18	Conf N	12	Conf N	18	WCh1	4	WCh1	4	WCh1	8	WCh1	2
FAC	2Q	FAC	3Q	FAC	1Pr	FAC	2Qr	FAC	2Q	FAC	4Q	FAV	1Q	FAV	2Q	FAV	2Q	FAV	1Q
FAT	3Qr	FAT	2P	FAT	3Q	FAT	1Pr	FAT	3Q	FAT	3Q								

WYTHENSHAWE AMATEURS

Founded: 1946   Nickname: The Ammies

Club Contact Details (T) 0161 428 0517   **(E)**

Ground: Hollyhedge Park, Altrincham Road, Wythenshawe M22 4US

Nearest Railway Station Benchill Metrolink   **Bus Route** 102, 103 to Altrincham Rd from Manc City Centre

HONOURS   **League:** Lancashire & Cheshire Division Two 1954-55, Division One 56-57, Premier 61-62.

FA Comps: None   Manchester Division One 1972-73, Premier 89-90, 92-93, 2002-03.

Colours(change): Blue & white

10 YEAR RECORD

08-09		09-10		10-11		11-12		12-13		13-14		14-15		15-16		16-17		17-18	
MancP	4	MancP	2	MancP	8	MancP	9	MancP	13	MancP	8	MancP	7	MancP	10	MancP	2	MancP	2

WYTHENSHAWE TOWN

Founded: 1946   Nickname:

Club Contact Details (T)   **(E)** info@wythenshawetownfc.co.uk

Ground: Ericstan Park, Timpson Road, Wythenshawe M23 9LL

Nearest Railway Station Baguley tram stop is only a 5-10minute walk from   **Bus Route** 11 / 11a / 109

HONOURS   **League:** Sth Manc & Wythen Div.2 1949-50. Lancs & Ches Div.C 1958-59, Div.3 59-60, Div.2 64-65, Div.1

FA Comps: None   66-67, 68-69, 69-70, 70-71. Manc Div.2 73-74, Div.1 2011-12. Cheshire Div.2 2014-15, Div.1 15-16.

Colours(change): Royal Blue

10 YEAR RECORD

08-09		09-10		10-11		11-12		12-13		13-14		14-15		15-16		16-17		17-18	
Manc1	8	Manc1	6	Manc1	4	Manc1	1	MancP	10	MancP	15	Ches2	1	Ches1	1	ChesP	7	ChesP	8

NORTHERN COUNTIES EAST LEAGUE

Founded: 1982 **Sponsored by:** Toolstation

Recent Champions: 2015: Shaw Lane Aquaforce **2016:** Tadcaster Albion **2017:** Cleethorpes Town

PREMIER DIVISION	P	W	D	L	F	A	GD	Pts	DIVISION ONE	P	W	D	L	F	A	GD	Pts
1 Pontefract Collieries	42	33	3	6	134	38	96	102	1 Knaresborough Town	42	31	7	4	91	30	61	100
2 Pickering Town	42	29	9	4	127	52	75	96	2 Yorkshire Amateur	42	27	7	8	132	55	77	88
3 AFC Mansfield	42	29	9	4	110	43	67	96	3 Grimsby Borough	42	26	7	9	113	56	57	85
4 Handsworth Parramore	42	27	4	11	99	56	43	85	4 Eccleshill United	42	26	7	9	109	61	48	85
5 Maltby Main	42	22	9	11	88	57	31	75	5 Shirebrook Town	42	25	6	11	91	60	31	81
6 Hemsworth Miners Welfare	42	22	6	14	104	77	27	72	6 Glasshoughton Welfare	42	23	8	11	85	54	31	77
7 Penistone Church	42	20	12	10	93	66	27	72	7 Selby Town	42	23	6	13	105	71	34	75
8 Bottesford Town	42	22	3	17	93	84	9	69	8 Hallam	42	21	10	11	100	58	42	73
9 Bridlington Town	42	18	10	14	81	60	21	64	9 Campion	42	22	7	13	95	65	30	73
10 Rainworth Miners Welfare	42	18	9	15	71	76	-5	63	10 Winterton Rangers	42	17	10	15	66	64	2	61
11 Liversedge	42	15	12	15	96	93	3	57	11 Swallownest	42	17	7	18	65	76	-11	58
12 Barton Town	42	17	5	20	64	76	-12	55*	12 AFC Emley	42	17	6	19	73	78	-5	57
13 Garforth Town	42	14	10	18	72	101	-29	52	13 Rossington Main	42	14	11	17	71	85	-14	53
14 Albion Sports	42	14	6	22	76	84	-8	48	14 Dronfield Town	42	16	4	22	62	75	-13	52
15 Thackley	42	13	8	21	76	85	-9	47	15 Ollerton Town	42	13	8	21	66	90	-24	47
16 Staveley Miners Welfare	42	13	8	21	52	83	-31	47	16 Armthorpe Welfare	42	13	7	22	72	97	-25	46
17 Athersley Recreation	42	13	7	22	66	89	-23	46	17 Nostell Miners Welfare	42	12	4	26	61	97	-36	40
18 Worksop Town	42	12	10	20	68	94	-26	46	18 East Yorkshire Carnegie	42	10	4	28	64	98	-34	34
19 Hall Road Rangers	42	16	7	19	83	84	-1	43*	19 Worsbrough Bridge Athletic	42	7	12	23	51	99	-48	33
20 Harrogate Railway Athletic	42	9	4	29	70	132	-62	31	20 FC Bolsover	42	11	3	28	48	124	-76	30
21 Parkgate	42	7	5	30	58	116	-58	26	21 Brigg Town	42	6	11	25	51	105	-54	29
22 Clipstone	42	0	2	40	37	172	-135	2	22 Retford United	42	6	6	30	42	115	-73	24

PREMIER DIVISION		1	2	3	4	5	6	7	8	9	10	11	12	13	14	15	16	17	18	19	20	21	22
1	AFC Mansfield		4-0	2-1	2-1	2-1	2-0	9-0	3-1	3-0	2-0	5-1	3-2	1-5	1-1	3-0	5-0	2-1	0-3	2-2	4-0	2-1	3-1
2	Albion Sports	3-0		3-1	1-2	0-6	1-4	5-2	3-0	3-1	2-1	0-1	0-1	0-3	1-3	2-3	1-3	2-2	0-1	1-2	3-2	3-0	1-1
3	Athersley Rec	1-5	2-0		1-1	1-0	0-1	3-0	6-1	0-1	2-1	2-4	0-0	2-5	0-3	2-1	1-0	2-6	1-1	1-3	1-3	1-1	5-2
4	Barton Town	0-2	1-0	1-2		2-5	1-3	4-1	4-1	1-2	1-1	1-0	2-1	0-6	1-2	5-1	3-0	1-1	0-6	0-0	1-0	1-0	2-3
5	Bottesford Town	1-4	4-2	4-0	3-2		2-1	3-1	4-3	2-2	2-4	3-2	0-3	5-0	1-4	5-0	3-2	0-4	2-4	2-1	0-1	2-0	4-0
6	Bridlington Town	1-1	0-0	3-1	2-1	1-1		2-1	5-0	6-1	0-0	5-2	2-4	1-1	1-0	2-1	2-2	1-3	1-3	1-2	2-0	2-1	3-1
7	Clipstone	1-3	1-6	0-3	1-5	0-1	1-8		0-4	2-2	2-3	1-2	2-7	1-5	3-10	0-4	1-2	2-4	2-5	1-2	0-2	0-6	0-5
8	Garforth Town	1-1	4-3	0-4	0-1	0-2	2-1	6-0		1-1	0-4	4-4	1-1	1-3	1-1	2-2	2-0	0-1	2-1	1-0	3-2	3-3	3-2
9	Hall Road Rangers	0-1	1-3	1-5	0-2	1-2	1-2	3-2	4-5		4-0	3-1	4-0	1-2	2-3	4-1	1-4	1-2	1-3	3-0	2-1	2-1	4-0
10	Handsworth Parr	0-3	3-2	5-0	4-0	5-1	2-0	6-1	3-0	1-4		3-1	4-1	3-1	0-1	3-0	3-2	1-3	1-3	4-0	2-3	4-1	2-1
11	Harrogate RA	0-4	0-0	3-1	2-3	2-3	1-3	5-2	0-2	1-2	2-4		1-4	0-3	2-2	2-3	2-2	2-9	1-6	4-1	0-3	4-3	0-1
12	Hemsworth MW	1-5	3-3	4-2	3-0	2-0	2-1	3-1	1-1	3-3	2-5	3-0		5-1	3-2	8-1	2-0	2-3	1-5	4-1	7-4	2-0	5-3
13	Liversedge	4-4	1-5	1-1	1-3	5-4	3-2	4-2	2-2	3-3	0-1	1-2	0-2		6-3	3-2	2-2	3-5	2-4	1-3	4-0	1-2	0-1
14	Maltby Main	0-2	2-0	3-1	3-1	4-2	1-1	4-1	2-3	2-1	0-0	3-0	3-1	3-1		3-2	0-2	0-0	0-2	2-3	1-1	3-1	1-1
15	Parkgate	2-4	2-4	0-1	3-1	1-2	3-2	4-1	1-2	1-1	2-4	2-6	2-2	0-1	1-2		1-1	2-5	2-6	0-2	0-1	0-6	3-1
16	Penistone Church	0-0	4-2	4-0	3-1	1-1	2-2	6-0	3-2	4-3	1-2	6-1	3-1	1-1	1-0	4-2		2-2	1-0	6-2	3-4	3-2	1-1
17	Pickering Town	2-3	5-1	2-0	2-1	4-0	2-2	4-0	7-0	1-1	3-0	9-1	1-0	2-2	2-3	3-0	3-2		3-2	3-2	2-1	3-1	5-1
18	Pontefract Colls	3-2	4-2	5-2	0-0	5-1	2-0	5-0	3-2	1-2	2-0	1-0	5-0	2-1	5-0	1-2	0-1		4-0	3-1	3-1	5-1	
19	Rainworth MW	1-1	0-3	2-1	3-2	3-2	0-0	4-1	2-2	2-0	1-1	6-1	2-1	1-1	0-2	1-1	1-2	1-4	0-5		2-1	2-0	1-1
20	Staveley MW	0-4	3-3	2-2	1-2	1-4	1-0	0-0	3-1	0-2	0-2	2-1	1-3	2-2	0-3	1-0	1-4	0-0	0-0	0-3		2-1	1-1
21	Thackley	0-0	1-0	2-2	4-0	4-0	2-3	2-1	4-2	2-4	0-2	5-3	1-3	2-2	2-2	2-1	1-1	4-2	0-8	4-3	0-1		2-2
22	Worksop Town	1-1	0-2	3-2	0-3	0-3	3-2	3-0	2-3	3-4	1-3	5-3	3-1	4-4	1-0	2-1	1-1	1-0	0-4	0-4	5-0	0-1	

LEAGUE CUP

HOLDERS: PENISTONE CHURCH

ROUND 1

Ollerton Town	v	Retford United	2-0
Armthorpe Welfare	v	Swallownest	0-2
Yorkshire Amateur	v	Brigg Town	6-1
FC Bolsover	v	Knaresborough	0-1
AFC Emley	v	Eccleshill United	0-2
Campion	v	Worsbrough Bridge	6-0

ROUND 2

Glasshoughton Welfare	v	Nostell MW	4-0
Hemsworth MW	v	Hallam	4-2
Winterton Rangers	v	Knaresborough	0-4
Albion Sports	v	Pontefract Collieries	1-2
Thackley	v	Swallownest	0-2
Athersley Recreation	v	Eccleshill United	3-1

ROUND 3

AFC Mansfield	v	Barton Town	2-0
Bottesford Town	v	Campion	0-3
Ollerton Town	v	Clipstone	4-3 aet
Hemsworth MW	v	Penistone Church	2-1
Swallownest	v	Dronfield Town	0-4
Knaresborough	v	Maltby Main	1-1, 6-5p
Pontefract Collieries	v	Pickering Town	4-3
Rossington Main	v	Rainworth MW	0-3
Yorkshire Amateur	v	Garforth Town	4-0
Harrogate RA	v	Staveley MW	0-1
Parkgate	v	Glasshoughton Welfare	2-0

Worksop Town	v	Bridlington Town	1-3
Athersley Recreation	v	Handsworth Parramore	0-4
Selby Town	v	Shirebrook Town	0-6
East Yorks Carnegie	v	Grimsby Borough	0-2

ROUND 4

AFC Mansfield	v	Staveley MW	2-1
Yorkshire Amateur	v	Hemsworth MW	1-4
Parkgate	v	Rainworth MW	0-3
Dronfield Town	v	Liversedge	2-3
Bridlington Town	v	Campion	1-0
Handsworth Parramore	v	Knaresborough	4-2
Shirebrook Town	v	Pontefract Collieries	5-1
Ollerton Town	v	Grimsby Borough	4-2

QUARTER FINALS

Rainworth MW	v	Liversedge	2-3
Shirebrook Town	v	Bridlington Town	2-3 aet
Hemsworth MW	v	AFC Mansfield	1-4
Handsworth Parramore	v	Ollerton Town	2-1

SEMI FINALS

Liversedge	v	Handsworth Parramore	5-2
Bridlington Town	v	AFC Mansfield	2-4

FINAL

AFC Mansfield	v	Liversedge

Final not played after Liversedge were found to have played an ineligible player in their Semi final against Handsworth Parramore.

CLUB MOVEMENTS

Premier Division - In: Eccleshill United (P), Goole AFC (R - NPLN), Knaresborough Town (P), Yorkshire Amateurs (P).
Out: AFC Mansfield (P - NPLE), Clipstone (R - EMC), Parkgate (R), Pickering Town (P - NPLE), Pontefract Collieries (P - NPLE).
Division One - In: Harworth Colliery (P - CMLN), Parkgate (R), Skegness Town (P - Lincs).
Out: Brigg Town (R - Lincs), Eccleshill United (P), Knaresborough Town (P), Retford United (R - CMN), Yorkshire Amateurs (P).

DIVISION ONE

		1	2	3	4	5	6	7	8	9	10	11	12	13	14	15	16	17	18	19	20	21	22
1	AFC Emley		0-4	5-2	0-2	2-1	3-1	2-2	2-1	2-1	1-2	0-4	0-0	0-2	2-1	2-3	2-2	0-4	3-0	0-1	1-0	1-3	1-8
2	Armthorpe Welfare	1-1		2-1	1-1	1-3	3-3	0-2	0-1	0-3	2-1	1-1	1-2	2-3	2-0	7-2	3-5	2-0	1-4	2-3	5-3	2-4	0-5
3	Brigg Town	2-0	1-1		2-2	4-0	2-1	0-2	0-4	0-3	2-2	0-4	1-2	1-5	2-2	2-2	3-3	3-1	2-2	0-1	1-4	0-2
4	Campion	2-3	2-4	3-2		2-1	3-2	1-2	11-1	1-1	3-1	3-2	0-2	4-0	4-1	2-1	2-2	0-2	2-4	0-2	0-1	6-0	2-3
5	Dronfield Town	3-2	1-0	2-0	3-1		3-0	1-2	4-2	0-3	0-2	0-2	0-2	1-0	2-0	2-0	2-2	1-4	1-2	2-1	1-2	2-2	1-1
6	East Yorks Carnegie	2-4	1-3	2-0	1-2	4-1		1-5	3-2	0-2	2-3	1-2	1-4	2-1	3-2	4-0	1-2	2-3	0-2	2-2	0-1	1-2	3-2
7	Eccleshill United	2-0	6-2	2-2	3-1	4-3	1-0		9-0	2-0	3-4	1-0	5-2	3-3	4-0	3-0	3-0	2-3	1-4	3-2	0-3	5-1	2-4
8	FC Bolsover	0-2	3-1	1-0	0-1	0-2	0-3	0-5		0-2	2-5	0-5	1-2	2-1	0-1	1-0	2-2	3-5	0-5	5-0	2-0	0-3	1-3
9	Glasshoughton Welf	2-2	0-2	1-1	2-3	4-1	4-1	2-0	2-0		0-3	2-2	2-2	4-1	2-3	3-0	5-1	2-1	4-1	1-0	0-0	1-3	0-4
10	Grimsby Borough	2-1	2-0	6-1	0-1	3-0	2-2	2-3	7-1	4-0		4-2	0-3	6-0	5-1	3-3	4-0	4-0	1-1	4-0	1-1	4-0	2-2
11	Hallam	3-4	3-1	5-1	2-2	1-4	2-1	3-1	5-1	0-3	3-2		2-3	1-0	3-0	2-0	4-0	2-2	1-1	3-0	4-3	7-0	0-1
12	Knaresborough	2-0	3-1	4-0	0-0	2-0	3-0	1-1	4-0	2-0	5-0	2-2		2-1	1-0	4-0	2-0	2-1	2-1	1-0	1-1	3-1	2-4
13	Nostell MW	0-5	6-3	2-3	0-3	0-1	3-1	1-2	1-1	1-3	1-2	1-5	0-3		0-2	2-1	0-2	4-1	2-3	1-1	1-5	0-0	2-1
14	Ollerton Town	1-2	1-0	3-0	4-3	4-1	2-2	1-3	1-1	1-4	0-3	1-2	0-2	2-0		1-1	0-1	3-2	2-1	2-2	1-1	2-1	3-3
15	Retford United	0-5	2-3	3-0	0-3	2-4	1-3	0-3	1-3	0-2	1-0	0-6	0-1	0-4	4-3		1-0	2-2	0-3	0-3	1-2	0-0	0-2
16	Rossington Main	2-0	2-3	2-2	1-1	1-0	4-0	0-2	3-2	4-5	1-1	1-0	0-0	1-5	4-0	2-0		0-5	1-3	0-2	2-2	4-0	1-7
17	Selby Town	2-1	2-1	4-2	1-3	2-1	1-3	3-1	8-0	0-1	2-3	2-1	2-1	8-1	3-3	3-2	2-1		4-2	3-1	2-2	4-1	1-2
18	Shirebrook Town	1-3	0-1	4-1	3-0	3-0	2-1	1-2	4-1	2-0	2-1	2-0	0-1	1-0	2-1	3-3	4-3	2-0		2-2	1-1	2-1	3-2
19	Swallownest	1-7	1-1	0-1	0-4	1-0	4-1	2-1	4-0	3-5	1-3	1-1	1-2	2-0	3-1	5-0	1-4	0-4	1-3		2-0	4-2	1-0
20	Winterton Rangers	2-1	6-0	3-0	3-5	2-1	1-0	1-1	2-3	1-0	1-3	1-2	0-3	0-5	2-3	1-0	2-2	0-2	2-2	1-2		2-0	1-0
21	Worsbrough Bridge	0-0	2-2	1-1	1-2	1-1	3-2	2-2	0-3	0-2	2-2	2-2	0-3	1-3	2-4	3-6	0-3	1-1	0-3	0-1	0-2		1-2
22	Yorkshire Amateur	4-1	5-1	5-2	1-2	2-5	6-1	3-3	4-0	1-1	2-3	1-1	2-1	6-1	6-1	8-0	3-1	3-1	5-1	2-0	4-1	1-1	

ALBION SPORTS

Founded: 1974   Nickname: Lions

Club Contact Details   **(T)** 0113 255 7292   **(E)** info@albionsports.co.uk
Ground: Throstle Nest, Newlands, Farsley, Leeds, LS28 5BE.
Nearest Railway Station New Pudsey - 1km
Capacity: 3,500   **Seats:** 1,750   **Covered:** 1,750   **Bus Route** Town St Slaters Rd - stop 340m away

Colours(change): Yellow/royal blue/royal blue (All red)
Previous Names: None
Previous Leagues: Bradford Amateur Sunday 1974-2007. West Riding County Amateur 2007-11.

HONOURS: FA Comps: None
       League: Bradford Amateur Sunday Premier Division 1995-96, 99-2000, 00-01, 02-03, 04-05, 05-06.

10 YEAR RECORD	Northern Counties East Division One 2012-13.								
08-09	09-10	10-11	11-12	12-13	13-14	14-15	15-16	16-17	17-18
		WRCP 2	NCE1 4	NCE1 1	NCEP 6	NCEP 10	NCEP 11	NCEP 8	NCEP 14
					FAC 1Q	FAC P	FAC EPr	FAC EPr	FAC 2Q
				FAV 2Q	FAV 2Q	FAV 2Q	FAV 1Q	FAV 1Q	FAV 1Q

ATHERSLEY RECREATION

Founded: 1979   Nickname: Penguins

Club Contact Details   **(T)** 07910 121 070   **(E)** petegoodlad@yahoo.co.uk
Ground: Sheerien Park, Ollerton Road, Athersley North, Barnsley, S71 3DP
Nearest Railway Station Barnsley - 3.4km
Capacity: 2,000   **Seats:** 150   **Covered:** 420   **Shop:** Yes   **Bus Route** Trowell Way - stop 80m away

Colours(change): Black and white
Previous Names: Athersley North Juniors 1979-86.
Previous Leagues: Barnsley Junior. Barnsley Association. Sheffield & Hallamshire County Senior 1997-2012.

HONOURS: FA Comps: None
       League: Barnsley Junior 1986-87. Barnsley Association 91-92, 92-93, 94-95, 95-96, 96-97. Sheffield & Hallamshire

10 YEAR RECORD	County Senior Division Two 1997-98, Premier Division 1999-2000, 03-04, 04-05, 06-07, 08-09, 11-12								
08-09	09-10	10-11	11-12	12-13	13-14	14-15	15-16	16-17	17-18
SHSP 1	SHSP 2	SHSP 2	SHSP 1	NCE1 2	NCEP 10	NCEP 13	NCEP 18	NCEP 10	NCEP 17
						FAC P	FAC EP	FAC EP	FAC EP
					FAV 2P	FAV 2Q	FAV 1P	FAV 1Q	FAV 1Q

BARTON TOWN

Founded: 1995   Nickname: Swans

Club Contact Details   **(T)** 01652 636 964   **(E)** bartontown@gmail.com
Ground: The Easy Buy Ground, Marsh Lane, Barton-on-Humber DN18 5JD
Nearest Railway Station Barton-on-Humber - 0.5km
Capacity: 3,000   **Seats:** 240   **Covered:** 540   **Shop:** No   **Bus Route** Butts Road - stop 133m away

Colours(change): Sky blue & navy blue
Previous Names: Barton Town Old Boys >2017.
Previous Leagues: Lincolnshire 1995-2000, Humber (Founder member) 2000-01, Central Midlands 2001-07.

HONOURS: FA Comps: None
       League: Lincolnshire 1996-97. Central Midlands Supreme Division 2005-06.

10 YEAR RECORD									
08-09	09-10	10-11	11-12	12-13	13-14	14-15	15-16	16-17	17-18
NCE1 5	NCE1 6	NCE1 2	NCEP 11	NCEP 8	NCEP 3	NCEP 5	NCEP 10	NCEP 20	NCEP 12
FAC EP	FAC 1Q	FAC P	FAC Pr	FAC P	FAC P	FAC P	FAC P	FAC EP	FAC EP
FAV 2Q	FAV 1Q	FAV 2P	FAV 2P	FAV 1Q	FAV 2Q	FAV 2P	FAV 1Q	FAV 1Q	FAV 2Q

BOTTESFORD TOWN

Founded: 1974   Nickname: The Poachers

Club Contact Details   **(T)** 01724 871 883   **(E)**
Ground: Birkdale Park, Ontario Road, Bottesford, Scunthorpe DN17 2TQ
Nearest Railway Station Scunthorpe - 3.6km
Capacity: 1,000   **Seats:** 90   **Covered:** 300   **Bus Route** Maple Leaf - stop 149m away

Colours(change): All blue & yellow
Previous Names: None
Previous Leagues: Lincolnshire 1974-2000. Central Midlands 2000-07.

HONOURS: FA Comps: None
       League: Lincolnshire 1989-90, 90-91, 91-92. Central Midlands Supreme Division 2006-07.

10 YEAR RECORD									
08-09	09-10	10-11	11-12	12-13	13-14	14-15	15-16	16-17	17-18
NCE1 6	NCE1 9	NCE1 17	NCE1 16	NCE1 15	NCE1 3	NCE1 8	NCE1 3	NCEP 12	NCEP 8
FAC Pr	FAC EP	FAC 1Q				FAC EP	FAC P	FAC P	FAC 1Q
FAV 1Q	FAV 1P	FAV 1Q	FAV 2Q	FAV 2P	FAV 1Q	FAV 1Pr	FAV 2Q	FAV 3P	FAV 2Q

BRIDLINGTON TOWN
Founded: 1918 Nickname: Seasiders

Club Contact Details (T) 01262 606 879 (E) secretary@bridtownafc.com
Ground: Neil Hudgell Law Stadium, Queensgate, Bridlington YO16 7LN

Capacity: 3,000 **Seats:** 500 **Covered:** 500 **Shop:** Yes
Colours(change): All red
Previous Names: Original Bridlington Town folded in 1994. Greyhound FC changed to Bridlington Town.
Previous Leagues: Yorkshire 1924-39, 59-82, NCEL 1982-90, 99-2003, Northern Premier 1990-94, 2003-08

HONOURS: FA Comps: FA Vase 1992-93
League: Yorkshire League 1974-75. Northern Counties East 1989-90, 2001-02, 09-10, NPL Division One 1992-93.

10 YEAR RECORD

	08-09	09-10	10-11	11-12	12-13	13-14	14-15	15-16	16-17	17-18
NCEP	4	1	3	2	3	12	8	5	3	9
FAC	1Qr	1Q	1Q	P	EP	Pr	1Q	EP	2Qr	P
FAV	2P	3P	1Pr	3P	1P	3P	1Q	2Q	1P	1P

ECCLESHILL UNITED
Founded: 1948 Nickname: The Eagles

Club Contact Details (T) 01274 615 739 (E)
Ground: Mitton Group Stadium, Kingsway, Wrose, Bradford, BD2 1PN
Nearest Railway Station Frizinghall - 1.7km
Capacity: 2,225 **Seats:** **Covered:** **Bus Route** Kingsway Plumpton Drive - stop 97m away
Colours(change): Blue & white
Previous Names:
Previous Leagues:

HONOURS: FA Comps: None
League: West Riding County Amateur 1976-77.

10 YEAR RECORD Northern Counties East Division One 1996-97.

	08-09	09-10	10-11	11-12	12-13	13-14	14-15	15-16	16-17	17-18
NCEP/NCE1	20	16	10	6	14	4	13	13	9	4
FAC	EP	EP		1Q	1Q		EP			
FAV	2Q	1Q	2P	2P	1Q	1P	1Q	EP	1Q	1Q

GARFORTH TOWN
Founded: 1964 Nickname: The Miners

Club Contact Details (T) (E) enquiries@garforthtown.net
Ground: Community Stadium, Cedar Ridge, Garforth, Leeds LS25 2PF
Nearest Railway Station East Garforth - 1km. Garforth - 1.2km.
Capacity: 3,000 **Seats:** 278 **Covered:** 200 **Bus Route** Aberford Road - stop 128m away
Colours(change): Yellow/blue/blue
Previous Names: Garforth Miners 1964-85
Previous Leagues: Leeds Sunday Comb. 1972-76, West Yorkshire 1976-78, Yorkshire 1978-82, NCE 1982-2007. Northern Premier 2007-13.

HONOURS: FA Comps: None
League: Northern Counties East Division 1 1997-98

10 YEAR RECORD

	08-09	09-10	10-11	11-12	12-13	13-14	14-15	15-16	16-17	17-18
NP1N/NCEP	16	20	13	5	22	14	14	16	15	13
FAC	2Qr	1Q	P	1Q	1Q	EP	P	EP	EP	EP
FAT/FAV	1Qr	1Q	1Qr	1Q	P	1P	2Q	2P	1Q	1P

GOOLE AFC
Founded: 1997 Nickname: The Vikings

Club Contact Details (T) 01405 762 794 (Match days) (E) andym236566609@aol.com
Ground: Victoria Pleasure Gardens, Marcus Road, Goole DN14 6TN
Nearest Railway Station Goole - 0.5km
Capacity: 3,000 **Seats:** 300 **Covered:** 800 Yes **Bus Route** Goole Newport Street - stop 200m away
Colours(change): Red & black
Previous Names: Goole Town > 1996.
Previous Leagues: Central Midlands 1997-98. Northern Counties East 2000-04. Northern Premier 2004-18.

HONOURS: FA Comps: None
League: Central Midlands 1997-98.

10 YEAR RECORD Northern Counties East Division One 1999-2000, Premier Division 2003-04.

	08-09	09-10	10-11	11-12	12-13	13-14	14-15	15-16	16-17	17-18
NP1S/NP1N	18	18	13	10	21	13	16	19	21	22
FAC	P	P	P	Pr	P	P	Pr	1Qr	P	P
FAT	1Q	1Q	Pr	1Q	Pr	P	2Q	1Q	1Qr	P

HALL ROAD RANGERS
Founded: 1959   Nickname: Rangers

Club Contact Details (T)   (E) hallroadrangers@live.co.uk
Ground: Hawroth Park, Dawson Drive, Hull HU6 7DY
Nearest Railway Station Cottingham - 3.5km
Capacity: **Seats:** 250   **Covered:** 750   **Shop:** Yes   **Bus Route** Larard Avenue - stop 158m away

Colours(change): Blue & white
Previous Names: None
Previous Leagues: Sunday League. East Riding County, Yorkshire 1968-82.

HONOURS: FA Comps: None
League: Yorkshire Division Three 1972-73, 79-80. Northern Counties East Division One 2016-17.

10 YEAR RECORD

08-09		09-10		10-11		11-12		12-13		13-14		14-15		15-16		16-17		17-18	
NCEP	16	NCEP	11	NCEP	14	NCEP	16	NCEP	22	NCE1	11	NCE1	17	NCE1	17	NCE1	1	NCEP	19
FAC	EP	FAC	EP	FAC	EPr	FAC	Pr	FAC	EP	FAC	EP							FAC	EP
FAV	2Q	FAV	1P	FAV	1Q	FAV	2Q	FAV	1P	FAV	1Q	FAV	2Q	FAV	2Q	FAV	2P	FAV	2P

HANDSWORTH PARRAMORE
Founded: 1936   Nickname: Amber Parras

Club Contact Details (T) 01909 479 955   (E)
Ground: The Windsor Foodservice Stadium, Sandy Land, Worksop S80 1UJ
Nearest Railway Station Worksop - 0.5km
Capacity: 2,500   **Seats:** 200   **Covered:** 750   **Shop:** No   **Bus Route** Grafton Street - stop 114m away

Colours(change): Amber & black
Previous Names: Parramore Sports > 2010. Sheffield Parramore 2010-2011. Worksop Parramore 2011-14.
Previous Leagues: Sheffield & Hallam County Senior 1985-2008. Central Midlands 2008-11

HONOURS: FA Comps: None
League: Central Midland Supreme Division 2010-11.

10 YEAR RECORD

08-09		09-10		10-11		11-12		12-13		13-14		14-15		15-16		16-17		17-18	
CM P	4	CM Su	8	CM Su	1	NCE1	3	NCEP	7	NCEP	4	NCEP	7	NCEP	2	NCEP	4	NCEP	4
												FAC	P	FAC	P	FAC	3Q	FAC	2Qr
												FAV	1P	FAV	3P	FAV	1P	FAV	1P

HARROGATE RAILWAY ATH.
Founded: 1935   Nickname: The Rail

Club Contact Details (T) 01423 883 104   (E)
Ground: Station View, Starbeck, Harrogate, North Yorkshire HG2 7JA
Nearest Railway Station Starbeck - 0.1km
Capacity: 3,500   **Seats:** 300   **Covered:** 600   **Shop:** Yes   **Bus Route** Henry Peacock - stop 134m away

Colours(change): Red and green
Previous Names: None
Previous Leagues: West Yorkshire, Harrogate & District, Yorkshire 1955-73, 80-82, Northern Counties East 1982-2006. Northern Premier 2006-16

HONOURS: FA Comps: None
League: West Yorkshire 1953-54.
10 YEAR RECORD   Northern Counties East Division Two North 1983-84, Division one 1989-99.

08-09		09-10		10-11		11-12		12-13		13-14		14-15		15-16		16-17		17-18	
NP1N	18	NP1N	17	NP1N	20	NP1N	21	NP1N	18	NP1N	13	NP1N	8	NP1N	21	NCEP	19	NCEP	20
FAC	P	FAC	1Q	FAC	P	FAC	1Q	FAC	Pr	FAC	P	FAC	P	FAC	P	FAC	P	FAC	Pr
FAT	1Q	FAT	1Q	FAT	3Q	FAT	1Q	FAT	1Q	FAT	P	FAT	P	FAT	P	FAV	2Q	FAV	1P

HEMSWORTH M.W.
Founded: 1981   Nickname: Wells

Club Contact Details (T) 01977 614 997   (E) beefy1986@hotmail.co.uk
Ground: Yorkshire NuBuilds Stadium, Wakefield Road, Fitzwilliam, Pontefract WF9 5AJ
Nearest Railway Station Fitzwilliam - 0.4km
Capacity: 2,000   **Seats:** 100   **Covered:** 100   **Shop:** Yes   **Bus Route** Wakefield Road - stop 22m away

Colours(change): Blue and white
Previous Names: None
Previous Leagues: Doncaster Senior. West Riding County Amateur 1995-2008.

HONOURS: FA Comps: None
League: West Riding County Amateur Division One 1996-97.
10 YEAR RECORD   Northern Counties East Division One 2015-16.

08-09		09-10		10-11		11-12		12-13		13-14		14-15		15-16		16-17		17-18	
NCE1	10	NCE1	7	NCE1	16	NCE1	8	NCE1	13	NCE1	17	NCE1	3	NCE1	1	NCEP	9	NCEP	6
				FAC	Pr	FAC	EP	FAC	P					FAC	EP	FAC	P	FAC	EP
		FAV	1P	FAV	1Q	FAV	2Q	FAV	1Q	FAV	2Q	FAV	2Q	FAV	2P	FAV	2P	FAV	2Q

KNARESBOROUGH TOWN
Founded: 1902 **Nickname:** The Boro

Club Contact Details (T) 01423 548 896 (E) knaresboroughtownafc@gmail.com
Ground: Manse Lane, Knaresborough, HG5 8LF
Nearest Railway Station Knaresborough - 1.5km
Capacity: 1,000 **Seats:** **Covered:** **Bus Route** Aspin Park School - stop 168 away

Colours(change): Red and black
Previous Names:
Previous Leagues: York. Harrogate & District. West Yorkshire.

HONOURS: FA Comps: None
League: York 1902-03, 03-04, 04-05, 08-09, 24-25, 25-26, 28-29, 33-34, 34-35, Div.2 51-52, Div.1 52-53. Harrogate & District 64-65,
65-66, 66-67. West Yorkshire Prem 2008-09. Northern Counties East Division One 2017-18.

08-09		09-10		10-11		11-12		12-13		13-14		14-15		15-16		16-17		17-18	
WYkP	1	WYkP	4	WYkP	2	WYkP	3	NCE1	8	NCE1	6	NCE1	12	NCE1	8	NCE1	7	NCE1	1
												FAC	P						
										FAV	2Q	FAV	1Q	FAV	1Q	FAV	1Q	FAV	2P

LIVERSEDGE
Founded: 1910 **Nickname:** Sedge

Club Contact Details (T) 01274 862 108 (E) liversedgefc@btinternet.com
Ground: Clayborn Ground, Quaker Lane, Hightown Road, Cleckheaton WF15 8DF
Nearest Railway Station Low Moor - 4.5km
Capacity: 2,000 **Seats:** 250 **Covered:** 750 **Shop:** Yes **Bus Route** Hightown Road - stop 142m away

Colours(change): Sky blue & black
Previous Names: None
Previous Leagues: Bradford 1919-22. West Riding Co. Amateur 1922-27, 49-72. Spen Valley 1947-49. Yorkshire 1972-82.

HONOURS: FA Comps: None
League: West Riding County Amateur 1923-24, 25-26, 26-27, 64-65, 65-66, 68-69.
Spen Valley 1948-49.

08-09		09-10		10-11		11-12		12-13		13-14		14-15		15-16		16-17		17-18	
NCEP	14	NCEP	9	NCEP	17	NCEP	14	NCEP	15	NCEP	20	NCEP	18	NCEP	14	NCEP	11	NCEP	11
FAC	EP	FAC	EP	FAC	EP	FAC	Pr	FAC	EP	FAC	EP	FAC	EP	FAC	EP	FAC	EP	FAC	1Qr
FAV	1P	FAV	1P	FAV	2Qr	FAV	2Q	FAV	2Q	FAV	1P	FAV	2Q	FAV	1Q	FAV	2Q	FAV	1P

MALTBY MAIN
Founded: 1916 **Nickname:** Miners

Club Contact Details (T) 07795 693 683 (E) john_mills_@hotmail.co.uk
Ground: Muglet Lane, Maltby, Rotherham S66 7JQ.
Nearest Railway Station Rotherham Central - 8 miles
Capacity: 2,000 **Seats:** 150 **Covered:** 300 **Shop:** No **Bus Route** Duke Avenue - stop 78m away

Colours(change): Red and black
Previous Names: Maltby Miners Welfare 1970-96
Previous Leagues: Sheffield Association 1919-29, 39-41, 45-49, 65-70, 72-73. Rotherham Minor 1929-36. Sheffield Amateur 1936-39.
Rotherham Association 1942-45, 55-58. Yorkshire League 1949-55, 73-82. Doncaster & District 1958-65.
HONOURS: FA Comps: None.
League: Sheffield Association 1925-26, 26-27.

08-09		09-10		10-11		11-12		12-13		13-14		14-15		15-16		16-17		17-18	
NCEP	12	NCEP	16	NCEP	11	NCEP	18	NCEP	14	NCEP	15	NCEP	19	NCEP	7	NCEP	14	NCEP	5
FAC	EP	FAC	EP	FAC	P	FAC	EP	FAC	1Q	FAC	EP	FAC	P	FAC	1Q	FAC	EP	FAC	EP
FAV	2Q	FAV	2Q	FAV	1Qr	FAV	1Q	FAV	2Q	FAV	1Q	FAV	2Qr	FAV	2P	FAV	1Q	FAV	2Q

PENISTON CHURCH
Founded: 1906 **Nickname:** None

Club Contact Details (T) (E) penistonechurchfc@gmail.com
Ground: Church View Road, Penistone, Sheffield S36 6AT
Nearest Railway Station Penistone - 0.2km
Capacity: 1,000 **Seats:** 100 **Covered:** Yes **Bus Route** Church View Road - stop 149m away

Colours(change): Black & white
Previous Names: Formed after the merger of Penistone Choirboys and Penistone Juniors.
Previous Leagues: Sheffield Junior 1906-07. Sheffield Amateur 1907-48. Hatchard League/Sheffield Association 1948-83. Sheffield & Hallamshire
County Senior (Founder Members) 1983-14.
HONOURS: FA Comps: None
League: Sheffield & Hallamshire County Senior Division One 1993-94, 2000-01.

08-09		09-10		10-11		11-12		12-13		13-14		14-15		15-16		16-17		17-18	
Sh&HP	10	Sh&HP	7	Sh&HP	3	Sh&HP	4	Sh&HP	3	Sh&HP	4	NCE1	9	NCE1	5	NCE1	6	NCEP	7
														FAC	EP	FAC	EP	FAC	2Q
										FAV	1Q	FAV	1Q	FAV	2Q	FAV	1P	FAV	1Q

STAVELEY MINERS WELFARE
Founded: 1989   Nickname: The Welfare

Club Contact Details (T) 01246 471 441
(E) staveleyed@hotmail.co.uk
Ground: Inkersall Road, Staveley, Chesterfield, S43 3JL
Nearest Railway Station Chesterfield - 5,4km
Capacity: 5,000 **Seats:** 220   **Covered:** 400   **Shop:** Yes   **Bus Route** Market Street - stop 156m away

Colours(change):   Blue & white
Previous Names: None
Previous Leagues: Chesterfield & District Amateur 1989-91. Sheffield & Hallamshire County Senior 1991-93.

HONOURS: FA Comps: None
       League: Sheffield & Hallamshire County Senior Division Three 1991-92, Division Two 1992-93.
10 YEAR RECORD   Northern Counties East Division One 2010-11.

08-09		09-10		10-11		11-12		12-13		13-14		14-15		15-16		16-17		17-18	
NCE1	4	NCE1	4	NCE1	1	NCEP	5	NCEP	13	NCEP	17	NCEP	9	NCEP	8	NCEP	6	NCEP	16
FAC	P	FAC	Pr	FAC	P	FAC	2Q	FAC	Pr	FAC	P	FAC	1Q	FAC	EP	FAC	EP	FAC	P
FAV	1Q	FAV	1Q	FAV	4P	FAV	SF	FAV	2P	FAV	3P	FAV	1Q	FAV	1Q	FAV	3P	FAV	1P

THACKLEY
Founded: 1930   Nickname: Dennyboys

Club Contact Details (T) 01274 615 571
(E) john_thackleyafc@yahoo.co.uk
Ground: Dennyfield, Ainsbury Avenue, Thackley, Bradford BD10 0TL
Nearest Railway Station Baildon - 1.4km
Capacity: 3000 **Seats:** 300   **Covered:** 600   **Bus Route** Thackley Road - stop 200m away

Colours(change):   Red and white
Previous Names: Thackley Wesleyians 1930-39
Previous Leagues: Bradford Amateur, West Riding County Amateur, West Yorkshire, Yorkshire 1967-82

HONOURS: FA Comps: None
       League: West Riding County Amateur x5. West Yorkshire 1965-66, 66-67. Yorkshire Division Two 1973-74.
10 YEAR RECORD

08-09		09-10		10-11		11-12		12-13		13-14		14-15		15-16		16-17		17-18	
NCEP	7	NCEP	4	NCEP	8	NCEP	10	NCEP	10	NCEP	13	NCEP	12	NCEP	12	NCEP	5	NCEP	15
FAC	EP	FAC	EP	FAC	2Q	FAC	P	FAC	EP	FAC	EP	FAC	EP	FAC	1Qr	FAC	EP	FAC	EP
FAV	2P	FAV	1Q	FAV	2P	FAV	1P	FAV	3P	FAV	3P	FAV	1Q	FAV	1Qr	FAV	1Q	FAV	2Q

WORKSOP TOWN
Founded: 1861   Nickname: Tigers

Club Contact Details (T) 01909 479 955
(E) wtfcsecretary@gmail.com
Ground: The Windsor Foodservice Stadium, off Sandy Lane, Worksop S80 1UJ
Nearest Railway Station Worksop - 0.5km
Capacity: 2,500 **Seats:** 200   **Covered:** 750   **Shop:** Yes   **Bus Route** Grafton Street - stop 114m away

Colours(change):   Amber & black
Previous Names: None
Previous Leagues: Sheffield Association. Midland 1949-60, 61-68, 69-74, Northern Premier 1968-69, 74-2004, 2007-14, Conf. 2004-07

HONOURS: FA Comps: None
       League: Sheffield Association 1898-99 (joint), 47-48, 48-49. Midland 1921-22, 65-66, 72-73.
10 YEAR RECORD

08-09		09-10		10-11		11-12		12-13		13-14		14-15		15-16		16-17		17-18	
NP P	17	NP P	18	NP P	7	NP P	15	NP P	9	NP P	4	NCEP	2	NCEP	4	NCEP	13	NCEP	18
FAC	2Q	FAC	1Qr	FAC	1Q	FAC	1Q	FAC	1Q	FAC	3Q	FAC	EP	FAC	EP	FAC	Pr	FAC	EP
FAT	2Q	FAT	1Qr	FAT	1P	FAT	2P	FAT	1P	FAT	1Q	FAV	4P	FAV	2P	FAV	2P	FAV	3P

YORKSHIRE AMATEUR
Founded: 1918   Nickname: Ammers

Club Contact Details (T) 0113 289 2886
(E)
Ground: Bracken Edge, Roxholme Road, Leeds, LS8 4DZ (Sat. Nav. LS7 4JG)
Nearest Railway Station Leeds - 3.5km
Capacity: 1,550 **Seats:**   **Covered:**   **Bus Route** Harehills Ln Roxholme Ave - stop 168m away

Colours(change):   White and red
Previous Names:
Previous Leagues: Yorkshire.

HONOURS: FA Comps: None
       League: Yorkshire 1931-32, Division Two 1958-59, Division Three 1977-78.
10 YEAR RECORD

08-09		09-10		10-11		11-12		12-13		13-14		14-15		15-16		16-17		17-18	
NCE1	18	NCE1	14	NCE1	3	NCE1	19	NCE1	21	NCE1	19	NCE1	10	NCE1	11	NCE1	13	NCE1	2
FAC	EP					FAC	EP							FAC	EP				
FAV	2Q	FAV	1Q	FAV	2Q	FAV	1P	FAV	1Q	FAV	1P	FAV	2Q	FAV	1Q				

AFC EMLEY

Founded: 2005   Nickname: Pewits

Club Contact Details (T) 01924 849 392   **(E)** office@afcemley.co.uk

Ground: The Welfare Ground, Off Upper Lane, Emley, nr Huddersfield HD8 9RE.   **Capacity:** 2,000

Nearest Railway Station Denby Dale - 5km   **Bus Route** Upper Lane Church Street - stop 61m away

HONOURS   **League:** None

FA Comps: None

Colours(change): Claret and sky blue

10 YEAR RECORD

08-09		09-10		10-11		11-12		12-13		13-14		14-15		15-16		16-17		17-18	
NCE1	8	NCE1	8	NCE1	8	NCE1	10	NCE1	7	NCE1	8	NCE1	5	NCE1	4	NCE1	3	NCE1	12
FAC	EP	FAC	EP	FAC	P	FAC	EP	FAC	EP	FAC	P	FAC	P	FAC	P	FAC	P	FAC	EP
FAV	2Q	FAV	2Q	FAV	2P	FAV	1P	FAV	4P	FAV	1P	FAV	1P	FAV	2Q	FAV	2P	FAV	1P

ARMTHORPE WELFARE

Founded: 1926   Nickname: Wellie

Club Contact Details (T)   **(E)** armthorpe.welfare@hotmail.co.uk

Ground: Welfare Ground, Church Street, Armthorpe, Doncaster DN3 3AG   **Capacity:** 2,500

Nearest Railway Station Kirk Sandall - 3.4km   **Bus Route** Beech Road - stop 13m away

HONOURS   **League:** Doncaster & District Senior 1952-53, 53-54, 54-55, 56-57, 57-58, 60-61, 61-62, 64-65, 82-83, Div.3 77-78,

FA Comps: None   Div.2 78-79, Div.1 81-82. NCE Div.1 Central 1984-85.

Colours(change): All blue

10 YEAR RECORD

08-09		09-10		10-11		11-12		12-13		13-14		14-15		15-16		16-17		17-18	
NCEP	15	NCEP	3	NCEP	13	NCEP	13	NCEP	20	NCEP	18	NCEP	17	NCEP	19	NCEP	21	NCE1	16
FAC	Pr	FAC	EP	FAC	P	FAC	1Qr	FAC	EP	FAC	EP	FAC	P	FAC	2Q	FAC	EP	FAC	EPr
FAV	2Q	FAV	4Pr	FAV	2Pr	FAV	3P	FAV	2P	FAV	2P	FAV	2Q	FAV	1P	FAV	1Q	FAV	2Q

CAMPION

Founded: 1963   Nickname:

Club Contact Details (T) 01274 491 919   **(E)** campionsecretary@gmail.com

Ground: Scotchman Road, Bradford, BD9 5DT.

Nearest Railway Station Frizinghall - 1.9km   **Bus Route** Toller Lane Masham Place - 109m away

HONOURS   **League:** West Riding Amateur Division Two 1989-90, Division One 92-93.

FA Comps: None

Colours(change): Red & black

10 YEAR RECORD

08-09	09-10	10-11		11-12		12-13		13-14		14-15		15-16		16-17		17-18	
		WRCP	3	WRCP	9	WRCP	12	WRCP	3	WRCP	3	WRCP	3	NCE1	8	NCE1	9
																FAV	1Q

DRONFIELD TOWN

Founded: 1998   Nickname: None

Club Contact Details (T)   **(E)** secretary@dronfieldtownfc.com

Ground: Stonelow Playing Fields, Stonelow Road, Dronfield, S18 2EU   **Capacity:** 500

Nearest Railway Station Dronfield - 0.9km   **Bus Route** Oakhill Road Bottom - stop 270m away

HONOURS   **League:** Hope Valley B Div 2001-02, A Div 2002-03, Prem 2003-04. Midland Regional Alliance Division One 2005-06,

FA Comps: None   Premier 2007-08. Central Midlands North 2012-13.

Colours(change): Red & black

10 YEAR RECORD

08-09	09-10		10-11		11-12		12-13		13-14		14-15		15-16		16-17		17-18	
	CM P	2	CM Su	7	CMN	3	CMN	1	NCE1	14	NCE1	19	NCE1	15	NCE1	19	NCE1	14
											FAV	1P	FAV	1P	FAV	1Q	FAV	1P

EAST YORKSHIRE CARNEGIE

Founded: 2016   Nickname: Carnegie, EYC

Club Contact Details (T)   **(E)** eastyorkshirecarnegie@hotmail.com

Ground: Dunswell Park, Dunswell HU6 0AA   **Capacity:** 2,000

Nearest Railway Station Hull (4 miles)

HONOURS   **League:** None

FA Comps: None

Colours(change): All black & white

10 YEAR RECORD

08-09	09-10	10-11	11-12	12-13	13-14	14-15	15-16	16-17		17-18	
								HumbP	5	NCE1	18

FC BOLSOVER

Founded: 2016   Nickname: None

Club Contact Details (T) 07950 682 973   **(E)** secretary.fcbolsover@gmail.com

Ground: Langwith Road Ground, Langwith Road, Shirebrook, NG20 8TF

Nearest Railway Station Shirebrook - 0.2km   **Bus Route** Langwith Road End - stop 36m away

HONOURS   **League:** Central Midlands North Division 2016-17.

FA Comps: None

Colours(change): Yellow & blue

10 YEAR RECORD

08-09	09-10	10-11	11-12	12-13	13-14	14-15	15-16	16-17	17-18
								CMN 1	NCE1 20
									FAV 1P

GLASSHOUGHTON WELFARE

Founded: 1964   Nickname: Welfare or Blues

Club Contact Details (T) 01977 511 234   **(E)** frank.maclachlan@btinternet.com

Ground: Glasshoughton Centre, Leeds Road, Glasshoughton, Castleford WF10 4PF   **Capacity:** 2,000

Nearest Railway Station Glasshoughton - 0.8km   **Bus Route** Leeds Road Carr Lane - stop 83m away

HONOURS   **League:** None

FA Comps: None

Colours(change): Royal blue & white

10 YEAR RECORD

08-09	09-10	10-11	11-12	12-13	13-14	14-15	15-16	16-17	17-18
NCE1 19	NCE1 13	NCE1 7	NCE1 2	NCEP 16	NCEP 16	NCEP 21	NCE1 16	NCE1 11	NCE1 6
FAC EPr			FAC Pr	FAC EP	FAC EP	FAC EP	FAC EPr		
FAV 1Q	FAV 1Q	FAV 1Q	FAV 2P	FAV 2Q	FAV 2Q	FAV 1Q	FAV 1Q	FAV 2Qr	FAV 2Q

GRIMSBY BOROUGH

Founded: 2003   Nickname: The Wilderness Boys

Club Contact Details (T) 07890 318 054   **(E)**

Ground: The Bradley Football Development Centre, Bradley Road, Grimsby, DN37 0AG   **Capacity:** 1,000

Nearest Railway Station Grimsby Town - 3km   **Bus Route** Crowland Avenue - stop 463m away

HONOURS   **League:** None

FA Comps: None

Colours(change): All red

10 YEAR RECORD

08-09	09-10	10-11	11-12	12-13	13-14	14-15	15-16	16-17	17-18
NCE1 13	NCE1 17	NCE1 15	NCE1 18	NCE1 17	NCE1 16	NCE1 22	NCE1 19	NCE1 4	NCE1 3
			FAC EP						FAC 1Q
	FAV 1P	FAV 2Q	FAV 2Q	FAV 1Q	FAV 2Q	FAV 1Q		FAV 2Q	FAV 1Q

HALLAM

Founded: 1860   Nickname: Countrymen

Club Contact Details (T) 0114 230 9484   **(E)** theclub@hallamfc.co.uk

Ground: Sandygate Road, Crosspool, Sheffield S10 5SE   **Capacity:** 1,000

Nearest Railway Station Sheffield - 4.5km   **Bus Route** Ringstead Crescent - stop 19m away

HONOURS   **League:** Hatchard 1902-03, 48-49. Sheffield Amateur 1922-23, 26-27.

FA Comps: None   Sheffield Association 1949-50. Yorkshire Division Two 1960-61.

Colours(change): Blue and white

10 YEAR RECORD

08-09	09-10	10-11	11-12	12-13	13-14	14-15	15-16	16-17	17-18
NCEP 10	NCEP 15	NCEP 19	NCE1 14	NCE1 12	NCE1 20	NCEP 14	NCE1 6	NCE1 5	NCE1 8
FAC EP	FAC 1Q	FAC EP	FAC EP	FAC EP				FAC EP	FAC P
FAV 1Pr	FAV 2P	FAV 1P	FAV 1Q	FAV 1Q	FAV 1Q	FAV 2Q	FAV 2P	FAV 2P	FAV 2Q

HARWORTH COLLIERY

Founded: 1931   Nickname:

Club Contact Details (T) 07979 958 255   **(E)** jonycw@hotmail.co.uk

Ground: Recreation Ground, Scrooby Road, Bircotes, Doncaster DN11 8JT   **Capacity:** 2,000

HONOURS   **League:** Doncaster Senior 1938-39, 39-40, 40-41, Division Two 49-50. Sheffield Association Division One

1964-65, 75-76. Central Midlands Supreme Division 1987-88, North 2017-18.

FA Comps: None

Colours(change): Orange and black

10 YEAR RECORD

08-09	09-10	10-11	11-12	12-13	13-14	14-15	15-16	16-17	17-18
CM Su 7	CM Su 12	CM Su 11	CMN 11	CMN 5	CMN 4	CMN 8	CMN 5	CMN 10	CMN 1
							FAV 2Q	FAV 1Q	

NOSTELL MINERS WELFARE

Founded: 1928   Nickname: The Welfare

Club Contact Details (T) 01924 866 010   (E) nostwellmwfc@hotmail.com

Ground: The Welfare Ground, Crofton Co. Centre, Middle Lane, New Crofton WF4 1LB   Capacity: 1500

Nearest Railway Station Streethouse - 2.9km   **Bus Route** The Slipper Pub - stop 372m away

HONOURS   **League:** West Yorkshire Premier Division 2004-05

FA Comps: None

Colours(change): Yellow and black

10 YEAR RECORD

	08-09		09-10		10-11		11-12		12-13		13-14		14-15		15-16		16-17		17-18	
	NCEP	13	NCEP	18	NCEP	9	NCEP	17	NCEP	18	NCEP	21	NCEP	15	NCEP	22	NCE1	22	NCE1	17
	FAC	Pr	FAC	P	FAC	EPr	FAC	EP	FAC	EP	FAC	EP	FAC	EP	FAC	EPr	FAC	EPr		
	FAV	3P	FAV	2Q	FAV	1Q	FAV	2Qr	FAV	1P	FAV	1Q	FAV	2Q	FAV	1Q	FAV	2Q	FAV	2Q

OLLERTON TOWN

Founded: 1988   Nickname: The Town

Club Contact Details (T)   (E)

Ground: The Lane, Walesby Lane, New Ollerton, Newark NG22 9UT

Nearest Railway Station Worksop   **Bus Route** Rosewood Centre - stop 214m away

HONOURS   **League:** Notts Alliance Division Two 1992-93, Division One 95-96.

FA Comps: None   Central Midlands Premier Division 2007-08.

Colours(change): Red and black

10 YEAR RECORD

	08-09		09-10		10-11		11-12		12-13		13-14		14-15		15-16		16-17		17-18	
	CM Su	4	CM Su	3	CM Su	13	CMN	7	CMN	6	CMN	8	CMN	10	CMN	2	NCE1	17	NCE1	15
	FAV	1Qr	FAV	2P	FAV	1Q	FAV	2Q	FAV	1Q	FAV	2Q			FAV	1Q	FAV	1Q	FAV	2Q

PARKGATE

Founded: 1969   Nickname: The Steelmen

Club Contact Details (T) 01709 826 600   (E) brucebickerdike@hotmail.co.uk

Ground: Roundwood Sports Complex, Green Lane, Rawmarsh, S62 6LA   1,000

Nearest Railway Station Swinton - 3.4km   **Bus Route** Roundwood Grove - stop 57m away

HONOURS   **League:** Northern Counties East Division One 2006-07.

FA Comps: None

Colours(change): Red & white

10 YEAR RECORD

	08-09		09-10		10-11		11-12		12-13		13-14		14-15		15-16		16-17		17-18	
	NCEP	11	NCEP	14	NCEP	2	NCEP	7	NCEP	9	NCEP	19	NCEP	16	NCEP	17	NCEP	17	NCEP	21
	FAC	EP	FAC	EP	FAC	1Q	FAC	1Q	FAC	EP	FAC	EP	FAC	EP	FAC	EP	FAC	P	FAC	P
	FAV	2Q	FAV	2Q	FAV	2Q	FAV	3P	FAV	3P	FAV	2P	FAV	1Q	FAV	1Q	FAV	1Q	FAV	2Q

ROSSINGTON MAIN

Founded: 1919   Nickname: The Colliery

Club Contact Details (T) 01302 864 870 (MD)   (E) g-parsons2@sky.com

Ground: Welfare Ground, Oxford Street, Rossington, Doncaster, DN11 0TE   Capacity: 2,000

Nearest Railway Station Doncaster - 6.4km   **Bus Route** Grantham Street - stop 149m away

HONOURS   **League:** Doncaster & District Senior 1944-45.

FA Comps: None   Central Midlands Premier Division 1984-85.

Colours(change): All blue

10 YEAR RECORD

	08-09		09-10		10-11		11-12		12-13		13-14		14-15		15-16		16-17		17-18	
	NCE1	11	NCE1	10	NCE1	14	NCE1	7	NCE1	18	NCE1	13	NCE1	15	NCE1	20	NCE1	15	NCE1	13
	FAC	EP	FAC	P	FAC	EP	FAC	EPr	FAC	EP										
	FAV	1P	FAV	1P	FAV	1Q	FAV	2Q	FAV	1Q	FAV	2Q	FAV	2Q	FAV	2Q	FAV	2Q	FAV	1P

SELBY TOWN

Founded: 1919   Nickname: The Robins

Club Contact Details (T) 01757 210 900   (E) toonarkley@yahoo.co.uk

Ground: The Fairfax Plant Hire Stadium, Richard Street, Scott Road, Selby YO8 4BN   Capacity: 5,000

Nearest Railway Station Selby - 0.8km   **Bus Route** Leisure Centre - stop 73m away

HONOURS   **League:** Yorkshire 1934-35, 35-36, 52-53, 53-54.

FA Comps: None   Northern Counties East Division One 1995-96.

Colours(change): All red

10 YEAR RECORD

	08-09		09-10		10-11		11-12		12-13		13-14		14-15		15-16		16-17		17-18	
	NCEP	3	NCEP	13	NCEP	15	NCEP	20	NCE1	16	NCE1	12	NCE1	11	NCE1	10	NCE1	10	NCE1	7
	FAC	1Q	FAC	P	FAC	P	FAC	EP	FAC	EP										
	FAV	1P	FAV	1P	FAV	2Qr	FAV	1P	FAV	2Q	FAV	1Q	FAV	1P	FAV	1P	FAV	1Q	FAV	1Q

SHIREBROOK TOWN

Founded: 1985   Nickname: None

Club Contact Details (T) 01623 742 535   **(E)** aimeeradford@yahoo.co.uk

Ground: Langwith Road, Shirebrook, Mansfield, NG20 8TF   **Capacity:** 2,000

Nearest Railway Station Shirebrook - 0.2km   **Bus Route** Langwith Road End - stop 36m away

HONOURS   **League:** Central Midlands League Supreme Division 2000-01, 01-02.

FA Comps: None   Northern Counties East Division One 2003-04.

Colours(change): Red and black

10 YEAR RECORD

	08-09	09-10	10-11	11-12	12-13	13-14	14-15	15-16	16-17	17-18
NCEP	17	NCEP 19	NCE1 13	NCE1 13	NCE1 6	NCE1 5	NCE1 4	NCE1 7	NCE1 18	NCE1 5
FAC	P	FAC P	FAC 1Q	FAC Pr	FAC EP	FAC Pr	FAC EPr	FAC EP	FAC EPr	
FAV	1Q	FAV 2Q	FAV 1Q	FAV 2Q	FAV 2Pr	FAV 2Q	FAV 1Q	FAV 2P	FAV 2Q	FAV 1P

SKEGNESS TOWN

Founded: 1947   Nickname: Lilywhites

Club Contact Details (T) 07960 756 351   **(E)** thegrays23@hotmail.com

Ground: Vertigo Stadium, Wainfleet Road, Skegness, Lincolnshire PE25 2EL

Nearest Railway Station Skegness ½ mile

HONOURS   **League:** Lincolnshire 1951-52, 55-56, 2006-07, 07-08, 13-14, 15-16, 16-17.

FA Comps: None

Colours(change): White & red

10 YEAR RECORD

08-09	09-10	10-11	11-12	12-13	13-14	14-15	15-16	16-17	17-18
Lincs 5	Lincs 5	Lincs 5	Lincs 12	Lincs 8	Lincs 1	Lincs 2	Lincs 1	Lincs 1	Lincs 2
									FAV 2Q

SWALLOWNEST

Founded: 2006   Nickname: None

Club Contact Details (T) 0114 287 2510   **(E)** glennwatts57@gmail.com

Ground: Rotherham Road, Sheffield S26 4UR.

Nearest Railway Station Woodhouse - 2.2km   **Bus Route** Park Street - stop 61m away

HONOURS   **League:** South Yorkshire Amateur Premier Division 2007-08.

FA Comps: None   Sheffield & Hallamshire County Senior Div.2 2008-09, Prem 10-11, 16-17.

Colours(change): All royal blue

10 YEAR RECORD

08-09	09-10	10-11	11-12	12-13	13-14	14-15	15-16	16-17	17-18
Sh&H2 1	Sh&H1 2	Sh&HP 1	Sh&HP 3	Sh&HP 6	Sh&HP 5	Sh&HP 3	Sh&HP 7	Sh&HP 1	NCE1 11

WINTERTON RANGERS

Founded: 1930   Nickname: Rangers

Club Contact Details (T) 01724 732 628   **(E)** wintertonrangers2018@mail.com

Ground: West Street, Winterton, Scunthorpe DN15 9QF.   **Capacity:** 3,000

Nearest Railway Station Scunthorpe - 6¼ miles   **Bus Route** Post Office - stop 150m away

HONOURS   **League:** Yprkshire Division One 1971-72, 76-77, 78-79.

FA Comps: None   Northern Counties East Division Two 1989-90, Premier 2007-08.

Colours(change): All blue

10 YEAR RECORD

	08-09	09-10	10-11	11-12	12-13	13-14	14-15	15-16	16-17	17-18
NCEP	5	NCEP 6	NCEP 5	NCEP 6	NCEP 19	NCEP 22	NCE1 18	NCE1 8	NCE1 12	NCE1 10
FAC	2Qr	FAC 1Q	FAC 1Qr	FAC EP	FAC EP	FAC EP	FAC P			
FAV	3P	FAV 1P	FAV 2P	FAV 2Q	FAV 2Q	FAV 2Q	FAV 1P	FAV 1Q	FAV 1Q	FAV 1Q

WORSBROUGH BRIDGE ATHLETIC

Founded: 1923   Nickname: The Briggers

Club Contact Details (T) 01226 284 452   **(E)** info@wbafc.org.uk

Ground: Park Road, Worsbrough Bridge, Barnsley S70 5LJ   **Capacity:** 2,000

Nearest Railway Station Barnsley - 3.1km   **Bus Route** West Street - stop 29m away

HONOURS   **League:** Barnsley Division One 1952-53, 58-59, 59-60.

FA Comps: None   Sheffield Association Division One 1965-66, 69-70.

Colours(change): All red

10 YEAR RECORD

08-09	09-10	10-11	11-12	12-13	13-14	14-15	15-16	16-17	17-18
NCE1 16	NCE1 18	NCE1 12	NCE1 11	NCE1 9	NCE1 10	NCE1 16	NCE1 21	NCE1 20	NCE1 19
FAV 2Q	FAV 1P	FAV 2Q	FAV 2Q	FAV 1Q	FAV 2Q	FAV 2Q	FAV 1Q		FAV 1Q

NORTHERN LEAGUE

Founded: 1889 **Sponsored by:** Ebac

Recent Champions: 2015: Marske United **2016:** Shildon **2017:** South Shields

DIVISION ONE	P	W	D	L	F	A	GD	Pts
1 Marske United	42	32	6	4	102	31	71	102
2 Morpeth Town	42	30	7	5	117	52	65	97
3 Shildon	42	24	8	10	93	55	38	80
4 Sunderland RCA	42	24	7	11	96	54	42	79
5 West Auckland Town	42	23	9	10	107	64	43	78
6 Stockton Town	42	23	2	17	91	72	19	71
7 Newcastle Benfield	42	22	5	15	90	71	19	71
8 North Shields	42	21	6	15	103	73	30	69
9 Consett	42	21	5	16	93	83	10	68
10 Dunston UTS	42	19	6	17	77	68	9	63
11 Ryhope CW	42	19	3	20	85	87	-2	60
12 Ashington	42	16	11	15	80	67	13	59
13 Team Northumbria	42	17	5	20	64	70	-6	56
14 Newton Aycliffe	42	13	13	16	53	58	-5	52
15 Guisborough Town	42	15	10	17	70	82	-12	52
16 Whitley Bay	42	15	6	21	73	91	-18	51
17 Penrith	42	15	3	24	71	85	-14	48
18 Seaham Red Star	42	12	7	23	57	90	-33	43
19 Bishop Auckland	42	13	4	25	68	112	-44	43
20 Jarrow Roofing BCA	42	11	6	25	70	102	-32	39
21 Washington	42	4	6	32	39	132	-93	18
22 Billingham Synthonia	42	2	7	33	28	128	-100	13

DIVISION TWO	P	W	D	L	F	A	GD	Pts
1 Blyth AFC	40	26	8	6	95	39	56	86
2 Hebburn Town	40	24	9	7	85	37	48	81
3 Whickham	40	25	5	10	80	52	28	80
4 Northallerton Town	40	25	4	11	99	64	35	79
5 Heaton Stannington	40	21	9	10	86	58	28	72
6 Thornaby	40	21	5	14	85	53	32	68
7 Willington	40	20	7	13	65	49	16	67
8 Tow Law Town	40	19	7	14	88	70	18	64
9 Billingham Town	40	17	10	13	81	60	21	61
10 Easington Colliery	40	16	9	15	78	75	3	57
11 Durham City	40	14	9	17	74	79	-5	51
12 Jarrow	40	13	11	16	56	69	-13	50
13 Esh Winning	40	14	8	18	76	90	-14	50
14 Chester-Le-Street	40	13	10	17	58	71	-13	49
15 West Allotment Celtic	40	13	6	21	64	86	-22	45
16 Bedlington Terriers	40	14	5	21	63	70	-7	44
17 Ryton & Crawcrook Albion	40	12	8	20	53	76	-23	44
18 Crook Town	40	12	6	22	62	104	-42	42
19 Brandon United	40	8	9	23	56	88	-32	33
20 Darlington RA	40	9	4	27	41	90	-49	31
21 Alnwick Town	40	6	7	27	51	116	-65	25

LEAGUE CUP

HOLDERS: SOUTH SHIELDS

ROUND 1

Durham City	v	Team Northumbria	3-2
Newton Aycliffe	v	Ryton & Crawcrook Albion	5-0
Washington	v	Chester-Le-Street	2-0
West Auckland	v	Consett	1-3
Whickham	v	Thornaby	3-2
Northallerton Town	v	Ashington	2-2, HWp
Hebburn Town	v	Alnwick Town	3-2
West Allotment Celtic	v	Dunston UTS	0-1
Brandon United	v	Willington	1-1, AWp
Easington Colliery	v	Jarrow Roofing	1-1, HWp
Crook Town	v	Newcastle Benfield	1-5

ROUND 2

Bedlington Terriers	v	Durham City	0-1
Billingham Town	v	Stockton Town	1-4
Marske United	v	North Shields	2-3
Newton Aycliffe	v	Dunston UTS	0-2
Whickham	v	Newcastle Benfield	0-0, HWp
Billingham Synthonia	v	Esh Winning	4-2
Darlington RA	v	Seaham Red Star	0-4
Hebburn Town	v	Ryhope CW	0-2
Jarrow	v	Penrith	1-4
Morpeth Town	v	Blyth AFC	1-0
Willington	v	Shildon	1-0
Guisborough Town	v	Northallerton Town	4-4
Easington Colliery	v	Washington	3-1
Consett	v	Tow Law Town	7-1
Bishop Auckland	v	Heaton Stannington	3-0
Whitley Bay	Bye		

ROUND 3

Consett	v	Newcastle Benfield	2-3
Dunston UTS	v	Billingham Synthonia	1-0
Seaham Red Star	v	Easington Colliery	4-1
North Shields	v	Stockton Town	1-2
Bishop Auckland	v	Guisborough Town	3-2
Durham City	v	Ryhope CW	1-4
Whitley Bay	v	Penrith	0-0, AWp
Morpeth Town	v	Willington	4-1

QUARTER FINALS

Newcastle Benfield	v	Ryhope CW	2-1
Seaham Red Star	v	Dunston UTS	0-3
Penrith	v	Bishop Auckland	1-2
Morpeth Town	v	Stockton Town	2-3

SEMI FINALS

Stockton Town	v	Dunston UTS	1-3
Bishop Auckland	v	Newcastle Benfield	1-1, HWp

FINAL

Bishop Auckland	v	Dunston UTS	0-1

ERNSET ARMSTRONG MEMORIAL CUP

HOLDERS: NORTHALLERTON TOWN

SEMI FINALS

Northallerton Town	v	Chester-Le-Street	0-1
Ryton & Crawcrook Albion	v	Hebburn Town	2-1

FINAL

Chester-Le-Street	v	Ryton & Crawcrook Albion	2-0

J.R. CLEATOR CUP

Morpeth Town	v	North Shields	3-0

CLUB MOVEMENTS

Division One - In: Blyth (P), Hebburn Town (P), Whickham (P).
Out: Billingham Synthonia (R), Jarrow Roofing BCA (F), Marske United (P - NPLE), Morpeth Town (P - NPLE), Team Northumbria (W), Washington (R).
Division Two - In: Billingham Synthonia (R), Birtley Town (P - NFA), Redcar Athletic (P - Wear), Washington (R).
Out: Blyth (P), Hebburn Town (P), Whickham (P).

ASHINGTON

Founded: 1883   Nickname: The Colliers

Club Contact Details   **(T)** 01670 811 991   **(E)** exec@ashingtonafc.com
Ground: Woodhorn Lane, Ashington NE63 9FW

Capacity: 2,000   **Seats:** 400   **Covered:** 900   **Shop:** Yes   **Bus Route** Wansbeck Hospital - stop 71m away

Colours(change): Black & White
Previous Names: None
Previous Leagues: East Northumberland. Northern Alliance, Football League, N. Eastern, Midland, Northern Counties, Wearside, N.P.L.

HONOURS: FA Comps: None
    League: East Northumberland 1897-98. Northern Alliance 1913-14.

10 YEAR RECORD   Northern Division Two 2000-01, 03-04.

	08-09		09-10		10-11		11-12		12-13		13-14		14-15		15-16		16-17		17-18	
NL 1	16	NL 1	6	NL 1	8	NL 1	5	NL 1	7	NL 1	6	NL 1	13	NL 1	12	NL 1	16	NL 1	12
FAC	1Q	FAC	EP	FAC	3Q	FAC	4Q	FAC	1Q	FAC	P	FAC	1Qr	FAC	P	FAC	EP	FAC	P
FAV	2P	FAV	2Q	FAV	4P	FAV	5P	FAV	4P	FAV	4P	FAV	2P	FAV	2P	FAV	2Q	FAV	1P

BISHOP AUCKLAND

Founded: 1886   Nickname: Two Blues

Club Contact Details   **(T)** 01388 604 605   **(E)**
Ground: Heritage Park, Bishop Auckland, Co. Durham DL14 9AE
Nearest Railway Station Bishop Auckland - 2.2km
Capacity: 2,004   **Seats:** 250   **Covered:** 722   **Bus Route** Bus stops right outside the ground.

Colours(change): Light & dark blue/blue/blue
Previous Names: Auckland Town 1889-1893
Previous Leagues: Northern Alliance 1890-91, Northern League 1893-1988, Northern Premier 1988-2006

HONOURS: FA Comps: FA Amateur Cup 1895-96, 1899-1900, 1913-14, 20-21, 21-22, 34-35, 38-39, 54-55, 55-56, 56-57.
    League: Northern League 1898-99, 1900-01, 01-02, 08-09, 09-10, 11-12, 20-21, 30-31, 38-39, 46-47, 49-50, 50-51,

10 YEAR RECORD   51-52, 53-54, 54-55, 55-56, 66-67, 84-85, 85-86.

	08-09		09-10		10-11		11-12		12-13		13-14		14-15		15-16		16-17		17-18	
NL 1	18	NL 1	13	NL 1	14	NL 1	8	NL 1	6	NL 1	8	NL 1	11	NL 1	8	NL 1	8	NL 1	19
FAC	Pr	FAC	1Q	FAC	Pr	FAC	EP	FAC	2Q	FAC	1Qr	FAC	1Q	FAC	P	FAC	4Q	FAC	EPr
FAV	2Q	FAV	2Q	FAV	1P	FAV	2Q	FAV	1P	FAV	2Q	FAV	2P	FAV	1P	FAV	2Q	FAV	2Q

BLYTH TOWN

Founded: 1995   Nickname:

Club Contact Details   **(T)**   **(E)** info@blythafc.co.uk
Ground: Woodhorn Lane, Ashington NE63 9FW
Nearest Railway Station Cramlington - 5.2km
Capacity: 2,000   **Seats:** 400   **Covered:** 900   **Bus Route** Wansbeck Hospital - stop 71m away

Colours(change): White with blue trim/white/blue hoops (Blue with white trim/blue/blue hoops)
Previous Names: None
Previous Leagues: Northern Alliance 2002-05

HONOURS: FA Comps: None
    League: Northern Alliance Division Two 2002-03, Premier 2013-14, 14-15, 15-16.

10 YEAR RECORD

	08-09		09-10		10-11		11-12		12-13		13-14		14-15		15-16		16-17		17-18	
NAl P	9	NAl P	4	NAl P	9	NAl P	11	NAl P	2	NAl P	1	NAl P	1	NAl P	1	NL 2	8	NL 2	1
																FAV	1Q	FAV	2Q

CONSETT

Founded: 1899   Nickname: Steelman

Club Contact Details   **(T)** 01207 588 886   **(E)** david_pyke@hotmail.co.uk
Ground: Belle Vue Park, Ashdale Road, Consett DH8 7JP

Capacity: 4,000   **Seats:** 400   **Covered:** 1000   **Shop:** No   **Bus Route** Mortons Garage - stop 174m away

Colours(change): All Red
Previous Names: Consett Celtic 1899-1922.
Previous Leagues: Northern Alliance 1919-26, 35-37, North Eastern 1926-35, 37-58, 62-64, Midland 1958-60,
    Northern Counties 1960-62, Wearside 1964-70.
HONOURS: FA Comps: None
    League: North Eastern 1939-40, Division Two 26-27. Northern Counties 1961-62. Northern Division Two 1988-89, 05-06.

10 YEAR RECORD

	08-09		09-10		10-11		11-12		12-13		13-14		14-15		15-16		16-17		17-18	
NL 1	2	NL 1	10	NL 1	2	NL 1	15	NL 1	9	NL 1	11	NL 1	9	NL 1	7	NL 1	7	NL 1	9
FAC	1Qr	FAC	Pr	FAC	EPr	FAC	EP	FAC	EPr	FAC	EP	FAC	1Q	FAC	2Q	FAC	2Qr	FAC	1Q
FAV	2P	FAV	1P	FAV	2Q	FAV	3P	FAV	2P	FAV	2Q	FAV	4P	FAV	2P	FAV	2Q	FAV	2Q

DUNSTON UTS

Founded: 1975 Nickname: The Fed

Club Contact Details (T) 0191 493 2935 (E) w.montague@sky.com
Ground: UTS Stadium, Wellington Road, Dunston, Gateshead NE11 9JL
Nearest Railway Station Metrocentre - 0.9km. Dunston - 1km.
Capacity: 2,000 **Seats:** 120 **Covered:** 400 **Shop:** No **Bus Route** Wellington Road - stop 24m away

Colours(change): All blue
Previous Names: Dunston Federation Brewery > 2007. Dunston Federation > 2009.
Previous Leagues: Northern Amateur & Wearside league

HONOURS: FA Comps: FA Vase 2011-12.
League: Wearside 1988-89, 89-90. Northern Division Two 1992-93, Division One 2003-04, 04-05.

10 YEAR RECORD

	08-09	09-10	10-11	11-12	12-13	13-14	14-15	15-16	16-17	17-18
	NL 1 6	NL 1 4	NL 1 7	NL 1 3	NL 1 5	NL 1 7	NL 1 6	NL 1 11	NL 1 15	NL 1 10
		FAC EPr	FAC 2Q	FAC 1Q	FAC 1Qr	FAC P	FAC 2Q	FAC 1Q	FAC 2Q	FAC P
		FAV 2P	FAV QF	FAV F	FAV 4P	FAV QF	FAV 5Pr	FAV 5Pr	FAV 3P	FAV 2P

GUISBOROUGH TOWN

Founded: 1973 Nickname: Priorymen

Club Contact Details (T) 01287 636 925 (E)
Ground: King George V Ground, Howlbeck Road, Guisborough TS14 6LE
Capacity: **Seats:** Yes **Covered:** Yes **Bus Route** Howlbeck Road - stop 49m away

Colours(change): Red & white
Previous Names: None
Previous Leagues: Middlesbrough & District 1973-77. Northern Alliance 1977-80. Midland 1980-82. Northern Counties East 1982-85.

HONOURS: FA Comps: None
League: Northern Alliance 1979-80.

10 YEAR RECORD

	08-09	09-10	10-11	11-12	12-13	13-14	14-15	15-16	16-17	17-18
	NL 2 7	NL 2 5	NL 2 2	NL 1 16	NL 1 11	NL 1 4	NL 1 3	NL 1 3	NL 1 20	NL 1 15
	FAC EP	FAC 1Q	FAC EP	FAC P	FAC Pr	FAC 3Q	FAC EPr	FAC 1Q	FAC P	FAC P
	FAV 1Pr	FAV 1P	FAV 1P	FAV 2Q	FAV 1Pr	FAV 1P	FAV 2P	FAV 2P	FAV 1P	FAV 1Q

HEBBURN TOWN

Founded: 1912 Nickname: Hornets

Club Contact Details (T) 0191 483 5101 (E) davepatter@yahoo.co.uk
Ground: Hebburn Sports & Social, Victoria Rd West, Hebburn, Tyne & Wear NE31 1UN
Nearest Railway Station Hebburn - 1km
Capacity: **Seats:** Yes **Covered:** Yes **Bus Route** Victoria Road West - stop 74m away

Colours(change): Yellow & black
Previous Names: Reyrolles, Hebburn Reyrolles > 1988, Hebburn 1988-2000.
Previous Leagues: Wearside 1960-89.

HONOURS: FA Comps: None
League: Tyneside1938-39. Northern Combination 1943-44. Wearside 1966-67.

10 YEAR RECORD

	08-09	09-10	10-11	11-12	12-13	13-14	14-15	15-16	16-17	17-18
	NL 2 10	NL 2 16	NL 2 10	NL 2 3	NL 1 18	NL 1 22	NL 2 5	NL 2 10	NL 2 11	NL 2 2
	FAC EP	FAC P	FAC EPr	FAC 4Q	FAC P	FAC P	FAC EPr	FAC EP		
	FAV 2Q	FAV 2Q	FAV 2P	FAV 1P	FAV 2Q	FAV 1Q	FAV 1Q	FAV 1P	FAV 1Q	FAV 2Q

NEWCASTLE BENFIELD

Founded: 1988 Nickname: The Lions

Club Contact Details (T) 07525 275 641 (E)
Ground: Sam Smiths Park, Benfield Road, Walkergate NE6 4NU
Nearest Railway Station Walkergate - 492m
Capacity: 2,000 **Seats:** 150 **Covered:** 250 **Bus Route** Benfield Comprehensive School - 96m away

Colours(change): Blue & white hoops/blue/blue
Previous Names: Heaton Corner House. Newcastle Benfield Saints.
Previous Leagues: Northern Alliance 1988-2003

HONOURS: FA Comps: None
League: Northern Alliance Division Two 1989-90, Division One 1994-95, 2002-03. Northern Division One 2008-09.

10 YEAR RECORD

	08-09	09-10	10-11	11-12	12-13	13-14	14-15	15-16	16-17	17-18
	NL 1 1	NL 1 5	NL 1 4	NL 1 12	NL 1 21	NL 1 14	NL 1 10	NL 1 18	NL 1 10	NL 1 7
	FAC 3Q	FAC P	FAC 2Q	FAC 1Q	FAC EP	FAC EP	FAC 2Q	FAC P	FAC 1Q	FAC 3Q
	FAV 2P	FAV 2P	FAV 2Q	FAV 4P	FAV 2P	FAV QF	FAV 3P	FAV 1P	FAV 2P	FAV 4P

NEWTON AYCLIFFE

Founded: 1965   Nickname: Aycliffe

Club Contact Details (T) 01325 312 768   (E) stecunliffe@aol.com
Ground: Moore Lane Park, Moore Lane, Newton Aycliffe, Co. Durham DL5 5AG
Nearest Railway Station Newton Aycliffe - 2km
Capacity: **Seats:** Yes   **Covered:** Yes   **Bus Route** Shafto Way - stop 271m away

Colours(change): Blue & black
Previous Names: None
Previous Leagues: Wearside 1984-94, 2008-09. Darlington & District. Durham Alliance > 2008.

HONOURS: FA Comps: None
League: Darlington & District Division 'A' 2004-05. Durham Alliance 2007-08. Wearside 2008-09.
Northern Division Two 2010-11.

10 YEAR RECORD	08-09	09-10	10-11	11-12	12-13	13-14	14-15	15-16	16-17	17-18
	Wear 1	NL 2 9	NL 2 1	NL 1 9	NL 1 17	NL 1 18	NL 1 18	NL 1 6	NL 1 9	NL 1 14
				FAC EP	FAC EPr	FAC Pr	FAC EP	FAC 2Qr	FAC EPr	FAC P
			FAV 1Q	FAV 1Qr	FAV 1P	FAV 1Q	FAV 1Q	FAT 5P	FAV 3P	FAV 1Q

NORTH SHIELDS

Founded: 1896   Nickname: Robins

Club Contact Details (T)   (E)
Ground: Daren Persson Staduim, West Percy Road, Chirton, North Shields NE29 6UA
Nearest Railway Station Meadow Well - 392m
Capacity: 1,500 **Seats:** Yes   **Covered:** Yes   **Bus Route** Waterville Road - stop 29m away

Colours(change): All red
Previous Names: North Shields Athletic 1896-15, Preston Colliery 1919-1928, North Shields FC 1928-92. North Shields Athletic 1995-99.
Previous Leagues: Northern Combination. Northern Alliance. North Eastern. Midland. Northern Counties/North Eastern 1960-64.
Northern 1964-89. Northern Counties East 1989-92. Wearside 1992-2004.
HONOURS: FA Comps: FA Amateur Cup 1968-69. FA Vase 2014-15.
League: Northern Alliance 1906-07, 07-08. North Eastern Div.2 28-29, Div.1 49-50. Northern Counties 60-61.
Northern Div.1 68-69, Div.2 2013-14. Northern Counties East Prem 91-92. Wearside 98-99, 01-02, 03-04.

10 YEAR RECORD	08-09	09-10	10-11	11-12	12-13	13-14	14-15	15-16	16-17	17-18
	NL 2 15	NL 2 6	NL 2 4	NL 2 8	NL 2 8	NL 2 1	NL 1 4	NL 1 5	NL 1 3	NL 1 8
	FAC EP		FAC Pr	FAC EPr	FAC EPr	FAC EP	FAC Pr	FAC Pr	FAC P	FAC EPr
	FAV 2Q	FAV 1P	FAV 1Q	FAV 1Q	FAV 1Q	FAV 1Pr	FAV F	FAV 4P	FAV 3P	FAV 3P

PENRITH

Founded: 1894   Nickname: Blues

Club Contact Details (T) 01768 865 990   (E) ianwhite77@hotmail.com
Ground: The Stadium, Frenchfield Park, Frenchfield, Penrith CA11 8UA
Nearest Railway Station Penrith North Lakes - 2.3km
Capacity: 1,500 **Seats:** 200   **Covered:** 1,000   **Shop:** No   **Bus Route** Oak Road - stop 727m away

Colours(change): White and blue
Previous Names: Penrith 1894-2007. Penrith Town 2007-08. Back to Penrith after a merger with Penrith United.
Previous Leagues: North Eastern. Northern 1947-82. North West Counties 1982-87, 90-97. Northern Premier League 1987-90.

HONOURS: FA Comps: None
League: Northern Division Two 2002-03, 07-08.

10 YEAR RECORD	08-09	09-10	10-11	11-12	12-13	13-14	14-15	15-16	16-17	17-18
	NL 1 7	NL 1 14	NL 1 17	NL 1 19	NL 1 13	NL 1 13	NL 1 14	NL 1 14	NL 1 12	NL 1 17
	FAC P	FAC P	FAC EP	FAC 1Q	FAC EP	FAC 3Q	FAC EP	FAC EP	FAC Pr	FAC Pr
	FAV 3P	FAV 3P	FAV 2Q	FAV 2Q	FAV 1P	FAV 1P	FAV 1Q	FAV 1Q	FAV 3P	FAV 2Q

RYHOPE COLLIERY WELFARE

Founded: 1892   Nickname: Colliery Welfare

Club Contact Details (T) 07901 545 760   (E)
Ground: Ryhope Recreation Park, Ryhope Street, Ryhope, Sunderland SR2 0AB
Nearest Railway Station Sunderland - 3.8km
Capacity: **Seats:** Yes   **Covered:** Yes   **Bus Route** Ryhope Street-post office - stop 79m away

Colours(change): Red & white
Previous Names: None
Previous Leagues: Wearside >2012, 2013-14.

HONOURS: FA Comps: None
League: Wearside 1927-28, 61-62, 62-63, 63-64, 65-66, 2010-11, 11-12.

10 YEAR RECORD	08-09	09-10	10-11	11-12	12-13	13-14	14-15	15-16	16-17	17-18
	Wear 8	Wear 2	Wear 1	Wear 1	NL 2 2	Wear 2	NL 2 6	NL 2 2	NL 1 17	NL 1 11
								FAC EPr	FAC EPr	FAC EP
							FAV 2P	FAV 1Q	FAV 2P	FAV 2P

SEAHAM RED STAR
Founded: 1973 Nickname: The Star

Club Contact Details (T) (E)
Ground: Seaham Town Park, Stockton Road, Seaham. Co.Durham SR7 0HY
Nearest Railway Station Seaham - 1.5km
Capacity: 500 **Seats:** Yes **Covered:** Yes **Bus Route** Mill Inn (Stockton Rd) - stop 201m away

Colours(change): Red & white
Previous Names: Seaham Colliery Welfare Red Star 1978-87.
Previous Leagues: Houghton & District 1973-74. Northern Alliance 1974-79. Wearside 1979-83.

HONOURS: FA Comps: None
League: Wearside 1981-82.
10 YEAR RECORD | Northern League Division Two 2014-15.

	08-09	09-10	10-11	11-12	12-13	13-14	14-15	15-16	16-17	17-18
NL	1 21	NL 2 12	NL 2 17	NL 2 20	NL 2 10	NL 2 4	NL 2 1	NL 1 9	NL 1 14	NL 1 18
FAC	EP	FAC EP	FAC EP	FAC P	FAC	FAC EP	FAC P	FAC EPr	FAC EP	FAC EP
FAV	2Q	FAV 2Q	FAV 1Q	FAV 1Q	FAV 1Q	FAV 1Q	FAV 3P	FAV 3P	FAV 1Q	FAV 2Q

SHILDON
Founded: 1890 Nickname: Railwaymen

Club Contact Details (T) 01388 773 877 (E)
Ground: Dean Street, Shildon, Co. Durham DL4 1HA
Nearest Railway Station Shildon - 1.2km
Capacity: 4,000 **Seats:** 480 **Covered:** 1000 **Bus Route** St. Johns Church - stop 149m away

Colours(change): Red and black
Previous Names: Shildon Athletic > 1923.
Previous Leagues: Auckland & Dist 1892-86, Wear Valley 1896-97, Northern 1903-07, North Eastern 1907-32

HONOURS: FA Comps: None
League: Northern 1933-34, 34-35, 35-36,36-37, 39-40, 2015-16, Division Two 2001-02.
10 YEAR RECORD

	08-09	09-10	10-11	11-12	12-13	13-14	14-15	15-16	16-17	17-18
NL	1 8	NL 1 2	NL 1 5	NL 1 10	NL 1 8	NL 1 3	NL 1 2	NL 1 1	NL 1 4	NL 1 3
FAC	1Q	FAC P	FAC 3Q	FAC 1Qr	FAC 2Q	FAC P	FAC 4Qr	FAC EPr	FAC 2Q	FAC 4Q
FAV	3P	FAV QF	FAV 3P	FAV 1P	FAV SF	FAV 2P	FAV 3P	FAV 1P	FAV 4P	FAV 2P

STOCKTON TOWN
Founded: 1979 Nickname:

Club Contact Details (T) 01642 604 915 (E) 1962.rvs@gmail.com
Ground: Bishopton Road West, Stockton-on-Tees TS19 0QD
Nearest Railway Station Stockton - 1.4km
Capacity: **Seats:** Yes **Covered:** Yes **Bus Route** Whitehouse Drive - stop 101m away

Colours(change): Yellow and blue
Previous Names: Hartburn Juniors 1979-2003.
Previous Leagues: Teeside 2009-10. Wearside 2010-2016.

HONOURS: FA Comps: None
League: Wearside 2012-13, 13-14, 14-15,15-16. Northern Division Two 2016-17.
10 YEAR RECORD

08-09	09-10	10-11	11-12	12-13	13-14	14-15	15-16	16-17	17-18
	Tee1 4	Wear 10	Wear 3	Wear 1	Wear 1	Wear 1	Wear 1	NL 2 1	NL 1 6
									FAC EP
								FAV 2P	FAV F

SUNDERLAND RYHOPE C.A.
Founded: 1961 Nickname: The CA

Club Contact Details (T) (E)
Ground: Meadow Park, Beachbrooke, Stockton Rd, Ryhope, Sunderland SR2 0NZ
Nearest Railway Station Seaham - 3.3km
Capacity: 1,500 **Seats:** 150 **Covered:** 200 **Bus Route** Ryhope Hospital - 94m away

Colours(change): Red & white
Previous Names: Ryhope Youth Club 1961-71. Ryhope Community Association 1971-99. Kennek Ryhope CA 1999-2007.
Previous Leagues: Seaham & District. Houghton & District. Northern Alliance 1978-82.

HONOURS: FA Comps: None
League: None
10 YEAR RECORD

	08-09	09-10	10-11	11-12	12-13	13-14	14-15	15-16	16-17	17-18
NL	2 4	NL 2 2	NL 1 13	NL 1 4	NL 1 22	NL 1 19	NL 1 16	NL 1 13	NL 1 11	NL 1
FAC	EP	FAC EP	FAC EP	FAC P	FAC EPr	FAC EP	FAC EPr	FAC EPr	FAC EP	FAC 2Q
FAV	1P	FAV 1Q	FAV 1Q	FAV 1P	FAV 2P	FAV 1P	FAV 2P	FAV 5P	FAV 5P	FAV 2Pr

WEST AUCKLAND TOWN
Founded: 1893   Nickname: West

Club Contact Details (T)   (E)
Ground: Darlington Road, West Auckland, Co. Durham DL14 9AQ
Nearest Railway Station Bishop Auckland - 4.1km
Capacity: 2,000 **Seats:** 250   **Covered:** 250   **Bus Route** Oakley Grange Farm - stop 128m away

Colours(change): Yellow and black
Previous Names: West Auckland 1893-1914.
Previous Leagues: Wear Valley 1896-1900. South Durham Alliance 1900-05. Mid Durham 1905-08.

HONOURS: FA Comps: None
League: Northern 1959-60, 60-61, Division Two 1990-91.

10 YEAR RECORD

	08-09	09-10	10-11	11-12	12-13	13-14	14-15	15-16	16-17	17-18
NL 1	20	16	6	2	4	5	5	17	18	5
FAC	P	EPr	2Q	EPr	2Qr	3Qr	Pr	P	P	EP
FAV	2Q	3P	2P	F	2P	F	2P	1P	2Q	4P

WHICKHAM
Founded: 1944   Nickname: The Home

Club Contact Details (T) 0191 4200 186   (E)
Ground: Glebe Sports Club, Rectory Lane, Whickham NE16 4PF
Nearest Railway Station Metrocentre - 2.1km
Capacity: **Seats:**   **Covered:**   **Bus Route** Whaggs Lane-south - stop 105m away

Colours(change): Black & white
Previous Names:
Previous Leagues: Northern Combination 1973-74.

HONOURS: FA Comps: FA Vase 1980-81.
League: Wearside 1977-78, 87-88. Northern Combination 1969-70, 72-73, 73-74.
Northern Division Two 1994-95.

10 YEAR RECORD

	08-09	09-10	10-11	11-12	12-13	13-14	14-15	15-16	16-17	17-18
NL 2	14	10	6	15	16	8	8	12	6	3
FAC	P	EP	EP	EP			P	EP		
FAV	1Qr	2P	1Q	1Q		4P	2P	2Q	1Q	1P

WHITLEY BAY
Founded: 1897   Nickname: The Seahorses

Club Contact Details (T) 0191 291 3637   (E) dbreakwell@hotmail.co.uk
Ground: Hillheads Park, Rink Way, Whitley Bay NE25 8HR
Nearest Railway Station Monkseaton - 768m
Capacity: 4,500 **Seats:** 450   **Covered:** 650   **Shop:** Yes   **Bus Route** Whitley Bay Ice Rink - stop 149m away

Colours(change): Royal blue & white
Previous Names: Whitley Bay Athletic 1950-58
Previous Leagues: Tyneside 1909-10, Northern Alliance 1950-55, North Eastern 1955-58, Northern 1958-88. Northern Premier League 1988-00.

HONOURS: FA Comps: FA Vase 2001-02, 08-09, 09-10, 10-11.
League: Northern Alliance 1952-53, 53-54. Northern 1964-65, 65-66, 06-07.
Northern Premier League Division One 1990-91.

10 YEAR RECORD

	08-09	09-10	10-11	11-12	12-13	13-14	14-15	15-16	16-17	17-18
NL 1	3	3	3	6	3	10	15	16	6	16
FAC	3Q	1Q	3Q	1Q	P	EP	EPr	3Q	EPr	1Q
FAV	F	F	F	5P	4P	3P	3P	2P	2Q	3P

BEDLINGTON TERRIERS

Founded: 1949   Nickname: Terriers

Club Contact Details (T) 07935 840 277   (E)

Ground: Doctor Pitt Welfare Park, Park Road, Bedlington NE22 5DP   **Capacity:** 3,000

Nearest Railway Station Cramlington - 5km   **Bus Route** Allgood Terrace - stop 216m away

HONOURS   **League:** Northern Combination 1954-55. Northern Alliance 1966-67.

FA Comps: None   Northern DivisioN Two 1993-94, Division One 97-98, 98-99, 99-00, 2000-01, 01-02.

Colours(change): All red.

10 YEAR RECORD

	08-09	09-10	10-11	11-12	12-13	13-14	14-15	15-16	16-17	17-18
NL	NL 1 14	NL 1 7	NL 1 9	NL 1 7	NL 1 15	NL 1 20	NL 1 17	NL 1 22	NL 2 12	NL 2 16
FAC	FAC 1Q	FAC P	FAC EP	FAC 2Q	FAC 1Q			FAC EPr	FAC EP	
FAV	FAV 1Pr	FAV 2P	FAV 1P	FAV 2P	FAV 2P			FAV 2Q	FAV 1Q	FAV 2P

BILLINGHAM SYNTHONIA

Founded: 1923   Nickname: Synners

Club Contact Details (T) 01642 530 203   (E)

Ground: Norton (Teesside) Sports Complex, Station Road, Norton TS20 1PE   **Capacity:** 2,000

Nearest Railway Station Billingham - 2.7km   **Bus Route** Jameson Road - stop 400m away

HONOURS   **League:** Teeside 1936-37.

FA Comps: None   Northern 1956-57, 88-89, 89-90, 95-96. Division Two 86-87.

Colours(change): Green & white

10 YEAR RECORD

	08-09	09-10	10-11	11-12	12-13	13-14	14-15	15-16	16-17	17-18
NL	NL 1 15	NL 1 12	NL 1 12	NL 1 11	NL 1 12	NL 1 20	NL 1 20	NL 2 5	NL 2 3	NL 1 22
FAC	FAC P	FAC P	FAC P	FAC P	FAC EP	FAC Pr	FAC EP	FAC EPr	FAC 1Qr	FAC EP
FAV	FAV 1Q	FAV 2Qr	FAV 5P	FAV 5Pr	FAV 3P	FAV 3P	FAV 1P	FAV 2Q	FAV 1P	FAV 2Qr

BILLINGHAM TOWN

Founded: 1967   Nickname: Billy Town

Club Contact Details (T)   (E)

Ground: Bedford Terrace, Billingham, Cleveland TS23 4AE   **Capacity:** 3,000

Nearest Railway Station Billingham - 0.4km   **Bus Route** Warwick Crescent - stop 136m away

HONOURS   **League:** Stockton & District Division Two 1968-69. Teesside 1978-79, 81-82.

FA Comps: None

Colours(change): All blue & white

10 YEAR RECORD

	08-09	09-10	10-11	11-12	12-13	13-14	14-15	15-16	16-17	17-18
NL	NL 1 17	NL 1 19	NL 1 15	NL 1 17	NL 1 20	NL 1 23	NL 2 18	NL 2 11	NL 2 5	NL 2 9
FAC	FAC P	FAC EP	FAC EP	FAC P	FAC P	FAC EP	FAC EP			FAC EP
FAV	FAV 2Q	FAV 1Q	FAV 1P	FAV 2P	FAV 1Q	FAV 2Qr	FAV 2Q	FAV 1Q	FAV 4P	FAV 2P

BIRTLEY TOWN

Founded: 1993   Nickname: The Hoops

Club Contact Details (T)   (E)

Ground: Birtley Sports Complex, Durham Road, Birtley DH3 2TB

HONOURS   **League:** Wearside Division Two 1994-95, Division One 2002-03, 06-07.

FA Comps: None

Colours(change): Green & white

10 YEAR RECORD

	08-09	09-10	10-11	11-12	12-13	13-14	14-15	15-16	16-17	17-18
NL	NL 2 8	NL 2 20	NL 2 13	NL 2 6	NL 2 17	NL 2 13	NL 2 17	NL 2 21	NAI P 8	NAI P 2
FAC		FAC EPr		FAC EP	FAC P					
FAV	FAV 2Q	FAV 2Q	FAV 1P	FAV 2Q	FAV 1Q	FAV 2Q	FAV 2Q	FAV 1Q	FAV 2Q	

BRANDON UNITED

Founded: 1968   Nickname: United

Club Contact Details (T) 07555 586 305   (E)

Ground: Welfare Park, Rear Commercial Street, Brandon DH7 8PL

Nearest Railway Station Durham - 4.4km   **Bus Route** S Lukes Church - stop 52m away

HONOURS   **League:** Durham & District Sunday Div.2 1969-70, Div.1 73-74, 74-75, 75-76, 76-77.

FA Comps: None   Northern Alliance Div.2 77-78, 78-79. Northern 2002-03, Div.2 84-85, 99-2000.

Colours(change): All red.

10 YEAR RECORD

	08-09	09-10	10-11	11-12	12-13	13-14	14-15	15-16	16-17	17-18
NL	NL 2 6	NL 2 15	NL 2 19	NL 2 17	NL 2 18	NL 2 19	NL 2 22	NL 2 15	NL 2 14	NL 2 19
FAC	FAC EPr	FAC P	FAC EP							
FAV	FAV 2Q	FAV 1Q	FAV 2Q	FAV 2Q	FAV 1Q		FAV 1Q	FAV 1Q	FAV 1Q	FAV 1Q

CHESTER-LE-STREET TOWN
Founded: 1972 **Nickname:** Cestrians

Club Contact Details (T) 0191 388 7283 **(E)**
Ground: Moor Park, Chester Moor, Chester-le-Street, Co.Durham DH2 3RW
Nearest Railway Station Chester-le-Street - 2.2km **Bus Route** Inn (A167) - stop 69m away
HONOURS **League:** Washington 1975-76. Wearside 1980-81.
FA Comps: None Northern Division Two 1983-84, 97-98.
Colours(change): Blue & white

10 YEAR RECORD
08-09	09-10	10-11	11-12	12-13	13-14	14-15	15-16	16-17	17-18
NL 1 13	NL 1 20	NL 2 8	NL 2 12	NL 2 13	NL 2 11	NL 2 13	NL 2 3	NL 1 21	NL 2 14
FAC EP	FAC P	FAC 1Q	FAC EPr	FAC EPr				FAC P	FAC EP
FAV 2Q	FAV 2Q	FAV 2Q	FAV 1Q	FAV 2Q	FAV 1Q	FAV 2Q	FAV 1P	FAV 2P	FAV 1Q

CROOK TOWN
Founded: 1889 **Nickname:** Black & Ambers

Club Contact Details (T) 01388 762 959 **(E)**
Ground: The Sir Tom Cowie Millfield, West Road, Crook, Co.Durham DL15 9PW **Capacity:** 1,500
Bus Route Bus stops right outside the ground
HONOURS **League:** Northern 1914-15, 26-27, 52-53, 58-59, 62-63, Division Two 2012-13.
FA Comps: FA Am C 00-01,53-54,
Colours(change): Amber and black

10 YEAR RECORD
08-09	09-10	10-11	11-12	12-13	13-14	14-15	15-16	16-17	17-18
NL 2 9	NL 2 13	NL 2 12	NL 2 10	NL 2 1	NL 1 15	NL 1 22	NL 2 18	NL 2 17	NL 2 18
FAC 1Q	FAC EP	FAC P	FAC EP	FAC Pr	FAC 1Q	FAC EP	FAC EP		
FAV 1P	FAV 3P	FAV 2Q	FAV 2P	FAV 1Q	FAV 2P	FAV 2Q	FAV 2Q	FAV 1Q	FAV 2Q

DURHAM CITY
Founded: 1949 **Nickname:** City

Club Contact Details (T) 01388 745 912 **(E)**
Ground: Hall Lane, Willington, County Durham DL15 0QG
Bus Route Mortons Garage - stop 174m away
HONOURS **League:** Northern 1994-95, 2007-08, Division Two 98-99.
FA Comps: None Northern Premier Division One North 2008-09.
Colours(change): Yellow/blue/yellow

10 YEAR RECORD
08-09	09-10	10-11	11-12	12-13	13-14	14-15	15-16	16-17	17-18
NP1N 1	NP P 20	NP1N 17	NP1N 9	NL 1 14	NL 1 9	NL 1 12	NL 1 20	NL 2 10	NL 2 11
FAC 4Qr	FAC 1Qr	FAC 1Q	FAC P	FAC 1Q	FAC Pr	FAC P	FAC EP	FAC EP	
FAT 2Pr	FAT 1Q	FAT 1Q	FAT 2Qr	FAV 1P	FAV 2Q	FAV 2Q	FAV 1P	FAV 1Q	FAV 2Q

EASINGTON COLLIERY
Founded: 1913 **Nickname:** The Colliery

Club Contact Details (T) **(E)**
Ground: Memorial Avenue, Seaside Lane, Easington Colliery SR8 3PL
Bus Route Black Diamond - stop 43m away
HONOURS **League:** Wearside 1929-30, 31-32, 32-33, 47-48, 48-49.
FA Comps: None
Colours(change): All green

10 YEAR RECORD
08-09	09-10	10-11	11-12	12-13	13-14	14-15	15-16	16-17	17-18
Wear 3	Wear 7	Wear 2	NL 2 22	Wear 21	Wear 6	Wear 2	NL 2 6	NL 2 7	NL 2 10
								FAC EP	
FAV 1Q	FAV 2Q	FAV 1P	FAV 2Q				FAV 2Q	FAV 1P	FAV 1Q

ESH WINNING
Founded: 1885 **Nickname:** Stags

Club Contact Details (T) 07432 648 072 **(E)**
Ground: West Terrace, Waterhouse, Durham DH7 9BQ **Capacity:** 3,500
Bus Route Church (Russell St) - stop 158m away
HONOURS **League:** Northern 1912-13.
FA Comps: None Durham & District Sunday 1978-79, 79-80, Division Two 72-73.
Colours(change): Yellow and green

10 YEAR RECORD
08-09	09-10	10-11	11-12	12-13	13-14	14-15	15-16	16-17	17-18
NL 2 3	NL 1 18	NL 1 21	NL 2 11	NL 2 20	NL 2 22	NL 2 20	NL 2 20	NL 2 21	NL 2 13
FAC EP	FAC EPr	FAC EP	FAC EP	FAC P					
FAV 1P	FAV 2Qr	FAV 2Q	FAV 2P	FAV 2P	FAV 1Q	FAV 2Q	FAV 1Q	FAV 2Q	FAV 1Q

HEATON STANNINGTON
Founded: 1910   Nickname: The Stan

Club Contact Details (T) 0191 281 9230   (E)
Ground: Grounsell Park, Newton Road, High Heaton, Newcastle upon Tyne NE7 7HP
Nearest Railway Station Longbenton - 1.2km   **Bus Route** No.38 stops at the ground
HONOURS   **League:** Northern Amateur 1936-37, 85-86. Tyneside Amateur 1983-84.
FA Comps: None   Northern Alliance Premier Division 2011-12, 12-13.
Colours(change): Black & white stripes

10 YEAR RECORD

08-09	09-10	10-11	11-12	12-13	13-14	14-15	15-16	16-17	17-18
NAI P 8	NAI P 7	NAI P 5	NAI P 1	NAI P 1	NL 2 5	NL 2 9	NL 2 9	NL 2 4	NL 2 5
							FAC P	FAC EP	FAC P
						FAV 2Q	FAV 2Q	FAV 2Q	FAV 1Q

JARROW
Founded: 1894   Nickname:

Club Contact Details (T) 0191 489 3743   (E)
Ground: Perth Green Community Assoc., Inverness Road, Jarrow NE32 4AQ
Nearest Railway Station Brockley Whins - 530m   **Bus Route** Inverness Road-youth club - stop 75m away
HONOURS   **League:** Northern Alliance 1898-99. Wearside 2016-17.
FA Comps: None
Colours(change): Royal blue & white

10 YEAR RECORD

08-09	09-10	10-11	11-12	12-13	13-14	14-15	15-16	16-17	17-18
Wear 5	Wear 10	Wear 5	Wear 6	Wear 9	Wear 10	Wear 12	Wear 8	Wear 1	NL 2 12

NORTHALLERTON TOWN
Founded: 1994   Nickname: Town

Club Contact Details (T) 01609 778 337   (E)
Ground: The Calvert Stadium, Ainderby Road, Northallerton DL7 8HA
Nearest Railway Station Northallerton - 0.3km   **Bus Route** Chantry Road - stop 81m away
HONOURS   **League:** Northern Division Two 1996-97.
FA Comps: None
Colours(change): Black & white

10 YEAR RECORD

08-09	09-10	10-11	11-12	12-13	13-14	14-15	15-16	16-17	17-18
NL 1 22	NL 2 8	NL 2 9	NL 2 9	NL 2 6	NL 2 7	NL 2 10	NL 2 8	NL 2 9	NL 2 4
FAC EP	FAC EPr	FAC 1Q	FAC P	FAC EP	FAC EP	FAC P		FAC P	
FAV 1Q	FAV 1P	FAV 1P	FAV 2Q	FAV 1Pr	FAV 1Q	FAV 1Q	FAV 1Q	FAV 2Q	FAV 2Q

REDCAR ATHLETIC
Founded: 1993   Nickname:

Club Contact Details (T) 01642 470 963   (E)
Ground: Green Lane, Redcar TS10 3RW

HONOURS   **League:** Wearside 2017-18.
FA Comps: None
Colours(change): Red and navy

10 YEAR RECORD

08-09	09-10	10-11	11-12	12-13	13-14	14-15	15-16	16-17	17-18
Wear 4	Wear 3	Wear 4	Wear 2	Wear 5	Wear 3	Wear 4	Wear 2	Wear 2	Wear 1

RYTON & CRAWCROOK ALBION
Founded: 1970   Nickname: The Albion

Club Contact Details (T) 0191 413 4448   (E)
Ground: Kingsley Park, Stannerford Road, Crawcrook NE40 3SN   **Capacity:** 2,000
Nearest Railway Station Wylam - 1.5km   **Bus Route** Stannerford Road - stop 121m away
HONOURS   **League:** Northern Alliance Division One 1996-97.
FA Comps: None
Colours(change): Black & royal blue

10 YEAR RECORD

08-09	09-10	10-11	11-12	12-13	13-14	14-15	15-16	16-17	17-18
NL 1 10	NL 1 10	NL 1 22	NL 2 18	NL 2 14	NL 2 21	NL 2 12	NL 2 16	NL 2 20	NL 2 17
FAC 1Q	FAC 1Q	FAC EP	FAC EP						
FAV 2Pr	FAV 2Q	FAV 2Q	FAV 2Q	FAV 2Q	FAV 2Q	FAV 1Qr	FAV 1Q	FAV 2Q	FAV 1Q

THORNABY

Founded: 1980   Nickname: The Blues

Club Contact Details (T) 01642 672 896   **(E)**
Ground: Teesdale Park, Acklam Road, Thornaby, Stockton on Tees TS17 7JU
Nearest Railway Station Thornaby - 1.2km   **Bus Route** Millfield Close - stop 143m away
HONOURS   **League:** Northern Division Two 1987-88, 91-92.
FA Comps: None
Colours(change): All blue

10 YEAR RECORD

08-09		09-10		10-11		11-12		12-13		13-14		14-15		15-16		16-17		17-18	
NL 2	20	NL 2	17	NL 2	14	NL 2	19	NL 2	19	NL 2	14	NL 2	7	NL 2	7	NL 2	16	NL 2	6
FAC	EP													FAC	EP	FAC	EP		
FAV	2Q	FAV	2Q	FAV	1Q	FAV	1Q	FAV	1Q	FAV	1Q	FAV	1Q	FAV	1Q	FAV	1Q	FAV	2P

TOW LAW TOWN

Founded: 1890   Nickname: Lawyers

Club Contact Details (T) 01388 731 443   **(E)**
Ground: Ironworks Ground, Tow Law, Bishop Auckland DL13 4EQ   **Capacity:** 3,000
Nearest Railway Station Wolsingham - 4.8km   **Bus Route** Mart (Castle Bank) - stop 241m away
HONOURS   **League:** Northern 1923-24, 24-25, 94-95.
FA Comps: None
Colours(change): Black & white stripes

10 YEAR RECORD

08-09		09-10		10-11		11-12		12-13		13-14		14-15		15-16		16-17		17-18	
NL 1	11	NL 1	9	NL 1	18	NL 1	21	NL 2	11	NL 2	10	NL 2	21	NL 2	14	NL 2	13	NL 2	8
FAC	P	FAC	EPr	FAC	EP	FAC	EP	FAC	EP	FAC	EP								
FAV	2Q	FAV	1P	FAV	1P	FAV	2Q	FAV	1Q	FAV	1Q	FAV	1Q	FAV	2Q	FAV	1Q	FAV	2P

WASHINGTON

Founded: 1947   Nickname: Mechanics

Club Contact Details (T)   **(E)**
Ground: Nissan Sports Complex, Washington Road Sunderland SR5 3NS   **Capacity:** 1,000
Nearest Railway Station East Boldon - 4.2km   **Bus Route** Ferryboat Lane - 453m away
HONOURS   **League:** North Eastern Division Two 1927-28. Washington Amateur 1955-56, 56-57,57-58, 58-59, 59-60, 61 -62,62-63.
FA Comps: None
Colours(change): All red

10 YEAR RECORD

08-09		09-10		10-11		11-12		12-13		13-14		14-15		15-16		16-17		17-18	
NL 2	7	NL 2	18	NL 2	16	NL 2	14	NL 2	12	NL 2	9	NL 2	2	NL 1	10	NL 1	19	NL 1	21
FAC	EPr							FAC	EP			FAC	P	FAC	2Qr	FAC	1Q	FAC	EP
FAV	1Q	FAV	1Q	FAV	1P	FAV	1Q	FAV	2Q	FAV	2Q	FAV	2Q	FAV	2Q	FAV	1Q	FAV	2Q

WEST ALLOTMENT CELTIC

Founded: 1928   Nickname: Celtic

Club Contact Details (T) 0191 250 7008   **(E)** tedilderton@gmail.com
Ground: Druid Park, Callerton Lane, Woolsington, Newcastle Upon Tyne NE13 8DF
Nearest Railway Station Callerton Parkway - 116m   **Bus Route** Bus stops 70m from the ground.
HONOURS   **League:** Northern Am. 1956-57, 57-58, 58-59, 59-60, 81-62, 82-83, Div 2: 38-39. Northern All. 1986-87, 90-91, 91-92, 97-98, 98-99, 99-2000, 01-02, 03-04. Northern Div 2 2004-05
FA Comps: None
Colours(change): Green & white

10 YEAR RECORD

08-09		09-10		10-11		11-12		12-13		13-14		14-15		15-16		16-17		17-18	
NL 1	9	NL 1	15	NL 1	20	NL 2	7	NL 2	7	NL 2	2	NL 1	19	NL 1	19	NL 1	22	NL 2	15
FAC	P	FAC	Pr	FAC	EP	FAC	EPr	FAC	P	FAC	EP	FAC	1Q	FAC	EP	FAC	EP	FAC	EP
FAV	1P	FAV	2Q	FAV	2Q	FAV	1Q	FAV	1Q	FAV	2Q	FAV	1P	FAV	2Q	FAV	1Q	FAV	1Q

WILLINGTON

Founded: 1906   Nickname: The Blue & Whites

Club Contact Details (T) 01388 745 912   **(E)** richtrem@icloud.com
Ground: Hall Lane, Willington, Co. Durham DL15 0QG   **Capacity:** 7,000
    Bus Route Police House - stop 129m away
HONOURS   **League:** Northern 1913-14, 25-26, 29-30.
FA Comps: FA Amateur Cup
Colours(change): Blue & white

10 YEAR RECORD

08-09		09-10		10-11		11-12		12-13		13-14		14-15		15-16		16-17		17-18	
Wear	19	Wear	19	Wear	14	Wear	5	Wear	2	NL 2	15	NL 2	11	NL 2	19	NL 2	18	NL 2	7
FAV	1Q	FAV	2Q	FAV	1Q	FAV	2Q	FAV	2Q	FAV	1Q	FAV	1Q	FAV	1Q	FAV	1Q	FAV	2Q

SOUTH WEST PENINSULA LEAGUE

Founded: 2007 **Sponsored by:** Carlsberg

Recent Champions: 2015: St Austell **2016:** Bodmin Town **2017:** Tavistock

PREMIER DIVISION

		P	W	D	L	F	A	GD	Pts
1	Plymouth Parkway	38	34	3	1	147	25	122	105
2	Tavistock	38	30	4	4	151	41	110	94
3	Falmouth Town	38	26	4	8	97	49	48	84*
4	Saltash United	38	24	7	7	127	55	72	79
5	Bodmin Town	38	24	7	7	96	50	46	79
6	St Austell	38	21	3	14	102	78	24	66
7	Launceston	38	20	5	13	89	54	35	65
8	Plymouth Argyle Res	38	20	7	11	113	58	55	64*
9	Helston Athletic	38	15	4	19	72	83	-11	49
10	Camelford	38	14	4	20	60	94	-34	46
11	Torpoint Athletic	38	12	9	17	63	77	-14	45
12	Stoke Gabriel	38	15	3	20	62	94	-32	45*
13	Cullompton Rangers	38	13	5	20	60	91	-31	44
14	Newquay	38	13	3	22	61	73	-12	42
15	Sticker	38	10	8	20	52	83	-31	38
16	Exmouth Town	38	10	7	21	48	91	-43	37
17	Godolphin Atlantic	38	10	6	22	59	116	-57	36
18	Ivybridge Town	38	10	5	23	52	92	-40	35
19	Callington Town	38	5	5	28	45	127	-82	20
20	Witheridge	38	2	5	31	34	159	-125	7*

DIVISION ONE EAST

		P	W	D	L	F	A	GD	Pts
1	St Martins	32	26	1	5	84	34	50	79
2	Newton Abbot Spurs	32	25	2	5	83	26	57	77
3	Bovey Tracey	32	20	1	11	70	54	16	61
4	Budleigh Salterton	32	18	4	10	89	47	42	58
5	University of Exeter	32	16	5	11	79	59	20	53
6	Crediton United	32	16	5	11	57	46	11	53
7	IlfracombeTown	32	15	5	12	52	54	-2	50
8	Torrideside AFC	32	15	4	13	67	56	11	49
9	Teignmouth	32	14	5	13	78	62	16	47
10	Axminster Town AFC	32	12	5	15	59	69	-10	41
11	Sidmouth Town	32	10	7	15	62	67	-5	37
12	Appledore AFC	32	10	6	16	49	73	-24	36
13	Brixham	32	8	10	14	48	65	-17	31*
14	Honiton Town	32	8	5	19	54	87	-33	29
15	Alphington AFC	32	7	6	19	43	82	-39	27
16	Galmpton & Roselands	32	8	2	22	43	70	-27	26
17	Liverton United	32	6	3	23	34	100	-66	21

DIVISION ONE WEST

		P	W	D	L	F	A	GD	Pts
1	Millbrook	32	21	7	4	100	40	60	70
2	Ludgvan	32	22	3	7	83	45	38	69
3	Elburton Villa	32	19	7	6	79	40	39	64
4	Mousehole	32	19	5	8	82	51	31	62
5	Liskeard Athletic	32	18	6	8	92	45	47	60
6	Porthleven	32	18	6	8	74	51	23	60
7	St Blazey	32	16	4	12	66	59	7	52
8	St Dennis	32	14	6	12	66	92	-26	48
9	Wadebridge Town	32	11	7	14	73	63	10	40
10	Penzance	32	12	4	16	83	78	5	40
11	Holsworthy	32	9	7	16	51	67	-16	34
12	Plymouth Marjons	32	9	5	18	43	59	-16	32
13	Wendron United	32	8	7	17	48	90	-42	31
14	Dobwalls	32	10	1	21	52	99	-47	31
15	Bude Town AFC	32	8	2	22	43	99	-56	26
16	Plymstock United	32	6	7	19	47	83	-36	25
17	Illogan RBL	32	6	8	18	43	64	-21	20*

PREMIER DIVISION

		1	2	3	4	5	6	7	8	9	10	11	12	13	14	15	16	17	18	19	20
1	Bodmin Town		4-3	3-2	2-1	1-1	0-4	5-1	4-0	1-1	1-0	2-1	2-2	1-1	1-2	4-1	1-0	7-1	0-3	1-1	8-0
2	Callington Town	1-6		3-4	4-0	1-1	2-6	2-3	1-3	2-5	1-4	0-2	1-0	1-7	2-2	0-7	0-2	1-2	2-4	1-2	5-2
3	Camelford	0-2	2-1		1-0	2-1	1-4	3-0	0-4	1-2	1-6	7-4	1-1	1-0	0-5	0-4	3-3	3-2	0-2	4-2	4-2
4	Cullompton Rangers	2-0	3-2	2-1		1-3	5-2	3-5	2-2	1-0	2-1	1-3	4-3	0-6	1-4	2-4	2-2	2-0	0-3	0-1	2-0
5	Exmouth Town	3-4	1-1	1-4	0-3		0-4	2-2	2-1	2-1	1-5	2-3	1-4	0-8	2-4	3-0	0-2	2-1	0-5	3-0	4-0
6	Falmouth Town	3-1	1-0	4-1	5-1	0-1		2-1	3-1	2-1	1-0	3-0	0-1	1-2	4-3	3-0	3-1	5-1	0-7	2-0	0-0
7	Godolphin Atlantic	1-2	4-0	5-1	3-2	0-2	3-3		1-3	7-1	1-3	3-0	1-4	0-11	1-1	2-3	2-1	1-2	0-6	1-1	3-0
8	Helston Athletic	1-2	3-0	2-1	1-2	5-1	0-2	4-0		1-1	4-1	3-2	1-4	0-1	0-2	1-4	2-1	1-2	0-4	4-1	2-0
9	Ivybridge Town	0-2	1-1	1-2	2-0	0-2	0-5	3-0	1-1		0-2	0-1	1-2	1-5	2-4	0-1	2-1	5-1	0-8	1-1	5-1
10	Launceston	1-2	3-0	3-1	1-0	3-0	0-0	6-1	5-3	2-1		2-0	7-0	0-2	1-3	1-3	1-3	4-1	1-3	1-1	6-0
11	Newquay	1-3	3-1	5-1	0-1	1-0	0-1	1-1	5-1	5-1	0-1		1-2	0-3	1-1	3-0	0-1	3-2	0-2	2-1	3-3
12	Plymouth Argyle Reserves	3-3	10-0	1-1	1-3	2-0	A-W	10-0	7-0	1-2	2-0	3-1		1-3	4-3	7-3	1-1	12-0	2-4	0-1	3-2
13	Plymouth Parkway	2-1	4-1	4-0	6-0	4-1	2-1	4-0	2-0	4-1	1-0	5-1	2-2		1-0	5-1	3-1	4-0	6-2	5-1	6-1
14	Saltash United	2-4	12-0	1-0	2-0	7-0	3-0	4-1	4-2	4-3	4-4	2-1	0-0	2-4		2-2	6-1	4-1	1-5	1-2	8-1
15	St Austell	0-3	4-0	3-1	2-1	1-1	5-5	6-1	5-1	4-0	1-3	2-1	2-4	1-2	2-3		4-3	2-3	2-3	6-1	3-0
16	Sticker	0-2	1-3	1-2	2-2	2-1	1-4	1-1	2-2	1-2	5-3	2-1	2-3	0-5	0-3	0-3		H-W	0-8	0-0	1-1
17	Stoke Gabriel	1-1	5-0	1-1	5-2	1-1	3-1	2-0	4-0	2-1	0-2	1-0	1-4	0-4	0-3	2-3	3-0		1-0	5-2	3-1
18	Tavistock	2-1	0-0	4-2	3-3	4-0	0-1	6-1	4-0	9-0	3-3	5-2	1-0	2-2	1-3	5-1	2-1	6-2		3-2	11-0
19	Torpoint Athletic	2-3	3-0	5-0	6-1	1-1	1-4	5-0	0-3	0-3	1-1	3-2	2-0	0-7	1-1	0-2	0-1	5-1	2-5		6-2
20	Witheridge	0-6	1-2	0-1	3-3	3-2	1-8	1-2	1-7	3-1	1-2	1-2	1-7	0-4	0-11	1-5	1-6	0-1	0-6	0-0	

WALTER C PARSON CUP

HOLDERS: ST AUSTELL

ROUND 1

St Austell	Bye		
Falmouth Town	v	Helston Athletic	2-0
Torridgeside AFC	v	Honiton Town	3-0
Alphington AFC	v	Axminster Town	0-1
Callington Town	v	Torpoint Athletic	1-2
Liverton United	v	Elburton Villa	3-2
Sidmouth Town	v	Crediton United	3-2
Stoke Gabriel	v	Witheridge	4-3
Plymouth Argyle Res	Bye		
Totnes & Dartington	v	Millbrook	AW
Godolphin Atlantic	v	Wadebridge Town	3-2
Penryn Athletic	v	Illogan RBL	AW
Dobwalls	v	Newton Abbot Spurs	1-5
Plymstock United	v	Plymouth Marjons	3-1
Ilfracombe Town	v	Budleigh Salterton	2-2, 4-3p
Appledore AFC	v	University of Exeter	1-6
Ludgvan	v	Mousehole	2-3
Wendron United	v	Camelford	2-4
Launceston	v	Brixham	2-1
Saltash United	Bye		
Holsworthy	v	St Martins	3-2
Bude Town	v	Teignmouth	0-5
Penzance	v	St Blazey	2-1
St Dennis	v	Newquay	2-1
Sticker	v	Porthleven	0-1
Bodmin Town	Bye		
Tavistock	Bye		
Ivybridge Town	v	Bovey Tracey	3-0
Exmouth Town	Bye		
Cullompton Rangers	Bye		
Plymouth Parkway	Bye		
Galmpton & Roselands	v	Liskeard Athletic	5-3

ROUND 2

St Austell	v	Falmouth Town	1-3
Torridgeside AFC	v	Axminster Town	4-3
Torpoint Athletic	v	Liverton United	2-1
Sidmouth Town	v	Stoke Gabriel	1-2

Plymouth Argyle Res	v	Millbrook	4-3
Godolphin Atlantic	v	Illogan RBL	2-1
Newton Abbot Spurs	v	Plymstock United	3-2
Ilfracombe Town	v	University of Exeter	1-3
Mousehole	v	Camelford	1-0
Launceston	v	Saltash United	3-2
Holsworthy	v	Teignmouth	1-5
Penzance	v	St Dennis	7-5
Porthleven	v	Bodmin Town	2-4
Tavistock	v	Ivybridge Town	3-2
Exmouth Town	v	Cullompton Rangers	1-2
Plymouth Parkway	v	Galmpton & Roselands	3-1

ROUND 3

Falmouth Town	v	Torridgeside AFC	4-1
Torpoint Athletic	v	Stoke Gabriel	2-1
Plymouth Argyle Res	v	Godolphin Atlantic	2-3
Newton Abbot Spurs	v	University of Exeter	3-2
Mousehole	v	Launceston	2-1
Teignmouth	v	Penzance	4-3
Bodmin Town	v	Tavistock	0-1
Cullompton Rangers	v	Plymouth Parkway	0-5

QUARTER FINALS

Falmouth Town	v	Torpoint Athletic	2-1
Godolphin Atlantic	v	Newton Abbot Spurs	2-1
Mousehole	v	Teignmouth	2-1
Tavistock	v	Plymouth Parkway	3-2

SEMI FINALS

Falmouth Town	v	Godolphin Atlantic	4-2
Mousehole	v	Tavistock	0-2

FINAL

Falmouth Town	v	Tavistock	4-2

CLUB MOVEMENTS

Premier Division
In: Elburton Villa (P), Millbrook (P),
Out: Plymouth Parkway (P - WLP). Stoke Gabriel (R).

Division One East- In: Elmore (P - D&E), Stoke Gabriel (R), Waldon Athletic (P - SDL).

Division One West - In: Bere Alston United (P - ECL).
Out: Elburton Villa (P), Illogan RBL (R), Millbrook (P).

BODMIN TOWN
Founded: 1896   Nickname: Black & Ambers

Club Contact Details (T) 01208 78165
(E) nickgiles@live.co.uk
Ground: Priory Park, Bodmin, Cornwall PL31 2AE
Nearest Railway Station Bodmin General - 587m

HONOURS
League: Bodmin & District 1922-23, 26-27. South Western 1990-91, 93-94, 2005-06.
South West Peninsula Premier Division 2007-08, 08-09, 11-12, 12-13, 15-16.
FA Comps: None
Colours(change): Yellow & black

10 YEAR RECORD

	08-09	09-10	10-11	11-12	12-13	13-14	14-15	15-16	16-17	17-18
SWPP	1	2	2	1	1	7	2	1	3	5
FAC	P	P	1Q	3Qr	1Qr	P	1Qr	2Q	Pr	2Qr
FAV	1P	1P	4P	2Pr	5P	4P	4P	4P	3P	2P

CALLINGTON TOWN
Founded: 1989   Nickname: The Pasty Men

Club Contact Details (T) 01579 382 647
(E) womble1954@me.com
Ground: Ginsters Marshfield Parc PL17 7DR

HONOURS
League: East Cornwall Combination 1997-98, 98-99.
South West Peninsula Division One West 2013-14.
FA Comps: None
Colours(change): Red & black

10 YEAR RECORD

08-09	09-10	10-11	11-12	12-13	13-14	14-15	15-16	16-17	17-18
SW1W 5	SW1W 10	SW1W 3	SW1W 6	SW1W 5	SW1W 1	SWPP 11	SWPP 16	SWPP 15	SWPP 19

CAMELFORD
Founded: 1893   Nickname: Camels

Club Contact Details (T)
(E) hilarykent35@gmail.com
Ground: Trelew Park, PL32 9TS

HONOURS
League: South West Peninsula Division One West 2010-11.
FA Comps: None
Colours(change): Blue

10 YEAR RECORD

	08-09	09-10	10-11	11-12	12-13	13-14	14-15	15-16	16-17	17-18
	SW1W 8	SW1W 8	SW1W 1	SWPP 9	SWPP 9	SWPP 14	SWPP 17	SWPP 15	SWPP 14	SWPP 10
FAV						2Q	1Qr	1P	1Q	2Q

CULLOMPTON RANGERS
Founded: 1945   Nickname: The Cully

Club Contact Details (T) 01884 33090
(E) alanslark1@tiscali.co.uk
Ground: Speeds Meadow, Cullompton EX15 1DW

HONOURS
League: East Devon Senior Division One 1950-51, 78-79.
Devon & Exeter Premier Division 1961-62, 63-64.
FA Comps: None
Colours(change): Red & black

10 YEAR RECORD

	08-09	09-10	10-11	11-12	12-13	13-14	14-15	15-16	16-17	17-18
SWPP	8	18	16	15	17	18	12	13	9	13
FAC		EP								
FAV	1P	2Q	2Q	2P	2Q	2Q	1Q	1Q	2Pr	2P

ELBURTON VILLA
Founded: 1982   Nickname: The Villa

Club Contact Details (T) 01752 480 025
(E) pope.n@sky.com
Ground: Haye Road, Elburton, Plymouth PL9 8HS
Capacity: 2,000

HONOURS
League: Plymouth & District Division One 1990-91.
FA Comps: None
Colours(change): Red & white stripes

10 YEAR RECORD

	08-09	09-10	10-11	11-12	12-13	13-14	14-15	15-16	16-17	17-18
	SWPP 18	SWPP 13	SWPP 19	SWPP 11	SWPP 3	SWPP 12	SWPP 18	SWPP 20	SW1W 2	SW1W 3
FAV							1Q	1Q	1Q	1Q

EXMOUTH TOWN

Founded: 1933 Nickname: The Town

Club Contact Details (T) 01395 263 348 (E) brian7645@btinternet.com
Ground: King George V, Exmouth EX8 3EE
Nearest Railway Station Exmouth - 0.6km **Bus Route** Exeter Road - stop 143m away
HONOURS **League:** Western 1983-84, 85-86.
FA Comps: None South West Peninsula Division One East 2012-13.
Colours(change): All royal blue

10 YEAR RECORD

08-09	09-10	10-11	11-12	12-13	13-14	14-15	15-16	16-17	17-18
SW1E 15	SW1E 8	SW1E 11	SW1E 5	SW1E 1	SWPP 2	SWPP 8	SWPP 12	SWPP 5	SWPP 16
									FAC EP
				FAV 1P	FAV 2Q		FAV 2Q	FAV 5P	FAV 2P

FALMOUTH TOWN

Founded: 1949 Nickname: The Ambers

Club Contact Details (T) 01326 375 156 (E) pascoerichard@hotmail.com
Ground: Bickland Park, Bickland Water Road, Falmouth TR11 4PB
Nearest Railway Station Penmere - 1.3km **Bus Route** Conway Road - stop 54m away
HONOURS **League:** South Western 1961-62, 65-66, 67-68, 70-71, 71-72, 72-73, 73-74, 85-86, 86-87, 88-89, 89-90, 91-92, 96-97, 99-2000. Western 74
FA Comps: None -75, 75-76, 76-77, 77-78. Cornwall Comb 83-84.
Colours(change): Amber & black

10 YEAR RECORD

08-09	09-10	10-11	11-12	12-13	13-14	14-15	15-16	16-17	17-18
SWPP 14	SWPP 3	SWPP 5	SWPP 3	SWPP 16	SWPP 16	SWPP 16	SWPP 11	SWPP 10	SWPP 3
FAC P	FAC Pr	FAC EPr	FAC EP						
FAV 2Q	FAV 2Q	FAV 1Qr	FAV 3P			FAV 1P	FAV 1Q		

GODOLPHIN ATLANTIC AFC

Founded: 1980 Nickname: G Army

Club Contact Details (T) (E) godolphin.arms@btconnect.com
Ground: Godolphin Way, Cornwall TR7 3BU
Nearest Railway Station Newquay - 1.2km **Bus Route** Brook House Inn - stop 136m away
HONOURS **League:** South West Peninsula Division One West 2012-13.
FA Comps: None
Colours(change): Sky blue & white

10 YEAR RECORD

08-09	09-10	10-11	11-12	12-13	13-14	14-15	15-16	16-17	17-18
SW1W 11	SW1W 6	SW1W 2	SW1W 4	SW1W 1	SWPP 5	SWPP 7	SWPP 5	SWPP 13	SWPP 17
									FAV 1Q

HELSTON ATHLETIC

Founded: 1896 Nickname: The Blues

Club Contact Details (T) 01326 573742 (Clubhouse) (E) paul.m.hendy@btinternet.com
Ground: Kellaway Park, Helston TR13 8PJ
 Bus Route Tesco - stop 101m away
HONOURS **League:** Cornwall Senior 1936-37, 37-38, 39-40. Cornwall Comb. 87-88, 2000-01, 10-11. South West
FA Comps: None Peninsula Division One West 2014-15.
Colours(change): All blue & white

10 YEAR RECORD

08-09	09-10	10-11	11-12	12-13	13-14	14-15	15-16	16-17	17-18
CornC 4	CornC 5	CornC 1	SW1W 2	SW1W 2	SW1W 3	SW1W 1	SWPP 10	SWPP 16	SWPP 9
								FAV 1P	FAV 1Q

IVYBRIDGE TOWN

Founded: 1925 Nickname: The Ivys

Club Contact Details (T) 01752 896 686 (E) secretary@ivybridgefc.com
Ground: Erme Valley, Ermington Road, Ivybridge PL21 9ES
Nearest Railway Station Ivybridge - 1.8km **Bus Route** Community Centre - stop 251m away
HONOURS **League:** Devon County 2005-06.
FA Comps: None
Colours(change): Green & black

10 YEAR RECORD

08-09	09-10	10-11	11-12	12-13	13-14	14-15	15-16	16-17	17-18
SWPP 4	SWPP 12	SWPP 7	SWPP 19	SWPP 13	SWPP 4	SWPP 4	SWPP 9	SWPP 17	SWPP 18
							FAV 2Q	FAV 1Q	FAV 1P

LAUNCESTON

Founded: 1891   Nickname: The Clarets

Club Contact Details (T) 01566 773 279
(E) launcestonfc@aol.com
Ground: Pennygillam Ind. Est., Launceston PL15 7ED

HONOURS   **League:** South Western 1994-95.
FA Comps: None

Colours(change): All claret

10 YEAR RECORD

08-09	09-10	10-11	11-12	12-13	13-14	14-15	15-16	16-17	17-18
SWPP 10	SWPP 11	SWPP 11	SWPP 5	SWPP 5	SWPP 8	SWPP 10	SWPP 14	SWPP 11	SWPP 7
FAC P	FAC P	FAC EP							
FAV 1P	FAV 2Q	FAV 2Q							

MILLBROOK AFC

Founded: 1888   Nickname: Magpies / Brook

Club Contact Details (T) 01752 822 113
(E) shaunhall86@hotmail.co.uk
Ground: Jenkins Park PL10 1EN

HONOURS   **League:** South West Peninsula Division One West 2017-18.
FA Comps: None

Colours(change): Black & white stripes

10 YEAR RECORD

08-09	09-10	10-11	11-12	12-13	13-14	14-15	15-16	16-17	17-18
SW1W 17	SW1W 15	EC1 5	EC1 2	ECP 6	ECP 3	SW1W 15	SW1W 13	SW1W 4	SW1W 1

NEWQUAY

Founded: 1890   Nickname: The Peppermints

Club Contact Details (T) 01637 872 935
(E) ruth_terry@btinternet.com
Ground: Mount Wise TR7 2BU

Nearest Railway Station Newquay - 0.8km   **Bus Route** Windsor Court - stop 117m away
HONOURS   **League:** South Western 1958-59, 59-60, 77-78, 79-80, 81-82, 83-84, 87-88.
FA Comps: None   South West Peninsula Division One West 2011-12.

Colours(change): Red & white (Blue & white)

10 YEAR RECORD

08-09	09-10	10-11	11-12	12-13	13-14	14-15	15-16	16-17	17-18
SW1W 2	SW1W 5	SW1W 9	SW1W 1	SWPP 12	SWPP 11	SWPP 15	SWPP 18	SWPP 19	SWPP 14
FAV 1Q	FAV 1P	FAV 1P			FAV EP	FAV 1P	FAV 2Q		

PLYMOUTH ARGYLE RESERVES

Founded: 1886   Nickname: The Pilgrims

Club Contact Details (T)
(E) chippycarps@gmail.com
Ground: Coach Road TQ12 1EJ

Nearest Railway Station Newton Abbot - 0.9km   **Bus Route** Decoy Road - stop 373m away
HONOURS   **League:** None
FA Comps: None

Colours(change): Green & white

10 YEAR RECORD

08-09	09-10	10-11	11-12	12-13	13-14	14-15	15-16	16-17	17-18
							SW1W 2	SWPP 6	SWPP 6

SALTASH UNITED

Founded: 1945   Nickname: The Ashes

Club Contact Details (T) 01752 845 746
(E) cooksleyscott@gmail.com
Ground: Kimberley Stadium, Callington Road, Saltash PL12 6DX

Nearest Railway Station Saltash - 0.9km   **Bus Route** Callington Road St Annes - stop 40m away
HONOURS   **League:** South Western 1953-54, 75-76. Western Division One 1976-77, Premier 1984-85, 86-87, 88-89.
FA Comps: None

Colours(change): Red & white stripes

10 YEAR RECORD

08-09	09-10	10-11	11-12	12-13	13-14	14-15	15-16	16-17	17-18
SWPP 5	SWPP 9	SWPP 6	SWPP 4	SWPP 6	SWPP 3	SWPP 3	SWPP 6	SWPP 2	SWPP 4
FAC EPr	FAC 1Qr	FAC EPr	FAC EP	FAC EP	FAC EP	FAC 1Q	FAC EP		
FAV 2P	FAV 2P	FAV 2P	FAV 2P	FAV 1P	FAV 3P	FAV 1P	FAV 1Q		FAV 2Q

ST. AUSTELL

Founded: 1890 Nickname: The Lily Whites

Club Contact Details (T) 01726 66099 (E) hotspurs403@gmail.com
Ground: Poltair Park, Trevarthian Road, St Austell PL25 4LR
Nearest Railway Station St Austell - 0.3km **Bus Route** Poltair Road - stop 33m away
HONOURS League: South Western 1968-69. South West Peninsula Premier 2014-15.
FA Comps: None
Colours(change): All white

10 YEAR RECORD

08-09	09-10	10-11	11-12	12-13	13-14	14-15	15-16	16-17	17-18
SW1W 3	SW1W 2	SWPP 10	SWPP 8	SWPP 4	SWPP 9	SWPP 1	SWPP 2	SWPP 4	SWPP 6
					FAC EP	FAC P	FAC P	FAC EPr	FAC EPr
				FAV 2P	FAV 1Q	FAV SF	FAV 2P	FAV 2Q	FAV 2Q

STICKER

Founded: 1911 Nickname: The Sticky

Club Contact Details (T) 01726 71003 (E) chrisjohnosborne@aol.com
Ground: Burngullow Park PL26 7EN
Nearest Railway Station St Austell - 4.4km **Bus Route** Hewas Inn (Fore St) - stop 1.1km away
HONOURS League: South West Peninsula Division One West 2016-17.
FA Comps: None
Colours(change): Yellow and blue

10 YEAR RECORD

08-09	09-10	10-11	11-12	12-13	13-14	14-15	15-16	16-17	17-18
ECP 4	ECP 8	ECP 3	ECP 2	SW1W 4	SW1W 4	SW1W 5	SW1W 3	SW1W 1	SWPP 15

TAVISTOCK

Founded: 1888 Nickname: The Lambs

Club Contact Details (T) 01822 614 447 (E) secretary@tavistockfc.com
Ground: Langsford Park, Red & Black Club, Crowndale Road, Tavistock PL19 8JR
Nearest Railway Station Gunnislake - 4.9km **Bus Route** Canons Way - stop 694m away
HONOURS League: Devon 1900-01. Plymouth Combination Division One 1950-51.
FA Comps: None South West Peninsula League Division One East 2014-15, Premier 16-17.
Colours(change): Red & black

10 YEAR RECORD

08-09	09-10	10-11	11-12	12-13	13-14	14-15	15-16	16-17	17-18
SWPP 6	SWPP 5	SWPP 13	SWPP 10	SWPP 10	SWPP 19	SW1E 1	SWPP 3	SWPP 1	SWPP 2
FAC P	FAC EP	FAC P	FAC 1Q	FAC EP	FAC EP				FAC 2Q
FAV 1P	FAV 2P	FAV 1P	FAV 1P	FAV 1Q	FAV 2P	FAV 1Q		FAV 1P	FAV 2P

TORPOINT ATHLETIC

Founded: 1887 Nickname: The Point

Club Contact Details (T) 01752 812 889 (E) robbietafc81@live.co.uk
Ground: The Mill, Mill Lane, Carbeile Road, Torpoint PL11 2RE
Nearest Railway Station Dockyard (plymouth) - 2.5km **Bus Route** Carbeile Inn - stop 338m away
HONOURS League: South Western 1964-65, 66-67.
FA Comps: None
Colours(change): Yellow & black

10 YEAR RECORD

08-09	09-10	10-11	11-12	12-13	13-14	14-15	15-16	16-17	17-18
SWPP 9	SWPP 8	SWPP 4	SWPP 12	SWPP 14	SWPP 10	SWPP 13	SWPP 8	SWPP 12	SWPP 11
		FAC 1Q	FAC P	FAC EP					
		FAV 2Q	FAV QF	FAV 2P	FAV 1Q	FAV 2Q	FAV 2P	FAV 3P	FAV 1Q

WITHERIDGE

Founded: 1920 Nickname: The Withy

Club Contact Details (T) 01884 861 511 (E) chriscole128@hotmail.com
Ground: Edge Down Park, Fore Street, Witheridge EX16 8AH
Bus Route School (B3137) - stop 174m away
HONOURS League: None
FA Comps: None
Colours(change): All blue

10 YEAR RECORD

08-09	09-10	10-11	11-12	12-13	13-14	14-15	15-16	16-17	17-18
SWPP 11	SWPP 10	SWPP 14	SWPP 13	SWPP 7	SWPP 6	SWPP 6	SWPP 7	SWPP 18	SWPP 20
						FAC 1Q	FAC 1Q		
		FAV 1Q	FAV 1P		FAV 1Q	FAV 2Qr	FAV 1P	FAV 2Q	FAV 1Q

Division One East 2018-19

1 Alphington AFC
2 Appledore AFC
3 Axminster Town AFC
4 Bovey Tracey
5 Brixham
6 Budleigh Salterton
7 Crediton United
8 Elmore
9 Honiton Town
10 Ilfracombe Town
11 Liverton United
12 Newton Abbot Spurs
13 Sidmouth Town
14 St Martins
15 Stoke Gabriel
16 Teignmouth
17 Torridgeside AFC
18 University of Exeter
19 Waldon Athletic

Division One West 2018-19

1 Bere Alston United
2 Bude Town AFC
3 Dobwalls
4 Holsworthy
5 Liskeard Athletic
6 Ludgvan
7 Mousehole
8 Penzance
9 Plymouth Marjons
10 Plymstock United
11 Porthleven
12 St Blazey
13 St Dennis
14 Wadebridge Town
15 Wendron United

DEVON & EXETER LEAGUE

Premier Division	P	W	D	L	F	A	GD	Pts
1 Elmore	30	28	2	0	121	19	102	86
2 Cronies	30	22	6	2	106	22	84	72
3 Newtown	30	18	6	6	106	49	57	60
4 Exwick Villa	30	17	4	9	73	43	30	55
5 Upottery	30	16	5	9	82	72	10	53
6 Heavitree United	30	12	10	8	75	51	24	46
7 Okehampton Argyle	30	12	7	11	70	71	-1	43
8 Witheridge 2nd	30	12	6	12	76	70	6	42
9 Beer Albion	30	10	10	10	48	68	-20	40
10 Newton St Cyres	30	10	3	17	45	74	-29	33
11 Feniton	30	8	6	16	69	90	-21	29*
12 Exmouth Town 2nd	30	9	3	18	39	73	-34	29*
13 Topsham Town	30	8	2	20	48	92	-44	26
14 Clyst Valley	30	6	6	18	44	94	-50	24
15 Seaton Town	30	6	4	20	57	110	-53	22
16 Hatherleigh Town	30	3	6	21	31	92	-61	15

Division One	P	W	D	L	F	A	GD	Pts
1 Colyton	22	14	6	2	72	31	41	48
2 University of Exeter 2nd	22	12	6	4	56	32	24	42
3 Lyme Regis	22	12	5	5	51	36	15	41
4 Perry Street & Yonder Hill	22	10	6	6	50	29	21	36
5 Heavitree United 2nd	22	9	5	8	45	61	-16	32
6 Lapford	22	8	7	7	61	49	12	31
7 Chard Town Reserves	22	7	7	8	31	45	-14	28
8 Cullompton Rangers 2nd	22	8	4	10	55	57	-2	27*
9 Sidmouth Town 2nd	22	8	3	11	50	52	-2	27
10 Chagford	22	6	1	15	46	62	-16	19
11 Wellington Reserves	22	5	4	13	42	76	-34	19
12 Alphington 2nd	22	4	4	14	30	59	-29	16

Division Two	P	W	D	L	F	A	GD	Pts
1 Bampton	28	22	3	3	101	40	61	69
2 Kentisbeare	28	18	4	6	96	50	46	58
3 Woodbury	28	16	6	6	66	44	22	54
4 Thorverton s	28	14	5	9	76	51	25	47
5 Dawlish FC	28	13	8	7	82	68	14	47
6 University of Exeter 3rd	28	14	4	10	87	71	16	46
7 Honiton Town 2nd	28	12	6	10	67	61	6	41
8 Bow AAC	28	10	8	10	44	63	-19	38
9 Newtown 2nd	28	10	5	13	69	72	-3	35
10 Uplowman Athletic	28	10	5	13	69	56	13	34
11 Axminster Town 2nd	28	9	5	14	60	69	-9	32
12 Halwill	28	8	5	15	53	73	-20	29
13 East Budleigh	28	6	9	13	62	71	-9	27
14 Axmouth United	28	4	5	19	42	92	-50	13
15 Newton Poppleford	28	4	2	22	37	130	-93	13

Division Three	P	W	D	L	F	A	GD	Pts
1 University of Exeter 4th	26	22	1	3	104	34	70	67
2 Crediton United 2nd	26	18	5	3	108	34	74	59
3 Royal Oak FC	26	18	3	5	94	44	50	57
4 Tipton St John	26	16	3	7	67	49	18	51
5 Priory	26	15	4	7	83	66	17	49
6 Ottery St Mary AFC	26	13	3	10	57	55	2	42
7 Otterton	26	10	6	10	59	61	-2	36
8 Tedburn St Mary	26	9	5	12	54	70	-16	32
9 Sandford	26	8	6	12	52	70	-18	29*
10 Budleigh Salterton 2nd	26	9	0	17	70	97	-27	26*
11 Countess Wear Dynamoes	26	5	7	14	47	74	-27	22
12 Lympstone	26	5	2	19	34	82	-48	17
13 Clyst Valley 2nd	26	4	5	17	49	84	-35	16*
14 Pinhoe	26	3	4	19	52	110	-58	12*

Division Four	P	W	D	L	F	A	GD	Pts
1 Whipton & Pinhoe	24	24	0	0	149	19	130	72
2 University of Exeter 5th	24	18	1	5	92	28	64	55
3 Winchester	24	14	4	6	68	57	11	46
4 North Tawton	24	14	3	7	80	47	33	45
5 Beer Albion 2nd	24	13	2	9	77	49	28	41
6 Newton St Cyres 2nd	24	11	1	12	77	84	-7	34
7 Alphington 3rd	24	11	0	13	62	69	-7	33
8 Feniton 2nd	24	9	5	10	50	62	-12	32
9 Teignmouth 2nd	24	10	2	12	55	58	-3	31*
10 Sampford Peverell	24	8	2	14	49	90	-41	26
11 Winkleigh	24	5	2	17	60	104	-44	16*
12 St Martins 2nd	24	5	0	19	37	74	-37	15
13 Starcross Generals	24	3	0	21	32	147	-115	8*

Division Five	P	W	D	L	F	A	GD	Pts
1 Elmore 2nd	24	20	1	3	105	20	85	61
2 Black Swan Town	24	19	1	4	121	41	80	58
3 Halwill 2nd	24	19	1	4	81	32	49	58
4 Lyme Regis Reserves	24	17	2	5	84	31	53	53
5 Millwey Rise	24	13	2	9	67	45	22	41
6 Hemyock	24	12	5	7	71	50	21	40*
7 Central	24	12	2	10	71	51	20	37*
8 Culm United	24	8	1	15	59	73	-14	25
9 Awliscombe	24	8	1	15	39	59	-20	25
10 Westexe Park Rangers	24	7	1	16	56	103	-47	21*
11 Ilminster Town Reserves	24	6	2	16	44	88	-44	19*
12 Dunkeswell Rovers	24	5	0	19	35	115	-80	15
13 Offwell Rangers FC	24	0	1	23	12	137	-125	0*

SOUTH WEST PENINSULA LEAGUE - STEP 6/7

Division Six

		P	W	D	L	F	A	GD	Pts
1	Upottery 2nd	20	13	3	4	63	29	34	42
2	Sidmouth Town 3rd	20	11	5	4	80	40	40	38
3	Exmouth Spartans	20	12	2	6	60	41	19	38
4	Cranbrook	20	11	3	6	66	35	31	36
5	Bravehearts	20	10	5	5	67	45	22	35
6	Queens Head	20	10	3	7	59	40	19	33
7	Bampton 2nd	20	9	4	7	41	48	-7	31
8	Wellington A	20	7	1	12	54	79	-25	22
9	Silverton	20	4	3	13	37	75	-38	14*
10	Cheriton Fitzpaine	20	3	5	12	37	78	-41	14
11	Seaton Town 2nd	20	1	4	15	25	79	-54	7

Division Seven

		P	W	D	L	F	A	GD	Pts
1	Spreyton FC	24	19	2	3	100	31	69	59
2	Bradninch Town	24	17	4	3	82	31	51	55
3	Witheridge 3rd	24	14	2	8	76	57	19	44
4	Amory Green Rovers	24	13	4	7	86	60	26	43
5	Kentisbeare 2nd	24	12	3	9	82	54	28	39
6	Lapford 2nd	24	10	6	8	47	39	8	36
7	Exeter United	24	14	3	7	58	36	22	32*
8	Willand XI	24	8	7	9	55	60	-5	31
9	Chagford 2nd	24	9	3	12	46	57	-11	29*
10	Colyton 2nd	24	5	5	14	40	69	-29	20
11	HT Dons	24	5	2	17	51	109	-58	17
12	Newton Poppleford 2nd	24	5	2	17	49	91	-42	16*
13	Kenn Valley United	24	3	1	20	36	114	-78	10

Division Eight

		P	W	D	L	F	A	GD	Pts
1	Thorverton 2nds	28	22	3	3	116	48	68	69
2	Okehampton Argyle 2nd	28	20	2	6	140	56	84	62
3	Culm United 2nds	28	19	4	5	102	53	49	61
4	Sidmouth Town 4ths	28	18	3	7	96	73	23	57
5	East Budleigh 2nd	28	15	3	10	107	67	40	48
6	Otterton 2nd	28	12	9	7	74	52	22	45
7	Cheriton Fitzpaine 2nds	28	12	4	12	70	65	5	40
8	Pinhoe 2nd	28	11	4	13	80	67	13	37
9	Honiton Town 3rd	28	10	5	13	80	79	1	34*
10	Millwey Rise 2nd	28	10	4	14	80	84	-4	33*
11	Central 2nd	28	9	4	15	60	81	-21	31
12	Tedburn St Mary 2nd	28	9	4	15	57	79	-22	31
13	Sandford 2nd	28	5	6	17	59	101	-42	21
14	Bradninch Villa	28	5	3	19	57	143	-86	21
15	Amory Green Rovers 2nd	28	2	2	24	37	167	-130	8

PLYMOUTH & WEST DEVON LEAGUE

Premier Division

		P	W	D	L	F	A	GD	Pts
1	Mount Gould FC	18	13	5	0	69	24	45	44
2	The Windmill FC (Devon)	18	14	2	2	58	26	32	38*
3	Plympton Athletic	18	9	2	7	61	38	23	29
4	Morley Rangers	18	9	2	7	59	55	4	29
5	Saltram Athletic	18	9	1	8	43	48	-5	28
6	The Navy Inn	18	8	3	7	51	38	13	27
7	Chaddlewood Miners Old Boys	18	7	4	7	53	46	7	25
8	Millbridge	18	5	3	10	43	52	-9	18
9	Plymouth Hope	18	2	0	16	28	84	-56	6
10	University of Plymouth	18	2	2	14	26	80	-54	-1*

Division One

		P	W	D	L	F	A	GD	Pts
1	Maristow	18	13	2	3	88	39	49	41
2	Signal Box Oak Villa	18	13	2	3	58	23	35	41
3	Millbridge 2nd	18	12	3	3	54	29	25	39
4	Pennycross SC	18	9	3	6	58	35	23	30
5	Plympton Athletic 2nd	18	9	2	7	55	34	21	29
6	DC Auto Repairs	18	6	2	10	39	52	-13	20
7	Lakeside Athletic 2nd	18	8	3	7	61	57	4	18*
8	SB Frankfort	18	3	2	13	23	54	-31	11
9	Cherry Tree	18	3	6	9	47	33	14	6*
10	Princetown	18	0	0	18	10	137	-127	-9*

Division Two

		P	W	D	L	F	A	GD	Pts
1	Millbridge 3rd	16	12	3	1	78	30	48	39
2	Plymouth Vaults	16	11	1	4	46	27	19	34
3	Hooe Rovers	16	10	3	3	76	27	49	33
4	Belgrave	16	9	3	4	51	24	27	30
5	SB Frankfort 2nd	16	9	2	5	81	43	38	26*
6	Kitto FC	16	4	4	8	33	67	-34	13*
7	Devonport FC	16	4	0	11	38	41	-3	12*
8	Victoria Park Rangers	16	3	2	11	25	68	-43	11
9	Woodford	16	0	0	16	9	110	-101	-9*

Division Three

		P	W	D	L	F	A	GD	Pts
1	Horrabridge Rangers	16	14	2	0	85	20	65	38*
2	The Windmill FC (Devon) Res	16	14	1	1	95	13	82	37*
3	Lakeside Athletic Res	16	10	1	5	67	32	35	25*
4	Morley Rangers 2nd	16	9	0	7	43	46	-3	24*
5	Drake FC	16	7	1	8	50	49	1	22
6	Tavistock Rovers	16	4	1	11	38	71	-33	13
7	Torpoint Athletic 4th	16	5	0	11	41	59	-18	9*
8	Central Park Rangers	16	3	0	13	26	87	-61	9
9	Team Carpy	16	3	0	13	28	96	-68	9

SOUTH DEVON LEAGUE

Premier Division

		P	W	D	L	F	A	GD	Pts
1	Ashburton Association	26	20	1	5	77	33	44	61
2	Waldon Athletic	26	19	3	4	83	33	50	60
3	Kingsteignton Athletic	26	16	7	3	78	29	49	55
4	Watcombe Wanderers	26	14	7	5	77	49	28	49
5	East Allington United	26	14	4	8	61	43	18	46
6	Dartmouth	26	14	3	9	62	52	10	45
7	Buckland Athletic 2nd	26	13	3	10	68	46	22	42
8	Upton Athletic	26	11	4	11	66	59	7	31*
9	Brixham AFC 2nd	26	9	4	13	53	60	-7	31
10	Roselands	26	7	2	17	46	83	-37	23
11	Paignton Villa	26	7	3	16	53	72	-19	21*
12	Kingskerswell & Chelston	26	6	5	15	63	76	-13	20*
13	Loddiswell Athletic	26	4	1	21	21	122	-101	13
14	Ivybridge Town 2nd	26	4	1	21	43	94	-51	10*

Division One

		P	W	D	L	F	A	GD	Pts
1	Harbertonford	24	16	4	4	91	42	49	52
2	Totnes & Dartington SC 2nd	24	17	1	6	79	33	46	52
3	Chudleigh Athletic	24	14	5	5	58	37	21	47
4	Salcombe Town	24	12	4	8	77	55	22	40
5	Buckland Athletic 3rd	24	10	8	6	51	33	18	38
6	Newton Abbot Spurs 2nd	24	11	3	10	55	53	2	36
7	Watcombe Wanderers 2nd	24	10	5	9	54	57	-3	35
8	Beesands Rovers	24	11	2	11	54	58	-4	35
9	Paignton Saints	24	10	3	11	78	60	18	33
10	Newton Abbot 66	24	8	2	14	71	58	13	23*
11	Babbacombe Corinthians	24	5	7	12	41	75	-34	22
12	Ipplepen Athletic	24	6	1	17	43	81	-38	19
13	Stoke Gabriel 2nd	24	3	1	20	22	132	-110	-2*

Division Two

		P	W	D	L	F	A	GD	Pts
1	Bovey Tracey 2nd	20	14	1	5	82	42	40	43
2	Bishopsteignton United	20	13	4	3	59	33	26	43
3	Torbay Police	20	12	4	4	73	27	46	40
4	Broadmeadow ST	20	9	3	5	77	50	27	37
5	Kingskerswell & Chelston 2nd	20	9	6	5	52	45	7	33
6	Buckfastleigh Rangers	20	10	2	8	56	47	9	32
7	Riviera United	20	9	2	9	45	48	-3	29
8	Kingsteignton Athletic 2nd	20	6	3	11	49	59	-10	21
9	Liverton United 2nd	20	6	3	11	38	45	-7	12*
10	Hookhills United	20	3	4	13	39	68	-29	10*
11	Newton United	20	0	1	19	17	123	-106	1

Division Three

		P	W	D	L	F	A	GD	Pts
1	Meadowbrook Athletic	22	19	0	3	99	22	77	57
2	Ashburton Association 2nd	22	16	2	4	78	33	45	50
3	Harbertonford 2nd	22	13	2	7	66	33	33	41
4	Abbotskerswell	22	12	3	7	62	50	12	39
5	Waldon Athletic 2nd	22	11	5	6	59	45	14	38
6	Barton Athletic	22	10	1	11	44	66	-22	31
7	Chudleigh Athletic 2nd	22	10	0	12	51	55	-4	30
8	Roselands 2nd	22	8	6	8	52	57	-5	30
9	Dartmouth 2nd	22	6	3	13	58	60	-2	21
10	Upton Athletic 2nd	22	8	1	13	53	65	-12	19*
11	Teign Village	22	6	0	16	37	87	-50	18
12	Ipplepen Athletic 2nd	22	1	1	20	26	112	-86	1*

Division Four

		P	W	D	L	F	A	GD	Pts
1	East Allington United 2nd	22	16	2	4	55	29	26	50
2	Paignton Villa 2nd	22	15	2	5	72	32	40	44*
3	Dittisham United	22	13	3	6	54	38	16	39*
4	Buckfastleigh Rangers 2nd	22	11	2	9	54	53	1	35
5	Riviera United 2nd	22	10	6	6	55	41	14	33*
6	Bishopsteignton United 2nd	22	11	2	9	67	61	6	32 *
7	Torquay Town	22	10	1	11	60	55	5	28*
8	Torbay Police 2nd	22	8	3	11	42	52	-10	27
9	Newton Rovers	22	8	3	11	46	63	-17	27
10	Newton Abbot 66 2nd	22	8	3	11	50	48	2	18*
11	Kingsbridge & Kellaton United	22	4	2	16	34	66	-32	14
12	Babbacombe Corinthians 2nd	22	2	3	17	25	76	-51	3*

Division Five

		P	W	D	L	F	A	GD	Pts
1	Watts Blake Bearne	20	15	2	3	108	20	88	47
2	Watcombe Wanderers 3rds	20	14	4	2	96	37	59	46
3	Paignton Saints 2nd	20	12	3	5	81	56	25	39
4	Barton Athletic 2nd	20	12	0	8	64	59	5	36
5	Stoke Fleming & Strete	20	11	2	7	53	36	17	35
6	Ilsington Villa	20	10	4	6	37	34	3	34
7	Broadhempston United	20	7	2	11	54	60	-6	23
8	Brixham AFC 3rds	20	8	2	10	48	59	-11	23*
9	Newton Rovers 2nd	20	3	3	14	25	71	-46	12
10	Chudleigh Athletic 3rds	20	4	1	15	30	74	-44	10*
11	Newton United 2nd	20	2	1	17	17	107	-90	-5*

SOUTH WEST PENINSULA LEAGUE - STEP 6/7
CORNWALL COMBINATION

Premier Division

		P	W	D	L	F	A	GD	Pts
1	Perranporth	38	31	5	3	147	34	113	95*
2	Falmouth Town Res	38	29	5	4	136	52	84	92
3	Carharrack	38	28	6	4	162	56	106	90
4	St Day	38	26	5	7	141	57	84	83
5	Hayle	38	22	4	12	88	68	20	70
6	Helston Athletic Res	38	21	4	13	101	70	31	67
7	Perranwell	38	20	3	15	90	65	25	63
8	Pendeen Rovers	38	16	8	14	92	74	18	56
9	Penryn Athletic	38	14	8	16	80	92	-12	50
10	Porthleven Res	38	15	4	19	102	106	-4	49
11	St Just	38	14	7	17	81	104	-23	49
12	St Agnes	38	15	3	20	82	97	-15	48
13	St Ives Town	38	14	4	20	50	82	-32	46
14	Mullion	38	13	4	21	74	95	-21	43
15	Illogan RBL Res	38	13	10	15	66	76	-10	41*
16	West Cornwall	38	11	4	23	57	113	-56	37
17	RNAS Culdrose	38	8	5	25	49	117	-68	31
18	Redruth United	38	7	7	24	44	115	-71	28
19	Goodhavern Athletic	38	9	1	28	48	127	-79	28
20	Holman SC	38	5	3	30	61	151	-90	18

EAST CORNWALL PREMIER LEAGUE

Premier Division

		P	W	D	L	F	A	GD	Pts
1	Torpoint Athletic	28	22	1	5	108	34	74	67
2	St Austell	28	21	1	6	81	25	56	64
3	Saltash United	28	20	3	5	91	35	56	63
4	Bere Alston United	28	17	4	7	81	39	42	55
5	Tavistock	28	15	6	7	68	60	8	51
6	Plymouth Parkway	28	14	6	8	73	39	34	48
7	Polperro	28	15	1	12	61	58	3	46
8	Plymstock United	28	12	8	8	67	56	11	44
9	Launceston	28	9	8	11	49	60	-11	35
10	Callington Town	28	11	4	13	50	42	8	34*
11	Looe Town	28	9	2	17	63	80	-17	23*
12	St Stephens Borough	28	6	4	18	51	78	-27	22
13	Liskeard Athletic	28	6	3	19	37	66	-29	18*
14	Pensilva	28	3	6	19	23	92	-69	12*
15	St Blazey FC	28	0	3	25	15	154	-139	0*

Division One

		P	W	D	L	F	A	GD	Pts
1	Wadebridge Town	22	19	1	2	97	28	69	58
2	Millbrook	22	17	1	4	74	39	35	52
3	Lakeside Athletic	22	15	3	4	88	30	58	45*
4	Lanreath	22	14	3	5	83	48	35	45
5	St Minver	22	13	2	7	75	49	26	41
6	Mevagissey	22	10	9	9	59	45	14	30*
7	Elburton Villa	22	7	4	11	64	58	6	22*
8	Newquay	22	6	3	13	54	89	-35	21
9	Morwenstow	22	5	5	12	51	72	-21	20
10	Padstow United	22	3	4	15	28	79	-51	13
11	Roche	22	3	3	16	30	99	-69	12
12	St Teath	22	3	2	17	28	95	-67	11

SOUTHERN COMBINATION FOOTBALL LEAGUE

Founded: 1920 (As Sussex County League >2015) **Sponsored by:** Macron Store
Recent Champions: 2015: Littlehampton Town **2016:** Horsham **2017:** Shoreham

PREMIER DIVISION	P	W	D	L	F	A	GD	Pts
1 Haywards Heath Town	38	26	5	7	88	34	54	83
2 Three Bridges	38	24	10	4	91	38	53	82
3 Pagham	38	22	9	7	100	42	58	75
4 Horsham YMCA	38	22	5	11	73	39	34	71
5 Eastbourne Town	38	19	12	7	81	40	41	69
6 Chichester City	38	20	8	10	86	54	32	68
7 Peacehaven & Tels	38	20	8	10	62	37	25	68
8 Saltdean United	38	19	8	11	58	43	15	65
9 Newhaven	38	18	7	13	77	58	19	61
10 Lancing	38	16	4	18	58	63	-5	52
11 Loxwood	38	15	6	17	61	78	-17	51
12 Crawley Down Gatwick	38	11	12	15	59	69	-10	45
13 East Preston	38	12	9	17	59	72	-13	45
14 AFC Uckfield Town	38	15	8	15	52	52	0	44*
15 Broadbridge Heath	38	10	7	21	51	81	-30	37
16 Eastbourne United	38	8	8	22	45	94	-49	32
17 Arundel	38	8	6	24	54	80	-26	30
18 Hassocks	38	8	4	26	38	92	-54	28
19 Worthing United	38	8	3	27	29	100	-71	27
20 Littlehampton Town	38	5	9	24	39	95	-56	24

LEAGUE CUP

HOLDERS: PAGHAM
ROUND 1

Billinghurst	v	Storrington	2-0
Kelsey	v	Midhurst & Easebourne	4-1
St Francis Rangers	v	Seaford Town	0-1
Oakwood	v	AFC Varndeanians	2-1
Southwick	v	Bexhill United	0-1
Langney Wanderers	v	Ringmer	4-2

ROUND 2

Haywards Heath Town	v	Eastbourne United	2-0
Billinghurst	v	Wick	2-3
Chichester City	v	Selsey	4-1
Newhaven	v	Seaford Town	7-2
Hailsham Town	v	Saltdean United	0-3
Mile Oak	v	Peacehaven & Telscombe	1-3
Oakwood	v	Lingfield	2-6
Littlehampton Town	v	Broadbridge Heath	2-3
East Preston	v	Arundel	1-2
Lancing	v	Steyning Town	4-3
Three Bridges	v	Crawley Down Gatwick	0-2
Loxwood	v	Pagham	0-0, 3-4p
Horsham YMCA	v	Worthing United	5-0
Hassocks	v	Bexhill United	0-1
Little Common	v	Langney Wanderers	2-0
AFC Uckfield Town	v	Eastbourne Town	2-0

(AFC Uckfield removed after playing an ineligible player)

ROUND 3

Haywards Heath Town	v	Wick	5-1
Chichester City	v	Newhaven	2-0
Saltdean United	v	Peacehaven & Telscombe	2-1
Lingfield	v	Broadbridge Heath	1-0
Arundel	v	Lancing	0-3
Crawley Down Gatwick	v	Pagham	5-1
Horsham YMCA	v	Bexhill United	3-0
Little Common	v	Eastbourne Town	0-2

QUARTER FINALS

Haywards Heath Town	v	Chichester City	2-1
Saltdean United	v	Lingfield	3-0
Lancing	v	Crawley Down Gatwick	0-3
Horsham YMCA	v	Eastbourne Town	4-0

SEMI FINALS

Haywards Heath Town	v	Saltdean United	2-1
Crawley Down Gatwick	v	Horsham YMCA	1-3

FINAL

Haywards Heath Town	v	Horsham YMCA	4-0

PREMIER DIVISION	1	2	3	4	5	6	7	8	9	10	11	12	13	14	15	16	17	18	19	20
1 AFC Uckfield Town		2-1	4-0	1-1	2-0	3-3	0-1	1-2	1-4	0-2	1-1	2-1	3-1	0-0	1-0	3-4	0-4	2-1	0-2	2-0
2 Arundel	0-1		3-3	3-4	2-3	1-1	0-3	2-3	0-3	1-2	3-1	3-4	1-0	1-1	2-2	1-1	2-0	1-4	0-3	1-2
3 Broadbridge Heath	4-1	3-2		2-0	0-0	0-2	1-4	1-1	2-0	0-4	1-2	2-1	3-1	1-2	2-1	1-2	0-2	2-3	1-5	1-0
4 Chichester City	4-0	5-2	0-0		3-2	4-3	0-0	1-1	1-2	1-4	1-1	5-0	0-1	5-0	0-2	0-5	1-0	3-0	3-1	5-3
5 Crawley Down Gatwick	2-1	2-2	3-0	2-2		3-4	2-2	2-1	1-1	1-1	0-2	2-2	1-1	3-0	2-0	1-3	2-0	0-4	0-0	3-0
6 East Preston	2-1	0-2	3-0	2-4	2-0		1-2	5-1	1-0	0-2	1-4	1-1	1-1	2-2	2-4	1-1	1-0	0-4	2-1	1-1
7 Eastbourne Town	1-1	4-1	5-0	0-1	3-2	4-2		8-1	3-1	1-1	0-2	2-0	2-2	1-1	2-1	0-2	1-1	0-2	1-2	1-2
8 Eastbourne United	0-0	1-3	2-2	1-2	2-1	1-2	3-5		0-1	0-1	0-5	2-1	3-3	1-2	2-3	1-5	2-2	0-0	0-3	0-1
9 Hassocks	1-3	0-4	3-2	0-4	1-3	2-2	0-4	1-2		1-4	0-2	0-4	3-1	0-3	2-3	0-3	0-6	0-1	0-2	2-0
10 Haywards Heath Town	1-2	2-0	5-1	2-1	2-2	3-0	2-3	5-1	5-0		2-0	2-0	2-1	4-2	3-0	1-0	3-0	1-4	1-4	4-0
11 Horsham YMCA	1-0	1-0	4-0	0-2	1-2	3-1	1-0	1-2	6-0	1-0		3-1	2-0	1-2	2-0	0-0	0-1	1-2	3-1	
12 Lancing	0-3	2-0	2-1	1-4	3-1	2-0	0-2	4-0	1-1	2-4		2-0	4-1	1-2	0-1	1-1	0-2	1-4	4-1	
13 Littlehampton Town	1-1	0-2	1-4	0-3	4-1	2-1	0-5	1-1	0-2	0-6	1-4	1-2		2-3	1-1	1-6	0-5	0-0	1-3	0-1
14 Loxwood	0-3	3-2	1-1	2-4	1-1	2-3	1-3	3-0	2-1	1-2	1-2	7-0		1-6	5-2	1-0	1-0			
15 Newhaven	1-0	3-0	1-1	3-2	4-0	1-0	0-0	5-2	2-2	3-1	0-1	1-3	1-5	6-1		2-5	1-2	1-2	1-1	4-0
16 Pagham	1-2	4-0	1-1	3-1	0-0	2-2	6-1	0-0	3-0	4-0	0-1	5-1	5-1	3-2		2-3	3-0	1-3	7-0	
17 Peacehaven & Tels	1-2	4-1	1-0	1-0	3-1	2-1	1-1	0-1	3-2	1-0	1-1	2-1	2-1	3-1	1-3	0-0		1-3	1-1	2-1
18 Saltdean United	1-0	1-0	2-0	1-0	2-2	1-0	0-0	3-0	3-0	1-1	1-3	1-1	4-0	0-1	3-3	1-3	0-2		1-1	0-1
19 Three Bridges	2-1	3-2	4-2	2-2	4-0	7-2	1-1	2-1	4-1	0-1	3-3	4-0	1-2	4-0	1-0	2-2	1-0	4-1		5-1
20 Worthing United	0-2	2-1	0-7	1-7	1-5	0-4	0-4	1-3	2-1	1-1	0-4	0-1	1-3	1-3	0-1	2-1	1-3	0-2	1-1	

SOUTHERN COMBINATION LEAGUE - STEP 5/6/7

DIVISION ONE	P	W	D	L	F	A	GD	Pts
1 Little Common	34	28	1	5	112	32	80	85
2 Langney Wanderers	34	26	4	4	123	57	66	82
3 Lingfield	34	25	4	5	114	46	68	79
4 Ringmer	34	21	1	12	83	52	31	64
5 Wick	34	18	7	9	86	55	31	61
6 Mile Oak	34	17	5	12	82	68	14	56
7 Bexhill United	34	17	4	13	72	52	20	55
8 Hailsham Town	34	15	4	15	74	75	-1	49
9 Selsey	34	13	8	13	54	52	2	47
10 St Francis Rangers	34	14	5	15	56	70	-14	47
11 Steyning Town	34	13	4	17	74	71	3	43
12 Seaford Town	34	12	6	16	56	69	-13	42
13 Midhurst & Easebourne	34	12	4	18	74	101	-27	40
14 AFC Varndeanians	34	10	5	19	51	85	-34	35
15 Storrington	34	7	6	21	39	96	-57	27
16 Billinghurst	34	6	6	22	51	98	-47	24
17 Oakwood	34	6	4	24	52	102	-50	22
18 Southwick	34	4	6	24	40	112	-72	18

DIVISION TWO	P	W	D	L	F	A	GD	Pts
1 Rustington	26	17	5	4	79	24	55	56
2 Sidlesham	26	16	5	5	63	21	42	53
3 Jarvis Brook	26	16	4	6	59	37	22	52
4 Alford	26	14	5	7	67	39	28	47
5 Bosham	26	14	5	7	62	43	19	47
6 Roffey	26	13	7	6	65	41	24	46
7 Cowfold	26	12	7	7	60	39	21	43
8 Westfield	26	12	4	10	60	47	13	40
9 Montpellier Villa	26	10	4	12	47	53	-6	34
10 Upper Beeding	26	9	4	13	36	44	-8	31
11 Worthign Town	26	7	4	15	44	81	-37	25
12 Rottingdean Village	26	7	2	17	36	89	-53	23
13 Clymping	26	4	1	21	48	91	-43	13
14 Ferring	26	1	3	22	28	105	-77	6

Lancing United withdrew - record expunged.

DIVISION ONE	1	2	3	4	5	6	7	8	9	10	11	12	13	14	15	16	17	18
1 AFC Varndeanians		1-4	4-1	2-2	1-3	4-2	1-4	3-7	2-1	1-1	0-3	5-0	1-2	5-1	1-2	2-1	2-2	0-4
2 Bexhill United	2-1		1-1	1-3	2-4	0-3	0-2	8-0	0-1	2-1	0-2	2-0	2-1	2-1	4-2	3-1	1-2	1-1
3 Billinghurst	1-3	1-0		1-3	1-5	2-1	1-3	3-4	3-4	3-2	1-2	2-2	1-1	1-3	0-1	2-1	1-1	2-2
4 Hailsham Town	3-1	1-1	3-2		3-3	0-6	1-3	3-2	5-1	4-2	0-2	3-0	0-2	6-2	1-2	2-0	2-1	2-7
5 Langney Wanderers	3-2	1-3	3-1	4-3		5-2	3-2	9-0	5-4	2-0	4-2	4-2	4-1	8-2	2-2	5-1	11-2	3-1
6 Lingfield	6-0	5-1	5-1	3-1	2-2		6-0	5-0	6-1	6-1	2-1	4-3	3-1	6-1	1-0	4-3	3-0	3-0
7 Little Common	5-0	2-0	8-0	3-0	2-1	1-2		2-0	3-1	6-1	2-3	4-1	4-1	3-2	8-1	1-0	3-0	2-0
8 Midhurst & Easebourne	2-3	2-4	5-1	4-2	4-5	2-2	0-5		2-2	2-1	5-4	3-1	1-2	0-2	1-3	2-1	3-2	
9 Mile Oak	1-0	3-1	4-2	2-2	1-3	2-1	0-5	5-2		5-0	0-1	2-3	3-1	1-1	2-0	3-2	7-1	3-3
10 Oakwood	3-1	0-7	4-2	1-2	1-3	1-3	1-5	3-4	2-2		1-6	1-3	0-2	5-2	2-3	2-5	5-1	2-3
11 Ringmer	0-0	2-1	7-0	1-0	0-2	0-1	0-5	6-2	0-1	4-2		3-1	2-3	5-0	1-2	2-1	5-0	1-3
12 Seaford Town	5-1	1-3	3-2	2-0	3-3	1-2	0-1	0-1	3-1	2-2	0-3		1-1	2-2	4-0	2-1	2-1	2-2
13 Selsey	2-0	1-3	2-2	2-0	0-1	1-4	1-2	2-1	3-2	0-2	0-2	2-0		7-0	3-1	1-1	3-0	2-2
14 Southwick	0-1	0-2	1-3	4-7	0-5	2-2	2-2	0-4	0-4	0-2	2-1	1-2	1-0		2-5	2-2	1-1	1-4
15 St Francis Rangers	1-1	1-1	3-1	1-2	2-4	4-4	0-6	1-0	0-5	2-1	2-3	2-0	1-1	5-0		0-2	2-3	0-2
16 Steyning Town	5-0	4-2	1-2	2-6	2-1	2-4	0-5	5-4	1-4	5-0	6-1	4-1	1-2	2-0	2-0		2-2	2-2
17 Storrington	1-2	0-3	1-0	3-2	2-0	1-4	1-3	2-2	2-3	0-0	1-5	0-2	2-0	3-1	0-3	1-3		0-1
18 Wick	5-0	1-5	5-4	2-0	0-2	2-1	2-0	2-1	3-1	4-0	2-3	1-2	1-1	3-1	1-3	2-1	6-1	

CLUB MOVEMENTS

Premier Division - In: Langney Wanderers (P), Lingfield (P), Little Common (P), Shoreham (R - Isth1S).
Out: Haywards Heath Town (P - IsthSE), Littlehampton Town (R), Three Bridges (P - IsthSE), Worthing United (R).

Division One - In: Alfold (P), Littlehampton Town (R), Sildlesham (P), Worthing United (R).
Out: Langney Wanderers (P), Lingfield (P), Little Common (P), Ringmer (W).

Division Two - In: Angmering Seniors (P - WSux), Copthorne (P - M-Sux), Littlehampton United (NC from Clymping).
Out: Alfold (P), Clymping (NC to Littlehampton United), Sildlesham (P).

AFC UCKFIELD TOWN

Founded: 1988   Nickname: The Oakmen

Club Contact Details (T) 01825 890 905   (E)
Ground: The Oaks, Old Eastbourne Road, Uckfield TN22 5QL
Nearest Railway Station Uckfield - 2.1km
Capacity: **Seats:** Yes   **Covered:** Yes

Colours(change):   Red & black
Previous Names: Wealden 1988-2010. AFC Uckfield & Uckfield Town merged in 2014.
Previous Leagues: None

HONOURS: FA Comps: None
League: Sussex County Division Two 2010-11.

10 YEAR RECORD

08-09		09-10		10-11		11-12		12-13		13-14		14-15		15-16		16-17		17-18	
SxC2	15	SxC2	8	SxC2	1	SxC1	8	SxC1	21	SxC1	10	SxC2	2	SCP	15	SCP	18	SCP	14
																FAC	EP	FAC	EPr
														FAV	1Q	FAV	2Q	FAV	2Q

ARUNDEL

Founded: 1889   Nickname: Mulletts

Club Contact Details (T) 01903 882 548   (E) mullets@btinternet.com
Ground: Mill Road, Arundel, W. Sussex BN18 9QQ
Nearest Railway Station Arundel - 1.6km
Capacity: 2,200 **Seats:** 100   **Covered:** 200

Colours(change):   Red and white
Previous Names: None
Previous Leagues: West Sussex (Founder Members) 1889-1949.

HONOURS: FA Comps: None
League: Sussex County Division One 1957-58, 58-59, 86-87.

10 YEAR RECORD

08-09		09-10		10-11		11-12		12-13		13-14		14-15		15-16		16-17		17-18	
SxC1	2	SxC1	12	SxC1	9	SxC1	17	SxC1	14	SxC1	12	SxC1	10	SCP	12	SCP	15	SCP	17
FAC	1Qr	FAC	EP	FAC	P	FAC	P	FAC	EP	FAC	EPr	FAC	EP	FAC	Pr	FAC	1Q	FAC	EP
FAV	3P	FAV	3P	FAV	2Q	FAV	2Q	FAV	2Q	FAV	2Q	FAV	1P	FAV	2Q	FAV	1Q	FAV	1Q

BROADBRIDGE HEATH

Founded: 1919   Nickname: The Bears

Club Contact Details (T) 01403 211 311   (E) crispandy@hotmail.com
Ground: Broadbridge Leisure Centre, Wickhurst Lane Broadbridge Heath Horsham RH12 3YS
Nearest Railway Station Christs Hospital - 1.5km
Capacity: **Seats:**   **Covered:**   **Bus Route** Tesco - stop 213m away

Colours(change):   All royal blue
Previous Names: None
Previous Leagues: Horsham & District >1971. West Sussex 1971-79. Southern Counties Combination 1979-83.

HONOURS: FA Comps: None
League: West Sussex Division One 1975-76.

10 YEAR RECORD

08-09		09-10		10-11		11-12		12-13		13-14		14-15		15-16		16-17		17-18	
SxC2	9	SxC2	14	SxC2	6	SxC2	5	SxC2	6	SxC2	2	SxC1	9	SCP	9	SCP	8	SCP	15
																		FAC	EP
												FAV	2Q	FAV	2Q	FAV	1Q	FAV	2P

CHICHESTER CITY

Founded: 2000   Nickname: Lillywhites

Club Contact Details (T) 01243 533 368   (E) secretary@chichestercityfc.co.uk
Ground: Oaklands Park, Chichester, W Sussex PO19 6AR
Nearest Railway Station Chichester - 1.2km
Capacity: 2,000 **Seats:** none **Covered:** 200   **Shop:** Yes   **Bus Route** University - stop 182m away

Colours(change):   White & green
Previous Names: Chichester FC (pre 1948), Chichester City 1948-2000. Merged with Portfield in 2000, Chicester City United 2000-09
Previous Leagues: None

HONOURS: FA Comps: None
League: Sussex County Division One 2003-04.

10 YEAR RECORD

08-09		09-10		10-11		11-12		12-13		13-14		14-15		15-16		16-17		17-18	
SxC1	7	SxC1	3	SxC1	14	SxC1	20	SxC1	19	SxC1	11	SxC1	14	SCP	5	SCP	3	SCP	6
FAC	P	FAC	P	FAC	EP	FAC	EPr	FAC	EP	FAC	EP	FAC	EP	FAC	P	FAC	EP	FAC	EP
FAV	2P	FAV	1P	FAV	1P	FAV	2P	FAV	2Q	FAV	1Q	FAV	1Q	FAV	1Q	FAV	4P	FAV	5P

CRAWLEY DOWN GATWICK
Founded: 1993　　Nickname: The Anvils

Club Contact Details (T) 01342 717 140　　(E) martinmd@btinternet.com
Ground: The Haven Centre, Hophurst Lane, Crawley Down RH10 4LJ

Capacity: 1,000　**Seats:** Yes　**Covered:** 50

Colours(change): All Red
Previous Names: Crawley Down United > 1993. Crawley Down Village > 1999. Crawley Down > 2012.
Previous Leagues: Mid Sussex, Sussex County > 2011. Isthmian 2011-14.

HONOURS: FA Comps: None
League: Mid-Sussex Premier Division 1994-95. Sussex County Division One 2010-11.

10 YEAR RECORD									
08-09	09-10	10-11	11-12	12-13	13-14	14-15	15-16	16-17	17-18
SxC2　3	SxC1　8	SxC1　1	Isth1S 16	Isth1S 13	Isth1S 23	SxC1 19	SC1　2	SCP 11	SCP 12
FAC EPr	FAC 1Q	FAC EP	FAC 1Q	FAC P	FAC P	FAC EPr	FAC EP	FAC P	FAC EP
FAV 2Q	FAV 2Q	FAV 1P	FAT P	FAT 1Q	FAT 1Q	FAV 2P	FAV 1Q	FAV 1Q	FAV 2Q

EAST PRESTON
Founded: 1966　Nickname: EP

Club Contact Details (T) 01903 776 026　　(E) keweia@btinternet.com
Ground: Roundstone Recreation Ground, Lashmar Road, East Preston BN16 1ES
Nearest Railway Station Angmering - 0.8km
Capacity:　**Seats:** Yes　**Covered:** Yes　　**Bus Route** Windlesham Gardens - stop 209m away

Colours(change): Black and white
Previous Names: None
Previous Leagues: Worthing & District 1966-68. West Sussex 1968-83.

HONOURS: FA Comps: None
League: West Sussex Premier Division 1977-78, 80-81, 81-82, 82-83.
10 YEAR RECORD　Sussex County Division Three 1983-84, Division Two 1997-98, 2011-12, Division One 2013-14.

08-09	09-10	10-11	11-12	12-13	13-14	14-15	15-16	16-17	17-18
SxC1 18	SxC2 14	SxC2 14	SxC2　1	SxC1　3	SxC1　1	SxC1 11	SCP 19	SC1　3	SCP 13
FAC P	FAC 2Q	FAC EP		FAC P	FAC 1Q	FAC 2Q	FAC EP	FAC 1Q	FAC P
FAV 1P	FAV 1Q	FAV 2Q	FAV 1P	FAV 2Q	FAV 5P	FAV 2P	FAV 1Q	FAV 2Q	FAV 1Qr

EASTBOURNE TOWN
Founded: 1881　　Nickname: Town

Club Contact Details (T) 01323 724 328　　(E) rb.marsh@talk21.com
Ground: The Saffrons, Compton Place Road, Eastbourne BN21 1EA
Nearest Railway Station Eastbourne - 0.4km
Capacity: 3,000　**Seats:** 200　**Covered:** Yes　　**Bus Route** Saffrons Road Cricket Club - stop 100m away

Colours(change): Yellow and blue
Previous Names: Devonshire Park 1881-89
Previous Leagues: Southern Amateur 1907-46, Corinthian 1960-63, Athenian 1963-76, Sussex County 1976-2007. Isthmian 2007-14.

HONOURS: FA Comps: None
League: Sussex County 1976-77, 2006-07.

10 YEAR RECORD									
08-09	09-10	10-11	11-12	12-13	13-14	14-15	15-16	16-17	17-18
Isth1S 13	Isth1S 22	Isth1S 18	Isth1S 14	Isth1S 11	Isth1S 24	SxC1　4	SCP　2	SCP　5	SCP　5
FAC 1Q	FAC P	FAC 1Q	FAC P	FAC 2Q	FAC 2Q	FAC P	FAC 3Q	FAC 1Q	FAC 1Q
FAT P	FAT P	FAT P	FAT 1Q	FAT 1Q	FAT 1Qr	FAV 1P	FAV 3P	FAV 4P	FAV 4P

EASTBOURNE UNITED
Founded: 1894　　Nickname: The U's

Club Contact Details (T) 01323 726 989　　(E) secretary@eastbourneunitedafc.com
Ground: The Oval, Channel View Road, Eastbourne, BN22 7LN
Nearest Railway Station Eastbourne - 2km
Capacity: 3,000　**Seats:** 160　**Covered:** 160　**Shop:** Yes　**Bus Route** Desmond Road - stop 241m away

Colours(change): White and black
Previous Names: 1st Sussex Royal Engineers. Eastbourne Old Comrades 1922. Eastbourne United (merged with Shinewater Assoc in 2000)
Previous Leagues: Sussex County 1921-28, 32-56. Spartan 1928-32. Metropolitan 1956-64. Athenian 1964-77. Isthmian 1977-92.
HONOURS: FA Comps: None
League: Athenian Division Two 1966-67, Division One 68-69. Sussex County Division One 1954-55, 55-56, 2008-09,
10 YEAR RECORD　Division Two 2013-14.

08-09	09-10	10-11	11-12	12-13	13-14	14-15	15-16	16-17	17-18
SxC1　1	SxC1　6	SxC1 20	SxC2　6	SxC2　4	SxC2　1	SxC1 12	SCP 10	SCP　7	SCP 16
FAC EP	FAC Pr	FAC EP			FAC 1Q	FAC P	FAC 1Q	FAC 1Q	FAC P
FAV 1Q	FAV 3P	FAV 2Q		FAV 1Q	FAV SF	FAV 2P	FAV 2Q	FAV 2P	FAV 1Q

HASSOCKS

Founded: 1902   **Nickname: The Robins**

Club Contact Details **(T)** 01273 846 040   **(E)** sarahajohn@btinternet.com
Ground: The Beacon, Brighton Road, Hassocks BN6 9NA
Nearest Railway Station Hassocks - 1.2km
Capacity: 1,800 **Seats:** 270   **Covered:** 100   **Bus Route** Friars Oak Cottages - stop 211m away

Colours(change): All Red
Previous Names: None
Previous Leagues: Mid Sussex, Brighton & Hove & District >1981.

HONOURS: FA Comps: None
League: Brighton, Hove & District Division Two 1965-66, Division One 71-72.
Sussex County Division Three 1991-92.

10 YEAR RECORD

08-09	09-10	10-11	11-12	12-13	13-14	14-15	15-16	16-17	17-18
SxC1 16	SxC1 14	SxC1 6	SxC1 4	SxC1 7	SxC1 6	SxC1 15	SCP 13	SCP 13	SCP 18
FAC EP	FAC EP	FAC 1Q	FAC EP	FAC EP	FAC 1Q	FAC EP			FAC EP
FAV 2Q	FAV 2Q	FAV 1Q	FAV 2Qr	FAV 1P	FAV 1P	FAV 2P		FAV 1Q	FAV 2Q

HORSHAM YMCA

Founded: 1898   **Nickname: YM's**

Club Contact Details **(T)** 01403 252 689   **(E)** ymcafootballclub@btconnect.com
Ground: Gorings Mead, Horsham, West Sussex RH13 5BP
Nearest Railway Station Horsham - 0.9km
Capacity: 1,575 **Seats:** 150   **Covered:** 200   **Bus Route** Brighton Road - stop 205m away

Colours(change): White and black
Previous Names: None
Previous Leagues: Horsham & District, Brighton & Hove, Mid Sussex, Sussex County > 2006, Isthmian 2006-11.

HONOURS: FA Comps: None
League: Sussex County 2004-05, 05-06.

10 YEAR RECORD

08-09	09-10	10-11	11-12	12-13	13-14	14-15	15-16	16-17	17-18
SxC1 3	Isth1S 11	Isth1S 22	SxC1 16	SxC1 10	SxC1 4	SxC1 5	SCP 7	SCP 10	SCP 4
FAC 1Qr	FAC 2Q	FAC P	FAC EPr	FAC EP	FAC EP	FAC Pr	FAC 2Qr	FAC EP	FAC EP
FAV 1P	FAT P	FAT P	FAV 1P	FAV 2P	FAV 1Q	FAV 2P	FAV 2Q	FAV 3P	FAV 1P

LANCING

Founded: 1941   **Nickname: The Lancers**

Club Contact Details **(T)** 01903 767 285   **(E)**
Ground: Culver Road, Lancing, West Sussex BN15 9AX
Nearest Railway Station Lancing - 0.2km
Capacity: 2,000 **Seats:**   **Covered:**   **Bus Route** North Road Post Office - stop 123m away

Colours(change): Yellow and blue
Previous Names: Lancing Athletic 1941-57
Previous Leagues: Brighton & Hove & District 1946-48.

HONOURS: FA Comps: None
League: Brighton 1946-47, 47-48. Sussex County Division Two 1957-58, 69-70.

10 YEAR RECORD

08-09	09-10	10-11	11-12	12-13	13-14	14-15	15-16	16-17	17-18
SxC2 9	SxC2 11	SxC1 2	SxC1 2	SxC1 13	SxC1 18	SxC1 8	SCP 4	SCP 12	SCP 10
FAC EP	FAC EP	FAC P	FAC P	FAC P	FAC EPr	FAC EP	FAC EP	FAC EPr	FAC EPr
FAV 2Q	FAV 2Q	FAV 4P	FAV 3P	FAV 1P	FAV 2Q	FAV 2Q	FAV 1P	FAV 2P	FAV 2Q

LANGNEY WANDERERS

Founded: 2010   **Nickname:**

Club Contact Details **(T)** 01323 766 265   **(E)** saunderstracey@sky.com
Ground: Langney Sports Club, Priory Lane, Eastbourne BN23 7QH
Nearest Railway Station Pevensey & Westham - 15-20 mins walk.
Capacity: 4,151 **Seats:** 542   **Covered:** 2,500   Yes **Bus Route** The LOOP Bus from the town centre.

Colours(change): White and red
Previous Names: None
Previous Leagues: East Sussex.

HONOURS: FA Comps: None
League: East Sussex Premier 2012-13. Sussex County Division Three 2013-14.

10 YEAR RECORD

08-09	09-10	10-11	11-12	12-13	13-14	14-15	15-16	16-17	17-18
				EsSuP 1	SxC3 1	SxC3 3	SC1 9	SC1 8	SC1 2
								FAV 1Qr	FAV 2Q

LINGFIELD
Founded: 1893   Nickname: The Lingers

Club Contact Details (T) 01342 834 269   (E) john.tovey@virginmedia.co.uk
Ground: Sports Pavillion, Godstone Road, Lingfield, Surrey RH7 6BT
Nearest Railway Station Lingfield - 1.2km
Capacity: 2,000 **Seats:** Yes **Covered:** Yes **Shop:** No   **Bus Route** Godstone Road - stop 391m away

Colours(change): Red & Yellow
Previous Names: None.
Previous Leagues: Redhill. Surrey Intermediate. Combined Counties. Mid Sussex. Sussex County > 2014. Southern Counties East 2014-15.

HONOURS: FA Comps: None
League: POST WAR: Edenbridge & Caterham 1952-53. Surrey Intermediate Prem B 76-77, Prem A 77-78, 78-79. Mid Sussex Prem 92-93. Sussex County Division Three 97-98.

10 YEAR RECORD

08-09		09-10		10-11		11-12		12-13		13-14		14-15		15-16		16-17		17-18	
SxC1	8	SxC1	10	SxC1	11	SxC1	7	SxC1	6	SxC1	15	SCE	17	SC1	8	SC1	5	SC1	3
FAC	EP	FAC	1Qr	FAC	P	FAC	1Qr	FAC	1Q	FAC	EP	FAC	EP	FAC	EP			FAC	EP
FAV	2Q	FAV	2Q	FAV	1Q	FAV	1Q	FAV	1P	FAV	1P	FAV	3P	FAV	2Q	FAV	1P	FAV	1Q

LITTLE COMMON
Founded: 1966   Nickname: The Green

Club Contact Details (T) 01424 845 861   (E) danieleldridge11@btinternet.com
Ground: Little Common Recreation Ground, Green Lane, Bexhill on Sea TN39 4PH
Nearest Railway Station Cooden Beach - 1.6km
Capacity: **Seats:** **Covered:**   **Bus Route** Green Lane - stop 183m away

Colours(change): Claret & blue
Previous Names:
Previous Leagues:

HONOURS: FA Comps: None
League: East Sussex 1975-76, 76-77, 2004-05. Southern Combination Division One 2017-18.

10 YEAR RECORD

08-09		09-10		10-11		11-12		12-13		13-14		14-15		15-16		16-17		17-18	
SxC3	2	SxC2	4	SxC2	13	SxC2	16	SxC2	3	SxC2	4	SxC2	7	SC1	7	SC1	2	SC1	1
																		FAC	EP
														FAV	1Q	FAV	2Q	FAV	1Q

LOXWOOD
Founded: 1920   Nickname: Magpies

Club Contact Details (T) 07791 766 857   (E) secretary@loxwoodfc.co.uk
Ground: Loxwood Sports Ass., Plaistow Road, Loxwood RH14 0RQ
Capacity: **Seats:** 100 **Covered:** Yes   **Bus Route** Plaistow Road - stop 28m away

Colours(change): White and black
Previous Names: None
Previous Leagues: West Sussex 1995-2006.

HONOURS: FA Comps: None
League: West Sussex Division Two North 1998-99, 2001-02.
10 YEAR RECORD Sussex County Division Three 2007-08.

08-09		09-10		10-11		11-12		12-13		13-14		14-15		15-16		16-17		17-18	
SxC2	10	SxC2	5	SxC2	6	SxC2	5	SxC2	9	SxC2	3	SxC1	6	SCP	8	SCP	6	SCP	11
														FAC	EP	FAC	P	FAC	P
												FAV	2P	FAV	2P	FAV	1Q	FAV	1Q

NEWHAVEN
Founded: 1887   Nickname: The Dockers

Club Contact Details (T) 01273 513 940   (E) martin.garry@premierfoods.co.uk
Ground: The Trafalgar Ground, Fort Road Newhaven East Sussex BN9 9DA
Nearest Railway Station Newhaven Harbour - 0.4km
Capacity: **Seats:** Yes **Covered:** Yes   **Bus Route** Court Farm Road - stop 20m away

Colours(change): Red & yellow
Previous Names: None
Previous Leagues: Brighton, Hove & District 1887-1920.

HONOURS: FA Comps: None
League: Sussex County Division One 1953-54, 73-74, Division Two 1971-72, 90-91, Division Three 2011-12.

10 YEAR RECORD

08-09		09-10		10-11		11-12		12-13		13-14		14-15		15-16		16-17		17-18	
SxC3	4	SxC3	9	SxC3	7	SxC3	1	SxC2	2	SxC1	13	SxC1	7	SCP	3	SCP	9	SCP	9
																FAC	EPr	FAC	Pr
FAV	2Q	FAV	1Q	FAV	1Q	FAV	2Q	FAV	1Q	FAV	1Pr	FAV	1Q	FAV	2P	FAV	3P	FAV	2Q

PAGHAM

Founded: 1903   Nickname: The Lions

Club Contact Details (T) 01243 266 112   (E) paghamfootballclub@outlook.com
Ground: Nyetimber Lane, Pagham, West Sussex PO21 3JY
Nearest Railway Station Bognor Regis - 4.3km
Capacity: 1,500 **Seats:** 200 **Covered:** 200   **Bus Route** The Bear Inn - stop 119m away

Colours(change): White and black
Previous Names: None
Previous Leagues: Bognor & Chichester 1903-50, West Sussex 50-69

HONOURS: FA Comps: None
 League: West Sussex Division One South 1962-63, Prmeier 65-66, 68-69, 69-70.
 Sussex County Division Two 1978-79, 86-87, 2006-07, Division One 80-81, 87-88, 88-89.

10 YEAR RECORD		08-09		09-10		10-11		11-12		12-13		13-14		14-15		15-16		16-17		17-18	
SxC1	11	SxC1	17	SxC1	4	SxC1	6	SxC1	5	SxC1	7	SxC1	3	SCP	6	SCP	4	SCP	3
FAC	EP	FAC	P	FAC	P	FAC	EP	FAC	1Qr	FAC	EP	FAC	1Q	FAC	1Q	FAC	1Q	FAC	1Q
FAV	2Q	FAV	1P	FAV	2Q	FAV	2P	FAV	1Pr	FAV	2Q	FAV	2P	FAV	2P	FAV	2Q	FAV	1P

PEACEHAVEN & TELSCOMBE

Founded: 1923   Nickname: The Tye

Club Contact Details (T) 01273 582 471   (E) danpalmer2008@hotmail.co.uk
Ground: The Sports Park, Piddinghoe Ave, Peacehaven, BN10 8RJ
Nearest Railway Station Newhaven - 3.2km
Capacity: 3,000 **Seats:** 350 **Covered:** Yes   **Bus Route** Slindon Avenue - stop 140m away

Colours(change): Black and white
Previous Names: Formed when Peacehaven Rangers and Telscombe Tye merged.
Previous Leagues: Sussex County > 2013. Isthmian 2013-16.

HONOURS: FA Comps: None
 League: Brighton, H&D Junior 1951-52, Intermediate 63-64, Senior 68-69. Sussex County Division One 1978-79, 81-82, 82-83, 91-92,
 92-93, 94-95, 95-96, 2012-13, Division Three 2005-06, Division Two 2008-09. Isthmian Division One South 2013-14.

10 YEAR RECORD		08-09		09-10		10-11		11-12		12-13		13-14		14-15		15-16		16-17		17-18	
SxC2	1	SxC1	2	SxC1	3	SxC1	5	SxC1	1	Isth1S	1	Isth P	21	Isth1S	24	SCP	14	SCP	7
FAC	Pr	FAC	EP	FAC	P	FAC	P	FAC	P	FAC	1Q	FAC	1Qr	FAC	P	FAC	1Q	FAC	EPr
FAV	2P	FAV	3P	FAV	2P	FAV	3P	FAT	1Q	FAT	3Q	FAT	1Q	FAV	2Q	FAV	1Q

SALTDEAN UNITED

Founded: 1966   Nickname: The Tigers

Club Contact Details (T) 01273 309 898   (E) bob.thomas@saltdeanunitedfc.co.uk
Ground: Hill Park, Coombe Vale Saltdean Brighton East Sussex BN2 8HJ
Nearest Railway Station Southease - 5km
Capacity: **Seats:** **Covered:**   **Bus Route** Saltdean Vale Shops - stop 175m away

Colours(change): Red & black
Previous Names: None
Previous Leagues: None

HONOURS: FA Comps: None
 League: Sussex County/Southern Combination Division Three 1988-89, Division Two 95-96 / Division One 2016-17.

10 YEAR RECORD		08-09		09-10		10-11		11-12		12-13		13-14		14-15		15-16		16-17		17-18	
SxC3	7	SxC3	8	SxC3	5	SxC3	2	SxC2	18	SxC2	13	SxC2	13	SC1	17	SC1	1	SCP	8
																		FAC	EP
FAV	2Q	FAV	2Q	FAV	2Q	FAV	1Q	FAV	1Q	FAV	1Q					FAV	1Q	FAV	1P

SHOREHAM

Founded: 1892   Nickname: Musselmen

Club Contact Details (T) 01273 454 261   (E) spencerdial@googlemail.com
Ground: Middle Road, Shoreham-by-Sea, West Sussex, BN43 6GA
Nearest Railway Station Shoreham-by-Sea - 1.1km
Capacity: 2,000 **Seats:** 150 **Covered:** 700 **Shop:** No **Bus Route** Hammy Lane - stop 150m away

Colours(change): All blue
Previous Names: None.
Previous Leagues: West Sussex. Sussex County/Southern Combination >2017. Isthmian 2017-18.

HONOURS: FA Comps: None
 League: West Sussex Junior Division 1897-98, Senior Division 1902-03, 04-05, 05-06. Sussex County Division One 1951
 -52, 52-53, 77-78, Division Two 1961-62, 76-77, 84-85, 93-94. Southern Combination Premier Division 2016-17.

10 YEAR RECORD		08-09		09-10		10-11		11-12		12-13		13-14		14-15		15-16		16-17		17-18	
SxC1	6	SxC1	9	SxC1	18	SxC1	18	SxC1	17	SxC1	14	SxC1	16	SCP	17	SCP	1	Isth1S	24
FAC	P	FAC	P	FAC	EP	FAC	1Q	FAC	EPr	FAC	1Q	FAC	P	FAC	1Q	FAC	P	FAC	1Q
FAV	3P	FAV	3P	FAV	1P	FAV	2Q	FAV	1Q	FAV	2Q	FAV	1Q	FAV	1Q	FAV	1P	FAT	P

DIVISION ONE

AFC VARNDEANIANS

Founded: 1929   **Nickname:**

Club Contact Details (T)   (E) stevematthews@utilitymatters.com

Ground: Withdean Stadium, Tongdean Lane, Brighton BN1 5JD

Nearest Railway Station Preston Park - 0.9km   **Bus Route** Bottom of Valley Drive - stop 91m away

HONOURS   **League:** Brighton & HD Division One 1973-74, 99-2000, 00-01, 02-03.

FA Comps: None   Mid Sussex Premier 03-04, 06-07, 08-09. Southern Combination Division Two 15-16.

Colours(change): Red & black

10 YEAR RECORD

08-09		09-10		10-11		11-12		12-13		13-14		14-15		15-16		16-17		17-18	
MSuxP	1	MSuxP	7	MSuxP	9	MSuxP	5	MSuxP	7	MSuxP	2	MSuxP	7	SC2	1	SC1	18	SC1	14

ALFOLD

Founded: 1923   **Nickname:**

Club Contact Details (T) 07836 553 594   (E) wayne.mouring@btopenworld.com

Ground: Recreation Ground, Dunsfold Road, Alfold, Surrey GU6 8JB

HONOURS   **League:** West Sussex Division Two 1980-81, 93-94, Division Four 1988-89, Premier 2002-03.

FA Comps: None

Colours(change): Red and blue

10 YEAR RECORD

08-09	09-10	10-11	11-12	12-13	13-14	14-15	15-16		16-17		17-18	
							SC2	13	SC2	14	SC2	4

BEXHILL UNITED

Founded: 2002   **Nickname:** The Pirates

Club Contact Details (T) 07791 368 049   (E) simon_dunne@hotmail.co.uk

Ground: The Polegrove, Brockley Road, Bexhill on Sea TN39 3EX

Nearest Railway Station Collington - 0.3km   **Bus Route** Polegrove - stop 91m away

HONOURS   **League:** Sussex County 1956-57, 65-66, 66-67.

FA Comps: None

Colours(change): White and black

10 YEAR RECORD

08-09		09-10		10-11		11-12		12-13		13-14		14-15		15-16		16-17		17-18	
SxC2	17	SxC3	2	SxC2	4	SxC2	7	SxC2	11	SxC2	8	SxC2	6	SC1	14	SC1	10	SC1	7
														FAC	P				
												FAV	2Q	FAV	1Q	FAV	1Q	FAV	2Q

BILLINGSHURST

Founded: 1891   **Nickname:** Hurst

Club Contact Details (T) 01403 786 445   (E) kevtilley@btinternet.com

Ground: Jubilee Fields, Newbridge Road, Billingshurst, West Sussex. RH14 9HZ

Nearest Railway Station Billinghurst - 1.7km   **Bus Route** Hole Farm - stop 126m away

HONOURS   **League:** West Sussex Premier Division 2011-12.

FA Comps: None

Colours(change): Red & black

10 YEAR RECORD

08-09	09-10	10-11	11-12		12-13		13-14		14-15		15-16		16-17		17-18	
			WSuxP	1	SxC3	4	SxC3	11	SxC3	6	SC2	5	SC1	15	SC1	16

HAILSHAM TOWN

Founded: 1885   **Nickname:** The Stringers

Club Contact Details (T) 01323 840 446   (E) stuartfairway1984@googlemail.com

Ground: The Beaconfield, Western Road, Hailsham BN27 3JF   **Capacity:** 2,000

Nearest Railway Station Polegate - 4.4km   **Bus Route** Bramble Drive - stop 190m away

HONOURS   **League:** Southern Counties Combination 1975-76.

FA Comps: None

Colours(change): Yellow & green

10 YEAR RECORD

08-09		09-10		10-11		11-12		12-13		13-14		14-15		15-16		16-17		17-18	
SxC1	15	SxC1	19	SxC1	16	SxC2	2	SxC1	12	SxC1	16	SxC1	17	SCP	18	SCP	20	SCP	8
FAC	P	FAC	EP	FAC	EP	FAC	EP	FAC	EP	FAC	EP	FAC	EP	FAC	EP	FAC	EP	FAC	EP
FAV	1Q	FAV	1Q	FAV	1Q	FAV	1Q	FAV	1Q	FAV	1Q	FAV	1P	FAV	2P	FAV	1Q	FAV	1Q

LITTLEHAMPTON TOWN
Founded: 1896   **Nickname:** Marigolds

Club Contact Details (T) 01903 716 390   **(E)** paulcox280458@yahoo.co.uk
Ground: St Flora Sportsfield, St Flora's Road, Littlehampton BN17 6BD   **Capacity:** 4,000
Nearest Railway Station Littlehampton - 1km   **Bus Route** Parkside Avenue - stop 79m away
HONOURS   **League:** Sussex County Division Two 1996-97, 2003-04, 12-13, Division One 1990-91, 2014-15.
FA Comps: None
Colours(change): Gold and black

10 YEAR RECORD

	08-09	09-10	10-11	11-12	12-13	13-14	14-15	15-16	16-17	17-18
	SxC2 14	SxC2 12	SxC2 11	SxC2 4	SxC2 1	SxC1 3	SxC1 1	SCP 11	SCP 16	SCP 20
FAC	EP	EPr	EPr	EP	1Q	1Q	1Q	P	EP	1Qr
FAV	1Q	1Q	1Q	2P	2Pr	2P	3Pr	1P	2Qr	1Q

MIDHURST & EASEBOURNE
Founded: 1946   **Nickname:** The Stags

Club Contact Details (T) 01730 816 557   **(E)** midhurstfc@gmail.com
Ground: Rotherfield, Dodsley Lane, Easebourne, Midhurst GU29 9BE
Bus Route Dodsley Grove - Stop 125m away
HONOURS   **League:** West Sussex 1955-56, 62-63, 64-65, Premier 67-68.
FA Comps: None   Sussex County Division Three 94-95, 2002-03.
Colours(change): All blue

10 YEAR RECORD

08-09	09-10	10-11	11-12	12-13	13-14	14-15	15-16	16-17	17-18
SxC2 16	SxC2 18	SxC2 15	SxC2 15	SxC2 8	SxC2 14	SxC2 8	SC1 15	SC1 9	SC1 13
									FAV 2Q

MILE OAK
Founded: 1960   **Nickname:** The Oak

Club Contact Details (T) 01273 423 854   **(E)** tewey62@virginmedia.com
Ground: Mile Oak Recreation Ground, Chalky Road, Portslade BN41 2YU
Nearest Railway Station Fishersgate - 2.1km   **Bus Route** New England Rise - stop 11m away
HONOURS   **League:** Brighton & Hove District Div.8 1960-61, Div.4 65-66, Div.2 72-73,
FA Comps: None   Div.1 73-74, Prem 1980-81. Sussex County Division Two 94-95.
Colours(change): Tangerine and black

10 YEAR RECORD

	08-09	09-10	10-11	11-12	12-13	13-14	14-15	15-16	16-17	17-18
	SxC2 2	SxC1 20	SxC2 7	SxC2 10	SxC2 7	SxC2 7	SxC2 5	SC1 6	SC1 4	SC1 6
FAC	P	P	EP	EPr				FAC EP	FAC EP	FAC EP
FAV	2P	1Q	2Q	2Q		1Qr	2Q	2Q	2Q	2Q

OAKWOOD
Founded: 1962   **Nickname:** The Oaks

Club Contact Details (T) 01293 515 742   **(E)** sarah.daly13@hotmail.co.uk
Ground: Tinsley Lane, Three Bridges, Crawley RH10 8AJ
Nearest Railway Station Three Bridges - 1.3km   **Bus Route** Maxwell Way - Stop 98m away
HONOURS   **League:** Crawley Division One 1973-74. Sussex County Division Three 1984-85, Division Two 2005-06.
FA Comps: None
Colours(change): Red & black

10 YEAR RECORD

	08-09	09-10	10-11	11-12	12-13	13-14	14-15	15-16	16-17	17-18
	SxC1 19	SxC2 9	SxC2 17	SxC2 18	SxC2 15	SxC2 12	SxC2 4	SC1 3	SC1 14	SC1 17
FAC			EP	EP					FAC EP	
FAV	1Qr	1Q	1Q	1Q	1Q	1Q	1Q	2Q	2Q	1Q

SEAFORD TOWN
Founded: 1888   **Nickname:** The Badgers

Club Contact Details (T) 01323 892 221   **(E)** andystiles@rocketmail.com
Ground: The Crouch, Bramber Road, Seaford BN25 1AG
Nearest Railway Station Seaford - 0.6km   **Bus Route** Seaford Head Lower School - stop 168m away
HONOURS   **League:** Lewes 1907-08.
FA Comps: None   Sussex County Division Three 1985-86, Division Two 1988-89, 2005-06.
Colours(change): All red

10 YEAR RECORD

08-09	09-10	10-11	11-12	12-13	13-14	14-15	15-16	16-17	17-18
SxC2 7	SxC2 10	SxC2 5	SxC2 17	SxC2 12	SxC2 17	SxC2 15	SC1 16	SC1 13	SC1 12
FAV 2Q			FAV 1P	FAV 2Q	FAV 1Q	FAV 2Q	FAV 1Q	FAV 2Q	FAV 1Q

SELSEY
Founded: 1903   Nickname: Blues
Club Contact Details (T) 01243 603 420   **(E)** selseyfootballclub@yahoo.com
Ground: The Bunn Leisure Stadium, High Street, Selsey, Chichester, PO20 0QH   **Capacity:** 1,000
Bus Route Medical Centre - stop 92m away
HONOURS   **League:** West Sussex Division One 1938-39, 54-55, 56-57, 57-58, 58-59, 60-61.
FA Comps: None   Sussex County Division Two 1963-64, 75-76.
Colours(change): All blue

10 YEAR RECORD

08-09		09-10		10-11		11-12		12-13		13-14		14-15		15-16		16-17		17-18	
SxC1	10	SxC1	11	SxC1	17	SxC1	12	SxC1	18	SxC1	17	SxC1	20	SC1	13	SC1	7	SC1	9
FAC	P	FAC	2Q	FAC	EP	FAC	P	FAC	EP	FAC	EP	FAC	EP	FAC	EP				
FAV	3P	FAV	2Q	FAV	1Q	FAV	1Q	FAV	1Q	FAV	1Q	FAV	1Q	FAV	2Q	FAV	2Q	FAV	2Q

SIDLESHAM
Founded: 1921   Nickname: The Sids
Club Contact Details (T) 07887 981 267   **(E)** michael.maiden@virgin.net
Ground: Recreation Ground, Selsey Road Sidlesham Nr Chichester PO20 7RD
HONOURS   **League:** West Sussex Division One 1963-64, Premier 2011-12.
FA Comps: None   Sussex County Division Three 1996-97, 2012-13, Division Two 99-2000
Colours(change): Yellow and green

10 YEAR RECORD

08-09		09-10		10-11		11-12		12-13		13-14		14-15		15-16		16-17		17-18	
SxC2	18	SxC2	11	SxC2	16	WSuxP	1	SxC3	1	SxC3	5	SxC3	2	SC1	11	SC2	3	SC2	2
																		FAV	1Q

SOUTHWICK
Founded: 1882   Nickname: The Wickers
Club Contact Details (T) 01273 701 010   **(E)** clive.harman.1966@btinternet.com
Ground: Old Barn Way, Southwick BN42 4NT
Nearest Railway Station Fishersgate - 0.4km   **Bus Route** Old Barn Way - stop 151m away
HONOURS   **League:** West Sussex Senior 1896-97, 97-98. Sussex County Div.1 25-26, 27-28, 29-30, 47-48, 68-69,
FA Comps: None   74-75, Div.2 2000-01, Div.3 14-15. Isthmian D2S 1985-86.
Colours(change): Red & black

10 YEAR RECORD

08-09		09-10		10-11		11-12		12-13		13-14		14-15		15-16		16-17		17-18	
SxC2	11	SxC2	16	SxC2	12	SxC2	8	SxC2	14	SxC3	9	SxC3	1	SC1	5	SC1	11	SC1	18
FAC	EPr	FAC	Pr	FAC	EP														
FAV	1Qr	FAV	1Q	FAV	2Q			FAV	1Q	FAV	2Q	FAV	2Q	FAV	1Q	FAV	1Q	FAV	1Q

ST. FRANCIS RANGERS
Founded: 2002   Nickname: Saints/Rangers
Club Contact Details (T) 01444 474 021   **(E)** j.goss@yahoo.co.uk
Ground: Colwell Ground, Princess Royal Hospital, Lewes Rd, Haywards Hth RH16 4EX   **Capacity:** 1,000
Nearest Railway Station Haywards Heath - 1.9km
HONOURS   **League:** None
FA Comps: None
Colours(change): Black & white

10 YEAR RECORD

08-09		09-10		10-11		11-12		12-13		13-14		14-15		15-16		16-17		17-18	
SxC1	12	SxC1	16	SxC1	19	SxC1	19	SxC1	11	SxC1	10	SxC1	13	SCP	20	SC1	17	SC1	10
		FAC	EP	FAC	EP	FAC	EP	FAC	EP	FAC	EP	FAC	P	FAC	EP	FAC	EP		
FAV	2P	FAV	1Q	FAV	1P	FAV	1Q	FAV	1P	FAV	1Q	FAV	2Q	FAV	2Q	FAV	1Q	FAV	1Qr

STEYNING TOWN
Founded: 1892   Nickname: The Barrowmen
Club Contact Details (T) 01903 814 601   **(E)** sensec@stcfc.co.uk
Ground: The Shooting Field, Steyning, West Sussex BN44 3RQ
Bus Route Middle Mead - stop 52m away
HONOURS   **League:** Brighton, H&D Division Two 1933-34, 38-39.
FA Comps: None   Sussex County Division Two 1977-78, Division One 1984-85, 85-86.
Colours(change): Red & white

10 YEAR RECORD

08-09		09-10		10-11		11-12		12-13		13-14		14-15		15-16		16-17		17-18	
SxC2	13	SxC2	17	SxC2	16	SxC2	13	SxC2	10	SxC2	11	SxC2	10	SC1	10	SC1	6	SC1	11
																		FAC	P
FAV	1Q					FAV	1Q	FAV	1Q	FAV	1Q	FAV	2Q	FAV	2P	FAV	1Q	FAV	2Q

STORRINGTON
Founded: 1920 **Nickname:** The Swans

Club Contact Details (T) 01903 745 860   **(E)** keithdalmon@btinternet.com
Ground: Recreation Ground, Pulborough Road, Storrington RH20 4HJ
Nearest Railway Station Pulborough - 5.6km   **Bus Route** Brow Close - stop 238m away
HONOURS   **League:** Sussex County Division Three 2004-05.
FA Comps: None
Colours(change): All blue

10 YEAR RECORD

08-09		09-10		10-11		11-12		12-13		13-14		14-15		15-16		16-17		17-18	
SxC2	12	SxC2	7	SxC2	8	SxC2	9	SxC2	10	SxC2	15	SxC2	14	SC1	4	SC1	12	SC1	15

WICK
Founded: 2013 **Nickname:**

Club Contact Details (T) 01903 713 535   **(E)** wickfootballclub@outlook.com
Ground: Crabtree Park, Coomes Way, Wick, Littlehampton, W Sussex BN17 7LS   **Capacity:** 1,000
Nearest Railway Station Littlehampton - 1.7km   **Bus Route** Seaton Road - stop 250 m away
HONOURS   **League:** Sussex County Division Two 1981-82, 85-86, 89-90, 93-94.
FA Comps: None
Colours(change): Red & black

10 YEAR RECORD

08-09		09-10		10-11		11-12		12-13		13-14		14-15		15-16		16-17		17-18	
SxC1	4	SxC1	4	SxC1	15	SxC1	14	SxC1	16	SxC2	6	SxC2	3	SCP	16	SCP	19	SC1	5
FAC	EP	FAC	P	FAC	EP	FAC	EP	FAC	EP							FAC	EP	FAC	EP
FAV	1Q	FAV	1P	FAV	1P	FAV	1Q	FAV	2Q							FAV	1P	FAV	1Q

WORTHING UNITED
Founded: 1952 **Nickname:** Mavericks

Club Contact Details (T) 01903 234 466   **(E)** secretary@worthingunitedfc.co.uk
Ground: The Robert Albon Memorial Ground, Lyons Way BN14 9JF
Nearest Railway Station East Worthing - 1.9km   **Bus Route** Lyons Farm Sainsbury's - stop 203m away
HONOURS   **League:** Sussex County Division Two 1973-74, 2014-15, Division Three 1989-90.
FA Comps: None
Colours(change): Sky blue & white

10 YEAR RECORD

08-09		09-10		10-11		11-12		12-13		13-14		14-15		15-16		16-17		17-18	
SxC1	20	SxC2	2	SxC2	3	SxC1	14	SxC1	22	SxC1	20	SxC2	1	SCP	14	SCP	17	SCP	19
FAC	EP	FAC	EP	FAC	P					FAC	EPr	FAC	EP	FAC	EPr	FAC	EP	FAC	EP
FAV	1Q	FAV	2Q	FAV	2Q			FAV	1Qr	FAV	2Q	FAV	2Q	FAV	1P	FAV	1Q	FAV	1Q

Division Two 2018-19

1	Angmering Seniors	8	Montpelier Villa
2	Bosham	9	Roffey
3	Copthorne	10	Rottingdean Village
4	Cowfold	11	Rustington
5	Ferring	12	Upper Beeding
6	Jarvis Brook	13	Westfield
7	Littlehampton United	14	Worthing Town

MID SUSSEX LEAGUE

Premier Division

		P	W	D	L	F	A	GD	Pts
1	Lindfield	24	16	5	3	87	34	53	53
2	Willingdon Athletic	24	15	4	5	59	31	28	49
3	Cuckfield Rangers	24	14	4	6	66	31	35	46
4	Copthorne	24	14	4	6	72	43	29	46
5	Balcombe	24	13	3	8	56	40	16	42
6	Sporting Lindfield	24	13	2	9	54	34	20	41
7	AFC Ringmer	24	12	5	7	52	45	7	41
8	Forest Row	24	11	7	6	55	30	25	40
9	AFC Uckfield Town Res	24	7	1	16	40	74	-34	22
10	Buxted	24	5	4	15	27	50	-23	19
11	Rotherfield	24	5	4	15	29	55	-26	19
12	Peacehaven & Telscombe Res	24	3	5	16	21	87	-66	-14
13	Portslade Athletic	24	3	2	19	36	100	-64	11

Championship

		P	W	D	L	F	A	GD	Pts
1	Copthorne Res	18	12	2	4	59	23	36	40*
2	Burgess Hill Albion	18	13	1	4	56	31	25	40
3	Eastbourne Rangers	18	12	0	6	48	30	18	36
4	Polegate Town	18	9	3	6	47	29	18	31*
5	Roffey Res	18	8	2	8	31	32	-1	27*
6	Godstone	18	8	2	8	36	41	-5	26
7	DCK Maidenbower	18	7	2	9	31	38	-7	23
8	Ashurst Wood	18	6	2	10	41	49	-8	20
9	Nutley	18	5	3	10	35	57	-22	18
10	AFC Haywards	18	1	1	16	15	69	-54	4

Division One	P	W	D	L	F	A	GD	Pts
1 Charlwood	18	14	1	3	55	30	25	43
2 Crawley Devils	18	11	3	4	47	21	26	37*
3 West Hoathly	18	8	5	5	32	25	7	30*
4 Hurstpierpont	18	8	5	5	46	39	7	29
5 Ardingly	18	8	3	7	45	40	5	28*
6 AFC Varndeanians 3rds	18	8	2	8	38	37	1	26
7 Ansty Sports & Social	18	5	6	7	24	33	-9	21
8 Brighton & Sussex Medical School	18	4	5	9	27	42	-15	17
9 Furnace Green Rovers	18	5	0	13	30	55	-25	15
10 Montpelier Villa Res	18	2	4	12	30	52	-22	10

Division Two	P	W	D	L	F	A	GD	Pts
1 Balcombe Res	16	11	3	2	46	27	19	36
2 Ridgewood	16	10	2	4	41	34	7	32
3 Cuckfield Town	16	9	3	4	36	24	12	30
4 Jarvis Brook Res	16	7	4	5	28	24	4	25
5 South Godstone	16	7	2	7	45	42	3	23
6 Bolney Rovers	16	6	4	6	46	37	9	22
7 Copthorne 3rds	16	5	1	10	27	35	-8	16
8 Eastbourne Rangers Res	16	4	1	11	32	62	-30	13
9 Plumpton Athletic	16	3	0	13	29	45	-16	9

Division Three	P	W	D	L	F	A	GD	Pts
1 Willingdon Athletic Res	16	12	2	2	54	26	28	38
2 Cuckfield Rangers Res	16	10	4	2	49	20	29	34
3 Lindfield Res	16	9	3	4	52	29	23	30
4 South Park 'A'	16	8	4	4	42	32	10	28
5 Walton Heath	16	5	4	7	33	32	1	19
6 Dormansland Rockets	16	5	2	9	20	32	-12	17
7 Wivelsfield Green	16	5	2	9	27	48	-21	17
8 Stones	16	2	6	8	24	42	-18	12
9 Buxted Res	16	2	1	13	15	55	-40	7

Division Four	P	W	D	L	F	A	GD	Pts
1 Chagossian & Mauritian Association	16	14	2	0	59	16	43	44
2 AFC Hurst	16	10	3	3	41	28	13	33
3 Burgess Hill Rhinos	16	9	2	5	61	35	26	29
4 Ashurst Wood Res	16	7	2	7	31	33	-2	23
5 Wisdom Sports	16	5	3	8	35	51	-16	18
6 Peacehaven & Telscombe 3rds	16	5	2	9	26	41	-15	17
7 Montpelier Villa 3rds	16	4	4	8	31	53	-22	16
8 East Court	16	4	3	9	31	40	-9	15
9 Rotherfield Res	16	3	1	12	29	47	-18	10

Division Five	P	W	D	L	F	A	GD	Pts
1 AFC Bolnore	18	15	3	0	50	13	37	48
2 Fletching	18	12	3	3	69	21	48	39
3 Forest Row Res	18	11	2	5	52	33	19	35
4 AFC Ringmer Res	18	9	2	7	38	37	1	29
5 Handcross Village	18	7	3	8	26	32	-6	24
6 DCK Maidenbower Res	18	6	4	8	38	41	-3	22
7 Ifield Albion	18	5	5	8	25	51	-26	20
8 Polegate Town Res	18	4	4	10	33	55	-22	16
9 Roffey 3rds	18	2	5	11	20	40	-20	11
10 Ansty Sports & Social Res	18	2	3	13	33	61	-28	9

Division Six	P	W	D	L	F	A	GD	Pts
1 Crawley Panthers	18	14	1	3	66	21	45	43
2 Scaynes Hill	18	14	1	3	48	30	18	43
3 AFC Uckfield Town 3rds	18	13	2	3	59	25	34	41
4 Burgess Hill Albion Res	18	9	4	5	40	32	8	31
5 Eastbourne Athletic	18	6	4	8	30	34	-4	22
6 Fairfield	18	5	3	10	33	42	-9	18
7 Willingdon Athletic 3rds	18	4	5	9	32	37	-5	17
8 Plumpton Athletic Res	18	4	3	11	23	62	-39	15
9 Nutley Res	18	3	4	11	19	32	-13	13
10 Ditchling Res	18	3	3	12	19	54	-35	12

Division Seven	P	W	D	L	F	A	GD	Pts
1 East Grinstead Town 3rds	18	12	4	2	52	21	31	40
2 Newick	18	11	3	4	49	24	25	36
3 Oakwood Res	18	10	4	4	46	49	-3	34
4 Crawley Albion	18	9	2	7	67	20	47	29
5 Ifield Galaxy	18	8	4	6	45	47	-2	28
6 Lindfield 3rds	18	7	1	10	36	60	-24	22
7 Maresfield Village	18	6	2	10	27	36	-9	20
8 DCK Maidenbower 3rds	18	5	5	8	27	50	-23	20
9 Handcross Village Res	18	4	3	11	25	42	-17	15
10 Hartfield	18	4	0	14	31	56	-25	12

Division Eight	P	W	D	L	F	A	GD	Pts
1 Cuckfield Rangers Dev	18	10	5	3	48	18	30	35
2 Hurstpierpont Res	18	10	3	5	44	35	9	33
3 Barcombe Res	18	9	5	4	46	33	13	32
4 AFC Uckfield Town IV	18	9	3	6	39	38	1	30
5 Crawley United	18	7	6	5	53	42	11	27
6 Keymer & Hassocks	18	6	8	4	40	25	15	26
7 Ringmer Res	18	6	4	8	46	40	6	22
8 Ardingly Res	18	5	2	11	39	58	-19	17
9 East Grinstead Meads	18	4	4	10	40	70	-30	16
10 Scaynes Hill Res	18	3	2	13	46	82	-36	11

Division Nine	P	W	D	L	F	A	GD	Pts
1 Ashurst Wood 3rds	16	12	3	1	59	26	33	39
2 Fletching Res	16	11	2	3	83	34	49	35
3 West Hoathly Res	16	10	3	3	49	28	21	33
4 Stones Res	16	10	1	5	41	25	16	31
5 Ifield Galaxy Res	16	10	0	6	54	38	16	30
6 Crawley United Res	16	5	1	10	40	54	-14	16
7 Scaynes Hill 3rds	16	3	0	13	27	57	-30	9
8 AFC Hurst Res	16	2	3	11	29	63	-34	9
9 Fairfield Res	16	2	1	13	18	75	-57	7

SOUTHERN COUNTIES EAST LEAGUE

Founded: As the Kent League in 1966 **Sponsored by:** None
Recent Champions: 2015: Phoenix Sports **2016:** Greenwich Borough **2017:** Ashford United

PREMIER DIVISION	P	W	D	L	F	A	GD	Pts
1 Sevenoaks Town	38	27	7	4	93	33	60	88
2 Whitstable Town	38	25	7	6	74	30	44	82
3 Crowborough Athletic	38	22	6	10	79	43	36	72
4 Beckenham Town	38	22	3	13	84	61	23	69*
5 Croydon	38	20	5	13	77	60	17	65
6 Cray Valley PM	38	19	6	13	69	58	11	63
7 Deal Town	38	18	6	14	67	61	6	60
8 Lordswood	38	16	11	11	60	57	3	59
9 Corinthian	38	17	5	16	59	54	5	56
10 Canterbury City	38	14	12	12	63	55	8	54
11 Sheppey United	38	14	9	15	73	62	11	51
12 Glebe	38	15	6	17	58	71	-13	51
13 AFC Croydon Athletic	38	14	8	16	52	68	-16	50
14 Bearsted	38	14	4	20	48	58	-10	46
15 Tunbridge Wells	38	12	10	16	49	65	-16	46
16 Chatham Town	38	11	10	17	44	56	-12	43
17 Erith Town	38	11	6	21	47	69	-22	39
18 Hollands & Blair	38	9	4	25	51	82	-31	31
19 Rushall	38	7	8	23	46	87	-41	29
20 Rochester United	38	3	7	28	45	108	-63	16*

DIVISION ONE	P	W	D	L	F	A	GD	Pts
1 Punjab United	36	28	6	2	96	36	60	90
2 K Sports	36	29	4	3	106	32	74	88*
3 Fisher	36	24	4	8	96	39	57	76
4 Erith & Belvedere	36	19	6	11	86	61	25	63
5 Bridon Ropes	36	19	4	13	93	69	24	61
6 Snodland Town	36	18	4	14	84	72	12	58
7 Holmesdale	36	17	5	14	84	55	29	56
8 FC Elmstead	36	16	7	13	65	58	7	55
9 Kent Football United	36	21	5	10	108	73	35	53*
10 Lydd Town	36	17	2	17	88	77	11	53
11 Sutton Athletic	36	14	6	16	69	68	1	48
12 Sporting Club Thamesmead	36	14	3	19	73	75	-2	45
13 Stansfeld	36	13	6	17	80	88	-8	45
14 Phoenix Sports Res	36	13	5	18	59	61	-2	44
15 Meridian VP	36	11	6	19	67	82	-15	39
16 Forest Hill Park	36	9	6	21	56	96	-40	33
17 Gravesham Borough	36	10	5	21	59	94	-35	32*
18 Lewisham Borough	36	4	2	30	42	131	-89	14
19 Crockenhill	36	3	0	33	29	173	-144	9

CLUB MOVEMENTS

Premier Division - In: Fisher (P), K Sports (P), Punjab United (P).
Out: Rochester United (R) Sevenoaks Town (P - IsthSE), Whitstable Town (P - IsthSE).
Division One - In: Greenways (P - KC), Kennington P - KC), Welling Town (N).
Out: Fisher (P), Gravesham Borough (Resigned), K Sports (P), Punjab United (P).

PREMIER DIVISION	1	2	3	4	5	6	7	8	9	10	11	12	13	14	15	16	17	18	19	20
1 AFC Croydon Athletic		2-1	1-2	1-1	0-2	3-1	2-1	0-2	0-2	2-0	1-1	2-2	0-0	2-3	2-2	1-1	0-2	4-2	3-2	2-4
2 Bearsted	0-0		2-0	2-2	2-2	0-2	1-3	1-0	2-3	0-1	3-0	3-1	2-1	0-1	1-0	2-0	0-5	0-2	1-0	1-2
3 Beckenham Town	1-2	3-2		2-1	4-2	2-0	3-2	2-3	0-1	6-1	0-3	6-0	2-1	1-3	4-2	3-1	2-3	1-2	2-3	3-1
4 Canterbury City	5-0	0-1	2-3		1-0	1-0	2-5	0-1	2-2	1-3	3-1	1-2	2-1	1-0	4-2	1-0	0-0	2-2	5-1	2-2
5 Chatham Town	0-2	1-0	1-4	2-0		1-2	0-0	1-3	1-1	1-3	1-0	1-2	2-1	0-0	0-0	0-0	0-3	1-1	1-0	1-3
6 Corinthian	3-4	1-0	2-1	0-0	1-0		1-1	0-2	2-0	0-1	2-1	3-1	0-0	1-2	2-3	5-0	1-2	3-0	1-3	0-5
7 Cray Valley PM	1-0	1-0	1-2	3-3	2-1	0-0		1-4	2-3	3-2	2-4	3-0	2-1	3-1	1-1	0-2	2-1	2-3	1-2	2-1
8 Crowborough Athletic	1-0	3-0	2-2	2-1	2-2	2-3	1-2		2-3	2-1	2-2	3-0	1-1	6-1	4-2	1-2	1-2	2-1	0-1	
9 Croydon	1-3	3-0	2-0	1-3	0-4	1-4	3-1	2-2		3-2	2-0	0-1	6-2	3-0	2-0	2-1	1-2	2-2	2-3	0-2
10 Deal Town	3-0	1-1	2-0	1-4	2-0	0-0	1-0	0-3	3-1		2-1	4-1	4-1	1-6	6-3	4-2	1-2	0-0	1-1	2-1
11 Erith Town	0-1	4-3	0-4	0-1	2-1	1-5	2-3	0-2	0-2	0-0		1-2	2-1	0-3	0-1	2-0	1-2	0-2	1-0	1-1
12 Glebe	3-1	3-1	1-3	3-0	0-2	2-3	1-2	0-1	0-1	2-1	2-4		1-0	1-3	3-2	2-2	0-0	2-0	0-0	1-3
13 Hollands & Blair	1-2	2-4	2-3	1-1	0-3	2-1	1-5	1-1	1-4	1-2	4-1	2-1		4-3	3-2	3-0	1-3	1-3	3-0	1-2
14 Lordswood	3-1	2-1	1-1	0-2	2-1	1-0	2-1	0-4	3-3	1-0	1-1	0-2	3-1		3-1	2-1	1-1	1-0	1-2	1-2
15 Rochester United	1-3	1-3	A-A	0-2	2-2	3-4	1-2	2-4	0-5	1-4	2-4	2-5	1-0	2-2		1-2	0-6	2-2	1-3	0-4
16 Rushall	2-2	1-2	1-3	2-2	1-4	2-3	1-2	3-2	2-7	0-2	1-1	0-2	2-3	2-2	3-2		0-3	2-1	0-0	0-3
17 Sevenoaks Town	7-0	1-0	4-2	2-2	2-0	2-0	2-2	1-0	3-0	4-0	1-2	1-1	4-1	3-0	3-0	3-1		2-5	6-2	2-1
18 Sheppey United	1-3	0-2	2-4	3-1	7-1	3-0	2-1	0-2	2-3	3-3	3-1	6-2	1-2	3-3	4-0	1-2	1-2		1-2	0-0
19 Tunbridge Wells	1-0	1-4	1-2	2-2	1-1	1-3	0-2	1-4	1-0	4-3	1-2	1-2	2-1	1-1	1-1	3-2	0-0	1-1		0-1
20 Whitstable Town	3-0	3-0	1-1	2-0	0-1	1-0	1-2	1-0	2-0	3-0	2-2	4-2	2-0	1-1	3-0	2-0	2-1	1-0	1-1	

LEAGUE CHALLENGE CUP

HOLDERS: SEVENOAKS TOWN

ROUND 1

Tunbridge Wells	v	Rochester United	2-1
Sporting Club Thamesmead	v	Phoenix Sports Res	1-0
Meridan VP	v	Snodland Town	1-3
Stansfeld	v	Punjab United	4-1
Fisher	v	Kent Football United	2-1
Beckenham Town	v	Lydd Town	3-4
Corinthian	v	Gravesham Borough	7-1

ROUND 2

K Sports	v	Crockenhill	6-1
Tunbridge Wells	v	Rusthall	3-2
Sheppey United	v	Cray Valley PM	2-2, 4-5p
Sporting Club Thamesmead	v	Bearsted	3-2
Sevenoaks Town	v	Erith Town	2-3
Bridon Ropes	v	Hollands & Blair	0-2
Crowborough Athletic	v	Canterbury City	3-1
AFC Croydon Athletic	v	Lewisham Borough	2-0
Chatham Town	v	Erith & Belvedere	3-1
Forest Hill Park	v	Snodland Town	0-3
FC Elmstead	v	Stansfeld	3-3, 3-5p
Lordswood	v	Fisher	3-0
Whitstable Town	v	Holmesdale	2-0
Lydd Town	v	Croydon	1-4
Sutton Athletic	v	Corinthian	2-2, 4-3p
Deal Town	v	Glebe	6-3

ROUND 3

K Sports	v	Tunbridge Wells	0-1
Cray Valley PM	v	Sporting Club Thamesmead	3-1
Erith Town	v	Hollands & Blair	3-0
Crowborough Athletic	v	AFC Croydon Athletic	3-2
Chatham Town	v	Snodland Town	4-1
Stansfeld	v	Lordswood	1-2
Whitstable Town	v	Croydon	4-0
Sutton Athletic	v	Deal Town	0-3

QUARTER FINALS

Tunbridge Wells	v	Cray Valley PM	2-1
Erith Town	v	Crowborough Athletic	2-6
Chatham Town	v	Lordswood	2-2, 1-4p
Whitstable Town	v	Deal Town	1-0

SEMI FINALS

Tunbridge Wells	v	Crowborough Athletic	3-0 / 2-0
Lordswood	v	Whitstable Town	2-3 / 0-1

FINAL

Tunbridge Wells	v	Whitstable Town	0-1

DIVISION ONE		1	2	3	4	5	6	7	8	9	10	11	12	13	14	15	16	17	18	19
1	Bridon Ropes		1-2	5-2	2-1	2-3	2-0	4-4	1-1	0-1	0-4	5-1	2-1	3-0	2-2	0-3	5-3	3-1	5-1	4-0
2	Crockenhill	3-1		0-3	3-4	1-5	2-6	0-4	1-12	0-8	1-2	3-1	2-6	2-5	0-4	1-2	0-5	0-4	0-7	0-6
3	Erith & Belvedere	1-6	7-1		4-1	0-0	4-1	3-3	4-3	2-1	3-2	8-1	1-3	4-2	3-1	4-2	2-3	1-2	1-1	3-0
4	FC Elmstead	1-1	4-1	0-0		2-3	0-0	3-0	2-4	1-3	1-2	4-4	1-0	3-2	1-0	1-3	1-3	2-0	2-2	5-2
5	Fisher	2-4	6-0	2-0	2-0		1-3	2-1	3-3	2-2	0-3	4-1	9-1	3-0	3-0	1-2	3-0	6-1	2-1	3-0
6	Forest Hill Park	2-5	3-0	1-1	2-0	0-3		1-2	2-3	1-5	4-4	3-0	1-9	3-1	0-3	1-2	1-4	0-3	0-5	3-1
7	Gravesham Borough	3-4	3-0	0-6	2-3	0-6	2-1		0-3	0-2	5-1	4-3	1-2	0-2	0-3	1-7	1-3	1-1	1-3	3-1
8	Holmesdale	4-2	3-0	0-1	0-1	1-0	1-2	1-0		4-2	2-2	4-2	2-3	3-1	2-1	1-1	1-3	5-1	2-0	1-2
9	K Sports	3-1	9-0	3-0	1-0	2-0	2-0	4-0	1-0		3-3	7-0	2-1	3-1	6-3	1-0	2-0	2-4	4-2	2-1
10	Kent Football United	3-2	9-1	1-3	0-2	2-0	5-2	5-1	2-1	2-4		4-1	4-0	3-3	4-2	2-6	4-3	3-3	0-2	1-2
11	Lewisham Borough	1-4	4-0	2-4	0-2	0-4	1-1	0-4	1-8	1-3	0-3		1-4	2-3	0-3	0-5	0-2	1-5	4-5	0-5
12	Lydd Town	1-2	8-1	3-0	0-1	1-3	5-0	3-2	3-0	1-3	3-2	2-3		3-2	0-1	1-1	2-2	3-2	4-2	1-3
13	Meridian VP	1-2	2-0	2-2	2-3	1-3	1-1	0-1	1-1	0-3	2-3	4-3	4-2		1-0	2-4	2-2	5-3	5-1	1-2
14	Phoenix Sports Reserves	1-4	6-0	0-2	1-5	1-1	0-2	3-0	0-3	0-3	1-5	7-0	2-1	1-1		0-1	2-1	2-2	1-1	2-0
15	Punjab United	2-1	5-0	3-1	2-2	1-0	5-2	5-1	1-0	0-0	4-2	3-0	4-3	2-1	2-0		2-0	2-1	5-1	3-2
16	Snodland Town	0-2	6-0	0-1	2-1	1-3	3-2	3-6	3-2	1-4	2-3	2-0	0-1	3-1	3-2	1-1		2-0	1-4	5-3
17	Sporting Club Thamesmead	5-3	3-1	1-3	1-0	0-2	4-1	3-0	0-1	0-2	1-4	0-2	3-1	6-0	0-2	0-2	2-5		5-1	2-1
18	Stansfeld	4-2	5-2	2-1	3-4	1-3	4-4	2-2	3-2	0-2	3-6	1-0	5-2	0-3	1-2	0-1	3-4	3-2		1-1
19	Sutton Athletic	2-1	4-1	3-1	1-1	1-3	3-0	1-1	3-0	1-1	0-3	1-2	3-4	2-3	1-0	2-2	3-3	3-2	3-0	

AFC CROYDON ATHLETIC

Founded: 2012   Nickname: The Rams

Club Contact Details   (T) 020 8689 5322   (E) secretary@afccroydonathletic.co.uk
Ground: Mayfield Stadium, off Mayfield Road, Thornton Heath CR7 6DN

Capacity: 3,000   **Seats:** 301   **Covered:** 660   **Shop:** Yes

Colours(change): All maroon
Previous Names: None
Previous Leagues: Combined Counties 2012-15.

HONOURS: FA Comps: None
        League: None

10 YEAR RECORD

08-09	09-10	10-11	11-12	12-13	13-14	14-15	15-16	16-17	17-18
				CC1 8	CC1 7	CC1 2	SCE 11	SCEP 7	SCEP 13
					FAC EP	FAC EP	FAC EP	FAC EP	FAC P
				FAV 1P	FAV 1P	FAV 2Q	FAV 1Pr	FAV 2Q	FAV 2Q

BEARSTED

Founded: 1895   Nickname: The Bears

Club Contact Details   (T) 07849 089 875   (E) benton951@aol.com
Ground: Otham Sports Ground, White Horse Lane, Otham ME15 8RJ
Nearest Railway Station Bearsted - 3.2km
Capacity: **Seats:** Yes   **Covered:** Yes   **Bus Route** Arriva No.13

Colours(change): White and blue
Previous Names: None
Previous Leagues: Maidstone & District. Kent County 1982-2011. Kent Invicta (Founder Member) 2011-16.

HONOURS: FA Comps: None
        League: Maidstone & District Div.6 1961-62, Div.3 73-74, Div.2 74-75, Div.1 77-78, Premier 79-80, 80-81, 81-82.
                 Kent County WD2 82-83, WD1 83-84, WPrem 87-87, WSen 87-88, D1W 96-97, Prem 2000-01, 01-02. Kent Invicta 2015-16.

10 YEAR RECORD

08-09	09-10	10-11	11-12	12-13	13-14	14-15	15-16	16-17	17-18
KC P 6	KC P 8	KC P 8	K_Iv 7	K_Iv 4	K_Iv 6	K_Iv 2	K_Iv 1	SCEP 12	SCEP 14
									FAC EP
								FAV 1Q	FAV 1Q

BECKENHAM TOWN

Founded: 1887   Nickname: Reds

Club Contact Details   (T) 07774 728 758   (E) peterpalmer3@sky.com
Ground: Eden Park Avenue, Beckenham Kent BR3 3JL
Nearest Railway Station Eden Park - 0.3km
Capacity: 4,000   **Seats:** 120   **Covered:** 120   **Shop:** Yes

Colours(change): All red
Previous Names: Original club folded in 1969 and reformed based on the Stanhope Rovers Junior team in 1971.
Previous Leagues: London 1923-35, 51-61. Kent County Amateur 1935-51. Aetolian 1961-64. Greater London 1964-69. South East London
                 Amateur 1971-75. London Spartan 1975-82.
HONOURS: FA Comps: None
        League: London Division One 1927-28.

10 YEAR RECORD

08-09	09-10	10-11	11-12	12-13	13-14	14-15	15-16	16-17	17-18
Kent P 15	Kent P 4	Kent P 10	Kent P 6	Kent P 11	SCE 8	SCE 9	SCE 12	SCEP 18	SCEP 4
		FAC 2Q	FAC 2Qr	FAC 1Q	FAC EP	FAC EP	FAC P	FAC P	FAC EP
	FAV 3P	FAV 3P	FAV 1P	FAV 1P	FAV 3P	FAV 2Q	FAV 2P	FAV 1P	FAV 3P

CANTERBURY CITY

Founded: 1904   Nickname:

Club Contact Details   (T) 01795 591 900   (E) mjsexton@btinternet.com
Ground: Shepherd Neame Stadium, Salters Lane, Faversham ME13 8ND

Capacity: 2,500   **Seats:** 180   **Covered:** 180   **Shop:** Yes

Colours(change): Burgundy/burgundy/white (All green)
Previous Names: None
Previous Leagues: Kent 1947-59, 94-01, Metropolitan 1959-60, Southern 1960-94, Kent County 2007-11.

HONOURS: FA Comps: None
        League: Kent County Division Two East 2007-08, One East 08-09.

10 YEAR RECORD

08-09	09-10	10-11	11-12	12-13	13-14	14-15	15-16	16-17	17-18
KC1E 1	KC P 5	KC P 2	Kent P 9	Kent P 9	SCE 12	SCE 12	SCE 8	SCEP 9	SCEP 10
					FAC EP	FAC P	FAC P	FAC Pr	FAC EP
				FAV 1P	FAV 1Q	FAV 1Q	FAV 3P	FAV 2P	FAV 2P

CHATHAM TOWN

Founded: 1882 Nickname: Chats

Club Contact Details (T) 01634 812 194 (E) secretary@chathamtownfc.com
Ground: CJ Doors Stadium, Maidstone Road, Chatham ME4 6LR
Nearest Railway Station Chatham - 1.4km
Capacity: 2,000 **Seats:** 600 **Covered:** 600 **Shop:** Yes **Bus Route** Bus stops outside the ground.

Colours(change): All red & black
Previous Names: Chatham FC 1882-1974, Medway FC 1974-79
Previous Leagues: Southern 1894-1900, 1920-21, 27-29, 83-88, 2001-06, Kent 1894-96, 1901-1905, 29-59, 68-83, 88-2001, Aetolian 1959-64, Metropolitan 1964-68, ISthmian 2006-17.
HONOURS: FA Comps: None
League: Kent 1894-95, 1903-04, 04-05, 71-72, 73-74, 75-76, 76-77, 79-80, 2000-01. Aetolian 1963-64.

10 YEAR RECORD

08-09	09-10	10-11	11-12	12-13	13-14	14-15	15-16	16-17	17-18
Isth1N 10	Isth1S 17	Isth1N 21	Isth1N 15	Isth1N 13	Isth1N 12	Isth1N 21	Isth1S 19	Isth1S 22	SCEP 16
FAC 1Q	FAC 1Qr	FAC P	FAC 1Q	FAC 1Q	FAC 4Q	FAC P	FAC 2Q	FAC Pr	FAC EPr
FAT 1Q	FAT P	FAT P	FAT P	FAT 1Q	FAT 2Q	FAT 1Qr	FAT 1Q	FAT P	FAV 2Q

CORINTHIAN

Founded: 1972 Nickname: The Hoops

Club Contact Details (T) 01474 573 116 (E) corinthians@billingsgroup.com
Ground: Gay Dawn Farm, Valley Road, Longfield DA3 8LY
Nearest Railway Station Longfield - 1.5 miles away
Capacity: **Seats:** Yes **Covered:** Yes

Colours(change): Green & white hoops
Previous Names: Welling United Reserves > 2009.
Previous Leagues: Southern 1985-91.

HONOURS: FA Comps: None
League: Southern Counties East 2003-04.

10 YEAR RECORD

08-09	09-10	10-11	11-12	12-13	13-14	14-15	15-16	16-17	17-18
Kent 2 6	Kent P 14	Kent P 12	Kent P 7	Kent P 4	SCE 5	SCE 6	SCE 6	SCEP 10	SCEP 9
			FAC P	FAC P	FAC P	FAC P	FAC P	FAC EP	FAC EPr
		FAV 1P	FAV 2Q	FAV 1Q	FAV 1P	FAV 1P	FAV 1P	FAV 4P	FAV 2P

CRAY VALLEY PAPER MILLS

Founded: 1919 Nickname: Millers

Club Contact Details (T) 07834 546 213 (E) jtaylor171.209@lgflmail.org
Ground: Badgers Sports, Middle Park Avenue, Eltham SE9 5HT
Nearest Railway Station Mottingham - 30min walk from ground.
Capacity: 1,000 **Seats:** 100 **Covered:** Yes **Bus Route** 160 stops outside the ground.

Colours(change): Green & black
Previous Names: None
Previous Leagues: Spartan 1991-97, Spartan South Midlands 1997-98, London Intermediate 1998-01, Kent County 2001-11.

HONOURS: FA Comps: None
League: Sidcup & Kent Division Two 1919-20. South Kent County Division Three (Western) 1933-37, Division One 2002
-03, Premier Division 2004-05. London Alliance Premier Division 1980-81.

10 YEAR RECORD

08-09	09-10	10-11	11-12	12-13	13-14	14-15	15-16	16-17	17-18
KC P 5	KC P 6	KC P 3	Kent P 11	Kent P 8	SCE 7	SCE 7	SCE 10	SCEP 4	SCEP 6
					FAC P	FAC EP	FAC P	FAC P	FAC 1Q
				FAV 1Q	FAV 2Pr	FAV 2Q	FAV 1P	FAV 1Q	FAV 1P

CROWBOROUGH ATHLETIC

Founded: 1894 Nickname: The Crows

Club Contact Details (T) 07879 434 467 (E) emgillett@hotmail.co.uk
Ground: Crowborough Co. Stadium, Alderbrook Rec, Fermor Road, TN6 3DJ

Capacity: 2,000 **Seats:** 150 **Covered:** 150

Colours(change): Navy blue and sky blue
Previous Names:
Previous Leagues: Sussex County 1974-2008. Isthmian 2008-09. Sussex County 2009-14.

HONOURS: FA Comps: None
League: Sussex County Division Two 1992-93, 2004-05, Division Three 2003-04, Division One 2007-08.

10 YEAR RECORD

08-09	09-10	10-11	11-12	12-13	13-14	14-15	15-16	16-17	17-18
Isth1S 22	SxC1 18	SxC1 12	SxC1 13	SxC1 15	SxC1 5	SCE 10	SCE 7	SCEP 2	SCEP 3
FAC 3Qr	FAC EPr	FAC EP	FAC EP	FAC P	FAC EPr	FAC EPr	FAC EPr	FAC EP	FAC 2Q
FAT 1Q	FAV 2P	FAV 1Q	FAV 1Q	FAV 1Q	FAV 2P	FAV 1Q	FAV 1Q	FAV 5P	FAV 4P

CROYDON

Founded: 1953   Nickname: The Trams

Club Contact Details **(T)** 02086 545524 (CH-0208 6548555)   **(E)** judy@kinetic-foundation.org.uk
Ground: Croydon Sports Arena, Albert Road, South Norwood SE25 4QL
Nearest Railway Station Croydon Tramlink - 1/4 mile
Capacity: 8,000 **Seats:** 500   **Covered:** 1,000   **Shop:** Yes   **Bus Route** No.312

Colours(change): Sky & navy blue
Previous Names: Croydon Amateurs 1953-73.
Previous Leagues: Surrey Senior 1953-63. Spartan 1963-64. Athenian 1964-74. Isthmian1974- 2006. Kent 2006-09. Combined Counties 2009-14.

HONOURS: FA Comps: None
League: Spartan 1963-64. Athenian Division Two 1965-66. Isthmian Division One 1999-00.

10 YEAR RECORD

	08-09		09-10		10-11		11-12		12-13		13-14		14-15		15-16		16-17		17-18	
	Kent P	9	CCP	16	CCP	20	CCP	16	CCP	14	CCP	13	SCE	18	SCE	18	SCEP	11	SCEP	5
FAC		P	FAC	EP	FAC	P	FAC	EP	FAC	EP	FAC	P	FAC	1Q	FAC	2Q	FAC	Pr	FAC	Pr
FAV		4P	FAV	2P	FAV	1P	FAV	1Q	FAV	3P	FAV	2Q	FAV	1Qr	FAV	1P	FAV	4P	FAV	2P

DEAL TOWN

Founded: 1908   Nickname: The Hoops

Club Contact Details **(T)** 01304 375 623   **(E)** secretary@dealtownfc.co.uk
Ground: Charles Sports Ground, St Leonards Road, Deal CT14 9AU
Nearest Railway Station Deal - 3/4 mile away
Capacity: 2,500 **Seats:** 180   **Covered:** 180   **Shop:** Yes

Colours(change): Black & white
Previous Names: Deal Cinque Ports FC > 1920
Previous Leagues: Thanet. East Kent. Kent. Aetolian. Southern. Greater London.

HONOURS: FA Comps: FA Vase 1999-2000
League: Kent 1953-54. Southern Counties East 1999-2000.

10 YEAR RECORD

	08-09		09-10		10-11		11-12		12-13		13-14		14-15		15-16		16-17		17-18	
	Kent P	12	Kent P	9	Kent P	11	Kent P	15	Kent P	12	SCE	13	SCE	13	SCE	9	SCEP	13	SCEP	7
FAC		EPr	FAC	1Qr	FAC	P	FAC	P	FAC	EP	FAC	P	FAC	Pr	FAC	2Q	FAC	EP	FAC	P
FAV		2Q	FAV	1Q	FAV	1Q	FAV	2P	FAV	2P	FAV	1Q	FAV	1Q	FAV	2P	FAV	2Qr	FAV	2P

ERITH TOWN

Founded: 1959   Nickname: The Dockers

Club Contact Details **(T)** 07877 766 794   **(E)** secretary@erithtown.co.uk
Ground: Erith Stadium, Avenue Road, Erith DA8 3AT
Nearest Railway Station Erith
Capacity: **Seats:** Yes   **Covered:** Yes

Colours(change): Red & black stripes
Previous Names: Woolwich Town 1959-89 and 1990-97.
Previous Leagues: London Metropolitan Sunday. London Spartan.

HONOURS: FA Comps: None
League: London Metropolitan Sunday Senior Section 1965-66, 70-71, 74-75.

10 YEAR RECORD

	08-09		09-10		10-11		11-12		12-13		13-14		14-15		15-16		16-17		17-18	
	Kent P	7	Kent P	12	Kent P	8	Kent P	4	Kent P	3	SCE	3	SCE	19	SCE	13	SCEP	17	SCEP	17
FAC		P	FAC	1Qr	FAC	2Q	FAC	2Q	FAC	EP	FAC	P	FAC	EP	FAC	P	FAC	P	FAC	1Q
FAV		2Q	FAV	1P	FAV	2Q	FAV	2P	FAV	2P	FAV	3P	FAV	2P	FAV	2Q	FAV	1Q	FAV	2P

FISHER

Founded: 1908   Nickname: The Fish

Club Contact Details **(T)**   **(E)** secretary.fisherfc@yahoo.com
Ground: St Pauls Sports Ground, Salter Road, Rotherhithe, London SE16

Capacity: **Seats:**   **Covered:**

Colours(change): Black & white stripes
Previous Names: Fisher Athletic. Reformed as Fisher F.C. in 2009.
Previous Leagues: Parthenon, Kent Amateur, London Spartan, Southern, Isthmian, Conference.

HONOURS: FA Comps: None
League: Southern Southern Division 1982-83, Premier 86-87, Eastern 2004-05.

10 YEAR RECORD

	08-09		09-10		10-11		11-12		12-13		13-14		14-15		15-16		16-17		17-18	
	Conf S	22	Kent P	13	Kent P	16	Kent P	10	Kent P	14	SCEP	14	SCEP	16	SCEP	17	SCEP	19	SCE1	3
FAC		2Q					FAC	P	FAC	EPr	FAC	EP	FAC	P	FAC	EP				
FAT		3Q			FAV	1P	FAV	2Q	FAV	2Q	FAV	2Q	FAV	1Pr	FAV	2P			FAV	1P

GLEBE

Founded: 2013   Nickname:

GLEBE FC

Club Contact Details (T) 07903 274 178
(E) Glebefc.clubsecretary@gmail.com
Ground: Foxbury Avenue, Chislehurst, Bromley BR7 6SD
Nearest Railway Station Sidcup - 1.9km
Capacity: 1,200 **Seats:** Yes **Covered:** Yes
Bus Route Nos. 269 & 260.

Colours(change): Red & black
Previous Names: Glebe Wickham Youth Team founded in 1995 with an adult side formed in 2013.
Previous Leagues: Kent Invicta 2013-16.

HONOURS: FA Comps: None
League: Southern Counties east Division One 2016-17.

10 YEAR RECORD									
08-09	09-10	10-11	11-12	12-13	13-14	14-15	15-16	16-17	17-18
					K_lv 10	K_lv 7	K_lv 3	SCE1 1	SCEP 12
							FAC EP	FAC EP	FAC 2Qr
					FAV 2Q	FAV 1Q	FAV 1Q	FAV 3P	FAV 1Qr

HOLLANDS & BLAIR

Founded: 1970   Nickname: Blair

HOLLANDS & BLAIR F.C.

Club Contact Details (T) 01634 573839
(E) laurence.plummer@btinternet.com
Ground: Star Meadow Sports Club, Darland Avenue, Gillingham, Kent ME7 3AN

Capacity: **Seats:** Yes **Covered:** Yes

Colours(change): All red
Previous Names: Hollands & Blair United 1970-74
Previous Leagues: Rochester & District 1970-2004. Kent County 2004-11

HONOURS: FA Comps: None
League: Rochester & District Premier 1989-90, 93-94, 2002-03, 03-04. Kent County Division Two Easy 2004-05, Division
One East 05-06, Premier 08-9, 10-11. Kent Invicta 2013-14, 14-15.

10 YEAR RECORD									
08-09	09-10	10-11	11-12	12-13	13-14	14-15	15-16	16-17	17-18
KC P 1	KC P 2	KC P 1	K_lv 3	K_lv 2	K_lv 1	K_lv 1	SCE 2	SCEP 8	SCEP 18
								FAC Pr	FAC P
							FAV 2Q	FAV 1P	FAV 1P

K SPORTS

Founded: 1919   Nickname: The

K SPORTS

Club Contact Details (T) 07725 941 711
(E) tonyhighsted@yahoo.co.uk
Ground: Cobdown Sports & Social Club, Station Road, Ditton, Aylesford, Kent ME20 6AU
Nearest Railway Station Aylesford
Capacity: **Seats:** **Covered:**

Colours(change): Black & white
Previous Names: Reeds International. APM. APM Contrast.
Previous Leagues: Kent County >2015.

HONOURS: FA Comps: None
League: Kent Division Two 1929-30, 30-31, 31-32, 46-47.
Kent County Senior Division West 1959-60, 63-64, Premier West 1990-91.

10 YEAR RECORD									
08-09	09-10	10-11	11-12	12-13	13-14	14-15	15-16	16-17	17-18
KC1E 5	KC1E 5	KC1E 2	KC P 6	KC P 6	KC P 3	KC P 4	K_lv 6	SCE1 5	SCE1 2
									FAV 1P

LORDSWOOD

Founded: 1968   Nickname: Lords

Club Contact Details (T) 01634 669 138
(E) slew1953@hotmail.co.uk
Ground: Martyn Grove, Northdane Way, Walderslade, ME5 8YE
Nearest Railway Station Chatham - 4.8km
Capacity: 600 **Seats:** 123 **Covered:** 123
Bus Route Lords Wood Leisure Centre - stop 30m away

Colours(change): Orange & black
Previous Names: None.
Previous Leagues: Rochester & Dist. Kent County.

HONOURS: FA Comps: None
League: None

10 YEAR RECORD									
08-09	09-10	10-11	11-12	12-13	13-14	14-15	15-16	16-17	17-18
Kent P 16	Kent P 16	Kent P 13	Kent P 12	Kent P 5	SCE 11	SCE 15	SCE 4	SCEP 16	SCEP 8
FAC EPr	FAC Pr	FAC EP	FAC P	FAC Pr	FAC EP	FAC Pr	FAC EP	FAC EPr	FAC EP
FAV 1P	FAV 1Q	FAV 1P	FAV 1P	FAV 4P	FAV 3P	FAV 1P	FAV 3P	FAV 1P	FAV 3P

PUNJAB UNITED
Founded: 2003   **Nickname:**

Club Contact Details   **(T)** 01474 323 817   **(E)** jindi_banwait@hotmail.com
Ground: Elite Venue, Hawkins Avenue, Dunkirk Close, Gravesend, Kent DA12 5ND
Nearest Railway Station Gravesend - 2.7km
Capacity: **Seats:**   **Covered:**

Colours(change):   All red with white trim
Previous Names: None
Previous Leagues: Kent County >2017.

HONOURS: FA Comps: None
       League: Kent County Premier 2016-17. Southern Counties East Division One 2017-18.

10 YEAR RECORD

08-09	09-10	10-11	11-12	12-13	13-14	14-15	15-16	16-17	17-18
								KC P 1	SCE1 1

RUSTHALL
Founded: 1899   **Nickname:** The Rustics

Club Contact Details   **(T)** 07976 386 527   **(E)** dean.Jacquin@optima-group.co.uk
Ground: Jockey Farm, Nellington Road, Rusthall, Tunbridge Wells, Kent TN4 8SH
Nearest Railway Station High Rocks - 1.5km
Capacity: **Seats:** Yes   **Covered:** Yes

Colours(change):   Green & white stripes
Previous Names: None
Previous Leagues: Tunbridge Wells 1899-1983. Kent County 1983-2011. Kent Invicta 2011-16.

HONOURS: FA Comps: None
       League: Tunbridge Wells 1904-05, 22-23, 23-24, 24-25, 25-26, 29-30, 30-31, 34-35, 37-38, 38-39, 51-52.
10 YEAR RECORD   Kent county Division Two West 1983-84, Division One West 1984-85, 2004-05.

08-09	09-10	10-11	11-12	12-13	13-14	14-15	15-16	16-17	17-18
KC P 11	KC P 7	KC P 14	K_lv 11	K_lv 12	K_lv 7	K_lv 13	K_lv 19	SCE1 2	SCEP 19
									FAC EPr
								FAV 2Q	FAV 1P

SHEPPEY UNITED
Founded: 1890   **Nickname:**

Club Contact Details   **(T)** 01795 669 547   **(E)** jon.longhurst@bond-group.co.uk
Ground: Havill Stadium, Holm Park, Queenborough Road ME12 3DB

Capacity: 1,450   **Seats:** 170   **Covered:** 470

Colours(change):   Red & white stripes
Previous Names: AFC Sheppy 2007-2010. Sheppey & Sheerness United after merger 2013-14.
Previous Leagues: Kent County > 2014.

HONOURS: FA Comps: None
       League: Kent 1905-06, 06-07, 72-73, 74-75, 78-79, 94-95. Greater London Section B 1964-65.
10 YEAR RECORD

08-09	09-10	10-11	11-12	12-13	13-14	14-15	15-16	16-17	17-18
KC1E 2	KC1E 11	KC1E 11	KC1E 4	KC P Exp	KC P 2	K_lv 5	K_lv 2	SCEP 6	SCEP 11
								FAC EP	FAC P
							FAV 2Q	FAV 2Q	FAV 2P

TUNBRIDGE WELLS
Founded: 1886   **Nickname:** The Wells

Club Contact Details   **(T)**   **(E)** secretary@twfcexec.com
Ground: Culverden Stadium, Culverden Down, Tunbridge Wells TN4 9SG
Nearest Railway Station Tunbridge Wells 1.5km. High Brooms - 1.8km
Capacity: 3,750   **Seats:** 250   **Covered:** 1,000

Colours(change):   All red
Previous Names: None.
Previous Leagues: South Eastern. Southern Amateur. Isthminan. Spartan. Kent.

HONOURS: FA Comps: None
       League: Southern Amateur Section B 1909-10. Kent Division One 1984-85.
10 YEAR RECORD

08-09	09-10	10-11	11-12	12-13	13-14	14-15	15-16	16-17	17-18
Kent P 10	Kent P 7	Kent P 6	Kent P 5	Kent P 7	SCE 4	SCE 5	SCE 14	SCEP 15	SCEP 15
FAC P	FAC P	FAC 1Q	FAC P	FAC EP	FAC 1Q	FAC EP	FAC Pr	FAC EPr	FAC 2Q
FAV 2P	FAV 2Q	FAV 3P	FAV 4P	FAV F	FAV 3P	FAV 4Pr	FAV 2P	FAV 1P	FAV 2Qr

DIVISION ONE

SOUTHERN COUNTIES EAST LEAGUE - STEP 5/6

BRIDON ROPES
Founded: 1935   Nickname: The Ropes

Club Contact Details (T) 0208 856 1923   (E) cburtonsmith@gmail.com
Ground: Meridian Sports & Social Club, Charlton Park Lane, Charlton, London SE7 8QS
Nearest Railway Station Charlton - 1.3km
HONOURS   **League:** Spartan Division Two 1991-92. Kent County Division One West 2009-10.
FA Comps: None

Colours(change): Blue and red

10 YEAR RECORD

08-09	09-10	10-11	11-12	12-13	13-14	14-15	15-16	16-17	17-18
KC1W 3	KC1W 1	KC P 4	K_lv 4	K_lv 7	K_lv 8	K_lv 10	K_lv 5	SCE1 7	SCE1 5
								FAC EP	
							FAV 1P	FAV 1P	FAV 2Q

ERITH & BELVEDERE
Founded: 1922   Nickname: Deres

Club Contact Details (T) 07584 302 210   (E) csec.thederes@mail.com
Ground: Park View Road, Welling DA16 1SY
Capacity: 4,000
Nearest Railway Station Welling - 1.1km
HONOURS   **League:** Kent Division One / Premier 1981-82 / 2012-13.
FA Comps: None

Colours(change): Blue & white

10 YEAR RECORD

08-09	09-10	10-11	11-12	12-13	13-14	14-15	15-16	16-17	17-18
Kent P 8	Kent P 12	Kent P 5	Kent P 2	Kent P 1	Isth1N 24	SCEP 3	SCEP 16	SCEP 20	SCE1 4
FAC 2Q	FAC P	FAC 2Q	FAC 1Q	FAC EP	FAC P	FAC Pr	FAC P	FAC EP	FAC P
FAV 1P	FAV 2P	FAV 2P	FAV 1Q	FAV 3P	FAT P	FAV QF	FAV 2P	FAV 1Q	FAV 1Pr

FC ELMSTEAD
Founded: 1958   Nickname: The Cocks

Club Contact Details (T) 07930 430 526   (E) beverley.carpenter@btinternet.com
Ground: Sutton Athletic FC, London Hire Ground, Lower Road, Hextable, Kent BR8 7RZ
Nearest Railway Station Swanley - 2.4km
HONOURS   **League:** None
FA Comps: None

Colours(change): Sky blue & red

10 YEAR RECORD

08-09	09-10	10-11	11-12	12-13	13-14	14-15	15-16	16-17	17-18
					KC3W 2	KC2W 2	K_lv 11	SCE1 11	SCE1 8
							FAV 1Q	FAV 1P	FAV 1Q

FOREST HILL PARK
Founded: 1992   Nickname:

Club Contact Details (T) 07774 294 236   (E) info@fhpfc.co.uk
Ground: Ladywell Arena, Silvermere Road, Catford, London SE6 4QX
Nearest Railway Station Ladywell and Catford Bridge.   **Bus Route** 47, 54, 75, 136, 181, 185, 199, 208
HONOURS   **League:** South London Alliance Division One 2005-06. Kent County Division Two West 2009-10.
FA Comps: None

Colours(change): All blue

10 YEAR RECORD

08-09	09-10	10-11	11-12	12-13	13-14	14-15	15-16	16-17	17-18
KC2W 4	KC2W 1	KC1W 9	KC P 6	KC P 7	KC1W 10	KC1W 5	K_lv 13	SCE1 12	SCE1 16
									FAV 2Q

GREENWAYS
Founded: 1965   Nickname:

Club Contact Details (T) 0844 880 0048   (E) greenwaysfc@hotmail.com
Ground: K Sports, Cobdown, Station Road, Ditton, Aylesford, Kent ME20 6AU
HONOURS   **League:** Gravesend Premier x7. Kent County Premier 1988-89.
FA Comps: None

Colours(change): Green and black

10 YEAR RECORD

08-09	09-10	10-11	11-12	12-13	13-14	14-15	15-16	16-17	17-18
KC1W 7	KC1W 8	KC1W 5	KC P 8	KC P 7	KC P 5	KC P 7	KC P 8	KC P 2	KC P 2

www.non-leagueclubdirectory.co.uk   479

HOLMESDALE

Founded: 1956   Nickname: The Dalers

Club Contact Details (T) 07875 730 862   **(E)** mitchell1982@sky.com

Ground: Holmesdale Sp.& Soc.Club, 68 Oakley Rd, Bromley BR2 8HG

Nearest Railway Station Hayes - 2.1km

HONOURS **League:** Thorton Heath & District Division Six 1956-57, Two 61-62, One 71-72, Premier 86-87. Surrey South Eastern

FA Comps: None   Comb. Prem 92-93. Kent County Div.1W 2005-06, Prem 06-07.

Colours(change): Green & yellow

10 YEAR RECORD

08-09	09-10	10-11	11-12	12-13	13-14	14-15	15-16	16-17	17-18
Kent P 5	Kent P 10	Kent P 14	Kent P 13	Kent P 16	SCE 10	SCE 14	SCE 19	SCE1 6	SCE1 7
	FAC P	FAC EP	FAC EP	FAC EP	FAC P	FAC P	FAC P	FAC EP	FAC EP
FAV 1Qr	FAV 2Q	FAV 1Q	FAV 1Q	FAV 2Q	FAV 2Q	FAV 1Q	FAV 1Qr	FAV 2Q	FAV 1Q

KENNINGTON

Founded: 1888   Nickname:

Club Contact Details (T) 01233 611 838   **(E)** kevin@lab-services.co.uk

Ground: Homelands Stadium, Ashford Road, Kingsnorth, Ashford, Kent, TN26 1NJ

HONOURS **League:** Kent County Premier 2017-18.

FA Comps: None

Colours(change): Amber & black

10 YEAR RECORD

08-09	09-10	10-11	11-12	12-13	13-14	14-15	15-16	16-17	17-18
KC1E 6	KC1E 12	KC1E 10	KC1E 11	KC1E 4	KC1E 4	KC1E 2	KC P 2	KC P 4	KC P 1

KENT FOOTBALL UNITED

Founded: 2010   Nickname:

Club Contact Details (T) 07875 488 856   **(E)** m.bolton.kfu@gmail.com

Ground: Glentworth Club, Lowfield Street, Dartford DA1 1JB

Nearest Railway Station Dartford - 0.8 km

HONOURS **League:** None

FA Comps: None

Colours(change): All blue

10 YEAR RECORD

08-09	09-10	10-11	11-12	12-13	13-14	14-15	15-16	16-17	17-18
			K_lv 13	K_lv 11	K_lv 11	K_lv 15	K_lv 17	SCE1 4	SCE1 9
			FAV 2Q	FAV 1Q	FAV 1Q				

LEWISHAM BOROUGH

Founded: 2003   Nickname: The Boro

Club Contact Details (T) 07958 946 236   **(E)** raymondsimpson40@yahoo.com

Ground: Ladywell Arena, Silvermere Road, Catford, London SE6 4QX

Nearest Railway Station Ladywell and Catford Bridge.   **Bus Route** 47, 54, 75, 136, 181, 185, 199, 208

HONOURS **League:** Kent County Division One West 2003-04, Premier 2005-06.

FA Comps: None

Colours(change): Navy and sky blue

10 YEAR RECORD

08-09	09-10	10-11	11-12	12-13	13-14	14-15	15-16	16-17	17-18
KC P 9	KC P 10	KC P 6	K_lv 8	K_lv 16	K_lv 13	K_lv 16	K_lv 20	SCE1 19	SCE1 18
									FAV 1Q

LYDD TOWN

Founded: 1885   Nickname: The Lydders

Club Contact Details (T) 01797 321 904   **(E)** brucemarchant@hotmail.com

Ground: The Lindsey Field, Dengemarsh Road, Lydd, Kent TN29 9JH

HONOURS **League:** Kent County Premier East 1969-70, 70-71, Senior East 1989-90, 90-91, 91-92, Division One East

FA Comps: None   92-93, 93-94.

Colours(change): Red and green

10 YEAR RECORD

08-09	09-10	10-11	11-12	12-13	13-14	14-15	15-16	16-17	17-18
KC1E 11	KC2E 11	KC2E 20	K_lv 12	K_lv 6	K_lv 2	K_lv 3	K_lv 8	SCE1 9	SCE1 10
									FAV 1Q

MERIDIAN VP
Founded: 1995   Nickname:

Club Contact Details (T) 0208 856 1923   **(E)** dtamna@globalnet.co.uk
Ground: Meridian Sports & Social Club, 110 Charlton Park Lane, London SE7 8QS
Nearest Railway Station Charlton - 1.3km
HONOURS   **League:** None
FA Comps: None

Colours(change): All sky blue

10 YEAR RECORD
08-09	09-10	10-11	11-12	12-13	13-14	14-15	15-16	16-17	17-18
KC2W 12	KC2W 11	KC2W 12	K_lv 15	K_lv 15	K_lv 14	K_lv 12	K_lv 12	SCE1 17	SCE1 15
							FAV 1P	FAV 1Q	FAV 2P

PHOENIX SPORTS RESERVES
Founded: 1935   Nickname:

Club Contact Details (T) 07795 182 927   **(E)** alf-levy@sky.com
Ground: Phoenix Sports Ground, Mayplace Road East, Barnehurst, Kent DA7 6JT
Nearest Railway Station Barnehurst - 1.1km. Crayford - 1.2km
HONOURS   **League:** Kent Division Two 2011-12. Kent County Division Two West 2013-14.
FA Comps: None

Colours(change): Green and black

10 YEAR RECORD
08-09	09-10	10-11	11-12	12-13	13-14	14-15	15-16	16-17	17-18
			Kent 2 1		KC2W 1	KC1W 8	K_lv 14	SCE1 13	SCE1 14

ROCHESTER UNITED
Founded: 1982   Nickname:

Club Contact Details (T) 07775 735 543   **(E)** tony.wheelerrufc@yahoo.co.uk
Ground: Rochester United Sports Ground, Rede Court Road, Strood, Kent ME2 3TU
Nearest Railway Station Strood - 2.1km
HONOURS   **League:** Rochester & District Division One 1997-98. Kent County Division One West 2007-08. Kent Invicta
2011-12.
FA Comps: None

Colours(change): Red and black

10 YEAR RECORD
08-09	09-10	10-11	11-12	12-13	13-14	14-15	15-16	16-17	17-18
KC P 10	KC P 12	KC P 15	K_lv 1	Kent P 13	SCE 15	SCE 20	SCE 15	SCEP 14	SCEP 20
							FAC 1Q	FAC Pr	FAC EPr
						FAV 1P	FAV 2Q	FAV 2Q	FAV 1Q

SNODLAND TOWN
Founded: 2012   Nickname:

Club Contact Details (T) 07999 457 864   **(E)** terry.reeves55@virginmedia.com
Ground: Potyns Field, Paddlesworth Road, Snodland ME6 5DP
Nearest Railway Station Snodland - 1.3km
HONOURS   **League:** None
FA Comps: None

Colours(change): Royal blue & yellow

10 YEAR RECORD
08-09	09-10	10-11	11-12	12-13	13-14	14-15	15-16	16-17	17-18
				KC P 11	KC P 4	KC P 9	KC1E 3	SCE1 8	SCE1 6
									FAV 1Q

SPORTING CLUB THAMESMEAD
Founded: 1900   Nickname: The Acre

Club Contact Details (T) 0208 320 4488   **(E)** lhsasfc@gmail.com
Ground: Sporting Club Thamesmead, Bayliss Avenue, Thamesmead, London SE28 8NJ
Nearest Railway Station Abbey Wood - 1.8km
HONOURS   **League:** South London Alliance Division One 2008-09.
FA Comps: None

Colours(change): Red & black

10 YEAR RECORD
08-09	09-10	10-11	11-12	12-13	13-14	14-15	15-16	16-17	17-18
SLAll1 1	KC2W 3	KC2W 4	K_lv 10	K_lv 5	K_lv 9	K_lv 6	K_lv 9	SCE1 10	SCE1 12
							FAC P	FAC EP	
						FAV 1Q	FAV 1Qr	FAV 2P	FAV 2Q

STANSFELD

Founded: 1961   Nickname: Palace

Club Contact Details (T) 07861 885 590   **(E)** stansfeldfc@hotmail.com
Ground: Glebe FC, Foxbury Avenue, Chislehurst, Bromley BR7 6HA

Nearest Railway Station Sidcup - 1.9km

HONOURS
FA Comps: None

League: Kent County Division Two (Western) 1958-59, Premier (Western) 62-63, 63-64, 77-78, Senior (Western) 84-85, 86-87, 88-89, 89-90, Premier 94-95, 2009-10.

Colours(change): Yellow & blue stripes

10 YEAR RECORD

08-09	09-10	10-11	11-12	12-13	13-14	14-15	15-16	16-17	17-18
KC P 3	KC P 1	KC P 13	KC P 2	KC P 9	KC P 6	KC P 2	KC P 4	KC P 9	SCE1 13
									FAV 2Q

SUTTON ATHLETIC

Founded: 1898   Nickname:

Club Contact Details (T) 01322 665 377   **(E)** guy.eldridge@btconnect.com
Ground: London Hire Stadium, Lower Road, Hextable, Kent BR8 7RZ

Nearest Railway Station Swanley - 2.4km

HONOURS
FA Comps: None

League: Dartford 1952-53, 53-54, 54-55, 56-57, 58-59, 59-60, 60-61, 61-62, 62-63, 63-64, 64-65. Kent County D2W 68-69, D1W 69-70, PremW 70-71, SeniorW 76-77.

Colours(change): Green & white

10 YEAR RECORD

08-09	09-10	10-11	11-12	12-13	13-14	14-15	15-16	16-17	17-18
KC1W 2	KC P 3	KC P 11	K_lv 6	K_lv 8	K_lv 3	K_lv 4	K_lv 4	SCE1 3	SCE1 11

WELLING TOWN

Founded: 2014   Nickname: The Boots

Club Contact Details (T) 07891 431 735   **(E)** wellingtownfootballclub@gmail.com
Ground: Bayliss Avenue, Thamesmead, London SE28 8NJ

HONOURS
FA Comps: None

League: Kent County Division Two West 2017-18.

Colours(change): Green and black

10 YEAR RECORD

08-09	09-10	10-11	11-12	12-13	13-14	14-15	15-16	16-17	17-18
								KC3W 2	KC2W 1

SPARTAN SOUTH MIDLANDS LEAGUE CLUB MOVEMENTS

Premier Division - In: Arlesey Town (R - Sth1S), Baldock Town (P), North Greenford United (LM - CCP), Potton United (P - UC1).
Out: Berkhamsted (P - SthE), Holmer Green (LM - HelP), Welwyn Garden City (P - SthE).

Division One - In: Amersham Town (P), Buckingham Town (LM - UC1), Park View (P).
Out: Baldock Town (P), St Neots Town Reserves (W).

Division Two - In: Bovingdon (LM - HertsP), Sarratt (P - Herts1).
Out: AFC Southgate (W), Amersham Town (P), Park View (P), Tring Town (W).

SPARTAN SOUTH MIDLANDS LEAGUE

Founded: 1998 **Sponsored by:** Molten

Recent Champions: 2015: Kings Langley **2016:** AFC Dunstable **2017:** London Colney

PREMIER DIVISION

		P	W	D	L	F	A	GD	Pts
1	Welwyn Garden City	40	32	4	4	100	33	67	100
2	Berkhamsted	40	26	10	4	113	54	59	88
3	Harpenden Town	40	27	5	8	97	55	42	86
4	Leighton Town	40	24	9	7	88	52	36	81
5	Biggleswade FC	40	22	7	11	96	61	35	73
6	Hadley	40	19	9	12	76	67	9	66
7	Leverstock Green	40	17	8	15	84	83	1	59
8	Biggleswade United	40	16	9	15	69	57	12	57
9	Wembley	40	15	8	17	76	68	8	53
10	Edgware Town	40	14	9	17	63	67	-4	51
11	Colney Heath	40	14	8	18	54	69	-15	50
12	Hoddesdon Town	40	14	6	20	64	72	-8	48
13	London Colney	40	14	6	20	55	72	-17	48
14	Holmer Green	40	11	13	16	53	75	-22	46
15	London Tigers	40	14	4	22	53	75	-22	46
16	St Margaretsbury	40	12	7	21	54	84	-30	43
17	Tring Athletic	40	11	9	20	59	71	-12	42
18	Crawley Green	40	10	6	24	59	90	-31	36
19	Oxhey Jets	40	8	11	21	56	89	-33	35
20	Cockfosters	40	9	8	23	52	85	-33	35
21	Stotfold	40	9	8	23	51	93	-42	35

Sun Sports withdrew - record expunged.

DIVISION ONE

		P	W	D	L	F	A	GD	Pts
1	Southall	38	30	4	4	116	36	80	94
2	Baldock Town	38	26	10	2	99	27	72	88
3	Winslow United	38	27	2	9	127	60	67	83
4	Broadfields United	38	23	6	9	94	59	35	75
5	Wodson Park	38	22	7	9	68	48	20	73
6	London Lions	38	22	3	13	93	73	20	69
7	Buckingham Athletic	38	18	11	9	77	51	26	65
8	Risborough Rangers	38	17	10	11	89	49	40	61
9	Harefield United	38	18	7	13	77	54	23	61
10	Enfield Borough	38	19	3	16	95	84	11	60
11	Brimsdown	38	13	9	16	80	84	-4	48
12	Bedford	38	14	6	18	55	90	-35	48
13	Rayners Lane	38	13	5	20	54	74	-20	44
14	Ampthill Town	38	11	8	19	70	77	-7	41
15	Hatfield Town	38	11	5	22	51	87	-36	38
16	Hillingdon Borough	38	11	4	23	60	106	-46	37
17	Langford	38	8	3	27	48	97	-49	27
18	Codicote	38	7	5	26	50	110	-60	26
19	FC Broxbourne Borough	38	7	2	29	58	104	-46	23
20	St. Neots Town Reserves	38	6	4	28	47	138	-91	22

DIVISION TWO

		P	W	D	L	F	A	GD	Pts
1	Park View	32	27	5	0	111	34	77	86
2	Aston Clinton	32	22	6	4	83	25	58	72
3	AFC Southgate	32	24	0	8	106	59	47	69*
4	Totternhoe	32	22	2	8	95	48	47	68
5	Old Bradwell United	32	18	6	8	77	42	35	60
6	Amersham Town	32	18	5	9	84	49	35	59
7	Mursley United	32	16	6	10	71	56	15	54
8	Loughton Manor	32	14	9	9	71	48	23	51
9	Unite MK	32	15	1	16	77	69	8	46
10	Pitstone & Ivinghoe	32	13	7	12	87	80	7	46
11	MK Gallacticos	32	13	6	12	87	85	2	45*
12	Clean Slate	32	7	5	20	35	101	-66	26
13	The 61FC (Luton)	32	6	5	21	38	93	-55	23
14	Grendon Rangers	32	5	4	23	39	81	-42	19
15	Berkhamsted Raiders CFC	32	5	4	23	41	96	-55	19
16	Tring Town AFC	32	3	5	23	27	86	-59	14*
17	Tring Corinthians	32	4	2	26	35	112	-77	14

PREMIER DIVISION

		1	2	3	4	5	6	7	8	9	10	11	12	13	14	15	16	17	18	19	20	21
1	Berkhamsted		4-2	2-0	3-1	3-2	6-0	2-2	4-0	4-1	8-0	3-1	2-2	5-5	7-0	2-1	2-4	4-1	3-1	3-1	0-4	2-1
2	Biggleswade FC	2-3		2-1	1-1	0-1	2-0	2-0	1-1	2-0	0-0	1-1	3-1	2-1	4-3	1-2	7-1	6-1	1-0	1-2	0-3	4-0
3	Biggleswade United	2-2	1-1		2-0	1-2	3-1	1-1	6-0	0-1	3-0	0-2	1-1	5-2	0-1	3-0	0-0	3-1	4-2	2-0	3-2	2-0
4	Cockfosters	0-4	1-2	3-2		0-1	3-0	0-1	0-5	2-1	2-4	1-1	2-3	2-2	0-1	1-1	4-2	0-0	3-1	2-2	1-2	1-3
5	Colney Heath	0-0	0-2	0-2	2-3		1-2	3-0	4-1	0-4	0-2	1-1	0-4	2-0	1-4	1-3	0-2	1-0	2-2	2-2	1-2	3-1
6	Crawley Green	1-1	1-3	3-2	3-0	2-2		1-1	1-2	1-2	3-2	5-0	1-2	2-2	1-4	2-3	0-1	3-0	3-2	4-2	0-2	1-2
7	Edgware Town	2-3	1-6	1-2	1-2	1-3	4-1		0-1	3-1	1-0	2-2	1-2	0-1	1-0	2-2	2-1	2-3	5-1	1-2	2-0	
8	Hadley	3-4	0-2	2-2	2-2	2-1	1-1	1-3		2-6	3-1	2-0	2-0	5-1	1-1	4-0	3-1	0-2	5-0	1-0	3-1	0-3
9	Harpenden Town	2-2	3-2	3-0	3-1	2-0	2-0	3-2	2-0		1-1	3-1	2-2	4-0	1-0	3-2	5-0	4-2	3-1	3-2	1-1	2-0
10	Hoddesdon Town	2-6	2-1	1-0	1-2	2-4	4-0	1-0	0-2	1-3		1-1	1-2	0-2	4-2	4-2	2-2	3-2	4-0	2-1	0-1	2-3
11	Holmer Green	0-3	2-7	2-4	4-0	2-2	1-1	1-0	1-0	0-0	0-4		1-0	1-3	0-0	1-1	0-4	0-2	3-0	2-1	1-2	
12	Leighton Town	0-0	3-3	4-0	2-1	1-0	3-2	1-3	0-0	4-1	1-0	4-0		6-2	3-2	4-1	2-0	3-1	0-1	3-1	0-2	2-1
13	Leverstock Green	2-2	5-3	3-1	3-4	1-1	1-2	3-0	4-2	1-2	3-2	1-4	1-3		2-2	3-0	3-2	3-0	0-1	1-0	0-2	2-2
14	London Colney	0-1	1-2	1-5	1-0	0-2	1-3	2-1	0-3	1-2	2-1	1-2	2-1			0-1	3-0	0-2	4-3	0-1	1-2	1-0
15	London Tigers	0-5	3-1	0-0	4-2	1-0	1-2	1-2	1-4	4-0	1-4	2-3	1-2	2-0	4-0		1-1	0-3	1-2	2-1	0-0	0-3
16	Oxhey Jets	0-1	0-2	0-0	3-2	1-2	4-2	2-2	3-4	1-2	3-0	2-2	1-4	1-4	0-4	4-1		2-3	1-1	1-5	1-4	0-1
17	St Margaretsbury	1-0	2-3	2-1	1-0	0-2	6-3	1-1	2-2	2-0	2-1	2-2	0-0	2-4	0-2	1-3	2-1		3-1	1-3	0-4	3-7
18	Stotfold	1-2	4-3	2-1	1-1	2-2	4-2	1-3	0-1	0-9	0-0	1-1	2-3	1-2	2-1	1-2	0-0			0-0	0-2	0-3
19	Tring Athletic	2-2	3-3	0-2	4-0	5-0	2-1	1-1	1-1	2-3	1-3	3-1	2-1	0-2	2-1	1-0	0-0	2-0	2-4		0-1	0-2
20	Welwyn Garden City	4-0	1-3	6-1	2-0	3-1	2-0	5-2	3-1	3-1	5-0	3-2	2-2	4-1	3-1	4-0	3-1	0-1				2-1
21	Wembley	1-3	2-3	1-1	4-2	3-0	4-0	1-2	2-2	3-7	1-1	3-1	3-3	1-2	1-1	0-2	2-2	6-1	2-0	0-1		

SPARTAN SOUTH MIDLANDS LEAGUE - STEP 5/6/7

CHALLENGE TROPHY

HOLDERS: LONDON COLNEY

ROUND 1

Aston Clinton	v	Harpenden Town	4-3
Edgware Town	v	Loughton Manor	2-1
Trying Athletic	v	Biggleswade United	1-1, 3-0p
Risborough Rangers	v	Leighton Town	3-2
Totternhoe	v	Oxhey Jets	1-2
Rayners Lane	v	Old Bradwell United	1-4
Bedford	v	Crawley Green	1-2
Holmer Green	v	Southall	2-4
Unite MK	v	Pitstone & Ivinghoe	2-2, 6-5p
Wembley	v	Ampthill Town	7-1
London Colney	v	Buckingham Athletic	3-1
Wodson Park	v	Berkhamsted Raiders CFC	4-0
London Lions	v	Codicote	2-1
Winslow United	v	New Bradwell St Peter	HW
London Tigers	v	St Margaretsbury	1-2
Hadley	v	Sun Sports	4-0
AFC Southgate	v	Grendon Rangers	3-2
Welwyn Garden City	v	St Neots Town Res	5-1
Clean Slate	v	Harefield United	2-8
Biggleswade FC	v	Amersham Town	2-0
Trying Town AFC	v	Park View	0-2
Cockfosters	v	MK Gallacticos	4-2
Hatfield Town	v	Hillingdon Borough	4-1
Colney Heath	v	Tring Corinthians	7-1
Langford	v	Stotfold	4-2
Enfield Borough	v	Broadfields United	2-3
Berkhamsted	v	Hoddesdon Town	2-2, 3-4p
Mursley United	v	Leverstock Green	0-3

ROUND 2

Aston Clinton	v	Edgware Town	0-2
Baldock Town	v	Tring Athletic	2-3
Risborough Rangers	v	Oxhey Jets	2-1
Brimsdown	v	Old Bradwell United	1-0
Crawley Green	v	FC Broxbourne Borough	1-1, 5-4p
Southall	v	United MK	2-1
Wembley	v	London Colney	1-1, 3-4p
Wodson Park	v	The 61FC (Luton)	3-0
London Lions	v	Winslow United	2-2, 3-4p
St Margretsbury	v	Hadley	1-4
AFC Southgate	v	Welwyn Garden City	2-7
Harefield United	v	Biggleswade FC	2-3

ROUND 3

Edgware Town	v	Tring Athletic	1-0
Risborough Rangers	v	Brimsdown	6-1
Crawley Green	v	Southall	0-3
London Colney	v	Wodson Park	1-0
Winslow United	v	Hadley	2-1
Welwyn Garden City	v	Biggleswade FC	2-3
Cockfosters	v	Colney Heath	1-0
Broadfields United	v	Hoddesdon Town	HW

QUARTER FINALS

Edgware Town	v	Risborough Rangers	2-3
Southall	v	London Colney	2-2, 4-5p
Winslow United	v	Biggleswade FC	1-2
Cockfosters	v	Broadfields United	0-4

SEMI FINALS

Risborough Rangers	v	London Colney	3-1
Biggleswade FC	v	Broadfields United	1-2

FINAL

Risborough Rangers	v	Broadfields United	1-3

(continued)

Park View	v	Cockfosters	1-3
Hatfield Town	v	Colney Heath	0-0, 4-5p
Langford	v	Broadfields United	0-5
Hoddesdon Town	v	Leverstock Green	5-0

PREMIER DIVISION CUP

HOLDERS: HODDESDON TOWN

SEMI FINALS

Welwyn Garden City	v	Hadley	3-0
Leighton Town	v	Harpenden Town	1-2

FINAL

Welwyn Garden City	v	Harpenden Town	1-3

DIVISION ONE CUP

HOLDERS: LANGFORD

SEMI FINALS

Baldock Town	v	London Lions	0-1
Ampthill Town	v	Southall	2-6

FINAL

London Lions	v	Southall	3-1

DIVISION ONE

		1	2	3	4	5	6	7	8	9	10	11	12	13	14	15	16	17	18	19	20
1	Ampthill Town		0-2	4-0	4-4	1-1	3-3	0-0	5-0	6-1	3-2	3-1	3-4	3-1	0-3	4-1	0-1	1-1	1-2	3-7	2-3
2	Baldock Town	4-1		7-0	3-0	4-2	1-0	4-1	4-0	3-1	0-0	2-1	3-0	3-0	3-0	0-0	1-1	1-1	4-0	2-0	2-1
3	Bedford	1-0	1-2		3-1	1-2	5-0	3-1	1-3	4-0	1-1	3-0	3-1	1-0	0-1	3-1	0-6	1-7	3-1	0-8	1-2
4	Brimsdown	0-2	2-2	1-1		3-2	A-W	2-0	3-1	5-3	3-2	2-2	1-3	5-2	2-1	2-2	1-6	2-6	1-1	4-2	2-3
5	Broadfields United	4-0	1-1	4-1	3-2		4-2	1-0	3-1	2-1	1-3	0-1	2-0	4-2	3-2	3-1	3-0	0-0	5-3	4-2	2-0
6	Buckingham Athletic	5-2	0-0	1-0	1-1	1-1		8-0	0-1	1-0	1-0	3-1	3-4	5-0	1-1	2-1	1-1	2-0	2-2	1-3	0-0
7	Codicote	1-0	0-6	3-1	0-6	2-3	1-2		0-5	2-2	3-3	0-1	1-3	1-2	2-6	1-2	3-4	0-2	4-2	1-4	1-2
8	Enfield Borough	0-3	0-2	8-0	2-1	0-4	2-2	1-3		2-1	1-1	8-4	2-2	4-1	4-2	3-2	2-0	1-4	3-0	2-3	6-2
9	FC Broxbourne Borough	3-0	0-2	1-2	1-4	0-4	1-3	4-5	3-4		1-3	2-3	3-0	3-2	2-1	2-1	1-6	0-4	7-0	0-4	1-2
10	Harefield United	3-0	1-3	1-2	1-0	2-2	1-3	1-0	4-3	4-2		2-1	2-0	3-0	1-2	3-1	2-2	2-4	7-1	1-2	1-2
11	Hatfield Town	2-2	0-7	2-3	4-1	1-1	1-1	1-1		3-2	1-3		3-2	1-3	4-0	4-3	1-1		0-3	0-2	
12	Hillingdon Borough	1-4	2-4	3-1	3-4	1-2	1-4	2-5	4-1	4-2	0-0	3-1		0-2	1-6	0-3	2-2	0-1	1-1	2-3	0-6
13	Langford	0-0	0-0	1-1	3-1	1-6	0-1	7-3	1-3	4-1	0-1	1-2	1-2		1-3	5-1	2-1	0-3	1-2	2-3	0-3
14	London Lions	2-1	1-4	3-3	3-3	6-3	3-1	3-1	4-2	4-2	0-3	3-1	4-2	4-0		3-0	2-0	4-6	0-1	3-2	2-0
15	Rayners Lane	2-0	1-2	0-0	1-3	4-0	1-1	1-1	0-2	4-1	1-4	1-0	1-3	2-1	1-0		1-0	0-4	4-0	5-3	1-2
16	Risborough Rangers	1-1	3-3	5-0	2-2	1-1	3-1	1-0	4-2	1-0	0-3	3-0	10-1	5-0	4-0	0-1		1-2	3-0	2-3	0-0
17	Southall	3-2	1-0	4-0	5-1	3-1	3-2	7-1	2-3	1-0	3-2	2-0	1-2	2-0	5-0	3-0	1-1		8-1	2-0	1-0
18	St. Neots Town Reserves	0-5	2-7	2-3	2-4	0-6	1-3	0-2	1-6	1-4	1-4	0-1	5-0	6-1	1-5	1-4	1-3	0-6		1-8	2-0
19	Winslow United	5-0	2-0	2-1	2-1	3-0	1-3	6-0	2-5	3-0	3-3	5-1	4-0	5-1	6-1	4-2	2-1	0-3	8-0		1-0
20	Wodson Park	3-1	1-1	1-1	1-0	3-2	1-7	2-0	3-0	1-1	1-0	1-0	2-1	3-0	1-2	5-0	1-1	2-1	3-2	3-3	

ARLESEY TOWN

Founded: 1891   Nickname: The Blues

Club Contact Details (T) 01462 734 504   (E)
Ground: New Lamb Meadow, Hitchin Road, Arlesey SG15 6RS
Nearest Railway Station Arlesey - 2.6km
Capacity: 2,920 **Seats:** 150 **Covered:** 600   Yes   **Bus Route** Prince of Wales - stop 100m away

Colours(change): Light & dark blue
Previous Names: None
Previous Leagues: Biggleswade & Dist., Bedfordshire Co. (South Midlands) 1922-26, 27-28, Parthenon, London 1958-60, United Co. 1933-36, 82-92, Spartan South Mid. 1992-2000, Isthmian 2000-04, 06-08, Southern 2004-07, 08-18.
HONOURS: FA Comps: FA Vase 1994-95.
League: South Midlands Premier 1951-52, 52-53, 94-95, 95-96. Spartan South Midlands Premier 1999-2000. United Counties Premier Division 1984-85. Isthmian Division Three 2000-01. Southern Division One Central 2010-11.

10 YEAR RECORD	08-09	09-10	10-11	11-12	12-13	13-14	14-15	15-16	16-17	17-18
	SthC 18	SthC 9	SthC 1	SthP 18	SthP 6	SthP 15	SthP 22	SthC 16	SthC 15	SthC 22
	FAC 2Q	FAC 1Q	FAC 1Q	FAC 1P	FAC 1P	FAC 3Q	FAC 1Q	FAC 1Q	FAC Pr	FAC 1Q
	FAT P	FAT 1Pr	FAT 2Qr	FAT 2Q	FAT 2Qr	FAT 1P	FAT 2Qr	FAT Pr	FAT Pr	FAT 1Q

BALDOCK TOWN

Founded: 1905   Nickname: The Reds

Club Contact Details (T) 07968 215 395   (E)
Ground: Arlesey Town FC, Armadillo Stadium, Hitchin Road, Arlesey SG15 6RS
Nearest Railway Station Arlesey - 2.6km
Capacity: 2,920 **Seats:** 150 **Covered:** 600   **Bus Route** Prince of Wales - stop 100m away

Colours(change): All red
Previous Names: Baldock 1905-21. Folded in 2001 reformed as Baldock 2003-06. Baldock Town 2006-08. Baldock Town Letchworth 2008-11.
Previous Leagues: Herts County 1905-25, 46-47, 2007-13. Beds & Dist/South Midlands 1925-39, 47-54, 64-83. Parthenon 1954-59. London 1959-64. United Counties 1983-87. Southern 1987-2001. North Herts 2003-06. North & Mid Herts (FM) 2006-07.
HONOURS: FA Comps: None
League: Herts Senior County Northern Div. 1920-21, Div.1 2007-08, Premier 11-12.
South Midlands Div.2 47-38, Div.1 49-50, Premier 27-28, 65-66, 67-68, 69-70.

10 YEAR RECORD	08-09	09-10	10-11	11-12	12-13	13-14	14-15	15-16	16-17	17-18
	HertP 3	HertP 3	HertP 4	HertP 1	HertP 2	SSM1 7	SSM1 10	SSM1 3	SSM1 3	SSM1 2
							FAC P	FAC EP	FAC EP	FAC 2Q
		FAV 1Q	FAV 1P			FAV 1P	FAV 1P	FAV 2Q	FAV 1P	FAV 1P

BIGGLESWADE FC

Founded: 2016   Nickname:

Club Contact Details (T) 01767 318 202   (E)
Ground: Biggleswade Town FC, Langford Road, Biggleswade SG18 9JT
Nearest Railway Station Biggleswade - 1km
Capacity: 3,000 **Seats:** 300 **Covered:** Yes   **Bus Route** Eldon Way - stop 260m away

Colours(change): Green & white
Previous Names: Based on Biggleswade Town's U18 side.
Previous Leagues: None

HONOURS: FA Comps: None
League: Spartan South Midlands Division One 2016-17.

10 YEAR RECORD	08-09	09-10	10-11	11-12	12-13	13-14	14-15	15-16	16-17	17-18
									SSM1 1	SSM P 5
										FAC EP
									FAV 2P	FAV 4P

BIGGLESWADE UNITED

Founded: 1959   Nickname: United

Club Contact Details (T) 07714 661 827   (E) info@biggleswadeunited.com
Ground: Second Meadow, Fairfield Rd, Biggleswade, Beds SG18 0BS
Nearest Railway Station Biggleswade - 0.9km
Capacity: 2,000 **Seats:** 260 **Covered:** 130   **Bus Route** Fairfield Road - stop 85m away

Colours(change): Red and navy
Previous Names: None
Previous Leagues: North Hertfordshire 1959-69. Midlands 1969-84. Hertfordshire Senior County 1984-86. Bedford & District 1986-96. South Midlands 1996-97.
HONOURS: FA Comps: None
League: Bedford & District Division Two 1990-91, Division One 91-92, Premier 94-95, 95-96.
South Midlands Division One 1996-97.

10 YEAR RECORD	08-09	09-10	10-11	11-12	12-13	13-14	14-15	15-16	16-17	17-18
	SSM P 1	SSM P 20	SSM P 20	SSM P 19	SSM P 18	SSM P 17	SSM P 13	SSM P 10	SSM P 9	SSM P 8
	FAC 1Q	FAC P	FAC EP	FAC P	FAC P	FAC 1Q	FAC 1Q	FAC 1Q	FAC 1Q	FAC EPr
	FAV 2P	FAV 2P	FAV 2Q	FAV 1P	FAV 2Q	FAV 1Q	FAV 2Q	FAV 2P	FAV 2Pr	FAV 1P

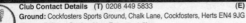

COCKFOSTERS
Founded: 1921   Nickname: Fosters

Club Contact Details (T) 0208 449 5833   (E) graham.bint@btinternet.com
Ground: Cockfosters Sports Ground, Chalk Lane, Cockfosters, Herts EN4 9JG
Nearest Railway Station New Barnet - 1.5km
Capacity: **Seats:** Yes   **Covered:** Yes   **Bus Route** Cockfosters - stop 200m away

Colours(change): All red
Previous Names: Cockfosters Athletic 1921-68.
Previous Leagues: Barnet 1921-30s. Wood Green 1930s-46. Northern Suburban Int. 1946-66. Hertfordshire County 1966-1991. Spartan 1991-97.

HONOURS: FA Comps: None
    League: Wood green DivisioN Two 1931-32, Division One 33-34, Premier 38-39. Northern Suburban Inter. Division One 1949-50, 60-61, Premier 61-62. Hertfordshire Senior County Division One 1966-67, Premier 78-79, 80-81, 83-84

10 YEAR RECORD

08-09		09-10		10-11		11-12		12-13		13-14		14-15		15-16		16-17		17-18	
SSM1	19	SSM1	11	SSM1	15	SSM1	9	SSM1	2	SSM P	8	SSM P	18	SSM P	9	SSM P	3	SSM P	20
FAC	EP	FAC	Pr	FAC	Pr	FAC	P	FAC	P	FAC	1Qr	FAC	P	FAC	1Q	FAC	EP	FAC	1Q
FAV	1Q	FAV	1P	FAV	1P	FAV	1Q	FAV	2P	FAV	2P	FAV	1P	FAV	1Qr	FAV	2P	FAV	1P

COLNEY HEATH
Founded: 1907   Nickname: Magpies

Club Contact Details (T) 01727 824 325   (E)
Ground: The Recreation Ground, High St, Colney Heath, St Albans AL4 0NP
Nearest Railway Station Welham Green - 3.6km
Capacity: **Seats:** Yes   **Covered:** Yes   **Bus Route** Crooked Billet Ph - stop 50m away

Colours(change): Black & white stripes
Previous Names: None
Previous Leagues: Herts Senior County League 1953-2000

HONOURS: FA Comps: None
    League: Herts County Division Two 1953-54 Division One 55-56, Prem 58-99, 99-00, Division One 88-89, Spartan South Midlands Division One 2005-06.

10 YEAR RECORD

08-09		09-10		10-11		11-12		12-13		13-14		14-15		15-16		16-17		17-18	
SSM P	12	SSM P	5	SSM P	5	SSM P	8	SSM P	13	SSM P	3	SSM P	14	SSM P	20	SSM P	18	SSM P	11
FAC	EP	FAC	EP	FAC	1Q	FAC	P	FAC	1Q	FAC	EP	FAC	P					FAC	2Qr
FAV	2Q	FAV	2Q	FAV	1P	FAV	1Q	FAV	2P	FAV	3Pr	FAV	1P			FAV	1P	FAV	1P

CRAWLEY GREEN
Founded: 1992   Nickname:

Club Contact Details (T)   (E) eddie.downey@hotmail.com
Ground: The Stadium at The Brache, Park Street, Luton LU1 3HH

Capacity: **Seats:**   **Covered:**

Colours(change): All maroon
Previous Names: None
Previous Leagues: None

HONOURS: FA Comps: None
    League: Spartan South Midlands Division Two 2004-05.

10 YEAR RECORD

08-09		09-10		10-11		11-12		12-13		13-14		14-15		15-16		16-17		17-18	
SSM1	16	SSM1	8	SSM1	4	SSM1	6	SSM1	4	SSM1	5	SSM1	7	SSM1	2	SSM P	11	SSM P	18
		FAC	P	FAC	1Qr	FAC	EP	FAC	EP	FAC	P	FAC	EP	FAC	EP	FAC	P	FAC	P
FAV	2Q	FAV	1Q	FAV	1Q	FAV	2Q	FAV	2Qr	FAV	1Q	FAV	2Q	FAV	2Q	FAV	1P	FAV	2P

EDGWARE TOWN
Founded: 1939   Nickname: The Wares

Club Contact Details (T) 0208 205 1645   (E) secretary@edgwaretownfc.co.uk
Ground: Silver Jubilee Park, Townsend Lane, London NW9 7NE
Nearest Railway Station Hendon - 1.1km
Capacity: 1,990 **Seats:** 298   **Covered:**   **Bus Route** Queensbury Road - stop 660m away

Colours(change): Green and white
Previous Names: Edgware 1972-87. Original Edgware Town folded in 2008 and re-formed in 2014.
Previous Leagues: Corinthian 1946-63. Athenian 1963-84. Spartan 1984-90, 2006-07. Isthmian 1990-2006, 2007-08.

HONOURS: FA Comps: None
    League: Middlesex Senior 1939-40, 43-44, 44-45 (shared). London Western Section 1945-46. London Spartan Premier 1987-88, 89 -90. Isthmian Division Three 1991-92. Spartan South Midlands Premier 2006-07, Division One 2015-16.

10 YEAR RECORD

08-09	09-10	10-11	11-12	12-13	13-14	14-15		15-16		16-17		17-18	
						SSM1	9	SSM1	1	SSM P	17	SSM P	10
										FAC	P	FAC	EPr
								FAV	3P	FAV	2Q	FAV	1P

HADLEY
Founded: 1882 Nickname: Bricks

Club Contact Details (T) (E) info@hadleyfc.co.uk
Ground: Hadley Sports Ground, Brickfield Lane, Arkley, Barnet EN5 3LD
Nearest Railway Station Elstree & Borehamwood - 2.8km
Capacity: 2,000 **Seats:** 150 **Covered:** 250 **Shop:** Yes **Bus Route** Brickfield Lane - stop 70m away
Colours(change): Red and black
Previous Names: None
Previous Leagues: Barnet & Dist. 1922-57, North Suburban 1957-70, Mid-Herts 1970-77, Herts Senior County 1977-85, 99-2007, Southern Olymian 1985-99, West Herts 2007-08.
HONOURS: FA Comps: None
League: Mid-Herts Premier 1975-76, 76-77. Hertfordshire Senior County Division Three 1977-78, Division One 2001-02, Premier 2003-04, 04-05. West Hertfordshire 2007-08.

10 YEAR RECORD	08-09	09-10	10-11	11-12	12-13	13-14	14-15	15-16	16-17	17-18
	SSM2 2	SSM1 2	SSM P 14	SSM P 15	SSM P 12	SSM P 13	SSM P 9	SSM P 6	SSM P 19	SSM P 6
			FAC EPr	FAC EPr	FAC P	FAC P	FAC EPr	FAC EP	FAC 3Qr	FAC 1Q
		FAV 2P	FAV 2Q	FAV 1P	FAV 1Pr	FAV 2P	FAV 2Qr	FAV 1P	FAV 1Q	FAV 2Qr

HARPENDEN TOWN
Founded: 1891 Nickname: Town

Club Contact Details (T) 07734700226/07702604771 (E)
Ground: Rothamstead Park, Amenbury Lane, Harpenden AL5 2EF
Nearest Railway Station Harpenden - 0.6km
Capacity: **Seats:** Yes **Covered:** Yes **Bus Route** Amenbury Lane - stop 250m away
Colours(change): Yellow & blue
Previous Names: Harpenden FC 1891-1908.
Previous Leagues: Herts Senior County (founder member) 1898-1900, 1908-22, 48-57. Mid-Herts 1900-08. South Midlands 1957-97.
HONOURS: FA Comps: None
League: Herts Senior County Western Division 1910-11, 11-12, 20-21, Premier 50-51, 52-53, 54-55. South Midlands Division One 1989-90, Premier 61-62, 64-65.

10 YEAR RECORD	08-09	09-10	10-11	11-12	12-13	13-14	14-15	15-16	16-17	17-18
	SSM1 8	SSM1 12	SSM1 7	SSM1 5	SSM1 7	SSM1 8	SSM1 6	SSM1 4	SSM1 2	SSM P 3
									FAC P	FAC EP
	FAV 1Q	FAV 2Q						FAV 2Q	FAV 1Q	FAV 1P

LEIGHTON TOWN
Founded: 1885 Nickname: Reds

Club Contact Details (T) 01525 373 311 (E)
Ground: Lake Street, Leighton Buzzard, Beds LU7 1RX
Nearest Railway Station Leighton Buzzard - 1.3km
Capacity: 2,800 **Seats:** 400 **Covered:** 300 **Bus Route** Morrisons (Lake St) - stop 60m away
Colours(change): Red & white
Previous Names: Leighton United 1922-63
Previous Leagues: Leighton & District, South Midlands 1922-24, 26-29, 46-54, 55-56, 76-92, Spartan 1922-53, 67-74,
HONOURS: FA Comps: None
League: South Midlands 1966-67, 91-92. Isthmian Division Two 2003-04.

10 YEAR RECORD	08-09	09-10	10-11	11-12	12-13	13-14	14-15	15-16	16-17	17-18
	SthM 8	SthM 10	SthC 7	SthC 13	SthC 21	SthC 19	SthC 18	SthC 21	SSM P 16	SSM P 4
	FAC 2Q	FAC Pr	FAC 1Q	FAC 3Q	FAC Pr	FAC P	FAC P	FAC 1Q	FAC EP	FAC P
	FAT 1Q	FAT 1Q	FAT 1Q	FAT 1Q	FAT P	FAT P	FAT 1Qr	FAT 1Q	FAV 2Q	FAV QF

LEVERSTOCK GREEN
Founded: 1895 Nickname: The Green

Club Contact Details (T) 01442 246 280 (E) levgreenfc@gmail.com
Ground: Pancake Lane, Leverstock Green, Hemel Hempstead, Herts HP2 4NQ
Nearest Railway Station Apsley - 3.2km
Capacity: 1,500 **Seats:** 50 **Covered:** 100 **Bus Route** Pancake Lane - stop 300m away
Colours(change): White and green
Previous Names: None
Previous Leagues: West Herts (pre 1954) & Herts Senior County 1954-91. South Midlands 1991-97.
HONOURS: FA Comps: None
League: Herts Senior County Division One 1978-79. South Midlands Senior Division 1996-97.

10 YEAR RECORD	08-09	09-10	10-11	11-12	12-13	13-14	14-15	15-16	16-17	17-18
	SSM P 6	SSM P 10	SSM P 4	SSM P 11	SSM P 15	SSM P 20	SSM P 15	SSM P 18	SSM P 12	SSM P 7
	FAC EP	FAC P	FAC EP	FAC EP	FAC EP	FAC EP	FAC 2Q	FAC EP	FAC EP	FAC Pr
	FAV 1P	FAV 1P	FAV 5P	FAV 2Pr	FAV 1Q	FAV 1Q	FAV 2Q	FAV 2Q	FAV 2P	FAV 2Q

LONDON COLNEY
Founded: 1907   Nickname: Blueboys

Club Contact Details (T) 01727 822 132   (E)
Ground: Cotlandswick Playing Fields, London Colney, Herts AL2 1DW
Nearest Railway Station Park Street - 2.3km
Capacity: 1,000   **Seats:** Yes   **Covered:** Yes   **Bus Route** Leisure Centre - stop 430m away

Colours(change): Royal blue and white
Previous Names: None
Previous Leagues: Herts Senior 1955-93.

HONOURS: FA Comps: None
League: Herts Senior County 1956-57, 59-60, 86-87, 88-89. 89-90. South Midlands Senior Division 1994-95. Spartan South Midlands Premier Division 2001-02, 16-17, Division One 2011-12.

10 YEAR RECORD	08-09	09-10	10-11	11-12	12-13	13-14	14-15	15-16	16-17	17-18
	SSM1	SSM1 5	SSM1	SSM1 1	SSM P 7	SSM P 7	SSM P 2	SSM P 2	SSM P 1	SSM P 13
	FAC EPr	FAC 1Qr	FAC 1Q	FAC EP	FAC	FAC EPr	FAC 1Q	FAC P	FAC 1Q	FAC EPr
	FAV 2Q	FAV 2P	FAV 1Q	FAV 1Q	FAV 2Q	FAV 1Q	FAV 3P	FAV 2P	FAV 3P	FAV 1Pr

LONDON TIGERS
Founded: 1986   Nickname: Tigers

Club Contact Details (T) 020 7289 3395 (10am-6pm)   (E) info@londontigers.org
Ground: Northwood Park, Cheshunt Avenue, Northwood HA6 1HR
Capacity: **Seats:** Yes   **Covered:** Yes

Colours(change): Amber and black
Previous Names: Marylebone 1986-97. London Tigers then merged with Kingsbury Town 2006. Kingsbury London Tigers 2006-11.
Previous Leagues: None

HONOURS: FA Comps: None
League: None

10 YEAR RECORD	08-09	09-10	10-11	11-12	12-13	13-14	14-15	15-16	16-17	17-18
	SSM P 5	SSM P 8	SSM P 12	SSM P 14	SSM P 20	SSM P 15	SSM P 17	SSM P 13	SSM P 21	SSM P 15
	FAC	FAC 1Q	FAC EP			FAC P	FAC 2Q	FAC EPr	FAC EPr	
	FAV 2Q	FAV 1P	FAV 1Q		FAV 2Q	FAV 1Q	FAV 1Q	FAV 1P	FAV 2Q	

NORTH GREENFORD UNITED
Founded: 1944   Nickname: Blues

Club Contact Details (T) 0208 422 8923   (E) barbarabivens@talktalk.net
Ground: Berkeley Fields, Berkley Avenue, Greenford UB6 0NX
Nearest Railway Station Greenford or Sudbury Hill (Piccadilly Line).
Capacity: 2,000   **Seats:** 150   **Covered:** 100   **Bus Route** No.92

Colours(change): Royal blue & white
Previous Names: None
Previous Leagues: London Spartan, Combined Counties 2002-10, 16-18. Southern 2010-16.

HONOURS: FA Comps: None
League: Combined Counties League Premier Division 2009-10

10 YEAR RECORD	08-09	09-10	10-11	11-12	12-13	13-14	14-15	15-16	16-17	17-18
	CCP 2	CCP 1	SthC 20	SthC 18	SthC 19	SthC 20	SthC 21	SthC 22	CCP 13	CCP 13
	FAC EP	FAC EP	FAC 3Q	FAC 3Qr	FAC P	FAC 3Q	FAC 2Q	FAC 1Qr	FAC 1Q	FAC P
	FAV 2Q	FAV 2P	FAT 1Q	FAT P	FAT P	FAT 2Q	FAT P	FAT P	FAV 2Q	FAV 1Q

OXHEY JETS
Founded: 1972   Nickname: Jets

Club Contact Details (T) 020 8421 6277   (E)
Ground: Boundary Stadium, Altham Way, South Oxhey, Watford WD19 6FW
Nearest Railway Station Carpenders Park - 1km
Capacity: 1,000   **Seats:** 150   **Covered:** 100   **Shop:** No   **Bus Route** Lytham Avenue - stop 75m away

Colours(change): Blue and white
Previous Names: None
Previous Leagues: Youth Leagues > 1981. Herts Senior County 1981-2004.

HONOURS: FA Comps: None
League: Herts Senior County Premier 2000-01, 01-02, 02-03. Spartan South Midladns Division One 2004-2005.

10 YEAR RECORD	08-09	09-10	10-11	11-12	12-13	13-14	14-15	15-16	16-17	17-18
	SSM P 13	SSM P 11	SSM P 19	SSM P 17	SSM P 3	SSM P 18	SSM P 12	SSM P 17	SSM P 15	SSM P 19
	FAC 1Q	FAC EP	FAC 1Q	FAC 2Q	FAC P	FAC EPr	FAC EP	FAC EPr	FAC P	FAC EP
	FAV 1P	FAV 2Q	FAV 1Q	FAV 1P	FAV 3P	FAV 2P	FAV 2P	FAV 2Q	FAV 1P	FAV 1P

POTTON UNITED
Founded: 1943   Nickname: Royals

Club Contact Details (T) 01767 261 100   **(E)** bev.strong@tiscali.co.uk
Ground: The Hutchinson Hollow, Bigglewade Road, Potton, Beds SG19 2LX
Nearest Railway Station Sandy - 4.4km
Capacity: 2,000 **Seats:**   **Covered:**   **Bus Route** The Ridgewy - stop 11m away

Colours(change): All blue
Previous Names: None
Previous Leagues: South Midlands 1946-55. United Counties 1961-2018.

HONOURS: FA Comps: None
League: United Counties 1986-87, 88-89, Division One 2003-04.

10 YEAR RECORD

08-09		09-10		10-11		11-12		12-13		13-14		14-15		15-16		16-17		17-18	
UCL P	20	UCL 1	11	UCL 1	15	UCL 1	15	UCL 1	16	UCL 1	10	UCL 1	3	UCL 1	7	UCL 1	6	UCL 1	2
FAC	EP	FAC	EPr	FAC	EP									FAC	EP			FAC	1Q
FAV	1P	FAV	2Q	FAV	1Q	FAV	2Q	FAV	2Q	FAV	1Q	FAV	2Q	FAV	2Q	FAV	1Q	FAV	2Q

STOTFOLD
Founded: 1904   Nickname: The Eagles

Club Contact Details (T) 01462 730 765   **(E)**
Ground: Roker Park, The Green, Stotfold, Hitchin, Herts SG5 4AN
Nearest Railway Station Arlesey - 2.9km
Capacity: 5,000 **Seats:** 300   **Covered:** 300   **Bus Route** The Green - stop 80m away

Colours(change): Amber and black
Previous Names: Stotfold Athletic.
Previous Leagues: Biggleswade & District, North Herts & South Midlands, United Counties > 2010

HONOURS: FA Comps: None
League: South Midlands 1980-81. United Counties Premier 2007-08.

10 YEAR RECORD

08-09		09-10		10-11		11-12		12-13		13-14		14-15		15-16		16-17		17-18	
UCL P	2	UCL P	7	SSM P	13	SSM P	9	SSM P	14	SSM P	19	SSM P	16	SSM P	15	SSM P	13	SSM P	21
FAC	1Q	FAC	EP	FAC	EP	FAC	1Q	FAC	Pr	FAC	P	FAC	EP	FAC	EP	FAC	1Q	FAC	EP
FAV	1P	FAV	4P	FAV	3P	FAV	1Q	FAV	1Q	FAV	1P	FAV	2Q	FAV	2P	FAV	1Qr	FAV	1Q

TRING ATHLETIC
Founded: 1958   Nickname: Athletic

Club Contact Details (T) 01442 891 144 (MD)   **(E)** tringathleticfc@hotmail.com
Ground: Grass Roots Stadium, Pendley Sports Centre, Cow Lane, Tring HP23 5NS
Nearest Railway Station Tring - 1.5km
Capacity: 2,000 **Seats:** 125   **Covered:** 100+   **Shop:** Yes   **Bus Route** Bus stops at the ground.

Colours(change): Red and black
Previous Names: Tring Athletic Youth 1958-71.
Previous Leagues: West Herts 1958-88.

HONOURS: FA Comps: None
League: West Herts Division One 1961-62, 64-65, 65-66.
Spartan South Midlands Senior Division 1999-2000.

10 YEAR RECORD

08-09		09-10		10-11		11-12		12-13		13-14		14-15		15-16		16-17		17-18	
SSM P	8	SSM P	3	SSM P	2	SSM P	6	SSM P	22	SSM P	10	SSM P	10	SSM P	12	SSM P	5	SSM P	17
FAC	P	FAC	P	FAC	1Q	FAC	P	FAC	Pr	FAC	P	FAC	EP	FAC	P	FAC	EP	FAC	EP
FAV	1Q	FAV	2Q	FAV	3P	FAV	2P	FAV	1Q	FAV	3P	FAV	3P	FAV	1P	FAV	4P	FAV	5P

WEMBLEY
Founded: 1946   Nickname: The Lions

Club Contact Details (T) 0208 904 8169   **(E)** general@wembleyfc.com
Ground: Vale Farm, Watford Road, Sudbury, Wembley HA0 3HG.
Nearest Railway Station Sudbury Town Underground - 1km Sudbury & Harrow Road
Capacity: 2450 **Seats:** 350   **Covered:** 950   **Shop:** No   **Bus Route** Butlers Green - stop 150m away

Colours(change): Red
Previous Names: None
Previous Leagues: Middlesex Senior. Spartan. Delphian. Corinthian. Athenian. Isthmian.

HONOURS: FA Comps: None
League: Middlesex Senior 1947-48. Spartan Western Division 1950-51.

10 YEAR RECORD

08-09		09-10		10-11		11-12		12-13		13-14		14-15		15-16		16-17		17-18	
CCP	17	CCP	15	CCP	14	CCP	10	CCP	15	CCP	9	SSM P	7	SSM P	11	SSM P	4	SSM P	9
FAC	EPr	FAC	EP	FAC	EP	FAC	1Q	FAC	Pr	FAC	1Q	FAC	EPr	FAC	Pr	FAC	Pr	FAC	P
FAV	2Q	FAV	2P	FAV	2Q	FAV	2Qr	FAV	1P	FAV	1P	FAV	2P	FAV	1Q	FAV	3P	FAV	2P

AMERSHAM TOWN
Founded: 1890   Nickname: The Magpies

Club Contact Details (T)   (E)

Ground: Spratleys Meadow, School Lane, Amersham, Bucks HP7 0EL   **Capacity:** 1,500

HONOURS
FA Comps: None

League: Wycombe & District Combination 1902-03, 19-20, 20.21.
Hellenic Division One 1962-63, Premier 63-64.

Colours(change): Black & white stripes

10 YEAR RECORD

08-09	09-10	10-11	11-12	12-13	13-14	14-15	15-16	16-17	17-18
SSM1 7	SSM1 17	SSM1 20	SSM1 20	SSM1 20	SSM1 16	SSM1 21	SSM2 12	SSM2 16	SSM2 6
			FAV 2Q	FAV 2P				FAV 1Q	FAV 1Q

AMPTHILL TOWN
Founded: 1881   Nickname: The Amps

Club Contact Details (T) 01525 404 440   (E)

Ground: Ampthill Park, Woburn Street, Ampthill MK45 2HX

Nearest Railway Station Flitwick - 3.1km. Millbrook - 3.4km   **Bus Route** Alameda Road - stop 117m away

HONOURS
FA Comps: None

League: South Midlands Premier Division 1959-60.

Colours(change): Amber and black

10 YEAR RECORD

08-09	09-10	10-11	11-12	12-13	13-14	14-15	15-16	16-17	17-18
SSM1 15	SSM1 13	SSM1 16	SSM1 2	SSM P 5	SSM P 2	SSM P 21	SSM1 14	SSM1 14	SSM1 14
FAC P	FAC EP	FAC EP		FAC EP	FAC P	FAC EP	FAC EP		
FAV 1Q	FAV 1Q	FAV 2Q	FAV 4P	FAV 5P	FAV QF	FAV 2P	FAV 1Q	FAV 1Q	FAV 1P

BEDFORD
Founded: 1957   Nickname: The B's

Club Contact Details (T) 07831 594 444   (E) bedfordfc@mail.com

Ground: McMullen Park, Meadow Lane, Cardington, Bedford, MK44 3SB

Nearest Railway Station Bedford St Johns - 3.8km   **Bus Route** Meadow Lane - stop 141m away

HONOURS
FA Comps: None

League: None

Colours(change): Black & white

10 YEAR RECORD

08-09	09-10	10-11	11-12	12-13	13-14	14-15	15-16	16-17	17-18
SSM1 14	SSM1 9	SSM1 13	SSM1 12	SSM1 5	SSM1 3	SSM1 3	SSM P 22	SSM1 19	SSM1 12
FAC EP	FAC EP	FAC EP	FAC EP			FAC EP	FAC EP	FAC EP	
FAV 1Q	FAV 2P	FAV 2Q	FAV 2Q		FAV 1Q	FAV 2Q	FAV 1Q	FAV 1Q	FAV 1Qr

BRIMSDOWN
Founded: 2013   Nickname: The Limers

Club Contact Details (T)   (E) gulayermiya1996@googlemail.com

Ground: Ware FC, Wodson Park, Wadesmill Road, Ware SG12 0UQ

Nearest Railway Station Ware - 1.9km   **Bus Route** Wodson Park - stop 100m away

HONOURS
FA Comps: None

League: None

Colours(change): Black and white

10 YEAR RECORD

08-09	09-10	10-11	11-12	12-13	13-14	14-15	15-16	16-17	17-18
					SSM2 13	SSM2 4	SSM1 15	SSM1 17	SSM1 11
							FAV 2Q		FAV 1Q

BROADFIELDS UNITED
Founded: 1993   Nickname: The Fighting Cocks

Club Contact Details (T) 01895 823 474   (E) websterlocke@aol.com

Ground: Harefield United FC, Breakspear Road North, Harefield, Middlesex UB9 6PE

Nearest Railway Station Denham - 3km   **Bus Route** Wickham Close - stop 150m away

HONOURS
FA Comps: None

League: Southern Olympian Division Four 1994-95.
Middlesex County Senior Division 1996-97.

Colours(change): Blue and white

10 YEAR RECORD

08-09	09-10	10-11	11-12	12-13	13-14	14-15	15-16	16-17	17-18
MidxP 9	MidxP Exp	MidxP 5	MidxP 8	MidxP 5	MidxP 15	MidxP 4	SSM1 11	SSM1 11	SSM1 4
					FAV 2Q	FAV 1Q	FAV 1Q	FAV 2P	FAV 1P

BUCKINGHAM ATHELTIC

Founded: 1933   **Nickname:** The Ath

Club Contact Details (T) 01280 816 945 (MD)   (E) info@buckinghamathletic.co.uk
Ground: Stratford Fields, Stratford Road, Buckingham MK18 1NY

Bus Route High Street - stop 206m away

HONOURS **League:** North Bucks Premier Division 1984-85. South Midlands Division One 1985-86, 90-91, Spartan
FA Comps: None   South Midlands Division Two 2002-03.

Colours(change): Sky blue & navy blue

10 YEAR RECORD

08-09	09-10	10-11	11-12	12-13	13-14	14-15	15-16	16-17	17-18
SSM1 19	SSM1 16	SSM1 18	SSM1 18	SSM1 11	SSM1 13	SSM1 15	SSM1 8	SSM1 10	SSM1 7
FAV 1Q	FAV 1Q	FAV 1Qr	FAV 1Q	FAV 2Q	FAV 2Q	FAV 1Qr	FAV 2Q	FAV 1Q	FAV 1P

BUCKINGHAM TOWN

Founded: 1883   **Nickname:** Robins

Club Contact Details (T) 01908 375 978   (E) buckinghamtownfc@hotmail.com
Ground: Irish Centre, Manor Fields, Bletchley, Milton Keynes MK2 2HX   **Capacity:** 2,500
Nearest Railway Station Fenny Stratford - 0.6km   **Bus Route** Wharfside - stop 300m away
HONOURS **League:** Aylesbury & Dist. 1902-03, 67-68. North Bucks 24-25, 28-29, 33-34, 35-36, 36-37, 38-39, 48-49, 49-50.
FA Comps: None   Southern Southern Division 90-91. United Counties 83-84, 85-86.

Colours(change): All red

10 YEAR RECORD

08-09	09-10	10-11	11-12	12-13	13-14	14-15	15-16	16-17	17-18
UCL 1 9	UCL 1 13	UCL 1 16	UCL 1 11	UCL 1 15	UCL 1 11	UCL 1 16	UCL 1 17	UCL 1 5	UCL 1 7
FAC EP	FAC EP								FAC EP
FAV 3P	FAV 1Q	FAV 1Q	FAV 2P		FAV 2Q		FAV 1Q	FAV 1P	FAV 1Q

CODICOTE

Founded: 1913   **Nickname:** The Cod

Club Contact Details (T) 01438 821 072   (E) codicote.fc@hotmail.co.uk
Ground: John Clements Memorial Ground, Bury Lane, Codicote SG4 8XY
Nearest Railway Station Knebworth - 3.5km   **Bus Route** St Giles Church - stop 16m away
HONOURS **League:** North Herts Division One 1929-30, 74-75, Division Two 68-69, Premier 77-78
FA Comps: None

Colours(change): Red & black

10 YEAR RECORD

08-09	09-10	10-11	11-12	12-13	13-14	14-15	15-16	16-17	17-18
HertP 5	HertP 7	HertP 5	HertP 3	SSM1 8	SSM1 10	SSM1 8	SSM1 10	SSM1 13	SSM1 18
					FAC EPr	FAC Pr	FAC EP		
FAV 1P	FAV 2Q	FAV 1Q	FAV 2Q	FAV 1P	FAV 2Q	FAV 1Q	FAV 1Q	FAV 1Q	FAV 2Q

ENFIELD BOROUGH

Founded: 2016   **Nickname:** Panthers

Club Contact Details (T) 07493 377 484   (E)
Ground: Wingate & Finchley FC, Maurice Rebak Stadium, Summers Lane, N12 0PD
Nearest Railway Station New Southgate - 2.3km
HONOURS **League:** None
FA Comps: None

Colours(change): Red & black

10 YEAR RECORD

08-09	09-10	10-11	11-12	12-13	13-14	14-15	15-16	16-17	17-18
								SSM2 3	SSM1 10
									FAV 2P

FC BROXBOURNE BOROUGH

Founded: 1959   **Nickname:** Boro

Club Contact Details (T)   (E)
Ground: Broxbourne Borough V & E Club, Goffs Lane, Cheshunt, Herts EN7 5QN   **Capacity:** 5,000
Nearest Railway Station Theobalds Grove - 2.3km   **Bus Route** Goffs School - stop 37m away
HONOURS **League:** Herts Senior County Division One 1993-94.
FA Comps: None

Colours(change): Blue and white

10 YEAR RECORD

08-09	09-10	10-11	11-12	12-13	13-14	14-15	15-16	16-17	17-18
SSM P 4	SSM P 9	SSM P 10	SSM P 13	SSM2 3	SSM1 6	SSM1 2	SSM P 16	SSM P 22	SSM1 19
FAC Pr	FAC EP	FAC EP	FAC EP				FAC EP	FAC EP	FAC EPr
FAV 2Q	FAV 1P	FAV 1Q	FAV 1Q		FAV 1Q	FAV 2Q	FAV 3P	FAV 2Q	FAV 1Q

HAREFIELD UNITED

Founded: 1868   Nickname: Hares

Club Contact Details (T) 01895 823 474   **(E)** rayigreen1@btinternet.com

Ground: Preston Park, Breakespeare Road North, Harefield, UB9 6NE   **Capacity:** 1,200

Nearest Railway Station Denham - 3km   **Bus Route** Wickham Close - stop 150m away

HONOURS   **League:** Great Western Comb. Division Two 1947-48, Division One 50-51.

FA Comps: None   Parthenon 1964-65.

Colours(change): Red & black

10 YEAR RECORD

08-09	09-10	10-11	11-12	12-13	13-14	14-15	15-16	16-17	17-18
SSM P 2	SSM P 6	SSM P 21	SSM P 18	SSM P 10	SSM P 14	SSM P 4	SSM P 21	SSM1 8	SSM1 9
FAC Pr	FAC 2Q	FAC P	FAC Pr	FAC 2Qr	FAC P	FAC P	FAC EPr	FAC 1Q	
FAV 3P	FAV 1P	FAV 2Q	FAV 1Q	FAV 1Q	FAV 1Q	FAV 1P	FAV 1P	FAV 2Q	FAV 1Q

HATFIELD TOWN

Founded: 1886   Nickname: Blue Boys

Club Contact Details (T)   **(E)** secretary@hatfieldtownfc.co.uk

Ground: Cotlandswick Playing Fields, North Orbital Road, London Colney AL2 1DW

HONOURS   **League:** Herts Senior Eastern Division 1911-12, 19-20, Premier 1935-36, 37-38, 38-39, 91-92, 2007-08, Division Two

FA Comps: None   89-90, Division One 90-91, 2001-02, 02-03.

Colours(change): Royal blue

10 YEAR RECORD

08-09	09-10	10-11	11-12	12-13	13-14	14-15	15-16	16-17	17-18
SSM1 3	SSM P 12	SSM P 11	SSM P 22	SSM P 21	SSM P 21	SSM1 4	SSM1 17	SSM1 20	SSM1 15
FAC P	FAC P	FAC EP	FAC 2Q	FAC EP	FAC EP	FAC EP			
FAV 1Q	FAV 1Q	FAV 1Q	FAV 2P	FAV 2Q	FAV 2Q	FAV 1Q		FAV 1Q	FAV 1Q

HILLINGDON BOROUGH

Founded: 1990   Nickname: The Hillmen, Boro

Club Contact Details (T) 01895 639 544   **(E)** accounts@middlesexstadium.com

Ground: Middlesex Stadium, Breakspear Rd, Ruislip HA4 7SB   **Capacity:** 1,500

Nearest Railway Station Willow Lawn - 737m   **Bus Route** Howletts Lane - stop 98m away

HONOURS   **League:** None

FA Comps: None

Colours(change): White & royal blue

10 YEAR RECORD

08-09	09-10	10-11	11-12	12-13	13-14	14-15	15-16	16-17	17-18
Isth1N 22	SSM P 18	SSM P 16	SSM P 10	SSM P 19	SSM P 11	SSM P 22	SSM1 16	SSM1 9	SSM1 16
FAC 1Q	FAC EP	FAC EP	FAC EP	FAC EP	FAC P	FAC EP	FAC EPr		
FAT P	FAV 1P	FAV 1P	FAV 1P	FAV 2Q	FAV 1P	FAV 2Q	FAV 1Q	FAV 2Q	FAV 2Q

LANGFORD

Founded: 1908   Nickname: Reds

Club Contact Details (T) 01462 816 106   **(E)**

Ground: Forde Park, Langford Road, Henlow, Beds SG16 6AF   **Capacity:** 2,000

Nearest Railway Station Arlesey - 1.9km   **Bus Route** Newtown (Langford Rd) - stop 24m away

HONOURS   **League:** Bedford & District 1931-32, 49-50. South Midlands Premier Division 1988-89.

FA Comps: None

Colours(change): Red & white stripes/red/red (All blue).

10 YEAR RECORD

08-09	09-10	10-11	11-12	12-13	13-14	14-15	15-16	16-17	17-18
SSM P 11	SSM P 19	SSM P 23	SSM1 10	SSM1 16	SSM1 19	SSM1 13	SSM1 18	SSM1 4	SSM1 17
FAC P	FAC EP	FAC EP	FAC EP						FAC EP
FAV 2Q	FAV 1P	FAV 1P	FAV 1Q	FAV 2Q	FAV 1Q	FAV 1Qr	FAV 1Q	FAV 1Q	FAV 2Q

LONDON LIONS

Founded: 1995   Nickname: Lions

Club Contact Details (T) 0208 441 6051   **(E)** clubsec@londonlions.com

Ground: Rowley Lane Sports Ground, Rowley Lane, Barnet EN5 3HW   **Capacity:** 1,500

Nearest Railway Station Elstree & Borehamwood - 2.4km   **Bus Route** Buses stop on Rowley Lane.

HONOURS   **League:** Hertfordshire Senior County Division One 1999-2000, Premier 09-10, 16-17. Spartan South

FA Comps: None   Midlands Division One 2012-13.

Colours(change): All blue

10 YEAR RECORD

08-09	09-10	10-11	11-12	12-13	13-14	14-15	15-16	16-17	17-18
HertP 2	HertP 1	SSM1 8	SSM1 7	SSM1 1	SSM P 22	SSM1 17	HertP 5	HertP 1	SSM1 6
				FAC 1Q	FAC EPr				
			FAV 1Q	FAV 2P	FAV 2Q			FAV 1Q	FAV 2P

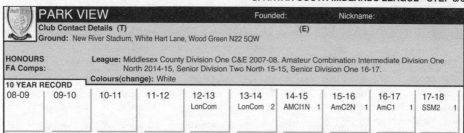

PARK VIEW

Founded: Nickname:

Club Contact Details (T)   **(E)**

Ground: New River Stadium, White Hart Lane, Wood Green N22 5QW

HONOURS   **League:** Middlesex County Division One C&E 2007-08. Amateur Combination Intermediate Division One

FA Comps: North 2014-15, Senior Division Two North 15-15, Senior Division One 16-17.

Colours(change): White

10 YEAR RECORD

08-09	09-10	10-11	11-12	12-13	13-14	14-15	15-16	16-17	17-18
				LonCom	LonCom 2	AMCI1N 1	AmC2N 1	AmC1 1	SSM2 1

RAYNERS LANE

Founded: 1933   Nickname: The Lane

Club Contact Details (T) 0208 868 8724   **(E)** richard.mitchell@tesco.net

Ground: Tithe Farm Social Club, Rayners Lane, South Harrow HA2 0XH

Nearest Railway Station Rayners Lane underground - 680m   **Bus Route** Clitheroe Avenue - stop 64m away

HONOURS   **League:** Hellenic Division One 1982-83, Division One East 2012-13.

FA Comps: None

Colours(change): Yellow and green

10 YEAR RECORD

08-09	09-10	10-11	11-12	12-13	13-14	14-15	15-16	16-17	17-18
Hel1E 14	Hel1E 12	Hel1E 7	Hel1E 3	Hel1E 1	Hel1E 9	Hel1E 7	Hel1E 5	Hel1E 11	SSM1 13
							FAV 2Q	FAV 2Q	FAV 2Q

RISBOROUGH RANGERS

Founded: 1971   Nickname: Rangers or Boro

Club Contact Details (T) 07849 843632 (MD only)   **(E)** nick@lloydlatchford.co.uk

Ground: "Windsors" Horsenden Lane, Princes Risborough. Bucks HP27 9NE   **Capacity:** 1,500

Nearest Railway Station Princes Rosborough - 0.2km   **Bus Route** Railway Station - stop 0.2km away

HONOURS   **League:** None

FA Comps: None

Colours(change): All red

10 YEAR RECORD

08-09	09-10	10-11	11-12	12-13	13-14	14-15	15-16	16-17	17-18
SSM2 10	SSM2 10	SSM2 5	SSM2 2	SSM2 4	SSM1 14	SSM1 5	SSM1 7	SSM1 6	SSM1 8
							FAC P	FAC EP	FAC EPr
						FAV 2Q	FAV 2Q	FAV 1Q	FAV 1Q

WINSLOW UNITED

Founded: 1891   Nickname: The Ploughmen

Club Contact Details (T) 01296 713 057   **(E)** garethrobins75@gmail.com

Ground: The Recreation Ground, Elmfields Gate, Winslow, Bucks MK18 3JG   **Capacity:** 2,000

Bus Route Elmside - stop 210m away

HONOURS   **League:** South Midlands Division One 1974-75.

FA Comps: None

Colours(change): Yellow and blue

10 YEAR RECORD

08-09	09-10	10-11	11-12	12-13	13-14	14-15	15-16	16-17	17-18
SSM1 12		SSM2 4	SSM2 7	SSM1 14	SSM1 9	SSM1 14	SSM1 19	SSM1 16	SSM1 3
	FAV 1Q		FAV 1P	FAV 2Q	FAV 2Q	FAV 1Qr	FAV 2Q	FAV 2Q	FAV 1Q

WODSON PARK

Founded: 1997   Nickname:

Club Contact Details (T) 07717 458 446   **(E)** lee.cook@wodsonmail.co.uk

Ground: Woodson Park Sports Centre, Wadesmill Road, Herts SG12 0UQ

Nearest Railway Station Ware - 2.1km   **Bus Route** Wodspn Park - stop 557m away

HONOURS   **League:** Hertford & District Division Three 1997-98.

FA Comps: None

Colours(change): Sky & navy blue

10 YEAR RECORD

08-09	09-10	10-11	11-12	12-13	13-14	14-15	15-16	16-17	17-18
SSM2 6	SSM2 4	SSM2 14	SSM1 16	SSM1 18	SSM1 17	SSM1 16	SSM1 6	SSM1 7	SSM1 5
			FAC EP	FAC EP					
		FAV 1P	FAV 1Q	FAV 1Q					FAV 2Qr

UNITED COUNTIES LEAGUE

Founded: 1895 **Sponsored by:** Future Lions

Recent Champions: 2015: AFC Rushden & Dia. **2016:** AFC Kempton Rovers **2017:** Peterborough Sports

PREMIER DIVISION	P	W	D	L	F	A	GD	Pts
1 Yaxley	42	29	6	7	135	40	95	93
2 Wisbech Town	42	29	6	7	122	48	74	93
3 Newport Pagnell Town	42	28	6	8	104	49	55	90
4 Holbeach United	42	26	5	11	97	37	60	83
5 Deeping Rangers	42	24	9	9	101	42	59	81
6 Leicester Nirvana	42	22	8	12	104	58	46	74
7 Eynesbury Rovers	42	21	12	9	81	52	29	72*
8 Cogenhoe United	42	22	5	15	73	57	16	71
9 Desborough Town	42	22	5	15	83	72	11	71
10 Daventry Town	42	19	10	13	70	60	10	67
11 Harborough Town	42	20	6	16	77	74	3	66
12 Kirby Muxloe	42	19	3	20	65	68	-3	60
13 Boston Town	42	15	7	20	70	70	0	52
14 Wellingborough Town	42	14	8	20	81	94	-13	50
15 Rothwell Corinthians	42	14	8	20	59	79	-20	50
16 Peterborough Northern Star	42	10	12	20	55	97	-42	42
17 Northampton ON Chenecks	42	11	5	26	66	108	-42	38
18 Sleaford Town	42	10	5	27	65	123	-58	35
19 Oadby Town	42	7	12	23	50	95	-45	33
20 Wellingborough Whitworth	42	9	6	27	59	105	-46	33
21 St Andrews	42	10	3	29	49	117	-68	33
22 Northampton Sileby Rangers	42	6	3	33	56	177	-121	21

DIVISION ONE	P	W	D	L	F	A	GD	Pts
1 Pinchbeck United	38	27	9	2	93	34	59	90
2 Potton United	38	24	7	7	110	47	63	79
3 Lutterworth Town	38	23	7	8	115	48	67	76
4 Raunds Town	38	22	6	10	96	54	42	72
5 Harrowby United	38	20	5	13	92	57	35	65
6 Olney Town	38	19	8	11	80	64	16	65
7 Buckingham Town	38	19	6	13	91	78	13	63
8 Blackstones	38	18	7	13	90	71	19	61
9 Rushden and Higham United	38	17	9	12	90	67	23	60
10 Bourne Town	38	17	8	13	82	70	12	59
11 Lutterworth Athletic	38	17	6	15	68	72	-4	57
12 Huntingdon Town	38	16	7	15	73	66	7	55
13 Irchester United	38	15	7	16	66	60	6	52
14 Burton Park Wanderers	38	13	7	18	72	110	-38	46
15 Thrapston Town	38	13	6	19	72	75	-3	45
16 Melton Town	38	10	7	21	64	95	-31	37
17 Long Buckby AFC	38	9	7	22	53	90	-37	34
18 Bugbrooke St Michaels	38	8	7	23	58	101	-43	31
19 Oakham United	38	6	2	30	42	123	-81	17*
20 Stewarts & Lloyds AFC	38	2	2	34	29	154	-125	8

ADDITIONAL CLUB MOVEMENTS

Premier Division - In: Pinchbeck United (P), Rugby Town (LM - MLP).
Out: Northampton Sileby Rangers (R), St Andrews (R), Wisbech Town (P - NPLE), Yaxley (P - SthE).
Division One - In: Anstey Nomads, Aylestone Park, Birstall United Social and Howell Sports (LM - EMCP), Northampton Sileby Rangers (R), St Andrews (R).
Out: Oakham United (R - P&DP), Olney Town (F), Pinchbeck United (P), Stewarts & Lloyds AFC (R - NCombP).

PREMIER DIVISION	1	2	3	4	5	6	7	8	9	10	11	12	13	14	15	16	17	18	19	20	21	22
1 Boston Town		0-1	0-0	0-0	4-1	2-0	1-2	1-0	0-1	3-0	0-1	3-4	5-0	1-2	1-1	1-2	3-2	2-0	2-2	3-1	3-2	2-2
2 Cogenhoe United	3-0		1-2	2-1	1-1	0-2	1-3	1-0	3-1	1-4	0-1	4-0	3-0	3-0	6-0	1-0	3-0	2-0	3-1	2-1	3-6	1-1
3 Daventry Town	1-3	1-1		2-1	0-1	3-2	3-3	1-2	3-2	2-2	1-2	1-1	1-0	3-1	1-0	2-1	3-2	3-1	2-1	4-0	0-1	1-4
4 Deeping Rangers	3-0	2-2	0-0		2-1	0-0	1-1	4-3	3-0	1-1	3-2	5-2	6-0	1-1	4-1	4-1	5-1	8-1	6-2	3-0	2-0	0-1
5 Desborough Town	1-1	1-2	1-0	2-0		0-3	1-2	3-1	0-1	0-5	0-1	3-5	8-0	3-2	2-0	3-0	2-1	0-1	6-1	2-1	1-0	1-4
6 Eynesbury Rovers	5-0	4-2	0-2	1-3	0-0		6-5	1-0	3-1	0-1	1-1	3-2	1-1	1-1	0-0	0-0	5-1	5-2	1-0	2-0	3-1	0-0
7 Harborough Town	2-1	0-4	3-1	1-2	1-3	1-1		0-2	2-1	3-1	0-1	1-1	8-1	1-0	1-1	0-1	4-0	1-0	0-4	6-3	2-1	1-2
8 Holbeach United	2-1	0-1	3-0	1-0	1-3	2-0	2-1		4-0	1-1	2-1	3-0	10-0	6-0	2-2	1-1	6-0	3-0	1-1	2-1	0-1	3-1
9 Kirby Muxloe	1-1	1-0	1-0	1-3	3-0	0-2	0-2	1-0		0-3	0-3	4-1	3-1	2-0	5-0	3-2	5-0	4-1	3-1	0-2	0-1	0-1
10 Leicester Nirvana	2-1	4-0	0-0	1-0	1-2	4-1	6-1	1-1	3-1		1-2	4-0	9-0	0-1	7-2	1-1	5-1	3-0	2-2	2-1	0-1	0-0
11 Newport Pagnell Town	1-0	0-3	1-3	2-2	7-0	3-1	1-0	0-2	4-3	1-0		6-1	3-2	4-1	4-0	4-0	4-0	7-1	4-1	2-2	2-3	
12 Northampton ON Chenecks	0-5	0-2	0-1	0-1	2-3	3-4	1-0	1-2	0-1	3-2	1-5		2-0	3-3	1-2	1-2	2-0	2-4	1-0	2-2	2-4	2-3
13 Northampton Sileby Rangers	0-7	3-1	3-8	0-5	0-5	2-3	1-0	1-7	2-2	2-6	2-6	4-3		2-3	1-4	3-3	5-0	2-4	1-3	2-5	0-2	
14 Oadby Town	4-1	1-2	2-1	0-3	0-5	2-2	1-0	0-1	1-1	0-1	0-3	1-1	2-1		1-1	5-0	1-4	2-2	0-1	1-1	1-1	1-3
15 Peterborough Northern Star	0-5	1-2	1-3	0-4	1-1	0-3	1-2	0-4	3-1	2-3	1-1	2-3	3-3	3-3		1-1	2-1	2-1	1-3	0-5	0-4	0-3
16 Rothwell Corinthians	2-1	2-4	1-2	1-0	2-4	1-1	5-0	2-0	0-1	0-1	1-1	1-0	4-1	2-3	1-1		3-4	4-1	1-5	2-1	0-1	2-4
17 Sleaford Town	1-0	1-0	1-4	1-1	2-3	0-4	2-2	0-2	2-5	5-1	2-1	2-0	2-3	2-0	1-2	2-4		4-2	2-2	3-3	1-2	0-3
18 St Andrews	4-1	3-1	1-1	1-4	1-1	1-3	2-3	0-4	2-3	3-0	0-1	1-2	2-1	2-4	0-2	2-1	1-3		0-1	0-3	0-5	
19 Wellingborough Town	4-0	3-0	3-1	2-4	4-6	2-1	4-1	1-3	2-0	1-3	2-2	2-3	3-6	1-1	1-4	1-1	5-0	2-4		0-0	1-3	0-2
20 Wellingborough Whitworth	1-2	1-1	1-1	2-1	1-3	0-2	1-3	0-6	2-0	1-9	2-4	0-2	4-2	2-1	0-1	2-4	2-3	3-1		1-2	2-5	
21 Wisbech Town	1-3	3-0	1-1	1-0	2-0	3-3	3-1	4-0	3-0	6-3	1-3	4-3	11-0	6-0	2-2	6-0	9-1	4-0	2-1	5-1		1-0
22 Yaxley	8-0	2-0	5-1	1-3	6-0	1-1	1-2	0-2	1-3	5-1	4-0	8-1	7-0	6-0	2-1	2-0	7-1	10-0	6-1	4-2	2-2	

DIVISION ONE

		1	2	3	4	5	6	7	8	9	10	11	12	13	14	15	16	17	18	19	20
1	Blackstones		3-4	4-1	2-0	5-2	0-3	3-3	0-2	1-1	4-0	3-0	2-2	9-0	1-1	2-5	3-2	1-2	2-0	5-0	4-3
2	Bourne Town	2-2		3-2	6-0	4-1	0-1	1-1	5-1	2-0	4-3	1-1	0-0	2-0	5-2	4-4	1-4	1-2	4-0	1-1	
3	Buckingham Town	3-1	2-2		3-3	1-2	4-0	5-2	3-4	2-1	4-1	1-0	4-2	5-0	2-3	2-1	3-2	2-2	5-2	5-1	2-1
4	Bugbrooke St Michaels	3-5	1-2	5-2		4-2	1-5	0-3	2-0	2-2	1-2	0-2	1-0	3-0	2-4	0-3	1-5	4-2	1-1	0-1	1-3
5	Burton Park Wanderers	0-3	3-0	0-3	3-1		0-15	3-3	1-1	0-5	1-2	1-4	6-2	4-2	2-1	2-2	0-3	3-1	2-5	4-2	1-2
6	Harrowby United	3-1	3-0	5-1	3-1	3-0		2-3	4-1	2-1	3-0	1-1	2-2	3-2	0-1	0-1	1-3	0-1	2-1	2-1	1-3
7	Huntingdon Town	1-2	2-1	1-2	1-1	1-2	1-2		2-1	5-3	0-1	0-1	7-0	4-2	2-1	0-0	2-1	0-1	2-1	4-0	2-5
8	Irchester United	1-2	4-2	1-2	3-1	1-2	0-2	4-3		2-3	0-0	3-0	3-2	0-0	4-1	1-1	0-0	1-0	1-0	4-0	2-0
9	Long Buckby AFC	1-2	1-0	1-3	2-2	1-1	2-2	0-5	1-1		1-2	0-3	0-5	2-0	1-2	0-1	1-4	2-4	0-4	3-2	1-1
10	Lutterworth Athletic	2-1	0-1	2-2	3-1	7-1	1-5	0-1	1-0	1-4		0-1	2-1	5-2	1-1	2-3	1-2	5-2	1-1	2-1	2-2
11	Lutterworth Town	7-1	4-4	2-1	7-1	5-1	4-2	2-0	2-1	9-1	3-2		6-0	3-1	1-3	1-2	1-2	3-2	0-0	10-0	2-1
12	Melton Town	1-1	0-3	2-4	1-0	1-4	1-0	1-2	0-5	2-4	1-2	5-2		1-2	2-0	0-2	2-2	3-1	2-2	3-0	3-1
13	Oakham United	0-2	0-2	9-1	1-3	1-1	0-1	2-1	2-5	0-3	1-3	0-3	2-6		0-4	0-3	0-7	1-6	0-4	3-3	2-3
14	Olney Town	2-1	2-5	0-0	1-1	2-2	2-1	2-1	3-1	2-0	2-3	2-1	5-1	2-0		2-3	1-1	2-1	3-4	4-1	2-3
15	Pinchbeck United	4-1	4-0	3-0	3-1	2-1	3-3	1-1	3-1	2-1	3-0	1-1	4-0	5-0	2-3		2-1	1-0	2-2	6-0	3-0
16	Potton United	4-1	5-0	3-3	3-1	3-1	3-1	3-0	2-1	5-0	1-0	1-1	5-0	4-0	4-2	0-3		0-3	4-4	7-0	3-0
17	Raunds Town	2-1	5-3	2-1	4-1	3-3	4-1	3-3	4-1	4-1	7-2	1-1	1-1	3-0	1-1	0-1	4-0		.	3-0	7-0	2-0
18	Rushden and Higham United	4-4	4-2	3-1	6-2	6-1	3-2	1-3	2-4	1-0	2-2	1-5	3-2	5-0	1-2	0-1	2-2	0-1		3-1	3-0
19	Stewarts & Lloyds AFC	0-4	0-1	1-4	3-4	0-5	3-3	1-1	0-3	1-2	1-10	1-7	2-6	1-5	0-1	0-4	3-2	1-5			1-8
20	Thrapston Town	0-1	0-3	1-0	2-2	3-4	1-3	6-0	1-0	4-0	1-3	1-6	4-0	5-1	2-2	2-2	1-5	1-3	0-2	2-0	

LEAGUE CUP

HOLDERS: YAXLEY

PRELIMINARY ROUND

Wisbech Town	v	Potton United	1-3
Newport Pagnell Town	v	Burton Park Wanderers	7-0
Bugbrooke St Michaels	v	Blackstones	1-4
Lutterworth Athletic	v	Eynesbury Rovers	1-6
Deeping Rangers	v	Cogenhoe United	1-3
Boston Town	v	Northampton Sileby Rangers	6-1
Pinchbeck United	v	St Andrews	10-1
Bourne Town	v	Harrowby United	0-3
Oakham United	v	Oadby Town	1-3
Sleaford Town	v	Melton Town	5-2 aet

ROUND 1

Wellingborough Town	v	Lutterworth Town	6-4 aet
Thrapston Town	v	Desborough Town	1-4
Northampton ON Chenecks	v	Long Buckby	1-4
Olney Town	v	Potton United	4-2
Newport Pagnell Town	v	Rothwell Corinthians	0-1
Rushden & Higham United	v	Leicester Nirvana	1-2
Blackstones	v	Huntingdon Town	4-1 aet
Peterborough Northern Star	v	Kirby Muxloe	3-2 aet
Eynesbury Rovers	v	Yaxley	1-4
Cogenhoe United	v	Harborough Town	1-3
Wellingborough Whitworth	v	Boston Town	3-5
Daventry Town	v	Stewarts & Lloyds	4-1
Raunds Town	v	Pinchbeck United	2-4
Irchester United	v	Harrowby United	2-3
Buckingham Town	v	Oadby Town	1-0
Holbeach United	v	Sleaford Town	4-1

ROUND 2

Wellingborough Town	v	Desborough Town	0-1
Long Buckby	v	Olney Town	1-3
Rothwell Corinthians	v	Leicester Nirvana	0-2
Blackstones	v	Peterborough Northern Star	2-1
Yaxley	v	Harborough Town	4-1
Boston Town	v	Daventry Town	1-5
Raunds Town	v	Harrowby United	0-1
Buckingham Town	v	Holbeach United	0-6

QUARTER FINALS

Desborough Town	v	Olney Town	2-1
Leicester Nirvana	v	Blackstones	5-2
Yaxley	v	Daventry Town	3-0
Harrowby United	v	Holbeach United	0-3

SEMI FINALS

Desborough Town	v	Leicester Nirvana	1-2
Yaxley	v	Holbeach United	3-0

FINAL

Leicester Nirvana	v	Yaxley	1-0

RESERVE DIVISION

		P	W	D	L	F	A	GD	Pts
1	Bugbrooke St Michaels Res	30	21	3	6	77	41	36	66
2	Oadby Town Res	30	19	6	5	72	34	38	63
3	Northampton ON Chenecks Res	30	18	7	5	83	41	42	61
4	Newport Pagnell Town Res	30	18	5	7	91	41	50	59
5	Raunds Town Res	30	15	8	7	71	49	22	53
6	Olney Town Res	30	17	2	11	67	53	14	53
7	Yaxley Res	30	14	7	9	64	45	19	49
8	Peterborough Northern Star Res	30	13	6	11	77	63	14	45
9	Potton United Res	30	12	6	12	56	55	1	42
10	Cogenhoe United Res	30	10	10	10	68	72	-4	40
11	Wellingborough Whitworth Res	30	11	6	13	59	63	-4	39
12	Rothwell Corinthians Res	30	9	5	16	58	73	-15	32
13	Irchester United Res	30	7	6	17	40	65	-25	27
14	Harborough Town Res	30	7	5	18	45	77	-32	26
15	Stewarts & Lloyds AFC Res	30	4	2	24	49	123	-74	14
16	Bourne Town Res	30	2	2	26	28	110	-82	8

PREMIER DIVISION

BOSTON TOWN
Founded: 1964   Nickname: Poachers

Club Contact Details (T) 01205 365 470   (E) btfcsec@hotmail.co.uk
Ground: DWB Stadium, Tattershall Road, Boston, Lincs PE21 9LR
Nearest Railway Station Boston - 1.6km
Capacity: 6,000 **Seats:** 450 **Covered:** 950   **Bus Route** Bus stops outside the ground

Colours(change): All blue
Previous Names: Boston 1964-1994
Previous Leagues: Lincolnshire, Central Alliance, Eastern Counties, Midland, Northern Counties East, Central Midlands.

HONOURS: FA Comps: None
League: Lincolnshire 1964-65. Central Alliance 1965-65. Midland 1974-75, 78-79, 80-81.
Central Midlands Supreme 1988-89. United Counties League 1994-95, 2000-01.

10 YEAR RECORD

	08-09	09-10	10-11	11-12	12-13	13-14	14-15	15-16	16-17	17-18
UCL P	5	5	7	14	10	14	12	16	20	13
FAC	1Q	1Q	Pr	P	EP	P	1Q	EP	EP	3Q
FAV	2P	2Q	2Q	2Q	2P	3P	1P	2Q	1Q	2Q

COGENHOE UNITED
Founded: 1967   Nickname: Cooks

Club Contact Details (T) 01604 890 521   (E) cogenhoeunited@outlook.com
Ground: Compton Park, Brafield Road, Cogenhoe NN7 1ND

Capacity: 5,000 **Seats:** 100 **Covered:** 200   **Bus Route** Orchard Way - stop 190m away

Colours(change): All blue
Previous Names: None
Previous Leagues: Central Northants Combination 1967-85.

HONOURS: FA Comps: None
League: Central Northants Combination Division Two 1951-52, Premier 80-81, 82-83, 83-84. United Counties 2004-05.

10 YEAR RECORD

	08-09	09-10	10-11	11-12	12-13	13-14	14-15	15-16	16-17	17-18
UCL P	9	8	15	12	8	5	5	5	13	8
FAC	EP	P	P	P	EP	EPr	P	2Q	P	P
FAV	4P	2P	1P	2P	2Q	1Q	1Q	1P	1Q	4P

DAVENTRY TOWN
Founded: 1886   Nickname: The Town

Club Contact Details (T) 01327 311 239   (E) club.secretary@dtfc.co.uk
Ground: Communications Park, Browns Road, Daventry, Northants NN11 4NS

Capacity: 2,000 **Seats:** 250 **Covered:** 250   **Bus Route** The Cherwell - stop 330m away

Colours(change): Purple and white
Previous Names: None
Previous Leagues: Northampton Town (pre-1987), Central Northways Comb 1987-89, United Counties 1989-2010. Southern 2010-15. Northern Premier 2015-16.
HONOURS: FA Comps: None
League: United Counties Division One 1989-90, 90-91, 2000-01, 2007-08, 16-17, Premier Division 2009-10.

10 YEAR RECORD

	08-09	09-10	10-11	11-12	12-13	13-14	14-15	15-16	16-17	17-18
	UCL P 7	UCL P 1	SthC 2	SthC 16	SthC 8	SthC 4	SthC 19	NP1S 21	UCL 1 1	UCL P 10
FAC		1Q	P	3Q	2Q	1P	1Q	P	EP	EP
	FAV 3P	FAV 5P	FAT 2Q	FAT 2Q	FAT P	FAT 1P	FAT P	FAT P	FAV 1P	FAV 2Q

DEEPING RANGERS
Founded: 1964   Nickname: Rangers

Club Contact Details (T) 01778 344 701   (E) drfcsecretary@gmail.com
Ground: The Haydon Whitham Stadium, Outgang Road, Market Deeping PE6 8LQ

Capacity: 2,000 **Seats:** 164 **Covered:** 250   **Bus Route** Buttercup Court - stop 720m away

Colours(change): Claret and blue
Previous Names: None
Previous Leagues: Peterborough & District 1966 - 1999.

HONOURS: FA Comps: None
League: United Counties Premier Division 2006-07.

10 YEAR RECORD

	08-09	09-10	10-11	11-12	12-13	13-14	14-15	15-16	16-17	17-18
UCL P	4	4	14	4	5	4	9	10	2	5
FAC	P	EPr	EP	2Q	EP	EP	EP	2Q	1Q	2Q
FAV	1Q	1P	1P	3P	2P	2Q	3P	2Q	1Qr	3P

DESBOROUGH TOWN

Founded: 1896   Nickname: Ar Tam

Club Contact Details (T) 01536 761 350   (E)
Ground: Waterworks Field, Braybrooke Road, Desborough NN14 2LJ

Capacity: 8,000 **Seats:** 250   **Covered:** 500   **Bus Route** Bus stops outside the ground.

Colours(change): All royal blue
Previous Names: None
Previous Leagues: Northamptonshire change name to United Counties in 1934.

HONOURS: FA Comps: None
League: Northamptonshire/United Counties 1900-01, 01-02, 06-07, 20-21, 23-24, 24-25, 27-28 / 48-49, 66-67.

10 YEAR RECORD

08-09	09-10	10-11	11-12	12-13	13-14	14-15	15-16	16-17	17-18
UCL P 11	UCL P 18	UCL P 19	UCL P 16	UCL P 11	UCL P 4	UCL P 14	UCL P 15	UCL P 4	UCL P 9
FAC EPr	FAC Pr	FAC 1Q	FAC EPr	FAC EPr	FAC P	FAC EP	FAC EP	FAC P	FAC P
FAV 1P	FAV 2Q	FAV 2Q	FAV 1P	FAV 2P	FAV 2P	FAV 2Q	FAV 1Q	FAV 1P	FAV 4P

EYNESBURY ROVERS

Founded: 1897   Nickname: Rovers

Club Contact Details (T) 07938 511 581uc   (E) erfcsecretary@gmail.com
Ground: Alfred Hall Memorial Ground, Hall Road, Eynesbury, St Neots PE19 2SF
Nearest Railway Station St Neots - 2.1km
Capacity: **Seats:** Yes   **Covered:** Yes   **Bus Route** Ernulf Academy Forecourt - stop 150m away

Colours(change): Royal blue & white
Previous Names: None
Previous Leagues: Biggleswade & District. St Neots Junior. Bed & District. South Midlands 1934-39. United Counties 1946-52. Eastern Counties 1952-63.
HONOURS: FA Comps: None
League: St Neots Junior 1910-11. Bedford & District Division Two 1926-27, 30-31, 31-32.
United Counties Division 1 1976-77.

10 YEAR RECORD

08-09	09-10	10-11	11-12	12-13	13-14	14-15	15-16	16-17	17-18
UCL 1 7	UCL 1 3	UCL 1 6	UCL 1 6	UCL 1 3	UCL 1 2	UCL P 11	UCL P 6	UCL P 5	UCL P 7
					FAC EP		FAC EP	FAC 1Q	FAC P
FAV 2Q	FAV 1P	FAV 2Q	FAV 1Q	FAV 1P	FAV 2P	FAV 1Qr	FAV 1P	FAV 1Q	FAV 1P

HARBOROUGH TOWN

Founded: 1976   Nickname: The Bees

Club Contact Details (T) 01858 467 339   (E)
Ground: Bowden's Park, Northampton Road, Market Harborough, Leics. LE16 9HF
Nearest Railway Station Market Harborough - 1.5km
Capacity: **Seats:** Yes   **Covered:** Yes   **Bus Route** Leisure Centre - stop 200m away

Colours(change): Yellow and black
Previous Names: Harborough Town Juniors 1976-2008. Juniors merged with adult team Spencer United to form today's club.
Previous Leagues: Northants Combination.

HONOURS: FA Comps: None
League: Northants Combination Premier Division 2009-10.

10 YEAR RECORD

08-09	09-10	10-11	11-12	12-13	13-14	14-15	15-16	16-17	17-18
NhCo 4	NhCo 1	UCL 1 17	UCL 1 2	UCL P 19	UCL P 17	UCL P 20	UCL P 11	UCL P 11	UCL P 11
					FAC P	FAC EPr	FAC P	FAC P	FAC P
			FAV 1Pr	FAV 2Q	FAV 1P	FAV 1Q	FAV 1Q	FAV 1P	FAV 1Q

HOLBEACH UNITED

Founded: 1929   Nickname: Tigers

Club Contact Details (T) 01406 424 761   (E)
Ground: Carters Park, Park Road, Holbeach, Lincs PE12 7EE

Capacity: 4,000 **Seats:** 200   **Covered:** 450   **Shop:** No   **Bus Route** Carter's Park - stop 70m away

Colours(change): Yellow & black
Previous Names: None
Previous Leagues: King's Lynn. Peterborough & District 1936-46. United Counties 1946-55, Eastern 1955-62, Midland Counties 1962-63.

HONOURS: FA Comps: None
League: United Counties 1989-90, 02-03, 12-13.

10 YEAR RECORD

08-09	09-10	10-11	11-12	12-13	13-14	14-15	15-16	16-17	17-18
UCL P 16	UCL P 16	UCL P 17	UCL P 6	UCL P 1	UCL P 11	UCL P 6	UCL P 4	UCL P 7	UCL P 4
FAC EP	FAC EPr	FAC EP	FAC Pr	FAC 1Q	FAC P	FAC P	FAC 2Qr	FAC 1Q	FAC 1Q
FAV 3P	FAV 2Q	FAV 2Q	FAV 1P	FAV 2Q	FAV 1P	FAV 5P	FAV 2P	FAV 2P	FAV 2P

KIRBY MUXLOE

Founded: 1910   Nickname:

Club Contact Details (T) 0116 239 2301   (E) kmfcsec@gmail.com
Ground: Kirby Muxloe Sports Club, Ratby Lane LE9 2AQ

Capacity: 1,000 **Seats:** Yes **Covered:** Yes   **Bus Route** Kirby Corner - stop 55m away

Colours(change): Yellow & blue stripes/blue/blue
Previous Names: None
Previous Leagues: Leicester Mutual. Leicester City. Leics Senior. East Mid Counties 2008-09. Midland All 2009-14. Midland Football 2014-15.

HONOURS: FA Comps: None
League: Leicestershire Senior Premier Division 2007-08.
10 YEAR RECORD | East Midlands Counties 2008-09.

08-09		09-10		10-11		11-12		12-13		13-14		14-15		15-16		16-17		17-18	
EMC	1	MidAl	10	MidAl	9	MidAl	11	MidAl	12	MidAl	14	MFLP	5	UCL P	9	UCL P	18	UCL P	12
				FAC	P	FAC	P	FAC	EP	FAC	P	FAC	P	FAC	P	FAC	Pr	FAC	P
FAV	1P	FAV	1P	FAV	1Q	FAV	2Q	FAV	1P	FAV	1P	FAV	2Q	FAV	2Q	FAV	1P	FAV	2Q

LEICESTER NIRVANA

Founded: 2008   Nickname:

Club Contact Details (T) 01162 660 009   (E) nirvanafc@hotmail.co.uk
Ground: Hamilton Park, Sandhills Avenue, Leicester LE5 1LU
Nearest Railway Station Syston - 3.9km
Capacity: **Seats:** Yes **Covered:** Yes   **Bus Route** Lakeview Chase - stop 70m away

Colours(change): All red
Previous Names: Thurnby Rangers and Leicester Nirvana merged to form today's club in 2008. Thurnby Nirvana 2008-15.
Previous Leagues: Leicestershire Senior >2010 East Midland Counties 2010-14

HONOURS: FA Comps: None
League: Leicestershire Senior Division One 1997-98, 2000-01, Premier Division 04-05. East Midland Counties 2013-14.
10 YEAR RECORD

08-09		09-10		10-11		11-12		12-13		13-14		14-15		15-16		16-17		17-18	
LeicSP	6	LeicSP	3	EMC	9	EMC	7	EMC	3	EMC	1	UCL P	2	UCL P	2	UCL P	17	UCL P	6
						FAC	1Qr	FAC	1Qr	FAC	EPr	FAC	P	FAC	P	FAC	EP	FAC	EP
				FAV	1P	FAV	1Q	FAV	1Q	FAV	2Q	FAV	4P	FAV	4P	FAV	2Q	FAV	2P

NEWPORT PAGNELL TOWN

Founded: 1963   Nickname: Swans

Club Contact Details (T) 01908 611 993   (E)
Ground: Willen Road, Newport Pagnell MK16 0DF

Capacity: 2,000 **Seats:** 100 **Covered:** 100   **Bus Route** Green Park Drive - stop 160m away

Colours(change): White & green
Previous Names: Newport Pagnell Wanderers > 1972.
Previous Leagues: North Bucks 1963-71. South Midlands 1971-73.

HONOURS: FA Comps: None
League: United Counties Division One 1981-82, 2001-02.
10 YEAR RECORD

08-09		09-10		10-11		11-12		12-13		13-14		14-15		15-16		16-17		17-18	
UCL P	3	UCL P	6	UCL P	3	UCL P	5	UCL P	6	UCL P	16	UCL P	10	UCL P	3	UCL P	10	UCL P	3
FAC	2Q	FAC	P	FAC	1Q	FAC	Pr	FAC	1Q	FAC	P	FAC	EP	FAC	Pr	FAC	EP	FAC	Pr
FAV	1Qr	FAV	3P	FAV	1P	FAV	4P	FAV	2P	FAV	2Q	FAV	2Q	FAV	1Q	FAV	QF	FAV	2P

NORTHAMPTON O.N.C.

Founded: 1946   Nickname: The Chens

Club Contact Details (T) 01604 634 045   (E)
Ground: Old Northamptonians Sports Ground, Billing Road, NN1 5RT
Nearest Railway Station Northampton - 2.7km
Capacity: 1,000 **Seats:** Yes **Covered:** Yes   **Bus Route** School for Boys - stop 80m away

Colours(change): White and navy
Previous Names: Chenecks FC 1946-60. ON (Old Northamptonians) Chenecks 1960-
Previous Leagues: Northampton Minor 1946-50. Northampton Town 1950-69.

HONOURS: FA Comps: None
League: United Counties Division One 1977-78, 79-80.
10 YEAR RECORD

08-09		09-10		10-11		11-12		12-13		13-14		14-15		15-16		16-17		17-18	
UCL 1	4	UCL 1	4	UCL 1	14	UCL 1	12	UCL 1	11	UCL 1	6	UCL 1	6	UCL 1	2	UCL P	12	UCL P	17
																FAC	EPr	FAC	P
														FAV	2Q	FAV	1P	FAV	1P

OADBY TOWN

Founded: 1937   Nickname: The Poachers

Club Contact Details (T) 01162 715 728   (E)
Ground: Freeway Park, Wigston Road, Oadby LE2 5QG
Nearest Railway Station South Wigston - 3.6km
Capacity: 5,000 **Seats:** 224 **Covered:** 224 **Shop:** Yes **Bus Route** Brabazon Road - stop 35m away

Colours(change): All red
Previous Names: Oadby Imperial > 1951.
Previous Leagues: Leicestershire Senior. Midland Alliance > 2011. East Midlands Counties 2011-12.

HONOURS: FA Comps: None
League: Leicestershire Senior Division Two 1951-52, Premier 63-64, 67-68, 68-69, 72-73, 94-95, 96-97, 97-98, 98-99.
10 YEAR RECORD Midland Alliance 99-00. United Counties Division One 2013-14.

08-09	09-10	10-11	11-12	12-13	13-14	14-15	15-16	16-17	17-18
MidAl 19	MidAl 14	MidAl 22	EMC 3	UCL 1 4	UCL 1 1	UCL P 13	UCL P 21	UCL P 19	UCL P 19
FAC EP	FAC EP	FAC 2Q	FAC Pr	FAC P	FAC EP	FAC EP	FAC 2Q	FAC EP	FAC P
FAV 2Q	FAV 2P	FAV 1Q	FAV 5P	FAV 2P	FAV 2P	FAV 1P	FAV 2Q	FAV 1Q	FAV 1Q

PETERBOROUGH NORTHERN STAR

Founded: 1900   Nickname: Star

Club Contact Details (T) 01733 552 416   (E) clubsecretary@pnsfc.co.uk
Ground: Branch Bros Stadium, Chestnut Avenue, Peterborough, Cambs PE1 4PE
Nearest Railway Station Peterborough - 2.6km
Capacity: 1,500 **Seats:** Yes **Covered:** yes **Bus Route** Hawthorn Road - stop 35m away

Colours(change): Black & white
Previous Names: Eye United 1900-31. Northam Star SC 1931-51. Eye United 1951-2005.
Previous Leagues: Peterborough Lge >2003

HONOURS: FA Comps: None
League: Peterborough 2002-03. United Counties League Division One 2008-09.
10 YEAR RECORD

08-09	09-10	10-11	11-12	12-13	13-14	14-15	15-16	16-17	17-18
UCL 1 1	UCL 1 2	UCL P 6	UCL P 7	UCL P 13	UCL P 9	UCL P 7	UCL P 17	UCL P 15	UCL P 16
				FAC 1Q	FAC P	FAC EP	FAC EP	FAC EP	FAC EP
			FAV QF	FAV 2P	FAV 2Q	FAV 3P	FAV 2Q	FAV 1P	FAV 2P

PINCHBECK UNITED

Founded: Nickname:

Club Contact Details (T)   (E)
Ground: Sir Harley Stewart Field, Winfrey Avenue, Spalding, PE11 1DA
Nearest Railway Station Spalding - 0.2km
Capacity: **Seats:** **Covered:** **Bus Route** Broad Street - stop 100m away

Colours(change): All red
Previous Names:
Previous Leagues: Peterborough & Distroct >2017

HONOURS: FA Comps: None
League: Peterborough & District Premier Division 1989-90, 90-91, 2011-12.
10 YEAR RECORD United Counties Division One 2017-18.

08-09	09-10	10-11	11-12	12-13	13-14	14-15	15-16	16-17	17-18
			P&D P 1	P&D P 15	P&D P 15	P&D P 7	P&D P 3	P&D P 2	UCL 1 1
									FAV 1Q

ROTHWELL CORINTHIANS

Founded: 1934   Nickname: Corinthians

Club Contact Details (T) 01536 711 706   (E) corinthsofficial@gmail.com
Ground: Sergeants Lawn, Desborough Road, Rothwell NN14 6JR
Nearest Railway Station Kettering - 5.6km
Capacity: **Seats:** 50 **Covered:** 200

Colours(change): Red/black/black
Previous Names: None
Previous Leagues: Kettering & District Amateur/East Midlands Alliance 1934-95.

HONOURS: FA Comps: None
League: None
10 YEAR RECORD

08-09	09-10	10-11	11-12	12-13	13-14	14-15	15-16	16-17	17-18
UCL P 21	UCL P 21	UCL P 21	UCL 1 8	UCL 1 17	UCL 1 15	UCL 1 2	UCL P 14	UCL P 16	UCL P 15
FAC EP	FAC Pr	FAC EP	FAC P	FAC EP			FAC EP	FAC EP	FAC EP
FAV 2Q	FAV 1P	FAV 1Qr	FAV 1Q	FAV 1Q	FAV 1Q	FAV 2Q	FAV 2Qr	FAV 2P	FAV 1Qr

RUGBY TOWN
Founded: 1956   Nickname: The Valley

Club Contact Details (T) 01788 844 806   (E) rugbytown@melbros.com
Ground: Butlin Road, Rugby, Warwicks CV21 3SD
Nearest Railway Station Rugby - 1km
Capacity: 6,000 **Seats:** 750   **Covered:** 1,000   **Shop:** Yes   **Bus Route** Jolly Brewers stop - 127m away

Colours(change): Sky blue and white
Previous Names: Valley Sports 1956-71, Valley Sport Rugby 1971-73, VS Rugby 1973-2000, Rugby United 2000-05
Previous Leagues: Rugby & District 1956-62, Coventry & Partnership, North Warwickshire 1963-69, United Counties 1969-75
West Midlands 1975-83. Southern 1983-2015. Northern Premier 2015-17. Midland Football 2017-18.
HONOURS: FA Comps: FA Vase 1982-83.
League: Southern Midland Division 1986-87. Midland Combination Division 1 2001-02.

10 YEAR RECORD

08-09	09-10	10-11	11-12	12-13	13-14	14-15	15-16	16-17	17-18
SthP 17	SthP 22	SthC 6	SthC 6	SthC 2	SthC 2	SthC 6	NP1S 9	NP1S 21	MFLP 6
FAC 3Q	FAC 2Q	FAC 1Q	FAC Pr	FAC 1Qr	FAC 3Qr	FAC P	FAC 2Q	FAC 2Q	FAC P
FAT 2Q	FAT 1Q	FAT 2Q	FAT Pr	FAT 1Qr	FAT P	FAT P	FAT P	FAT Pr	FAV 2Pr

SLEAFORD TOWN
Founded: 1968   Nickname: Town

Club Contact Details (T) 01529 415 951   (E)
Ground: Eslaforde Park, Boston Road, Sleaford, Lincs NG34 9GH
Nearest Railway Station Sleaford - 1.4km
Capacity: 1,000 **Seats:** 88   **Covered:** 88   **Bus Route** Eslaforde Park - stop 90m away

Colours(change): Green and black
Previous Names: None
Previous Leagues: Lincolnshire 1968-2003.

HONOURS: FA Comps: None
League: United Counties Division One 2005-06.

10 YEAR RECORD

08-09	09-10	10-11	11-12	12-13	13-14	14-15	15-16	16-17	17-18
UCL P 15	UCL P 9	UCL P 18	UCL P 19	UCL P 18	UCL P 13	UCL P 19	UCL P 7	UCL P 14	UCL P 18
FAC 1Q	FAC 1Qr	FAC EP	FAC EP	FAC P	FAC 1Q	FAC EP	FAC EP	FAC P	FAC EP
FAV 1Q	FAV 3P	FAV 1Q	FAV 2Q	FAV 1P	FAV 2Q	FAV 2Q	FAV 4P	FAV 3Pr	FAV 1Q

WELLINGBOROUGH TOWN
Founded: 1867   Nickname: Doughboys

Club Contact Details (T) 01933 441 388   (E)
Ground: Dog and Duck, London Road, Wellingborough NN8 2DP
Nearest Railway Station Wellingborough - 1.2km
Capacity: 2,500 **Seats:** Yes   **Covered:** Yes   **Bus Route** The Dog & Duck Pub - stop 50m away

Colours(change): Yellow & blue
Previous Names: Original team (Formed 1867) folded in 2002 reforming in 2004
Previous Leagues: Metropolitan. Southern.

HONOURS: FA Comps: None
League: United Counties 1964-65.

10 YEAR RECORD

08-09	09-10	10-11	11-12	12-13	13-14	14-15	15-16	16-17	17-18
UCL P 18	UCL P 11	UCL P 5	UCL P 8	UCL P 15	UCL P 8	UCL P 15	UCL P 20	UCL P 9	UCL P 14
FAC P	FAC EP	FAC 1Q	FAC EP	FAC P	FAC EPr	FAC EP	FAC EP	FAC EP	FAC P
FAV 2P	FAV 2P	FAV 1P	FAV 1Q	FAV 1Q	FAV 2Q	FAV 2Q	FAV 2Q	FAV 2Q	FAV 1Q

WELLINGBOROUGH WHITWORTH
Founded: 1973   Nickname: Flourmen

Club Contact Details (T) 07825 632 545   (E) whitworthfc@yahoo.co.uk
Ground: Victoria Mill Ground, London Road, Wellingborough NN8 2DP
Nearest Railway Station Wellingborough - 1.2km
Capacity: 2,500 **Seats:** Yes   **Covered:** Yes   **Bus Route** The Dog & Duck Pub - stop 50m away

Colours(change): Red & black
Previous Names: None
Previous Leagues: Rushden & District 1973-77. East Midlands Alliance 1977-85.

HONOURS: FA Comps: None
League: Rushden & District 1975-76, 76-77. United Counties Division One 2006-07.

10 YEAR RECORD

08-09	09-10	10-11	11-12	12-13	13-14	14-15	15-16	16-17	17-18
UCL 1 8	UCL 1 12	UCL 1 13	UCL 1 4	UCL 1 13	UCL 1 17	UCL 1 7	UCL 1 15	UCL 1 2	UCL P 20
				FAC EP			FAC EP	FAC EP	FAC EP
			FAV 1Q	FAV 2Q	FAV 2Q	FAV 1Q	FAV 1Q	FAV 2Q	FAV 2Q

ANSTEY NOMADS

Founded: 1947   Nickname: Nomads

Club Contact Details (T)   (E)
Ground: Davidson Homes Park, Cropston Road, Anstey, Leicester LE7 7BP   **Capacity:** 1000
Nearest Railway Station Leicester - 6.2km
HONOURS   **League:** Leicestershire Senior 1951-52, 53-54, 81-82, 82-83, 2008-09, Division Two 1973-74.
FA Comps: None
Colours(change): Red & white

10 YEAR RECORD

08-09	09-10	10-11	11-12	12-13	13-14	14-15	15-16	16-17	17-18
LeicSP 1	EMC 20	EMC 12	EMC 9	EMC 14	EMC 17	EMC 14	EMC 4	EMC 17	EMC 2
			FAC EP	FAC EP				FAC EP	
FAV 2Q	FAV 1Q	FAV 1P	FAV 2Q	FAV 2Q	FAV 1Q	FAV 1Q	FAV 1P	FAV 2Q	FAV 1Q

AYLESTONE PARK

Founded: 1968   Nickname:

Club Contact Details (T) 0116 278 5485   (E)
Ground: Mary Linwood Recreation Ground, Saffron Lane, Leicester LE2 6TG
Nearest Railway Station South Wigston - 1.1km
HONOURS   **League:** None
FA Comps: None
Colours(change): Red and white

10 YEAR RECORD

08-09	09-10	10-11	11-12	12-13	13-14	14-15	15-16	16-17	17-18
LeicSP 11	LeicSP 14	LeicSP 8	LeicSP 3	EMC 7	EMC 18	EMC 19	EMC 5	EMC 4	EMC 9
								FAC EP	FAC P
			FAV 2Q		FAV 2Q	FAV 1Q	FAV 2Q	FAV 1Q	FAV 1Q

BIRSTALL UNITED SOCIAL

Founded: 1961   Nickname:

Club Contact Details (T) 0116 267 1230   (E)
Ground: Meadow Lane, Birstall LE4 4FN
Nearest Railway Station Syston
HONOURS   **League:** Leicester Mutual Division One 1972-73, 73-74, 75-76.
          Leicestershire Senior Division Two 1976-77, Premier 2015-16.
FA Comps: None
Colours(change): White and navy

10 YEAR RECORD

08-09	09-10	10-11	11-12	12-13	13-14	14-15	15-16	16-17	17-18
LeicSP 10	LeicSP 9	LeicSP 9	LeicSP 6	LeicSP 11	LeicSP 4	LeicSP 4	LeicSP 1	EMC 3	EMC 8
									FAC P
FAV 1Q	FAV 1Q		FAV 2Q	FAV 1Q				FAV 2Qr	FAV 1Q

BLACKSTONES

Founded: 1920   Nickname: Stones

Club Contact Details (T) 01780 757 835   (E) imacgilli@outlook.com
Ground: Lincoln Road, Stamford, Lincs PE9 1SH   **Capacity:** 1,000
Nearest Railway Station Stamford - 1.5km   **Bus Route** Junction with Kesteven Rd - stop 75m away
HONOURS   **League:** Peterborough & District 1918-19, Division Two 1961-62, Division One 75-76.
FA Comps: None
Colours(change): Black & green

10 YEAR RECORD

08-09	09-10	10-11	11-12	12-13	13-14	14-15	15-16	16-17	17-18
UCL P 13	UCL P 13	UCL P 9	UCL P 11	UCL P 20	UCL 1 20	UCL 1 17	UCL 1 10	UCL 1 14	UCL 1 8
FAC EP	FAC 1Q	FAC EPr	FAC EP	FAC P	FAC EP				
FAV 3P	FAV 1P	FAV 2Qr	FAV 1Q	FAV 2Q	FAV 2Q	FAV 2Q	FAV 1P	FAV 2Q	FAV 1Q

BOURNE TOWN

Founded: 1883   Nickname: Wakes

Club Contact Details (T)   (E)
Ground: Abbey Lawn, Abbey Road, Bourne, Lincs PE10 9EN   **Capacity:** 2,000
          Bus Route Nowells Lane - stop 105m away
HONOURS   **League:** Peterborough & District 1933-34, 39-40, 45-46, 46-47. Central Alliance Division One South 59-60. United
FA Comps: None   Counties Premier 65-66, 68-69, 69-70, 71-72, 90-91.
Colours(change): Claret & sky blue

10 YEAR RECORD

08-09	09-10	10-11	11-12	12-13	13-14	14-15	15-16	16-17	17-18
UCL P 19	UCL P 17	UCL 1 12	UCL 1 14	UCL 1 10	UCL 1 21	UCL 1 10	UCL 1 5	UCL 1 15	UCL 1 10
FAC EP	FAC 2Q								
FAV 1Q	FAV 1P						FAV 2Q	FAV 1Q	FAV 2Q

BUGBROOKE ST MICHAELS

Founded: 1929   Nickname: Badgers

Club Contact Details (T) 01604 830 707   (E) graybags05@btinternet.com

Ground: Birds Close, Gayton Road, Bugbrooke NN7 3PH   **Capacity:** 2,500

Bus Route Bakers Arms Pub - stop 500m away

HONOURS   **League:** Central Northants Combination 1968-69, 69-70, 71-72, 76-77, 85-86.

FA Comps: None   United Counties Division One 1998-99.

Colours(change): White and black

10 YEAR RECORD

08-09	09-10	10-11	11-12	12-13	13-14	14-15	15-16	16-17	17-18
UCL 1 10	UCL 1 7	UCL 1 3	UCL 1 3	UCL 1 7	UCL 1 18	UCL 1 11	UCL 1 18	UCL 1 3	UCL 1 18
			FAC P	FAC 1Q	FAC EP				
FAV 2Q	FAV 2P	FAV 2Q	FAV 1P	FAV 2Q	FAV 2Q	FAV 1Q	FAV 1Q		

BURTON PARK WANDERERS

Founded: 1961   Nickname: The Wanderers

Club Contact Details (T)   (E)

Ground: Latimer Park, Polwell Lane, Burton Latimer, Northants NN15 5PS

Nearest Railway Station Kettering - 4.1km   **Bus Route** Station Road - stop 120m away

HONOURS   **League:** None

FA Comps: None

Colours(change): Blue & black

10 YEAR RECORD

08-09	09-10	10-11	11-12	12-13	13-14	14-15	15-16	16-17	17-18
UCL 1 13	UCL 1 15	UCL 1 8	UCL 1 9	UCL 1 19	UCL 1 8	UCL 1 18	UCL 1 19	UCL 1 19	UCL 1
						FAV 2Q	FAV 1Qr	FAV 1Q	FAV 2Q

HARROWBY UNITED

Founded: 1949   Nickname: The Arrows

Club Contact Details (T) 01476 401 201   (E)

Ground: Environcom Stadium, Harrowby Lane, Grantham NG31 9QY

Nearest Railway Station Grantham - 2.6km   **Bus Route** St Wulframs School - stop 100m away

HONOURS   **League:** Midlands Regional Alliance Premier Division 1989-90.

FA Comps: None   United Counties Division One 1991-92.

Colours(change): Blue

10 YEAR RECORD

08-09	09-10	10-11	11-12	12-13	13-14	14-15	15-16	16-17	17-18
CM Su 17	CM Su 18			UCL 1 6	UCL 1 3	UCL P 17	UCL P 18	UCL P 21	UCL 1 5
						FAC EP	FAC EP	FAC P	FAC EP
				FAV 1P	FAV 2Q	FAV 1P	FAV 1P	FAV 1Q	FAV 1P

HOLWELL SPORTS

Founded: 1902   Nickname:

Club Contact Details (T) 01664 812 080   (E)

Ground: Welby Road, Asfordby Hill, Melton Mowbray, Leicestershire LE14 3RD   **Capacity:** 1000

Nearest Railway Station Melton Mowbray - 2.8km

HONOURS   **League:** Leic Senior Premier 1911-12, 87-88, 91-92, 92-93. Division One 1984-85.

FA Comps: None   Leicester & District 1907-08, 08-09. Melton Mowbray & Dist Am 1933-34.

Colours(change): Green & gold

10 YEAR RECORD

08-09	09-10	10-11	11-12	12-13	13-14	14-15	15-16	16-17	17-18
LeicSP 4	EMC 13	EMC 13	EMC 11	EMC 5	EMC 9	EMC 8	EMC 16	EMC 16	EMC 18
	FAC EPr	FAC EPr		FAC EP	FAC EP	FAC 1Q	FAC 1Qr		
FAV 1Q	FAV 2Q	FAV 2P	FAV 1P	FAV 1Q	FAV 3P	FAV 2Q	FAV 2Q	FAV 1P	FAV 2Q

HUNTINGDON TOWN

Founded: 1995   Nickname: The Hunters

Club Contact Details (T)   (E)

Ground: Jubilee Park, Kings Ripton Road,, Huntingdon, Cambridgeshire PE28 2NR

Nearest Railway Station Huntingdon - 3.4km   **Bus Route** Newnham Close - stop 1km away

HONOURS   **League:** Cambridgeshire Division 1B 1999-2000.

FA Comps: None   United Counties Division One 2011-12.

Colours(change): Red & black

10 YEAR RECORD

08-09	09-10	10-11	11-12	12-13	13-14	14-15	15-16	16-17	17-18
UCL 1 14	UCL 1 8	UCL 1 5	UCL 1 1	UCL P 4	UCL P 2	UCL P 16	UCL P 22	UCL P 22	UCL 1 12
			FAC 1Q	FAC 1Q	FAC 1Q	FAC EP	FAC EPr	FAC EP	FAC EP
FAV 2Q	FAV 1Q	FAV 2Q	FAV 2Q	FAV 1Q	FAV 3P	FAV 2P	FAV 1Q	FAV 2Q	FAV 2Q

IRCHESTER UNITED

Founded: 1885   Nickname: The Romans

Club Contact Details (T) 01933 312 877   **(E)**

Ground: Alfred Street, Irchester NN29 7DR   **Capacity:** 1,000

Nearest Railway Station Wellingborough - 3.1km   **Bus Route** Alfred Street - stop 100m away

HONOURS   **League:** Rushden & District 1928-29, 29-30, 36-37. Northants / United Counties Division Two 1930-31, 31

FA Comps: None   -32 / United Counties Division One 2009-10.

Colours(change): Red and black

10 YEAR RECORD

08-09	09-10	10-11	11-12	12-13	13-14	14-15	15-16	16-17	17-18
UCL 1 16	UCL 1 1	UCL P 10	UCL P 20	UCL P 21	UCL 1 19	UCL 1 15	UCL 1 16	UCL 1 8	UCL 1 13
			FAC EP	FAC EP	FAC EP				
		FAV 1Q	FAV 2Q	FAV 2Q	FAV 2Q	FAV 1P	FAV 1Q	FAV 2Q	FAV 2Q

LONG BUCKBY AFC

Founded: 1937   Nickname: Bucks

Club Contact Details (T) 07749 393 045   **(E)** lbafc.dja@gmail.com

Ground: Station Road, Long Buckby NN6 7QA   **Capacity:** 2,000

Nearest Railway Station Long Buckby - 0.3km   **Bus Route** Watson Road - stop 70m away

HONOURS   **League:** United Counties Division Three 1969-70, Division Two 70-71, 71-72, Premier Division 2011-12.

FA Comps: None

Colours(change): All claret

10 YEAR RECORD

08-09	09-10	10-11	11-12	12-13	13-14	14-15	15-16	16-17	17-18
UCL P 8	UCL P 3	UCL P 4	UCL P 1	UCL P 16	UCL P 18	UCL P 21	UCL 1 6	UCL 1 13	UCL 1 17
FAC EP	FAC 1Qr	FAC EP	FAC EP	FAC 3Q	FAC EP	FAC EPr	FAC 1Q		
FAV 3P	FAV 5P	FAV 5P	FAV 3P	FAV 1Pr	FAV 1Q	FAV 2Q	FAV 2Q	FAV 1Q	FAV 1Q

LUTTERWORTH ATHLETIC

Founded: 1983   Nickname: The Athletic

Club Contact Details (T) 01455 554 046   **(E)** djones20335783@aol.com

Ground: Weston Arena, Hall Park, Hall Lane, Bitteswell, Lutterworth LE17 4LN

Bus Route Manor Farm - stop 1.5km away

HONOURS   **League:** Leicester & District Division Two 1994-95, Premier 2004-05.

FA Comps: None

Colours(change): Green & white hoops/white/white

10 YEAR RECORD

08-09	09-10	10-11	11-12	12-13	13-14	14-15	15-16	16-17	17-18
LeicS1 2	LeicSP 6	LeicSP 6	LeicSP 2	EMC 13	UCL 1 5	UCL 1 4	UCL 1 11	UCL 1 12	UCL 1 11
		FAV 1Q	FAV 1P	FAV 2Q	FAV 1Q		FAV 1Q	FAV 1Q	FAV 1Q

LUTTERWORTH TOWN

Founded: 1955   Nickname: The Swifts

Club Contact Details (T)   **(E)** lutterworthtownfc@hotmail.com

Ground: Dunley Way, Lutterworth, Leicestershire, LE17 4NP

Bus Route Elizabethan Way - stop 300m away

HONOURS   **League:** Leicestershire Senior Division Two 1980-81, Premier 90-91, 2016-17.

FA Comps: None

Colours(change): Orange and black

10 YEAR RECORD

08-09	09-10	10-11	11-12	12-13	13-14	14-15	15-16	16-17	17-18
LeicS1 13	LeicS1 8	LeicS1 15	LeicS1 14	LeicS1 6	LeicS1 6	LeicS1 7	LeicS1 3	LeicSP 1	UCL 1 3
									FAV 1P

MELTON TOWN

Founded: 2004   Nickname:

Club Contact Details (T) 01664 480 576   **(E)** secretarymeltonmowbrayfc@hotmail.com

Ground: Melton Sports Village, Burton Road, Melton Mowbray LE13 1DR

HONOURS   **League:** None

FA Comps: None

Colours(change): Red and white

10 YEAR RECORD

08-09	09-10	10-11	11-12	12-13	13-14	14-15	15-16	16-17	17-18
	LeicS1 9	LeicS1 12	LeicS1 6	LeicS1 2	LeicSP 2	LeicSP 2	LeicSP 3	UCL 1 9	UCL 1 16
									FAV 2Q

UNITED COUNTIES LEAGUE - STEP 5/6

NORTHAMPTON SILEBY RANGERS Founded: 1968   Nickname: Rangers
Club Contact Details (T) 01604 670 366   **(E)**
Ground: Fernie Fields Sports Ground, Moulton, Northampton NN3 6FR
Nearest Railway Station Northampton - 5.5km   **Bus Route** Booth Rise - stop 205m away
HONOURS   **League:** Northampton Town 1988-89 89-90. United Counties Division One 1993-94, 2002-03, 04-05, 12-13.
FA Comps: None
Colours(change): Red and black

10 YEAR RECORD
08-09	09-10	10-11	11-12	12-13	13-14	14-15	15-16	16-17	17-18
UCL 1 3	UCL 1 9	UCL 1 9	UCL 1 16	UCL 1 1	UCL P 15	UCL P 18	UCL P 19	UCL P 8	UCL P 22
						FAC 1Q	FAC P	FAC P	FAC EP
FAV 2Q	FAV 1Q				FAV 1P	FAV 1Q	FAV 2P	FAV 2P	FAV 2Q

RAUNDS TOWN   Founded: 1946   Nickname: Shopmates
Club Contact Details (T) 01933 623 351   **(E)**
Ground: Kiln Park, London Road, Raunds, Northants NN9 6EQ   **Capacity:** 3,000
Bus Route Bus stops outside the ground.
HONOURS   **League:** United Counties Division One 1982-83.
FA Comps: None
Colours(change): Red & black

10 YEAR RECORD
08-09	09-10	10-11	11-12	12-13	13-14	14-15	15-16	16-17	17-18
UCL P 10	UCL P 20	UCL P 20	UCL 1 13	UCL 1 14	UCL 1 12	UCL 1 9	UCL 1 8	UCL 1 7	UCL 1 4
FAC 1Q	FAC EPr	FAC EP	FAC EP				FAC P	FAC EP	FAC EPr
FAV 2P	FAV 1Q	FAV 2Q	FAV 2Q	FAV 2Q		FAV 1Q	FAV 1P	FAV 1Q	FAV 2Q

RUSHDEN & HIGHAM UNITED   Founded: Formed: 2007 Nickname: The Lankies
Club Contact Details (T) 01933 410 036   **(E)** rhufcsec@yahoo.co.uk
Ground: Hayden Road, Rushden, Northants NN10 0HX   **Capacity:** 1,500
Bus Route Ashwell Road - stop 60m away
HONOURS   **League:** None
FA Comps: None
Colours(change): Orange and black

10 YEAR RECORD
08-09	09-10	10-11	11-12	12-13	13-14	14-15	15-16	16-17	17-18
UCL 1 6	UCL 1 16	UCL 1 10	UCL 1 5	UCL 1 8	UCL 1 14	UCL 1 13	UCL 1 13	UCL 1 16	UCL 1 9
			FAC EP	FAC EP	FAC EP				
FAV 2Q	FAV 2Q	FAV 1Q	FAV 2Q	FAV 2Q	FAV 1Q		FAV 1Q	FAV 1Q	FAV 1P

ST. ANDREWS   Founded: 1973   Nickname: The Saints
Club Contact Details (T) 0116 283 9298   **(E)** standrewsfc@btconnect.com
Ground: Canal Street, Aylestone, Leicester LE2 8LX
Nearest Railway Station South Wigston - 3km
HONOURS   **League:** Leicestershire City Premier x4. Leicestershire Senior 1989-90, 93-94, 95-96.
FA Comps: None   East Midlands Counties 2015-16.
Colours(change): Black & white

10 YEAR RECORD
08-09	09-10	10-11	11-12	12-13	13-14	14-15	15-16	16-17	17-18
EMC 9	EMC 15	EMC 17	EMC 4	EMC 16	EMC 7	EMC 2	EMC 1	MFLP 9	UCL P 21
	FAC P	FAC EP		FAC EP		FAC EPr	FAC EP	FAC EP	FAC EPr
FAV 2Qr	FAV 2Q	FAV 2Q	FAV 2P	FAV EP	FAV SF	FAV 2P	FAV 3P	FAV 1P	FAV 2Q

THRAPSTON TOWN   Founded: 1960   Nickname: Venturas
Club Contact Details (T) 01832 732 470   **(E)**
Ground: Chancery Lane, Thrapston, Northants NN14 4JL   **Capacity:** 1,000
Bus Route Library - stop 170m away
HONOURS   **League:** Kettering Amateur League 1970-71, 72-73, 73-74, 77-78.
FA Comps: None
Colours(change): All blue

10 YEAR RECORD
08-09	09-10	10-11	11-12	12-13	13-14	14-15	15-16	16-17	17-18
UCL 1 11	UCL 1 6	UCL 1 2	UCL 1 21	UCL 1 12	UCL 1 13	UCL 1 8	UCL 1 9	UCL 1 10	UCL 1 15
			FAC 1Q	FAC P			FAC P		
FAV 1P	FAV 2Q	FAV 1P	FAV 2Q	FAV 2Q	FAV 2Q	FAV 1Q	FAV 1Q	FAV 1P	FAV 1Q

WESSEX LEAGUE

Founded: 1986 **Sponsored by:** Sydenhams

Recent Champions: 2015: Petersfield Town **2016:** Salisbury **2017:** Portland United

PREMIER DIVISION	P	W	D	L	F	A	GD	Pts
1 Blackfield & Langley	42	31	7	4	118	28	90	100
2 Andover Town	42	32	3	7	116	56	60	99
3 Sholing	42	28	7	7	100	34	66	91
4 Horndean	42	24	7	11	94	55	39	79
5 Hamworthy United	42	24	4	14	83	72	11	76
6 AFC Portchester	42	23	5	14	81	53	28	74
7 Alresford Town	42	20	10	12	89	59	30	70
8 Lymington Town	42	20	11	11	82	57	25	68*
9 Baffins Milton Rovers	42	20	5	17	85	77	8	65
10 Hamble Club	42	18	9	15	104	72	32	63
11 Bemerton Heath Harlequins	42	19	8	15	76	80	-4	62*
12 Shaftesbury	42	16	8	18	63	75	-12	56
13 Brockenhurst	42	15	9	18	66	74	-8	54
14 Bashley	42	15	7	20	77	87	-10	52
15 Portland United	42	12	14	16	73	76	-3	50
16 Fareham Town	42	15	5	22	77	92	-15	50
17 Team Solent	42	12	10	20	95	107	-12	46
18 Bournemouth	42	11	9	22	54	78	-24	42
19 Cowes Sports	42	9	6	27	61	97	-36	33
20 Amesbury Town	42	8	5	29	64	130	-66	29
21 Newport (IoW)	42	7	5	30	49	117	-68	26
22 Petersfield Town	42	4	4	34	39	170	-131	16

DIVISION ONE	P	W	D	L	F	A	GD	Pts
1 Christchurch	34	23	8	3	88	33	55	77
2 Andover New Street	34	24	0	10	82	56	26	72
3 Tadley Calleva	34	22	4	8	96	45	51	70
4 United Services Portsmouth	34	20	5	9	74	47	27	65
5 AFC Stoneham	34	18	8	8	75	38	37	62
6 Romsey Town	34	18	6	10	74	51	23	60
7 Laverstock & Ford	34	18	5	11	79	56	23	59
8 Alton	34	16	6	12	73	64	9	54
9 Fawley	34	16	3	15	53	56	-3	51
10 New Milton Town	34	13	7	14	55	63	-8	46
11 Ringwood Town	34	14	3	17	81	93	-12	45
12 Downton	34	12	2	20	51	77	-26	38
13 Whitchurch United	34	10	5	19	45	77	-32	35
14 Totton & Eling	34	9	6	19	55	82	-27	33
15 Hythe & Dibden	34	8	7	19	48	65	-17	31
16 East Cowes Victoria	34	7	7	20	53	78	-25	28
17 Verwood Town	34	8	3	23	47	83	-36	27
18 Folland Sports	34	5	5	24	42	107	-65	17*

CLUB MOVEMENTS

Premier Division

In: Andover New Street (P), Christchurch (P), Tadley Calleva (P).
Out: Amesbury Town (R), Andover Town (D), Blackfield & Langley (P - SthWl), Newport (IOW) (R), Petersfield Town (R).

Division One

In: Amesbury Town (R), Andover Town (D), Newport (IOW) (R), Petersfield Town (R).
Out: Andover New Street (P), Christchurch (P), Tadley Calleva (P).

PREMIER DIVISION	1	2	3	4	5	6	7	8	9	10	11	12	13	14	15	16	17	18	19	20	21	22
1 AFC Portchester		0-1	3-1	1-0	1-0	4-0	3-0	0-2	1-0	0-0	3-2	0-1	2-3	3-1	0-1	1-0	7-0	3-1	4-2	0-1	0-1	3-0
2 Alresford Town	2-2		5-0	3-0	4-3	5-0	1-1	0-0	6-0	2-5	5-0	1-0	1-1	1-3	0-0	1-3	3-0	3-1	1-3	2-3	1-4	4-0
3 Amesbury Town	3-2	2-6		0-4	1-2	4-3	3-4	0-2	0-2	2-1	3-3	2-1	0-3	3-4	3-5	1-2	4-2	3-1	2-2	0-2	1-3	1-3
4 Andover Town	3-2	5-2	2-0		0-3	5-1	6-1	5-3	2-1	3-0	2-1	4-3	6-1	1-2	2-0	2-1	5-3	4-0	2-0	3-1	3-3
5 Baffins Milton Rovers	3-4	2-1	3-3	1-4		5-2	3-1	4-2	1-1	1-3	5-0	3-2	2-2	1-3	1-5	0-2	2-1	3-0	0-6	0-2	1-3	5-1
6 Bashley	0-1	4-2	6-5	1-2	0-5		1-1	1-2	3-4	0-1	3-2	2-5	0-2	1-2	5-0	0-5	3-1	6-0	2-1	2-1	1-1	3-2
7 Bemerton Heath Harlequins	1-2	2-2	5-0	1-3	1-0	1-0		0-8	6-0	3-0	2-2	2-1	0-3	0-3	3-0	2-1	3-2	4-1	0-0	1-1	4-0	3-0
8 Blackfield & Langley	3-0	0-2	1-0	3-1	2-0	2-1	3-0		3-0	6-0	2-2	3-2	1-1	1-0	6-0	4-0	3-0	10-0	2-3	4-0	2-0	3-0
9 Bournemouth	0-0	1-2	4-0	1-2	0-3	2-2	1-2	0-4		1-0	3-1	0-3	2-2	0-2	0-1	1-2	1-2	3-1	0-2	4-2	0-2	1-1
10 Brockenhurst	4-1	0-1	1-1	0-2	1-2	1-1	0-1	1-1	2-2		4-3	0-1	2-3	4-1	2-4	0-2	3-0	2-1	2-1	4-1	1-4	1-6
11 Cowes Sports	1-2	2-3	2-0	3-5	2-2	0-4	3-0	0-1	2-1	0-1		1-1	2-1	3-2	1-4	0-1	2-0	0-1	1-1	4-1	0-2	4-0
12 Fareham Town	0-2	3-0	2-3	1-4	2-5	1-2	0-2	0-5	0-5	3-2	4-1		0-2	1-0	1-2	2-2	2-1	5-2	3-1	1-2	2-2	3-6
13 Hamble Club	0-1	1-2	6-2	2-2	1-1	1-2	4-2	0-4	0-1	2-1	3-2	3-1		5-0	1-3	3-5	2-2	8-0	5-2	5-0	1-1	6-2
14 Hamworthy United	1-3	1-0	2-1	1-4	0-1	3-1	4-4	3-2	2-1	2-2	2-0	2-0	2-1		2-4	0-0	4-1	9-0	1-0	2-1	1-0	5-4
15 Horndean	2-0	0-1	2-2	3-2	2-0	0-0	3-0	0-0	3-0	1-1	4-1	2-3	1-0	6-0		1-0	7-0	4-2	1-1	1-2	3-4	5-1
16 Lymington Town	3-1	1-1	3-0	1-2	2-0	1-5	2-3	0-0	2-2	0-0	4-0	4-2	3-2	3-3	1-0		2-2	8-1	2-2	1-2	1-3	3-1
17 Newport (IoW)	0-7	3-1	2-4	0-4	0-4	3-1	4-2	0-0	2-0	0-3	2-4	2-5	3-2	1-2	1-5	1-2		2-2	0-2	0-0	0-1	2-4
18 Petersfield Town	1-3	0-7	4-1	1-2	1-3	0-3	0-5	0-4	2-1	2-6	2-0	3-4	0-7	0-3	1-5	0-0	0-6		1-3	2-0	0-6	0-3
19 Portland United	0-4	1-1	6-1	1-1	0-1	0-2	0-1	1-5	3-5	0-0	4-0	3-2	2-2	0-2	3-4	2-2	1-0	2-2		2-2	2-1	6-1
20 Shaftesbury	5-1	1-1	3-2	1-2	4-2	0-0	1-2	2-3	1-0	0-3	3-1	1-2	1-3	0-2	1-0	0-1	5-0	3-0	1-1		1-1	3-1
21 Sholing	1-1	2-0	4-0	2-0	4-0	1-0	3-2	2-4	0-1	1-2	1-0	0-0	2-1	3-0	0-0	3-2	5-0	6-0	4-0	3-0		3-0
22 Team Solent	3-3	2-2	7-0	1-3	1-1	3-3	2-2	0-2	0-0	7-0	3-2	1-2	3-3	5-1	1-0	1-2	0-4	8-1	1-1	7-2	0-6	

LEAGUE CUP

HOLDERS: SHOLING

ROUND 1

Blackfield & Langley	v	Hythe & Dibden	6-0
New Milton Town	v	Laverstock & Ford	1-1, 4-5p
Bournemouth	v	AFC Porchester	2-3
Portland United	v	Amesbury Town	2-5
Alresford Town	v	Christchurch	1-0
Shaftesbury	v	Whitchurch United	3-2
East Cowes Victoria	v	Fawley	AW
Downton	v	Ringwood Town	1-1, 3-4p
Totton & Eling	v	Sholing	1-4

ROUND 2

Blackfield & Langley	v	Romsey Town	4-0
United Services Portsmouth	v	Alton	2-0
Verwood Town	v	Laverstock & Ford	1-0
Weymouth Res	v	Hamworthy United	AW
Horndean	v	Brockenhurst	3-1
AFC Porchester	v	Cowes Sports	12-2
Andover New Street	v	Folland Sports	2-1
Lymington Town	v	Amesbury Town	5-0
Bemerton Heath Harlequins	v	Hamble Club	0-4
Bashley	v	Alresford Town	1-2
Shaftesbury	v	Fawley	0-0, 2-4p
Fareham Town	v	AFC Stoneham	1-2
Newport (IOW)	v	Tadley Calleva	4-3
Team Solent	v	Baffins Milton Rovers	1-3
Ringwood Town	v	Sholing	0-2
Petersfield Town	v	Andover Town	2-2, 7-6p

ROUND 3

Blackfield & Langley	v	United Services Portsmouth	5-1
Verwood Town	v	Hamworthy United	2-7
Horndean	v	AFC Porchester	1-4
Andover New Street	v	Lymington Town	1-0
Hamble Club	v	Alresford Town	2-1
Fawley	v	AFC Stoneham	2-2, 5-4p
Newport (IOW)	v	Baffins Milton Rovers	2-0
Sholing	v	Petersfield Town	3-0

QUARTER FINALS

Blackfield & Langley	v	Hamworthy United	5-0
AFC Porchester	v	Andover New Street	1-0
Hamble Club	v	Fawley	0-0, 5-6p
Newport (IOW)	v	Sholing	1-6

SEMI FINALS

Blackfield & Langley	v	AFC Porchester	1-1, 2-3p
Fawley	v	Sholing	2-1

FINAL

AFC Porchester	v	Fawley	4-0

DIVISION ONE	1	2	3	4	5	6	7	8	9	10	11	12	13	14	15	16	17	18
1 AFC Stoneham		5-1	1-2	2-2	1-2	3-2	2-0	2-2	0-0	0-1	1-0	2-2	6-1	0-2	2-0	1-3	4-0	4-0
2 Alton	4-1		2-1	0-0	0-3	2-1	7-1	2-1	2-1	2-2	4-0	8-4	3-2	3-2	2-2	0-1	4-2	4-0
3 Andover New Street	0-4	2-1		1-0	0-1	6-2	1-0	2-1	5-2	2-1	2-0	0-4	3-2	1-0	4-2	2-3	2-0	1-2
4 Christchurch	4-2	1-1	4-1		6-0	3-2	3-1	5-0	2-0	1-0	3-0	5-1	1-0	2-0	7-1	1-2	1-0	2-1
5 Downton	0-1	0-3	1-4	1-3		1-2	3-2	2-1	2-1	2-0	1-3	1-3	0-3	0-3	2-1	2-0	0-2	3-3
6 East Cowes Victoria	1-5	2-2	1-3	0-0	1-4		1-1	2-3	1-1	1-3	0-0	5-1	3-0	2-3	3-2	1-2	4-4	3-0
7 Fawley	1-0	0-2	4-0	0-4	2-1	3-1		1-0	1-0	2-0	1-2	2-1	0-1	2-0	3-2	2-5	4-1	2-1
8 Folland Sports	0-4	3-1	3-7	1-4	1-3	0-3	2-4		1-1	1-1	5-1	1-5	1-5	0-3	0-1	1-5	1-1	0-0
9 Hythe & Dibden	1-1	0-2	1-4	1-5	6-5	4-0	1-1	5-0		1-3	0-2	4-3	2-0	2-5	3-0	1-2	0-1	0-2
10 Laverstock & Ford	2-2	4-2	2-4	2-2	3-2	0-4	3-0	9-0	1-0		2-1	0-2	4-1	5-6	5-1	2-2	5-0	1-0
11 New Milton Town	0-1	5-1	1-0	1-3	3-1	1-1	3-3	6-1	3-2	0-5		1-1	1-2	1-5	1-0	2-3	3-1	1-1
12 Ringwood Town	1-3	2-1	1-3	2-3	5-1	3-1	2-0	4-2	0-2	3-5	2-3		1-3	0-5	0-0	2-1	4-3	5-1
13 Romsey Town	0-0	3-0	4-2	2-4	1-1	1-0	2-1	0-2	1-1	3-1	3-3	6-2		0-1	2-1	1-0	5-0	4-1
14 Tadley Calleva	0-2	6-1	1-2	0-0	4-1	2-1	3-2	6-1	2-0	2-0	1-1	7-0	1-2		2-2	4-2	2-0	5-0
15 Totton & Eling	2-3	4-0	0-5	1-1	3-2	5-0	1-4	3-2	2-2	2-4	0-4	5-2	0-7	2-4		1-3	2-0	4-0
16 United Services Portsmouth	1-1	1-1	2-3	3-0	3-0	4-1	1-0	3-1	3-0	0-1	3-1	4-2	3-3	5-2	0-0		0-2	2-0
17 Verwood Town	0-5	2-1	1-4	2-4	1-2	4-0	0-2	2-3	0-2	4-0	0-1	3-7	0-2	2-2	1-3	4-1		3-0
18 Whitchurch United	1-4	0-4	2-3	2-2	2-1	2-1	0-1	4-1	3-1	1-2	4-0	2-4	2-2	1-5	2-0	2-1	3-1	

AFC PORTCHESTER
Founded: 1971　　Nickname: Portchy/Royals

Club Contact Details **(T)** 01329 233 833 (Clubhouse)　　**(E)** secretary@afcportchester.co.uk
Ground: Teh Crest Finance Stadium, Cranleigh Road, Portchester, Hampshire PO16 9DP
Nearest Railway Station Porchester - 15.km
Capacity:　**Seats:** Yes　**Covered:** Yes　　**Bus Route** Sandport Grove stop

Colours(change): Tangerine and black
Previous Names: Loyds Sports 1971-73. Colourvison Rangers 1973-76. Wilcor Mill 1976-2003.
Previous Leagues: City of Portsmouth Sunday. Portsmouth & District >1998. Hampshire 1998-2004.

HONOURS: FA Comps: None
League: Portsmouth & Football 1997-98. Hampshire Division One 2001-02.

10 YEAR RECORD

08-09	09-10	10-11	11-12	12-13	13-14	14-15	15-16	16-17	17-18
Wex1 19	Wex1 6	Wex1 3	Wex1 2	WexP 15	WexP 8	WexP 3	WexP 6	WexP 8	WexP 6
			FAC Pr	FAC EP	FAC 2Q	FAC P	FAC 2Q	FAC 2Q	FAC 2Q
		FAV 2Q	FAV 2Q	FAV 2Q	FAV 3P	FAV 3P	FAV 1P	FAV 2Q	FAV 1P

ALRESFORD TOWN
Founded: 1898　　Nickname: The Magpies

Club Contact Details **(T)** 01962 735 100 or 07703 346 672　　**(E)** secretary.alresfordtownfc@gmail.com
Ground: Arlebury Park, The Avenue, Alresford, Hants SO24 9EP
Nearest Railway Station Alresford - 620m
Capacity:　**Seats:** Yes　**Covered:** Yes　　**Bus Route** Bridge Road stop

Colours(change): Black & white stripes
Previous Names: None
Previous Leagues: Winchester League, North Hants league, Hampshire League

HONOURS: FA Comps: None
League: North Hampshire 1999-2000.

10 YEAR RECORD

08-09	09-10	10-11	11-12	12-13	13-14	14-15	15-16	16-17	17-18
WexP 18	WexP 17	WexP 15	WexP 15	WexP 2	WexP 2	WexP 16	WexP 20	WexP 5	WexP 7
FAC EP	FAC P	FAC Pr	FAC P	FAC P	FAC EP	FAC Pr	FAC EP	FAC 2Q	FAC P
FAV 2Q	FAV 1Pr	FAV 1Q	FAV 1P	FAV 2Q	FAV 4P	FAV 3P	FAV 1Q	FAV 2P	FAV 2Q

ANDOVER NEW STREET
Founded: 1895　　Nickname: The Street

Club Contact Details **(T)** 01264 358 358 (Wkends from 12)　　**(E)** andovernewstreetfc@hotmail.co.uk
Ground: Foxcotte Park Charlton Andover Hampshire SP11 0TA
Nearest Railway Station Andover - 2.4km
Capacity:　**Seats:**　**Covered:**　　**Bus Route** Charlton Cemetery - stop 120m away

Colours(change): Green & black
Previous Names: St Mary's Youth 1890s. New Street 1961-2001.
Previous Leagues: Andover & District. North Hants >1976. Hampshire 1976-2004.

HONOURS: FA Comps: None
League: None

10 YEAR RECORD

08-09	09-10	10-11	11-12	12-13	13-14	14-15	15-16	16-17	17-18
Wex1 20	Wex1 19	Wex1 17	Wex1 10	Wex1 15	Wex1 15	Wex1 13	Wex1 16	Wex1 19	Wex1 2
FAV 2Q		FAV 1P	FAV 2Q	FAV 1Q			FAV 1Q	FAV 1Q	FAV 1Q

BAFFINS MILTON ROVERS
Founded: 2011　　Nickname: None

Club Contact Details **(T)**　　**(E)** baffinsmiltonrovers@hotmail.co.uk
Ground: The Kendall Stadium, Eastern Road, Portsmouth PO3 5LY
Nearest Railway Station Hilsea - 1.3km
Capacity:　**Seats:** 120　**Covered:** Yes　　**Bus Route** Robinson Way - stop 420m away

Colours(change): All royal blue
Previous Names: Formed when Sunday league teams Baffins Milton and Milton Rovers merged.
Previous Leagues: Hampshire Premier >2016

HONOURS: FA Comps: None
League: Portsmouth Saturday Premier Division 2011-12.
Hampshire Premier Senior Division , 2013-14, 15-16.

10 YEAR RECORD

08-09	09-10	10-11	11-12	12-13	13-14	14-15	15-16	16-17	17-18
			PorS P 1	PorS P 2	HantP 1	HantP 2	HantP 1	Wex1 2	WexP 9
									FAV 3P

BASHLEY — Founded: 1947 — Nickname: The Bash

Club Contact Details (T) 01425 620 280 (E) footballsecretary@bashleyfc.org.uk
Ground: Bashley Road Ground, Bashley Road, New Milton, Hampshire BH25 5RY
Nearest Railway Station New Milton - 1.9km
Capacity: 4,250 **Seats:** 250 **Covered:** 1,200 **Shop:** Yes **Bus Route** Village Store & PO - stop 230m away
Colours(change): Gold and black
Previous Names: None
Previous Leagues: Bournemouth 1953-83, Hampshire 1983-86, Wessex 1986-89, Southern 1989-2004, 06-16. Isthmian 2004-06

HONOURS: FA Comps: None
League: Hampshire Division Three 1984-85. Wessex 1986-87, 87-88, 88-89. Southern Southern Division 1989-90, Division One South & West 2006-07.

10 YEAR RECORD

	08-09	09-10	10-11	11-12	12-13	13-14	14-15	15-16	16-17	17-18
	SthP 14	SthP 7	SthP 11	SthP 13	SthP 17	SthP 23	Sthsw 22	Sthsw 22	WexP 14	WexP 14
FAC	3Qr	2Q	3Q	1Q	1Qr	2Q	P	P	EP	EP
FAT	1Pr	1P	1Q	1Qr	1Qr	1Q	P	1Q		
FAV									2Q	1P

BEMERTON HEATH HARLEQUINS — Founded: 1989 — Nickname: Quins

Club Contact Details (T) 01722 331 925 (E) sec.bhhfc@hotmail.co.uk
Ground: The Clubhouse, Western Way, Bemerton Heath Salisbury SP2 9DT
Nearest Railway Station Salisbury - 2.1km
Capacity: 2,100 **Seats:** 250 **Covered:** 350 **Bus Route** Winding Way - stop 75m away
Colours(change): Black & white
Previous Names: Bemerton Athletic, Moon FC & Bemerton Boys merged in 1989
Previous Leagues: Salisbury & Wilts Combination, Salisbury & Andover Sunday.

HONOURS: FA Comps: None
League: None

10 YEAR RECORD

	08-09	09-10	10-11	11-12	12-13	13-14	14-15	15-16	16-17	17-18
	WexP 12	WexP 3	WexP 2	WexP 2	WexP 5	WexP 7	WexP 13	WexP 9	WexP 11	WexP 11
FAC	EP	P	EP	EP	EP	EP	1Q	P	1Q	EP
FAV	2P	2P	4P	3P	5P	2P	2P	2Q	3P	1Q

BOURNEMOUTH — Founded: 1875 — Nickname: Poppies

Club Contact Details (T) 01202 515 123 (E) bournemouthwessex@gmail.com
Ground: Victoria Park, Namu Road, Winton, Bournemouth BH9 2RA
Capacity: 3,000 **Seats:** 205 **Covered:** 205 **Shop:** Yes
Colours(change): Red and white
Previous Names: Bournemouth Rovers, Bournemouth Wanderers, Bournemouth Dean Park.
Previous Leagues: Hampshire

HONOURS: FA Comps: None
League: None

10 YEAR RECORD

	08-09	09-10	10-11	11-12	12-13	13-14	14-15	15-16	16-17	17-18
	WexP 15	WexP 4	WexP 5	WexP 9	WexP 13	WexP 15	WexP 18	WexP 18	WexP 17	WexP 18
FAC	P	EP	P	2Qr	EP	P	Pr	EP	EP	EP
FAV	1Q	2Q	3P	QF	2P	1Q	2Q	2Q	1P	2Q

BROCKENHURST — Founded: 1898 — Nickname: The Badgers

Club Contact Details (T) 01590 623 544 (E) info@brockenhurstfc.co.uk
Ground: Grigg Lane, Brockenhurst, Hants SO42 7RE
Nearest Railway Station Brockenhurst - 0.5km
Capacity: 2,000 **Seats:** 200 **Covered:** 300 **Bus Route** Brockenhurst College - stop 260m away
Colours(change): Blue and white
Previous Names: None
Previous Leagues: Hampshire

HONOURS: FA Comps: None
League: Hampshire Division Three 1959-60, Division Two 70-71, Division One 75-76. Wessex Division One 2012-13.

10 YEAR RECORD

	08-09	09-10	10-11	11-12	12-13	13-14	14-15	15-16	16-17	17-18
	WexP 5	WexP 13	WexP 22	Wex1 5	Wex1 1	WexP 11	WexP 14	WexP 14	WexP 10	WexP 13
FAC	Pr	1Q	EP	1Q	EP	1Q	EP	3Q	P	P
FAV	1Q	3P	2Q	1P	1Q	2Q	1Q	1Q	1Q	2P

CHRISTCHURCH

Founded: 1885   Nickname: The Church

Club Contact Details   (T) 01202 473 792   **(E)** secretary@christchurchfc.co.uk
Ground: Hurn Bridge S.C, Avon Causeway, Christchurch BH23 6DY
Nearest Railway Station Christchurch - 4.6km
Capacity: 1,200 **Seats:** 215   **Covered:** 265   **Bus Route** Post Office - stop 100m away

Colours(change):   All Blue
Previous Names: None
Previous Leagues: Hampshire

HONOURS: FA Comps: None
       League: Hampshire Division Two 1937-38, 47-48, 85-86, Division Three 52-53.
10 YEAR RECORD | Wessex Division One 2017-18.

08-09	09-10	10-11	11-12	12-13	13-14	14-15	15-16	16-17	17-18
WexP 7	WexP 5	WexP 6	WexP 3	WexP 3	WexP 16	WexP 21	Wex1 6	Wex1 4	Wex1 1
FAC P	FAC EP	FAC EP	FAC EP	FAC 1Q	FAC EP	FAC EPr	FAC P	FAC EP	FAC EP
FAV 5P	FAV 2P	FAV 1Pr	FAV 3P	FAV 1P	FAV 1Pr	FAV 2Q	FAV 1Q	FAV 2Q	FAV 3P

COWES SPORTS

Founded: 1881   Nickname: Yachtsmen

Club Contact Details   (T) 01983 718 277   **(E)** secretary.cowessportsfc@outlook.com
Ground: Westwood Park Reynolds Close off Park Rd Cowes Isle of Wight PO31 7NT

Capacity: **Seats:** Yes   **Covered:** Yes   **Bus Route** Parklands Avenue - stop 100m away

Colours(change):   Blue & White
Previous Names: None
Previous Leagues: Hampshire (Founding members) 1896-98, 1903-94. Southern 1898-1900.

HONOURS: FA Comps: None
       League: Hampshire Division One 1896-97, 1926-27, 27-28, 30-31, 36-37, 55-56, 93-94, Division Two 1974-75.
10 YEAR RECORD | Southern Division Two South West 1998-99.

08-09	09-10	10-11	11-12	12-13	13-14	14-15	15-16	16-17	17-18
WexP 13	WexP 22	Wex1 8	Wex1 6	Wex1 4	Wex1 3	Wex1 2	WexP 11	WexP 18	WexP 19
FAC 1Q	FAC EP	FAC EP	FAC EP	FAC EP	FAC P	FAC P	FAC P	FAC EP	FAC EP
FAV 2Q	FAV 2Q	FAV 2Q	FAV 3P	FAV 2Q	FAV 2Q	FAV 1P	FAV 2Q	FAV 2Q	FAV 1Q

FAREHAM TOWN

Founded: 1947   Nickname: Creeksiders

Club Contact Details   (T) 07445 805 122   **(E)** farehamtnfc@gmail.com
Ground: Cams Alders, Palmerston Drive, Fareham, Hants PO14 1RH
Nearest Railway Station Fareham - 0.9km
Capacity: 2,000 **Seats:** 450   **Covered:** 500   **Shop:** Yes   **Bus Route** Fairfield Avenue - stop 250m away

Colours(change):   Red & black stripes
Previous Names: Formed when Fareham FC, Fareham Brotherhood and Fareham Youth Centre merged.
Previous Leagues: Portsmouth 1946-49. Hampshire 1949-79. Southern 1979-98.

HONOURS: FA Comps: None
       League: Hampshire League Division 3 East 1949-50, Premier 1959-60, 62-63, 63-64, 64-65, 65-66, 66-67, 72-73, 74-75.
10 YEAR RECORD

08-09	09-10	10-11	11-12	12-13	13-14	14-15	15-16	16-17	17-18
WexP 10	WexP 6	WexP 8	WexP 12	WexP 9	WexP 10	WexP 19	WexP 12	WexP 12	WexP 16
FAC EP	FAC EP	FAC P	FAC EP	FAC 2Q	FAC 1Q	FAC EP	FAC EP	FAC 1Qr	FAC P
FAV 1Pr	FAV 2P	FAV 2Q	FAV 1P	FAV 2Q	FAV 2P	FAV 1P	FAV 1Q	FAV 2Q	FAV 2P

HAMBLE CLUB

Founded: 1969   Nickname: The Monks

Club Contact Details   (T) 07977 324 923   **(E)** secretary.hambleclubfc@gmail.com
Ground: Hamble Community Facility, Hamble Lane SO31 4TS
Nearest Railway Station Hamble - 0.4km
Capacity: **Seats:** Yes   **Covered:** Yes   **Bus Route** Hamble Lane School - stop 500m away

Colours(change):   All yellow
Previous Names: None
Previous Leagues: Hampshire Premier 1993-2016.

HONOURS: FA Comps: None
       League: Hampshire Premier 2014-15. Wessex Division One 2016-17.
10 YEAR RECORD

08-09	09-10	10-11	11-12	12-13	13-14	14-15	15-16	16-17	17-18
HantP 17	HantP 12	HantP 16	HantP 15	HantP Exp	Hant1 2	HantP 1	HantP 3	Wex1 1	WexP 10
									FAV 5P

HAMWORTHY UNITED

Founded: 1926   Nickname: The Hammers

Club Contact Details (T) 01202 674 974   (E) hamworthyutdsecretary@gmail.com
Ground: The County Ground, Blandford Close, Hamworthy, Poole BH15 4BF
Nearest Railway Station Poole - 1.4km
Capacity: 2,000 **Seats:**   **Covered:** Yes   **Shop:** No   **Bus Route** Carter School - stop 100m away
Colours(change): Maroon & sky blue
Previous Names: Hamworthy St. Michael merged with Trinidad Old Boys 1926
Previous Leagues: Dorset Combination (Founder Member) / Dorset Premier 1957-2004.

HONOURS: FA Comps: None
League: Dorset Premier 2002-03, 03-04.

10 YEAR RECORD

08-09	09-10	10-11	11-12	12-13	13-14	14-15	15-16	16-17	17-18
WexP 8	WexP 16	WexP 9	WexP 7	WexP 10	WexP 12	WexP 10	WexP 16	WexP 16	WexP 5
FAC 2Q	FAC 1Q	FAC Pr	FAC EP	FAC 2Q	FAC P	FAC 2Q	FAC 1Q	FAC 1Q	FAC 1Q
FAV 3P	FAV 1Q	FAV 2Q	FAV 1Q	FAV 2Q	FAV 1P	FAV 2Q	FAV 1Q	FAV 1Q	FAV 2Q

HORNDEAN

Founded: 1887   Nickname: Deans

Club Contact Details (T) 02392 591 363   (E) horndeanfc1887@gmail.com
Ground: Five Heads Park Five Heads Road Horndean Hampshire PO8 9NZ
Nearest Railway Station Rowlands Castle - 4.5km
Capacity: **Seats:** Yes   **Covered:** Yes   **Bus Route** Horndean Com. School - stop 560m away
Colours(change): All red (All yellow)
Previous Names: None
Previous Leagues: Waterlooville & District. Portsmouth. Hampshire 1972-86, 1995-2004. Wessex 1986-95

HONOURS: FA Comps:
League: Waterlooville & District 1926-27, 29-30, 30-31, 31-32. Portsmouth Division Two 1953-54, Premier 68-69, 69-70,
70-71. Hampshire Division Four 1974-75, Division Three 75-76, Division Two 79-80.

10 YEAR RECORD

08-09	09-10	10-11	11-12	12-13	13-14	14-15	15-16	16-17	17-18
WexP 22	Wex1 12	Wex1 2	WexP 17	WexP 11	WexP 17	WexP 11	WexP 5	WexP 6	WexP 4
			FAC 1Q	FAC 1Q	FAC 1Q	FAC 1Q	FAC EP	FAC EP	FAC 1Q
		FAV 1Q	FAV 2Q	FAV 3P	FAV 2Q	FAV 2P	FAV 1P	FAV 1P	FAV 3P

LYMINGTON TOWN

Founded: 1998   Nickname: Town

Club Contact Details (T) 01590 671 305   (E) Secretary.lymingtontownfc@yahoo.com
Ground: The Sports Ground, Southampton Road, Lymington SO41 9ZG
Nearest Railway Station Lymington Town - 0.6km
Capacity: 3,000 **Seats:** 200   **Covered:** 300   **Bus Route** Town Hall - Stop 110m away
Colours(change): Red and white
Previous Names: None
Previous Leagues: Hampshire 1998-2004.

HONOURS: FA Comps: None
League: Wessex Division Two 2004-05.

10 YEAR RECORD

08-09	09-10	10-11	11-12	12-13	13-14	14-15	15-16	16-17	17-18
WexP 18	WexP 20	WexP 11	WexP 14	WexP 19	WexP 14	WexP 9	WexP 13	WexP 9	WexP 8
FAC Pr	FAC EP	FAC Pr	FAC EP	FAC P	FAC 1Q	FAC EP	FAC EP	FAC EPr	FAC EP
FAV 2P	FAV 2Q	FAV 1P	FAV 1Q	FAV 2Q	FAV 1P	FAV 2Qr	FAV 2P	FAV 1Q	FAV 1P

PORTLAND UNITED

Founded: 1921   Nickname: Blues

Club Contact Details (T) 01305 861 489   (E) secretary.portlandutdfc@aol.com
Ground: New Grove Corner, Grove Road, Portland DT5 1DP

Capacity: 2,000 **Seats:** Yes   **Covered:** Yes   **Bus Route** Clifton Hotel - stop 280m away
Colours(change): All royal blue
Previous Names: None
Previous Leagues: Western 1925-70. Dorset Combination 1970-76, 77-2001, Dorset Premier 2006-07. Wessex 2001-02.

HONOURS: FA Comps: None
League: Western Division Two 1930-31, 31-32. Dorset Combination 1998-99, 99-2000, Dorset Premier 2007-08, 08-09,
12-13, 13-14. Wessex Division One 2015-16, Premier 2016-17.

10 YEAR RECORD

08-09	09-10	10-11	11-12	12-13	13-14	14-15	15-16	16-17	17-18
Dor P 1	Dor P 8	Dor P 4	Dor P 3	Dor P 1	Dor P 1	Dor P 2	Wex1 1	WexP 1	WexP 15
									FAC P
								FAV 2P	FAV 2Q

SHAFTESBURY
Founded: 1888   **Nickname:** The Rockies

Club Contact Details (T) 07917 652 438
(E) secretary@shaftesburyfc.co.uk
Ground: Cockrams, Coppice Street, Shaftesbury SP7 8PF

Capacity: **Seats:** Yes   **Covered:** Yes   **Bus Route** Linden Park - stop 100m away

Colours(change): Red & white
Previous Names: Shaftesbury Town.
Previous Leagues: Dorset Junior. Dorset Senior 1931-57. Dorset Combination 1957-62, 76-2004. Wessex 2004-11. Dorset Premier 2011-16.

HONOURS: FA Comps: None
League: Dorset Junior 1905-06, 62-63. Dorset Senior 1932-33. Dorset Combination 1988-89, 96-97.
10 YEAR RECORD Dorset Premier 2015-16. Wessex Division One 2016-17.

08-09	09-10	10-11	11-12	12-13	13-14	14-15	15-16	16-17	17-18
Wex1 15	Wex1 20	Wex1 19	Dor P 18	Dor P 11	Dor P 14	Dor P 4	Dor P 1	Wex1 3	WexP 12
FAC EPr	FAC EP	FAC							FAC P
FAV 1P	FAV 2Q	FAV 2Q					FAV 2Q	FAV 2P	FAV 1Q

SHOLING
Founded: 1884   **Nickname:** The Boatmen

Club Contact Details (T) 02380 403 829
(E) secretary.sholingfc@gmail.com
Ground: The Universal Stadium, Portsmouth Road, Sholing, SO19 9PW
Nearest Railway Station Netley - 1.9km
Capacity: 1,000 **Seats:** Yes   **Covered:** Yes   **Bus Route** Bus stop outside the ground.

Colours(change): Red & white stripes
Previous Names: Woolston Works, Thornycrofts (Woolston) 1918-52, Vospers 1960-2003, Vosper Thorneycroft FC/VTFC 2003-10
Previous Leagues: Hampshire 1991-2004, Wessex 2004-09, 2013-14. Southern 2009-13, 2014-15.

HONOURS: FA Comps: FA Vase 2013-14.
League: Hampshire Premier Division 2000-01, 03-04.
10 YEAR RECORD Wessex Premier 2013-14.

08-09	09-10	10-11	11-12	12-13	13-14	14-15	15-16	16-17	17-18
WexP 2	Sthsw 4	Sthsw 2	Sthsw 4	Sthsw 7	WexP 1	Sthsw 17	WexP 2	WexP 3	WexP 3
FAC EP	FAC 2Q	FAC 2Qr	FAC 2Q	FAC 3Q	FAC 2Q	FAC 1Q	FAC P	FAC 1Q	FAC EP
FAV 4P	FAV P	FAT P	FAT 1Q	FAT 3Q	FAV F	FAT 3Q	FAV 2P	FAV 1P	FAV 3P

TADLEY CALLEVA
Founded: 1989   **Nickname:** The Tadders

Club Contact Details (T) 07787 501 028
(E) secretarytcfc@gmail.com
Ground: Barlows Park Silchester Road Tadley Hampshire RG26 3PX
Nearest Railway Station Midgham - 5.1km
Capacity: 1,000 **Seats:**   **Covered:**   **Bus Route** Tadley Common Road - stop 60m away

Colours(change): All yellow
Previous Names: Tadley FC 1989-99. Tadley Town 1999-2004.
Previous Leagues: Hampshire 1994-2004

HONOURS: FA Comps: None
League: Wessex Division One 2007-08.
10 YEAR RECORD

08-09	09-10	10-11	11-12	12-13	13-14	14-15	15-16	16-17	17-18
Wex1 16	Wex1 15	Wex1 16	Wex1 17	Wex1 7	Wex1 5	Wex1 3	Wex1 3	Wex1 7	Wex1 3
					FAC P	FAC EPr	FAC EP	FAC EP	
FAV 1Q				FAV 1Q	FAV 2Q	FAV 2Q	FAV 3Pr	FAV 1Q	FAV 2Q

TEAM SOLENT
Founded: 2007   **Nickname:** The Sparks

Club Contact Details (T)
(E) secretary.teamsolent@solent.ac.uk
Ground: Test Park, Lower Broomhill Road, Southampton SO16 9BP
Nearest Railway Station Redbridge - 1.2km
Capacity: **Seats:** Yes   **Covered:** Yes   **Bus Route** The Saints - stop 450m away

Colours(change): All red
Previous Names: None
Previous Leagues: Hampshire Premier 2007-11.

HONOURS: FA Comps: None
League: Wessex Division One 2014-15.
10 YEAR RECORD

08-09	09-10	10-11	11-12	12-13	13-14	14-15	15-16	16-17	17-18
HantP 3	HantP 2	HantP 2	Wex1 3	Wex1 3	Wex1 6	Wex1 1	WexP 7	WexP 7	WexP 17
					FAC EP	FAC EP	FAC EP	FAC P	FAC EP
				FAV 1Q	FAV 1Q	FAV 1Qr	FAV 1P	FAV 5P	FAV 3P

DIVISION ONE

AFC STONEHAM
Founded: 1919   Nickname: The Purples

Club Contact Details (T) 07765 046 429   **(E)** secretary@afcstoneham.co.uk

Ground: The HP Arena, Jubilee Park, Chestnut Avenue, Eastleigh SO50 9PF

Nearest Railway Station Southampton Airport Parkway - 1.6km   **Bus Route** Golf Driving Range stop

HONOURS   **League:** Southampton Senior 1982-83, 92-93, 96-97. Hampshire Premier 2007-08.

FA Comps: None

Colours(change): All purple

10 YEAR RECORD

08-09	09-10	10-11	11-12	12-13	13-14	14-15	15-16	16-17	17-18
HantP 4	HantP 6	HantP 8	HantP 4	HantP 2	HantP 12	HantP 4	Wex1 8	Wex1 8	Wex1 5
								FAV 1P	FAV 1Q

ALTON TOWN
Founded: 1947   Nickname: The Brewers

Club Contact Details (T)   **(E)** secretary.altontownfc@hotmail.com

Ground: Anstey Park Enclosure, Anstey Road, Alton, Hants GU34 2NB   **Capacity:** 2,000

Nearest Railway Station Alton - 0.6km   **Bus Route** Anstey Lane - stop 32m away

HONOURS   **League:** Athenian Division Two 1973-74. Hampshire Division Two 1986-87, Division One 98-99, Premier

FA Comps: None   2001-02.

Colours(change): White and black

10 YEAR RECORD

08-09	09-10	10-11	11-12	12-13	13-14	14-15	15-16	16-17	17-18
WexP 19	WexP 18	WexP 13	WexP 10	WexP 18	CCP 21	CC1 13	Wex1 7	Wex1 12	Wex1 8
FAC EP	FAC P	FAC 2Qr	FAC P	FAC P	FAC P	FAC 1Q	FAC EP		
FAV 2Q	FAV 2Q	FAV 2Q	FAV 2Pr	FAV 1P	FAV 1P	FAV 1Q	FAV 1P	FAV 1P	FAV 1P

AMESBURY TOWN
Founded: 1904   Nickname: Blues

Club Contact Details (T) 01980 623 489   **(E)** amesburytownfc@gmail.com

Ground: Bonnymead Park Recreation Road Amesbury SP4 7BB

Bus Route Mandalay Guest House - stop 600m away

HONOURS   **League:** Salisbury & District Division Two 1954-55, Division One 55-56. Wiltshire Division One 1959-60.

FA Comps: None   Wiltshire Combination/County 1974-75, 79-80 / Division One 90-91, 91-92. Hampshire Premier

Colours(change): Royal blue & white

10 YEAR RECORD

08-09	09-10	10-11	11-12	12-13	13-14	14-15	15-16	16-17	17-18
Wex1 12	Wex1 11	Wex1 13	Wex1 14	Wex1 14	Wex1 10	Wex1 4	Wex1 2	WexP 19	WexP 20
FAC EP	FAC EP	FAC EP					FAC EP	FAC P	FAC P
FAV 2Q	FAV 1Q	FAV 1Q	FAV 1Q	FAV 1Q	FAV 1Q	FAV 2Q	FAV 1Q	FAV 1P	FAV 2Q

ANDOVER TOWN
Founded: 2013   Nickname:

Club Contact Details (T)   **(E)** secretary@andovertownfc.co.uk

Ground: Portway Stadium, West Portway, Portway Industrial Estate, Andover SP10 3LF   **Capacity:** 3,000

Nearest Railway Station Andover - 1.8km   **Bus Route** Arkwright Gate - stop 130m away

HONOURS   **League:** None

FA Comps: None

Colours(change): All blue

10 YEAR RECORD

08-09	09-10	10-11	11-12	12-13	13-14	14-15	15-16	16-17	17-18
						WexP 12	WexP 4	WexP 13	WexP 2
							FAC Pr	FAC 1Q	FAC 1Q
						FAV 2Q	FAV 1P	FAV 2P	FAV 1Q

DOWNTON
Founded: 1905   Nickname: The Robins

Club Contact Details (T) 01725 512 162   **(E)** info@downtonfc.com

Ground: Brian Whitehead Sports Ground Wick Lane Downton Wiltshire SP5 3NF   **Capacity:** 2,000

Bus Route The Bull - stop 180m away

HONOURS   **League:** Wessex League Division One 2010-11.

FA Comps: None

Colours(change): All red

10 YEAR RECORD

08-09	09-10	10-11	11-12	12-13	13-14	14-15	15-16	16-17	17-18
Wex1 17	Wex1 4	Wex1 1	WexP 6	WexP 8	WexP 21	Wex1 12	Wex1 10	Wex1 11	Wex1 12
FAC 1Q	FAC EPr	FAC EP	FAC EPr	FAC EP	FAC EP	FAC EP	FAC EP		
FAV 1Q	FAV 1P	FAV 2P	FAV 2P	FAV 3P	FAV 2Q		FAV 1Q	FAV 1Q	FAV 1P

EAST COWES VICTORIA ATHLETIC

Founded: 1885   Nickname: The Vics

Club Contact Details (T) 01983 297 165   (E) ecvafc@outlook.com

Ground: Beatrice Avenue Whippingham East Cowes Isle of Wight PO32 6PA   **Capacity:** 1,000

Bus Route Osborne House - stop 400m away

HONOURS   **League:** Hampshire Division Two 1947-48, 63-64, 71-72, Division One 85-86, 86-87.

FA Comps: None

Colours(change): Red & white

10 YEAR RECORD

08-09		09-10		10-11		11-12		12-13		13-14		14-15		15-16		16-17		17-18	
Wex1	18	Wex1	17	Wex1	15	Wex1	4	Wex1	8	Wex1	16	Wex1	15	Wex1	18	Wex1	20	Wex1	16
								FAC	P	FAC	EP								
				FAV	2Q	FAV	1Q	FAV	1Q	FAV	2Q	FAV	2Q	FAV	1Q	FAV	2Q	FAV	1Q

FAWLEY

Founded: 1923   Nickname: Oilers

Club Contact Details (T) 02380 893 750 (Club)   (E) fawleyafc@aol.com

Ground: Waterside Spts & Soc. club, 179 Long Lane, Holbury, Soto, SO45 2PA

Nearest Railway Station Netley - 5.3km   **Bus Route** New Forest Academy - stop 100m away

HONOURS   **League:** Hampshire Division Three 1994-95.

FA Comps: None

Colours(change): Sky and navy blue

10 YEAR RECORD

08-09		09-10		10-11		11-12		12-13		13-14		14-15		15-16		16-17		17-18	
Wex1	9	Wex1	2	WexP	20	WexP	19	WexP	17	WexP	20	WexP	17	WexP	19	WexP	20	Wex1	9
								FAC	EP	FAC	EP	FAC	EP	FAC	EP	FAC	EP	FAC	EP
						FAV	2P	FAV	1P	FAV	2Q	FAV	1Q	FAV	1Q	FAV	1Q	FAV	2Q

FOLLAND SPORTS

Founded: 1938   Nickname: Planemakers

Club Contact Details (T) 02380 452 173   (E) follandsportsfc@hotmail.co.uk

Ground: Folland Park, Kings Ave, Hamble, Southampton SO31 4NF   **Capacity:** 1,000

Nearest Railway Station Hamble - 1km   **Bus Route** Verdon Avenue - stop 300m away

HONOURS   **League:** Hampshire 1941-42, Division Four 79-80, Division Three 80-81. Southampton Senior 1961-62, 67 -68. Wessex Division One 2009-10.

FA Comps: None

Colours(change): All red

10 YEAR RECORD

08-09		09-10		10-11		11-12		12-13		13-14		14-15		15-16		16-17		17-18	
WexP	21	Wex1	1	WexP	12	WexP	5	WexP	7	WexP	3	WexP	8	WexP	21	Wex1	17	Wex1	18
FAC	EPr	FAC	EPr	FAC	3Q	FAC	EP	FAC	P	FAC	P	FAC	2Qr	FAC	EP	FAC	EP		
FAV	1Q	FAV	2P	FAV	1P	FAV	2Q	FAV	3P	FAV	2P	FAV	2P	FAV	2Q	FAV	1Q	FAV	1Q

HYTHE & DIBDEN

Founded: 1902   Nickname: The Boatmen

Club Contact Details (T) 07825 550 624   (E) hythedibdenfc@aol.com

Ground: Clayfields, Claypit Lane, Dibden SO45 5TN

Nearest Railway Station Southampton Town Quay - 3.5km   **Bus Route** Drapers Copse - stop 200m away

HONOURS   **League:** Hampshire Division Three West 1949-50. Southampton Division Two 1970-71, 75-76.

FA Comps: None

Colours(change): Green and white

10 YEAR RECORD

08-09		09-10		10-11		11-12		12-13		13-14		14-15		15-16		16-17		17-18	
Wex1	7	Wex1	16	Wex1	14	Wex1	18	Wex1	16	Wex1	4	Wex1	7	Wex1	11	Wex1	18	Wex1	15
												FAC	EP	FAC	EP				
				FAV	2Q			FAV	1Q	FAV	1P	FAV	1Q	FAV	1Q	FAV	1Q	FAV	2Q

LAVERSTOCK & FORD

Founded: 1956   Nickname: The Stock

Club Contact Details (T) 01722 327 401   (E) sec.laverstockandfordfc@gmail.com

Ground: The Dell, Church Road, Laverstock, Salisbury, Wilts SP1 1QX

Nearest Railway Station Salisbury - 2.5km   **Bus Route** St Andrews School - stop 40m away

HONOURS   **League:** Hampshire Division Two 2002-03.

FA Comps: None

Colours(change): Green & white hoops

10 YEAR RECORD

08-09		09-10		10-11		11-12		12-13		13-14		14-15		15-16		16-17		17-18	
WexP	20	WexP	21	WexP	17	WexP	22	Wex1	13	Wex1	9	Wex1	8	Wex1	5	Wex1	6	Wex1	7
		FAC	EP	FAC	P											FAC	EP	FAC	P
FAV	2Q	FAV	1P	FAV	1P			FAV	1Q	FAV	1P	FAV	2Q	FAV	1P	FAV	1Q	FAV	1Q

NEW MILTON TOWN

Founded: 1998 — Nickname: The Linnets

Club Contact Details (T) 01425 628 191 — **(E)** enquiries@newmiltontownfc.com
Ground: Fawcetts Fields, Christchurch Road, New Milton BH25 6QB — **Capacity:** 1,500
Nearest Railway Station New Milton - 1.1km — **Bus Route** Old Milton Green - stop 150m away
HONOURS — **League:** Wessex 1998-99, 2004-05.
FA Comps: None
Colours(change): Maroon & blue

10 YEAR RECORD

08-09	09-10	10-11	11-12	12-13	13-14	14-15	15-16	16-17	17-18
WexP 9	WexP 19	WexP 19	WexP 20	WexP 21	Wex1 11	Wex1 6	Wex1 14	Wex1 14	Wex1 10
FAC P	FAC P	FAC EPr	FAC EPr	FAC EP			FAC EP		
FAV 3P	FAV 2Q	FAV 1Q	FAV 2Q	FAV 2P		FAV 2Q	FAV 1P	FAV 1Q	FAV 1Q

NEWPORT (I.O.W.)

Founded: 1888 — Nickname: The Port

Club Contact Details (T) 01983 525 027 — **(E)** secretary@niowfc.com
Ground: St George's Park, St George's Way, Newport PO30 2QH — **Capacity:** 4,000
Bus Route St Georges Park - stop 70m away
HONOURS — **League:** Isle of Wight 1907-08, 08-09, 09-10, 23-24. Hampshire 1929-30, 32-33, 38-39, 47-48, 49-50, 52-53, 53-54, 56-57, 79-79, 79-80, 80-81. Southern Eastern Division 2000-01.
FA Comps: None
Colours(change): Yellow and blue

10 YEAR RECORD

08-09	09-10	10-11	11-12	12-13	13-14	14-15	15-16	16-17	17-18
WexP 6	WexP 9	WexP 10	WexP 13	WexP 6	WexP 4	WexP 7	WexP 10	WexP 15	WexP 21
FAC EP	FAC P	FAC 1Q	FAC 1Q	FAC 2Q	FAC P	FAC 2Qr	FAC EP	FAC EP	FAC EP
FAV 1P	FAV 2Q	FAV 3P	FAV 1Q	FAV 5Pr	FAV 2P	FAV 3P	FAV 4P	FAV 2P	FAV 4P

PETERSFIELD TOWN

Founded: 1993 — Nickname: Rams

Club Contact Details (T) 01730 233 416 — **(E)** secretary.petersfieldtownfc@outlook.com
Ground: Love Lane, Petersfield, Hampshire GU31 4BW — **Capacity:** 3000
Nearest Railway Station Petersfield - 0.8km — **Bus Route** Madeline Road - stop 140m away
HONOURS — **League:** Wessex Division One 2013-14, Premier Division 2014-15.
FA Comps: None
Colours(change): Red & black

10 YEAR RECORD

08-09	09-10	10-11	11-12	12-13	13-14	14-15	15-16	16-17	17-18
Wex1 4	Wex1 8	Wex1 11	Wex1 12	Wex1 6	Wex1 1	WexP 1	SthC 13	SthC 22	WexP 22
	FAC EP	FAC EP	FAC EP	FAC EPr	FAC P	FAC EP	FAC 3Q	FAC P	FAC EP
FAV 2Q	FAV 1Q	FAV 1Q	FAV 2Q	FAV 1P	FAV 1P	FAV 2Q	FAT P	FAT Pr	FAV 2Q

RINGWOOD TOWN

Founded: 1879 — Nickname: The Peckers

Club Contact Details (T) 01425 473 448 — **(E)** ringwoodtownfc@live.co.uk
Ground: The Canotec Stadium, Long Lane, Ringwood, Hampshire BH24 3BX — **Capacity:** 1,000
Bus Route Crow Crossroads - stop 100m away
HONOURS — **League:** Hampshire Division three 1995-96.
FA Comps: None
Colours(change): Red and white

10 YEAR RECORD

08-09	09-10	10-11	11-12	12-13	13-14	14-15	15-16	16-17	17-18
Wex1 11	Wex1 5	Wex1 6	Wex1 9	Wex1 9	Wex1 13	Wex1 11	Wex1 13	Wex1 5	Wex1 11
FAC Pr	FAC P	FAC 1Q	FAC EP	FAC EP					FAC EP
FAV 1Q	FAV 2Q	FAV 1Q	FAV 2Q	FAV 1Q	FAV 1Q	FAV 1P	FAV 2Q	FAV 1Q	FAV 2Q

ROMSEY TOWN

Founded: 1886 — Nickname: Town

Club Contact Details (T) 01794 516 691 — **(E)** romseytownfc@gmail.com
Ground: The By-Pass Ground, South Front, Romsey SO51 8GJ — **Capacity:** 1,500
Nearest Railway Station Romsey - 0.5km — **Bus Route** Linden Road - stop 100m away
HONOURS — **League:** Post War: Southampton West 1951-52, Senior Div.2 72-73, Senior Div.1 73-74, 76-77, Prem 80-81, 83-84. Hampshire Div.4 75-76, Div.2 78-79. Wessex 89-90.
FA Comps: None
Colours(change): Red & black

10 YEAR RECORD

08-09	09-10	10-11	11-12	12-13	13-14	14-15	15-16	16-17	17-18
WexP 11	WexP 10	WexP 16	WexP 8	WexP 20	WexP 22	Wex1 14	Wex1 9	Wex1 13	Wex1 6
	FAC P	FAC EPr	FAC EP	FAC P	FAC EP	FAC EP			
FAV 1Q	FAV 1Q	FAV 2Q	FAV 2Q	FAV 2Q	FAV 2Q	FAV 1Q	FAV 2Q	FAV 1P	FAV 1P

TOTTON & ELING

Founded: 1925   Nickname: The Millers

Club Contact Details (T) 07545 182 379   **(E)** tefcsecretary@gmail.com

Ground: Millers Park,Little Tesrwood Farm Salisbury Road Totton SO40 2RW   **Capacity:** 1,500

Nearest Railway Station Totton - 2.9km   **Bus Route** Cooks Lane - stop 280m away

HONOURS   **League:** Hampshire Division three 1974-75, Division One 1987-88, 88-89.

FA Comps: None   Wessex Division One 2008-09.

Colours(change): Red & black

10 YEAR RECORD

	08-09	09-10	10-11	11-12	12-13	13-14	14-15	15-16	16-17	17-18
	Wex1 1	WexP 7	WexP 18	WexP 11	WexP 12	WexP 8	WexP 20	Wex1 15	Wex1 15	Wex1 14
		FAC P	FAC 1Q	FAC P	FAC 1Qr	FAC Pr	FAC EP			
	FAV 1P	FAV 2Q	FAV 1Q	FAV 1Q	FAV 1Q	FAV 1Q	FAV 1Q			

UNITED SERVICES PORTSMOUTH

Founded: 1962   Nickname: The Navy

Club Contact Details (T) 02392 573 041 (Gr'sman)   **(E)** usportsmouthfc@hotmail.co.uk

Ground: Victory Stadium HMS Temeraire Burnaby Road Portsmouth PO1 2HB

Nearest Railway Station Portsmouth Harbour - 0.7km   **Bus Route** University - stop 120m away

HONOURS   **League:** Hampshire Division Two 1967-68, 77-78, 80-81.

FA Comps: None

Colours(change): Royal blue & red

10 YEAR RECORD

	08-09	09-10	10-11	11-12	12-13	13-14	14-15	15-16	16-17	17-18
	Wex1 3	Wex1 9	Wex1 5	Wex1 13	Wex1 12	Wex1 7	Wex1 5	Wex1 4	Wex1 9	Wex1 4
								FAC EP	FAC P	
	FAV 2Q	FAV 1P	FAV 1Q	FAV 2Q	FAV 2Q	FAV 2Q	FAV 2P	FAV 2Qr	FAV 1Q	FAV 1P

VERWOOD TOWN

Founded: 1920   Nickname: The Potters

Club Contact Details (T) 01202 814 007   **(E)** secretary@vtfc.co.uk

Ground: Potterne Park Potterne Way Verwood Dorset BH21 6RS

Bus Route Potterne Bridge - stop 280m away

HONOURS   **League:** Wessex Division One 2011-12.

FA Comps: None

Colours(change): Red & black

10 YEAR RECORD

	08-09	09-10	10-11	11-12	12-13	13-14	14-15	15-16	16-17	17-18
	Wex1 13	Wex1 7	Wex1 9	Wex1 1	WexP 14	WexP 19	WexP 15	WexP 17	WexP 22	Wex1 17
			FAC EPr	FAC EP	FAC EP	FAC EP	FAC EP	FAC P	FAC Pr	FAC EPr
		FAV 1P	FAV 3P	FAV 1Q	FAV 1Qr	FAV 2P	FAV 3P	FAV 2Q	FAV 1Q	FAV 1Q

WHITCHURCH UNITED

Founded: 1903   Nickname: Jam Boys

Club Contact Details (T) 01256 892 493   **(E)** secretary.wufc@gmail.com

Ground: Longmeadow Winchester Road Whitchurch Hampshire RG28 7RB   **Capacity:** 1,500

Nearest Railway Station Whitchurch - 1.7km   **Bus Route** Charcot Close - stop 100m away

HONOURS   **League:** Hampshire Division Two 1989-90.

FA Comps: None

Colours(change): Red & white stripes

10 YEAR RECORD

	08-09	09-10	10-11	11-12	12-13	13-14	14-15	15-16	16-17	17-18
	Wex1 6	Wex1 10	Wex1 7	Wex1 8	Wex1 2	WexP 13	WexP 6	WexP 15	WexP 21	Wex1 13
				FAC 2Q	FAC EP	FAC EPr	FAC EPr	FAC EPr	FAC P	FAC EP
			FAV 1Q	FAV 2Q	FAV 2Q	FAV 1Q	FAV 2Q	FAV 1Pr	FAV 2Q	FAV 2Q

WEST MIDLANDS (REGIONAL) LEAGUE

Founded: 1889 **Sponsored by:** None

Recent Champions: 2015: Sporting Khalsa **2016:** Shawbury United **2017:** Haughmond

PREMIER DIVISION	P	W	D	L	F	A	GD	Pts
1 Wolverhampton Sporting Community	38	34	2	2	148	29	119	104
2 Tividale	38	28	5	5	121	49	72	89
3 Malvern Town	38	26	5	7	113	65	48	83
4 Black Country Rangers	38	23	8	7	111	56	55	77
5 Wednesfield	38	23	5	10	101	63	38	74
6 Ellesmere Rangers	38	22	5	11	106	68	38	71
7 Bewdley Town	38	19	6	13	91	70	21	63
8 Cradley Town	38	19	5	14	85	63	22	62
9 Wolverhampton Casuals	38	18	3	17	121	95	26	57
10 Wellington	38	17	5	16	82	75	7	56
11 Bilston Town Community	38	16	5	17	80	85	-5	53
12 Hereford Lads Club	38	16	3	19	73	90	-17	51
13 Stone Old Alleynians	38	14	3	21	76	92	-16	45
14 Smethwick Rangers	38	9	6	23	49	85	-36	33
15 Shifnal Town	38	10	3	25	58	111	-53	33
16 Dudley Sports	38	9	5	24	61	110	-49	32
17 Dudley Town	38	8	7	23	44	100	-56	31
18 AFC Bridgnorth	38	8	6	24	50	91	-41	30
19 Pegasus Juniors	38	7	7	24	37	109	-72	28
20 Wellington Amateurs	38	3	8	27	38	139	-101	17

DIVISION ONE	P	W	D	L	F	A	GD	Pts
1 Wem Town	32	23	4	5	95	34	61	73
2 Newport Town	32	21	6	5	106	39	67	69
3 Old Wulfrunians	32	20	8	4	58	27	31	68
4 St Martins	32	20	0	12	87	46	41	60
5 Gornal Athletic	32	18	5	9	71	47	24	59
6 Darlaston Town (1874)	32	17	7	8	79	63	16	58
7 Worcester Raiders	32	17	7	8	72	59	13	58
8 Team Dudley	32	15	7	10	90	68	22	52
9 Allscott	32	13	3	16	55	65	-10	42
10 Tipton Town	32	12	4	16	60	71	-11	40
11 Bustleholme	32	12	3	17	68	85	-17	39
12 Wrens Nest	32	11	2	19	56	79	-23	35
13 Bromyard Town	32	10	3	19	60	87	-27	33
14 Kington Town	32	8	3	21	51	81	-30	27
15 Telford Juniors	32	7	3	22	48	87	-39	24
16 Wyrley	32	6	5	21	39	86	-47	23
17 Willenhall Town	32	3	8	21	34	105	-71	17

DIVISION TWO	P	W	D	L	F	A	GD	Pts
1 Sikh Hunters	28	23	4	1	105	25	80	73
2 Wolverhampton United	28	20	4	4	85	26	59	64
3 Gornal Colts	28	19	5	4	92	57	35	62
4 Bewdley Town Res	28	15	7	6	93	48	45	52
5 Warstone Wanderers	28	17	1	10	114	71	43	52
6 Rock Rovers	28	14	4	10	75	71	4	46
7 Church Stretton	28	13	5	10	68	49	19	44
8 Oldbury United	28	10	5	13	56	61	-5	35
9 AFC Bilbrook	28	9	6	13	51	74	-23	33
10 Ludlow	28	8	5	15	58	79	-21	29
11 F C Darlaston	28	8	5	15	51	76	-25	29
12 Wonder Vaults	28	8	3	17	56	83	-27	27
13 AFC Broseley	28	7	6	15	43	92	-49	27
14 Market Drayton Town Res	28	4	6	18	45	93	-48	18
15 AFC Bridgnorth Development	28	1	2	25	29	116	-87	5

Premier Division League Cup Final
Wolverhampton SC   v   Black County Rangers   3-0

PREMIER DIVISION	1	2	3	4	5	6	7	8	9	10	11	12	13	14	15	16	17	18	19	20
1 AFC Bridgnorth		0-2	0-3	1-3	0-5	1-2	1-2	0-2	3-0	0-2	1-0	3-2	2-3	0-1	1-4	4-0	0-3	0-1	3-3	1-1
2 Bewdley Town	2-2		0-3	7-1	1-4	3-1	5-1	7-1	3-1	2-6	7-0	5-2	2-0	3-2	0-1	6-5	1-3	0-3	1-4	2-0
3 Bilston Town Community	3-3	1-2		1-1	0-3	3-2	0-3	3-2	4-1	3-4	2-2	3-1	1-0	1-3	2-4	3-2	0-8	1-2	3-2	8-0
4 Black Country Rangers	4-0	4-1	2-0		1-1	3-1	5-3	3-2	6-1	2-2	2-1	6-1	1-2	1-1	2-2	0-0	0-2	1-1	4-0	8-0
5 Cradley Town	1-0	1-1	3-0	0-2		3-1	3-2	3-4	2-0	1-3	3-1	1-2	1-1	3-2	3-5	2-5	0-2	0-2	2-2	4-1
6 Dudley Sports	2-0	2-2	2-2	1-5	2-6		2-2	0-6	2-1	0-4	1-2	1-0	4-1	1-2	3-4	0-5	1-4	0-3	1-1	
7 Dudley Town	2-1	0-3	0-5	0-4	4-2	2-2		1-5	1-4	0-4	1-1	3-1	1-0	1-8	2-2	0-4	0-3	0-2	3-1	1-1
8 Ellesmere Rangers	9-2	2-0	3-2	3-2	3-1	4-0	1-0		4-1	6-2	10-0	4-0	1-0	3-3	4-6	2-3	1-2	2-1	0-3	1-1
9 Hereford Lads Club	1-2	0-3	1-2	1-1	2-2	2-0	3-1	3-2		2-3	2-3	1-3	5-2	1-3	2-1	2-2	0-2	5-2	2-1	3-1
10 Malvern Town	4-0	1-1	5-1	2-2	2-1	7-1	3-0	1-3	4-5		3-0	4-2	7-0	4-1	0-6	6-1	2-1	3-2	2-1	3-1
11 Pegasus Juniors	1-1	2-3	2-2	0-5	1-3	0-5	0-1	0-1	1-2	0-3		2-1	2-1	1-1	1-2	1-0	0-4	2-5	0-4	6-0
12 Shifnal Town	4-0	0-4	1-4	3-4	0-2	1-6	3-0	0-0	2-3	0-1	1-1		3-2	1-4	3-0	4-6	0-6	0-9	0-2	2-2
13 Smethwick Rangers	2-1	1-1	1-2	0-3	1-1	0-0	0-0	4-3	2-3	0-0	0-1	3-1		2-1	0-4	2-6	1-6	0-2	1-1	4-0
14 Stone Old Alleynians	3-5	0-3	1-3	1-5	3-4	4-0	4-3	1-2	2-4	2-3	1-0	1-2	3-1		0-2	2-1	0-3	0-3	2-1	1-3
15 Tividale	3-1	2-0	5-1	3-1	1-0	6-2	5-1	1-2	3-2	10-1	4-0	6-1	3-1	1-2		3-3	1-1	2-2	4-2	3-0
16 Wolverhampton Casuals	1-4	4-2	2-1	2-7	1-3	7-2	4-1	2-2	3-4	1-4	9-0	3-4	6-0	1-4	1-3		0-1	6-0	2-4	7-0
17 Wolverhampton Sporting Community	4-0	6-2	4-1	3-1	3-2	2-0	2-0	4-2	6-1	3-0	6-0	5-1	3-2	5-0	2-3	4-2		6-1	4-0	2-2
18 Wednesfield	2-0	2-2	2-0	2-3	0-3	4-3	3-1	2-2	4-0	1-1	5-1	2-0	1-2	7-3	2-1	1-3	1-3		3-1	5-2
19 Wellington	3-3	1-0	5-2	1-3	1-0	4-2	1-1	3-0	1-2	3-2	6-1	1-0	1-3	5-1	0-2	3-4	2-8	1-3		3-1
20 Wellington Amateurs	1-4	1-2	1-4	0-3	1-5	2-4	2-0	1-2	1-0	2-5	1-1	1-4	3-3	0-4	0-7	1-4	0-11	2-7	1-2	

AFC BRIDGNORTH

Founded: 2013 Nickname: Meadow Men

Club Contact Details (T) 07748 302 650 **(E)** steve_groorne2003@yahoo.co.uk
Ground: Crown Meadow, Innage Lane, Bridgnorth WV16 4HS **Capacity:** 2,000

Bus Route Bus stops outside the ground.

HONOURS **League:** West Midlands (Reg) Division One 2013-14.
FA Comps: None

Colours(change): Blue & white

10 YEAR RECORD									
08-09	09-10	10-11	11-12	12-13	13-14	14-15	15-16	16-17	17-18
					WM1 1	WMP 2	WMP 2	WMP 8	WMP 18
							FAC P	FAC EP	
						FAV 1P	FAV 2P	FAV 1Q	FAV 1Q

BEWDLEY TOWN

Founded: 1978 Nickname: None

Club Contact Details (T) 07739 626 169 **(E)** stevegodfrey09@gmail.com
Ground: Ribbesford Meadows, Ribbesford, Bewdley, Worcs DY12 2TJ

Bus Route Burlish Farm - stop 1km away

HONOURS **League:** West Midlands (Reg) Division One South 2002-03, Division One 2004-05.
FA Comps: None

Colours(change): Royal blue & yellow

10 YEAR RECORD									
08-09	09-10	10-11	11-12	12-13	13-14	14-15	15-16	16-17	17-18
WMP 3	WMP 12	WMP 6	WMP 4	WMP 8	WMP 7	WMP 17	WMP 16	WMP 6	WMP 7
	FAC EP	FAC P	FAC 1Q	FAC 1Q	FAC EP	FAC EP			FAC EP
FAV 2Q	FAV 2P	FAV 2Q	FAV 1Q	FAV 1P	FAV 1Q	FAV 1Q	FAV 1Q	FAV 2Q	FAV 1Q

BILSTON TOWN COMMUNITY

Founded: 1894 Nickname: The Steelmen

Club Contact Details (T) **(E)** w.l.smith@outlook.com
Ground: Queen Street Stadium, Queen Street, Bilston WV14 7EX **Capacity:** 4,000
Nearest Railway Station Bilston Central - 550m **Bus Route** Bus stops outside the ground
HONOURS **League:** Walsall & District 1895-96, 1900-01, 01-02, 32-33, 35-36, 47-48. Birmingham & District/West Mids
FA Comps: None (Reg) Division One 1956-57, Premier 60-61, 72-73.

Colours(change): Orange & black

10 YEAR RECORD									
08-09	09-10	10-11	11-12	12-13	13-14	14-15	15-16	16-17	17-18
WM1 5	WM1 12	WM1 9	WM1 9	WM1 2	WMP 16	WMP 13	WMP 20	WMP 15	WMP 11
				FAV 1P	FAV 2Q	FAV 1Q	FAV 2Q	FAV 2Q	FAV 2Q

BLACK COUNTRY RANGERS

Founded: 1996 Nickname:

Club Contact Details (T) 07891 128 896 **(E)** bcrfc@outlook.com
Ground: Halesowen Town F C, The Grove, Old Hawne Lane, Halesowen B63 3TB
Nearest Railway Station Old Hill - 1.8km **Bus Route** Cranmoor Crescent - stop 50m away
HONOURS **League:** West Midlands (Reg) Division Two 2009-10, Division One 10-11.
FA Comps: None

Colours(change): Red

10 YEAR RECORD									
08-09	09-10	10-11	11-12	12-13	13-14	14-15	15-16	16-17	17-18
WM2 5	WM2 1	WM1 1	WMP 2	WMP 5	WMP 5	WMP 10	WMP 15	WMP 13	WMP 4
					FAC P	FAC EP			
				FAV 2P	FAV 1Q	FAV 1Q	FAV 1Pr	FAV	

CRADLEY TOWN

Founded: 1948 Nickname: The Lukes or Hammers

Club Contact Details (T) 07708 659 636 **(E)** d.attwood@sky.com
Ground: The Beeches, Beeches View Avenue, Cradley, Halesowen B63 2HB **Capacity:** 3,000
Nearest Railway Station Cradley Heath - 2km **Bus Route** Hedgefield Grove - stop 200m away
HONOURS **League:** West Midlands (Reg) Division One 1990-91.
FA Comps: None

Colours(change): Red and black

10 YEAR RECORD									
08-09	09-10	10-11	11-12	12-13	13-14	14-15	15-16	16-17	17-18
MidAl 16	MidAl 22	WMP 8	WMP 8	WMP 9	WMP 10	WMP 15	WMP 8	WMP 10	WMP 8
FAC 2Q	FAC 1Q	FAC EP	FAC EPr	FAC Pr	FAC EP			FAC EPr	
FAV 2Q	FAV 2Q	FAV 1Q	FAV 1Q	FAV 2Q	FAV 1P	FAV 2Q	FAV 1P	FAV 1Q	FAV 2Q

DUDLEY SPORTS

Founded: 1925   Nickname: The Piemen

Club Contact Details (T) 01384 349 413   **(E)** kath-john.lewis@blueyonder.co.uk

Ground: Hillcrest Avenue, Brierley Hill, West Mids DY5 3QH   **Capacity:** 2,000

Nearest Railway Station Lye - 2.1km Stourbridge - 2.5km Cradley Heath -   **Bus Route** Lancaster Road - stop 60m away

HONOURS   **League:** None

FA Comps: None

Colours(change): Green & white

10 YEAR RECORD

08-09		09-10		10-11		11-12		12-13		13-14		14-15		15-16		16-17		17-18	
WMP	12	WMP	15	WMP	14	WMP	12	WMP	17	WMP	17	WMP	12	WMP	6	WMP	17	WMP	16
FAC	EP	FAC	1Q					FAC	EPr							FAC	P		
FAV	1Q	FAV	1Q	FAV	1Q	FAV	2Q	FAV	1Q	FAV	2Q	FAV	1Q	FAV	2Q	FAV	2Q	FAV	2Q

DUDLEY TOWN

Founded: 1888   Nickname: The Duds or Robins

Club Contact Details (T) 07986 549 675   **(E)** davef.dtfc@blueyonder.co.uk

Ground: The Dell Stadium, Bryce Road, Brierley Hill, West Mids DY5 4NE

Nearest Railway Station Lye - 3.7km Cradley Heath 3.9km Stourbridge - 4km   **Bus Route** Rookery Park - stop 200m away

HONOURS   **League:** Birmingham Combination 1933-34. Southern Midland Division 1984-85.

FA Comps: None

Colours(change): Red & black

10 YEAR RECORD

08-09		09-10		10-11		11-12		12-13		13-14		14-15		15-16		16-17		17-18	
WMP	5	WMP	5	WMP	13	WMP	7	WMP	6	WMP	9	WMP	14	WMP	13	WMP	18	WMP	17
FAC	EP	FAC	Pr	FAC	P			FAC	1Q	FAC	EPr	FAC	P						
FAV	2P	FAV	2Qr	FAV	2Qr	FAV	2Q	FAV	1Q	FAV	2P	FAV	2Q	FAV	1Q	FAV	1Q	FAV	2Q

HAUGHMOND

Founded: 1980   Nickname: Academicals

Club Contact Details (T) 07785 531 754   **(E)** stuartlwilliams@btinternet.com

Ground: Sundorne Sports Village, Sundorne Road, Shrewsbury. SY1 4RQ

Nearest Railway Station Shrewsby - 2.6km   **Bus Route** Ta Centre stop - 109m away

HONOURS   **League:** Shropshire County Premier Division 2010-11. West Midlands Division Two 2011-12, Premier

FA Comps: None   Division 2016-17.

Colours(change): White and black

10 YEAR RECORD

08-09		09-10		10-11		11-12		12-13		13-14		14-15		15-16		16-17		17-18	
ShCP	2	ShCP	2	ShCP	1	WM2	1	WM1	4	WM1	2	WMP	8	WMP	5	WMP	1	MFLP	20
																FAC	EP	FAC	2Qr
														FAV	2P	FAV	1P	FAV	1P

HEREFORD LADS CLUB

Founded: 1925   Nickname:

Club Contact Details (T) 07542 581 976   **(E)** stevenbelly@icloud.com

Ground: Hereford Lads Club, Widemarsh Common, Hereford HR4 9NA

Nearest Railway Station Hereford - 1km   **Bus Route** Priory Place - stop 150m away

HONOURS   **League:** Herefordshire Division One 2002-03.

FA Comps: None   West Midlands Division One 2016-17.

Colours(change): Blue and white

10 YEAR RECORD

08-09		09-10		10-11		11-12		12-13		13-14		14-15		15-16		16-17		17-18	
						WM2	2	WM2	3	WM1	10	WM1	5	WM1	2	WM1	1	WMP	12
																		FAV	1Q

MALVERN TOWN

Founded: 1947   Nickname: The Hillsiders

Club Contact Details (T) 07944 110 402   **(E)** marg@malverntown.co.uk

Ground: HD Anywhere Community Stadium, Lamgland Avenue, Malvern WR14 2EQ   **Capacity:** 2,500

Nearest Railway Station Great Malvern - 1.2km. Malvern Link - 1.5km   **Bus Route** Bus stops outside the ground

HONOURS   **League:** Midland Combination Division One 1955-56.

FA Comps: None

Colours(change): Sky blue and claret

10 YEAR RECORD

08-09		09-10		10-11		11-12		12-13		13-14		14-15		15-16		16-17		17-18	
SthC	22	MidAl	19	MidAl	23	WMP	13	WMP	13	WMP	14	WMP	5	WMP	3	WMP	4	WMP	3
FAC	P	FAC	Pr	FAC	P	FAC	EPr							FAC	2P	FAC	EP	FAC	P
FAT	P	FAV	1P	FAV	1P	FAV	1Q	FAV	1Q	FAV	1Q	FAV	1Q	FAV	2Q	FAV	1P	FAV	P

PEGASUS JUNIORS

Founded: 1955   Nickname: The Redmen

Club Contact Details (T) 07816 121 248
(E) nikmarsh1982@gmail.com
Ground: Old School Lane, Hereford HR1 1EX   **Capacity:** 1,000
Nearest Railway Station Hereford - 1.3km   **Bus Route** Bus stops outside the ground
HONOURS   **League:** Hellenic Division One 1984-85, 98-99.
FA Comps: None

Colours(change): Red and white

10 YEAR RECORD

08-09		09-10		10-11		11-12		12-13		13-14		14-15		15-16		16-17		17-18	
Hel P	10	Hel P	14	Hel P	22	WMP	17	WMP	7	WMP	2	WMP	9	WMP	9	WMP	9	WMP	19
FAC	EP	FAC	2Q	FAC	EPr	FAC	EPr	FAC	P	FAC	EP	FAC	EPr	FAC	EP				
FAV	1Q	FAV	2Q	FAV	2Q	FAV	1Q	FAV	1P	FAV	1Q	FAV	2P	FAV	1Q	FAV	2Q	FAV	1Q

PERSHORE TOWN

Founded: 1988   Nickname: Town

Club Contact Details (T)
(E) cindywebb1@hotmail.co.uk
Ground: King George V Playing Field, King George's Way, Pershore WR10 1QU   **Capacity:** 1,000
Nearest Railway Station Pershore - 2.1km   **Bus Route** Abbey Tea Rooms stop - 167m away
HONOURS   **League:** Midland Combination Division Two 1989-90, Premier 1993-94.
FA Comps: None

Colours(change): Blue & white

10 YEAR RECORD

08-09		09-10		10-11		11-12		12-13		13-14		14-15		15-16		16-17		17-18	
MCmP	13	MCmP	20	MCmP	13	MCmP	16	MCmP	13	MCmP	15	MFL1	11	MFL1	14	MFL1	18	MFL1	18
FAC	EP	FAC	EP																
FAV	2Q	FAV	2Q	FAV	2Q	FAV	2Q	FAV	2Q	FAV	2Q	FAV	2Q	FAV	1Q	FAV	1Q	FAV	2Q

SHAWBURY UNITED

Founded: 1992   Nickname:

Club Contact Details (T) 01939 233 287
(E) daibando161274@aol.com
Ground: Butler Sports Ground, Bowensfield, Wem, Shrewsbury SY4 5AP   1,000
Nearest Railway Station Wem - 0.6km   **Bus Route** Adams School stop - 161m away
HONOURS   **League:** West Midlands (Regional) Premier Division 2015-16.
FA Comps: None

Colours(change): Black & white

10 YEAR RECORD

08-09		09-10		10-11		11-12		12-13		13-14		14-15		15-16		16-17		17-18	
WMP	10	WMP	21	WMP	17	WMP	10	WMP	4	WMP	4	WMP	7	WMP	1	MFLP	19	MFLP	21
																FAC	EPr	FAC	EP
FAV	2Pr	FAV	2Q	FAV	1Q	FAV	2Q	FAV	2P	FAV	1P	FAV	2Q	FAV	1Q	FAV	1P	FAV	1Q

SHIFNAL TOWN

Founded: 1964   Nickname: The Town or Reds

Club Contact Details (T) 07986 563 156
(E) eve.ronfinney@hotmail.co.uk
Ground: Phoenix Park, Coppice Green Lane, Shifnal, Shrops TF11 8PD
Nearest Railway Station Shifnal - 0.8km   **Bus Route** Green (Barn Rd) - stop 100m away
HONOURS   **League:** West Midlands (Regional) Division One 1978-79, 2015-16, Premier Division 2006-07.
FA Comps: None

Colours(change): Red & white stripes/black/red (Pale blue/navy/navy)

10 YEAR RECORD

08-09		09-10		10-11		11-12		12-13		13-14		14-15		15-16		16-17		17-18	
MidAl	8	MidAl	21	WMP	9	WMP	16	WMP	19	WMP	19	WMP	21	WM1	1	WMP	11	WMP	15
FAC	1Q	FAC	EP	FAC	EPr	FAC	EPr	FAC	EP										
FAV	1P	FAV	1Q	FAV	2Pr	FAV	1Q	FAV	1P	FAV	1Q	FAV	2Q	FAV	1Q	FAV	1P	FAV	1P

SMETHWICK

Founded: 1977   Nickname:

Club Contact Details (T) 01384 826 420
(E)
Ground: Hillcrest Avenue, Brierley Hill, West Mids. DY5 3QH   **Capacity:** 2,000
Nearest Railway Station Lye - 2.1km Stourbridge 2.5km Cradley Heath -   **Bus Route** Lancaster Road - stop 60m away
HONOURS   **League:** Midland Combination Division Three 2007-08.
FA Comps: None   West Midlands Division One 2012-13.

Colours(change): Blue & yellow

10 YEAR RECORD

08-09		09-10		10-11		11-12		12-13		13-14		14-15		15-16		16-17		17-18	
MCm2	6	MCm2	10	WM2	4	WM1	4	WM1	1	WMP	12	WMP	19	WMP	12	WMP	16	WMP	14
																FAV	1Q	FAV	2Q

TIVIDALE
Founded: 1953 Nickname: The Dale

Club Contact Details (T) 07939 234 813   **(E)** leon@tividalefc.com
Ground: The Beeches, Packwood Road, Tividale, West Mids B69 1UL   Capacity: 3,000
Nearest Railway Station Dudley Port - 1.6km   **Bus Route** Regent Road - stop 100m away
HONOURS **League:** Warwickshire & West Midlands Alliance Premier 1964-65. West Midlands (Reg) Division One 1972-73, Premier
FA Comps: None   Division 2010-11. Midland Alliance 2013-14.
Colours(change): All yellow

10 YEAR RECORD
08-09	09-10	10-11	11-12	12-13	13-14	14-15	15-16	16-17	17-18
WMP 13	WMP 7	WMP 1	MidAl 4	MidAl 8	MidAl 1	NP1S 8	NP1S 22	MFLP 22	WMP 2
FAC EP	FAC 1Qr	FAC EP	FAC EP	FAC 2Q	FAC 1Q	FAC 2Qr	FAC 1Q	FAC P	FAC 1Q
FAV 2Q	FAV 2P	FAV 1P	FAV 5P	FAV 2Q	FAV 2Q	FAT P	FAT P	FAV 1Q	FAV 1Q

WEDNESFIELD
Founded: 1961 Nickname: The Cottagers

Club Contact Details (T) 07807 868 763   **(E)** meridithgill@gmail.com
Ground: Cottage Ground, Amos Lane, Wednesfield WV11 1ND
Nearest Railway Station Wolverhampton - 3km   **Bus Route** Cottages Homes - stop 20m away
HONOURS **League:** West Midlands Division One A 1976-77, Division One 77-78, Premier 95-96, 96-97.
FA Comps: None
Colours(change): Red & white

10 YEAR RECORD
08-09	09-10	10-11	11-12	12-13	13-14	14-15	15-16	16-17	17-18
WMP 9	WMP 11	WMP 4	WMP 6	WMP 18	WMP 15	WMP 22	WM1 4	WM1 2	WMP 5
	FAC EP	FAC 2Q							
FAV 2Q	FAV 1P	FAV 2P		FAV 1Q	FAV 1Q	FAV 1Q	FAV 1Q	FAV 1Q	FAV 1P

WELLINGTON
Founded: 1968 Nickname: The Wellies

Club Contact Details (T) 07842 186 643 (MD)   **(E)** perkinsmj49@gmail.com
Ground: Wellington Playing Field, Wellington, Hereford HR4 8AZ   Capacity: 1,000
Bus Route Wellington Village - stop 270m away
HONOURS **League:** West Midlands (Reg) Division One South 1998-99.
FA Comps: None
Colours(change): Orange

10 YEAR RECORD
08-09	09-10	10-11	11-12	12-13	13-14	14-15	15-16	16-17	17-18
WMP 6	WMP 6	WMP 10	WMP 11	WMP 15	WMP 8	WMP 11	WMP 11	WMP 5	WMP 10
FAC EP	FAC EP	FAC EPr	FAC EP	FAC P		FAC P			FAC EP
FAV 1Q	FAV 3P	FAV 1Q	FAV 2Q	FAV 1Q	FAV 1Q	FAV 1P	FAV 2Q	FAV 2Q	FAV 1P

WEM TOWN
Founded: Nickname:

Club Contact Details (T) 07875 483 534   **(E)** jessgoughwemtownfc@gmail.com
Ground: Butler Sports Centre, Bowens Field, Wem SY4 5AP
HONOURS **League:** West Midlands (Reg) Division One 2017-18.
FA Comps: None
Colours(change): Red

10 YEAR RECORD
08-09	09-10	10-11	11-12	12-13	13-14	14-15	15-16	16-17	17-18
	WM2 22	WM1 4	WM1 12	WM1 3	WM1 4	WM1 7	WM1 9	WM1 9	WM1 1

WOLVERHAMPTON CASUALS
Founded: 1899 Nickname: The Cassies

Club Contact Details (T) 07870 737 229   **(E)** mickgreen7@hotmail.com
Ground: Brinsford Stadium, Brinsford Lane, Wolverhampton WV10 7PR
Nearest Railway Station Billbrook - 4.8km   **Bus Route** Old Heath House - stop 350m away
HONOURS **League:** West Midlands (Reg) Division One 1994-95.
FA Comps: None
Colours(change): Green

10 YEAR RECORD
08-09	09-10	10-11	11-12	12-13	13-14	14-15	15-16	16-17	17-18
WMP 19	WMP 16	WMP 12	WMP 3	WMP 3	WMP 3	WMP 6	WMP 7	WMP 2	WMP 9
			FAC EP	FAC 1Qr	FAC P	FAC EP	FAC EP	FAC EPr	FAC P
FAV 1Q	FAV 1P	FAV 1P	FAV 1Q	FAV 1Q	FAV 2Q	FAV 1Q	FAV 2Q	FAV 2P	FAV 1Q

WEST MIDLANDS (REGIONAL) LEAGUE

CLUB MOVEMENTS

Premier Division - In: Haughmond (R - MLP), Pershore Town (LM - ML1), Shawbury Town (R - MLP), Wem Town (P).

Out: Ellesmere Rangers (LM - NWCS), Stone Old Alleynians (LM - NWCS), Wolverhampton CS (P - MLP).

Division One - In: Sikh Hunters (P), Wellington Amateurs (R).

Out: St Martins (P - NWCS), Wem Town (P).

Division One 2018-19

1   Allscott
2   Bromyard Town
3   Bustleholme
4   Darlaston Town (1874)
5   Droitwich Spa
6   Gornal Athletic
7   Newport Town
8   Old Wulfrunians
9   Sikh Hunters
10 Team Dudley
11 Telford Juniors
12 Tipton Town
13 Wellington Amateurs
14 Willenhall Town
15 Worcester Raiders
16 Wrens Nest
17 Wyrley

AFC Kilburn v Blidworth Welfare game in the Central Midlands League South - Kilburn's 'keeper gets a good strong punch to this Blidworth attack to help his side to a 1-0 win. Photo: Bill Wheatcroft.

WESTERN LEAGUE

Founded: 1892 **Sponsored by:** Toolstation

Recent Champions: 2015: Melksham Town **2016:** Odd Down (Bath) **2017:** Bristol Manor Farm

PREMIER DIVISION	P	W	D	L	F	A	GD	Pts
1 Street	38	32	3	3	100	31	69	99
2 Melksham Town	38	26	6	6	99	39	60	84
3 Willand Rovers	38	24	6	8	93	37	56	78
4 Bradford Town	38	23	9	6	88	47	41	78
5 Buckland Athletic	38	25	3	10	84	54	30	78
6 Shepton Mallet	38	20	2	16	63	52	11	62
7 Bridport	38	18	4	16	82	62	20	58
8 Bridgwater Town	38	18	4	16	61	51	10	58
9 Hengrove Athletic	38	16	8	14	73	60	13	56
10 Bitton	38	14	11	13	58	66	-8	53
11 Cribbs	38	14	8	16	75	62	13	50
12 Clevedon Town	38	13	8	17	56	63	-7	47
13 Chipping Sodbury Town	38	13	6	19	65	76	-11	45
14 Odd Down (BATH)	38	12	8	18	55	62	-7	44
15 Wellington	38	12	6	20	52	73	-21	42
16 Brislington	38	10	10	18	51	71	-20	40
17 Hallen	38	8	10	20	44	80	-36	34
18 Cadbury Heath	38	8	8	22	62	115	-53	32
19 Longwell Green Sports	38	5	5	28	33	111	-78	20
20 Wells City	38	3	7	28	33	115	-82	12*

DIVISION ONE	P	W	D	L	F	A	GD	Pts
1 Westbury United	42	28	11	3	97	29	68	95
2 Roman Glass St George	42	28	9	5	120	49	71	93
3 Keynsham Town	42	27	8	7	120	62	58	89
4 Cheddar	42	21	9	12	90	61	29	72
5 Devizes Town	42	20	10	12	90	65	25	70
6 Radstock Town	42	19	10	13	86	67	19	67
7 Oldland Abbotonians	42	19	7	16	83	74	9	64
8 Welton Rovers	42	18	9	15	80	65	15	63
9 Chard Town	42	17	11	14	70	59	11	62
10 Wincanton Town	42	17	10	15	63	71	-8	61
11 Chippenham Park	42	13	15	14	57	70	-13	54
12 Bishop Sutton	42	16	6	20	70	91	-21	54
13 Almondsbury	42	15	8	19	60	64	-4	53
14 Bishops Lydeard	42	16	5	21	74	96	-22	53
15 Malmesbury Victoria	42	14	9	19	69	97	-28	51
16 Bristol Telephones	42	14	8	20	74	98	-24	50
17 Calne Town	42	14	7	21	66	94	-28	49
18 Ashton & Backwell United	42	12	10	20	42	61	-19	46
19 Sherborne Town	42	13	6	23	78	95	-17	45
20 Corsham Town	42	10	9	23	43	71	-28	39
21 Portishead Town	42	8	8	26	45	89	-44	31*
22 Warminster Town	42	6	9	27	54	103	-49	27

CLUB MOVEMENTS Premier Division - In: Plymouth Parkway (P - SWPP), Roman Glass St George (P), Shortwood United (R - Sth1W), Westbury (P). **Out:** Long Green Sports (R), Melksham Town (P - SthW), Street (P - SthW), Wells (R).

Division One - In: Long Green Sports (R), Wells (R). **Out:** Roman Glass St George (P), Westbury (P).

LES PHILLIPS CUP

HOLDERS: MELKSHAM TOWN

PRELIMINARY ROUND

Hengrove Athletic	v	Almondsbury UWE	2-3
Bitton	v	Welton Rovers	4-0
Malmesbury Victoria	v	Bishops Lydeard	2-4
Cadbury Heath	v	Bishop Sutton	5-0
Roman Glass St George	v	Chard Town	0-2
Bridport	v	Keynsham Town	5-2
Calne Town	v	Bradford Town	2-4
Chippenham Park	v	Longwell Green Sports	2-1
Hallen	v	Radstock Town	3-2
Clevedon Town	v	Wincanton Town	2-1

ROUND 1

Bridgwater Town	v	Chipping Sodbury Town	4-0
Wellington	v	Westbury United	4-0
Almondsbury UWE	v	Bitton	2-3
Bishops Lydeard	v	Portishead Town	5-2
Cadbury Heath	v	Chard Town	0-3
Bridport	v	Willand Rovers	2-1
Ashton & Backwell United	v	Shepton Mallet	1-3
Bristol Telephones	v	Devizes Town	1-3
Street	v	Bradford Town	3-2 aet
Oldland Abbotonians	v	Chippenham Park	0-2
Hallen	v	Wells City	1-2
Cribbs	v	Clevedon Town	2-1
Warminster Town	v	Cheddar	2-1
Buckland Athletic	v	Corsham Town	2-0
Brislington	v	Sherborne Town	4-1
Odd Down (Bath)	v	Melksham Town	0-2

ROUND 2

Bridgwater Town	v	Wellington	5-3
Bitton	v	Bishops Lydeard	3-0
Chard Town	v	Bridport	0-1
Shepton Mallet	v	Devizes Town	2-0
Street	v	Chippenham Park	1-0
Wells City	v	Cribbs	0-5
Warminster Town	v	Buckland Athletic	0-1
Brislington	v	Melksham Town	2-1

QUARTER FINALS

Bridgwater Town	v	Bitton	4-0
Bridport	v	Shepton Mallet	2-2, 3-1p
Street	v	Cribbs	3-0
Buckland Athletic	v	Brislington	4-1

SEMI FINALS

Bridgwater Town	v	Shepton Mallet	1-1, 3-4p
Street	v	Buckland Athletic	0-1 aet

FINAL

Shepton Mallet	v	Buckland Athletic	2-2, 2-4p

BITTON　　　　Founded: 1892　　Nickname: The Ton

Club Contact Details **(T)** 01179 323 222　　**(E)** dan_langdon@hotmail.co.uk
Ground: Rapid Solicitors Ground, Bath Road, Bitton, Bristol BS30 6HX.
Nearest Railway Station Bitton - 500m
Capacity: 1,000 **Seats:** 48　　**Covered:** 200　　**Bus Route** Cherry Garden Road - stop 50m away

Colours(change): Red & white/black/black (Yellow/green/yellow)
Previous Names: None
Previous Leagues: Avon Premier Combination, Gloucestershire County 1995-97.

HONOURS: FA Comps: None
League: Western League Premier Division 2008-09.

10 YEAR RECORD

08-09		09-10		10-11		11-12		12-13		13-14		14-15		15-16		16-17		17-18	
WestP	1	WestP	8	WestP	2	WestP	2	WestP	7	WestP	6	WestP	7	WestP	14	WestP	19	WestP	10
FAC	2Q	FAC	EPr	FAC	1Q	FAC	EPr	FAC	P	FAC	P	FAC	EP	FAC	P	FAC	P	FAC	EPr
FAV	5P	FAV	2P	FAV	4P	FAV	4P	FAV	4P	FAV	3P	FAV	1Q	FAV	2Q	FAV	2Q	FAV	1Q

BRADFORD TOWN　　　　Founded: 1992　　Nickname: Bobcats

Club Contact Details **(T)** 07801 499 168　　**(E)** bradfordtownfc@gmail.com
Ground: Bradford Sports & Social Club, Trowbridge Rd, Bradford on Avon BA15 1EE
Nearest Railway Station Bradford-upon-Avon - 0.3km
Capacity:　　**Seats:** Yes　**Covered:** Yes　　**Bus Route** Junction Road _ stop 30m away

Colours(change): All royal blue (All sky blue)
Previous Names: None
Previous Leagues: Wiltshire County 1992-2005.

HONOURS: FA Comps: None
League: Western Division One 2013-14.

10 YEAR RECORD

08-09		09-10		10-11		11-12		12-13		13-14		14-15		15-16		16-17		17-18	
West1	3	West1	4	West1	6	West1	5	West1	3	West1	1	WestP	8	WestP	8	WestP	5	WestP	4
				FAC	EPr	FAC	EP	FAC	EP	FAC	EP	FAC	1Q	FAC	2Q	FAC	EP	FAC	EP
		FAV	2P	FAV	2Q	FAV	1P	FAV	2Q	FAV	1P	FAV	5P	FAV	4P	FAV	4P	FAV	5P

BRIDGWATER TOWN　　　　Founded: 1984　　Nickname: The Robins

Club Contact Details **(T)** 01278 446 899　　**(E)** ianbarber4@gmail.com
Ground: Fairfax Park, College Way, Bath Road, Bridgwater, Somerset TA6 4TZ
Nearest Railway Station Bridgwater - 0.7km
Capacity: 2,500 **Seats:** 128　　**Covered:** 500　　**Shop:** Yes

Colours(change): Red & white
Previous Names: Bridgwater Town
Previous Leagues: Somerset Senior 1984-94. Western 1994-2007. Southern 2007-2017.

HONOURS: FA Comps: None
League: Somerset Senior Division One 1986-87, Premier 89-90, 90-91, 91-92. Western Division One 1995-96.

10 YEAR RECORD

08-09		09-10		10-11		11-12		12-13		13-14		14-15		15-16		16-17		17-18	
Sthsw	7	Sthsw	3	Sthsw	18	Sthsw	15	Sthsw	19	Sthsw	14	Sthsw	12	Sthsw	19	Sthsw	22	WestP	8
FAC	1Q	FAC	3Q	FAC	1Q	FAC	1Q	FAC	P	FAC	3Q	FAC	2Q	FAC	P	FAC	P	FAC	1Q
FAT	P	FAT	1Qr	FAT	1Q	FAT	P	FAT	2Q	FAT	1Q	FAT	P	FAT	Pr	FAT	Pr	FAV	3Pr

BRIDPORT　　　　Founded: 1885　　Nickname: Bees

Club Contact Details **(T)** 01308 423 834　　**(E)** sevie@tiscali.co.uk
Ground: St Mary's Field, Bridport, Dorset DT6 5LN

Capacity: 2,000 **Seats:** 150　　**Covered:** Yes　　**Bus Route** Leisure Centre - stop 20m away

Colours(change): Red and black
Previous Names: None
Previous Leagues: Dorset. South Dorset. West Dorset. Perry Street. Dorset Combination (Founding Memeber) 1957-61, 84-88. Western 1961-84.

HONOURS: FA Comps: None
League: Dorset Combination 1985-86, 86-87, 87-88.

10 YEAR RECORD

08-09		09-10		10-11		11-12		12-13		13-14		14-15		15-16		16-17		17-18	
West1	13	West1	10	West1	3	WestP	14	WestP	14	WestP	12	WestP	14	WestP	16	WestP	16	WestP	7
FAC	1Q	FAC	1Qr	FAC	P	FAC	P	FAC	EP	FAC	P	FAC	EP	FAC	1Q	FAC	EP	FAC	3Q
FAV	1Q	FAV	2Q	FAV	1P	FAV	1P	FAV	2Q	FAV	1Q	FAV	2P	FAV	1P	FAV	1Q	FAV	1Q

BRISLINGTON
Founded: 1956   Nickname: Bris

Club Contact Details (T) 01179 774 030   (E) brislingtonsecretary@icloud.com
Ground: Ironmould Lane, Brislington, Bristol BS4 4TZ
Nearest Railway Station Keynsham - 3km
Capacity: 2,000 **Seats:** 144   **Covered:** 1,500   **Bus Route** Ironmould Lane - stop 100m away

Colours(change): Red & black
Previous Names: Formed as an U16 team.
Previous Leagues: Bristol Church of England. Bristol & Suburban. Somerset Senior until 1991.

HONOURS: FA Comps: None
League: Somerset Senior 1988-89. Western Division One 1994-95.

10 YEAR RECORD

	08-09		09-10		10-11		11-12		12-13		13-14		14-15		15-16		16-17		17-18	
WestP	10	WestP	9	WestP	15	WestP	7	WestP	2	WestP	10	WestP	10	WestP	11	WestP	10	WestP	16
FAC	P	FAC	EPr	FAC	EP	FAC	1Q	FAC	EP	FAC	4Q	FAC	P	FAC	EP	FAC	2Q	FAC	P
FAV	2P	FAV	2P	FAV	1P	FAV	1Q	FAV	1P	FAV	2P	FAV	1P	FAV	1Q	FAV	2Q	FAV	2Q

BUCKLAND ATHLETIC
Founded: 1977   Nickname: The Bucks

Club Contact Details (T) 01626 361 020   (E) phardingham@virginmedia.com
Ground: Homers Heath, South Quarry, Kingskerswell Road, Newton Abbot TQ12 5JU
Nearest Railway Station Newton Abbot approx 2 miles from the ground.
Capacity: 1,000 **Seats:** Yes   **Covered:** Yes

Colours(change): Yellow with black trim
Previous Names: None
Previous Leagues: Torbay Pioneer 1977-87. Devon & Exeter 1987-2000. Devon County 2000-07. South West Peninsula 2007-12.

HONOURS: FA Comps: None
League: Devon & Exeter Senior Third Division 1987-88, Premier 94-95, 99-00.
10 YEAR RECORD South West Peninsula Premier 2009-10, 10-11.

	08-09		09-10		10-11		11-12		12-13		13-14		14-15		15-16		16-17		17-18	
SWPP	3	SWPP	1	SWPP	1	SWPP	2	WestP	10	WestP	11	WestP	2	WestP	4	WestP	4	WestP	5
		FAC	EPr	FAC	EPr	FAC	Pr	FAC	1Q	FAC	2Q	FAC	EP	FAC	P	FAC	EP	FAC	EP
FAV	2Q	FAV	2Q	FAV	2Q	FAV	1P	FAV	2P	FAV	2P	FAV	3P	FAV	3P	FAV	QF	FAV	2P

CADBURY HEATH
Founded: 1894   Nickname: The Heathens

Club Contact Details (T) 07971 399 268   (E) martinbristol1955@hotmail.com
Ground: Springfield, Cadbury Heath Road, Bristol BS30 8BX
Nearest Railway Station Oldland - 1.2km
Capacity: 2,000 **Seats:** Yes   **Covered:** Yes   **Bus Route** The King William IV - stop 100m away

Colours(change): Red & white
Previous Names: None
Previous Leagues: Gloucestershire County 1968-75, 80-2000. Midland Combination 1975-77.

HONOURS: FA Comps: None
League: Gloucestershire County 1970-71, 71-72, 72-73, 73-74, 93-94, 97-98, 98-99.
10 YEAR RECORD Western League Division One 2011-12.

	08-09		09-10		10-11		11-12		12-13		13-14		14-15		15-16		16-17		17-18	
West1	4	West1	11	West1	4	West1	1	WestP	4	WestP	13	WestP	11	WestP	12	WestP	11	WestP	18
						FAC	2Q	FAC	P	FAC	EP	FAC	EP	FAC	EP	FAC	3Q	FAC	2Qr
				FAV	4P	FAV	2P	FAV	2P	FAV	1P	FAV	2Q	FAV	2P	FAV	2Q	FAV	1P

CHIPPING SODBURY TOWN
Founded: 1885   Nickname: The Sods

Club Contact Details (T) 07778 678 823   (E) g.endicott@btopenworld.com
Ground: The Ridings, Wickwar Road, Chipping Sodbury, Bristol BS37 6BQ
Nearest Railway Station Yate - 2.7km
Capacity: **Seats:** Yes   **Covered:** Yes   **Bus Route** Wickwar Road - stop 50m away

Colours(change): Black & white
Previous Names: None
Previous Leagues: Gloucester County 2008-2015.

HONOURS: FA Comps: None
League: Western Division One 2015-16.
10 YEAR RECORD

	08-09		09-10		10-11		11-12		12-13		13-14		14-15		15-16		16-17		17-18	
GlCo	17	GlCo	8	GlCo	3	GlCo	18	GlCo	15	GlCo	11	GlCo	3	West1	1	WestP	13	WestP	13
																		FAC	P
																FAV	1Q	FAV	1Q

CLEVEDON TOWN
Founded: 1880   Nickname: Seasiders

Club Contact Details   **(T)** 01275 871 600   **(E)** erichowe@hotmail.co.uk
Ground: Everyone Active Stadium, Davis Lane, Clevedon BS21 6TG
Nearest Railway Station Yatton - 4km
Capacity: 3,500   **Seats:** 300   **Covered:** 1,600   **Shop:** Yes   **Bus Route** Sercombe Park - stop 400m away

Colours(change): Blue with white
Previous Names: Clevedon FC and Ashtonians merged in 1974
Previous Leagues: Western (Founder Members 1892), 1945-58, 73-93. Bristol & District. Bristol Suburban. Somerset Senior. Southern 1993-2015.

HONOURS: FA Comps: None
     League: Bristol & Suburban 1925-26, 27-28, 28-29. Somerset Senior 36-37. Bristol Charity 37-38, 40-41. Western 92-93. Southern Midland Division 98-99, Divions 1W 2005-06.

10 YEAR RECORD

08-09		09-10		10-11		11-12		12-13		13-14		14-15		15-16		16-17		17-18	
SthP	18	SthP	21	Sthsw	20	Sthsw	20	Sthsw	15	Sthsw	17	Sthsw	18	WestP	19	WestP	14	WestP	12
FAC	2Q	FAC	2Q	FAC	3Q	FAC	2Q	FAC	2Q	FAC	3Qr	FAC	P	FAC	3Q	FAC	P	FAC	P
FAT	1Q	FAT	1Q	FAT	P	FAT	P	FAT	Pr	FAT	2Q	FAT	P	FAV	1Q	FAV	2P	FAV	2Q

CRIBBS
Founded: 1976   Nickname: Cribbs

Club Contact Details   **(T)** 0117 950 2303   **(E)** welshwizard1973@aol.com
Ground: The Lawns, Station Road, Henbury, Bristol BS10 7TB
Nearest Railway Station Pilning - 4.3km. Sea MIlls - 4.5km. Patchway - 4.5km
Capacity: 1,000   **Seats:** 100   **Covered:** Yes   **Bus Route** Rugby Club - stop 400m away

Colours(change): Blue
Previous Names: Sun Life Assurance 1976. AXA>2011. Cribbs Friends Life 2011-13
Previous Leagues: Bristol & Avon. Avon Premier Combination. Gloucestershire County > 2012.

HONOURS: FA Comps: None
     League: Gloucester County 2011-12.

10 YEAR RECORD

08-09		09-10		10-11		11-12		12-13		13-14		14-15		15-16		16-17		17-18	
GlCo	6	GlCo	11	GlCo	2	GlCo	1	West1	8	West1	5	West1	3	WestP	5	WestP	8	WestP	11
												FAC	P	FAC	EP	FAC	EPr	FAC	EP
										FAV	2Q	FAV	1Q	FAV	1Q	FAV	1Q	FAV	2Q

HALLEN
Founded: 1949   Nickname: The Armadillos

Club Contact Details   **(T)** 01179 505 559   **(E)** sinbad88@hotmail.co.uk
Ground: Hallen Centre, Moorhouse Lane, Hallen Bristol   BS10 7RU
Nearest Railway Station St Andrews Road - 2.7km
Capacity: 2,000   **Seats:** 200   **Covered:** 200   **Bus Route** Moorhouse Park - stop 250m away

Colours(change): Blue and black
Previous Names: Lawrence Weston Athletic, Lawrence Weston Hallen
Previous Leagues: Bristol & District. Bristol Premier. Gloucestershire County 1987-92. Hellenic 1992-2000.

HONOURS: FA Comps: None
     League: Gloucestershire County 1988-89, 92-93. Hellenic Division One 1996-97. Western Division One 2003-04.

10 YEAR RECORD

08-09		09-10		10-11		11-12		12-13		13-14		14-15		15-16		16-17		17-18	
WestP	9	WestP	12	WestP	16	WestP	4	WestP	9	WestP	15	WestP	17	WestP	17	WestP	18	WestP	17
FAC	EP	FAC	2Q	FAC	P	FAC	1Qr	FAC	P	FAC	1Q	FAC	P	FAC	EPr	FAC	EP	FAC	EPr
FAV	2Q	FAV	2Q	FAV	2Qr	FAV	2Q	FAV	1P	FAV	5P	FAV	2P	FAV	2P	FAV	2Q	FAV	1Q

HENGROVE ATHLETIC
Founded: 1948   Nickname: The Grove

Club Contact Details   **(T)** 07884 492 217   **(E)** secretary@hengroveathletic.com
Ground: Norton Lane, Whitchurch, Bristol BS14 0BT
Nearest Railway Station Bedminster - 2.5km
Capacity: **Seats:** Yes   **Covered:** Yes   **Bus Route** Wooton Park - stop 100m away

Colours(change): Green & white
Previous Names: None
Previous Leagues: Bristol & Suburban >1974. Somerset County 1974-2006.

HONOURS: FA Comps: None
     League: Somerset County Premier Division 2005-06.

10 YEAR RECORD

08-09		09-10		10-11		11-12		12-13		13-14		14-15		15-16		16-17		17-18	
West1	6	West1	7	West1	10	West1	10	West1	2	WestP	21	West1	12	West1	7	West1	2	WestP	9
						FAC	EP	FAC	P	FAC	EP	FAC	EPr			FAC	P	FAC	P
				FAV	2Pr	FAV	2Q	FAV	2Q	FAV	2Q	FAV	2Q	FAV	3P	FAV	1P	FAV	2P

ODD DOWN (BATH)
Founded: 1901   Nickname: The Down

Club Contact Details (T) 01225 832 491   (E) lorainebrown@btinternet.com
Ground: Lew Hill Memorial Ground, Combe Hay Lane, Odd Down BA2 8PA
Nearest Railway Station Oldfield Park - 2.9km
Capacity: 1,000 **Seats:** 160 **Covered:** 250   **Bus Route** St Gregory's School - stop 50m away

Colours(change): All blue
Previous Names: None
Previous Leagues: Bath & District. Wiltshire. Somerset Senior. Mid-Somerset.

HONOURS: FA Comps: None
    League: Western Division One 1992-93, Premier Division 2015-16.

10 YEAR RECORD

	08-09		09-10		10-11		11-12		12-13		13-14		14-15		15-16		16-17		17-18	
	West1	19	West1	2	WestP	8	WestP	9	WestP	8	WestP	4	WestP	5	WestP"	1	WestP	7	WestP	14
FAC		P	FAC	Pr	FAC	Pr	FAC	P	FAC	P	FAC	EPr	FAC	P	FAC	P	FAC	P	FAC	1Q
FAV			FAV	2Q	FAV	2P	FAV	2P	FAV	2Q	FAV	2P	FAV	2P	FAV	3P	FAV	2P	FAV	1P

PLYMOUTH PARKWAY AFC
Founded: 1988   Nickname: The Parkway

Club Contact Details (T) 07786 571 308   (E) gennyt@sky.com
Ground: Bolitho Park, St Peters Road, Manadon, Plymouth PL5 3JG
Nearest Railway Station St Budeaux Road - 2.8km
Capacity: **Seats:** Yes **Covered:** Yes   **Bus Route** St Peters Road - stop 10m away

Colours(change): All Yellow
Previous Names: None
Previous Leagues: Plymouth & District. South West Peninsula >2018.

HONOURS: FA Comps: None
    League: Plymouth & District Division Two 1990-91.
    South West Peninsula Premier Division 2013-14, 17-18.

10 YEAR RECORD

	08-09		09-10		10-11		11-12		12-13		13-14		14-15		15-16		16-17		17-18	
	SWPP	2	SWPP	6	SWPP	3	SWPP	6	SWPP	2	SWPP	1	SWPP	5	SWPP	4	SWPP	7	SWPP	1
									FAC	1Qr	FAC	1Q	FAC	P	FAC	1Q	FAC	1Q	FAC	EP
FAV	2Q	FAV	4P	FAV	3P	FAV	1P	FAV	1Q	FAV	3P	FAV	2P	FAV	2P	FAV	1Pr	FAV	3P

ROMAN GLASS ST GEORGE
Founded: 1872   Nickname: The Glass

Club Contact Details (T) 07770 331 491   (E) adamwolves2@hotmail.com
Ground: Oaklands Park, Gloucester Road, Alomndsbury BS32 4AG
Nearest Railway Station Patchway - 2.6km
Capacity: 2,000 **Seats:** **Covered:**   **Bus Route** Alondsbury Depot - stop 100m away

Colours(change): White and black
Previous Names: St George. Bristol St George. Merged with Roman Glass in 1995 to form today's club.
Previous Leagues: Bristol & District/Western (Founder Members) 1892-1903, 1928-35. Bristol & District 1935-57. Bristol Premier Combination
(FM) 1957-68. Gloucestershire County (FM) 1968-87, 99-2007. County of Avon Premier Comb 1987-95.
HONOURS: FA Comps: None
    League: Bristol & District Div.1 1949-50. Bristol Premier Com. Div.1 1963-64, 64-65, 65-66, 66-67, 67-68, 88-89, Prem 92-93. .
    Gloucestershire County 1969-70, 2001-02, 06-07.

10 YEAR RECORD

	08-09		09-10		10-11		11-12		12-13		13-14		14-15		15-16		16-17		17-18	
	West1	16	West1	18	West1	15	West1	8	West1	17	West1	12	West1	20	West1	18	West1	15	West1	2
									FAV	2Q	FAV	2Q	FAV	2Q	FAV	1Qr	FAV	2Q	FAV	2Q

SHEPTON MALLET
Founded: 1986   Nickname: The Mallet

Club Contact Details (T) 01749 344 609   (E) gkrkb@tiscali.co.uk
Ground: Playing Fields, Old Wells Road, West Shepton, Shepton Mallet BA4 5XN
Capacity: 2,500 **Seats:** 120 **Covered:** Yes   **Bus Route** West Lodge - stop 180m away

Colours(change): Black & white
Previous Names: None
Previous Leagues: Somerset Senior.

HONOURS: FA Comps: None
    League: Somerset Senior League 2000-01.

10 YEAR RECORD

	08-09		09-10		10-11		11-12		12-13		13-14		14-15		15-16		16-17		17-18	
	West1	17	West1	17	West1	14	West1	16	West1	7	West1	2	WestP	9	WestP	10	WestP	12	WestP	6
FAC	EP	FAC	EP							FAC	EPr	FAC	Pr	FAC	EP	FAC	P	FAC	EP
FAV	2Q	FAV	2Q	FAV	1Q	FAV	1Q	FAV	1Q	FAV	2P	FAV	3P	FAV	2Q	FAV	1Q	FAV	2Q

SHORTWOOD UNITED

Founded: 1900   Nickname: The Wood

Club Contact Details (T) 01453 833 936
(E) jimcunneen1951@gmail.com
Ground: Meadowbank, Shortwood, Nailsworth GL6 0SJ

Capacity: 2,000 **Seats:** 50   **Covered:** 150   No   **Bus Route** Homefield Turn - stop 250m away

Colours(change): Red and white
Previous Names: None.
Previous Leagues: Stroud & District. Gloucestershire Northern Senior. Gloucestershire County. Hellenic >2012. Southern 2012-18.

HONOURS: FA Comps: None
League: Gloucestershire 1981-82. Hellenic 1984-85, 91-92.

10 YEAR RECORD

08-09	09-10	10-11	11-12	12-13	13-14	14-15	15-16	16-17	17-18
Hel P 2	Hel P 2	Hel P 6	Hel P 2	Sthsw 8	Sthsw 6	Sthsw 11	Sthsw 7	Sthsw 9	Sthsw 17
FAC 2Qr	FAC 1Qr	FAC Pr	FAC Pr	FAC P	FAC 1P	FAC 3Qr	FAC 2Q	FAC P	FAC P
FAV 1P	FAV 4P	FAV 2P	FAV QF	FAT 3Qr	FAT 1Q	FAT 1Q	FAT P	FAT P	FAT 3Q

WELLINGTON

Founded: 1892   Nickname: Wellie

Club Contact Details (T) 01823 664 810
(E) jeffandjane@talktalk.net
Ground: Wellington Playing Field, North Street, Wellington TA21 8NE

Capacity: 1,500 **Seats:** 200   **Covered:** 200   **Bus Route** Nth St Police Station - stop 150m away

Colours(change): Orange and black
Previous Names: None
Previous Leagues: Taunton Saturday, Somerset Senior.

HONOURS: FA Comps: None
League: Western Division One 2007-08, 16-17.

10 YEAR RECORD

08-09	09-10	10-11	11-12	12-13	13-14	14-15	15-16	16-17	17-18
WestP 7	WestP 13	WestP 18	West1 18	West1 18	West1 8	West1 6	West1 12	West1 1	WestP 15
	FAC EP	FAC P	FAC EP						FAC EP
FAV 2Q	FAV 3P	FAV 2P	FAV 2Q	FAT 2Q		FAV 2Q		FAV 1Q	FAV 2P

WESTBURY UNITED

Founded: 1920   Nickname: White Horse

Club Contact Details (T) 01373 764 197
(E) secretary@westburyunited.co.uk
Ground: Meadow Lane, Westbury, Wiltshire BA13 3AF
Nearest Railway Station Westbury - 1.1km
Capacity: **Seats:** **Covered:** **Bus Route** Springfield Road - stop 200m away

Colours(change): Green and black
Previous Names: Formed after the merger of Westbury Old Comrades FC and Westbury Great Western Railway XI
Previous Leagues: Wiltshire County 1920-1984.

HONOURS: FA Comps: None
League: Wiltshire 1934-35, 37-38, 38-39, 49-50, 50-51, 55-56.
10 YEAR RECORD Western Division One 1991-92, 2017-18.

08-09	09-10	10-11	11-12	12-13	13-14	14-15	15-16	16-17	17-18
West1 9	West1 5	West1 17	West1 17	West1 19	West1 20	West1 22	West1 22	West1 12	West1 1
FAC P	FAC EPr	FAC P							
FAV 2Qr	FAV 1P	FAV 1Q	FAV 1Q	FAV 1P	FAV 1Q	FAV 1Q	FAV 1Q	FAV 2Q	FAV 2Q

WILLAND ROVERS

Founded: 1946   Nickname: Rovers

Club Contact Details (T) 01884 33885
(E) domclarkwillandrovers@gmail.com
Ground: Silver Street, Willand, Collumpton, Devon EX15 2RH
Nearest Railway Station Tiverton Parkway - 3.2km
Capacity: 1,000 **Seats:** 75   **Covered:** 150   **Bus Route** Garage (Silver St) - stop 50m away

Colours(change): White and blue
Previous Names: None.
Previous Leagues: Devon & Exeter >1992. Devon County (Founder Members) 1992-2001.

HONOURS: FA Comps: None
League: Devon County 1998-99, 00-01, Western Division One 2004-05.

10 YEAR RECORD

08-09	09-10	10-11	11-12	12-13	13-14	14-15	15-16	16-17	17-18
WestP 3	WestP 2	WestP 4	WestP 5	WestP 11	WestP 8	WestP 6	WestP 6	WestP 6	WestP 3
FAC P	FAC 2Q	FAC 1Q	FAC EP	FAC EP	FAC EP	FAC 4Q	FAC EP	FAC EPr	FAC 1Q
FAV 3P	FAV 5Pr	FAV 4P	FAV 4P	FAV 2P	FAV 1P	FAV 1Q	FAV 2Q	FAV 1P	FAV 2P

DIVISION ONE

ASHTON & BACKWELL UNITED
Founded: 2010   Nickname: The Stags

Club Contact Details (T) 01275 461 273   **(E)** ashtonbackwellsecretary@gmail.com

Ground: The Lancer Scott Stadium, West Town Road, Backwell. BS48 3HQ   **Capacity:** 1,000

Nearest Railway Station Nailsea & Backwell - 0.9km   **Bus Route** Spar (Rodney Rd) - stop 150m away

HONOURS   **League:** None

FA Comps: None

Colours(change): Maroon & blue

10 YEAR RECORD

08-09	09-10	10-11	11-12	12-13	13-14	14-15	15-16	16-17	17-18
		SomP 7	SomP 3	SomP 3	West1 14	West1 8	West1 8	West1 7	West1 18
							FAC EP	FAC EP	
			FAV 2Q	FAV 2Q	FAV 1P	FAV 2Q	FAV 2Q	FAV 2Q	FAV 2Q

BISHOP SUTTON
Founded: 1977   Nickname: Bishops

Club Contact Details (T) 01275 332 855   **(E)** bishopsuttonafcsecretary@hotmail.co.uk

Ground: Lakeview, Wick Road, Bishops Sutton, Bristol BS39 5XN.   **Capacity:** 1,500

Bus Route Butchers Arms Pub - stop 50m away

HONOURS   **League:** Western Division One 1997-98, Premier Division 2012-13.

FA Comps: None

Colours(change): All blue

10 YEAR RECORD

08-09	09-10	10-11	11-12	12-13	13-14	14-15	15-16	16-17	17-18
WestP 15	WestP 4	WestP 5	WestP 6	WestP 1	WestP 9	WestP 19	West1 21	West1 16	West1 12
FAC EP	FAC EP	FAC P	FAC 1Q	FAC Pr	FAC P	FAC EP	FAC EP		
FAV 1Q	FAV 1P	FAV 1Pr	FAV 2P	FAV 2Q	FAV 1P	FAV 1Q	FAV 1P	FAV 2Q	FAV 2Q

BISHOPS LYDEARD
Founded: 1912   Nickname:

Club Contact Details (T)   **(E)** itspeebee@gmail.com

Ground: Cottlestone Road, Bishops Lydeard, Taunton, TA4 3BA   **Capacity:** 1,000

Nearest Railway Station Bishops Lydeard - 1.5km   **Bus Route** Darby Way - 80m away

HONOURS   **League:** Somerset County Division One 2004-05, Premier Division 15-16.

FA Comps: None

Colours(change): Red & black stripes/

10 YEAR RECORD

08-09	09-10	10-11	11-12	12-13	13-14	14-15	15-16	16-17	17-18
SomP 4	SomP 2	SomP 12	SomP 11	SomP 13	SomP 10	SthP 6	SomP 1	West1 6	West1 14

BRISTOL TELEPHONES
Founded: 1948   Nickname: The Phones

Club Contact Details (T) 01275 891 776   **(E)** steve.watkins56@talktalk.net

Ground: BTRA Sports Ground, Stockwood Lane, Stockwood, Bristol BS14 8SJ

Nearest Railway Station Keynsham - 3.6km   **Bus Route** Battson Road - stop 50m away

HONOURS   **League:** Bristol & Suburban Premier Division 2010-11, 12-13.

FA Comps: None   Gloucestershire County 2016-17.

Colours(change): All pale blue

10 YEAR RECORD

08-09	09-10	10-11	11-12	12-13	13-14	14-15	15-16	16-17	17-18
Br&SuP2 11	Br&SuP2 3	Br&SuP1 1	Br&SuP1 3	Br&SuP1 1	GlCo 3	GlCo 8	GlCo 10	GlCo 1	West1 16

CALNE TOWN
Founded: 1886   Nickname: Lilywhites

Club Contact Details (T) 07795 833 702   **(E)** wmm498@msn.com

Ground: Bremhill View, Calne, Wiltshire SN11 9EE   **Capacity:** 2,500

Bus Route Northend - stop 80m away

HONOURS   **League:** None

FA Comps: None

Colours(change): White and black

10 YEAR RECORD

08-09	09-10	10-11	11-12	12-13	13-14	14-15	15-16	16-17	17-18
WestP 16	WestP 20	West1 11	West1 4	West1 9	West1 13	West1 15	West1 15	West1 21	West1 17
FAC 1Q	FAC P	FAC EP	FAC EP	FAC EP	FAC EP				
FAV 1P	FAV 1Q	FAV 1P	FAV 2Q	FAV 1P	FAV 1Q	FAV 2Q	FAV 1P	FAV 1P	FAV 2Q

CHARD TOWN
Founded: 1920   Nickname: The Robins

Club Contact Details (T) 01460 61402
(E) chardtownfcsecretary@outlook.com
Ground: Denning Sports Field, Zembard Lane, Chard, Somerset TA20 1JL
Capacity: 1,500
Bus Route Holyrood School - stop 100m away

HONOURS   **League:** Perry Street & District 1939-40.
FA Comps: None   Somerset Senior 1949-50, 53-54, 59-60, 67-68, 69-70.
Colours(change): All red

10 YEAR RECORD

08-09		09-10		10-11		11-12		12-13		13-14		14-15		15-16		16-17		17-18	
WestP	20	West1	16	West1	13	West1	6	West1	6	West1	15	West1	7	West1	3	West1	10	West1	9
FAC	EPr	FAC	EP			FAC	EP	FAC	P										
FAV	2Q	FAV	2Q	FAV	2Q	FAV	1Q	FAV	1Q										

CHEDDAR
Founded: 1892   Nickname: The Cheesemen

Club Contact Details (T) 01934 707 271
(E) secretarycheddarfc@gmail.com
Ground: Bowdens Park, Draycott Road, Cheddar BS27 3RL
Capacity: 1,105
Bus Route Church Street - stop 400m away

HONOURS   **League:** Cheddar Valley 1910-11.
FA Comps: None   Somerset Senior Division One 2003-04.
Colours(change): Yellow and black

10 YEAR RECORD

08-09		09-10		10-11		11-12		12-13		13-14		14-15		15-16		16-17		17-18	
SomP	8	SomP	7	SomP	4	SomP	2	West1	11	West1	17	West1	10	WestP	5	West1	3	West1	4
																FAC	EPr	FAC	EP
										FAV	1Q	FAV	1Q	FAV	1Q	FAV	2Q	FAV	1Q

CHIPPENHAM PARK
Founded: 2012   Nickname: The Park

Club Contact Details (T) 01249 650 400
(E) eede.martin@gmail.com
Ground: Hardenhuish Park, Bristol Road, Chippenham SN14 6LR
Capacity: 2,800
Nearest Railway Station Chippenham - 1km   **Bus Route** Fenway Park - stop 170m away
HONOURS   **League:** None
FA Comps: None
Colours(change): All blue

10 YEAR RECORD

08-09	09-10	10-11	11-12		12-13		13-14		14-15		15-16		16-17		17-18	
			Wilt	3	West1	10	West1	11	West1	14	West1	8	West1	11		
					FAV	1Q	FAV	2P	FAV	2Q	FAV	1Q	FAV	2Q		

CORSHAM TOWN
Founded: 1883   Nickname: The Peacocks

Club Contact Details (T)
(E) les.bateman63@btinternet.com
Ground: Southbank Ground, Lacock Road, Corsham SN13 9HS
Capacity: 1,200
Nearest Railway Station Chippenham - 5.8km   **Bus Route** St Patrick's School - stop 50m away
HONOURS   **League:** Wiltshire Division Two 1960-61, Division One 97-98.
FA Comps: None   Western Premier Division 2006-07.
Colours(change): Red & white

10 YEAR RECORD

08-09		09-10		10-11		11-12		12-13		13-14		14-15		15-16		16-17		17-18	
WestP	19	WestP	17	WestP	10	WestP	18	West1	4	West1	7	West1	9	West1	10	West1	19	West1	20
FAC	EP	FAC	EP	FAC	P	FAC	EP	FAC	EP	FAC	1Qr	FAC	EP						
FAV	1Q	FAV	1P	FAC	2Q	FAV	1Qr	FAV	1Q	FAV	2Q	FAV	2Q	FAV	1P	FAV	2Q	FAV	1Q

DEVIZES TOWN
Founded: 1885   Nickname: The Town

Club Contact Details (T) 01380 722 817
(E) neil@hallmarkflooring.co.uk
Ground: Nursteed Road, Devizes, Wiltshire SN10 3DX
Capacity: 2,500
Bus Route Eastleigh Road - stop 80m away

HONOURS   **League:** Wiltshire Senior 1895-96, 89-99, 35-36, 48-49, 51-52, 53-54, Premier 61-62, 63-64. Western
FA Comps: None   Premier Division 1972-73, Division One 99-2000.
Colours(change): Red & white stripes

10 YEAR RECORD

08-09		09-10		10-11		11-12		12-13		13-14		14-15		15-16		16-17		17-18	
WestP	21	WestP	19	West1	5	West1	19	West1	21	West1	11	West1	18	West1	19	West1	11	West1	5
FAC	EP	FAC	EPr			FAC	EP												
FAV	2Q	FAV	2Q	FAV	2Q	FAV	1P	FAV	1Q	FAV	1Q	FAV	1Q	FAV	1Q	FAV	1P	FAV	1Q

KEYNSHAM TOWN

Founded: 1895   Nickname: K's

Club Contact Details (T)   (E) jules1233@live.com

Ground: AJN Stadium, Bristol Road, Keynsham BS31 2BE   Capacity: 3,000

Nearest Railway Station Keynsham - 0.7km   **Bus Route** Rugby Club - stop 50m away

HONOURS   **League:** Western Division One 1977-78.

FA Comps: None

Colours(change): Amber and black

10 YEAR RECORD

	08-09	09-10	10-11	11-12	12-13	13-14	14-15	15-16	16-17	17-18
	West1 5	West1 8	West1 16	West1 13	West1 13	West1 19	West1 17	West1 9	West1 4	West1 3
FAC	EP	EP	EP						EP	EP
FAV	2Q	1P	2P	2Q	1Q	2Q	2Q	2Qr	2Q	1Q

LONGWELL GREEN SPORTS

Founded: 1966   Nickname: The Green

Club Contact Details (T)   (E) daveheal04@gmail.com

Ground: Longwell Green Com. Centre, Shellards Road BS30 9DU   1,000

Nearest Railway Station Bitton - 1.4km   **Bus Route** Sally Barn Close - stop 500m away

HONOURS   **League:** Bristol & District Division Four 1982-83.

FA Comps: None

Colours(change): Blue & white

10 YEAR RECORD

	08-09	09-10	10-11	11-12	12-13	13-14	14-15	15-16	16-17	17-18
	West1 2	WestP 11	WestP 17	WestP 13	WestP 15	WestP 14	WestP 16	WestP 18	WestP 17	WestP 19
FAC		EP	P	P	EPr	Pr	1Q	P	EP	EP
FAV	1P	2P	2Q	1Qr	2Pr	1P	1P	2Qr	2Q	2Q

OLDLAND ABBOTONIANS

Founded: 1910   Nickname: The O's

Club Contact Details (T) 01179 328 263   (E) secretary@oldlandfootball.com

Ground: Aitchison Playing Field, Castle Road, Oldland Common, Bristol BS30 9SZ

Nearest Railway Station Oldland - 400m   **Bus Route** The Clamp - stop 130m away

HONOURS   **League:** Somerset County Division One 2004-05.

FA Comps: None

Colours(change): Blue & white

10 YEAR RECORD

	08-09	09-10	10-11	11-12	12-13	13-14	14-15	15-16	16-17	17-18
	West1 7	West1 6	West1 2	West1 11	West1 5	West1 21	West1 14	West1 4	West1 17	West1 7
FAC						EP			P	
FAV					1Q	1Q	1Q	2Q	2Q	2Q

PORTISHEAD TOWN

Founded: 1912   Nickname: Posset

Club Contact Details (T) 01275 817 600   (E) andy.carling@yahoo.co.uk

Ground: Bristol Road, Portishead, Bristol BS20 6QG   Capacity: 1,400

Nearest Railway Station Avonmouth - 5.1km   **Bus Route** Glebe Road - stop 50m away

HONOURS   **League:** Somerset County 1993-94, 94-95, 95-96, 97-98.

FA Comps: None

Colours(change): White and black

10 YEAR RECORD

	08-09	09-10	10-11	11-12	12-13	13-14	14-15	15-16	16-17	17-18
	West1 11	West1 12	West1 18	West1 12	West1 14	West1 22	West1 21	West1 6	West1 14	West1 21
FAC			P	EP					1Q	
FAV	2Q	1Q	2Q	1Q	1Q	1Q	2Q	1P	2Q	2Q

RADSTOCK TOWN

Founded: 1895   Nickname: The Miners

Club Contact Details (T) 01761 435 004   (E) rtfcsecretary@outlook.com

Ground: Southfields Recreation Ground, Southfields, Radstock BA3 3NZ   Capacity: 1,250

Bus Route Withies Park - stop 80m away

HONOURS   **League:** Somerset Senior Division One 1996-97.

FA Comps: None

Colours(change): Red and black

10 YEAR RECORD

	08-09	09-10	10-11	11-12	12-13	13-14	14-15	15-16	16-17	17-18
	WestP 17	WestP 16	WestP 12	WestP 16	WestP 17	WestP 1	West1 13	West1 13	West1 5	West1 6
FAC	EP	EP	P	P	EP	EP	EP			
FAV	2Q	1Q	1P	1Q	2Q	2Q	1P	2Q	1Q	1P

SHERBORNE TOWN

Founded: 1894   Nickname:

Club Contact Details (T) 01935 816 110   (E) secretary@sherbornetownfc.co.uk
Ground: Raleigh Grove, Terrace Playing Field, Sherborne DT9 5NS   **Capacity:** 1,200
Nearest Railway Station Sherborne - 0.5km   **Bus Route** Sherborne Station - stop 0.5km away
HONOURS   **League:** Dorset Premier 1981-82. Western Division One 2012-13.
FA Comps: None
Colours(change): Black & white

10 YEAR RECORD

08-09		09-10		10-11		11-12		12-13		13-14		14-15		15-16		16-17		17-18	
WestP	12	WestP	18	WestP	14	WestP	17	West1	1	WestP	9	WestP	12	WestP	13	WestP	20	WestP	19
FAC	EP	FAC	P	FAC	2Q	FAC	EP	FAC	1Q	FAC	P	FAC	1Q	FAC	Pr	FAC	EP	FAC	EP
FAV	1P	FAV	2Q	FAV	1Pr	FAV	2Q	FAV	2P	FAV	2Q	FAV	1P	FAV	1Q	FAV	1P	FAV	1Q

WARMINSTER TOWN

Founded: 1878   Nickname: The Red & Blacks

Club Contact Details (T) 01985 217 828   (E) chrisjrobbins58@gmail.com
Ground: Weymouth Street, Warminster BA12 9NS
Nearest Railway Station Warminster - 0.9km   **Bus Route** Glebe Field - stop 80m away
HONOURS   **League:** None
FA Comps: None
Colours(change): Red & black stripes

10 YEAR RECORD

08-09		09-10		10-11		11-12		12-13		13-14		14-15		15-16		16-17		17-18	
Wex1	5	Wex1	14	Wex1	12	Wex1	16	West1	15	West1	18	West1	16	West1	17	West1	18	West1	22
		FAC	Pr	FAC	EP														
FAV	1P	FAV	1Q	FAV	2Q			FAV	2Q	FAV	1P	FAV	1Q	FAV	2Q	FAV	1Q	FAV	2Q

WELLS CITY

Founded: 1890   Nickname:

Club Contact Details (T) 01749 679 971   (E) daveg55@hotmail.co.uk
Ground: Athletic Ground, Rowdens Road, Wells, Somerset BA5 1TU   **Capacity:** 1,500
Bus Route The Police Station - stop 20m away
HONOURS   **League:** Western Division One 1949-50, 2009-10.
FA Comps: None
Colours(change): All blue

10 YEAR RECORD

08-09		09-10		10-11		11-12		12-13		13-14		14-15		15-16		16-17		17-18	
West1	10	West1	1	WestP	9	WestP	12	WestP	19	West1	6	West1	19	West1	2	WestP	15	WestP	20
						FAC	2Q	FAC	P	FAC	1Q					FAC	EPr	FAC	P
		FAV	2P	FAV	1Q	FAV	1P	FAV	2Q	FAV	1Q	FAV	1P	FAV	1Q	FAV	2Q	FAV	1Q

WELTON ROVERS

Founded: 1887   Nickname: Rovers

Club Contact Details (T) 02762 412 097   (E) malcolm@weltonr.plus.com
Ground: West Clewes, North Road, Midsomer Norton, Bath BA3 2QD   **Capacity:** 2,400
Bus Route Elm View - 50m away
HONOURS   **League:** Western 1911-12, 64-65, 65-66, 66-67, 73-74, Division One 59-60, 87-88.
FA Comps: None
Colours(change): Green & white

10 YEAR RECORD

08-09		09-10		10-11		11-12		12-13		13-14		14-15		15-16		16-17		17-18	
WestP	8	WestP	5	WestP	19	West1	7	West1	16	West1	6	West1	2	WestP	20	West1	20	West1	8
FAC	EP	FAC	EP	FAC	EP	FAC	EP	FAC	EP					FAC	EP	FAC	EP	FAC	EP
FAV	2Q	FAV	3P	FAV	1Q	FAV	1Q	FAV	2Q	FAV	1Q	FAV	2P	FAV	3P	FAV	1Q	FAV	1Q

WINCANTON TOWN

Founded: 1890   Nickname: Winky

Club Contact Details (T) 01963 31815   (E) cmartin10101981@gmail.com
Ground: Wincanton Sports Ground, Moor Lane, Wincanton. BA9 9EJ
Nearest Railway Station Templecombe - 4.9km   **Bus Route** Balsam Lane - stop 1.2km away
HONOURS   **League:** Yeovil & District Division Two 1988-89, Division One 89-90, Premier 90-91.
FA Comps: None   Dorset Senior Division 2006-07.
Colours(change): Yellow & black

10 YEAR RECORD

08-09		09-10		10-11		11-12		12-13		13-14		14-15		15-16		16-17		17-18	
Dor P	8	Dor P	9	Dor P	7	Dor P	4	Dor P	2	West1	4	West1	4	West1	16	West1	13	West1	10
														FAC	P				
												FAV	1Q	FAV	EP	FAV	1Q	FAV	2Q

ANGLIAN COMBINATION

PREMIER DIVISION

		P	W	D	L	F	A	GD	Pts
1	Harleston Town	30	26	2	2	118	33	85	80
2	Mulbarton Wands	30	25	2	3	89	22	67	77
3	Norwich CEYMS	30	18	6	6	76	45	31	60
4	Long Stratton	30	15	2	13	42	49	-7	47
5	Bradenham Wands	30	15	1	14	61	58	3	46
6	Hellesdon	30	13	5	12	59	42	17	44
7	Waveney	30	12	6	12	50	52	-2	42
8	St Andrews	30	12	5	13	47	41	6	41
9	Caister	30	12	4	14	55	63	-8	40
10	Wroxham Res	30	11	7	12	61	53	8	39*
11	Beccles Town	30	10	8	12	53	62	-9	38
12	Blofield United	30	9	6	15	48	63	-15	33
13	Mattishall	30	10	3	17	45	73	-28	33
14	Acle United	30	9	4	17	52	63	-11	31
15	Stalham Town	30	7	6	17	54	88	-34	27
16	Reepham Town	30	1	3	26	29	132	-103	6

DIVISION ONE

		P	W	D	L	F	A	GD	Pts
1	Wymondham Town	28	22	3	3	97	29	68	69
2	Sheringham	28	18	6	4	82	34	48	60
3	Scole United	28	17	4	7	65	31	34	55
4	Mundford	28	16	5	7	69	37	32	53
5	UEA	28	15	5	8	57	32	25	50
6	Aylsham	28	13	7	8	70	46	24	46
7	Attleborough Town	28	11	5	12	54	51	3	38
8	Bungay Town	28	9	8	11	46	35	11	35
9	Yelverton	28	9	8	11	58	58	0	35
10	North Walsham Town	28	9	5	14	51	80	-29	32
11	Kirkley & Pakefield Res	28	9	5	14	39	75	-36	32
12	Watton United	28	8	4	16	44	72	-28	28
13	Hindringham	28	5	9	14	40	58	-18	24
14	Cromer Town	28	7	1	20	30	120	-90	22
15	Loddon United	28	4	1	23	40	84	-44	8*

DIVISION TWO

		P	W	D	L	F	A	GD	Pts
1	Easton	28	22	3	3	113	43	70	69
2	Fakenham Town Res	28	22	1	5	109	32	77	67
3	East Harling	28	17	6	5	61	29	32	57
4	Thetford Rovers	28	16	5	7	80	60	20	53
5	Poringland Wands	28	15	5	8	70	57	13	50
6	Holt United	28	14	4	10	80	50	30	46
7	Martham	28	12	3	13	80	61	19	39
8	Gayton United	28	10	8	10	72	50	22	38
9	Wells Town	28	11	3	14	105	79	26	36
10	Caister Res	28	10	3	15	55	60	-5	32*
11	Brandon Town	28	8	6	14	61	81	-20	29*
12	Mattishall Res	28	7	6	15	70	85	-15	26*
13	Sprowston Athletic	28	7	4	17	38	76	-38	25
14	Horsford United	28	4	3	21	26	201	-175	13*
15	Acle United Res	28	3	4	21	45	101	-56	12*

DIVISION THREE

		P	W	D	L	F	A	GD	Pts
1	Gorleston Res	28	23	1	4	111	35	76	70
2	Buxton	28	19	1	8	81	43	38	58
3	Freethorpe	28	17	3	8	57	42	15	54
4	Hingham Athletic	28	14	7	7	75	48	27	49
5	Swaffham Town Res	28	15	4	9	66	44	22	49
6	Beccles Caxton	28	14	7	7	62	60	2	49
7	Earsham	28	11	6	11	50	58	-8	39
8	Norwich CEYMS Res	28	11	6	11	51	53	-2	38*
9	Hempnall	28	10	2	16	47	75	-28	32
10	South Walsham	28	8	7	13	49	59	-10	31
11	Redgate Rangers	28	10	2	16	49	62	-13	31*
12	Hemsby	28	9	4	15	59	85	-26	31
13	Long Stratton Res	28	8	6	14	58	62	-4	29*
14	Blofield United Res	28	7	4	17	61	84	-23	25
15	Costessey Sports	28	3	2	23	35	101	-66	11

DIVISION FOUR

		P	W	D	L	F	A	GD	Pts
1	Bradenham Wands Res	28	23	1	4	102	44	58	70
2	Gt Yarmouth Town Res	28	19	5	4	93	39	54	62
3	Heacham	28	18	2	8	74	44	30	55*
4	Aylsham Res	28	17	4	7	80	33	47	54*
5	Gayton United Res	28	15	3	10	58	56	2	48
6	Waveney Res	28	14	6	8	50	50	0	47*
7	Mulbarton Wands Res	28	12	8	8	79	61	18	43*
8	Downham Town Res	28	13	3	12	73	64	9	42
9	Wymondham Town Res	28	11	5	12	68	65	3	38
10	St Andrews Res	28	11	5	12	48	49	-1	37*
11	Bungay Town Res	28	10	4	14	46	64	-18	34
12	Sheringham Res	28	10	2	16	44	78	-34	30*
13	North Walsham Town Res	28	5	5	18	42	81	-39	17*
14	Stalham Town Res	28	4	1	23	27	79	-52	8*
15	Reepham Town Res	28	0	2	26	28	105	-77	0*

DIVISION FIVE NORTH

		P	W	D	L	F	A	GD	Pts
1	UEA Res	22	18	1	3	83	28	55	55
2	Mundford Res	22	16	2	4	90	26	64	50
3	Castle Acre Swifts	22	16	2	4	67	26	41	50
4	Dussindale Rovers	22	15	3	4	64	22	42	48
5	Hellesdon Res	22	14	3	5	73	31	42	45
6	Norwich Eagles	22	8	7	7	62	65	-3	31
7	Hindringham Res	22	8	3	11	44	47	-3	27
8	Narborough	22	7	4	11	28	47	-19	25
9	Easton Res	22	6	5	11	37	46	-9	23
10	Necton	22	4	2	16	29	89	-60	13*
11	Thorpe Village	22	3	0	19	14	94	-80	9
12	Wells Town Res	22	1	0	21	15	85	-70	-1*

DIVISION FIVE SOUTH

		P	W	D	L	F	A	GD	Pts
1	UEA Res	22	18	1	3	83	28	55	55
2	Mundford Res	22	16	2	4	90	26	64	50
3	Castle Acre Swifts	22	16	2	4	67	26	41	50
4	Dussindale Rovers	22	15	3	4	64	22	42	48
5	Hellesdon Res	22	14	3	5	73	31	42	45
6	Norwich Eagles	22	8	7	7	62	65	-3	31
7	Hindringham Res	22	8	3	11	44	47	-3	27
8	Narborough	22	7	4	11	28	47	-19	25
9	Easton Res	22	6	5	11	37	46	-9	23
10	Necton	22	4	2	16	29	89	-60	13*
11	Thorpe Village	22	3	0	19	14	94	-80	9
12	Wells Town Res	22	1	0	21	15	85	-70	-1*

CENTRAL & SOUTH NORFOLK LEAGUE

Division One

		P	W	D	L	F	A	GD	Pts
1	Longham	18	17	1	0	86	27	59	52
2	Dereham Taverners	18	16	0	2	105	19	86	48
3	Watton Utd Res	17	9	4	4	39	39	0	31
4	Attleborough Town A	18	8	0	10	35	46	-11	24
5	Rockland Utd	18	6	4	8	36	47	-11	22
6	Mulbarton Wdrs A	18	5	4	9	33	53	-20	19
7	Hethersett Ath	18	5	3	10	36	58	-22	18
8	Morley Village	18	4	4	10	38	48	-10	16
9	Shipdham	17	4	3	10	29	63	-34	15
10	North Elmham	18	2	3	13	21	58	-37	9

Hethersett Ath OB withdrew - record expunged.
Sporle withdrew - record expunged.

Division Two

		P	W	D	L	F	A	GD	Pts
1	Briston	24	19	3	2	113	35	78	60
2	UEA A	24	16	4	4	79	37	42	52
3	Castle Acre Swifts Res	24	15	1	8	79	47	32	46
4	Norwich Medics	24	13	6	5	69	37	32	45
5	Bridgham Utd	24	12	2	10	69	73	-4	38
6	Hockering	24	10	6	8	64	59	5	36
7	Yaxham	24	9	3	12	53	62	-9	30
8	Dereham Taverners Res	24	8	4	12	61	83	-22	28
9	Dussindale Rovers Res	24	7	4	13	53	76	-23	25
10	Brandon Town Res	24	7	2	15	59	83	-24	23
11	Tacolneston Res	24	6	4	14	51	85	-34	22
12	Bar 33	24	5	5	14	47	79	-32	20
13	Mundford Exiles	24	5	4	15	42	83	-41	19

Division Three East

		P	W	D	L	F	A	GD	Pts
1	Redgrave Rangers	20	19	0	1	92	22	70	57
2	Briston Res	20	14	1	5	104	33	71	43
3	Wensum Albion	20	12	1	7	62	49	13	37
4	Longham Res	20	11	2	7	77	55	22	35
5	Taverham	20	8	2	10	64	58	6	26
6	Bowthorpe Rovers	20	8	2	10	37	52	-15	26
7	Morley Village Res	20	8	1	11	61	65	-4	25
8	Home Care Utd	20	8	0	12	48	93	-45	24
9	Bacton	20	7	1	12	48	88	-40	22
10	Hockering Res	20	4	2	14	42	75	-33	14
11	Bar 33 Reserves	20	3	4	13	27	72	-45	13

Division Three West

		P	W	D	L	F	A	GD	Pts
1	Tugas United F.C.	14	12	0	2	77	14	63	36
2	Gressenhall	14	10	2	2	53	18	35	32
3	AFC Weeting	14	8	3	3	36	20	16	27
4	Hingham Ath Res	14	7	3	4	61	30	31	24
5	Cockers	14	7	1	6	39	25	14	22
6	Narborough Res	14	4	1	9	18	42	-24	13
7	Colkirk	14	2	0	12	16	74	-58	6
8	Necton Res	14	1	0	13	10	87	-77	3

Rampant Horse withdrew - record expunged.
Yaxham Res withdrew - record expunged.

NORTH EAST NORFOLK LEAGUE

Division One

		P	W	D	L	F	A	GD	Pts
1	Runton United	23	23	0	0	150	19	131	69
2	Cromer Youth Old Boys	23	19	2	2	112	19	93	59
3	Gimingham United	24	16	2	6	132	35	97	50
4	Aylsham A	24	16	1	7	103	32	71	49
5	Hickling	24	13	2	9	79	64	15	41
6	Southrepps	24	11	4	9	55	54	1	37
7	East Ruston	24	11	2	11	56	41	15	35
8	North Walsham Town A	24	10	3	11	68	67	1	29*
9	Holt United Reserves	24	8	3	13	72	57	15	25*
10	Erpingham United	24	4	3	17	43	112	-69	15
11	Gimingham United Res	24	5	2	17	45	66	-21	14*
12	Holt United Colts	24	6	2	16	48	94	-46	14*
14	Erpingham United Res	24	0	0	24	10	313	-303	-2*

Haisboro Athletic withdrew - record expunged.

NORTH WEST NORFOLK LEAGUE

Division One

		P	W	D	L	F	A	GD	Pts
1	AFC Lynn	15	13	1	1	76	10	66	40
2	Terrington	16	10	2	4	60	25	35	32
3	Denver	16	9	4	3	40	28	12	31
4	Birchwood	16	7	1	8	30	34	-4	22
5	Snettisham	15	6	3	6	23	30	-7	21
6	Ingoldisthorpe	16	5	3	8	28	33	-5	18
7	Thornham	16	5	1	10	32	59	-27	16
8	Heacham Reserves	16	4	0	12	34	66	-32	12
9	Bishops Lynn	16	3	3	10	28	66	-38	12

Division Two

		P	W	D	L	F	A	GD	Pts
1	Hunstanton	19	16	1	2	89	33	56	49
2	AFC Walpole	20	15	3	2	73	35	38	48
3	AFC Lynn Reserves	20	11	5	4	56	40	16	38
4	Gayton United 'A'	20	10	4	6	41	43	-2	34
5	Docking Rangers	20	9	4	7	54	38	16	31
6	Watlington Sports & Social Club	19	9	1	9	52	47	5	28
7	The Woottons	20	6	5	9	63	80	-17	23
8	Marshland Saints	20	5	5	10	35	53	-18	20
9	F.C. International	20	4	5	11	41	67	-26	17
10	Pentney	20	4	3	13	35	54	-19	15
11	South Creake	20	2	0	18	44	93	-49	6

FINAL TABLES

Division Three

		P	W	D	L	F	A	GD	Pts
1	Ingoldisthorpe Reserves	16	13	1	2	60	17	43	40
2	Reffley	16	11	0	5	64	32	32	33
3	West Winch	16	10	1	5	67	38	29	31
4	Terrington Reserves	16	9	2	5	59	38	21	29
5	Heacham Social Club	16	7	1	8	46	36	10	22
6	Hungate Rovers	16	7	1	8	41	61	-20	22
7	The Woottons Reserves	16	6	1	9	31	64	-33	19
8	Birchwood Reserves	16	3	3	10	25	56	-31	12
9	Hunstanton Town	16	0	2	14	19	70	-51	2

BEDFORDSHIRE COUNTY

PREMIER DIVISION

		P	W	D	L	F	A	GD	Pts
1	Shefford Town & Campton	28	20	4	4	89	28	61	64
2	AFC Kempston Town & BC	28	16	4	8	62	42	20	52
3	AFC Oakley M&DH (Sat)	28	15	5	8	73	51	22	50
4	Ickwell & Old Warden	28	16	2	10	71	65	6	49*
5	Crawley Green Reserves	28	14	6	8	66	45	21	46*
6	Caldecote	28	13	7	8	63	56	7	46
7	Wilstead	28	13	7	8	60	59	1	46
8	Flitwick Town	28	12	4	12	60	66	-6	40
9	Cranfield United	28	10	9	9	56	51	5	39
10	Wootton Blue Cross	28	12	3	13	60	64	-4	39
11	Stevington	28	10	7	11	54	52	2	36*
12	Queens Park Crescents	28	7	4	17	48	82	-34	25
13	Marston Shelton Rovers	28	5	8	15	48	54	-6	23
14	Sharnbrook	28	5	6	17	35	72	-37	18*
15	Kempston Rovers Dev	28	2	4	22	28	86	-58	6*

Renhold United withdrew - record expunged

DIVISION ONE

		P	W	D	L	F	A	GD	Pts
1	Totternhoe Res	26	20	2	4	102	34	68	62
2	Riseley Sports	26	18	4	4	78	34	44	58
3	AFC Kempston Town & BC Res	26	16	2	8	88	55	33	50
4	Cranfield United Res	26	15	4	7	59	41	18	49
5	Wixams	26	16	1	9	72	55	17	49
6	Lea Sports PSG	26	15	2	9	56	53	3	47
7	Flitwick Town Res	26	11	4	11	56	60	-4	37
8	Sandy	26	11	4	11	67	55	12	36*
9	Cople & Bedford SA	26	10	6	10	73	65	8	35*
10	Biggleswade Res	26	8	6	12	54	60	-6	30
11	Shefford Town & Campton Res	26	8	2	16	67	68	-1	26
12	Henlow	26	8	4	14	52	57	-5	26*
13	The 61 FC (Luton) Res	26	3	1	22	32	118	-86	10
14	Meltis Albion	26	2	0	24	24	125	-101	5*

DIVISION TWO

		P	W	D	L	F	A	GD	Pts
1	Bedford Albion	24	19	2	3	70	29	41	59
2	Wilstead Res	24	17	1	6	83	44	39	52
3	Henlow Res	24	16	3	5	81	45	36	51
4	Marston Shelton Rovers Res	24	14	3	7	69	52	17	40*
5	Elstow Abbey	24	11	4	9	40	41	-1	37
6	Caldecote Res	24	10	5	9	50	46	4	34*
7	Houghton Athletic	24	9	4	11	39	48	-9	29*
8	CS Rovers	24	9	1	14	56	75	-19	28
9	AFC Oakley M&DH Res	24	8	2	14	29	59	-30	25*
10	Atletico Europa	24	7	3	14	44	66	-22	23*
11	Sundon Park Rovers	24	5	7	12	38	67	-29	22
12	Luton Leagrave AFC	24	5	3	16	51	74	-23	18
13	Westoning	24	5	4	15	43	47	-4	7*

Wixams Wanderers withdrew - record expunged.
Renhold United Res withdrew - record expunged.

DIVISION THREE

		P	W	D	L	F	A	GD	Pts
1	Kempston Athletic	28	23	3	2	118	50	68	72
2	Harlington	28	20	3	5	92	47	45	63
3	Black Swan (Luton)	28	18	2	8	93	50	43	56
4	Clifton	28	16	8	4	87	54	33	56
5	Caldecote 'A'	28	14	7	7	65	57	8	48*
6	Bedford Albion Res	28	13	8	7	71	47	24	46*
7	Shefford Town & Campton 'A'	28	13	3	12	60	49	11	42
8	Lidlington United Sports Club	28	13	3	12	67	62	5	42
9	Sandy Res	28	13	3	12	65	66	-1	42
10	AFC Kempston Town & BC 'A'	28	8	6	14	57	108	-51	30
11	Flitwick Town 'A'	28	8	4	16	59	67	-8	23*
12	Wootton Village	28	6	2	20	36	80	-44	20
13	Stevington Res	28	6	2	20	49	81	-32	13*
14	Dinamo Flitwick	28	5	2	21	47	115	-68	13*
15	White Eagles	28	6	0	22	55	88	-33	7*

LUTON DISTRICT & SOUTH BEDFORDSHIRE LEAGUE

		P	W	D	L	F	A	GD	Pts
1	Christians in Sport	18	16	0	2	89	23	66	48
2	Sporting Lewsey Park	18	13	0	5	88	39	49	39
3	St Josephs	18	12	1	5	86	43	43	37
4	FC Kokan	18	12	1	5	50	45	5	37
5	Farley Boys	18	11	1	6	57	28	29	34
6	FC Polonia	18	5	2	11	38	71	-33	17
7	Jedenastka	18	4	3	11	50	68	-18	15
8	Square FC	18	4	1	13	37	66	-29	13
9	Houghton Hatters	18	4	0	14	33	100	-67	12
10	Farley Boys 2nd X1	18	4	1	13	48	93	-45	11*

CAMBRIDGESHIRE COUNTY

PREMIER DIVISION

		P	W	D	L	F	A	GD	Pts
1	West Wratting	30	25	3	2	85	29	56	78
2	Great Shelford	30	18	10	2	90	33	57	64
3	Brampton	30	17	5	8	80	46	34	56
4	Linton Granta	30	16	6	8	80	50	30	54
5	Cambridge University Press	30	15	5	10	75	59	16	50
6	Fulbourn Institute	30	13	9	8	56	44	12	48
7	Eaton Socon	30	14	5	11	61	53	8	47
8	Lakenheath	30	12	7	11	72	57	15	43
9	Hemingfords United	30	12	4	14	48	72	-24	40
10	Gamlingay United	30	11	4	15	51	72	-21	37
11	Cherry Hinton	30	10	4	16	52	57	-5	34
12	Comberton United	30	8	7	15	55	85	-30	31
13	Foxton	30	9	2	19	42	73	-31	29
14	Cambridge City Dev	30	7	6	17	48	74	-26	24*
15	Sawston United	30	5	6	19	35	75	-40	21
16	Chatteris Town	30	5	3	22	30	81	-51	18

SENIOR DIVISION A

		P	W	D	L	F	A	GD	Pts
1	Bar Hill	26	21	2	3	58	22	36	65
2	Ely City Res	26	19	4	3	84	29	55	61
3	Milton	26	15	6	5	56	41	15	51
4	Over Sports	26	15	5	6	61	33	28	50
5	Fowlmere	26	14	4	8	73	56	17	46
6	Soham United	26	13	4	9	63	41	22	43
7	Orwell	26	13	4	9	61	54	7	43
8	Somersham Town	26	10	3	13	42	47	-5	33
9	Haverhill Borough Res	26	10	3	13	52	64	-12	23*
10	Hundon	26	5	8	13	41	64	-23	23
11	Fulbourn Institute Res	26	5	4	17	40	73	-33	19
12	Girton United	26	5	3	18	27	68	-41	18
13	Soham Town Rangers Res	26	5	2	19	36	71	-35	17
14	Cottenham United	26	4	4	18	43	74	-31	16

Burwell Swifts withdrew - record expunged

SENIOR DIVISION B

		P	W	D	L	F	A	GD	Pts
1	Huntingdon United First	30	22	4	4	108	42	66	70
2	Whittlesford United First	30	20	6	4	65	39	26	66
3	Red Lodge F.C. First	30	21	3	6	91	46	45	63*
4	Newmarket Town F.C Res	30	19	2	9	110	71	39	59
5	Royston Town FC A	30	17	1	12	71	69	2	52
6	Witchford 96 First	30	12	5	13	60	69	-9	41
7	Great Chishill First	30	12	3	15	71	68	3	39
8	Steeple Bumpstead First	30	12	2	16	52	58	-6	38
9	March Town United Res	29	11	4	14	64	60	4	37
10	Bluntisham Rangers	30	12	1	17	69	91	-22	37
11	Wisbech St Mary Res	30	10	4	16	68	74	-6	34
12	Cambridge University Press Res	30	9	6	15	57	72	-15	33
13	Lakenheath F.C. Res	29	11	3	15	54	70	-16	33*
14	Needingworth United	30	7	11	12	63	73	-10	31*
15	Sawston Rovers	30	7	4	19	40	76	-36	25
16	Godmanchester Rovers Res	30	7	1	22	40	105	-65	22

DIVISION ONE A

		P	W	D	L	F	A	GD	Pts
1	West Wratting Res	24	19	3	2	82	32	50	60
2	Thaxted Rangers	24	14	5	5	79	39	40	47
3	Linton Granta Res	24	12	4	8	52	40	12	40
4	Cherry Hinton Res	24	12	1	11	78	58	20	37
5	Clare Town F.C.	24	11	4	9	68	55	13	37
6	Exning United F.C.	24	12	1	11	70	80	-10	37
7	Steeple Morden	24	11	1	12	42	48	-6	34
8	Ashdon Villa	24	11	2	11	53	45	8	29*
9	Debden	24	7	6	11	51	63	-12	27
10	Milton Res	24	7	4	13	46	66	-20	25
11	Hardwick FC	24	7	3	14	49	79	-30	24
12	Duxford United	24	8	0	16	37	79	-42	24
13	Balsham	24	6	4	14	46	69	-23	22

DIVISION ONE B

		P	W	D	L	F	A	GD	Pts
1	St Ives Rangers	18	12	2	4	59	24	35	38
2	AFC Barley Mow	18	11	2	5	63	26	37	35
3	Eaton Socon Res	18	11	2	5	48	35	13	35
4	Alconbury	18	11	2	5	46	34	12	35
5	Houghton & Wyton	17	9	2	6	49	38	11	29
6	Mildenhall Town F.C. Res	17	6	4	7	35	37	-2	22
7	Fordham	18	5	6	7	31	35	-4	21
8	Fenstanton	18	5	4	9	39	45	-6	19
9	Chatteris Town Res	18	3	2	13	22	66	-44	11
10	Hemingfords United Res	18	3	0	15	25	77	-52	9

Buckden withdrew - record expunged

Little Downham Swifts withdrew - record expunged

Littleport Town withdrew - record expunged

DIVISION TWO A

		P	W	D	L	F	A	GD	Pts
1	Cambourne Rovers	24	19	2	3	88	38	50	59
2	Bassingbourn	24	16	0	8	48	28	20	48
3	Bar Hill SSC Res	24	14	4	6	64	38	26	46
4	Mott MacDonald	24	12	6	6	57	38	19	42
5	Over Sports Res	24	12	2	10	58	39	19	38
6	Whittlesford United Res	24	11	2	11	42	39	3	35
7	Great Shelford Res	24	12	1	11	51	42	9	34*
8	Linton Granta A	24	10	2	12	62	86	-24	32
9	Gamlingay United Res	24	9	4	11	58	57	1	31
10	Papworth	24	9	2	13	53	66	-13	29
11	Litlington Athletic	24	8	1	15	43	86	-43	25
12	City Life	24	5	2	17	37	71	-34	8*
13	Sawston United Res	24	5	0	19	44	77	-33	3*

DIVISION TWO B

		P	W	D	L	F	A	GD	Pts
1	Tuddenham 08 F.C. (Sat)	22	15	4	3	61	30	31	49
2	Isleham United	22	13	3	6	56	40	16	42
3	Ramsey Pavilion	22	12	4	6	68	45	23	40
4	Mepal Sports	22	11	5	6	63	41	22	38
5	Brampton Res	22	9	7	6	55	36	19	34
6	Wimblington	22	8	8	6	55	57	-2	32
7	Wisbech St Mary A Team	22	8	4	10	53	48	5	25*
8	Swavesey Institute	22	7	4	11	40	54	-14	25
9	Doddington United	22	9	1	12	44	64	-20	25*
10	Soham United Res	22	7	2	13	40	50	-10	23
11	March Rangers	22	6	4	12	40	56	-16	22
12	Manea United	22	4	0	18	28	82	-54	12

Mildenhall United F.C. withdrew - record expunged

FINAL TABLES

DIVISION THREE A

		P	W	D	L	F	A	GD	Pts
1	Meldreth	24	17	5	2	86	32	54	56
2	Comberton United Res	24	17	2	5	96	42	54	53
3	Steeple Morden Res	24	14	4	6	71	48	23	46
4	Foxton Res	24	14	4	6	65	47	18	46
5	Haverhill Rovers F.C. 'A'	24	14	3	7	54	42	12	45
6	Great Paxton 1sts	24	13	2	9	84	58	26	38*
7	Eaton Socon A Team	24	12	0	12	65	65	0	36
8	Hundon F.C. Res (Sat)	24	9	7	8	44	49	-5	34
9	Girton United Res	24	7	4	13	55	65	-10	22*
10	Cherry Hinton A team	24	6	3	15	43	77	-34	21
11	Melbourn	24	7	1	16	34	74	-40	19*
12	Duxford United Res	24	4	2	18	34	73	-39	11*
13	Abington United	24	3	1	20	33	92	-59	10

DIVISION THREE B

		P	W	D	L	F	A	GD	Pts
1	Wisbech Town Acorns 1st	22	17	2	3	79	22	57	53
2	Burwell Swifts Res	22	15	2	5	79	31	48	44*
3	Chatteris Town Youth Fen Tigers	22	13	5	4	67	33	34	44
4	Burwell Tigers Men	22	12	5	5	50	35	15	41
5	Ely Crusaders	22	10	6	6	60	43	17	36
6	The Eagle (Ely)	22	9	5	8	56	60	-4	32
7	Alconbury Res	22	9	4	9	46	44	2	31
8	Benwick Athletic	22	6	3	13	51	68	-17	21
9	Somersham Town Res	22	4	5	13	29	59	-30	17
10	Wisbech St Mary B	22	7	1	14	35	60	-25	16*
11	Cottenham United Res	22	4	4	14	32	65	-33	16
12	Bluntisham Rangers Res	22	4	2	16	40	104	-64	14
13	Guyhirn withdrew - record expunged								

DIVISION FOUR A

		P	W	D	L	F	A	GD	Pts
1	Fulbourn Institute A Team	24	18	5	1	70	23	47	59
2	Suffolk Punch Haverhill	24	20	1	3	107	35	72	49*
3	Milton A Team	24	13	3	8	83	71	12	42
4	Buckden Res	24	12	4	8	57	64	-7	40
5	Papworth Res	24	11	6	7	49	45	4	39
6	Harston Bostocks	24	12	1	11	61	50	11	37
7	Cambridge Ambassadors	24	10	4	10	49	48	1	34
8	Kedington F.C.	24	10	3	11	42	40	2	27*
9	Guilden Morden Team	24	6	6	12	56	69	-13	24
10	Wickhambrook F.C.	24	9	1	14	64	66	-2	22*
11	Sawston Rovers Res	24	6	3	15	38	74	-36	18*
12	Saffron Dynamos	24	3	5	16	40	83	-43	8*
13	Bassingbourn Res	24	3	4	17	28	76	-48	7*

DIVISION FOUR B

		P	W	D	L	F	A	GD	Pts
1	Fordham Res	26	24	2	0	87	23	64	74
2	Outwell Swifts Res	26	19	3	4	109	25	84	60
3	Huntingdon United Res	26	19	1	6	97	44	53	58
4	Houghton & Wyton Res	26	16	0	10	75	46	29	48
5	Needingworth United Res	26	15	2	9	73	58	15	47
6	Isleham United Res	26	15	2	9	58	46	12	47
7	Coldham United	26	12	3	11	76	74	2	39
8	Ely Crusaders Res	26	12	1	13	65	63	2	37
9	Wisbech Town Acorns Res	26	10	3	13	64	64	0	33
10	Wimblington Res	26	9	1	16	60	70	-10	28
11	Hemingfords United A Team	25	5	2	18	43	126	-83	17
12	Witchford 96 Res	26	7	0	19	48	63	-15	12*
13	Chatteris Town A Team	26	3	3	20	42	90	-48	9*
14	March Rangers Res	25	3	1	21	33	138	-105	7*

DIVISION FIVE A

		P	W	D	L	F	A	GD	Pts
1	Barrington 1st	24	18	1	5	83	41	42	55
2	Oakington Vikings	24	16	4	4	47	30	17	52
3	Longstanton FC	24	13	5	6	79	53	26	44
4	Histon Hornets	24	12	3	9	67	45	22	39
5	Clare Town F.C. Res	24	12	3	9	64	57	7	39
6	Orwell Res	24	11	5	8	55	52	3	38
7	Hardwick FC Res	24	11	3	10	60	61	-1	36
8	Milton B Team	24	10	3	11	38	57	-19	32*
9	Mott MacDonald Res	24	6	5	13	33	51	-18	23
10	Thaxted Rangers Res	24	7	4	13	52	61	-9	22*
11	Barton Mills F.C.	24	6	1	17	54	86	-32	19
12	Harston Bostocks Res	24	4	6	14	29	57	-28	17*
13	Steeple Bumpstead Res	24	7	3	14	38	48	-10	15*
14	Bottisham Men	0	0	0	0	0	0	0	0

DIVISION FIVE B

		P	W	D	L	F	A	GD	Pts
1	St Ives Rangers Res	24	18	2	4	105	36	69	56
2	March Soccer School Academy	24	16	3	5	91	35	56	51
3	Littleport Town Res	24	16	2	6	78	55	23	50
4	Fenstanton Res	24	14	3	7	81	58	23	45
5	AFC Christchurch The Magpies	24	14	0	10	82	60	22	42
6	Little Downham Swifts Res	24	17	2	5	107	58	49	41*
7	Wicken	24	10	4	10	73	66	7	34
8	Chatteris Town Youth Fen Tigers Res	24	10	1	13	55	82	-27	31
9	Marchester United	24	6	6	12	56	68	-12	21*
10	Cottenham United A Team	24	5	4	15	33	72	-39	19
11	Benwick Athletic Res	24	6	1	17	44	103	-59	16*
12	Coldham United Res	24	4	3	17	38	92	-54	15
13	Somersham Town A Team	24	3	3	18	29	87	-58	12

CENTRAL MIDLANDS

NORTH DIVISION

		P	W	D	L	F	A	GD	Pts
1	Harworth Colliery	34	26	5	3	116	34	82	83
2	Clay Cross Town	34	27	2	5	119	48	71	83
3	AFC Bentley	34	20	10	4	97	51	46	70
4	Collingham	34	21	3	10	110	56	54	66
5	Retford	34	20	5	9	89	46	43	65
6	Lincoln Moorlands Railway	34	20	3	11	109	67	42	63
7	Staveley Miners Welfare Res	34	16	6	12	89	62	27	54
8	Dinnington Town	34	16	5	13	73	64	9	53
9	Tideswell United	34	18	3	13	67	69	-2	53*
10	Appleby Frodingham	34	15	7	12	63	55	8	52
11	Thorne Colliery	34	13	4	17	82	93	-11	42*
12	Phoenix	34	13	0	21	70	99	-29	39
13	Dronfield Town Res	34	11	4	19	55	68	-13	36*
14	Askern	34	11	2	21	60	82	-22	35
15	Renishaw Rangers	34	9	3	22	40	149	-109	30
16	Brodsworth Welfare	34	7	4	23	51	90	-39	15*
17	Newark Town	34	4	4	26	48	125	-77	14*
18	Welbeck Lions	34	2	4	28	39	119	-80	10

SOUTH DIVISION

		P	W	D	L	F	A	GD	Pts
1	Eastwood Community	28	26	0	2	98	23	75	78
2	Sherwood Colliery	28	24	3	1	84	18	66	75
3	Hucknall Town	28	20	2	6	71	24	47	62
4	Pinxton	28	19	2	7	87	45	42	59
5	Matlock Town Reserves	28	16	2	10	66	47	19	50
6	Swanwick Pentrich Road	28	14	4	10	64	45	19	46
7	Blidworth Welfare	28	12	4	12	54	47	7	40
8	Hilton Harriers	28	10	8	10	51	62	-11	38
9	Mickleover RBL	28	8	6	14	45	55	-10	30
10	Keyworth United	28	7	6	15	55	95	-40	27
11	AFC Kilburn	28	7	3	18	39	86	-47	24
12	Holbrook St Michaels	28	5	5	18	52	81	-29	20
13	Linby Colliery Welfare	28	5	5	18	26	65	-39	20
14	Teversal Reserves	28	5	3	20	42	97	-55	18
15	Aslockton & Orston	28	4	3	21	33	77	-44	15

MIDLANDS REGIONAL ALLIANCE

Premier Division

		P	W	D	L	F	A	GD	Pts
1	Rowsley '86	20	19	1	0	84	14	70	58
2	Castle Donington Cobras	20	14	4	2	70	30	40	46
3	Melbourne Dynamo	20	13	1	6	70	31	39	40
4	Castle Donington	20	9	4	7	42	47	-5	31
5	Derby Singh Brothers	20	10	3	7	60	39	21	27 *
6	Shirebrook Rangers	20	7	3	10	36	51	-15	24
7	Wirksworth Ivanhoe	20	5	5	10	33	50	-17	20
8	Chesterfield Town	20	5	3	12	40	55	-15	18
9	Newhall United	20	5	2	13	22	56	-34	17
10	Moira United	20	4	4	12	22	59	-37	16
11	Allestree	20	4	0	16	24	71	-47	12

Matlock United withdrew - record expunged.

Division One

		P	W	D	L	F	A	GD	Pts
1	Burton Town	18	14	2	2	60	21	39	44
2	Rolls-Royce Leisure	18	13	2	3	71	35	36	41
3	Mayfield	18	10	4	4	56	37	19	34
4	Ripley Town	18	8	4	6	39	38	1	28
5	Rowsley '86 Res	18	8	3	7	37	45	-8	27
6	Wirksworth Town Res	18	7	3	8	30	28	2	24
7	Ashbourne Reserves	18	5	4	9	32	45	-13	19
8	Little Eaton	18	4	6	8	35	41	-6	18
9	Willington Sports	18	3	3	12	38	62	-24	12
10	Punjab United	18	1	3	14	20	66	-46	6

Division Two

		P	W	D	L	F	A	GD	Pts
1	Melbourne Dynamo Rese	14	13	1	0	66	14	52	40
2	Little Eaton Reserves	14	9	2	3	44	21	23	29
3	Wirksworth Ivanhoe Res	14	7	3	4	42	30	12	24
4	Sherwin	14	6	3	5	32	39	-7	21
5	Newhall United Dev	14	4	5	5	35	26	9	17
6	Derby Athletic	14	5	1	8	31	35	-4	16
7	South Normanton United	14	2	1	11	21	61	-40	7
8	Willington Sports Res	14	1	2	11	15	60	-45	5

CHESHIRE LEAGUE

PREMIER DIVISION

		P	W	D	L	F	A	GD	Pts
1	Knutsford FC	28	24	1	3	91	33	58	73
2	Malpas FC	28	16	4	8	76	43	33	52
3	Whaley Bridge Athletic	28	16	4	8	69	40	29	52
4	Linotype - Cheadle H.N.	28	14	5	9	50	47	3	47
5	Billinge First	28	14	3	11	52	50	2	45
6	Ashton Town	28	13	3	12	66	55	11	42
7	Congleton VR	28	12	4	12	45	52	-7	40
8	Wythenshawe Town	28	11	4	13	45	53	-8	37
9	Greenalls Padgate St Oswalds	28	10	6	12	46	73	-27	36
10	Eagle Sports	28	10	5	13	44	50	-6	35
11	Rylands	28	10	4	14	50	53	-3	34
12	Altrincham FC Reserves	28	9	4	15	42	60	-18	31
13	Crewe FC	28	8	7	13	47	68	-21	31
14	Poynton FC	28	9	3	16	53	63	-10	30
15	Denton Town	28	4	3	21	46	82	-36	14*

DIVISION ONE

		P	W	D	L	F	A	GD	Pts
1	Daten FC	28	16	9	3	72	37	35	57
2	Pilkington FC	28	17	3	8	88	56	32	54
3	F.C. St. Helens	28	16	5	7	73	43	30	53
4	Middlewich Town	28	16	5	7	72	42	30	53
5	Egerton FC	28	17	2	9	84	58	26	53
6	Lostock Gralam	28	15	6	7	58	46	12	51
7	Windle Labour	28	13	3	12	74	83	-9	42
8	Mersey Valley	28	11	6	11	64	58	6	39
9	Styal FC	28	12	3	13	63	62	1	39
10	West Didsbury & Chorlton Res	28	11	6	11	61	64	-3	39
11	AFC Macclesfield	28	12	3	13	74	79	-5	39
12	Halebank	28	8	5	15	65	86	-21	29
13	Garswood United	28	5	3	20	37	76	-39	18
14	Golborne Sports	28	4	4	20	51	101	-50	16
15	Cheadle Town Res	28	3	5	20	35	80	-45	14

FINAL TABLES

DIVISION TWO

		P	W	D	L	F	A	GD	Pts
1	Ford Motors	28	22	3	3	102	36	66	69
2	Vulcan FC	28	19	4	5	83	36	47	61
3	Blacon Youth Club	28	18	6	4	101	55	46	60
4	Broadheath Central JFC	28	17	5	6	101	56	45	56
5	Unicorn Athletic JFC	28	17	1	10	72	51	21	52
6	Buxton FC Res	28	15	3	10	66	56	10	48
7	Grappenhall Sports	28	13	3	12	60	65	-5	42
8	Moore United FC	28	12	4	12	76	69	7	40
9	Orford FC	28	13	1	14	71	72	-1	40
10	Tarporley Victoria	28	10	2	16	39	88	-49	32
11	Winstanley Warriors	28	7	6	15	58	81	-23	27
12	Maine Road Res	28	6	1	19	60	76	-16	25
13	Cuddington FC	28	7	4	17	73	94	-21	25
14	Sandbach United Res	28	7	1	20	70	102	-32	22
15	St Helens Town Res	28	2	2	24	135	-95	8	

RESERVE DIVISION

		P	W	D	L	F	A	GD	Pts
1	Knutsford A	32	21	7	4	81	31	50	70
2	Garswood United Res	32	21	3	8	86	52	34	66
3	Eagle Sports Res	32	19	5	8	79	46	33	62
4	Rylands Res	32	17	6	9	85	54	31	57
5	Middlewich Town Res	32	17	4	11	82	56	26	55
6	Poynton Res	32	17	4	11	77	60	17	55
7	Pilkington Res	32	16	6	10	96	72	24	54
8	F.C. St. Helens Res	32	17	3	12	62	49	13	54
9	Daten FC Res	32	15	7	10	78	56	22	52
10	Styal FC Res	32	15	2	15	51	64	-13	47
11	Greenalls Padgate St Oswalds Res	32	12	4	16	61	72	-11	40
12	Billinge Res	32	11	3	18	63	95	-32	36
13	Moore United FC Res	32	10	3	19	57	69	-12	33
14	Vulcan FC Res	32	9	6	17	48	73	-25	33
15	Orford Res	32	7	4	21	61	105	-44	25
16	Linotype - Cheadle H.N. Res	32	6	4	22	56	101	-45	22
17	Golborne Sports Res	32	4	5	23	39	107	-68	17

DORSET PREMIER LEAGUE

		P	W	D	L	F	A	GD	Pts
1	Hamworthy Recreation	32	26	1	5	100	42	58	79
2	Westland Sports	32	24	2	6	95	29	66	74
3	Gillingham Town	32	20	4	8	86	55	31	64
4	Merley Cobham Sports	32	19	3	10	89	50	39	60
5	Holt United	32	18	8	6	82	42	40	59*
6	Dorchester Sports	32	19	2	11	94	65	29	59
7	Swanage Town & Herston	32	20	0	12	81	62	19	54*
8	Balti Sports	32	15	4	13	90	76	14	49
9	Mere Town	32	14	6	12	69	70	-1	48
10	Hamworthy United Res	32	14	4	14	87	82	5	46
11	Shaftesbury Town Res	32	12	7	13	70	79	-9	40*
12	Parley Sports	32	11	4	17	72	84	-12	37
13	Bridport Res	32	8	4	20	53	93	-40	28
14	Sturminster Newton United	32	6	6	20	49	97	-48	24
15	Blandford United	32	6	4	22	58	111	-53	22
16	Wareham Rangers	32	5	2	25	47	108	-61	11*
17	Sherborne Town Res	32	2	5	25	34	111	-77	11

DORSET LEAGUE

Senior Division

		P	W	D	L	F	A	GD	Pts
1	Corfe Castle	24	18	2	4	63	29	34	56
2	Chickerell United	24	15	4	5	69	34	35	49
3	Portland United Res	24	16	1	7	69	38	31	49
4	Westland Sports Res	24	14	2	8	58	43	15	44
5	Beaminster	24	12	3	9	51	44	7	39
6	Corfe Mullen United	24	11	4	9	52	45	7	37
7	Poole Borough	24	10	3	11	58	60	-2	33
8	Witchampton United	24	9	5	10	49	54	-5	32
9	Broadstone FC Seniors	24	7	4	13	39	50	-11	25
10	Allendale	24	6	5	13	42	69	-27	23
11	Wincanton Town Res	24	8	4	12	38	61	-23	22*
12	Cranborne	24	5	2	17	33	75	-42	17
13	Dorchester Sports Res	24	3	5	16	26	45	-19	14

Division One

		P	W	D	L	F	A	GD	Pts
1	AFC Blandford	24	21	2	1	100	33	67	65
2	Tisbury United	24	19	3	2	67	29	38	60
3	Wool United	24	16	3	5	63	44	19	51
4	Wareham Rangers Res	24	13	3	8	73	55	18	42
5	Portland United A Team	24	12	3	9	67	55	12	39
6	Stalbridge	24	10	3	11	56	55	1	33
7	Blandford United Res	24	9	4	11	44	57	-13	30*
8	Weymouth FC Colts	24	8	3	13	55	65	-10	27
9	Allendale Res	24	8	3	13	40	55	-15	27
10	Swanage Town & Herston Res	24	8	2	14	37	57	-20	26
11	Canford United	24	7	4	13	65	69	-4	25
12	Boscombe Polonia	24	5	1	18	37	91	-54	15*
13	Parley Sports Res	24	1	4	19	22	61	-39	7

Division Two

		P	W	D	L	F	A	GD	Pts
1	Sturminster Marshall	26	23	2	1	122	24	98	71
2	Wimborne Phoenix	26	20	0	6	117	31	86	60
3	Portland Town	26	18	4	4	88	38	50	58
4	Shaftesbury Town Colts	26	14	6	6	68	41	27	48
5	Portesham United	26	12	4	10	66	47	19	40
6	Maiden Newton & Cattistock	26	10	4	12	56	80	-24	34
7	Broadstone FC Seniors Res	26	10	3	13	56	61	-5	33
8	Broadmayne	26	6	11	9	61	69	-8	33
9	Piddlehinton United	26	9	4	13	54	72	-18	31
10	Gillingham Town Res	26	9	2	15	49	83	-34	29
11	Chickerell United Res	26	7	7	12	53	62	-9	28
12	Sturminster Newton United Res	26	6	5	15	41	89	-48	23
13	Marnhull	26	6	2	18	46	104	-58	20
14	Okeford United	26	3	3	20	23	99	-76	12

Division Three

		P	W	D	L	F	A	GD	Pts
1	Gill Dons	24	21	1	2	99	36	63	64
2	Bridport 3rd Team	24	17	4	3	76	32	44	55
3	Verwood All Stars	24	16	1	7	84	38	46	49
4	AFC Blandford Res	24	13	2	9	79	55	24	41
5	South Cheriton United	24	11	3	10	49	49	0	36
6	Donhead United	24	11	3	10	61	66	-5	36
7	Corfe Castle Res	24	11	3	10	47	59	-12	36
8	Wimborne Phoenix Res	24	10	2	12	61	59	2	32
9	Portland Town Res	24	7	6	11	57	70	-13	27
10	Bere Regis	24	5	5	14	40	83	-43	20
11	Wool United Res	24	4	6	14	47	79	-32	18
12	Handley Sports	24	3	3	16	38	79	-41	18
13	Pimperne Sports Society	24	3	5	16	53	86	-33	13*

Division Four

		P	W	D	L	F	A	GD	Pts
1	Piddlehinton United Res	26	23	1	2	114	18	96	70
2	Corfe Mullen United Res	26	17	2	7	59	33	26	53
3	Verwood All Stars Dev	26	16	3	7	86	52	34	51
4	Portland United Youth Panthers	26	15	5	6	80	48	32	50
5	Puddletown FC	26	14	3	9	63	41	22	45
6	Portland Town A Team	26	12	5	9	58	53	5	41
7	Shillingstone	26	11	6	9	57	59	-2	39
8	Tisbury United Res	26	11	5	10	44	45	-1	38
9	Redlands Rebels	26	11	1	14	71	79	-8	34
10	Crossways Spitfires	26	9	5	12	61	65	-4	32
11	Chickerell United A	26	8	4	14	41	64	-23	28
12	Lytchett and Upton Red Triangle	26	6	5	15	43	73	-30	19*
13	Portesham United Res	26	3	3	20	35	82	-47	12
14	Wool and Winfrith	26	1	2	23	23	123	-100	2*

ESSEX & SUFFOLK BORDER LEAGUE

PREMIER DIVISION

		P	W	D	L	F	A	GD	Pts
1	Gas Recreation	28	23	3	2	113	34	79	72
2	Coggeshall United	28	23	3	2	101	22	79	72
3	West Bergholt	28	17	0	11	56	42	14	51
4	White Notley	28	14	4	10	67	53	14	46
5	Alresford Colne Rangers	28	14	3	11	58	59	-1	45
6	Brantham Athletic Res	28	14	2	12	65	62	3	44
7	Little Oakley Res	28	14	1	13	51	53	-2	43
8	Wormingford Wanderers	28	11	7	10	55	65	-10	40
9	Hatfield Peverel	28	11	4	13	54	44	10	37
10	Harwich & Parkeston	28	10	7	11	55	51	4	37
11	Hedinghams United	28	8	7	13	46	78	-32	31
12	Kelvedon Social	28	7	4	17	35	53	-18	25
13	Dedham Old Boys	28	5	6	17	37	71	-34	21
14	Earls Colne	28	5	5	18	33	84	-51	20
15	Barnston	28	3	6	19	30	85	-55	15

DIVISION ONE

		P	W	D	L	F	A	GD	Pts
1	Great Bentley	26	23	3	0	91	20	71	72
2	Lawford Lads	26	20	2	4	88	18	70	62
3	Brightlingsea Regent Res	26	17	3	6	74	42	32	54
4	Tiptree Engaine	26	15	3	8	71	38	33	48
5	Cressing United	26	15	1	10	69	40	29	46
6	West Bergholt Res	26	14	1	11	61	58	3	43
7	Tiptree Jobserve	26	11	2	13	64	53	11	35
8	Little Oakley A	26	11	2	13	66	64	2	35
9	Boxted Lodgers	26	10	2	14	63	75	-12	32
10	Holland Res	26	8	5	13	56	61	-5	29
11	Alresford Colne Rangers Res	26	8	3	15	49	79	-30	27
12	Bradfield Rovers	26	7	1	18	33	121	-88	22
13	Gas Recreation Res	26	5	1	20	42	72	-30	16
14	FC Clacton Res	26	3	1	22	28	114	-86	10

DIVISION TWO

		P	W	D	L	F	A	GD	Pts
1	Tiptree Heath	22	21	0	1	129	16	113	63
2	Bures United	22	19	2	1	78	11	67	59
3	Flitch United	22	16	3	3	87	23	64	51
4	Belle Vue Social Club	22	14	1	7	57	44	13	43
5	Connaught Red Star	22	12	2	8	58	39	19	38
6	Brantham Athletic F.C. 'A'	22	11	1	10	48	53	-5	34
7	Hatfield Peverel Res	22	10	1	11	38	50	-12	31
8	Mersea Island	22	5	3	14	30	79	-49	18
9	Kelvedon Social Res	22	4	1	17	31	78	-47	13
10	Colne Engaine	22	3	4	15	28	81	-53	13
11	Lawford Lads Res	22	3	2	17	26	81	-55	11
12	Boxted Lodgers Res	22	3	2	17	25	80	-55	11

DIVISION THREE

		P	W	D	L	F	A	GD	Pts
1	Colne Athletic	22	22	0	0	146	15	131	66
2	Tollesbury	22	15	3	4	100	39	61	48
3	Rowhedge	22	15	2	5	69	29	40	47
4	Wormingford Wanderers Res	22	14	2	6	69	42	27	44
5	Ramsey & Mistley	22	12	1	9	90	68	22	37
6	Oyster	22	9	5	8	55	57	-2	32
7	Dedham Old Boys Res	22	9	1	12	78	61	17	28
8	Tiptree Jobserve Res	21	7	3	11	49	73	-24	24
9	Great Bentley Res	21	7	2	12	43	61	-18	23
10	Bradfield Rovers Res	22	4	1	17	30	146	-116	13
11	Barnston Res	22	4	0	18	30	91	-61	12
12	Hedinghams United Res	22	3	0	19	29	106	-77	9

COLCHESTER AND EAST ESSEX FOOTBALL LEAGUE

Premier Division

		P	W	D	L	F	A	GD	Pts
1	Harwich Rangers	16	13	0	3	47	22	25	39
2	Tavern	16	12	2	2	53	26	27	38
3	Riverbank Athletic	16	9	3	4	57	38	19	30
4	Abbey Fields	16	8	3	5	35	26	9	27
5	Cavendish	16	9	0	7	32	26	6	27
6	Tiptree Park Reserves	16	4	1	11	37	51	-14	13
7	Sporting Rebels	16	4	1	11	36	61	-25	13
8	Nayland Rangers	16	4	1	11	29	54	-25	13
9	Mistley	16	3	1	12	22	44	-22	10

Division One

		P	W	D	L	F	A	GD	Pts
1	St Osyth	16	13	3	1	78	21	57	39
2	Stanway Athletic	16	12	2	2	56	25	31	38
3	Langham Lodgers	16	10	2	4	41	27	14	32
4	Ramsey Mill Reserves	16	9	0	7	44	51	-7	27
5	Old Memorial Services	16	7	1	8	38	38	0	22
6	Stoke by Nayland .	16	6	0	10	20	42	-22	18
7	Cavendish Reserves	16	5	1	10	31	36	-5	18
8	Oyster Reserves	16	4	0	12	22	55	-33	12
9	Mersea Island Reserves	16	2	1	13	21	56	-35	7

FINAL TABLES
ESSEX OLYMPIAN LEAGUE

PREMIER DIVISION

		P	W	D	L	F	A	GD	Pts
1	Catholic United	24	15	6	3	52	26	26	51
2	Frenford	24	15	3	6	56	26	30	48
3	Springfield	24	13	6	5	59	30	29	45
4	White Ensign	24	14	2	8	57	38	19	44
5	Harold Wood Athletic	24	13	4	7	63	46	17	43
6	Kelvedon Hatch	24	12	6	6	55	42	13	42
7	May & Baker E.C.	24	10	4	10	53	46	7	34
8	Leigh Ramblers	24	8	6	10	49	47	2	30
9	Bishop's Stortford Swifts	24	8	5	11	41	49	-8	29
10	Manford Way	24	9	3	12	39	45	-6	28*
11	Canning Town	24	7	3	14	28	56	-28	24
12	Rayleigh Town	24	4	3	17	32	61	-29	15
13	Basildon Town	24	2	1	21	18	90	-72	7

DIVISION ONE

		P	W	D	L	F	A	GD	Pts
1	Buckhurst Hill	23	20	2	1	79	26	53	62
2	Hutton	24	16	4	4	66	30	36	52
3	Great Baddow	24	16	3	5	71	42	29	51
4	Sungate	23	11	4	8	56	46	10	37
5	Old Southendian	24	11	4	9	53	49	4	37
6	Shenfield AFC	24	11	3	10	50	53	-3	36
7	FC Hamlets	24	10	4	10	46	39	7	34
8	Newbury Forest	24	8	4	12	58	66	-8	28
9	Snaresbrook	24	8	3	13	31	56	-25	27
10	Galleywood	24	7	5	12	34	51	-17	26
11	Old Chelmsfordians	24	7	3	14	36	55	-19	22*
12	Harold Hill	24	5	2	17	32	64	-32	11*
13	Runwell Sports	24	3	3	18	25	60	-35	10*

DIVISION TWO

		P	W	D	L	F	A	GD	Pts
1	May & Baker E.C. Res	22	16	3	3	62	26	36	51
2	Herongate Athletic	22	15	4	3	89	43	46	49
3	Ramsden Scotia	22	15	2	5	63	29	34	45*
4	Benfleet	22	12	5	5	70	33	37	41
5	Rayleigh Town Res	22	10	7	5	61	43	18	37
6	Ongar Town	22	12	0	10	52	59	-7	36
7	Toby	22	9	6	7	55	41	14	33
8	Newham United	22	8	4	10	42	42	0	26*
9	A1 Sports	22	7	3	12	41	51	-10	20*
10	Upminster	22	3	4	15	31	63	-32	11*
11	Rochford Town	22	4	1	17	34	79	-45	11*
12	Ryan	22	1	1	20	34	125	-91	4

DIVISION THREE

		P	W	D	L	F	A	GD	Pts
1	Manford Way Res	22	19	1	2	85	31	54	58
2	Shoebury Town	22	16	3	3	71	34	37	51
3	Harold Wood Athletic Res	22	12	2	8	50	43	7	38
4	Beacon Hill Rovers	22	11	3	8	66	43	23	36
5	White Ensign Res	22	13	0	10	62	41	21	34*
6	Hutton Res	22	9	4	9	61	40	21	31
7	Leigh Town	22	10	2	10	59	42	17	30*
8	Old Chelmsfordians Res	22	9	5	8	50	41	9	30*
9	Frenford Res	22	9	2	11	53	47	6	29
10	Roydon	22	8	4	10	46	58	-12	28
11	Debden Sports	22	2	1	19	26	58	-32	-5*
12	Leytonstone United	22	1	1	20	8	159	-151	-8*

DIVISION FOUR

		P	W	D	L	F	A	GD	Pts
1	Chingford Athletic	20	17	1	2	86	23	63	52
2	Old Southendian Res	20	14	2	4	60	26	34	42*
3	Southend Sports	20	11	1	8	57	47	10	34
4	Basildon Town Res	20	10	2	8	59	35	24	32
5	Toby Res	20	9	5	6	58	41	17	32
6	Old Barkabbeyans	20	9	3	8	51	53	-2	30
7	Leigh Ramblers Res	20	8	1	11	32	49	-17	23*
8	Epping	20	9	2	9	39	31	8	21*
9	Canning Town Res	20	7	0	13	36	63	-27	21
10	Galleywood Res	20	4	0	16	14	63	-49	10*
11	Sungate Res	20	3	1	16	17	78	-61	8*

DIVISION FIVE

		P	W	D	L	F	A	GD	Pts
1	Westhamians	22	19	3	0	80	19	61	60
2	Academy Soccer	22	18	3	1	118	17	101	57
3	Shenfield AFC Res	22	15	1	6	68	37	31	46
4	Catholic United Res	22	13	6	3	57	33	24	43*
5	Dagenham United	22	10	2	10	56	51	5	30*
6	Herongate Athletic Res	22	8	4	10	59	63	-4	28
7	Collier Row	22	9	1	12	56	85	-29	28
8	Southend Sports Res	22	8	1	13	44	61	-17	21*
9	Bishop's Stortford Swifts Res	22	7	0	15	37	86	-49	17*
10	Newbury Forest Res	22	8	0	14	58	60	-2	16*
11	Old Barkabbeyans Res	22	5	1	16	51	81	-30	14*
12	Springfield Res	22	1	0	21	20	111	-91	3

GLOUCESTERSHIRE COUNTY LEAGUE

		P	W	D	L	F	A	GD	Pts
1	Thornbury Town	32	26	4	2	95	22	73	82
2	Lebeq United	32	21	4	7	94	39	55	67
3	Frampton United	32	20	5	7	76	41	35	65
4	Stonehouse Town	32	19	6	7	86	56	30	63
5	Hardwicke	32	18	4	10	72	54	18	58
6	AEK Boco	32	16	8	8	73	39	34	56
7	Broadwell Amateurs	32	16	8	8	49	29	20	56
8	Wick	32	17	2	13	82	49	33	53
9	Ruardean Hill Rangers	32	16	5	11	55	41	14	53
10	Henbury	32	14	7	11	64	51	13	45*
11	Little Stoke	32	11	8	13	55	56	-1	41
12	Rockleaze Rangers	32	11	2	19	57	80	-23	35
13	Gala Wilton	32	5	7	20	43	88	-45	22
14	Kingswood	32	5	6	21	37	81	-44	21
15	Patchway Town	32	5	4	23	39	106	-67	16*
16	Southmead CS Athletic	32	6	1	25	24	114	-90	16*
17	Hanham Athletic	32	3	5	24	27	82	-55	14

BRISTOL SUBURBAN LEAGUE

Premier Division One		P	W	D	L	F	A	GD	Pts
1	St Aldhelms	22	17	2	3	69	26	43	53
2	Ashton United	22	16	1	5	45	23	22	49
3	Filton Athletic	22	12	3	7	44	32	12	39
4	Easton Cowboys	22	12	3	7	40	35	5	39
5	Lawrence Weston	22	11	3	8	42	41	1	36
6	Rockleaze Rangers Res	22	9	6	7	45	31	14	33
7	Old Georgians	22	8	5	9	34	44	-10	29
8	Bristol Bilbao	22	5	7	10	36	41	-5	22
9	AFC Mangotsfield	22	6	3	13	42	56	-14	21
10	Avonmouth	22	5	5	12	36	56	-20	20
11	Mangotsfield Sports	22	4	4	14	28	50	-22	16
12	Fishponds Old Boys	22	2	8	12	22	48	-26	14

Sartan United withdrew - record expunged

THORNBURY TOWN GLOUCESTERSHIRE COUNTY LEAGUE CHAMPIONS

Premier Two	P	W	D	L	F	A	GD	Pts
1 Bromley Heath United	22	18	2	2	75	24	51	56
2 Old Cothamians	22	17	2	3	79	25	54	53
3 Stoke Gifford United	22	15	2	5	72	31	41	47
4 Almondsbury Res	22	11	4	7	55	44	11	37
5 Parson Street Old Boys	22	11	3	8	71	57	14	36
6 Cadbury Heath Res	22	10	2	10	56	57	-1	32
7 Fry's Club OB	22	9	4	9	52	58	-6	31
8 AFC Hartcliffe	22	8	2	12	55	57	-2	25
9 Glenside 5 Old Boys	22	7	4	11	35	54	-19	25
10 Ridings High	22	5	2	15	42	77	-35	17
11 Port of Bristol	22	4	3	15	33	59	-26	15
12 AFC Brislington Res	22	1	2	19	24	106	-82	5

Division One	P	W	D	L	F	A	GD	Pts
1 North Bristol United	22	17	1	4	82	40	42	52
2 Oldbury FC	22	15	3	4	79	30	49	48
3 Bristol Spartak	22	14	3	5	72	36	36	45
4 Wessex Wanderers	22	13	3	6	72	31	41	42
5 Rockleaze Rangers A	22	11	4	7	52	42	10	37
6 St Aldhelms AFC	22	10	3	9	64	60	4	33
7 Stockwood Wanderers Res	22	9	3	10	37	45	-8	30
8 Bristol Telephone Res	22	9	2	11	54	71	-17	29
9 AFC Mangotsfield Res	22	5	6	11	43	51	-8	21
10 Ashton United Res	22	5	4	13	40	70	-30	19
11 Easton Cowboys Res	22	3	4	15	33	69	-36	12
12 Avonmouth Res	22	2	2	18	29	112	-83	8

Division Two	P	W	D	L	F	A	GD	Pts
1 Stoke Rangers	18	15	1	2	61	30	31	46
2 Keynsham Town A	18	14	1	3	51	23	28	43
3 North Bristol Trust	18	11	2	5	42	23	19	35
4 Wanderers	18	9	4	5	45	40	5	31
5 Corinthian Sports	18	8	4	6	35	36	-1	28
6 Bromley Heath United Res	18	6	2	10	43	55	-12	20
7 Long Ashton Res	18	5	3	10	37	43	-6	18
8 Old Cothamians Res	18	4	6	8	33	43	-10	18
9 Bikkle Sports	18	4	1	13	43	53	-10	13
10 Fishponds Old Boys Res	18	1	2	15	18	62	-44	5

DivisioN Three	P	W	D	L	F	A	GD	Pts
1 Bedminster Cricketers	18	14	0	4	62	32	30	42
2 Park Knowle	18	12	2	4	58	29	29	38
3 Stoke Gifford United Res	18	10	3	5	39	32	7	33
4 Cosmos	18	10	2	6	61	34	27	32
5 Little Stoke Res	18	9	5	4	46	21	25	32
6 Rockleaze Rangers Res	18	7	2	9	32	46	-14	23
7 Filton Athletic Res	18	5	4	9	39	53	-14	19
8 Imperial Res	18	4	4	10	29	36	-7	16
9 Glenside 5 Old Boys Res	18	5	1	12	31	66	-35	16
10 Old Georgians Res	18	2	1	15	21	69	-48	7

Division Four	P	W	D	L	F	A	GD	Pts
1 Port of Bristol Res	20	15	2	3	64	27	37	47
2 Lockleaze Community	20	11	5	4	76	43	33	38
3 Broad Plain Res	20	10	5	5	48	33	15	35
4 North Bristol Trust Res	20	10	2	8	55	44	11	32
5 Oldbury FC Res	20	9	4	7	55	52	3	31
6 AFC Hartcliffe Res	20	8	5	7	46	56	-10	29
7 RR Athletic	20	7	4	9	68	54	14	25
8 Brandon Sports	20	7	4	9	47	59	-12	25
9 TC Sports	20	7	1	12	52	62	-10	22
10 EAston Cowboys A	20	6	2	12	57	76	-19	20
11 St Aldhelms A	20	2	2	16	29	91	-62	8

FINAL TABLES

Division Five

		P	W	D	L	F	A	GD	Pts
1	Lawrence Weston Res	20	14	3	3	86	35	51	45
2	Cadbury Heath A	20	13	4	3	71	41	30	43
3	Cosmos Res	20	12	2	6	60	44	16	38
4	Parson Street Old Boys Res	20	9	3	8	61	61	0	30
5	Wessex Wanderers Res	20	8	3	9	45	53	-8	27
6	Corinthian Sports Res	20	7	5	8	43	56	-13	26
7	North Bristol Trust A	20	7	3	10	54	60	-6	24
8	Kellaway Rangers	20	6	4	10	44	46	-2	22
9	Socius United	20	6	4	10	61	67	-6	22
10	Bristol Phoenix	20	7	1	12	47	68	-21	22
11	Avonmouth A	20	4	2	14	31	72	-41	14

BRISTOL PREMIER COMBINATION

Premier Division

		P	W	D	L	F	A	GD	Pts
1	Olveston United	26	19	4	3	79	22	57	61
2	Cribbs Reserves	26	17	4	5	101	53	48	55
3	Hallen Reserves	26	17	2	7	70	49	21	53
4	Shaftesbury Crusade	26	11	6	9	50	38	12	39
5	Longwell Green Res	26	10	5	11	53	57	-4	35
6	Sea Mills Park	26	11	2	13	43	62	-19	35
7	Talbot Knowle Utd	26	11	1	14	54	66	-12	34
8	AEK Boco Reserves	26	8	8	10	45	51	-6	32
9	Totterdown United	26	9	5	12	40	54	-14	32
10	Chipping Sodbury Town Res	26	9	4	13	50	61	-11	31
11	Lebeq (Saturday) FC	26	8	6	12	45	62	-17	30
12	Highridge United	26	9	2	15	43	58	-15	29
13	Old Sodbury	26	8	3	15	48	72	-24	27
14	Winterbourne United	26	8	2	16	48	64	-16	26

Division One

		P	W	D	L	F	A	GD	Pts
1	Seymour United	22	17	4	1	54	24	30	55
2	Stapleton	22	15	7	0	64	24	40	52
3	Hambrook	22	12	5	5	48	30	18	41
4	Bitton Reserves	22	13	5	4	62	47	15	41*
5	De Veys	22	12	4	6	61	39	22	40
6	Real Thornbury	22	9	8	5	62	42	20	35
7	Bristol Manor Farm Res	22	6	5	11	32	46	-14	23
8	Oldland Abbotonians Res	22	5	4	13	39	64	-25	19
9	D R G (Frenchay)	22	6	1	15	35	67	-32	19
10	Greyfriars Athletic	22	5	3	14	38	60	-22	18
11	Roman Glass/St George Res	22	4	3	15	30	60	-30	15
12	Shirehampton Res	22	2	3	17	24	46	-22	7*

BRISTOL & DISTRICT LEAGUE

Senior Division

		P	W	D	L	F	A	GD	Pts
1	Iron Acton	24	17	5	2	92	36	56	56
2	Pucklechurch Sports	24	16	5	3	87	35	52	53
3	Hillfields Old Boys	24	17	2	5	69	44	25	53
4	St Nicholas Old Boys	24	15	1	8	88	38	50	46
5	Nicholas Wanderers	24	13	5	6	100	39	61	44
6	Bradley Stoke Town	24	13	3	8	86	52	34	42
7	Wick Res	23	11	3	9	43	53	-10	36
8	Mendip Broadwalk Res	24	9	4	11	53	64	-11	31
9	Cribbs 'A'	24	8	2	14	42	65	-23	26
10	Bristol Barcelona	24	6	4	14	34	71	-37	22
11	Longwell Green Sports 'A'	23	4	3	16	33	85	-52	15
12	Lebeq (Saturday) FC.Res	24	3	2	19	39	111	-72	11
13	Patchway Town Res	24	3	1	20	38	111	-73	10

Division One

		P	W	D	L	F	A	GD	Pts
1	AEK Boco 'A'	26	23	1	2	109	26	83	70
2	Made for Ever	26	22	1	3	89	16	73	67
3	Stapleton Res	26	18	1	7	65	41	24	55
4	AFC Mangotsfield	26	17	3	6	59	39	20	54
5	Yate Athletic	26	12	3	11	87	57	30	39
6	Seymour United Res	26	12	2	12	72	60	12	38
7	Rangeworthy	26	11	3	12	61	72	-11	36
8	Greyfriars Athletic Res	26	9	8	9	42	52	-10	35
9	Henbury Res	26	10	1	15	74	63	11	31
10	Totterdown United Res	26	9	2	15	55	72	-17	29
11	Frys Club 'A'	26	8	2	16	57	73	-16	26
12	Soundwell Victoria	26	7	4	15	65	88	-23	25
13	Hanham Athletic Res	26	6	3	17	36	93	-57	21
14	Zimba FC	26	1	0	25	21	140	-119	3

Division Two

		P	W	D	L	F	A	GD	Pts
1	Bendix	24	21	3	0	78	25	53	66
2	Nicholas Wanderers Res	24	17	2	5	84	32	52	53
3	Bradley Stoke Town Res	23	14	3	6	63	35	28	45
4	Tormarton	24	12	3	9	69	48	21	39
5	Lawrence Rovers	24	11	3	10	59	56	3	36
6	Chipping Sodbury Town 'A'	24	10	3	11	51	56	-5	33
7	Olveston United Res	24	9	6	9	46	57	-11	33
8	Iron Acton Res	24	8	4	12	36	39	-3	28
9	Highridge United Res	24	8	2	14	43	54	-11	23*
10	Frampton Athletic	23	6	5	12	38	51	-13	23
11	Hartcliffe	24	7	1	16	34	68	-34	22
12	Sea Mills Park Res	24	5	5	14	30	62	-32	20
13	Old Sodbury Res	24	5	4	15	40	88	-48	19

Division Three

		P	W	D	L	F	A	GD	Pts
1	University of Bristol	22	16	1	5	114	37	77	49
2	Hambrook Res	22	15	3	4	66	29	37	48
3	Rangeworthy Res	22	15	2	5	60	30	30	47
4	Westerleigh Sports	22	12	2	8	57	54	3	38
5	Brimsham Green	22	11	2	9	62	47	15	35
6	Real Thornbury Res	22	11	2	9	36	32	4	35
7	De Veys Res	22	8	4	10	55	55	0	28
8	Talbot Knowle United	22	7	1	14	45	94	-49	22
9	Wick 'A'	22	6	3	13	42	75	-33	21
10	Mendip Broadwalk 'A'	22	5	5	12	42	61	-19	20
11	Greyfriars Athletic 'A'	22	5	5	12	45	88	-43	20
12	Roman Glass St George 'A'	22	6	0	16	33	55	-22	18

Division Four

		P	W	D	L	F	A	GD	Pts
1	Hillfields OB Res	20	16	1	3	70	19	51	49
2	Nicholas Wanderers 'A'	20	16	0	4	77	27	50	48
3	Bristol Eagles	20	11	3	6	66	41	25	36
4	Cribbs 'B'	20	12	0	8	56	45	11	36
5	Pucklechurch Sports Res	20	9	2	9	46	34	12	29
6	Crosscourt United	20	9	1	10	50	40	10	28
7	Yate Athletic Res	20	8	2	10	48	47	1	26
8	DRG Frenchay	20	7	3	10	39	80	-41	24
9	Frys Club 'B'	20	6	1	13	31	64	-33	19
10	Colerne FC	20	5	3	12	30	61	-31	18
11	Cutters Friday	20	2	2	16	20	75	-55	8

Division Five

	P	W	D	L	F	A	GD	Pts
1 Stokeside FC	24	22	2	0	156	41	115	68
2 Shaftesbury Crusade Res	24	21	1	2	96	23	73	64
3 Iron Acton A	24	14	1	9	73	53	20	43
4 AFC Mangotsfield Res	24	12	5	7	50	48	2	41
5 Bradley Stoke Town 'A'	24	12	2	10	56	48	8	38
6 The Phoenix FC	24	12	0	12	53	40	13	36
7 Hanham Abbotonians	23	11	3	9	62	54	8	36
8 Seymour United 'A'	23	10	1	12	64	60	4	31
9 Highridge Colts	24	7	5	12	29	48	-19	26
10 Greyfriars Athletic 'B'	24	6	2	16	41	102	-61	20
11 Bristol Eagles Res	24	6	0	18	52	103	-51	18
12 AFC Grace	24	5	1	18	29	72	-43	16
13 westerleigh Res	22	4	1	17	23	92	-69	13

GLOUCESTERSHIRE SENIOR LEAGUE

Division One

	P	W	D	L	F	A	GD	Pts
1 Charlton Rovers	28	20	5	3	94	22	72	65
2 FC Barometrics	28	20	2	6	97	45	52	62
3 Chalford	28	16	7	5	67	39	28	55
4 Cam Bulldogs	28	17	3	8	70	54	16	54
5 Sharpness	28	16	5	7	59	36	23	53
6 Longlevens Reserves	28	16	3	9	53	43	10	51
7 Brockworth Albion	28	12	3	13	57	51	6	39
8 Berkeley Town	28	10	7	11	62	50	12	37
9 Taverners	28	9	3	16	47	64	-17	30
10 Harrow Hill	28	7	8	13	45	58	-13	29
11 Tuffley Rovers Reserves	28	8	5	15	42	67	-25	29
12 Quedgeley Wanderers	28	7	5	16	53	79	-26	26
13 Stroud Harriers	28	5	7	16	43	75	-32	22
14 Leonard Stanley	28	5	7	16	33	66	-33	22
15 Bibury	28	4	6	18	34	107	-73	15*

Division Two

	P	W	D	L	F	A	GD	Pts
1 Welland	30	22	4	4	79	35	44	70
2 Upton St Leonards	30	15	5	10	86	60	26	50
3 Whaddon United	30	15	5	10	72	47	25	50
4 Whitecroft	30	15	5	10	68	49	19	50
5 English Bicknor	30	15	5	10	59	52	7	50
6 Woolaston	30	14	4	12	57	48	9	46
7 Lydney Town Reserves	30	14	4	12	68	64	4	46
8 Smiths Athletic	30	12	8	10	60	52	8	44
9 Falcons	30	12	5	13	61	63	-2	41
10 FC Lakeside	30	12	4	14	67	68	-1	40
11 Bredon	30	11	6	13	47	50	-3	39
12 Lydbrook Athletic	30	11	5	14	41	59	-18	38
13 Abbeymead Rovers	30	10	7	13	51	72	-21	37
14 Winchcombe Town	30	9	7	14	50	57	-7	34
15 Broadwell Amateurs Res	30	9	7	14	44	72	-28	34
16 Dursley Town	30	1	5	24	36	98	-62	5*

Division One

	P	W	D	L	F	A	GD	Pts
1 Cheltenham Civil Service	20	18	0	2	76	19	57	54
2 Andoversford	20	11	6	3	60	30	30	39
3 Upton Town	20	12	3	5	47	30	17	39
4 Bishops Cleeve FC Thirds	20	11	4	5	56	33	23	37
5 Tewkesbury Town	20	10	2	8	56	33	23	32
6 Newton	20	7	4	9	27	41	-14	25
7 Dowty Dynamos	20	7	2	11	36	52	-16	23
8 Shurdington Rovers	20	6	3	11	38	47	-9	21
9 Kings	20	4	6	10	31	56	-25	18
10 Whaddon United Res	20	4	2	14	21	47	-26	14
11 RSG	20	3	2	15	28	88	-60	8*

Division Two

	P	W	D	L	F	A	GD	Pts
1 Cheltenham Civil Service Res	22	19	1	2	78	13	65	58
2 The Beeches	22	19	1	2	92	34	58	58
3 FC Barometrics Res	22	13	3	6	77	33	44	42
4 Hanley Swan	22	13	1	8	79	60	19	40
5 Fintan	22	13	0	9	50	45	5	39
6 Southside Star FC	22	11	1	10	68	58	10	34
7 Gala Wilton Res	22	9	5	8	54	46	8	32
8 Bredon Res	22	7	5	10	48	51	-3	26
9 Prestbury Rovers	22	5	3	14	36	67	-31	17*
10 Pittville United	22	5	0	17	34	89	-55	12*
11 Andoversford Res	22	3	2	17	29	94	-65	11
12 Tewkesbury Town Res	22	2	4	16	28	83	-55	10

Division Three

	P	W	D	L	F	A	GD	Pts
1 St Pauls United	24	20	3	1	106	28	78	63
2 AFC Renegades	24	18	3	3	104	31	73	57
3 Charlton Rovers Res	24	13	4	7	67	52	15	43
4 Brockworth Albion Res	24	12	7	5	67	60	7	43
5 FC Barometrics Thirds	24	13	3	8	60	44	16	42
6 Leckhampton Rovers	24	10	3	11	60	69	-9	32*
7 Dowty Dynamos Res	24	9	4	11	52	70	-18	31
8 Falcons Res	24	9	2	13	45	63	-18	29
9 Cheltenham Civil Service 3rds	24	8	4	12	54	65	-11	28
10 Windyridge Rovers	24	9	1	14	59	72	-13	25*
11 Kings Res	24	7	3	14	44	66	-22	24
12 Cheltenham United	24	3	3	18	37	90	-53	12
13 FC Lakeside Res	24	2	2	18	39	84	-45	11*

Division Four

	P	W	D	L	F	A	GD	Pts
1 Prestbury Rovers Res	24	20	0	4	93	18	75	60
2 Malvern Vale FC Academy	24	19	1	4	107	33	74	58
3 Welland Res	24	15	2	7	88	57	31	47
4 Malvern Vale FC First	24	14	2	8	76	50	26	44
5 Woodmancote United	24	13	0	11	65	58	7	39
6 Smiths Athletic Res	24	11	2	11	67	56	11	35
7 Gala Wilton Thirds	24	11	2	11	57	72	-15	35
8 Winchcombe Town Res	24	10	1	13	60	68	-8	30*
9 Bishops Cleeve Dev Res	24	10	0	14	53	72	-19	30
10 Fintan Res	24	10	0	14	52	63	-11	27*
11 Cheltenham Saracens 3rds	24	7	0	17	38	91	-53	20*
12 Andoversford Thirds	24	4	4	16	39	82	-43	16
13 Charlton Rovers Thirds	24	4	2	18	32	107	-75	13*

FINAL TABLES

NORTH GLOUCESTERSHIRE LEGAGUE

Premier Division

		P	W	D	L	F	A	GD	Pts
1	Ellwood	24	18	3	3	52	32	20	57
2	Huntley	24	17	1	6	93	42	51	52
3	Redbrook Rovers	24	15	4	5	85	37	48	49
4	Staunton & Corse	24	15	3	6	77	34	43	48
5	Coleford Town	24	15	1	8	60	37	23	46
6	Howle Hill	24	13	3	8	79	44	35	42
7	Ruardean Hill Rangers Res	24	12	4	8	56	40	16	40
8	Mushet & Coalway Utd	24	10	4	10	52	58	-6	34
9	Bream Amts	24	7	3	14	48	60	-12	24
10	Westbury Utd	24	5	5	14	44	65	-21	20
11	Harrow Hill Res	24	4	5	15	33	71	-38	17
12	Lydney Town A	24	4	4	16	28	67	-39	16
13	Lydbrook Athletic Res	24	1	0	23	19	139	-120	3

Division One

		P	W	D	L	F	A	GD	Pts
1	Redmarley	22	18	2	2	71	24	47	56
2	Worrall Hill	22	17	3	2	76	34	42	54
3	Viney St Swithins	22	14	1	7	78	45	33	43
4	Whitecroft Res	22	12	2	8	39	27	12	38
5	Milkwall	22	12	1	9	45	46	-1	37
6	Mitcheldean	22	11	0	11	53	57	-4	33
7	Woolaston Res	22	9	4	9	49	40	9	31
8	Blakeney	22	9	2	11	43	54	-11	29
9	Tidenham	22	8	3	11	37	64	-27	27
10	Westbury Utd Res	22	4	3	15	33	76	-43	15
11	Coleford Town Res	22	4	1	17	29	46	-17	13
12	English Bicknor Res	22	2	2	18	22	62	-40	8

Division Two

		P	W	D	L	F	A	GD	Pts
1	Ross Juniors	24	15	5	4	97	39	58	50
2	Broadwell A	24	15	5	4	79	28	51	50
3	Whitecroft A	24	14	6	4	63	35	28	48
4	Rank Outsiders	24	13	5	6	56	41	15	44
5	Lydbrook Athletic A	24	14	2	8	59	62	-3	44
6	Mushet & Coalway Utd Res	24	11	5	8	55	70	-15	38
7	Longhope	24	11	4	9	53	53	0	37
8	Redbrook Rovers Res	24	9	3	12	58	68	-10	30
9	Bream Amts Res	24	8	5	11	38	46	-8	29
10	Ruardean Hill Rangers A	24	7	5	12	48	46	2	26
11	Puma	24	7	4	13	59	88	-29	25
12	Milkwall Res	24	3	4	17	39	66	-27	13
13	Ruardean Utd	24	2	1	21	34	96	-62	7

Division Three

		P	W	D	L	F	A	GD	Pts
1	Staunton & Corse Res	26	24	1	1	123	12	111	73
2	Yorkley	26	20	2	4	96	27	69	62
3	Viney St Swithins Res	26	16	4	6	63	37	26	52
4	Ellwood Res	26	16	1	9	70	53	17	49
5	Lydney Town B	26	13	5	8	73	55	18	44
6	Blakeney Res	26	14	1	11	60	58	2	43
7	Newent Town A	26	13	1	12	83	77	6	40
8	Sling	26	12	2	12	57	43	14	38
9	Mitcheldean Res	26	12	1	13	58	65	-7	37
10	Tidenham Res	26	8	3	15	50	56	-6	27
11	Harrow Hill B	26	8	2	16	61	80	-19	26
12	Littledean	26	6	3	17	43	116	-73	21
13	St Briavels	26	5	2	19	29	79	-50	17
14	Rank Outsiders Res	26	1	0	25	19	127	-108	3
15	Weston Under Penyard withdrew - record expunged								

STROUD & DISTRICT LEAGUE

Division One

		P	W	D	L	F	A	GD	Pts
1	Barnwood United	24	16	4	4	62	24	38	52
2	Frampton United Res	24	16	4	4	66	30	36	52
3	Tredworth Tigers	24	13	5	6	59	37	22	44
4	Stonehouse Town Res	24	12	6	6	45	29	16	42
5	Kings Stanley	24	10	6	8	63	43	20	36
6	Hardwicke Res	24	10	6	8	47	41	6	36
7	Charfield	24	12	3	9	45	42	3	36*
8	Old Richians	24	9	4	11	46	56	-10	31
9	Tetbury Town	24	7	8	9	40	43	-3	29
10	Randwick	24	6	6	12	44	63	-19	24
11	Kingswood Res	24	7	4	13	30	60	-30	19*
12	Wotton Rovers	24	5	2	17	41	71	-30	17
13	Stroud United	24	3	2	19	24	73	-49	11

Division Two

		P	W	D	L	F	A	GD	Pts
1	Rodborough Old Boys	24	19	2	3	78	41	37	59
2	Longlevens 3rds	24	18	3	3	93	38	55	57
3	Minchinhampton	24	17	3	4	82	41	41	54
4	Cam Bulldogs Res	24	13	3	8	64	46	18	42
5	Eastcombe	24	13	1	10	72	68	4	40
6	Quedgeley Wanderers Res	24	12	4	8	70	38	32	37*
7	Sharpness Res	24	9	7	8	51	42	9	34
8	Didmarton	24	10	1	13	48	52	-4	31
9	Trident	24	7	5	12	51	61	-10	26
10	Tibberton United	24	8	3	13	54	60	-6	24*
11	Bush	24	6	4	14	47	66	-19	16*
12	Longford	24	4	1	19	29	83	-54	13
13	Horsley United	24	1	1	22	22	125	-103	4

Division Three

		P	W	D	L	F	A	GD	Pts
1	Ramblers	22	14	5	3	78	30	48	47
2	Taverners Res	22	15	2	5	63	35	28	47
3	Chalford Res	22	14	3	5	67	37	30	45
4	Upton St Leonards Res	22	13	3	6	65	37	28	42
5	Tuffley Rovers 3rds	22	11	3	8	67	42	25	36
6	Thornbury Town Res	22	10	6	6	48	36	12	36
7	Tetbury Town Res	22	9	2	11	48	59	-11	29
8	Uley	22	7	1	14	54	83	-29	22
9	Whitminster	22	5	6	11	38	47	-9	21
10	Quedgeley Wanderers 3rds	22	6	3	13	50	65	-15	21
11	McCadam	22	5	4	13	42	75	-33	13*
12	Cotswold Rangers	22	3	2	17	27	101	-74	11

Division Four

		P	W	D	L	F	A	GD	Pts
1	Tredworth Tigers Res	24	21	3	0	101	27	74	66
2	Kingsway Rovers	24	18	2	4	115	25	90	56
3	Wickwar Wanderers	24	14	5	5	78	47	31	44*
4	Barnwood United Res	24	13	5	6	66	52	14	44
5	Old Richians Res	24	12	5	7	43	35	8	41
6	Avonvale United	24	10	4	10	47	51	-4	31*
7	Frampton United 3rds	24	9	2	13	49	68	-19	29
8	Alkerton Rangers	24	9	1	14	50	69	-19	28
9	Hardwicke 3rds	24	8	3	13	44	59	-15	27
10	Saintbridge	24	7	4	13	50	74	-24	25
11	Tuffley Rovers 4ths	24	7	4	13	32	63	-31	25
12	Abbeymead Rovers Res	24	2	2	20	26	91	-65	8
13	Dursley Town Res	24	4	4	16	35	75	-40	7*

Division Five

		P	W	D	L	F	A	GD	Pts
1	Charfield Res	24	17	1	6	88	42	46	52
2	Stonehouse Town 3rds	24	16	2	6	97	44	53	50
3	Stroud Harriers Res	24	16	3	5	81	53	28	45*
4	Chalford 3rds	24	13	5	6	70	42	28	41*
5	Longlevens 4ths	24	13	2	9	66	50	16	41
6	Rodborough Old Boys Res	24	11	3	10	61	47	14	36
7	Wotton Rovers Res	24	10	5	9	56	54	2	35
8	Kings Stanley Res	24	11	6	7	68	65	3	33*
9	Painswick	24	10	3	11	61	59	2	27*
10	Berkeley Town Res	24	6	5	13	41	60	-19	23
11	Randwick Res	24	5	5	14	34	66	-32	20
12	Leonard Stanley Res	24	5	1	18	27	70	-43	13*
13	Longford Res	24	1	3	20	13	117	-104	0*

Division Six

		P	W	D	L	F	A	GD	Pts
1	North Nibley	22	19	1	2	121	25	96	58
2	Bridgeway	22	16	3	3	96	25	71	51
3	Kingsway Rovers Res	22	16	1	5	121	37	84	49
4	Minchinhampton Res	22	15	1	6	62	48	14	46
5	Gloster Rovers	22	10	4	8	56	47	9	34
6	Uley Res	22	9	3	10	55	67	-12	30
7	Cam Bulldogs 3rds	22	9	2	11	51	52	-1	29
8	Sharpness 3rds	22	8	2	12	70	77	-7	26
9	Brockworth Albion 3rds	22	7	3	12	55	78	-23	24
10	Eastcombe Res	22	7	2	13	55	62	-7	20*
11	Horsley United Res	22	4	1	17	26	110	-84	13
12	Stroud United Res	22	0	1	21	14	154	-140	-5*

Division Seven

		P	W	D	L	F	A	GD	Pts
1	Cotswold Rangers Res	22	19	0	3	94	27	67	57
2	Tuffley Rovers 5ths	22	18	0	4	94	39	55	54
3	Cashes Green	22	17	1	4	91	30	61	52
4	Abbeymead Rovers 3rds	22	14	1	7	89	58	31	43
5	Ramblers Res	22	14	0	8	107	42	65	39*
6	Tetbury Town 3rds	22	12	1	9	59	54	5	37
7	Cam Everside Wanderers	22	8	1	13	52	75	-23	25
8	Stonehouse Town 4ths	22	7	1	14	58	75	-17	19*
9	Randwick 3rds	22	5	2	15	44	88	-44	17
10	Rodborough Old Boys 3rds	22	5	2	15	47	99	-52	17
11	Woodchester	22	4	1	17	52	119	-67	13
12	Uley 3rds	22	4	0	18	34	117	-83	12

HAMPSHIRE PREMIER LEAGUE

SENIOR DIVISION

		P	W	D	L	F	A	GD	Pts
1	Paulsgrove	30	26	1	3	101	29	72	79
2	Bush Hill	30	19	9	2	103	33	70	66
3	Infinity	30	21	3	6	101	35	66	66
4	Liphook United	30	16	4	10	85	59	26	52
5	QK Southampton	30	15	7	8	60	45	15	52
6	Liss Athletic	30	16	2	12	74	60	14	50
7	Stockbridge	30	14	4	12	65	67	-2	46
8	Clanfield	30	13	5	12	71	64	7	44
9	Locks Heath	30	13	5	12	54	54	0	44
10	Hayling United	30	12	7	11	68	72	-4	43
11	Sway	30	14	1	15	69	81	-12	43
12	Overton United	30	13	2	15	47	58	-11	41
13	Fleetlands	30	8	2	20	48	96	-48	23*
14	Colden Common	30	6	1	23	43	94	-51	19
15	Winchester Castle	30	4	2	24	35	85	-50	14
16	Hedge End Rangers	30	1	3	26	30	122	-92	6

DIVISION ONE

		P	W	D	L	F	A	GD	Pts
1	Netley Central Sports	21	15	3	3	64	31	33	48
2	Four Marks	21	13	3	5	51	33	18	42
3	Lyndhurst	21	13	2	6	65	34	31	41
4	South Wonston Swifts	21	10	3	8	50	26	24	33
5	Upham	21	9	1	11	48	43	5	28
6	Headley United	21	7	3	11	31	49	-18	24
7	AFC Petersfield	21	6	2	13	32	52	-20	20
8	Michelmersh & Timsbury	21	1	3	17	28	101	-73	6

RESERVE DIVISION

		P	W	D	L	F	A	GD	Pts
1	Paulsgrove Res	18	15	1	2	51	20	31	46
2	Overton United Res	18	13	2	3	63	28	35	41
3	Liphook United Res	18	12	2	4	51	27	24	38
4	Bush Hill Res	18	11	3	4	44	21	23	36
5	Clanfield Res	18	9	2	7	36	31	5	29
6	Fleetlands Res	18	5	2	11	34	51	-17	17
7	Headley United Res	18	4	4	10	27	49	-22	16
8	Winchester Castle Res	18	4	2	12	29	55	-26	14
9	Hayling United Res	18	3	2	13	21	62	-41	11
10	QK Southampton Res	18	2	4	12	21	33	-12	10

ALDERSHOT & DISTRICT LEAGUE

Senior Division

		P	W	D	L	F	A	GD	Pts
1	Yateley United A	16	12	2	2	51	15	36	38
2	Frimley Select	16	10	5	1	45	22	23	35
3	Hartley Wintney A	16	10	0	6	45	42	3	30
4	Rushmoor Community	16	9	1	6	36	20	16	28
5	Normandy Spartans	16	9	1	6	34	33	1	28
6	Fleet Spurs A	16	5	2	9	24	32	-8	17
7	Alton	16	4	3	9	38	44	-6	15
8	Wey Valley	16	3	2	11	33	51	-18	11
9	Cove Development	16	2	0	14	14	61	-47	6

Division One

		P	W	D	L	F	A	GD	Pts
1	Traco Athletic	18	16	1	1	82	23	59	49
2	Sandhurst Sports	18	12	1	5	64	30	34	37
3	AFC Laffans	18	12	1	5	48	44	4	37
4	Mytchett Athletic	18	11	1	6	66	43	23	34
5	Four Marks Reserves	18	10	0	8	49	38	11	30
6	Yateley United B	18	7	2	9	52	55	-3	23
7	Letef Select	18	7	1	10	42	63	-21	22
8	Wey Valley Reserves	18	6	1	11	43	59	-16	19
9	Hindhead Athletic	18	3	2	13	19	39	-20	11
10	Fleet Spurs Veterans	18	1	0	17	14	85	-71	3

FINAL TABLES

BASINGSTOKE & DISTRICT LEAGUE

Division One	P	W	D	L	F	A	GD	Pts
1 Twentyten	14	12	1	1	54	17	37	37
2 Hook	14	11	1	2	59	17	42	34
3 AFC Aldermaston Res	14	9	0	5	40	41	-1	27
4 Overton Utd A	14	7	2	5	28	28	0	23
5 Herriard Sports	14	7	0	7	27	31	-4	21
6 Tadley Calleva A	14	4	2	8	27	36	-9	14
7 Bounty Utd	14	2	0	12	17	39	-22	6
8 Winklebury Wizards	14	1	0	13	12	55	-43	3

Division Two	P	W	D	L	F	A	GD	Pts
1 AFC Berg	18	16	2	0	106	21	85	50
2 Sherborne Saints	18	14	0	4	78	40	38	42
3 Twentyten Res	18	12	0	6	47	36	11	36
4 Basingstoke Athletic	18	10	2	6	42	46	-4	32
5 Somesay	18	8	3	7	50	31	19	27
6 Long Dog Soldiers	18	7	2	9	43	58	-15	23
7 Basingstoke Town Colts	18	4	3	11	34	59	-25	15
8 Chineham	18	5	0	13	33	75	-42	15
9 AFC Aldermaston A	18	3	3	12	47	64	-17	12
10 Origin Headley	18	3	1	14	31	81	-50	10

ISLE OF WIGHT

Division One	P	W	D	L	F	A	GD	Pts
1 Whitecroft & Barton	22	18	3	1	74	13	61	57
2 Brading Town	22	14	5	3	55	22	33	47
3 E.C.S.	22	13	3	6	54	35	19	42
4 West Wight	22	11	7	4	37	24	13	37*
5 Shanklin	22	10	6	6	54	37	17	36
6 Northwood St Johns	22	10	4	8	55	37	18	34
7 Binstead & COB	22	8	5	9	51	38	13	29
8 Ventnor	22	8	2	12	44	64	-20	26
9 Sandown	22	6	5	11	33	40	-7	23
10 Cowes Sports	22	6	2	14	33	63	-30	23*
11 Ryde Saints	22	4	2	16	24	83	-59	14
12 Oakfield	22	0	4	18	17	75	-58	4

Division Two	P	W	D	L	F	A	GD	Pts
1 Pan Sports	26	25	0	1	80	24	56	75
2 Osborne Coburg	26	23	2	1	120	24	96	71
3 Bembridge	26	17	3	6	89	32	57	54
4 Niton Community	26	16	3	7	90	50	40	48*
5 Carisbrooke Utd	26	12	6	8	81	50	31	42
6 Seaview	26	10	6	10	62	60	2	36
7 AFC Wootton	26	9	7	10	69	54	15	34
8 East Cowes Vics A	26	9	6	11	64	59	5	33
9 Wroxall	26	7	5	14	59	76	-17	26
10 Newchurch	26	7	5	14	57	87	-30	26
11 Brighstone	26	6	4	16	63	73	-10	25*
12 Newport IOW A	26	4	9	13	50	106	-56	21
13 Royal Canaries	26	5	4	17	54	110	-56	19
14 Yarmouth & Calb	26	2	0	24	49	182	-133	6

SOUTHAMPTON FOOTBALL LEAGUE

Premier Division	P	W	D	L	F	A	GD	Pts
1 Athletico Romsey	16	11	0	5	43	23	20	33
2 Chamberlayne AFC	16	9	4	3	31	17	14	31
3 Bishops Waltham Dynamos	16	8	4	4	22	22	0	28
4 BTC (Southampton)	16	8	3	5	25	20	5	27
5 Comrades Sports	16	8	0	8	21	33	-12	24
6 AFC Gulf Western	16	6	3	7	25	23	2	21
7 Soton University	16	5	2	9	23	32	-9	17
8 Braishfield	16	3	7	6	16	25	-9	16
9 Nursling	16	2	1	13	13	24	-11	7

Senior One	P	W	D	L	F	A	GD	Pts
1 Alderbury	16	15	1	0	60	18	42	46
2 Compton	16	10	3	3	57	25	32	33
3 Priory Rovers	16	10	1	5	43	33	10	31
4 Montefiore Halls	16	8	3	5	31	31	0	27
5 Hedge End Town	16	5	1	10	48	45	3	16
6 Warsash Wasps	16	5	1	10	38	49	-11	16
7 Upham Res	16	4	2	10	25	44	-19	14
8 Durley	16	4	1	11	19	46	-27	13
9 Comrades Sports Res	16	4	1	11	24	54	-30	13

Junior One	P	W	D	L	F	A	GD	Pts
1 BTC Soton Res	16	12	1	3	75	19	56	37
2 Knightwood Utd	16	12	0	4	76	28	48	36
3 FC Independence	16	9	2	5	43	25	18	29
4 Hamble United	16	9	1	6	30	31	-1	28
5 Capital	16	7	0	9	30	44	-14	21
6 Redlynch & W Utd	16	6	2	8	37	30	7	20
7 Athletico Romsey Res	16	5	1	10	24	63	-39	16
8 West End Rovers	16	5	0	11	39	71	-32	15
9 Lyndhurst Res	16	2	3	11	20	63	-43	9

Junior Two	P	W	D	L	F	A	GD	Pts
1 Nursling Vets	16	15	0	1	66	21	45	45
2 Southbrook Utd	16	8	4	4	51	41	10	28
3 AFC Hiltingbury	16	9	0	7	54	39	15	27
4 Gosport FC Vets	16	8	3	5	41	31	10	27
5 Athletico Romsey A	16	6	3	7	37	39	-2	21
6 Whiteley Wanderers	16	7	0	9	33	50	-17	21
7 Forest Edge Rovers	16	5	1	10	36	58	-22	16
8 Hedge End Town Res	16	5	0	11	29	45	-16	15
9 Sporting Wessex	16	2	3	11	32	55	-23	9

Junior Three

	P	W	D	L	F	A	GD	Pts
1 Durley Res	18	10	6	2	46	25	21	36
2 Hythe Aztecs	18	11	2	5	51	35	16	35
3 AFC Station	18	9	4	5	31	35	-4	31
4 Braishfield Res	18	7	4	7	39	36	3	25
5 Bishops Waltham Dyn Res	18	5	3	10	34	44	-10	18
6 Redlynch & W Utd Res	18	4	5	9	37	36	1	17
7 Michelmersh & T A	18	3	4	11	46	73	-27	13

Junior Four

	P	W	D	L	F	A	GD	Pts
1 Hythe Aztecs Res	15	14	0	1	59	18	41	42
2 Botley Village	15	10	3	2	38	18	20	33
3 Inmar	15	6	1	8	55	42	13	19
4 Shield	15	6	0	9	34	45	-11	18
5 Compton Res	15	3	4	8	67	48	19	13
6 Hamble United Res	15	1	2	12	19	101	-82	5

HERTS SENIOR COUNTY LEAGUE

Premier Division

	P	W	D	L	F	A	GD	Pts
1 Bovingdon	28	25	1	2	116	26	90	76
2 Letchworth Garden City Eagles (HSCL)	28	18	4	6	57	27	30	58
3 Ware Sports FC	28	16	4	8	73	48	25	52
4 Belstone	28	14	7	7	55	41	14	49
5 Wormley Rovers	28	14	4	10	64	50	14	46
6 Sandridge Rovers	28	12	8	8	45	33	12	44
7 Broadfields	28	11	11	6	37	27	10	44
8 Cuffley (Saturday)	28	10	7	11	62	52	10	37
9 Standon & Puckeridge	28	10	7	11	46	61	-15	37
10 Bushey Sports Club	28	11	1	16	61	64	-3	34
11 Knebworth	28	8	5	15	45	61	-16	29
12 Chipperfield Corinthians	28	9	2	17	52	78	-26	29
13 FC Lemsford	28	7	4	17	45	81	-36	25
14 Evergreen FC (HSCL)	28	5	4	19	33	83	-50	19
15 Buntingford Town	28	3	5	20	21	80	-59	14

Division One

	P	W	D	L	F	A	GD	Pts
1 Bovingdon Res	26	20	3	3	78	29	49	63
2 Weston FC	26	16	6	4	88	40	48	54
3 Sun Sports Res	26	17	3	6	83	41	42	54
4 Hadley Res	25	15	6	4	53	28	25	51
5 Cheshunt FC A	26	14	5	7	53	29	24	47
6 Sarratt	26	13	3	10	62	42	20	42
7 Hinton	25	12	4	9	49	52	-3	40
8 Rayners Lane Res	26	9	2	15	48	62	-14	29
9 Oxhey Jets Res	26	7	6	13	44	54	-10	27
10 Hatfield Social	25	8	3	14	39	64	-25	27
11 Wodson Park Res	25	7	4	14	40	55	-15	25
12 Hampstead Heath Lions	26	5	5	16	38	83	-45	20
13 Lemsford	26	5	3	18	32	91	-59	18
14 Bengeo Trinity	26	3	5	18	37	74	-37	14

HUMBER PREMIER LEAGUE

Premier Division

	P	W	D	L	F	A	GD	Pts
1 Chalk Lane	26	19	1	6	61	20	41	58
2 Pocklington Town	26	15	5	6	73	27	46	50
3 Beverley Town	26	14	4	8	60	34	26	46
4 Sculcoates Amateurs	26	14	4	8	58	48	10	46
5 Reckitts AFC	26	11	7	8	45	41	4	40
6 AFC Walkington	26	12	4	10	59	56	3	40
7 Hedon Rangers	26	12	1	13	51	60	-9	37
8 Hessle Rangers	26	9	6	11	40	56	-16	33
9 Crown FC	26	10	3	13	37	54	-17	33
10 Westella & Willerby AFC	26	8	8	10	51	55	-4	32
11 South Cave United	26	7	9	10	60	64	-4	30
12 East Riding Rangers	26	6	7	13	43	71	-28	25
13 Hornsea Town	26	6	5	15	50	77	-27	23
14 North Ferriby Athletic	26	4	6	16	38	63	-25	18

Division One

	P	W	D	L	F	A	GD	Pts
1 LIV Supplies	24	20	3	1	88	38	50	63
2 Hull United AFC	24	19	2	3	76	30	46	59
3 North Ferriby United Res	24	15	1	8	90	57	33	46
4 Bridlington Town Res	24	15	1	8	65	37	28	46
5 Brandesburton AFC	24	13	4	7	67	53	14	43
6 Easington United	24	8	8	8	51	46	5	32
7 Blackburn Athletic	24	7	6	11	46	60	-14	27
8 Driffield Evening Institute	24	8	3	13	38	55	-17	27
9 Howden AFC	24	8	2	14	60	78	-18	26
10 Driffield Junior Football Club	24	6	2	16	38	57	-19	20
11 Hall Road Rangers Res	24	6	6	12	50	66	-16	18*
12 Barton Town FC Res	24	6	2	16	54	79	-25	17*
13 Hessle Sporting United	24	4	2	18	45	112	-67	14

KENT COUNTY LEAGUE

Premier Division

	P	W	D	L	F	A	GD	Pts
1 Kennington	28	25	0	3	88	26	62	75
2 Greenways	28	20	3	5	87	48	39	63
3 Bexley	28	16	5	7	51	37	14	53
4 Peckham Town	28	14	5	9	61	39	22	47
5 Tudor Sports	28	12	6	10	56	50	6	41*
6 Staplehurst Monarchs United	28	11	5	12	65	70	-5	38
7 Borden Village	28	12	4	12	67	65	2	37*
8 New Romney	28	10	7	11	45	52	-7	37
9 Stansfeld (Oxford & Bermondsey)	28	10	7	11	58	71	-13	37
10 Otford United	28	11	3	14	61	58	3	36
11 Fleetdown United	28	8	6	14	35	44	-9	30
12 Farnborough Old Boys Guild	28	7	7	14	39	55	-16	27*
13 Metrogas	28	8	3	17	55	78	-23	27
14 Faversham Strike Force Seniors	28	6	5	17	41	77	-36	23
15 Lydd Town Reserves	28	5	4	19	53	92	-39	19

Lewisham Athletic withdrew - record expunged

ANDREAS CARTER KENT COUNTY LEAGUE
SEASON 2017-2018

Kennington FC
Premier Division Champions

Dan Scorer - Manager
Kennington FC
Premier Division Champions

Kent County League Representative XI
Semi-Finalists - FA Inter League Cup

Ben Williams & Craig Penfold
Sporting Club Thamesmead FC Reserves
Aford Awards Joint Manager of the Year

Sporting Club Thamesmead FC Reserves
Division Three West Winners

Welling Town FC
'Barry Bundock' West Kent Challenge Shield Winners

Woodnesborough FC
Division Three Central & East - Promoted

Anne Ambrose - Woodnesborough FC
Secretary of the Year

Club Langley FC
'Bill Manklow' Inter-Regional
Challenge Cup Winners

Tonbridge Invicta FC
Eastern Section 'Les Leckie' Cup Winners
Ashford FC
Eastern Section 'Les Leckie' Cup Finalists

Club Langley FC
'Bill Manklow' Inter-Regional Challenge Cup Winners

Kiara Gallagher
Assistant Referee of the Year

Mr & Mrs Jerry Carter - League Sponsor
with Dean Saunders at Annual Presentation Dinner

Daniel Barham - Referee of the Year

ANDREAS CARTER KENT COUNTY LEAGUE

LEAGUE CONTACT
Philip Smith - Marketing & Communications Officer
Telephone: 07939 046182
Email: philip.smith@kentcountyfootballleague.co.uk

FINAL TABLES

Division One Central & East

		P	W	D	L	F	A	GD	Pts
1	Kings Hill	18	14	1	3	65	22	43	43
2	Hawkinge Town	18	14	0	4	60	26	34	42
3	Deal Sports	18	12	2	4	56	25	31	38
4	K Sports Reserves	18	12	2	4	51	35	16	38
5	Cuxton 91	18	11	2	5	56	19	37	35
6	Herne Bay Reserves	18	5	2	11	25	54	-29	14*
7	Rolvenden	18	4	2	12	27	50	-23	13*
8	Guru Nanak	18	3	3	12	21	48	-27	12
9	Hollands & Blair Reserves	18	3	4	11	22	59	-37	12*
10	Hildenborough Athletic	18	2	2	14	25	70	-45	5*

Hildenborough Athletic Withdrawn - Having played 75% of matches un-played fixture awarded to opponents

Division One West

		P	W	D	L	F	A	GD	Pts
1	Old Bromleians	24	20	2	2	80	24	56	62
2	Chipstead	24	15	3	6	80	42	38	48
3	Halls AFC	24	15	2	7	51	40	11	47
4	Ide Hill	24	14	3	7	86	43	43	45
5	Club Langley	24	13	3	8	57	41	16	42
6	Welling Park	24	12	4	8	70	51	19	40
7	Halstead United	24	12	4	8	55	38	17	40
8	Sutton Athletic Reserves	24	11	3	10	49	33	16	36
9	Old Roan	24	10	0	14	48	51	-3	30
10	Long Lane	24	8	4	12	52	58	-6	27*
11	AFC Mottingham	24	4	4	16	30	59	-29	16
12	Stansfeld (O & B) Res	24	5	0	19	28	84	-56	12*
13	Orpington	24	1	0	23	20	142	-122	3

Old Roan Withdrawn - Having played 75% of matches un-played fixtures awarded to opponents

Division Two Central & East

		P	W	D	L	F	A	GD	Pts
1	Wateringbury	20	17	1	2	71	26	45	52
2	Rochester City	20	16	1	3	95	24	71	49
3	Burgess Hodgson	20	12	4	4	69	47	22	40
4	Lordswood Res	20	12	2	6	53	42	11	38
5	Snodland Town Res	20	8	4	8	53	55	-2	28
6	Ashford	20	7	4	9	55	45	10	25
7	West Farleigh	20	7	5	8	47	43	4	25*
8	Tonbridge Invicta	20	7	2	11	51	54	-3	23
9	Rusthall Reserves	20	7	2	11	43	52	-9	23
10	Larkfield And New Hythe Wanderers	20	1	4	15	17	89	-72	7
11	New Romney Res	20	1	1	18	35	112	-77	-2*

Division Two West

		P	W	D	L	F	A	GD	Pts
1	Welling Town	22	17	4	1	86	13	73	55
2	Sydenham Sports	22	18	1	3	80	22	58	55
3	South East Athletic	22	14	2	6	50	40	10	44
4	Johnson & Phillips	22	12	4	6	46	30	16	40
5	Fleetdown United Res	22	11	4	7	38	36	2	37
6	FC Elmstead Res	22	9	4	9	43	39	4	31
7	Crayford Arrows	22	9	3	10	41	45	-4	29*
8	Metrogas Res	22	7	2	13	35	65	-30	20*
9	Nomads	22	5	4	13	47	58	-11	19
10	Dulwich Village	22	4	4	14	23	50	-27	16
11	Belvedere	22	3	5	14	20	74	-54	14
12	Long Lane Res	22	2	5	15	18	55	-37	11

Division Three Central & East

		P	W	D	L	F	A	GD	Pts
1	AEI Sports	22	18	3	1	91	22	69	57
2	Deal Sports Res	22	14	4	4	79	35	44	46
3	Deal Town Rangers	22	13	2	7	74	53	21	41
4	AFC Ashford Athletic	22	12	4	6	61	35	26	40
5	Faversham Town Res	22	11	5	6	61	48	13	38
6	University Of Kent	22	11	5	6	67	45	22	32*
7	Bromley Green	22	9	2	11	50	51	-1	27*
8	CC Sport	22	6	5	11	58	66	-8	23
9	Woodnesborough	22	7	2	13	36	58	-22	23
10	Staplehurst Monarchs United Res	22	6	3	13	51	73	-22	20*
11	Tenterden Town	22	5	2	15	49	81	-32	17
12	Aylesford	22	1	1	20	26	136	-110	4

Division Three West

		P	W	D	L	F	A	GD	Pts
1	Sporting Club Thamesmead Res	26	22	3	1	107	35	72	69
2	Red Velvet	26	21	3	2	97	24	73	66
3	HFSP & Ten-Em-Bee	26	18	2	6	92	44	48	56
4	Drummond Athletic	26	17	3	6	75	41	34	54
5	Bexley Reserves	26	16	1	9	68	51	17	49
6	Parkwood Rangers	26	12	2	12	61	67	-6	38
7	Old Bromleians Res	26	11	0	15	55	68	-13	33
8	Welling Town Res	26	9	5	12	51	53	-2	32
9	AFC Bexley	26	11	2	13	56	66	-10	32*
10	Bridon Ropes Res	26	9	2	15	61	65	-4	29
11	Farnborough Old Boys Guild Res	26	8	1	17	54	77	-23	25
12	South East Athletic Res	26	6	3	17	37	91	-54	21
13	Peckham Town Res	26	6	2	18	48	81	-33	20
14	AFC Lewisham	26	1	1	24	40	139	-99	4

BROMLEY AND SOUTH LONDON LEAGUE

Premier Division

		P	W	D	L	F	A	GD	Pts
1	Tudor Sports Res	16	14	1	1	69	15	54	43
2	Ten Em Bee	18	13	3	2	65	27	38	42
3	EFC	17	11	3	3	51	27	24	36
4	Eltham Town	17	10	2	5	25	18	7	32
5	Centresports	18	9	1	8	41	32	9	28
6	Eden Park Rangers	18	7	1	10	33	63	-30	22
7	Old Colfeians Green	18	6	0	12	38	49	-11	18
8	Red Velvet Res	18	4	2	12	13	26	-13	14
9	West Bromley Albion	18	3	2	13	19	71	-52	11
10	Croydon BR	18	3	1	14	26	52	-26	10

Division One

		P	W	D	L	F	A	GD	Pts
1	Danson Sports	16	13	1	2	54	16	38	40
2	Meridian Sports	16	10	2	4	43	20	23	32
3	Kingsdale	16	8	1	7	36	32	4	25
4	Farnborough OBG 4th	16	8	0	8	29	34	-5	24
5	Crayford Arrows Red	16	4	6	6	33	31	2	18
6	Rutland Rangers	16	5	3	8	18	22	-4	18
7	River Plate	16	6	0	10	26	50	-24	18
8	Lewisham Athletic Res	16	5	2	9	23	34	-11	17*
9	Crofton Albion	16	3	3	9	36	59	-23	15

Division Two

		P	W	D	L	F	A	GD	Pts
1	Farnborough OBG 3rd	14	9	4	1	54	28	26	31
2	Old Colfeians Blue	14	10	1	3	44	28	16	31
3	Frazier FC	14	8	3	3	58	36	22	27
4	Russellers	14	5	2	7	30	39	-9	17
5	South Dulwich FC	14	5	1	8	34	43	-9	16
6	Junior Reds	14	4	1	9	17	31	-14	13
7	KSG Falcons	14	4	1	9	34	52	-18	13
8	Ground Hoppers	14	2	5	7	43	57	-14	11

Division Three

		P	W	D	L	F	A	GD	Pts
1	Eltham Town Res	18	14	1	3	73	23	50	43
2	Old Bromleians 3rd	18	13	1	4	66	30	36	40
3	Old Roan Res	18	12	2	4	66	31	35	38
4	AFC London	18	11	2	5	65	38	27	35*
5	Seven Acre Sports	18	9	2	7	57	44	13	29
6	Welling Park Res	18	7	2	9	51	54	-3	23
7	Dulwich Village Res	18	7	1	10	46	63	-17	22
8	Highfield and Welling	18	7	0	11	52	56	-4	21
9	Latter Day Saints	18	2	1	15	31	88	-57	7
10	Slade Green Knights	18	1	2	15	38	118	-80	5

LEICESTERSHIRE SENIOR LEAGUE

Premier Division

		P	W	D	L	F	A	GD	Pts
1	Ingles FC	28	21	3	4	90	23	67	66
2	Bardon Hill	28	21	3	4	92	38	54	66
3	FC Khalsa GAD	28	17	4	7	87	50	37	55
4	Allexton & New Parks	28	15	5	8	96	45	51	50
5	Saffron Dynamo	28	15	3	10	86	59	27	48
6	Barlestone St Giles	28	14	4	10	58	61	-3	46
7	Coalville Town Dev	28	14	4	10	70	60	10	43*
8	Hathern FC	28	12	4	12	66	70	-4	40
9	Friar Lane & Epworth	28	11	5	12	60	64	-4	38
10	Ellistown FC	28	11	4	13	55	72	-17	37
11	Cottesmore Amateurs	28	9	3	16	58	72	-14	30
12	Sileby Town	28	9	3	16	55	60	-5	27*
13	FC GNG	28	7	5	16	47	73	-26	26
14	Kirby Muxloe Res	28	4	4	20	38	110	-72	13*
15	Ashby Ivanhoe Res	28	3	0	25	28	129	-101	6*

Ibstock United withdrew - record expunged

Division One

		P	W	D	L	F	A	GD	Pts
1	Rugby Borough	31	26	2	3	195	27	168	80
2	Thurnby Rangers	31	22	4	5	146	41	105	70
3	Asfordby FC	32	20	7	5	95	63	32	67
4	Desford FC	32	20	5	7	99	47	52	65
5	County Hall	32	18	5	9	107	55	52	59
6	Birstall United Res	32	19	4	9	81	43	38	58*
7	Lutterworth Town Res	31	15	5	11	81	67	14	50
8	Anstey Nomads Res	31	14	7	10	96	52	44	49
9	Aylestone Park Res	32	14	5	13	83	87	-4	47
10	St Andrews Res	31	14	7	10	75	100	-25	46*
11	Loughborough FC	32	12	1	19	71	86	-15	37
12	Caterpillar FC	32	10	6	16	68	62	6	36
13	Barrow Town Res	32	9	7	16	92	80	12	31*
14	Anstey Town	32	7	4	21	46	102	-56	25
15	Holwell Sports Dev	31	8	0	23	41	123	-82	15*
16	Highfield Rangers	32	3	2	27	30	181	-151	11
17	Earl Shilton Albion	32	2	1	29	33	223	-190	4*

LIVERPOOL COUNTY PREMIER LEAGUE

Premier Division

		P	W	D	L	F	A	GD	Pts
1	Lower Breck	24	22	2	0	95	17	78	68
2	East Villa	24	16	5	3	57	28	29	53
3	Alder	24	16	4	4	69	43	26	52
4	Waterloo Dock	24	15	1	8	69	45	24	46
5	Old Xaverians	24	10	5	9	39	38	1	35
6	Liverpool NALGO	24	10	4	10	44	57	-13	34
7	Custy's	24	9	3	12	49	64	-15	30
8	Aigburth PH	24	9	2	13	53	27	26	29
9	MSB Woolton	24	9	2	13	57	67	-10	28*
10	South Sefton Borough	24	7	5	12	33	45	-12	26
11	Alumni	24	5	4	15	29	72	-43	21*
12	AFC Liverpool Res	24	4	4	16	22	54	-32	16
13	Waterloo GSOB	24	2	3	19	32	91	-59	9

Division One

		P	W	D	L	F	A	GD	Pts
1	British Rail	20	17	3	0	103	20	83	54
2	Knowsley North	20	15	2	3	112	39	73	47
3	Bankfield OB	20	14	3	3	71	36	35	45
4	Waterloo Dock Res	20	10	4	6	50	35	15	34
5	Liver Academy	20	7	6	6	41	46	-5	27*
6	Lower Breck Res	20	7	3	10	41	51	-10	24
7	South Garston	20	7	2	10	51	58	-7	23*
8	Edge Hill BCOB	20	6	2	12	39	57	-18	20
9	ROMA	20	5	3	12	31	65	-34	18
10	BRNESC	20	5	2	13	41	65	-24	17
11	Warbreck	20	1	0	19	20	128	-108	3

Division Two

		P	W	D	L	F	A	GD	Pts
1	Quarry Bank Old Boys	20	18	0	2	68	14	54	54
2	The Saddle	20	15	2	3	66	26	40	47
3	Aintree Villa	20	13	2	5	52	32	20	41
4	FC Pilchy	20	13	1	6	63	29	34	40
5	AFC Kirkby	20	8	4	8	58	53	5	28
6	Waterloo GSOB Res	20	8	3	9	57	49	8	27
7	Botanic	20	7	2	11	34	69	-35	23
8	City of Liverpool Res	20	6	3	11	47	59	-12	21
9	Roby	20	5	5	10	36	50	-14	20
10	Red Rum	20	3	1	16	32	88	-56	10
11	Fantail	20	1	3	16	22	66	-44	6

FINAL TABLES

MANCHESTER LEAGUE

Premier Division

		P	W	D	L	F	A	GD	Pts
1	Avro	28	25	1	2	105	34	71	76
2	Wythenshawe Amateurs	28	20	2	6	84	37	47	62
3	East Manchester	28	17	5	6	76	43	33	56
4	Springhead	28	17	4	7	63	39	24	55
5	Hindsford	28	13	6	9	77	55	22	45
6	Heyside	28	11	9	8	55	45	10	42
7	Rochdale Sacred Heart	28	10	6	12	66	64	2	35*
8	Stockport Georgians	28	10	5	13	54	65	-11	35
9	Walshaw Sports	28	10	4	14	50	64	-14	34
10	Dukinfield Town	28	10	3	15	58	63	-5	33
11	Bolton County	28	9	6	13	49	64	-15	33
12	Royton Town	28	8	2	18	49	70	-21	26
13	Manchester Gregorians	28	7	4	17	39	71	-32	25
14	AFC Monton	28	6	4	18	39	104	-65	22
15	Old Altrinchamians	28	3	7	18	40	86	-46	16
"

Division One

		P	W	D	L	F	A	GD	Pts
1	Chadderton Reserves	22	15	4	3	91	30	61	49
2	Manchester Central	22	13	3	6	60	33	27	42
3	Beechfield United	22	15	1	6	60	31	29	38*
4	Elton Vale	22	12	2	8	55	41	14	37*
5	Pennington	22	11	1	10	53	52	1	34
6	Boothstown	22	8	5	9	39	57	-18	29
7	Atherton Town	22	8	4	10	47	47	0	28
8	Chapel Town	22	8	4	10	46	56	-10	27*
9	Leigh Athletic	22	8	3	11	43	62	-19	26*
10	Wilmslow Albion	22	5	4	13	41	64	-23	19
11	Hollinwood	22	6	2	14	50	75	-25	18*
12	Westbury Sports Club	22	5	3	14	43	80	-37	17*
"

Division Two

		P	W	D	L	F	A	GD	Pts
1	Altrincham Hale	20	14	2	4	60	31	29	44
2	Tintwistle Athletic	20	13	3	4	62	39	23	42
3	Bolton Lads and Girls Club	20	13	3	4	61	39	22	42
4	Radcliffe Juniors	20	12	2	6	62	38	24	38
5	Govan Athletic	20	11	4	5	73	34	39	37
6	Heywood St James	20	8	3	9	40	46	-6	27
7	Uppermill	20	6	3	11	54	48	6	21
8	Atherton LR Dev	20	6	4	10	29	56	-27	21*
9	Breightmet United	20	5	2	13	31	63	-32	17
10	Irlam Steel	20	4	4	12	32	61	-29	15*
11	Hindley Juniors	20	2	2	16	24	73	-49	7*
"

Division Three

		P	W	D	L	F	A	GD	Pts
1	Rochdale Sacred Heart Res	20	18	0	2	97	22	75	54
2	Wythenshawe Amateurs Res	20	14	1	5	70	32	38	43
3	Avro Res	20	12	4	4	56	27	29	36*
4	Atherton Town Res	20	10	3	7	42	32	10	33
5	Manchester Gregorians Res	20	8	4	8	34	34	0	28
6	Hindsford Res	20	9	1	10	46	48	-2	28
7	Walshaw Sports Res	20	8	4	8	38	56	-18	28
8	Dukinfield Town Res	20	7	3	10	50	49	1	24
9	Wilmslow Albion Res	20	5	1	14	32	80	-48	16
10	Stockport Georgians Res	20	2	5	13	28	58	-30	10*
11	Springhead Res	20	3	2	15	21	76	-55	10*
"

Division Four

		P	W	D	L	F	A	GD	Pts
1	East Manchester Academy	15	11	1	3	71	21	50	34
2	Elton Vale Res	16	11	1	4	50	29	21	34
3	Rochdale Sacred Heart A	16	10	3	3	42	28	14	33
4	Leigh Athletic Res	16	7	1	8	38	60	-22	22
5	Pennington Res	16	5	3	8	35	51	-16	18
6	AFC Monton Res	16	5	2	9	32	43	-11	16*
7	Bolton County Res	16	4	3	9	38	41	-3	15
8	Old Altrinchamians Res	16	3	4	9	16	41	-25	13
9	Hollinwood Res	15	5	2	8	40	48	-8	9*
"

Division Five

		P	W	D	L	F	A	GD	Pts
1	Chadderton EDS	18	15	1	2	117	23	94	46
2	Uppermill Res	18	15	1	2	81	29	52	46
3	Boothstown Res	18	11	2	5	45	33	12	35
4	Heywood St James Res	18	8	4	6	52	48	4	28
5	Altrincham Hale Res	18	8	2	8	62	60	2	26
6	Atherton Town A	18	7	3	8	39	45	-6	24
7	Bolton Lads and Girls Club Res	18	8	0	10	55	66	-11	23*
8	Tintwistle Athletic Res	18	6	2	10	54	55	-1	20
9	Govan Athletic Res	18	2	1	15	22	66	-44	6*
10	Breightmet United Res	18	2	0	16	30	132	-102	6

MIDDLESEX COUNTY LEAGUE

Premier Division

		P	W	D	L	F	A	GD	Pts
1	British Airways	26	19	4	3	79	36	43	61
2	Brentham	26	16	5	5	66	34	32	53
3	Cricklewood Wanderers	26	14	7	5	69	51	18	49
4	FC Assyria	26	15	3	8	76	49	27	48
5	Indian Gymkhana Club	26	13	6	7	57	36	21	45
6	Lampton Park	26	12	5	9	48	45	3	41
7	Sporting Hackney	26	11	4	11	48	53	-5	37
8	Pitshanger Dynamo	26	10	6	10	55	54	1	36
9	Tottenham Hale Rangers	26	12	5	9	46	54	-8	29*
10	Kensington Dragons	26	9	1	16	49	60	-11	28
11	Hillingdon	26	7	13	6	43	65	-22	25
12	C.B. Hounslow United Res	26	5	5	15	34	57	-23	20
13	Stonewall	26	5	5	16	34	58	-24	20
14	South Kilburn	26	1	4	23	25	77	-52	7
15	Tooting & Mitcham Wanderers withdrew - record expunged								

Division One Central & East

		P	W	D	L	F	A	GD	Pts
1	St Panteleimon	22	18	4	0	102	17	85	46*
2	AEK London	22	14	6	2	72	25	47	36*
3	AFC United	22	13	4	5	85	43	42	31*
4	Fire United Christian	22	12	7	3	48	26	22	31*
5	The Wilberforce Wanderers	22	8	5	9	41	42	-1	29
6	Mile End Park Rangers	22	9	4	9	42	44	-2	28*
7	NW London FC	22	8	4	10	39	71	-32	28
8	Hackney Wick Res	22	5	4	13	41	81	-40	19
9	J L Rovers	22	4	4	11	43	48	-5	13*
10	London Samurai Utd	22	6	5	11	63	55	8	9*
11	London United	22	3	3	15	29	63	-34	-1*
12	SJ Global United	22	1	4	17	25	115	-90	-5*

Division One West

		P	W	D	L	F	A	GD	Pts
1	Larkspur Rovers	22	16	2	4	71	32	39	50
2	PFC Victoria London	22	16	2	3	64	23	41	38*
3	South Kilburn 3rds	22	10	4	7	46	56	-10	34
4	VOS	22	14	3	4	60	20	40	33*
5	FC IGK	22	10	3	9	49	42	7	33
6	Kodak (Harrow)	22	10	2	10	39	47	-8	32
7	New Hanford	22	7	1	13	33	50	-17	22
8	Chape London	22	10	2	10	46	43	3	20*
9	North Acton	22	5	5	12	50	72	-22	20
10	Alpha & Omega	22	5	2	15	27	59	-32	17
11	FC Deportivo Galicia Res	22	8	2	12	57	66	-9	14*
12	Hounslow Wanderers	22	4	2	16	38	70	-32	14

Division Two

		P	W	D	L	F	A	GD	Pts
1	Hilltop	22	18	1	3	90	23	67	55
2	Western Athletic	22	17	2	3	82	38	44	53
3	Harrow Bhoys	22	15	3	4	57	48	9	48
4	AFC Hanwell & Hayes	22	14	1	7	71	54	17	43
5	Harrow Rangers	22	10	0	11	47	54	-7	30
6	Hillingdon Abbots	22	8	1	12	30	47	-17	25
7	St Nicholas	22	8	1	13	38	67	-29	25
8	C.B. Hounslow United 3rds	22	7	3	12	61	70	-9	24
9	Sudbury Court	22	7	4	11	43	52	-9	22*
10	Heston Bombers	22	7	1	14	33	56	-23	22
11	West SL Benfica	22	4	3	15	33	76	-43	3*
12	Cranford Park	22	5	2	15	42	42	0	2*

Combination

		P	W	D	L	F	A	GD	Pts
1	Lampton Park Res	20	15	0	5	50	24	26	45
2	Brentham Res	20	14	1	5	73	30	43	43
3	Pitshanger Dynamo Res	20	12	4	4	51	27	24	40
4	London Titans	20	12	3	5	65	30	35	39
5	LNER	20	12	2	6	54	50	4	38
6	Ruislip	20	11	4	5	73	35	38	37
7	Centenary Park	20	7	3	10	43	50	-7	24
8	Stonewall Res	20	6	4	10	34	48	-14	22
9	C.B. Hounslow United 5ths	20	5	4	11	34	49	-15	19
10	Hillingdon Res	20	1	3	16	15	54	-39	6
11	AFC Heathrow	20	0	2	18	16	111	-95	2

NORTH RIDING LEAGUE

Premier Division

		P	W	D	L	F	A	GD	Pts
1	Boro Rangers	24	21	0	3	116	28	88	63
2	Stockton West End 'A'	24	17	1	6	80	50	30	52
3	Redcar Town	24	12	5	7	47	32	15	41
4	Fishburn Park	24	13	2	9	48	48	0	41
5	Redcar Newmarket	24	11	4	9	65	64	1	37
6	Guisborough United	24	10	8	6	66	46	20	35*
7	Thornby Dubliners	24	10	5	9	68	56	12	35
8	St Marys 1947	24	10	3	11	65	66	-1	33
9	Yarm & Eaglescliffe	24	7	4	13	46	64	-18	25
10	Beads	24	8	4	12	60	94	-34	25*
11	Grangetown Boys Club	24	6	5	13	49	80	-31	23
12	Staithes Athletic	24	6	3	15	54	74	-20	21
13	Nunthorpe Athletic	24	2	2	20	45	107	-62	5*

Division One

		P	W	D	L	F	A	GD	Pts
1	Bedale AFC	14	13	0	1	56	19	37	39
2	New Marske Lakes United	14	8	2	4	38	29	9	26
3	Redcar Athletic Res	14	7	3	4	48	38	10	24
4	Great Ayton United	14	7	2	5	31	26	5	23
5	Whitby Fishermans Society	14	5	2	7	34	38	-4	17
6	Lingdale Village	14	4	1	9	24	40	-16	13
7	Loftus Athletic	14	4	1	9	24	44	-20	13
8	Stokesley Sports Club Res	14	2	1	11	26	47	-21	7

NORTHAMPTONSHIRE COMBINATION

Premier Division

		P	W	D	L	F	A	GD	Pts
1	James King Blisworth	24	20	3	1	92	29	63	63
2	Moulton	24	16	5	3	81	38	43	53
3	Harpole	24	14	5	5	55	36	19	47
4	Earls Barton United	24	12	6	6	50	31	19	42
5	Roade	24	10	6	8	46	43	3	36
6	Heyford Athletic	24	11	2	11	64	64	0	35
7	Kettering Nomads	24	9	6	9	50	43	7	33
8	Woodford United	24	5	10	9	47	37	10	32
9	Corby Pegasus	24	9	4	11	43	56	-13	31
10	Wollaston Victoria	24	7	4	13	40	58	-18	25
11	Burton United	24	3	14	7	58	71	-13	24
12	Spratton	24	9	15	12	27	68	-41	9
13	Brixworth All Saints	24	2	2	20	28	107	-79	8

Division One

		P	W	D	L	F	A	GD	Pts
1	Wootton St George	20	17	2	1	77	26	51	53
2	Desborough & Rothwell United	20	15	1	4	68	30	38	46
3	West Haddon Albion	20	14	1	5	52	38	14	43
4	Corby Kingswood	20	10	4	6	41	30	11	34
5	Wellingborough Rising Sun	20	10	3	7	67	59	8	33
6	AFC Houghton Magna	20	8	3	9	42	42	0	27
7	Weldon United	20	7	4	9	51	41	10	25
8	Bugbrooke St Michaels 'A'	20	6	2	12	29	49	-20	20
9	Roade Res	20	4	5	11	35	53	-18	14*
10	AFC Woodford Wolves	20	2	0	18	31	99	-68	· 6
11	Milton	20	3	3	14	28	54	-26	3*

FINAL TABLES

Division Two

		P	W	D	L	F	A	GD	Pts
1	Finedon Volta	26	21	3	2	89	41	48	66
2	Corby Strip Mills	26	20	3	3	100	31	69	63
3	Higham Town	26	18	4	4	89	35	54	58
4	Northampton Spartak	26	16	6	4	80	45	35	54
5	Corby Pegasus Res	26	15	4	7	69	60	9	49
6	Kettering Nomads Res	26	11	8	7	68	47	21	41
7	Wollaston Victoria Res	26	11	4	11	63	48	15	34*
8	FC FotoGold	26	9	4	13	58	64	-6	31
9	Corby White Hart Locos	26	7	7	12	49	62	-13	28
10	Daventry Cummins	26	7	5	14	39	55	-16	26
11	Bugbrooke St Michaels 'B'	26	7	3	16	57	86	-29	24
12	Kettering Orchard Park	26	7	1	18	50	101	-51	22
13	Brixworth All Saints Res	26	2	4	20	25	70	-45	10
14	Medbourne	26	2	2	22	45	136	-91	8

Division Three

		P	W	D	L	F	A	GD	Pts
1	Weldon United Res	28	21	3	4	85	26	59	66
2	Yelvertoft	28	19	4	5	93	45	48	61
3	Earls Barton United Res	28	18	4	6	94	56	38	58
4	Harpole Res	28	18	3	7	88	45	43	57
5	Desborough & Rothwell United Res	28	14	3	11	62	57	5	45
6	Corby United	28	13	5	10	70	67	3	44
7	Irthlingborough Rangers	28	12	4	12	51	41	10	40
8	Corby Ravens	28	10	7	11	46	44	2	37
9	Stanwick Rovers	28	11	4	13	63	75	-12	37
10	Woodford United Res	28	9	8	11	55	52	3	32*
11	FC Siam	28	7	10	11	58	85	-27	31
12	Delapre Dragons	28	7	5	16	55	89	-34	26
13	Finedon Volta Res	28	4	9	15	30	75	-45	21
14	Spratton Res	28	6	1	21	30	83	-53	16*
15	Heyford Athletic Res	28	3	6	19	36	76	-40	15

Division Four

		P	W	D	L	F	A	GD	Pts
1	Moulton Res	26	20	2	4	115	54	61	62
2	FC Siam Res	26	20	2	4	112	61	51	62
3	Thrapston Venturas	26	17	4	5	75	38	37	55
4	Corby Ravens Res	26	17	2	7	121	64	57	53
5	Corby White Hart Locos Res	26	14	4	8	82	69	13	46
6	Corby Rising Hope	26	14	3	9	66	58	8	45
7	Kettering Ise Lodge	26	11	4	11	68	64	4	37
8	Corby Strip Mills Res	26	11	3	12	69	67	2	36
9	Higham Town Res	26	9	6	11	66	72	-6	33
10	Corby Trades & Labour	26	10	0	16	46	81	-35	30
11	Corby United Res	26	7	4	15	73	91	-18	25
12	Great Doddington	26	4	5	17	36	87	-51	17
13	Wilby	26	2	5	19	34	84	-50	11
14	West Haddon Albion Res	26	3	2	21	46	119	-73	11

NORTHERN ALLIANCE

Premier Division

		P	W	D	L	F	A	GD	Pts
1	Newcastle University	30	25	2	3	123	31	92	77
2	Birtley Town	30	22	3	5	91	42	49	69
3	Ponteland United	30	17	6	7	68	49	19	57
4	Wellington	30	17	5	8	86	54	32	56
5	Whitley Bay A	30	17	3	10	86	63	23	54
6	Seaton Delaval AFC	30	18	2	10	100	63	37	53*
7	Killingworth Town	30	13	5	12	59	54	5	44
8	Shankhouse	30	13	5	12	52	48	4	44
9	Ashington Colliers	30	14	4	12	68	61	7	43*
10	Gateshead Rutherford	30	11	5	14	52	62	-10	38
11	Percy Main Ams	30	12	2	16	58	72	-14	38
12	AFC Newbiggin	30	11	2	17	56	88	-32	29*
13	Gateshead A	30	8	3	19	67	72	-5	27
14	Northbank	30	8	4	18	57	72	-15	22*
15	North Shields Athletic	30	7	1	22	49	106	-57	19*
16	FC United of Newcastle	30	0	2	28	25	160	-135	-1*

Division One

		P	W	D	L	F	A	GD	Pts
1	Killingworth YPC	30	27	2	1	144	29	115	83
2	Hazlerigg Victory	30	24	2	4	131	32	99	74
3	Newcastle Chemfica	30	18	6	6	115	50	65	60
4	Felling Magpies	30	16	3	11	88	67	21	51
5	Wallsend Community	30	15	6	9	89	66	23	48*
6	Seaton Burn	30	14	5	11	73	65	8	47
7	Forest Hall	30	14	3	13	61	58	3	45
8	New Fordley	30	16	2	12	75	52	23	44*
9	Hexham	30	14	2	14	77	65	12	44
10	Red Row Welfare	30	13	3	14	74	77	-3	39*
11	Wallsend Boys Club	30	11	5	14	66	62	4	35*
12	Gosforth Bohemians	30	10	4	16	46	70	-24	34
13	Hebburn Reyrolle	30	8	3	19	53	121	-68	27
14	Cullercoats	30	8	4	18	49	79	-30	25*
15	Newcastle East End	30	3	3	24	34	152	-118	9*
16	Cramlington Town	30	2	1	27	30	160	-130	7

Division Two

		P	W	D	L	F	A	GD	Pts
1	Blyth Spartans Res	28	23	4	1	126	33	93	73
2	Prudhoe YC Seniors	28	20	1	7	98	47	51	61
3	Winlaton Vulcans	28	16	6	6	93	50	43	54
4	Bedlington	28	16	4	8	91	55	36	52
5	Blyth Town	28	15	7	6	83	51	32	52
6	Cramlington United	28	14	6	8	79	70	9	48
7	Blyth FC	28	14	1	13	58	63	-5	43
8	Whitburn Athletic	28	11	4	13	51	57	-6	37
9	Whitley Bay Sporting Club	28	10	6	12	62	68	-6	36
10	Coundon and Leeholme	28	9	7	12	54	63	-9	34
11	Wideopen & District	28	7	4	17	44	72	-28	25
12	Spittal Rovers	28	6	7	15	43	82	-39	22*
13	Willington Quay Saints	28	6	3	19	44	84	-40	21
14	Seghill	28	4	7	17	37	70	-33	19
15	Gateshead Redheugh 1957	28	4	3	21	39	137	-98	15

NOTTINGHAMSHIRE SENIOR

OXFORDSHIRE SENIOR LEAGUE

Premier Division

		P	W	D	L	F	A	GD	Pts
1	Newark Flowserve	34	31	0	3	135	28	107	93
2	Awsworth Villa	34	21	5	8	105	52	53	68
3	FC Cavaliers	34	19	7	8	68	42	26	64
4	Bingham Town	34	19	5	10	77	56	21	62
5	Southwell City	34	17	6	11	72	58	14	57
6	Basford United Community	34	17	5	12	82	45	37	56
7	Calverton Miners Welfare	34	17	5	12	72	62	10	56
8	Cotgrave	34	13	10	11	61	56	5	49
9	Sandiacre Town	34	13	5	16	68	78	-10	44
10	Wollaton	34	13	5	16	79	91	-12	44
11	Kimberley Miners Welfare AFC	34	13	4	17	54	75	-21	43
12	Attenborough First	34	12	5	17	61	87	-26	41
13	AFC Dunkirk	34	10	7	17	80	86	-6	37
14	Underwood Villa	34	11	3	20	61	90	-29	36
15	Magdala Amateurs	34	5	5	19	67	99	-32	35
16	Gedling Southbank	34	8	6	20	57	94	-37	30
17	Bilborough Town	34	9	3	22	56	101	-45	30
18	Ruddington Village	34	6	8	20	64	119	-55	26

Division One

		P	W	D	L	F	A	GD	Pts
1	Stapleford Town Senior	28	21	2	5	86	34	52	65
2	Ashland Rovers	28	18	5	5	81	45	36	59
3	Keyworth United Res	28	18	4	6	92	54	38	58
4	Netherfield Albion	28	18	6	4	68	39	29	57*
5	Kirton Brickworks	28	13	7	8	60	51	9	46
6	Selston Reserves	28	13	4	11	58	54	4	43
7	Mansfield Hosiery Mills	28	12	3	13	71	67	4	39
8	Ravenshead	28	11	4	13	65	66	-1	37
9	Beeston Rylands	28	11	2	15	67	88	-21	35
10	Wollaton Reserves	28	9	5	14	59	67	-8	32
11	Ruddington Village Res	28	9	3	16	39	75	-36	30
12	Southwell City Res	28	8	5	15	48	60	-12	29
13	Real Community	28	9	2	17	52	66	-14	29
14	Awsworth Villa Res	28	7	2	19	50	80	-30	23
15	AFC Bridgford	28	3	6	19	28	78	-50	15

Division Two

		P	W	D	L	F	A	GD	Pts
1	Woodthorpe Park Rangers	28	25	1	2	125	32	93	76
2	Bridgford United	28	20	4	4	105	42	63	64
3	Burton Joyce	28	15	6	7	106	44	62	51
4	Southwell City Dev	28	16	2	10	76	53	23	50
5	Newark Flowserve Res	28	16	4	8	77	51	26	49*
6	Barrowby	28	13	6	9	80	73	7	45
7	Sneinton Town	28	11	6	11	75	76	-1	39
8	Keyworth United Dev	28	12	2	14	63	75	-12	38
9	Bingham Town Res	28	9	10	9	58	53	5	37
10	AFC Clifton	28	10	6	12	62	81	-19	36
11	Kirton Brickworks Res	28	9	2	17	55	106	-51	29
12	Welbeck Lions Res	28	9	1	18	53	87	-34	28
13	Magdala Amateurs Res	28	7	3	18	46	90	-44	24
14	Gedling Southbank Res	28	6	3	19	75	101	-26	21
15	Nottingham City	28	2	4	22	43	135	-92	10

Premier Division

		P	W	D	L	F	A	GD	Pts
1	Heyford Athletic	24	19	3	2	57	14	43	60
2	Freeland	24	17	5	2	60	18	42	56
3	Kennington Athletic	24	16	3	5	70	29	41	51
4	Cropredy	24	16	2	6	75	38	37	50
5	Adderbury Park	24	12	5	7	44	28	16	41
6	Mansfield Rd	24	9	6	9	44	38	6	33
7	Yarnton	24	10	3	11	44	63	-19	33
8	Chalgrove	24	9	4	11	55	57	-2	31
9	OUP	24	8	3	13	39	54	-15	27
10	Charlton	24	5	8	11	29	41	-12	23
11	Horspath	24	3	5	16	32	63	-31	14
12	Marston Sts	24	4	1	19	24	71	-47	13
13	Launton Sports	24	2	4	18	19	78	-59	10

Division One

		P	W	D	L	F	A	GD	Pts
1	Bicester United FC	18	12	3	3	40	18	22	39
2	Garsington	18	12	2	4	53	39	14	38
3	Middleton Cheney	18	12	1	5	50	19	31	37
4	Summertown AFC	18	9	0	9	44	37	7	27
5	Adderbury Res	18	8	1	9	51	47	4	25
6	OUP Res	18	6	5	7	29	36	-7	23
7	Woodstock Town Res	18	6	2	10	35	54	-19	20
8	Lusitanos Oxford	18	6	1	11	37	54	-17	19
9	Long Crendon FC	18	5	2	11	35	52	-17	17
10	Eynsham	18	4	3	11	29	47	-18	15

Zubry Oxford FC withdrew - record expunged

Division Two

		P	W	D	L	F	A	GD	Pts
1	Freeland Res	22	16	5	1	66	26	40	53
2	Kennington Athletic Res	22	16	3	3	70	31	39	51
3	Cropedy Res	22	13	3	6	66	38	28	42
4	Heyford Athletic Res	22	13	2	7	60	48	12	41
5	Marston Sts Res	22	11	2	9	41	37	4	35
6	Launton Sports Res	22	10	4	8	57	47	10	34
7	Yarnton Res	22	7	5	10	43	45	-2	26
8	Charlton Res	22	5	10	7	46	54	-8	25
9	Mansfield Rd Res	22	6	4	12	30	54	-24	22
10	Chinnor Development	22	6	2	14	25	40	-15	20
11	Chalgrove Res	22	4	3	15	34	53	-19	15
12	Horspath Res	22	3	1	18	31	96	-65	10

Eynsham Res withdrew - record expunged

FINAL TABLES

WITNEY & DISTRICT LEAGUE

Premier Division	P	W	D	L	F	A	GD	Pts
1 Hanborough	20	18	2	0	60	14	46	56
2 FC Hollybush	20	14	3	3	43	24	19	45
3 Charlbury Town	20	7	7	6	40	37	3	28
4 Kirtlington	20	8	1	11	59	57	2	25
5 Hailey	20	7	4	9	45	50	-5	25
6 Chipping Norton Town	20	6	7	7	43	51	-8	25
7 Spartan Rangers	20	6	6	8	31	45	-14	24
8 Minster Lovell	20	6	5	9	43	57	-14	23
9 Carterton Rangers	20	6	4	10	32	31	1	22
10 Carterton Town A	20	6	3	11	44	56	-12	21
11 Combe	20	4	2	14	36	54	-18	14

Division One	P	W	D	L	F	A	GD	Pts
1 Aston	18	15	3	0	56	11	45	48
2 Tower Hill	18	13	3	2	59	29	30	42
3 Stonesfield	18	13	2	3	45	24	21	41
4 Chadlington	18	8	2	8	33	32	1	26
5 Witney Royals	18	7	2	9	51	49	2	23
6 Milton	18	5	5	8	31	55	-24	20
7 Tower Hill Stars	18	6	1	11	37	34	3	18*
8 Eynsham SSC	18	4	3	11	30	51	-21	15
9 Bampton Utd	18	4	3	11	36	58	-22	15
10 FC Nomads	18	2	2	14	28	63	-35	10*

FC Ascott withdrew - record expunged

Division Two	P	W	D	L	F	A	GD	Pts
1 Bletchington	22	17	1	4	69	35	34	52
2 Moreton Rangers	22	15	4	3	44	17	27	49
3 Bourton Rovers	22	14	5	3	64	30	34	46*
4 Middle Barton	22	13	4	5	43	29	14	43
5 Kingham All Blacks	22	11	2	9	57	39	18	37
6 Charlbury Town Res	22	9	2	11	40	39	1	29
7 Witney Wanderers	22	8	2	12	37	50	-13	26
8 Hailey Res	22	7	1	14	41	57	-16	25
9 Brize Norton	22	8	3	11	41	40	1	24*
10 Hanborough Res	22	7	2	13	38	70	-32	23
11 Aston Res	22	3	3	15	40	68	-28	15
12 Spartan Rangers Res	22	4	1	17	25	65	-40	13

Division Three	P	W	D	L	F	A	GD	Pts
1 Siege FC	22	18	2	2	91	38	53	56
2 FC Hollybush Res	22	17	1	4	79	39	40	52
3 Ducklington	22	14	3	5	74	49	25	45
4 Corinthians	22	13	4	5	72	35	37	43
5 Minster Lovell Res	22	13	1	8	72	45	27	40
6 Wootton	22	12	3	7	76	52	24	39
7 Bourton Rovers Res	22	8	2	12	55	86	-31	26
8 Chipping Norton Town Res	22	7	0	15	39	84	-45	21
9 Combe Res	22	6	2	14	48	69	-21	20
10 Witney Royals Res	22	5	5	12	50	77	-27	20
11 FC Mills	22	5	2	15	47	84	-37	17
12 Milton Res	22	1	1	20	20	65	-45	4

Division Four	P	W	D	L	F	A	GD	Pts
1 Carterton Town B	24	21	1	2	129	24	105	64
2 Bletchington Res	24	18	1	5	104	40	64	55
3 Kingham All Blacks Res	24	18	0	6	89	39	50	54
4 Wootton Res	24	16	0	8	58	34	24	48
5 Stonesfield Res	24	14	2	8	57	58	-1	44
6 Brize Norton Res	24	12	3	9	68	60	8	39
7 Chadlington Res	24	11	2	11	46	43	3	35
8 FC Ascott Res	24	11	2	11	48	49	-1	35
9 Bampton Utd Res	24	11	1	12	63	56	7	34
10 Spartan Rangers A	24	7	2	15	56	66	-10	23
11 Siege FC Res	24	4	1	19	37	109	-72	13
12 Eynsham SSC Res	24	4	1	19	43	137	-94	13
13 FC Ascott Rangers	24	1	0	23	19	102	-83	3

PETERBOROUGH & DISTRICT LEAGUE

Premier Division	P	W	D	L	F	A	GD	Pts
1 Netherton United	30	24	4	2	137	29	108	76
2 Moulton Harrox	30	21	4	4	87	31	56	70*
3 Whittlesey Athletic	30	18	7	4	75	40	35	64*
4 Stamford Lions	30	16	6	7	90	41	49	57*
5 Thorney	30	15	5	9	81	51	30	53*
6 Peterborough ICA Sports	30	16	4	10	76	47	29	52
7 Leverington Sports	30	12	4	13	65	77	-12	43*
8 Holbeach United Res	30	12	6	12	68	57	11	42
9 Sutton Bridge United	30	13	3	13	71	72	-1	39*
10 Peterborough Sports Res	30	13	1	15	67	77	-10	39*
11 Ketton	30	12	3	15	63	86	-23	39
12 Warboys Town	30	10	4	16	56	114	-58	34
13 Sawtry	30	8	5	17	59	75	-16	29
14 Deeping Rangers Res	30	8	4	18	58	94	-36	28
15 AFC Stanground Sports	30	5	3	20	48	102	-54	14*
16 Langtoft Utd (Sat) First	30	0	1	28	22	130	-108	-2*

Division One	P	W	D	L	F	A	GD	Pts
1 Moulton Harrox Res	24	18	4	0	84	26	58	64*
2 Tydd St Mary	24	17	0	7	81	44	37	51
3 Long Sutton Athletic	24	14	2	7	72	43	29	47*
4 Wittering Harriers	24	14	2	8	79	56	23	44
5 Peterborough Polonia	24	12	6	6	81	43	38	42
6 Ramsey Town	24	12	2	9	68	58	10	37*
7 Oundle Town	24	10	4	10	61	52	9	34
8 Stamford Belvedere	24	10	3	11	61	55	6	33
9 Crowland Town	24	9	4	11	58	58	0	31
10 Uppingham Town	24	7	3	14	49	73	-24	24
11 Netherton United Res	24	6	2	16	51	112	-61	20
12 Kings Cliffe	24	4	1	19	28	78	-50	13
13 Oakham United Res	24	3	1	18	23	98	-75	8*

Division Two

		P	W	D	L	F	A	GD	Pts
1	FC Parson Drove	26	21	1	3	117	20	97	65*
2	Eye United	26	20	3	3	116	25	91	63
3	Whittlesey Athletic Res	26	18	3	4	79	38	41	60*
4	Bretton North End	26	17	2	5	70	44	26	55*
5	Spalding Town	26	15	3	6	65	35	30	50*
6	FC Peterborough	26	14	3	8	56	51	5	43*
7	Rippingale & Folkingham	26	11	1	13	61	66	-5	35*
8	Parkway Eagles	26	9	4	13	62	92	-30	31
9	Netherton United 'A'	26	7	4	13	43	61	-18	27*
10	Stamford Lions Res	26	7	3	16	58	67	-9	24
11	Spalding United Res	26	8	2	16	49	75	-26	21*
12	Ketton Res	26	6	3	16	39	64	-25	20*
13	Stilton United	26	4	1	21	38	93	-55	13
14	Langtoft Utd (Sat) Res	26	1	1	21	18	140	-122	5*

Division Three

		P	W	D	L	F	A	GD	Pts
1	Cardea	26	21	2	2	135	35	100	68*
2	Premiair	26	18	3	4	116	35	81	60*
3	Oundle Town Res	26	16	3	6	91	63	28	54*
4	Whaplode Drove	26	16	3	7	98	63	35	51
5	Feeder	26	14	3	8	84	52	32	48*
6	Brotherhood Sports	26	14	6	5	102	53	49	45*
7	Farcet United	26	9	5	10	52	57	-5	34*
8	Leverington Sports Res	26	8	3	13	50	89	-39	33*
9	Whittlesey Athletic 'A'	26	8	5	13	58	84	-26	29
10	Stamford Belvedere Res	26	6	6	14	51	76	-25	24
11	Thorpe Wood Rangers	26	6	4	12	47	73	-26	22*
12	Holbeach Bank	26	5	3	16	47	103	-56	20*
13	Uppingham Town Res	26	6	2	17	47	78	-31	19*
14	Riverside	26	2	0	22	22	139	-117	0*

Division Four

		P	W	D	L	F	A	GD	Pts
1	Eunice Huntingdon	22	17	1	1	65	12	53	58*
2	Stamford Lions 'A'	22	17	3	2	78	23	55	54
3	Peterborough NECI	22	15	0	5	75	42	33	47*
4	Whittlesey Athletic 'B'	22	13	1	7	62	41	21	43*
5	FC Peterborough Res	22	10	1	7	42	32	10	40*
6	Long Sutton Athletic Res	22	11	2	9	42	49	-7	35
7	Parkside	22	10	2	10	55	52	3	32
8	Huntingdon Rovers	22	7	1	13	35	65	-30	22*
9	Orton Rangers ORFC	22	4	2	14	32	46	-14	20*
10	Holbeach United 'A'	22	3	1	17	29	71	-42	7*
11	Tydd St Mary Res	22	1	4	15	29	77	-48	5*
12	Ramsey Town Res	22	3	2	11	20	54	-34	4*

Division Five

		P	W	D	L	F	A	GD	Pts
1	AFC Orton	9	8	1	0	51	11	40	25
2	Glinton & Northborough Res	9	8	0	1	30	10	20	24
3	Kings Cliffe Res	9	5	1	3	32	13	19	16
4	Spalding United 'A'	9	5	1	3	25	20	5	16
5	Premiair Res	8	5	0	3	23	13	10	15
6	Wittering Harriers Res	9	2	2	3	17	23	-6	14*
7	Hampton	9	3	1	5	25	20	5	10
8	Gunthorpe Harriers	9	1	0	7	15	49	-34	6*
9	FC Peterborough 'A'	9	0	0	7	8	39	-31	2*
10	Leverington Sports 'A'	8	0	0	5	1	29	-28	-3*

Division Five A

		P	W	D	L	F	A	GD	Pts
1	Glinton & Northborough Res	10	8	0	2	26	14	12	24
2	Premiair Res	10	7	1	2	30	19	11	22
3	AFC Orton	10	4	2	4	39	25	14	14
4	Wittering Harriers Res	10	3	2	5	22	29	-7	11
5	Kings Cliffe Res	10	3	1	5	18	26	-8	9*
6	Spalding United 'A'	10	1	0	8	16	38	-22	6*

Division Five B

		P	W	D	L	F	A	GD	Pts
1	FC Parson Drove Res	10	7	2	0	69	11	58	26*
2	Stanground Sports	10	6	2	0	39	11	28	22*
3	Hampton	10	3	1	4	25	20	5	16*
4	Leverington Sports 'A'	10	4	0	5	28	28	0	11*
5	FC Peterborough 'A'	10	2	0	7	15	57	-42	3*
6	Gunthorpe Harriers	10	1	1	7	13	62	-49	3*

SHEFFIELD COUNTY SENIOR

Premier Division

		P	W	D	L	F	A	GD	Pts
1	Swinton Athletic	28	21	2	5	83	33	50	65
2	Stocksbridge Park Steels Res	28	21	1	6	88	36	52	64
3	AFC Penistone Church Res	28	17	6	5	86	25	61	57
4	North Gawber Colliery	28	16	7	5	77	48	29	55
5	Frecheville CAFC	28	15	6	7	71	39	32	53*
6	Grimethorpe Sports	28	15	7	6	85	37	48	51*
7	Jubilee Sports	28	15	4	9	96	53	43	49
8	Oughtibridge WMFC	28	10	6	12	60	34	26	37*
9	South Kirkby Colliery	28	10	6	12	37	52	-15	35*
10	Wombwell Main	28	9	7	12	43	49	-6	34
11	Handsworth Parramore Res	28	8	8	12	40	41	-1	32
12	Denaby United	28	5	10	13	55	88	-33	25
13	Denaby Main	28	3	4	21	30	116	-86	15*
14	Houghton Main	28	4	2	22	25	78	-53	14
15	Millmoor Juniors	28	2	2	24	18	165	-147	8

Division One

		P	W	D	L	F	A	GD	Pts
1	Dodworth Miners Welfare	22	19	2	1	70	22	48	59
2	High Green Villa	22	14	2	6	54	41	13	44
3	Hepworth United	22	13	4	5	48	32	16	43
4	Kiveton Park	22	10	3	9	63	56	7	33
5	Ecclesfield Red Rose 1915	22	9	3	10	41	45	-4	30
6	Sheffield Medics	22	8	4	10	35	46	-11	28
7	AFC Dronfield	22	8	3	11	58	56	2	27
8	Hemsworth Miners Welfare Res	22	7	5	10	45	56	-11	26
9	Caribbean Sports	22	6	4	11	34	39	-5	25
10	Brinsworth Whitehill	22	7	3	12	36	49	-13	24
11	Stocksbridge Park Steels Dev	22	6	12	52	52	-24	18	
12	Silkstone United	22	4	5	13	36	54	-18	17

FINAL TABLES

Division Two

		P	W	D	L	F	A	GD	Pts
1	Burngreave FC	26	20	2	4	119	48	71	65*
2	Wombwell Main Dev	26	17	2	7	80	53	27	50*
3	Boynton Sports	26	14	6	6	95	48	47	48
4	Manor Hotel	26	15	3	8	88	63	25	48
5	Sheffield Bankers Res	26	15	2	9	74	68	6	47
6	Swinton Athletic Res	26	13	4	9	62	48	14	45*
7	Caribbean Sports Res	26	12	5	9	94	61	33	41
8	New Bohemians	26	13	2	11	61	55	6	41
9	Worsbrough Bridge Athletic Dev	26	10	3	13	71	82	-11	33
10	Maltby Main Res	26	9	6	11	39	50	-11	33
11	Working Wonders	26	8	6	12	71	63	8	30
12	North Gawber Colliery Res	26	3	7	16	24	91	-67	16
13	AFC Dronfield Res	26	3	6	17	38	88	-50	14*
14	Thurcroft Miners Institute	26	1	4	21	25	123	-98	7

Division One West

		P	W	D	L	F	A	GD	Pts
1	Worle	30	22	5	3	99	30	69	71
2	Somerton Town	30	22	4	4	117	29	88	70
3	Uphill Castle	30	22	4	4	102	35	67	70
4	Yatton & Cleeve United	30	19	2	9	109	51	58	59
5	Winscombe	30	17	5	8	74	57	17	56
6	Minehead AFC	30	15	6	9	76	52	24	51
7	Nailsea & Tickenham Res	30	15	5	10	75	61	14	50
8	Burnham United	30	14	3	13	64	48	16	45
9	Glastonbury	30	13	6	11	66	55	11	45
10	Street Res	30	12	2	16	78	74	4	38
11	Portishead Town Res	30	11	3	16	83	85	-2	36
12	Ashton & Backwell United Res	30	8	3	19	48	71	-23	27
13	Weston St Johns	30	7	4	19	60	103	-43	22*
14	Clevedon United Res	29	6	5	18	33	105	-72	17*
15	Combe St Nicholas	29	5	2	22	29	116	-87	14*
16	Congresbury	30	1	1	28	23	164	-141	4

SOMERSET COUNTY LEAGUE

Premier Division

		P	W	D	L	F	A	GD	Pts
1	Chilcompton Sports	32	26	3	3	107	29	78	81
2	Watchet Town	32	24	4	4	84	24	60	76
3	Nailsea & Tickenham	32	20	6	6	83	29	54	66
4	Fry Club	32	19	8	5	80	41	39	65
5	Middlezoy Rovers	32	17	8	7	52	30	22	59
6	Shirehampton	32	16	5	11	69	57	12	50*
7	Nailsea United	32	12	7	13	51	48	3	43
8	Clevedon United	32	10	8	14	47	59	-12	38
9	Odd Down (BATH) Res	32	9	11	12	39	59	-20	37*
10	Stockwood Green	32	7	13	12	38	51	-13	34
11	Wrington Redhill	32	9	7	16	46	70	-24	34
12	Stockwood Wanderers	32	7	12	13	43	47	-4	33
13	Ilminster Town	32	7	11	14	44	68	-24	32
14	Clutton	32	8	6	18	40	69	-29	30
15	Bridgwater Town FC Res	32	11	4	17	44	67	-23	29*
16	Wells City Res	32	5	3	24	38	92	-54	17*
17	Staplegrove	32	5	4	23	37	102	-65	16*

Division One East

		P	W	D	L	F	A	GD	Pts
1	Westfield	32	27	4	1	141	41	100	85
2	Saltford	32	23	3	6	88	43	45	72
3	Timsbury Athletic	32	22	5	5	113	31	82	71
4	Keynsham Town Res	32	20	6	6	104	43	61	66
5	Mendip Broadwalk	32	16	7	9	79	61	18	55
6	Hengrove Athletic Res	32	15	5	12	84	55	29	50
7	Long Ashton	32	14	7	11	74	75	-1	49
8	Purnell Sports	32	14	2	16	73	82	-9	44
9	Castle Cary	32	10	10	12	55	69	-14	40
10	Imperial	32	11	6	15	57	59	-2	39
11	Brislington Res	32	9	6	17	62	63	-1	33
12	Broad Plain House	32	11	3	18	51	73	-22	33*
13	Frome Town Sports	32	9	4	19	43	92	-49	31
14	Fry Club Res	32	8	6	18	40	85	-45	30
15	Welton Rovers Res	32	8	5	19	47	75	-28	29
16	Peasedown Miners Welfare	32	8	8	16	44	84	-40	29*
17	Cutters Friday	32	1	5	26	34	158	-124	8

Division Two

		P	W	D	L	F	A	GD	Pts
1	AFC Brislington	24	20	3	1	93	21	72	63
2	Radstock Town Res	24	19	1	4	91	31	60	58
3	Hutton	24	13	3	8	49	50	-1	42
4	Chew Magna	24	12	3	9	72	34	38	39
5	Draycott	24	11	6	7	63	48	15	39
6	Banwell	24	11	2	11	44	43	1	35
7	Cheddar Res	24	10	3	11	38	40	-2	33
8	Nailsea United Res	24	9	5	10	45	45	0	32
9	Burnham United Res	24	8	5	11	29	54	-25	29
10	Winscombe Res	24	8	2	14	43	58	-15	26
11	Yatton & Cleeve United Res	24	7	4	13	44	56	-12	25
12	Tunley Athletic	24	5	1	18	27	101	-74	16
13	Stockwood Green Res	24	3	2	19	22	79	-57	11

MID-SOMERSET LEAGUE

Premier Division

		P	W	D	L	F	A	GD	Pts
1	Frome Collegians	18	17	0	1	79	14	65	51
2	Coleford Athletic	18	13	2	3	44	29	15	41
3	Victoria Sports	18	12	1	5	57	37	20	37
4	Radstock Town A	18	9	3	6	39	37	2	30
5	Westfield Res	18	9	2	7	43	38	5	29
6	Westhill Sports	18	9	2	7	32	29	3	29
7	Purnell Sports Res	18	4	4	10	39	50	-11	16
8	Mells & Vobster Utd	18	3	1	14	22	57	-35	10
9	Temple Cloud	18	5	1	12	25	37	-12	6*
10	Wells City A	18	0	2	16	18	70	-52	2

Division One

		P	W	D	L	F	A	GD	Pts
1	Bath Villa	18	14	2	2	71	30	41	43*
2	Peasedown Albion	18	12	2	4	63	24	39	38
3	Pilton United	18	11	1	6	68	38	30	34
4	Chilcompton Sports Res	18	9	3	6	62	51	11	27*
5	Clutton Res	18	7	3	8	40	52	-12	24
6	Chew Magna Res	18	6	4	8	49	43	6	19*
7	Somer Valley Sports	18	5	3	10	39	67	-28	18
8	Meadow Rangers	18	4	4	10	31	52	-21	16
9	High Littleton	18	4	3	11	26	55	-29	15
10	Belrose	18	4	3	11	25	62	-37	14*

Division Two	P	W	D	L	F	A	GD	Pts
1 Evercreech Rovers	18	11	3	4	59	29	30	36
2 Peasedown Albion Res	18	10	3	5	45	29	16	33
3 Timsbury Athletic Res	18	9	5	4	59	30	29	32
4 Coleford Athletic Res	18	8	5	5	41	25	16	26*
5 Wessex	18	6	3	9	44	42	2	21
6 Westhill Sports Res	18	5	1	12	21	74	-53	16
7 Saltford Res	18	3	2	13	23	63	-40	8*

Division Three	P	W	D	L	F	A	GD	Pts
1 Weston	16	13	3	0	46	18	28	42
2 Stoke Rovers	16	11	1	4	46	22	24	34
3 Farrington Gurney	16	9	1	6	33	29	4	25*
4 Timsbury Athletic A	16	5	5	6	28	34	-6	20
5 Glastonbury Res	16	7	1	8	35	39	-4	19*
6 Westfield A	16	6	1	9	33	42	-9	19
7 Purnell Sports A	16	4	3	9	24	35	-11	14*
8 Chilcompton United	16	3	4	9	21	37	-16	13
9 Pilton United Res	16	3	3	10	26	36	-10	12

PERRY STREET & DISTRICT LEAGUE

Premier Division	P	W	D	L	F	A	GD	Pts
1 Barrington	20	16	2	2	79	25	54	50
2 Merriott Rovers	20	15	3	2	59	33	26	44*
3 South Petherton	20	14	1	5	61	31	30	43
4 Chard Utd.	20	13	2	5	68	32	36	41
5 West & Middle Chinnock	20	11	4	5	61	46	15	37
6 Misterton	20	10	1	9	46	38	8	31
7 Shepton Beauchamp	20	8	1	11	53	49	4	25
8 Winsham	20	6	3	11	38	45	-7	19*
9 Pymore	20	4	0	16	31	67	-36	12
10 Netherbury	20	3	1	16	28	86	-58	10
11 Combe Res	20	0	2	18	15	87	-72	0*

Division One	P	W	D	L	F	A	GD	Pts
1 Halstock	18	15	2	1	90	23	67	47
2 Farway United	18	11	5	2	62	29	33	38
3 Forton Rangers	18	11	4	3	55	35	20	37
4 Ilminster Colts	18	10	2	6	55	47	8	32
5 Waytown Hounds	18	9	4	5	52	33	19	31
6 Perry Street Res	18	5	6	7	44	52	-8	21
7 Uplyme	18	5	3	10	42	54	-12	18
8 Hawkchurch	18	4	4	10	46	65	-19	16
9 Shepton Res	18	2	3	13	34	68	-34	9
10 Chard Rangers	18	1	1	16	18	92	-74	4

Division Two	P	W	D	L	F	A	GD	Pts
1 Thorncombe	20	17	3	0	114	23	91	54
2 Crewkerne Rangers	20	15	3	2	80	25	55	48
3 Misterton Res	20	14	3	3	86	31	55	45
4 Forton Rangers Res	20	12	1	7	58	35	23	37
5 Charmouth	20	10	3	7	59	60	-1	33
6 South Petherton Res	20	9	2	9	56	45	11	29
7 Dowlish & Donyatt	20	6	2	12	47	75	-28	20
8 Kingsbury	20	5	2	13	46	69	-23	17
9 Chard Utd. Res	20	3	2	15	46	90	-44	11
10 Combe A	20	4	2	14	35	101	-66	9*
11 Winsham Res	20	3	1	16	32	105	-73	9*

Division Three	P	W	D	L	F	A	GD	Pts
1 Ilminster Town A	18	15	0	3	59	22	37	45
2 Donyatt United	18	14	2	2	68	26	42	40*
3 Crewkerne Rangers Res	18	12	1	5	58	31	27	37
4 Merriott Dynamos	18	10	1	7	46	46	0	30*
5 Lyme Rovers	18	8	2	8	61	60	1	26
6 Farway Res	18	8	2	8	60	51	9	24*
7 Thorncombe Res	18	5	4	9	31	55	-24	19
8 Netherbury Res	18	4	3	11	49	49	0	11*
9 Chard Rangers Res	18	3	1	14	29	79	-50	10
10 Chard United All Stars	18	2	2	14	27	69	-42	7*

TAUNTON LEAGUE

Premier Division	P	W	D	L	F	A	GD	Pts
1 Middlezoy Rovers Res	22	18	3	1	82	18	64	57
2 Bishops Lydeard Res	22	14	3	5	84	26	58	45
3 Bridgwater Sports s	22	14	1	7	82	40	42	43
4 Westonzoyland	22	12	5	5	56	30	26	41
5 Wembdon	22	12	3	7	50	35	15	39
6 Alcombe Rovers	22	11	6	5	43	38	5	39
7 Morganians	22	9	0	13	57	60	-3	27
8 Ash Rangers	22	7	4	11	44	62	-18	22*
9 North Petherton (Mens)	22	5	3	14	52	54	-2	18
10 Porlock	22	4	5	13	32	78	-46	17
11 Creech Cougars	22	5	4	13	43	71	-28	16*
12 Woolavington	22	2	1	19	18	131	-113	4*

Division One	P	W	D	L	F	A	GD	Pts
1 Redgate	24	19	1	4	82	31	51	58
2 Watchet Town Res	24	16	4	4	85	37	48	52
3 Galmington	24	14	7	3	64	37	27	49
4 Staplegrove Res	24	13	6	5	79	48	31	39*
5 Bridgwater Sports Res	24	12	3	9	64	55	9	39
6 Minehead AFC Res	24	10	4	10	54	56	-2	34
7 Dulverton Town	24	9	3	12	49	53	-4	30
8 White Eagles (Taunton)	24	10	2	12	53	80	-27	29*
9 Stogursey	24	9	6	9	57	51	6	27*
10 Bridgwater Grasshoppers	24	7	3	14	59	83	-24	24
11 Butlins Saturday	24	5	5	14	39	63	-24	20
12 Norton Fitzwarren	24	3	5	16	44	84	-40	14
13 Porlock Res	24	4	1	19	31	82	-51	13

FINAL TABLES

Division Two

		P	W	D	L	F	A	GD	Pts
1	FC Castlemoat	24	20	3	1	130	36	94	63
2	North Curry (Sat)	24	15	3	6	93	31	62	48
3	Wembdon Res	24	16	2	6	89	41	48	47*
4	Sydenham Rangers	24	14	2	8	92	68	24	44
5	Middlezoy Rovers Athletic	24	13	2	9	70	64	6	41
6	Bridgwater Sports Colts	24	13	2	9	70	67	3	41
7	Norton Fitzwarren Res	24	12	4	8	85	60	25	40
8	Morganians Res	24	9	3	12	40	63	-23	27*
9	Nether Stowey Tigers	24	7	5	12	56	66	-10	20*
10	Hamilton Athletic Foxes	24	6	2	16	53	139	-86	20
11	Wyvern United	24	6	6	12	41	75	-34	18*
12	Exmoor Rangers	24	4	3	17	39	82	-43	12*
13	North Petherton Res	24	2	1	21	32	98	-66	7

WESTON-SUPER-MARE & DISTRICT LEAGUE

Division One

		P	W	D	L	F	A	GD	Pts
1	Portishead Caledonian Thistle	18	16	1	1	80	23	57	49
2	Locking Park	18	13	1	4	72	44	28	40
3	Westend	18	10	1	7	74	54	20	31
4	K V F C	18	10	1	7	41	46	-5	31
5	Sporting Weston	18	8	5	5	41	41	0	29
6	Uphill Castle Res	18	7	2	9	47	48	-1	23
7	Wedmore	18	6	3	9	39	54	-15	21
8	Portishead Town A	18	5	2	11	32	51	-19	17
9	Nailsea United A	18	4	2	12	37	48	-11	14
10	Wrington Redhill Res	18	2	0	16	23	77	-54	6

Division Two

		P	W	D	L	F	A	GD	Pts
1	St George Easton In Gordano	20	17	2	1	66	23	43	53
2	Worle Res	20	13	1	6	52	28	24	40
3	Clapton In Gordano	20	9	6	5	57	43	14	33
4	Yatton & Cleeve United A	20	10	1	9	55	50	5	31
5	South Park Rangers	20	9	1	10	50	48	2	28
6	Churchill Club 70	20	7	4	9	35	42	-7	25
7	Axbridge Town	20	6	5	9	43	45	-2	23
8	Banwell Res	20	7	2	11	43	52	-9	23
9	Worle Rangers	20	6	2	12	40	70	-30	20
10	Locking Park Res	20	7	1	12	42	57	-15	19*
11	Winscombe A	20	6	1	13	32	57	-25	19

Division Three

		P	W	D	L	F	A	GD	Pts
1	Portishead Town B	16	12	1	3	57	22	35	37
2	Nailsea United B	16	11	1	4	33	21	12	34
3	Congresbury Res	16	10	2	4	33	19	14	32
4	St George Easton In Gordano Res	16	9	3	4	60	35	25	30
5	Selkirk United	16	9	0	7	50	32	18	27
6	Shipham	16	8	2	6	53	38	15	26
7	Kewstoke Lions	16	4	2	10	43	60	-17	14
8	Worle Rangers Res	16	2	0	14	17	65	-48	6
9	"Wrington Redhill ""A"""	16	1	1	14	17	71	-54	4

Division Four

		P	W	D	L	F	A	GD	Pts
1	Burnham United A	16	14	0	2	68	22	46	42
2	Uphill Castle A	16	11	1	4	65	35	30	34
3	Hutton Res	16	10	0	6	60	37	23	30
4	Cheddar A	16	8	1	7	42	37	5	25
5	AFC Nailsea	16	8	1	7	18	22	-4	25
6	Sporting Weston Res	16	7	2	7	43	48	-5	23
7	Congresbury A	16	7	1	8	38	38	0	17*
8	Axbridge Town Res	16	2	1	13	22	80	-58	7
9	Banwell A	16	1	1	14	21	58	-37	4

Division Five

		P	W	D	L	F	A	GD	Pts
1	West Wick	16	11	5	0	63	18	45	38
2	Banwell B	16	11	2	3	47	24	23	34*
3	Lodway	16	10	2	4	61	29	32	32
4	Clevedon United A	16	7	5	4	45	37	8	26
5	Burnham United B	16	7	3	6	50	49	1	24
6	Yatton & Cleeve United B	16	7	2	7	29	22	7	19*
7	Weston Celtic	16	3	2	11	19	35	-16	11
8	Wedmore Res	16	3	2	11	22	72	-50	11
9	Nailsea United C	16	1	1	14	25	75	-50	4

YEOVIL & DISTRICT LEAGUE

Premier Division

		P	W	D	L	F	A	GD	Pts
1	Somerton Town Res	18	17	0	1	75	12	63	51
2	Templecombe Rovers	18	13	1	4	63	24	39	40
3	Ashcott	18	11	1	6	60	26	34	34
4	Pen Mill	18	8	2	8	43	31	12	25*
5	East Coker	18	7	4	7	45	54	-9	25
6	Montacute	18	8	1	9	41	51	-10	25
7	Castle Cary Res	18	5	3	10	42	60	-18	18
8	Stoke	18	5	3	10	26	59	-33	18
9	Wagtail Athletic	18	3	3	12	26	60	-34	11*
10	Martock United	18	3	2	13	36	80	-44	11

Division One

		P	W	D	L	F	A	GD	Pts
1	Pen Mill Athletic	20	15	2	3	78	34	44	47
2	Bradford Abbas	20	14	4	2	79	35	44	46
3	Keinton Park Rangers	20	13	1	6	68	52	16	40
4	Manor Athletic	20	10	4	6	59	52	7	34
5	Milborne Port Res	20	8	5	7	56	54	2	29
6	Ashcott Res	20	9	1	10	45	50	-5	28
7	Bruton United	20	7	3	10	43	59	-16	24
8	Charlton United	20	6	4	10	43	71	-28	22
9	Odcombe	20	6	3	11	54	63	-9	21
10	Barwick & Stoford	20	2	2	16	32	69	-37	8
11	Brhoden United	20	4	3	13	36	54	-18	7*

Division Two

		P	W	D	L	F	A	GD	Pts
1	Langport & Huish Sports	20	17	2	1	90	26	64	53
2	Huish AFC	20	14	3	3	78	38	40	45
3	Pen Mill Res	20	13	3	4	83	35	48	42
4	Crewkerne Rangers Colts	20	12	2	6	69	44	25	38
5	Keinton Park Rangers Res	20	11	1	8	67	51	16	34
6	Wyndham Athletic	20	8	1	11	57	70	-13	25
7	Odcombe Res	20	6	3	11	54	64	-10	21
8	Martock United Res	20	5	2	13	49	68	-19	16*
9	Stoke Res	20	3	5	12	53	76	-23	14
10	Milborne Port A	20	3	5	12	31	76	-45	13*
11	Bruton United Res	20	4	1	15	24	107	-83	8*

STAFFORDSHIRE COUNTY SENIOR

Premier Division

		P	W	D	L	F	A	GD	Pts
1	Wolstanton United	30	25	4	1	105	41	64	79
2	Foley Meir	30	21	5	4	118	49	69	68
3	Silverdale Athletic	30	21	3	6	94	39	55	66
4	Leek CSOB	30	18	5	7	79	48	31	59
5	Eastwood Hanley	30	14	7	9	64	45	19	49
6	Redgate Clayton	30	14	5	11	76	73	3	47
7	Alsager Town Res	30	13	5	12	52	48	4	44
8	Ball Haye Green	30	14	2	14	84	76	8	41
9	Newcastle Town Res	30	10	6	14	64	70	-6	36
10	Ashbourne FC	30	10	6	14	59	66	-7	36
11	Stone Dominoes Res	30	10	4	16	55	79	-24	34
12	Walsall Phoenix	30	10	2	18	79	88	-9	32
13	Cheadle Town Res	30	9	4	17	55	82	-27	31
14	Hanley Town Res	30	6	8	16	46	72	-26	26
15	Knypersley Victoria	30	6	3	21	67	117	-50	21
16	Florence FC	30	4	1	25	56	160	-104	13

Division One

		P	W	D	L	F	A	GD	Pts
1	Ossma Blurton TT	26	22	4	0	83	19	64	70
2	Brereton Social	26	18	4	4	64	27	37	58
3	Shenstoen Pathfinder	26	18	1	7	79	33	46	55
4	Penkridge FC	26	12	5	9	62	52	10	41
5	Market Drayton Tigers	26	11	7	8	47	37	10	40
6	Foley Meir Res	26	12	3	11	44	53	-9	39
7	Abbey Hulton United	26	12	3	11	51	37	14	36
8	Audley	26	10	6	10	41	41	0	36
9	Leek CSOB Res	26	9	3	14	51	61	-10	30
10	Redgate Clayton Res	26	10	3	13	52	50	2	27
11	Milton United	26	6	6	14	38	51	-27	27
12	Keele University	26	6	3	17	33	63	-30	21
13	Walsall Phoenix Res	26	6	1	19	45	89	-44	19
14	Cheadle Town Res	26	4	3	19	24	101	-77	12

Division Two

		P	W	D	L	F	A	GD	Pts
1	Whittington	26	17	5	4	86	40	46	56
2	Goldenhill Wanderers	26	17	2	7	74	38	36	53
3	Red Star Alma	26	17	1	8	80	55	25	52
4	Staffordshire Moorlands	26	14	4	8	93	58	35	46
5	AFC Alsager	26	14	3	9	76	57	19	45
6	Acorn Albion	26	13	1	12	60	60	0	40
7	NDFC	26	11	4	11	64	68	-4	37
8	Hilton Harriers	26	11	3	12	46	51	-5	36
9	Cannock United	26	9	4	13	61	73	-12	31
10	Keele University Res	26	9	4	13	58	74	-16	31
11	Featherstone FC	26	8	5	13	52	73	-21	29
12	Chesterton AFC	26	6	7	13	70	89	-19	25
13	Audley Res	26	5	6	15	41	69	-28	21
14	AFC Fenton	26	5	3	18	44	100	-56	18

SUFFOLK & IPSWICH LEAGUE

Premier Division

		P	W	D	L	F	A	GD	Pts
1	Achilles	30	25	2	3	137	45	92	77
2	Crane Sports	30	19	5	6	89	38	51	62
3	Henley Athletic	30	18	5	7	80	40	40	59
4	Coplestonians	30	17	6	7	93	45	48	57
5	Felixstowe Harpers United	30	18	3	9	77	58	19	57
6	Capel Plough	30	15	6	9	53	45	8	51
7	Wenhaston United	30	15	4	11	59	50	9	49
8	Benhall St Mary	30	14	4	12	60	65	-5	46
9	Bramford United	30	12	5	13	64	73	-9	41
10	East Bergholt United	30	11	7	12	48	55	-7	40
11	AFC Hoxne	30	9	7	14	58	66	-8	34
12	Westerfield United	30	8	7	15	56	68	-12	31
13	Grundisburgh	30	7	4	19	48	80	-32	25
14	Leiston St Margarets	30	5	8	17	40	80	-40	23
15	Haughley United	30	4	5	21	51	105	-54	17
16	Ransomes Sports	30	3	2	25	39	139	-100	11

Division One

		P	W	D	L	F	A	GD	Pts
1	Claydon	26	22	1	3	73	21	52	67
2	Trimley Red Devils	26	20	5	1	75	27	48	65
3	Bildeston Rangers	26	17	2	7	70	51	19	53
4	Old Newton United	26	15	1	10	66	42	24	46
5	Bacton United 89	26	14	2	10	50	48	2	44
6	Sporting 87	26	11	6	9	61	41	20	39
7	AFC Kesgrave	24	12	2	10	42	32	10	38
8	Stanton	25	11	4	10	44	39	5	37
9	Barham Athletic	26	8	7	11	42	52	-10	31
10	Wickham Market	25	8	1	16	40	60	-20	25
11	Mendlesham	26	6	5	15	40	62	-22	23
12	Stowupland Falcons	26	2	17	45	77	-32	15	
13	Ipswich Athletic	26	5	0	21	34	91	-57	15
14	Trimley Athletic	26	3	4	19	20	59	-39	13

Division Two

		P	W	D	L	F	A	GD	Pts
1	Cedars Park	22	19	2	1	74	16	58	59
2	Coddenham Athletic	22	19	1	2	86	35	51	58
3	Saxmundham Sports	22	13	1	8	64	40	24	40
4	Tacket Street BBOB	22	10	3	9	66	52	14	33
5	Cockfield United	21	10	1	10	68	57	11	31
6	Shotley	22	10	1	11	43	62	-19	31
7	Stonham Aspal	22	10	3	9	55	55	0	27*
8	Halesworth Town	22	7	2	13	37	52	-15	23
9	Ipswich Valley Rangers	21	7	3	11	44	59	-15	22*
10	Bramford Road Old Boys	22	6	4	12	40	60	-20	22
11	Somersham	22	6	3	13	38	53	-15	21
12	Witnesham Wasps	22	1	2	19	24	98	-74	5

Division Three

		P	W	D	L	F	A	GD	Pts
1	Kesgrave Kestrels	22	19	2	1	131	32	99	59
2	AFC YourShirts	22	18	3	1	102	16	86	57
3	Tattingstone United	22	14	3	5	74	38	36	45
4	Felixstowe Rangers	22	12	0	10	91	53	38	36
5	Thurston	22	11	2	9	60	51	9	35
6	Sproughton Sports	22	10	3	9	51	43	8	33
7	Elmswell	22	10	3	9	58	71	-13	30*
8	Woolverstone United	22	9	6	7	62	49	13	27*
9	Ufford Sports	22	8	2	12	45	60	-15	26
10	Sutton Heath Saxons	22	3	3	16	37	88	-51	12
11	Chantry Grasshoppers	22	3	2	17	37	104	-67	11
12	Salvation Army	22	0	1	21	20	163	-143	1

FINAL TABLES

Division Four

		P	W	D	L	F	A	GD	Pts
1	Wortham	24	22	1	1	111	27	84	67
2	Trimley Sports & Social Club	24	19	1	4	132	38	94	58
3	Bardwell Sports	24	19	0	5	109	36	73	57
4	Coplestonians 'B'	24	17	3	4	108	42	66	54
5	Framlingham Town 'A'	24	14	1	9	114	53	61	39*
6	Hope Church	24	10	2	12	58	58	0	29*
7	Elmswell Res	23	8	4	11	61	58	3	28
8	Whitton United 'A'	24	8	3	13	58	67	-9	25*
9	BROB Res	24	7	3	14	47	78	-31	22*
10	Bacton United 89 'A'	24	7	1	16	60	96	-36	22
11	Saxmundham Sports Res	23	6	4	13	50	86	-36	22
12	Sutton Heath Saxons Res	23	2	2	19	28	133	-105	4*
13	AFC Orwell	23	2	1	20	26	190	-164	3*

Intermediate A

		P	W	D	L	F	A	GD	Pts
1	Old Newton United Res	24	17	2	5	84	41	43	53
2	Framlingham Town Res	24	17	2	5	78	37	41	53
3	AFC. Hoxne Res	22	14	3	5	83	38	45	45
4	Achilles Res	23	13	3	7	70	49	21	42
5	Coplestonians Res	24	12	5	7	70	46	24	41
6	Westerfield United Res	24	12	4	8	56	46	10	40
7	Wenhaston United Res	24	10	8	6	40	40	0	38
8	Sporting 87 Res	24	9	6	9	49	58	-9	33
9	East Bergholt United Res	23	9	4	10	57	55	2	29*
10	Bramford United Res	24	5	7	12	45	60	-15	22
11	Henley Athletic Res	24	4	4	16	51	94	-43	16
12	Mendlesham Res	24	3	4	17	32	94	-62	11*
13	Ipswich Athletic Res	24	3	0	21	20	77	-57	9

Intermediate B

		P	W	D	L	F	A	GD	Pts
1	Coplestonians 'A'	24	19	0	5	65	21	44	57
2	Bacton United 89 Res	24	18	1	5	69	41	28	55
3	Trimley Red Devils Res	24	15	3	6	75	29	46	48
4	Claydon Res	24	15	3	6	67	35	32	48
5	Wickham Market Res	23	14	2	7	63	48	15	40*
6	Stonham Aspal Res	24	10	7	7	61	44	17	37
7	Cockfield United Res	24	10	4	10	65	67	-2	34
8	Haughley United Res	24	8	5	11	51	59	-8	27*
9	Cedars Park Res	22	6	3	13	39	64	-25	21
10	Trimley Athletic Res	23	8	1	14	65	82	-17	19*
11	Benhall St Mary Res	24	6	0	18	36	76	-40	18
12	East Bergholt United 'A'	24	4	4	16	50	94	-44	16
13	Stowupland Falcons Res	24	1	7	16	26	72	-46	5*

Intermediate C

		P	W	D	L	F	A	GD	Pts
1	Barham Athletic Res	22	19	1	2	91	26	65	58
2	Capel Plough Res	22	17	1	4	66	24	42	52
3	AFC Kesgrave Res	22	15	2	5	86	38	48	47
4	Leiston St Margarets Res	22	14	4	4	82	33	49	46
5	Kesgrave Kestrels Res	22	11	3	8	58	41	17	36
6	Stonham Aspal 'A'	22	8	4	10	66	69	-3	28
7	Sporting 87 'A'	22	6	4	12	47	66	-19	22
8	Ufford Sports Res	22	7	1	14	47	71	-24	22
9	Sprouighton Sports Res	20	6	2	12	38	72	-34	18*
10	Ransomes Sports Res	21	6	3	12	47	50	-3	15*
11	Halesworth Town Res	21	4	4	13	29	100	-71	14*
12	Somersham Res	22	1	3	18	28	95	-67	4*

LOWESTOFT & DISTRICT LEAGUE

Division One

		P	W	D	L	F	A	GD	Pts
1	Mutford & Wrentham FC	20	16	2	2	102	23	79	50
2	Oulton Broad	20	15	2	3	85	36	49	47
3	Southwold Town	20	13	4	3	74	28	46	43
4	Stanford	20	12	0	8	53	52	1	36
5	Oxford Arms	20	12	0	8	75	39	36	30*
6	Norton Athletic	20	8	4	8	45	42	3	28
7	Spexhall	20	8	3	9	45	45	0	27
8	Kirkley & Pakefield U21s	20	7	2	11	43	56	-13	23
9	First & Last	20	7	1	12	43	90	-47	22
10	Hearts of Oak	20	1	2	17	33	103	-70	5
11	Barsham	20	1	0	19	19	103	-84	-6*

Division Two

		P	W	D	L	F	A	GD	Pts
1	Hopton	20	15	2	3	103	37	66	47
2	Beccles Caxton Res	20	14	4	2	75	34	41	46
3	"Waveney ""A"""	20	14	1	5	41	29	12	43
4	Kirkley & Pakefield B	20	10	3	7	52	47	5	33
5	Carlton Colville Town	20	10	2	8	58	36	22	32
6	Ellingham	20	9	2	9	68	53	15	29
7	Earsham Res	20	8	4	8	32	33	-1	25*
8	Bungay Town A	20	7	3	10	49	56	-7	24
9	Norton Athletic Res	20	6	3	11	52	60	-8	21
10	Crusaders	20	4	1	15	39	102	-63	13
11	Spexhall Res	20	0	1	19	18	100	-82	1

Division Three

		P	W	D	L	F	A	GD	Pts
1	Celt Rangers	26	25	0	1	190	15	175	75
2	Mariners	26	16	4	6	73	47	26	52
3	Stanford Res	26	16	2	8	102	73	29	50
4	Gentlemens Club	26	15	2	9	82	66	16	47
5	Redwood United	26	13	5	8	85	67	18	44
6	East Coast	26	13	5	8	62	67	-5	44
7	AC Mill Lane Res	26	13	0	13	75	67	8	39
8	Carlton Colville Town Res	26	10	6	10	78	83	-5	36
9	Mutford & Wrentham Res	26	12	3	11	56	69	-13	36*
10	Art Eternal	26	10	3	13	67	66	1	30*
11	AFC Oulton	26	9	1	16	72	76	-4	28
12	Loddon United Res	26	8	3	15	59	74	-15	27
13	Hempnall Res	26	4	2	20	39	82	-43	5*
14	Hawthorn United	26	0	0	26	18	206	-188	-3*

ST EDMUNDSBURY LEAGUE

Division One

		P	W	D	L	F	A	GD	Pts
1	St Edmunds 1965	16	15	0	1	84	16	68	45
2	Vipers FC	16	14	0	2	71	19	52	42
3	Bedricks Worth	16	13	0	3	108	22	86	39
4	RF Saints FC	16	9	0	7	56	49	7	27
5	Walsham Le Willows B	16	7	0	9	65	41	24	21
6	Bury Town Rams	16	6	0	10	26	47	-21	17*
7	Eriswell Village	16	4	0	12	30	86	-56	11*
8	Bury Wanderers	16	2	1	13	28	116	-88	4*
9	Beck Row F.C.	16	1	1	14	16	88	-72	1*

SURREY ELITE INTERMEDIATE

Intermediate Division	P	W	D	L	F	A	GD	Pts
1 Tooting Bec	26	19	5	2	81	22	59	62
2 Royal Holloway Old Boys	26	18	3	5	53	29	24	57
3 Battersea Ironsides	26	17	1	8	61	45	16	52
4 Chessington KC	26	12	7	7	62	51	11	43
5 Laleham	26	12	5	9	52	47	5	41
6 AFC Cubo	26	12	4	10	65	51	14	40
7 N P L	26	12	2	12	62	57	5	38
8 Godalming & Farncombe Athletic	26	12	4	10	55	45	10	37*
9 Ripley Village	26	10	3	13	61	52	9	36*
10 AFC Spelthorne Sports	26	10	3	13	51	55	-4	33
11 Spartans Youth	26	9	4	13	51	53	-2	31
12 Westside	26	9	2	15	45	56	-11	29
13 Merrow	26	5	2	19	35	81	-46	17
14 Reigate Priory	26	2	1	23	25	115	-90	7

SURREY COUNTY INTERMEDIATE (WESTERN)

Premier Division	P	W	D	L	F	A	GD	Pts
1 Horsley	24	16	5	3	80	36	44	53
2 West End Village	24	13	6	5	66	45	21	45
3 Lyne Seniors	24	13	5	6	84	43	41	44
4 University of Surrey	24	11	6	7	57	37	20	36 *
5 Chobham Burymead	24	11	6	7	64	47	17	36 *
6 Woking & Horsell	24	12	4	8	62	43	19	34 *
7 Shottermill & Haslemere	24	9	7	8	45	56	-11	34
8 Yateley United (Sat)	24	8	5	11	36	61	-25	29
9 Milford & Witley	24	7	7	10	40	61	-21	28
10 Cranleigh	24	7	5	12	34	50	-16	26
11 Worplesdon Phoenix	24	7	4	13	50	60	-10	25
12 Knaphill Athletic	24	7	3	14	48	53	-5	24
13 Chiddingfold	24	2	3	19	27	101	-74	9

Division One	P	W	D	L	F	A	GD	Pts
1 Guildford United	18	13	1	4	47	22	25	40
2 Parkside United	18	12	2	4	47	28	19	38
3 Windlesham United	18	10	2	6	36	22	14	32
4 Old Salesians	18	10	2	6	40	37	3	32
5 Keens Park Rangers	18	10	1	7	56	37	19	31
6 Manorcroft United	18	8	3	7	31	35	-4	24*
7 Hambledon	18	5	5	8	47	41	6	20
8 Burpham	18	4	6	8	26	34	-8	18
9 Weysiders	18	1	5	12	22	58	-36	8
10 Lightwater United	18	1	5	12	22	60	-38	8

Premier Reserves	P	W	D	L	F	A	GD	Pts
1 Woking & Horsell Res	16	11	3	2	44	20	24	36
2 Worplesdon Phoenix Res	16	9	3	4	53	31	22	30
3 Hambledon Res	16	9	2	5	28	23	5	29
4 Windlesham United Res	16	8	3	5	39	32	7	27
5 Knaphill Athletic Res	16	7	3	6	39	35	4	24
6 University of Surrey Res	16	8	1	7	39	29	10	22*
7 Chobham Burymead Res	16	4	3	9	30	42	-12	15
8 Yateley United Res (Sat)	16	2	3	11	29	56	-27	9
9 Chiddingfold Res	16	2	3	11	16	49	-33	9

Division One Reserves	P	W	D	L	F	A	GD	Pts
1 Horsley Res	16	13	2	1	66	14	52	41
2 Cranleigh Res	16	11	1	4	44	35	9	34
3 Keens Park Rangers Res	16	9	2	5	44	32	12	29
4 Milford & Witley Res	16	8	4	4	50	29	21	27*
5 Shottermill & Haslemere Res	16	8	2	6	38	31	7	26
6 Old Salesians Res	16	4	4	8	26	38	-12	16
7 West End Village Res	16	3	3	10	21	43	-22	12
8 Lightwater United Res	16	2	5	9	31	54	-23	11
9 Weysiders Res	16	2	1	13	26	70	-44	7

SURREY SOUTH EASTERN COMBINATION

Intermediate Division One	P	W	D	L	F	A	GD	Pts
1 Old Rutlishians	20	16	1	3	77	21	56	49
2 Hanworth Sports	20	14	6	0	33	14	19	48
3 Wandgas Sport	20	13	4	3	50	24	26	43
4 Westminster Casuals	20	9	4	7	45	35	10	31
5 Old Plymouthians	20	9	4	7	37	31	6	31
6 West Fulham	20	8	2	10	46	38	8	26
7 LDN South West	20	8	4	8	32	39	-7	25
8 A.M.Y	20	6	3	11	58	58	0	21
9 Bermondsey Town	20	5	4	11	43	50	-7	19
10 Ashtead	20	3	0	17	21	71	-50	9
11 Forestdale	20	2	2	16	20	81	-61	8

Intermediate Division Two	P	W	D	L	F	A	GD	Pts
1 Frenches Athletic	20	15	2	3	65	26	39	47
2 Balham Res	20	12	3	5	65	35	30	39
3 Raynes Park Vale Res	20	11	3	6	47	28	19	36
4 Oxted & District	20	11	2	7	39	44	-5	35
5 AFC Ewell	20	8	6	6	34	29	5	30
6 Claygate Royals	20	9	2	9	37	39	-2	29
7 Southwark Borough 2009	20	9	0	11	53	50	3	27
8 Merton Social	20	7	4	9	47	49	-2	25
9 Kew Park Rangers	20	7	2	11	51	59	-8	23
10 Old Wimbledonians	20	4	4	12	25	43	-18	16
11 AC Malden	20	3	0	17	21	82	-61	9

THAMES VALLEY PREMIER

Premier Division	P	W	D	L	F	A	GD	Pts
1 Reading YMCA	26	24	2	0	97	12	85	74
2 Woodcote Stoke Row	26	20	4	2	87	42	45	64
3 Westwood United	26	15	5	6	67	47	20	50
4 Wright & Unity Sports	26	15	2	9	52	41	11	47
5 Newbury FC	26	13	6	7	69	50	19	45
6 Marlow United	26	13	4	9	66	45	21	43
7 Cookham Dean	26	12	2	12	54	50	4	38
8 Mortimer	26	10	4	12	50	60	-10	34
9 Wraysbury Village	26	5	5	14	52	65	-13	26
10 Berks County FC	26	6	6	14	41	58	-17	24
11 Wokingham & Emmbrook Res	26	7	3	16	36	67	-31	24
12 Highmoor Ibis United	26	6	5	15	31	61	-30	20*
13 Woodley United Royals	26	6	1	19	39	65	-26	19
14 Taplow United	26	2	3	21	24	102	-78	12*

FINAL TABLES

Division One

		P	W	D	L	F	A	GD	Pts
1	Richings Park	22	13	3	6	55	35	20	42
2	Burghfield FC	22	12	4	6	41	28	13	42*
3	Cookham Dean Res	22	11	7	4	34	24	10	40
4	FC Imaan Lions	22	12	3	7	55	35	20	39
5	Eldon Celtic	22	9	5	8	46	44	2	31*
6	Finchampstead	22	9	4	9	45	44	1	31
7	Hurst	22	10	1	11	31	47	-16	31
8	Westwood United Res	22	9	3	10	45	51	-6	30
9	Reading YMCA Rapids	22	7	6	9	26	24	2	27
10	Rotherfield United	22	5	6	11	32	42	-10	21
11	Maidenhead Town	22	6	3	13	37	50	-13	21
12	Frilsham & Yattendon	22	5	3	14	27	50	-23	18

Division Two

		P	W	D	L	F	A	GD	Pts
1	FC Woodley	20	16	3	1	68	28	40	51
2	South Reading	20	13	4	3	55	27	28	43
3	White Eagles	20	11	3	6	42	40	2	36
4	AFC Corinthians	20	8	4	8	46	55	-9	28
5	Mortimer Res	20	7	5	8	54	55	-1	26
6	Woodcote Stoke Row Res	20	8	2	10	44	46	-2	26
7	Harchester Hawks	20	8	1	11	41	40	1	25
8	Brimpton Athletic	20	6	4	10	54	49	5	22
9	Hurst Res	20	6	4	10	42	49	-7	22
10	Marlow United Res	20	7	1	12	37	56	-19	22
11	Berks County Res	20	4	1	15	33	71	-38	13

Division Three

		P	W	D	L	F	A	GD	Pts
1	Wargrave	16	11	2	3	46	34	12	35
2	Maidenhead Town Res	16	10	3	3	46	19	27	33
3	Goring United	16	10	2	4	56	20	36	32
4	Braybrooke	16	9	0	7	37	31	6	27
5	Henley Town Res	16	8	2	6	38	27	11	26
6	Hurst 'A'	16	6	5	5	36	35	1	23
7	Woodley United 'A'	16	4	3	9	48	40	8	15
8	Taplow United Res	16	3	2	11	19	57	-38	11
9	Highmoor Ibis Athletic	16	1	1	14	14	77	-63	4

Division Four

		P	W	D	L	F	A	GD	Pts
1	Twyford & Ruscombe	20	19	0	1	82	27	55	57
2	Taplow United 'A'	20	15	1	4	69	40	29	46
3	Maidenhead Town 'A'	20	10	3	7	56	50	6	33
4	Goring United Res	20	9	3	8	54	48	6	30
5	Cintra Park Rovers	20	9	2	9	39	40	-1	29
6	Berks County Rovers	20	8	3	9	54	51	3	27
7	Woodley United 'B'	20	7	5	8	44	43	1	26
8	White Eagles Res	20	6	5	9	45	61	-16	23
9	AFC Corinthians 'A'	20	4	4	12	35	56	-21	16
10	Harchester Hawks Dev	20	4	3	13	36	63	-27	15
11	Farnham Royal Mavericks	20	3	3	14	37	72	-35	11*

WEARSIDE LEAGUE

		P	W	D	L	F	A	GD	Pts
1	Redcar Athletic	32	25	5	2	98	32	66	80
2	Cleator Moor Celtic	32	25	4	3	112	26	86	79
3	Sunderland West End	32	20	6	6	105	42	63	66
4	Hebburn Town Res	32	20	4	8	74	38	36	64
5	Boldon CA	32	19	7	6	68	43	25	64
6	Richmond Town	32	16	5	11	73	49	24	53
7	Silksworth Colliery Welfare	32	15	5	12	70	54	16	50
8	Wolviston	32	16	2	14	73	64	9	50
9	Hartlepool	32	14	5	13	80	55	25	47
10	Gateshead Leam Rangers	32	12	5	15	46	64	-18	41
11	Darlington Reserves	32	12	4	16	76	63	13	40
12	Harton & Westoe CW	32	8	7	17	49	83	-34	31
13	Annfield Plain	32	8	2	22	38	102	-64	26
14	Stokesley Sports Club	32	7	4	21	56	112	-56	25
15	South Shields Res	32	8	0	24	50	106	-56	24
16	Windscale	32	6	5	21	46	107	-61	23
17	Coxhoe Athletic	32	4	4	24	42	116	-74	16

Prudhoe Town withdrew - record expunged

DURHAM ALLIANCE COMBINATION

		P	W	D	L	F	A	GD	Pts
1	Wheatley Hill WMC	16	14	1	1	85	20	65	43
2	Horden Community Welfare	16	13	0	3	85	23	62	36*
3	West Auckland Tunns	16	11	1	4	68	29	39	34
4	Hylton Sports Club	16	9	3	4	68	54	14	30
5	Hall Farm Glasshus	16	9	2	5	68	32	36	26*
6	Seaton United	16	4	1	11	37	64	-27	13
7	Durham City Res	16	3	2	11	39	50	-11	11
8	Farringdon Detached	16	3	2	11	34	67	-33	11
9	Jarrow FC Res	16	0	0	16	15	160	-145	0

WEST CHESHIRE LEAGUE

Division One

		P	W	D	L	F	A	GD	Pts
1	South Liverpool	30	22	5	3	81	31	50	71
2	Vauxhall Motors	30	17	7	6	72	39	33	58
3	Mossley Hill Athletic	30	18	3	9	78	36	42	57
4	Newton	30	17	3	10	80	53	27	54
5	Rainhill Town	30	15	7	8	71	50	21	52
6	Richmond Raith Rovers	30	14	4	12	59	75	-16	46
7	Maghull	30	13	5	12	48	42	6	44
8	Upton AA	30	14	1	15	51	47	4	43
9	Neston Nomads	30	13	2	15	66	73	-7	41
10	Redgate Rovers	30	13	2	15	66	90	-24	41
11	Chester Nomads	30	9	8	13	33	50	-17	35
12	Marshalls	30	10	2	18	55	60	-5	32
13	Ashville	30	14	3	13	45	36	9	30*
14	West Kirby	30	6	4	20	27	62	-35	22
15	Heswall	30	10	2	18	52	64	-12	17*
16	Mallaby	30	4	4	22	42	118	-76	16

Division Two

		P	W	D	L	F	A	GD	Pts
1	Hale	26	17	4	5	58	28	30	55
2	Maghull Res	26	15	7	4	50	31	19	52
3	Ellesmere Port Town	26	14	9	3	60	37	23	51
4	Cheshire Lines	26	14	7	5	60	41	19	49
5	Mossley Hill Athletic Res	26	13	5	8	58	42	16	44
6	South Liverpool Res	26	13	4	9	48	39	9	43
7	Ashville Res	26	12	5	9	48	33	15	41
8	Vauxhall Motors Res	26	11	5	10	64	49	15	38
9	Capenhurst Villa	26	11	5	10	55	42	13	38
10	Prescot Cables Res	26	11	2	13	50	58	-8	35
11	Heswall Res	26	10	2	14	33	42	-9	32
12	Rainhill Town Res	26	7	3	16	42	57	-15	24
13	Willaston	26	2	1	23	39	96	-57	7
14	West Kirby Res	26	1	3	22	15	85	-70	6

Division Three

		P	W	D	L	F	A	GD	Pts
1	Page Celtic	24	18	2	4	99	37	62	56
2	Litherland Remyca Res	24	17	4	3	96	45	51	55
3	Wirral SB	24	15	7	2	56	30	26	52
4	Mersey Royal	24	15	2	7	81	44	37	47
5	Poulton Royal	24	14	2	8	54	39	15	44
6	Marshalls Res	24	13	2	9	65	54	11	41
7	Chester Nomads Res	24	10	3	11	49	47	2	33
8	Burscough Dynamo	24	9	2	13	52	73	-21	29
9	Cheshire Lines Res	24	7	2	15	41	66	-25	23
10	Neston Nomads Res	24	6	5	13	40	76	-36	23
11	Redgate Rovers Res	24	6	2	16	42	72	-30	20
12	Capenhurst Villa Res	24	5	1	18	37	63	-26	16
13	Ellesmere Port Town Res	24	3	2	19	21	87	-66	11

WEST LANCASHIRE LEAGUE

Premier Division

		P	W	D	L	F	A	GD	Pts
1	Garstang	30	22	5	3	96	24	72	71
2	Blackpool Wren Rovers	30	22	3	5	87	35	52	69
3	Longridge Town	30	17	4	9	66	47	19	55
4	Euxton Villa	30	14	10	6	60	50	10	52
5	Tempest United	30	15	6	9	69	49	20	51
6	Fulwood Amateurs	30	14	2	14	59	55	4	44
7	Southport Hesketh	30	11	10	9	61	64	-3	43
8	Slyne with Hest	30	12	5	13	62	73	-11	41
9	Haslingden St. Marys	30	12	4	14	61	67	-6	40
10	Turton	30	10	5	15	44	55	-11	35
11	Thornton Cleveleys	30	10	4	16	57	54	3	34
12	Hesketh Bank	30	9	7	14	52	63	-11	34
13	Vickerstown	30	10	2	18	55	69	-14	32
14	Coppull United	30	9	4	17	44	79	-35	31
15	Burscough Richmond	30	5	9	16	38	78	-40	24
16	Whitehaven	30	6	4	20	42	91	-49	22

Division One

		P	W	D	L	F	A	GD	Pts
1	Poulton	29	22	5	2	105	25	80	71
2	Hurst Green	30	22	2	6	75	31	44	68
3	CMB	30	21	5	4	68	29	39	68
4	Milnthorpe Corinthians	30	20	4	6	93	35	58	64
5	Eagley	30	16	6	8	88	59	29	50*
6	Lostock St Gerards	29	14	7	8	63	38	25	49
7	Hawcoat Park	30	13	6	11	82	55	27	45
8	Stoneclough	30	11	6	13	59	74	-15	39
9	Lytham Town	30	9	11	10	56	68	-12	38
10	Kendal County	30	9	5	16	59	72	-13	32
11	Crooklands Casuals	30	9	5	16	50	67	-17	32
12	GSK Ulverston Rangers	30	9	6	15	53	57	-4	30*
13	Wyre Villa	30	8	2	20	42	96	-54	26
14	Askam United	30	7	4	19	55	98	-43	25
15	Fulwood Amateurs Res	30	4	7	19	42	95	-53	19
16	Mill Hill St Peters	30	3	3	24	26	117	-91	12

Division Two

		P	W	D	L	F	A	GD	Pts
1	Leyland United	28	22	3	3	99	35	64	69
2	Millom	28	21	3	4	80	30	50	66
3	Ladybridge	28	18	4	6	91	51	40	58
4	Charnock Richard Res	28	17	5	6	67	40	27	56
5	Walney Island	28	10	9	9	64	53	11	39
6	Lostock St Gerards Res	28	12	3	13	53	63	-10	39
7	Dalton United	28	12	3	13	46	57	-11	39
8	Thornton Cleveleys Res	28	11	1	16	54	91	-37	34
9	Kendal United	28	10	3	15	59	64	-5	30*
10	Furness Rovers	28	8	6	14	37	74	-37	30
11	Croston Sports	28	8	13	14	43	58	-15	27
12	Tempest United Res	28	6	15	14	47	61	-14	27
13	Furness Cavaliers	28	7	5	16	53	83	-30	26
14	Padiham Res	28	8	4	16	63	58	5	25*
15	Euxton Villa Res	28	6	5	17	43	81	-38	23

Division Three

		P	W	D	L	F	A	GD	Pts
1	Garstang Res	30	23	2	5	109	38	71	71
2	Poulton Res	31	20	5	6	83	48	35	65
3	Hurst Green Res	32	19	4	9	96	52	44	61
4	Longridge Town Res	32	15	6	11	94	71	23	51
5	Haslingden St. Marys Res	31	14	8	9	75	66	9	50
6	Turton Res	30	13	8	9	80	67	13	47
7	Burscough Richmond Res	30	14	5	11	79	77	2	47
8	Eagley Res	29	14	3	12	71	74	-3	45
9	CMB Res	31	13	4	14	66	73	-7	43
10	Milnthorpe Corinthians Res	32	12	5	15	69	92	-23	41
11	Lytham Town Res	26	12	4	10	65	45	20	40
12	Coppull United Res	30	12	4	14	57	54	3	37*
13	Thornton Cleveleys A	31	8	5	18	61	93	-32	29
14	Hesketh Bank Res	26	8	4	14	57	85	-28	28
15	Mill Hill St Peters Res	32	7	5	20	54	93	-39	23*
16	Croston Sports Res	32	8	2	22	63	104	-41	23*
17	Wyre Villa Res	29	6	4	19	52	99	-47	22

Stoneclough Res withdrew - record expunged

FINAL TABLES

WEST RIDING LEAGUE

Premier Division	P	W	D	L	F	A	GD	Pts
1 Golcar United	22	17	3	2	61	28	33	54
2 Salts	22	16	2	4	69	37	32	50
3 Steeton	22	15	4	3	60	34	26	49
4 Route One Rovers	22	14	3	5	79	47	32	45
5 Littletown	22	11	2	9	68	45	23	35
6 Campion Development	22	10	2	10	61	37	24	32
7 Lower Hopton	22	8	3	11	44	64	-20	27
8 Lepton Highlanders	22	7	3	12	47	59	-12	24
9 Wibsey	22	7	3	12	47	69	-22	24
10 Britannia Sports	22	3	5	14	36	56	-20	14
11 Wakefield City	22	3	3	16	31	73	-42	12
12 DRAM Community	22	3	3	16	35	89	-54	12

Honley withdrew - records expunged
Thornton United withdrew - records expunged

Division One	P	W	D	L	F	A	GD	Pts
1 Wakefield City	26	19	3	4	91	54	37	60
2 Thornton United	25	17	3	5	113	44	69	59*
3 Route One Rovers	24	18	2	4	96	40	56	56
4 Holmfirth Town	26	16	4	6	96	43	53	52
5 Golcar United Reserves	26	15	5	6	67	40	27	50
6 Britannia Sports	26	14	5	7	75	47	28	47
7 PFC	26	14	3	9	99	62	37	45
8 Wibsey	26	10	6	10	71	67	4	39
9 Ventus & Yeadon Celtic	25	9	0	16	54	83	-29	27
10 Steeton Reserves	26	7	5	14	52	68	-16	26
11 Tyersal	26	7	3	16	51	105	-54	15
12 Churwell Lions	26	4	3	19	37	104	-67	15
13 Hunsworth	26	4	3	19	37	95	-58	14
14 Westbrook YMCA	26	2	3	21	24	111	-87	12

Lower Hopton Reserves withdrew - records expunged
UNITA withdrew - records expunged

CRAVEN & DISTRICT LEAGUE

Premier Division	P	W	D	L	F	A	GD	Pts
1 Settle Utd	16	12	2	2	73	26	47	38
2 Silsden Whitestar	16	12	2	2	66	20	46	38
3 Grassington Utd	16	9	4	3	59	32	27	31
4 Trawden Celtic	16	8	2	6	32	37	-5	26
5 Rolls	16	6	2	8	47	36	11	20
6 FC Sporting Keighley	16	6	1	9	42	82	-40	19
7 Cowling	16	4	3	9	33	48	-15	15
8 Pendle Renegades	16	4	2	10	33	66	-33	14
9 Cross Hills	16	1	2	13	30	68	-38	5

Division One	P	W	D	L	F	A	GD	Pts
1 Carleton	20	18	1	1	95	27	68	55
2 Skipton Town	20	15	2	3	84	24	60	47
3 Rolls Res	20	13	2	5	67	39	28	41
4 Broomhill	20	13	0	7	64	49	15	39
5 Settle Utd Res	20	10	4	6	60	38	22	34
6 Hellifield Sports FC	20	8	1	11	39	50	-11	25
7 Cononley Sports	20	8	0	12	62	58	4	24
8 AFC Colne	20	8	0	12	67	73	-6	24
9 Bradley	20	6	1	13	33	65	-32	19
10 Chatburn	20	4	3	13	35	66	-31	15
11 Earby Town	20	0	0	20	9	126	-117	0

Division Two	P	W	D	L	F	A	GD	Pts
1 Bingley Town First	20	20	0	0	73	21	52	60
2 Silsden Whitestar Res	20	15	1	4	89	40	49	46
3 Trawden Celtic Res	20	13	2	5	79	43	36	41
4 Grassington Utd Res	20	12	3	5	74	43	31	39
5 AFC Barnoldswick	20	10	3	7	58	37	21	33
6 Ilkley Town	20	9	2	9	62	46	16	29
7 Skipton Town Res	20	7	3	10	39	50	-11	24
8 Salts	20	4	3	13	55	64	-9	15
9 Barlick Wanderers	20	4	2	14	35	86	-51	14
10 Pendle Renegades Res	20	3	3	14	36	84	-48	12
11 Barnoldswick Barons	20	1	2	17	27	113	-86	5

Division Three	P	W	D	L	F	A	GD	PTS
1 Cowling Res	20	16	3	1	67	22	45	51
2 Burnley Belvedere FC	19	14	1	4	80	24	56	43
3 Salts Res	20	12	2	6	53	38	15	38
4 Broomhill Res	20	11	1	8	69	54	15	34
5 Cross Hills Res	20	9	4	7	56	45	11	31
6 Iplay FC Barrowford	20	9	3	8	48	57	-9	30
7 Bingley Town Res	19	6	3	10	34	53	-19	21
8 Sutton	20	6	3	11	44	69	-25	21
9 Horton	18	4	4	10	26	49	-23	16
10 Settle Utd 3rds FC	20	4	3	13	32	70	-38	15
11 Otley Town	20	2	3	15	40	68	-28	9

HALIFAX & DISTRICT LEAGUE

Premier Division	P	W	D	L	F	A	GD	Pts
1 Shelf FC	20	17	1	2	99	31	68	52
2 Ryburn United	20	16	2	2	61	27	34	50
3 Sowerby Bridge	20	12	5	3	69	41	28	41
4 Shelf United	20	11	0	9	54	43	11	33
5 Midgley United	20	9	2	9	41	50	-9	29
6 Hebden Royd RS	20	8	4	8	64	58	6	28
7 Greetland AFC	20	5	5	10	40	66	-26	20
8 Sowerby United	20	4	5	11	39	72	-33	17
9 Calder 76	20	4	3	13	30	57	-27	15
10 Northowram	20	4	2	14	46	67	-21	14
11 Illingworth St Marys	20	3	5	12	40	71	-31	14

Division One	P	W	D	L	F	A	GD	Pts
1 Denholme United	20	19	0	1	75	19	56	57
2 Copley United	20	14	0	6	67	39	28	42
3 Brighouse Sports AFC	20	12	3	5	61	41	20	39
4 Holmfield	20	11	1	8	60	49	11	34
5 Salem	20	11	0	9	73	75	-2	33
6 AFC Illingworth St Mary's Res	20	10	1	8	63	39	24	31*
7 Elland Allstars	20	8	3	9	65	65	0	27
8 Ivy House FC	20	6	3	11	48	64	-16	21
9 Ryburn United Res	20	5	3	11	44	51	-7	18*
10 Calder 76 Reserves	20	2	2	16	27	61	-34	8
11 AFC Crossleys	20	2	2	16	40	120	-80	8

Division Two

		P	W	D	L	F	A	GD	Pts
1	FC Plummet Line	20	18	1	1	85	26	59	55
2	St Columbas	20	17	1	2	66	19	47	52
3	Junction Inn Rastrick	20	14	1	5	93	32	61	43
4	Greetland AFC Res	20	10	0	10	60	63	-3	30
5	Midgley United Res	20	9	1	10	47	50	-3	28
6	Northowram Res	20	9	0	11	66	61	5	27
7	Sowerby Bridge Res	20	7	3	10	44	51	-7	24
8	Sowerby United Res	20	7	2	11	57	93	-36	23
9	Shelf United Res	20	7	0	13	52	66	-14	21
10	AFC Crossleys Res	20	4	0	16	43	87	-44	12
11	Hebden Royd Red Star Res	20	3	1	16	34	99	-65	10

Division Three

		P	W	D	L	F	A	GD	Pts
1	Mixenden United	18	16	1	1	77	25	52	49
2	Stainland United AFC	18	12	1	5	54	43	11	37
3	FC Ovenden	18	10	0	8	66	52	14	30
4	Shelf FC Reserves	18	8	2	8	50	53	-3	26
5	Flying Dutchman AFC	18	8	0	10	34	35	-1	24
6	Brighouse Sports Res	18	3	2	13	32	54	-22	11
7	Warley Rangers 2017	18	3	0	15	29	80	-51	9

HUDDERSFIELD & DISTRICT LEAGUE

Premier Division

		P	W	D	L	F	A	GD	Pts
1	Heywood Irish Centre FC22	22	16	6	0	59	22	37	54
2	Holmbridge	22	13	5	4	52	33	19	44
3	Shepley	22	12	4	6	72	38	34	40
4	Linthwaite Athletic	22	12	3	7	69	54	15	39
5	Hepworth Utd	22	12	1	9	40	33	7	37
6	Berry Brow	22	11	3	8	67	44	23	36
7	Newsome	22	11	3	8	43	34	9	36
8	Diggle	22	10	3	9	47	46	1	33
9	Skelmanthorpe	22	4	6	12	37	53	-16	18
10	AFC Lindley	22	4	5	13	31	54	-23	17
11	Meltham Athletic	22	4	1	17	34	82	-48	13
12	Kirkheaton Rovers	22	2	2	18	26	84	-58	8

Division Two

		P	W	D	L	F	A	GD	Pts
1	Slaithwaite Utd	26	19	3	4	77	42	35	60
2	Colne Valley	26	19	3	4	76	42	34	60
3	Honley	26	19	2	5	94	45	49	59
4	Scholes	26	14	5	7	67	59	8	47
5	Marsden	26	14	2	10	73	63	10	44
6	Netherton	26	10	4	12	65	62	3	34
7	H.V.Academicals	26	9	6	11	67	58	9	33
8	Lepton Highlanders	26	9	5	12	65	68	-3	32
9	Shelley	26	9	5	12	66	78	-12	32
10	Britannia Sports	26	9	4	13	58	79	-21	31
11	Almondbury Woolpack	26	7	8	11	57	73	-16	29
12	AFC Dalton	26	6	9	11	55	68	-13	27
13	Moorside	26	6	3	17	47	68	-21	21
14	Scissett	26	1	3	22	23	85	-62	6

Division Three

		P	W	D	L	F	A	GD	Pts
1	Fothergill-Whittles	24	18	3	3	96	37	59	56*
2	Dalton Dynamos	24	15	8	1	98	36	62	53
3	Littleborough	24	16	1	7	91	48	43	49
4	Brook Motors	24	13	5	6	78	57	21	44
5	Junction	24	13	3	8	77	44	33	42
6	Cumberworth	24	13	3	8	64	41	23	42
7	3D Dynamos	24	12	3	9	71	70	1	39
8	Hade Edge	24	11	3	10	52	55	-3	36
9	Uppermill	24	9	5	10	50	70	-20	32
10	Almondbury WMC	24	8	2	14	65	83	-18	26
11	Deighton FC	24	4	4	16	47	79	-32	15*
12	Brighouse Athletic	24	2	3	19	26	99	-73	9
13	Wooldale Wanderers	24	0	1	23	9	105	-96	1

Division Four

		P	W	D	L	F	A	GD	Pts
1	Dewsbury Town	20	16	2	2	93	37	56	50
2	Golcar Utd	20	14	2	4	73	36	37	44
3	Rose and Crown	20	11	3	6	62	48	14	36
4	Grange Moor Saints	20	10	2	8	47	32	15	32
5	Cleckheaton AFC	20	9	4	7	59	56	3	31
6	Kirkburton	20	8	4	8	52	43	9	28
7	Flockton FC	20	8	4	8	63	71	-8	28
8	Westend	20	7	4	9	46	70	-24	25
9	Sporting CAV	20	5	3	12	44	57	-13	18
10	Cartworth Moor	20	4	1	15	48	78	-30	13
11	Mount	20	2	3	15	22	81	-59	9

Reserve Divisin One

		P	W	D	L	F	A	GD	Pts
1	Newsome Res	22	18	4	0	60	29	31	58
2	Netherton Res	22	12	5	5	78	53	25	41
3	Moorside Res	22	13	2	7	74	53	21	41
4	Linthwaite Athletic Res	22	11	3	8	53	39	14	36
5	Heywood Irish Centre Res	22	10	6	6	50	55	-5	36
6	Diggle Res	22	10	4	8	42	46	-4	34
7	Meltham Athletic Res	22	10	3	9	48	43	5	33
8	Shelley Res	22	9	4	9	48	51	-3	31
9	Shepley Res	22	7	5	10	47	54	-7	26
10	Berry Brow Res	22	7	4	11	31	55	-24	25
11	AFC Lindley Res	22	3	0	19	34	70	-36	9
12	Kirkheaton Rovers Res	22	2	0	20	10	27	-17	6

Reserve Division Two

		P	W	D	L	F	A	GD	Pts
1	Honley Res	16	12	3	1	62	25	37	39
2	Holmbridge Res	16	11	0	5	54	39	15	33
3	Cumberworth Res	16	10	1	5	55	40	15	31
4	AFC Dalton Res	16	9	3	4	40	30	10	30
5	H.V.Academicals Res	16	8	2	6	38	29	9	26
6	Uppermill Res	16	5	3	8	37	43	-6	18
7	Britannia Sports Res	16	5	1	10	41	44	-3	16
8	Brook Motors Res	16	4	1	11	32	69	-37	13
9	Scholes Res	16	1	0	15	20	60	-40	3

FINAL TABLES

Reserve Division Three

		P	W	D	L	F	A	GD	Pts
1	Fothergill-Whittles Res	18	16	0	2	90	15	75	48
2	Junction Res	18	14	0	4	66	37	29	42
3	Berry Brow 'A'	18	11	1	6	39	32	7	34
4	Littleborough Res	18	10	1	7	69	42	27	31
5	Deighton FC Res	18	9	0	9	48	36	12	27
6	Slaithwaite Utd Res	18	6	5	7	41	73	-32	23
7	Hade Edge Res	18	4	4	10	41	72	-31	16
8	Almondbury Woolpack Res	18	4	3	11	41	60	-19	15
9	Cumberworth 'A'	18	4	3	11	18	48	-30	15
10	Scissett Res	18	2	3	13	22	60	-38	9

Reserve Division Four

		P	W	D	L	F	A	GD	Pts
1	Dalton Dynamos Res	18	16	1	1	93	19	74	49
2	Cumberworth 'B'	18	15	2	1	113	40	73	47
3	Almondbury WMC Res	18	11	1	6	75	44	31	34
4	3D Dynamos Res	18	9	4	5	83	43	40	31
5	Littleborough 'A'	18	7	4	7	57	54	3	25
6	Honley 'A'	18	6	1	11	40	67	-27	19
7	Cartworth Moor Res	18	6	0	12	76	95	-19	18
8	Westend Res	18	5	1	12	45	117	-72	16
9	Mount Res	18	4	3	11	42	96	-54	15
10	Hade Edge 'A'	18	2	1	15	35	84	-49	7

WAKEFIELD & DISTRICT LEAGUE

Premier Division

		P	W	D	L	F	A	GD	Pts
1	Rock Inn FC	12	11	1	0	68	12	56	34
2	Royston Cross FC	12	9	1	2	52	16	36	28
3	Crackenedge FC	12	9	0	3	64	24	40	27
4	Crofton Sports FC	12	3	2	7	26	39	-13	11
5	Eastmoor FC	12	2	2	8	25	60	-35	8
6	Halton Moor FC	12	4	2	6	31	48	-17	5*
7	Pontefract Town	12	0	0	12	19	86	-67	-12*

Division One

		P	W	D	L	F	A	GD	Pts
1	Snydale Athletic	20	14	1	5	79	31	48	43
2	FC Prince	20	13	2	5	78	45	33	41
3	Ryhill FC	19	13	2	4	68	36	32	41
4	Durkar FC	20	12	3	5	66	38	28	39
5	Fox & Hounds (Batley) FC	20	12	3	5	74	50	24	39
6	Red Lion Alverthorpe FC	20	11	1	8	53	52	1	34
7	Ossett Dynamos	20	7	1	12	41	65	-24	22
8	White Swan FC	20	5	3	12	45	52	-7	18
9	Pontefract Sports & Social	20	4	5	11	50	56	-6	17
10	Fieldhead Hospital	20	3	3	14	38	119	-81	12
11	Walton Sports & Social	19	2	2	15	32	80	-48	2*

Division Two

		P	W	D	L	F	A	GD	Pts
1	AFC Heckmondwike	27	21	1	5	96	42	54	64
2	Nostell Miners Welfare	28	21	3	4	132	32	100	60*
3	Waterloo FC	28	19	2	7	90	57	33	59
4	AFC Sheaf	28	16	4	8	85	61	24	52
5	Horbury Athletic	28	14	7	7	99	58	41	49
6	FC Thornes	28	14	3	11	103	64	39	45
7	Thornhill United	28	13	4	11	84	71	13	43
8	Snydale Athletic Res	28	12	6	10	114	64	50	42
9	West End Terriers FC	28	19	5	4	119	57	62	33*
10	New Carlton FC	28	10	3	15	75	112	-37	33
11	Dewsbury Westside	27	9	4	14	81	100	-19	28*
12	Overthorpe SC Res	28	5	4	19	53	112	-59	19
13	Crofton Sports FC Res	28	3	4	21	36	129	-93	13
14	Middleton Old Boys	28	4	3	21	35	118	-83	12*
15	Howden Clough	28	2	1	25	40	165	-125	7

YORKSHIRE AMATEUR LEAGUE

Premier Division

		P	W	D	L	F	A	GD	Pts
1	Drighlington FC	22	17	3	2	84	36	48	54
2	Stanley United	22	16	2	4	59	32	27	50
3	Leeds Medics & Dentists	22	13	4	5	49	23	26	43
4	Alwoodley FC	22	13	3	6	68	34	34	42
5	Farsley Celtic Juniors	22	12	2	8	63	43	20	38
6	Grangefield OB	22	11	3	8	54	45	9	36
7	Ealandians	22	9	2	11	51	62	-11	29
8	Athletico	22	8	1	13	60	71	-11	25
9	Stanningley OB	22	5	5	12	36	50	-14	20
10	Beeston Juniors	22	6	2	14	45	78	-33	20
11	Morley Town AFC	22	5	2	15	46	92	-46	17
12	St. Nicholas	22	1	3	18	37	86	-49	6

Championship

		P	W	D	L	F	A	GD	Pts
1	Horsforth St. Margaret's	22	16	2	4	65	38	27	50
2	Calverley United	22	14	2	6	76	54	22	44
3	Gildersome Spurs OB	22	15	1	6	87	49	38	43*
4	St. Bedes AFC	22	13	2	7	62	39	23	41
5	Shire Academics	22	10	4	8	63	53	10	34
6	Mount St. Mary's	22	9	3	10	48	48	0	30
7	Leeds Medics & Dentists Res	22	8	2	12	36	45	-9	26
8	Wortley	22	8	1	13	53	60	-7	25
9	Beeston St. Anthony's	22	8	1	13	46	55	-9	25
10	Leeds Independent	22	7	3	12	40	54	-14	24
11	Collingham Juniors OB	22	6	2	14	53	77	-24	20
12	Thornesians	22	5	3	14	48	105	-57	18

Division One

		P	W	D	L	F	A	GD	Pts
1	Leeds City OB	20	16	1	3	83	28	55	49
2	Ealandians Res	20	15	3	2	82	31	51	48
3	Idle FC	20	15	2	3	68	37	31	47
4	Rothwell	20	13	1	6	59	41	18	40
5	Sky Blue FC	20	9	2	9	45	49	-4	29
6	Collegians	20	8	2	10	46	58	-12	26
7	Farsley Celtic Juniors Res	20	6	2	12	51	72	-21	20
8	Dewsbury Rangers FC	20	5	2	13	32	67	-35	17
9	Alwoodley FC Res	20	5	1	14	38	63	-25	16
10	Leeds Medics & Dentists III	20	5	3	12	29	41	-12	15*
11	Garforth Rangers	20	3	1	16	30	76	-46	10

Division Two

		P	W	D	L	F	A	GD	PTS
1	Garforth Crusaders	18	14	1	3	60	27	33	43
2	Woodkirk Valley	18	12	2	4	78	41	37	38
3	Morley Town AFC Res	18	11	3	4	75	48	27	36
4	Colton Athletic	18	10	2	6	67	56	11	32
5	Fairbank United	18	8	4	6	57	48	9	28
6	Sandal Wanderers	18	5	2	11	42	59	-17	17
7	Tyersal	18	5	2	11	41	59	-18	17
8	Trinity & All Saints COB	18	4	6	8	41	42	-1	15*
9	Huddersfield Amateur	18	4	3	11	33	61	-28	15
10	Farnley Sports	18	3	3	12	34	87	-53	12

DivisioN Three

		P	W	D	L	F	A	GD	PTS
1	Shire Academics Res	22	16	3	3	78	31	47	51
2	Horsforth St. Margaret's Res	22	15	5	2	71	44	27	50
3	Leeds City OB Res	22	11	7	4	68	44	24	40
4	Norristhorpe	22	10	6	6	78	54	24	36
5	North Leeds	22	10	6	6	56	51	5	36
6	Morley Town AFC III	22	10	4	8	51	52	-1	34
7	Tingley Athletic	22	9	4	9	56	58	-2	31
8	Lepton Highlanders	22	10	3	9	48	47	1	27*
9	Ealandians III	22	9	2	11	58	75	-17	26*
10	Leeds Modernians	22	7	1	14	44	57	-13	22
11	Colton Athletic Res	22	2	2	18	43	79	-36	8
12	Leeds Medics & Dentists IV	22	1	1	20	23	82	-59	-5*

Division Four

		P	W	D	L	F	A	GD	Pts
1	Leeds City OB III	20	17	1	2	108	19	89	52
2	Prospect FC	20	15	3	2	105	37	68	48
3	Morley Amateur	20	10	4	6	66	46	20	34
4	Middleton Park	20	10	3	7	56	30	26	33
5	Gildersome Spurs OB Res	20	11	3	6	59	38	21	33*
6	Drighlington FC Res	20	10	1	9	64	54	10	31
7	Beeston Juniors Res	20	9	0	11	49	93	-44	27
8	Shire Academics III	20	7	4	9	46	59	-13	25
9	Calverley United Res	20	7	1	12	28	51	-23	19*
10	Dewsbury Rangers FC Res	20	3	0	17	28	106	-78	9
11	Thornesians Res	20	0	2	18	24	100	-76	2

Division Five

		P	W	D	L	F	A	GD	Pts
1	Rothwell Res	24	17	5	2	90	28	62	56
2	Norristhorpe Res	24	18	1	5	80	43	37	55
3	St. Bedes AFC Res	24	15	2	7	70	55	15	47
4	North Leeds Res	24	13	3	8	82	59	23	42
5	Old Batelians Res	23	14	1	8	82	56	26	40*
6	Tyersal Res	23	14	2	7	71	58	13	38*
7	West End Park	24	10	2	12	68	77	-9	32
8	Shire Academics IV	24	8	4	12	60	69	-9	28
9	Thornesians III	24	7	3	14	49	81	-32	21*
10	Leeds Modernians Res	24	5	3	16	36	75	-39	18
11	Huddersfield Amateur Res	24	8	2	14	39	52	-13	17*
12	Leeds City OB IV	24	5	2	17	46	81	-35	17
13	Old Centralians	24	5	2	17	47	86	-39	17

WEST YORKSHIRE LEAGUE

Premier Division

		P	W	D	L	F	A	GD	Pts
1	Carlton Athletic	30	23	3	4	100	35	65	72
2	Leeds City	30	22	3	5	84	40	44	69
3	Beeston St Anthony's	30	21	1	8	92	49	43	64
4	Horbury Town	30	13	7	10	58	53	5	46
5	Ilkley Town	30	13	6	11	68	59	9	45
6	Huddersfield Amateur	30	13	2	15	60	85	-25	41
7	Field	30	12	4	14	58	62	-4	40
8	Robin Hood Athletic	30	10	10	10	50	57	-7	40
9	Knaresborough Town	30	10	8	12	57	55	2	38
10	Shelley	30	11	4	15	52	54	-2	37
11	Hunslet Club	30	10	7	13	58	62	-4	37
12	Sherburn White Rose	30	11	2	17	57	85	-28	35
13	Headingley	30	9	6	15	44	62	-18	33
14	Hartshead	30	8	5	17	49	77	-28	28
15	Pool	30	7	7	16	46	70	-24	28
16	Hall Green United	30	8	3	19	47	75	-28	27

Division One

		P	W	D	L	F	A	GD	Pts
1	Rawdon Old Boys	28	22	4	2	75	22	53	70
2	Whitkirk Wanderers	28	23	0	5	79	31	48	69
3	Wyke Wanderers	28	19	3	6	67	42	25	60
4	East End Park	28	17	2	9	76	48	28	56*
5	Featherstone Colliery	28	17	3	8	86	62	24	54
6	Aberford Albion	28	15	3	10	102	48	54	48
7	Wetherby Athletic	28	15	2	11	67	49	18	47
8	Boroughbridge	28	14	5	9	60	51	9	47
9	Oxenhope Recreation	28	9	4	15	66	78	-12	31
10	Kippax	28	9	4	15	52	78	-26	31
11	Rothwell	28	9	3	16	51	79	-28	27*
12	Leeds Modernians	28	7	2	19	52	78	-26	23
13	Howden Clough	28	6	2	20	49	93	-44	20
14	Altofts	28	5	2	21	40	83	-43	17
15	Brighouse Old Boys	28	3	1	24	35	115	-80	10

Division Two

		P	W	D	L	F	A	GD	Pts
1	Newsome	22	18	1	3	101	30	71	55
2	Otley Town	22	15	4	3	72	36	36	49
3	Kirk Deighton Rangers	22	15	3	4	74	29	45	48
4	Knaresborough Celtic	22	11	5	6	68	48	20	38
5	Huddersfield YM	22	11	4	7	61	39	22	37
6	Swillington Saints	22	11	1	10	58	66	-8	34
7	Ripon City	22	10	2	10	43	57	-14	32
8	Old Centralians	22	8	3	12	41	70	-29	24
9	Hampsthwaite United	22	6	3	13	56	70	-14	21
10	Kellingley Welfare	22	7	3	12	45	61	-16	21*
11	Baildon Trinity Athletic	22	3	3	14	47	72	-25	18
12	Garforth Rangers	22	0	0	22	20	108	-88	0

FINAL TABLES

Alliance Division One

		P	W	D	L	F	A	GD	PTS
1	Field Res	30	26	2	2	148	38	110	80
2	Beeston St. Anthony's Res	30	25	2	3	117	38	79	77
3	Leeds City Res	30	22	3	5	107	42	65	69
4	Shelley Res	30	22	3	5	94	40	54	69
5	Headingley Res	30	14	6	10	79	64	15	48
6	Hunslet Club Res	30	11	5	14	65	76	-11	41*
7	Carlton Athletic Res	30	11	6	13	78	86	-8	39
8	Horbury Town Res	30	13	4	13	79	78	1	37*
9	Hartshead Res	30	8	6	16	76	100	-24	33*
10	Huddersfield Amateur Res	30	9	5	16	67	96	-29	32
11	Oxenhope Recreation Res	30	9	4	17	67	103	-36	31
12	Robin Hood Athletic Res	30	10	3	17	70	87	-17	30*
13	Leeds Modernians Res	30	7	6	17	62	100	-38	27
14	Kippax Res	30	7	4	19	61	107	-46	25
15	East End Park Res	30	6	4	20	52	120	-68	25*
16	Pool Res	30	7	3	20	43	90	-47	24

Alliance Division Two

		P	W	D	L	F	A	GD	Pts
1	Whitkirk Wanderers Res	28	20	3	5	136	43	93	63
2	Hall Green United Res	28	17	3	8	60	55	5	54
3	Aberford Albion Res	28	16	4	8	79	45	34	52
4	Kirk Deighton Rangers Res	28	15	5	8	75	55	20	50
5	Ilkley Town Res	28	15	4	9	86	65	21	49
6	Huddersfield YM Res	28	15	3	10	87	72	15	48
7	Otley Town Res	28	14	5	9	81	63	18	47
8	Boroughbridge Res	28	13	4	11	66	53	13	43
9	Sherburn White Rose Res	28	12	3	13	77	96	-19	39
10	Wyke Wanderers Res	28	12	0	16	63	101	-38	36
11	Wetherby Athletic Res	28	11	1	16	75	66	9	34
12	Hampsthwaite United Res	28	9	1	18	54	72	-18	28
13	Howden Clough Res	28	8	2	18	54	102	-48	26
14	Old Centralians Res	28	7	1	20	46	112	-66	22
15	Altofts Res	28	5	3	20	48	87	-39	15*

HARROGATE & DISTRICT LEAGUE

Premier Division

		P	W	D	L	F	A	GD	Pts
1	Harlow Hill	24	20	3	1	94	24	70	63
2	Thirsk Falcons	24	20	2	2	110	24	86	62
3	Kirkby Malzeard	24	14	2	8	64	53	11	44
4	Knaresborough Celtic Res	24	13	2	9	63	57	6	41
5	Beckwithshaw Saints	24	12	2	10	56	54	2	38
6	Burley Trojans	24	11	3	10	55	45	10	36
7	Pateley Bridge	24	9	8	7	46	39	7	35
8	Bramhope	24	8	3	13	52	69	-17	27
9	Bardsey FC	24	7	4	13	29	52	-23	25
10	Hampsthwaite FC	24	5	6	13	44	74	-30	21
11	Pannal Sports	24	5	4	15	44	73	-29	19
12	Addingham	24	3	3	16	44	92	-48	18
13	Helperby United	24	5	2	17	51	96	-45	17

Division One

		P	W	D	L	F	A	GD	Pts
1	Ventus Yeadon Celtic	20	15	1	4	68	34	34	46
2	Bedale AFC Res	20	13	1	6	67	37	30	40
3	Thirsk Falcons Res	20	13	1	6	65	42	23	40
4	Beckwithshaw Saints Res	20	11	3	6	60	44	16	36
5	Bardsey Res	20	11	2	7	65	49	16	35
6	Dalton Athletic	20	8	1	11	55	45	10	25
7	Harlow Hill Res	20	7	2	11	55	65	-10	23
8	Pool AFC A Team	20	7	1	12	37	70	-33	22
9	Boroughbridge A Team	20	7	0	13	53	71	-18	21
10	Ripon City Res	20	7	0	13	34	70	-36	21
11	Kirkstall Crusaders	20	4	2	14	43	75	-32	14

WILTSHIRE SENIOR LEAGUE

Premier Division

		P	W	D	L	F	A	GD	Pts
1	Kintbury Rangers	32	25	3	4	126	31	95	78
2	Melksham Town Res	32	24	1	7	111	38	73	73
3	Cricklade Town	32	21	5	6	110	39	71	68
4	Shrewton United	32	23	1	8	115	60	55	68*
5	Wroughton	32	20	4	8	102	62	40	61*
6	Purton	32	19	3	10	65	50	15	58*
7	Westbury United Res	32	16	8	8	86	51	35	52*
8	Marlborough Town	32	14	4	14	57	72	-15	46
9	Corsham Town Res	32	14	5	13	68	67	1	45*
10	Royal Wootton Bassett Town Dev	32	14	3	15	71	77	-6	45
11	Ludgershall Sports	32	10	4	18	59	101	-42	34
12	Trowbridge Town	32	8	7	17	45	71	-26	31
13	Devizes Town Res	32	10	6	16	43	76	-33	30*
14	Malmesbury Victoria Dev	32	6	5	21	49	103	-54	21*
15	Pewsey Vale Dev	32	5	6	21	38	93	-55	19*
16	Bremhill	32	5	5	22	59	98	-39	18*
17	Bassett Bulldogs	32	2	2	28	18	133	-115	6*

SWINDON & DISTRICT LEAGUE

Premier Division

		P	W	D	L	F	A	GD	Pts
1	Tawny Owl	21	18	1	2	131	39	92	55
2	FC Dorcan	22	18	1	3	69	36	33	55
3	Bakers Arms	22	15	3	4	74	41	33	48
4	Ashton Keynes	22	13	2	7	77	47	30	41
5	Wheatsheaf	22	12	1	9	70	51	19	37
6	Lower Stratton	22	9	2	11	57	61	-4	29
7	Stratton Juniors	22	8	4	10	32	60	-28	28
8	Swindon Spitfires	21	8	3	10	56	67	-11	27
9	Swindon Supermarines DC	22	7	1	14	61	103	-42	22
10	Wroughton Res	22	5	5	12	60	64	-4	20
11	Ramsbury	22	3	2	17	47	96	-49	11
12	Swindon Centurians Spectrum	22	2	1	19	20	89	-69	7

Division One

		P	W	D	L	F	A	GD	Pts
1	Ruby Removals	22	20	1	1	143	24	119	61
2	Marlborough Res	22	17	1	4	81	31	50	52
3	Highworth Town Dev	22	11	2	9	49	33	16	35
4	Village Inn	22	11	1	10	43	56	-13	34
5	Chiseldon	22	10	3	9	62	47	15	33
6	North Swindon WMC	22	11	0	11	64	79	-15	33
7	Swindon AFC	22	10	1	11	48	58	-10	31
8	Redhouse	22	8	4	10	69	64	5	28
9	Haydon Wick	22	8	4	10	42	68	-26	28
10	New Town All Stars	22	8	2	12	49	57	-8	26
11	Moredon FC	22	6	3	13	49	95	-46	21
12	Brockhill United	22	1	0	21	14	101	-87	3

TROWBRIDGE & DISTRICT LEAGUE

Division One

		P	W	D	L	F	A	GD	Pts
1	Freshford United	20	16	1	3	71	24	47	49
2	Luxol St Andrews FC	20	12	5	3	65	21	44	41
3	Stockton & Codford FC	20	13	1	6	60	30	30	40
4	Melksham Town 'A'	20	11	4	5	59	35	24	37
5	Hilperton United	20	9	3	8	52	54	-2	30
6	Semington Magpies	20	7	5	8	40	43	-3	26
7	Warminster Town Res	20	6	3	11	31	67	-36	24*
8	Three Daggers FC	20	8	4	8	57	37	20	22*
9	Calne Eagles	20	5	3	12	34	64	-30	18
10	Trowbridge Town Res	20	3	5	12	27	69	-42	14
11	Westbury United Dev	20	2	2	16	32	84	-52	7*

Division Two

		P	W	D	L	F	A	GD	Pts
1	Holt FC	14	11	1	2	59	20	39	34
2	Heytesbury	14	10	2	2	70	24	46	32
3	Melksham Town 'B' FC	14	7	5	2	48	29	19	26
4	Aces FC	14	7	2	5	36	31	5	23
5	Zeals FC	14	6	2	6	54	43	11	20
6	Trowbridge Wanderers Dev	14	5	1	8	37	64	-27	16
7	Greyhound FC	14	2	2	10	32	53	-21	8
8	The Stiffs	14	0	1	13	14	86	-72	1

YORK LEAGUE

Premier Division

		P	W	D	L	F	A	GD	Pts
1	Wigginton GH	28	23	3	2	97	23	74	72
2	Old Malton	28	20	2	6	99	31	68	62
3	Huntington Rovers	28	16	5	7	74	46	28	53
4	Dringhouses	28	15	4	9	60	51	9	49
5	F1 Racing	28	14	6	8	98	59	39	48
6	Dunnington	28	14	7	7	59	38	21	46*
7	Osbaldwick	28	14	2	12	57	48	9	44
8	Hemingbrough United	28	14	0	14	64	87	-23	42
9	Tadcaster Magnets	28	11	3	14	45	66	-21	36
10	Church Fenton FC	28	9	8	11	47	54	-7	35
11	Poppleton United	28	9	3	16	46	65	-19	30
12	Copmanthorpe	28	7	4	17	46	83	-37	25
13	Sporting Knavesmire	28	6	6	16	49	75	-26	24
14	Malton & Norton	28	6	2	20	51	80	-29	20
15	York RI	28	2	5	21	25	111	-86	8*

Division One

		P	W	D	L	F	A	GD	Pts
1	Thorpe United	20	16	3	1	71	27	44	51
2	Pocklington Town 2nd	20	16	1	3	69	18	51	49
3	Kirkbymoorside	20	12	3	5	53	33	20	39
4	Rawcliffe	20	11	3	6	53	34	19	36
5	Easingwold Town	20	8	6	6	48	46	2	30
6	Tockwith AFC	20	9	2	9	44	34	10	26*
7	Cliffe	20	8	2	10	47	50	-3	26
8	Riccall United	20	7	1	12	39	52	-13	22
9	Harrison Signs FC	20	6	1	13	32	51	-19	19
10	Brooklyn FC	20	3	1	16	28	68	-40	10
11	Wilberfoss	20	2	1	17	31	102	-71	7

Division Two

		P	W	D	L	F	A	GD	Pts
1	Haxby Town	16	12	1	3	93	29	64	37
2	Heworth AFC	16	12	1	3	70	30	40	37
3	Strensall Tigers	16	11	2	3	85	38	47	35
4	Bishopthorpe United	16	9	1	6	55	36	19	28
5	Barmby Moor	16	9	1	6	40	35	5	28
6	Stamford Bridge	16	6	2	8	51	47	4	20
7	Civil Service	16	6	2	8	51	51	0	20
8	Heslington	16	1	1	14	16	92	-76	1*
9	Crayke United	16	1	0	15	16	119	-103	-2*

Division Three

		P	W	D	L	F	A	GD	Pts
1	Malt Shovel FC	14	12	2	0	75	13	62	38
2	Rufforth United	14	10	0	4	72	27	45	30
3	Cawood	14	9	3	2	42	23	19	30
4	Bubwith White Swan FC	14	8	2	4	53	33	20	26
5	The Beagle FC	14	5	0	9	27	52	-25	15
6	Fulford FC	14	3	1	10	15	61	-46	10
7	Moor Lane	14	3	1	10	37	71	-34	7*
8	Selby Olympia	14	1	1	12	22	63	-41	4

Division Four

		P	W	D	L	F	A	GD	Pts
1	Clifford FC	14	10	2	2	48	27	21	32
2	Pollington FC	14	7	5	2	36	20	16	26
3	Stillington S&C	14	7	1	6	35	30	5	22
4	LNER Builders	14	5	5	4	31	41	-10	20
5	Elm Park	14	6	2	6	34	34	0	17*
6	Swinton AFC	14	4	2	8	36	38	-2	14
7	Huntington FC	14	5	0	9	28	42	-14	12*
8	Wheldrake	14	3	1	10	30	46	-16	10

Reserves A

		P	W	D	L	F	A	GD	Pts
1	Wigginton Grasshoppers Res	20	16	3	1	80	23	57	51
2	Huntington Rovers Res	20	16	1	3	69	24	45	49
3	Pocklington Town 3rd Res	20	13	5	2	58	25	33	44
4	Dunnington Res	20	11	3	6	50	43	7	36
5	Thorpe United Res	20	11	1	8	68	46	22	34
6	Old Malton Res	20	10	2	8	47	38	9	32
7	Easingwold Town Res	20	5	1	14	25	53	-28	16
8	Hemingbrough Utd Res	20	5	3	12	34	61	-27	15*
9	Church Fenton FC Res	20	2	6	12	27	54	-27	12
10	Malton & Norton Res	20	3	3	14	35	83	-48	12
11	Copmanthorpe Res	20	3	2	15	18	61	-43	11

FINAL TABLES

Reserves B

		P	W	D	L	F	A	GD	Pts
1	Osbaldwick Res	18	12	2	4	67	26	41	38
2	Poppleton United Res	18	11	3	4	61	42	19	36
3	Dringhouses Res	18	9	1	8	58	44	14	28
4	F1 Racing FC Res	18	8	4	6	55	44	11	28
5	Haxby Town Res	18	9	0	9	36	41	-5	27
6	Tockwith AFC Res	18	7	4	7	40	35	5	25
7	Bishopthorpe United Res	18	7	3	8	48	56	-8	24
8	Tadcaster Magnets Res	18	7	1	10	40	61	-21	22
9	Harrison Signs FC Res	18	8	3	7	47	56	-9	21*
10	Heworth AFC Res	18	1	1	16	34	81	-47	1*

Reserves C

		P	W	D	L	F	A	GD	Pts
1	Wilberfoss Res	18	15	2	1	103	22	81	47
2	Malt Shovel Res	18	13	2	3	67	23	44	41
3	Stamford Bridge Res	18	11	3	4	59	34	25	36
4	Cliffe Res	18	9	4	5	55	33	22	31
5	Brooklyn Res	18	9	2	7	53	42	11	29
6	York Railway Institute Res	18	9	5	4	51	45	6	29*
7	Civil Service Res	18	5	3	10	39	75	-36	18
8	Rufforth United Res	18	3	3	12	23	66	-43	9*
9	Fulford Res	18	2	1	15	17	49	-32	4*
10	Wheldrake Res	18	1	1	16	11	89	-78	4

AMATEUR FOOTBALL ASSOCIATION

AMATEUR FOOTBALL COMBINATION

Premier Division

		P	W	D	L	F	A	GD	Pts
1	Old Hamptonians	20	11	4	5	65	26	39	37
2	Dorkinians	20	10	5	5	41	31	10	35
3	Honourable Artillery Co	20	9	5	6	45	44	1	32
4	Old Thorntonians	20	9	4	7	41	32	9	31
5	Old Meadonians	20	8	5	7	37	38	-1	29
6	Old Suttonians	20	8	3	9	38	41	-3	27
7	Old Wokingians	20	8	3	9	29	33	-4	27
8	Old Parmiterians	20	7	6	7	44	41	3	24*
9	UCL Academicals	20	6	5	9	22	34	-12	23
10	Old Minchendenians	20	6	5	9	27	41	-14	23
11	Clapham Old Xaverians	20	4	3	13	29	57	-28	15

SENIOR ONE

		P	W	D	L	F	A	GD	Pts
1	Southgate Olympic	20	14	1	5	38	25	13	43
2	Wandsworth Borough	20	13	3	4	50	19	31	42
3	Reigatians	20	12	5	3	53	25	28	41
4	Bealonians	20	11	5	4	45	28	17	38
5	Fulham Compton Old Boys	20	11	1	8	39	34	5	34
6	Old Ignatian	20	8	3	9	44	42	2	27
7	Queen Mary College Old Boys	20	7	4	9	42	42	0	25
8	Old Manorians	20	6	6	8	45	36	9	24
9	Economicals	20	3	5	12	30	51	-21	14
10	Old Salvatorians	20	3	4	13	20	52	-32	13
11	Kings Old Boys	20	2	3	15	19	71	-52	9

SENIOR TWO NORTH

		P	W	D	L	F	A	GD	Pts
1	Albanian	18	15	1	2	73	31	42	46
2	Altis FC	18	12	1	5	63	39	24	37
3	Enfield Old Grammarians	18	11	2	5	45	32	13	35
4	Southgate County	18	11	0	7	45	37	8	33
5	IB Albion	18	8	2	8	38	41	-3	26
6	Old Aloysians	18	6	5	7	37	42	-5	23
7	Latymer Old Boys	18	7	1	10	35	47	-12	22
8	Hale End Athletic	18	4	1	13	34	51	-17	13
9	UCL Academicals II	18	3	4	11	20	44	-24	13
10	Old Woodhouseians	18	4	1	13	23	49	-26	13

SENIOR TWO SOUTH

		P	W	D	L	F	A	GD	Pts
1	Old Meadonians II	20	14	3	3	54	24	30	45
2	Fitzwilliam Old Boys	20	13	6	1	44	17	27	45
3	Glyn Old Boys	20	11	2	7	61	33	28	35
4	Old Hamptonians II	20	11	1	8	50	43	7	34
5	Old Thorntonians II	20	9	4	7	45	40	5	31
6	Old Tenisonians	20	6	7	7	39	36	3	25
7	Honourable Artillery Co II	20	7	3	10	38	42	-4	24
8	Worcester College Old Boys	20	6	5	9	43	48	-5	23
9	Shene Old Grammarians	20	5	6	9	28	40	-12	21
10	Old Pauline	20	4	5	11	26	50	-24	17
11	London Lawyers	20	2	2	16	12	67	-55	-3*

SENIOR THREE NORTH

		P	W	D	L	F	A	GD	Pts
1	Old Minchendenians II	20	14	2	4	84	39	45	44
2	Bealonians II	20	12	5	3	48	22	26	41
3	Old Salvatorians II	20	12	2	6	48	30	18	38
4	Globe Rangers	20	10	3	7	54	49	5	33
5	Spaniards	20	8	7	5	48	39	9	31
6	Old Manorians II	20	9	3	8	50	44	6	30
7	Albanian II	20	7	6	7	43	49	-6	27
8	Hale End Athletic II	20	8	2	10	40	51	-11	24*
9	Old Ignatian II	20	6	4	10	44	60	-16	22
10	Enfield Old Grammarians II	20	2	6	12	31	54	-23	12
11	Old Vaughanians	20	1	2	17	36	89	-53	5

SENIOR THREE SOUTH

		P	W	D	L	F	A	GD	Pts
1	Economicals II	18	16	0	2	58	17	41	48
2	Royal Bank of Scotland	18	15	0	3	48	21	27	41*
3	Old Suttonians II	18	10	1	7	53	39	14	31
4	Mickleham Old Boxhillians	18	8	4	6	42	39	3	28
5	Old Strand Academicals	18	8	1	9	53	59	-6	25
6	Old Meadonians III	18	6	4	8	42	48	-6	22
7	Old Sedcopians	18	6	4	8	36	43	-7	22
8	New-Magdalen AFC	18	6	3	9	52	53	-1	21
9	Dorkinians II	18	3	2	13	38	58	-20	11
10	Old St Marys	18	1	3	14	21	66	-45	6

INTERMEDIATE NORTH

		P	W	D	L	F	A	GD	Pts
1	Old Uffingtonians	18	14	0	4	81	38	43	42
2	Bealonians III	18	12	1	5	80	28	52	37
3	Leyton County Old Boys	18	11	3	4	60	45	15	36
4	Old Tollingtonians	18	8	5	5	50	38	12	29
5	UCL Academicals III	18	8	4	6	53	48	5	28
6	Lea Valley	18	8	2	8	54	45	9	26
7	Southgate Olympic II	18	7	2	9	51	63	-12	23
8	Wood Green Old Boys	18	6	2	10	41	50	-9	20
9	Old Parmiterians II	18	3	1	14	37	116	-79	10
10	Somerville Old Boys	18	2	2	14	32	68	-36	8

INTERMEDIATE SOUTH

		P	W	D	L	F	A	GD	Pts
1	Royal Bank of Scotland II	18	15	1	2	53	20	33	46
2	Rob Roy Reds	18	9	6	3	42	30	12	33
3	Clissold Park Rangers	18	9	3	6	33	26	7	30
4	Reigatians II	18	8	5	5	41	32	9	29
5	Old Wokingians II	18	7	3	8	42	34	8	24
6	Clapham Old Xaverians II	18	6	4	8	30	39	-9	22
7	Witan	18	6	2	10	37	38	-1	20
8	Heathrow Seniors	18	5	1	12	32	50	-18	16
9	Old Meadonians IV	18	5	1	12	36	63	-27	16
10	London Welsh	18	5	4	9	35	49	-14	15*

ONE NORTH

		P	W	D	L	F	A	GD	Pts
1	University of Hertfordshire	18	14	2	2	75	34	41	44
2	Old Manorians III	18	10	3	5	47	37	10	33
3	Queen Mary College Old Boys II	18	9	5	4	52	39	13	32
4	Old Kingsburians	18	9	4	5	53	40	13	31
5	UCL Academicals IV	18	9	3	6	65	41	24	30
6	Old Parmiterians III	18	7	3	8	48	45	3	21*
7	Albanian III	18	8	1	9	51	56	-5	21*
8	Latymer Old Boys II	18	4	5	9	38	50	-12	17
9	Old Salvatorians III	18	5	0	13	33	70	-37	15
10	Old Magdalenians	18	1	2	15	23	73	-50	-3*

ONE SOUTH

		P	W	D	L	F	A	GD	Pts
1	Old Tenisonians II	18	14	1	3	56	30	26	43
2	Old Thorntonians III	18	12	2	4	58	35	23	38
3	Dorkinians III	18	9	3	6	38	30	8	30
4	Glyn Old Boys II	18	7	3	8	43	38	5	24
5	Sinjuns Grammarians	18	7	3	8	39	37	2	24
6	Old Pauline II	18	7	3	8	27	28	-1	24
7	Economicals III	18	7	3	8	28	43	-15	24
8	Old Tiffinians	18	7	1	10	33	49	-16	22
9	Wandsworth Borough II	18	6	2	10	41	36	5	20
10	Old Sedcopians II	18	3	1	14	25	62	-37	10

TWO NORTH

		P	W	D	L	F	A	GD	Pts
1	Mayfield Athletic	18	13	2	3	66	39	27	41
2	Old Minchendenians III	18	12	2	4	67	43	24	38
3	Mill Hill Village	18	10	4	4	61	46	15	32*
4	Hale End Athletic III	18	9	4	5	66	47	19	31
5	Old Aloysians II	18	8	3	7	51	53	-2	27
6	Hinton & Finchley Revolution OB	18	6	4	8	50	56	-6	22
7	Queen Mary College Old Boys III	18	7	1	10	47	52	-5	17*
8	Old Parmiterians IV	18	4	1	13	35	76	-41	13
9	Egbertian	18	6	1	11	37	47	-10	10*
10	Southgate Olympic III	18	3	2	13	37	58	-21	5*

TWO SOUTH

		P	W	D	L	F	A	GD	Pts
1	Old Wokingians III	18	12	4	2	58	21	37	40
2	Old Whitgiftian	18	13	1	4	41	18	23	40
3	Brent	18	10	4	4	53	26	27	34
4	Shene Old Grammarians II	18	8	3	7	41	35	6	27
5	Old Meadonians V	18	8	2	8	50	53	-3	26
6	Fulham Compton Old Boys II	18	7	3	8	33	37	-4	24
7	Tilburg Regents	18	8	1	9	36	34	2	23*
8	Kings Old Boys II	18	5	3	10	26	41	-15	18
9	Old Guildfordians	18	5	2	11	31	55	-24	17
10	Old Pauline III	18	1	3	14	20	69	-49	3*

THREE NORTH

		P	W	D	L	F	A	GD	Pts
1	Old Salvatorians IV	16	9	6	1	45	26	19	33
2	Old Challoners	16	9	4	3	43	26	17	31
3	Old Manorians IV	16	9	3	4	67	23	44	30
4	Old Parmiterians V	16	10	3	3	61	25	36	30*
5	Wood Green Old Boys II	16	7	2	7	46	52	-6	23
6	Old Kingsburians II	16	5	5	6	40	36	4	17*
7	Old Woodhouseians II	16	5	2	9	36	40	-4	17
8	Southgate County II	16	3	2	11	29	65	-36	11
9	Old Vaughanians II	16	1	1	14	23	97	-74	-3*

FINAL TABLES

THREE SOUTH

		P	W	D	L	F	A	GD	Pts
1	London Welsh II	20	16	2	2	81	25	56	50
2	Blackheath Wanderers SC	20	15	0	5	75	45	30	45
3	Old Thorntonians IV	20	10	3	7	58	54	4	33
4	Old Meadonians VI	20	9	4	7	51	47	4	31
5	Reigatians III	20	8	3	9	48	44	4	27
6	Royal Sun Alliance	20	7	2	11	50	60	-10	23
7	Old St Marys II	20	6	5	9	42	55	-13	23
8	National Westminster Bank	20	6	5	9	36	53	-17	23
9	Old Suttonians III	20	6	4	10	44	61	-17	22
10	Sinjuns Grammarians II	20	6	3	11	33	48	-15	21
11	Glyn Old Boys III	20	5	1	14	31	57	-26	16

FIVE SOUTH

		P	W	D	L	F	A	GD	Pts
1	Old Suttonians V	20	17	3	0	74	31	43	54
2	Clapham Old Xaverians IV	20	14	1	5	66	35	31	43
3	Shene Old Grammarians III	20	12	3	5	67	44	23	39
4	John Fisher Old Boys	20	9	5	6	62	44	18	32
5	Witan II	20	6	7	7	43	44	-1	25
6	Old Wokingians V	20	7	3	10	42	45	-3	24
7	Old Tiffinians II	20	5	6	9	53	69	-16	21
8	Old Tenisonians III	20	6	2	12	51	69	-18	20
9	Dorkinians V	20	5	4	11	35	59	-24	19
10	Clissold Park Rangers II	20	5	4	11	31	51	-20	17*
11	Wandsworth Borough IV	20	4	2	14	38	71	-33	14

FOUR NORTH

		P	W	D	L	F	A	GD	Pts
1	Parkfield	20	15	2	3	62	31	31	47
2	Enfield Old Grammarians III	20	12	3	5	54	26	28	39
3	Old Ignatian III	20	11	5	4	57	37	20	38
4	Old Aloysians III	20	11	4	5	55	45	10	37
5	Old Parmiterians VI	20	11	2	7	56	47	9	32*
6	UCL Academicals V	20	8	3	9	40	46	-6	27
7	University of Hertfordshire II	20	7	5	8	50	49	1	26
8	Bealonians IV	20	7	5	8	39	39	0	26
9	Albanian IV	20	7	3	10	37	41	-4	24
10	Old Tollingtonians II	20	3	0	17	42	89	-47	9
11	Latymer Old Boys III	20	1	2	17	36	78	-42	5

SIX NORTH

		P	W	D	L	F	A	GD	Pts
1	Old Salvatorians V	18	14	1	3	79	22	57	43
2	Old Minchendenians IV	18	13	2	3	72	30	42	41
3	Bealonians VI	18	10	0	8	60	48	12	30
4	Wood Green Old Boys III	18	9	1	8	65	54	11	28
5	UCL Academicals VI	18	8	3	7	58	51	7	27
6	Parkfield II	18	9	2	7	66	70	-4	27*
7	Old Parmiterians VIII	18	8	2	8	56	48	8	23*
8	Latymer Old Boys IV	18	6	3	9	46	54	-8	21
9	Southgate Olympic VI	18	3	3	12	38	67	-29	10*
10	Old Ignatian V	18	1	1	16	23	119	-96	4

FOUR SOUTH

		P	W	D	L	F	A	GD	Pts
1	Clapham Old Xaverians III	20	15	4	1	71	35	36	49
2	Old Hamptonians III	20	11	3	6	46	37	9	36
3	Old Sedcopians III	20	10	4	6	42	28	14	34
4	Old Crosbeians	20	10	3	7	43	32	11	33
5	Old Suttonians IV	20	9	5	6	38	32	6	32
6	Fulham Compton Old Boys III	20	9	2	9	47	46	1	29
7	Old Wokingians IV	20	7	2	11	35	51	-16	23
8	Wandsworth Borough III	20	5	7	8	39	47	-8	22
9	Old Thorntonians V	20	5	6	9	42	51	-9	21
10	Dorkinians IV	20	5	3	12	36	51	-15	14*
11	Old Meadonians VII	20	3	3	14	41	70	-29	12

SIX SOUTH

		P	W	D	L	F	A	GD	Pts
1	Mickleham Old Boxhillians II	18	13	1	4	58	31	27	40
2	Old Wokingians VI	18	12	2	4	61	41	20	38
3	Brent II	18	11	3	4	51	30	21	36
4	Glyn Old Boys IV	18	7	6	5	49	45	4	27
5	Shene Old Grammarians IV	18	8	2	8	46	49	-3	26
6	Old Pauline IV	18	7	3	8	47	42	5	19*
7	Old Suttonians VI	18	5	4	9	36	45	-9	19
8	Old Meadonians VIII	18	5	3	10	41	56	-15	18
9	Sinjuns Grammarians III	18	5	3	10	38	55	-17	18
10	Reigatians IV	18	2	3	13	38	71	-33	9

FIVE NORTH

		P	W	D	L	F	A	GD	Pts
1	Bealonians V	20	16	2	2	69	21	48	50
2	Old Pegasonians	20	15	1	4	95	36	59	46
3	Old Kingsburians III	20	12	5	3	63	33	30	41
4	Mill Hill Village II	20	12	3	5	80	44	36	39
5	Old Ignatian IV	20	11	2	7	43	38	5	35
6	Old Woodhouseians III	20	9	2	9	46	38	8	29
7	London Hospital Old Boys	20	6	4	10	50	62	-12	22
8	Old Aloysians IV	20	5	2	13	48	77	-29	14*
9	Southgate Olympic V	20	5	2	13	33	67	-34	14*
10	Old Parmiterians VII	20	3	2	15	32	91	-59	8*
11	Leyton County Old Boys II	20	2	3	15	39	91	-52	6*

SEVEN NORTH

		P	W	D	L	F	A	GD	Pts
1	Old Parmiterians IX	22	19	0	3	99	40	59	54*
2	Old Vaughanians III	22	18	1	3	110	35	75	52*
3	Ravenscroft Old Boys	22	17	0	5	117	54	63	51
4	Albanian V	22	13	3	6	80	46	34	42
5	Old Manorians V	22	10	6	6	79	44	35	36
6	Enfield Old Grammarians IV	22	11	2	9	69	59	10	35
7	Southgate County III	22	5	6	11	42	69	-27	21
8	Bealonians VII	22	6	3	13	37	73	-36	21
9	Old Ignatian VI	22	6	1	15	49	110	-61	19
10	Old Challoners II	22	4	7	11	52	87	-35	17*
11	Old Woodhouseians IV	22	4	4	14	40	81	-41	16
12	Old Minchendenians V	22	2	1	19	43	119	-76	4*

SEVEN SOUTH

		P	W	D	L	F	A	GD	Pts
1	Witan III	22	16	3	3	100	40	60	51
2	Old Suttonians VII	22	15	3	4	62	26	36	48
3	Old Wokingians VII	22	10	5	7	54	49	5	35
4	Wandsworth Borough V	22	10	4	8	46	36	10	34
5	Reigatians V	22	9	4	9	64	61	3	31
6	Old Sedcopians IV	22	9	4	9	54	61	-7	31
7	Old Thorntonians VI	22	8	6	8	61	48	13	30
8	Brent III	22	8	6	8	61	58	3	30
9	Old Grantonians	22	9	4	9	56	69	-13	26*
10	Dorkinians VI	22	7	2	13	40	70	-30	23
11	Old Tenisonians IV	22	3	5	14	23	61	-38	14
12	Old Tiffinians III	22	4	2	16	39	81	-42	14

EIGHT SOUTH

		P	W	D	L	F	A	GD	Pts
1	Reigatians VI	18	12	4	2	64	39	25	40
2	John Fisher Old Boys II	18	11	3	4	65	34	31	36
3	Old Tiffinians IV	18	11	1	6	58	38	20	34
4	Old Guildfordians II	18	10	3	5	67	44	23	33
5	Old Whitgiftian II	18	8	4	6	46	30	16	28
6	Old Meadonians IX	18	7	4	7	39	49	-10	25
7	Old Sedcopians V	18	6	3	9	40	52	-12	21
8	Old St Marys III	18	6	3	9	46	64	-18	21
9	Wandsworth Borough VI	18	3	2	13	28	53	-25	11
10	Old Wokingians VIII	18	2	1	15	31	81	-50	7

ARTHURIAN LEAGUE

Premier Division

		P	W	D	L	F	A	GD	Pts
1	Old Foresters	18	14	3	1	48	13	35	45
2	Old Carthusians	18	11	7	0	50	20	30	40
3	Old Tonbridgians	18	9	4	5	47	30	17	31
4	Old Wykehamists	18	9	2	7	34	36	-2	29
5	Kings College Wimbledon	18	6	5	7	27	34	-7	23
6	Old Etonians	18	6	4	8	31	46	-15	22
7	Old Chigwellians	18	6	2	10	29	30	-1	20
8	Old Salopians	18	3	8	7	35	43	-8	17
9	Lancing Old Boys	18	4	4	10	27	46	-19	16
10	Old Marlburians	18	1	3	14	21	51	-30	6

Division One

		P	W	D	L	F	A	GD	Pts
1	Old Bradfieldians	16	16	0	0	68	25	43	48
2	Old Brentwoods	16	12	0	4	56	27	29	36
3	Old Harrovians	16	10	1	5	59	34	25	31
4	Old Berkhamstedians	16	9	0	7	43	36	7	27
5	Old Aldenhamians	16	6	1	9	27	61	-34	19
6	Old Cholmeleians	16	4	5	7	32	36	-4	17
7	Old Reptonians	16	5	1	10	36	42	-6	16
8	Old Malvernians	16	3	3	10	28	49	-21	12
9	Old Wellingtonians	16	1	1	14	25	64	-39	1*

Division Two

		P	W	D	L	F	A	GD	Pts
1	Old Alleynians AFC	18	14	3	1	57	20	37	45
2	Old Radleians	18	11	2	5	57	36	21	35
3	Old Foresters II	18	8	5	5	34	31	3	29
4	Old Carthusians II	18	8	4	6	44	28	16	28
5	Old Westminsters	18	7	6	5	45	37	8	27
6	Old Etonians II	18	6	3	9	26	37	-11	21
7	Kings College Wimbledon II	18	5	3	10	31	38	-7	18
8	Old Harrovians II	18	5	2	11	30	44	-14	17
9	Lancing Old Boys II	18	5	1	12	24	52	-28	16
10	Old Carthusians III	18	5	3	10	23	48	-25	14*

Division Three

		P	W	D	L	F	A	GD	Pts
1	Old Citizens	18	13	2	3	67	29	38	41
2	Old Chigwellians II	18	13	2	3	48	17	31	41
3	Old Merchant Taylors	18	9	2	7	42	29	13	29
4	Old Tonbridgians II	18	8	4	6	36	36	0	28
5	Old Salopians II	18	7	4	7	31	43	-12	25
6	Old Epsomians	18	7	2	9	33	41	-8	23
7	Old Sennockians	18	7	1	10	35	36	-1	22
8	Old Aldenhamians II	18	5	5	8	33	51	-18	20
9	Old Haberdashers	18	5	1	12	35	62	-27	16
10	Old Eastbournians	18	3	3	12	32	48	-16	12

Division Four

		P	W	D	L	F	A	GD	Pts
1	Old Johnians FC	14	10	3	1	39	16	23	33
2	Old Rugbeians	14	9	2	3	40	15	25	29
3	Old Suttonians SV	14	8	2	4	40	25	15	26
4	Old Stoics	14	6	1	7	41	37	4	19
5	Old Bancroftians AFC	14	4	3	7	24	40	-16	15
6	Old Alleynians AFC II	14	4	2	8	35	41	-6	14
7	Old Merchant Taylors II	14	4	2	8	28	38	-10	14
8	Old Wykehamists II	14	3	1	10	24	59	-35	10

Division Five North

		P	W	D	L	F	A	GD	Pts
1	Old Columbans	12	10	1	1	45	16	29	31
2	Old Brentwoods III	12	8	1	3	38	20	18	25
3	Old Albanians SA	12	6	3	3	29	27	2	21
4	Old Brentwoods II	12	3	6	3	24	23	1	15
5	Old Cholmeleians II	12	3	3	6	29	32	-3	12
6	Old Chigwellians III	12	2	3	7	15	37	-22	9
7	Old Foresters III	12	1	1	10	12	37	-25	4

FINAL TABLES

Division Five South

		P	W	D	L	F	A	GD	Pts
1	Old Harrovians III	12	10	1	1	36	13	23	31
2	Old Shirburnians	12	7	1	4	38	24	14	22
3	Old Westminsters II	12	6	1	5	32	26	6	19
4	Old Amplefordians	12	6	1	5	23	22	1	19
5	Old King's Scholars	12	4	2	6	20	30	-10	14
6	Old Epsomians II	12	3	0	9	9	22	-13	9
7	Kings College Wimbledon III	12	2	2	8	17	38	-21	8

SOUTHERN AMATEUR LEAGUE

Senior Division One

		P	W	D	L	F	A	GD	Pts
1	Polytechnic	20	15	3	2	71	14	57	48
2	Alleyn Old Boys	20	12	4	4	45	22	23	40
3	Nottsborough	20	12	3	5	54	21	33	39
4	West Wickham	20	9	5	6	35	36	-1	32
5	Old Wilsonians	20	7	7	6	39	31	8	28
6	Old Parkonians	20	6	6	8	32	43	-11	24
7	Old Garchonians	20	6	5	9	34	44	-10	23
8	Old Owens	20	5	5	10	36	43	-7	20
9	Winchmore Hill	20	4	6	10	37	51	-14	18
10	East Barnet Old Grammarians	20	5	3	12	31	73	-42	18
11	Bank of England	20	4	3	13	21	57	-36	15

Southern Division Two

		P	W	D	L	F	A	GD	Pts
1	Actonians Association	20	16	3	1	84	23	61	51
2	Civil Service	20	11	7	2	47	17	30	40
3	NUFC Oilers	20	10	6	4	49	30	19	36
4	Alexandra Park	20	10	3	7	37	38	-1	33
5	Ibis Eagles	20	8	5	7	36	38	-2	29
6	HSBC	20	8	2	10	40	48	-8	26
7	Merton	20	7	3	10	29	36	-7	24
8	Norsemen	20	7	3	10	35	46	-11	24
9	Old Finchleians	20	5	3	12	30	44	-14	18
10	Old Lyonians	20	4	4	12	42	61	-19	16
11	Crouch End Vampires	20	4	1	15	20	68	-48	13

Southern Division Three

		P	W	D	L	F	A	GD	Pts
1	Carshalton	18	13	2	3	42	21	21	41
2	Cambridge Heath	18	11	3	4	30	18	12	36
3	South Bank Cuaco	18	10	2	6	40	23	17	32
4	Broomfield	18	9	2	7	44	32	12	29
5	Old Blues	18	8	3	7	39	36	3	27
6	The Warren	18	8	2	8	41	38	3	26
7	Weirside Rangers	18	7	4	7	31	26	5	25
8	Old Stationers	18	5	6	7	31	44	-13	21
9	Kew Association	18	3	1	14	28	44	-16	10
10	AFC Oldsmiths	18	2	3	13	18	62	-44	9

Intermediate Division One

		P	W	D	L	F	A	GD	Pts
1	West Wickham Res	18	13	4	1	56	18	38	43
2	Alleyn Old Boys Res	18	12	1	5	49	26	23	37
3	Polytechnic Res	18	9	5	4	37	18	19	32
4	NUFC Oilers Res	18	9	5	4	54	37	17	32
5	Old Wilsonians Res	18	7	2	9	33	36	-3	23
6	Nottsborough Res	18	6	4	8	34	35	-1	22
7	Actonians Association Res	18	5	5	8	27	38	-11	20
8	Winchmore Hill Res	18	6	2	10	24	36	-12	20
9	Civil Service Res	18	4	5	9	30	50	-20	17
10	East Barnet Old Grammarians Res	18	1	3	14	20	70	-50	6

Intermediate Division Two

		P	W	D	L	F	A	GD	Pts
1	Crouch End Vampires Res	18	13	4	1	74	27	47	43
2	Bank of England Res	18	12	3	3	64	22	42	39
3	Alexandra Park Res	18	11	4	3	56	26	30	37
4	Old Parkonians Res	18	11	3	4	73	35	38	36
5	Old Lyonians Res	18	6	5	7	36	48	-12	23
6	AFC Oldsmiths Res	18	7	0	11	37	57	-20	21
7	Ibis Eagles Res	18	6	3	9	37	62	-25	21
8	Old Finchleians Res	18	4	2	12	31	69	-38	14
9	South Bank Cuaco Res	18	3	2	13	30	54	-24	11
10	HSBC Res	18	2	4	12	24	62	-38	10

Intermediate Division Three

		P	W	D	L	F	A	GD	Pts
1	Old Owens Res	18	13	2	3	71	23	48	38*
2	Carshalton Res	18	10	3	5	50	36	14	33
3	Norsemen Res	18	10	3	5	29	32	-3	30*
4	Weirside Rangers Res	18	9	0	9	32	46	-14	27
5	Merton Res	18	7	5	6	28	34	-6	26
6	Cambridge Heath Res	18	5	4	9	37	39	-2	19
7	St. James' Old Boys	18	5	3	10	33	53	-20	18
8	Old Blues Res	18	4	5	9	29	44	-15	17
9	Hampstead Heathens	18	5	2	11	31	40	-9	14*
10	The Warren Res	18	8	1	9	37	30	7	10*

Intermediate Division Four

		P	W	D	L	F	A	GD	Pts
1	West Wickham 3rd	20	19	0	1	56	16	40	57
2	Polytechnic 3rd	20	14	1	5	72	37	35	43
3	Alleyn Old Boys 3rd	20	10	5	5	52	34	18	35
4	Old Parkonians 3rd	20	9	4	7	52	41	11	31
5	Civil Service 3rd	20	9	2	9	50	51	-1	29
6	Nottsborough 3rd	20	8	4	8	52	46	6	25*
7	Actonians Association 3rd	20	7	3	10	46	59	-13	24
8	Old Salesians	20	6	2	12	39	66	-27	20
9	Alexandra Park 3rd	20	6	1	13	38	50	-12	19
10	Old Finchleians 3rd	20	5	3	12	44	69	-25	18
11	Bank of England 3rd	20	2	5	13	32	64	-32	8*

Junior Division One North

		P	W	D	L	F	A	GD	Pts
1	Winchmore Hill 3rd	18	14	1	3	77	28	49	43
2	Alexandra Park 4th	18	11	2	5	63	46	17	35
3	Old Garchonians 3rd	18	10	3	5	58	31	27	33
4	Old Finchleians 4th	18	9	2	7	54	43	11	29
5	East Barnet Old Grammarians 3rd	18	7	1	10	37	53	-16	22
6	Norsemen 4th	18	5	1	12	35	65	-30	16
7	Old Garchonians 4th	18	1	2	15	28	86	-58	5

Junior Division Two North

		P	W	D	L	F	A	GD	Pts
1	Winchmore Hill 5th	18	15	3	0	69	16	53	48
2	Old Parkonians 4th	18	9	4	5	49	36	13	31
3	Old Owens 3rd	18	11	0	7	65	37	28	30*
4	Crouch End Vampires 4th	18	8	5	5	47	37	10	29
5	Old Finchleians 5th	18	8	4	6	56	41	15	28
6	Alexandra Park 5th	18	6	6	6	44	38	6	21*
7	Winchmore Hill 6th	18	5	6	7	38	46	-8	21
8	Alexandra Park 6th	18	7	0	11	36	53	-17	21
9	St. James' Old Boys Res	18	5	0	13	31	84	-53	15
10	Tansley	18	0	4	14	37	84	-47	4

Junior Division Three North

		P	W	D	L	F	A	GD	Pts
1	East Barnet Old Grammarians 4th	16	13	0	3	77	43	34	39
2	Old Finchleians 6th	16	12	2	2	61	23	38	38
3	Broomfield Res	16	12	1	3	86	34	52	37
4	Old Parkonians 5th	16	10	1	5	57	38	19	31
5	Winchmore Hill 7th	16	5	1	10	38	66	-28	16
6	East Barnet Old Grammarians 5th	16	4	2	10	34	73	-39	14
7	Old Lyonians 3rd	16	4	1	11	42	60	-18	13
8	Old Parkonians 6th	16	4	0	12	31	72	-41	12
9	Norsemen 5th	16	3	2	11	41	58	-17	11

Junior Division Four North

		P	W	D	L	F	A	GD	Pts
1	Old Parkonians 7th	18	15	0	3	64	35	29	45
2	Old Owens 4th	18	13	3	2	72	24	48	42
3	Broomfield 3rd	18	13	1	4	88	31	57	40
4	Norsemen 6th	18	11	1	6	67	57	10	34
5	Old Parkonians 8th	18	9	3	6	50	43	7	30
6	Old Lyonians 4th	18	6	2	10	61	49	12	20
7	Alexandra Park 7th	18	4	3	11	27	47	-20	15
8	Alexandra Park 8th	18	3	5	10	31	67	-36	14
9	Winchmore Hill 8th	18	4	1	13	35	62	-27	13
10	Old Stationers 3rd	18	1	3	14	27	107	-80	6

Junior Division Five North

		P	W	D	L	F	A	GD	Pts
1	Old Parkonians 10th	14	10	2	2	48	22	26	32
2	Old Lyonians 5th	14	10	0	4	55	38	17	30
3	Crouch End Vampires 6th	14	7	2	5	41	37	4	23
4	Crouch End Vampires 5th	14	5	4	5	38	31	7	19
5	Norsemen 7th	14	5	3	6	38	43	-5	18
6	Alexandra Park 9th	14	6	1	7	28	36	-8	16*
7	Winchmore Hill 9th	14	3	4	7	29	49	-20	13
8	Alexandra Park 10th	14	1	2	11	22	43	-21	-1*

Junior Division One South

		P	W	D	L	F	A	GD	Pts
1	Polytechnic 4th	20	16	3	1	50	15	35	51
2	Alleyn Old Boys 4th	20	14	2	4	67	42	25	44
3	Nottsborough 4th	20	11	3	6	54	34	20	36
4	City of London	20	10	4	6	39	25	14	34
5	South Bank Cuaco 3rd	20	9	5	6	42	40	2	32
6	Carshalton 3rd	20	9	2	9	47	42	5	29
7	Actonians Association 4th	20	7	4	9	34	37	-3	25
8	Old Wilsonians 3rd	20	4	6	10	33	40	-7	18
9	Kew Association Res	20	6	0	14	37	52	-15	18
10	Merton 3rd	20	5	1	14	31	59	-28	16
11	HSBC 3rd	20	3	2	15	23	71	-48	11

Junior Division Two South

		P	W	D	L	F	A	GD	Pts
1	Alleyn Old Boys 5th	18	15	0	3	63	30	33	45
2	West Wickham 4th	18	12	4	2	63	28	35	40
3	Polytechnic 5th	18	9	1	8	45	44	1	28
4	Carshalton 4th	18	8	4	6	52	61	-9	28
5	Actonians Association 5th	18	6	3	9	32	38	-6	21
6	Civil Service 5th	18	6	3	9	37	51	-14	21
7	AFC Oldsmiths 3rd	18	6	5	7	41	34	7	20*
8	Civil Service 4th	18	6	2	10	54	51	3	20
9	Weirside Rangers 3rd	18	6	2	10	40	52	-12	20
10	Ibis Eagles 3rd	18	4	0	14	25	63	-38	12

Junior Division Three South

		P	W	D	L	F	A	GD	Pts
1	Actonians Association 6th	16	12	3	1	48	25	23	39
2	Ibis Eagles 4th	16	9	4	3	42	23	19	31
3	West Wickham 5th	16	8	2	6	44	27	17	26
4	Alleyn Old Boys 6th	16	6	5	5	41	39	2	23
5	HSBC 4th	16	7	0	9	36	43	-7	21
6	Old Wilsonians 4th	16	5	6	5	34	40	-6	20
7	Bank of England 4th	16	4	3	9	24	29	-5	15
8	Polytechnic 6th	16	3	5	8	25	51	-26	14
9	City of London Res	16	3	3	10	24	41	-17	12

FINAL TABLES

Junior Division Four South

		P	W	D	L	F	A	GD	Pts
1	Old Salesians Res	18	10	3	5	74	43	31	33
2	South Bank Cuaco 4th	18	10	2	6	47	33	14	32
3	Ibis Eagles 5th	18	11	2	5	49	35	14	31*
4	Merton 4th	18	10	1	7	56	45	11	31
5	Kew Association 3rd	18	9	2	7	45	55	-10	29
6	Actonians Association 7th	18	9	5	4	42	18	24	28*
7	Polytechnic 7th	18	9	1	8	56	52	4	28
8	West Wickham 6th	18	5	1	12	40	54	-14	16
9	Civil Service 6th	18	4	2	12	30	61	-31	14
10	Polytechnic 8th	18	3	1	14	26	69	-43	7*

Junior Division Five South

		P	W	D	L	F	A	GD	Pts
1	Merton 6th	16	11	3	2	67	31	36	36
2	Old Wilsonians 5th	16	11	2	3	34	31	3	35
3	Actonians Association 8th	16	8	2	6	50	39	11	26
4	HSBC 5th	16	7	2	7	43	35	8	23
5	Old Wilsonians 6th	16	7	2	7	37	39	-2	23
6	South Bank Cuaco 5th	16	4	5	7	31	41	-10	17
7	Merton 5th	16	5	2	9	25	41	-16	17
8	Civil Service 7th	16	5	1	10	30	34	-4	16
9	City of London 3rd	16	2	5	9	22	48	-26	11

Junior Division Six South

		P	W	D	L	F	A	GD	Pts
1	Alleyn Old Boys 7th	20	17	1	2	77	31	46	52
2	Old Blues 3rd	20	11	3	6	55	43	12	36
3	Old Wilsonians 7th	20	10	3	7	49	59	-10	33
4	South Bank Cuaco 6th	20	9	5	6	62	46	16	32
5	Bank of England 5th	20	9	2	9	51	43	8	29
6	South Bank Cuaco 7th	20	8	4	8	63	50	13	28
7	Civil Service 8th	20	8	4	8	48	41	7	28
8	Old Salesians 3rd	20	7	2	11	46	51	-5	23
9	Merton 7th	20	6	3	11	63	74	-11	21
10	HSBC 6th	20	5	3	12	55	69	-14	18
11	Old Wilsonians 8th	20	4	2	14	38	100	-62	14

ISLAND FOOTBALL

ISLE OF MAN LEAGUE

Premier Division

		P	W	D	L	F	A	GD	Pts
1	St Georges	23	21	1	1	140	30	110	64
2	Peel	24	18	2	4	111	36	75	56
3	Rushen Utd	24	18	1	5	91	32	59	55
4	Corinthians	23	17	1	5	100	22	78	52
5	St Johns Utd	24	10	8	6	75	57	18	38
6	DHSOB	24	10	7	7	51	41	10	37
7	St Marys	24	11	3	10	77	66	11	36
8	Laxey	24	10	1	13	64	83	-19	31
9	Douglas Athletic	24	9	1	14	55	83	-28	28
10	Douglas Royal	24	4	3	17	39	112	-73	15
11	Braddan	24	4	2	18	33	104	-71	14
12	Ramsey	24	3	2	19	26	103	-77	11
13	Colby	24	3	2	19	29	122	-93	11

Division Two

		P	W	D	L	F	A	GD	Pts
1	Marown	24	18	2	4	98	36	62	56
2	Castletown	24	18	2	4	90	33	57	56
3	Foxdale	24	17	3	4	102	33	69	54
4	Pulrose United	24	17	1	6	91	38	53	52
5	Onchan	24	14	2	8	60	42	18	44
6	RYCOB	24	13	4	7	92	38	54	43
7	Malew	24	13	2	9	79	68	11	41
8	Union Mills	24	12	4	8	88	69	19	40
9	Douglas & District	24	7	2	15	43	85	-42	23
10	Ayre United	24	5	2	17	45	93	-48	17
11	Michael United	24	3	4	17	33	113	-80	13
12	Gymnasium	24	3	1	20	41	108	-67	10
13	Governors Athletic	24	1	1	22	36	142	-106	4

Combination One

		P	W	D	L	F	A	GD	Pts
1	Rushen Utd Res	24	21	1	2	130	25	105	64
2	DHSOB Res	24	20	0	4	79	32	47	60
3	Corinthians Res	24	18	0	6	103	44	59	54
4	Douglas Athletic Res	24	13	3	8	75	64	11	42
5	St Georges Res	24	11	4	9	62	34	28	37
6	Peel Res	24	12	1	11	70	46	24	37
7	St Johns Utd Res	24	12	0	12	66	70	-4	36
8	Douglas Royal Res	24	10	1	13	64	88	-24	31
9	St Marys Res	24	9	1	14	70	73	-3	28
10	Laxey Res	24	9	1	14	65	70	-5	28
11	Ramsey Res	24	5	2	17	40	96	-56	17
12	Braddan Res	24	5	2	17	39	109	-70	17
13	Colby Res	24	3	0	21	42	154	-112	9

Combination Two

		P	W	D	L	F	A	GD	Pts
1	RYCOB Res	24	23	1	0	141	27	114	70
2	Onchan Res	24	17	4	3	90	47	43	55
3	Malew Res	24	14	1	9	88	49	39	43
4	Marown Res	24	12	3	9	98	71	27	39
5	Pulrose United Res	24	12	2	10	70	66	4	38
6	Ayre United Res	24	11	3	10	63	80	-17	36
7	Douglas & District Res	24	11	2	11	64	63	1	35
8	Castletown Res	24	11	0	13	54	59	-5	33
9	Union Mills Res	24	10	2	12	60	69	-9	32
10	Foxdale Res	24	6	3	15	39	76	-37	21
11	Gymnasium Res	24	6	3	15	46	88	-42	21
12	Governors Athletic Res	24	5	1	18	47	117	-70	16
13	Michael United Res	24	3	5	16	38	86	-48	14

GUERNSEY LEAGUE

Priaulx League

		P	W	D	L	F	A	GD	Pts
1	Rovers AC	24	18	3	3	69	21	48	57
2	St Martins AC	24	17	3	4	69	30	39	54
3	Northerners AC	24	15	1	8	70	35	35	46
4	Vale Recreation	24	8	8	8	48	41	7	32
5	Manzur	24	9	5	10	49	63	-14	32
6	Rangers FAC	24	9	4	11	52	49	3	31
7	Alderney	24	8	4	12	32	52	-20	28
8	UCF Sylvans	24	7	2	15	46	60	-14	23
9	Belgrave Wanderers	24	1	2	21	28	112	-84	5

Division One

		P	W	D	L	F	A	GD	Pts
1	Vale Recreation	14	12	0	2	57	18	39	36
2	BW Rangers	14	9	2	3	47	23	24	29
3	St Martins AC	14	9	1	4	42	26	16	28
4	UCF Sylvans	14	6	3	5	17	19	-2	21
5	Rovers AC	14	6	2	6	26	24	2	20
6	Manzur	14	4	0	10	14	27	-13	12
7	Northerners AC	14	4	0	10	5	40	-35	12
8	Belgrave Wanderers	14	1	2	11	19	50	-31	5

Division Two

		P	W	D	L	F	A	GD	Pts
1	Red Lion FC	16	15	1	0	71	13	58	46
2	Manzur	16	11	3	2	55	25	30	36
3	Rovers AC	16	9	3	4	45	34	11	30
4	UCF Sylvans	16	9	0	7	38	30	8	27
5	Northerners AC	16	7	1	8	40	55	-15	22
6	Centrals	16	5	2	9	33	40	-7	17
7	Vale Recreation	16	4	3	9	41	46	-5	15
8	Rangers FAC	16	4	1	11	31	58	-27	13
9	CF Independant	16	0	2	14	20	73	-53	2

Division Three

		P	W	D	L	F	A	GD	Pts
1	Police	16	12	1	3	51	27	24	37
2	London House Bels	16	11	2	3	65	35	30	35
3	Rovers AC	16	10	1	5	68	42	26	31
4	Rocquaine Pirates	16	10	0	6	49	26	23	30
5	Centrals	16	9	1	6	63	45	18	28
6	Manor Farm Saints	16	6	3	7	50	36	14	21
7	CF Independant	16	5	1	10	36	64	-28	16
8	Thrive Physiotherapy	16	3	1	12	32	53	-21	10
9	Vale Recreation	16	1	0	15	17	103	-86	3

JERSEY FOOTBALL COMBINATION

Premiership

		P	W	D	L	F	A	GD	Pts
1	St Paul's	18	14	2	2	59	20	39	44
2	St Peter	18	10	5	3	55	22	33	35
3	JTC Jersey Wanderers	18	9	2	7	56	28	28	29
4	St Clement	18	9	2	7	41	38	3	29
5	St Ouen	18	9	1	8	34	31	3	28
6	Rozel Rovers	18	4	3	11	21	44	-23	15
7	Grouville	18	0	1	17	9	92	-83	1

NON LEAGUE DAY
13.10.18
Support your
LOCAL
FOOTBALL CLUB
nonleagueday.co.uk

NORTHERN IRELAND TABLES 2017-18

IRELAND FOOTBALL ASSOCIATION

Premiership

		P	W	D	L	F	A	GD	Pts
1	Crusaders	38	28	7	3	106	38	68	91
2	Coleraine	38	26	11	1	76	31	45	89
3	Glenavon	38	19	12	7	85	52	33	69
4	Linfield	38	20	7	11	72	45	27	67
5	Cliftonville	38	20	5	13	68	45	23	65
6	Glentoran	38	14	9	15	52	52	0	51
7	Ballymena United	38	14	6	18	53	65	-12	48
8	Dungannon Swifts	38	13	6	19	42	62	-20	45
9	Ards	38	12	4	22	42	74	-32	40
10	Warrenpoint Town	38	8	6	24	52	86	-34	30
11	Carrick Rangers	38	6	5	27	31	78	-47	23
12	Ballinamallard United	38	5	8	25	38	89	-51	23

Championship

		P	W	D	L	F	A	GD	Pts
1	Institute	32	21	5	6	55	36	19	68
2	Newry City	32	17	8	7	58	31	27	59
3	HW Welders	32	16	8	8	54	42	12	56
4	Portadown	32	14	9	9	61	36	25	51
5	Ballyclare Comrades	32	15	3	14	56	52	4	48
6	Larne	32	12	11	9	59	47	12	47
7	PSNI	32	11	8	13	55	50	5	41
8	Loughgall	32	12	2	18	45	59	-14	38
9	Limavady United	32	10	7	15	52	58	-6	37
10	Knockbreda	32	9	9	14	50	54	-4	36
11	Dergview	32	9	9	14	49	59	-10	36
12	Lurgan Celtic	32	3	7	22	32	102	-70	16

Premier Intermediate League

		P	W	D	L	F	A	GD	Pts
1	Dundela	25	17	6	2	70	27	43	57
2	Queens University	25	16	2	7	58	32	26	50
3	Lisburn Distillery	25	14	3	8	43	33	10	45
4	Banbridge Town	25	11	9	5	44	34	10	42
5	Moyola Park	25	10	5	10	46	38	8	35
6	Portstewart	25	9	4	12	32	48	-16	31
7	Armagh City	25	9	3	13	35	39	-4	30
8	Sport and Leisure Swifts	25	8	5	12	39	56	-17	29
9	Annagh United	25	9	2	14	39	57	-18	29
10	Tobermore United	25	7	7	11	45	55	-10	28
11	Newington YC	25	6	9	12	37	52	-15	27
12	Donegal Celtic	25	5	4	16	32	49	-17	19

BALLYMENA & PROVINCIAL LEAGUE

Intermediate Division

		P	W	D	L	F	A	GD	Pts
1	Glebe Rangers	24	19	2	3	74	30	44	59
2	Bangor	24	18	4	2	82	14	68	58
3	St James Swifts	24	16	3	5	66	28	38	51
4	Newtowne	24	13	1	10	54	42	12	40
5	Desertmartin	24	12	3	9	59	59	0	39
6	Dunloy	24	11	5	8	57	38	19	38
7	Coagh United	24	10	7	7	74	39	35	37
8	Brantwood	24	7	5	12	49	47	2	26
9	Cookstown Youth	24	7	4	13	48	56	-8	25
10	Ballynure OB	24	7	3	14	31	62	-31	24
11	Cookstown Royal British Legion	24	4	8	12	32	57	-25	20
12	Sofia Farm	24	5	2	17	31	95	-64	17
13	Chimney Corner	24	2	1	21	18	106	-88	7

Junior Division One

		P	W	D	L	F	A	GD	Pts
1	Newington YC II	18	16	0	2	72	22	50	48
2	Woodlands	18	11	3	4	58	35	23	36
3	Brantwood Res	18	10	2	6	45	31	14	32
4	Antrim Rovers	18	8	6	4	44	37	7	30
5	FC Whiteabbey	18	8	3	7	44	38	6	27
6	3rd Ballyclare OB	18	6	6	6	36	39	-3	24
7	Desertmartin Swifts	18	5	3	10	41	57	-16	18
8	Cookstown Olympic	17	3	6	8	35	47	-12	15
9	Sport & Leisure II	18	4	3	11	41	74	-33	15
10	Ballynure OB B	17	0	4	13	24	60	-36	4

Junior Division Two

		P	W	D	L	F	A	GD	Pts
1	Killmoon Rangers	17	14	1	2	62	23	39	43
2	Castle Star	17	12	2	3	65	22	43	38
3	Cookstown Youth Colts	18	11	5	2	64	28	36	38
4	Clough Rangers Athletic	16	9	4	3	55	29	26	31
5	Mallusk Athletic	18	8	2	8	37	37	0	26
6	Brantwood / Loughside	18	6	4	8	31	52	-21	22
7	North End United Youth	18	4	5	9	39	60	-21	17
8	Antrim Rovers Swifts	18	4	3	11	23	48	-25	15
9	Cookstown RBL Reserves	18	3	1	14	26	69	-43	10
10	68th Newtownabbey OB 'A'	18	2	3	13	23	57	-34	9

Junior Division Three

		P	W	D	L	F	A	GD	Pts
1	Rathcoole	12	11	1	0	76	12	64	34
2	Carrickfergus Athletic	12	8	1	3	39	31	8	25
3	North Belfast United	12	6	2	4	39	24	15	20
4	Ballyclare North End	12	5	1	6	21	27	-6	16
5	Red Star (Carrick)	12	3	2	7	19	55	-36	11
6	Carnlough Swifts	12	2	2	8	20	33	-13	8
7	68th Newtownabbey OB 'B'	12	1	1	10	18	64	-46	4

MID ULSTER LEAGUE

Intermediate A

		P	W	D	L	F	A	GD	Pts
1	Dollingstown	24	17	5	2	72	26	46	56
2	Banbridge Rangers	24	18	1	5	57	27	30	55
3	Crewe United	24	15	5	4	59	35	24	50
4	Hanover	24	15	3	6	61	33	28	48
5	Valley Rangers	24	13	1	10	49	48	1	40
6	Windmill Stars	24	10	5	9	49	38	11	35
7	Moneyslane	24	10	4	10	42	41	1	34
8	Fivemiletown United	24	9	3	12	33	56	-23	30
9	Tandragee Rovers	24	6	9	9	50	44	6	27
10	Ballymacash Rangers	24	6	3	15	40	59	-19	21
11	Richhill AFC	24	6	2	16	38	53	-15	20
12	St Marys	24	4	6	14	31	62	-31	18
13	AFC Silverwood	24	3	1	20	24	83	-59	10

Intermediate B

		P	W	D	L	F	A	GD	Pts
1	Laurelvale	24	16	4	4	59	35	24	52
2	Bourneview Mill	24	13	6	5	63	32	31	45
3	Oxford Sunnyside	24	13	6	5	59	39	20	45
4	Tullyvallen	24	13	3	8	60	41	19	42
5	Lower Maze	24	12	4	8	63	48	15	40
6	Seagoe	24	11	7	6	48	40	8	40
7	Markethill Swifts	24	9	7	8	52	47	5	34
8	Craigavon City	24	9	6	9	54	58	-4	33
9	Lurgan Town	24	9	5	10	56	49	7	32
10	Dungannon Tigers	24	8	8	8	54	51	3	32
11	Seapatrick	24	5	3	16	40	75	-35	18
12	Broomhedge Maghaberry	24	3	3	18	31	75	-44	12
13	Dromore Amateurs	24	4	0	20	22	71	-49	12

Division One

		P	W	D	L	F	A	GD	Pts
1	Hill Street	22	15	5	2	94	28	66	50
2	Rectory Rangers	22	14	4	4	57	25	32	46
3	Ballyoran	22	15	0	7	70	36	34	45
4	Caledon Rovers	22	10	5	7	38	29	9	35
5	Ambassadors	22	9	6	7	39	40	-1	33
6	Coalisland Athletic	22	10	2	10	69	52	17	32
7	Sandy Hill	22	7	5	10	31	44	-13	26
8	Glenavy	22	8	2	12	40	56	-16	26
9	Lurgan BBOB	22	7	5	10	35	54	-19	26
10	Red Star	22	8	1	13	47	89	-42	25
11	Portadown BBOB	22	6	1	15	40	67	-27	19
12	Donaghmore	22	4	2	16	26	66	-40	14

Division Two

		P	W	D	L	F	A	GD	Pts
1	Armagh Celtic	24	17	2	5	77	43	34	53
2	Newmills	24	16	2	6	73	50	23	50
3	Keady Celtic	24	15	4	5	99	62	37	49
4	Stranmillis	24	13	4	7	88	69	19	43
5	Knockmenagh Swifts	24	12	2	10	62	60	2	38
6	Scarva Rangers	24	11	4	9	63	49	14	37
7	Hillsborough Boys	24	10	7	7	64	52	12	37
8	Donacloney	24	8	7	9	62	59	3	31
9	White City	24	9	3	12	61	64	-3	30
10	West End Hibs	24	9	3	12	64	73	-9	30
11	Goodyear	24	5	6	13	45	75	-30	21
12	Derryhirk United	24	3	3	18	49	95	-46	12
13	Lurgan United	24	1	7	16	35	91	-56	10

Division Three

		P	W	D	L	F	A	GD	Pts
1	Banbridge YCOB	20	15	2	3	61	27	34	47
2	Ballymacash YM	20	14	1	5	70	40	30	43
3	United LT	20	13	2	5	67	32	35	41
4	Gilford Crusaders	20	13	2	5	64	31	33	41
5	Annalong	20	12	4	4	82	36	46	40
6	Armagh Blues	20	13	0	7	63	28	35	39
7	Glenavy Youth	20	7	3	10	51	58	-7	24
8	Sporting Lisburn	20	6	1	13	38	68	-30	19
9	The Dons	20	5	1	14	29	84	-55	16
10	Damolly	20	3	0	17	42	80	-38	9
11	Moira Albion	20	1	0	19	30	113	-83	3

NORTHERN AMATEUR LEAGUE

Premier Division

		P	W	D	L	F	A	GD	Pts
1	Crumlin Star	26	20	5	1	79	29	50	65
2	Rathfriland Rangers	26	18	3	5	79	31	48	57
3	East Belfast	26	15	7	4	84	42	42	52
4	Immaculata F.C.	26	16	1	9	75	54	21	49
5	1st Bangor Old Boys	26	11	5	10	45	45	0	38
6	Ards Rangers	26	10	5	11	52	47	5	35
7	Albert Foundry F.C.	26	10	5	11	50	52	-2	35
8	Crumlin United	26	10	5	11	43	54	-11	35
9	Downpatrick F.C.	26	9	5	12	61	56	5	32
10	Shankill United	26	10	2	14	50	52	-2	32
11	Drumaness Mills	26	9	3	14	39	73	-34	30
12	Derriaghy C C	26	7	5	14	39	57	-18	26
13	Malachians	26	6	3	17	42	98	-56	21
14	Lisburn Rangers	26	3	2	21	40	88	-48	11

Division One A

		P	W	D	L	F	A	GD	Pts
1	Ballynahinch Olympic	24	16	6	2	61	22	39	54
2	Islandmagee	24	16	3	5	56	33	23	51
3	Larne Tech O.B.	24	13	7	4	50	31	19	46
4	Abbey Villa	24	10	7	7	42	33	9	37
5	Rathfern Rangers	24	11	2	11	60	48	12	35
6	Killyleagh Y.C	24	10	4	10	53	49	4	34
7	Dunmurry Rec	24	11	1	12	37	40	-3	34
8	Sirocco Wks	24	10	4	10	52	59	-7	34
9	Comber Rec F.C.	24	9	1	14	39	56	-17	28
10	Orangefield Old Boys	24	7	4	13	40	57	-17	25
11	Kilmore Rec	24	7	2	15	37	53	-16	23
12	Newcastle	24	6	4	14	45	62	-17	22
13	St Patricks Y.M. F.C.	24	5	5	14	44	73	-29	17*

NORTHERN IRELAND FOOTBALL

Division One B

		P	W	D	L	F	A	GD	Pts
1	Uni of Ulster at Jordanstown	26	19	3	4	71	30	41	60
2	Rosario Y.C.	26	17	5	4	57	26	31	56
3	Ballywalter Rec. F.C.	26	16	4	6	68	22	46	52
4	Dromara Village	26	13	3	10	61	46	15	42
5	Portaferry Rovers	26	12	5	9	39	38	1	41
6	St Lukes F.C.	26	12	4	10	59	41	18	40
7	Dunmurry Y. M.	26	11	6	9	65	65	0	39
8	Grove United	26	11	4	11	41	47	-6	37
9	Colin Valley F.C.	26	7	8	11	59	52	7	29
10	Barn United	26	8	5	13	60	59	1	29
11	Mossley F.C.	26	6	6	14	38	57	-19	24
12	Downshire YM	26	7	3	16	43	65	-22	24
13	Dundonald	26	6	4	16	31	99	-68	22
14	Ballynahinch United	26	5	4	17	29	74	-45	19

Division One C

		P	W	D	L	F	A	GD	Pts
1	18th Newtownabbey O.B.	24	22	2	0	86	32	54	68
2	Bryansburn Rangers	24	16	6	2	72	32	40	54
3	Rosemount Rec	24	16	1	7	87	47	40	49
4	Bangor Amateurs F.C.	24	12	9	3	62	37	25	45
5	Suffolk F.C.	24	14	2	8	63	33	30	44
6	Shorts FC	24	11	5	8	68	43	25	38
7	Wellington Rec	24	9	4	11	49	50	-1	31
8	Saintfield United	24	8	5	11	61	69	-8	29
9	Bloomfield F.C.	24	7	7	10	53	58	-5	28
10	Holywood F.C.	24	7	2	15	33	63	-30	23
11	Bangor Swifts	24	5	5	14	41	76	-35	20
12	Groomsport	23	1	3	19	31	92	-61	3*
13	Iveagh United	23	1	1	21	25	99	-74	1*

Division Two A

		P	W	D	L	F	A	GD	Pts
1	Tullycarnet FC	22	15	5	2	67	27	40	50
2	Aquinas FC	22	16	1	5	64	21	43	49
3	Woodvale F.C.	22	13	7	2	59	27	32	46
4	Greenisland F.C.	22	13	6	3	57	22	35	45
5	St Oliver Plunkett F.C.	22	13	4	5	56	25	31	43
6	Ballysillan Swifts	22	9	3	10	40	49	-9	30
7	Ford	22	7	8	7	55	44	11	29
8	Finaghy F.C.	22	8	4	10	40	36	4	28
9	Lower Shankill FC	22	7	3	12	50	51	-1	24
10	Queens Grads.	22	6	1	15	30	61	-31	19
11	Newington Rangers	22	2	0	20	23	90	-67	6
12	Kircubbin F.C.	22	2	0	20	15	103	-88	6

Division Two B

		P	W	D	L	F	A	GD	Pts
1	Portavogie Rangers F.C.	22	17	4	1	58	19	39	55
2	Donaghadee F.C.	22	16	3	3	65	27	38	51
3	Bangor Rangers	22	15	4	3	63	38	25	49
4	Shamrock FC	22	13	0	9	75	65	10	39
5	Ardoyne	22	12	4	6	71	48	23	37*
6	Queens University Res	22	8	5	9	59	60	-1	29
7	Kelvin Old Boys	22	6	7	9	45	59	-14	25
8	Bangor Y.M.	22	8	0	14	44	58	-14	24
9	St Teresas Y.C.	22	6	2	14	51	76	-25	20
10	Castlewellan Town FC	22	6	2	14	36	63	-27	20
11	Newtownbreda F C	22	5	2	15	36	60	-24	17
12	Civil Service	22	3	1	18	39	69	-30	10

Division Two C

		P	W	D	L	F	A	GD	Pts
1	Willowbank FC	22	19	0	3	102	21	81	57
2	Nortel	22	18	2	2	88	28	60	56
3	St Matthews	22	17	3	2	101	19	82	54
4	Whitehead Eagles	22	13	2	7	59	43	16	41
5	Carryduff Colts	22	11	5	6	61	38	23	38
6	St Mary's	22	9	1	12	53	55	-2	28
7	4th Newtownabbey F.C.	22	8	4	10	47	53	-6	28
8	22nd Old Boys	22	7	6	9	41	37	4	27
9	Suffolk Swifts	22	7	2	13	50	57	-7	23
10	Ravenhill YM FC	22	6	4	12	52	66	-14	22
11	Rooftop	22	1	1	20	29	123	-94	4
12	Grange Rangers	22	1	0	21	16	159	-143	3

Division Three A

		P	W	D	L	F	A	GD	Pts
1	Crumlin Utd Res	26	20	1	5	83	32	51	61
2	Crumlin Star Res	26	17	6	3	86	38	48	57
3	Woodvale F.C.Res	26	14	4	8	64	51	13	46
4	St Oliver Plunkett F.C.Res	26	14	3	9	70	47	23	45
5	St Lukes F.C. Res	26	14	3	9	74	61	13	45
6	Immaculata F.C.Res	26	14	3	9	73	56	17	42*
7	Comber Rec F.C.Res	26	12	3	11	60	56	4	39
8	Albert Foundry F.C.Res	26	12	2	12	55	58	-3	38
9	Ards Rangers Res	26	11	2	13	46	58	-12	35
10	Malachians Res	26	9	2	15	49	70	-21	29
11	St Patricks YM Res	26	9	0	17	45	79	-34	27
12	Lisburn Rgs Res	26	7	2	17	47	81	-34	23
13	Rosario Y.C. Res	26	6	4	16	47	61	-14	22
14	Barn Utd Res	26	5	1	20	35	86	-51	13*

Division Three B

		P	W	D	L	F	A	GD	Pts
1	Rathfern Rgs Res	26	20	4	2	100	34	66	64
2	Sirocco Wks Res	26	19	2	5	88	47	41	59
3	Derriaghy CC Res	26	19	0	7	92	36	56	57
4	Larne Tech O.B. Res	26	18	1	7	93	42	51	55
5	Bangor Swifts Res	26	14	2	10	71	62	9	44
6	Shankill Utd. Res	26	13	2	11	97	56	41	41
7	Bloomfield F.C.Res	26	9	2	15	70	70	0	29
8	Orangefield O.B. Res	26	8	5	13	53	72	-19	29
9	Lower Shankill Res	26	9	2	15	64	89	-25	29
10	Grove Utd Res	26	9	2	15	45	77	-32	29
11	Tullycarnet FC Res	26	9	1	16	66	122	-56	28
12	Dunmurry Rec Res	26	7	3	16	50	92	-42	24
13	U.U.Jordanstown Res	26	8	0	18	52	100	-48	24
14	Killyleagh Y.C. Res	26	5	4	17	55	97	-42	19

Division Three C

		P	W	D	L	F	A	GD	Pts
1	East Belfast FC Res	26	22	1	3	105	32	73	67
2	Colin Valley F.C.Res	26	17	2	7	87	41	46	53
3	Abbey Villa Res	26	14	5	7	62	43	19	47
4	Islandmagee Res	26	14	3	9	85	52	33	45
5	Shamrock FC Res	26	13	2	11	82	71	11	41
6	Saintfield Utd Res	26	10	6	10	76	65	11	36
7	Bangor Rgs Res	26	10	5	11	66	56	10	35
8	Queens Grads Res	26	9	4	13	67	57	10	31
9	Dunmurry Y.M.Res	26	9	4	13	57	83	-26	31
10	Shorts Res	26	9	4	13	52	81	-29	31
11	Ford F.C. Res	26	7	8	11	60	75	-15	29
12	1st Bangor Old Boys Res	26	9	2	15	58	77	-19	29
13	Bangor YM Res	26	7	4	15	49	78	-29	25
14	Wellington Rec Res	26	6	2	18	38	133	-95	20

Division Three D

		P	W	D	L	F	A	GD	Pts
1	Rosemount Rec Res	22	18	1	3	79	44	35	55
2	Aquinas FC Res	22	16	2	4	86	31	55	50
3	Bangor Amateurs Res	22	13	3	6	72	42	30	42
4	Mossley FC Res	22	12	4	6	70	42	28	40
5	Ballywalter Rec. F.C.Res	22	12	3	7	53	47	6	39
6	Portaferry Rovers Res	22	11	2	9	47	50	-3	35
7	Suffolk FC Res	22	9	5	8	70	49	21	32
8	St Teresas Y.C.Res	22	8	1	13	42	73	-31	25
9	Bryansburn Rgs. Res	22	7	3	12	49	60	-11	24
10	18th Newtownabbey O.B	22	6	4	12	45	65	-20	22
11	Downshire YM. Res	22	3	1	18	22	83	-61	10
12	Iveagh Utd Res	22	2	1	19	30	79	-49	7

Division Three E

		P	W	D	L	F	A	GD	Pts
1	Ballysillan Swifts Res	20	17	1	2	88	28	60	52
2	Greenisland F.C.Res	20	17	0	3	102	21	81	51
3	Holywood F.C. Res	20	11	3	6	74	46	28	36
4	Donaghadee FC Res	20	10	2	8	54	50	4	32
5	Newtownbreda Res	20	10	1	9	51	46	5	31
6	Kelvin OB Res	20	8	1	11	54	66	-12	25
7	Whitehead Eagles Res	20	7	2	11	39	68	-29	23
8	Ravenhill YM FC Res	20	7	3	10	41	65	-24	21*
9	4th Newtownabbey O.B. Res	20	5	3	12	32	53	-21	18
10	Suffolk Swifts Res	20	5	1	14	27	85	-58	16
11	Civil Service Res	20	3	3	14	23	57	-34	12

Division Three F

		P	W	D	L	F	A	GD	Pts
1	Willowbank FC Res	14	12	2	0	77	28	49	38
2	St Matthews Res	14	8	4	2	43	28	15	28
3	St Mary's Res	14	8	1	5	37	33	4	25
4	Groomsport Res	14	6	1	7	37	43	-6	19
5	22nd Old Boys Res	14	4	3	7	27	38	-11	15
6	Nortel Res	14	4	2	8	37	42	-5	14
7	Finaghy F.C. Res	14	2	5	7	30	49	-19	11
8	Carryduff Colts Res	14	1	4	9	29	56	-27	7

NORTHERN IRELAND INTERMEDIATE LEAGUE

		P	W	D	L	F	A	GD	Pts
1	Magherafelt Sky Blues	16	13	2	1	40	23	17	41
2	Ardstraw	16	11	1	4	45	21	24	34
3	Strabane Athletic	16	10	3	3	42	14	28	33
4	Maiden City	16	10	1	5	44	17	27	31
5	Newbuildings United	16	6	1	9	24	33	-9	19
6	Dungiven	16	5	3	8	24	35	-11	18
7	Trojans	16	5	1	10	30	46	-16	16
8	Ballymoney United	16	2	4	10	17	43	-26	10
9	Oxford United Stars	16	1	2	13	19	53	-34	5

BELFAST & DISTRICT LEAGUE

Premier Division

		P	W	D	L	F	A	GD	Pts
1	Beann Mhadaghain	18	14	2	2	79	25	54	44
2	Cumann Spoirt an Phobail	18	13	2	3	79	28	51	41
3	Tullymore Swifts	18	11	3	4	79	47	32	36
4	Newhill YC	18	9	1	8	53	49	4	28
5	St James Swifts II	18	8	2	8	54	44	10	26
6	St Malachys OB	18	2	0	16	21	103	-82	6
7	Belfast Deaf United	18	1	0	17	37	106	-69	3

Division One

		P	W	D	L	F	A	GD	Pts
1	Realtá	20	16	2	2	77	34	43	50
2	Crosscollyer	20	13	1	6	77	34	43	40
3	Cumann Spoirt an Phobail II	20	11	3	6	64	45	19	36
4	Kashmir Bilbao	20	11	3	6	41	39	2	36
5	Tullymore Swifts II	20	8	4	8	49	50	-1	28
6	Newhill YC II	20	8	3	9	47	58	-11	27
7	Sporting Belfast	20	5	8	7	48	46	2	23
8	Bheann Mhadigan II	20	5	7	8	50	44	6	22
9	Willowbank III	20	6	4	10	56	75	-19	22
10	Collingwood Holylands	20	4	5	11	52	66	-14	17
11	Riverside FC	20	2	2	16	31	101	-70	8

Division Two

		P	W	D	L	F	A	GD	Pts
1	Glenpark	23	17	3	3	87	40	47	54
2	Glanville Rec	23	13	4	6	86	41	45	43
3	Realtá II	23	14	1	8	68	58	10	43
4	Shankill Elim	23	11	5	7	69	40	29	38
5	Clarawood FC	23	10	3	10	70	55	15	33
6	St James Swifts III	21	9	3	9	52	53	-1	30
7	Crosscollyer II	23	8	4	11	46	53	-7	28
8	St Marys III	16	2	3	11	36	58	-22	9
9	Grove Athletic	21	1	0	20	29	145	-116	3

IRISH CUP

HOLDERS: LINFIELD

FIRST ROUND

Ballymacash Rangers v	Shankill United	3-4
Bryansburn Rangers v	St. Mary's Youth	3-1
Rathfern Rangers v	Lisburn Rangers	4-5
Crumlin Star v	Shorts	9-1
Coagh United v	Ballymoney	6-1
18th Newtownabbey v	Comber Rec.	3-2
Bloomfield v	Craigavon City	1-3
Laurelvale v	Broomhedge	6-1
Windmill Stars v	St. James' Swifts	2-1
Ardstraw v	Richhill A.F.C.	10-2
Magherafelt Sky Blues v	Colin Valley	AW
Ballynahinch United v	Rosario YC	AW
Seagoe v	Larne Tech. OB	1-12
Crewe United v	Drumaness Mills	2-3
Killyleagh YC v	Newbuildings United	5-1
Glebe Rangers v	Bangor	2-0
1st Bangor Old Boys v	Tullyvallen Rangers	2-3
Orangefield OB v	Dunmurry YM	3-0
Seapatrick v	Ballynure OB	1-4
Maiden City v	Dollingstown	3-1
Bangor Amateurs v	Newtowne	0-3
Malachians v	Downshire YM	AWp
Moneyslane v	Sirocco Works	1-4
Royal British Legion v	Dromara Village	1-2
Markethill Swifts v	Grove United	2-1
Fivemiletown United v	Islandmagee	1-4
Dunmurry Rec. v	Dromore Amateurs	4-0
Saintfield United v	Tandragee Rovers	2-4
Hanover v	Chimney Corner	8-2
Lower Maze v	St. Patrick's YM	1-2
Suffolk v	Dungiven	2-3
Coagh United v	Ballymoney United	6-1
Rosemount Rec. v	St. Luke's	3-1
Lurgan Town v	Groomsport	3-1
Valley Rangers v	Oxford Sunnyside	5-0
Abbey Villa v	Immaculata	0-3
Portaferry Rovers v	Ballynahinch Olympic	3-1
Derriaghy Cricket Club v	Bourneview Mill	3-1
Dunloy v	Banbridge Rangers	3-1
Crumlin United v	A.F.C. Silverwood	3-2
Barn United v	Rathfriland Rangers	3-8
Oxford United Stars v	Trojans	4-3

ROUND 2A

Strabane Athletic were originally excluded from the competition, but were reinstated after the first-round draw, necessitating a 'Round 2A' involving Strabane and the eleven clubs that had received first-round byes. One tie was drawn

Ards Rangers v	Iveagh United	9-0

SECOND ROUND

18th Newtownabbey OB v	UUJ	1-2
Annagh United v	Markethill Swifts	4-2
Ardstraw v	Dundela	2-6
Armagh City v	Coagh United	2-0
Ballywalter Rec v	Ballynure OB	6-3
Bryansburn Rangers v	Albert Foundry	3-4
Colin Valley v	Valley Rangers	1-4
Cookstown Youth v	Craigavon City	6-7
Crumlin Star v	Oxford United Stars	5-0
Crumlin United v	Donegal Celtic	2-0
Derriaghy CC v	Shankill United	1-2
Downshire YM v	Moyola Park	1-10
Dromara Village v	Banbridge Town	0-1
Drumaness Mills v	Hanover	0-2
Dunloy v	Portstewart	1-2
Dunmurry Rec v	Tobermore United	0-7
Glebe Rangers v	Rosemount Rec	3-0
Immaculata v	Larne Tech. OB	2-1
Islandmagee v	Ards Rangers	1-2
Laurelvale v	Tullyvallen Rangers	5-2
Maiden City v	Lurgan Town	7-1
Newington v	Lisburn Distillery	0-3
Newtowne v	Desertmartin	4-2
Portaferry Rovers v	Mossley	2-0
Queen's University v	Dungiven	7-2
Rathfriland Rangers v	Orangefield OB	4-1
Rosario YC v	Brantwood	4-0
Sport & Leisure Swifts v	Windmill Stars	2-0
St. Patrick's YM v	Wellington Rec	3-2
Tandragee Rovers v	Lisburn Rangers	3-2
Killyleagh YC v	Sirocco Works	2-0
Newcastle v	Strabane Athletic	3-1

THIRD ROUND

Armagh City	v	Crumlin Star	1-2
Ballywalter Rec	v	Ards Rangers	3-2
Banbridge Town	v	Queen's University	1-2
Craigavon City	v	Albert Foundry	1-4
Crumlin United	v	Valley Rangers	2-0
Glebe Rangers	v	UUJ	w/o
Hanover	v	Shankill United	2-3
Immaculata	v	Brantwood AET	3-1
Killyleagh YC	v	Tobermore United	3-1
Laurelvale	v	Moyola Park	0-5
Newcastle	v	Rathfriland Rangers	3-0
Newtowne	v	Lisburn Distillery	0-2
Portstewart	v	Portaferry Rovers	2-1
Sport & Leisure Swifts	v	Dundela	0-2
St. Patrick's YM	v	Annagh United	2-5
Tandragee Rovers	v	Maiden City	1-2 aet

FOURTH ROUND

Crumlin United	v	Immaculata	2-4
Dundela	v	Newcastle	5-0
Glebe Rangers	v	Annagh United	2-1
Lisburn Distillery	v	Albert Foundry	3-1
Moyola Park	v	Ballywalter Rec	2-0
Portstewart	v	Maiden City	1-1, AWp
Queen's University	v	Killyleagh YC	3-1
Shankill United	v	Crumlin Star	0-4

FIFTH ROUND

Knockbreda	v	Institute	0-2
Queen's University	v	Dundela	0-1
Lurgan Celtic	v	Glentoran	1-2
Larne	v	Dergview	3-0
Carrick Rangers	v	Glenavon	1-3 aet
Coleraine	v	Lisburn Distillery	7-0
Crusaders	v	Maiden City	2-0
Ballinamallard United	v	Immaculata	4-2
Cliftonville	v	Warrenpoint Town	4-3 aet
Loughgall	v	PSNI	4-1
Ballymena United	v	Moyola Park	4-0
Newry City AFC	v	H&W Welders	2-0
Portadown	v	Ballyclare Comrades	1-2 aet
Ards	v	Crumlin Star	4-1
Linfield	v	Glebe Rangers	5-0
Dungannon Swifts	v	Limavady United	4-0

SIXTH ROUND

Linfield	v	Newry City	1-0
Cliftonville	v	Crusaders	4-1
Loughgall	v	Ards	2-1
Ballyclare Comrades	v	Glentoran	0-4
Coleraine	v	Institute	4-0
Ballymena United	v	Ballinamallard Utd	2–2, 4-3p
Larne	v	Dundela	6-1
Glenavon	v	Dungannon Swifts	3-0

QUARTER FINALS

Ballymena United	v	Larne	1-2
Coleraine	v	Glentoran	1-0
Glenavon	v	Loughgall	1-2
Linfield	v	Cliftonville	0-1

SEMI FINALS

Cliftonville	v	Loughgall	4-1
Coleraine	v	Larne	3-1

FINAL
Saturday 5th May 2018

Cliftonville	v	Coleraine	1-3

SCOTTISH TABLES 2017-18

HIGHLAND LEAGUE

		P	W	D	L	F	A	GD	Pts
1	Cove Rangers	34	29	3	2	127	22	105	90
2	Formartine United	34	26	1	7	124	41	83	79
3	Inverurie Loco Works	34	25	3	6	104	37	67	78
4	Fraserburgh	34	23	4	7	101	38	63	73
5	Forres Mechanics	34	23	4	7	88	45	43	73
6	Brora Rangers	34	20	3	11	87	39	48	63
7	Buckie Thistle	34	15	6	13	80	56	24	51
8	Deveronvale	34	16	3	15	72	75	-3	51
9	Nairn County	34	16	3	15	61	71	-10	51
10	Rothes	34	15	4	15	77	70	7	49
11	Huntly	34	15	4	15	66	81	-15	49
12	Wick Academy	34	12	10	12	67	54	13	46
13	Clachnacuddin	34	11	8	15	54	69	-15	41
14	Turriff United	34	11	4	19	54	70	-16	37
15	Keith	34	4	4	26	45	104	-59	16
16	Lossiemouth	34	4	3	27	40	124	-84	15
17	Strathspey Thistle	34	4	2	28	26	124	-98	14
18	Fort William	34	0	5	29	31	184	-153	5

LOWLAND LEAGUE

		P	W	D	L	F	A	GD	Pts
1	The Spartans	30	23	4	3	64	17	47	73
2	East Kilbride	30	22	5	3	76	23	53	71
3	BSC Glasgow	30	20	5	5	71	27	44	65
4	East Stirlingshire	30	19	7	4	67	31	36	64
5	Selkirk	30	15	3	12	63	50	13	48
6	Cumbernauld Colts	30	11	8	11	53	54	-1	41
7	Civil Service Strollers	30	11	7	12	47	44	3	40
8	Gretna 2008	30	12	4	14	50	56	-6	40
9	University of Stirling	30	11	5	14	45	49	-4	38
10	Edusport Academy	30	9	7	14	46	49	-3	34
11	Edinburgh University	30	9	7	14	40	45	-5	34
12	Whitehill Welfare	30	11	1	18	50	66	-16	34
13	Gala Fairydean Rovers	30	8	7	15	43	63	-20	31
14	Dalbeattie Star	30	7	8	15	46	65	-19	29
15	Vale of Leithen	30	8	5	17	44	76	-32	29
16	Hawick Royal Albert	30	1	3	26	18	108	-90	6

EAST OF SCOTLAND LEAGUE

Premier Division

		P	W	D	L	F	A	GD	Pts
1	Kelty Hearts	24	23	0	1	143	12	131	69
2	Lothian Thistle Hutchison Vale	24	22	1	1	97	20	77	67
3	Preston Athletic	24	16	3	5	74	36	38	51
4	Leith Athletic	24	15	4	5	78	39	39	49
5	Tynecastle	24	13	0	11	79	48	31	39
6	Heriot-Watt University	24	11	6	7	59	53	6	39
7	Peebles Rovers	24	12	2	10	59	73	-14	38
8	Burntisland Shipyard	24	8	1	15	52	69	-17	25
9	University of Stirling Res	24	6	6	12	48	73	-25	24
10	Coldstream	24	5	3	16	52	79	-27	18
11	Eyemouth United	24	6	0	18	44	114	-70	18
12	Ormiston	24	3	3	18	17	68	-51	12
13	Tweedmouth Rangers	24	1	1	22	21	139	-118	4

SOUTH OF SCOTLAND LEAGUE

		P	W	D	L	F	A	GD	Pts
1	Threave Rovers	28	24	1	3	94	21	73	73
2	Mid-Annandale	28	21	3	4	107	42	65	66
3	Lochar Thistle	28	20	3	5	89	40	49	63
4	St Cuthbert Wanderers	28	17	3	8	87	57	30	54
5	Abbey Vale	28	15	4	9	78	50	28	49
6	Bonnyton Thistle	28	14	4	10	89	41	48	46
7	Heston Rovers	28	15	1	12	75	71	4	46
8	Stranraer reserves	28	12	6	10	90	77	13	42
9	Newton Stewart	28	12	2	14	65	64	1	38
10	Upper Annandale	28	11	4	13	66	74	-8	37
11	Nithsdale Wanderers	28	11	3	14	77	81	-4	36
12	Lochmaben	28	10	3	15	61	75	-14	33
13	Creetown	28	3	2	23	32	97	-65	11
14	Annan Athletic reserves	28	3	1	24	41	139	-98	10
15	Dumfries YMCA	28	2	0	26	26	148	-122	6

If licensed, Champions of East of Scotland and South of Scotland Leagues play-off for a place in the Lowland League.

NORTH CALEDONIAN LEAGUE

		P	W	D	L	F	A	GD	Pts
1	Orkney	16	13	0	3	82	16	66	39
2	Invergordon	16	12	2	2	48	21	27	38
3	Golspie Sutherland	16	11	2	3	51	23	28	35
4	Thurso	16	9	2	5	38	23	15	29
5	Alness United	16	8	1	7	31	55	-24	25
6	St Duthus	16	4	2	10	28	28	0	14
7	Inverness Athletic	16	4	1	11	31	56	-25	13
8	Halkirk United	16	4	1	11	23	54	-31	13
9	Bunillidh Thistle	16	1	1	14	17	73	-56	4

SJFA EAST REGION

Superleague

		P	W	D	L	F	A	GD	Pts
1	Bonnyrigg Rose Athletic	30	20	9	1	83	23	60	69
2	Linlithgow Rose	30	21	2	7	69	37	32	65
3	Penicuik Athletic	30	17	6	7	55	31	24	57
4	Dundonald Bluebell	30	18	1	11	58	45	13	55
5	Broxburn Athletic	30	13	10	7	76	55	21	49
6	Lochee United	30	14	3	13	58	50	8	45
7	Hill of Beath Hawthorn	30	11	9	10	54	47	7	42
8	Bo'ness United	30	12	5	13	57	53	4	41
9	Camelon Juniors	30	13	2	15	55	57	-2	41
10	Broughty Athletic	30	11	7	12	48	56	-8	40
11	Newtongrange Star	30	12	3	15	55	59	-4	39
12	Carnoustie Panmure	30	12	3	15	50	63	-13	39
13	Sauchie	30	9	6	15	36	55	-19	33
14	Jeanfield Swifts	30	9	4	17	44	71	-27	31
15	Kennoway Star Hearts	30	5	6	19	42	89	-47	21
16	Forfar West End	30	4	2	24	18	67	-49	14

Premier Division

		P	W	D	L	F	A	GD	Pts
1	Musselburgh Athletic	30	25	4	1	85	28	57	79
2	Fauldhouse United	30	18	4	8	72	56	16	58
3	Haddington Athletic	30	16	7	7	66	47	19	55
4	Tayport	30	14	8	8	68	51	17	50
5	Blackburn United	30	14	5	11	41	38	3	47
6	Thornton Hibs	30	12	9	9	59	47	12	45
7	Dunbar United	30	13	6	11	57	49	8	45
8	Tranent	30	12	4	14	54	57	-3	40
9	Glenrothes Juniors	30	11	4	15	68	66	2	37
10	Downfield Juniors	30	10	5	15	55	72	-17	35
11	St Andrews United	30	10	5	15	47	68	-21	35
12	Arniston Rangers	30	7	13	10	41	44	-3	34
13	Bathgate Thistle	30	7	9	14	39	55	-16	30
14	Dalkeith Thistle	30	8	4	18	51	69	-18	28
15	Whitburn Juniors	30	7	7	16	55	77	-22	28
16	Kirriemuir Thistle	30	7	4	19	30	64	-34	25

North Division

		P	W	D	L	F	A	GD	Pts
1	Dundee North End	26	21	2	3	89	25	64	65
2	Luncarty	26	19	3	4	84	26	58	60
3	Dundee Violet	26	18	3	5	66	25	41	57
4	Kinnoull Juniors	26	17	5	4	67	39	28	56
5	Dundee East Craigie	26	15	3	8	56	43	13	48
6	Scone Thistle	26	15	2	9	58	34	24	47
7	Blairgowrie Juniors	26	13	2	11	73	55	18	41
8	Lochee Harp	26	12	3	11	62	58	4	39
9	Lochore Welfare	26	8	3	15	43	60	-17	27
10	Arbroath Victoria	26	8	2	16	38	72	-34	26
11	Coupar Angus	26	7	1	18	46	66	-20	22
12	Brechin Victoria	26	6	1	19	40	89	-49	19
13	Newburgh Juniors	26	4	2	20	28	85	-57	14
14	Forfar Albion	26	2	2	22	33	106	-73	8

South Division

		P	W	D	L	F	A	GD	Pts
1	Pumpherston Juniors	26	20	3	3	91	27	64	63
2	Armadale Thistle	26	17	5	4	74	36	38	56
3	Edinburgh United	26	17	4	5	82	31	51	55
4	Oakley United	26	16	4	6	71	40	31	52
5	West Calder United	26	15	3	8	79	43	36	48
6	Lochgelly Albert	26	14	5	7	57	46	11	47
7	Crossgates Primrose	26	14	1	11	74	46	28	43
8	Harthill Royal	26	12	2	12	66	56	10	38
9	Craigroyston	26	11	3	12	44	67	-23	36
10	Rosyth	26	10	2	14	60	67	-7	32
11	Easthouses Lily MW	26	7	1	18	45	60	-15	22
12	Livingston United	26	7	0	19	55	77	-22	21
13	Stoneyburn Juniors	26	3	4	19	29	86	-57	13
14	Kirkcaldy YM	26	0	1	25	11	156	-145	1

SJFA NORTH REGION

Superleague

		P	W	D	L	F	A	GD	Pts
1	Banks o' Dee	26	22	3	1	91	22	69	69
2	Hermes	26	14	8	4	68	41	27	50
3	Dyce Juniors	26	13	6	7	57	38	19	45
4	Culter	26	14	2	10	52	40	12	44
5	Ellon United	26	12	3	11	41	41	0	39
6	Maud Juniors	26	11	3	12	45	56	-11	36
7	Montrose Roselea	26	9	8	9	36	31	5	35
8	Dufftown	26	11	2	13	50	57	-7	35
9	Stonehaven Juniors	26	8	8	10	50	55	-5	32
10	Hall Russell United	26	8	7	11	29	41	-12	31
11	Colony Park	26	8	5	13	43	63	-20	29
12	Newburgh Thistle	26	7	6	13	45	49	-4	27
13	Banchory St Ternan	26	6	4	16	41	71	-30	22
14	Inverness City	26	5	3	18	31	74	-43	18

Division One East

		P	W	D	L	F	A	GD	Pts
1	Aberdeen East End	20	18	2	0	70	17	53	56
2	Sunnybank	20	13	2	5	61	30	31	41
3	Longside	20	13	1	6	63	26	37	40
4	Fraserburgh United	20	10	5	5	49	28	21	35
5	Stoneywood Parkvale	20	10	3	7	60	38	22	33
6	Glentanar	20	9	4	7	51	57	-6	31
7	Aberdeen University	20	9	3	8	48	43	5	30
8	Buchanhaven Hearts	20	8	1	11	34	55	-21	25
9	Newmachar United	20	4	3	13	29	58	-29	12*
10	Lewis United	20	1	3	16	15	81	-66	6
11	Cruden Bay Juniors	20	0	3	17	10	57	-47	3

Runners-up play-off Sunnybank 1-0 Deveronside. Promotion/Relegation Play-off Final Newburgh Thistle 1-1, 6-5p Sunnybank.

SCOTTISH FOOTBALL

Division One West

		P	W	D	L	F	A	GD	Pts
1	Nairn St Ninian	24	20	2	2	88	19	69	62
2	Deveronside	24	17	1	6	76	27	49	52
3	Forres Thistle	24	16	2	6	60	32	28	50
4	Buckie Rovers	24	13	1	10	54	41	13	40
5	Burghead Thistle	24	12	2	10	51	44	7	38
6	Islavale	24	10	2	12	45	40	5	32
7	New Elgin	24	8	4	12	48	70	-22	28
8	Spey Valley United	24	3	0	21	32	101	-69	6*
9	Whitehills	24	2	0	22	28	108	-80	6

SJFA WESTERN REGION

Super League Premier

		P	W	D	L	F	A	GD	Pts
1	Beith Juniors	22	14	3	5	61	21	40	45
2	Auchinleck Talbot	22	14	2	6	56	25	31	44
3	Pollok	22	11	7	4	46	27	19	40
4	Kilwinning Rangers	22	12	4	6	43	29	14	40
5	Kilbirnie Ladeside	22	9	7	6	35	37	-2	34
6	Kirkintilloch Rob Roy	22	9	4	9	45	53	-8	31
7	Glenafton Athletic	22	8	6	8	30	30	0	30
8	Hurlford United	22	8	5	9	37	36	1	29
9	Cumnock Juniors	22	7	6	9	36	40	-4	27
10	Clydebank	22	7	3	12	32	44	-12	24
11	Girvan	22	2	6	14	24	59	-35	12
12	Arthurlie	22	2	5	15	20	64	-44	11

Division One

		P	W	D	L	F	A	GD	Pts
1	Petershill	26	19	4	3	65	30	35	61
2	Cambuslang Rangers	26	16	2	8	62	39	23	50
3	Largs Thistle	26	15	5	6	42	27	15	50
4	Renfrew	26	15	4	7	48	36	12	49
5	Irvine Meadow XI	26	15	4	7	45	33	12	49
6	Troon	26	14	5	7	62	42	20	47
7	Rutherglen Glencairn	26	13	4	9	56	46	10	43
8	Cumbernauld United	26	13	2	11	51	45	6	41
9	Darvel	26	9	4	13	48	55	-7	31
10	Kilsyth Rangers	26	8	4	14	42	53	-11	28
11	Larkhall Thistle	26	7	4	15	45	62	-17	25
12	Kello Rovers	26	6	5	15	38	55	-17	23
13	Maryhill	26	2	6	18	24	62	-38	12
14	Shettleston	26	2	3	21	19	62	-43	9

Central District Division One

		P	W	D	L	F	A	GD	Pts
1	Rossvale	28	20	4	4	65	33	32	64
2	St Roch's	28	19	5	4	73	40	33	62
3	Benburb	28	18	4	6	81	38	43	58
4	Neilston Juniors	28	16	4	8	75	46	29	52
5	Blantyre Victoria	28	14	4	10	61	47	14	46
6	Wishaw Juniors	28	13	2	13	68	48	20	41
7	Glasgow Perthshire	28	11	6	11	52	47	5	39
8	Port Glasgow Juniors	28	12	3	13	38	50	-12	39
9	Shotts Bon Accord	28	12	1	15	58	52	6	37
10	Yoker Athletic	28	10	6	12	53	58	-5	36
11	East Kilbride Thistle	28	11	3	14	47	61	-14	36
12	Greenock Juniors	28	10	4	14	38	52	-14	34
13	Forth Wanderers	28	9	3	16	53	77	-24	30
14	Thorniewood United	28	5	3	20	44	89	-45	18
15	Lesmahagow Juniors	28	3	2	23	35	103	-68	11

Central District Division Two

		P	W	D	L	F	A	GD	Pts
1	Royal Albert	22	16	4	2	65	25	40	52
2	Gartcairn Juniors	22	16	3	3	75	27	48	51
3	Bellshill Athletic	22	14	2	6	49	29	20	44
4	St Anthony's	22	12	1	9	43	32	11	37
5	Ashfield	22	11	2	9	42	31	11	35
6	Lanark United	22	8	7	7	52	40	12	31
7	Vale of Clyde	22	9	2	11	53	45	8	29
8	Vale of Leven	22	9	2	11	49	41	8	29
9	Johnstone Burgh	22	8	4	10	41	55	-14	28
10	Carluke Rovers	22	7	5	10	39	41	-2	26
11	Dunipace	22	5	2	15	27	51	-24	17
12	Newmains United	22	0	0	22	15	133	-118	0

Ayrshire District League

		P	W	D	L	F	A	GD	Pts
1	Dalry Thistle	20	16	3	1	80	17	63	51
2	Irvine Victoria	20	15	1	4	60	30	30	46
3	Craigmark Burntonians	20	14	1	5	50	27	23	43
4	Whitletts Victoria	20	12	4	4	44	33	11	40
5	Lugar Boswell Thistle	20	10	1	9	55	47	8	31
6	Ardrossan Winton Rovers	20	8	3	9	45	41	4	27
7	Maybole Juniors	20	8	2	10	55	36	19	26
8	Muirkirk Juniors	20	6	3	11	33	59	-26	21
9	Saltcoats Victoria	20	4	1	15	22	73	-51	13
10	Ardeer Thistle	20	4	0	16	23	51	-28	12
11	Annbank United	20	3	1	16	31	84	-53	10

SCOTTISH AMATEUR FOOTBALL LEAGUE

Premier Division

		P	W	D	L	F	A	GD	Pts
1	Goldenhill	16	16	0	0	55	9	46	48
2	St. Joseph's FP	16	13	0	3	50	17	33	39
3	Alba Thistle	16	11	1	4	41	30	11	34
4	Inverclyde	16	7	1	8	36	30	6	22
5	Motherwell Thistle	16	7	1	8	29	36	-7	22
6	Oban Saints	16	6	1	9	25	33	-8	19
7	EKRR	16	4	1	11	17	40	-23	13
8	East Kilbride FC	16	3	3	10	22	38	-16	12
9	Hillington	16	1	0	15	22	64	-42	3

Drumchapel Colts withdrew - record expunged

ABERDEENSHIRE AMATEUR FOOTBALL ASSOCIATION

Premier Division

		P	W	D	L	F	A	GD	Pts
1	Woodside	26	19	5	2	86	32	54	62
2	Sportsmans Club	26	20	1	5	93	46	47	61
3	Rothie Rovers	26	18	4	4	84	48	36	58
4	Cowie Thistle	26	15	5	6	78	39	39	50
5	Old Aberdonians	26	13	5	8	54	42	12	44
6	MS United	26	10	3	13	53	70	-17	33
7	Cove Thistle	26	9	6	11	69	69	0	33
8	Newtonhill	26	10	2	14	55	80	-25	32
9	RGU	26	10	1	15	49	59	-10	31
10	Westhill	26	8	4	14	51	64	-13	28
11	University	26	6	9	11	46	73	-27	27
12	Echt	26	8	2	16	53	73	-20	26
13	Ellon Amateurs	26	5	4	17	41	70	-29	19

Division One North

		P	W	D	L	F	A	GD	Pts
1	Stoneywood East End	22	17	2	3	73	25	48	53
2	St Laurence	22	15	3	4	68	30	38	48
3	Bervie Caledonian	22	12	5	5	69	47	22	41
4	Sheddocksley	22	11	2	9	48	53	-5	35
5	Rattrays XI	22	9	6	7	46	44	2	33
6	Tarves	22	9	5	8	57	45	12	32
7	Kincorth	22	9	5	8	58	52	6	32
8	Beacon Rangers	22	9	3	10	50	60	-10	30
9	Newburgh Thistle	22	8	4	10	42	51	-9	28
10	Nicolls Amateurs	22	5	3	14	29	58	-29	18
11	Burghmuir	22	5	1	16	40	69	-29	16
12	Stonehaven Athletic	22	2	3	17	28	74	-46	9

Division One East

		P	W	D	L	F	A	GD	Pts
1	Insch	24	20	2	2	68	20	48	Insch
2	Don Athletic	24	16	4	4	65	38	27	52
3	Westdyke	24	15	4	5	73	32	41	49
4	Bridge of Don	24	13	3	8	73	49	24	42
5	Glendale	24	10	8	6	56	45	11	38
6	Westdyce	24	10	4	10	46	55	-9	34
7	Ellon Thistle	24	8	4	12	37	44	-7	28
8	Alford	24	7	7	10	40	49	-9	28
9	Kaimhill United	24	8	1	15	40	76	-36	25
10	Halliburton	24	5	9	10	37	44	-7	24
11	AC Mill Inn	24	7	1	16	43	60	-17	19*
12	Bon Accord City	24	5	3	16	46	88	-42	18

Division Two North

		P	W	D	L	F	A	GD	Pts
1	Turriff Thistle	18	15	1	2	62	32	30	46
2	JS XI	18	12	3	3	53	29	24	39
3	Continental	18	10	3	5	46	28	18	33
4	Faithlie United	18	8	2	8	52	48	4	26
5	Kintore	18	6	5	7	34	30	4	23
6	Glentanar Reflex	18	7	1	10	50	52	-2	22
7	Postal ALC	18	5	2	11	37	54	-17	17
8	West End	18	4	4	10	40	53	-13	16
9	University Strollers	18	6	3	9	35	49	-14	15*
10	Abergeldie	18	4	2	12	33	67	-34	14

Division Two East

		P	W	D	L	F	A	GD	Pts
1	Tolbooth	22	20	0	2	87	27	60	60
2	BSFC	22	17	1	4	71	36	35	49*
3	Dyce ITC Hydraulics	22	13	2	7	57	41	16	41
4	Torphins	22	11	5	6	59	37	22	38
5	Lads Club Amateurs	22	10	2	10	51	48	3	32
6	Colony Park	22	9	3	10	49	58	-9	30
7	Auchnagatt Barons	22	8	2	12	41	66	-25	23*
8	Powis	22	6	4	12	47	62	-15	22
9	University Colts	22	7	3	12	33	37	-4	21*
10	Great Western United	22	6	2	14	61	61	0	20
11	FC Polska	22	6	1	15	47	101	-54	19
12	Aboyne	22	5	3	14	37	66	-29	18

Division Three

		P	W	D	L	F	A	GD	Pts
1	AFC Murdos	24	21	0	3	105	41	64	63
2	St Marnans	24	18	2	4	83	27	56	56
3	Monymusk	24	13	4	7	70	46	24	43
4	Grammar FP's	24	13	2	9	67	63	4	41
5	Kemnay Amateurs	24	12	5	7	53	36	17	41
6	Glendale Youth	24	11	5	8	67	48	19	38
7	Feughside	24	11	4	9	56	41	15	37
8	Kemnay Youth	24	9	4	11	44	55	-11	31
9	Theologians	24	9	3	12	46	59	-13	30
10	Jesus House	24	9	2	13	51	71	-20	29
11	Ferryhill	24	4	7	13	45	70	-25	19
12	West End United	24	2	5	17	35	90	-55	11
14	Middlefield Wasps	24	1	3	20	29	104	-75	6

BORDER AMATEUR LEAGUE

A League

		P	W	D	L	F	A	GD	Pts
1	Hawick Waverley	18	14	3	1	83	25	58	45
2	Chirnside United	18	13	1	4	63	28	35	40
3	Hawick United	18	11	3	4	42	32	10	36
4	Jed Legion	18	8	2	8	38	41	-3	26
5	Greenlaw	18	7	4	7	44	39	5	25
6	Tweeddale Rovers	18	8	1	9	40	46	-6	25
7	Gordon	18	7	0	11	42	54	-12	21
8	Stow	18	5	1	12	18	44	-26	16
9	Coldstream Ams	18	4	2	12	30	59	-29	14
10	Newtown	18	3	3	12	32	64	-32	12

B League

		P	W	D	L	F	A	GD	Pts
1	Gala Hotspur	22	15	3	4	72	37	35	48
2	Langholm Legion	22	14	4	4	80	46	34	46
3	Hawick Legion	22	14	3	5	69	48	21	45
4	Kelso Thistle	22	13	4	5	76	43	33	43
5	Tweedmouth Ams	22	13	1	8	63	48	15	43
6	Leithen Rovers	22	9	3	10	58	61	-3	30
7	Earlston Rhymers	22	9	2	11	46	71	-25	29
8	Duns Ams	22	8	1	13	54	76	-22	25
9	Biggar United	22	7	1	14	46	61	-15	22
10	Lauder	22	4	8	10	58	71	-13	20
11	Linton Hotspur	22	4	4	14	37	67	-30	16
12	St.Boswells	22	4	2	16	42	72	-30	14

SCOTTISH FOOTBALL

C League		P	W	D	L	F	A	GD	Pts
1	Langlee Ams	20	17	3	0	111	24	87	54
2	Berwick Colts	20	15	0	5	52	42	10	45
3	Gala Fairydean Rovers	20	14	2	4	75	37	38	44
4	Ancrum	20	10	3	7	62	39	23	33
5	Selkirk Victoria	20	9	6	5	54	35	19	33
6	Highfields United	20	10	2	8	62	51	11	32
7	Melrose	20	7	2	11	48	73	-25	23
8	Hawick Legion Rovers	20	7	1	12	39	61	-22	22
9	Gala Thistle	20	4	2	14	43	82	-39	14
10	Tweeddale Rovers Colts	20	2	4	14	26	63	-37	10
11	Kelso Ams	20	1	3	16	23	88	-65	6

SCOTTISH JUNIOR CUP

HOLDERS: Glenafton Athletic

ROUND 1

Maryhill	v	Irvine Meadow	0-0
Culter	v	East Kilbride Thistle	2-3
Dunipace Juniors	v	Dunbar United	0-4
Kirkintilloch Rob Roy	v	Glenrothes	5-0
Glasgow Perthshire	v	Dundee North End	2-2
Rutherglen Glencairn	v	Kirriemuir Thistle	4-0
Arniston Rangers	v	St Andrews United	1-0
Ardeer Thistle	v	Yoker Athletic	0-1
Penicuik Athletic	v	Livingston United	7-0
Kello Rovers	v	Arthurlie	3-4
Longside	v	Deveronside	2-1
Troon	v	Renfrew	1-1
Bonnyrigg Rose	v	Shettleston	5-0
Lochee Harp	v	Bo'ness United	2-4
Tayport	v	Cumbernauld United	1-2
Burghead Thistle	v	Shotts Bon Accord	2-5
Thornton Hibs	v	Ellon United	2-0
Kilwinning Rangers	v	Saltcoats Victoria	HW
Musselburgh Athletic	v	Newburgh Thistle	4-0
Ardrossan Winton Rovers	v	Banchory St Ternan	6-2
Broxburn Athletic	v	Fraserburgh	6-0
Rosyth	v	Dundee East Craigie	2-2
Pumpherston	v	Cambuslang Rangers	1-3
Aberdeen University	v	Kirkcaldy YMCA	5-0
Irvine Victoria	v	Maybole	0-0
Lewis United	v	Bathgate Thistle	1-2
Rossvale	v	Greenock Juniors	1-0
Hill of Beath Hawthorn	v	New Elgin	5-0
Newmains United Com.	v	Annbank United	2-4

REPLAYS

Irvine Meadow	v	Maryhill	0-0, 3-2p
Dundee East Craigie	v	Rosyth	4-3
Dundee North End	v	Glasgow Perthshire	0-1
Maybole	v	Irvine Victoria	0-3
Renfrew	v	Troon	2-2, 2-4p

ROUND 2

Shotts Bon Accord	v	Muirkirk	13-0
Newmachar United	v	Dyce	2-7
Lanark United	v	Dalkeith Thistle	2-1
Longside	v	Carnoustie Panmure	1-4
Vale of Clyde	v	Arbroath Victoria	4-1
West Calder United	v	Scone Thistle	3-6
Tranent	v	Easthouses Lily Miners Wel.	5-1
Kirkintilloch Rob Roy	v	Carluke Rovers	6-0
Lochee United	v	Armadale Thistle	1-0
Hill of Beath Hawthorn	v	Buckie Rovers	4-0
Lesmahagow	v	Arthurlie	3-3
Auchinleck Talbot	v	Forres Thistle	8-0
Dufftown	v	Oakley United	1-1
Forfar Albion	v	Haddington Athletic	0-6
Kilsyth Rangers	v	Stoneywood Parkvale	3-1
Sunnybank	v	Ashfield	1-6
Glasgow Perthshire	v	Kinnoull	4-0
Hermes	v	Blairgowrie	3-1
Fauldhouse United	v	Bonnyrigg Rose	2-3
Irvine Meadow	v	Broxburn Athletic	5-2
St Roch's	v	Bellshill Athletic	0-1
Neilston	v	Downfield	2-3
Dundee East Craigie	v	Newtongrange Star	1-2
Troon	v	Stoneyburn	3-1
Montrose Roselea	v	Coupar Angus	1-3
Port Glasgow	v	Petershill	0-0
Rossvale	v	Edinburgh United	3-1
Wishaw	v	Arniston Rangers	1-1
Thorniewood United	v	Dundonald Bluebell	1-0
Maud	v	Harthill Royal	5-3
Broughty Athletic	v	Bathgate Thistle	1-3
Rutherglen Glencairn	v	Glentanar	11-0
Craigmark Burntonians	v	Cumnock	0-5
Cruden Bay	v	Banks o' Dee	AW
Crossgate Primrose	v	Newburgh	1-0
Kilwinning Rangers	v	Larkhall Thistle	2-1
Brechin Victoria	v	Bo'ness United	0-4
Girvan	v	East Kilbirde Thistle	2-3
Gartcairn	v	Whitehills	9-0
Kennoway Star Hearts	v	Clydebank	3-2
Camelon	v	Hall Russell United	4-1
Whitletts Victoria	v	Jeanfield Swifts	1-2
St Anthony's	v	Yoker Athletic	1-3
Ardrossan Winton Rovers	v	Dunbar United	2-4
Lochore Welfare	v	Spey Valley United	3-1
Beith	v	Inverness City	12-0
Royal Albert	v	Pollok	1-4
Vale of Leven	v	Luncarty	3-2
Cambuslang Rangers	v	Stonehaven	1-3
Benburb	v	Craigroyston	3-2
Blantyre Victoria	v	Lochgelly Albert	3-0
Aberdeen University	v	Johnstone Burgh	1-2
Thornton Hibs	v	Cumbernauld United	0-2
Aberdeen East End	v	Blackburn United	0-6
Sauchie	v	Largs Thistle	3-1
Hurlford United	v	Nairn St Ninian	2-0
Dundee Violet	v	Forfar West End	2-2
Musselburgh Athletic	v	Darvel	3-2
Lugar Boswell Thistle	v	Linlithgow Rose	1-3

Buchanhaven Hearts	v	Whitburn	2-2
Kilbirnie Ladeside	v	Penicuik Athletic	2-2
Dalry Thistle	v	Glenafton Athletic	1-5
Forth Wanderers	v	Irvine Victoria	1-0
Annbank United	v	Colony Park	1-2

REPLAYS

Oakley United	v	Dufftown	3-2
Petershill	v	Port Glasgow	3-0
Arniston Rangers	v	Wishaw	2-3
Forfar West End	v	Dundee Violet	1-0
Whitburn	v	Buchanhaven Hearts	9-1
Arthurlie	v	Lesmahagow	4-3
Penicuik Athletic	v	Kilbirnie Ladeside	3-3, 3-4p

ROUND 3

Glasgow Perthshire	v	Pollok	3-3
Haddington Athletic	v	Vale of Clyde	3-1
Hermes	v	Dunbar United	1-1
Rossvale	v	Banks o' Dee	3-2
Troon	v	Yoker Athletic	0-3
Arthurlie	v	Coupar Angus	3-1
Vale of Leven	v	Bonnyrigg Rose	2-3
Bo'ness United	v	Kilwinning Rangers	3-0
Tranent	v	Jeanfield Swifts	0-3
Blackburn United	v	Colony Park	5-1
Forth Wanderers	v	Lochore Welfare	2-2
Cumnock	v	Bathgate Thistle	5-1
Kilbirnie Ladeside	v	Lanark United	4-1
Kennoway Star Hearts	v	Blantyre Victoria	4-0
Gartcairn	v	Maud	3-1
Rutherglen Glencairn	v	Stonehaven	6-0
Forfar West End	v	Shotts Bon Accord	4-2
Kirkintilloch Rob Roy	v	Glenafton Athletic	1-0
Scone Thistle	v	Kilsyth Rangers	0-3
Sauchie	v	Camelon	3-1
Bellshill Athletic	v	Ashfield	3-0
Oakley United	v	Linlithgow Rose	0-3
Downfield	v	Wishaw	2-2
Whitburn	v	Benburb	4-1
Thorniewood United	v	East Kilbride Thistle	0-0
Newtongrange Star	v	Cumbernauld United	0-0
Hurlford United	v	Musselburgh Athletic	2-1
Carnoustie Panmure	v	Petershill	2-1
Lochee United	v	Johnstone Burgh	HW
Crossgates Primrose	v	Beith	1-5
Hill of Beath Hawthorn	v	Auchinleck Talbot	0-2

REPLAYS

Pollok	v	Glasgow Perthshire	5-0
Dunbar United	v	Hermes	4-0
Lochore Welfare	v	Forth Wanderers	1-2
East Kilbride Thistle	v	Thorniewood United	7-1
Cumbernauld United	v	Newtongrange Star	0-4
Wishaw	v	Downfield	5-1

ROUND 4

Irvine Meadow	v	Dunbar United	6-2
Bonnyrigg Rose	v	Newtongrange Star	5-2
Lochee United	v	East Kilbride Thistle	5-0
Blackburn United	v	Linlithgow Rose	0-5
Cumnock	v	Auchinleck Talbot	1-5
Bellshill Athletic	v	Sauchie	1-2
Whitburn	v	Yoker Athletic	1-2
Gartcairn	v	Arthurlie	2-2
Kirkintilloch Rob Roy	v	Kennoway Star Hearts	6-2
Rossvale	v	Pollok	0-3
Kilsyth Rangers	v	Carnoustie Panmure	0-2
Jeanfield Swifts	v	Beith	2-6
Rutherglen Glencairn	v	Bo'ness United	0-3
Hurlford United	v	Haddington Athletic	3-0
Kilbirnie Ladeside	v	Forfar West End	2-1
Wishaw	v	Forth Wanderers	1-0

REPLAY

Arthurlie	v	Gartcairn	2-1

ROUND 5

Kirkintilloch Rob Roy	v	Linlithgow Rose	4-3
Bonnyrigg Rose	v	Beith	1-2
Irvine Meadow	v	Lochee United	0-2
Kilbirnie Ladeside	v	Bo'ness United	0-3
Auchinleck Talbot	v	Pollok	4-1
Carnoustie Panmure	v	Arthurlie	3-0
Sauchie	v	Hurlford United	0-1
Yoker Athletic	v	Wishaw	1-3

QUARTER FINALS

Beith	v	Lochee United	1-4
Carnoustie Panmure	v	Auchinleck Talbot	0-2
Bo'ness United	v	Hurlford United	2-2
Wishaw	v	Kirkintilloch Rob Roy	2-0

REPLAY

Hurlford United	v	Bo'ness United	2-1

SEMI FINALS 1st LEG

Auchinleck Talbot	v	Lochee United	0-1
Wishaw	v	Hurlford United	0-1

SEMI FINALS 2nd LEG

Lochee United	v	Auchinleck Talbot	0-2
Hurlford United	v	Wishaw	1-1

FINAL

Auchinleck Talbot	v	Hurlford United	3-2

Hyslop 37, Wilson 90+1   *Robertson 5 (pen), McKenzie 64*
McCracken 90+3

WELSH TABLES 2017-18

WELSH PREMIER

		P	W	D	L	F	A	GD	Pts
1	The New Saints	32	23	5	4	83	32	51	74
2	Bangor City	32	19	3	10	49	32	17	60
3	Connah's Quay Nomads	32	17	6	9	46	29	17	57
4	Bala Town	32	15	4	13	37	48	-11	49
5	Cefn Druids	32	12	8	12	38	41	-3	44
6	Cardiff Metropolitan	32	12	7	13	46	41	5	43
7	Barry Town United	32	16	5	11	39	31	8	53
8	Newtown	32	12	4	16	52	55	-3	40
9	Aberystwyth Town	32	10	7	15	47	56	-9	37
10	Llandudno	32	9	9	14	39	44	-5	36
11	Carmarthen Town	32	8	5	19	35	62	-27	29
12	Prestatyn Town	32	4	7	21	27	67	-40	19

Ater 22 games the League splits into two. The top six then play each other twice again and the bottom six do the same. However, once split, no team can climb back into the top six no matter what points they finish on.

CYMRU ALLIANCE

		P	W	D	L	F	A	GD	Pts
1	Caernarfon Town	28	19	8	1	98	31	67	65
2	Denbigh Town	28	19	3	6	69	43	26	60
3	Airbus UK Broughton	28	17	3	8	67	42	25	54
4	Guilsfield	28	15	8	5	54	38	16	53
5	Holywell Town	28	14	8	6	75	37	38	50
6	Rhyl	28	13	8	7	62	44	18	47
7	Porthmadog	28	13	5	10	70	46	24	44
8	Gresford Athletic	28	12	6	10	57	57	0	39*
9	Penrhyncoch	28	10	9	9	45	46	-1	39
10	Ruthin Town	28	10	5	13	51	49	2	35
11	Flint Town United	28	10	6	12	49	42	7	30*
12	Holyhead Hotspur	28	9	3	16	39	57	-18	30
13	Caerws	28	5	3	20	39	72	-33	18
14	Queens Park	28	2	3	23	26	110	-84	9
15	Llandudno Junction	28	1	4	23	28	115	-87	7

Rhayader Town resigned.

WELSH LEAGUE

Division One

		P	W	D	L	F	A	GD	Pts
1	Llanelli Town	30	24	3	3	87	33	54	75
2	Haverfordwest County	30	19	3	8	65	37	28	60
3	Penybont	30	18	6	6	64	37	27	57*
4	Cambrian & Clydach	30	17	3	10	58	39	19	54
5	Afan Lido	30	15	4	11	61	48	13	49
6	Goytre	30	15	3	12	51	62	-11	48
7	Goytre United	30	13	8	9	53	52	1	47
8	Cwmbran Celtic	30	14	4	12	67	51	16	46
9	Undy Athletic	30	13	5	12	62	60	2	44
10	Taffs Well	30	11	5	14	52	48	4	38
11	Briton Ferry Llansawel	30	10	7	13	58	64	-6	37
12	Cwmamman United	30	8	6	16	38	59	-21	30
13	Port Talbot Town	30	9	11	10	58	53	5	29*
14	Monmouth Town	30	7	4	19	44	73	-29	25
15	Caerau (Ely)	30	5	3	22	32	78	-46	18
16	Ton Pentre	30	1	7	22	26	82	-56	10

Division Two

		P	W	D	L	F	A	GD	Pts
1	Llantwit Major	30	21	6	3	70	27	43	69
2	Pontypridd Town	30	22	1	7	93	31	62	67
3	Ammanford	30	20	3	7	74	37	37	63
4	STM Sports	30	18	6	6	94	36	58	60
5	Aberbargoed Buds	30	18	3	9	54	33	21	57
6	Garden Village	30	17	3	10	59	46	13	54
7	Caldicot Town	30	17	2	11	50	35	15	53
8	Risca United	30	13	7	10	53	48	5	46
9	Pontardawe Town	30	13	3	14	51	51	0	42
10	Abergavenny Town	30	11	6	13	43	48	-5	39
11	Aberdare Town	30	9	6	15	42	56	-14	33
12	Croesyceiliog	30	9	2	19	36	56	-20	29
13	AFC Llwydcoed	30	8	4	18	41	60	-19	28
14	West End	30	8	5	17	40	80	-40	26*
15	Dinas Powys	30	4	3	23	25	80	-55	15
16	AFC Porth	30	1	2	27	24	125	-101	5

Division Three

		P	W	D	L	F	A	GD	Pts
1	Swansea University	30	24	3	3	100	27	73	75
2	Bridgend Street	30	23	5	2	105	41	64	74
3	Trefelin Boys & Girls Club	30	23	5	2	81	33	48	74
4	Treharris Athletic Western	30	17	3	10	76	64	12	54
5	Penrhiwceiber Rangers	30	12	6	12	59	60	-1	42
6	Pontyclun	30	11	8	11	53	61	-8	41
7	Ynysygerwn	30	10	10	10	53	53	0	40
8	Trethomas Bluebirds	30	11	5	14	50	48	2	38
9	Panteg	30	11	5	14	59	70	-11	38
10	Tredegar Town	30	7	13	10	48	59	-11	37
11	Caerau	30	11	2	17	48	72	-24	35
12	Newport City	30	9	5	16	52	69	-17	32
13	Treowen Stars	30	9	3	18	42	68	-26	30
14	Chepstow Town	30	7	6	17	57	84	-27	27
15	Ely Rangers	30	6	3	21	45	92	-47	21
16	Neuadd wen	30	4	8	18	44	71	-27	20

WELSH NATIONAL LEAGUE

Premier

		P	W	D	L	F	A	GD	Pts
1	Buckley Town	28	21	3	4	83	22	61	66
2	Brickfield Rangers	28	19	6	3	78	30	48	63
3	Corwen	28	16	3	9	73	45	28	51
4	Cefn Albion	28	16	3	9	73	52	21	51
5	Mold Alexandra	28	15	2	11	64	56	8	47
6	Llanuwchllyn	28	14	3	11	56	44	12	45
7	Saltney Town	28	12	5	11	56	54	2	41
8	Lex Glyndwr	28	11	7	10	57	47	10	40
9	Chirk AAA	28	11	5	12	50	42	8	38
10	Hawarden Rangers	28	12	2	14	52	56	-4	38
11	Rhostyllen	28	11	2	15	50	64	-14	35
12	FC Nomads of Connah's Quay	28	11	2	15	44	61	-17	35

Division One

		P	W	D	L	F	A	GD	Pts
1	Brymbo	20	16	2	2	78	23	55	50
2	Rhos Aelwyd	20	14	4	2	65	24	41	46
3	Cefn Mawr Rangers	20	10	5	5	55	34	21	35
4	Llangollen Town	20	11	1	8	67	45	22	34
5	New Brighton Villa	20	10	3	7	41	43	-2	33
6	Mynydd Isa Spartans	20	9	3	8	48	41	7	30
7	Maesgwyn	20	8	1	11	58	74	-16	25
8	Castell Alun Colts	20	7	2	11	36	57	-21	23
9	Rhydymwyn	20	4	6	10	47	63	-16	18
10	Overton Recreational	20	4	2	14	29	59	-30	14
11	Johnstown Youth	20	1	3	16	26	87	-61	6

Point of Ayr, Penley and Acrefair Youth all withdrew - records expunged.

NORTH EAST WALES LEAGUE

Division One

		P	W	D	L	F	A	GD	Pts
1	Plas Madoc	26	23	0	3	130	36	94	69
2	Penyffordd Lions	26	19	3	4	120	39	81	60
3	Offa Athletic	26	18	3	5	99	31	68	57
4	Airbus UK Broughton Youth	26	16	1	9	98	44	54	49
5	Connah's Quay Nomads U1826	16	1	9	96	47	49	49
6	Acton	26	14	4	8	92	54	38	46
7	Flint Mountain	26	14	2	10	98	51	47	44
8	Rhosllanerchrugog	26	12	3	11	77	56	21	39
9	Caerwys	26	11	3	12	85	80	5	36
10	Brymbo Victoria	26	8	4	14	62	73	-11	28
11	Mostyn Dragons	26	8	3	15	57	63	-6	27
12	Mold Town United	26	5	3	18	44	105	-61	18
13	Bradley Park	26	2	1	23	35	151	-116	7
14	Bellevue	26	0	1	25	15	278	-263	1

CPD Sychdyn, Marchwiel Villa, Aston Park and Halkyn United all withdrew - records expunged.

Division One

		P	W	D	L	F	A	GD	Pts
1	Conwy Borough	28	20	4	4	107	37	70	64
2	Llangefni Town	28	19	4	5	68	25	43	61
3	Llanrug United	28	12	12	4	64	51	13	48
4	Llanberis	28	14	4	10	43	55	-12	46
5	Greenfield	28	14	5	9	82	53	29	44*
6	Llanrwst United	28	12	8	8	63	54	9	44
7	Llandudno Albion	28	13	6	9	76	52	24	42*
8	Penrhyndeudraeth	28	11	5	12	55	49	6	38
9	Barmouth & Dyffryn United	28	12	2	14	38	49	-11	38
10	Mynydd Llandegai	28	10	5	13	57	72	-15	35
11	Llandyrnog United	28	8	6	14	51	63	-12	30
12	St Asaph City	28	7	8	13	49	60	-11	29
13	Nantlle Vale	28	6	5	17	32	74	-42	23
14	Trearddur Bay	28	7	1	20	42	83	-41	22
15	Pwllheli	28	6	3	19	47	97	-50	21

Glantraeth withdrew - record expunged.

Division Two

		P	W	D	L	F	A	GD	Pts
1	Prestatyn Sports	28	24	3	1	117	30	87	72*
2	Bodedern Athletic	28	21	1	6	78	41	37	64
3	Glan Conwy	28	19	2	7	74	35	39	59
4	Llannefydd	28	15	7	6	65	35	30	52
5	Amlwch Town	28	16	4	8	66	47	19	52
6	Y Felinheli	28	16	1	11	71	49	22	49
7	Meliden	28	12	4	12	70	67	3	40
8	Gaerwen	28	12	3	13	47	58	-11	39
9	Aberffraw	28	11	2	15	53	61	-8	35
10	Penmaenmawr Phoenix	28	10	4	14	58	59	-1	34
11	Blaenau Amateurs	28	9	4	15	70	98	-28	31
12	Pentraeth	28	8	4	16	40	67	-27	28
13	Mochdre Sports	28	7	3	18	53	84	-31	24
14	Llannerchymedd	28	4	2	22	19	78	-59	14
15	Llanfairpwll	28	2	4	22	25	97	-72	10

Cemaes Bay withdrew - record expunged.

GWYNEDD LEAGUE

		P	W	D	L	F	A	GD	Pts
1	Holyhead Town	22	17	1	4	95	40	55	52
2	Bro Goronwy	22	16	3	3	87	32	55	51
3	Llanystumdwy	22	14	2	6	83	48	35	44
4	Bontnewydd	22	14	0	8	67	35	32	42
5	Gwalchmai	22	13	3	6	60	38	22	42
6	Nefyn United	22	11	4	7	58	34	24	37
7	Waunfawr	22	9	2	11	58	59	-1	29
8	Llangoed & District	22	9	2	11	45	58	-13	29
9	Menai Bridge Tigers	22	7	5	10	48	50	-2	26
10	Talysarn Celts	22	7	0	15	34	72	-38	21
11	Beaumaris Town	22	2	4	16	40	91	-51	7*
12	Llanllyfni	22	0	0	22	18	136	-118	0

ANGLESEY LEAGUE

		P	W	D	L	F	A	GD	Pts
1	Mynydd Tigers	16	12	2	2	80	21	59	38
2	Bryngwran Bulls	16	12	0	4	72	25	47	36
3	Valley Athletic	16	11	1	4	93	37	56	34
4	Caergybi	16	11	1	4	81	30	51	34
5	Arriva Bangor	16	8	1	7	67	41	26	25
6	Llangoed & District Reserves	16	6	2	8	42	55	-13	17*
7	Bodorgan	16	3	3	10	32	70	-38	12
8	Pentraeth Reserves	16	2	2	12	22	74	-52	8
9	Llandegfan	16	1	0	15	19	155	-136	3

Action, above and below, from Bow Street v Llandrindod Wells. Photo: Bill Wheatcroft.

Above:
Carroll (Aberystwyth)
Webbe (Barry).

McLaggan (Barry) gets
his shot in under pressure
from McKenna
(Aberystwyth).

Davies (Denbigh) tries to get
between Edwards and Crowther
(Airbus)

Main Stand Denbigh

WELSH FOOTBALL

MID WALES LEAGUE

Division One

		P	W	D	L	F	A	GD	Pts
1	Llanrhaeadr YM	30	26	1	3	117	30	87	79
2	Welshpool Town	30	17	8	5	99	46	53	59
3	Llanidloes Town	30	17	6	7	60	40	20	57
4	Llanfair United	30	18	2	10	79	58	21	56
5	Bow Street	30	15	6	9	73	47	26	51
6	Aberaeron	30	15	6	9	67	53	14	51
7	Carno	30	14	7	9	73	48	25	49
8	Radnor Valley	30	15	4	11	70	54	16	49
9	Berriew	30	12	6	12	66	58	8	42
10	Knighton Town	30	13	3	14	68	61	7	42
11	Tywyn Bryncrug	30	11	3	16	64	83	-19	36
12	Kerry	30	11	3	16	64	87	-23	36
13	Llandrindod Wells	30	11	0	19	44	59	-15	33
14	Churchstoke	30	6	8	16	53	81	-28	26
15	Machynlleth	30	4	2	24	32	117	-85	14
16	Borth United	30	2	1	27	23	130	-107	7

Division Two

		P	W	D	L	F	A	GD	Pts
1	Builth Wells	22	19	2	1	72	16	56	59
2	Llansantffraid Village	22	16	3	3	71	29	42	51
3	Brecon Northcote	22	12	3	7	50	36	14	39
4	Hay St Mary's	22	11	4	7	45	38	7	37
5	Abermule	22	10	2	10	47	50	-3	32
6	Dolgellau Athletic	22	9	4	9	37	43	-6	31
7	Aberystwyth University	22	9	3	10	54	43	11	30
8	Dyffryn Banw	22	8	3	11	34	43	-9	27
9	Presteigne St. Andrews	22	7	3	12	28	56	-28	24
10	Newbridge-on-Wye	22	6	3	13	50	56	-6	21
11	Montgomery Town	22	6	5	11	44	59	-15	20*
12	Penybont	22	1	1	20	24	87	-63	4

Talgarth Town withdrew - record expunged.

VALE OF CLYWD & CONWY LEAGUE

Premier Division

		P	W	D	L	F	A	GD	Pts
1	Kinmel Bay	18	15	2	1	87	27	60	47
2	Llanfairfechan Town	18	15	1	2	80	22	58	46
3	Llansannan	18	10	1	7	46	43	3	31
4	Cerrig-y-Drudion	18	7	5	6	48	42	6	26
5	Rhyl Youth	18	8	1	9	47	56	-9	22*
6	Machno United	18	7	1	10	36	56	-20	22
7	Bro Cernyw	18	5	1	12	36	51	-15	16
8	Old Colwyn	18	8	2	8	48	77	-29	14*
9	Y Glannau	18	4	0	14	39	69	-30	12
10	Abergele	18	3	2	13	37	61	-24	11

Division One

		P	W	D	L	F	A	GD	PTS
1	Llandudno Amateurs	22	20	1	1	128	24	104	61
2	Llandudno Athletic	22	17	3	2	93	30	63	54
3	Llanrwst United Res	22	14	3	5	80	52	28	45
4	Rhuddlan Town	22	14	2	6	94	52	42	44
5	Rhos United	22	11	4	7	68	57	11	37
6	Llandyrnog United Res	22	8	8	6	58	55	3	32
7	Henllan	22	9	2	11	64	58	6	29
8	Llysfaen	22	6	4	12	49	59	-10	22
9	St Asaph City Reserves	22	5	5	12	65	76	-11	20
10	Denbigh Development	22	5	3	14	38	79	-41	18
11	Betws-y-Coed	22	2	1	19	37	117	-80	7
12	Llanfairfechan Town Res	22	3	0	19	35	150	-115	6*

NEWPORT & DISTRICT FOOTBALL LEAGUE

Premier X

		P	W	D	L	F	A	GD	Pts
1	Cromwell AFC	22	12	6	4	86	51	35	42
2	Whiteheads Rhisga	22	13	1	8	67	46	21	40
3	Pontnewydd United	22	12	4	6	59	61	-2	40
4	Llanyrafon AFC	22	12	3	7	80	51	29	39
5	Docks Cons	22	9	5	8	58	54	4	32
6	Fairwater FC	22	9	4	9	66	60	6	31
7	Riverside Rovers	22	9	1	12	55	71	-16	28
8	Rogerstone AFC	22	7	5	10	68	70	-2	26
9	West of St Julians	22	8	2	12	49	76	-27	26
10	Civil Service	22	8	1	13	53	75	-22	25
11	Croesyceiliog Athletic	22	8	1	13	61	81	-20	25
12	Crindau Corries	22	7	3	12	66	72	-6	24

Premier Y

		P	W	D	L	F	A	GD	pts
1	Caerleon AFC	20	16	1	3	85	41	44	49
2	Albion Rovers	20	14	3	3	77	36	41	45
3	AC Pontymister	20	13	3	4	70	35	35	42
4	Cwmbran Celtic	20	12	3	5	91	58	33	39
5	Lliswerry FC	20	8	4	8	54	69	-15	28
6	Trethomas Bluebirds	20	9	0	11	84	41	43	27
7	Pill AFC	20	7	2	11	62	89	-27	23
8	Newport Corinthians	20	6	2	12	48	76	-28	20
9	Coed Eva Athletic	20	6	2	12	40	81	-41	20
10	Villa Dino C/C	20	5	3	12	53	68	-15	18
11	Lucas Cwmbran	20	3	1	16	40	110	-70	10

Division 1

		P	W	D	L	F	A	GD	pts
1	Recrite Scaffolding	16	12	3	1	69	22	47	39
2	River Usk AFC	16	12	0	4	59	25	34	36
3	Machen FC	16	10	3	3	58	25	33	33
4	Albion Rovers	16	7	2	7	55	41	14	23
5	Gaer Park AFC	16	6	1	9	51	75	-24	19
6	Marshfield AFC	15	5	3	8	33	65	-32	18
7	The Docks Cons	16	4	4	8	32	55	-23	16
8	AC Pontymister	16	4	2	10	41	57	-16	14
9	Cwmcarn Athletic	16	1	4	11	40	73	-33	7

Glenside Rovers withdrew - record expunged.

Villa Dino C/C withdrew - record expunged

Division 2

		P	W	D	L	F	A	GD	pts
1	Baneswell Social	18	16	0	2	75	30	45	48
2	Glan Usk FC	18	15	1	2	91	25	66	46
3	Spencer Boys & Dev	18	14	2	2	97	31	66	44
4	Llanyrafon AFC	18	8	2	8	66	52	14	26
5	Caerleon Town	18	8	1	9	69	62	7	25
6	Newport Corinthians	18	7	2	9	48	48	0	23
7	Albion Rovers	18	7	1	10	64	69	-5	22
8	Cromwell Youth	18	5	2	11	36	73	-37	17
9	Rogerstone	18	2	2	14	31	73	-42	8
10	Newport Eagles	18	1	1	16	21	135	-114	4

PEMBROKESHIRE LEAGUE

Division One

		P	W	D	L	F	A	GD	Pts
1	Hakin United	24	21	1	2	125	25	100	64
2	Goodwick United	24	19	4	1	113	23	90	61
3	Merlins Bridge	24	18	3	3	96	24	72	57
4	Carew	24	15	3	6	89	41	48	48
5	Clarbeston Road	24	12	4	8	86	50	36	40
6	Narberth	24	11	1	12	57	66	-9	34
7	Monkton Swifts	24	12	1	11	66	68	-2	31
8	Neyland	24	8	4	12	59	86	-27	28
9	Pennar Robins	24	7	2	15	37	83	-46	23
10	Lamphey	24	6	4	14	42	85	-43	22
11	Angle	24	4	3	17	30	124	-94	12
12	Milford United	24	3	2	19	21	70	-49	11
13	Herbrandston	24	3	2	19	26	102	-76	11

Division Two

		P	W	D	L	F	A	GD	Pts
1	Hakin United Res	26	22	3	1	111	26	85	69
2	St Clears	26	20	1	5	126	51	75	61
3	Saundersfoot Sports	26	19	2	5	97	37	60	59
4	Kilgetty	26	17	3	6	85	40	45	54
5	Fishguard Sports	26	16	2	8	68	46	22	50
6	Merlins Bridge Res	26	12	1	13	59	72	-13	37
7	St Ishmaels	26	8	5	13	44	57	-13	29
8	Prendergast Villa	26	8	5	13	55	82	-27	29
9	Lawrenny	26	8	3	15	64	82	-18	27
10	Johnston	26	7	6	13	50	72	-22	27
11	Hundleton	26	7	3	16	50	88	-38	24
12	Solva	26	7	2	17	55	101	-46	23
13	Llangwm	26	5	5	16	48	84	-36	20
14	Letterston	26	5	1	20	29	103	-74	16

Division Three

		P	W	D	L	F	A	GD	Pts
1	Camrose	22	19	1	2	110	21	89	58
2	Broad Haven	22	18	2	2	113	27	86	56
3	Pennar Robins Res	22	17	0	5	72	30	42	51
4	Goodwick UNited Res	22	13	0	9	52	34	18	39
5	Carew Res	22	11	1	10	67	51	16	34
6	Milford Athletic	22	8	5	9	54	53	1	29
7	Pembroke Boro	22	9	0	13	57	70	-13	27
8	Clarbeston Road Res	22	8	1	13	38	66	-28	25
9	Narberth Res	22	5	5	12	36	50	-14	20
10	Pendine	22	6	1	15	38	97	-59	19
11	Milford United Res	22	5	1	16	29	72	-43	16
12	St Florence	22	4	1	17	30	125	-95	7

Division Four

		P	W	D	L	F	A	GD	Pts
1	Mokton Swifts Res	22	17	4	1	128	37	91	52
2	Fishguard Sports Res	22	15	4	3	69	40	29	49
3	St Clears Res	22	11	3	8	105	51	54	36
4	Solva Res	22	11	4	7	95	70	25	34
5	Pennar Robins 3rds	22	10	6	6	64	39	25	33
6	Neyland Res	22	9	5	8	65	63	2	32
7	Herbrandston Res	22	9	2	11	67	66	1	29
8	Kilgetty Res	22	8	2	12	98	73	25	26
9	Broad Haven Res	22	7	5	10	65	60	5	26
10	Llangwm Res	22	7	4	11	61	60	1	25
11	St Ishmaels Res	22	7	1	14	63	74	-11	22
12	Angle Res	22	1	0	21	12	259	-247	-6

Division Five

		P	W	D	L	F	A	GD	Pts
1	Coheston AFC	20	17	2	1	101	28	73	53
2	Hundleton Res	20	12	0	8	75	39	36	36
3	Camrose Res	20	11	3	6	58	38	20	36
4	Pembroke Boro Res	20	10	0	10	44	61	-17	30
5	Johnston Res	20	9	1	10	61	58	3	28
6	Carew 3rds	20	9	3	8	62	56	6	27
7	Lawrenny Res	20	8	3	9	64	64	0	27
8	Milford United 3rds	20	7	4	9	57	49	8	25
9	Letterston Res	20	4	4	12	43	85	-42	16
10	Milford Athletic 3rds	20	4	3	13	42	92	-50	15
11	Saundersfoot Sports Res	20	6	3	11	52	89	-37	12

WELSH CUP

HOLDERS: BALA TOWN

FIRST QUALIFYING ROUND
SOUTH EAST REGION

Villa Dino Christchurch	v	Neuadd Wen	4–1
Abertillery Bluebirds	v	Chepstow Town	5–4
Panteg	v	Newport City	2–0
Newport YMCA	v	Machen	1–4
FC Tredegar	v	Tredegar Town	3-3, 6-7p
Cwmbrân Town	v	Caerleon	3–1

SOUTH CENTRAL REGION

Butetown	v	Aberfan SDC	3–2
Cardiff Draconians	v	Canton Liberal	8–1
Llantwit Fardre	v	Grange Allstars	1–0
Merthyr Saints	v	Tiger Bay	6–4
Treharris Athletic Western	v	Llanrumney United	7–0

Llanrumney Utd awarded the tie after Treharris played an ineligible player.

Blaenrhondda	v	Brecon Corries	3–4
Trethomas Bluebirds	v	Ely Rangers	3–4
Aber Valley	v	Cardiff Corinthians	3–4
Penydarren	v	Penrhiwceiber Rangers	5–3
Trebanog	v	Caerphilly Athletic	0–2
Treforest	v	Brecon Northcote	1–3 aet
Rumney Juniors	v	Ferndale and District	4–2
Pontlottyn	v	Bridgend Street	2–6
Pontyclun	v	Garw	2–0
Clwb Cymric	v	Penrhiwfer	0–1

SOUTH WEST REGION

Penlan Club	v	Caerau	1–4
Llangynwyd Rangers	v	Porthcawl Town	2–3
Trefelin	v	Ynysygerwn	1-1, 1-3p
Newcastle Emlyn	v	Pencoed Athletic	0–2

WELSH FOOTBALL

Carmarthen Stars	v	CRC Rangers	4–3
Swansea University	v	Cefn Cribwr Boys Club	2-2, 1-4p

CENTRAL REGION

Kerry	v	Hay St Marys	2–1
Abermule	v	Tywyn Bryncrug	1–0
Llansantffraid Village	v	Montgomery Town	6–0
Borth United	v	Trewern United	5–3
Churchstoke	v	Welshpool Town	2-3 aet
Machynlleth	v	Llandrindod Wells	0–5

NORTH EAST REGION

Lex Glyndwr	v	Greenfield	2–1
Penyffordd Lions	v	Cefn Albion	3–2
Rhydymwyn	v	Cefn Mawr Rangers	3–2
Rhostyllen	v	Llangollen Town	4–2
Brymbo Victoria	v	Acton	3-6 aet
Penycae	v	Castell Alun Colts	5–3
St Asaph City	v	Llay Welfare	1–2
FC Penley	v	Mostyn Dragons	4-4, 4-3p
Rhos Aelwyd	v	Coedpoeth United	1–2
New Brighton Villa	v	Brymbo	0–2
Mynydd Isa Spartans	v	Rhosllanerchrugog	1–3

NORTH WEST REGION

Barmouth & Dyffryn United	v	Llanfairpwll	1–0
Cemaes Bay	v	Llannefydd	0–5
Llanberis	v	Llandudno Albion	2–3
Waunfawr	v	Llanrwst United	4-6 aet
Nantlle Vale	v	Llanystumdwy	5–1
Blaenau Ffestiniog Am.	v	Llandyrnog United	3–12
Trearddur Bay United	v	Aberffraw	1–3
Llandudno Albion	v	Llangefni Town	3-1 aet
Penrhyndeudraeth	v	Bodedern Athletic	2–3
Llanrug United	v	Pentraeth	4-2 aet
Holyhead Town	v	Gaewen	2–4

SECOND QUALIFYING ROUND

SOUTH EAST REGION

Bridgend Street	v	Llanrumney United	7–0
Rumney Juniors	v	Caerphilly Athletic	1–4
Butetown	v	STM Sports	3–5
Machen	v	Ely Rangers	4–0
Abertillery Bluebirds	v	Cardiff Corinthians	1–2
Llwydcoed	v	Panteg	3-4 aet
Risca United	v	Croesyceiliog	1-2 aet
Cwmbrân Town	v	Aberbargoed Buds	1–7
Abergavenny Town	v	Porth	7–0
Villa Dino Christchurch	v	Caldicot Town	2–5
Cardiff Draconians	v	Tredegar Town	5–1
Aberdare Town	v	Dinas Powys	2–1

SOUTH WEST REGION

West End	v	Ynysygerwn	1-1, 1-3p
Caerau	v	Pontyclun	2–6
Penrhiwfer	v	Pontypridd Town	1-3 aet
Pontardawe Town	v	Garden Village	3-4 aet
Brecon Corries	v	Penydarren	1–3
Carmarthen Stars	v	Porthcawl Town	5-4 aet
Llantwit Major	v	Cefn Cribwr Boys Club	2–1
Ammanford	v	Merthyr Saints	5–2
Pencoed Athletic	v	Llantwit Fardre	2–0

CENTRAL REGION

Knighton Town	v	Bow Street	0–2
Llansantffraid Village	v	Berriew	0–7
Llanrhaeadr	v	Kerry	3–1
Welshpool Town	v	Aberaeron	3–4
Abermule	v	Borth United	3–2
Carno	v	Llandrindod Wells	2–1
Rhayader Town	v	Brecon Northcote	3-2 aet
Llanidloes Town	v	Barmouth & Dyffryn United)	3–0

NORTH EAST REGION

Rhosllanerchrugog	v	Penyffordd Lions	2–3
Lex Glyndwr	v	Hawarden Rangers	1–0
FC Penley	v	Brymbo	3–2
Saltney Town	v	Coedpoeth United (3	3–2
Penycae	v	Llay Welfare	1–3
Rhostyllen	v	Brickfield Rangers	2–7
Mold Alexandra	v	Acton	5–0
Corwen	v	Nomads of Connahs Quay	3-1 aet
Llanuwchllyn	v	Chirk AAA	0–1
Rhydymwyn	v	Buckley Town	0–2

NORTH WEST REGION

Meliden	v	Nantlle Vale	3-3, 4-3p
Gaewen	v	Pwllheli	6–5
Llanrug United	v	Llandyrnog United	5–1
Penmaenmawr Phoenix	v	Llanrwst United	1–4
Bodedern Athletic	v	Aberffraw (4	2–0
Llandudno Albion	v	Llannefydd	1-1 5-4p
Conwy Borough	v	Amlwch Town	4–1
Mynydd Llandygai	v	Mochdre Sports	0–3

ROUND 1

Aberdare Town	v	Ammanford	0-0, 2-3p
Caersws	w/o		
Conwy Borough	v	Bodedern Athletic	5-1
Aberbargoed Buds	v	Port Talbot Town	2-0
STM Sports	v	Afan Lido	5-2
Caldicot Town	v	Goytre	2-3
Porthmadog	v	Penyffordd	3-0
Garden Village	v	Penrhyncoch	3-4
Brickfield Rangers	v	Chirk AAA	1-0
Mochdre Sports	v	F.C. Penley	1-1, 3-5p
Pontypridd Town	v	Cambrian & Clydach Vale	2-1 aet
Llay Welfare	v	Llanrug United	1-0
Buckley Town	v	Llanidloes Town	2-1
Gaerwen	v	Llandudno Junction	1-3
Haverfordwest County	v	Croesyceiliog	2-1
Guilsfield	v	Mold Alexandra	4-0
Llandudno Albion	v	Rhyl	3-2
Cwmamman United	v	Rhayader Town	3-1
Carno (3}	v	Gresford Athletic	0-4
Bridgend Street	v	Machen	4-3
Cardiff Draconians	v	Ton Pentre	1-2
Llanrhaeadr	v	FC Queens Park	3-0
Caerau (Ely)	v	Cwmbran Celtic	0-1
Briton Ferry Llansawel	v	Goytre United	3-1
Abergavenny Town	v	Panteg	1-3
Denbigh Town	v	Holyhead Hotspur	4-3
Aberaeron	v	Llanelli Town	1-6
Flint Town United	v	Llanfair United	3-0
Cardiff Corinthians	v	Penydarren	0-4
Monmouth Town	v	Ynysygerwn	4-1
Abermule	v	Berriew	0-4
Saltney Town	v	Llanrwst United	6-0
Caerphilly Athletic	v	Carmarthen Stars	4-1 aet
Caernarfon Town	v	Lex XI	5-1
Llantwit Major	v	Taff's Well	3-2
Meliden	v	Ruthin Town	0-4
Pontyclun	v	Pencoed Athletic	0-0, 7-8p
Holywell Town	v	Corwen	3-0
Pen-y-Bont	v	Undy Athletic	1-0 aet
Airbus UK Broughton	v	Bow Street	3-0

ROUND 2

Goytre	v	Briton Ferry Llansawel	2-1
Haverfordwest County	v	Aberbargoed Buds	2-0
Airbus UK Broughton	v	Saltney Town	4-0
Pen-y-Bont	v	Monmouth Town	2-1
Brickfield Rangers	v	Ruthin Town	2-3 aet
Buckley Town	v	Llandudno Albion	2-1
Ton Pentre	v	Panteg	1-2
Caernarfon Town	v	Berriew	4-1
Caersws	v	Llanrhaeadr	1-2
Porthmadog	v	F.C. Penley	10-0
Gresford Athletic	v	Conwy Borough	5-1
Holywell Town	v	Guilsfield	2-3
Llay Welfare	v	Flint Town United	1-3
Ammanford	v	Llantwit Major	1-1, 3-2p
Caerphilly Athletic	v	Penrhyncoch	2-4
Cwmamman United	v	Bridgend Street	3-0
Cwmbran Celtic	v	Llanelli Town	2-1
Pencoed Athletic	v	Pontypridd Town	1-3
Penydarren	v	STM Sports	2-1
Llandudno Junction	v	Denbigh Town	3-2 aet

ROUND 3

The New Saints	v	Penrhyncoch	6-0
Llandudno	v	Gresford Athletic	4-0
Newtown	v	Guilsfield	2-0
Llandudno Junction	v	Penydarren	0-4
Pontypridd Town	v	Haverfordwest County	3-1
Ammanford	v	Carmarthen Town	2-3
Buckley Town	v	Flint Town United	0-1
Pen-y-Bont	v	Cardiff Metropolitan University	1-3
Bangor City	v	Cwmamman United	4-3
Aberystwyth Town	v	Bala Town	4-0
Prestatyn Town	v	Ruthin Town	0-3
Llanrhaeadr	v	Cefn Druids	3-2
Connah's Quay Nomads	v	Cwmbran Celtic	3-0
Porthmadog	v	Panteg	7-2
Airbus UK Broughton	v	Goytre	3-2 aet
Caernarfon Town	v	Barry Town United	2-0

ROUND 4

Caernarfon Town	v	The New Saints	1-3
Llanrhaeadr	v	Bangor City	2-3
Pontypridd Town	v	Penydarren	1-2
Flint Town United	v	Newtown	2-2, 3-4p
Connah's Quay Nomads	v	Porthmadog	3-1
Cardiff Metropolitan Uni.	v	Aberystwyth Town	0-1
Llandudno	v	Ruthin Town	4-3 aet
Airbus UK Broughton	v	Carmarthen Town	1-4

QUARTER FINALS

Bangor City	v	Penydarren	7-0
Connah's Quay Nomads	v	The New Saints	2-1
Carmarthen Town	v	Aberystwyth Town	1-3
Llandudno	v	Newtown	0-2

SEMI FINALS

Connah's Quay Nomads	v	Bangor City	6-1
Newtown	v	Aberystwyth Town	1-2

FINAL

Aberystwyth Town	v	Connah's Quay Nomads	1-4

WELSH TROPHY

HOLDERS: CHIRK AAA

ROUND 1

ABER VALLEY	v	ST JOSEPHS A	0 - 4
ABERFAN	v	YNYSDDU WELFARE CRUSADERS	1 - 6
BRYN ROVERS	v	KILVEY UNITED	5 - 3
CAERPHILLY ATHLETIC	v	COGAN CORONATION	2 - 1
CANTON LIBERAL	v	ST ALBANS	7 - 3
CANTON RANGERS	v	CWMCARN ATHLETIC	1 - 4
CLWB CYMRIC	v	CADOXTON BARRY	0 - 6
CORWEN	v	CPD LLANNEFYDD	3 - 0
CPD IEUENCTID BONTNEWYDD	v	TALYSARN CELTS	2 - 1
CRC RANGERS	v	CARMARTHEN STARS	1 - 2
CWMAMAN	v	GRAIG	13 - 0
PORTHCAWL	v	NORTH END	1 - 0
FERNDALE AND DISTRICT BGC	v	GLAMORGAN ATHLETIC	4 - 5
GARW	v	PORT TENNANT COLTS	3 - 2
GOODWICK UNITED	v	YNYSTAWE ATHLETIC	3 - 1
HAKIN UNITED	v	BONYMAEN COLTS	14 - 0
LLANRUMNEY UNITED	v	CARNETOWN	2 - 0
LUCAS CWMBRAN	v	MACHEN A	5 - 1
MALTSTERS SPORTS	v	CEFN CRIBBWR	2 - 4
MENAI BRIDGE TIGERS	v	HOLYWELL TOWN	1 - 2
MERTHYR SAINTS	v	WHITEHEADS RHISGA	4 - 1
MOSTYN DRAGONS	v	ACTON	1 - 2
MUMBLES RANGERS	v	PENCOED ATHLETIC AMATEUR	1 - 6
PENYDARREN BOYS & GIRLS	v	CAERPHILLY TOWN	8 - 0
PILL	v	FAIRFIELD UNITED	2 - 5 aet
PLAS MADOC	v	BRYMBO VICTORIA	6 - 3
RAGGED SCHOOL	v	CWM WANDERERS	4 - 3
RHOSLLANERCHRUGOG	v	OFFA ATHLETIC	2 - 0
ROCKSPUR	v	LLANGYNWYD RANGERS	3 - 1
SOUTH GOWER	v	MORRISTON OLYMPIC	5 - 1
TALBOT GREEN	v	BLAENRHONDDA	0 - 3
TONYPANDY ALBION	v	ABERCARN UNITED	1 - 3
TREBANOG	v	CLYDACH WASPS	2 - 0
TREFOREST	v	TREDEGAR	2 - 0
TREWERN	v	CEFN MAWR RANGERS	5 - 1
VILLA DINO CHRISTCHURCH	v	LLANTWIT FARDRE A	8 - 1
WEST END RANGERS	v	MERLIN'S BRIDGE	2 - 3

ROUND 2

ABERCARN UNITED	v	CADOXTON BARRY	2-5
BLAENAU FFESTINIOG	v	PENTRAETH	0-2
BOW STREET	v	CHURCHSTOKE	4-1
BRICKFIELD RANGERS	v	MOLD ALEXANDRA	2-3 aet
CAERPHILLY ATHLETIC	v	NEUADD WEN	2-0
CANTON LIBERAL	v	CWMAMAN	1-5
CARDIFF CORINTHIANS	v	YNYSDDU WELFARE	2-3
CARMARTHEN STARS	v	BAGLAN DRAGONS	5-4 aet
CEFN ALBION	v	PLAS MADOC	5-0
CONWY BOROUGH	v	HOLYHEAD TOWN	4-3 aet
CORWEN	v	RHOSLLANERCHRUGOG	6-0
CPD LLANNEFYDD	v	TREARDDUR BAY UNITED	2-1
CWMCARN ATHLETIC	v	LUCAS CWMBRAN	3-2
DYFFRYN BANW	v	LLANIDLOES TOWN	1-3
ELY RANGERS	v	GRANGE ALBION	1-2
FAIRFIELD UNITED	v	GLAMORGAN ATHLETIC	2-1
NOMADS OF CONNAH'S QUAY	v	CASTELL ALUN COLTS	5-0
PORTHCAWL	v	MERLIN'S BRIDGE	0-2
GAERWEN	v	MYNYDD LLANDEGAI	3-2
GARDEN VILLAGE	v	SWANSEA UNIVERSITY	4-3
GOODWICK UNITED	v	ROCKSPUR	4-0

WELSH FOOTBALL

HAKIN UNITED	v	PENCOED ATHLETIC AMATEUR	2-1
HAWARDEN RANGERS	v	ACTON	4-0
JOHNSTOWN YOUTH	v	BUCKLEY TOWN	0-9
KNIGHTON TOWN	v	TYWYN BRYNCRUG	4-2
LLANBERIS	v	AMLWCH TOWN	4-1
LLANDRINDOD WELLS	v	BERRIEW	0-3
LLANDUDNO ALBION	v	PENRHYNDEUDRAETH	2-4
LLANFAIR UNITED	v	CARNO	3-1
LLANGOLLEN TOWN	v	COEDPOETH UNITED	6-2 aet
LLANRHAEADR YM MOCHNANT	v	MONTGOMERY TOWN	4-1
LLANRUG UNITED	v	BODEDERN	6-0
LLANRUMNEY UNITED	v	TON & GELLI BOYS CLUB	2-6
LLANSANTFFRAID VILLAGE	v	PRESTEIGNE ST ANDREWS	4-2
LLANUWCHLLYN	v	RHYDYMWYN	5-1
LLAY WELFARE	v	MYNYDD ISA SPARTANS	2-3
NEW BRIGHTON VILLA	v	PENLEY	10-4
NEWPORT CITY	v	MERTHYR SAINTS	3-3, 4-3p
PENMAENMAWR PHOENIX	v	CLWB IEUENCTID BONTNEWYDD	4-3
PENYDARREN BOYS & GIRLS	v	STM SPORTS	3-2
PONTLOTTYN	v	ST JOSEPHS A	4-2
PRESTATYN SPORTS	v	ABERFFRAW	4-2 aet
PWLLHELI	v	LLANRWST UNITED	5-1
RADNOR VALLEY	v	BRECON NORTHCOTE	4-1
RAGGED SCHOOL	v	GARW SBGC	4-2
RHOS AELWYD	v	PENYCAE	2-0
RHOSTYLLEN	v	LEX GLYNDWR	0-1
SALTNEY TOWN	v	OVERTON RECREATIONAL	4-0
SOUTH GOWER	v	BRYN ROVERS	2-1
ST ASAPH CITY	v	GREENFIELD	1-2
TREBANOG	v	ABERTILLERY BLUEBIRDS	1-2
TREOWEN STARS	v	BLAENRHONDDA	3-3, 5-4p
TREWERN	v	MACHYNLLETH	2-1 aet
VILLA DINO CHRISTCHURCH	v	TREFOREST	8-4
Y FELINHELI	v	LLANYSTUMDWY	3-4
YNYSGERWN	v	CEFN CRIBWR	2-1

ROUND 3

ABERTILLERY BLUEBIRDS	v	SOUTH GOWER	5-1
BUCKLEY TOWN	v	SALTNEY TOWN	6-0
CEFN ALBION	v	PENAMENMAWR PHOENIX	8-3
CHIRK AAA	v	PENRHYNDEUDRAETH	5-2
COEDPOETH UNITED	v	CONWY BOROUGH	2-7
CORWEN	v	CPD LLANNEFYDD	3-0
CWMCARN ATHLETIC	v	HAKIN UNITED	1-8
FAIRFIELD UNITED	v	YNYSDDU WELFARE	0-1
NOMADS OF CONNAH'S QUAY	v	PRESTATYN SPORTS	3-1
GAERWEN	v	GREENFIELD	1-5
GARDEN VILLAGE	v	PONTLOTTYN	5-1
GOODWICK UNITED	v	PENLAN SOCIAL	3-2
GRANGE ALBION	v	MERLIN'S BRIDGE	2-1
KNIGHTON TOWN	v	LLANRHAEADR YM MOCHNANT	3-1
LEX GLYNDWR	v	LLANRUG UNITED	0-3
LLANFAIR UNITED	v	BOW STREET	2-1
LLANGEFNI TOWN	v	HAWARDEN RANGERS	3-1
LLANIDLOES TOWN	v	LLANSANTFFRAID VILLAGE	4-1
LLANUWCHLLYN	v	BRYMBO	3-3, 3-4p
MELIDEN	v	LLANYSTUMDWY	4-5
MOLD ALEXANDRA	v	CPD DYFFRYN NANTLLE	2-1
MYNYDD ISA SPARTANS	v	PENTRAETH	6-0
NEW BRIGHTON VILLA	v	PWLLHELI	3-2
NEWPORT CITY	v	CAERPHILLY ATHLETIC	2-3 aet
PENYDARREN BOYS & GIRLS	v	YNYSGERWN	4-0
RADNOR VALLEY	v	BERRIEW	0-2
RAGGED SCHOOL	v	CWMAMAN	3-1
RHOS AELWYD	v	LLANBERIS	2-1
SULLY SPORTS	v	CARMARTHEN STARS	2-2, 2-4p
TREOWEN STARS	v	TON & GELLI BOYS CLUB	2-1

TREWERN	v	MOCHDRE SPORTS	1-5
VILLA DINO CHRISTCHURCH	v	CADOXTON BARRY	4-3

ROUND 4

ABERTILLERY BLUEBIRDS	v	RAGGED SCHOOL	2-0
BERRIEW	v	BRYMBO	0-1 aet
BUCKLEY TOWN	v	NOMADS OF CONNAH'S QUAY	2-1 aet
CAERPHILLY ATHLETIC	v	HAKIN UNITED	2-3
CARMARTHEN STARS	v	PENYDARREN BOYS & GIRLS	0-5
CHIRK AAA	v	NEW BRIGHTON VILLA	4-0
CONWY BOROUGH	v	CEFN ALBION	2-1
GARDEN VILLAGE	v	VILLA DINO CHRISTCHURCH	8-0
GRANGE ALBION	v	TREOWEN STARS	2-1
LLANFAIR UNITED	v	CORWEN	3-2 aet
LLANGEFNI TOWN	v	LLANYSTUMDWY	4-0
LLANIDLOES TOWN	v	LLANRUG UNITED	2-5 aet
MOLD ALEXANDRA	v	GREENFIELD	2-5
MYNYDD ISA	v	KNIGHTON TOWN	4-1
RHOS AELWYD	v	MOCHDRE SPORTS	2-0
YNYSDDU WELFARE	v	GOODWICK UNITED	0-1

ROUND 5

ABERTILLERY BLUEBIRDS	v	RHOS AELWYD	1-3
BRYMBO	v	GREENFIELD	2-4
BUCKLEY TOWN	v	GARDEN VILLAGE	2-1
CONWY BOROUGH	v	LLANFAIR UNITED	5-4
GOODWICK UNITED	v	PENYDARREN BOYS & GIRLS	1-1
LLANGEFNI TOWN	v	HAKIN UNITED	3-1
LLANRUG UNITED	v	CHIRK AAA	2-2, HWp
MYNYDD ISA SPARTANS	v	GRANGE ALBION	1-3

QUARTER FINALS

CONWY BOROUGH	v	GRANGE ALBION	7-1
LLANRUG UNITED	v	GREENFIELD	2-5
PENYDARREN BOYS & GIRLS	v	LLANGEFNI TOWN	2-0
RHOS AELWYD	v	BUCKLEY TOWN	1-0

SEMI FINALS

GREENFIELD	v	RHOS AELWYD	2-3
PENYDARREN BOYS & GIRLS	v	CONWY BOROUGH	0-3

FINAL

RHOS AELWYD	v	CONWY BOROUGH	1-4

ENGLAND C

RESULTS 2017-18

8 November 2017 - International Challenge Trophy Final - Ziar nad Hronon Stadium, Slovakia.

SOLVAKIA U21	v	ENGLAND C	4-0

Orsula, Ivan, Fasko, Herc   *Cartwright (Red Card 44)*

England: *Grant Smith* (Boreham Wood) - Sub 82 *Brandon Hall* (Kidderminster Harriers), *Andrew Cartwright* (Blyth Spartans), *David Ferguson* (York City), *Louis John* (Sutton United), *Alex Wynter* (Maidstone United), *Jake Gallagher* (Aldershot Town) - Sub 67 *Jack Powell* (Ebbsfleet United), *Sam Barratt* (Maidenhead United) - Sub 46 *Johnson, Ryan Croasdale* (Kidderminster Harriers), *Morgan Ferrier* (Dagenham & Redbridge), *Joshua Rees* (Bromley) - Sub 46 *Joseph Ward* (Woking), *Fejiri Okenabirhie* (Dagenham & Redbridge) - Sub 76 *Oladapo Afolayan* (Solihull Moors).

20 March 2018 - International National Game - Jenner Park, Barry, Wales.

WALES C	v	ENGLAND C	2-3

Jones, Venables   *Okenabirhie 10, 53, 75*

England: *Grant Smith* (Boreham Wood) - Sub 81 *James Montgomery* (Gateshead), *Sam Ling* (Leyton Orient), *Fraser Horsfall* (Kidderminster Harriers) - Sub 73 *James Jones* (Chester), *Joshua Stanton* (Woking), *Daniel Jones* (Barrow), *Robert Ramshaw* (Spennymoor Town) - Sub 62 *Charlee Adams* (Dagenham & Redbridge), *Ryan Croasdale* (Kidderminster Harriers), *Mitchell Pinnock* (Dover Athletic), *James Hardy* (AFC Flylde), *Daniel Maguire* (Blyth Spartans) - Sub 77 *Jason Gilchrist* (Southport), *Fejiri Okenabirhie* (Dagenham & Redbridge FC) - Sub 81 *Samuel Barratt* (Maidenhead United).

27 May 2018 - International National Game - Whitehall Stadium, Dublin, Ireland.

REPUBLIC OF IRELAND	v	ENGLAND C	4-2

Stritch 15, Murphy 46, Hayes 81, 86   *Pennell 39, Walker 58*

England: **England C:** *Thomas McHale* (Truro City) - Sub 46 *Euan Van der Vliet* (St Paul's Jersey), *Sam Ling* (Leyton Orient) - Sub 56 *Alex Brown* (Sheffield FC), *Joshua Staunton* (Woking), *Fraser Horsfall* (Kidderminster Harriers), *Luke Pennell* (Dagenham & Redbridge), *Cavaghn Miley* (Eastleigh), *Charlee Adams* (Dagenham & Redbridge) - Sub 76 *Josef Wheatley* (Darlington), *Thomas Wright* (Sutton United) - Sub 67 *Thomas Crawford* (Chester), *Joshua Koroma* (Leyton Orient) - sub 46 *Thomas Walker* (Salford City), *Fejiri Okenabirhie* (Dagenham & Redbridge FC), *Kyjuan Marsh-Brown* (Whitehawk).

GOALSCORERS 1979 - 2018

13 GOALS...
Carter, Mark

7 GOALS...
Cole, Mitchell

6 GOALS...
Ashford, Noel

5 GOALS...
Davison, Jon
Williams, Colin

4 GOALS...
Culpin, Paul
D'Sane, Roscoe
Johnson, Jeff
Mackhail-Smith, Craig
Norwood, James

3 GOALS...
Adamson, David
Guinan, Steve
Grayson, Neil
Hatch, Liam
Kirk, Jackson
Morison, Steve
Morrison, Michael
Okenabirhie, Fejiri (Hatrick)
Opponents
Taylor, Matt
Watkins, Dale

2 GOALS...
Alford, Carl
Barnes-Homer, Matthew
Barrett, Keith
Bishop, Andrew
Burgess, Andrew
Casey, Kim
Cordice, Neil
Elding, Anthony
Gray, Andre
Hayles, Barry
Hill, Kenny
Howell, David
John, Louis
McQueen, Darren
Mutrie, Les
Patmore, Warren
Pearson, Matty
Richards, Justin
Seddon, Gareth
Southam, Glen
Watson, John
Weatherstone, Simon
Whitbread, Barry
Yiadom, Andy

1 GOAL...
Agana, Tony
Anderson, Dale
Ashton, John
Beautyman, Harry
Benson, Paul
Berry
Blackburn, Chris
Boardman, Jon
Bogle, Omar
Bolton, Jimmy
Boyd, George
Bradshaw, Mark
Briscoe, Louis
Brown, Paul
Browne, Corey
Carey-Bertram, Daniel
Carr, Michael
Cavell, Paul
Charles, Lee
Charley, Ken
Charnock, Kieran
Constable, James
Crittenden, Nick
Davies, Paul
Day, Matt
Densmore, Shaun
Drummond, Stewart
Fleming, Andrew
Franks, Franks
Furlong, Paul

Grant, John
Guthrie, Kurtis
Harrad, Shaun
Hine, Mark
Holland, Jack
Holroyd, Chris
Humphreys, Delwyn
Howells, Jake
Jackson, Kayden
Jackson, Marlon
James, Kingsley
Jennings, Connor
Kennedy, John
Kerr, Scott
Kimmins, Ged
King, Simon
Leworthy, David
Lowe, Jamal
McDougald, Junior
McFadzean, Kyle
Mayes, Bobby
Moore, Neil
Moore, Luke
Newton, Sean
O'Keefe, Eamon
Oli, Dennis
Penn, Russell
Pennell, Luke
Pitcher, Geoff
Porter, Max

Ricketts, Sam
Robbins, Terry
Roberts, Jordan
Robinson, Mark
Roddis, Nick
Rodgers, Luke
Rodman, Alex
Rogers, Paul
Ryan, Tim
Sarcevic, Antoni
Sellars, Neil
Shaw, John
Sheldon, Gareth
Simpson, Josh
Sinclair, Dean
Smith, Ian
Smith, Ossie
Spencer, Scott
Stansfield, Adam
Stephens, Mickey
Stott, Steve
Taylor, Steve
Thurgood, Stuart
Tubbs, Matthew
Venables, David
Walker, Thomas
Watkins, Adam
Way, Darren
Webb, Paul
Whitehouse, Elliott
Wilcox, Russ

ENGLAND'S RESULTS 1979 - 2018

BARBADOS
02.06.08	Bridgetown	2 - 0

BELGIUM
11.02.03	KV Ostend	1 - 3
04.11.03	Darlington	2 - 2
15.11.05	FC Racing Jets	2 - 0
19.05.09	Oxford United	0 - 1
09.02.11	Luton Town	1 - 0
12.09.12	Gemeentelijk Sportstadion	2 - 1

BERMUDA
04.06.13	Hamilton	6 - 1

BOSNIA & HERZEGOVINA
16.09.08	Grbavia Stadium	2 - 6

CYPRUS U21
17.02.15	Larnaca	1 - 2

CZECH REPUBLIC UNDER-21
19.11.13	Home	2 - 2

ESTONIA
12.10.10		1 - 0

UNDER-23
18.11.14	FC Halifax Town	4 - 2
15.11.16	A Le Coq Arena, Tallinn	2 - 1

FINLAND UNDER-21
14.04.93	Woking	1 - 3
30.05.94	Aanekoski	0 - 2
01.06.07	FC Hakka	1 - 0
15.11.07	Helsinki	2 - 0

GIBRALTAR
27.04.82	Gibraltar	3 - 2
31.05.95	Gibraltar	3 - 2
21.05.08	Colwyn Bay	1 - 0
15.11.11	Gibraltar	1 - 3

GRENADA
31.05.08	St. George's	1 - 1

HOLLAND
03.06.79	Stafford	1 - 0
07.06.80	Zeist	2 - 1
09.06.81	Lucca	2 - 0
03.06.82	Aberdeen	1 - 0
02.06.83	Scarborough	6 - 0
05.06.84	Palma	3 - 3
13.06.85	Vleuten	3 - 0
20.05.87	Kirkaldy	4 - 0
11.04.95	Aalsmeer	0 - 0
02.04.96	Irthlingborough	3 - 1
18.04.97	Appingedam	0 - 0
03.03.98	Crawley	2 - 1
30.03.99	Genemuiden	1 - 1
21.03.00	Northwich	1 - 0
22.03.01	Wihemina FC	3 - 0
24.04.02	Yeovil Town	1 - 0
25.03.03	BV Sparta 25	0 - 0
16.02.05	Woking	3 - 0
29.11.06	Burton Albion	4 - 1

HUNGARY
15.09.09	Szekesfehervar	1 - 1
28.05.14	Budapest	2 - 4

IRAQ
27.05.04	Macclesfield	1 - 5

IRISH PREMIER LEAGUE XI
13.02.07	Glenavon FC	1 - 3

ITALY
03.06.80	Zeist	2 - 0
13.06.81	Montecatini	1 - 1
01.06.82	Aberdeen	0 - 0
31.05.83	Scarborough	2 - 0
09.06.84	Reggio Emilia	0 - 1
11.06.85	Houten	2 - 2
18.05.87	Dunfermline	1 - 2
29.01.89	La Spezia	1 - 1
25.02.90	Solerno	0 - 2
05.03.91	Kettering	0 - 0
01.03.99	Hayes	4 - 1
01.03.00	Padova	1 - 1
20.11.02	AC Cremonese	3 - 2
11.02.04	Shrewsbury	1 - 4
10.11.04	US Ivrea FC	1 - 0
15.02.06	Cambridge United	3 - 1
12.11.08	Benevento	2 - 2
28.02.12	Fleetwood Town	1 - 1

JORDAN UNDER-23
04.03.14	Jordan	1 - 0

LATVIA UNDER-23
10.09.13	Latvia	0 - 1

MALTA UNDER-21
17.02.09	Malta	4 - 0

NORWAY UNDER-21
01.06.94	Slemmestad	1 - 2

PANJAB
28.05.17	Solihull Moors	1 - 2

POLAND
17.11.09	Gradiszk Wielpolski	2 - 1

PORTUGAL
19.05.11	Sixfields Stadium	0 - 1

REPUBLIC OF IRELAND
24.05.86	Kidderminster	2 - 1
26.05.86	Nuneaton	2 - 0
25.05.90	Dublin	2 - 1
27.05.90	Cork	3 - 0
27.02.96	Kidderminster	4 - 0
25.02.97	Dublin	0 - 2
16.05.02	Boston	1 - 2
20.05.03	Merthyr Tydfil	4 - 0
18.05.04	Deverondale	2 - 3
24.05.05	Cork	1 - 0
23.05.06	Eastbourne Boro'	2 - 0
22.05.07	Clachnacuddin	5 - 0
26.05.10	Waterford United	2 - 1

UNDER-21
01.06.15	Galway	2 - 1

AMATEURS
27.05.18	Whitehall Stadium	2 - 4

RUSSIA
05.06.12	Russia	0 - 4

SCOTLAND
31.05.79	Stafford	5 - 1
05.06.80	Zeist	2 - 4
11.06.81	Empoli	0 - 0
05.06.82	Aberdeen	1 - 1
04.06.83	Scarborough	2 - 1
07.06.84	Modena	2 - 0
15.06.85	Harderwijk	1 - 3
23.05.87	Dunfermline	2 - 1
18.05.02	Kettering	2 - 0
24.05.03	Carmarthen Town	0 - 0
23.05.04	Deverondale	3 - 1
28.05.05	Cork	3 - 2
27.05.06	Eastbourne Boro'	2 - 0
25.05.07	Ross County	3 - 0
22.05.08	Colwyn Bay	1 - 0

SLOVAKIA UNDER-21/23
24.05.14	Slovakia	0 - 1
05.06.16	Sutton United	3 - 4
08.11.17	Ziar nad Hronon Stadium	0 - 4

SPARTA PRAGUE B
21.05.14	Prague	2 - 2

TURKEY U23
05.02.13	Dartford FC	0 - 1
14.10.14	Istanbul	0 - 2

UKRAINE
22.03.16	Kiev	2 - 0

USA
20.03.02	Stevenage Boro.	2 - 1
09.06.04	Charleston USA	0 - 0

WALES
27.03.84	Newtown	1 - 2
26.03.85	Telford	1 - 0
18.03.86	Merthyr Tydfil	1 - 3
17.03.87	Gloucester	2 - 2
15.03.88	Rhyl	2 - 0
21.03.89	Kidderminster	2 - 0
06.03.90	Merthyr Tydfil	0 - 0
17.05.91	Stafford	1 - 2
03.03.92	Aberystwyth	1 - 0
02.03.93	Cheltenham	2 - 1
22.02.94	Bangor	2 - 1
28.02.95	Yeovil Town	1 - 0
23.05.99	St Albans	2 - 1
16.05.00	Llanelli	1 - 1
13.02.01	Rushden & Dia.	0 - 0
14.05.02	Boston	1 - 1
22.05.03	Merthyr Tydfil	2 - 0
20.05.04	Keith FC	0 - 2
26.05.05	Cork	1 - 0
25.05.06	Eastbourne Boro'	1 - 1
27.05.07	Clachnacuddin	3 - 0
21.02.08	Exeter City	2 - 1
24.05.08	Rhyl	3 - 0
15.09.10	Newtown FC	2 - 2

WALES C
20.03.18	Barry FC	3 - 2

RESULTS SUMMARY 1979 - 2017	P	W	D	L	F	A
Barbados	1	1	0	0	2	0
Belgium	6	3	1	2	8	7
Bermuda	1	1	0	0	6	1
Bosnia & Herzegovina	1	0	0	1	2	6
Cyprus U21	1	0	0	1	1	2
Czech Republic U21	1	0	2	0	2	2
Finland Under-21	4	2	0	2	4	5
Estonia	1	1	0	0	1	0
Estonia Under-23	2	2	0	0	6	3
Grenada	1	0	1	0	1	1
Gibraltar	4	3	0	1	8	7
Holland	19	14	5	0	40	8
Hungary	2	0	1	1	3	5
Iraq	1	0	0	1	1	5
Irish Premier League XI	1	0	0	1	1	3
Italy	18	5	8	4	24	22
Jordan U23	1	1	0	0	1	0
Latvia U23	1	0	0	1	0	1
Malta	1	1	0	0	4	0
Norway Under-21	1	0	0	1	1	2
Panjab	1	1	0	0	2	1
Poland	1	1	0	0	2	1
Portugal	1	0	0	1	0	1
Republic of Ireland	13	10	0	3	30	11
Republic of Ireland U21	1	1	0	0	2	1
Republic of Ireland Amateurs	1	0	0	1	2	4
Russia	1	0	0	1	0	4
Scotland	15	10	3	2	30	15
Slovakia U21/U23	3	0	0	3	3	9
Sparta Prague B	1	0	2	0	2	2
Turkey U23	2	0	0	2	0	3
Ukraine	1	1	0	0	2	0
USA	2	1	1	0	2	1
Wales	24	13	7	4	34	20
Wales C	1	1	0	0	3	2
TOTALS	**136**	**73**	**31**	**33**	**230**	**155**

MANAGERS 1979 - 2017		P	W	D	L	F	A	*Win%
1979	Howard Wilkinson	2	2	0	0	6	1	-
1980 - 1984	Keith Wright	17	9	5	3	30	16	53
1985 - 1988	Kevin Verity	12	7	2	3	23	15	58
1989 - 1996	Tony Jennings	19	10	4	5	27	18	53
1997	Ron Reid	2	0	1	1	0	2	-
1998 - 2002	John Owens	14	8	5	1	22	10	57
2002 -	Paul Fairclough	71	38	12	21	122	91	54

*Calculated for those who managed for 10 games or more.

the
FOOTBALL
ASSOCIATION
COMPETITIONS

CUP

TROPHY

VASE

YOUTH CUP

COUNTY YOUTH CUP

SUNDAY CUP

WOMEN'S CUP

FACEP - Rusthalls Michael Tubb goes past CB Hounslows Stef Nor. Photo: Alan Coomes

THE FA CUP
2017-18

FAC2P - Great save from Oualah (Leatherhead) from Akinfenwa (Wycombe). Photo: Keith Clayton.

EXTRA PRELIMINARY ROUND
SATURDAY 5 AUGUST 2017 - WINNING CLUBS TO RECEIVE £1,500

#	Home		Away	Score	Att
1	Penrith	v	West Auckland Town	2-1	213
2	Billingham Town	v	Pickering Town	0-3	134
3	Barnoldswick Town	v	Jarrow Roofing Boldon CA	3-1	207
4	Sunderland RCA	v	Garforth Town	3-1	122
5	Shildon	v	Morpeth Town	2-0	269
6	Consett	v	Bishop Auckland	3-3	394
	Bishop Auckland	v	Consett (9/8)	2-5	432
7	Washington	v	Dunston UTS	0-3	148
8	Bridlington Town	v	Billingham Synthonia	2-0	190
9	Newton Aycliffe	v	Chester-Le-Street Town	1-0	131
10	Seaham Red Star	v	Whitley Bay	1-1	180
	Whitley Bay	v	Seaham Red Star (8/8)	4-1	259
11	Thackley	v	Harrogate Railway Athletic	3-4	112
12	Guisborough Town	v	Stockton Town	4-2	256
13	Ashington	v	Sunderland Ryhope CW	1-0	211
14	Newcastle Benfield	v	West Allotment Celtic	1-0	102
15	Albion Sports	v	Nelson	2-0	78
16	Team Northumbria	v	Heaton Stannington	0-1	95
17	Marske United	v	North Shields	4-4	217
	North Shields	v	Marske United (9/8)	0-1	279
18	Litherland Remyca	v	AFC Liverpool	2-0	312
	(Live on BBC Sport)				
19	AFC Emley	v	Burscough (6/8)	0-3	306
20	Squires Gate	v	Ashton Athletic	0-4	102
21	Cammell Laird 1907	v	Maltby Main	4-1	102
22	Padiham	v	City of Liverpool	1-2	357
23	Pontefract Collieries	v	Alsager Town	1-0	91
24	Hallam	v	Bootle (6/8)	3-0	310
25	Runcorn Town	v	AFC Darwen	3-2	120
26	Northwich Victoria	v	1874 Northwich	2-2	510
	1874 Northwich	v	Northwich Victoria (8/8)	2-0	429
27	Widnes	v	Handsworth Parramore (6/8)	0-5	165
28	Congleton Town	v	New Mills	4-2	193
29	Irlam	v	Abbey Hey	1-2	204
30	Armthorpe Welfare	v	Liversedge	1-1	45
	Liversedge	v	Armthorpe Welfare (8/8)	5-3	91
31	Parkgate	v	Barnton	4-2	83
32	Athersley Recreation	v	West Didsbury & Chorlton	0-5	113
33	Charnock Richard	v	Penistone Church	3-4	254
34	Maine Road	v	Winsford United	3-2	165
35	Runcorn Linnets	v	Hemsworth MW	2-0	324
36	Hanley Town	v	Atherstone Town	4-1	181
37	Coventry United	v	Rugby Town	1-2	315
38	Sporting Khalsa	v	Stourport Swifts	2-2	57
	Stourport Swifts	v	Sporting Khalsa (8/8)	2-3aet	114
39	AFC Wulfrunians	v	Shawbury United	3-0	72
40	Wolverhampton SC	v	Haughmond	2-3	55
41	Tividale	v	Highgate United	1-1	104
	Highgate United	v	Tividale (8/8)	2-3	110
42	Walsall Wood	v	Whitchurch Alport	3-1	203
43	Coventry Sphinx	v	Boldmere St Michaels	0-2	117
44	Daventry Town	v	Worcester City	0-1	244
45	Wolverhampton Casuals	v	Malvern Town	7-0	82
46	Westfields	v	Bewdley Town	3-1	219
47	Coleshill Town	v	Wellington	6-2	82
48	Bromsgrove Sporting	v	Rocester	2-2	602
	Rocester	v	Bromsgrove Sporting (8/8)	0-3	196
49	Brocton	v	Cadbury Athletic	3-0	67
50	Kimberley MW	v	Blaby & Whetstone Athletic	2-4	101
	(tie awarded to Kimberley MW – Blaby & Whetstone Athletic removed)				
51	Oadby Town	v	St Andrews	1-1	189
	St Andrews	v	Oadby Town (8/8)	2-2aet	136
	(Oadby Town won 3-1 on kicks from the penalty mark – at Oadby Town FC)				
52	Birstall United	v	South Normanton Athletic	3-0	190
53	Bottesford Town	v	Long Eaton United	6-0	69
54	Leicester Road	v	Sleaford Town	2-1	54
55	Dunkirk	v	Leicester Nirvana	2-1	63
56	Kirby Muxloe	v	Barton Town	4-2	61
57	AFC Mansfield	v	Hall Road Rangers	2-1	70
58	Staveley MW	v	Loughborough University	2-1	160
59	Retford United	v	Quorn	1-1	170
	Quorn	v	Retford United (9/8)	3-0	153
60	Clipstone	v	West Bridgford	3-1	72
61	Heanor Town	v	Aylestone Park (4/8)	0-1	213
62	Worksop Town	v	Hinckley	1-2	435
63	Boston Town	v	Radford	2-2	81
	Radford	v	Boston Town (15/8)	2-2aet	107
	(Boston Town won 4-3 on kicks from the penalty mark)				
64	Rainworth MW	v	Shepshed Dynamo	0-1	95
65	Harrowby United	v	Grimsby Borough	0-3	75
66	Biggleswade	v	Wisbech Town	1-4	149
67	Swaffham Town	v	Rothwell Corinthians	3-1	80
68	Raunds Town	v	Yaxley	1-1	85
	Yaxley	v	Raunds Town (8/8)	4-2aet	70
69	Peterborough Northern Star	v	Deeping Rangers	2-3	92
70	Cogenhoe United	v	Godmanchester Rovers	3-0	64
71	Ely City	v	Holbeach United	0-2	114
72	Huntingdon Town	v	Newport Pagnell Town	1-4	72
73	Eynesbury Rovers	v	Thetford Town	3-2	93
74	Northampton Sileby Rangers	v	Harborough Town	0-5	72
75	Wellingborough Whitworths	v	Desborough Town	0-4	52
76	Fakenham Town	v	Wellingborough Town	0-2	85
77	Histon	v	Northampton On Chenecks	0-1	110
78	Potton United	v	Biggleswade United (4/8)	0-0	252
	Biggleswade United	v	Potton United (8/8)	1-2	142
79	Hoddesdon Town	v	Haverhill Rovers	1-2	76
80	Sawbridgeworth Town	v	West Essex	0-3	115
81	Enfield 1893	v	Haverhill Borough	1-2	41
82	Redbridge	v	Stansted	3-1	82
83	Takeley	v	Wivenhoe Town	3-1	86
84	Kirkley & Pakefield	v	Saffron Walden Town	1-2	98
85	Southend Manor	v	Wroxham	1-0	58
86	Framlingham Town	v	Wadham Lodge	0-0	246
	Wadham Lodge	v	Framlingham Town (9/8)	1-3	82
	(at Aveley FC)				
87	FC Broxbourne Borough	v	Tower Hamlets	1-1	58
	Tower Hamlets	v	FC Broxbourne Borough (7/8)	1-0	68
88	Barkingside	v	Stowmarket Town (6/8)	0-4	215
89	Ilford	v	Woodbridge Town	1-0	72
90	FC Clacton	v	Clapton	0-1	203
91	Hadleigh United	v	Sporting Bengal United	3-2	87
92	FC Romania	v	Waltham Forest	2-2	52
	Waltham Forest	v	FC Romania (15/8)	1-2	46
93	Hackney Wick	v	Long Melford	0-1	267
	(at Clapton FC)				
94	Felixstowe & Walton United	v	Brantham Athletic	2-7	252
95	Stanway Rovers	v	Gorleston	2-4	92
96	Hullbridge Sports	v	Ipswich Wanderers	5-1	70
97	St Margetsbury	v	Burnham Ramblers (6/8)	3-2	135
98	Great Yarmouth Town	v	Diss Town	5-0	176
99	Newmarket Town	v	Great Wakering Rovers	5-1	88
100	Walsham Le Willows	v	Basildon United	2-2	130
	Basildon United	v	Walsham Le Willows (8/8)	3-0	184
101	Welwyn Garden City	v	North Greenford United	2-4	160

EXTRA PRELIMINARY ROUND

102	Cockfosters	v	Risborough Rangers	1-1	120
	Risborough Rangers	v	Cockfosters (8/8)	2-2aet	131
	(Cockfosters won 4-2 on kicks from the penalty mark)				
103	Holmer Green	v	AFC Hayes	4-0	71
104	Lydney Town	v	Wantage Town	1-3	107
105	Langford	v	Hadley	1-9	63
106	Highworth Town	v	London Colney (6/8)	1-1	174
	London Colney	v	Highworth Town (8/8)	2-4	82
107	Stotfold	v	Berkhamsted	1-12	86
108	Woodley United	v	Tuffley Rovers	1-2	108
109	Southall	v	Harpenden Town	5-1	43
	(at North Greenford United FC)				
110	Flackwell Heath	v	Burnham (4/8)	5-0	202
111	Highmoor Ibis	v	Buckingham Town (6/8)	3-1	52
112	Fairford Town	v	Longlevens	1-1	104
	Longlevens	v	Fairford Town (8/8)	5-1	132
113	Edgware Town	v	Leverstock Green	1-1	68
	Leverstock Green	v	Edgware Town (15/8)	5-3	68
	(8/8 – tie abandoned due to serious injury to player, 2-3)				
114	Chipping Sodbury Town	v	Brackley Town Saints	3-1	161
115	Leighton Town	v	Oxhey Jets	4-0	72
	(at Berkhamsted FC)				
116	Windsor	v	Wembley	1-4	136
117	Brimscombe & Thrupp	v	Sun Sports	4-0	65
118	Royal Wootton Bassett Town	v	Crawley Green	1-2	89
119	Colney Heath	v	Tring Athletic	1-0	115
120	Ardley United	v	Baldock Town	1-3	52
121	Corinthian	v	Deal Town	2-2	71
	Deal Town	v	Corinthian (8/8)	4-1	120
122	Hassocks	v	Hollands & Blair	2-3	112
123	Sheppey United	v	AFC Croydon Athletic	3-2	263
124	Crowborough Athletic	v	Lingfield (4/8)	2-0	152
125	Sutton Common Rovers	v	Canterbury City	2-0	73
	(at Banstead Athletic FC)				
126	Newhaven	v	Peacehaven & Telscombe	0-0	504
	Peacehaven & Telscombe	v	Newhaven (8/8)	0-2	439
127	Colliers Wood United	v	AFC Uckfield Town	2-2	54
	AFC Uckfield Town	v	Colliers Wood United (8/8)	0-2	71
128	Chessington & Hook United	v	Lancing	2-2	101
	Lancing	v	Chessington & Hook United (8/8)	1-3	104
129	East Preston	v	Saltdean United	2-1	104
130	Epsom & Ewell	v	Banstead Athletic (6/8)	1-2	123
131	Hailsham Town	v	Redhill	1-8	86
132	Loxwood	v	Holmesdale	3-1	97
133	Tunbridge Wells	v	Beckenham Town	1-0	271
134	Walton & Hersham	v	Mile Oak	7-0	91
135	Sevenoaks Town	v	Broadbridge Heath	3-1	113
136	Hanworth Villa	v	Bedfont & Feltham	5-0	94
137	Glebe	v	Lordswood	1-0	102
138	Whitstable Town	v	Croydon	2-3	187
139	Worthing United	v	Steyning Town	2-4	128
140	Arundel	v	Pagham	0-4	150
141	Horley Town	v	Raynes Park Vale	5-1	83
142	Abbey Rangers	v	Cray Valley (PM)	1-3	60
143	Eastbourne Town	v	Bearsted	2-1	211
144	Spelthorne Sports	v	Chertsey Town	1-3	97
145	Rochester United	v	Erith Town	1-1	74
	Erith Town	v	Rochester United (15/8)	5-0	75
146	Erith & Belvedere	v	Wick	4-0	45
147	AC London	v	Crawley Down Gatwick	3-2	61
	(at Crawley Down Gatwick FC)				
148	Chatham Town	v	Littlehampton Town	1-1	202
	Littlehampton Town	v	Chatham Town (16/8)	2-1	158
149	Little Common	v	Eastbourne United	1-2	116
150	Rusthall	v	CB Hounslow United (6/8)	0-0	282
	(at Tunbridge Wells FC)				
	CB Hounslow United	v	Rusthall (8/8)	2-1	143
151	Haywards Heath Town	v	Bedfont Sports (8/8)	5-2	84
	(5/8 - tie abandoned after 45 minutes due to waterlogged pitch, 1-1)				
152	Horsham YMCA	v	Three Bridges	0-2	175
153	Bracknell Town	v	Cowes Sports (2.00)	3-0	276
154	Thatcham Town	v	Petersfield Town	5-0	122
155	Christchurch	v	AFC Portchester	1-5	82
156	Farnham Town	v	Fawley	3-2	71
157	Bashley	v	Fareham Town	2-4	160
158	Hamworthy United	v	Bemerton Heath Harlequins	4-1	100
159	Team Solent	v	Brockenhurst	2-5	71
160	Badshot Lea	v	Verwood Town (6/8)	1-1	101
	Verwood Town	v	Badshot Lea (8/8)	3-3aet	40
	(Badshot Lea won 3-1 on kicks from the penalty mark)				
161	Amesbury Town	v	Eversley & California	4-0	56
162	Camberley Town	v	Blackfield & Langley	0-0	98
	Blackfield & Langley	v	Camberley Town (8/8)	1-2aet	86
163	Whitchurch United	v	Laverstock & Ford	0-3	91
164	Ringwood Town	v	Ascot United	0-6	84
165	Binfield	v	Chichester City	4-3	101
166	Horndean	v	Melksham Town	2-1	68
167	Knaphill	v	Bournemouth	0-0	105
	Bournemouth	v	Knaphill (8/8)	0-2	52
168	Newport (IW)	v	Guildford City	2-2	174
	Guildford City	v	Newport (IW) (16/8)	3-0	153
	(at Godalming Town FC)				
169	Godalming Town	v	Westfield	2-1	96
170	Sholing	v	Alresford Town (4/8)	1-2	302
171	Lymington Town	v	Andover Town	0-2	85
	(at New Milton Town FC)				
172	Clevedon Town	v	Bitton	2-2	99
	Bitton	v	Clevedon Town (8/8)	0-1	60
173	Cadbury Heath	v	Longwell Green Sports	4-1	112
174	Plymouth Parkway	v	Portland United	0-1	229
175	AFC St Austell	v	Bridport	1-1	292
	Bridport	v	AFC St Austell (9/8)	1-0	212
176	Wells City	v	Cribbs	2-1	62
177	Shaftesbury	v	Exmouth Town	0-0	155
	Exmouth Town	v	Shaftesbury (9/8)	1-2aet	175
178	Shepton Mallet	v	Tavistock	1-4	88
179	Buckland Athletic	v	Bodmin Town	2-3	169
180	Cheddar	v	Willand Rovers	0-2	173
181	Wellington AFC	v	Hengrove Athletic	1-3	40
	(at Witheridge FC)				
182	Street	v	Hallen	1-1	94
	Hallen	v	Street (8/8)	1-4	65
183	Brislington	v	Sherborne Town	6-1	41
184	Bridgwater Town	v	Keynsham Town	5-2	211
185	Bradford Town	v	Odd Down	3-4	151
			Total Attendance		**31,169**

FACEP - It's a race for the ball during Briscombe & Thrupp's tie verses Sun Sports. Photo: Peter Barnes.

FACEP - Erith & Belvederes Max Williams takes on Eddie Beck (stripes) of Wick. Photo: Alan Coomes.

FACP - The Slimbridge player gets in a shot against Cinderford Town. Photo: Peter Barnes.

FACP - Billy Bennett of Sevenoaks Town fires in a shot past two Cray Wanderers defenders. Photo: Alan Coomes.

PRELIMINARY ROUND
SATURDAY 19 AUGUST 2017 - WINNERS RECEIVE £1,925

#	Home		Away	Score	Att
1	Albion Sports	v	Newton Aycliffe	2-1	75
2	South Shields	v	Bridlington Town	3-1	1420
	(Live on BBC Sport)				
3	Pickering Town	v	Clitheroe (20/8)	1-2	133
4	Sunderland RCA	v	Ashington	4-0	98
5	Guisborough Town	v	Shildon	1-5	204
6	Goole	v	Newcastle Benfield	1-2	143
7	Barnoldswick Town	v	Dunston UTS	2-1	193
8	Tadcaster Albion	v	Colne	0-1	200
9	Harrogate Railway Athletic	v	Kendal Town	1-1	107
	Kendal Town	v	Harrogate Railway Athletic (22/8)	4-1	105
10	Scarborough Athletic	v	Marske United	1-1	885
	Marske United	v	Scarborough Athletic (22/8)	1-2aet	415
11	Consett	v	Heaton Stannington	4-0	349
12	Penrith	v	Whitley Bay	1-1	221
	Whitley Bay	v	Penrith (22/8)	3-1	351
13	Abbey Hey	v	Maine Road	2-2	134
	Maine Road	v	Abbey Hey (28/8)	1-2	189
	(21/8 – tie abandoned after 99 mins due to serious injury to player, 1-1)				
14	Sheffield	v	Ossett Town	0-2	229
15	Penistone Church	v	Litherland Remyca	2-0	208
16	Bamber Bridge	v	Brighouse Town	3-2	220
17	Hallam	v	Atherton Collieries (20/8)	1-4	302
18	Frickley Athletic	v	Runcorn Town	2-1	188
19	Ramsbottom United	v	Liversedge	2-3	202
20	Pontefract Collieries	v	Skelmersdale United	1-2	99
21	Ashton Athletic	v	Runcorn Linnets	4-2	201
22	Parkgate	v	Handsworth Parramore	2-4	116
23	Trafford	v	Kidsgrove Athletic	2-2	197
	Kidsgrove Athletic	v	Trafford (23/8)	2-0	164
24	Prescot Cables	v	City of Liverpool (18/8)	2-2	973
	City of Liverpool	v	Prescot Cables (22/8)	8-2	956
25	1874 Northwich	v	West Didsbury & Chorlton	3-3	247
	West Didsbury & Chorlton	v	1874 Northwich (22/8)	1-3	304
26	Glossop North End	v	Mossley	0-2	450
27	Hyde United	v	Congleton Town	4-2	332
28	Ossett Albion	v	Droylsden	3-4	89
29	Colwyn Bay	v	Stocksbridge Park Steels	3-0	207
30	Radcliffe Borough	v	Burscough	1-1	114
	Burscough	v	Radcliffe Borough (22/8)	0-3	92
31	Leek Town	v	Cammell Laird 1907	2-0	242
32	Sporting Khalsa	v	Market Drayton Town	1-1	64
	Market Drayton Town	v	Sporting Khalsa (22/8)	1-1aet	145
	(Market Drayton Town won 4-1 on kicks from the penalty mark)				
33	Alvechurch	v	Hanley Town	2-0	211
34	Walsall Wood	v	Tividale	0-1	162
35	Bedworth United	v	Haughmond	0-2	108
36	Rugby Town	v	Romulus	2-3	201
37	Bromsgrove Sporting	v	Coleshill Town	3-4	708
38	Wolverhampton Casuals	v	Boldmere St Michaels	2-2	55
	Boldmere St Michaels	v	Wolverhampton Casuals (22/8)	5-0	94
39	Worcester City	v	Chasetown (20/8)	1-1	572
	Chasetown	v	Worcester City (22/8)	2-0	266
40	Brocton	v	Gresley	2-0	99
41	Newcastle Town	v	Evesham United	1-1	123
	Evesham United	v	Newcastle Town (23/8)	2-3aet	235
42	AFC Wulfrunians	v	Westfields	1-1	87
	Westfields	v	AFC Wulfrunians (23/8)	1-0	157
43	Birstall United	v	Cleethorpes Town	0-3	216
44	Shepshed Dynamo	v	Kimberley MW	3-0	174
45	Kirby Muxloe	v	Dunkirk	0-2	50
46	Grimsby Borough	v	Leicester Road	4-1	73
47	Oadby Town	v	Loughborough Dynamo	1-3	139
48	Hinckley	v	Aylestone Park	4-1	172
49	Quorn	v	AFC Mansfield (20/8)	1-3	160
50	Staveley MW	v	Basford United	0-1	135
51	Boston Town	v	Carlton Town	3-2	56
52	Lincoln United	v	Belper Town	0-0	140
	Belper Town	v	Lincoln United (22/8)	1-4	142
53	Bottesford Town	v	Clipstone	4-1	53
54	Wisbech Town	v	Spalding United	2-2	266
	Spalding United	v	Wisbech Town (22/8)	0-2	303
55	Dereham Town	v	Corby Town	3-0	164
56	Cambridge City	v	Stamford (18/8)	1-0	236
57	Barton Rovers	v	Deeping Rangers	1-2	71
58	Yaxley	v	Harborough Town	5-3	68
59	Holbeach United	v	Northampton On Chenecks	6-1	98
60	Potton United	v	AFC Dunstable (18/8)	2-0	170
61	Newport Pagnell Town	v	Kempston Rovers	3-3	152
	Kempston Rovers	v	Newport Pagnell Town (22/8)	4-1	142
62	Arlesey Town	v	Desborough Town	3-1	80
63	Soham Town Rangers	v	Cogenhoe United	3-2	123
64	Eynesbury Rovers	v	Peterborough Sports	1-1	207
	Peterborough Sports	v	Eynesbury Rovers (22/8)	2-0	218
65	Wellingborough Town	v	AFC Rushden & Diamonds	0-4	513
66	Bedford Town	v	Swaffham Town	3-1	180
67	St Margaretsbury	v	Hullbridge Sports (20/8)	2-2	118
	Hullbridge Sports	v	St Margaretsbury (22/8)	1-1aet	104
	(St Margaretsbury won 5-4 on kicks from the penalty mark)				
68	Bury Town	v	Tilbury	1-2	233
69	Southend Manor	v	Gorleston	2-3	64
70	Bowers & Pitsea	v	Haringey Borough	0-2	174
71	Maldon & Tiptree	v	Waltham Abbey	5-1	73
72	AFC Hornchurch	v	Brentwood Town	2-0	309
73	Canvey Island	v	Witham Town	0-2	224
74	Clapton	v	Norwich United	2-0	122
75	Framlingham Town	v	Mildenhall Town	0-1	278
76	Haverhill Rovers	v	Heybridge Swifts	1-1	188
	Heybridge Swifts	v	Haverhill Rovers (22/8)	6-1	187
77	Newmarket Town	v	Ware	1-2	100
78	Tower Hamlets	v	Takeley	0-4	55
79	Brantham Athletic	v	Cheshunt	3-6	70
80	Stowmarket Town	v	Romford	1-1	106
	(at Ipswich Wanderers FC)				
	Romford	v	Stowmarket Town (23/8)	3-1	110
81	AFC Sudbury	v	Aveley	4-0	174

FAC1Q - Midfield action from Cinderford Town's match against Moneyfields. Photo: Peter Barnes.

FAC2Q - Phoenix Sports keeper Steve Phillips gets this shot from Glebes Jason Goodchild square in the face.
Photo: Alan Coomes.

FAC1Q - The Dunkirk defender gets up unchallenged to clear this AFC Mansfield attack. Photo: Bill Wheatcroft.

PRELIMINARY ROUND
SATURDAY 19 AUGUST 2017 - WINNERS RECEIVE £1,925

No.	Home		Away	Score	Att
82	Ilford	v	Haverhill Borough	1-1	82
	Haverhill Borough	v	Ilford (22/8)	5-2	115
83	Hertford Town	v	Hadleigh United	4-1	260
84	Great Yarmouth Town	v	Basildon United	1-0	163
85	Grays Athletic	v	Redbridge	2-0	174
86	Long Melford	v	FC Romania	1-2	84
87	Barking	v	Saffron Walden Town	0-0	76
	Saffron Walden Town	v	Barking (22/8)	3-4	343
88	Potters Bar Town	v	West Essex	4-1	121
89	Slimbridge	v	Cinderford Town	1-2	164
90	Flackwell Heath	v	Didcot Town	1-2	118
91	Baldock Town	v	North Greenford United (20/8)	3-1	120
92	Chalfont St Peter	v	Beaconsfield Town	2-2	87
	Beaconsfield Town	v	Chalfont St Peter (21/8)	3-1	127
93	Ashford Town (Middx)	v	Wembley	3-0	104
94	Colney Heath	v	Shortwood United	2-0	145
95	Kidlington	v	Wantage Town	1-0	109
96	Swindon Supermarine	v	Northwood	1-0	132
97	Hayes & Yeading United	v	Brimscombe & Thrupp	1-0	201
98	Leighton Town	v	Tuffley Rovers	2-3	118
99	Crawley Green	v	Berkhamsted (20/8)	2-3	76
100	Chipping Sodbury Town	v	Bishop's Cleeve	1-3	135
101	Leverstock Green	v	Aylesbury United	1-1	108
	Aylesbury United	v	Leverstock Green (23/8)	4-1	149
102	Southall	v	Hadley	2-4	37
	(at Hillingdon Borough FC)				
103	Aylesbury	v	Cirencester Town	2-1	72
104	Uxbridge	v	Thame United	0-4	85
105	Highworth Town	v	Marlow (20/8)	2-3	173
106	Hanwell Town	v	Longlevens	1-0	75
107	Highmoor Ibis	v	North Leigh	1-3	42
108	Cockfosters	v	Holmer Green	3-0	112
109	Pagham	v	Sittingbourne	1-1	124
	Sittingbourne	v	Pagham (22/8)	0-1	152
110	Hollands & Blair	v	Crowborough Athletic	1-4	155
111	Erith & Belvedere	v	Cray Valley (PM) (20/8)	1-4	98
112	Whyteleafe	v	Erith Town	1-1	107
	Erith Town	v	Whyteleafe (23/8)	3-3	94
	(Erith Town won 4-1 on kicks from the penalty mark)				
113	Carshalton Athletic	v	Walton & Hersham	1-1	263
	Walton & Hersham	v	Carshalton Athletic (22/8)	1-1aet	148
	(Carshalton Athletic won 5-4 on kicks from the penalty mark)				
114	Haywards Heath Town	v	South Park	2-0	114
115	Colliers Wood United	v	Shoreham	1-1	65
	Shoreham	v	Colliers Wood United (22/8)	3-1aet	78
116	Sutton Common Rovers	v	Eastbourne Town	1-2	101
117	Corinthian-Casuals	v	Hythe Town	1-1	115
	Hythe Town	v	Corinthian-Casuals (22/8)	1-3	278
118	Greenwich Borough	v	Three Bridges	4-1	74
119	Deal Town	v	Glebe	2-2	121
	Glebe	v	Deal Town (22/8)	3-0	140
120	Walton Casuals	v	Molesey	3-1	81
	(at Cobham FC)				
121	Redhill	v	Ashford United	1-3	178
122	Ramsgate	v	Hanworth Villa	3-1	183
123	East Grinstead Town	v	VCD Athletic	3-2	75
124	Cray Wanderers	v	Sevenoaks Town (20/8)	2-3	162
125	Banstead Athletic	v	Loxwood	6-3	89
126	East Preston	v	Thamesmead Town	0-8	89
127	Littlehampton Town	v	Eastbourne United (20/8)	3-2	177
128	Chipstead	v	Horley Town	2-0	105
129	Tunbridge Wells	v	Rusthall	3-1	241
130	Steyning Town	v	Phoenix Sports	0-5	89
131	Chertsey Town	v	Horsham	1-3	120
132	Herne Bay	v	Chessington & Hook United (20/8)	2-1	204
133	Lewes	v	Newhaven	3-3	446
	Newhaven	v	Lewes (22/8)	1-4	364
134	Sheppey United	v	Hastings United	0-2	397
135	Croydon	v	Faversham Town	0-0	110
	Faversham Town	v	Croydon (22/8)	2-1	187
136	AC London	v	Egham Town (18/8)	1-5	47
137	Bracknell Town	v	Winchester City	0-4	238
138	Fleet Town	v	AFC Totton	1-1	130
	AFC Totton	v	Fleet Town (22/8)	5-0	195
139	Andover Town	v	Wimborne Town	3-3	163
	Wimborne Town	v	Andover Town (22/8)	1-2	248
140	Godalming Town	v	Farnham Town	3-0	155
141	AFC Portchester	v	Amesbury Town	3-1	107
142	Hamworthy United	v	Ascot United	4-1	65
143	Binfield	v	Horndean	1-1	120
	Horndean	v	Binfield (22/8)	3-0	91
144	Brockenhurst	v	Hartley Wintney	1-5	133
145	Guildford City	v	Camberley Town (20/8)	4-0	163
	(at Godalming Town FC)				
146	Salisbury	v	Fareham Town	3-2	505
147	Badshot Lea	v	Moneyfields	0-3	56
148	Laverstock & Ford	v	Knaphill	2-4	84
149	Alresford Town	v	Thatcham Town	0-2	80
150	Portland United	v	Paulton Rovers	0-3	221
151	Barnstaple Town	v	Clevedon Town	1-0	119
152	Tavistock	v	Shaftesbury	2-1	105
153	Bideford	v	Wells City	6-0	281
154	Cadbury Heath	v	Yate Town	1-0	132
155	Bridgwater Town	v	Brislington	1-0	41
156	Hengrove Athletic	v	Bodmin Town	1-4	50
157	Willand Rovers	v	Bristol Manor Farm	2-1	100
158	Odd Down	v	Mangotsfield United	1-0	99
159	Taunton Town	v	Larkhall Athletic	3-0	368
160	Bridport	v	Street	3-1	210
			Total Attendance		**35,568**

FAC2Q - It's the Kettering player that connects with this corner to fire a header towards the Kidsgrove Athletic goal. Photo: Peter Barnes.

FAC3Q - The Cinderford 'keeper tips this Hampton & Richmond Borough chance over the bar. Photo: Peter Barnes.

FAC3Q - The Lancaster City striker tries to get the final touch under pressure from two Shaw Lane defenders and the goalkeeper. Photo: Peter Barnes.

FIRST QUALIFYING ROUND
SATURDAY 2 SEPTEMBER 2017 - WINNERS RECEIVE £3,000

#	Home	v	Away	Score	Att
1	Penistone Church	v	Whitby Town	3-2	496
2	Albion Sports	v	Barnoldswick Town	3-2	124
3	City of Liverpool	v	Nantwich Town (1/9)	1-2	1024
4	Warrington Town	v	Grimsby Borough	1-0	297
5	Ashton Athletic	v	Bamber Bridge	2-1	202
6	Kidsgrove Athletic	v	Clitheroe	3-2	156
7	Stalybridge Celtic	v	Farsley Celtic	2-1	289
8	Marine	v	Ashton United	1-3	324
9	Shaw Lane	v	Radcliffe Borough	3-1	183
10	Scarborough Athletic	v	Workington	1-0	794
11	Bottesford Town	v	Shildon	0-1	141
12	Cleethorpes Town	v	Atherton Collieries	1-2	196
13	Colne	v	Lancaster City	0-1	301
14	Ossett Town	v	Consett	2-1	279
15	Hyde United	v	Kendal Town	1-0	305
16	Droylsden	v	Colwyn Bay	4-3	174
17	Abbey Hey	v	Altrincham	3-3	371
	Altrincham	v	Abbey Hey (5/9)	2-1	520
18	Skelmersdale United	v	Handsworth Parramore	1-2	165
19	Buxton	v	Frickley Athletic	3-2	242
20	Whitley Bay	v	Newcastle Benfield	0-2	608
21	Sunderland RCA	v	Liversedge	0-0	176
	Liversedge	v	Sunderland RCA (5/9)	0-4	235
22	Mossley	v	1874 Northwich	2-2	355
	1874 Northwich	v	Mossley (5/9)	2-0	348
23	Witton Albion	v	South Shields	0-2	534
24	Halesowen Town	v	Basford United	0-3	359
25	Boston Town	v	Hednesford Town	2-0	157
26	Kempston Rovers	v	Wisbech Town	2-1	161
27	Loughborough Dynamo	v	Stourbridge	1-3	262
28	Market Drayton Town	v	Alvechurch	1-5	82
	(at Nantwich Town FC)				
29	AFC Mansfield	v	Dunkirk	4-0	130
30	Soham Town Rangers	v	Westfields	0-0	163
	Westfields	v	Soham Town Rangers (6/9)	1-0	202
31	Peterborough Sports	v	Stafford Rangers	3-4	284
32	Rushall Olympic	v	Potton United	1-0	139
33	Sutton Coldfield Town	v	Barwell	0-2	186
34	St Ives Town	v	Coalville Town	1-0	203
35	Grantham Town	v	Holbeach United	2-1	302
36	Haughmond	v	Matlock Town	3-2	236
37	Tividale	v	AFC Rushden & Diamonds	2-3	325
38	Lincoln United	v	Redditch United	0-1	114
39	Shepshed Dynamo	v	Leek Town	6-1	262
40	Romulus	v	Kettering Town (3/9)	0-3	249
41	Stratford Town	v	Newcastle Town	4-0	187
42	King's Lynn Town	v	Coleshill Town	4-1	817
43	Mickleover Sports	v	Hinckley	2-1	305
44	Boldmere St Michaels	v	Chasetown	0-3	359
45	Yaxley	v	Dereham Town	0-1	125
46	Brocton	v	Deeping Rangers	2-4	127
47	Cambridge City	v	St Neots Town (1/9)	3-1	312
48	Maldon & Tiptree	v	Hayes & Yeading United	3-3	91
	Hayes & Yeading United	v	Maldon & Tiptree (5/9)	4-3aet	201
49	Tilbury	v	Aylesbury United	0-1	115
50	North Leigh	v	Biggleswade Town	2-2	92
	Biggleswade Town	v	North Leigh (5/9)	3-2	113
51	Romford	v	AFC Hornchurch (3/9)	0-1	333
52	Baldock Town	v	Thame United (3/9)	4-3	161
53	Hendon	v	Wingate & Finchley	1-1	298
	Wingate & Finchley	v	Hendon (5/9)	4-2aet	266
54	Beaconsfield Town	v	Marlow	0-2	218
55	Colney Heath	v	Cockfosters	3-0	140
56	Berkhamsted	v	Slough Town	1-3	366
57	Clapton	v	Needham Market	0-3	143
58	Royston Town	v	Dunstable Town	2-0	234
59	Billericay Town	v	Didcot Town	5-0	1159
	(Live on BBC Sport)				
60	Bedford Town	v	Lowestoft Town	0-2	264
61	Ware	v	Witham Town	2-1	101
62	Thurrock	v	Harlow Town	1-1	159
	Harlow Town	v	Thurrock (5/9)	2-1	230
63	Hadley	v	FC Romania	2-3	125
64	Great Yarmouth Town	v	Chesham United	0-2	277
65	Hertford Town	v	Grays Athletic	1-1	315
	Grays Athletic	v	Hertford Town (6/9)	2-3aet	232
66	Haringey Borough	v	Hitchin Town	1-1	171
	Hitchin Town	v	Haringey Borough (4/9)	1-1aet	201
	(Haringey Borough won 3-2 on kicks from the penalty mark)				
67	Potters Bar Town	v	Bishop's Stortford	1-0	181
68	Gorleston	v	Barking	0-4	192
69	Arlesey Town	v	Heybridge Swifts	0-7	163
70	AFC Sudbury	v	Mildenhall Town	1-1	239
	Mildenhall Town	v	AFC Sudbury (5/9)	2-4	280
71	Aylesbury	v	Leiston	1-3	109
72	Hanwell Town	v	Brightlingsea Regent	4-1	142
73	St Margaretsbury	v	Kidlington	1-6	105
74	Cheshunt	v	Takeley	2-0	185
75	Haverhill Borough	v	Kings Langley	0-8	126
76	Enfield Town	v	Harrow Borough	2-1	421
77	Littlehampton Town	v	Chipstead (3/9)	2-2	229
	Chipstead	v	Littlehampton Town (5/9)	4-0	128
78	Ashford Town (Middx)	v	Corinthian Casuals	2-0	125
79	Phoenix Sports	v	Eastbourne Town	2-0	177
80	Ramsgate	v	Egham Town	3-3	204
	Egham Town	v	Ramsgate (5/9)	2-4	98
81	Margate	v	East Grinstead Town	3-1	458
82	Faversham Town	v	Tonbridge Angels	3-1	346
83	Crowborough Athletic	v	Sevenoaks Town	2-0	107
84	Dulwich Hamlet	v	Hastings United	3-1	1294
85	Tooting & Mitcham United	v	Merstham	2-0	256
86	Thamesmead Town	v	Lewes	3-0	104
87	Herne Bay	v	Walton Casuals	3-1	192
88	Metropolitan Police	v	Staines Town	3-2	153
89	Folkestone Invicta	v	Greenwich Borough	3-2	351
90	Dorking Wanderers	v	Worthing	3-2	281
91	Horsham	v	Ashford United	6-0	243
92	Haywards Heath Town	v	Tunbridge Wells	2-2	202
	Tunbridge Wells	v	Haywards Heath Town (5/9)	3-0aet	254
93	Banstead Athletic	v	Glebe	0-4	79
94	Carshalton Athletic	v	Pagham	5-3	225
95	Kingstonian	v	Shoreham (1/9)	3-2	218
96	Leatherhead	v	Cray Valley (PM)	6-0	283
97	Erith Town	v	Burgess Hill Town	0-3	102
98	Hereford	v	Godalming Town	8-0	1737
99	Banbury United	v	Tiverton Town	4-2	436
100	Bridport	v	Barnstaple Town	1-0	246
101	Gosport Borough	v	Bridgwater Town	1-0	250
102	Frome Town	v	AFC Totton	2-1	191
103	AFC Portchester	v	Dorchester Town	1-0	391
104	Farnborough	v	Salisbury	2-3	396
105	Odd Down	v	Weymouth	0-5	190
106	Tavistock	v	Taunton Town	2-2	380
	Taunton Town	v	Tavistock (5/9)	1-2	373
107	Merthyr Town	v	Willand Rovers	6-1	303
108	Tuffley Rovers	v	Swindon Supermarine	0-5	221
109	Horndean	v	Bodmin Town	0-2	68
110	Paulton Rovers	v	Winchester City	1-0	129
111	Guildford City	v	Knaphill	1-3	198
112	Basingstoke Town	v	Hartley Wintney	2-2	554
	Hartley Wintney	v	Basingstoke Town (5/9)	1-0	640
113	Bideford	v	Bishop's Cleeve	5-1	231
114	Hamworthy United	v	Thatcham Town	1-5	185
115	Cinderford Town	v	Moneyfields	2-1	116
116	Andover Town	v	Cadbury Heath	1-2	309
			Total Attendance		**36,688**

SECOND QUALIFYING ROUND
SATURDAY 16 SEPTEMBER 2017 - WINNERS RECEIVE £4,500

No	Home		Away	Score	Att
1	Salford City	v	York City	1-2	1350
2	Darlington	v	South Shields	0-3	1814
3	Southport	v	Bradford (Park Avenue)	0-3	496
4	Ossett Town	v	Atherton Collieries	1-0	244
5	Newcastle Benfield	v	Ashton United	2-1	149
6	Warrington Town	v	Hyde United	1-1	429
	Hyde United	v	Warrington Town (19/9)	2-0	433
7	Harrogate Town	v	Penistone Church	3-0	653
8	Spennymoor Town	v	Gainsborough Trinity	1-2	403
9	Handsworth Parramore	v	FC United Of Manchester	1-1	434
	FC United Of Manchester	v	Handsworth Parramore (19/9)	6-2	623
10	Albion Sports	v	Ashton Athletic (17/9)	0-4	203
11	Shildon	v	Altrincham	1-0	345
12	Scarborough Athletic	v	Sunderland RCA	2-0	932
13	Blyth Spartans	v	Shaw Lane	1-2	573
14	1874 Northwich	v	North Ferriby United (17/9)	1-0	439
15	Stockport County	v	Curzon Ashton	1-0	1922
16	Stalybridge Celtic	v	Chorley	1-3	551
17	Lancaster City	v	Droylsden	4-0	303
18	Stafford Rangers	v	Tamworth	1-0	782
19	Boston United	v	Haughmond	1-1	726
	Haughmond	v	Boston United (19/9)	0-5	768
20	Shepshed Dynamo	v	Nantwich Town	0-1	318
21	Deeping Rangers	v	Kidderminster Harriers (12.30)	2-4	696
	(Live on BBC Sport)				
22	AFC Mansfield	v	Rushall Olympic	0-0	110
	Rushall Olympic	v	AFC Mansfield (19/9)	1-2	114
23	Kempston Rovers	v	Hereford	0-4	429
24	Stratford Town	v	Redditch United	4-1	326
25	AFC Telford United	v	Barwell	2-0	541
26	Nuneaton Town	v	King's Lynn Town	3-1	613
27	Kettering Town	v	Kidsgrove Athletic	2-0	543
28	Basford United	v	Mickleover Sports	1-0	217
29	Alfreton Town	v	AFC Rushden & Diamonds	2-2	403
	AFC Rushden & Diamonds	v	Alfreton Town (19/9)	1-3	609
30	Westfields	v	Leamington	0-2	365
31	Grantham Town	v	Alvechurch	3-4	332
32	Buxton	v	Chasetown	4-1	314
33	Stourbridge	v	St Ives Town (17/9)	2-0	765
34	Dereham Town	v	Boston Town	1-2	246
35	Leiston	v	Crowborough Athletic	4-2	234
36	Concord Rangers	v	Tunbridge Wells	4-0	191
37	Braintree Town	v	Royston Town	2-2	256
	Royston Town	v	Braintree Town (19/9)	1-2	251
38	AFC Sudbury	v	Chipstead	3-0	169
39	Biggleswade Town	v	East Thurrock United	0-1	191
40	St Albans City	v	Cambridge City	3-3	561
	Cambridge City	v	St Albans City (18/9)	0-2	276
41	Horsham	v	Herne Bay	2-5	200
42	Hemel Hempstead Town	v	Wingate & Finchley	0-0	377
	Wingate & Finchley	v	Hemel Hempstead Town (19/9)	1-2aet	251
43	Lowestoft Town	v	Harlow Town	0-1	395
44	Metropolitan Police	v	Heybridge Swifts	2-2	84
	Heybridge Swifts	v	Metropolitan Police (26/9)	1-1aet	277
	(Heybridge Swifts won 4-3 on kicks from the penalty mark)				
45	Chelmsford City	v	Ramsgate	7-0	578
46	Ware	v	Leatherhead	2-5	149
47	Kings Langley	v	Margate	0-1	258
48	Thamesmead Town	v	Billericay Town (17/9)	1-1	433
	Billericay Town	v	Thamesmead Town (19/9)	5-0	774
49	Baldock Town	v	Aylesbury United	1-2	335
50	Hertford Town	v	AFC Hornchurch	1-2	308
51	Glebe	v	Phoenix Sports	2-2	224
	Phoenix Sports	v	Glebe (19/9)	1-1aet	183
	(Phoenix Sports won 5-4 on kicks from the penalty mark)				
52	FC Romania	v	Hayes & Yeading United (17/9)	2-2	168
	Hayes & Yeading United	v	FC Romania (19/9)	2-0aet	207
53	Kingstonian	v	Brackley Town	0-3	289
54	Eastbourne Borough	v	Carshalton Athletic	4-3	438
55	Folkestone Invicta	v	Tooting & Mitcham United	3-1	335
56	Cheshunt	v	Dorking Wanderers	1-3	170
57	Wealdstone	v	Faversham Town	4-0	414
58	Colney Heath	v	Burgess Hill Town	3-3	153
	Burgess Hill Town	v	Colney Heath (19/9)	3-0	255
59	Welling United	v	Haringey Borough	1-2	329
60	Dartford	v	Barking	3-1	652
61	Hampton & Richmond Boro	v	Potters Bar Town	1-1	392
	Potters Bar Town	v	Hampton & Richmond Boro (19/9)	0-3	179
62	Whitehawk	v	Oxford City	1-3	295
63	Marlow	v	Ashford Town (Middx)	0-2	161
64	Needham Market	v	Chesham United	2-0	166
65	Slough Town	v	Dulwich Hamlet	3-2	712
66	Hanwell Town	v	Enfield Town	0-0	210
	Enfield Town	v	Hanwell Town (19/9)	5-0	278
67	Havant & Waterlooville	v	Merthyr Town	2-1	296
68	Bodmin Town	v	Bideford (20/9)	1-1	260
	Bideford	v	Bodmin (26/9)	1-0	237
69	Bridport	v	Cadbury Heath	2-2	262
	Cadbury Heath	v	Bridport (20/9)	2-3aet	203
70	Gosport Borough	v	Swindon Supermarine	1-2	231
71	Bognor Regis Town	v	Weston Super Mare	2-1	397
72	Cinderford Town	v	Hartley Wintney	1-0	167
73	Tavistock	v	Frome Town	1-2	410
74	Weymouth	v	Chippenham Town	2-0	609
75	Banbury United	v	Thatcham Town	2-0	450
76	Bath City	v	Knaphill	6-0	497
77	Truro City	v	AFC Portchester	2-0	302
78	Salisbury	v	Poole Town	0-2	995
79	Paulton Rovers	v	Kidlington	3-2	155
80	Gloucester City	v	Hungerford Town	0-3	275
			Total Attendance		40,017

THIRD QUALIFYING ROUND
SATURDAY 30 SEPTEMBER 2017 - WINNERS RECEIVE £7,500

#	Home		Away	Score	Att
1	1874 Northwich	v	Ossett Town	2-2	387
	Ossett Town	v	1874 Northwich (3/10)	0-0aet	341
	(Ossett Town won 5-4 on kicks from the penalty mark)				
2	AFC Mansfield	v	Boston United	0-2	613
3	Stafford Rangers	v	AFC Telford United	1-1	1137
	AFC Telford United	v	Stafford Rangers (3/10)	4-1	869
4	Newcastle Benfield	v	Kidderminster Harriers	0-1	403
5	Nantwich Town	v	Nuneaton Town	3-1	479
6	Boston Town	v	Hyde United	2-3	410
7	Banbury United	v	Shildon	2-3	700
8	Scarborough Athletic	v	Stratford Town	2-2	1180
	Stratford Town	v	Scarborough Athletic (3/10)	1-4aet	498
9	Basford United	v	Kettering Town	2-3	525
10	Shaw Lane	v	Lancaster City	2-1	314
11	Buxton	v	Alvechurch	2-1	309
12	Stockport County	v	FC United Of Manchester	3-3	3034
	FC United of Manchester	v	Stockport County (3/10)	1-0	1688
13	Ashton Athletic	v	Chorley	0-1	602
	(Live on BBC Sport)				
14	Leamington	v	Gainsborough Trinity	0-0	459
	Gainsborough Trinity	v	Leamington (3/10)	2-0	380
15	Stourbridge	v	Alfreton Town	3-1	646
16	South Shields	v	York City	3-2	2806
17	Harrogate Town	v	Bradford (Park Avenue)	0-0	911
	Bradford (Park Avenue)	v	Harrogate Town (2/10)	0-2	393
18	Swindon Supermarine	v	Paulton Rovers	2-3	214
19	Enfield Town	v	Phoenix Sports	3-0	501
20	Hayes & Yeading United	v	Havant & Waterlooville	0-4	241
21	Hereford	v	AFC Hornchurch	2-0	2440
22	Slough Town	v	Poole Town	2-1	680
23	Brackley Town	v	Braintree Town	4-1	383
24	Concord Rangers	v	Dorking Wanderers	3-0	141
25	East Thurrock United	v	Harlow Town	2-2	222
	Harlow Town	v	East Thurrock United (3/10)	1-2	329
26	Chelmsford City	v	Weymouth	2-1	664
27	Cinderford Town	v	Hampton & Richmond Boro	2-3	233
28	Oxford City	v	Leiston	4-2	185
29	Margate	v	Herne Bay	2-0	1009
30	St Albans City	v	Bridport	2-1	683
31	Heybridge Swifts	v	Frome Town	2-1	244
32	Truro City	v	AFC Sudbury	4-1	359
33	Eastbourne Borough	v	Bognor Regis Town	0-2	762
34	Bath City	v	Hemel Hempstead Town	3-0	510
35	Needham Market	v	Dartford	1-6	379
36	Haringey Borough	v	Bideford	4-1	267
37	Folkestone Invicta	v	Aylesbury United	2-1	473
38	Hungerford Town	v	Billericay Town	1-1	507
	Billericay Town	v	Hungerford Town (3/10)	6-1	1024
39	Burgess Hill Town	v	Wealdstone	1-0	590
40	Ashford Town (Middx)	v	Leatherhead	1-2	277
			Total Attendance		**32,401**

FOURTH QUALIFYING ROUND
SATURDAY 14 OCTOBER 2016 - WINNERS RECEIVE £12,500

#	Home		Away	Score	Att
1	FC Halifax Town	v	Tranmere Rovers	1-3	1630
2	Solihull Moors	v	Ossett Town	1-1	415
	Ossett Town	v	Solihull Moors (17/10)	1-2	1176
3	South Shields	v	Hartlepool United	1-2	2887
4	Shaw Lane	v	Barrow (15/10)	2-1	864
5	Chorley	v	Boston United	0-0	1204
	Boston United	v	Chorley (17/10)	3-4aet	1132
6	AFC Telford United	v	FC United of Manchester	3-1	1451
7	Harrogate Town	v	Gainsborough Trinity	1-2	927
8	Nantwich Town	v	Kettering Town	1-1	760
	Kettering Town	v	Nantwich Town (17/10)	0-1	903
9	Buxton	v	Gateshead	1-2	653
10	Guiseley	v	Shildon	6-0	772
11	AFC Fylde	v	Wrexham	1-0	1390
12	Kidderminster Harriers	v	Chester	2-0	1896
13	Scarborough Athletic	v	Hyde United	0-2	2003
14	Stourbridge	v	Macclesfield Town	0-5	1152
15	Brackley Town	v	Billericay Town	3-3	741
	Billericay Town	v	Brackley Town (17/10)	2-1	1464
16	Dagenham & Redbridge	v	Leyton Orient	0-0	2529
	Leyton Orient	v	Dagenham & Redbridge (17/10)	1-0	2013
17	Eastleigh	v	Hereford	1-2	1345
18	Aldershot Town	v	Torquay United	1-0	1583
19	Bath City	v	Chelmsford City	0-0	878
	Chelmsford City	v	Bath City	1-0	645
20	Oxford City	v	Bognor Regis Town	1-0	406
21	Maidenhead United	v	Havant & Waterlooville	2-1	753
22	Haringey Borough	v	Heybridge Swifts	2-4	401
23	Woking	v	Concord Rangers	1-1	1004
	Concord Rangers	v	Woking (17/10)	1-2aet	382
24	Hampton & Richmond Boro	v	Truro City	0-2	784
25	Dover Athletic	v	Bromley	0-0	923
	Bromley	v	Dover Athletic (17/10)	3-0	828
26	Slough Town	v	Folkestone Invicta	1-0	926
27	Burgess Hill Town	v	Dartford	0-1	873
28	St Albans City	v	Boreham Wood	1-3	1418
	(Live on BBC Sport)				
29	Maidstone United	v	Enfield Town	2-2	1495
	Enfield Town	v	Maidstone United (17/10)	1-3aet	820
30	Margate	v	Leatherhead	1-2	879
31	Paulton Rovers	v	Sutton United	2-3	601
32	East Thurrock United	v	Ebbsfleet United	0-0	669
	Ebbsfleet United	v	East Thurrock United (17/10)	3-0	866
			Total Attendance		**44,428**

FIRST ROUND PROPER
SATURDAY 4 NOVEMBER 2017 - WINNERS RECEIVE £18,000

#	Home	v	Away	Score	Att
1	Stevenage	v	Nantwich Town	5-0	1436
2	Bradford City	v	Chesterfield	2-0	4747
3	Port Vale	v	Oxford United (3/11)	2-0	3443
4	Newport County	v	Walsall	2-1	2701
	(Live on S4C)				
5	Morecambe	v	Hartlepool United	3-0	2004
6	Yeovil Town	v	Southend United	1-0	2079
7	Peterborough United	v	Tranmere Rovers	1-1	3758
	Tranmere Rovers	v	Peterborough United (15/11)	0-5	4199
	(Live on BT Sport 1)				
8	Cambridge United	v	Sutton United (5/11)	1-0	3070
9	Forest Green Rovers	v	Macclesfield Town	1-0	1387
10	AFC Fylde	v	Kidderminster Harriers	4-2	1480
11	Luton Town	v	Portsmouth	1-0	5333
12	Shrewsbury Town	v	Aldershot Town	5-0	3859
13	Hereford	v	AFC Telford United	1-0	4712
14	Guiseley	v	Accrington Stanley (5/11)	0-0	1611
	Accrington Stanley	v	Guiseley (14/11)	1-1aet	1166
	(Guiseley won 4-3 on kicks from the penalty mark)				
15	Blackburn Rovers	v	Barnet	3-1	3710
16	Ebbsfleet United	v	Doncaster Rovers	2-6	2069
17	Leatherhead	v	Billericay Town (5/11)	1-1	1797
	Billericay Town	v	Leatherhead (16/11)	1-3	3400
	(Live on BT Sport 1)				
18	Boreham Wood	v	Blackpool	2-1	1041
19	Shaw Lane	v	Mansfield Town	1-3	1700
	(Live on BT Sport 1)				
20	Colchester United	v	Oxford City	0-1	1775
21	Plymouth Argyle	v	Grimsby Town	1-0	5137
22	AFC Wimbledon	v	Lincoln City	1-0	3394
23	Rochdale	v	Bromley	4-0	2241
24	Coventry City	v	Maidenhead United (5/11)	2-0	3370
25	Chorley	v	Fleetwood Town (6/11)	1-2	3526
	(Live on BT Sport 1)				
26	Carlisle United	v	Oldham Athletic	3-2	3900
27	Notts County	v	Bristol Rovers (3/11)	4-2	4288
28	Dartford	v	Swindon Town (5/11)	1-5	2705
29	Cheltenham Town	v	Maidstone United	2-4	2799
30	Woking	v	Bury (5/11)	1-1	1858
	Bury	v	Woking (14/11)	0-3	1513
31	Crewe Alexandra	v	Rotherham United	2-1	2597
32	Gillingham	v	Leyton Orient	2-1	3659
33	Hyde United	v	Milton Keynes Dons (3/11)	0-4	3123
	(Live on BBC Two)				
34	Gainsborough Trinity	v	Slough Town	0-6	1630
35	Solihull Moors	v	Wycombe Wanderers (5/11)	0-2	1545
36	Northampton Town	v	Scunthorpe United	0-0	2820
	Scunthorpe United	v	Northampton Town (14/11)	1-0	1880
37	Charlton Athletic	v	Truro City	3-1	4494
38	Wigan Athletic	v	Crawley Town	2-1	3288
39	Gateshead	v	Chelmsford City	2-0	732
40	Exeter City	v	Heybridge Swifts (5/11)	3-1	3004
			Total Attendance		125,980

SECOND ROUND PROPER
SATURDAY 2 DECEMBER 2017 - WINNERS RECEIVE £27,000

#	Home	v	Away	Score	Att
1	Woking	v	Peterborough United (3/12)	1-1	3032
	Peterborough United	v	Woking (12/12)	5-2	3022
2	Milton Keynes Dons	v	Maidstone United	4-1	4804
3	Newport County	v	Cambridge United (3/12)	2-0	2748
4	Wycombe Wanderers	v	Leatherhead (3/12)	3-1	3835
5	Port Vale	v	Yeovil Town	1-1	3316
	Yeovil Town	v	Port Vale (12/12)	3-2aet	1588
6	Shrewsbury Town	v	Morecambe	3-0	3184
7	Doncaster Rovers	v	Scunthorpe United (3/12)	3-0	5251
8	Slough Town	v	Rochdale (4/12)	0-4	1950
	(Live on BT Sport 1)				
9	AFC Wimbledon	v	Charlton Athletic (3/12)	3-1	3270
10	Stevenage	v	Swindon Town	5-2	1883
11	Mansfield Town	v	Guiseley (3/12)	3-0	4081
12	Gateshead	v	Luton Town (3/12)	0-5	1339
13	Bradford City	v	Plymouth Argyle	3-1	4957
14	Blackburn Rovers	v	Crewe Alexandra (3/12)	3-3	4472
	Crewe Alexandra	v	Blackburn Rovers (13/12)	0-1	2241
15	AFC Fylde	v	Wigan Athletic (1/12)	1-1	3351
	(Live on BBC Two)				
	Wigan Athletic	v	AFC Fylde (12/12)	3-2	3124
16	Gillingham	v	Carlisle United	1-1	3178
	Carlisle United	v	Gillingham (19/12)	3-1	2357
17	Notts County	v	Oxford City	3-2	5092
	(Live on BT Sport 1)				
18	Forest Green Rovers	v	Exeter City	3-3	2250
	Exeter City	v	Forest Green Rovers (12/12)2-1aet		
19	Fleetwood Town	v	Hereford	1-1	2567
	Hereford	v	Fleetwood Town (14/12)	0-2	4235
	(Live on BT Sport 1)				
20	Coventry City	v	Boreham Wood (3/12)	3-0	2985
			Total Attendance		84,112

THIRD ROUND PROPER
SATURDAY 6 JANUARY 2018 - WINNERS RECEIVE £67,500

#	Home	v	Away	Score	Att
1	Ipswich Town	v	Sheffield United	0-1	12057
2	Watford	v	Bristol City	3-0	13269
3	Birmingham City	v	Burton Albion	1-0	7623
4	Liverpool	v	Everton (5/1)	2-1	50427
	(Live on BBC One)				
5	Brighton & Hove Albion	v	Crystal Palace (8/1)	2-1	14507
	(Live on BT Sport 1)				
6	Aston Villa	v	Peterborough United	1-3	21677
7	AFC Bournemouth	v	Wigan Athletic	2-2	9894
	Wigan Athletic	v	AFC Bournemouth (17/1)	3-0	4709
8	Coventry City	v	Stoke City	2-1	14199
9	Newport County	v	Leeds United (7/1)	2-1	6887
	(Live on BBC Wales)				
10	Bolton Wanderers	v	Huddersfield Town	1-2	11574
11	Yeovil Town	v	Bradford City	2-0	3040
12	Nottingham Forest	v	Arsenal (7/1)	4-2	27182
	(Live on BT Sport 1)				
13	Brentford	v	Notts County	0-1	6935
14	Queens Park Rangers	v	Milton Keynes Dons	0-1	6314
15	Manchester United	v	Derby County (5/1)	2-0	73899
16	Exeter City	v	West Bromwich Albion	0-2	5638
17	Doncaster Rovers	v	Rochdale	0-1	4513
18	Tottenham Hotspur	v	AFC Wimbledon (7/1)	3-0	47527
19	Middlesbrough	v	Sunderland	2-0	26399
20	Fleetwood Town	v	Leicester City	0-0	5001
	(Live on BBC One)				
	Leicester City	v	Fleetwood Town (16/1)	2-0	17237
	(Live on BT Sport 2)				
21	Blackburn Rovers	v	Hull City	0-1	6777
22	Cardiff City	v	Mansfield Town	0-0	6378
	Mansfield Town	v	Cardiff City (16/1)	1-4	5736
23	Manchester City	v	Burnley	4-1	53356
24	Shrewsbury Town	v	West Ham United (7/1)	0-0	9535
	(Live on BBC One)				
	West Ham United	v	Shrewsbury Town (16/1)	1-0aet	39867
25	Wolverhampton Wanderers	v	Swansea City	0-0	22976
	Swansea City	v	Wolverhampton Wanderers (17/1)	2-1	8294
26	Stevenage	v	Reading	0-0	3877
	Reading	v	Stevenage (16/1)	3-0	4986
27	Newcastle United	v	Luton Town	3-1	47069
28	Millwall	v	Barnsley	4-1	5319
29	Fulham	v	Southampton	0-1	17327
30	Wycombe Wanderers	v	Preston North End	1-5	4928
31	Chelsea	v	Norwich City	0-0	23598
	(Live on BT Sport 1)				
	Chelsea	v	Norwich City (17/1)	1-1aet	39684
	(Chelsea won 5-3 on kicks from the penalty mark – Live on BBC One)				
32	Carlisle United	v	Sheffield Wednesday	0-0	7793
	Sheffield Wednesday	v	Carlisle United (16/1)	2-0	12003
			Total Attendance		710,011

FOURTH ROUND PROPER
SATURDAY 27 JANUARY 2018 - WINNERS RECEIVE £90,000

1	Liverpool (Live on BT Sport 2)	v	West Bromwich Albion (7.45)	2-3 53342
2	Peterborough United (Live on BT Sport 2)	v	Leicester City (12.30)	1-5 13193
3	Huddersfield Town	v	Birmingham City	1-1 13047
	Birmingham City	v	Huddersfield Town (6/2)	1-4aet 13175
4	Notts County	v	Swansea City	1-1 9802
	Swansea City (Live on BBC One)	v	Notts County (6/2)	8-1 7822
5	Yeovil Town (Live on BBC One)	v	Manchester United (7.55)	0-4 9195
6	Sheffield Wednesday	v	Reading	3-1 14148
7	Cardiff City (Live on BBC One)	v	Manchester City (4.00)	0-2 32339
8	Milton Keynes Dons	v	Coventry City	0-1 14925
9	Millwall	v	Rochdale	2-2 8346
	Rochdale	v	Millwall (6/2)	1-0 2790
10	Southampton	v	Watford	1-0 25195
11	Middlesbrough	v	Brighton & Hove Albion	0-1 20475
12	Wigan Athletic	v	West Ham United	2-0 14194
13	Hull City	v	Nottingham Forest	2-1 13450
14	Newport County (Live on BBC One)	v	Tottenham Hotspur (5.30)	1-1 9836
	Tottenham Hotspur (Live on BT Sport 2)	v	Newport County (7/2)	2-0 38947
15	Chelsea (Live on BT Sport 2)	v	Newcastle United (1.30)	3-0 41049
16	Sheffield United	v	Preston North End	1-0 15680
			Total Attendance	**370,950**

FIFTH ROUND PROPER
SATURDAY 17 FEBRUARY 2018 - WINNERS RECEIVE £180,000

1	Sheffield Wednesday (Live on BT Sport 2)	v	Swansea City	0-0 19427
	Swansea City (Live on BBC One)	v	Sheffield Wednesday (27/2)	2-0 8198
2	West Bromwich Albion	v	Southampton	1-2 17600
3	Chelsea (Live on BT Sport 2)	v	Hull City (16/2)	4-0 39591
4	Leicester City	v	Sheffield United (16/2)	1-0 28336
5	Huddersfield Town (Live on BT Sport 2)	v	Manchester United	0-2 17861
6	Rochdale (Live on BBC One)	v	Tottenham Hotspur (18/2)	2-2 8480
	Tottenham Hotspur (Live on BT Sport 2)	v	Rochdale (28/2)	6-1 24627
7	Brighton & Hove Albion	v	Coventry City	3-1 26966
8	Wigan Athletic (Live on BBC One)	v	Manchester City (19/2)	1-0 19242
			Total Attendance	**210,328**

QUARTER FINALS
SATURDAY 17 MARCH 2018 - WINNERS RECEIVE £360,000

1	Swansea City (Live on BT Sport 1)	v	Tottenham Hotspur	0-3 17498
2	Manchester United (Live on BT Sport 1)	v	Brighton & Hove Albion	2-0 74241
3	Leicester City (Live on BBC One)	v	Chelsea (18/3)	1-2aet 31792
4	Wigan Athletic (Live on BBC One)	v	Southampton (18/3)	0-2 17110
			Total Attendance	**208,568**

SEMI FINALS
WINNERS RECEIVE £900,000   RUNNERS-UP £450,000

SATURDAY 21 APRIL 2018 - at Wembley Stadium				
1	Manchester United (Live on BBC One)	v	Tottenham Hotspur (5.15)	2-1 84667
SUNDAY 22 APRIL 2018 - at Wembley Stadium				
2	Chelsea (Live on BT Sport 1)	v	Southampton	2-0 73416
			Total Attendance	**158,083**

THE FINAL
SATURDAY 19 MAY 2018   WINNERS RECEIVE £1.8m   RUNNERS-UP £900,000

CHELSEA	1	0	MANCHESTER UNITED
Hazard 22 (pen)			

AT WEMBLEY STADIUM ~ ATTENDANCE: 87,647

FAC4Q - Gateshead score against Buxton during their 2-1 victory.

Photo: Bill Wheatcroft.

EXTRA PRELIMINARY ROUND DRAW 2018-19
SATURDAY 11 AUGUST 2018 ~ WINNERS RECEIVE £2,250   LOSERS RECEIVE £750

1 Consett v North Shields	47 Ellesmere Rangers v Leicester Road
2 Thackley v Whitley Bay	48 Sporting Khalsa v Tividale
3 Hebburn Town v Dunston UTS	49 Long Eaton United v St Andrews
4 Ashington v Knaresborough Town	50 Sleaford Town v South Normanton Athletic
5 Goole v Morpeth Town	51 Heather St Johns v Kimberley Miners Welfare
6 Glasshoughton Welfare v Blyth	52 Kirby Muxloe v AFC Mansfield
7 Newcastle Benfield v Stockton Town	53 Clipstone v Barton Town
8 Selby Town v Whickham	54 Lutterworth Town v Heanor Town
9 Seaham Red Star v Heaton Stannington	55 Hinckley v Anstey Nomads
10 Team Northumbria v Shildon	56 Worksop Town v Shepshed Dynamo
11 Northallerton Town v Garforth Town	57 Rainworth MW v Dunkirk
12 Guisborough Town v Newton Aycliffe	58 Staveley MW v Boston Town
13 Barnoldswick Town v Billingham Synthonia	59 Teversal v Loughborough University
14 Washington v West Auckland Town	60 Oadby Town v Shirebrook Town
15 Sunderland RCA v Sunderland Ryhope CW	61 Bottesford Town v Radford
16 Bridlington Town v Harrogate Railway Athletic	62 Quorn v Belper United
17 Penrith v Albion Sports	63 Leicester Nirvana v Grimsby Borough
18 Bishop Auckland v Pickering Town	64 Cogenhoe United v Wisbech Town
19 AFC Darwen v Barnton	65 Wellingborough Whitworth v Harborough Town
20 Liversedge v Padiham	66 Deeping Rangers v Holbeach United
21 City of Liverpool v Silsden	67 Raunds Town v Eynesbury Rovers
22 AFC Liverpool v Ashton Athletic	68 Arlesey Town v Desborough Town
23 Widnes v Northwich Victoria	69 Thetford Town v Fakenham Town
24 Burscough v 1874 Northwich	70 Northampton Sileby Rangers v Ely City
25 Congleton Town v Eccleshill United	71 Godmanchester Rovers v Newport Pagnell Town
26 Prestwich Heys v Abbey Hey	72 Biggleswade United v Wellingborough Town
27 West Didsbury & Chorlton v Squires Gate	73 Histon v Peterborough Northern Star
28 Winsford United v Irlam	74 Daventry Town v Potton United
29 Penistone Church v Bootle	75 Biggleswade v Northampton On Chenecks
30 Hemsworth Miners Welfare v Runcorn Town	76 Swaffham Town v Yaxley
31 Hallam v Runcorn Linnets	77 Rothwell Corinthians v Pinchbeck United
32 Maltby Main v Athersley Recreation	78 Hullbridge Sports v Gorleston
33 Parkgate v Sandbach United	79 Wroxham v Saffron Walden Town
34 Litherland Remyca v Charnock Richard	80 Great Yarmouth Town v Hadleigh United
35 Maine Road v Handsworth Parramore	81 Walthamstow v Walsham Le Willows
36 Walsall Wood v Worcester City	82 Kirkley & Pakefield v FC Clacton
37 Highgate United v AFC Wulfrunians	83 Wodson Park v Hoddesdon Town
38 Boldmere St Michaels v Malvern Town	84 Tower Hamlets v Stanway Rovers
39 Atherstone Town v Hanley Town	85 Norwich United v Takeley
40 Stourport Swifts v Shawbury United	86 St Margaretsbury v Enfield 1893
41 Wednesfield v Rocester	87 Framlingham Town v Whitton United
42 Coventry United v Rugby Town	88 Southend Manor v FC Romania
43 Coventry Sphinx v Whitchurch Alport	89 Wivenhoe Town v Brantham Athletic
44 Haughmond v Wolverhampton SC	90 Stowmarket Town v Basildon United
45 Racing Club Warwick v Coleshill Town	91 Sporting Bengal United v Ilford
46 Romulus v Westfields	92 Haverhill Rovers v Haverhill Borough

93 Ipswich Wanderers v Baldock Town
94 Barkingside v Wadham Lodge
95 Cockfosters v Newmarket Town
96 Woodbridge Town v Clapton
97 Burnham Ramblers v West Essex
98 Stansted v Sawbridgeworth Town
99 Redbridge v Long Melford
100 Oxhey Jets v Wantage Town
101 Tuffley Rovers v Colney Heath
102 Winslow United v Easington Sports
103 Harpenden Town v Edgware Town
104 Hadley v Fairford Town
105 Brackley Town Saints v London Colney
106 London Lions v Wembley
107 Windsor v Highworth Town
108 Bishops Cleeve v Stotfold
109 AFC Hayes v Lydney Town
110 Flackwell Heath v North Greenford United
111 Tring Athletic v Berkhamsted
112 Southall v Leverstock Green
113 Holmer Green v Longlevens
114 Ardley United v Shortwood United
115 Holyport v Brimscombe & Thrupp
116 Abingdon United v Burnham
117 Crawley Green v Woodley United
118 Reading City v Chipping Sodbury Town
119 Leighton Town v Royal Wootton Bassett Town
120 Arundel v Chertsey Town
121 Sutton Common Rovers v CB Hounslow United
122 Broadbridge Heath v Shoreham
123 Langney Wanderers v Epsom & Ewell
124 Bearsted v Chichester City
124 Redhill v Horley Town
126 AFC Croydon Athletic v Rochester United
127 Spelthorne Sports v Peacehaven & Telescombe
128 Hassocks v Erith Town
129 Worthing United v Littlehampton Town
130 Little Common v Bedfont Sports
131 Crowborough Athletic v Hanworth Villa
132 Raynes Park Vale v Lingfield
133 AFC Uckfield Town v Glebe
134 Abbey Rangers v Newhaven
135 Cobham v Sheppey United
136 Fisher v Horsham YMCA
137 Loxwood v Hollands & Blair
138 Sevenoaks Town v Lordswood
139 Crawley Down Gatwick v Three Bridges
140 Eastbourne United v Hackney Wick

141 Cray Valley (PM) v Eastbourne Town
142 Croydon v Tunbridge Wells
143 Erith & Belvedere v Saltdean United
144 Haywards Heath Town v Lancing
145 Rusthall v Wick
146 East Preston v Balham
147 K Sports v Pagham
148 Deal Town v Whitstable Town
149 Broadfields United v Banstead Athletic
150 Chatham Town v Walton & Hersham
151 Corinthian v Canterbury City
152 Beckenham Town v Colliers Wood United
153 Hamworthy United v Team Solent
154 Melksham Town v Badshot Lea
155 AFC Stoneham v AFC Portchester
156 Newport (IW) v Amesbury Town
157 Knaphill v Sholing
158 Guildford City v Petersfield Town
159 Tadley Calleva v Baffins Milton Rovers
160 Bemerton Heath Harlequins v Cowes Sports
161 Andover New Street v Romsey Town
162 United Services Portsmouth v Andover Town
163 Horndean v Godalming Town
164 Hamble Club v Alresford Town
165 Farnham Town v Binfield
166 Brockenhurst v Christchurch
167 Bashley v Bournemouth
168 Fareham Town v Frimley Green
169 Ascot United v Camberley Town
170 Sandhurst Town v Lymington Town
171 Clevedon Town v Portland United
172 Westbury United v Cribbs
173 Hallen v Longwell Green Sports
174 Wells City v Shaftesbury
175 Bodmin Town v Keynsham Town
176 Cheddar v Bridgwater Town
177 Shepton Mallet v Willand Rovers
178 Bitton v Tavistock
179 Buckland Athletic v Pewsey Vale
180 Bridport v Wellington AFC
181 Hengrove Athletic v Plymouth Parkway
182 Saltash United v Odd Down
183 Brislington v Cadbury Heath
184 Bradford Town v Roman Glass St George

PRELIMINARY ROUND DRAW 2018-19
SATURDAY 25 AUGUST 2018 ~ WINNERS RECEIVE £2,890 LOSERS RECEIVE £960

1 Ashington or Knaresborough Town v Glasshoughton Welfare or Blyth

2 Bridlington Town v Northallerton Town or Garforth Town
or Harrogate Railway Athletic

3 Hebburn Town or Dunston UTS v Pontefract Collieries

4 Newcastle Benfield v Washington or West Auckland Town or Stockton Town

5 Thackley or Whitley Bay v Barnoldswick Town or Billingham Synthonia

6 Goole or Morpeth Town v Marske United

7 Consett or North Shields v Seaham Red Star or Heaton Stannington

8 Tadcaster Albion v Team Northumbria or Shildon

9 Clitheroe v Sunderland RCA or Sunderland Ryhope CW

10 Kendal Town v Selby Town or Whickham

11 Bishop Auckland or Pickering Town v Colne

12 Penrith or Albion Sports v Guisborough Town or Newton Aycliffe

13 AFC Liverpool or Ashton Athletic v Skelmersdale United

14 Ossett United v Mossley

15 Burscough or 1874 Northwich v Widnes or Northwich Victoria

16 Atherton Collieries v Colwyn Bay

17 Kidsgrove Athletic v Ramsbottom United

18 Stocksbridge Park Steels v Bamber Bridge

19 Prescot Cables v Winsford United or Irlam

20 Brighouse Town v Parkgate or Sandbach United

21 Prestwich Heys or Abbey Hey v Radcliffe

22 Droylsden v West Didsbury & Chorlton or Squires Gate

23 Hyde United v Sheffield

24 Maine Road v Congleton Town or Eccleshill United
or Handsworth Parramore

25 Frickley Athletic v Liversedge or Padiham

26 Hallam or Runcorn Linnets v Maltby Main or Athersley Recreation

27 Penistone Church or Bootle v Hemsworth Miners Welfare or Runcorn Town

28 Litherland Remyca v Leek Town or Charnock Richard

29 AFC Darwen or Barnton v Trafford

30 City of Liverpool or Silsden v Glossop North End

31 Stourport Swifts or Shawbury United v Sporting Khalsa or Tividale

32 Sutton Coldfield Town v Gresley

33 Alvechurch v Bromsgrove Sporting

34 Boldmere St Michaels v Racing Club Warwick or Coleshill Town
or Malvern Town

35 Bedworth United v Atherstone Town or Hanley Town

36 Romulus or Westfields v Newcastle Town

37 Walsall Wood or Worcester City v Coventry Sphinx or Whitchurch Alport

38 Highgate United or AFC Wulfrunians v Ellesmere Rangers or Leicester Road

39 Wednesfield or Rocester v Chasetown

40 Coventry United or Rugby Town v Evesham United

41 Haughmond or Wolverhampton SC v Market Drayton Town

42 Heather St Johns v Oadby Town or Shirebrook Town
or Kimberley Miners Welfare

43 Loughborough Dynamo v Bottesford Town or Radford

44 Staveley MW or Boston Town v Lutterworth Town or Heanor Town

45 Belper Town v Lincoln United

46 Worksop Town v Carlton Town or Shepshed Dynamo

47 Teversal v Cleethorpes Town or Loughborough University

48 Kirby Muxloe or AFC Mansfield v Rainworth MW or Dunkirk

49 Hinckley or Anstey Nomads v Clipstone or Barton Town

50 Leicester Nirvana v Long Eaton United or St Andrews or Grimsby Borough

51 Quorn or Belper United v Sleaford Town or South Normanton Athletic

52 Stamford v Peterborough Sports

53 Northampton Sileby Rangers v Cogenhoe United or Wisbech Town or Ely City

54 Deeping Rangers v AFC Rushden & Diamonds or Holbeach United

55 Wellingborough Whitworth v Cambridge City or Harborough Town

56 Corby Town v Dunstable Town

57 Biggleswade v Soham Town Rangers
or Northampton On Chenecks

58 Thetford Town or Fakenham Town v Godmanchester Rovers or
Newport Pagnell Town

59 Arlesey Town or Desborough Town v Kempston Rovers

60 Bedford Town v Dereham Town

61 Histon v Raunds Town or Eynesbury Rovers
or Peterborough Northern Star

62 Daventry Town or Potton United v Swaffham Town or Yaxley

63 Barton Rovers v Rothwell Corinthians or Pinchbeck United

64 Spalding United v Biggleswade United or Wellingborough Town

65 Waltham Abbey v Bury Town

66 Felixstowe & Walton United v Walthamstow or Walsham Le Willows

67 AFC Sudbury v Mildenhall Town

68 Heybridge Swifts v Burnham Ramblers or West Essex

69 Aveley v Potters Bar Town

70 Hertford Town v Tilbury

71 Stansted or Sawbridgeworth Town v Norwich United or Takeley

72 Redbridge or Long Melford v St Margaretsbury or Enfield 1893

73 Bowers & Pitsea v Barking

74 Coggeshall Town v Witham Town

75 Haverhill Rovers v Maldon & Tiptree or Haverhill Borough

76 Wivenhoe Town v Welwyn Garden City or Brantham Athletic

77 Haringey Borough v Tower Hamlets or Stanway Rovers

78 Cheshunt v Canvey Island

79 Southend Manor or FC Romania v Grays Athletic

80 Woodbridge Town or Clapton v Great Yarmouth Town or Hadleigh United

81 Stowmarket Town v Framlingham Town or Whitton United or Basildon United

82 Great Wakering Rovers v Barkingside or Wadham Lodge

83 Kirkley & Pakefield or FC Clacton v Ware

84 Cockfosters or Newmarket Town v Hullbridge Sports or Gorleston

85 Wroxham or Saffron Walden Town v Wodson Park or Hoddesdon Town

86 Brentwood Town v Sporting Bengal United or Ilford

87 Romford v Ipswich Wanderers or Baldock Town

88 Winslow United or Easington Sports v Reading City or Chipping Sodbury Town

89 Northwood v Holmer Green or Longlevens

90 Ardley United or Shortwood United v Abingdon United or Burnham

91 AFC Dunstable v Swindon Supermarine

92 Crawley Green or Woodley United v Aylesbury United

93 Kidlington v Marlow

94 Thame United v Tring Athletic or Berkhamsted

95 Bishops Cleeve or Stotfold v Flackwell Heath or North Greenford United

96 Didcot Town v Aylesbury

97 Brackley Town Saints v Hadley or Fairford Town or London Colney

98 Slimbridge v Oxhey Jets or Wantage Town

99 Chalfont St Peter v London Lions or Wembley

100 Beaconsfield Town v Uxbridge

101 Tuffley Rovers or Colney Heath v Cinderford Town

102 Harpenden Town or Edgware Town v Southall or Leverstock Green

103 Holyport or Brimscombe & Thrupp v Hayes & Yeading United

104 North Leigh v Hanwell Town

105 Cirencester Town v Windsor or Highworth Town

106 Leighton Town v AFC Hayes or Lydney Town or Royal Wootton Bassett Town

107 Tooting & Mitcham United v Redhill or Horley Town

108 East Grinstead Town v South Park

109 Walton Casuals v Broadbridge Heath or Shoreham

110 Beckenham Town v Langney Wanderers or Epsom & Ewell or Colliers Wood United

111 Crawley Down Gatwick v Phoenix Sports or Three Bridges

112 Arundel or Chertsey Town v Herne Bay

113 Sittingbourne v Bearsted or Chichester City

114 Abbey Rangers or Newhaven v K Sports or Pagham

115 Cobham or Sheppey United v Egham Town

116 Cray Valley (PM) v Ashford Town (Middx) or Eastbourne Town

117 Molesey v Lewes

118 AFC Croydon Athletic v Crowborough Athletic or Hanworth Villa or Rochester United

119 Raynes Park Vale or Lingfield v Spelthorne Sports or Peacehaven & Telescombe

120 Carshalton Athletic v Horsham

121 Ashford United v Fisher or Horsham YMCA

122 AFC Uckfield Town or Glebe v Broadfields United or Banstead Athletic

123 Greenwich Borough v Haywards Heath Town or Lancing

124 Chipstead v Corinthian or Canterbury City

125 Loxwood or Hollands & Blair v Hassocks or Erith Town

126 Hythe Town v Worthing United or Littlehampton Town

127 Whytleafe v Erith & Belvedere or Saltdean United

128 Corinthian Casuals v Croydon or Tunbridge Wells

129 Ramsgate v Chatham Town or Walton & Hersham

130 Sutton Common Rovers v Deal Town or Whitstable Town or CB Hounslow United

131 Cray Wanderers v Rusthall or Wick

132 Faversham Town v Eastbourne United or Hackney Wick

133 East Preston or Balham v Thamesmead Town

134 Hastings United v VCD Athletic

135 Sevenoaks Town or Lordswood v Little Common or Bedfont Sports

136 Thatcham Town v Bemerton Heath Harlequins or Cowes Sports

137 Salisbury v Hamble Club or Alresford Town

138 Farnham Town or Binfield v Brockenhurst or Christchurch

139 Moneyfields v Andover New Street or Romsey Town

140 Hamworthy United or Team Solent v AFC Totton

141 Sandhurst Town or Lymington Town v Fareham Town or Frimley Green

142 Fleet Town v Guildford City or Petersfield Town

143 United Services Portsmouth v Knaphill or Sholing or Andover Town

144 AFC Stoneham or AFC Portchester v Westfield

145 Tadley Calleva v Hartley Wintney or Baffins Milton Rovers

146 Wimborne Town v Newport (IW) or Amesbury Town

147 Melksham Town or Badshot Lea v Blackfield & Langley

148 Ascot United or Camberley Town v Horndean or Godalming Town

149 Winchester City v Bashley or Bournemouth

150 Bodmin Town or Keynsham Town v Brislington or Cadbury Heath

151 Bideford v Bristol Manor Farm

152 Bradford Town v Paulton Rovers or Roman Glass St George

153 Hallen or Longwell Green Sports v Bridport or Wellington AFC

154 Barnstaple Town v Wells City or Shaftesbury

155 Hengrove Athletic v Larkhall Athletic or Plymouth Parkway

156 Clevedon Town or Portland United v Bitton or Tavistock

157 Westbury United or Cribbs v Saltash United or Odd Down

158 Cheddar or Bridgwater Town v Yate Town

159 Shepton Mallet or Willand Rovers v Street

160 Buckland Athletic or Pewsey Vale v Mangotsfield United

FAC4Q - Goalmouth action from the Bath City v Chelmsford City tie. Photo: Peter Barnes.

FAC1P - Truros Billy Palfrey,Ed Palmer and Ben Gerring surround Charltons Ricky Holmes. Photo: Alan Coomes.

FAC1P - Harvey (Truro) gets his shot on target despite Konsa (Charlton). Photo: Keith Clayton.

FAC1P - Rowe (Fylde) scores the first goal past O'Connor (Kidderminster). Photo: Keith Clayton. (RIGHT) More First Round Proper action from the Forest Green Rovers v Macclsfield Town match. Photo: Peter Barnes.

THE FA TROPHY 2017-18

PRELIMINARY ROUND
SATURDAY 7 OCTOBER 2017 - WINNERS RECEIVE £3,000

#	Home		Away	Score	Att
1	Ossett Albion	v	Droylsden	1-1	139
	Droylsden	v	Ossett Albion (10/10)	1-1aet	120
	(Droylsden won 4-2 on kicks from the penalty mark)				
2	Ramsbottom United	v	Colwyn Bay	3-0	282
3	Bamber Bridge	v	Brighouse Town	4-2	304
4	Cleethorpes Town	v	Hyde United	2-1	297
5	Mossley	v	Skelmersdale United	3-1	138
6	Kendal Town	v	Radcliffe Borough	2-1	111
7	Stocksbridge Park Steels	v	Atherton Collieries	1-4	
8	Scarborough Athletic	v	South Shields	2-5	
9	Tadcaster Albion	v	Glossop North End	0-2	227
10	Ossett Town	v	Goole	3-0	154
11	Prescot Cables	v	Trafford	3-1	
12	Clitheroe	v	Colne	3-0	
13	Sheffield	v	Frickley Athletic	0-3	402
14	Romulus	v	Corby Town (8/10)	0-2	139
15	Newcastle Town	v	Soham Town Rangers	3-0	
16	Chasetown	v	Market Drayton Town	2-0	
17	AFC Rushden & Diamonds	v	Kidsgrove Athletic	1-3	
18	Basford United	v	Peterborough Sports	5-0	139
19	Stamford	v	Loughborough Dynamo	3-0	
20	Belper Town	v	Alvechurch	1-2	
21	Gresley	v	Bedworth United	0-1	
22	Leek Town	v	Lincoln United	4-1	
23	Thamesmead Town	v	AFC Hornchurch (8/10)	1-1	
	AFC Hornchurch	v	Thamesmead Town (10/10)	1-2	126
24	Greenwich Borough	v	Hanwell Town	0-1	80
25	Heybridge Swifts	v	Carshalton Athletic	2-0	
26	Hertford Town	v	Guernsey		
	(walkover for Hertford Town – Guernsey withdrawn)				
27	Kempston Rovers	v	Hythe Town	0-1	132
28	Potters Bar Town	v	Tilbury	4-0	89
29	Ashford United	v	Sittingbourne	0-3	325
30	Egham Town	v	Shoreham	7-1	68
31	Northwood	v	Maldon & Tiptree	2-5	
32	AFC Sudbury	v	Aylesbury United	2-2	
	Aylesbury United	v	AFC Sudbury (11/10)	1-2	
33	Waltham Abbey	v	Faversham Town	2-1	75
34	Romford	v	Hastings United (8/10)	0-1	130
35	VCD Athletic	v	Bedford Town	0-1	65
36	Haringey Borough	v	Whyteleafe	3-0	
37	Bowers & Pitsea	v	Dereham Town	2-2	173
	Dereham Town	v	Bowers & Pitsea (10/10)	1-4	180
38	Cray Wanderers	v	Horsham	8-0	
39	Chipstead	v	Barking	1-1	
	Barking	v	Chipstead (10/10)	2-1	67
40	East Grinstead Town	v	Lewes	2-4	203
41	Corinthian-Casuals	v	AFC Dunstable	2-0	153
42	Cheshunt	v	Herne Bay	3-0	144
43	Ramsgate	v	Bury Town	3-5	
44	Hayes & Yeading United	v	Barton Rovers	3-1	116
45	Brentwood Town	v	South Park	3-3	113
	South Park	v	Brentwood Town (10/10)	2-7	
46	Walton Casuals	v	Canvey Island	3-0	
47	Phoenix Sports	v	Chalfont St Peter	0-3	
48	Ashford Town (Middx)	v	Uxbridge	4-1	121
49	Grays Athletic	v	Norwich United	4-3	201
50	Aylesbury	v	Molesey	4-3	77
51	Marlow	v	Aveley	0-0	101
	Aveley	v	Marlow (9/10)	5-3aet	115
52	Taunton Town	v	AFC Totton	1-1	335
	AFC Totton	v	Taunton Town (10/10)	1-2aet	228
53	Mangotsfield United	v	Thame United	0-1	110
54	Bishop's Cleeve	v	Larkhall Athletic	0-1	
55	Shortwood United	v	Didcot Town	0-1	
56	Fleet Town	v	Yate Town	1-1	89
	Yate Town	v	Fleet Town (10/10)	2-1	
57	Evesham United	v	Cirencester Town (8/10)	2-3	236
58	North Leigh	v	Wimborne Town	1-3	85
59	Moneyfields	v	Bideford	4-2	185
60	Swindon Supermarine	v	Barnstaple Town	1-0	
61	Salisbury	v	Paulton Rovers	2-3	
62	Slimbridge	v	Hartley Wintney	0-1	106
63	Bristol Manor Farm	v	Cinderford Town	4-1	160
64	Kidlington	v	Winchester City	3-1	

FAT1Q - The Frome forward gets up highest against Shortwood United. Photo: Peter Barnes.

FAT1Q - Thamesmeads Bode Anidugbe shields the ball from Conor Witherspoon of Brightlingsea Regent. Photo: Alan Coomes.

FAT2P - Hereford's No.11 sends his header towards the Potter Bar goal. Photo: Peter Barnes.

FIRST QUALIFYING ROUND
SATURDAY 28 OCTOBER 2017 - WINNERS RECEIVE £3,250

#	Home		Away	Score	Att
1	Ashton United	v	Frickley Athletic	4-1	
2	Glossop North End	v	Matlock Town	3-2	310
3	Mossley	v	Lancaster City	0-1	174
4	Ossett Town	v	Droylsden	1-3	139
5	Altrincham	v	Clitheroe	3-0	
6	Farsley Celtic	v	South Shields	1-1	382
	South Shields	v	Farsley Celtic (31/10)	4-3aet	
7	Buxton	v	Cleethorpes Town	1-2	261
8	Warrington Town	v	Bamber Bridge	2-1	239
9	Shaw Lane	v	Ramsbottom United	2-2	183
	Ramsbottom United	v	Shaw Lane (31/10)	4-1aet	
10	Whitby Town	v	Marine	1-3	
11	Prescot Cables	v	Stalybridge Celtic	0-0	
	Stalybridge Celtic	v	Prescot Cables (31/10)	5-1	171
12	Kendal Town	v	Atherton Collieries	2-4	
13	Workington	v	Witton Albion	4-0	
14	Grantham Town	v	Halesowen Town	1-0	236
15	Rushall Olympic	v	Nantwich Town	2-0	
16	Hednesford Town	v	Mickleover Sports	1-0	
17	Newcastle Town	v	Kidsgrove Athletic	2-2	
	Kidsgrove Athletic	v	Newcastle Town (1/11)	2-1	189
18	Stratford Town	v	Bedworth United	2-1	176
19	Chasetown	v	Spalding United	2-1	
20	Stafford Rangers	v	St Ives Town	6-0	495
21	Barwell	v	Carlton Town	1-0	138
22	Stamford	v	Sutton Coldfield Town	3-0	
23	St Neots Town	v	Corby Town	3-2	275
24	Redditch United	v	Coalville Town	0-1	
25	Cambridge City	v	Alvechurch	0-2	171
26	Leek Town	v	Kettering Town	3-2	390
27	Stourbridge	v	Basford United	1-0	404
28	Hitchin Town	v	Cheshunt	5-0	
29	Dorking Wanderers	v	Ware	5-0	
30	Maldon & Tiptree	v	Walton Casuals	3-0	105
31	Billericay Town	v	Tooting & Mitcham United	3-1	
32	Leatherhead	v	Hythe Town	1-0	201
33	Sittingbourne	v	Merstham (2.30)	1-1	165
	Merstham	v	Sittingbourne (31/10)	0-2	126
34	Bishop's Stortford	v	Hanwell Town	4-0	
35	Needham Market	v	Arlesey Town	3-1	173
36	King's Lynn Town	v	Mildenhall Town	0-1	534
37	Hendon	v	Kings Langley	3-1	171
38	Aylesbury	v	Harlow Town	0-0	91
	Harlow Town	v	Aylesbury (31/10)	4-2	121
39	Barking	v	Beaconsfield Town	0-2	71
40	Brentwood Town	v	Bedford Town	0-0	
	Bedford Town	v	Brentwood Town (31/10)	2-4	145
41	Tonbridge Angels	v	Heybridge Swifts	3-3	
	Heybridge Swifts	v	Tonbridge Angels (31/10)	2-1	224
42	Bury Town	v	Chalfont St Peter	1-1	
	Chalfont St Peter	v	Bury Town (31/10)	0-3	81
43	Hastings United	v	Ashford Town (Middx)	3-4	
44	Metropolitan Police	v	AFC Sudbury	3-0	90
45	Dunstable Town	v	Lewes	1-4	102
46	Corinthian-Casuals	v	Hertford Town	3-1	150
47	Cray Wanderers	v	Grays Athletic	2-2	133
	Grays Athletic	v	Cray Wanderers (1/11)	0-2	152
48	Worthing	v	Lowestoft Town	3-0	
49	Staines Town	v	Margate	0-3	247
50	Waltham Abbey	v	Dulwich Hamlet	0-3	
51	Thamesmead Town	v	Brightlingsea Regent (29/10)	3-1	156
52	Royston Town	v	Enfield Town	2-0	
53	Potters Bar Town	v	Witham Town	3-0	83
54	Harrow Borough	v	Haringey Borough	1-1	103
	Haringey Borough	v	Harrow Borough (30/10)	1-0	
55	Leiston	v	Folkestone Invicta	1-1	191
	Folkestone Invicta	v	Leiston (31/10)	1-1aet	
	(Leiston won 6-5 on kicks from the penalty mark)				
56	Burgess Hill Town	v	Aveley	2-0	
57	Bowers & Pitsea	v	Egham Town	1-1	102
	Egham Town	v	Bowers & Pitsea (7/11)	3-5aet	
	(tie awarded to Egham Town – Bowers & Pitsea removed)				
58	Biggleswade Town	v	Wingate & Finchley	0-5	
59	Kingstonian	v	Thurrock (27/10)	3-3	225
	Thurrock	v	Kingstonian (31/10)	1-4	84
60	Hayes & Yeading United	v	Chesham United	0-3	182
61	Taunton Town	v	Merthyr Town	2-1	456
62	Dorchester Town	v	Basingstoke Town	2-1	290
63	Paulton Rovers	v	Cirencester Town	2-2	119
	Cirencester Town	v	Paulton Rovers (31/10)	0-4	109
64	Gosport Borough	v	Bristol Manor Farm	1-0	
65	Yate Town	v	Moneyfields	0-1	118
66	Thame United	v	Wimborne Town	5-0	99
67	Larkhall Athletic	v	Farnborough	1-3	
68	Swindon Supermarine	v	Hartley Wintney	0-3	157
69	Hereford	v	Weymouth	4-1	1552
70	Tiverton Town	v	Banbury United	2-2	248
	Banbury United	v	Tiverton Town (31/10)	3-2	230
71	Kidlington	v	Slough Town	1-4	201
72	Shortwood United	v	Frome Town	2-0	

SECOND QUALIFYING ROUND
SATURDAY 11 NOVEMBER 2017 - WINNERS RECEIVE £4,000

#	Home		Away	Score	Att
1	Lancaster City	v	Stratford Town	3-0	252
2	Kidsgrove Athletic	v	Grantham Town	0-2	242
3	Alvechurch	v	Coalville Town	1-5	213
4	Warrington Town	v	Ashton United	1-1	313
	Ashton United	v	Warrington Town (14/11)	2-2aet	163
	(Warrington Town won 4-2 on kicks from the penalty mark)				
5	Altrincham	v	Ramsbottom United	4-1	
6	Stalybridge Celtic	v	Rushall Olympic	3-2	240
7	Glossop North End	v	Leek Town	4-3	469
8	Stamford	v	Droylsden	1-2	
9	Chasetown	v	Workington	1-3	
10	Hednesford Town	v	Cleethorpes Town	1-1	369
	Cleethorpes Town	v	Hednesford Town (15/11)	2-1	225
11	Atherton Collieries	v	Marine	1-5	
12	St Neots Town	v	Stourbridge	2-3	323
13	Barwell	v	Mildenhall Town	0-1	176
14	Stafford Rangers	v	South Shields	3-1	955
15	Chesham United	v	Hitchin Town	3-1	297
16	Taunton Town	v	Beaconsfield Town	1-1	476
	Beaconsfield Town	v	Taunton Town (13/11)	1-1aet	86
	(Taunton Town won 7-6 on kicks from the penalty mark)				
17	Brentwood Town	v	Needham Market	3-1	
18	Hereford	v	Potters Bar Town	0-0	1368
	Potters Bar Town	v	Hereford (14/11)	1-2	230
19	Corinthian-Casuals	v	Wingate & Finchley	1-3	180
20	Lewes	v	Bishop's Stortford	2-0	568
21	Dorchester Town	v	Heybridge Swifts	1-2	319
22	Harlow Town	v	Dulwich Hamlet	2-1	363
23	Hendon	v	Burgess Hill Town	3-0	165
24	Ashford Town (Middx)	v	Kingstonian	2-2	183
	Kingstonian	v	Ashford Town (Middx) (13/11)	2-0	175
25	Maldon & Tiptree	v	Slough Town	1-4	179
26	Sittingbourne	v	Haringey Borough	1-1	134
	Haringey Borough	v	Sittingbourne (13/11)	1-0	
27	Thamesmead Town	v	Metropolitan Police	0-1	82
28	Royston Town	v	Leatherhead	3-2	219
29	Hartley Wintney	v	Gosport Borough	3-0	
30	Farnborough	v	Banbury United	3-3	269
	Banbury United	v	Farnborough (25/11)	2-3aet	
31	Thame United	v	Worthing	1-0	136
32	Paulton Rovers	v	Shortwood United	1-2	163
33	Margate	v	Egham Town (25/11)	2-0	
34	Billericay Town	v	Bury Town	6-2	
35	Dorking Wanderers	v	Leiston	4-1	
36	Moneyfields	v	Cray Wanderers (14/11)	1-1	
	Cray Wanderers	v	Moneyfields (22/11)	4-1	

THIRD QUALIFYING ROUND
SATURDAY 25 NOVEMBER 2017 - WINNERS RECEIVE £5,000

#	Home		Away	Score	Att
1	Brackley Town	v	Salford City	4-0	
2	York City	v	Coalville Town	3-1	1001
3	Cleethorpes Town	v	Spennymoor Town	1-2	306
4	Grantham Town	v	Chorley	3-4	361
5	Tamworth	v	Warrington Town	2-2	468
	Warrington Town	v	Tamworth (28/11)	3-0	223
6	AFC Telford United	v	Droylsden	4-2	
7	Darlington	v	Harrogate Town (24/11)	2-3	1127
8	Gainsborough Trinity	v	Stafford Rangers	2-0	299
9	Bradford (Park Avenue)	v	Stourbridge	1-1	
	Stourbridge	v	Bradford (Park Avenue) (27/11)	2-1	385
10	Boston United	v	Kidderminster Harriers	2-2	
	Kidderminster Harriers	v	Boston United (28/11)	2-0	604
11	Nuneaton Town	v	North Ferriby United	5-1	
12	Stockport County	v	Southport	2-2	
	Southport	v	Stockport County (29/11)	0-3	424
13	Blyth Spartans	v	Stalybridge Celtic	2-1	
14	Glossop North End	v	Workington	0-0	368
	Workington	v	Glossop North End (28/11)	5-1	351
15	Alfreton Town	v	Altrincham	0-2	329
16	Leamington	v	Curzon Ashton	3-1	249
17	Lancaster City	v	Mildenhall Town	1-0	242
18	Marine	v	FC United Of Manchester	1-0	778
19	Lewes	v	Truro City	1-3	619
20	Havant & Waterlooville	v	Dorking Wanderers	3-1	233
21	East Thurrock United	v	Shortwood United	3-1	
22	Taunton Town	v	Concord Rangers	3-2	
23	Hemel Hempstead Town	v	Bognor Regis Town	1-1	
	Bognor Regis Town	v	Hemel Hempstead Town (28/11)	1-0	
24	Farnborough	v	Hartley Wintney (29/11)	1-2	255
25	Oxford City	v	Hereford	1-2	
26	Hendon	v	Slough Town	1-1	251
	Slough Town	v	Hendon (28/11)	1-1aet	626
	(Hendon won 3-0 on kicks from the penalty mark)				
27	Braintree Town	v	Cray Wanderers	3-0	
28	Welling United	v	Weston Super Mare	0-1	
29	St Albans City	v	Poole Town	3-1	317
30	Metropolitan Police	v	Wingate & Finchley	0-1	63
31	Whitehawk	v	Chippenham Town	2-1	138
32	Haringey Borough	v	Thame United	3-1	
33	Brentwood Town	v	Dartford	1-2	296
34	Chesham United	v	Gloucester City	2-1	246
35	Hungerford Town	v	Billericay Town	0-2	
36	Hampton & Richmond Boro	v	Harlow Town	5-1	289
37	Bath City	v	Margate (28/11)	0-0	
	Margate	v	Bath City (5/12)	2-2aet	275
	(Bath City won 5-4 on kicks from the penalty mark)				
38	Wealdstone	v	Chelmsford City	1-1	
	Chelmsford City	v	Wealdstone (29/11)	1-2	367
39	Eastbourne Borough	v	Royston Town	1-1	277
	Royston Town	v	Eastbourne Borough (28/11)	2-2aet	189
	(Eastbourne Borough won 4-3 on kicks from the penalty mark)				
40	Kingstonian	v	Heybridge Swifts (26/11)	2-2	251
	Heybridge Swifts	v	Kingstonian (29/11)	5-1	187

FIRST ROUND PROPER
SATURDAY 16 DECEMBER 2017 - WINNERS RECEIVE £6,000

#	Home		Away	Score	Att
1	Solihull Moors	v	Tranmere Rovers (18/12)	2-0	215
2	Blyth Spartans	v	AFC Telford United (19/12)	1-0	476
3	Kidderminster Harriers	v	York City	2-1	1138
4	Chorley	v	Marine	1-3	708
5	FC Halifax Town	v	Macclesfield Town (9/1)	1-0	503
6	Spennymoor Town	v	Gainsborough Trinity (9/1)	4-4aet	360
	(Spennymoor Town won 5-3 on kicks from the penalty mark)				
7	Chester	v	AFC Fylde	2-2aet	886
	(Chester won 5-4 on kicks from the penalty mark)				
8	Wrexham	v	Harrogate Town	0-2	1370
9	Leamington	v	Stourbridge	0-1	404
10	Lancaster City	v	Stockport County	1-3	578
11	Warrington Town	v	Altrincham	0-0	545
	Altrincham	v	Warrington Town (19/12)	1-2	453
12	Gateshead	v	Guiseley+ (20/12)	2-1aet	290
13	Nuneaton Town	v	Barrow	0-1	415
14	Workington	v	Hartlepool United	1-0	771
15	Haringey Borough	v	Leyton Orient	1-2	1133
16	Dover Athletic	v	Eastbourne Borough	3-0	424
17	Wealdstone	v	Wingate & Finchley	1-0	371
18	Billericay Town	v	Havant & Waterlooville	3-1	705
19	Chesham United	v	Weston Super Mare (19/12)	0-2	193
20	Sutton United	v	Truro City	1-0	576
21	Woking	v	Maidenhead United	0-2	648
22	Whitehawk	v	St Albans City	1-2	143
23	East Thurrock United	v	Aldershot Town	4-0	252
24	Hendon	v	Bath City	2-1	256
25	Ebbsfleet United	v	Eastleigh	2-1	733
26	Hereford	v	Dagenham & Redbridge (17/12)	3-2	1518
27	Torquay United	v	Maidstone United	0-4	804
28	Hartley Wintney	v	Bromley	0-2	482
29	Braintree Town	v	Brackley Town	0-0	249
	Brackley Town	v	Braintree Town (19/12)	2-0	238
30	Taunton Town	v	Bognor Regis Town	1-4	508
31	Hampton & Richmond Boro	v	Heybridge Swifts	1-1	294
	Heybridge Swifts	v	Hampton & Richmond Boro (19/12)	3-2	
32	Dartford	v	Boreham Wood	1-1	607
	Boreham Wood	v	Dartford (19/12)	2-2aet	173
	(Boreham Wood won 3-1 on kicks from the penalty mark)				

SECOND ROUND PROPER
SATURDAY 13 JANUARY 2018 - WINNERS RECEIVE £7,000

#	Home		Away	Score	Att
1	Ebbsfleet United	v	Warrington Town	1-1	911
	Warrington Town	v	Ebbsfleet United (16/1)	2-0	334
2	Kidderminster Harriers	v	Stockport County	2-2	1348
	Stockport County	v	Kidderminster Harriers (16/1)	3-0	883
3	East Thurrock United	v	Chester	1-0	347
4	Bognor Regis Town	v	Leyton Orient	1-2aet	1371
5	Brackley Town	v	Barrow	0-0	512
	Barrow	v	Brackley Town (16/1)	0-2	430
6	Weston Super Mare	v	Workington	1-1	361
	Workington	v	Weston Super Mare (16/1)	2-1	576
7	Billericay Town	v	Stourbridge	3-2	1081
8	FC Halifax Town	v	Maidenhead United	1-4	802
9	Maidstone United	v	Heybridge Swifts	2-1	1276
10	Dover Athletic	v	Marine	4-3	565
11	Gateshead	v	Boreham Wood	3-3	284
	Boreham Wood	v	Gateshead (16/1)	1-2	183
12	Wealdstone	v	Hereford	1-0	909
13	Sutton United	v	Hendon	3-0	785
14	Blyth Spartans	v	Bromley	1-4	647
15	Spennymoor Town	v	Solihull Moors	2-0	570
16	St Albans City	v	Harrogate Town	1-1	634
	Harrogate Town	v	St Albans City (16/1)	5-0	362

THIRD ROUND PROPER
SATURDAY 3 FEBRUARY 2018 - WINNERS RECEIVE £8,000

#	Home		Away	Score	Att
1	Harrogate Town	v	Billericay Town	2-2	864
	Billericay Town	v	Harrogate Town (6/2)	3-2	820
2	Maidstone United	v	Gateshead	2-2	1186
	Gateshead	v	Maidstone United (6/2)	3-0	338
3	Maidenhead United	v	Stockport County	1-1	855
	Stockport County	v	Maidenhead United (6/2)	3-2aet	1131
4	Wealdstone	v	Warrington Town	2-1	601
5	Brackley Town	v	Sutton United	3-1	767
6	Dover Athletic	v	Leyton Orient	3-4	1016
7	Spennymoor Town	v	East Thurrock United	1-1	743
	East Thurrock United	v	Spennymoor Town (6/2)	2-5	238
8	Workington	v	Bromley	1-1	890
	Bromley	v	Workington (6/1)	7-1	

FOURTH ROUND PROPER
SATURDAY 24 FEBRUARY 2018 - WINNERS RECEIVE £10,000

#	Home		Away	Score	Att
1	Stockport County	v	Brackley Town	1-1	2213
	Brackley Town	v	Stockport County (6/3)	2-1	513
2	Billericay Town	v	Wealdstone	2-5	1823
3	Leyton Orient	v	Gateshead	3-3	3771
	Gateshead	v	Leyton Orient (6/3)	3-2	684
4	Bromley	v	Spennymoor Town	0-0	830
	Spennymoor Town	v	Bromley (14/3) @ Darlington FC	1-2	

SEMI FINALS
1ST LEG SATURDAY 17 MARCH / 2ND LEG SATURDAY 24 MARCH 2018 - WINNERS RECEIVE £20,000

Home		Away	Score	Att
Brackley Town	v	Wealdstone	1-0	1250
Wealdstone	v	Brackley Town	0-2	2008
Brackley Town through 3-0 on aggregate.				3258
Bromley	v	Gateshead	3-2	1254
Gateshead	v	Bromley	1-1	2264
Bromley through 4-3 on aggregate.				3518

THE FINAL...

BRACKLEY TOWN   1, 5p
R Johnson (og) 90+6

BROMLEY   1, 4p
Bugiel 19

Wembley Stadium ~ Att: 31,430
*combined Trophy/Vase attendance

THE SQUADS

BRACKLEY TOWN	BROMLEY
Danny Lewis	David Gregory
Matt Lowe	Jack Holland (c)
Connor Franklin (sub 77)	Raymond Raymond
Shane Byrne	Louis Dennis (sub 68)
Alex Gudger	Adam Mekki (sub 72)
Gareth Dean (c)	Jordan Higgs
Glenn Walker	Tyrone Sterling
James Armson	George Porter (sub 61)
Lee Ndlovu (sub 53)	Roger Johnson
Aaron Williams	Frankie Sutherland
Adam Walker	Omar Bugiel
Substitutes	**Substitutes**
Andy Brown (53)	Josh Rees (61)
Ellis Myles (77)	Brandon Hanlan (68)
Luke Graham	Ben Chorley (72)
Theo Streete	Alan Dunne
Steve Diggin	Dan Johnson

Referee Chris Kavanagh.
Assisted by Dan Cook & Daniel Robathan.
Fourth official Michael Salisbury.

Step 2 Brackley, a small town in Northamptonshire, versus Step 1 Bromley, a Kent town larger than many whose teams are Football League stalwarts. Surely, no contest. But wait. What about the clichés, "Football/ The Cup is a great leveller"? Well, it certainly was here in an entertaining and spirited game played in a sporting manner, with plenty of effort and skill to match. For three quarters of the normal ninety minutes Bromley had the lead but with just seconds of the added on five minutes at the end of the ninety Brackley got the equaliser few would claim they did not deserve. Another half an hour with no additional score and it was on to penalties. Giving my nearest press colleague the benefit of my recent wisdom, gained by experience in such matters, I declared, "The first to miss will prove the winner." Thus when Brackley's first, Shane Byrne's, penalty was saved by David Gregory I was convinced Brackley would be the ultimate victors. And that is the way it was. 4-4 after the first five of each side's spot kicks, Bromley's sixth kick hit the post and Andy Brown smashed his contribution home to set the Brackley players storming towards their delighted supporters while Bromley were left stunned that a seeming victory, anticipated only a short time before, had been snatched from their grasp with that last gasp equaliser followed by a second snatch when it came to penalties.

There was goalmouth action right from the kick off. Bromley's George Porter's header flew over in the opening attack and Matt Lowe retaliated with a dangerous cross which, with keeper David Gregory out of position, went begging with no Brackley forward on hand to take advantage. The lively Omar Bugiel had already shot narrowly wide but with nineteen minutes gone he fastened on to an Adam Mekki (later, but nearly an hour before the end, named man of the match) through ball and was able to thump the ball low and hard to Danny Lewis' left and put the Kent side into the lead. Bromley continued to have the greater proportion of chances and looked sharper in front of goal, with Lebanon international

Lewis (Brackley) saves from Porter (Bromley). Photo: Keith Clayton.

Bugiel a continuing threat, whereas Brackley's build up play and interpassing was the more impressive, often engineered by Byrne whose volley from the edge of the area brought the first half to a close.

Lewis was called on to make an instinctive save with his fists from Jack Holland's close range header, the result of a corner, as the second half opened. At the other end a screamer from James

Substitute Andy Brown (Brackley), scores the winning penalty. Photo: Peter Barnes.

Armson was only inches wide before Bromley's Louis Dennis made a chance which Frankie Sutherland hit firmly within a whisker of the far post. No one in the crowd could complain about any lack of action as the balance of chances began to tilt Brackley's way. Armson hit the post, Aaaron Williams had a shot cleared off the line and Glenn Walker provided several teasing crosses. Sub Brandon Hanlan added some zip to the Bromley attacks, a last ditch block by Gareth Dean stopping his most dangerous foray and Lewis blocking another effort with his legs. The announcement of five minutes of added time spurred Brackley to greater efforts, even goalkeeper Lewis venturing upfield for a corner. Then, with seconds to go, Matt Lowe's shot from distance bounced back off a post to his skipper Dean who prodded the ball goalwards, where it glanced off Bromley's Roger Johnson to bring Brackley level via an own goal.

Extra time saw half chances at both ends, Hanlan twice for Bromley and Lowe for Brackley coming closest but penalties were ever looming and duly arrived. As in the game itself Bromley looked home and dry when they took the lead but, just as they had in the ninety minutes, Brackley levelled in the nick of time and when Bromley missed their sixth there was

Brown to coolly ensure the Trophy travelled north rather than east. The Saints had triumphed over The Ravens. Congratulations to both teams on their behaviour. It was good to see that a hard and earnestly fought final could be played without rancour to opponent or officials, a tribute also to their respective managers.

Naturally Brackley manager Kevin Wilkin, who had managed Wrexham when they had lost the 2015 Trophy final on penalties to North Ferriby, a defeat which brought about his departure from Wrexham the very next day, was euphoric about his team's success. Many of this squad had played under Kevin at other clubs such as Telford and Nuneaton so this victory was very much a triumph brought about by his ability to spot, recruit and motivate. Wilkin's counterpart, Neil Smith, in his eighth season with the club, was naturally disappointed, particularly for his players who had been so close to success, but praised the brilliance of his squad who had served Bromley so well during the season, only narrowly missing out on the play offs for a League Two spot, and had taken the club to Wembley.

Arthur Evans

Photo: Alan Coomes.

PAST FINALS

1970 MACCLESFIELD TOWN 2 (Lyons, B Fidler)   TELFORD UNITED 0   Att: 28,000
Northern Premier League   *Southern League*
Macclesfield: Cook, Siew right, Bennett, Beaumont, Collins Roberts Lyons, B Fidler,Young, Corfield, D Fidler.
Telford: Irvine, Harris Croft, Flowers Coton, Ray,Fudge, Hart, Bentley, Murray, Agger.   Ref: K Walker

1971 TELFORD UTD 3 (Owen, Bentley, Fudge)   HILLINGDON BORO. 2 (Reeve, Bishop)   Att: 29,500
Southern League   *Southern League*
Telford: Irvine, Harris Croft, Ray, Coton, Carr, Fudge, Owen, Bentley, Agger ,Murray.
Hillingdon B.: Lowe, Batt, Langley, Higgins n, Newcombe, Moore, Fairbild,Bishop, Reeve, Carter, Knox   Ref: D Smith

1972 STAFFORD RANGERS 3 (Williams 2, Cullerton)   BARNET 0   Att: 24,000
Northern Premier League   *Southern League*
Stafford R.: Alek c Chadwik Clayon, Sargeant, Aston, Mab in, Cullerton, Chapman,Williams Bayley, Jones
Barnet: MC lelland, Ly , Jenkins Ward, Embrey, King, Powell, Ferry, Flatt, Easton, Plume .   Ref: P Partridge

1973 SCARBOROUGH 2 (Leask, Thompson)   WIGAN ATHLETIC 1 (Rogers) aet   Att:23,000
Northern Premier League   *Northern Premier League*
Scarborough: Garrow, Appleton, Shoulder, Dunn, Siddle, Fagan, Donoghue, Frank Leask (Barmby , Thompe n, Hewitt.
Wigan: Reeves, Morris, Sutherland, Taylor,Jackson, Gillibrand, Clements, Oats (McCunnell), Rogers, King, Worswick.   Ref: H Hackney

1974 MORECAMBE 2 (Richmond, Sutton)   DARTFORD 1 (Cunningham)   Att: 19,000
Northern Premier League   *Southern League*
Morecambe: Coates Pearson, Bennett, Sutton, Street, Baldwin, Done, Webber,Roberts (Galley , Kershaw, Richmond.
Dartford: Morton, Read, Payne, Carr, Burns,Binks, Light, Glozier, Robinson (Hearne), Cunningham, Halleday.   Ref: B Homewood

1975(1) MATLOCK TOWN 4 (Oxley, Dawson, T Fenoughty, N Fenoughty) SCARBOROUGH 0   Att: 21,000
Northern Premier League   *Northern Premier League*
Matlock Fell, MK ay, Smith, Stuart, Dawson, Swan, Okey, N Fenoughy, So tt, T Fenoughty, M Fenoughty.
Scarborough: Williams Hewitt, Rettitt, Dunn, Marshall, Todd, Houghton, Woodall, Davidson, Barnby, Award.   Ref: K Styes

1976 SCARBOROUGH 3 (Woodall, Abbey, Marshall(p)) STAFFORD R. 2 (Jones 2) aet   Att: 21,000
Northern Premier League   *Northern Premier League*
Scarborough: Barnard, Johnn, Marshall, H Dunn, Ayre (Donoghue), HA Dunn, Dale,Barmby, Woodall, Abbey, Hilley.
Stafford: Arnold, Ritbie, Ribards Sargeant,Seddon, Morris Chapman, Lowe, Jones Hutbine n, Chadwik   Ref: R Challis

1977 SCARBOROUGH 2 (Dunn(p), Abbey)   DAGENHAM 1 (Harris)   Att: 21,500
Northern Premier League   *Isthmian League*
Scarborough: Chapman, Smith, Marshall (Barmby , Dunn, Ayre, Deere, Award,Donoghue, Woodall, Abbey, Dunn.
Dagenham: Hutley, Wellman, P Currie, Dunwell,Moore, W Currie, Harkns Saul, Fox Harris Holder.   Ref: G Courtney

1978 ALTRINCHAM 3 (King, Johnson, Rogers)   LEATHERHEAD 1 (Cook)   Att: 20,000
Northern Premier League   *Isthmian League*
Altrincham: Eales Allan, Crosley, Bailey, Owens King, Morris Heatho te,Johnson, Rogers Davidson (Flaherty .
Leatherhead: Swannell, Cooper, Eaton, Davies Reid, Malley, Cook Salkeld, Baler, Boyle (Bailey).   Ref: A Grey

1979 STAFFORD RANGERS 2 (A Wood 2)   KETTERING TOWN 0   Att: 32,000
Northern Premier League   *Southern League*
Stafford: Arnold, F Wood, Willis Sargeant, Seddon, Ritbie, Sel r, Chapman, A Wood, Cullerton, Chadwik (Jones .
Kettering: Lane, Ashby, Lee, Eastell, Dixey,Suddards, Flannagan, Kellock, Phipps, Clayton, Evans (Hughes).   Ref: D Richardson

1980(2) DAGENHAM 2 (Duck, Maycock)   MOSSLEY 1 (Smith)   Att: 26,000
Isthmian League   *Northern Premier League*
Dagenham: Huttley, Wellman, Seles Dunwell, Moore, Durrell, Mayck Horan,Duk Kidd, Jones (Holder).
Mossley Fitton, Brown, Vaughan, Gorman, Salter, Polliot, Smith, Moore, Skeete, O'Connor, Keelan (Wiles n).   Ref: K Baler

1981(3) BISHOP'S STORTFORD 1 (Sullivan)   SUTTON UNITED 0   Att: 22,578
Isthmian League   *Isthmian League*
Bishop's Stortford: Moore, Blakman, Brame, Smith (Worrell), Bradford, Abery, Sullivan,Knapman, Radford, Simmonds Mitbell.
Sutton Utd.: Collyer, Rogers, Green, J Rains,T Rains, Stephens (Sunnucks), Waldon, Pritchard, Cornwell, Parsons, Dennis.   Ref: J Worrall

1982 ENFIELD 1 (Taylor)   ALTRINCHAM 0   Att: 18,678
Alliance Premier League   *Alliance Premier League*
Enfield: Jobs Barrett, Tone, Jennings Waite, Ironton, Ab ford, Tayor,Holmes Oliver (Flint), King.   Ref: B Steve ns
Altrincham: Connaughton, Crosley, Davien, Bailey, Cuddy, King (Whitbread), Allan, Heatho te, Johnson, Rogers Howard.

Notes:
1   The only oa s on three members of the ame family played in the ame FA Trophy Final team.
2   The firs of the Amateurs from the Isthmian League to win the FA Trophy.
3   Goalkeeper Terry Moore had also won an Amateur Cup Winners Medal with Bishop's Stortford in 1974.
     All games played at Wembley (old & new) unless stated.

THE FA TROPHY

1983 TELFORD UTD 2 (Mather 2)   NORTHWICH VICTORIA 1 (Bennett)   **Att: 22,071**
Alliance Premier League   *Alliance Premier League*
Telford: Charlton, Lewis Turner, Mayman (d e ph), Walker, Eaton, Barnett,Williams Mather, Hogan, Alo k
Northwib : Ryan, Fretwell, Murphy, d nes Fors aw, Ward, Andere n, Abel (Bennett), Reid, Chesters Wile n.   Ref: B Hill

1984 NORTHWICH VICTORIA 1 (Chester)   BANGOR CITY 1 (Whelan)   **Att: 14,200**
Replay NORTHWICH VICTORIA 2 (Chesters(p), Anderson) BANGOR CITY 1 (Lunn)   **Att: 5,805 (at Stoke)**
Alliance Premier League   *Alliance Premier League*
Northwib : Ryan, Fretwell, Dean, d nes Fors aw (Power 65), Bennett, Andere n,Abel, Reid, Chesters Wile n.   Ref: J Martin
Bangor: Letheren, Cau nagh, Gray, Whelan, Bank Lunn, Urqhart, Morris Carter, Howat, Sutb iffe (Wes wood 105) . Same in replay.

1985 WEALDSTONE 2 (Graham, Holmes)   BOSTON UNITED 1 (Cook)   **Att: 20,775**
Alliance Premier League   *Alliance Premier League*
Wealdstone: Iles, Perkins, Bowgett, Byatt, Davies, Greenaway, Holmes, Wainwright,Donnellan, Graham (N Cordice 89), A Cordice.
Boston: Blackwell, Casey, Ladd,Creane, O'Brien, Thommson, Laverick (Mallender 78), Simpsom, Gilbert, Lee, Cook.   Ref: J Bray

1986 ALTRINCHAM 1 (Farrelly)   RUNCORN 0   **Att: 15,700**
Gola League   *Gola League*
Altrinb am: Wealands Gardner, Denn ore, d hne n, Farrelly, Conning, Cuddy,Dai e n, Reid, Ellis Andere n. Sub: Newton.
Runcorn: McBride, Lee, Roberts,Jones, Fraser, Smith, S Crompton (A Crompton), Imrie, Carter, Mather, Carrodus.   Ref: A Ward

1987 KIDDERMINSTER HARRIERS 0   BURTON ALBION 0   **Att: 23,617**
Replay KIDDERMINSTER HARRIERS 2 (Davies 2)   BURTON ALBION 1 (Groves)   **Att: 15,685 (at West Brom)**
Conference   *Southern League*
Kiddermint er: Arnold, Barton, Boa ll, Braiz er (s b Haz ewood in rep), Collins (s b Peare n 90 at Wembley , Woodall, MK eniz e,
O'Dowd, Tuohy, Cas y, Dai es s b:d nes
Burton: New, Essex, Kamara, Vaughan, Simms, Groves, Bancroft, Land, Dorsett, Redfern, (sub Wood in replay), Gauden.
Sub: Patterson.   Ref: D Shaw

1988 ENFIELD 0   TELFORD UNITED 0   **Att: 20,161**
Replay ENFIELD 3 (Furlong 2, Howell)   TELFORD UNITED 2 (Biggins, Norris(p))   **Att: 6,912 (at W Brom)**
Conference   *Conference*
Enfield: Pape, Cottington, Howell, Keen (s b Edmonds in rep), Sparrow (s b Haz eden at Wembley , Lewis (s b Edmonds at
Wembley , Harding, Cooper, King,Furlong, Franc s
Telford: Charlton, MG inty, Storton, Nele n, Wiggins Mayn an (s b Cunningham in rep (s b Hano k), Sank y, d e ph, Stringer (s b
Griffiths at Wembley, Griffiths in replay , Biggins Norris   Ref: L Dille s

1989 TELFORD UNITED 1 (Crawley)   MACCLESFIELD TOWN 0   **Att: 18,102**
Conference   *Conference*
Telford: Charlton, Lee, Brindley, Hancock, Wiggins, Mayman, Grainger, Joseph, Nelson, Lloyd, Stringer. Subs: Crawley, Griffiths.
Macclesfield: Zelem, Roberts, Tobin, Edwards, Hardman, Askey, Lake, Hanton, Imrie, Burr, Timmons. Subs: Devonshire, Kendall.

1990 BARROW 3 (Gordon 2, Cowperthwaite)   LEEK TOWN 0   **Att: 19,011**
Conference   *Northern Premier League*
Barrow: McDonnell, Higgins, Chilton, Skivington, Gordon, Proctor, Doherty (Burgess), Farrell (Gilmore), Cowperthwaite, Lowe, Ferris.
Leek: Simpson, Elsby (Smith), Pearce, McMullen, Clowes, Coleman (Russell),Mellor, Somerville, Sutton, Millington, Norris   Ref: T Simpson

1991 WYCOMBE W. 2 (Scott, West)   KIDDERMINSTER HARRIERS 1 (Hadley)   **Att: 34,842**
Conference   *Conference*
Wy mbe: Granv lle, Cros ey, Cab , Kerr, Creae r, Carroll, Ry n, Stapleton,Wes , So tt, Guppy (Hutb ine n).   Ref: J Wate n
Kidderminster: Jones, Kurila, McGrath, Weir, Barnett, Forsyth, Joseph (Wilcox), Howell (Whitehouse), Hadley, Lilwall, Humphries

1992 COLCHESTER UTD* 3 (Masters, Smith, McGavin)   WITTON ALBION 1 (Lutkevitch)   **Att: 27,806**
Conference   *Conference*
Colchester: Barrett, Donald, Roberts, Knsella, English, Martin, Cook, Masters,McDonough (Bennett 65), McGavin, Smith.   Ref: K P Barratt
Witton: Mason, Halliday, Coathup, McNeilis, Jim Connor, Anderson, Thomas, Rose, Alford, Grimshaw (Joe Connor), Lutkevitch (McCluskie)

1993 WYCOMBE W*. 4 (Cousins, Kerr, Thompson, Carroll) RUNCORN 1 (Shaughnessy)   **Att: 32,968**
Conference   *Conference*
Wycombe: Hyde, Cousins, Cooper, Kerr, Crossley, Thompson (Hayrettin 65),Carroll, Ryan, Hutchinson, Scott, Guppy. Sub: Casey.
Runcorn: Williams, Bates, Robertson, Hill, Harold (Connor 62), Anderson, Brady (Parker 72), Brown, Shaughnessy, McKenna, Brabin

1994 WOKING 2 (D Brown, Hay)   RUNCORN 1 (Shaw (pen))   **Att: 15,818**
Conference   *Conference*
Woking: Batty, Tucker, L Wye, Berry, Brown, Clement, Brown (Rattray 32), Fielder, Steele, Hay (Puckett 46), Walker.   Ref: Paul Durkin
Runcorn: Williams, Bates, Robertson, Shaw, Lee, Anderson, Thomas, Connor, McInerney (Hill 71), McKenna, Brabin. Sub: Parker

1995 WOKING 2 (Steele, Fielder)   KIDDERMINSTER HARRIERS 1 aet (Davies)   **Att: 17,815**
Conference   *Conference*
Woking: Batty, Tucker, L Wye, Fielder, Brown, Crumplin (Rattray 42), S Wye, Ellis, Steele, Hay (Newberry 112), Walker. (Sub: Read(gk)
Kiddermint er: Roe , Hode n, Banc oft, Webb, Brindley (Cartwright 94), Fors h, Deak n, Yates Humphrey (Hughes 105), Dai es
Purdie. Sub: Dearloe (gk   Ref: D J Gallagher

1996 MACCLESFIELD TOWN 3 (Payne, OG, Hemmings) **NORTHWICH VICTORIA** 1 (Williams) **Att: 8,672**
Conference   *Conference*
Macclesfield: Price, Edey, Gardiner, Payne, Howarth(C), Sorvel, Lyons, Wood (Hulme 83), Coates, Power, Hemmings (Cavell 88).
Northwib : Greg oos , Ward, Duffy, Burges (Simpe n 87), Abel (Steele), Walters Williams Butler (C), Cool , Humphries Via ry.
Ref: M Reed

1997 WOKING 1 (Hay 112)   **DAGENHAM & REDBRIDGE** 0   **Att: 24,376**
Conference   *Isthmian League*
Wok ng: Batty, Brown, Howard, Fos er, Tay or, S Wy , Thompe n (a b d nes 115), Ellis Steele (L Wy 108), Walk r, a b n (Hay 77).
Dagenham: Gothard, Cule rhoue , Connor, Creae r, a q ues (a b Double 75), Daï de n, Pratt (Nay or 81), Parratt, Broom, Rogers
Stime n (d hn 65).   Ref: J Winter

1998 CHELTENHAM TOWN 1 (Eaton 74)   **SOUTHPORT** 0   **Att: 26,387**
Conference   *Conference*
Cheltenham: Book Duff, Freeman, Bank Vic ory, Knight (Smith 78), Howells Bloomer, Walk r (a b Milton 78), Eaton, Watk ns Sub:
Wright.
Southport: Stewart, Horner, Futb er, Ry n, Farley, Kielty, Butler, Gamble, Formby (a b Whittak r 80), Thompe n (a b Bollard 88),
Ros Sub: Mitten.   Ref: G S Willard

1999 KINGSTONIAN 1 (Mustafa 49)   **FOREST GREEN ROVERS** 0   **Att: 20,037**
Conference   *Conference*
Kings onian: Farrelly, Mus afa, Lule tt, Cros ey, Stewart, Harris Patterson, Pitb er, Rattray, Leworthy (Franc s 87), Al amoah. Subs
(not ue d): d hn, Corbett, Brown, Tranter
Forest Green Roe rs Shuttlewood, Hedges Forbes Bailey (Smart 76), Kilgour, Wigg (Cook 58), Honor (Winter 58), Dry ale,
MG regor, Mehew, Sp s Subs (not ue d): Perrin, Coupe   Ref: A B Wilk e

2000 KINGSTONIAN 3 (Akuamoah 40, 69, Simba 75) **KETTERING TOWN** 2 (Vowden 55, Norman 64p) **Att: 20,034**
Conference   *Conference*
Kings onian: Farelly, Mus afa, Lule tt, Cros ey, Stewart (Saunders 77), Harris Kadi (Leworthy 83), Pitb er, Green (Bas ord 86),
Smiba, Al amoah. Subs (not ue d): Hurs , Allan
Kettering Town: Sollit, Ml amara, Adams Perk ns Vowden, Norman (Duik 76), Fisher, Brown, Shutt, Watk ns (Hude n 46), Setb ell
(Hopk n 81). Subs (not ue d): Ridgway, Wile n   Ref: S W Dunn

2001 CANVEY ISLAND 1 (Chenery)   **FOREST GREEN ROVERS** 0   **Att: 10,007**
Isthmian League   *Conference*   **at Villa Park**
Forest Green Roe rs Perrin, Cous ns Low ood, Fos er, Clark Burns Daley, Dry ale (Bennett 46), Fos er (Hunt 75), Meeb am,
Slater. Subs (not ue d): Hedges Prine , Ghent
Cane y ls and: Harrie n, Duffy, Chenery, Bodley, Ward, Tile n, Stime n (Tanner 83), Gregory, Vaughan (d nes 76), Parmenter. Subs
(not ue d): Bennett, Miller, Thompe n.   Ref: A G Wiley

2002 YEOVIL TOWN 2 (Alford, Stansfield) **STEVENAGE BOROUGH** 0   **Att: 18,809**
Conference   *Conference*   **at Villa Park**
Yeovi l Town: Weale, Locw ood, Tonk n, Ske rton, Plut (White 51), Way, Stans ield, d hne n, Alford (Giles 86), Crittenden (Lindegaard
83), Mc ndoe. Subs (not ue d): O'Brien, Sheffield
Stee nage Borough: Wilk re n, Hamb er, Goodliffe, Trott, Frae r, Fib er, Wormull (Stirling 71), Ee rs (Williams 56), a b n, Sigere
(Campbell 74), Clark . Subs (not ue d): Campbell, Greg oos   Ref: N S Barry

2003 BURSCOUGH 2 (Martindale 25, 55)   **TAMWORTH** 1 (Cooper 78)   **Att: 14,265**
Northern Premier   *Southern Premier*   **at Villa Park**
Bure ugh: Tay or, Teale, Tay or, Maa uley (White 77), Lawles Bowen, Wright, Norman, Martindale (Mcl ale 80), By ne (Bluk 84),
Burns Subs (not ue d): MG uire (g/k Moly eux
Tamworth: Ac on, Warner, Follett, Robine n, Walb , Cooper, Colley, Ea ns (Turner 64), Rib rds (Hatton 88), MG orry,
Sale (Hallam 54). Subs (not ue d): Groo tt, Barnes (g/k .   Ref: U D Rennie

2004 HEDNESFORD TOWN 3 (Maguire 28, Hines 53, Brindley 87) **CANVEY ISLAND** 2 (Boylan 46, Brindley 48 og) **Att: 6,635**
Southern Premier   *Isthmian Premier Champions*   **at Villa Park**
Hednes ord Town: Young, Simk n, Hines King, Brindley, Ry er (Barrow 59), Palmer, Anthrobus Dank (Pieare 78), Maguire,
Charie (Ea ns 55). Subs (not ue d): Ea ns (g/k MG hee.
Cane y ls and: Potter, Kennedy, Duffy, Chenery, Cowan, Gooden (Dobine n 89), Minton, Gregory (Mcl ougald 80), Boy an,
Midgley (Berquez 73), Ward. Subs (not ue d): Theobald, Harrie n (g/k .
Ref: M L Dean

2005 GRAYS ATHLETIC 1 (Martin 65) Pens: 6 **HUCKNALL TOWN** 1 (Ricketts 75) Pens: 5 **Att: 8,116**
Conference South   *Conference North*   **at Villa Park**
Gray Athletic Bay s Brennan, Nutter, Stuart, Matthews Thurgood, Oli (Powell 80), Hopper (Carthy 120), Batterb y (a b Web 61),
Martin, Cole. Subs (not ue d): Embere n, Brue ..
Huk all Town: Smith, Ab er, Barris (Plummer 30), Hunter, Timons Cook , Smith (Ward 120), Palmer (Heatho te 94), Rib tts
Bao n, Todd. Subs (not ue d): Winder, Lindley.   Ref: P Dowd

2006 GRAYS ATHLETIC 2 (Oli, Poole)   **WOKING** 0   **Att: 13,997**
Conference   *Conference*   **at Upton Park**
Gray Athletic Bay s Sambrook Nutter, Stuart, Hane n, Kightly (Williame n 90), Thurgood, Martin, Poole, Oli, Mc ean.
Subs (not ue d): Ey e (g/k , Hooper, Olay nk , Mawer.
Wok ng: a lal, a cb n, Mad onald, Nethero tt (Wate n 60), Hutb ine n, Murray, Smith (Cok rill 60), Ea ns (Blas an 85),
Fergue n, MA llis er, d s in Rib ards. Subs (not ue d): Daï s (g/k , El-Salahi.

                                                                Ref: Howard Webb (Sheffield)

2007 STEVENAGE BOROUGH 3 (Cole, Dobson, Morrison) **KIDDERMINSTER HARRIERS** 2 (Constable 2)   Att: 53,262
Conference   *Conference*   **(New Trophy record)**
Stevenage Borough: Julian, Fuller, Nutter, Oliver, Gaia, Miller, Cole, Morrison, Guppy (Dobson 63), Henry, Beard.
Subs not used: Potter, Slabber, Nurse, McMahon.
Kidderminster Harriers Bevan, Kenna, Hurren, Creighton, Whitehead, Blackwood, Russell, Penn, Smikle (Reynolds 90),
Christie (White 75) , Constable.
Subs not used: Taylor, Sedgemore, McGrath.
                                                                        Ref: Chris Foy (Merseyside)

2008 EBBSFLEET UNITED 1 (McPhee)   **TORQUAY UNITED** 0   Att: 40,186
Blue Square Premier   *Blue Square Premier*
Ebbsfleet United: Cronin, Hawkins McCarthy, Smith, Opinel, McPhee, Barrett, Bostwick Long (MacDonald 84), Moore, Akinde.
Subs not used: Eribenne, Purdie, Ricketts Mott.
Torquay United: Rice , Manel, Todd, Woods Nibole n, D'Sane (Benyon 66), Hargreaves Adams Zebroski, Sills (Hill 88),
Phillips (Stevens 46). Subs not used: Hockey and Robertson.
                                                                        Ref: Martin Atkinson (West Riding)

2009 STEVENAGE BOROUGH 2 (Morison, Boylan)   **YORK CITY** 0   Att: 27,102
Blue Square Premier   *Blue Square Premier*
Stevenage Borough: Day, Henry, Bostwick Roberts Wilson, Mills Murphy, Drury, Vincenti (Anaba et 86), Boylan, Morison.
Subs not used: Bayes Albrighton, Maamria and Willock
York City Ingham, Purkis McGurk Parslow, Pejic Mackin, Greaves McWilliams 74), Ruse (Russell 80), Brodie, McBreen (Sodje 60),
Boyes Subs not used – Mimms and Robinson.
                                                                        Referee: Michael Jones

2010 BARROW 2 (McEvilly 79, Walker 117)   **STEVENAGE BOROUGH** 1 (Drury 10)   Att: 21,223
Blue Square Premier   *Blue Square Premier*
Barrow: Stuart Tomlinson, Simon Spender, Paul Jones Phil Bolland, Paul Edwards Simon Wiles (s b Carlos Logan 63rd min),
Robin Hulbert, Andy Bond, Paul Rutherford (s b Mark Boyd 109th min), Jason Walker, Gregg Blundell (s b Lee McEvilly 73rd min).
Subs not used – Tim Deasy and Mike Pearson.
Stevenage Borough: Chris Day (s b Ashley Bayes 90th min), Ronnie Henry, John Ashton, Mark Roberts Scott Laird,
Joel Byrom (s b Lawrie Wilson 58th min), David Bridges Michael Bostwick Andy Drury, Chris Beardsley (s b Charlie Griffin 64th min),
Yemi Odubade. Subs not used – Stacey Long and Peter Vincenti.
Man of the match - Paul Rutherford.
                                                                        Referee Lee Probert.

2011 DARLINGTON 1 (Senior 120)   **MANSFIELD TOWN** 0   Att: 24,668
Blue Square Premier   *Blue Square Premier*
Darlington: Sam Russell, Paul Arnison, Ian Miller, Liam Hatch, Aaron Brown, Jamie Chandler, Chris Moore, Marc Bridge-Wilkinson (sub
Paul Terry 100th min), Gary Smith (sub Arman Verma 38th min), John Campbell (sub Chris Senior 75th min), Tommy Wright.
Subs not used – Danzelle St Louis-Hamilton (gk) and Phil Gray.
Mansfield Town: Alan Marriott, Gary Silk, Stephen Foster, Tom Naylor, Dan Spence, Louis Briscoe, Tyrone Thompson, Kyle Nix, Adam
Smith (sub Ashley Cain 95th min), Adam Murray (sub Danny Mitchley 108th min), Paul Connor
Subs not used – Paul Stonehouse and Neil Collett (gk)
Man of the match - Jamie Chandler.
                                                                        Referee Stuart Atwell

2012 YORK CITY 2 (Blair 61, Oyebanjo 68)   **NEWPORT COUNTY** 0   Att: 19,844
Blue Square Premier   *Blue Square Premier*
York City: Michael Ingham, Jon Challinor, Chris Smith, Daniel Parslow, Ben Gibson, Matty Blair, Lanre Oyebanjo, Patrick McLaughlan
(sub Jamal Fyfield 82nd min), James Meredith, Ashley Chambers (Adriano Moke 89th min), Jason Walker (Jamie Reed 90th min).
Subs not used – Paul Musselwhite (g/k), Michael Potts.
Newport County: Glyn Thompson, David Pipe, Ismail Yakubu, Gary Warren, Andrew Hughes, Sam Foley, Lee Evans, Nat Jarvis (sub
Jake Harris 68th min), Max Porter (sub Darryl Knights 79th min), Romone Rose (sub Elliott Buchanan 68th min), Lee Minshull.
Subs not used – Matthew Swan (g/k), Paul Rodgers.
Man of the match - Lanre Oyebanjo.
                                                                        Referee Anthony Taylor

2013 WREXHAM 1 (Thornton 82 (pen))   **GRIMSBY TOWN** 1 (Cook 71)   Att: 35,226
Wrexham won 4-1 on kicks from the penalty mark after extra time.
Blue Square Premier   *Blue Square Premier*
Wrexham: Chris Maxwell, Stephen Wright, Martin Riley, Jay Harris, Danny Wright, Brett Ormerod (Robert Ogleby 77 min),
Andy Morrell (Adrian Cieslewicz 61 min), Dean Keates, Johnny Hunt, Chris Westwood, Kevin Thornton (Joe Clarke 89 min).
Subs not used - Andy Coughlin (gk) Glen Little.
Grimsby Town: Sam Hatton, Aswad Thomas, Shaun Pearson, Ian Miller, Joe Colbeck, Craig Disley, Frankie Artus, Andy Cook, James
McKeown, Ross Hannah (Andi Thanoj 55 min), Marcus Marshall (Richard Brodie 87 min).
Subs not used - Jamie Devitt, Bradley Wood, Lenell John-Lewis.
                                                                        Referee Jonathan Moss

2014 CAMBRIDGE UNITED 4 (Bird 38, Donaldson 50,59, Berry 78 (pen)) **GOSPORT BOROUGH** 0   Att: 18,120
Conference Premier   *Conference South*
Cambridge United: Will Norris, Greg Taylor, Jock Coulson (Tom Bonner 87 min), Ian Miller, Ryan Donaldson, Tom Champion,
Richard Tait, Liam Hughes (Nathan Arnold 73 min), Luke Berry, Ryan Bird, Josh Gillies (Andy Pugh 61 min).
Subs not used - Kevin Roberts, Mitch Austin.
Gosport Borough: Nathan Ashmore, Lee Molyneaux, Andy Forbes, Jamie Brown (Rory Williams 57 min), Brett Poate, Sam Pearce,
Josh Carmichael, Danny Smith, Tim Sills (Dan Woodward 57 min), Justin Bennett, Michael Gosney (Dan Wooden 72 min).
Subs not used - Ryan Scott, Adam Wilde.

                                                                        Referee Craig Pawson

2015 **NORTH FERRIBY UNITED** 3 (King 76 (pen), Kendall 86, 111) **WREXHAM** 3 (Moult 11, 118, Harris 59) **Att: 14,548**
Conference North *Conference National*

North Ferriby United: Adam Nicklin, Sam Topliss, Danny Hone, Matt Wilson, Josh Wilde (Nathan Peat 90), Liam King, Adam Bolder (Nathan Jarman 62), Russell Fry (Ryan Kendall 80), Danny Clarke, Tom Denton, Jason St Juste.
Subs not used - Tom Nicholson and Mark Gray.
Wrexham: Andy Coughlin, Steve Tomassen, Manny Smith, Blaine Hudson, Neil Ashton, Jay Harris, Dean Keates (Robbie Evans 73), Joe Clarke (Andy Bishop 102), Kieron Morris (Wes York 87), Louis Moult, Connor Jennings.
Subs not used - Mark Carrington and Luke Waterfall.
Referee Michael Oliver

2016 **FC HALIFAX TOWN** 1 (McManus 48) **GRIMSBY TOWN** 0 **Att: 46,781** (Inaugural Non-League finals day
Conference National *Conference National*

FC Halifax Town: Sam Johnson, Matty Brown, Hamza Bencherif, Kevin Roberts, James Bolton, Nicky Wroe, Jake Hibbs, Scott McManus (Kingsley James 73), Josh McDonald (Sam Walker 63), Jordan Burrow, Richard Peniket (Connor Hughes 86).
Subs not used - Jordan Porter and Shaquille McDonald.
Grimsby Town: James McKeown, Richard Tait (Danny East 81), Shaun Pearson, Aristote Nsiala, Gregor Robertson, Andy Monkhouse (Jon-Paul Pitman 68), Craig Disley, Craig Clay (Nathan Arnold 63), Jon Nolan, Omar Bogle, Padraig Amond.
Subs not used - Josh Gowling and Josh Venney.
Referee Lee Mason

2017 **YORK CITY** 3 (Parkin 8, Oliver 22, Connolly 86) **MACCLESFIELD TOWN** 2 (Browne 13, Norburn 45+1)
Conference National *Conference National* **Att: 38,224** (Combined Trophy Vase att.)

York City: Kyle Letheren, Asa Hall (Aidan Connolly 69), Yan Klukowski (Adriano Moke 46), Hamza Bencherif, Danny Holmes (Shaun Rooney 76), Amari Morgan-Smith, Simon Heslop, Sean Newton, Daniel Parslow, Jon Parkin, Vadaine Oliver.
Subs not used - Luke Simpson, Scott Fenwick.
Macclesfield Town: Scott Flinders, Andy Halls, David Fitzpatrick, Neill Byrne (John McCombe 68), George Pilkington, Rhys Browne, Chris Holroyd, Kingsley James, Ollie Norburn (Anthony Dudley 89), Mitch Hancox (Luke Summerfield 86), Danny Whitaker.
Subs not used - Craig Ross, Danny Whitehead.
Referee Paul Tierney

All Finals at Wembley unless otherwise stated.

FAT2P - Action from the 2-2 draw between Kidderminster Harriers and Stockpotr County.. Photo: Peter Barnes.

FATP - The Evsham striker lines up to shoot under pressure from the Cirencester player. Photo: Peter Barnes.

FAT3Q - Marshall's (No.2) own goal gives Altrincham the lead, whilst below Johnson (7) scores their 2nd from the penalty spot to beat Alfreton 0-2.
Photo: Bill Wheatcroft.

FATF - Bromley's Jack Holland (White) gets in a header against Brackley at Wembley. Photo: Alan Coomes.

EXTRA PRELIMINARY ROUND 2018-19
SATURDAY 29 SEPTEMBER 2018 ~ WINNERS RECEIVE £2,000

1 Atherton Collieries v Runcorn Linnets
2 Cleethorpes Town v Mossley
3 Sheffield v Prescot Cables
4 Trafford v Colne
5 Glossop North End v Brighouse Town
6 Droylsden v Widnes
7 Bromsgrove Sporting v Corby Town
8 Loughborough Dynamo v Market Drayton Town
9 Peterborough Sports v Sutton Coldfield Town
10 Coleshill Town v Kidsgrove Athletic
11 Witham Town v Coggeshall Town
12 Uxbridge v Chalfont St Peter
13 Felixstowe & Walton United v Grays Athletic
14 Romford v Great Wakering Rovers

15 Bedford Town v Cheshunt
16 Bury Town v Horsham
17 Aveley v Tooting & Mitcham United
18 Didcot Town v Thamesmead Town
19 Ashford Town (Middx) v Heybridge Swifts
20 Barton Rovers v Kempston Rovers
21 Whyteleafe v Bowers & Pitsea
22 Waltham Abbey v Hastings United
23 AFC Sudbury v Egham Town
24 Ashford United v Haywards Heath Town
25 Blackfield & Langley v Highworth Town
26 Evesham United v Moneyfields
27 Slimbridge v Winchester City

PRELIMINARY ROUND 2018-19
SATURDAY 13 OCTOBER 2018 ~ WINNERS RECEIVE £3,000

1 Sheffield or Prescot Cables v Kendal Town
2 Pickering Town v Stocksbridge Park Steels
3 Marske United v Atherton Collieries
          or Runcorn Linnets
4 Radcliffe v Cleethorpes Town or Mossley
5 Droylsden or Widnes v Tadcaster Albion
6 Trafford or Colne v Ramsbottom United
7 Skelmersdale United v Frickley Athletic
8 Ossett United v Colwyn Bay
9 Morpeth Town v Glossop North End
          or Brighouse Town
10 Clitheroe v Pontefract Collieries
11 Spalding United v Carlton Town
12 Wisbech Town v Coleshill Town
              or Kidsgrove Athletic
13 Peterborough Sports v Cambridge City
or Sutton Coldfield Town
14 Gresley v Newcastle Town
15 Belper Town v Stamford
16 Chasetown v Lincoln United
17 Soham Town Rangers v AFC Mansfield
18 Leek Town v Loughborough Dynamo
              or Market Drayton Town
19 Bromsgrove Sporting or Corby Town v Yaxley
20 Chipstead v Welwyn Garden City
21 Berkhamsted v South Park
22 Barking v Hayes & Yeading United
23 AFC Dunstable v Witham Town
              or Coggeshall Town
24 Hythe Town v FC Romania
25 Felixstowe & Walton United v Sevenoaks Town
              or Grays Athletic
26 Aylesbury United v Mildenhall Town
27 Didcot Town or Thamesmead Town v Hertford Town
28 Greenwich Borough v AFC Sudbury
              or Egham Town
29 Dunstable Town v Northwood
30 Ashford United v Bracknell Town
or Haywards Heath Town

31 Faversham Town v Sittingbourne
32 Phoenix Sports v Ramsgate
33 Bedfont Sports v Whitstable Town
34 Canvey Island v Cray Wanderers
35 Tilbury v Bedford Town or Cheshunt
36 Bury Town or Horsham v Ware
37 Romford or Great Wakering Rovers
      v East Grinstead Town
38 Dereham Town v Barton Rovers
                  or Kempston Rovers
39 VCD Athletic v Hanwell Town
40 Aylesbury v Herne Bay
41 Three Bridges v Molesey
42 Waltham Abbey or Hastings United v
      Whyteleafe or Bowers & Pitsea
43 Ashford Town (Middx) v Westfield
or Heybridge Swifts
44 Uxbridge or Chalfont St Peter v Maldon & Tiptree
45 Brentwood Town v Marlow
46 Aveley or Tooting & Mitcham United v Basildon
United
47 Slimbridge or Winchester City v Melksham Town
48 AFC Totton v North Leigh
49 Yate Town v Blackfield & Langley
              or Highworth Town
50 Cinderford Town v Evesham United
                  or Moneyfields
51 Bideford v Street
52 Thatcham Town v Cirencester Town
53 Mangotsfield United v Kidlington
54 Larkhall Athletic v Thame United
55 Fleet Town v Barnstaple Town
56 Bristol Manor Farm v Paulton Rovers

2018-19 EXEMPT CLUBS

24 CLUBS EXEMPT TO FIRST ROUND PROPER
AFC Fylde
Aldershot Town
Barnet
Barrow AFC
Boreham Wood
Braintree Town
Bromley
Chesterfield
Dagenham & Redbridge
Dover Athletic
Eastleigh
Ebbsfleet United
FC Halifax Town
Gateshead
Harrogate Town
Hartlepool United
Havant & Waterlooville
Leyton Orient
Maidenhead United
Maidstone United
Salford City
Solihull Moors
Sutton United
Wrexham

44 CLUBS EXEMPT TO THIRD ROUND QUALIFYING
AFC Telford United
Alfreton Town
Altrincham
Ashton Untied
Bath City
Billericay Town
Blyth Spartans AFC
Boston United
Brackley Town
Bradford (Park Avenue)
Chelmsford City
Chester
Chippenham Town
Chorley
Concord Rangers
Curzon Ashton
Darlington
Dartford
Dulwich Hamlet
East Thurrock United
Eastbourne Borough
FC United Of Manchester
Gloucester City
Guiseley AFC
Hampton & Richmond Borough
Hemel Hempstead Town
Hereford

Hungerford Town
Kidderminster Harriers
Leamington
Nuneaton Borough
Oxford City
Slough Town
Southport
Spennymoor Town
St Albans City
Stockport County
Torquay United
Truro City
Wealdstone
Welling United
Weston Super Mare
Woking
York City

88 CLUBS EXEMPT TO FIRST ROUND QUALIFYING
AFC Hornchurch
AFC Rushden & Diamonds
Alvechurch
Bamber Bridge
Banbury United
Barwell
Basford United
Basingstoke Town
Beaconsfield Town
Bedworth United
Biggleswade Town
Bishop's Stortford
Bognor Regis Town
Brightlingsea Regent
Burgess Hill Town
Buxton
Carshalton Athletic
Chesham United
Coalville Town
Corinthian Casuals
Dorchester Town
Dorking Wanderers
Enfield Town
Farnborough
Farsley Celtic
Folkestone Invicta
Frome Town
Gainsborough Trinity
Gosport Borough
Grantham Town
Halesowen Town
Haringey Borough
Harlow Town
Harrow Borough
Hartley Wintney
Hednesford Town

Hendon
Hitchin Town
Hyde United
Kettering Town
King's Lynn Town
Kings Langley
Kingstonian
Lancaster City
Leatherhead
Leiston
Lewes
Lowestoft Town
Margate
Marine
Matlock Town
Merstham
Merthyr Town
Metropolitan Police
Mickleover Sports
Nantwich Town
Needham Market
North Ferriby United
Poole Town
Potters Bar Town
Redditch United
Royston Town
Rushall Olympic
Salisbury
Scarborough Athletic
South Shields
St Ives Town
St Neots Town
Stafford Rangers
Staines Town
Stalybridge Celtic
Stourbridge
Stratford Town
Swindon Supermarine
Tamworth
Taunton Town
Tiverton Town
Tonbridge Angels
Walton Casuals
Warrington Town
Weymouth
Whitby Town
Whitehawk
Wimborne Town
Wingate & Finchley
Witton Albion
Workington AFC
Worthing

THE FA VASE 2017-18

FIRST QUALIFYING ROUND
SATURDAY 9 SEPTEMBER 2017 - WINNING CLUB TO RECEIVE £550 LOSING CLUB TO RECEIVE £175

1	Stokesley SC v Hebburn Town	0-8	37
2	Chester-Le-Street Town v Silsden	2-3	101
3	Sunderland Ryhope CW v Guisborough Town	7-1	
4	Seaham Red Star v Albion Sports	2-0	103
5	Whickham v Newton Aycliffe (8/9)	3-1	225
6	Padiham v Thackley (12/9)	5-0	
	(tie awarded to Thackley – Padiham removed)		
7	Garforth Town v Holker Old Boys	3-1	68
8	Blyth AFC v West Allotment Celtic (12.00)	2-1	
9	Esh Winning v Penrith	0-2	
10	Heaton Stannington v Carlisle City	1-3	
11	Tow Law Town v Crook Town	3-2	
12	Brandon United v Bishop Auckland	2-3	
13	Ashington v Easington Colliery	3-0	
14	Northallerton Town v Alnwick Town	4-2	
15	Marske United v Ryton & Crawcrook Albion	2-0	
16	Barnoldswick Town v Dunston UTS	0-1	
17	Darlington Railway Athletic v Harrogate Railway Athletic	4-6	
18	Eccleshill United v Jarrow Roofing Boldon CA	0-2	
19	Campion v Bedlington Terriers	1-2	
20	Widnes v Glasshoughton Welfare	1-2	
21	Alsager Town v New Mills	3-2	
22	Vauxhall Motors v 1874 Northwich	4-5aet	
23	Maltby Main v Cammell Laird 1907	4-2	
24	Northwich Victoria v Stockport Town (8/9)	3-4	
25	Hallam v Abbey Hey (10/9)	1-1aet	180
	Abbey Hey v Hallam (13/9)	0-1	60
26	St Helens Town v Hemsworth MW	1-2	
27	Selby Town v Charnock Richard	1-7	
28	Rossington Main v Cheadle Town	4-1	
29	Barnton v Peniston Church (12/9)	3-1	35
30	Maine Road v Pontefract Collieries	1-5	
31	Prestwich Heys v Liversedge (12/9)	1-2	39
32	Atherton LR v Irlam (12/9)	1-2	
33	Litherland Remyca v Ashton Town	1-0aet	
34	Parkgate v Daisy Hill	4-0	
35	Worsbrough Bridge Athletic v Dronfield Town (10/9)	2-3	
36	AFC Liverpool v Athersley Recreation (10/9)	3-2	118
37	AFC Blackpool v West Didsbury & Chorlton	1-6	
38	Squires Gate v Congleton Town	2-6	
39	Cadbury Athletic v Littleton	2-3	
40	Pegasus Juniors v Droitwich Spa	1-3aet	
41	Lutterworth Athletic v AFC Wulfrunians	2-4	
42	Boldmere St Michaels v Coventry Alvis	6-1	
43	Coventry United v Tipton Town (10/9)	3-1	282
44	Bewdley Town v Rugby Town	1-4	
45	Heather St Johns v Coventry Sphinx	5-4	
46	Barnt Green Spartak v Walsall Wood	0-1	
47	Westfields v Stapenhill	4-2	
48	Wellington Amateurs v Dudley Town	0-0aet	
	Dudley Town v Wellington Amateurs (13/9)	3-1aet	
49	Hereford Lads Club v Stone Old Alleynians	2-5	41
50	Studley v Long Buckby	3-0	
51	Leicester Road v Racing Club Warwick	1-4	
52	Malvern Town v Smethwick	1-4	
53	Chelmsley Town v AFC Bridgnorth	4-1	
54	Uttoxeter Town v Gornal Athletic	4-1	
55	Ellesmere Rangers v Highgate United	0-7	
56	Nuneaton Griff v Rocester (8/9)	5-8aet	88
57	Ashby Ivanhoe v St Martins	3-1	
58	Paget Rangers v Wolverhampton Casuals (8/9)	3-0	
59	Hanley Town v Lichfield City	5-1	
60	Ellistown & Ibstock United v Eccleshall	3-2	
61	Wolverhampton SC v FC Oswestry Town	5-0	
62	Shawbury United v Wellington	2-4	
63	Whitchurch Alport v Pershore Town	4-4aet	
	(Whitchurch Alport won 4-3 on kicks from the penalty mark - tie awarded to Pershore Town - Whitchurch Alport removed)		
64	Cradley Town v Bromyard Town	7-1	
65	Bilston Town v Bolehall Swifts	3-2	
66	Coton Green v Heath Hayes	2-5	
67	Tividale v Brocton	0-2	
68	Long Eaton United v Rainworth MW	2-0	
69	Hall Road Rangers v Gedling MW	2-0	
70	Quorn v Oadby Town	2-1	
71	Clifton All Whites v Harrowby United	2-2aet	
	Harrowby United v Clifton All Whites (12/9)	4-0	
72	Friar Lane & Epworth v Lutterworth Town	0-3	
73	Kimberley MW v Barrow Town	1-2	
	(tie awarded to Kimberley MW – Barrow Town removed)		
74	South Normanton v Melton Town	2-3	
75	Radcliffe Olympic v Belper United	0-6	17
76	Kirby Muxloe v Anstey Nomads	3-2	
77	Ilkeston v Clipstone		
	(walkover for Clipstone – Ilkeston removed)		
78	Leicester Nirvana v Graham St Prims	5-1	
79	Loughborough University v Winterton Rangers	5-0	
80	Worksop Town v Aylestone Park	5-2	
81	Grimsby Borough v Shirebrook Town (10/9)	0-3	80
82	Hucknall Town v Clay Cross Town	2-1	
83	Heanor Town v Holbrook Sports	0-2	
84	Collingham v Radford		
	(walkover for Radford – Collingham removed)		
85	Bottesford Town v West Bridgford	5-1	
86	Birstall United v South Normanton Athletic	1-6	
87	Skegness Town v Sleaford Town	3-0	
88	Westella & Willerby v Arnold Town	1-1aet	
	(Westella & Willerby won 5-4 on kicks from the penalty mark)		
	(at Arnold Town FC)		
89	Blaby & Whetstone Athletic v Blidworth Welfare	6-0	
90	Raunds Town v Wellingborough Town	2-0	
91	Stewarts & Lloyds v Swaffham Town	1-6	
92	Fakenham Town v Huntingdon Town	2-3	
93	Downham Town v Biggleswade United	0-2	
94	Histon v Blackstones	5-1	
95	Potton United v Netherton United	1-1aet	
	Netherton United v Potton United (13/9)	0-3	
96	Pinchbeck United v Holbeach United (8/9)	1-5	262
97	Bourne Town v Harborough Town	3-2	
98	March Town United v Peterborough Northern Star	2-3	
99	Cogenhoe United v Rothwell Corinthians	1-1aet	
	Rothwell Corinthians v Cogenhoe United (12/9)	1-2	
100	Stansted v Wodson Park	0-3	
101	Basildon United v St Margaretsbury	1-1aet	
	St Margaretsbury v Basildon United (12/9)	1-2	
102	Barkingside v Southend Manor (10/9)	2-1	80
103	Framlingham Town v Waltham Forest	2-0	
104	Brimsdown v Debenham LC	1-2	
105	FC Clacton v Coggeshall Town	0-2aet	
106	Hadleigh United v Wadham Lodge	2-1	

FAV1Q - Goal mouth action between Radcliffe Olympic (defending) and Belper United. Photo: Bill Wheatcroft.

FAV1Q - Horsham YMCAs Dean Carden gets in a tackle against Snodland Towns Liam Wilkins. Photo: Alan Coomes.

FAV1Q - Former Aston Villa forward, Julian Joachim in action for Radcliffe Olympic v Belper United. Photo: Bill Wheatcroft.

FAV2Q - Leicester Nirvana look to have beaten the Belper United 'keeper with this effort. Photo: Bill Wheatcroft.

FIRST QUALIFYING ROUND
SATURDAY 9 SEPTEMBER 2017 - WINNING CLUB TO RECEIVE £550 LOSING CLUB TO RECEIVE £175

No	Home		Away	Score	
107	Ilford	v	Cornard United	2-0	
108	Redbridge	v	Brantham Athletic	6-1	
109	Enfield 1893	v	Haverhill Borough (10/9)	1-0	72
110	Norwich CBS	v	Ipswich Wanderers	2-0	
111	Saffron Walden Town	v	Sawbridgeworth Town	1-2	
112	Enfield Borough	v	Canning Town	4-2	
113	Tower Hamlets	v	Hackney Wick (8/9)	2-1	102
114	Woodbridge Town	v	Hoddesdon Town	2-0	
115	Stowmarket Town	v	Team Bury (10/9)	7-0	120
	(at Bury Town FC)				
116	Long Melford	v	Halstead Town	1-2aet	
117	Great Yarmouth Town	v	FC Broxbourne Borough	3-1	
118	Haverhill Rovers	v	Whitton United	1-3	
119	Wivenhoe Town	v	Holland	0-2	
120	Great Wakering Rovers	v	Sporting Bengal United	6-1	
121	Wootton Blue Cross	v	London Lions	2-3aet	
122	Welwyn Garden City	v	Brackley Town Saints	3-1	
123	AFC Hayes	v	Hatfield Town	1-1aet	27
	Hatfield Town	v	AFC Hayes (12/9)	0-3	23
124	Hillingdon Borough	v	Marston Shelton Rovers	2-1	
125	Malmesbury Victoria	v	Chipping Sodbury Town	5-3aet	
126	New College Swindon	v	Ampthill Town	0-10	
127	Baldock Town	v	Buckingham Town (10/9)	1-0	
128	North Greenford United	v	Harpenden Town	3-4	
129	Oxford City Nomads	v	Woodley United (10/9)	3-1	19
130	Royal Wootton Bassett Town	v	Fairford Town (8/9)	3-1	159
131	Clanfield 85	v	Holmer Green	2-1	
132	Colney Heath	v	Harefield United	1-0	
133	Abingdon United	v	Highmoor Ibis	1-0	
134	Hadley	v	Milton United	2-0	
135	Edgware Town	v	Risborough Rangers	2-1	
136	Cricklewood Wanderers	v	Stotfold	7-2	
137	Crawley Green	v	Tuffley Rovers	2-1	
138	Highworth Town	v	Easington Sports	4-0	
139	Leighton Town	v	Brimscombe & Thrupp	3-1	
140	Ardley United	v	Longlevens	2-4	
141	Lydney Town	v	Winslow United	4-2	
142	Buckingham Athletic	v	Bedford	1-1aet	
	Bedford	v	Buckingham Athletic (12/9)	1-6	
143	Broadfields United	v	Pitshanger Dynamo	3-1	22
144	Amersham Town	v	Langford	1-3	
145	Rochester United	v	Lancing	3-5	
146	Southwick	v	Broadbridge Heath	2-7	
147	Hollands & Blair	v	Tooting & Mitcham Wanderers		
	(tie awarded to Hollands & Blair - Tooting & Mitcham Wanderers removed)				
148	AFC Croydon Athletic	v	Bearsted (10/9)	2-1	68
149	Eastbourne United	v	Newhaven	1-2aet	
150	Ringmer	v	AC London	1-3	
151	Erith & Belvedere	v	Holmesdale (10/9)	4-2aet	
152	Glebe	v	Deal Town	3-3aet	
	Deal Town	v	Glebe (12/9)	7-2	79
153	East Preston	v	Forest Hill Park	4-4aet	
	Forest Hill Park	v	East Preston (13/9)	1-0	
154	Sheppey United	v	Loxwood	5-1	
155	Oakwood	v	Langney Wanderers	2-4	
156	FC Elmstead	v	Whitstable Town	1-5	
157	Hailsham Town	v	Abbey Rangers	2-3	
158	Banstead Athletic	v	Fisher	1-2	
159	Westside	v	Steyning Town	0-2	
160	Snodland Town	v	Horsham YMCA	0-3	
161	Chessington & Hook United	v	Lydd Town	2-1	
162	Worthing United	v	Horley Town	2-4	
163	Colliers Wood United	v	K Sports	0-2	
164	Bridon Ropes	v	Wick	2-0	
165	FC Deportivo Galicia	v	Lewisham Borough (Com) (10/9)	6-3aet	
166	Walton & Hersham	v	Little Common	7-1	
167	Spelthorne Sports	v	Sutton Athletic		
	(walkover for Spelthorne Sports – Sutton Athletic removed)				
168	CB Hounslow United	v	Peacehaven & Telscombe	2-1	
169	St Francis Rangers	v	Erith Town	1-1aet	
	Erith Town	v	St Francis Rangers (13/9)	2-0	39
170	Seaford Town	v	Saltdean United	1-3	
171	Mile Oak	v	Chertsey Town	2-1	
172	Arundel	v	Lordswood	0-4	
173	Canterbury City	v	Sutton Common Rovers	4-3	
174	Stansfeld	v	Bedfont & Feltham (10/9)	4-0	84
175	Gravesham Borough	v	Cobham	1-3	
176	Tooting Bec	v	Littlehampton Town	3-1	
177	AFC Uckfield Town	v	Raynes Park Vale	2-0	
178	Redhill	v	Chatham Town	1-3	
179	Beckenham Town	v	Lingfield	3-2aet	
180	Bedfont Sports	v	Three Bridges	1-2	
181	Tadley Calleva	v	Andover New Street	3-2	
182	Shaftesbury	v	Brockenhurst	4-5aet	
183	Horndean	v	Andover Town	4-3aet	
184	Windsor	v	Devizes Town	2-1	
185	Hamble Club	v	Bemerton Heath Harlequins	3-1	
186	Ascot United	v	Farnham Town (10/9)	1-3	105
187	Hamworthy United	v	AFC Stoneham	5-2	
188	Amesbury Town	v	New Milton Town	3-0	
189	East Cowes Victoria Athletic	v	Calne Town	1-3	
190	AFC Aldermaston	v	Romsey Town	2-3	
191	Petersfield Town	v	Corsham Town	1-0	
192	Swanage Town & Herston	v	Ash United	4-3aet	
193	Cove	v	Westbury United	0-3	
194	Warminster Town	v	Folland Sports	3-1	
195	Knaphill	v	Sidlesham	1-0	
196	Pewsey Vale	v	Chippenham Park	0-2	
197	Newport (IW)	v	Fleet Spurs	5-2	
198	Guildford City	v	Lymington Town	1-2	
199	United Services Portsmouth	v	Verwood Town	2-1aet	25
200	Ringwood Town	v	Eversley & California	1-0	
201	Laverstock & Ford	v	Fawley	1-2	
202	Cowes Sports	v	Baffins Milton Rovers	1-3	
203	Hythe & Dibden	v	Bagshot	4-3	
204	Camelford	v	Helston Athletic	3-2	
205	Cullompton Rangers	v	Torpoint Athletic	1-0	
206	Wellington AFC	v	Wells City	3-1	
207	Cheddar	v	Radstock Town	1-3	
208	Bovey Tracey	v	Keynsham Town	3-1	
209	Witheridge	v	Cribbs	1-9	
210	Plymouth Parkway	v	Sherborne Town	4-1	
211	Axminster Town	v	Crediton United	2-4	
212	Tavistock	v	Hallen	2-0	
213	Almondsbury UWE	v	Clevedon Town	1-2	
214	Bitton	v	Brislington	1-3	
215	Welton Rovers	v	Willand Rovers	0-1	
216	Bridport	v	Wincanton Town	1-2	
217	AFC St Austell	v	Bishops Lydeard	9-1	
218	Cadbury Heath	v	St Blazey	3-1	
219	Roman Glass St George	v	Elburton Villa	2-0aet	
220	Ashton & Backwell United	v	Godolphin Atlantic	2-1	

SECOND QUALIFYING ROUND
SATURDAY 23 SEPTEMBER 2017 - WINNING CLUB TO RECEIVE £725 LOSING CLUB TO RECEIVE £250

No	Home		Away	Score	Att
1	Sunderland Ryhope CW	v	Northallerton Town	2-0aet	
2	Team Northumbria	v	Durham City	2-0	85
3	Stockton Town	v	Consett	4-3aet	
4	Garforth Town	v	Nelson	3-2	72
5	Hebburn Town	v	Newcastle Benfield	1-3	
6	Billingham Synthonia	v	Whitley Bay	2-2aet	125
	Whitley Bay	v	Billingham Synthonia (26/9)	3-0	233
7	Willington	v	Harrogate Railway Athletic	0-1	
8	Tow Law Town	v	Penrith	5-1	138
9	Carlisle City	v	Thornaby	2-3	66
10	Marske United	v	Seaham Red Star	2-0aet	170
11	Whickham	v	Blyth AFC (22/9)	3-2	150
12	West Auckland Town	v	Silsden	3-0	
13	Thackley	v	Ashington	2-3aet	96
14	Dunston UTS	v	Washington	5-0	235
15	Jarrow Roofing Boldon CA	v	Knaresborough Town	1-2	53
16	Bedlington Terriers	v	Bishop Auckland	2-0	
17	Rossington Main	v	Hallam	2-2aet	
	Hallam	v	Rossington Main (26/9)	0-2	105
18	Litherland Remyca	v	Chadderton	3-2	39
19	Irlam	v	Parkgate	2-1	68
20	Winsford United	v	Pontefract Collieries	1-4	
21	Alsager Town	v	Nostell MW	5-1	58
22	1874 Northwich	v	Congleton Town (24/9)	1-1aet	313
	Congleton Town	v	1874 Northwich (26/9)	0-1	218
23	AFC Liverpool	v	City of Liverpool	0-2	492
24	Sandbach United	v	AFC Emley	0-2	123
25	Ashton Athletic	v	Maltby Main	3-1	64
26	Charnock Richard	v	Bacup Borough	3-0	118
27	Burscough	v	Armthorpe Welfare	6-0	56
28	West Didsbury & Chorlton	v	Stockport Town	4-3	183
29	Glasshoughton Welfare	v	AFC Darwen	2-4	65
30	Dronfield Town	v	Barnton	4-2aet	
31	Hemsworth MW	v	Liversedge	2-3aet	82
32	Highgate United	v	Pershore Town (3/10)	6-2	
33	Bilston Town	v	Haughmond	1-4	74
34	Dudley Town	v	Atherstone Town	0-4	75
35	Wellington	v	Littleton	2-1	63
36	Chelmsley Town	v	AFC Wulfrunians	2-4	45
37	Dudley Sports	v	Brocton	0-6	
38	Shifnal Town	v	Droitwich Spa	3-2aet	
39	Cradley Town	v	Walsall Wood	0-2	67
40	Ellistown & Ibstock United	v	Wednesfield	0-5	33
41	Heather St Johns	v	Rocester	3-0	51
42	Westfields	v	Daventry Town	6-0	137
43	Stourport Swifts	v	Paget Rangers	5-1	79
44	Smethwick	v	Rugby Town (at Sporting Khalsa FC)	1-4	
45	Stafford Town	v	Ashby Ivanhoe	4-1	48
46	Studley	v	Hanley Town	0-2	
47	Boldmere St Michaels	v	Worcester City	3-4aet	
48	Racing Club Warwick	v	Coventry Copsewood	7-1	
49	Heath Hayes	v	Wolverhampton SC	0-3	
50	Uttoxeter Town	v	Bardon Hill (24/9)	0-1	135
51	Coventry United	v	Stone Old Alleynians (24/9)	2-1	170
52	Barton Town Old Boys	v	Clipstone	1-2	
53	Retford United	v	Pinxton	1-2	
54	Westella & Willerby	v	Ollerton Town (24/9)	4-0	39
55	Leicester Nirvana	v	Belper United	4-2	
56	Lutterworth Town	v	Teversal	7-0	
57	Shirebrook Town	v	Long Eaton United	3-1	153
58	Hall Road Rangers	v	Skegness Town	4-1	
59	Hucknall Town	v	Eastwood Community	1-4	214
60	Holwell Sports	v	Dunkirk	0-1	45
61	Melton Town	v	FC Bolsover	1-4	
62	Holbrook Sports	v	Quorn	1-2	53
63	Blaby & Whetstone Athletic	v	Bottesford Town	4-0	36
64	Loughborough University	v	Staveley MW	2-4	95
65	Worksop Town	v	Kirby Muxloe	3-0	339
66	Boston Town	v	South Normanton Athletic	1-2	
67	Sandiacre Town	v	Sherwood Colliery	1-3	
68	Harrowby United	v	St Andrews	4-1	
69	Radford	v	Kimberley MW	1-4	55
70	Godmanchester Rovers	v	Raunds Town	1-0	
71	Northampton On Chenecks	v	Irchester United	2-1	34
72	Swaffham Town	v	Rushden & Higham United	4-5aet	58
73	Biggleswade	v	Northampton Sileby Rangers	5-3	
74	Histon	v	Cogenhoe United	0-1	
75	Potton United	v	Peterborough Northern Star	1-2	
76	Bourne Town	v	Wisbech Town	0-5	151
77	Eynesbury Rovers	v	Burton Park Wanderers	2-1	
78	Biggleswade United	v	Thrapston Town	2-0	
79	Holbeach United	v	Huntingdon Town	2-1	
80	Thetford Town	v	Oakham United		
	(walkover for Thetford Town – Oakham United withdrawn)				
81	Wellingborough Whitworths	v	Wisbech St Mary	1-3	
82	Redbridge	v	Coggeshall Town	2-2aet	
	Coggeshall Town	v	Redbridge (26/9)	3-1	
83	Tower Hamlets	v	Little Oakley	10-1	56
84	Enfield Borough	v	Woodbridge Town	6-2	
85	Wroxham	v	Norwich CBS	0-3	151
86	Basildon United	v	Walsham Le Willows	2-1aet	
87	Barkingside	v	Whitton United (24/9)	2-3	90
88	Halstead Town	v	Stanway Rovers	2-1	128
89	West Essex	v	Great Wakering Rovers	1-2	
90	Diss Town	v	Framlingham Town	2-3aet	98
91	Ilford	v	Hullbridge Sports	0-3	40
92	Kirkley & Pakefield	v	Burnham Ramblers	2-3	66
93	Great Yarmouth Town	v	Debenham LC	1-1aet	
	Debenham LC	v	Great Yarmouth Town (26/9)	2-0aet	
94	Wodson Park	v	Holland	2-2aet	37
	Holland	v	Wodson Park (28/9)	4-1	
95	Stowmarket Town	v	Enfield 1893	4-5aet	132
96	Hadleigh United	v	Sawbridgeworth Town	1-2aet	84
97	Buckingham Athletic	v	AFC Hayes	1-0	72
98	Ampthill Town	v	Clanfield 85	4-0	
99	Highworth Town	v	Burnham	5-1	81
100	Abingdon United	v	Welwyn Garden City	0-2	
101	Broadfields United	v	Holyport	7-0	
102	Wantage Town	v	Lydney Town	2-0	68
103	Cricklewood Wanderers	v	Rayners Lane	7-2	
104	Hadley	v	Colney Heath	5-5aet	54
	Colney Heath	v	Hadley (26/9)	3-0	
105	Hillingdon Borough	v	Harpenden Town	0-3	
106	Wallingford Town	v	Oxhey Jets	1-2aet	43
107	Tytherington Rocks	v	Longlevens	1-8	
108	Oxford City Nomads	v	Baldock Town	1-5	
109	Royal Wootton Bassett Town	v	Codicote	5-0	62
110	London Lions	v	Malmesbury Victoria (1/10)	3-1	
	(23/9 – tie abandoned after 61 mins, due to serious injury to player, 0-1)				
111	Langford	v	Crawley Green	3-1	
	(tie awarded to Crawley Green – Langford removed)				
112	Edgware Town	v	Henley Town	4-0	49
113	Leighton Town	v	Leverstock Green	2-0	
114	Whitstable Town	v	Lancing	6-5aet	
115	Cobham	v	Bexhill United	2-0	67
116	AC London	v	Horley Town (22/9)	0-5	
117	Rusthall	v	Crawley Down Gatwick	2-1	
118	Hassocks	v	Spelthorne Sports	0-3	
119	Saltdean United	v	Stansfeld	3-1	
120	Balham	v	Forest Hill Park	5-0	
121	Horsham YMCA	v	Langney Wanderers	3-1	
122	Broadbridge Heath	v	AFC Croydon Athletic	3-2aet	
123	Billingshurst	v	Lordswood	1-2	
124	Steyning Town	v	Three Bridges	0-3	

SECOND QUALIFYING ROUND
SATURDAY 23 SEPTEMBER 2017 - WINNING CLUB TO RECEIVE £725 LOSING CLUB TO RECEIVE £250

125	Sporting Club Thamesmead	v	Walton & Hersham	0-8	
126	Meridian VP	v	FC Deportivo Galicia	0-0aet	
	(Meridian VP won 3-1 on kicks from the penalty mark)				
127	Beckenham Town	v	Bridon Ropes	1-0	
128	Erith & Belvedere	v	Chessington & Hook United	4-2aet	27
129	K Sports	v	Abbey Rangers	4-2	
130	Chatham Town	v	Kensington Borough	2-4aet	
131	Tooting Bec	v	Fisher	0-3	99
132	Newhaven	v	Hollands & Blair	1-2	84
133	Deal Town	v	CB Hounslow United	2-1	83
134	Erith Town	v	Mile Oak (24/9)	1-0	78
135	Sheppey United	v	Tunbridge Wells	2-2aet	331
	Tunbridge Wells	v	Sheppey United (26/9)	1-5	
136	Canterbury City	v	AFC Uckfield Town (24/9)	3-0	72
137	Newport (IW)	v	Alresford Town	2-1	100
138	Badshot Lea	v	Frimley Green	2-3	56
139	Romsey Town	v	Bournemouth	2-0	70
140	AFC Portchester	v	Tadley Calleva	3-0	
141	Knaphill	v	Horndean	0-2	105
142	Fareham Town	v	Binfield	4-2	
143	Godalming Town	v	Brockenhurst	3-5	
144	Alton Town	v	Amesbury Town	7-3	
145	Baffins Milton Rovers	v	Selsey	1-0	
146	Hamworthy United	v	Lymington Town	2-6	92
147	Calne Town	v	Downton	0-1	75
148	Sandhurst Town	v	Ringwood Town	2-1	
149	Warminster Town	v	Farnham Town	0-4	81
150	Midhurst & Easebourne	v	United Services Portsmouth	0-2	
151	Swanage Town & Herston	v	Fawley	3-2	
152	Windsor	v	Whitchurch United	8-0	96
153	Westbury United	v	Christchurch (11/10)	0-1	89
	(23/9 5-2aet – tie ordered to be replayed – at Christchurch FC)				
154	Bashley	v	Hythe & Dibden	4-0	
155	Chippenham Park	v	Camberley Town (24/9)	0-2	60
156	Hamble Club	v	Petersfield Town	5-0	
157	Willand Rovers	v	Saltash United	4-1	
158	Odd Down	v	Oldland Abbotonians	3-1	33
159	Radstock Town	v	Roman Glass St George	2-0	41
160	Hengrove Athletic	v	Ashton & Backwell United	3-1	55
161	Cadbury Heath	v	Shepton Mallet	3-1	69
162	Clevedon Town	v	Wellington AFC	0-1	
163	Bovey Tracey	v	Bishop Sutton	1-0	
164	AFC St Austell	v	Bridgwater Town	4-5aet	267
165	Wincanton Town	v	Plymouth Parkway	0-3	
166	Tavistock	v	Camelford (27/9)	3-2	
167	Cullompton Rangers	v	Cribbs	2-1	62
168	Portishead Town	v	Bodmin Town	1-6	
169	Longwell Green Sports	v	Ivybridge Town	2-3aet	
170	Crediton United	v	Brislington	0-0aet	57
	(Crediton United won 6-5 on kicks from the penalty mark)				

FIRST ROUND PROPER
SATURDAY 21 OCTOBER 2017 - WINNING CLUB TO RECEIVE £825 LOSING CLUB TO RECEIVE £275

1	Ashton Athletic	v	Liversedge (26/10)	4-2	75
	(21/10 – tie abandoned after 70 mins due to waterlogged pitch, 3-0)				
2	West Didsbury & Chorlton	v	West Auckland Town	0-3	
3	Irlam	v	1874 Northwich	1-4	174
4	Garforth Town	v	Knaresborough Town	2-3aet	
5	Team Northumbria	v	Runcorn Linnets	1-1aet	
	Runcorn Linnets	v	Team Northumbria (24/10)	3-2	261
6	AFC Emley	v	Thornaby	2-6	140
7	Rossington Main	v	Bootle	3-4aet	
8	Sunderland Ryhope CW	v	Harrogate Railway Athletic	10-1	48
9	Pickering Town	v	Newcastle Benfield	3-4aet	184
10	Dunston UTS	v	Burscough	2-1	182
11	Ashington	v	Hall Road Rangers	1-2	228
12	Tow Law Town	v	Bridlington Town	2-1	175
13	Bedlington Terriers	v	Charnock Richard	1-0	
14	Whickham	v	Stockton Town	0-2	84
15	North Shields	v	Handsworth Parramore	4-2	
16	AFC Darwen	v	Marske United (25/10)	2-3	135
17	Alsager Town	v	Runcorn Town	5-2	73
18	Westella & Willerby	v	Whitley Bay	1-5	
19	Pontefract Collieries	v	Litherland Remyca	3-1	99
20	City of Liverpool	v	Dronfield Town	7-0	372
21	Blaby & Whetstone Athletic	v	Northampton On Chenecks	3-1	44
22	Walsall Wood	v	Atherstone Town	1-0	133
23	Lutterworth Town	v	Coventry United	2-3	
24	Westfields	v	Shifnal Town	6-0	96
25	Brocton	v	Wednesfield	4-1	54
26	Stourport Swifts	v	Shirebrook Town	3-2	108
27	Worcester City	v	Sherwood Colliery	4-3	408
28	Wolverhampton SC	v	Staveley MW (25/10)	4-2	
29	Rugby Town	v	Harrowby United	2-0aet	
30	Pinxton	v	Heather St Johns	3-1	112
31	Hanley Town	v	Godmanchester Rovers	1-3	82
32	Racing Club Warwick	v	Clipstone	2-0	
33	Haughmond	v	Worksop Town	1-2	155
34	Wellington	v	Desborough Town	0-2	45
35	Eastwood Community	v	Dunkirk	3-2	120
36	Bardon Hill	v	Quorn	3-4	54
37	Stafford Town	v	Kimberley MW	0-1	58
38	AFC Wulfrunians	v	Leicester Nirvana	1-1aet	
	Leicester Nirvana	v	AFC Wulfrunians (24/10)	4-1	
39	Rushden & Higham United	v	Highgate United	0-2	
40	FC Bolsover	v	Deeping Rangers	1-3	67
41	Holbeach United	v	South Normanton Athletic	1-0	
42	Hullbridge Sports	v	Colney Heath	1-1aet	
	Colney Heath	v	Hullbridge Sports (24/10)	0-1	
43	Holland	v	Great Wakering Rovers (20/10)	1-2	100
44	Burnham Ramblers	v	Leighton Town	0-1	
45	London Colney	v	Cogenhoe United	4-4aet	
	Cogenhoe United	v	London Colney (24/10)	1-0	
46	Basildon United	v	Biggleswade	0-2	95
47	Enfield 1893	v	Coggeshall Town (22/10)	1-0aet	113
48	Enfield Borough	v	Newmarket Town	4-2	
49	Framlingham Town	v	Cockfosters	2-0	
50	Wisbech St Mary	v	Whitton United	2-1	
51	Norwich CBS	v	Oxhey Jets	1-0	
52	Thetford Town	v	Debenham LC	1-1aet	
	Debenham LC	v	Thetford Town (24/10)	0-2	
53	Welwyn Garden City	v	Takeley	3-0	
54	Halstead Town	v	Tower Hamlets	2-2aet	
	(Tower Hamlets won 6-5 on kicks from the penalty mark)				
55	Peterborough Northern Star	v	Baldock Town	1-0	74
56	Biggleswade United	v	Yaxley	0-1	
57	Crawley Green	v	Harpenden Town	3-0	
58	Wisbech Town	v	Felixstowe & Walton United	4-0	
59	FC Romania	v	Eynesbury Rovers (22/10)	2-0	
60	Edgware Town	v	Walton & Hersham	1-3	
61	Haywards Heath Town	v	Camberley Town	2-0	93
62	Cobham	v	Westfield	0-4	
63	Bracknell Town	v	Buckingham Athletic	6-2	232
64	Erith & Belvedere	v	Horley Town	2-2aet	
	Horley Town	v	Erith & Belvedere (24/10)	3-2aet	
65	Balham	v	Deal Town	1-3	
66	Thatcham Town	v	Horsham YMCA	2-1	
67	London Lions	v	Clapton	3-2	
68	Sevenoaks Town	v	Longlevens	2-1	66
69	Broadbridge Heath	v	Kensington Borough	3-0	61
70	Beckenham Town	v	Sawbridgeworth Town	2-0	
71	Saltdean United	v	Whitstable Town	0-1aet	

FAV2Q - Walton & Hershams Jamie Thoroughgood heads clear from SC Thamesmeads Josh Patrick. Photo: Alan Coomes.

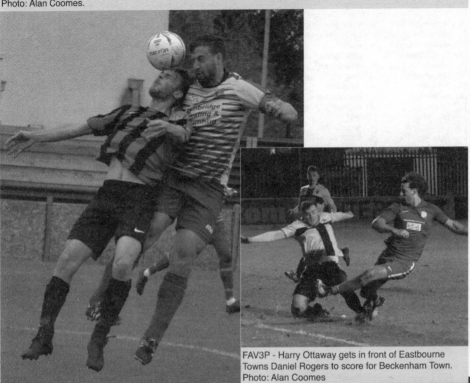

FAV3P - Harry Ottaway gets in front of Eastbourne Towns Daniel Rogers to score for Beckenham Town. Photo: Alan Coomes

FAV2P - Leicester Nirvana's No.9 fires in on goal but the Eastwood Community stand firm to go through to the third round.
Photo: Bill Wheatcroft.

FAV2P - Meridians Harvey Brinkley blocks a cross from Horley Towns Tate Greenaway. Photo: Alan Coomes.

FIRST ROUND PROPER
SATURDAY 21 OCTOBER 2017 - WINNING CLUB TO RECEIVE £825 LOSING CLUB TO RECEIVE £275

72	Cray Valley (PM)	v	Cricklewood Wanderers	3-1	40
	(tie awarded to Cricklewood Wanderers – Cray Valley PM removed – subject to appeal)				
73	Rusthall	v	Epsom & Ewell	2-7	
74	Canterbury City	v	K Sports	4-3	42
75	Royal Wootton Bassett Town	v	Ampthill Town	2-1	
76	Spelthorne Sports	v	Lordswood	0-1	48
77	Sheppey United	v	Fisher	2-1	
78	Erith Town	v	Pagham	4-0	42
79	Wembley	v	Broadfields United	3-0	44
80	Hanworth Villa	v	Three Bridges	3-2	72
81	Flackwell Heath	v	Windsor	2-5	102
82	Meridian VP	v	Hollands & Blair	2-0	30
83	Bodmin Town	v	Swanage Town & Herston (28/10)	2-1	
84	Odd Down	v	Tavistock	1-2	36
85	AFC Portchester	v	Cullompton Rangers	2-3	173
86	Wellington AFC	v	Downton	4-3aet	
87	Highworth Town	v	Sholing	1-3	122
88	Christchurch	v	United Services Portsmouth	3-0	56
89	Romsey Town	v	Hamble Club	2-3	
90	Portland United	v	Horndean (24/10)	0-1	91
91	Fareham Town	v	Ivybridge Town	4-3	
92	Wantage Town	v	Cadbury Heath	4-3	53
93	Baffins Milton Rovers	v	Radstock Town	1-0	
94	Hengrove Athletic	v	Alton Town	4-2aet	
95	Newport (IW)	v	Bovey Tracey	7-2	110
96	Plymouth Parkway	v	Sandhurst Town	6-1	221
97	Brockenhurst	v	Crediton United	2-1aet	
98	Willand Rovers	v	Street	7-1	
99	Farnham Town	v	Lymington Town	2-0	83
100	Frimley Green	v	Blackfield & Langley	0-2	
101	Bashley	v	Bridgwater Town	2-3aet	

SECOND ROUND PROPER
SATURDAY 11 NOVEMBER 2017 - WINNING CLUB TO RECEIVE £900 LOSING CLUB TO RECEIVE £300

1	Stockton Town	v	Bootle	4-2aet	360
2	North Shields	v	Knaresborough Town	2-1	372
3	Dunston UTS	v	Worksop Town	0-1	368
4	Marske United	v	Shildon	2-1aet	431
5	Sunderland Ryhope CW	v	City of Liverpool	1-2	245
6	1874 Northwich	v	Tow Law Town (14/11)	5-1	229
7	Hall Road Rangers	v	Pontefract Collieries	2-4	96
8	West Auckland Town	v	Billingham Town	3-2	
9	Runcorn Linnets	v	Sunderland RCA	1-1aet	
	Sunderland RCA	v	Runcorn Linnets (14/11)	1-2	
10	Ashton Athletic	v	Morpeth Town	1-0	
11	Bedlington Terriers	v	Newcastle Benfield	0-3	
12	Thornaby	v	Whitley Bay	2-4	230
13	Wolverhampton SC	v	Rugby Town	2-2aet	107
	Rugby Town	v	Wolverhampton SC (14/11)	0-2	
14	Hinckley	v	AFC Mansfield	2-0	
15	Coleshill Town	v	Blaby & Whetstone Athletic	8-1	
16	Godmanchester Rovers	v	Deeping Rangers	3-4	
17	Brocton	v	Shepshed Dynamo	3-5	102
18	Desborough Town	v	Pinxton	7-4aet	
19	Quorn	v	Coventry United	0-6	
20	Racing Club Warwick	v	Alsager Town	2-1	186
21	Leicester Nirvana	v	Eastwood Community	0-2	134
22	Walsall Wood	v	Holbeach United	5-0	171
23	Worcester City	v	Highgate United	1-2	
24	Kimberley MW	v	Stourport Swifts	0-2	109
25	Sporting Khalsa	v	Bromsgrove Sporting	0-1	
26	Tring Athletic	v	Ely City	4-1	
27	Welwyn Garden City	v	Newport Pagnell Town	2-1	
28	Thetford Town	v	Wisbech Town	1-4	286
29	Biggleswade	v	Crawley Green	2-0	
30	Yaxley	v	Peterborough Northern Star	3-0	
31	Leighton Town	v	London Lions	1-0	140
32	Hullbridge Sports	v	Wembley	3-2	
33	Sun Sports	v	Cogenhoe United		
	(walkover for Cogenhoe United – Sun Sports removed)				
34	Tower Hamlets	v	Enfield 1893	1-2	77
35	Enfield Borough	v	Berkhamsted	2-4aet	
36	Gorleston	v	Framlingham Town	2-1	127
37	Wisbech St Mary	v	Norwich CBS	1-4	
38	Great Wakering Rovers	v	FC Romania	2-2aet	115
	FC Romania	v	Great Wakering Rovers (15/11) 0-1		
39	Erith Town	v	Windsor	1-2	
40	Walton & Hersham	v	Hanworth Villa	2-1	142
41	Haywards Heath Town	v	Sevenoaks Town (14/11)	1-2	78
42	Whitstable Town	v	Epsom & Ewell	3-2aet	186
43	Meridian VP	v	Horley Town	0-3	41
44	Sheppey United	v	Beckenham Town	2-3	318
45	Westfield	v	Canterbury City	1-0	
46	Thatcham Town	v	Broadbridge Heath	8-2	
47	Southall	v	Lordswood	1-2	
48	Crowborough Athletic	v	Croydon	5-0	205
49	Bracknell Town	v	Cricklewood Wanderers	8-0	282
50	Corinthian	v	Eastbourne Town	3-4	74
51	Chichester City	v	Deal Town (14/11)	3-0	
52	Christchurch	v	Fareham Town	3-2	126
53	Team Solent	v	Tavistock (14/11)	2-0	
54	Exmouth Town	v	Blackfield & Langley	1-3	
55	Sholing	v	Wellington AFC	2-1	128
56	Wantage Town	v	Melksham Town	1-4	108
57	Newport (IW)	v	Hengrove Athletic	6-2	
58	Baffins Milton Rovers	v	Cullompton Rangers	3-1	
59	Buckland Athletic	v	Bradford Town	1-2	
60	Hamble Club	v	Brockenhurst	5-4aet	
61	Willand Rovers	v	Westfields	1-2	
62	Farnham Town	v	Bridgwater Town	2-3	
63	Plymouth Parkway	v	Bodmin Town	4-2	435
64	Horndean	v	Royal Wootton Bassett Town (14/11) 3-2		

FAV4P - Desborough Town on the attack against Stourport Swifts. Photo: Bill Wheatcroft.

FAV5P - Action from the Melksham v Tring tie. Photo: Peter Barnes.

FAVQF - Melksham take on eventual FA Vase winners Thatcham Town (Stripes). Photo: Peter Barnes.

THIRD ROUND PROPER
SATURDAY 2 DECEMBER 2017 - WINNING CLUB TO RECEIVE £1,125 LOSING CLUB TO RECEIVE £375

#	Home		Away	Score	Att
1	1874 Northwich	v	Ashton Athletic	2-0	248
2	Stockton Town	v	City Of Liverpool	1-0	527
3	West Auckland Town	v	Whitley Bay	4-3	
4	Pontefract Collieries	v	Worksop Town	3-0	270
5	Newcastle Benfield	v	North Shields	3-1	298
6	Runcorn Linnets	v	Marske United	2-3	369
7	Stourport Swifts	v	Walsall Wood	3-1	141
8	Bromsgrove Sporting	v	Coventry United	1-1aet	834
	Coventry United	v	Bromsgrove Sporting (6/12)	3-3aet	205
	(Bromsgrove Sporting won 4-3 on kicks from the penalty mark)				
9	Wolverhampton SC	v	Shepshed Dynamo	5-0	98
10	Desborough Town	v	Eastwood Community	4-1	194
11	Highgate United	v	Coleshill Town	1-2	
12	Hinckley	v	Deeping Rangers	3-1	193
13	Racing Club Warwick	v	Wisbech Town	0-2	229
14	Gorleston	v	Leighton Town	2-4	124
15	Hullbridge Sports	v	Enfield 1893	3-2	
16	Yaxley	v	Norwich CBS	2-3	
17	Great Wakering Rovers	v	Cogenhoe United	0-2	98
18	Tring Athletic	v	Berkhamsted	1-0	
19	Welwyn Garden City	v	Biggleswade	1-2	
20	Lordswood	v	Bracknell Town	0-1	
21	Beckenham Town	v	Eastbourne Town	2-3	
22	Horley Town	v	Baffins Milton Rovers	4-1	207
23	Walton & Hersham	v	Windsor	1-2	
24	Crowborough Athletic	v	Westfield	1-0	
25	Whitstable Town	v	Chichester City	0-2	
26	Thatcham Town	v	Sevenoaks Town	3-1	
27	Christchurch	v	Newport (IW)	0-1	92
28	Sholing	v	Blackfield & Langley	0-1	169
29	Plymouth Parkway	v	Westfields	2-3	253
30	Hamble Club	v	Horndean	2-1	
31	Bridgwater Town	v	Melksham Town	2-2aet	247
	Melksham Town	v	Bridgwater Town (4/12)	2-0	204
32	Bradford Town	v	Team Solent	4-0	143

FOURTH ROUND PROPER
SATURDAY 6 JANUARY 2018 - WINNING CLUB TO RECEIVE £1,875 LOSING CLUB TO RECEIVE £625

#	Home		Away	Score	Att
1	Newcastle Benfield	v	Coleshill Town	1-1aet	203
	Coleshill Town	v	Newcastle Benfield (13/1)	1-1aet	224
	(Coleshill Town won 4-2 on kicks from the penalty mark)				
2	Wisbech Town	v	Bromsgrove Sporting	1-3	650
3	Cogenhoe United	v	Wolverhampton SC	2-3	155
4	Marske United	v	Hinckley (13/1)	5-0	252
	(at Billingham Town FC)				
5	1874 Northwich	v	Pontefract Collieries (7/1)	3-1	625
	(at Witton Albion FC)				
6	Stockton Town	v	West Auckland Town	2-1aet	537
7	Desborough Town	v	Stourport Swifts	2-4aet	292
8	Melksham Town	v	Crowborough Athletic	2-1	686
9	Westfields	v	Hamble Club	1-4	242
10	Blackfield & Langley	v	Bracknell Town	3-3aet	145
	Bracknell Town	v	Blackfield & Langley (9/1)	2-1	396
11	Leighton Town	v	Norwich CBS	5-2aet	260
12	Newport (IW)	v	Bradford Town (13/1)	0-1	249
13	Eastbourne Town	v	Windsor	1-3	596
14	Horley Town	v	Chichester City	1-2	317
15	Tring Athletic	v	Hullbridge Sports	5-1	217
16	Thatcham Town	v	Biggleswade	2-1	

FIFTH ROUND PROPER
SATURDAY 3 FEBRUARY 2018 - WINNING CLUB TO RECEIVE £2,250 LOSING CLUB TO RECEIVE £750

#	Home		Away	Score	Att
1	Wolverhampton SC	v	Leighton Town (10/2)	3-4	158
2	Thatcham Town	v	Bromsgrove Sporting	2-1	
3	Marske United	v	Bradford Town	2-0	383
4	Coleshill Town	v	Bracknell Town	2-4aet	285
5	1874 Northwich	v	Chichester City	1-0	580
	(at Witton Albion FC)				
6	Stockton Town	v	Stourport Swifts	3-0	663
7	Windsor	v	Hamble Club	2-0	625
8	Melksham Town	v	Tring Athletic	2-1	1236

QUARTER FINALS
SATURDAY 24 FEBRUARY 2018 - WINNING CLUB TO RECEIVE £4,125 LOSING CLUB TO RECEIVE £1,375

#	Home		Away	Score	Att
1	Bracknell Town	v	Marske United	0-3	1082
2	Melksham Town	v	Thatcham Town	0-1	2208
3	Stockton Town	v	Windsor	2-0	1213
4	Leighton Town	v	1874 Northwich	0-1	1109

SEMI FINALS
1ST LEG SATURDAY 17 MARCH / 2ND LEG SATURDAY 24 MARCH 2018 - WINNERS RECEIVE £5,500 LOSING CLUB TO RECEIVE £1,750

Home		Away	Score	Att
Marske United	v	Stockton Town	0-2	1500
Stockton Town	v	Marske United	1-2	1800
Stockton Town through 3-2 on aggregate.				3300
Thatcham Town	v	1874 Northwich	1-0	1134
1874 Northwich	v	Thatcham Town	2-3	1693
Thatcham Town through 4-2 on aggregate.				2827

THE FINAL...

STOCKTON TOWN 0

THATCHAM TOWN 1

Cooper-Clark 23 (pen)

Wembley Stadium ~ Att: 31,430*
*combined Trophy/Vase attendance

THE SQUADS

STOCKTON TOWN	THATCHAM TOWN
Michael Arthur	Chris Rackley
Joe Carter (sub 61)	Lewis Brownhill
James Ward (sub 79)	Curtis Angell
Nathan Mulligan	Tom Melledew (c) (sub 81)
Dale Mulligan	Baboucarr Jarra
Tom Coulthard (c)	Tom Moran
Kevin Hayes	Harrison Bayley
Fred Woodhouse	Shane Cooper-Clark (sub 89)
Jamie Owens	Gavin James
James Risbrough	Ekow Elliott
Chris Stockton (67)	Jordan Brown (sub 70)

Substitutes	Substitutes
Matthew Garbutt (61)	Jemel Johnson (70)
Sonni Coleman (67)	Ashleigh James (81)
Adam Nicholson (79)	Ross Cook (89)
Alan Cossavella	Harry Grant
Chris Dunwell	Gareth Thomas

Referee Darren England
Assisted by Matthew Jones and Marc Wilson
4th official, Robert Jones

With 619 teams originally entering this year's Vase these two teams, which had successfully come through to make the final, were each appearing at this stage for the first time. Fittingly we had one from the south, The Kingfishers, and one from the north of the country, The Anchors, to bring some balance, especially for the non-committed. Previously, Stockton's home, the Northern League, having won 8 out of the last 9 finals, had dominated but Thatcham, having had a forty game unbeaten run during the season, were the favourites. They were already Hellenic League champions and, after a season long stay at Step Five, the blue and whites are set for return to the Southern League. As a result boss Danny Robinson, who described his club's achievement as "once in a lifetime", had recently signed for a further two year stint as manager. He particularly praised his central defenders. On the other hand Stockton had actually made a remarkable recovery after losing their first nine games of the season and, in the Vase, having, not once but several times, needed extra time to win through, including a last minute winner versus Consett in their first match in the season's competition. For many years Stockton did not have an adult team, only a number of junior sides

so they have made good progress. To their credit, additionally most, if not all, of their players have come up through the club's own ranks. Manager Michael Dunwell, ex Hartlepool player, with a brother on the bench, was rightly pleased by his players' performances and thought they had been a good advert for the club which, despite those early losses, had finished seventh in their league. Certainly they could not have given any more effort than they expended here.

It was the yellow and blue clad Stockton who dominated the early moments as Joe Carter found ample space on the right to despatch a low cross into the area. Fortunately Baboucarr Jarra was alert and able to clear. A similar move down the left was again thwarted by the resolute Jarra while Gavin James had a shot blocked at the other end. There were some very competitive challenges early on from both sides, Thatcham's Curtis Angell looking most fortunate to escape a yellow card. His team mate, Ekow Elliott, was notably lively on the left and it was his team which took the lead in the 23rd minute. Jordan Brown was clearly brought down in the penalty area by James Ward and up stepped leading scorer Shane Cooper-Clark to score, the

Arthur (Stockton) saves at the feet of James (Thatcham). Photo: Keith Clayton.

forcefulness of his spot kick paying dividends as goalkeeper Michael Arthur's strong arm all but halted its progress before it spun wildly into the opposite corner.

The extreme heat led to a water break just after the half hour but the brief rest did little to threaten Thatcham's dominance, their interpassing being more accurate and promising than that of their opponents. Tom Moran spoilt his good approach work with a misplaced final pass and two good Elliott raids also failed to find a team mate. A free kick, as the half ended, bounced off the Stockton wall and the follow up was blocked at the foot of his post by Arthur before anyone could pounce on the loose ball.

The second half opened with Stockton looking more dangerous. Angell was forced to hoof clear and Jamie Owens shot just wide. A Carter foray produced a low cross which eluded his team mates but raised the hopes of Stockton supporters, although their hearts were thumping a few moments later as Thatcham nearly scored a second when Arthur's clearance went straight to Gavin James in front of goal. His fierce shot hit the bar and, at first sight, appeared to bounce behind the line but replays showed the officials

Stocktons Jamie Owens is tackled by Thatchams Tom Moran. Photo: Alan Coomes.

had been correct in continuing play. James next almost presented his newly arrived team mate, Jemel Johnson, with a scoring opportunity whilst Kevin Hayes was now looking more prominent for the northerners, in creating some half chances.

As the minutes ebbed away Stockton were definitely in the ascendancy and raised their supporters' spirits. A couple of corners exerted pressure on the Thatcham back line. There were appeals for handball as a corner was cleared and goalkeeper Chris Rackley eagerly fell on the ball to waste a few seconds. The outstanding Jarra, deservedly awarded man of the match, blocked one shot at point blank range and then cleared over his own bar as the pressure mounted. A third successive corner was headed over by Dale Mulligan. In the dying minutes goalkeeper Arthur, to add pressure, ventured upfield for a further corner. As this was cleared newly arrived sub Ross Cook securing the ball, raced towards Arthur's now unguarded goal and rolled the ball goalwards. Only a miraculous last ditch slide from Matthew Garbutt managed to divert the ball and prevent a further Thatcham score. Still that one score from the penalty spot meant the 2018 Vase ended up in Berkshire hands.

Arthur Evans.

Jarra (Thatcham) clears with the keeper well beaten. Photo: Keith Clayton.

Thatcham Town celebrate their FA Vase final win. Photo: Peter Barnes.

PAST FINALS

1975 HODDESDON TOWN 2 *(South Midlands)*   **EPSOM & EWELL 1** *(Surrey Senior)*   Att: 9,500
Sedgwick 2   Wales   Ref: Mr R Toseland
Hoddesdon: Galvin, Green, Hickey, Maybury, Stevenson, Wilson, Bishop, Picking, Sedgwick, Nathan, Schofield
Epsom & Ewell: Page, Bennett, Webb, Wales, Worby, Jones, O'Connell, Walker, Tuite, Eales, Lee

1976 BILLERICAY TOWN 1 *(Essex Senior)*   **STAMFORD 0 (aet)** *(United Counties)*   Att: 11,848
Aslett   Ref: Mr A Robinson
Billericay: Griffiths, Payne, Foreman, Pullin, Bone, Coughlan, Geddes, Aslett, Clayden, Scott, Smith
Stamford: Johnson, Kwiatowski, Marchant, Crawford, Downs, Hird, Barnes, Walpole, Smith, Russell, Broadbent

1977 BILLERICAY TOWN 1 *(Essex Senior)*   **SHEFFIELD 1 (aet)** *(Yorkshire)*   Att: 14,000
Clayden   Coughlan og   Ref: Mr J Worrall
Billericay: Griffiths, Payne, Bone, Coughlan, Pullin, Scott, Wakefield, Aslett, Clayden, Woodhouse, McQueen. Sub: Whettell
Sheffield: Wing, Gilbody, Lodge, Hardisty, Watts, Skelton, Kay, Travis, Pugh, Thornhill, Haynes. Sub: Strutt

Replay BILLERICAY TOWN 2   **SHEFFIELD 1**   Att: 3,482
Aslett, Woodhouse   Thornhill   at Nottingham Forest
Billericay: Griffiths, Payne, Pullin, Whettell, Bone, McQueen, Woodhouse, Aslett, Clayden, Scott, Wakefield
Sheffield: Wing, Gilbody, Lodge, Strutt, Watts, Skelton, Kay, Travis, Pugh, Thornhill, Haynes

1978 NEWCASTLE BLUE STAR 2 *(Wearside)*   **BARTON ROVERS 1** *(South Midlands)*   Att: 16,858
Dunn, Crumplin   Smith   Ref: Mr T Morris
Newcastle: Halbert, Feenan, Thompson, Davidson, S Dixon, Beynon, Storey, P Dixon, Crumplin, Callaghan, Dunn. Sub: Diamond
Barton Rovers: Blackwell, Stephens, Crossley, Evans, Harris, Dollimore, Dunn, Harnaman, Fossey, Turner, Smith. Sub: Cox

1979 BILLERICAY TOWN 4 *(Athenian)*   **ALMONDSBURY GREENWAY 1** *(Glos. Co)*   Att: 17,500
Young 3, Clayden   Price   Ref: Mr C Steel
Billericay: Norris, Blackaller, Bingham, Whettell, Bone, Reeves, Pullin, Scott, Clayden, Young, Groom. Sub: Carrigan
Almondsbury: Hamilton, Bowers, Scarrett, Sullivan, Tudor, Wookey, Bowers, Shehean, Kerr, Butt, Price. Sub: Kilbaine

1980 STAMFORD 2 *(United Counties)*   **GUISBOROUGH TOWN 0** *(Northern Alliance)*   Att: 11,500
Alexander, McGowan   Ref: Neil Midgeley
Stamford: Johnson, Kwiatkowski, Ladd, McGowan, Bliszczak I, Mackin, Broadhurst, Hall, Czarnecki, Potter, Alexander. Sub: Bliszczak S
Guisborough: Cutter, Scott, Thornton, Angus, Maltby, Percy, Skelton, Coleman, McElvaney, Sills, Dilworth. Sub: Harrison

1981 WHICKHAM 3 *(Wearside)*   **WILLENHALL 2 (aet)** *(West Midlands)*   Att: 12,000
Scott, Williamson, Peck og   Smith, Stringer   Ref: Mr R Lewis
Whickham: Thompson, Scott, Knox, Williamson, Cook, Ward, Carroll, Diamond, Cawthra, Robertson, Turnbull. Sub: Alton
Willenhall: Newton, White, Darris, Woodall, Heath, Fox, Peck, Price, Matthews, Smith, Stringer. Sub: Trevor

1982 FOREST GREEN ROVERS 3 *(Hellenic)*   **RAINWORTH M.W 0** *(Notts Alliance)*   Att: 12,500
Leitch 2, Norman   Ref: Mr K Walmsey
Forest Green: Moss, Norman, Day, Turner, Higgins, Jenkins, Guest, Burns, Millard, Leitch, Doughty. Sub: Dangerfield
Rainworth M.W: Watson, Hallam, Hodgson, Slater, Sterland, Oliver, Knowles, Raine, Radzi, Reah, Comerford. Sub: Robinson

1983 V.S. RUGBY 1 *(West Midlands)*   **HALESOWEN TOWN 0** *(West Midlands)*   Att: 13,700
Crawley   Ref: Mr B Daniels
VS Rugby: Burton, McGinty, Harrison, Preston, Knox, Evans, ingram, Setchell, Owen, Beecham, Crawley. Sub: Haskins
Halesowen Town: Coldicott, Penn, Edmonds, Lacey, Randall, Shilvock, Hazelwood, Moss, Woodhouse, P Joinson, L Joinson. Sub: Smith

1984 STANSTED 3 *(Essex Senior)*   **STAMFORD 2** *(United Counties)*   Att: 8,125
Holt, Gillard, Reading   Waddicore, Allen   Ref: Mr T Bune
Stanstead: Coe, Williams, Hilton, Simpson, Cooper, Reading, Callanan, Holt, Reevs, Doyle, Gillard. Sub: Williams
Stamford: Parslow, Smitheringate, Blades, McIlwain, Lyon, Mackin, Genovese, Waddicore, Allen, Robson, Beech. Sub: Chapman

1985 HALESOWEN TOWN 3 *(West Midlands)*   **FLEETWOOD TOWN 1** *(N W Counties)*   Att: 16,715
L Joinson 2, Moss   Moran   Ref: Mr C Downey
Halesowen: Coldicott, Penn, Sherwood, Warner, Randle, Heath, Hazlewood, Moss (Smith), Woodhouse, P Joinson, L Joinson
Fleetwood Town: Dobson, Moran, Hadgraft, Strachan, Robinson, Milligan, Hall, Trainor, Taylor (Whitehouse), Cain, Kennerley

1986 HALESOWEN TOWN 3 *(West Midlands)*   **SOUTHALL 0** *(Isthmian 2 South)*   Att: 18,340
Moss 2, L Joinson   Ref: Mr D Scott
Halesowen: Pemberton, Moore, Lacey, Randle (Rhodes), Sherwood, Heath, Penn, Woodhouse, P Joinson, L Joinson, Moss
Southall: Mackenzie, James, McGovern, Croad, Holland, Powell (Richmond), Pierre, Richardson, Sweales, Ferdinand, Rowe

1987 ST. HELENS 3 *(N W Counties)*   **WARRINGTON TOWN** 2 *(N W Counties)*   Att: 4,254
Layhe 2, Rigby   Reid, Cook   Ref: Mr T Mills
St Helens: Johnson, Benson, Lowe, Bendon, Wilson, McComb, Collins (Gledhill), O'Neill,Cummins, Lay, Rigby. Sub: Deakin
Warrington: O'Brien. Copeland, Hunter, Gratton, Whalley, Reid, Brownville (Woodyer), Cook,Kinsey, Looker (Hill), Hughes

1988 COLNE DYNAMOES 1 *(N W Counties)*   **EMLEY** 0 *(Northern Counties East)*   Att: 15,000
Anderson   Ref: Mr A Seville
Colne Dynamoes: Mason, McFafyen, Westwell, Bentley, Dunn, Roscoe, Rodaway, Whitehead (Burke),Diamond, Anderson, Wood (Coates)
Emley: Dennis, Fielding, Mellor, Codd, Hirst (Burrows), Gartland (Cook), Carmody,Green, Bramald, Devine, Francis

1989 TAMWORTH 1 *(West Midlands)*   **SUDBURY TOWN** 1 (aet) *(Eastern)*   Att: 26,487
Devaney   Hubbick   Ref: Mr C Downey
Tamworth: Bedford, Lockett, Atkins, Cartwright, McCormack, Myers, Finn, Devaney, Moores,Gordon, Stanton. Subs: Rathbone, Heaton
Sudbury Town: Garnham, Henry, G Barker, Boyland, Thorpe, Klug, D Barker, Barton, Oldfield,Smith, Hubbick. Subs: Money, Hunt
Replay **TAMWORTH** 3   **SUDBURY TOWN** 0   Att: 11,201
Stanton 2, Moores   at Peterborough
Tamworth: Bedford, Lockett, Atkins, Cartwright, Finn, Myers, George, Devaney, Moores,Gordon, Stanton. Sub: Heaton
Sudbury Town: Garnham, Henry, G Barker, Boyland, Thorpe, Klug, D Barker, Barton, Oldfield,Smith, Hubbick. Subs: Money, Hunt

1990 YEADING 0 *(Isthmian 2 South)*   **BRIDLINGTON TOWN** 0 (aet) *(N Co East)*   Att: 7,932
                                                                                                 Ref: Mr R Groves
Yeading: Mackenzie, Wickens, Turner, Whiskey (McCarthy), Croad, Denton, Matthews, James(Charles), Sweates, Impey, Cordery
Bridlington: Taylor, Pugh, Freeman, McNeill, Warburton, Brentano, Wilkes (Hall), Noteman,Gauden, Whiteman, Brattan (Brown)
Replay **YEADING** 1   **BRIDLINGTON TOWN** 0   Att: 5,000
Sweales   at Leeds Utd FC
Yeading: Mackenzie, Wickens, Turner, Whiskey, Croad (McCarthy), Schwartz, Matthews,James, Sweates, Impey (Welsh), Cordery
Bridlington: Taylor, Pugh, Freeman, McNeill, Warburton, Brentano, Wilkes (Brown), Noteman,Gauden (Downing), Whiteman, Brattan

1991 GRESLEY ROVERS 4 *(West Midlands)*   **GUISELEY** 4 (aet) *(Northern Co East)*   Att: 11,314
Rathbone, Smith 2, Stokes   Tennison 2, Walling, A Roberts   Ref: Mr C Trussell
Gresley: Aston, Barry, Elliott (Adcock), Denby, Land, Astley, Stokes, K Smith, Acklam,Rathbone, Lovell (Weston)
Guiseley: Maxted, Bottomley, Hogarth, Tetley, Morgan, McKenzie, Atkinson (Annan),Tennison, Walling, A Roberts, B Roberts
Replay **GUISELEY** 3   **GRESLEY ROVERS** 1   Att: 7,585
Tennison, Walling, Atkinson   Astley   at Bramall Lane
Guiseley: Maxted, Annan, Hogarth, Tetley, Morgan, McKenzie (Bottomley), Atkinson,Tennison (Noteman), Walling, A Roberts, B Roberts
Gresley: Aston, Barry, Elliott, Denby, Land, Astley, Stokes (Weston), K Smith, Acklam, Rathbone, Lovell (Adcock)

1992 WIMBORNE TOWN 5 *(Wessex)*   **GUISELEY** 3 *(Northern Premier Div 1)*   Att: 10,772
Richardson, Sturgess 2, Killick 2   Noteman 2, Colville   Ref: Mr M J Bodenham
Wimborne: Leonard, Langdown, Wilkins, Beacham, Allan, Taplin, Ames, Richardson, Bridle,Killick, Sturgess (Lovell), Lynn
Guiseley: Maxted, Atkinson, Hogarth, Tetley (Wilson), Morgan, Brockie, A Roberts,Tennison, Noteman (Colville), Annan, W Roberts

1993 BRIDLINGTON TOWN 1 *(NPL Div 1)*   **TIVERTON TOWN** 0 *(Western)*   Att: 9,061
Radford   Ref: Mr R A Hart
Bridlington: Taylor, Brentano, McKenzie, Harvey, Bottomley, Woodcock, Grocock, A Roberts, Jones, Radford (Tyrell), Parkinson. Sub: Swailes
Tiverton Town: Nott, J Smith, N Saunders, M Saunders, Short (Scott), Steele, Annunziata, KSmith, Everett, Daly, Hynds (Rogers)

1994 DISS TOWN 2 *(Eastern)*   **TAUNTON TOWN** 1 *(Western)*   Att: 13,450
Gibbs (p), Mendham   Fowler   Ref: Mr K. Morton
Diss Town: Woodcock, Carter, Wolsey (Musgrave), Casey (Bugg), Hartle, Smith, Barth, Mendham, Miles, Warne, Gibbs
Taunton Town: Maloy, Morris, Walsh, Ewens, Graddon, Palfrey, West (Hendry), Fowler, Durham, Perrett (Ward), Jarvis

1995 ARLESEY TOWN 2 *(South Midlands)*   **OXFORD CITY** 1 *(Ryman 2)*   Att: 13,670
Palma, Gyalog   S Fontaine   Ref: Mr G S Willard
Arlesey: Young, Cardines, Bambrick, Palma (Ward), Hull, Gonsalves, Gyalog, Cox, Kane,O'Keefe, Marshall (Nicholls). Sub: Dodwell
Oxford: Fleet, Brown (Fisher), Hume, Shepherd, Muttock, Hamilton (Kemp), Thomas, Spittle, Sherwood, S Fontaine, C Fontaine. Sub: Torres

1996 BRIGG TOWN 3 *(N Co East)*   **CLITHEROE** 0 *(N W Counties)*   Att: 7,340
Stead 2, Roach   Ref: Mr S J Lodge
Brigg: Gawthorpe, Thompson, Rogers, Greaves (Clay), Buckley (Mail), Elston, C Stead, McLean, N Stead (McNally), Flounders, Roach
Clitheroe: Nash, Lampkin, Rowbotham (Otley), Baron, Westwell, Rovine, Butcher, Taylor (Smith), Grimshaw, Darbyshire, Hill (Dunn)

1997 WHITBY TOWN 3 *(Northern)*   **NORTH FERRIBY UTD.** 0 *(N Co East)*   Att: 11,098
Williams, Logan, Toman   Ref: Graham Poll
North Ferriby: Sharp, Deacey, Smith, Brentano, Walmsley, M Smith, Harrison (Horne), Phillips (Milner), France (Newman), Flounders, Tennison
Whitby Town: Campbell, Williams, Logan, Goodchild, Pearson, Cook, Goodrick (Borthwick), Hodgson, Robinson, Toman (Pyle), Pitman (Hall)

1998 TIVERTON TOWN 1 *(Western)*   **TOW LAW TOWN 0** *(Northern Division 1)*   **Att: 13,139**
Varley   **Ref: M A Riley**
Tiverton Town: Edwards, Felton, Saunders, Tatterton, Smith J, Conning, Nancekivell (Rogers), Smith K (Varley), Everett, Daly, Leonard (Waters)
Tow Law Town: Dawson, Pickering, Darwent, Bailey, Hague, Moan, Johnson, Nelson, Suddick, Laidler (Bennett), Robinson.

1999 TIVERTON TOWN 1 *(Western)*   **BEDLINGTON TERRIERS 0** *(Northern)*   **Att: 13, 878**
Rogers 88   **Ref: W. C. Burns**
Bedlington Terriers: O'Connor, Bowes, Pike, Boon (Renforth), Melrose, Teasdale, Cross, Middleton (Ludlow), Gibb, Milner, Bond. Subs:
Pearson, Cameron, Gowans
Tiverton Town: Edwards, Fallon, Saunders, Tatterton, Tallon, Conning (Rogers), Nancekivell (Pears), Varley, Everett, Daly, Leonard. Subs:
Tucker, Hynds, Grimshaw

2000 DEAL TOWN 1 *(Kent)*   **CHIPPENHAM TOWN 0** *(Western)*   **Att: 20,000**
Graham 87   **Ref: D Laws**
Deal Town: Tucker, Kempster, Best, Ash, Martin, Seager, Monteith, Graham, Lovell, Marshall, Ribbens. Subs: Roberts, Warden, Turner
Chippenham Town: Jones, James, Andrews, Murphy, Burns, Woods, Brown, Charity, Tweddle, Collier, Godley. Subs: Tiley, Cutler

2001 TAUNTON TOWN 2 *(Western)*   **BERKHAMPSTED TOWN 1** *(Isthmian 2)*   **(at Villa Park) Att: 8,439**
Fields 41, Laight 45   Lowe 71   **Ref: E. K. Wolstenholme**
Taunton Town: Draper, Down, Chapman, West, Hawkings, Kelly, Fields (Groves), Laight, Cann (Tallon), Bastow, Lynch (Hapgood).
Subs: Ayres, Parker
Berkhampsted Town: O'Connor, Mullins, Lowe, Aldridge, Coleman, Brockett, Yates, Adebowale, Richardson, Smith, Nightingale.
Subs: Ringsell, Hall, Knight, Franklin, Osborne

2002 WHITLEY BAY 1 *(Northern)*   **TIPTREE UNITED 0** *(Eastern)*   **(at Villa Park) Att: 4742**
Chandler 97   **Ref: A Kaye**
Whitley Bay: Caffrey, Sunderland, Walmsley, Dixon (Neil), Anderson, Locker, Middleton, Bowes (Carr), Chandler, Walton, Fenwick (Cuggy).
Subs: Cook, Livermore
Tiptree United: Haygreen, Battell, Wall, Houghton, Fish, Streetley (Gillespie), Wareham (Snow), Daly, Barefield, Aransibia (Parnell), Brady.
Subs: Powell, Ford.

2003 BRIGG TOWN 2 *(Northern Co.East)*   **A.F.C SUDBURY 1** *(Eastern Counties)*   **(at Upton Park) Att: 6,634**
Housham 2, Carter 68   Raynor 30   **Ref: M Fletcher**
Brigg Town:- Steer, Rap in, Rowland, Thompe n, Blanb ard, Stones Stead (Thompe n 41), Houb am,
Borman (Dray on 87), Roab , Carter. Subs (not ue d) Nei s Gawthorpe.
AFC Sudbury - Greg ooe , Head (Norfolk 63), Spearing, Trae y, Bib op, Andere n (Owen 73), Rap er,
Gardiner (Bana 79), Bennett, Clay on, Bete n. Subs (not ue d) Tay or, Hy e.

2004 WINCHESTER CITY 2 *(Wessex)*   **A.F.C SUDBURY 0** *(Eastern Counties)*   **(at St Andrews) Att: 5,080**
Forbes 19, Smith 73 (pen)   **Ref: P Crossley**
Winb es er City - Arthur, Dyke (Tate 83), Bicknell, Redwood, Goss, Blake, Webber, Green, Mancey, Forbes (Rogers 70),
Smith (Green 90). Subs (not used) - Lang and Rastall.
AFC Sudbury - Greygoose, Head, Wardley, Girling, Tracey, Norfolk, Owen (Banya 62), Hyde (Calver 57), Bennett, Claydon,
Betson (Francis 73n). Subs (not used) - Rayner, Nower.

2005 DIDCOT TOWN 3 *(Hellenic)*   **A.F.C SUDBURY 2** *(Eastern Counties)*(at White Hart Lane)   **Att: 8,662**
Beavon (2), Wardley (og)   Wardley, Calver (pen)   **Ref: R Beeeby**
Dido t Town:- Webb, Goodall, Heapy, Campbell, Green, Parrott, Hannigan, Ward, Concannon (Jones 88), Beavon (Bianchini 90), Powell.
Subs (not used) – Cooper, Allen, Spurrett.
AFC Sudbury - Greygoose, Girling, Wardley, Bennett, Hyde (Hayes 78), Owen (Norfolk 65), Claydon (Banya 59), Head, Calver, Betson,
Terry Rayner. Subs (not used) – Howlett, Nower.

2006 NANTWICH TOWN 3 *(NWC 1)*   **HILLINGDON BOROUGH 1** *(Spartan S.Mids P.)*(at St Andrews) **Att: 3,286**
Kinsey (2), Scheuber   Nelson
Nantwib Town:- Hab ey, A.Tay or, T.Tay or, Smith, Dai s Donnelly, Beab ey, Sb euber (Park ne n 69), Kine y (Marrow 69),
Blab (Sa rlett 86) and Griggs Subs (not ue d): O'Connor and Read.
Hillingdon Borough:- Brown, Rundell (Fenton 80),Kide n, Phillips Croft, Lawrene , Dune n (Nele n 46), Tilbury, Hibbs
Wharton (Ly ns 38). Subs (not ue d): O'Grady, White.

2007 TRURO 3 *(Western Division 1)*   **AFC TOTTON 1** *(Wessex Division 1)* **Att: 27,754 (New Vase record)**
Wills (2), Broad   Potter   **Ref: P Joslin**
AFC Totton: Brunnschweiler, Reacord, Troon (Stevens 60), Potter (Gregory 82), Bottomley, Austen, Roden, Gosney, Hamodu (Goss 89), Osman, Byres.
Subs not used: Zammit, McCormack.
Truro City: Stevenson, Ash, Power, Smith, Martin (Pope 84), Broad, Wills, Gosling, Yetton, Watkins, Walker (Ludlam 90).
Subs not used: Butcher, Routledge, Reski.

2008 **KIRKHAM & WESHAM** 2 *(North West Co. Div.2)*   **LOWESTOFT TOWN** 1 *(Eastern Co. Premier)*   Att: 19,537
Walwyn (2)   Thompson (og)   Ref: A D'Urso

Kirkham and Wesham: Summerfield, Jackson (Walwyn 79), Keefe (Allen 55), Thompson, Shaw, Eastwood, Clark, Blackwell, Wane, Paterson (Sheppard 90), Smith. Subs not used: Moffat and Abbott

Lowestoft Town: Reynolds, Poppy, Potter, Woodrow, Saunders, Plaskett (McGee 79), Godbold, Darren Cockrill (Dale Cockrill 46), Stock, Hough, King (Hunn 55). Subs not used: McKenna and Rix.

2009 **WHITLEY BAY** 2 *(Northern Division One)*   **GLOSSOP NORTH END** 0 *(North West Co. Prem)*   Att: 12,212
Kerr, Chow   Ref: K Friend

Whitley Bay: Burke, Taylor, Picton, McFarlane (Fawcett 60), Coulson, Ryan, Moore, Robson, Kerr, Chow (Robinson 73), Johnston (Bell 60). Subs not used: McLean and Reay.

Glossop North End: Cooper, Young, Kay, Lugsden, Yates, Gorton, Bailey (Hind 57), Morris, Allen (Balfe 65), Hamilton (Bailey 72), Hodges. Subs not used: Whelan and Parker.

2010 **WHITLEY BAY** 6 *(Northern Division One)*   **WROXHAM** 1 *(Eastern Counties Premier Division)*   Att: 8,920
Chow 21(sec), Easthaugh 16 (og), Kerr, Johnston,   Cook 12   Ref: A Taylor
Robinson, Gillies

Whitley Bay: Terry Burke, Craig McFarlane, Callum Anderson, Richard Hodgson, (sub Lee Picton 69th min), Darren Timmons, Leon Ryan, Adam Johnston (sub Joshua Gillies 77th min), Damon Robson, Lee Kerr, Paul Chow (sub Phillip Bell 61st min), Paul Robinson. Subs not used – Tom Kindley and Chris Reid.

Wroxham: Scott Howie, Gavin Pauling (sub Ross Durrant 57th min), Shaun Howes, Graham Challen, Martin McNeil (sub Josh Carus 46th min), Andy Easthaugh (sub Owen Paynter 69th min), Steve Spriggs, Gavin Lemmon, Paul Cook, Danny White, Gary Gilmore. Subs not used – Danny Self and Gareth Simpson.

2011 **WHITLEY BAY** 3 *(Northern Division One)*   **COALVILLE TOWN** 2 *(Midland Alliance)*   Att: 8,778
Chow 28, 90, Kerr 61   Moore 58, Goodby 80   Ref: S Mathieson

Whitley Bay: Terry Burke, Craig McFarlane (sub Steve Gibson 90th min), Callum Anderson, Darren Timmons, Gareth Williams (sub David Coulson 68th min), Damon Robson, Lee Kerr, Paul Chow, Paul Robinson, David Pounder (sub Brian Smith 68th min), Gary Ormston.
Subs not used – Kyle Hayes (gk) and Brian Rowe. Coalville Town: Sean Bowles, Ashley Brown (sub Matthew Gardner 88th min), Cameron Stuart, Adam Goodby, Zach Costello, Lee Miveld,
Callum Woodward, Anthony Carney (sub Craig Attwood 90th min), Ryan Robbins (sub Ashley Wells 66th min), Matt Moore, Jerome Murdock. Subs not used – Richard Williams (gk) and James Dodd.

2012 **DUNSTON UTS** 2 *(Northern Division One)*   **WEST AUCKLAND TOWN** 0 *(Northern Division One)*   Att: 5,126
Bulford 32, 79   Ref: R East

Dunston UTS: Liam Connell, Ben Cattenach, Terry Galbraith, Michael Robson, Chris Swailes, Kane Young, Steven Shaw, Michael Dixon, Stephen Goddard (sub Sreven Preen 84th min), Andrew Bulford (sub Danny Craggs 88th min), Lee McAndrew.
Subs not used – Andrew Clark (g/k), Ian Herron, Jack Burns.

West Auckland Town: Mark Bell, Neil Pattinson, Andrew Green, Jonny Gibson, John Parker, Mark Stephenson (sub Daniel Hindmarsh 76th min), Stuart Banks, Mark Hudson, Mattie Moffatt, Michael Rae, Adam Nicholls (sub Martin Young 60th min).
Subs not used – Daryll Hall, Ross Preston, Matthew Coad.

2013 **SPENNYMOOR TOWN** 2 *(Northern Division One)*   **TUNBRIDGE WELLS** 1 *(Kent League)*   Att: 16,751
Cogdon 18, Graydon 80   Stanford 78   Ref: M Naylor

Spennymoor Town: Robert Dean, Kallum Griffiths, Leon Ryan, Chris Mason, Stephen Capper, Keith Graydon, Lewis Dodds, Wayne Phillips (Anthony Peacock 64 min), Joe Walton (Andrew Stephenson 73 min), Mark Davison, (Michael Rae 76 min), Gavin Congdon.
Subs not used - David Knight (g/k), Steven Richardson.

Tunbridge Wells: Chris Oladogba, Jason Bourne, Scott Whibley, Perry Spackman, Lewis Mingle, Jon Pilbeam (Richard Sinden 85 min), Andy McMath, Joe Fuller (Tom Davey 58 min), Andy Irvine, Carl Connell (Jack Harris 58 min), Josh Stanford.
Subs not used - Michael Czanner (gk), Andy Boyle.

2014 **SHOLING** 1 *(Wessex Premier Division - 1st)*   **WEST AUCKLAND TOWN** 0 *(Northern Division One - 5th)*   Att: 5,432
McLean 71   Ref: D Coote

Sholing: Matt Brown, Mike Carter, Marc Diaper, Peter Castle (Dan Miller 53 min), Lee Bright, Tyronne Bowers (Kevin Brewster 75 min), Barry Mason, Lewis Fennemore (Alex Sawyer 78 min), Lee Wort, Byron Mason, Marvin McLean.
Subs not used - Ashley Jarvis, Nick Watts.

West Auckland Town: Jordan Nixon, Neil Pattinson, Andrew Green (Jonathan Gibson 63 min), Daryll Hall, Lewis Galpin, Brian Close, Shaun Vipond (Stuart Banks 76 min), Robert Briggs, Mattie Moffat (Steven Richardson 74 min). John Campbell, Dennis Knight.
Subs not used - Paul Garthwaite, Adam Wilkinson..

2015 **NORTH SHIELDS** 2 *(Northern Division One - 4th)*   **GLOSSOP NORTH END** 1 *(North West Co. Premier - 1st)*   Att: 9,674
Bainbridge 80, Forster 96   Bailey 55   Ref: A Madley

North Shields: Christopher Bannon, Stuart Donnison, John Parker, Kevin Hughes, John Grey, James Luccock (Ryan Carr 59), Ben Richardson, Mciahel McKeown, Dean Holmes (Adam Forster 69), Denver Morris, Gareth Bainbridge (Kieran Wrightson 107).
Subs not used - Curtis Coppen and Marc Lancaster.

Glossop North End: Greg Hall, Michael Bowler, Matthew Russell, Kevin Lugsden, Dave Young, Martin Parker, Lee Blackshaw (Samuel Grimshaw 69), Samuel Hare (Samuel Hind 82), Tom Bailey, Kieran Lugsden, Eddie Moran (Daniel White 60).
Subs not used - Benjamin Richardson and Richard Gresty.

2016 **MORPETH TOWN** 4 *(Northern Division One - 4th)*   HEREFORD 1 *(Midland League - 1st)*   **Att: 46,781**
     Swailes 34, Carr 47, Taylor 59, Bell 92   Purdie 2   *(Inaugural Non-League finals day)*
                                                         Ref: S Atwelly

Morpeth Town: Karl Dryden, Stephen Forster, James Novak, Ben Sayer, Chris Swailes, Michael Hall, Sean Taylor (sub Damien Mullen 78),
Keith Graydon, Luke Carr (sub Shaun Bell 88), Michael Chilton (sub Steven Anderson 69), Jordan Fry.
Subs not used - Dale Pearson and Niall Harrison.
Hereford: Martin Horsell, Jimmy Oates, Joel Edwards, Rob Purdie, Ryan Green, Aaron Birch, Pablo Haysham, Mike Symons,
Jamie Willets (sub John Mills 70), Joe Tumelty (sub Mustapha Bundu 55), Sirdic Grant.
Subs not used - Nathan Summers, Dylan Bonella and Ross Staley.

2017 **SOUTH SHIELDS** 4 *(Northern Division One - 1st)*   CLEETHORPES TOWN 0 *(Northern Counties East Premier - 1st)*   **Att: 38,224**
     Finnigan 43 (pen), Morse 80, Foley 86, 89)   *(Combined FA trophy Vase att.)*
                                                              Ref: D England

South Shields: Liam Connell, Alex Nicholson, Darren Lough, Jon Shaw, Dillon Morse, Julio Arca, Andrew Stephenson (sub Robert Briggs 56),
Wayne Phillips (sub Barrie Smith 82), Gavin Congdon, Carl Finnigan (sub Michael Richardson 71), David Foley.
Subs not used - Louis Storey and Darren Holden.
Cleethorpes Town: Liam Higton, Tim Lowe, Peter Winn, Liam Dickens, Matt Bloomer, Matty Coleman (sub Luke Mascall 70),
Liam Davis (sub Jack Richardson 73), Alex Flett, Marc Cooper (Andy Taylor 61), Brody Richardson, Jon Oglesby.
Subs not used - Gary King and Kieran Wressell.

All Finals at Wembley unless otherwise stated.

FIRST QUALIFYING ROUND 2018-19
SATURDAY 1 SEPTEMBER 2018 ~ WINNING CLUB TO RECEIVE £550 LOSING CLUB TO RECEIVE £175

1 Alnwick Town v Charnock Richard
2 Stokesley SC v Guisborough Town
3 Holker Old Boys v Prestwich Heys
4 Goole v Barnoldswick Town
5 Whickham v Jarrow
6 West Allotment Celtic v Yorkshire Amateur
7 Darlington Railway Athletic v Bedlington Terriers
8 Chester-Le-Street Town v Sunderland Ryhope CW
9 Esh Winning v Whitley Bay
10 Bishop Auckland v Newton Aycliffe
11 North Shields v Consett
12 Daisy Hill v Whitehaven
13 Harrogate Railway Athletic v Silsden
14 Thackley v Thornaby
15 Dunston UTS v Heaton Stannington
16 Team Northumbria v Garforth Town
17 Billingham Town v Campion
18 Blyth v Crook Town
19 Billingham Synthonia v Knaresborough Town
20 Durham City v Seaham Red Star
21 Eccleshill United v Hebburn Town
22 Northallerton Town v Willington
23 Lower Breck v West Didsbury & Chorlton
24 Longridge Town v Vauxhall Motors
25 Worksop Town v Grimsby Borough
26 Burscough v Alsager Town
27 Wythenshawe Town v Rylands
28 Winsford United v Liversedge
29 Maltby Main v Ashton Athletic
30 Ashton Town v St Helens Town
31 Barton Town v AFC Liverpool
32 AFC Blackpool v Nostell MW
33 Sandbach United v Athersley Recreation
34 Shelley v Penistone Church
35 AFC Emley v Litherland Remyca
36 Swallownest v Abbey Hey
37 Cammell Laird 1907 v Harworth Colliery
38 Armthorpe Welfare v Worsbrough Bridge Athletic
39 Parkgate v Chadderton
40 Congleton Town v Bootle
41 Selby Town v Stavely MW
42 Kirby Muxloe v Brocton
43 Nuneaton Griff v Coton Green
44 Littleton v Lichfield City

45 Coventry Sphinx v Sporting Khalsa
46 FC Stratford v Bewdley Town
47 Abbey Hulton United v Whitchurch Alport
48 AFC Bridgnorth v Wolverhampton Casuals
49 Ellesmere Rangers v Birstall United Social
50 Rugby Borough v Malvern Town
51 Stafford Town v Wednesfield
52 Droitwich Spa v Coventry United
53 Boldmere St Michaels v GNP Sports
54 Heather St Johns v Rocester
55 Rugby Town v Team Dudley
(walkover for Rugby Town – Team Dudley not accepted into Competition)
56 Racing Club Warwick v Pegasus Juniors
57 Melton Town v Ingles
58 Lutterworth Athletic v Cradley Town
59 Wellington FC v St Martins
60 Dudley Sports v Shawbury United
61 Coventry Copsewood v Eccleshall
62 NKF Burbage v Lutterworth Town
63 Gornal Athletic v Stone Old Alleynians
64 Wellington Amateurs v Ellistown
(walkover for Wellington Amateurs – Ellistown not accepted into Competition)
65 Heath Hayes v Shifnal Town
66 Dudley Town v Bardon Hill
67 Pershore Town v Hanley Town
68 Ashby Ivanhoe v Friar Lane & Epworth
69 Bolehall Swifts v Tipton Town
70 Haughmond v Saffron Dynamo
71 Gedling MW v Ilkeston Town
72 Rainworth MW v Teversal
73 Newark Flowserve v Harrowby United
74 Leicester Road v Bottesford Town
75 Loughborough University v West Bridgford
76 Ollerton Town v New Mills
77 Skegness Town v Clay Cross Town
78 Anstey Nomads v Eastwood Community
79 Borrowash Victoria v Hucknall Town
80 Clifton All Whites v Belper United
81 Blidworth Welfare v Blaby & Whetstone Athletic
82 Clipstone v Aylestone Park
83 South Normanton Athletic v St Andrews
84 Oadby Town v Sherwood Colliery
85 Dunkirk v Stapenhill

86 Quorn v Retford United
87 Holwell Sports v Pinxton
88 Lincoln Moorlands Railway v Kimberley Miners Welfare
89 Radford v Selston
90 Framlingham Town v Wisbech St Mary
91 Deeping Rangers v Blackstones
92 Woodbridge Town v Eynesbury Rovers
93 Gorleston v Boston Town
94 Peterborough Northern Star v Fakenham Town
95 Walsham Le Willows v Diss Town
96 Newmarket Town v Downham Town
97 Bourne Town v March Town United
98 Huntingdon Town v Wroxham
99 Ely City v Norwich United
100 Stotfold v Wadham Lodge
101 St Margaretsbury v Hadleigh United
102 Newbury Forest v Wivenhoe Town
103 Wormley Rovers v Biggleswade United
104 Enfield Borough v Halstead Town
105 Clapton v Woodford Town 2017
106 May & Baker Eastbrook Community v Burnham Ramblers
107 Stanway Rovers v White Ensign
108 Baldock Town v Long Melford
109 Haverhill Rovers v Ilford
110 Holland v Cornard United
111 Walthamstow v Takeley
112 Langford v Tower Hamlets
113 Southend Manor v Ipswich Wanderers
114 Stansted v Brantham Athletic
115 London Colney v Cockfosters
116 Whitton United v Hatfield Town
117 British Airways v Harefield United
118 Rothwell Corinthians v CB Hounslow United
119 Spelthorne Sports v Northampton On Chenecks
120 FC Deportivo Galicia v London Tigers
121 Sandhurst Town v Kensington Borough
122 Wellingborough Whitworth v Bugbrooke St Michaels
123 Hanworth Villa v Bedford
124 Ampthill Town v Edgware Town
125 Broadfields United v Daventry Town
126 AFC Hayes v Wembley
127 Rushden & Higham United v Winslow United
128 Raunds Town v Cranfield United
129 Bicester Town v AFC Spelthorne Sports Club
130 Southall v Reading City
131 Leverstock Green v Unite MK
132 Cricklewood Wanderers v Risborough Rangers
133 Burnham v Hillingdon
(walkover for Burnham – Hillingdon not accepted into Competition)
134 St Panteleimon v Holmer Green
135 Shrivenham v Tytherington Rocks
136 Bashley v AFC Portchester
137 Binfield v Frimley Green
138 Tadley Calleva v Ascot United
139 Milton United v Clanfield 85
140 Chertsey Town v Woodley United
141 Brimscombe & Thrupp v Ash United
142 Wallingford Town v Abingdon United
143 Penn & Tylers Green v AFC Stoneham
144 Lydney Town v Abbey Rangers
145 Cove v Fleet Spurs
146 Royal Wootton Bassett Town v Oxford City Nomads
(walkover for Royal Wootton Bassett Town – Oxford City
Nomads withdrawn)
147 Ardley United v Holyport
148 Fairford Town v Baffins Milton Rovers
149 Colliers Wood United v Stansfeld
150 Bagshot v Sidlesham
151 Raynes Park Vale v Cobham
152 Lingfield v Epsom & Ewell
153 Croydon v Little Common

154 Sutton Athletic v Cray Valley (PM)
155 Hassocks v K Sports
156 St Francis Rangers v FC Elmstead
157 Knaphill v AFC Varndeanians
158 Wick v Godalming Town
159 Mile Oak v Selsey
160 Billingshurst v Tunbridge Wells
161 Lordswood v Fire United Christian
162 Sheerwater v Lancing
163 Meridian VP v Southwick
164 Chessington & Hook United v Oakwood
165 Erith Town v Arundel
166 Lewisham Borough (Com) v Broadbridge Heath
167 Kent Football United v Steyning Town Community
168 SC Thamesmead v Midhurst & Easebourne United
169 Westside v AC London
170 AFC Croydon Athletic v Worthing United
171 AFC Uckfield Town v Hollands & Blair
172 Glebe v Loxwood
173 Seaford Town v Tooting Bec
174 Lydd Town v Punjab United
175 Snodland Town v Newhaven
176 Erith & Belvedere v Rusthall
177 Fisher v Corinthian
178 East Preston v Eastbourne United
179 Bearsted v Bexhill United
180 Sheppey United v Balham
181 Langney Wanderers v Canterbury City
182 Saltdean United v Crawley Down Gatwick
183 Redhill v Holmesdale
184 Guildford City v Rochester United
185 Whitchurch United v Almondsbury
186 Devizes Town v Warminster Town
187 Calne Town v Fawley
188 Christchurch v Folland Sports
189 Cowes Sports v Westbury United
190 Chippenham Park v Bitton
191 Lymington Town v Portland United
192 Oldland Abbotonians v Totton & Eling
193 Hamworthy United v Amesbury Town
194 Romsey Town v Bridport
195 Ringwood Town v Alresford Town
196 Stockbridge v Roman Glass St George
197 Hallen v Fareham Town
198 East Cowes Victoria Athletic v Pewsey Vale
199 Team Solent v Longwell Green Sports
200 Eversley & California v Downton
201 Bournemouth v Bristol Telephones
202 Hythe & Dibden v Bemerton Heath Harlequins
203 Corsham Town v Laverstock & Ford
204 Exmouth Town v Callington Town
205 Plymouth Parkway v Brislington
206 Tavistock v Helston Athletic
207 Keynsham Town v Sidmouth Town
208 Bishops Lydeard v Bishop Sutton
209 Godolphin Atlantic v Portishead Town
210 Hengrove Athletic v Newquay
211 Wellington AFC v Saltash United
212 Liskeard Athletic v Bovey Tracey
213 Crediton United v Clevedon Town
214 AFC St Austell v Ilfracombe Town
215 Wincanton Town v Radstock Town
216 Witheridge v Wells City
217 Odd Down v Shepton Mallet
218 Elburton Villa v Launceston

SECOND QUALIFYING ROUND 2018-19
SATURDAY 15 SEPTEMBER 2018 ~ WINNING CLUB TO RECEIVE £725 LOSING CLUB TO RECEIVE £250

1 Northallerton Town or Willington v Steeton
2 Ashington v Blyth or Crook Town
3 Nelson v Tow Law Town
4 Thackley or Thornaby v Carlisle City
5 Whickham or Jarrow v Esh Winning or Whitley Bay
6 Billingham Town or Campion v Birtley Town
7 Albion Sports v Harrogate Railway Athletic or Silsden
8 Chester-Le-Street Town v Dunston UTS or Heaton Stannington or Sunderland Ryhope CW
9 Bishop Auckland or Newton Aycliffe v West Allotment Celtic or Yorkshire Amateur
10 Brandon United v Washington
11 Penrith v Alnwick Town or Charnock Richard
12 Padiham v Holker Old Boys or Prestwich Heys
13 Eccleshill United or Hebburn Town v Billingham Synthonia or Knaresborough Town
14 Ryton & Crawcrook Albion v Team Northumbria or Garforth Town
15 Stokesley SC or Guisborough Town v Goole or Barnoldswick Town
16 Darlington Railway Athletic v Redcar Athletic or Bedlington Terriers
17 Bridlington Town v North Shields or Consett
18 Daisy Hill or Whitehaven v Durham City or Seaham Red Star
19 AFC Darwen v Garstang
20 Northwich Victoria v Maltby Main or Ashton Athletic
21 Swallownest or Abbey Hey v AFC Blackpool or Nostell MW
22 Avro v Barnton
23 Irlam v Burscough or Alsager Town
24 Bacup Borough v AFC Emley or Litherland Remyca
25 Cammell Laird 1907 v Shelley or Penistone Church or Harworth Colliery
26 Glasshoughton Welfare v Parkgate or Chadderton
27 Cheadle Town v Longridge Town or Vauxhall Motors
28 Congleton Town or Bootle v Hallam
29 Armthorpe Welfare v Squires Gate or Worsbrough Bridge Athletic
30 Selby Town or Stavely MW v Maine Road
31 Wythenshawe Town or Rylands v Hemsworth Miners Welfare
32 Barton Town or AFC Liverpool v Ashton Town or St Helens Town
33 Atherton LR v Sandbach United or Athersley Recreation
34 Winsford United or Liversedge v Worksop Town or Grimsby Borough
35 Winterton Rangers v Rossington Main
36 Lower Breck v Stockport Town or West Didsbury & Chorlton
37 Chelmsley Town v Tividale
38 Dudley Sports or Shawbury United v Pershore Town or Hanley Town
39 Rugby Borough or Malvern Town v Bustleholme
40 Abbey Hulton United v Shepshed Dynamo or Whitchurch Alport
41 Littleton or Lichfield City v Smethwick
42 Ellesmere Rangers v Heather St Johns or Rocester or Birstall United Social
43 Coventry Copsewood or Eccleshall v Hereford Lads Club
44 Boldmere St Michaels v Studley or GNP Sports
45 Lye Town v Bolehall Swifts or Tipton Town
46 Stafford Town or Wednesfield v Bromyard Town
47 Uttoxeter Town v Walsall Wood
48 Wellington Amateurs v Racing Club Warwick or Pegasus Juniors
49 NKF Burbage or Lutterworth Town v Lutterworth Athletic or Cradley Town
50 Kirby Muxloe or Brocton v Nuneaton Griff or Coton Green

51 Cadbury Athletic v Wem Town
52 Droitwich Spa or Coventry United v Atherstone Town
53 Paget Rangers v Kington Town
54 Haughmond or Saffron Dynamo v Heath Hayes or Shifnal Town
55 Melton Town or Ingles v Rugby Town
56 Ashby Ivanhoe v FC Stratford or Bewdley Town or Friar Lane & Epworth
57 Black Country Rangers v Dudley Town or Bardon Hill
58 AFC Bridgnorth v Romulus or Wolverhampton Casuals
59 AFC Wulfrunians v Wellington FC or St Martins
60 Gornal Athletic v Coventry Sphinx or Sporting Khalsa or Stone Old Alleynians
61 Borrowash Victoria v Newark Flowserve or Harrowby United or Hucknall Town
62 Clipstone or Aylestone Park v Lincoln Moorlands Railway or Kimberley Miners Welfare
63 Holwell Sports or Pinxton v Leicester Road or Bottesford Town
64 Holbrook Sports v Blidworth Welfare or Blaby & Whetstone Athletic
65 Clifton All Whites or Belper United v Rainworth MW or Teversal
66 Quorn or Retford United v Skegness Town or Clay Cross Town
67 Barrow Town v Shirebrook Town
68 Heanor Town v Dunkirk or Stapenhill
69 South Normanton Athletic v Radford or Selston or St Andrews
70 Ollerton Town or New Mills v Long Eaton United
71 Arnold Town v Loughborough University or West Bridgford
72 Sleaford Town v Sandiacre Town
73 Anstey Nomads v Oadby Town or Sherwood Colliery or Eastwood Community
74 Graham St Prims v Gedling MW or Ilkeston Town
75 Dronfield Town v Harborough Town
76 FC Bolsover v Leicester Nirvana
77 Peterborough Northern Star v Bourne Town or March Town United or Fakenham Town
78 Histon v Team Bury
79 Walsham Le Willows or Diss Town v Deeping Rangers or Blackstones
80 Huntingdon Town or Wroxham v Mulbarton Wanderers
81 Framlingham Town v Swaffham Town or Wisbech St Mary
82 Woodbridge Town v Pinchbeck United or Eynesbury Rovers
83 Great Yarmouth Town v Thetford Town
84 Gorleston or Boston Town v Kirkley & Pakefield
85 Newmarket Town v Ely City or Norwich United or Downham Town
86 Saffron Walden Town v May & Baker Eastbrook Community or Burnham Ramblers
87 Southend Manor v Haverhill Rovers or Ilford or Ipswich Wanderers
88 Hoddesdon Town v FC Clacton
89 London Lions v Wormley Rovers or Biggleswade United
90 Colney Heath v Langford or Tower Hamlets
91 Stansted or Brantham Athletic v Walthamstow or Takeley
92 Haverhill Borough v Whitton United or Hatfield Town
93 Little Oakley v St Margaretsbury or Hadleigh United
94 Barkingside v Wodson Park
95 London Colney or Cockfosters v FC Broxbourne Borough
96 Coggeshall United v Sawbridgeworth Town
97 Enfield Borough or Halstead Town v Sporting Bengal United

98 Baldock Town or Long Melford v Stanway Rovers or White Ensign

99 Codicote v Holland or Cornard United

100 Clapton or Woodford Town 2017 v Newbury Forest or Wivenhoe Town

101 Hadley v Enfield 1893

102 Stotfold or Wadham Lodge v West Essex

103 Amersham Town v Hanworth Villa or Bedford

104 Southall or Reading City v AFC Hayes or Wembley

105 Brackley Town Saints v Crawley Green

106 Burton Park Wanderers v FC Deportivo Galicia or London Tigers

107 Brimsdown v Bicester Town or AFC Spelthorne Sports Club

108 Leverstock Green or Unite MK v Raunds Town or Cranfield United

109 Wellingborough Town v Burnham

110 Potton United v Rothwell Corinthians or CB Hounslow United

111 St Panteleimon or Holmer Green v Long Buckby

112 Cricklewood Wanderers v North Greenford United
or Risborough Rangers

113 Arlesey Town v Irchester United

114 Sandhurst Town v Northampton Sileby Rangers
or Kensington Borough

115 Broadfields United v Ampthill Town or Edgware Town
or Daventry Town

116 Bedfont & Feltham v Rushden & Higham United or Winslow United

117 Wellingborough Whitworth v Spelthorne Sports or Northampton On Chenecks
or Bugbrooke St Michaels

118 Rayners Lane v Thrapston Town

119 British Airways or Harefield United v Oxhey Jets

120 Easington Sports v Brimscombe & Thrupp or Ash United

121 Fairford Town v New College Swindon
or Baffins Milton Rovers

122 Royal Wootton Bassett Town v Bashley or AFC Portchester

123 Thame Rangers v Farnham Town

124 Tadley Calleva or Ascot United v Chertsey Town or Woodley United

125 Wallingford Town v Alton
or Abingdon United

126 Penn & Tylers Green v Binfield or Frimley Green
or AFC Stoneham

127 Chipping Sodbury Town v Lydney Town or Abbey Rangers

128 Milton United or Clanfield 85 v Buckingham Athletic

129 Shrivenham or Tytherington Rocks v Badshot Lea

130 Malmesbury Victoria v Virginia Water

131 Cheltenham Saracens v Flackwell Heath

132 Longlevens v Tuffley Rovers

133 Ardley United or Holyport v Cove or Fleet Spurs

134 Redhill or Holmesdale v Forest Hill Park

135 Kent Football United v Lydd Town or Punjab United
or Steyning Town Community

136 Knaphill or AFC Varndeanians v Langney Wanderers or Canterbury City

137 Sutton Athletic or Cray Valley (PM) v Hailsham Town

138 Raynes Park Vale v Gravesham Borough
or Cobham

139 St Francis Rangers or FC Elmstead v Lordswood or Fire United Christian

140 Sporting Club Thamesmead v Banstead Athletic
or Midhurst & Easebourne United

141 Billingshurst or Tunbridge Wells v Bridon Ropes

142 Guildford City or Rochester United v Erith & Belvedere or Rusthall

143 Wick or Godalming Town v Hackney Wick

144 Peacehaven & Telscombe v Shoreham

145 AFC Uckfield Town v Meridian VP or Southwick
or Hollands & Blair

146 Westside or AC London v Erith Town or Arundel

147 Colliers Wood United or Stansfeld v Bagshot or Sidlesham

148 Saltdean United v Littlehampton Town
or Crawley Down Gatwick

149 Mile Oak or Selsey v Bearsted or Bexhill United

150 Chatham Town v Camberley Town

151 Fisher or Corinthian v Glebe or Loxwood

152 Chessington & Hook United v Sheerwater or Lancing
or Oakwood

153 Snodland Town or Newhaven v Croydon or Little Common

154 Sheppey United or Balham v Seaford Town or Tooting Bec

155 Hassocks or K Sports v Deal Town

156 East Preston or Eastbourne United v Lewisham Borough (Community) or Broadbridge Heath

157 AFC Croydon Athletic v Lingfield or Epsom & Ewell
or Worthing United

158 Hamworthy United v Calne Town or Fawley
or Amesbury Town

159 Stockbridge v Hythe & Dibden or Bemerton Heath Harlequins
or Roman Glass St George

160 Bournemouth or Bristol Telephones v Christchurch or Folland Sports

161 Verwood Town v Ringwood Town or Alresford Town

162 Romsey Town or Bridport v Devizes Town or Warminster Town

163 Eversley & California or Downton v Lymington Town or Portland United

164 Shortwood United v Cribbs

165 Swanage Town & Herston v Team Solent or Longwell Green Sports

166 Hallen or Fareham Town v Corsham Town or Laverstock & Ford

167 Chippenham Park or Bitton v Bishops Cleeve

168 Petersfield Town v Cowes Sports or Westbury United

169 New Milton Town v Cadbury Heath

170 Oldland Abbotonians v East Cowes Victoria Athletic or Pewsey Vale
or Totton & Eling

171 Sherborne Town v Whitchurch United or Almondsbury

172 Shaftesbury v Andover New Street

173 United Services Portsmouth v Brockenhurst

174 Buckland Athletic v Hengrove Athletic or Newquay

175 Odd Down or Shepton Mallet v Welton Rovers

176 Wincanton Town or Radstock Town v Plymouth Parkway or Brislington

177 Cullompton Rangers v Ivybridge Town

178 Keynsham Town or Sidmouth Town v Godolphin Atlantic or Portishead Town

179 Wellington AFC or Saltash United v Axminster Town

180 Liskeard Athletic or Bovey Tracey v Tavistock or Helston Athletic

181 Falmouth Town v Crediton United or Clevedon Town

182 Bishops Lydeard or Bishop Sutton v Elburton Villa or Launceston

183 Exmouth Town or Callington Town v Bridgwater Town

184 Cheddar v Newton Abbot Spurs

185 Camelford v Bodmin Town

186 Porthleven v Torpoint Athletic

187 Witheridge or Wells City v AFC St Austell or Ilfracombe Town

PRELIMINARY ROUND

1	Durham City	v	Spennymoor Town (4/9)	0-2	60
2	Morpeth Town	v	Hebburn Town (4/9)	3-0	
3	Curzon Ashton	v	Nelson (4/9)	0-1	141
4	Ashton Athletic	v	Witton Albion (4/9)	1-0	45
5	AFC Darwen	v	Daisy Hill (6/9)	0-4	119
6	Irlam	v	St Helens Town (7/9)	2-1	67
7	West Didsbury & Chorlton	v	Warrington Town		
	(walkover for Warrington Town – West Didsbury & Chorlton withdrawn)				
8	Burscough	v	Lancaster City		
	(walkover for Burscough – Lancaster City withdrawn)				
9	Hyde United	v	Chorley (8/9)	2-1	67
10	Skelmersdale United	v	FC United of Manchester		
	(walkover for FC United of Manchester – Skelmersdale United withdrawn)				
11	Ashton United	v	Chadderton		
	(walkover for Ashton United – Chadderton withdrawn)				
12	Stockport County	v	Stockport Town (8/9)	3-5	162
13	Salford City	v	Mossley (7/9)	1-0	196
14	Radcliffe Borough	v	Nantwich Town (18/9)	2-5	
15	Bamber Bridge	v	Altrincham		
	(walkover for Altrincham – Bamber Bridge withdrawn)				
16	Ossett Town	v	Harrogate Town (7/9)	1-3aet	53
17	Staveley MW	v	Stocksbridge Park Steels (4/9)	4-0	147
18	Silsden	v	Glasshoughton Welfare		
	(walkover for Silsden – Glasshoughton Welfare withdrawn)				
19	Worksop Town	v	Garforth Town (7/9)	3-1	77
20	North Ferriby United	v	Nostell MW		
	(walkover for Nostell MW – North Ferriby United withdrawn)				
21	Worsbrough Bridge Athleticv		Bottesford Town (5/9)	1-2	
22	Sheffield	v	Hall Road Rangers (7/9)	4-3	90
23	York City	v	Tadcaster Albion (6/9)	4-0	
24	Eastwood Community	v	Deeping Rangers (8/9)	5-2	
25	Harborough Town	v	Leicester Road (7/9)	5-2	
26	Ilkeston	v	Boston United		
	(walkover for Boston United – Ilkeston removed)				
27	Long Eaton United	v	Anstey Nomads (7/9)	9-4	79
28	Aylestone Park	v	Grantham Town (7/9)	3-2	70
29	West Bridgford	v	Lincoln United (6/9)	3-0	46
30	Dunkirk	v	Leicester Nirvana (6/9)	5-2	36
31	Ashby Ivanhoe	v	Belper Town (6/9)	0-2	57
32	Alfreton Town	v	Mickleover Sports (6/9)	2-1aet	119
33	Sporting Khalsa	v	Lichfield City (5/9)	2-3	
34	Nuneaton Griff	v	Hereford (6/9)	2-3	52
35	Racing Club Warwick	v	Walsall Wood (6/9)	2-3	
36	Sutton Coldfield Town	v	Wolverhampton Casuals		
	(walkover for Sutton Coldfield Town – Wolverhampton Casuals withdrawn)				
37	Newcastle Town	v	Wednesfield (12/9)	2-2aet	50
	(Newcastle Town won 4-2 on kicks from the penalty mark)				
38	Bedworth United	v	Kidsgrove Athletic		
	(walkover for Bedworth United – Kidsgrove Athletic withdrawn)				
39	Stafford Town	v	Worcester City (5/9)	1-3	40
40	Bromsgrove Sporting	v	Leek Town (6/9)	1-2	137
41	Leamington	v	Stratford Town (6/9)	2-3	23
42	Kidderminster Harriers	v	Alvechurch (7/9)	3-0	
43	AFC Telford United	v	Bromyard Town (6/9)	3-2	
44	Bilston Town	v	Coten Green (4/9)	3-2	
45	Tipton Town	v	Tamworth		
	(4/9 – tie abandoned after 76 mins due to serious injury to player, 1-5 – tie awarded to Tamworth)				
46	Rushall Olympic	v	Dudley Town (6/9)	2-3	
47	Malvern Town	v	Rugby Town (4/9)	3-1	
48	Highgate United	v	Boldmere St Michaels (7/9)	4-5	
49	AFC Rushden & Diamondsv		Rushden & Higham United (7/9)12-0		
50	Peterborough Northern Star v		St Neots Town (7/9)	2-1	76
51	Brackley Town	v	Yaxley (6/9)	5-0	84
52	Biggleswade Town	v	Huntingdon Town (7/9)	6-0	
53	Cogenhoe United	v	Biggleswade United (7/9)	1-3	
54	Cambridge City	v	Felixstowe & Walton United (7/9)3-2aet		64
	(at Huntingdon Town FC)				
55	Framlingham Town	v	Dereham Town (7/9)	1-3	
56	Wisbech St Mary	v	Swaffham Town (5/9)	0-9	
57	Histon	v	Gorleston (4/9)	0-6	
58	AFC Sudbury	v	King's Lynn Town (7/9)	8-1	
59	Whitton United	v	Leiston (7/9)	0-2	
60	Bury Town	v	Wroxham (5/9)	0-2	54
61	Fakenham Town	v	Haverhill Rovers (4/9)	1-4	
62	Ipswich Wanderers	v	Newmarket Town (7/9)	4-2	

63	Woodbridge Town	v	Walsham Le Willows (7/9)	3-1	62
64	Basildon United	v	Witham Town		
	(walkover for Witham Town – Basildon United withdrawn)				
65	Saffron Walden Town	v	Potters Bar Town (7/9)	3-1	110
66	Hoddesdon Town	v	Barkingside (7/9)	5-2	
67	Hitchin Town	v	Little Oakley		
	(walkover for Hitchin Town – Little Oakley withdrawn)				
68	Barking	v	Ware (4/9)	3-1	45
69	AFC Hornchurch	v	Takeley (12/9)	2-0	
70	Hullbridge Sports	v	Waltham Forest (7/9)	1-0	54
71	Ilford	v	Cheshunt (6/9)	0-5	22
72	Harlow Town	v	Brightlingsea Regent		
	(walkover for Brightlingsea Regent – Harlow Town withdrawn)				
73	Halstead Town	v	Bishop's Stortford (7/9)	1-5	
74	Brentwood Town	v	Stanway Rovers (6/9)	2-1	57
75	Concord Rangers	v	Waltham Abbey (7/9)	3-0	90
76	Great Wakering Rovers	v	Hadley		
	(walkover for Hadley – Great Wakering Rovers withdrawn)				
77	Royston Town	v	Redbridge (6/9)	4-1	
78	Heybridge Swifts	v	Romford (7/9)	2-5	51
79	Tower Hamlets	v	Grays Athletic (4/9)	5-3	64
80	Coggeshall Town	v	Sawbridgeworth Town (14/9)	6-0	
81	Thurrock	v	Aveley (6/9)	9-1	70
82	Northwood	v	Haringey Borough (7/9)	5-1	30
83	Kings Langley	v	Colney Heath (7/9)	3-2	79
84	Hemel Hempstead Town	v	Sun Sports (4/9)	4-0	144
85	Staines Town	v	Harrow Borough (5/9)	5-3aet	
86	Bedfont Sports	v	Winslow United		
	(walkover for Bedfont Sports – Winslow United withdrawn)				
87	Edgware Town	v	Cockfosters (4/9)	5-3	31
88	Buckingham Athletic	v	Oxhey Jets (7/9)	7-0	40
89	Harefield United	v	Spelthorne Sports (4/9)	4-0	24
90	Hendon	v	North Greenford United (6/9)	7-0	60
91	Flackwell Heath	v	Newport Pagnell Town (7/9)	2-1	83
92	Wealdstone	v	Uxbridge (6/9)	1-2	
93	Wingate & Finchley	v	Chalfont St Peter (7/9)	10-0	62
94	Leverstock Green	v	Aylesbury (7/9)	0-4	36
95	Carshalton Athletic	v	Eastbourne Town		
	(walkover for Carshalton Athletic – Eastbourne Town withdrawn)				
96	Erith Town	v	Dulwich Hamlet (4/9)	2-10	116
97	Phoenix Sports	v	VCD Athletic (7/9)	2-1	139
98	Lingfield	v	Croydon (8/9)	1-4	
	(at Croydon FC)				
99	Ashford United	v	Chatham Town (5/9)	8-2	63
100	East Grinstead Town	v	Lewisham Borough (Community)		
	(walkover for Lewisham Borough (Community) – East Grinstead Town withdrawn)				
101	Lordswood	v	Glebe		
	(walkover for Lordswood – Glebe withdrawn)				
102	Corinthian	v	Eastbourne Borough (7/9)	0-3	36
103	Sevenoaks Town	v	Dartford (8/9)	0-2	110
104	Ramsgate	v	Hollands & Blair (7/9)	2-2aet	90
	(Hollands & Blair won 4-2 on kicks from the penalty mark)				
105	Margate	v	Thamesmead Town (5/9)	3-0	65
106	Hampton & Richmond Boro	v	Chertsey Town (6/9)	2-1	101
107	Steyning Town	v	Chichester City (5/9)	5-1	46
108	Camberley Town	v	Raynes Park Vale (7/9)	7-3	
109	Whitehawk	v	Worthing (6/9)	4-1	
110	Whyteleafe	v	Balham (6/9)	4-1	32
111	Dorking Wanderers	v	Bognor Regis Town (7/9)	1-5	
112	Ash United	v	Newhaven (4/9)	4-0	
113	Knaphill	v	Metropolitan Police (5/9)	5-4aet	59
114	Chessington & Hook United	v	East Preston (7/9)	4-1aet	
115	Shoreham	v	Three Bridges (4/9)	2-3	
116	Frimley Green	v	Worthing United (4/9)	1-4	63
117	Corinthian-Casuals	v	Merstham (7/9)	1-1aet	89
	(Corinthian-Casuals won 6-5 on kicks from the penalty mark)				
118	Guildford City	v	Hastings United (6/9)	0-1	
119	Crowborough Athletic	v	Horley Town (6/9)	4-0	
120	Walton & Hersham	v	Westfield (6/9)	3-1	31
121	Oxford City	v	Basingstoke Town (4/9)	6-5	
122	Bracknell Town	v	Highmoor Ibis (5/9)	5-1	93
123	Ascot United	v	Marlow (7/9)	0-3	50
124	Alton Town	v	Slough Town		
	(walkover for Alton Town – Slough Town withdrawn)				
125	Kidlington	v	Fleet Spurs (7/9)	0-2	30

THE FA YOUTH CUP

126 Poole Town v Farnborough (6/9) 4-4aet 72
(Farnborough won 5-4 on kicks from the penalty mark)
127 Havant & Waterlooville v Salisbury (6/9) 0-1 51
128 Christchurch v Team Solent (7/9) 1-2 62
129 Cirencester Town v Oldland Abbotonians (14/9) 5-2 39
(6/9 – tie abandoned after 56 mins due to floodlight failure, 3-0)
130 Gloucester City v Bristol Manor Farm (4/9) 3-2
(at Tuffley Rovers FC)
131 Paulton Rovers v Wellington AFC (7/9) 1-2 47
132 Ashton & Backwell United v Wells City (7/9) 1-6
133 Welton Rovers v Willand Rovers
(walkover for Welton Rovers – Willand Rovers withdrawn)
134 Keynsham Town v Tavistock (7/9) 0-2 53
(at Bishop Sutton FC)
135 Weston Super Mare v Portishead Town (7/9) 4-2
136 Bridgwater Town v Radstock Town (7/9) 1-3

FIRST ROUND QUALIFYING

1 Carlisle City v Morpeth Town (19/9) 2-6 52
2 Workington v Ryton & Crawcrook Albion
(walkover for Workington – Ryton & Crawcrook Albion withdrawn)
3 Shildon v Darlington (18/9) 4-2
4 Stockton Town v Spennymoor Town (18/9) 0-2 168
5 South Shields v Chester-Le-Street Town (20/9) 10-0 124
6 Ashton United v Altrincham
(walkover for Altrincham – Ashton United withdrawn)
7 Irlam v Prescot Cables (21/9) 0-6 85
8 Warrington Town v Colne (20/9) 1-0aet
9 Vauxhall Motors v Ashton Athletic (20/9) 2-1
10 Nantwich Town v Southport (25/9) 3-1 125
11 Abbey Hey v Ashton Town (22/9) 3-1 42
12 Marine v Bootle (20/9) 2-6
13 Burscough v FC United of Manchester (20/9) 0-6 60
14 Stalybridge Celtic v Nelson (18/9) 1-5 34
15 Hyde United v Stockport Town (22/9) 3-1 75
16 Daisy Hill v Salford City (20/9) 1-4 133
17 Rossington Main v AFC Emley (18/9) 2-0 32
18 Harrogate Railway Athletic v Nostell MW (21/9) 6-1 41
19 Farsley Celtic v Handsworth Parramore (19/9) 0-12 34
20 York City v Harrogate Town (19/9) 5-0
21 Bottesford Town v Worksop Town (28/9) 3-1 57
22 Ossett Albion v Staveley MW (21/9) 6-3 59
23 Selby Town v Sheffield
(walkover for Sheffield – Selby Town withdrawn)
24 Maltby Main v Silsden (18/9) 4-1
25 Matlock Town v Alfreton Town (20/9) 0-1
26 Blaby & Whetstone Athletic v Aylestone Park (20/9) 0-7 40
27 Sandiacre Town v Buxton (19/9) 4-1
28 Belper Town v Eastwood Community (18/9) 3-2
29 West Bridgford v Long Eaton United (19/9) 3-4 100
30 Bourne Town v Harborough Town (21/9) 1-7 65
31 Basford United v Dunkirk (21/9) 0-3 130
32 Gresley v Boston United (20/9) 0-4
33 Newcastle Town v Boldmere St Michaels (21/9) 3-1 81
34 Worcester City v Bilston Town (18/9) 4-4aet 61
(Worcester City won 5-3 on kicks from the penalty mark – at Stourport Swifts FC)
35 Nuneaton Town v Stratford Town (19/9) 2-0 54
36 Romulus v Walsall Wood (19/9) 1-4 60
37 Halesowen Town v Kidderminster Harriers (20/9) 2-1 121
38 Tamworth v Leek Town (18/9) 3-2
39 AFC Telford United v Lichfield City (21/9) 2-1aet
40 Hereford v Stourbridge (18/9) 1-2aet 92
41 Malvern Town v Sutton Coldfield Town
(walkover for Sutton Coldfield Town – Malvern Town withdrawn)
42 Ellesmere Rangers v Dudley Town (21/9) 3-4
43 Bedworth United v Pegasus Juniors (20/9) 5-2 17
44 Evesham United v Eccleshall (20/9) 4-0 54
45 Wellingborough Town v Kempston Rovers (21/9) 2-1
46 AFC Dunstable v Brackley Town (21/9) 5-1 76
47 AFC Rushden & Diamonds v Rothwell Corinthians (18/9) 3-2
48 Kettering Town v St Ives Town (21/9) 1-3 47
49 Biggleswade Town v Biggleswade United (21/9) 4-0
50 Peterborough Sports v Corby Town (21/9) 3-4
51 Godmanchester Rovers v Peterborough Northern Star (19/9) 1-1aet
(Peterborough Northern Star won 5-4 on kicks from the penalty mark)
52 Brantham Athletic v Woodbridge Town (20/9) 2-4

53 Ely City v Needham Market (21/9) 1-12
54 Haverhill Rovers v Cornard United (18/9) 2-0 31
55 Gorleston v Wroxham (21/9) 1-0 79
56 March Town United v Swaffham Town (21/9) 4-1
57 Cambridge City v Hadleigh United (20/9) 7-0 64
58 Leiston v Mildenhall Town (20/9) 1-0 67
59 Ipswich Wanderers v AFC Sudbury (21/9) 0-7 92
60 Stowmarket Town v Dereham Town (21/9) 3-8 68
(at Dereham Town FC)
61 Coggeshall Town v St Margaretsbury (21/9) 3-0
62 Barking v Chelmsford City (18/9) 6-0 78
63 Tilbury v Codicote
(walkover for Codicote – Tilbury withdrawn)
64 Royston Town v Bishop's Stortford (20/9) 0-2 78
65 Thurrock v Clapton (18/9) 7-2 82
66 East Thurrock United v FC Broxbourne Borough (20/9) 1-3 110
67 Cheshunt v Hullbridge Sports (21/9) 5-0 91
68 Hadley v Tower Hamlets (20/9) 1-3 54
69 Romford v Witham Town (25/9) 1-0 54
70 Brentwood Town v AFC Hornchurch (19/9) 1-3 93
71 Braintree Town v Hoddesdon Town (20/9) 1-5
72 Concord Rangers v Hitchin Town (21/9) 3-4 65
73 Saffron Walden Town v Brightlingsea Regent (21/9) 3-1 100
74 Hendon v Aylesbury (20/9) 4-2aet 41
75 Staines Town v Hanwell Town (20/9) 5-2 52
76 Bedfont Sports v St Albans City (18/9) 2-3aet 31
77 Sandhurst Town v Kings Langley (18/9) 1-7
78 Wingate & Finchley v Ashford Town (Middx) (27/9) 4-1 68
79 Hayes & Yeading United v Brimsdown (21/9) 7-1 46
80 Enfield Town v CB Hounslow United (20/9) 5-0 51
81 Edgware Town v Harefield Town (21/9) 10-2 46
82 Chesham United v Northwood (21/9) 4-3aet 51
83 Buckingham Athletic v Flackwell Heath (21/9) 3-1
84 Hemel Hempstead Town v Uxbridge (21/9) 2-0 40
85 Lewisham Borough (Community) v Lordswood (18/9) 4-2 64
86 Ashford United v Folkestone Invicta (19/9) 1-5 62
87 Carshalton Athletic v Dulwich Hamlet (22/9) 3-2aet 102
88 Eastbourne Borough v Welling United (19/9) 0-1 92
89 Croydon v AFC Croydon Athletic (20/9) 3-2 73
90 Margate v Hollands & Blair (21/9) 3-0 60
91 Tooting & Mitcham United v Cray Wanderers (18/9) 1-3
92 Tonbridge Angels v Greenwich Borough
(walkover for Greenwich Borough – Tonbridge Angels withdrawn)
93 Phoenix Sports v Dartford (21/9) 2-1
94 Faversham Town v Chipstead (21/9) 1-6
95 Kingstonian v Mile Oak (21/9) 6-1 46
96 Whyteleafe v South Park (20/9) 4-2
97 Burgess Hill Town v Haywards Heath Town (21/9) 2-0 41
98 Crowborough Athletic v Three Bridges (21/9) 1-6
(at Three Bridges FC)
99 Leatherhead v Wick (18/9) 7-0 35
100 Arundel v Lewes
(walkover for Lewes – Arundel withdrawn)
101 Knaphill v Ash United (19/9) 1-2 106
102 Hastings United v Abbey Rangers (22/9) 2-1
103 Walton & Hersham v Hampton & Richmond Boro (20/9) 2-4 50
104 Worthing United v Bognor Regis Town (18/9) 1-5 56
105 Redhill v Camberley Town (20/9) 1-4
106 Corinthian-Casuals v Whitehawk (20/9) 1-7 67
107 Steyning Town v Chessington & Hook United (19/9) 6-2 45
108 Hartley Wintney v Holmer Green (21/9) 1-3
109 Fleet Town v Fleet Spurs (18/9) 3-1 77
110 Andover Town v Hungerford Town (25/9) 2-3 85
111 Didcot Town v Oxford City (21/9) 1-4 84
112 Windsor v Alton Town (18/9) 4-0
113 Clanfield 85 v Bracknell Town (21/9) 5-2aet
114 Thame United v Binfield (21/9) 5-2
115 Thatcham Town v Marlow (18/9) 1-3aet
116 Salisbury v Winchester City (21/9) 3-2 71
117 Brockenhurst v AFC Totton (21/9) 4-6aet
118 Farnborough v Fareham Town
(walkover for Farnborough – Fareham Town withdrawn)
119 Team Solent v AFC Stoneham (21/9) 4-2
120 AFC Portchester v Romsey Town (18/9) 1-1aet
(AFC Portchester won 4-3 on kicks from the penalty mark)
121 Sholing v Wimborne Town (21/9) 3-1 105

122	Cirencester Town	v	Chippenham Town (20/9)	2-4	57
123	Gloucester City (at Tuffley Rovers FC)	v	Bishop's Cleeve (18/9)	6-0	
124	New College Swindon (at Malmesbury Victoria FC)	v	Malmesbury Victoria (21/9)	1-3	
125	Tuffley Rovers	v	Yate Town (20/9)	2-3	54
126	Welton Rovers	v	Wells City (21/9)	4-7aet	
127	Tavistock	v	Elburton Villa (18/9)	3-1	
128	Bath City	v	Radstock Town (20/9)	3-2aet	
129	Odd Down	v	Wellington AFC (21/9)	4-0	37
130	Clevedon Town	v	Weston Super Mare (18/9)	5-2	

SECOND ROUND QUALIFYING

1	Barrow	v	Gateshead (2/10)	1-5	159
2	South Shields	v	Spennymoor Town (9/10)	1-2	277
3	Shildon	v	Workington (5/10)	3-0	
4	Morpeth Town	v	Hartlepool United (2/10)	0-3	78
5	Nelson (at Hyde United FC)	v	Hyde United (13/10)	8-0	
6	Nantwich Town	v	Tranmere Rovers (11/10)	0-1	223
7	Prescot Cables	v	FC United Of Manchester (4/10)	3-1aet	
8	Bootle	v	Altrincham (5/10)	2-3	
9	AFC Fylde (at Kellamergh Park)	v	Chester (5/10)	1-3	
10	Salford City	v	Warrington Town (3/10)	2-1	129
11	Vauxhall Motors	v	Wrexham (3/10)	0-4	
12	FC Halifax Town	v	Abbey Hey (4/10)	4-1	113
13	Handsworth Parramore	v	Ossett Albion (2/10)	2-1	88
14	Rossington Main	v	Guiseley (5/10)	0-5	63
15	Sheffield	v	Alfreton Town (6/10)	0-3	104
16	York City	v	Harrogate Railway Athletic (3/10)	3-1	186
17	Maltby Main (at Bottesford Town FC)	v	Bottesford Town (3/10)	1-6	159
18	Belper Town	v	Sandiacre Town (5/10)	1-0	
19	Tamworth	v	Boston United (6/10)	3-1	
20	Dunkirk	v	Harborough Town (5/10)	7-1	43
21	Long Eaton United	v	Aylestone Park (5/10)	2-1	74
22	Worcester City	v	Sutton Coldfield Town (4/10)	0-1	48
23	Evesham United	v	Walsall Wood (2/10)	4-0	77
24	Newcastle Town	v	Bedworth United (5/10)	1-3	
25	Solihull Moors	v	Nuneaton Town (5/10)	0-2	87
26	Halesowen Town	v	AFC Telford United (5/10)	0-2	73
27	Stourbridge	v	Dudley Town (4/10)	3-0	
28	Corby Town	v	AFC Rushden & Diamonds (2/10)	1-2aet	128
29	AFC Dunstable	v	St Ives Town (5/10)	1-0	
30	Biggleswade Town	v	Wellingborough Town (5/10)	2-0	47
31	Haverhill Rovers	v	Cambridge City (4/10)	0-2	
32	Woodbridge Town	v	Peterborough Northern Star (5/10)	6-1	58
33	Leiston	v	Dereham Town (5/10)	1-0	59
34	Gorleston	v	Needham Market (5/10)	3-2	50
35	AFC Sudbury	v	March Town United (5/10)	5-0	46
36	Tower Hamlets	v	Leyton Orient (9/10)	0-3	218
37	AFC Hornchurch	v	FC Broxbourne Borough (5/10)	4-1	90
38	Dagenham & Redbridge	v	Coggeshall Town (5/10)	6-0	117
39	Cheshunt	v	Romford (3/10)	4-1aet	88
40	Saffron Walden Town	v	Hitchin Town (5/10)	2-3	113
41	Thurrock	v	Bishop's Stortford (4/10)	0-2	
42	Barking	v	Hoddesdon Town (4/10)	0-2aet	
43	Hampton & Richmond Boro	v	Codicote (4/10)	3-2	
44	Edgware Town	v	Wingate & Finchley (4/10)	1-2	49
45	Boreham Wood	v	Hendon (5/10)	2-1	103
46	Hayes & Yeading United	v	Enfield Town (4/10)	2-3	27
47	Hemel Hempstead Town	v	Chesham United (5/10)	6-0	57
48	Kings Langley	v	St Albans City (5/10)	2-8	88
49	Staines Town	v	Carshalton Athletic (2/10)	3-2	52
50	Ebbsfleet United	v	Phoenix Sports (5/10)	0-2	167
51	Chipstead	v	Lewisham Borough (Comm) (5/10)	4-1	56
52	Dover Athletic	v	Cray Wanderers (4/10)	1-0	81
53	Bromley	v	Maidstone United (2/10)	3-1	286
54	Folkestone Invicta	v	Welling United (5/10)	0-2	
55	Greenwich Borough	v	Margate (4/10)	0-4	81
56	Whitehawk	v	Woking (5/10)	3-1	70
57	Camberley Town	v	Three Bridges (5/10)	4-0	70
58	Sutton United	v	Croydon (5/10)	2-1	
59	Leatherhead	v	Lewes (2/10)	1-2aet	51
60	Bognor Regis Town	v	Hastings United (6/1)	0-3	63

61	Burgess Hill Town	v	Whyteleafe (5/10)	3-2	53
62	Kingstonian (at Colliers Wood United FC)	v	Steyning Town (5/10)	1-2	50
63	Windsor	v	Buckingham Athletic (4/10)	4-7aet	70
64	Marlow	v	Thame United (4/10)	2-0	51
65	Clanfield 85	v	Oxford City (5/10)	4-2	46
66	Holmer Green	v	Maidenhead United (5/10)	2-1aet	33
67	Fleet Town	v	AFC Portchester (2/10)	4-1	50
68	Ash United	v	Farnborough (5/10)	4-2	115
69	Eastleigh (at Malmesbury Victoria FC)	v	Malmesbury Victoria (3/10)	3-1	84
70	Aldershot Town	v	Hungerford Town (4/10)	5-3	72
71	Salisbury	v	AFC Totton (3/10)	1-4	93
72	Team Solent (Sholing won 8-7 on kicks from the penalty mark)	v	Sholing (4/10)	2-2aet	71
73	Wells City	v	Yate Town (4/10)	4-3	
74	Chippenham Town	v	Clevedon Town (4/10)	1-2	52
75	Odd Down	v	Bath City (5/10)	1-2	74
76	Tavistock	v	Gloucester City (5/10)	1-3	47

THIRD ROUND QUALIFYING

1	Gateshead	v	Wrexham (20/10)	2-3	
2	Nelson	v	Prescot Cables (31/10)	1-2	
3	Altrincham	v	Chester (20/10)	1-3	
4	York City	v	Salford City (17/10)	0-1	
5	Spennymoor Town	v	Tranmere Rovers (18/10)	0-1	155
6	Shildon	v	Guiseley (11/10)	1-3	
7	Hartlepool United	v	FC Halifax Town (18/10)	2-1	240
8	Nuneaton Town	v	Long Eaton United (17/10)	1-2	126
9	Belper Town	v	Bottesford Town (17/10)	2-3	
10	Dunkirk	v	AFC Rushden & Diamonds (26/10)	2-1	63
11	Handsworth Parramore	v	AFC Telford United (16/10)	2-1	88
12	Evesham United	v	Bedworth United (16/10)	2-0	100
13	Sutton Coldfield Town	v	Stourbridge (19/10)	0-2	78
14	Tamworth	v	Alfreton Town (20/10)	2-0	
15	Cambridge City (at Huntingdon Town FC)	v	Leiston (18/10)	1-0aet	90
16	Gorleston	v	Dagenham & Redbridge (19/10)	1-7	235
17	Hitchin Town	v	Hoddesdon Town (19/10)	6-1	
18	Woodbridge Town	v	Bishop's Stortford (19/10)	0-2	75
19	Leyton Orient	v	AFC Hornchurch (25/10)	4-0	285
20	Cheshunt	v	AFC Sudbury (19/10)	5-2	
21	Holmer Green (Marlow won 5-4 on kicks from the penalty mark)	v	Marlow (17/10)	0-0aet	93
22	Buckingham Athletic	v	Hampton & Richmond Boro (18/10)	7-1	
23	St Albans City	v	Biggleswade Town (18/10)	0-2	76
24	Clanfield 85 (Clanfield 85 won 5-3 on kicks from the penalty mark)	v	Hemel Hempstead Town (19/10)	0-0aet	
25	Boreham Wood	v	Enfield Town (16/10)	2-0	
26	Wingate & Finchley	v	AFC Dunstable (18/10)	2-0	
27	Phoenix Sports	v	Whitehawk (18/10)	3-4	203
28	Chipstead	v	Sutton United (19/10)	4-2	98
29	Hastings United	v	Bromley (19/10)	1-2	
30	Margate	v	Staines Town (19/10)	3-0	73
31	Lewes	v	Steyning Town (19/10)	3-0	
32	Camberley Town	v	Burgess Hill Town (19/10)	3-1	
33	Welling United (Welling United won 2-1 on kicks from the penalty mark)	v	Dover Athletic (16/10)	1-1aet	
34	Eastleigh (at Wells City FC)	v	Wells City (17/10)	3-0	90
35	Bath City	v	Clevedon Town (17/10)	3-4	116
36	Aldershot Town (Sholing won 4-3 on kicks from the penalty mark)	v	Sholing (16/10)	2-2aet	
37	Fleet Town	v	Gloucester City (16/10)	0-2	
38	AFC Totton (AFC Totton won 5-4 on kicks from the penalty mark)	v	Ash United (30/10)	2-2aet	

FIRST ROUND PROPER

1	Tranmere Rovers	v	Blackburn Rovers (1/11)	0-1	251
2	Morecambe	v	Wigan Athletic (31/10)	0-4	168
3	Carlisle United	v	Prescot Cables (13/11)	5-1	150
4	Bradford City	v	Blackpool (1/11)	0-3	248
5	Oldham Athletic	v	Bury (1/11)	0-3	299
6	Accrington Stanley	v	Rochdale (1/11)	1-0	
7	Hartlepool United	v	Chester (1/11)	3-1	228
8	Guiseley (Fleetwood Town won 4-3 on kicks from the penalty mark)	v	Fleetwood Town (31/10)	0-0aet	161
9	Wrexham (Wrexham won 5-4 on kicks from the penalty mark)	v	Salford City (31/10)	2-2aet	146
10	Evesham United (tie awarded to Evesham United – Shrewsbury Town removed)	v	Shrewsbury Town (1/11)	0-3	219
11	Rotherham United	v	Bottesford Town (1/11)	7-0	303

12	Doncaster Rovers	v	Walsall (26/10)	4-3	
13	Dunkirk	v	Tamworth (3/11)	0-2	109
14	Stourbridge	v	Port Vale (30/10)	2-3aet	353
15	Grimsby Town	v	Mansfield Town (5/11)	0-1	152
16	Long Eaton United	v	Scunthorpe United (2/11)	0-3	
17	Chesterfield	v	Notts County (2/11)	3-1	200
18	Lincoln City	v	Coventry City (31/10)	1-2	345
19	Handsworth Parramore	v	Crewe Alexandra (1/11)	0-2	204
20	Barnet	v	Wingate & Finchley (1/11)	4-0	256
21	Colchester United	v	Cheshunt (31/10)	5-4	227
22	Milton Keynes Dons	v	Southend United (31/10)	1-0	372
23	Leyton Orient	v	Biggleswade Town (8/11)	5-0	237
24	Peterborough United	v	Cambridge United (31/10)	1-2aet	612
25	Hitchin Town	v	Dagenham & Redbridge (2/11)	4-6	256
26	Buckingham Athletic	v	Northampton Town (2/11)	2-4	345
27	Clanfield 85	v	Cambridge City (2/11)	2-1	162
28	Luton Town	v	Stevenage (1/11)	1-2	392
29	Bishop's Stortford	v	Boreham Wood (1/11)	3-1aet	157
30	Charlton Athletic	v	Whitehawk (8/11)	4-1	167
	(at Welling United FC)				
31	Bromley	v	Chipstead (30/10)	2-0	
32	Marlow	v	AFC Wimbledon (1/11)	0-3	231
33	Welling United	v	Margate (30/10)	3-1	113
34	Gillingham	v	Portsmouth (31/10)	1-2aet	
35	Lewes	v	Camberley Town (30/10)	4-3	88
36	Bristol Rovers	v	Forest Green Rovers (2/11)	1-1aet	321
	(Bristol Rovers won 3-1 on kicks from the penalty mark)				
37	Swindon Town	v	Newport County (4/11)	6-2	251
38	AFC Totton	v	Cheltenham Town (6/11)	0-9	
39	Plymouth Argyle	v	Eastleigh (31/10)	7-2	232
40	Sholing	v	Clevedon Town (2/11)	2-0	227
41	Gloucester City	v	Oxford United (2/11)	1-2aet	153
	(at Tuffley Rovers FC)				
42	Yeovil Town	v	Exeter City (31/10)	0-3	

SECOND ROUND PROPER

1	Evesham United	v	Crewe Alexandra (21/11)	0-4	205
2	Cambridge United	v	Scunthorpe United (14/11)	0-1	
3	Chesterfield	v	Port Vale (14/11)	2-1	
4	Wigan Athletic	v	Bury (17/11)	1-3	155
	(at Lancashire FA County Ground)				
5	Blackburn Rovers	v	Wrexham (15/11)	3-1	338
6	Accrington Stanley	v	Coventry City (9/11)	2-3	174
7	Carlisle United	v	Hartlepool United (28/11)	0-2	167
8	Tamworth	v	Fleetwood Town (14/11)	1-2aet	
9	Rotherham United	v	Mansfield Town (15/11)	0-1	335
10	Doncaster Rovers	v	Blackpool (14/11)	0-2	
11	Colchester United	v	Bishop's Stortford (13/11)	5-0	
12	Swindon Town	v	Northampton Town (14/11)	1-0	281
13	Plymouth Argyle	v	AFC Wimbledon (14/11)	3-2	252
14	Exeter City	v	Charlton Athletic (14/11)	1-2	
15	Cheltenham Town	v	Welling United (16/11)	2-0	
16	Oxford United	v	Bristol Rovers (15/11)	3-1	344
	(at Oxford City FC)				
17	Portsmouth	v	Lewes (10/11)	3-1	474
18	Dagenham & Redbridge	v	Clanfield 85 (16/11)	7-1	150
19	Leyton Orient	v	Sholing (22/11)	5-0	254
20	Barnet	v	Milton Keynes Dons (14/11)	1-3	246
21	Bromley	v	Stevenage (16/11)	1-4	

THIRD ROUND PROPER

1	Sheffield United	v	Burton Albion (12/12)	2-0	337
2	Queens Park Rangers	v	Charlton Athletic (12/12)	1-3	337
3	Tottenham Hotspur	v	Preston North End (12/12)	5-0	78
	(at Tottenham Hotspur FC Training Centre)				
4	Mansfield Town	v	Crystal Palace (7/12)	2-2aet	450
	(Crystal Palace won 6-5 on kicks from the penalty mark)				
5	Burnley	v	Leeds United (27/11)	1-0	
6	Cheltenham Town	v	Bury (13/12)	1-2	172
7	Brighton & Hove Albion	v	Newcastle United (7/12)	0-5	253
8	Oxford United	v	Dagenham & Redbridge (21/12)	0-3	233
	(at Oxford City FC)				
9	Blackburn Rovers	v	Stoke City (13/12)	2-1	
10	Fleetwood Town	v	Stevenage (11/12)	1-5	251
11	West Bromwich Albion	v	Leyton Orient (5/12)	4-0	206
12	Plymouth Argyle	v	Manchester City (14/12)	0-0aet	1842
	(Plymouth Argyle won 6-5 on the penalty mark)				
13	Huddersfield Town	v	Fulham (15/12)	1-1aet	173
	(Fulham won 4-3 on kicks from the penalty mark)				
14	AFC Bournemouth	v	Hull City (8/12)	3-0	545
15	Portsmouth	v	Leicester City (5/12)	1-2	603
16	Chelsea	v	Scunthorpe United (15/12)	4-0	107
	(at Aldershot Town FC)				
17	Watford	v	Sunderland (7/1)	1-0	227
18	Swindon Town	v	Nottingham Forest (9/12)	1-3	178
19	Milton Keynes Dons	v	Cardiff City (12/12)	1-0	265
20	Swansea City	v	Chesterfield (15/12)	2-0	69
	(at Landore Training Ground)				
21	Middlesbrough	v	Bolton Wanderers (14/12)	2-0	254
22	Reading	v	Millwall (14/12)	2-1	379
23	Derby County	v	Manchester United (13/12)	2-2	
	(Derby County won 3-1 on kicks from the penalty mark)				
24	Norwich City	v	Barnsley (12/12)	4-1	
25	Everton	v	Ipswich Town (8/12)	1-2	
26	Bristol City	v	Birmingham City (5/12)	1-2	230
27	Colchester United	v	Crewe Alexandra (14/12)	2-0	153
28	West Ham United	v	Blackpool (15/12)	0-1	265
	(at Dagenham & Redbridge FC)				
29	Southampton	v	Wolverhampton Wanderers (14/12)	4-1	312
30	Arsenal	v	Sheffield Wednesday (13/12)	2-1	343
	(at Boreham Wood FC)				
31	Aston Villa	v	Coventry City (13/12)	2-1	482
32	Hartlepool United	v	Liverpool (13/12)	1-5	989

FOURTH ROUND PROPER

1	Liverpool	v	Arsenal (20/1)	2-3aet	
2	Burnley	v	Plymouth Argyle (5/1)	0-1	
3	Crystal Palace	v	Newcastle United (19/1)	2-3aet	1774
4	Blackpool	v	Southampton (16/1)	1-1aet	223
	(Blackpool won 4-2 on kicks from the penalty mark)				
5	Stevenage	v	Middlesbrough (11/1)	1-2	636
6	Chelsea	v	West Bromwich Albion (17/1)	7-0	157
	(at Aldershot Town FC)				
7	Ipswich Town	v	Dagenham & Redbridge (16/1)	2-1	585
8	Charlton Athletic	v	Reading (16/1)	3-4aet	
	(at Welling United FC)				
9	Bury	v	Aston Villa (22/1)	1-0	502
10	Colchester United	v	Milton Keynes Dons (16/1)	2-0	262
11	Birmingham City	v	Sheffield United (16/1)	1-0	553
12	Nottingham Forest	v	Leicester City (16/1)	1-1aet	654
	(Nottingham Forest won 5-4 on kicks from the penalty mark)				
13	Blackburn Rovers	v	Watford (17/1)	2-0	278
14	Swansea City	v	Fulham (17/1)	0-2	
	(at Landore Training Ground)				
15	Norwich City	v	Derby County (12/1)	4-2aet	
16	AFC Bournemouth	v	Tottenham Hotspur (16/1)	0-3	1362

FIFTH ROUND PROPER

1	Colchester United	v	Reading (6/2)	1-4	337
	(tie awarded to Colchester United – Reading removed)				
2	Plymouth Argyle	v	Fulham (7/2)	1-3aet	1517
3	Bury	v	Birmingham City (16/2)	1-3	
4	Middlesbrough	v	Arsenal (2/2)	2-3	471
	(at Bishop Auckland FC)				
5	Blackburn Rovers	v	Nottingham Forest (6/2)	5-1	482
6	Norwich City	v	Newcastle United (7/2)	4-3aet	
7	Tottenham Hotspur	v	Chelsea (13/2)	0-2	899
	(at Stevenage FC)				
8	Ipswich Town	v	Blackpool (30/1)	0-2	627

SIXTH ROUND PROPER

1	Fulham	v	Chelsea (27/2)	0-6	1582
2	Norwich City	v	Birmingham City (27/2)	1-3	
3	Colchester United	v	Arsenal (6/3)	1-5	918
4	Blackburn Rovers	v	Blackpool (6/3)	2-3	526

THE FA COUNTY YOUTH CUP

FIRST ROUND
1 Isle Of Man v Cumberland (30/9) 4-2aet
(at The Bowl, Douglas)
2 Leicestershire & Rutland v Nottinghamshire (7/10) 4-0
(at Holmes Park)
3 Guernsey v Hertfordshire (30/9) 1-3
(at Track Cycling Ground, Guernsey)
4 Devon v Kent (30/9) 1-2
(at Devon County FA)
5 London v Berks & Bucks (1/10) 2-5aet
(at Beckenham Town FC)
6 Somerset v Northamptonshire (30/9) 0-2

SECOND ROUND
1 Northumberland v West Riding (28/10) 3-0
(at Northumberland FA)
2 Sheffield & Hallamshire v Durham (4/11) 4-6
(at Staveley MW FC)
3 Isle Of Man v Lancashire (28/10) 3-0
(at The Bowl, Douglas)
4 Leicestershire & Rutland v Liverpool (4/11) 1-2 52
(at Holmes Park)
5 Westmorland v Birmingham (4/11) 0-1
(at Kendal Town FC)
6 Cheshire v North Riding (4/11) 3-2
(at Vauxhall Motors FC)
7 Staffordshire v Manchester (29/10) 2-1
(at Hednesford Town FC)
8 Cambridgeshire v Suffolk (9/11) 4-3
(at Histon FC)
9 Norfolk v Jersey (4/11) 2-1 73
(at FDC, Norwich)
10 Gloucestershire v Amateur Football Alliance (28/10)2-0
(at Gloucestershire FA)
11 Middlesex v Wiltshire (4/11) 4-2
(at Uxbridge FC)
12 Herefordshire v Oxfordshire (29/10) 0-5
(at Bromyard Town FC)
13 Essex v Bedfordshire (22/10) 5-1
(at Aveley FC)
14 Kent v Cornwall (28/10) 1-3
(at Margate FC)
15 Berks & Bucks v Sussex (5/11) 5-1aet
(at Slough Town FC)
16 Hertfordshire v Northamptonshire (4/11) 0-1
(at Bishop's Stortford FC)

PREVIOUS TEN FINALS
2017 Middlesex v Cornwall 2-1
2016 Liverpool v Sussex 2-0
2015 Cheshire v Middlesex 3-2
2014 Lancashire v Suffolk 3-2 aet
2013 Bedfordshire v Manchester 4-4, 4-2p
2012 Essex v West Riding 4-2 aet
2011 Norfolk v Staffordshire 4-2
2010 Kent v Sheffield & Hallamshire 1-0
2009 Birmingham v Kent 2-1
2008 Suffolk v Cambridgeshire 2-1

THIRD ROUND
1 Staffordshire v Northamptonshire (3/12) 1-0 36
(at Stafford Rangers FC)
2 Isle Of Man v Middlesex (25/11) 4-3aet
(at The Bowl, Douglas)
3 Gloucestershire v Cornwall (9/12) 5-3aet
(at Gloucestershire FA, Oaklands Park)
4 Cheshire v Liverpool (9/1) 2-3
(at Vauxhall Motors FC)
5 Birmingham v Oxfordshire (6/1) 1-1aet 32
(Oxfordshire won 4-1 on kicks from the penalty mark)
6 Essex v Durham (9/12) 0-4
(at Maldon & Tiptree FC)
7 Northumberland v Norfolk (25/11) 0-2
(at Northumberland FA)
8 Cambridgeshire v Berks & Bucks (14/1) 0-4
(at Cambourne Fitness and Sports Centre)

FOURTH ROUND
1 Staffordshire v Oxfordshire (28/1) 2-2aet 50
(Staffordshire won 3-1 on kicks from the penalty mark)
(at Hednesford Town FC)
2 Isle of Man v Norfolk (20/1) 1-2
(at The Bowl, Douglas)
3 Berks & Bucks v Liverpool (28/1) 5-1
(at Slough Town FC)
4 Gloucestershire v Durham (13/1) 5-1 35
(at Cirencester Town FC)

SEMI FINALS
1 Norfolk v Gloucestershire (10/3) 3-1aet 134
(at The FDC, Norwich)
2 Berks & Bucks v Staffordshire (25/2) 2-5
(at Bracknell Town FC)

THE FINAL
Saturday 14 APRIL 2018 at Stoke City FC
1 Staffordshire v Norfolk 0-2 300

FA YOUTH CUP

SEMI FINALS
				1st Leg		2nd Leg	
1	Blackpool	v	Arsenal	2-2	849	0-5	2083
2	Birmingham City	v	Chelsea	0-3	1568	0-4	4445

THE FINAL
			1st Leg		2nd Leg	
Chelsea	v	Arsenal	3-1	4878	4-0	3877

PREVIOUS TEN FINALS
Aggregate Score
2017 Chelsea v Manchester City 6-2
2016 Chelsea v Manchester City 4-2
2015 Chelsea v Manchester City 5-2
2014 Chelsea v Fulham 7-6
2013 Norwich City v Chelsea 4-2
2012 Chelsea v Blackburn Rovers 4-1
2011 Manchester Utd v Sheffield United 4-1
2010 Chelsea v Aston Villa 3-2
2009 Arsenal v Liverpool 6-2
2008 Manchester City v Chelsea 4-2

FIRST ROUND

1 Burradon & New Fordley v Wrekenton Blue Star 3-1
(at Morpeth Town FC)

2 Newton Aycliffe Huntsman v Southwick (Sunderland) 0-0aet
(Newton Aycliffe Huntsman won 4-3 on kicks from the penalty mark)
(at Shildon AFC)

3 Dawdon Welfare Park v Amble Tavern 2-1
(at Seaham Red Star FC)

4 Garston v FC Dovecot 1-3
(at Tetleys Carlsberg Club, Warrington)

5 The Georgies v Mottram 3-1aet
(at Lower Breck)

6 Lobster v Kirkdale 4-2
(at St John Bosco School)

7 FC Walkers Hounds v Ferrybridge Progressive 4-2aet
(at Golcar United FC)

8 West Kirby (Sunday) v Rock Ferry Social 1-5
(at West Kirby FC)

9 Chapeltown Fforde Grene v Oyster Martyrs 1-3
(at Yorkshire Amateur FC)

10 Thornton United v Hope Inn Whites 0-2
(at Manningham Mills)

11 Mayfair v AFC Blackburn Leisure 7-0 30
(at Anfield Sports Centre)

12 St John Fisher OB v Oakenshaw
(walkover for Oakenshaw – St John Fisher OB withdrawn)

13 Kent v Melling Victoria 2-2aet
(Melling Victoria won 5-4 on kicks from the penalty mark)
(at Jericho Lane)

14 Campfield v Dock 3-2
(at Litherland Sports Park)

15 Leeds City Rovers v Pineapple 1-6 80
(at Adel Memorial Ground, Leeds)

16 Kensington Fields v HT Sports 6-0
(at Skelmersdale United FC)

17 Home Bargains v Linthwaite 3-2
(at Alder Sports & Social Club)

18 Attenborough Cavaliers v Austin Ex Apprentices 0-1
(at Radford FC)

19 Sporting Dynamo v Penn Tandoori Sundats 0-2
(at Ibstock Welfare FC)

20 BGIS Fairfield v Carlton Top Spot 4-1
(at Fairfield Villa FC)

21 RHP Sports & Social v Oadby Athletic 2-4
(at Newark Flowserve FC)

22 FC Brimington v OJM 0-6
(at Shirebrook Town FC)

23 Quorn Royals v Highgate Dynamos 1-2 129
(at Riverside Park, Leicester)

24 Rempstone v Hampton Sunday 0-1
(at Costock Road, East Leake, Nottingham)

25 Black Horse (Redditch) v AFC Jacks 0-6 55
(at Studley FC)

26 Halfway v Nuthall 3-1
(at Boldmere St Michaels FC)

27 Olympia v Gym United 0-3
(at Haringey Borough FC)

28 Asianos v Hertford Stags 1-0
(at Barking FC)

29 Old Southall v AC Sportsman 5-3 46
(at AFC Hayes)

30 North Wembley v St Josephs (Luton)
(walkover for St Josephs (Luton) – North Wembley withdrawn)

31 Broadfields United (Sunday) v Real Milan 2-4
(at Harefield United FC)

32 Harpole v FC Bengals 1-2
(at Harpole FC)

33 Reed Rangers v Club Lewsey 0-4
(at Sun Postal Sports & Social Club)

34 AFC Bevendean v White Hart 1-4
(at Southwick FC)

35 AFC Links v Shire United 3-1 17
(at Colliers Wood United FC)

36 Market Hotel v Eden Park Rangers 2-6 49
(at Lydd Town FC)

37 Barnes AFC v Real Rosehill 7-1
(at Hanworth Villa FC)

38 London St Georges v Broadwater 3-2
(at AFC Croydon Athletic)

39 AFC Kumazi Strikers v Portland 2-3
(at Peckham Town FC)

40 Dolphin v Lebeqs Tavern Courage 1-2
(at Weymouth College Sports Centre)

SECOND ROUND

1 FC Walkers Hounds v Mayfair 0-5
(at Huddersfield Amateurs FC)

2 Queens Park v FC Soho (19/11) 6-2
(at Newton FC)

3 FC Dovecot v Hope Inn Whites (2.00) 1-3
(at Tetley Walker Recreation Club)

4 Canada v Allerton (2.00) 4-2 86
(at Lower Breck)

5 Pineapple v Home Bargains 1-3aet
(at South Liverpool FC)

6 Burradon & New Fordley v Melling Victoria 3-2aet
(at Heaton Stannington FC)

7 Oyster Martyrs v Lobster (11.30) 4-1
(at St John Bosco School)

8 Hartlepool Lion Hillcarter v Newton Aycliffe Huntsman 1-4
(at Hartlepool FC)

9 Rock Ferry Social v Campfield 2-4 90
(at Cammell Laird 1907 FC)

10 Dawdon Welfare Park v Custys 2-1 110
(at Seaham Red Star FC)

11 The Georgies v Dengo United (11.00) 0-2
(at Lower Breck)

12 Toller v Kensington Fields 1-4
(at Manningham Mills)

13 Hardwick Social v Oakenshaw 3-0
(at Stockton Town FC)

14 Halfway v Austin Ex Apprentices (2.00) 0-2
(at Boldmere St Michaels FC)

15 Oadby Athletic v St Josephs (Luton) 1-4aet
(at Oadby Town FC)

16 Hampton Sunday v FC Topps 0-2
(at Hampton FC)

17 Penn Tandoori Sundats v Club Lewsey 2-1
(at Wolverhampton Casuals FC)

18 Highgate Dynamos v Enderby Social 4-0
(at Highgate United FC)

19 Leighton Madrid v AFC Jacks 1-1aet
(AFC Jacks won 5-3 on kicks from the penalty mark)
(at Leighton Town FC)

20 Falcons v Birstall Stamford 4-2 10
(at Potton United FC)

21 OJM v BGIS Fairfield (19/11) 1-4
(at GKN Thimble Mill Recreation Ground, Smethwick)

22 Aylesbury Flooring v Gym United 1-2
(at Aylesbury FC)

23 Larkspur Rovers v Real Milan (19/11) 2-4aet
(at Rayners Lane FC)

24	Manor House	v	Eden Park Rangers	0-1	
	(at Redbridge FC)				
25	London St Georges	v	Asianos	0-4	
	(at AFC Croydon Athletic)				
26	NLO	v	Old Southall (19/11)	5-1	
	(at Northwood FC)				
27	New Salamis	v	Portland (2.00)	5-4	45
	(at White Hart Lane Community Sports Centre)				
28	Priory Sports	v	FC Bengals	0-1	43
	(at Maldon & Tiptree FC)				
29	White Hart	v	AFC Links	1-0	38
	(at Peacehaven & Telscombe FC)				
30	Barnes AFC	v	Barnes Albion FC	2-0	
	(at Hanworth Villa FC)				
31	Navy Inn	v	Chessington United (19/11)	4-1	
	(at Launceston FC)				
32	Talbot Rangers	v	Lebeqs Tavern Courage (2.00)	1-6	
	(at Verwood Town FC)				

THIRD ROUND

1	Oyster Martyrs	v	Dawdon Welfare Park	2-0	
	(at JMO Sports Park, Skelmersdale)				
2	Burradon & New Fordley	v	Mayfair (7/1)	2-3	
	(tie reversed – at Anfield Sports & Community Centre)				
3	Hope Inn Whites	v	Dengo United	0-1	
	(at Yorkshire Amateur FC)				
4	Hardwick Social	v	Canada	2-1	
	(at Stockton Town FC)				
5	Newton Aycliffe Huntsman	v	Campfield (17/12)	2-3	
	(at Shildon AFC)				
6	Kensington Fields	v	Home Bargains (17/12)	2-3	
	(at St John Bosco School)				
7	Penn Tandoori Sundats	v	Queens Park (17/12)	2-1	
	(at Wolverhampton Casuals FC)				
8	St Josephs (Luton)	v	FC Topps (17/12)	3-1	20
	(at Arlesey Town FC)				
9	Highgate Dynamos	v	BGIS Fairfield (7/1)	5-1	
	(at Coleshill Town FC)				
10	AFC Jacks	v	Austin Ex Apprentices (7/1)	1-0	
	(tie reversed – at Pilkington XXX FC)				
11	Falcons	v	Asianos (17/12)	2-3	
	(at Newmarket Town FC)				
12	FC Bengals	v	Real Milan (17/12)	5-2	
	(at Brunel Sports Complex)				
13	Gym United	v	Eden Park Rangers (14/1)	2-5	
	(tie reversed – at Beckenham Town FC)				
14	NLO	v	New Salamis (17/12)	0-3	
	(tie reversed – at Haringey Borough FC)				
15	White Hart	v	Navy Inn	3-1	8
	(at Southwick FC)				
16	Barnes AFC	v	Lebeqs Tavern Courage (2.00)	3-4	25
	(at Hanworth Villa FC)				

FOURTH ROUND

1	Mayfair	v	Campfield (2.00)	1-0	
	(at Anfield Sports & Community Centre)				
2	Oyster Martyrs	v	Penn Tandoori Sundats	5-1	
	(at JMO Sports Park, Skelmersdale)				
3	Dengo United	v	AFC Jacks (1.30)	2-2aet	
	(Dengo United won 3-2 on kicks from the penalty mark - at St Helens Town FC)				
4	Hardwick Social	v	Home Bargains	1-0	
	(at Stockton Town FC)				
5	Highgate Dynamos	v	St Josephs (Luton)	2-1aet	
	(at Highgate United FC)				
6	Asianos	v	New Salamis (2.00)	0-4	
	(at Barking FC)				
7	Lebeqs Tavern Courage	v	FC Bengals	0-3	60
	(tie awarded to Lebeqs Tavern Courage – FC Bengals removed)				
	(at Bristol Manor Farm FC)				
8	Gym United	v	White Hart (21/1)	4-0	
	(at Thetford Town FC)				

FIFTH ROUND

1	Mayfair	v	Dengo United	2-1	
	(at Liverpool Soccer Centre)				
2	Hardwick Social	v	Oyster Martyrs	2-1	
	(at Stockton Town FC)				
3	New Salamis	v	Highgate Dynamos	5-1	
	(at Haringey Borough FC)				
4	Lebeqs Tavern Courage	v	Gym United	1-3	80
	(at Bristol Manor Farm FC)				

SEMI FINALS

1	Gym United	v	Mayfair	2-1	88
	(at Solihull Moors FC)				
2	New Salamis	v	Hardwick Social (25/3)	1-2	250
	(at Alfreton Town FC)				

THE FINAL

SUNDAY 29 APRIL 2018

| | Gym United | v | Hardwick Social | 0-2aet | 422 |
| | (at Sheffield United FC) | | | | |

PREVIOUS TEN FINALS

2017	Hardwick Social	v New Salamis	1-1, 3-1p
2016	New Salamis	v Barnes	1-1, 4-3p
2015	Campfield	v OJM	2-0
2014	Humbledon Plains Farm	v Oyster Martyrs	5-2
2013	Oyster Martyrs	v Barnes Albion	4-3
2012	Hetton Lyons C.C.	v Canada	5-1
2011	Oyster Martyrs	v Paddock	1-0
2010	Hetton Lyons C.C.	v Magnet Tavern	4-2
2009	Scots Grey	v Oyster Martyrs	4-3 aet
2008	Hetton Lyons C.C.	v Coundon Conservative	3-2

THE FA WOMEN'S CUP

FIRST QUALIFYING ROUND

1. Alnwick Town Juniors v Washington — 3-2 — 53
(at Alnwick Town FC)
2. Blyth Town Lions v South Shields — 0-3
(at Blyth AFC)
3. RACA Tynedale v Norton & Stockton Ancients
(walkover for Norton & Stockton Ancients – RACA Tynedale withdrawn)
4. Penrith v South Park Rangers — 4-2
(at Penrith AFC)
5. Workington Reds v Redcar Town — 1-2
(at Workington FC)
6. Prudhoe Town v Chester-Le-Street
(3/9 – tie abandoned after 116 minutes due to serious injury to player, 2-5 – tie awarded to Chester-Le-Street)
(at Prudhoe Town FC)
7. Bishop Auckland v Gateshead Leam Rangers — 4-2
(at Bishop Auckland FC)
8. Carlisle United v Wallsend Boys Club — 3-1 — 48
(at Creighton Rugby Club)
9. Sheffield Wednesday v Yorkshire Amateur — 2-1
(at Sheffield Hallam University Sports Park)
10. Altofts v Bradford Park Avenue
(walkover for Altofts – Bradford Park Avenue withdrawn)
11. Malet Lambert v Wakefield — 4-5aet
(at Andrew Marvell College, Hull)
12. Ossett Albion v Farsley Celtic — 0-5
(at Ossett Albion FC)
13. Dronfield Town v Harworth Colliery
(3/9 – tie abandoned after 68 minutes due to serious injury to player, 0-5 – tie awarded to Harworth Colliery)
(at Dronfield Town FC)
14. Nelson v Blackpool — 0-14
(at Nelson FC)
15. Merseyrail Bootle v Stockport County — 4-2
(at Bootle FC)
16. Wigan Athletic v Accrington — 7-0
(at Billange Soccer Centre, Billange)
17. FC United Of Manchester v Altrincham — 13-1
(at FC United Of Manchester)
18. West Didsbury & Chorlton v Warrington Wolverines — 3-2
(at West Didsbury & Chorlton FC)
19. Manchester Stingers v Blackburn Community Sports Club — 2-1
(at Whalley Range FC)
20. Fleetwood Town Wrens v Burnley — 0-6
(at Brews Park)
21. Lincoln Moorlands Railway v Cosby United — 4-3
(at Lincoln Moorlands Railway FC)
22. Loughborough Students v Mansfield Town — 4-2 — 20
(at Holywell Park)
23. AFC Leicester v Leicester City Women Development — 0-2
(at Judge Meadow College, Leicester)
24. Rise Park v Teversal — 7-3
(at Arnold Town FC)
25. Market Warsop v Nettleham — 0-5
(at Rainworth MW FC)
26. Eastwood Ladies v Arnold Town — 3-0
(at Eastwood Community FC)
27. Leafield Athletic v Knowle — 5-1 — 39
(at Dickens Heath Sports Club)
28. Leek Town v Solihull United — 2-1 — 68
(at Leek Town FC)
29. Wryley v Lye Town — 0-3
(at Wyrley Juniors FC)
30. Redditch United v Stockingford AA Pavilion — 2-1
(at Redditch United FC)
31. Shrewsbury Town v Wolverhampton Sporting C. — 4-2 — 68
(at Shrewsbury College)
32. Solihull Sporting v Coventry Sphinx — 0-8
(at Sedgemere Sports & Social)
33. Crusaders v Abbey Hulton United — 6-2 — 30
(at Rowheath Pavillion)
34. Shrewsbury Juniors v Brereton Town — 0-3
(at Shrewsbury Sports Village)
35. Coundon Court v Goldenhill Wanderers — 2-6 — 42
(at Coventry Colliery Sports Ground)
36. Rugby Town v Worcester United — 1-4

37. Sutton Coldfield Town v Bedworth United (2.30) — 0-4
(at Bedworth United FC)
38. Gornal v Stone Dominoes
(walkover for Gornal – Stone Dominoes withdrawn)
39. Newmarket Town v Histon — 4-2 — 85
(at Newmarket Town FC)
40. Kettering Town v Woodford United — 10-0 — 35
(at Kettering Town FC)
41. Sprowston v Wymondham Town — 0-4
(at Sprowston Sports & Social Club)
42. Roade v St Ives Town — 0-1
(at Roade FC)
43. Oadby & Wigston v King's Lynn Town — 1-3
(at Oadby & Wigston FC)
44. Peterborough Northern Star v Netherton United
(walkover for Peterborough Northern Star – Netherton United withdrawn)
45. Cambridge City v Moulton — 8-2
(at Trinity College, Cambridge)
46. Riverside v Corby Town — 2-1
(at Queens Park, Yaxley)
47. March Town United v Peterborough United — 0-5 — 80
(at March Town United FC)
48. Acle United v Thrapston Town — 4-1 — 85
(at Great Yarmouth Town FC)
49. Colchester Town v Bungay Town — 2-4
(at Cage Lane, Boxted)
50. Harlow Town v Little Thurrock Dynamos — 4-0
(at Harlow Town FC)
51. Brentwood Town v Corringham Cosmos — 6-0
(at Garon Park)
52. AFC Sudbury v Writtle — 4-3
(at AFC Sudbury FC)
53. Billericay Town v Chelmsford City (2.30) — 8-0
(at Nursery Playing Fields, Ramsden Heath)
54. Milton Keynes City v Bedford — 2-4aet — 50
(at Tattnehoe Lane Playing Fields)
55. Sandy v Hemel Town
(walkover for Hemel Town – Sandy withdrawn)
56. AFC Dunstable v Houghton Athletic (7.30) — 5-0
(at AFC Dunstable)
57. Royston Town v Watford Ladies Development — 7-0 — 80
(at Royston Town FC)
58. Hertford Town v Bishop's Stortford — 0-1
(at Wodson Park FC)
59. Garston v Colney Heath — 1-4
(at Bushey Sports Club)
60. Brentford v Chesham United — 1-7 — 25
(at Lampton School, Hounslow)
61. Headington v Ashford Town (Middx) — 0-17
(at Ashford Town (Middx) FC)
62. Ascot United v Newbury — 1-1aet — 73
(Ascot United won 4-3 on kicks from the penalty mark)
(at Ascot United FC)
63. Benson Lionesses v Wargrave — 4-2
(at RAF Benson)
64. Fleet Town v Alton — 1-8
(at Fleet Town FC)
65. Oxford City v Woodley United — 9-0
(tie awarded to Woodley United – Oxford City removed)
66. Chinnor v New London Lionesses — 0-12
(at Chinnor FC)
67. Queens Park Rangers Girls v Hampton & Richmond Borough — 0-1
(at Bedfont Sports FC)
68. Meridian v Fulham Foundation — 2-1 — 20
(at The Victory Academy School)
69. Ashford v Aylesford — 2-3aet — 25
(at Charing Playing Fields, Ashford)
70. Kent Football United v London Kent Football United — 0-4 — 30
71. Worthing v Godalming Town — 1-2
(at Godalming Town FC)
72. Eastbourne Town v Dartford — 7-0
(at Eastbourne Town FC)
73. Worthing Town v Parkwood Rangers — 1-7
(at Worthing Town FC)

74	Victoire	v	Burgess Hill Town	2-2aet	
	(Burgess Hill Town won 4-2 on kicks from the penalty mark)				
	(at Croygas Sports Club)				
75	Whyteleafe	v	Bexhill United	1-0	
	(at Whyteleafe FC)				
76	Abbey Rangers	v	Eastbourne	1-2	63
	(at Abbey Rangers FC)				
77	Carshalton Athletic	v	Herne Bay (3.30)	3-0	35
	(tie awarded to Herne Bay – Carshalton Athletic removed for playing ineligible player)				
78	Frampton Rangers	v	New Milton Town	2-3	
	(at Gloucestershire FA, Oaklands Park)				
79	Buckland Athletic	v	Exeter City (10/9)	9-2	
	(at Buckland Athletic FC)				
80	AEK Boco	v	Downend Flyers	0-9	
	(at AEK Boco)				
81	FC Chippenham	v	Team Solent	4-3aet	
	(at Stanley Park, Chippenham)				
82	Middlezoy Rovers	v	Marine Academy Plymouth	1-7	20
	(at The Aerodrome, Westonzoyland)				
83	Royal Wootton Bassett Town	v	AFC Bournemouth	2-5	
	(at Royal Wootton Bassett Town FC)				
84	Warsash Wasps	v	Ilminster Town	4-0	54
	(at New Road, Warsash)				
85	Winchester City Flyers	v	Frome Town	5-0	
	(at Winchester City FC)				
86	Bournemouth Sports	v	Keynsham Town Development	3-1	
	(at Bournemouth Sports Club)				
87	Eastleigh	v	Torquay United	0-6	
	(at Eastleigh FC)				

SECOND QUALIFYING ROUND

1	Alnwick Town Juniors	v	Redcar Town	1-0	57
	(at Alnwick Town FC)				
2	Cramlington United	v	Carlisle United	1-7	
	(at Northburn Sports & Community Centre)				
3	Bishop Auckland	v	South Shields	1-6	48
	(at King James Academy)				
4	Chester-Le-Street	v	Hartlepool United	0-9	
	(at East Durham College)				
5	Norton & Stockton Ancients	v	Penrith	3-2aet	150
	(at Norton & Stockton Ancients FC)				
6	Worksop Town	v	Farsley Celtic	3-5	
	(at Worksop Town FC)				
7	Altofts	v	Sheffield Wednesday	4-3aet	
	(at Altofts FC)				
8	Wakefield	v	Harworth Colliery	4-3	
	(at Nostell MW FC)				
9	Blackpool	v	West Didsbury & Chorlton	2-2aet	52
	(West Didsbury & Chorlton won 3-2 on kicks from the penalty mark)				
10	CMB Ladies	v	Tranmere Rovers	2-1	40
11	Burnley	v	Merseyrail Bootle	4-3	40
	(at Barden Athletics Ground, Burnley)				
12	Manchester Stingers	v	MSB Woolton	0-6	
	(at Whalley Range FC)				
13	Wigan Athletic	v	FC United Of Manchester	1-0	
	(at Billinge Soccer Centre)				
14	Eastwood Ladies	v	Rise Park	4-0	
	(at Eastwood Community FC)				
15	Loughborough Students	v	Lincoln Moorlands Railway	6-3	25
	(at Loughborough University)				
16	Leicester City Women Dev	v	Nettleham	2-3aet	45
	(at Riverside Pavilion)				
17	Shrewsbury Town	v	Leek Town	5-2	
	(at Shrewsbury College)				
18	Redditch United	v	Goldenhill Wanderers	5-1	
	(at Redditch United FC)				
19	Leafield Athletic	v	Lye Town	1-2	
	(at Dickens Heath Sports Club)				
20	Bedworth United	v	Gornal	2-0aet	62
	(at Bedworth United FC)				
21	Worcester United	v	Coventry Sphinx	2-8	
	(at Worcester University)				
22	Brereton Town	v	Crusaders	2-1	
	(at Brereton Town FC)				

23	Newmarket Town	v	King's Lynn Town	4-3aet	
	(at Newmarket Town FC)				
24	Acle United	v	Riverside		
	(walkover for Acle United – Riverside withdrawn)				
25	Cambridge City	v	Kettering Town	5-2	
	(at Trinity College)				
26	Peterborough Northern Star	v	Peterborough United	4-2	
	(at Peterborough Northern Star FC)				
27	Wymondham Town	v	St Ives Town	7-1	
	(at Wymondham Town FC)				
28	Frontiers	v	AFC Sudbury	1-8	49
	(at Takeley FC)				
29	Harlow Town	v	Bungay Town	3-2	45
	(at Harlow Town FC)				
30	Brentwood Town	v	Billericay Town	2-3	
	(at Brentwood Town FC)				
31	Colney Heath	v	Royston Town	0-4	
	(at Colney Heath FC)				
32	Hemel Town	v	Bedford	0-12	
	(at Hemel Hempstead Town FC)				
33	AFC Dunstable	v	Bishop's Stortford	7-1	
	(at AFC Dunstable)				
34	Benson Lionesses	v	Ashford Town (Middx)	1-12	
	(at RAF Benson)				
35	New London Lionesses	v	Hampton & Richmond Boro	2-0	
	(at Regents Park)				
36	Ascot United	v	Chesham United	0-2	
	(at Ascot United FC)				
37	Woodley United	v	Alton (24/9)	2-1	35
	(at Woodley United FC)				
38	Eastbourne Town	v	Aylesford	5-2	
	(at Eastbourne Town FC)				
39	Godalming Town	v	Eastbourne	3-2aet	
	(at Godalming Town FC)				
40	Meridian	v	London Kent Football United	2-3	20
	(at The Victory Academy)				
41	Hassocks	v	Margate	5-1	
	(at Hassocks FC)				
42	Herne Bay	v	Parkwood Rangers (2.30)	1-3	32
	(at Herne Bay FC)				
43	Whyteleafe	v	Burgess Hill Town	6-0	
	(at Farleigh Rovers FC)				
44	Marine Academy Plymouth	v	Buckland Athletic		
	(walkover for Buckland Athletic – Marine Academy Plymouth withdrawn)				
45	FC Chippenham	v	Bournemouth Sports	2-1	
	(at Stanley Park, Chippenham)				
46	New Milton Town	v	Downend Flyers	5-4	50
	(at New Milton Town FC)				
47	Pen Mill	v	Forest Green Rovers	1-4	76
	(at Johnson Park, Yeovil)				
48	Torquay United	v	AFC Bournemouth	1-0	
	(at Torquay United FC)				
49	Winchester City Flyers	v	Warsash Wasps	5-1	
	(at Totton & Eling FC)				

THIRD QUALIFYING ROUND

1	Alnwick Town Juniors	v	Rotherham United	5-0	82
	(at Alnwick Town FC)				
2	Farsley Celtic	v	Hartlepool United	1-3	
	(at Farsley Celtic FC)				
	(tie awarded to Farsley Celtic - Hartlepool United removed)				
3	Burnley	v	Wigan Athletic (15/10)	4-1	35
	(at Barden Sports Club, Burnley)				
4	West Didsbury & Chorlton	v	MSB Woolton	6-3	
	(at West Didsbury & Chorlton FC)				
5	Brighouse Town	v	Wakefield (3.00)	6-1	
	(at Brighouse Town FC)				
6	Altofts	v	Chorley	1-5	
	(at Altofts FC)				
7	Chester-Le-Street Town	v	Barnsley	2-1	
	(at Chester-Le-Street Town FC)				
8	Crewe Alexandra	v	Hull City	1-4	32
	(at Cumberland Arena, Crewe)				
9	South Shields	v	Norton & Stockton Ancients	0-3	
	(at Harton & Westoe Miners Welfare, South Shields)				

10	CMB v Bolton Wanderers (15/10) (at CMB Sports Club)	2-5	42
11	Liverpool Marshalls Feds v Mossley Hill (at IM Marsh, Barkhill Road, Liverpool)	7-0	
12	Steel City Wanderers v Morecambe (at SGP Thorncliffe, Sheffield)	2-1	40
13	Sheffield United v Leeds United (12.00) (Sheffield United won 3-2 on kicks from the penalty mark – at Sheffield United FC)	3-3aet	
14	Newcastle United v Carlisle United (at Newcastle University, Cochrane Park)	9-1	
15	Redditch United v Solihull Moors (at Redditch United FC)	5-2	
16	Sporting Khalsa v Lye Town (at University Of Wolverhampton)	6-1	40
17	The New Saints v Shrewsbury Town (at Foxen Manor)	3-1	
18	Eastwood v Coventry Sphinx (at Play Soccer 3G Arena, Eastwood)	5-3	
19	Long Eaton United v Leicester City Ladies (at Long Eaton United FC)	3-1	
20	Bedworth United v Birmingham & West Midlands (at Bedworth United FC)	2-1	53
21	Radcliffe Olympic v Loughborough Foxes (walkover for Loughborough Foxes – Radcliffe Olympic withdrawn)		
22	Loughborough Students v Brereton Town (at Loughborough University FC)	3-0	
23	Burton Albion v Nettleham (at Stafford Rangers FC)	0-4	30
24	Milton Keynes Dons v Actonians (at Newport Pagnell Town FC)	2-0	76
25	Cambridge City v Ipswich Town (at Trinity College Sports Ground)	1-5	
26	Maidenhead United v Luton Town (at Maidenhead United FC)	0-1	
27	Cambridge United v Norwich City (at Mildenhall Town FC)	4-0	
28	Peterborough Northern Star v Acle United (at Peterborough Northern Star FC)	1-3	
29	Harlow Town v Denham United (at Harlow Town FC)	1-0	90
30	Wymondham Town v Newmarket Town (at Wymondham Town FC)	9-2aet	175
31	Enfield Town v AFC Sudbury (at Enfield Town FC)	1-0	
32	Godalming Town v Haringey Borough (at Godalming Town FC)	5-0	
33	Ashford Town (Middx) v London Kent Football United (at Ashford Town (Middx) FC)	6-4	
34	AFC Dunstable v Eastbourne Town (at AFC Dunstable)	2-0	49
35	New London Lionesses v Parkwood Rangers (at Regents Park, London)	3-1aet	
36	Leyton Orient v Billericay Town (2.30) (at Leyton Orient FC)	7-0	
37	Hassocks v Stevenage (at Hassocks FC)	0-8	
38	Bedford v Royston Town (at Kempston Rovers FC)	2-3	
39	Chesham United v Whyteleafe (at Chesham United FC)	2-1	
40	AFC Wimbledon v Woodley United (at Sutton United FC)	14-1	50
41	Cheltenham Town v Southampton Saints (at Cheltenham Saracens FC)	1-4	
42	FC Chippenham v Basingstoke Town (at Stanley Park, Chippenham)	1-6	
43	Poole Town v Plymouth Argyle (at Milborne St Andrew FC)	2-5	34
44	St Nicholas v Keynsham Town (at Yate Town FC)	0-1	55
45	New Milton Town v Buckland Athletic (at New Milton Town FC)	1-4	60
46	Winchester City Flyers v Southampton Women (at Winchester City FC)	0-7	
47	Forest Green Rovers v Larkhall Athletic (at Slimbridge FC)	0-3	

48	Brislington v Torquay United (Brislington won 4-2 on kicks from the penalty mark – at Brislington FC)	0-0aet	63

FIRST ROUND

1	Alnwick Town Juniors v Burnley (2.00) (at Alnwick Town FC)	0-4	
2	Liverpool Marshalls Feds v Bolton Wanderers (at IM Marsh Playing Fields)	1-0aet	
3	Hull City v Steel City Wanderers (12.30) (at Hull University)	4-1	
4	Norton & Stockton Ancients v Chorley (at Norton & Stockton Ancients FC)	0-4	70
5	Farsley Celtic v West Didsbury & Chorlton (at Farsley Celtic FC)	6-4aet	
6	Newcastle United v Sheffield United (2.00) (at Newcastle University)	3-0	
7	Brighouse Town v Chester-Le-Street Town (at Brighouse Town AFC)	6-1	43
8	Bedworth United v The New Saints (2.00) (at Bedworth United FC)	0-2	85
9	Redditch United v Loughborough Foxes (at Redditch United FC)	2-4	
10	Nettleham v Loughborough Students (2.00) (at Nettleham FC)	3-0	
11	Sporting Khalsa v Eastwood (2.00) (at University of Wolverhampton)	5-1	
12	Cambridge United v Long Eaton United (at Mildenhall Town FC)	0-1	85
13	Enfield Town v Wymondham Town (at Enfield Town FC)	3-2	
14	Harlow Town v Royston Town (2.00) (at Harlow Town FC)	2-1	133
15	Stevenage v Acle United (at Hertford Town FC)	4-1	25
16	Ipswich Town v Leyton Orient (2.00) (at Felixstowe & Walton United FC)	4-2aet	
17	Ashford Town (Middx) v Milton Keynes Dons (at Ashford Town (Middx) FC)	0-6	
18	Chesham United v New London Lionesses (at Chesham United FC)	1-2aet	
19	AFC Wimbledon v Godalming Town (2.00) (at Sutton United FC)	5-0	90
20	AFC Dunstable v Luton Town (2.00) (at AFC Dunstable)	0-4	102
21	Larkhall Athletic v Southampton Women (2.00) (at Larkhall Athletic FC)	2-3	40
22	Buckland Athletic v Brislington (2.00) (at Buckland Athletic FC)	1-4	
23	Plymouth Argyle v Basingstoke Town (19/11) (walkover for Plymouth Argyle – Basingstoke Town withdrawn)		
24	Southampton Saints v Keynsham Town (2.00) (at Sholing FC)	1-3	

SECOND ROUND

1	Middlesbrough v Farsley Celtic (at MFC Foundation, 3G)	8-1	
2	Sporting Khalsa v The New Saints (2.00) (The New Saints won 4-1 on kicks from the penalty mark) (at University of Wolverhampton)	2-2aet	45
3	Derby County v Hull City (Derby County won 3-2 on kicks from the penalty mark) (at Mickleover Sports FC)	1-1aet	81
4	Huddersfield Town v West Bromwich Albion (at The Stafflex Arena, Huddersfield)	7-0	79
5	Nettleham v Liverpool Marshalls Feds (at Nettleham FC)	1-3	
6	Nottingham Forest v Newcastle United (2.00) (at Basford United FC)	0-2	
7	Bradford City v Long Eaton United (at Eccleshill United FC)	5-0	
8	Blackburn Rovers v Loughborough Foxes (2.00) (at Bamber Bridge FC)	4-1	77
9	Fylde Ladies v Guiseley AFC Vixens (at AFC Fylde)	2-0	43
10	Stoke City v Burnley (Burnley won 4-1 on kicks from the penalty mark – at Norton United FC)	0-0aet	

11	Brighouse Town (at Brighouse Town FC)	v	Wolverhampton Wanderers (17/12)	6-3	123
12	Chorley (at Euxton Villa FC)	v	Leicester City Women	0-3	102
13	Keynsham Town (at Keynsham Town FC)	v	Southampton Women	2-1	
14	Milton Keynes Dons (at Newport Pagnell Town FC)	v	Cardiff City (2.00)	0-1	110
15	Lewes (at Lewes FC)	v	Enfield Town	7-0	
16	Charlton Athletic (at Sporting Club Thamesmead FC)	v	Queens Park Rangers (2.00)	5-0	66
17	Gillingham (at Chatham Town FC)	v	Plymouth Argyle	1-3aet	
18	Brislington (at Brislington FC)	v	Swindon Town (2.00)	3-2aet	67
19	AFC Wimbledon (at Sutton United FC)	v	Portsmouth (2.00)	1-2	70
20	New London Lionesses (at Northwood FC)	v	Crystal Palace	0-3	
21	Luton Town (at Stockwood Park Athletics Stadium)	v	Harlow Town	3-2aet	51
22	Coventry United (at Butts Park Arena)	v	West Ham United (2.00)	6-1	
23	Chichester City (at Chichester City FC)	v	C&K Basildon	4-2	120
24	Stevenage (Ipswich Town won 3-0 on kicks from the penalty mark – at Hertford Town FC)	v	Ipswich Town	1-1aet	80

THIRD ROUND

1	Cardiff City (at Centre of Sporting Excellence, Cardiff)	v	Burnley	3-2	
2	Fylde Ladies (at University of Central Lancashire Sports Arena)	v	Plymouth Argyle (2.00)	1-3	58
3	Keynsham Town (at Keynsham Town FC)	v	Brislington	8-1	70
4	Huddersfield Town (at Shelley FC)	v	Lewes	1-2	96
5	Leicester City Women (at Quorn FC)	v	Bradford City	2-1	78
6	Newcastle United (at Newcastle University)	v	The New Saints	1-2	153
7	Blackburn Rovers (at JMO Sports Park, Skelmersdale)	v	Portsmouth (2.00)	7-0	
8	Derby County (at Mickleover Sports FC)	v	Brighouse Town (14/1)	1-3	
9	Ipswich Town (at Felixstowe & Walton United FC)	v	Charlton Athletic	2-5aet	110
10	Crystal Palace (Coventry United won 3-2 on kicks from the penalty mark - at Glebe FC)	v	Coventry United (2.00)	1-1aet	
11	Middlesbrough (at Thornaby FC)	v	Liverpool Marshall Feds	4-3aet	
12	Chichester City (at Chichester City FC)	v	Luton Town	2-0	100

FOURTH ROUND

1	Durham (at New Ferens Park, Durham)	v	Sheffield (1.00)	2-1	
2	Aston Villa (at Tamworth FC)	v	Middlesbrough	4-0	
3	Sunderland (at South Shields FC)	v	Brighouse Town	13-0	
4	Keynsham Town (at Keynsham Town FC)	v	Lewes	0-3	75
5	Tottenham Hotspur (at Cheshunt FC)	v	Doncaster Rovers Belles	0-3	
6	Liverpool (at Liverpool County FA)	v	Watford (1.00)	5-0	
7	Cardiff City (Cardiff City won 5-4 on kicks from the penalty mark)	v	Oxford United	0-0aet	
8	The New Saints (Chichester City won 5-4 on kicks from the penalty mark)	v	Chichester City (12.00)	1-1aet	
9	Millwall Lionesses (at St Pauls Sports Ground)	v	Coventry United (3.00)	4-1	
10	Reading (at Wycombe Wanderers FC)	v	Birmingham City	0-1	

11	Plymouth Argyle (at Devon FA)	v	Leicester City Women (11/2)	2-3	208
12	Brighton & Hove Albion (at Sussex County FA)	v	Manchester City	0-2	1400
13	Blackburn Rovers (at Bamber Bridge FC)	v	Charlton Athletic	2-3aet	
14	Yeovil Town (at Weston Super Mare FC)	v	Arsenal	0-3	323
15	London Bees (at Barnet FC)	v	Chelsea	0-10	486
16	Everton (at Marine FC)	v	Bristol City	3-1	712

FIFTH ROUND

1	Arsenal (at Boreham Wood FC)	v	Millwall Lionesses	1-0	
2	Cardiff City (at Centre of Sporting Excellence, Cardiff)	v	Charlton Athletic	1-3	
3	Lewes (at Lewes FC)	v	Everton	0-6	975
4	Sunderland (at South Shields FC)	v	Aston Villa	3-2	
5	Chichester City (at Chichester City FC)	v	Liverpool	0-3	
6	Birmingham City (at Solihull Moors FC)	v	Manchester City	1-3aet	
7	Chelsea (at AFC Wimbledon)	v	Doncaster Rovers Belles	6-0	
8	Durham (at New Ferens Park, Durham)	v	Leicester City	5-2	

QUARTER FINALS

1	Sunderland (at South Shields FC)	v	Manchester City (25/3)	2-4aet	
2	Liverpool (at Prescot Cables FC)	v	Chelsea	0-3	358
3	Arsenal (at Boreham Wood FC)	v	Charlton Athletic (25/3)	5-0	
4	Durham (at New Ferens Park, Durham)	v	Everton (25/3)	1-6	502

SEMI FINALS

| 1 | Everton (at Marine FC – Live on BBC Red Button) | v | Arsenal (12.30) | 1-2 | 1457 |
| 2 | Chelsea (at AFC Wimbledon – Live on BBC Two) | v | Manchester City (3.30) | 2-0 | 3048 |

THE FINAL

Saturday 5 May - @ Wembley Stadium

Arsenal	v	Chelsea	1-3	45,423
Miedema 73		Bachmann 48, 60, Kirby 76		
		New record crowd for Women's FA Cup		

FIRST ROUND

1   Northern Football Alliance   v   Lincolnshire
    (walkover for Lincolnshire – Northern Football Alliance withdrawn)

2   Isle of Man   v   Peterborough & District (7/10) 4-1
    (at The Bowl, Douglas, Isle Of Man)

3   Liverpool County Premier   v   West Yorkshire Association (14/10)   3-2
    (at Liverpool County FA)

4   Staffordshire County Senior   v   Lancashire Amateur (30/9)   5-0
    (at Newcastle Town FC)

5   Northamptonshire Combination v   Humber Premier (7/10)   1-2
    (at Wellingborough Whitworths FC)

6   Chester & Wirral   v   Cheshire (14/10)   6-3aet
    (at Cammell Laird 1907 FC)

7   Cumberland County   v   North Riding Football (4/11) 3-2
    (tie awarded to North Riding Football – Cumberland County removed)
    (at County Ground, Whitehaven)

8   York Football   v   West Riding County Am. (14/10) 2-1   72
    (at Tadcaster Albion FC)

9   Jersey Football Combination v   Essex Olympian (30/9)   3-2
    (at Springfield Stadium, Jersey)

10   Dorset Premier   v   Kent County (14/10)   2-3   72
    (at Swanage Town & Herston FC)

11   Guernsey County Senior   v   Surrey Elite Intermediate
    (walkover for Guernsey County Senior – Surrey Elite Intermediate withdrawn)

12   Somerset County   v   Essex & Suffolk Border (30/9) 3-3aet
    (Essex & Suffolk Border won 3-0 on kicks from the penalty mark)
    (at Hengrove Athletic FC)

13   Hampshire Premier   v   Cambridgeshire County (30/9) 1-2
    (at Hamble Club FC)

14   Anglian Combination   v   Amateur Football Combination (30/9) 0-5
    (at FDC, Bowthorpe, Norwich)

15   Bedfordshire County   v   Southern Amateur (7/10)   6-4
    (at Cranfield United FC)

16   Thames Valley Premier   v   Spartan South Midlands (14/10) 3-2
    (at Rivermoor Stadium, Reading)

SECOND ROUND

1   Isle of Man   v   Liverpool County Premier (18/11)   2-1
    (at The Bowl, Douglas)

2   Lincolnshire   v   Staffordshire County Senior (20/1) 2-5aet

3   Humber Premier   v   North Riding Football (13/1)   1-5
    (at East Riding County FA)

4   Chester & Wirral   v   York Football (13/1)   1-8
    (tie reversed – at Harrogate Town FC)

5   Bedfordshire County   v   Amateur Football Com (25/11) 4-5aet   62
    (at Cranfield United FC)

6   Jersey Football Combination v   Kent County (16/12)   1-3
    (at Springfield Stadium, St Helier)

7   Essex & Suffolk Border   v   Guernsey County Senior (2/12) 5-0
    (at Coggeshall Town FC)

8   Cambridgeshire County   v   Thames Valley Premier (13/1) 2-5
    (at Histon FC)

THIRD ROUND

1   York Football   v   Staffordshire County (17/2)   4-0   50
    (at Harrogate Town FC)

2   North Riding Football   v   Isle of Man (18/2)   5-2
    (at Stokesley FC)

3   Essex & Suffolk Border   v   Kent County (17/2)   1-1
    (Kent County won 4-3 on kicks from the penalty mark)
    (at Brantham Athletic FC)

4   Amateur Football Com.   v   Thames Valley Premier (4/2) 5-4
    (at Corinthian Casuals FC)

SEMI FINALS

1   York Football   v   Kent County (17/3)   4-1aet   90
    (at Harrogate Town)

2   Amateur Football Com.   v   North Riding Football (24/3) 4-3aet   80
    (tie awarded to North Riding Football – Amateur Football Com. removed)

FINAL

Sunday 6 May 2018
    North Riding Football   v   York Football   4-2   314
    (at Sheffield United)

THE FA DISABILTY FINALS DAY

Saturday 16 and Sunday 17 June
At St. George's Park

Amputee Final
Everton 2-3 Peterborough United Amputees
Blind Final
RNC Leicestershire Foxes 1-0 West Bromwich Albion
Cerebral Palsy Final
North East & Yorkshire Disability 2-0 Chelsea Blues
Deaf Final
Derby County Com. Trust 9-0 Braidwood Trust School
Partially Sighted Final
North West Scorpions 1-4 Birmingham Futsal
Powerchair Final
Aspire PFC 0-1 West Bromwich Albion

Peterborough

Tweed (Everton) gets in his shot against Peterborough.

Plesca (Foxes) scores the only goal of the game.

Leicestershire Foxes

North East and Yorkshire

Taylor-West (Chelsea) Brown (NEY).

Derby County Community Trust

Birmingham Futsal

Bolding (Aspire) and Gordon (WBA) pass each other.

West Bromwich Albion. All photos: Keith Clayton

COUNTY FOOTBALL ASSOCIATION CONTACTS

AMATEUR FOOTBALL ALLIANCE
Tel: 020 8733 2613 Fax: 020 7250 1338
Website: www.amateur-fa.com
Email: info@amateur-fa.com

ARMY FA
Tel: 01252 787 067 Fax: 01252 787 072
Website: www.armyfa.com
Email: info@armyfa.com

BEDFORDSHIRE FA
Tel: 01582 565 111 Fax: 01582 565 222
Website: www.bedfordshirefa.com
Email: info@bedfordshirefa.com

BERKS & BUCKS FA
Tel: 01367 242 099 Fax: 01367 242 158
Website: www.berks-bucksfa.com
Email: info@berks-bucksfa.com

BIRMINGHAM FA
Tel: 0121 357 4278 Fax: 0121 358 1661
Website: www.birminghamfa.com
Email: info@birminghamfa.com

CAMBRIDGESHIRE FA
Tel: 01223 209 025 Fax: 01223 209 030
Website: www.cambridgeshirefa.com
Email: info@cambridgeshirefa.com

CHESHIRE FA
Tel: 01606 871 166 Fax: 01606 871 292
Website: www.cheshirefa.com
Email: info@cheshirefa.com

CORNWALL FA
Tel: 01208 269010 Fax: 01208 892665
Website: www.cornwallfa.com
Email: info@cornwallfa.com

CUMBERLAND FA
Tel: 01900 872 310
Fax: 01900 616 470
Website: www.cumberlandfa.com
Email: info@cumberlandfa.com

DERBYSHIRE FA
Tel: 01332 361 422 Fax: 01332 360 130
Website: www.derbyshirefa.com
Email: info@derbyshirefa.com

DEVON FA
Tel: 01626 332 077 Fax: 01626 336 814
Website: www.devonfa.com
Email: info@devonfa.com

DORSET FA
Tel: 01202 682 375 Fax: 01202 666 577
Website: www.dorsetfa.com
Email: info@dorsetfa.com

DURHAM FA
Tel: 01913 872 929
Website: www.durhamfa.com
Email: info@durhamfa.com

EAST RIDING FA
Tel: 01482 221 158 Fax: 01482 221 169
Website: www.eastridingfa.com
Email: info@eastridingfa.com

ENGLISH SCHOOLS FA
Tel: 01785 785 970 Fax: 01785 785 971
Website: www.esfa.co.uk
Email: info@schoolsfa.com

ESSEX FA
Tel: 01245 465 271 Fax: 01245 393 089
Website: www.essexfa.com
Email: info@essexfa.com

GLOUCESTERSHIRE FA
Tel: 01454 615 888 Fax: 01454 618 088
Website: www.gloucestershirefa.com
Email: info@gloucestershirefa.com

GUERNSEY FA
Tel: 01481 200 443 Fax: 01481 200 451
Website: www.guernseyfa.com
Email: info@guernseyfa.com

HAMPSHIRE FA
Tel: 01256 853 000 Fax: 01256 357 973
Website: www.hampshirefa.com
Email: info@hampshirefa.com

HEREFORDSHIRE FA
Tel: 01432 342 179 Fax: 01432 279 265
Website: www.herefordshirefa.com
Email: info@herefordshirefa.com

HERTFORDSHIRE FA
Tel: 01462 677622 Fax: 01462 677624
Website: www.hertfordshirefa.com
Email: info@hertfordshirefa.com

HUNTINGDONSHIRE FA
Website: www.huntsfa.com
Email: info@huntsfa.com

ISLE OF MAN FA
Tel: 01624 615 576 Fax: 01624 615 578
Website: www.isleofmanfa.com
Email: info@isleofmanfa.com

JERSEY FA
Tel: 01534 730 433 Fax: 01534 500 029
Website: www.jerseyfa.com
Email: info@jerseyfa.com

KENT FA
Tel: Governance 01622 791850,
Development 01622 792140
Fax: 01622 790658
Website: www.kentfa.com
Email: info@kentfa.com

LANCASHIRE FA
Tel: 01772 624 000 Fax: 01772 624 700
Website: www.lancashirefa.com
Email: info@lancashirefa.com

LEICESTERSHIRE & RUTLAND FA
Tel: 01162 867 828
Website: www.leicestershirefa.com
Email: info@leicestershirefa.com

LINCOLNSHIRE FA
Tel: 01522 524 917 Fax: 01522 528 859
Website: www.lincolnshirefa.com
Email: info@lincolnshirefa.com

LIVERPOOL FA
Tel: 01515 234 488 Fax: 01515 234 477
Website: www.liverpoolfa.com
Email: info@liverpoolfa.com

LONDON FA
Tel: 020 7610 8360 Fax: 020 7610 8370
Website: www.londonfa.com
Email: info@londonfa.com

MANCHESTER FA
Tel: 01616 047 620 Fax: 01616 047 622
Website: www.manchesterfa.com
Email: info@manchesterfa.com

MIDDLESEX FA
Tel: 020 8515 1919 Fax: 020 8515 1910
Website: www.middlesexfa.com
Email: info@middlesexfa.com

NORFOLK FA
Tel: 01603 704 050 Fax: 01603 704 059
Website: www.norfolkfa.com
Email: info@norfolkfa.com

NORTHAMPTONSHIRE FA
Tel: 01604 670 741 Fax: 01604 670 742
Website: www.northamptonshirefa.com
Email: info@northamptonshirefa.com

NORTH RIDING FA
Tel: 01642 717 770 Fax: 01642 717 776
Website: www.northridingfa.com
Email: info@northridingfa.com

NORTHUMBERLAND FA
Tel: 01912 700 700 Fax: 01912 700 700
Website: www.northumberlandfa.com
Email: info@northumberlandfa.com

NOTTINGHAMSHIRE FA
Tel: 0115 983 7400 Fax: 0115 946 1977
Website: www.nottinghamshirefa.com
Email: info@nottinghamshirefa.com

OXFORDSHIRE FA
Tel: 01993 894400 Fax: 01993 772 191
Website: www.oxfordshirefa.com
Email: info@oxfordshirefa.com

RAF FA
Tel: 01993 895 704 Fax: 01993 895 545
Website: www.royalairforcefa.com
Email: info@royalairforcefa.com

ROYAL NAVY FA
Tel: 02392 722 671 Fax: 02932 724 923
Website: www.royalnavyfa.com
Email: info@navyfa.com

SHEFFIELD & HALLAMSHIRE FA
Tel: 0114 261 5500
Website: www.sheffieldfa.com
Email: info@sheffieldfa.com

SHROPSHIRE FA
Tel: 01743 362 769 Fax: 01743 270 494
Website: www.shropshirefa.com
Email: info@shropshirefa.com

SOMERSET FA
Tel: 01458 832359 Fax: 01458 835588
Website: www.somersetfa.com
Email: info@somersetfa.com

STAFFORDSHIRE FA
Tel: 01785 256 994 Fax: 01785 279 837
Website: www.staffordshirefa.com
Email: info@staffordshirefa.com

SUFFOLK FA
Tel: 01449 616 606 Fax: 01449 616 607
Website: www.suffolkfa.com
Email: info@suffolkfa.com

SURREY FA
Tel: 01372 373 543 Fax: 01372 361 310
Website: www.surreyfa.com
Email: info@surreyfa.com

SUSSEX FA
Tel: 01903 753 547 Fax: 01903 761 608
Website: www.sussexfa.com
Email: info@sussexfa.com

WESTMORLAND FA
Tel: 01539 730 946 Fax: 01539 740 567
Website: www.westmorlandfa.com
Email: info@westmorlandfa.com

WEST RIDING FA
Tel: 01132 821 222 Fax: 01132 821 525
Website: www.wrcfa.com
Email: info@wrcfa.com

WILTSHIRE FA
Tel: 01793 486 047 Fax: 01793 692 699
Website: www.wiltshirefa.com
Email: info@wiltshirefa.com

WORCESTERSHIRE FA
Tel: 01905 827 137 Fax: 01905 798 963
Website: www.worcestershirefa.com
Email: info@worcestershirefa.com

COUNTY CUPS

A.F.A. Senior Cup
HOLDERS: Polytechnic
Quarter Finals
Old Meadonians	v	Polytechnic	2-2, 5-4p
Nottsborough	v	Old Garchonians	1-3
Old Wilsonians	v	Old Wokingians	3-0
KCS Old Boys	v	Actonians Association	3-4

Semi Finals
Old Meadonians	v	Old Garchonians	4-3
Old Wilsonians	v	Actonians Association	0-2

Final
Old Meadonians	v	Actonians Association	2-4

A.F.A. Middlesex/Essex Senior Cup
HOLDERS: Actonians Association
Quarter Finals
Old Meadonians	v	Albanian	2-3
Old Hamptonians	v	Actonians Association	3-2
Southgate County	v	Old Manorians	0-2
Old Parkonians	v	Old Ignations	2-1

Semi Finals
Albanian	v	Old Hamptonians	2-3
Old Manorians	v	Old Parkonians	2-5

Final
Old Hamptonians	v	Old Parkonians	1-3

A.F.A. Surrey/Kent Senior Cup
HOLDERS: Nottsborough
Quarter Finals
Old Thorntonians	v	Dorkinians	2-6
Wandsworth Borough	v	Old Wokingians	1-2
Reigatians	v	Old Tenisonians	3-2 aet
Honourable Artillery Co	v	Kings Old Boys	8-1

Semi Finals
Dorkinians	v	Old Wokingians	4-2
Reigatians	v	Honourable Artillery Co	3-2

Final
Dorkinians	v	Reigatians	2-0

Arthur Dunn Cup
HOLDERS: Old Carthusians
Quarter Finals
Lancing Old Boys	v	Old Foresters	0-2
Old Carthusians	v	Old Alleynians	4-1
Old Westminsters	v	Old Reptonians	0-3
Old Tonbridgians	v	Old Salopians	1-0

Semi Finals
Old Foresters	v	Old Carthusians	1-2
Old Tonbridgians	v	Old Reptonians	2-1

Final
Old Carthusians	v	Old Tonbridgians	3-3, 5-3p

Berks & Bucks Senior Cup
HOLDERS: Maidenhead United
Quarter Finals
Thatcham Town	v	Woodley United	AW
Windsor	v	Milton Keynes Dons	0-5
Bracknell Town	v	Slough Town	2-3
Didcot Town	v	Chesham United	0-1

Semi Finals
Slough Town	v	Milton Keynes Dons	1-4
Woodley United	v	Chesham United	0-2

Final
Chesham United	v	Milton Keynes Dons	2-2, 4-3p

Berks & Bucks Senior Trophy
HOLDERS: Bracknell Town
Quarter Finals
Buckingham Athletic	v	Marlow United	0-1
Chalvey (WMC)	v	Newport Pagnell Town Res	3-3, 3-5p
Saxton Rovers	v	Kintbury Rangers	5-0
Winslow United	v	Langley	2-1

Semi Finals
Saxton Rovers	v	Winslow United	1-1, 6-5p
Marlow United	v	Newport Pagnell Town Res	2-0

Final
Saxton Rovers	v	Marlow United	3-1

Berks & Bucks Intermediate Cup
HOLDERS: Risborough Rangers
Penn & Tylers Green Res	v	Delaford Colts	1-2

Berks & Bucks Junior Cup
HOLDERS: New Zealand C (Aylesbury)
Final
Tattenhoe Res	v	FC Tradesman	2-2, 4-2p

Birmingham Senior Cup
HOLDERS: Leamington
Quarter Finals
Hednesford Town	v	Burton Albion	4-1
Nuneaton Town	v	Walsall	2-0
Alvechurch	v	West Bromwich Albion	2-3
Coleshill Town	v	Stourbridge	2-3

Semi Finals
Stourbridge	v	West Bromwich Albion	3-1
Hednesford Town	v	Nuneaton Town	4-0

Final
Hednesford Town	v	Stourbridge	1-2

Birmingham Vase
HOLDERS: Wednesfield
Final
Northfield Town	v	Smithswood Firs	1-1, 3-4p

Birmingham Amateur Cup
HOLDERS: Coventry United U21
Final
Claverdon AFC	v	Tamworth U21	2-1

Channel Islands - Muratti Vase
HOLDERS: Guernsey
Round One
Alderney	v	Guernsey	0-2

Final
Jersey	v	Guernsey	1-0

Break down of Muratti Vase Wins
Jersey	54	Guernsey	46	Shared	1	Alderney	1

Cambridgeshire Invitational Cup

Quarter Finals

Cambridge City	v	West Wratting	5-0
Wisbech Town	v	Soham Town Rangers	AW
Wisbech St Mary	v	Ely City	1-3
March Town United	v	Cambridge United Dev	0-3

Semi Finals

Cambridge City	v	Cambridge United Dev	1-3
Soham Town Rangers	v	Ely City	2-2, 3-5p

Final

Cambridge United Dev	v	Ely City	TBC

Cheshire Senior Cup

HOLDERS: Stockport County

Quarter Finals

Stalybridge Celtic	v	Barnton	6-1
Stockport Town	v	Hyde United	1-1, 4-3p
Nantwich Town	v	Crewe Alexandra	2-1
Altrincham	v	Winsford United	0-1

Semi Finals

Nantwich Town	v	Stalybridge Celtic	4-3 aet
Winsford United	v	Stockport Town	1-2

Final

Nantwich Town	v	Stockport Town	3-0

Cornwall Senior Cup

HOLDERS: Bodmin Town

Quarter Finals

AFC St Austell	v	Falmouth Town	3-0
Mousehole	v	Newquay	5-0
Torpoint Athletic	v	Bodmin Town	3-2
Saltash United	v	Sticker	6-1

Semi Finals

Torpoint Athletic	v	Saltash United	1-3
AFC St Austell	v	Mousehole	1-3 aet

Final

Saltash United	v	Mousehole	3-2

Cornwall Junior Cup

HOLDERS: St Minver

Final

St Stephen	v	Torpoint Athletic 3rd	2-0

Cumberland Senior Cup

HOLDERS: Workington

Quarter-Finals

Workington Athletic	v	Workington	0-1
Cleator Moor Celtic	v	Pirelli	4-0
Aspatria	v	Netherhall	1-3
Penrith	v	Windscale	7-0

Semi-Finals

Penrith	v	Netherhall	1-0
Cleator Moor Celtic	v	Workington	1-1, 5-3p

Final

Cleator Moor Celtic	v	Penrith	2-1 aet

Derbyshire Senior Challenge Cup

HOLDERS: Matlock Town

Quarter-Finals

Buxton	v	Mickleover Sports	3-1
Chesterfield	v	Belper Town	0-0, 3-1p
Ilkeston Town	v	Whaley Bridge	4-3 aet
New Mills	v	Alfreton Town	1-4

Semi-Finals

Buxton	v	Chesterfield	0-1
Alfreton Town	v	Ilkeston Town	2-0

Final

Alfreton Town	v	Chesterfield	0-1

Devon St Lukes Cup

HOLDERS: Tiverton Town

Quarter-Finals

Bideford	v	Tiverton Town	1-1, 5-4p
Exmouth Town	v	Cullompton Rangers	0-2
Willand Rovers	v	Plymouth Argyle	3-2
Plymouth Parkway	v	Tavistock	2-0

Semi-Finals

Cullompton Rangers	v	Plymouth Parkway	0-2
Bideford	v	Willand Rovers	3-2

Final

Bideford	v	Plymouth Parkway	1-4

Devon Premier Cup

HOLDERS: University of Exeter

Quarter-Finals

Budleigh Salterton	v	Teignmouth	0-1
Bovey tracy	v	Newton Abbot Spurs	2-1
Brixham AFC	v	Torridgside	0-3
Plymstock United	v	University of Exeter	0-8

Semi-Finals

Torridgeside	v	University of Exeter	1-1, 4-2p
Teignmouth	v	Bovey Tracey	4-0

Final

Teignmouth	v	Torridgeside	2-0

Devon Senior Cup

HOLDERS: Cronies

Quarter-Finals

Plympton Athletic	v	Harbertonford	1-3 aet
Chagford	v	Colyton	1-2
Lakeside Athletic	v	Watcombe Wanderers	4-0
Sidmouth Town Res	v	Maristow	3-0

Semi-Finals

Colyton	v	Harbertonford	3-3, 4-2p
Sidmouth Twon Res	v	Lakeside Athletic	1-1, 4-2p

Final

Colyton	v	Sidmouth Town Res	0-2

Devon Intermediate Cup

HOLDERS: Royal Oak

Final

Black Swan Town	v	Elmore Res	3-4

CHESTERFIELD
Derbyshire Senior Cup
Winners
Photo: Bill Wheatcroft

COTTERED
Hertfordshire Junior Cup
Winners

HENLON RESERVES
Bedfordshire Junior Cup
Winners

TOTTERNHOE
Bedfordshire Senior Trophy
Winners

AFC DUNSTABLE U21
Bedfordshire Intermediate Cup
Winners

Photos: Gordon Whittington

Dorset Senior Cup
HOLDERS: Weymouth
Quarter-Finals

Hamworthy United	v	Poole Town	2-10
Wimborne Town	v	Dorchester Town	2-0
Portland United	v	Verwood Town	4-2
Shaftesbury Town	v	Bridport	3-1

Semi-Finals

Shaftesbury Town	v	Portland United	2-1
Poole Town	v	Wimborne Town	1-1, 2-4p

Final

Shaftesbury Town	v	Wimborne Town	0-7

Dorset Senior Trophy
HOLDERS: Parley Sports
Quarter-Finals

Parley Sports	v	Poole Town Dev	4-5
Westland Sports Res	v	Dorchester Sports	2-1
Wareham Rangers	v	Holt United	1-3
Merley Cobham Sports	v	Portland United Res	7-1

Semi-Finals

Merley Cobham Sports	v	Holt United	1-2
Westland Sports Res	v	Poole Town Dev	3-1

Final

Holt United	v	Westland Sports Res	4-1

Dorset Intermediate Cup
HOLDERS: Lower Parkstone CFC
Final

Wareham Rangers Res	v	AFC Blandford	2-2, 4-3p

Dorset Junior Cup
HOLDERS: Okeford United
Final

Verwood All Stars	v	Gill Dons	2-0

Durham Senior Challenge Cup
HOLDERS: South Shields
Final

Consett AFC	v	Dunston UTS	4-2

East Riding Senior Cup
HOLDERS: Bridlington Town
Quarter-Finals

Hedon Rangers	v	Bridlington Town	0-6
Beverley Town	v	Hessle Rangers	2-0
Hull City	v	Hall Road Rangers	3-1
East Riding Rangers	v	Dunnington	1-2

Semi-Finals

Bridlington Town	v	Dunnington	6-1
Beverley Town	V	Hull City	0-4

Final

Bridlington Town	v	Hull City	1-2

Essex Senior Cup
HOLDERS: Chelmsford City
Quarter-Finals

East Thurrock United	v	Concord Rangers	1-0
Billericay Town	v	Harlow Town	3-0
Colchester Untied	v	Chelmsford City	0-1
Romford	v	Grays Athletic	1-0

Semi-Finals

Billericay Town	v	Romford	6-1
East Thurrock United	v	Chelmsford City	0-2

Final

Billericay Town	v	Chelmsford City	2-1

Essex Premier Cup
HOLDERS: Harold Wood Athletic
Quarter-Finals

Waltham Abbey Res	v	May & Baker Eastbrook Comm.	5-2
Catholic United	v	Shenfield Association	5-1
Buckhurst Hill	v	Kelvedon Hatch	5-0
Old Southendian	v	Manford Way	2-1

Semi-Finals

Old Southendian	v	Catholic United	0-1
Waltham Abbey Res	v	Buckhurst Hill	1-3

Final

Buckhurst Hill	v	Catholic United	2-0

Essex Junior Cup
HOLDERS: May & Baker Eastbrook Community
Final

Chingford Athletic	v	Oracle Components	3-5 aet

Gloucestershire Senior Challenge Cup
HOLDERS: Bristol City U23/Res
Quarter-Finals

Bristol City U23	v	Bristol Rovers U23/Res	1-1, 4-2p
Gloucester City	v	Shortwood United	4-0
Cinderford Town	v	Forest Green Rovers U23/Res	1-2
Bristol Manor Farm	v	Bishops Cleeve	6-1

Semi-Finals

Bristol Manor Farm	v	Gloucester City	0-4
Forest Green Rovers U23/Res	v	Bristol City U23	0-3

Final

Gloucester City	v	Bristol City U23	1-1, 6-7p

Hampshire Senior Cup
HOLDERS: Basingstoke Town
Quarter-Finals

Winchester City	v	Alresford Town	4-3
Blackfield & Langley	v	AFC Porchester	3-0
Eastleigh	v	AFC Bournemouth	0-2
Havant & Waterlooville	v	Hamble Club	8-1

Semi-Finals

Winchester City	v	Blackfield & Langley	0-1
Havant & Waterlooville	v	AFC Bournemouth	2-0

Final

Blackfield & Langley	v	Havant & Waterlooville	0-3

Herefordshire Challenge Cup
HOLDERS: Hereford
Quarter-Finals

Hereford	v	Tenbury United	15-1
Ewyas Harold	v	Leominster Town	0-0, 3-0p
Malvern Town Res	v	Hereford Lads Club	0-5
Wellington	v	Pegasus Juniors	1-0

Semi-Finals

Hereford	v	Ewyas Harold	7-0
Hereford Lads Club	v	Wellington	3-1

Final

Hereford	v	Hereford Lads Club	6-0

Huntingdonshire Senior Cup
HOLDERS: Eynesbury Rovers
Quarter-Finals

Eynesbury Rovers	v	Godmanchester Rovers	1-0
St Ives Town	v	Huntington Town	4-2

Semi-Finals

St Ives Town	v	St Neots Town	0-2
Yaxley	v	Eynesbury Rovers	0-2

Final

St Neots Town	v	Eynesbury Rovers	6-1

Huntingdonshire Intermediate Cup
HOLDERS: Easton Socon
Final

Eaton Socon	v	Somersham Town	3-1

Huntingdonshire Junior Cup
HOLDERS: Eaton Socon Res
Final

AFC Barley Mow	v	St Ives Rangers	3-3, 2-4p

Isle of Man FA Cup
HOLDERS: St Georges
Quarter-Finals

Braddan	v	St Georges	AW
St Marys	v	Corinthians	2-4
Peel	v	Douglas Athletic	7-1
St Johns United	v	Castletown	6-2

Semi-Finals

Corinthians	v	St Georges	2-1
Peel	v	St Johns United	1-0

Final

Corinthians	v	Peel	3-2

Kent Senior Cup
HOLDERS: Dover Athletic
Final

Maidstone United	v	Folkestone Invicta	0-0, 4-3p

Lancashire Senior Cup
HOLDERS: Liverpool
Quarter-Finals

Fleetwood Town	v	Blackpool	3-0
Morecambe	v	Blackburn Rovers	0-3
Bury	v	Preston North End	2-1
Oldham Athletic	v	AFC Fylde	1-3

Semi-Finals

Fleetwood Town	v	AFC Fylde	2-0
Blackburn Rovers	v	Bury	0-0, 1-3

Final

Bury	v	Fleetwood Town	4-2

Lancashire Challenge Trophy
HOLDERS: Ashton Athletic
Quarter-Finals

Clitheroe	v	Radcliffe	4-0
Padiham	v	Charnock Richard	1-3
Bamber Bridge	v	Chorley	1-2
AFC Darwen	v	Lancaster City	2-3

Semi-Finals

Charnock Richard	v	Clitheroe	0-0, 4-5p
Chorley	v	Lancaster City	1-0

Final

Chorley	v	Clitheroe	3-2

Leicestershire Challenge Cup
HOLDERS: Bawell
Quarter-Finals

Shepshed Dynamo	v	Loughborough	3-2
Barwell	v	Kirby Muxloe	4-1
Loughborough Dynamo	v	Aylestone Park Youth Seniors	1-0
Colaville Town	v	Leicester Road	4-1

Semi-Finals

Shepshed Dyanmo	v	Loughborough Dynamo	1-4
Coalville Town	v	Barwell	3-2

Final

Loughborough Dynamo	v	Coalville Town	2-2, 6-7p

Leicestershire Senior Cup
HOLDERS: Leicester Road
Quarter-Finals

Melton Town	v	FC Khalsa	3-2
Anstey Nomads	v	Ketton	8-0
Lutterworth Athletic	v	NKF Burbage	2-3
Barrow Town	v	Heather St John's	1-9

Semi Finals

Heather St John's	v	Anstey Nomads	3-2
Melton Town	v	NKF Burbage	1-2

Final

Heather St John's	v	NKF Burbage	2-3 aet

Lincolnshire Senior Cup
HOLDERS: Lincoln United
Quarter-Finals

Grantham Town	v	Spalding United	3-0
Grimsby Town	v	Scunthorpe United	4-0
Lincoln United	v	Boston United	0-1
Gainsborough Trinity	v	Lincoln City	4-1

Semi-Finals

Gainsborough Trinity	v	Grantham Town	3-2
Boston United	v	Grimsby Town	3-0

Final

Gainsborough Trinity	v	Boston United	2-2, 3-1p

Lincolnshire Senior Trophy
HOLDERS: Cleethorpes Town
Quarter-Finals

Cleethorpes Town	v	Winterton Rangers	3-2
Grimsby Borough	v	Bottesford Town	1-0
Bourne Town	v	Sleaford Town	3-1
Holbeach United	v	Deeping Rangers	0-0, 4-2p

Semi-Finals

Cleethorpes Town	v	Grimsby Borough	1-0
Bourne Town	v	Holbeach United	1-2

Final

Holbeach United	v	Grimsby Borough	1-1, 4-1p

Liverpool Senior Cup
HOLDERS: Prescot Cables
Quarter-Finals

Widnes	v	Southport	5-1
Tranmere Rovers	v	Marine	0-1
Burscough	v	Litherland Remyca	2-2, 3-4p
Everton	v	Prescot Cables	1-3

Semi-Finals

Widnes	v	Marine	1-2
Litherland Remyca	v	Prescot Cables	0-4

Final

Marine	v	Prescot Cables	0-4

London Senior Cup
HOLDERS: Cray Valley (PM)
Quarter-Finals

Met Police	v	Tooting & Mitcham	0-1
Cray Valley (PM)	v	Croydon	2-1
Dulwich Hamlet	v	Harrow Borough	4-2
Hendon	v	Balham	1-2

Semi-Finals

Tooting & Mitcham	v	Cray Valley (PM)	0-2
Dulwich Hamlet	v	Balham	0-1

Final

Balham	v	Cray Valley (PM)	4-1

London Senior Trophy
HOLDERS: Balham
Quarter-Finals

Fisher	v	Forest Hill Park	3-4
Tooting Bec	v	Sporting Hackney	2-1
Lewisham Borough	v	Phoenix Sports	0-3
Erith & Belvedere	v	FC Elmstead	2-0

Semi-Finals

Tooting Bec	v	Erith & Belvedere	1-7
Firest Hill Park	v	Phoenix Sports	1-3

Final

Erith & Belvedere	v	Phoenix Sports	2-3 aet

Manchester Premier Cup
HOLDERS: FC United of Manchester
Quarter-Finals

Hyde United	v	West Didsbury Chorlton	5-2
Abbey Hey	v	Trafford	2-3
Salford City	v	FC United of Manchester	0-3
Mossley	v	Droylsden	1-1, 4-5p

Semi-Finals

Hyde United	v	FC United of Manchester	0-1
Droylsden	v	Trafford	2-2, 1-3p

Final

FC United of Manchester	v	Trafford	2-2, 3-2p

Middlesex Senior Challenge Cup
HOLDERS: Hampton & Richmond Borough
Quarter-Finals

Wealdstone	v	Hampton & Richmond Borough	1-0
Staines Town	v	Uxbridge	2-2, 3-2p
Enfield 1893	v	Barnet	2-3
Hendon	v	Spelthorne Sports	9-1

Semi-Finals

Wealdstone	v	Staines Town	3-3, 5-6p
Hendon	v	Barnet	2-0

Final

Staines Town	v	Hendon	0-0, 4-5p

Middlesex Premier Cup
HOLDERS: Broadfields United
Quarter-Finals

Brimsdown	v	Southall	0-1
Broadfields United	v	Bedfont & Feltham	4-0
FC Deportivo Galicia	v	Hillingdon Borough	3-2
Harefield United	v	Kensington Borough	3-0

Semi-Finals

Southall	v	Broadfields United	2-3
FC Deportivo Galicia	v	Harefield United	0-1

Final

Broadfields United	v	Harefield United

Norfolk Senior Cup
HOLDERS: King's Lynn Town
Quarter-Finals

Great Yarmouth	v	Downham Town	2-3
Wymondham Town	v	Thetford Town	2-1 aet
Norwich United	v	King's Lynn Town	5-0
Wroxham	v	Dereham Town	2-3

Semi-Finals

Downham Town	v	Wymondham Town	3-0
Norwich United	v	Dereham Town	4-0

Final

Dowham Town	v	Norwich United	2-4 aet

Northamptonshire Senior Cup
HOLDERS: Kettering Town
Quarter-Finals

Daventry Town	v	Kettering Town	1-6
AFC Rushden & Diamonds	v	Wellingborough Town	6-1
Brackley Town	v	Peterborough Northern Star	3-1
Peterborough Sports	v	Cogenhoe United	7-0

Semi-Finals

Peterborough Sports	v	Brackley Town	0-0, 9-10p
Kettering Town	v	AFC Rushden & Diamonds	3-3, 5-4p

Final

Kettering Town	v	Brackley Town	2-1

Northamptonshire Junior Cup
HOLDERS: James King Bilsworth
Final

Moulton	v	Netherton United	2-3

North Riding Senior Cup
HOLDERS: Whitby Town
Quarter-Finals

York City	v	Boro Rangers	2-1
Scarborough Athletic	v	Pickering Town Community	2-1
Nothallerton Town	v	Thornaby	1-1, 2-4p
Middlesbrough U23/Res	v	Redcar Athletic	7-0

Semi-Finals

Thornaby	v	Scarborough Ahtletic	0-7
York City	v	Middlesbrough U23/Res	3-3, 0-3p

Final

Scarborough Athletic	v	Middlesbrough U23/Res	0-1

Northumberland Senior Cup
HOLDERS: Blyth Spartans
Quarter-Finals

Newcastle United U23	v	Blyth AFC	7-2
Morpeth Town	v	North Shields	3-2
Blyth Spartans	v	Bedlington Terriers	4-0
Team Northumbria	v	Newcastle Benfield	2-2, 5-6p

Semi-Finals

Newcastle United U23	v	Newcastle Benfield	3-0
Morpeth Town	v	Blyth Spartans	8-2

Final

Newcastle United U23	v	Morpeth Town	3-1

Nottinghamshire Senior Cup
HOLDERS: Carlton Town
Quarter-Finals

Dunkirk	v	Clipstone	3-3, 4-3p
Radford	v	Carlton Town	1-6
Retford United	v	Teversal	2-3
Basford United	v	Kimberley Miners Welfare	7-0

Semi-Finals

Basford United	v	Teversal	3-1
dunkirk	v	Carlton Town	2-1

Final

Dunkirk	v	Basford United	1-5

Oxfordshire Senior Cup
HOLDERS: North Leigh
Quarter-Finals

Ardley United	v	Oxford United	1-3
Kidlington	v	Thame United	3-1
North Leigh	v	Oxford City	AW
Easington Sports	v	Banbury United	1-2

Semi-Finals

Oxford City	v	Oxford United	1-0
Banbury United	v	Kidlington	2-3

Final

Oxford City	v	Kidlington	5-3

Sheffield & Hallamshire Senior Challenge Cup
HOLDERS: Shaw Lane Association
Quarter-Finals

Swallownest	v	Frickley Athletic	1-2
Shaw Lane	v	North Gawber	4-1
Penistone Church	v	AFC Emley	3-0
Stocksbridge Park Steels	v	Maltby Main	2-3

Semi-Finals

Penistone Church	v	Maltby Main	2-0
Shaw Lane	v	Frickley Athletic	3-1

Final

Penistone Church	v	Shaw Lane	3-4 aet

Somerset Premier Cup
HOLDERS: Taunton Town
Quarter-Finals

Odd Down (BATH)	v	Paulton Rovers	0-2
Wincanton Town	v	Weston-Super-Mare	0-6
Wellington	v	Clevedon Town	3-2
Bath City	v	Welton Rovers	8-1

Semi-Finals

Weston-Super-Mare	v	Bath City	2-2, 5-4p
Paulton Rovers	v	Wellington	4-1

Final

Paulton Rovers	v	Weston-Super-Mare	2-3

Somerset Senior Cup
HOLDERS: Odd Down (BATH) Res
Quarter-Finals

Worle	v	Nailsea United	2-1
Nailsea & Tickenham	v	Weston St Johns	5-0
Westland Sports	v	Stockwood Green	5-2
Chilcompton Sports	v	Keynsham Town Res	5-0

Semi-Finals

Westland Sports	v	Chilcompton Sports	0-2
Worle	v	Nailsea & Tickenham	0-1

Final

Nailsea & Tickenham	v	Chilcompton Sports	2-0

Staffordshire Senior Cup
HOLDERS: Stoke City
Quarter-Finals

Newcastle Town	v	Hednesford Town	1-2
Leek Town	v	Stoke City	2-4
Stafford Rangers	v	Kidsgrove Athletic	4-0
Wolverhampton Sporting C.	v	Walsall	3-2

Semi-Finals

Hednesford Town	v	Stoke City	2-0
Stafford Rangers	v	Wolverhampton Sporting C.	3-1

Final

Stafford Rangers	v	Hednesford Town	3-2

(Staffordshire) Walsall Senior Cup
HOLDERS: Walsall
Quarter-Finals

Stafford Rangers	v	Rushall Olympic	2-3
Sutton Coldfield Town	v	Walsall	1-1, 4-2p
Romulus	v	Wolverhampton Casuals	2-1
Sporting Khalsa	v	Walsall Wood	1-2

Semi-Finals

Sutton Coldfield Town	v	Rushall Olympic	2-6
Romulus	v	Walsall Wood	AW

Final

Rushall Olympic	v	Walsall Wood	2-2, 4-3p

Suffolk Premier Cup
HOLDERS: Needham Market
Quarter-Finals

Haverhill Rovers	v	Kirkley & Pakefield	2-5
Brantham Athletic	v	Bury Town	1-3
Leiston	v	Ipswich Town	2-1
Needham Market	v	Felixstowe & Walton United	3-2

Semi-Finals

Bury Town	v	Needham Market	0-0, 5-4p
Leiston	v	Kirkley & Pakefield	3-1

Final

Bury Town	v	Leiston	0-3

Suffolk Senior Cup
HOLDERS: Achilies
Quarter-Finals

Achilies	v	Felixstowe Harpers United	6-1
Bramford United	v	Woodbridge Town	2-5
Lakenheath	v	Bungay Town	2-4
Leiston Res	v	Brantham Athletic	4-1

Semi-Finals

Achilies	v	Woodbridge Town	1-3
Bungay Town	v	Brantham Athletic	7-1

Final

Bungay Town	v	Woodbridge Town	0-3

Surrey Senior Cup
HOLDERS: Woking
Quarter Finals

Met Poluce	v	Leatherhead	1-1, 2-4p
Colliers Wood United	v	Dorking Wanderers	0-6
Sutton United	v	Merstham	1-2
Chipstead	v	South Park	0-1

Semi-Finals

Dorking Wanderers	v	Leatherhead	0-1
Merstham	v	South Park	6-0

Final

Leatherhead	v	Merstham	1-3

Surrey Premier Cup
HOLDERS: Worcester Park
Quarter Finals

Old Wilsonians	v	Worcester Park	1-8
Nottsborough	v	Chessington & Hook United	6-0
Lingfield	v	Westfield Res	5-1
Raynes Park Vale	v	Corinthian-Casuals Res	1-0

Semi-Finals

MWorcester Park	v	Lingfield	5-0
Raynes Park Vale	v	Nottsborough	1-1, AWp

Final

Nottsborough	v	Worcester Park	2-0

Surrey Intermediate Cup
HOLDERS: Chessington
Final

Wandgas Sport	v	Old Rustishians	0-2

Surrey Junior Cup
HOLDERS: Woodmansterne Hyde
Final

Ottershaw	v	Sporting Kitz Vets	1-0

Sussex Senior Challenge Cup
HOLDERS: Brighton & Hove Albion U23
Quarter-Finals

Pagham	v	Horsham	3-0
Burgess Hill Town	v	Saltdean United	0-2
Whitehawk	v	Brighton & Hove Albion U23	1-3
Eastbourne Borough	v	Crawley Town	3-4

Semi-Finals

Brighton & Hove Albion U23	v	Pagham	6-0
Saltdean United	v	Crawley Town	0-6

Final

Brighton & Hove Albion U23	v	Crawley Town	2-1

Sussex Intermediate Cup
HOLDERS: Cowfold
Final

Rustington	v	Eastbourne Rangers	2-1

Sussex Junior Cup
HOLDERS: Romans United
Final

Whyke United	v	Sovereign Saints	1-4

West Riding County Cup

HOLDERS: Farsley Celtic

Quarter-Finals

FC Halifax Town	v	Selby Town	2-4
Campion	v	Farsley Celtic	2-3
Tadcaser Albion	v	Guiseley	2-1
Harrogate Town	v	Pontefract Collieries	1-5

Semi-Finals

Tadcaster Albion	v	Selby Town	0-2
Pontefract Collieries	v	Farsley Celtic	1-2

Final

Selby Town	v	Farsley Celtic

Westmorland Senior Challenge Cup

HOLDERS: Milnthorpe Corinthians

Quarter-Finals

Kendal County	v	Keswick	2-2, 4-3p
Ambleside United	v	Appleby	0-6
Shap	v	Endmoor KGR	1-3
Milnthorpe Corinthians	v	Castletown United	4-1

Semi-Finals

Appleby	v	Milnthorpe Corinthians	3-2
Endmoor KGR	v	Kendal County	1-2

Final

Kendal County	v	Appleby	1-3

Wiltshire Senior Cup

HOLDERS: Swindon Supermarine

Quarter-Finals

Royal Wotton Bassett Town	v	Highworth Town	2-5
Chippenham Town	v	Chippenham Park	3-1
Bremhill	v	Bemerton Heath Harlequins	0-3
Westbury United	v	Salisbury	0-1

Semi-Finals

Chippenham Town	v	Bemerton Heath Harlequins	8-0
Salisbury Town	v	Highworth Town	1-2

Final

Chippenham Town	v	Highworth Town	3-0

Wiltshire Junior Cup

HOLDERS: Luxol UK

Final

Luxol UK	v	Tawny Owl	2-3

Worcestershire Senior Invitation Cup

HOLDERS: Kidderminster Harriers

Semi-Finals

Redditch United	v	Kidderminster Harriers	2-3
Evesham United	v	Worcester City	1-1, 3-1p

Final

Kidderminster Harriers	v	Evesham United	1-2

Worcestershire Senior Invitation Urn

HOLDERS: Highgate United

Quarter-Finals

Malvern Town	v	Stourport Swifts	1-3
Bromsgrove Sporting	v	Dudley Sports	HW
Alvechurch	v	Lye Town	0-0, 2-3p
Littleton	v	Bewdley Town	2-1

Semi-Finals

Stourport Swifts	v	Bromsgrove Sporting	2-2, 5-6p
Lye Town	v	Littleton	3-0

Final

Bromsgrove Sporting	v	Lye Town	0-0, 4-2p

POTTON UNITED
North Bedfordshire Charity Cup
Winners

SANDY FC
East Bedfordshire Charity Cup
Winners

Photos: Gordon Whittington

CLUB INDEX

Numbers with (L) relate to the page number of the league the club are featured in.
Leagues with (T) following it, denotes club featured in the 2017-18 league table.

CLUB INDEX	LEAGUE	PAGE

National Division Players

Following this title page is a database of every player that took part in the 2017-18 season in the National Division. Whether they played or just sat on the bench they should be there, along with their age, position and total appearances (League & FA competitions) and goals, should they have made any or scored. Below that is the players' club history, with (L) indicating a loan period. If a player has '(Lx2)' next to a club, it indicates that he had to separate loan spells during the same season.

For a break down of these appearances, and for which club(s) they made them, turn to page 67 for the details.

It is the intension to build on this database by adding the National North and South players next year, and, if time and an efficient system of logging, allows, it is hoped that players for the up and coming season (i.e. 2019-20) could be included too.

Action the National League game between Maidstone Utd and Aldershot Town. Photo: Bill Wheatcroft

SURNAME Clubs Played for	FIRST NAME	AGE	POSITION	2017-18 TOTAL Apps Gls	

◊ **Acton** — Darren — 45 — Goalkeeper
Burton, Kidderminster, Tamworth, Nuneaton, Brackley (L), Brackley, Chasetown, Solihull M

◊ **Adams** — Blair — 26 — Defender — 36 — 1
Sunderland, Brentford (L), Northampton (L), Coventry (L), Coventry, Notts Co, Mansfield (L), Cambridge U, Hamilton, Hartlepool

◊ **Adams** — Charlee — 23 — Midfielder — 24 — 2
Birmingham, Lincoln (L), Lincoln (L),Kilmarnock (L), Dagenham & R

◊ **Adams** — Ebou — 22 — Midfielder — 20
Dartford, Norwich, Braintree (L), Shrewsbury (L), Leyton Orient (L)

◊ **Adebowale** — Emmanuel (Manny) — 20 — Defender
West Ham, Sheffield United, Goole AFC (L), Sheffield FC (L), Dover, Bognor Regis (L)

◊ **Adeloye** — Tomi — 22 — Forward — 10
Stoke, Macclesfield (L), Chelmsford, Dover, Welling, Altrincham, FC Utd, Hartlepool, Whitehawk

◊ **Adeyinka** — Tashan — Forward
Maidenhead United, Welling, Bishop's Stortford, Bromley

◊ **Afolayan** — Oladapo — 21 — Forward — 33 — 11
Loughborough Uni, Solihull M, West Ham

◊ **Ainge** — Simon — 30 — Forward — 10
Bradford, Halifax (L), Cambridge U (L), Guiseley, Luton (L), Halifax, Bradford PA, Harrogate T, Wrexham (L)

◊ **Akintunde** — Oluwaseun (James) — 22 — Forward — 43 — 8
Cambridge, AFC Sudbury (L), Histon (L), Chester

◊ **Alabi** — James — 23 — Forward — 22 — 1
Stoke, Scunthorpe (L), Mansfield (L), Forest Green (L), Scunthorpe (L), Accrington (L), Ipwsich, Grimsby (L), Chester, Tranmere, Dover (L)Leyton Orient

◊ **Alexander** — Cheye — 23 — Defender — 46
Port Vale, Concord R, Bishop's St., Aldershot, Barnet

◊ **Allen** — Ifeanyi (Iffy) — 24 — Midfielder — 15 — 1
Barnet, Yeovil, Torquay (L), Aldershot, Wrexham, Bromley, Wealdstone (L)

◊ **Allen** — Jamie — 23 — Forward — 12 — 1
Fleetwood, AFC Fylde (L), Stalybridge (L), Southport, Dover

◊ **Amankwaah** — Kevin — 36 — Defender — 3
Bristol C, Torquay (L), Cheltenham (L), Yeovil (L), Yeovil, Swansea, Burton (L), Rochdale, Exeter, Northampton, Salisbury, Sutton U, Bath

◊ **Amond** — Padraig — 30 — Forward — 4 — 1
Sligo Rovers, Pacos Ferreira, Accrington (L), Accrington, Morecambe, Grimsby, Hartlepool, Newport Co

◊ **Anderson** — Joe — 28 — Defender — 50 — 2
Fulham, Woking (L), Lincoln (L), Lincoln, Cambridge U, Bromley, Maidstone

◊ **Anderson** — Myles — 28 — Defender — 27
Leyton OrientAberdeen, Blackburn R, Aldershot (L), Exeter, Monza, Chievo, Barrow, Torquay, Chester (L), Chester, Hartlepool

◊ **Anderson** — Tahjay — Forward
Bromley

◊ **Andrade** — Bruno — 24 — Midfielder — 55 — 28
QPR, Aldershot (L), Wycombe (L), Stevenage (L), Stevenage (L), Woking (L), Boreham W

PLAYER DATABASE

SURNAME Clubs Played for	FIRST NAME	AGE	POSITION	2017-18 TOTAL Apps	Gls
◊ Andersson Reading, Bath (L), Torquay (L)	Axel	20	Defender	6	
◊ Appau Woking	Declan	19	Midfielder	12	1
◊ Archer Bedworth United, Stourbridge, Chester	Jordan		Forward	20	4
◊ Arnold Reading, Wycombe (L), Woking, Whitehawk, Aldershot	Nick	25	Defender	7	
◊ Arnold Norwich, Grays, Eastleigh (L), Wycombe, Hayes & Y (L), Stevenage, Forest Green, Dover, Gillingham, Barrow, Shrewsbury	Steve	28	Goalkeeper	17	
◊ Arthur Kettering, QPR, Rushden (L), Northampton, Havant & W, AFC Wimbledon, Woking, Crawley, Woking, Aldershot, Whitehawk (L)	Chris	28	Defender	13	
◊ Arthur Birmingham, Lincoln (L), Cheltenham (L), Cheltenham (L), Macclesfield	Koby	22	Midfielder	16	2
◊ Asante Birmingham, Northampton (L), Shrewsbury (L), Shrewsbury (L), Kidderminster, Solihull M, Grimsby, Solihull M (L), Tamworth	Akwasi	25	Forward	11	
◊ Ashmore Havant & W, Gosport B, Ebbsfleet	Nathan	28	Goalkeeper	54	
◊ Astles Rhyl, Northwich V, Chester	Ryan	24	Defender	43	2
◊ Atkinson Halifax	Jack		Goalkeeper		
◊ Atkinson Barnsley, Scarborough (L), Halifax (L), Grimsby (L), Grimsby, Fleetwood, Accrington (L), Accrington, Guiseley	Rob	31	Defender	11	
◊ Atkinson West Brom, Cambridge U (L), Notts Co, Eastleigh (L), Gateshead (L), Alfreton (L), Solihull M (L), Boston U	Wesley	23	Defender	3	1
◊ Audel Auxerre, Izola, Triestina, San Marino (L), Pisa, Macclesfield, Crewe, Lincoln (L), Lincoln (L), Macclesfield , Notts Co, Barrow	Thierry	31	Defender	9	
◊ Azeez Charlton, Wycombe (L), Leyton O (L), Torquay (L), Dagenham & R (L), AFC Wimbledon, Partick, Cambridge U, Dover (L)	Ade	24	Forward	12	1
◊ Baba Fulham, Birmingham, Macclesfield (L)	Noe	21	Defender	15	
◊ Bailey Sutton U, Barnet, Southend, Charlton, Middlesbrough, Millwall, Barnet, Sutton U	Nicky	34	Midfielder	34	1
◊ Balanta QPR, Wycombe (L), MK Dons (L), MK Dons (L), MK Dons (L), Yeovil (L), Bristol R, Carlisle, Boreham W	Angelo	28	Midfielder	42	12
◊ Balatoni Hearts, Partick (L), Partick (L), Partick, Kilmarnock, Ayr, Falkirk, Torquay	Conrad	27	Defender	16	

SURNAME Clubs Played for	FIRST NAME	AGE	POSITION	2017-18 TOTAL Apps	Gls
◊ Banks	Oliver	25	Midfielder	9	1
Rotherham, Chesterfield, Northampton (L), Oldham, Tranmere (L), Swindon (L)					
◊ Bannister	Charlie	21	Goalkeeper	3	
Kidderminster, Solihull M					
◊ Banton	Jason	25	Midfielder	29	3
Arsenal, Blackburn, Liverpool, Leicester, Burton (L), Crystal Palace, Plymouth (L), MK Dons (L),					
Plymouth, Wycombe, Hartlepool (L), Notts Co (L), Crawley, Partick (L), Woking					
◊ Barker	Charley	19	Midfielder		
Leyton Orient, Wingate (L), Northwood (L),					
◊ Barnard	Christopher		Midfielder		
Dover					
◊ Barnes	Aaron	21	Defender	16	1
Charlton, Torquay (L), Colchester, Torquay (L)					
◊ Barnum-Bobb	Jazzi	22	Defender	8	
Cardiff, Newport Co (L), Newport Co, Torquay (L), Chelmsford					
◊ Barratt	Ben		Defender		
Wrexham					
◊ Barratt	Sam	22	Midfielder	35	7
Maidenhead, Southend					
◊ Barrow	Scott	29	Defender	45	3
Tamworth, Macclesfield, Newport, Gateshead					
◊ Barrows	Ross		Defender		
Halifax, North Ferriby (L)					
◊ Barthram	Jack	24	Midfielder	33	1
Tottenham, Swindon, Cheltenham, Barrow					
◊ Bartlett	Rhys	18	Midfielder	1	
Maidstone					
◊ Baskerville	Guy		Defender		
Bromley					
◊ Batty	Daniel	20	Midfielder	5	2
Hull, Halifax (L)					
◊ Bauress	Bradley		Midfielder	32	
Blackburn, Colwyn Bay, Witton, Barrow					
◊ Bawling	Bobson	22	Midfielder	12	
Watford, Crawley, Woking					
◊ Baxter	Nathan	19	Goalkeeper	48	
Chelsea, Solihull M (L), Woking (L)					
◊ Beautyman	Harry	26	Midfielder	17	1
Leyton O, Sutton U, Welling, Peterborough, Northampton, Stevenage, Sutton U					
◊ Beckwith	Dean	34	Defender	18	1
Gillingham, Margate (L), Hereford U, Northampton, Luton, Eastleigh, Sutton U, Maidstone (L)					
◊ Bell	Nyal	21	Forward	16	1
Rochdale, Chester (L), Gateshead, Chester (L)Alfreton (L)					
◊ Bellamy	Liam	26	Midfielder	18	
Charlton,Brentford, Cray W (L), Ebbsfleet (L), Ebbsfleet, Dover, Aldershot, Farnborough, Dover					
◊ Benbow	Luke	26	Forward	3	
Solihull M, Redditch, Stourbridge, Hednesford, Stourbridge, Solihull M, Stourbridge (L)					

| SURNAME | FIRST NAME | AGE | POSITION | 2017-18 TOTAL | |
Clubs Played for				Apps	Gls
◊ Benson	Paul	39	Forward	14	1

White Ensign, Dagenham & R, Chalton, Swindon, Portsmouth (L), Cheltenham (L), Luton (L), Luton, Dagenham & R, Boreham W, Bedford T (L)

| ◊ Bentley | Jordan | 19 | Defender | | |

Plymouth, Sutton U (L)

| ◊ Bignot | Paul | 32 | Defender | 14 | |

Crewe , Kidderminster (L), Kidderminster, Newport Co, Blackpool, Plymouth (L), Grimsby, Solihull M, Newport Co, Barrow, Telford

| ◊ Bird | Ryan | 30 | Forward | 51 | 20 |

Burnham, Portsmouth, Cambridge U (L), Cambridge U, Hartlepool (L), Yeovil, Eastleigh, Newport Co, Dover

| ◊ Blanchfield | James | 20 | Midfielder | 1 | |

Arsenal, Ipswich,Aldershot (L)

| ◊ Blinkhorn | Matt | 33 | Forward | 25 | |

Blackpool, Luton (L), Bury (L), Morecambe (L), Morecambe, Sligo Rovers (Ireland), York, HydeAFC Fylde

| ◊ Blissett | Nathan | 27 | Forward | 16 | 5 |

Kidderminster, Cambridge U (L), Bristol R, Tranmere (L), Lincoln (L), Torquay (L), Torquay, Plymouth, Macclesfield (L)

| ◊ Bloomfield | Mason | 21 | Forward | 29 | 3 |

Dagenham & R, Chatham (L), Erith & Bel (L), Maldon & Tiptree (L), Chelmsford, Billericay, Grays, Witham,Brentwood, Aveley, Dagenham & R

| ◊ Boco | Romuald | 33 | Midfielder | 20 | 2 |

Accrington, Sligo Rovers, Burton (L), Accrington, Plymouth, Chesterfield, Portsmouth, Accrington, Leyton Orient

| ◊ Boden | Scott | 28 | Forward | 36 | 3 |

Chesterfield, Macclesfield (L), Macclesfield, Halifax, Newport Co, Inverness CT, Wrexham

| ◊ Bolarinwa | Tom | 28 | Midfielder | 27 | 8 |

Sutton U, Grimsby, Sutton U (L)

| ◊ Bond | Andy | 32 | Midfielder | 48 | 5 |

Crewe , Barrow, Colchester, Crewe (L), Bristol R (L), Chester, Stevenage, Chorley, Crawley, AFC Fylde

| ◊ Bonne | Macauley | 22 | Forward | 52 | 25 |

Colchester, Lincoln (L), Woking (L), Leyton Orient

| ◊ Bonos | Elliott | | Midfielder | 5 | |

Dagenham & R

| ◊ Boucaud | Andre | 33 | Midfielder | 44 | |

QPR,Reading, Peterborough (L), Peterborough (L), Peterborough, Aldershot (L), Kettering, York (L), York, Luton, Notts Co (L), Notts Co, Dagenham & R

| ◊ Bowen | James | 22 | Defender | 10 | |

Cheltenham, Gloucester (L), Gloucester (L), Hereford FC, Solihull M

| ◊ Boyce | Andrew | 28 | Defender | 40 | |

Gainsborough, Lincoln, Scunthorpe (L), Scunthorpe, Grimsby (L), Grimsby (L), Hartlepool (L), Notts Co (L), Grimsby, Eastleigh

| ◊ Bozhurt | Erbil | 28 | Goalkeeper | | |

Hayes & Y, Haringey, Hampton & R, Boreham W,

SURNAME	FIRST NAME	AGE	POSITION	2017-18 TOTAL	
Clubs Played for				Apps	Gls
◊ Bozier	Matt		Defender	3	
Aldershot					
◊ Brandy	Febian	29	Forward	2	
Manchester U, Swansea (L), Hereford (L), Gillingham (L), Notts Co, Panetolikos, Walsall,					
Sheffield U, Rotherham, Crewe, Rochdale,Ubon UMT Utd (Thailand), Ebbsfleet					
◊ Brill	Dean	32	Goalkeeper	29	
Luton, Gillingham (L), Oldham, Barnet, Luton, Inverness Cal (L), Inverness Cal, Motherwell,					
Colchester, Leyton Orient					
◊ Brodie	Richard	31	Forward	5	
Newcastle B, York, Barrow, Crawley, Fleetwood (L), Morecambe (L), Grimsby (L), Gateshead,					
Hereford (L), Southport (L), Southport, Aldershot, Stockport, York, Macclesfield (L), Boston U,					
Southport (L), Solihull M (L)					
◊ Broom	Ryan	21	Midfielder	13	3
Bristol R, Bath (L), Eastleigh (L), Cheltenham					
◊ Brophy	James	24	Midfielder	27	3
Swindon, Leyton Orient (L)					
◊ Brown	Connor	25	Defender	25	
Sheffield U, Oldham, Carlisle (L), Guiseley, York (L)					
◊ Brown	Matt	28	Defender	42	4
Manchester C, Chesterfield, Southport (L), Chester (L), Chester, Halifax					
◊ Brown	Nathan	19	Forward	6	1
Man City, Chester					
◊ Brown	Sebastian	28	Goalkeeper		
AFC Wimbledon, Woking (L), Bromley, Whitehawk (L), Hampton & R, Whitehawk, Hampton & R,					
Sutton U					
◊ Brundle	Mitch	23	Midfielder	51	5
Yeovil, Bristol C, Cheltenham, Braintree, Hemel H (L), Gateshead, Dover					
◊ Bubb	Bradley	30	Forward	7	
Farnborough, Aldershot, Woking (L), Havant & W, Oxford C, Ebbsfleet, Wealdstone					
◊ Bugiel	Omar	23	Forward	22	5
Forest Green Rovers, Bromley (L),					
◊ Burbidge	Fred		Goalkeeper		
Boreham W					
◊ Burgess	Scott	20	Midfielder	33	1
Bury, Stalybridge (L), Macclesfield (L)					
◊ Burke	Luke	20	Defender	35	
Wigan Athletic, BarrowAFC Fylde					
◊ Burrow	Jordan	25	Forward	56	16
Chesterfield, Morecambe, Stevenage, Lincoln, Halifax, Gateshead					
◊ Burrows	Brandan			1	
Wrexham					
◊ Bush	Chris	26	Defender	40	1
Brentford, Wimbledon (L), Wimbledon, Gateshead, Hereford, Welling, Lincoln, Chelmsford,					
Ebbsfleet					
◊ Butler	Jamie	26	Goalkeeper	48	
Met Police, Concord R, Hemel H, Braintree (L), Sutton U					

PLAYER DATABASE

| SURNAME | FIRST NAME | AGE | POSITION | 2017-18 TOTAL | |
Clubs Played for				Apps	Gls
◊ Buxton	Adam	26	Defender	41	2
Wigan, Burton (L), Accrington (L), Accrington, Portsmouth, Tranmere					
◊ Byrne	Neill	25	Defender	51	2
Nottingham Forest, Rochdale, Barrow (L), Southport (L), Telford, Macclesfield, Gateshead					
◊ Cadogan	Kieron	27	Midfielder	45	6
Crystal Palace, Burton (L), Rotherham (L), Aldershot (L), Barnet (L), Sutton U					
◊ Campbell	Kristian		Defender	2	
Merstham, Bromley, Bognor R (L)					
◊ Campbell	Tahvon	21	Forward	14	1
West Brom, Kidderminster (L), Yeovil (L), Yeovil (L), Notts Co (L), Solihull M (L), Forest Green (L)					
◊ Camwell	Chris	19	Defender	4	
Coventry, Solihull M (L)					
◊ Capel	Elliott	18	Midfielder		
Maidstone					
◊ Caprice	Jake	25	Defender	42	
Crystal Palace, Blackpool, Dag & Red (L), St Mirren (L), Tamworth (L), Lincoln, Woking, Leyton Orient					
◊ Carline	George	25	Midfielder	38	
Solihull M					
◊ Carrington	Mark	31	Defender	28	
Crewe, MK Dons, Hamilton, Bury, Wrexham					
◊ Carter	Charlie	21	Midfielder	46	12
Woking					
◊ Carter	Darren	34	Midfielder	49	8
Birmingham, Sunderland (L), West Brom, Preston, Millwall (L), Cheltenham, Northampton, Forest Green, Solihull M					
◊ Cassidy	Jake	25	Forward	36	5
llandudno J, Airbus, Wolves, Tranmere (Lx3), Notts Co (L), Southend (L), Oldham, Guiseley, Hartlepool					
◊ Catterick	Ryan	19	Goalkeeper		
Hartlepool					
◊ Champion	Tom	32	Midfielder	52	1
Dartford, Cambridge U, Barnet, Lincoln (L), Boreham W					
◊ Chaney	Sam	22	Midfielder	6	
Torquay, Whitehawk (L)					
◊ Chapman	Louie		Goalkeeper		
Dagenham & R					
◊ ChapPell	Jordan	26	Midfielder	10	
Sheffield Utd, Burton (L), Torquay (L), Torquay, Grimsby (L), Chester					
◊ Charles	Dion	22	Forward	12	
Blackpool, Fylde (L), Fylde, Fleetwood, Halifax (L), Southport					
◊ Charles-Cook	Regan	21	Midfielder	29	6
Charlton, Solihull M (L), Woking (Lx2)					
◊ Cheek	Michael	26	Forward	36	14
Heybridge S, Stanway R, Chelmsford, Braintree, Dagenham & R					
◊ Cheidu Dixon	Bohan	28	Midfielder	4	
Accrington, Lincoln, Stalybridge, Fylde, Halifax, Stockport					

SURNAME Clubs Played for	FIRST NAME	AGE	POSITION	2017-18 TOTAL Apps	Gls
◊ Chesmain Millwall,Welling (L), Boreham W (L)	Noah	20	Defender	4	1
◊ Chettle Peterborough, AFC Fylde (L)	Callum	21	Midfielder	9	
◊ Childs Eastleigh, Gosport B (L)	Mark		Goalkeeper	1	
◊ Chorley Arsenal, Brentford (L), Wimbledon, MK Dons, Gillingham (L), Tranmere, Leyton O, Stevenage, Portsmouth, Stevenage (L), Bromley	Ben	35	Defender	28	
◊ Clackstone Hull,Notts Co (L), Halifax (L)	Josh	21	Midfielder	5	
◊ Clark Dagenham & R, Thurrock, Chelmsford, Dartford,Ebbsfleet	Kenny	29	Defender	44	2
◊ Clark Leyton Orient, East Thurrock (L), Braintree	Michael	20	Defender	3	
◊ Clarke Hull United, Frickley, Hall Road R, Winterton R, North Ferriby, Halifax	Danny	33	Midfielder	19	1
◊ Clarke Tranmere	Eddie	19	Defender	16	
◊ Clarke Bristol R, Southend (L), Kidderminster (L), Forest Green (L), Salisbury, Northwich, Oxford U, Northampton, AFC Wimbledon, Eastleigh, Torquay	Ryan	36	Goalkeeper	11	
◊ Clay Chesterfield, Barrow (L), Alfreton (L), York, Halifax, Worksop, Grimsby, Motherwell, Leyton Orient	Craig	26	Midfielder	48	4
◊ Clayden Leyton Orient	Charles		Forward	1	
◊ Cleary Liverpool, Birmingham, Solihull M (L), Dundalk	Dan	22	Defender	2	
◊ Clements Crewe, Hednesford, Mansfield, Grimsby, Barrow (L), Forest Green (L),	Chris	28	Midfielder	8	
◊ Clerima Histon, Braintree, Maidenhead	Remy	28	Defender	38	2
◊ Clifton Maidenhead, Havant & W, Maidenhead	Adrian	29	Midfielder	41	8
◊ Cockerline Sheffield Utd, Curzon Ashton (L), Barrow, Stalybridge (L), Southport	Daniel	21	Forward	5	
◊ Coddington Middlesbrough, Huddersfield, Northampton, Wrexham (L), Guiseley (L)	Luke	23	Goalkeeper	16	
◊ Coker Crystal Palace, Maidstone (L)	Andre	20	Forward	8	
◊ Cole Staines, Eastleigh, Hampton & R, Torquay	Chinua	24	Defender	3	
◊ Cole QPR, Hayes (L), Farnborough, Plymouth, Woking, Aldershot	Jake	32	Goalkeeper	23	
◊ Cole Man Utd, Fulham, MK Dons (L), Shrewsbury (Lx2), Inverness CT (Lx2), Tranmere	Larnell	25	Midfielder	17	4

SURNAME	FIRST NAME	AGE	POSITION	2017-18 TOTAL	
Clubs Played for				Apps	Gls
◊ Collins	Aaron	21	Forward	6	1
Newport Co, Wolves, Notts Co (L), Tranmere (L), Maidstone (L), Newport Co (L)					
◊ Collins	Jamie	33	Midfielder	46	4
Watford, Newport Co, Aldershot, Forest Green, Eastleigh, Sutton U					
◊ Collins	Michael	32	Midfielder	23	
Huddersfield, Scunthorpe, Wimbledon (L), Oxford U, York, Leyton Orient, Halifax					
◊ Comley	James	27	Midfielder	37	1
Crystal Palace, St Albans, Maidenhead					
◊ Connors	Jack	23	Defender	31	1
Fulham, Dagenham & R, Hendon (L), Boreham W (L), Ebbsfleet					
◊ Constable	James	33	Forward	27	2
Chippenham, Walsall, Kidderminster (L), Kidderminster, Shrewsbury, Oxford U (L), Oxford U,					
Eastleigh, Poole (L)					
◊ Cook	Andy	27	Forward	47	29
Carlisle, Barrow (L), Barrow (L), Barrow, Grimsby, Barrow, Tranmere, Walsall					
◊ Cook	Anthony	28	Midfielder	27	
Dagenham & R, Chelmsford, Bromley, Ebbsfleet, Woking					
◊ Cook	Ollie	20	Defender	13	
Southampton, Barrow (L)					
◊ Coombes	Adam	27	Midfielder	16	1
Chelsea, Yeovil (L), Notts Co, Bromley, Welling, Sutton U, Hampton & R (L), Welling (L)					
◊ Correia	Raul	25	Forward	12	1
Chorley, Blackpool, Guiseley (L), York					
◊ Coulson	Josh	29	Defender	31	2
Cambridge U, Leyton Orient					
◊ Coulson	Luke	24	Midfielder	54	13
Cardiff, Oxford C, Eastleigh, Barnet, Ebbsfleet					
◊ Cousins	Mark	31	Goalkeeper	49	
Fulham, Colchester U, Dagenham & R					
◊ Coyle	Callum	22	Midfielder	1	
Solihull M					
◊ Crawford	Tom	19	Midfielder	17	1
Stoke City, Chester, Notts Co					
◊ Cresswell	Ryan	30	Defender	13	1
Sheffield U, Halifax (L), Rotherham (L), Morecambe (L), Macclesfield (L), Bury, Rotherham,					
Southend, Fleetwood, Northampton, Eastleigh					
◊ Crookes	Adam	20	Defender	16	
Nottingham Forest, Guiseley (L)					
◊ Crump	Ryan	22	Goalkeeper		
Liverpool U18, Blackburn U21Southport, Chester					
◊ Cullinane-Liburd	Jordan	23	Defender	13	
Redditch, Solihull M, Rushall, Hereford					
◊ Cunningham	Aaron	20	Defender	1	
Hartlepool					
◊ Cunningham	Karl	24	Midfielder	2	
Lincoln, Chester					

SURNAME Clubs Played for	FIRST NAME	AGE	POSITION	2017-18 TOTAL Apps	Gls
◊ Dalby Leyton Orient, Leeds	Sam	18	Forward	2	
◊ Daly Evesham, Corby, Redditch, Solihull M, Halesowen, Leamington, Barwell, Leamington, Solihull M, Kidderminster, Solihull M	Liam	30	Defender	43	1
◊ Daniel Crystal Palace, Charlton, Hayes & Y (L), Torquay (L), Woking, Welling, Dover	Kadell	24	Midfielder	44	2
◊ Davey Chelsea, Scunthorpe (L), Peterborough (L), Stabæk (Norway) (L), Crawley (L), Cheltenham, Torquay (L), Boreham W (L)	Alex	23	Defender	22	1
◊ Davies Tranmere, Chester	Liam	22	Midfielder	2	
◊ Davies Morecambe, Fleetwood, Morecambe (L), Accrington (L), Tranmere	Scott	31	Goalkeeper	45	
◊ Davis Grays, Braintree, Boreham W, Sutton U	Kenny	30	Midfielder	42	2
◊ Davis Coventry, Peterborough (L), Northampton, Oxford U, Yeovil, Cleethorpes T, Cheltneham, Torquay	Liam	31	Defender	34	
◊ Dawson Stoke, Carlisle, Nuneaton, AFC Telford, Chester	Lucas	24	Midfielder	38	5
◊ Dayton Crystal Palace, Yeovil (L), Crawley (L), Kilmarnock, Oldham, St Mirren (L), Swindon, Cheltenham, Leyton Orient	James	29	Midfielder	32	3
◊ De Havilland Millwall, Sheffield W, Wycombe, Aldershot (L), Maidstone (L)	Will	23	Defender	18	
◊ Deen-Conteh Chelsea, FC Ergotelis, Port Vale, Boston (L), Zaria Balti, FC Zugdidi, Dover	Aziz	25	Defender	5	
◊ Del Girolamo Sheff Utd, York (lx2), Northampton (L), Bristol C, Cheltenham (L), Chesterfield (L), Macclesfield	Diego	22	Forward		
◊ Dennet Eastleigh	Oliver		Forward	1	
◊ Dennis Dagenham & R, Bromley	Louis	25	Forward	53	21
◊ Denton Wakefield, Huddersfield, Woking (L), Cheltenham (L), Wakefield (L), Alfreton, North Ferriby, Halifax	Tom	29	Forward	33	10
◊ Devericks Gretna, Barnet, Alfreton, Dover, Hartlepool, Dover (L), Wrexham	Nicky	30	Midfielder	44	4
◊ Diagne Nottingham, Abervilliers, Macclesfield, Lincoln (L), Morecambe, Lincoln, Macclesfield (L), Hemel H, Barrow	Tony	27	Defender	19	
◊ Diarra St Albans, Hemel H, Hampton & R (L), Hampton & R, Barrow	Moussa	28	Defender	41	3
◊ Dibble Bury, Barnsley, Nuneaton (L), Chelmsford (L), Boston Utd, Nuneaton, Chorley (L), Wrexham	Christian	24	Goalkeeper	6	
◊ Dixon Sunderland, Workington (L), Hartlepool (L), Boston (L), Gateshead (L), Barrow	Joel	24	Goalkeeper	15	

PLAYER DATABASE

SURNAME Clubs Played for	FIRST NAME	AGE	POSITION	2017-18 TOTAL Apps Gls	
◊ Doe	Scott	29	Defender	24	1
Weymouth, Dagenham & Redbridge, Boreham Wood, Dagenham & Redbridge, Whitehawk (L), Boreham W,					
◊ Donaldson	Ryan	27	Midfielder	19	2
Newcastle, Hartlepool (L), Tranmere (L), Gateshead, Cambridge U, Plymouth, Hartlepool					
◊ Donnelly	Liam	22	Defender	29	3
Fulham, Crawley (L), Hartlepool					
◊ Dorel	Vincent	26	Goalkeeper	35	
Plymouth, Torquay					
◊ Dowling	George	19	Defender	22	2
Bristol C, Weston-S-M (L), Torquay (L)					
◊ Downer	Simon	36	Defender	18	
Leyton O, Aldershot (L), Weymouth, Grays, Rushden, Sutton U, Maidenhead, Sutton U					
◊ Downes	Alex	18	Defender	1	
Chester					
◊ Drury	Andy	34	Midfielder	46	6
Sittingbourne, Ebbsfleet, Lewes, Stevenage, Luton, Ipswich, Crawley (L), Crawley, Luton, Eastleigh, Ebbsfleet					
◊ Drysdale	Declan		Defender	1	
Tranmere					
◊ Duckworth	Michael	26	Defender	18	
York, Harrogate Railway, Bradford PA, Hartlepool, Fleetwood, Morecambe (L), Halifax					
◊ Duggan	Mitch	21	Forward	12	
Tranmere					
◊ Dundas	Craig	37	Forward	41	8
Sutton U					
◊ Dunkley	Tristan	25	Forward	10	
Loughborough, Worcester, Hednesford, Halesowen (L), Solihull M, Rushall					
◊ Dunn	Chris	30	Goalkeeper	36	
Northampton, Coventry, Yeovil, Cambridge U, Wrexham					
◊ Dunn	Jack	23	Forward	6	
Liverpool, Cheltenham (L), Burton (L), Morecambe (L), Tranmere (L), Tranmere					
◊ Dunne	Alan	35	Defender	19	
Millwall, Leyton O, Bromley,					
◊ Dunne	Jimmy	20	Defender	23	2
Burnley, Barrow (L), Accrington (L)					
◊ Durrell	Elliott	28	Midfielder	38	9
Hednesford, Wrexham, Tamworth, Chester, Macclesfield					
◊ East	Danny	26	Defender	5	
Hull City, Northampton (L), Gillingham (L), Portsmouth, Aldershot (L), Grimsby, Guiseley					
◊ Eastmond	Craig	27	Midfielder	41	5
Arsenal, Millwall (L), Wycombe (L), Colchester (L), Colchester, Yeovil, Sutton U					
◊ Edmundson	Samuel George	20	Defender	14	
Oldham, Alfreton (L), AFC Fylde (L)					
◊ Edwards	Jack	26	Midfielder	6	
Leamington, Solihull M, Leamington					

SURNAME Clubs Played for	FIRST NAME	AGE	POSITION	2017-18 TOTAL Apps Gls	
◊ Edwards	Jonathan	21	Forward	14	2
Peterborough, Ilkeston (L), Scarborough (L), St Albans (L), Hull, Accrington (L), Woking (L)					
◊ Edwards	Opanin	19	Midfielder	4	
Bristol C, Bath (L), Solihull M (L), Bath (L)					
◊ Efete	Michee	21	Defender	27	
Norwich, Torquay (L)					
◊ Effiong	Inih	27	Forward	35	12
Boreham W, Barrow, Woking, Ross Co					
◊ Egan	Alfie	20	Midfielder	4	
AFC Wimbledon, Sutton U (L)					
◊ Ekpiteta	Marvin	22	Defender	6	
Chelmsford, Concord R, E Thurrock, Leyton Orient					
◊ Ellis	Mark	29	Defender	7	1
Exeter, Bolton, Torquay (L), Torquay, Forest Green (L), Crewe, Shrewsbury, Carlisle (L), Carlisle, Forest Green (L), Leyton Orient (L), Tranmere					
◊ Elokobi	George	32	Defender	23	3
Dulwich H, Colchester, Chester (L), Wolves, Nottingham F (L), Bristol C, Oldham, Colchester, Braintree (L), Leyton Orient					
◊ Enver	Aiden		Midfielder		
Bromley					
◊ Essam	Connor	26	Defender	51	1
Gillingham, Luton (L), Crawley, Dartford (L), Dover, Leyton O, Dover (L), Eastleigh, Woking (L), Dover (L), Dover					
◊ Essuman	George	21	Defender	1	
Hemel H, AveleyLeverstock Green, London Colney, Waltham F, Ware, Maldon & Tiptree, Grays, VCD Ath, Dover,Oxford C (L), Whitehawk (L), Margate (L), Torquay					
◊ Evans	Callum	22	Defender	26	
Barnsley, Macclesfield (L), Forest Green, Torquay (L), Macclesfield (L)					
◊ Evans	Owen	21	Goalkeeper	4	
Hereford, Wigan, Rhyl (L), North Ferriby (L), Sutton U (L),					
◊ Evans	Will	26	Defender	37	2
Swindon, Hereford (L), Hereford, Newport Co (L), Eastleigh, Aldershot					
◊ Ezewele	Josh	21	Defender	9	
West Brom, Yeovil, Kidderminster (L), AFC Fylde					
◊ Fallon	Rory	36	Forward	5	
Barnsley, Shrewsbury (L), Swindon, Yeovil (L), Swansea, Plymouth, Ipswich (L), Yeovil, Aberdeen, St JohnstoneCrawley, Scunthorpe, Bristol R, Truro, Torquay, Dorchester					
◊ Fazakerley	Loui	34	Defender	11	
Eastbourne B, Welling, Dover					
◊ Featherstone	Nicky	29	Midfielder	38	
Hull, Grimsby (L),Hereford, Walsall, Scunthorpe, Hartlepool					
◊ Fenelon	Shamir	23	Forward	38	10
Brighton, Torquay (L), Rochdale (L), Tranmere (L), Dagenham & R (L), Crawley, Whitehawk (L), Aldershot					
◊ Ferdinand	Kane	25	Midfielder	50	4
Southend, Peterborough, Northampton (L), Luton (L), Cheltenham (L), Dagenham & R, East Thurrock, Woking					

PLAYER DATABASE

SURNAME Clubs Played for	FIRST NAME	AGE	POSITION	2017-18 TOTAL Apps	Gls
◊ Ferrier	Morgan	23	Forward	48	15
Arsenal, Nottingham, Bishop's St, Hemel H, Boreham W, Dagenham & R, Boreham W					
◊ Finley	Sam	25	Midfielder	38	7
The New Saints, WrexhamAFC Fylde					
◊ Finney	Alex	22	Defender	31	3
Leyton Orient, Bolton, QPR, Maidstone (L)					
◊ Firth	Andrew	21	Goalkeeper	11	
Liverpool, Chester (L), Barrow					
◊ Fitzpatrick	David	23	Midfielder	5	
QPR, AFC Wimbledon, Tonbridge A (L), Torquay (L), Barrow					
◊ Fitzpatrick	David	28	Defender	48	1
Southport, Macclesfield, Torquay (L)					
◊ Fletcher	Alex	19	Forward	3	
Plymouth, Torquay (L)					
◊ Flintney	Ross	34	Goalkeeper	21	
Fulham, Brighton (L), Brighton (L), Doncaster (L), Barnet, Grays, Dover, Gillingham, Eastleigh, Whitehawk, Bromley, Eastleigh					
◊ Flores	Jordan	22	Midfielder	1	
Wigan, Blackpool (L), Chesterfield (L), AFC Fylde (L)					
◊ Flowers	Harry	22	Defender	13	
Burnley, Guiseley					
◊ Folivi	Michael	20	Forward	18	3
Watford, Coventry (L), Boreham W (L)					
◊ Fondop-Talom	Mike	24	Forward	35	9
Whitehawk, Billericay, Oxford C, Guiseley (L), Halifax (L)					
◊ Fowler	George	?	Defender	27	
Ipswich, Aldershot (L), Aldershot					
◊ Fox	Ben	20	Midfielder	17	2
Burton, Tamworth (L), Solihull (L), Gateshead (L)					
◊ FranCIs-Angol	Zaine	25	Defender	48	2
Tottenham, Motherwell, Kidderminster, AFC Fylde					
◊ Franks	Jonathan	28	Midfielder	30	6
Middlesbrough, Oxford U (L), Yeovil (L), Hartlepool, Ross Co, Hartlepool, Wrexham					
◊ Freestone	Lewis	18	Defender	4	
Peterborough, St Albans (L), Guiseley (L)					
◊ Frempah	Ben	23	Midfielder	4	
Cray Wanderers, Leicester, Ross County, Hendon, Solihull M, Guiseley					
◊ Fyfield	Jamal	29	Defender	40	1
York, Grimsby, Welling, Wrexham, Gateshead					
◊ Gallagher	Jake	25	Midfielder	38	2
Millwall, Welling, Aldershot					
◊ Gallifuoco	Giancarlo	24	Defender	49	5
Tottenham, Swansea, Melbourne Victory, Torquay, Dover					
◊ Garner	Scott	28	Defender	33	2
Leicester, Mansfield, Grimsby, Cambridge U, Lincoln (L), Boston, Halifax					
◊ George	Luke	25	Midfielder	8	
Southport, Chester, Hartlepool					

SURNAME Clubs Played for	FIRST NAME	AGE	POSITION	2017-18 TOTAL Apps	Gls
◊ Ginnelly Shrewsbury, Burnley, Altrincham (L), Walsall (L), Lincoln (L), Lincoln (L), Tranmere (L)	Josh	21	Midfielder	12	3
◊ Gnabouyou Marseille, US Orleans 45, Paris FC, FC Inter, AEL Kalloni, Sliema Wanderers, FC Inter, Torquay, Unattached, IBV	Guy Kassa	28	Forward	6	
◊ Gomis FC Lens, Puertollano, Almeria, Southend, Sutton, Barrow	Bedsente	30	Midfielder	47	5
◊ Goodman Millwall, Luton (L), Aldershot (L), AFC Wimbledon (L), Margate, Braintree, Maidenhead, Bromley	Jake	24	Defender	43	2
◊ Gordon Dagenham & R, Whitehawk (L)	Liam	19	Defender	2	1
◊ Gordon Boreham WHaringey (L)	Quba	20	Defender		
◊ Gosling Exeter, Dorchester (L), Bristol R, Newport Co (L), Cambrideg U (L)Forest Green (L), Torquay	Jake	24	Midfielder	14	
◊ Gough Gresley, Solihull M, Brackley, AFC Telford, Chester	Jordan	28	Defender	18	
◊ Gowling West Brom, Herfolge, Bournemouth, Carlisle, Hereford (L), Gillingham (L), Gillingham, Lincoln (L), Lincoln, Kidderminster (L), Kidderminster, Grimsby (L), Grimsby, Torquay	Josh	34	Defender	26	
◊ Graham Cheltenham, Telford (L), Chelmsford, Ebbsfleet, Chelmsford (L)	Bagasan	25	Midfielder	5	
◊ Graham Sheffield U, Halifax (L)	Sam	17	Defender	7	
◊ Grainger Leyton Orient, Farnborough (L), Hampton & R (L)	Charlie	21	Goalkeeper	23	
◊ Grand Rochdale, Carlisle, Grimsby, Morecambe, Northwich, Fleetwood, Mansfield (L), Aldershot (L), Southport, AFC Telford, Barrow, Salford, AFC Fylde	Simon	34	Defender	41	5
◊ Gray Darlington, Kettering (L), Accrington, Northampton (L), Wrexham, Southport, Glenavon, Torquay, York (L), Tamworth (L)	James	26	Forward	13	2
◊ Green Blackburn, Tranmere	Devarn	21	Forward	3	1
◊ Green Lincoln C, Eastwood (L), Sheffield (L), Grantham (L), Lincoln U, Ange IF (Swe), Whitecaps (US), Guiseley	Elliot	24	Defender	2	
◊ Green Mustangs (US)Newport Co, Handsworth P, Scarborough Ath, Guiseley	Joe	22	Goalkeeper	19	
◊ Green Hartlepool, Gateshead (L), Gateshead, Blyth Spartans (L)	Kieran	21	Midfielder	8	
◊ Green Halesowen, Stourbridge, Solihull M	Kristian	27	Defender	35	
◊ Green Bristol R, Port Vale, Eastleigh	Mike	29	Defender	18	
◊ Green Aston Villa, Lincoln, Tamworth, Forest Green, Hereford U (L), Tamworth, Solihull M	Paul	31	Defender	26	

PLAYER DATABASE

SURNAME / Clubs Played for	FIRST NAME	AGE	POSITION	2017-18 TOTAL Apps	Gls
◊ Greenwood	Rees	21	Midfielder	11	
Sunderland, Gateshead					
◊ Grego-Cox	Reece	21	Forward	18	4
QPR, Newport Co (L), Woking (L)					
◊ Gregory	David	23	Goalkeeper	58	
Crystal Palace, Eastbourne (L), Leyton O (L), Cambridge U, Bromley					
◊ Gumbs	Evan	21	Defender	4	
Tranmere, Bradford PA (L)					
◊ Hall	Asa	31	Midfielder	38	3
Birmingham , Boston (L), Shrewsbury (L), Luton, Oxford U, Shrewsbury, Aldershot (L), Oxford U (L), Cheltenham, York (L), Barrow					
◊ Hall-Johnson	Reece	23	Defender	12	1
Norwich, Maidstone, Bishop's St, Braintree, Grimsby, Chester (L)					
◊ Halls	Andy	26	Defender		
Stockport, Macclesfield, Chester					
◊ Hamann	Nick	30	Goalkeeper		
Basingstoke, Braintree, Woking, Hemel H, Maidenhead					
◊ Hammond	James	28	Defender		
Colchester, Wealdstone, Concord R, Maidenhead					
◊ Hancox	Mitch	24	Defender	41	7
Birmingham, Crawley (L), Macclesfield					
◊ Hanford	Dan	27	Goalkeeper	26	
Hereford, Floriana, Carlisle, Gateshead					
◊ Hanlan	Brandon	21	Forward	22	5
Charlton, Bromley (L), Colchester (L), Bromley (L)					
◊ Hanley	Raheem	24	Defender	7	
Blackburn, Swansea, Northampton, Halifax (L)					
◊ Hannah	Ross	32	Forward	32	9
Matlock, Bradford, Grimsby, Chester, Barrow, Chester					
◊ Hannant	Luke	24	Midfielder	24	3
Gateshead, Port Vale					
◊ Hanson	Jacob	20	Defender	2	
Huddersfield, Bradford, Halifax (L)					
◊ Happe	Daniel	19	Defender	33	
Leyton Orient, Gateshead (L)					
◊ Hardy	James	22	Forward	25	
Man City, AFC Fylde					
◊ Hare	Josh	23	Defender	33	3
Gillingham, Eastbourne, Maidstone					
◊ Harfield	Ollie	20	Defender	1	
Bournemouth, Poole (L), Boreham W (L)					
◊ Harris	Jay	31	Midfielder	42	
Everton, Accrington, Chester, Wrexham, Tranmere					
◊ Harrison	Byron	31	Forward	42	13
Havant & W, Worthing, Boreham Wd, Harrow B, Ashford (Mx), Carshalton, Stevenage, AFC Wimbledon, Cheltenham, Chesterfield,Stevenage (L), Barrow, Sutton U (L)					

SURNAME Clubs Played for	FIRST NAME	AGE	POSITION	2017-18 TOTAL Apps Gls	
◊ Harrison	Scott	24	Defender	29	
Darlington, Sunderland, Bury (L), Hartlepool (L), Hartlepool (L), Hartlepool					
◊ Harrold	Matt	34	Forward	30	5
Harlow, Brentford, Dagenham & R (L), Grimsby (L), Yeovil, Southend, Wycombe, Shrewsbury, Bristol R, Crawley, Cambridge U (L), Leyton Orient					
◊ Harvey	Alex-Ray	28	Midfielder	34	
Burnley, Fleetwood Town (L), Fleetwood Town (L), Barrow (L), Barrow, Guiseley					
◊ Hatfield	Will	26	Midfielder	30	3
Leeds, York (L), Accrington (L), Accrington, Halifax (L), Guiseley					
◊ Hawkes	Josh	19	Midfielder	11	2
Hartlepool					
◊ Hawkins	Lewis	25	Defender	37	
Horden CW, Hartlepool					
◊ Hawkins	Oliver	26	Forward	7	
Hemel Hempstead Town, Dagenham & Redbridge, Portsmouth					
◊ Haworth	Andy	29	Midfielder	16	1
Blackburn, Gateshead (L), Rochdale (L), Bury, Oxford U (L), Bradford (L), Falkirk, Rochdale, Notts Co, Tamworth (L), Tamworth, Cheltenham, Barrow (L), Barrow, Macclesfield, Torquay, Guiseley					
◊ Healey	Rhys	23	Forward	8	6
Cardiff, Colchester (L), Dundee (L), Newport Co (L), Torquay (L)					
◊ Healy	Joe	31	Forward		
Millwall, Crawley (L), Welling, Maidstone, Dover, Welling, Maidstone, Unattached					
◊ Hellawell	Rhain		Midfielder		
Stockport Town, Chester					
◊ Heslop	Simon	31	Midfielder	5	1
Barnsley, Kidderminster (L), Tamworth (L), Northwich (L), Halifax (L), Grimsby (L), Kettering (L), Luton (L), Oxford U, Stevenage, Mansfield, Torquay, Wrexham, York, Eastleigh (L)					
◊ Hibbs	Jake	22	Midfielder	27	
Halifax, Droylsden (L), Hyde (L), Telford (L), Bradford PA (L),					
◊ Higgins	Ryan	24	Defender	18	
Birmingham, Tamworth (L), Telford (L), Chester, Southport, Torquay					
◊ Higgs	Jordan	21	Midfielder	42	3
Bromley, Carshalton, Bromley,					
◊ Higgs	Kieran	19	Forward	1	
Norwich, Solihull M (L)					
◊ Hines	Zavon	29	Forward	24	8
West Ham, Coventry (L), Burnley, Bournemouth (L), Bradford, Dagenham & R, Southend, Maidstone, Chesterfield					
◊ Hobson	Shaun	20	Defender	13	
Burnley, Bournemouth, Eastbourne B (L), Chester (L)					
◊ Hodgkiss	Jared	31	Defender	32	1
West Brom, Aberdeen (L), Northampton (L), Forest Green, Kidderminster, Torquay (L), Macclesfield					
◊ Holden	Darren	24	Defender	22	
Hartlepool, Ross County, Gateshead, South Shields, Guiseley					

PLAYER DATABASE

SURNAME Clubs Played for	FIRST NAME	AGE	POSITION	2017-18 TOTAL Apps Gls	
◊ Holland	Jack	26	Defender	57	9
Bromley, Crystal Palace, Eastbourne (L), Bromley,					
◊ Hollands	Danny	32	Midfielder	34	
Chelsea, Torquay (L), Bournemouth, Charlton, Swindon (L), Gillingham (L), Portsmouth (L),					
Portsmouth, Crewe, Eastleigh					
◊ Holman	Dan	28	Forward	27	6
Braintree, Colchester, Wrexham (L), Aldershot (L), Dover (L), Woking (L), Cheltenham (L),					
Cheltenham, Boreham W (L), Leyton O (L)					
◊ Holroyd	Chris	31	Forward	35	13
Chester, Cambridge U, Brighton (L), Brighton, Stevenage (L), Bury (L), Rotherham, Preston,					
Macclesfield (L), Morecambe, Macclesfield, Wrexham					
◊ Holt	Grant	37	Forward	23	
Workington, Halifax, Barrow (L), Barrow, Sheffield Wed, Rochdale, Nottingham, Blackpool					
(L), Shrewsbury, Norwich, Wigan, Aston Villa (L), Huddersfield (L), Wolves (L), Rochdale (L),					
Hibernian, King's Lynn, Barrow					
◊ Hornby	Sam	23	Goalkeeper	15	
Burton, Brackley (L), Kidderminster (L), Port Vale, Chester (L)					
◊ Horsfall	Fraser	21	Defender		
Huddersfield, Stalybridge (L), Gateshead (L), Kidderminster (L)					
◊ Hotte	Nathan	30	Defender	33	1
Hull, Scarborough, Farsley Celtic, Bradford PA, North Ferriby, Halifax					
◊ Howe	Callum	24	Defender	28	4
Scunthorpe, Gateshead (L), Alfreton (L), Lincoln, Southport (L), Eastleigh (L),Port Vale					
◊ Howell	Luke	31	Midfielder	35	4
Gillingham, MK Dons, Lincoln (L), Lincoln, Dagenham & R, Boreham W, Dagenham & R,					
Aldershot					
◊ Howells	Jake	27	Midfielder	46	
Luton, Yeovil (L), EastleighDagenham & R, Ebbsfleet (L)					
◊ Hoyte	Gavin	28	Defender	33	1
Arsenal, Watford (L), Brighton (L), Lincoln (L), AFC Wimbledon (L), Dagenham & R, Gillingham,					
Barnet, Eastleigh					
◊ Hudson	Ellis	19	Midfielder	2	
Bradford, Harrogate (L), Guiseley (L)					
◊ Hudson-Odoi	Bradley	29	Forward	9	
Hereford, Grays (L), Histon, Grays (L), Met Police, Wealdstone, Sutton U, Maidstone (L),					
Hampton & R (L), Eastleigh (L), Hampton & R (L)					
◊ Hughes	Jeff	33	Midfielder	35	2
Lincoln, Crystal Palace, Peterborough (L), Bristol R (L), Bristol R, Notts Co, Fleetwood,					
Cambridge U, Tranmere (L), Tranmere					
◊ Hughes	Liam	25	Midfielder	15	
Cambridge U, Inverness CT, Barrow, Guiseley					
◊ Humphrey	Chris	30	Midfielder	4	
Shrewsbury, Stafford (L), Motherwell, PNE, Hibernian, Bury, Barrow (L)					
◊ Hunter	Max		Goalkeeper		
Bromley					

| SURNAME | FIRST NAME | AGE | POSITION | 2017-18 TOTAL | |
Clubs Played for				Apps	Gls
◊ Hurst	James	26	Defender	19	

Portsmouth, West Brom, Blackpool (L), Shrewsbury (L), Chesterfield (L), Birmingham (L), Shrewsbury (L), Crawley, Northampton (L), Hednesford, Torquay, Guiseley (L), Telford, Dover, Wrexham

| ◊ Hurst | Kevan | 32 | Midfielder | 25 | 1 |

Sheffield U, Boston (L), Stockport (L), Chesterfield (L), Scunthorpe (L), Scunthorpe, Carlisle, Morecambe (L), Walsall, Southend, Mansfield, Guiseley (L), Guiseley

| ◊ Hyde | Jake | 28 | Forward | 37 | 7 |

Swindon, Weymouth (L), Weymouth (L), Barnet, Hayes & Yeading, Dundee, Dunfermline, Dundee, Barnet, York, Stevenage, Maidenhead (L), Maidenhead

| ◊ Hyde | Tyrique | 19 | Midfielder | | |

Dagenham & Redbridge, Whitehawk (L), Ware (L)

| ◊ Hylton | Jermaine | 25 | Forward | 32 | 4 |

Swindon, Guiseley (L), Solihull M

| ◊ Ilesanmi | Femi | 27 | Defender | 50 | 2 |

AFC Wimbledon, QPR, Ashford T (Kent), Dagenham & R, Histon (L), York, Boreham W, Dover

| ◊ Inman | Dean | 27 | Defender | 13 | 1 |

Hampton & R, Hayes & Yeading, Maidenhead, Billericay

| ◊ Isaac | Chez | 25 | Midfielder | 44 | |

Watford, Tamworth (L), Boreham W, Braintree, Woking

| ◊ Jaaskelainen | Will | 20 | Goalkeeper | | |

Bolton Wanderers, Crewe Alexandra, Nantwich Town (L), Chester (L)

| ◊ Jalal | Shwan | 34 | Goalkeeper | 43 | |

Tottenham, Woking (L), Woking, Sheff Wed (L), Peterborough, Morecambe (L), Bounremouth, Oxford U (L), Leyton Orient (L), Bury, Northampton, Macclesfield, Wrexham, Macclesfield, Chesterfield

| ◊ James | Kingsley | 26 | Midfielder | 47 | 2 |

Sheffield Utd, Port Vale, Hereford (L), Hereford, Chester, Halifax, Macclesfield, Chester, Barrow (L)

| ◊ James | Luke | 23 | Forward | 17 | 7 |

Hartlepool, Peterborough (L), Bradford (L), Hartlepool (L), Bristol (L), Forest Green, Barrow (L)

| ◊ Janata | Arthur | | Goalkeeper | | |

Leyton Orient

| ◊ Jarvis | Aaron | 20 | Forward | 4 | |

Basingstoke, Luton, Boreham W (L)

| ◊ Jeffers | Shaun | 26 | Forward | 31 | 5 |

Coventry, Cheltenham (L), Cambridge U (L), Tamworth (L), Peterborough, Newport Co, Yeovil, Woking (L), Chelmsford, Boreham W, Hampton & R (L)

| ◊ Jeffrey | Anthony | 23 | Midfielder | 36 | 1 |

Arsenal, Stevenage (L), Boreham W (L), Wycombe (L), Boreham W, Welling, Concord R, Boreham W (L), Boreham W, Forest Green, Boreham W (L), Boreham W (L),Sutton, Dover (L),

| ◊ Jennings | Connor | 26 | Forward | 48 | 9 |

Scunthorpe, Stockport (L), Macclesfield (L), Grismby (L), Wrexham, Tranmere, Macclesfield (L)

| ◊ Jennings | James | 30 | Defender | 41 | 4 |

Macclesfield, Altrincham (L), Kettering, Cambridge U, Mansfield (L), Mansfield, Forest Green, Cheltenham (L), Morecambe (L), Wrexham (L), Wrexham

PLAYER DATABASE

SURNAME Clubs Played for	FIRST NAME	AGE	POSITION	2017-18 TOTAL Apps	Gls
◊ John Sutton U, Hemel H (L), Hampton & R (L), Ebbsfleet (L)	Louis	24	Defender	39	3
◊ Johnson Bromley	Dan	22	Defender	26	
◊ Johnson Tranmere, Stevenage (L), Gateshead, Motherwell	Danny	25	Forward	45	21
◊ Johnson Amiens, Plymouth, Sheffield Wed, Coventry, Eastleigh	Reda	30	Defender	13	1
◊ Johnson Wycombe, Cardiff, Birmingham, Wolves, Sheffield Wed (L), West Ham (L), Charlton, Bromley	Roger	35	Defender	28	1
◊ Johnson Stevenage Borough, St Albans City (L), Boreham Wood (L), Nuneaton Town (L)	Ryan	21	Defender	2	
◊ Johnson Stoke, Port Vale, Stafford (L), Alfreton (L), Halifax (L), Gateshead (L), Halifax (L), Halifax	Sam	25	Goalkeeper	47	
◊ Jones Hartlepool, Grimsby, Gateshead (L), AFC Fylde (L), Barrow	Dan	23	Defender	35	3
◊ Jones Swansea, Bangor, AFC Fylde	Henry	24	Midfielder	24	5
◊ Jones Chester, Salford	James	19	Defender	17	
◊ Jones Yeovil, Woking (L), Woking	Joseph	24	Defender	36	1
◊ Jordan Arsenal, Yeovil (L), Chesterfield, Stevenage, Lewes, Eastbourne, Farnborough, Boreham W, Concord R, Ebbsfleet	Michael	32	Goalkeeper		
◊ Joyce Oldham, Stockport, Chester	Wade	24	Midfielder	11	
◊ Judd Leyton Orient	Myles	18	Midfielder	15	
◊ Justham Waltham F, Leyton, Redbridge, Brentwood,East Thurrock,Luton, Dagenham & R	Elliot	28	Goalkeeper		
◊ Kabamba Hayes, Uxbridge, AFC Hayes, Burnham, Hemel H (L), Hampton & R (L), Hampton & R, Portsmouth, Colchester (L), Aldershot (L)	Nike	25	Forward	11	3
◊ Kandi Birmingham, Chelsea, West Brom, Brighton, Bognor Regis (Lx2), Woking, Leatherhead, Dagenham & R	Chike	22	Forward	18	1
◊ Kay AFC Fylde, Barnsley, AFC Fylde (L), Tranmere (L), Chesterfield (L)	Josh	21	Midfielder	2	
◊ Keating Sligo Rovers, Galway, Finn Harps, Torquay	Ruairi	23	Forward	41	4
◊ Kedwell Herne Bay, Welling, Grays, Wimbledon, Gillingham, Ebbsfleet	Danny	34	Forward	53	21
◊ Keita Boreham W, Potters Bar (L), Wingate & F (L), Hayes & Y	Frank	20	Forward	1	
◊ Kelleher Celtic, Peterhead (L), Oxford U (L), Solihull M (L)	Fiacre	22	Defender	42	2

SURNAME Clubs Played for	FIRST NAME	AGE	POSITION	2017-18 TOTAL	
				Apps	Gls
◊ Kellerman Aldershot	Jim	20	Midfielder	41	7
◊ Kelly Rushden, Oxford U, Kettering, Mansfield (L), Tamworth, Forest Green, Wrexham	Marcus	32	Midfielder	44	2
◊ Kennedy Leicester, Motherwell, AFC Fylde, Macclesfield	Kieran	24	Defender	35	1
◊ Kerr Birmingham, Motherwell, Cowdenbeath, Stenhousemuir, Gateshead	Fraser	25	Defender	38	1
◊ Kettle Solihull M, Tamworth (L)	Joel	27	Defender	18	2
◊ Khan Halifax	Shiraz		Midfielder	2	
◊ Kilman Maidenhead	Max	21	Defender	38	1
◊ King Rotherham, Altrincham (L), North Ferriby, Halifax, Gainsborough (L)	Liam	30	Midfielder	3	
◊ Kinsella Arsenal, Aston Villa, Luton (L), Kidderminster (L), Colchester, Aldershot (L)	Lewis	23	Defender	19	
◊ Kirby Tranmere, Stockport (L)	Jake	24	Midfielder	3	
◊ Kirwan Aldershot	Eoin	18	Forward		
◊ Klukowski Forest Green, Newport Co, York, Torquay, Kidderminster (L)	Yan	31	Midfielder	8	
◊ Koroma Leyton Orient	Josh	19	Forward	34	6
◊ Kosylo Stockport, Ashton, Hyde, Nantwich, Halifax	Matt	25	Midfielder	35	11
◊ Koue Niate Solihull M, Oxford C, Guiseley	Jean-Yves	25	Defender	7	
◊ Lafayette Wealdstone, Welling, Luton, Woking (L), Welling (L), Eastleigh, Aldershot (L), Dover, Sutton U, Maidstone (L)	Ross	32	Forward	42	12
◊ Laing Sunderland, Wycombe (L), Nottingham F, Notts Co (L), Motherwell (L), Motherwell, Notts Co (L), Inverness CT, Hartlepool	Louis	25	Defender	42	1
◊ Lait Stourbridge, Solihull M	Chris	25	Midfielder	6	1
◊ Langley Wigan, AFC Fylde (L), AFC Fylde	Josh	25	Defender	4	
◊ Langstaff Gateshead, Blyth (L)	Macaulay	21	Forward	4	
◊ Lathrope Norwich, Torquay, Hereford (L), Aldershot, Torquay, Woking (L)	Damon	28	Midfielder	24	
◊ Lavercombe Torquay, Wigan, Torquay (L), Torquay (L), Rhyl (L), Torquay (L)	Dan	21	Goalkeeper	2	

| SURNAME | FIRST NAME | AGE | POSITION | 2017-18 TOTAL | |
Clubs Played for				Apps	Gls
◊ Lawless	Alex	33	Midfielder	30	
Fulham, Torquay, Forest Green, York, Luton (L), Luton, Yeovil, Leyton Orient					
◊ Lawlor	Jake	27	Midfielder	32	2
Guiseley, AFC Fylde (L)					
◊ Ledger	Michael	21	Defender	12	
Sunderland, Viking (L), Hartlepool (L)					
◊ Lee	Charlie	31	Midfielder	8	1
Tottenham, Millwall (L), Peterborough, Gillingham (L), Gillingham, Stevenage, Leyton Orient					
◊ Lee	Jordan	21	Defender	2	
Bournemouth, Torquay (L), Torquay (L)					
◊ Lema	Crossley	19	Defender		
Sutton U					
◊ Lemonheigh-Evans	Connor	21	Forward	15	1
Bristol C, Bath (L), Torquay (L)					
◊ Lenighan	Simon	24	Midfielder	24	1
Leeds, Bradford PA (L), Halifax (L), Harrogate T, Alfreton (L), Frickley A, Rotherham, Warrington T, Altrincham, Shaw Lane, Glossop NE, Guiseley					
◊ Lewington	Chris	29	Goalkeeper		
Charlton, Dulwich, Fisher Ath, Sittingbourne, Leatherhead, Dagenham & R, Colchester, Margate, Welling, Dover					
◊ Lewis	Paul	23	Midfielder	8	1
Macclesfield, Cambridge U, Dover (L)					
◊ Lewis	Stuart	30	Midfielder	49	4
Tottenham, Barnet, Stevenage, Gillingham, Dagenham & R, Wycombe (L), Wycombe, Ebbsfleet, Maidstone (L), Maidstone					
◊ Liburd	Rowan	25	Forward	29	8
Billericay, Reading, Wycombe (L), Stevenage, Leyton Orient (L), Hemel H (L), Guiseley (L), Guiseley					
◊ Ling	Sam	21	Defender	45	3
Leyton O, Dagenham & R, Leyton O					
◊ Lloyd	Ryan	24	Midfielder	28	4
Port Vale, Tamworth (L), Chester (Lx2), Macclesfield					
◊ Loach	Scott	30	Goalkeeper	49	
Ipswich, Lincoln C, Watford, Stafford (L), Morecambe (L), Bradford (L), Ipswich, Rotherham, Bury (L), Peterborough (L), Yeovil (L), Notts Co, York (L), Hartlepool					
◊ Lokko	Kevin	22	Defender	40	3
Colchester, Welling, Maidstone, Stevenage, Dagenham & R (L), Dover (L), Dover					
◊ Lowe	Daniel	34	Defender	15	
Northampton, Halifax, Guiseley					
◊ Lowe	Keith	32	Defender	48	1
Wolves, Burnley (L), QPR (L), Swansea (L), Brighton (L), Cheltenham (Lx2)Port Vale (L), Kidderminster, Hereford, Cheltenham, York (L), York, Kidderminster, Macclesfield					
◊ Loza	Jamar	24	Forward	36	3
Norwich, Coventry (L), Leyton Orient (L), Southend (L), Yeovil (L), Stevenage (L), Southend (L), Maidstone					

SURNAME Clubs Played for	FIRST NAME	AGE	POSITION	2017-18 TOTAL Apps Gls	
◊ Luer	Greg	23	Forward	6	
Hull, Port Vale (L), Scunthorpe (L), Stevenage (L), Maidstone (L)					
◊ Lynch	Alex	23	Goalkeeper	15	
Peterborough United, Wycombe Wanderers, Wealdstone (L), Bala Town (L), Chester, Llandudno					
◊ Lynch	Dave	25	Midfielder	14	
Workington, Altrincham, Halifax, Southport					
◊ Lynch	Jay	25	Goalkeeper	41	
Man Utd, Bolton, Accrington, Salford, AFC Fylde					
◊ Lyons-Foster	Kodi		Defender	7	
Aldershot, Whitehawk (L)					
◊ M'Boungou	Chris	26	Defender	9	
Staines, Bishop's St, Whitehawk, Guiseley					
◊ MacDonald	Calum	20	Defender	24	1
Derby, Barrow (L)					
◊ MacDonald	Josh	23	Midfielder	32	1
Middlesbrough, Marske Utd, Halifax					
◊ Mackreth	Jack	26	Midfielder	34	
Tranmere, Barrow, Macclesfield, Grimsby, Tranmere, Macclesfield, Bury, Macclesfield (L), Wrexham					
◊ MacLeod	Ian	19	Goalkeeper		
Gateshead					
◊ MagnAy	Carl	29	Defender	35	1
Leeds, Chelsea, MK Dons (L), Northampton (L), Gateshead, Grimsby, Hartlepool					
◊ Magri	Sam	24	Defender	39	
Portsmouth, QPR, Nuneaton (L), Dover (L), Dover, Ebbsfleet					
◊ Maher	Niall	22	Defender	9	
Bolton, Blackpool (L), Bury, Galway, Telford, Halifax					
◊ Mahon	Craig	29	Midfielder	33	1
Wigan, Accrington (L), Salford, Vauxhall M, Chester					
◊ Makoma	Donovan	19	Midfielder	19	1
FC Lens, Barrow					
◊ Mambo	Yado	26	Defender	10	
Charlton, Welling (L), Eastbourne (L), Ebbsfleet (L), Wimbledon (L), Shrewsbury (L), Ebbsfleet (L), Dover, Chelmsford, Hayes & Y, Margate, Bishop's S, Ebbsfleet					
◊ Mangan	Andy	31	Forward	19	1
Blackpool, Accrington, Bury, Accrington, Forest Green, Wrexham, Fleetwood, Forest Green, Shrewsbury, Tranmere, Shrewsbury, TranmereAFC Fylde (L)					
◊ Marks	Sean	32	Forward	38	6
Braintree, Maidenhead					
◊ Marsh	Tyrone	24	Forward	44	10
Oxford U, Welling (L), Torquay, Dover, Macclesfield					
◊ Marsh-Brown	Keanu	25	Midfielder	6	4
FulhamMK Dons (L), Dundee U (L), Oldham, Yeovil, Barnet (L), Barnet, Forest Green, Dover (L)					
◊ Marsh-Hughes	Lloyd	17	Forward		
Chester					
◊ Martin	Romario	18	Midfielder	4	
Solihull M					

PLAYER DATABASE

SURNAME Clubs Played for	FIRST NAME	AGE	POSITION	2017-18 TOTAL Apps Gls	
◊ Martinez Solihull M, Telford (L)	Sheridan	25	Goalkeeper	2	
◊ Marx Wrexham, Southport (L)	Oliver	20	Defender	2	
◊ Mason Woking	Sam	18	Goalkeeper	3	
◊ Massanka Burnley, York (L), Morecambe (L), Wrexham (L), Wrexham (L)	Ntumba	21	Midfielder	25	3
◊ Massey Wealdstone, Braintree (L), Braintree, Maidenhead	Alan	29	Defender	50	
◊ Matthews Bournemouth, Braintree (L), Eastleigh (L), Eastleigh (L)	Sam	21	Midfielder	39	6
◊ Maxted Doncaster, Hartlepool, Forest Green, Guiseley, Accrington	Jonathan	24	Goalkeeper	21	
◊ Maxwell Kidderminster, Birmingham, Kidderminster (L), Grimsby (L), Gateshead (L)	Luke	21	Midfielder	11	
◊ Maye Solihull M	Simeon	24	Midfielder	3	
◊ McAllister Basingstoke,Stevenage, Ebbsfleet (L), Woking, Grays, Rushden (L), Oxford U, Exeter, Barnet (L), Rotherham (L), Crawley, Newport Co, Luton (L), Eastleigh, Sutton, Eastbourne (L), Eastleigh	Craig	38	Forward	24	2
◊ McAnuff Wimbledon, West Ham, Cardiff, Crystal Palace, Watford, Reading, Leyton Orient, Stevenage, Leyton Orient	Jobi	36	Midfielder	40	6
◊ McCallum Dulwich H, West Ham, Rochdale (L), AFC Wimbledon (L), Aldershot (L), Torquay (L), Hearts (L), Portsmouth (L), Leyton OrientEastleigh	Paul	25	Forward	28	8
◊ McClure Wycombe, Hayes & Y Utd (L), Dagenham & R, Aldershot	Matt	26	Forward	36	6
◊ McCombe Huddersfield, Torquay (L), Hereford, Port Vale, Mansfield, York, Macclesfield, Chester, Harrogate T	John	33	Defender	24	
◊ McCorkell Maidstone	Andrew	20	Goalkeeper		
◊ McCoy Arsenal, Watford, Wealdstone, Wycombe, York, Ebbsfleet, Aldershot	Marvin	29	Defender	22	
◊ McCready Everton, Chester, Morecambe, Exeter, AFC Fylde	Tom	27	Midfielder	10	
◊ McDonagh Nottingham F, Wrexham (L), Cambridge U (L), Tranmere (L)	Gerry	20	Forward	11	
◊ McDonald Birmingham, Nuneaton (L), Solihull M (L)	Wesley	21	Midfielder	5	
◊ McDonnell Ipswich, Aldershot (L)	Adam	21	Midfielder	34	4
◊ McEveley Blackburn, Burnley (L), Gillingham (L), Ipswich (L), Derby, PNE (L), Charlton (L), Barnsley, Swindon (L), Swindon, Sheffield U, Ross County, Tranmere	James	33	Defender	13	2

SURNAME Clubs Played for	FIRST NAME	AGE	POSITION	2017-18 TOTAL Apps Gls	
◊ McFadzean	Callum	24	Midfielder	26	1
Sheffield U, Chesterfield (L), Burton (L), Burton (L), Stevenage (L), Kilmarnock, Alfreton, Guiseley,					
◊ McGinty	Sean	24	Defender	48	4
Man Utd, Morecambe (L), Oxford U (L), Carlisle (L), Tranmere (L), Sheffield U, Northampton (L), Rochdale (L), Rochdale, Halifax (L), Aldershot (L), Aldershot, Torquay					
◊ Mcgregor	Callum		Midfielder	1	
Wrexham					
◊ McKenzie	Chinedu		Forward	2	
Maidenhead, Bognor R (L)					
◊ McLaughlin	Patrick	27	Midfielder	57	6
Newcastle, York, Grimsby, Harrogate T (L), Gateshead, Hartlepool					
◊ McLean	Aaron	35	Forward	11	2
Leyton Orient, Aldershot, Grays, Peterborough, Hull, Ipswich (L), Birmingham (L), Bradford, Peterborough, Barnet, Ebbsfleet					
◊ McLoughlin	Shane	21	Midfielder	2	
Ipswich, Bromley (L), Bromley (L)					
◊ McManus	Scott	29	Defender	39	3
Stenhausemuir, Crewe, Stenhausemuir (L), Stranraer, FC Utd, Halifax					
◊ McNall	Lewis	19	Midfielder	11	2
Newcastle, Gateshead (L)					
◊ McNamara	Ben	29	Goalkeeper		
Newcastle U21 (Aus)Rockdale CS, B. White Eagles, NuneatonBarwell (L), Northampton, Hendon, Concord R, Braintree, Dagenham & R, Harlow (L)					
◊ McNulty	Steve	34	Defender	47	1
Fleetwood, Luton, Tranmere					
◊ McQueen	Darren	23	Forward	12	2
Tottenham, Ipswich, Maldon & Tiptree, Ebbsfleet					
◊ McQuoid	Josh	28	Midfielder	32	3
Bournemouth, Millwall (L), Millwall, Burnley (L), Bournemouth, Peterborough (L), Coventry (L), Luton, Stevenage, Torquay (L), Aldershot (L)					
◊ McSheffrey	Gary	35	Forward	12	2
Coventry, Stockport (L), Luton (L), Luton (L), Birmingham, Nottingham F (L), Leeds (L), Coventry, Chesterfield, Scunthorpe, Doncaster (L), Doncaster, Eastleigh, Grimsby					
◊ Mekki	Adam	26	Midfielder	44	4
Aldershot Town, Barnet, Dover Athletic, Tranmere Rovers, Bromley					
◊ Mellish	Jon	20	Defender	10	
Gateshead					
◊ Mensah	Bernard	23	Forward	17	4
Watford, Braintree (L), V Guimaraes (L), V Guimaraes (L), Barnet (L), Braintree (L), Aldershot, Bristol R					
◊ Middleton	Harry	23	Midfielder	6	
Doncaster, Port Vale, Halifax (L)					
◊ Miles	Jonathan	25	Goalkeeper		
Tottenham, Dagenham & R (L), Whitehawk (L), Brentwood (L), Ebbsfleet, Concord (L), Gosport (L), Margate (L), Welling (L),					

PLAYER DATABASE

SURNAME Clubs Played for	FIRST NAME	AGE	POSITION	2017-18 TOTAL Apps	Gls
◊ Miley	Cavanagh	23	Midfielder	38	3
Jersey, Eastleigh					
◊ Miller	George	20	Forward	6	
Bury, Middlesbrough, Wrexham (L), Bury (L)					
◊ Mills	Danny	26	Forward	12	1
Crawley, Peterborough, Torquay (L), Rushden (L), Histon (L), Kettering (L), Tamworth (L),					
Kettering (L), Carshalton, Whitehawk, Ebbsfleet, Dartford (L)					
◊ Mitchell	Conor	22	Goalkeeper	8	
BurnleyBradford PA (L), Chester (L)					
◊ Mitchell	Tallen		Midfielder	2	
Truro, Torquay					
◊ Molyneux	Lee	29	Defender	24	2
Everton, Southampton, Port Vale (L), Plymouth, Accrington, Crewe, Rochdale (L), Accrington (L),					
Accrington (L), Tranmere, Morecambe, Guiseley, Chorley (L)					
◊ Monakana	Jeffrey	24	Midfielder	1	
Arsenal, PNE, Colchester (L), Brighton, Crawley (L), Aberdeen (L), Mansfield (L), Carlisle (L),					
Bristol R (L), Voluntari (Rom), Sutton U, Margate (L), Welling (L), Wealdstone (L)					
◊ Moncur	Freddy	21	Midfielder		
Leyton Orient, Bishop's St. (L)					
◊ Mongoy	Jordy	19	Forward	1	
Dagenham & R					
◊ Montgomery	James	24	Goalkeeper	34	
Telford, Gateshead					
◊ Monthe	Emmanuel	23	Midfielder	6	
Southport, Hayes & Y, Havant & W, Hayes & Y (L), Bath, Forest Green, Tranmere (L)					
◊ Montrose	Lewis	29	Midfielder	48	3
Man City, Wigan, Rochdale (L), Cheltenham (L), Cheltenham (L), Chesterfield (L), Wycombe,					
Gillingham, Oxford U (L), York , Stockport, AFC Fylde					
◊ Mooney	David	33	Forward	42	6
Reading, Stockport (L), Norwich (L), Charlton (L), Colchester (L), Leyton Orient, Southend,					
Leyton Orient					
◊ Moore	Lewis	21	Goalkeeper		
Swansea, Dagenham & R					
◊ Moore	Stuart	23	Goalkeeper	18	
Reading, Basingstoke (L), Peterborough (L), Luton (L), Barrow, Swindon					
◊ Morgan	Adam	24	Forward	21	4
LiverpoolRotherham (L), Yeovil (L), Yeovil, St Johnstone (L), Accrington, Hemel H, Curzon A,					
Halifax, Sligo Rovers					
◊ Morris	Chad		Midfielder		
West Ham, Sutton U					
◊ Morrison	Curtis	20	Forward	3	
Chesterfield, Matlock (L), Matlock (L), Guiseley					
◊ Moses	Ademola	29	Forward	34	8
Brentford, Woking (L), Woking, Bromley, Dover, Sutton (L), Maidenhead					
◊ Mottley-Henry	Dylan	20	Midfielder	16	1
Bradford, Altrincham (L), Bradford PA (L), Barnsley, Tranmere (L), Chesterfield (L)					

SURNAME Clubs Played for	FIRST NAME	AGE	POSITION	2017-18 TOTAL Apps Gls	
◊ Moyo	Cliff	25	Defender	24	
Alfreton, Barrow, Northwich, Drolsden, Trafford, Halifax					
◊ Muldoon	Jack	29	Forward	49	10
Worksop, Rochdale, FC Halifax, Lincoln, AFC Fylde					
◊ Muldoon	Oliver	23	Midfielder	7	
Charlton, Gillingham (L), Dagenham & R (L), Braintree (L), Gillingham, Maidstone					
◊ Mulhern	Euan (Frank)	21	Forward	11	2
Leeds, Southport (L), Huddersfield, Guiseley, Stockport					
◊ Mulley	James	29	Midfielder	17	
Hayes & Yeading, Chelmsford (L), AFC Wimbledon, Hayes & Yeading (L), Braintree, Maidenhead, Hampton & R					
◊ Munns	Jack	24	Midfielder	19	1
Leyton O, Tottenham, Aldershot, Charlton, Cheltenham, Hartlepool					
◊ Murombedzi	Shepherd	23	Midfielder	9	1
Reading, Torquay, Nuneaton, Hayes & Y, Solihull M, Chester, Brackley					
◊ Murphy	Rhys	27	Forward	9	1
Arsenal, Brentford (L), Preston (L), Dagenham & R, Oldham, Crawley (L), AFC Wimbledon (L), Forest Green, York (L), Crawley (L), Torquay (L), Gillingham					
◊ Murtagh	Keiran	29	Midfielder	53	2
Charlton, Fisher, Yeovil, Wycombe, Cambridge U, Macclesfield, Mansfield, Woking (L), Woking, Boreham W					
◊ Myrie-Williams	Jennison	30	Midfielder	12	
Bristol C, Cheltenham (L), Tranmere (L), Cheltenham (L), Carlisle (L), Hereford (L), Dundee Utd, St Johnstone, Stevenage, Port Vale (L), Port Vale, Scunthorpe, Tranmere (L), Sligo Rovers, Newport Co, Torquay					
◊ N'Gala	Bondz	28	Defender	16	
West Ham, Weymouth (L), MK Dons (L), Scunthorpe (L), Plymouth (L), Plymouth, Yeovil, Stevenage, Barnet (L), Portsmouth, Barnet, Eastleigh, Dover, Dagenham & R, Leyton O (L)					
◊ Newton	Conor	26	Midfielder	28	3
Newcastle, St Mirren (L), Rotherham, Cambridge U, Hartlepool					
◊ Nicholson	Tom	30	Goalkeeper	3	
Scarborough, Garforth, Hull City, North Ferriby, Halifax					
◊ Nieskens	Dave	24	Defender	8	1
Barrow					
◊ Nirennold	Victor	27	Midfielder	3	
Fleetwood, Guiseley (L)					
◊ Noble	Cain		Midfielder	1	
Chester					
◊ Norburn	Oliver	25	Midfielder	47	4
Leicester, Bristol R, Bristol R, Plymouth, Guiseley, Macclesfield, Tranmere					
◊ Nortey	Nortei	23	Midfielder	38	5
Chelsea, Welling, Wrexham, Solihull M, Dover					
◊ Norwood	James	27	Forward	48	27
Exeter, Forest Green (L), Eastbourne (L), Forest Green, Tranmere					
◊ Nsimbi	Ivan	18	Forward		
Woking					

PLAYER DATABASE

| SURNAME | FIRST NAME | AGE | POSITION | 2017-18 TOTAL | |
Clubs Played for				Apps	Gls
◊ Nunn	Ben	28	Defender	25	
Boston, Chelmsford, Boreham W (L), Boreham W, St Albans (L), Dagenham & R					
◊ O'Brien	Billy	22	Goalkeeper	3	
Man City, Hyde (L), St Mirren (L), Macclesfield					
◊ O'Donnell	Jonathan	26	Midfielder	12	
Luton, Hyde (L), Gateshead (L), Gateshead					
◊ O'Leary	Max	21	Goalkeeper	25	
Bristol C, Kidderminster (L), Bath (L), Solihull M (L)					
◊ O'Sullivan	Tommy	23	Midfielder	7	
Cardiff, Port Vale (L), Newport Co (Lx2), Colchester, Torquay (L)					
◊ Oates	Rhys	23	Forward	39	7
Barnsley, Grimsby (L), Chester (L), HartlepoolGateshead (L)					
◊ Obileye	Ayo	23	Defender	34	7
Sheffield Wed, Dagenham & Red (L), Dagenham & Red (L), Eastleigh, Dover (L)					
◊ Ochieng	Henry	19	Midfielder	6	
Leyton Orient					
◊ Odametey	Harold	25	Midfielder	50	2
Hampton & R, Maidenhead					
◊ Odejayi	Kayode	36	Forward	41	2
Bristol C, Forest Green (L), Forest Green, Cheltenham, Barnsley, Scunthorpe (L), Colchester, Rotherham, Accrington (L), Accrington (L), Tranmere, Stockport, Guiseley					
◊ Ofori-Twumasi	Nathan	28	Defender	38	1
Chelsea, Dagenham & R (L), Peterborough, Northampton (L), Northampton, Yeovil, Newport Co, Maidstone					
◊ Okenabirhie	Fejiri	22	Forward	39	12
Arsenal, Stevenage , Bedford (L), Cambridge (L), Royston T (L), Farnborough (L), Millwill U21, Harrow B, Dagenham & R, Shrewsbury					
◊ Okojie	Shaun		Forward	9	1
Aldershot, Wealdstone (L), Eastbourne (L)					
◊ Okosieme	Ejiro	25	Defender	9	
Bishop's St, Macclesfield, Dover					
◊ Okuonghoe	Magnus	32	Defender	27	2
Aldershot, St Albans, Crawley, Dagenham & R, Weymouth, Dagenham & R, Colchester, Luton, Hartlepool (L), Dagenham & R, Maidstone, Welling (L)					
◊ Oliver	Connor	24	Midfielder	33	
Sunderland, Hartlepool (L), Blackpool, Morecambe (L), North Ferriby, Halifax					
◊ Orlu	Richard	30	Defender	32	1
Dover, Woking					
◊ Orrell	Lewis		Midfielder		
Hartlepool					
◊ Osborn	Neal	19	Goalkeeper		
Southampton, Torquay, Barnstaple (L)					
◊ Osborne	Jamey	26	Midfielder	24	3
Hednesford, Ringmer (L), Redditch, Solihull M, Grimsby, Solihull M (L), Solihull M					
◊ Osei	Darius	20	Forward	9	1
Stalybridge, Oldham, Maidstone					

SURNAME Clubs Played for	FIRST NAME	AGE	POSITION	2017-18 TOTAL Apps Gls	
◊ Osho Reading, Maidenhead (L)	Gabriel	19	Defender	3	
◊ Owen Hartlepool	Jacob		Defender	1	
◊ Owusu Tranmere, Maidenhead	Nana	22	Defender	10	1
◊ Oyeleke Brentford, Northampton (L), Aldershot (L), Aldershot (L), Woking (L), Exeter, Aldershot	Emmanuel	25	Midfielder	44	3
◊ Palmer Scunthorpe, Southport (L), Droylsden, Buxton, North Ferriby, Guiseley	Ashley	25	Defender	41	1
◊ Panayiotou Leicester, Port Vale (L),Raith (L), Barrow, Salford City (L)	Harrison (Harry)	23	Forward	33	2
◊ Parry Millwall, Stoke, Maidenhead (L), Nuneaton T (L), Weston-S-M (L), Worcester (L), Grays Ath, Maidstone, Margate, Braintree, Dover	Immanuel (Manny)	24	Defender	51	6
◊ Passley Fulham, Shrewsbury (L), Portsmouth (L), Dagenham & R, Whitehawk, Dover	Josh	23	Defender	38	
◊ Paxman Maidstone, East Thurrock (L)	Jack	24	Midfielder	28	1
◊ Payne Gillingham, Peterborough (L), Peterborough, Leyton Orient (L), Blackpool, Ebbsfleet	Jack	26	Midfielder	25	
◊ Payne Barnet, Solihull M (L)	Joe	19	Defender	3	
◊ Pearson Grimsby, Wrexham	Shaun	29	Defender	45	5
◊ Peniket Fulham, Hereford (L), Kidderminster (L), Telford (L), Tamworth, Halifax, Telford (L), Gateshead	Richard	25	Forward	50	12
◊ Penn Scunthorpe, Kidderminster, Alvechurch (L), Burton, Cheltenham, York, Carlisle, Gateshead (L), Wrexham (L), Gateshead	Russell	32	Midfielder	52	
◊ Pennell MK Dons, Rushden, Banbury United, Wolverton, Dunstable, Dagenham & R	Luke	22	Defender	22	
◊ Pentney Leicester, York (Lx2)Ilkeston (L), Woking (L), Colchester, Bath (L), Hayes & Yeading (L), Chelmsford, Braintree, Maidenhead	Carl	28	Goalkeeper	52	
◊ Peters Brentford, Ebbsfleet (L), Crawley (L), Margate, Braintree, Maidenhead	Ryan	30	Midfielder	15	
◊ Phillips Crystal Palace, Maidstone	Michael	20	Midfielder	8	1
◊ Philpot Millwall, Bromley (L), Woking (L)	Jamie	21	Forward	33	7
◊ Phipps Margate, Maidstone, Welling (L), East Thurrock (L)	Harry	19	Midfielder	2	
◊ Pigott Charlton, Gillingham (L), Newport Co (L), Southend (L), Southend (L), Luton (L), Cambridge U, Maidstone (L), Maidstone, AFC Wimbledon	Joe		Forward	34	14

PLAYER DATABASE

SURNAME Clubs Played for	FIRST NAME	AGE	POSITION	2017-18 TOTAL Apps Gls	
◊ Pilkington	George	36	Defender	35	
Everton, Exeter (L), Port Vale, Luton, Mansfield, Forest Green (L), Macclesfield (L), Macclesfield					
◊ Pilling	Luke	21	Goalkeeper	4	
Tranmere					
◊ Pinnock	Mitchell	23	Midfielder	48	11
Southend, Bromley, Concord R (L), Maidstone, Dover, AFC Wimbledon					
◊ Pittman	Jon-Paul	31	Midfielder	19	3
Nottingham F, Hartlepool (L), Bury (L), Doncaster, Crawley, Wycombe, Oxford U, Crawley (L), Wycombe, Grimsby, Harrogate T, Torquay					
◊ Pollock	Aron	20	Defender		
Leyton Orient, Wingate (L), Wealdstone (L), Leatherhead (L), Leatherhead					
◊ Porter	George	26	Forward	46	8
Leyton O, Burnley, Colchester (L), AFC Wimbledon (L), Rochdale, Dagenham & R, Welling, Bromley					
◊ Powell	Jack	24	Midfielder	49	
West Ham, Millwall, Concord R (L), Braintree (L), Ebbsfleet					
◊ Prestedge	Reece	32	Midfielder	36	1
Bishop's St, Bromley, Chelmsford (L), Maidstone					
◊ Preston	Callum	22	Goalkeeper	1	
Birmingham, Telford (L), Crawley, Stevenage, Altrincham, Stevenage, Wrexham					
◊ Preston	Jordan	22	Forward	54	5
Blackburn, Ayr (L), Ayr, Guiseley, Gateshead					
◊ Pring	Cameron		Defender	1	
Bristol C, Aldershot (L), Hereford (L)					
◊ Pritchard	Harry	25	Midfielder	47	15
Maidenhead					
◊ Pritchard	Liam		Forward		
Hartlepool					
◊ Purver	Alex	22	Midfielder	30	2
Leeds, Guiseley (L), Guiseley					
◊ Quigley	Joe	21	Forward	14	2
Bournemouth, Torquay (L), Wrexham (L), Woking (L), Woking (L), Gillingham (L), Gillingham (L), Newport Co (L), Boreham W (L)					
◊ Quigley	Scott	25	Forward	17	8
The New Saints, Blackpool, Wrexham (L)					
◊ Rainey	Ryan	21	Midfielder	2	
Wolves, Chester (L)					
◊ Ralph	Nathan	25	Midfielder	39	
Peterborough, Kettering (L), Northampton, Yeovil, Newport Co, Aldershot (L), Woking					
◊ Ramsbottom	Sam	22	Goalkeeper	7	
Tranmere, Galway FC, Barrow, Macclesfield					
◊ Ramsey	Louis	20	Defender	30	
Norwich, Woking (L)					
◊ Rance	Dean	26	Midfielder	41	3
Gillingham, Maidstone (L), Bishop's S (L), Dover (L), Dover, Ebbsfleet					
◊ Raven	David	33	Defender	7	
Liverpool, Tranmere (L), Carlisle, Shrewsbury, Tranmere, Inverness CT, Wrexham					

SURNAME Clubs Played for	FIRST NAME	AGE	POSITION	2017-18 TOTAL Apps Gls	
◊ Raymond	Frankie	25	Midfielder	47	3
Reading, Dagenham & R, Bromley					
◊ Read	Harvey	19	Defender	1	
Eastleigh, Hungerford (L),					
◊ Reason	Jai	28	Midfielder	50	5
Ipswich, Cambridge U (L), Cambridge U, Crawley, Braintree, Eastleigh, Boreham W, Maidstone					
◊ Reckord	Jamie	26	Defender	19	1
Wolves, Northampton (L), Scunthorpe (L), Coventry (L), Plymouth (L), Swindon (L), Ross Co, Oldham, Solihull M					
◊ Rees	Josh	18	Midfielder	54	20
Nottingham F, Nuneaton (L), Torquay (L), Torquay, Chelmsford, Bromley, Gillingham					
◊ Reid	Alex	22	Forward	33	7
Fleetwood, Wrexham (L), Solihull M (L)					
◊ Reid	Jamie	24	Forward	43	6
Exeter, Dorchester (L), Torquay (L), Truro (L), Torquay (L), Torquay (L)					
◊ Reid	Paul	36	Defender		
Carlisle, Rangers, Preston (L), Northampton (L), Northampton, Barnsley, Carlisle (L), Colchester, Scunthorpe, Northampton, Eastleigh, Whitehawk (L)					
◊ Rendell	Scott	31	Forward	41	13
Aldershot, Forest Green, Crawley, Cambridge U, Peterborough (L), Peterborough, Yeovil (L), Cambridge U (L), Torquay (L), Wycombe, Bristol R (L), Oxford U (L), Luton, Woking, Aldershot					
◊ Reynolds	Callum	28	Defender	42	2
Rushden, Portsmouth, Luton (L), Tamworth, Corby (L), Boreham W, Aldershot, Barnet					
◊ Reynolds	Lamar	22	Midfielder	12	
Newport Co, Leyton Orient (L)					
◊ Richards	Courtney	24	Midfielder	19	
Brighton, Torquay, Macclesfield, Solihull M (L)					
◊ Richards	Jack	19	Forward	14	1
Maidstone, Welling (L), Eastbourne (L)					
◊ Richards	Jordan	25	Defender	14	
Hartlepool, Alfreton (L), Darlington, AFC Fylde, Southport					
◊ Richards	Kane	24	Forward	17	1
Derby, Ilkeston, Chester, Dover, AFC Telford (L)					
◊ Richardson	Kenton	19	Defender	7	
Hartlepool					
◊ Ricketts	Mark	33	Midfielder	51	1
Charlton, MK Dons (L), Ebbsfleet, WokingBoreham W					
◊ Ridehalgh	Liam	27	Defender	42	1
Huddersfield, Swindon (L), Chesterfield (L), Chesterfield (L), Rotherham (L), Tranmere (L), Tranmere					
◊ Riley	Martin	31	Defender	3	
Wolves, Shrewsbury (L), Kidderminster, Cheltenham, Mansfield, Wrexham, Mansfield, Tranmere, Wrexham, Halifax					
◊ Robert	Fabien	29	Midfielder	25	2
Lorient, Boulogne (L), Doncaster (L), Swindon, Forest Green, Aldershot (L)					
◊ Roberts	Gary	31	Midfielder	13	
Crewe, Yeovil, Rotherham, Port Vale, Mansfield, Connah's Q, Bangor, Southport, Chester					

PLAYER DATABASE

| SURNAME | FIRST NAME | AGE | POSITION | 2017-18 TOTAL | |
Clubs Played for				Apps	Gls
◊ Roberts	James	22	Forward	3	
Wycombe, Oxford U, Chester (L), Oxford C (L), Barnet (L), Oxford C (L), Chelmsford (L), Guiseley (L)					
◊ Roberts	Kevin	28	Defender	40	
Chester, Cambridge U, Halifax, Wrexham					
◊ Robinson	Matt	24	Midfielder	35	
Leicester, Luton, Kidderminster (L), Grimsby (L), Woking (L), Dagenham & R					
◊ Robson	Craig	26	Defender	46	3
Havant & W, Sorrento FC (W.Aus), Bognor Regis, Dagenham & R					
◊ Rodney	Devante	20	Forward	44	3
Man City, Sheff Wed, Hartlepool					
◊ Rokka	Elliot	22	Midfielder	1	
Radcliffe B, Tranmere					
◊ Romaine	Elliott	26	Forward	25	5
Brighton, Millwall, Three Bridges, Lewes, Horsham YMCA (L), Eastbourne B, Dagenham & R, Welling (L), Torquay (L),					
◊ Rooney	John	27	Midfielder	34	8
Macclesfield, Barnsley, Bury, Chester, Wrexham, Guiseley					
◊ Rowe	Danny M	26	Forward	52	30
Stockport, Barrow, Macclesfield, AFC Fylde					
◊ Rowe	James	26	Midfielder	43	3
Forest Green, Tranmere, Cheltenham, Aldershot					
◊ Rowe-turner	Lathaniel	28	Defender	31	
Leicester City, Cheltenham Town (L), Torquay United (L), Torquay United, Luton Town, Alfreton Town (L), Alfreton Town, Kidderminster Harriers, Nuneaton (L), Torquay United, Chester					
◊ Rutherford	Paul	31	Midfielder	44	2
Chester, Barrow, Southport, Wrexham					
◊ Sach	Bradley	17	Forward	7	1
Boreham W					
◊ Sam-Yorke	Delano	29	Forward	39	3
Woking, AFC Wimbledon, Basingstoke, Cambridge U, Lincoln (L), Lincoln (L), Forest Green, Boreham W (L), Woking, Maidstone (L)Maidstone, Dartford					
◊ Sammons	Ashley	26	Midfielder	2	
Birmingham, Hereford U, Worcester, Redditch, Worcester, Redditch, Corby, Redditch, Hednesford, Solihull M, Redditch (L),					
◊ Saraiva	Fabio	24	Forward	20	
Merstham, Maidstone, Merstham, Woking					
◊ Sargeant	Sam	20	Goalkeeper	3	
Leyton Orient					
◊ Sendles-White	Jamie	24	Defender	16	
QPR, Colchester (L), Mansfield (L), Hamilton, Swindon, Leyton Orient, St Albans					
◊ Shakes	Ricky	33	Midfielder	50	4
Bolton, Bristol R (L), Bury (L), Swindon, Brentford, Ebbsfleet, Kidderminster, Boreham W					
◊ Shaw	Frazer	23	Defender	6	
Dulwich H, Leyton Orient, Accrington, Woking, Eastleigh					
◊ Shaw	Tom	31	Midfielder	15	
Kidderminster Harriers, Cambridge United, Alfreton Town, Chester, Tamworth					

SURNAME Clubs Played for	FIRST NAME	AGE	POSITION	2017-18 TOTAL Apps Gls	
◇ Sheppard	Jack	21	Defender	2	1
Reading, Hayes & Yeading (L), Eastbourne (L), Dagenham & R (L), Guiseley (L), Wealdstone (L)					
◇ Sheron	Nathan	20	Defender	3	
Fleetwood, Chorley (L), Chester (L), Southport (L)					
◇ Shields	Sean	26	Midfielder	38	5
Tottenham, Potters Bar, St Albans, Dagenham & R, St Albans (L), Ebbsfleet (L), Ebbsfleet,					
Chelmsford (L), Margate (L), Hemel (L)					
◇ Sho-Silva	Tobi	23	Forward	14	1
CharltonWelling (L), Welling (L), Inverness CT (L), Bromley, Dover					
◇ Simpson	Connor	18	Forward	7	1
Hartlepool, PNE					
◇ Skinner	Luke		Goalkeeper		
Aldershot					
◇ Slew	Jerome		Forward	2	
Chester, North Ferriby					
◇ Smith	Christian	30	Midfielder	36	2
Port Vale, Cambridge U (L), Northwich (L), Clyde, Wrexham, York, Wrexham, Newport Co (L),					
Barrow (L), Tamworth (L), Telford, Chelmsford, Hayes & Yeading, Bishop's St, Maidenhead					
◇ Smith	Emanuel	29	Defender	45	2
Walsall, Notts Co, Wrexham, Barrow, Gateshead, Wrexham					
◇ Smith	Grant	24	Goalkeeper	56	
Fulham, Brighton, Hayes & Y (L), Bognor (L), Bognor, Boreham W					
◇ Smith	Jonathan	21	Midfielder	50	10
Wrexham, Cheltenham TownAFC Fylde					
◇ Smith	Kane	22	Defender	51	3
Boreham W					
◇ Smith	Leo	20	Midfielder	8	
Wrexham					
◇ Smith	Mark	22	Goalkeeper	2	
Brentford, Lowestoft (L), Aldershot, Eastbourne B (L)					
◇ Sodeinde	Victor		Midfielder		
Maidstone					
◇ Sokolik	Jakub	24	Defender	5	
Liverpool, Southend (L), Yeovil, Southend (L), Southend, Plymouth, Torquay					
◇ Soloman-Davies	Josh	18	Defender	1	
Tranmere					
◇ Sotiriou	Ruel	16	Forward	6	
Leyton Orient					
◇ Southwell	Dayle	24	Forward	18	7
Grimsby, Harrogate (L), Boston U, Wycombe, Guiseley					
◇ Sparkes	Daniel	26	Midfielder	26	4
Histon, Braintree, Torquay, Dagenham & R					
◇ Spellman	Carl		Midfielder	1	
Tranmere					
◇ Spence	Daniel	28	Defender	17	
Reading, Salisbury (L), Salisbury, Hayes & Y, Eastleigh, Sutton U, Hemel H (L)					

PLAYER DATABASE

SURNAME Clubs Played for	FIRST NAME	AGE	POSITION	2017-18 TOTAL Apps Gls	
◊ St Ledger Peterborough, Stevenage (L), PNE, Middlesbrough (L), Leciester, Millwall (L), Ipswich, Orlando City, Colorado, Solihull M, Guiselsey	Sean	33	Defender	8	
◊ Stack Arsenal, Beveren (L), Millwall (L), Reading (L), Reading, Leeds (L), Wolves (L), Plymouth, Blackpool (L), Wolves (L), Hibernian, Barnet, Eastleigh	Graham	36	Goalkeeper	28	
◊ Staunton Gillingham, St Albans (L), Dagenham & R, Woking	Joshua	22	Defender	41	3
◊ Stearn Forest Green, Sutton U, Eastleigh, Sutton U, Bath (L)	Ross	27	Midfielder	16	1
◊ Steer Arsenal, Gillingham (L), Oldham, Boston Utd, Maidenhead	Rene	28	Defender	37	
◊ Stephens Norwich , Lincoln (L), Hibernian, Barnet, Boreham W	Dave	26	Defender	49	1
◊ Sterling Cray W, Dartford, Dover, Bromley	Tyrone	30	Defender	55	
◊ Sterling-James Birmingham, Cheltenham, Oxford C (L), Gloucester (L), Solihull M, Mansfield, Solihull M (L)	Omari	24	Forward	8	1
◊ Stojsavljevic Woking	Lazar	20	Defender	6	1
◊ Storer Stevenage, Birmingham, Yeovil (L), Gloucester (L), Solihull M (L)	Jack	20	Defender	19	
◊ Stott Oldham, Curzon A (L), AFC Fylde (L), Curzon A (L), Stockport (L)	Jamie	20	Defender	1	
◊ Strevens BarnetSlough (L), St Albans (L), Crawley, Dagenham & R, Brentford, Wycombe, Gillingham, Dagenham & R, Eastleigh, Whitehawk (L),	Ben	38	Forward	8	1
◊ Stubbs Wigan, Crewe (L), AFC Fylde (L)	Sam	19	Defender	7	
◊ Sutherland QPR, Portsmouth (L), Leyton O (L), AFC Wimbledon (L), Dagenham & R (L), Crawley Town (L), Woking, Whitehawk, Bromley	Frankie	24	Forward	40	1
◊ Sutton Stafford, Northwich, Port Vale, Mansfield, Tranmere, Barrow (L)	Richard	32	Defender	49	5
◊ Takyi Braunschweig B, Farnborough, Walton C, Spartaks, Oberneuland, Bognor Regis, Wrexham	Ferdinand	23	Forward	1	
◊ Tarpey Maidenhead, Barnet	Dave	29	Forward	6	7
◊ Tasdemir AFC Fylde	Serhat		Midfielder	28	5
◊ Taylor Cambridge, Bishop's St (L), Maidstone, Aldershot	Bobby-Joe	23	Midfielder	26	1
◊ Taylor Oldham , Stockport (L), Stockport, Rotherham, Rochdale (L), Cheltenham, Northampton, EastleighAFC Fylde	Jason	31	Midfielder	21	
◊ Taylor Halifax, Sutton U, Hampton & R (L)	Josh	23	Forward	32	1

SURNAME Clubs Played for	FIRST NAME	AGE	POSITION	2017-18 TOTAL Apps Gls	
◊ Taylor	Rhys	28	Goalkeeper	17	
Chelsea, QPR (L), Crewe (L), Crewe (L), Rotherham (L), Southend, PNE, Macclesfield, Newport Co, Wrexham (L), AFC FyldeTranmere (L)					
◊ Taylor	Tommy	18	Goalkeeper		
Maidstone					
◊ ter Horst	Johan	23	Forward	22	2
Hull, York (L), MaidstoneFolkstone Inv (L), Folkstone Inv					
◊ Tharme	Douglas		Defender		
Wrexham					
◊ Theophanous	Louie	26	Forward	11	
Histon, Staines, Bromley, Staines, Farnborough, Sutton (L), St Albans, Chelmsford, Billericay, Kingstonian (L), Woking, Kingstonian					
◊ Thomas	Aswad	28	Defender	41	1
Charlton, Accrington (L), Barnet (L), Woking, Braintree, Grimsby, Woking, Dover (L), Dover, Sutton U					
◊ Thomas	Kalern	24	Defender	6	
Quorn, Loughborough, Corby, Boston U, Solihull M, Halesowen, Kettering					
◊ Thomas	Kwame	22	Forward	30	4
Derby, Notts Co (L), Blackpool (L), Coventry, Sutton U (L), Solihull M (L)					
◊ Thomas	Sorba		Midfielder	6	
Boreham W					
◊ Thomas	Terell	22	Defender	21	1
Charlton, Woking, Wigan, Sutton U (L)					
◊ Thompson	Jordan	19	Defender	9	
Coventry, Barrow (L)					
◊ Thompson	Josh	27	Defender		
Stockport, Celtic, Rochdale (L), Peterborough (L), Chesterfield (L), Portsmouth, Colchester, Tranmere, Southport, Macclesfield					
◊ Thompson	Reece	24	Forward	13	1
York, North Ferriby, Guiseley, Boston Utd (L)					
◊ Thomson	Connor	22	Defender	11	1
Carlisle, Blackburn, Barrow (L), Halifax					
◊ Thomson	Matthew		Defender	2	
Chester					
◊ Thorne	James	22	Forward	2	
Nottingham F, Macclesfield (L), Hartlepool					
◊ Tinkler	Robbie	22	Defender	17	
Middlesbrough, North Ferriby (L), Gateshead (L)					
◊ Togwell	Sam	33	Midfielder	22	
Crystal Palace, Oxford U (L), Northampton (L), Port Vale (L), Barnsley, Scunthorpe, Chesterfield, Wycombe (L), Barnet, Eastleigh					
◊ Tollitt	Ben	23	Midfielder	12	
Skelmersdale, Portsmouth, Tranmere					
◊ Tomlinson	Ben	28	Forward	35	3
Worksop, Macclesfield, Alfreton, Lincoln, Barnet, Grimsby (L), Tranmere (L), Barrow (L), Carlisle, Halifax					

SURNAME Clubs Played for	FIRST NAME	AGE	POSITION	2017-18 TOTAL	
				Apps	Gls
◊ Tonks Halesowen, Stourbridge, Solihull M, Stourbridge	Tom	26	Midfielder	3	
◊ Toure BrestViry-Chatillon, West Brom, La Roche Vendee, Fontenay-Foot-Vendee, Macclesfield	Gime	24	Forward	12	
◊ Townsend Birmingham, Lincoln (L), Lincoln (L), Barnsley (L), Barnsley (L), Barnsley, Solihull M (L)	Nick	23	Goalkeeper	5	
◊ Traore Notts Co, Swindon, Forest Green, Tranmere	Drissa	26	Midfielder	3	
◊ Trueman Birmingham, Solihull M (L)	Connal	22	Goalkeeper	4	
◊ Tulian Bromley	Santi	21	Goalkeeper		
◊ Tunnicliffe West Brom, Barnsley, Kidderminster, Hednesford (L), AFC Fylde	Jordan	24	Defender	50	6
◊ Turgott West Ham, Bradford (L), Colchester (L), Rotherham(L), Dagenham & R (L), Coventry, Leyton Orient, Bromley, Stevenage, Boreham Wood, Maidstone (L)Maidstone	Blair	24	Midfielder	31	6
◊ Turley Wycombe, Salisbury, Forest Green, Eastleigh, Newport Co, Boreham W (L)	Jamie	28	Defender	37	5
◊ Turnbull Stockport, Altrincham (L), Northampton, Stockport (L), Stockport (L), Lincoln (L), Macclesfield, Barrow, Chester, Stokcport	Paul	29	Midfielder	24	
◊ Tuton Halifax, Barnsley, Grimsby (L), Barrow (L), Halifax (L)	Shaun	26	Forward	7	
◊ Udoh Crewe Alexandra, Solihull Moors (L), Chester (L), Leamington (L)	Daniel	21	Forward	4	
◊ Upward Maidenhead	Ryan	26	Midfielder	44	8
◊ Vassell Oldham, Chorley (L), Walsall, Chester (L), Gateshead, Port Vale	Theo	21	Defender	41	3
◊ Vaughan Kidderminster, Worcester (L), Worcester, Solihull M, Worcester (L), Chester, Kidderminster	Nathan	37	Goalkeeper	13	1
◊ Vose Braintree, Barnet, Colchester, Welling, Wrexham, Scunthorpe, Grimsby (L), Whitehawk, Bromley, Chester	Dominic	24	Forward	18	2
◊ Wabo Southend, Cambridge C (L), Ebbsfleet (L)	Norman	20	Forward	8	
◊ Walker Brighton, Eastbourne B (L), Dover	Mitch	26	Goalkeeper	51	
◊ Walker-Rice Tranmere	Danny		Forward	1	
◊ Wallace Everton, Bury (L), Stockport (L), Shrewsbury (L), Stevenage (L), Tranmere (L), Tranmere, Sheff Utd, Shrewsbury (L), Tranmere (L), Tranmere	James	26	Midfielder	2	
◊ Walters Leeds, Nottingham F, Barrow (L)	Lewis	23	Forward	16	1

SURNAME Clubs Played for	FIRST NAME	AGE	POSITION	2017-18 TOTAL Apps	Gls
◊					
◊ Walton	Simon	30	Midfielder	32	3
Leeds, Charlton, Ipswich (L), Cardiff (L), QPR, Hull (L), Plymouth, Blackpool (L), Crewe (L), Sheff U (L), Hartlepool, Stevenage, Crawley, Guiseley, Sutton U					
◊ Wanadio	Luke	25	Midfielder	48	8
Staines, Welling, Dartford, Bromley, Aldershot					
◊ Ward	Joe	22	Midfielder	34	8
Chelmsford, Brighton, Lincoln (L), Woking, Peterborough					
◊ Ward	Lewis	21	Goalkeeper	25	
Reading, Sutton (L), Fylkir (Iceland) (L), Margate (L), Hungerford (L), Aldershot (L)					
◊ Waring	George	23	Forward	13	2
Stoke, Barnsley (L), Oxford U (L), Shrewsbury (L), Carlisle (L), Tranmere (L), Halifax (L), Kidderminster (L)					
◊ Waters	Matty	20	Midfielder	8	2
Chester					
◊ Waterston	Nathan	21	Forward	9	1
Workington, Barrow					
◊ Watson	Keith	28	Defender	9	3
Dundee Utd, Forfar (L), East Fife (L), Hibernian (L), St Mirren, St Johnsonte, Hartlepool					
◊ Wedgbury	Samuel	29	Midfielder	42	1
Sheff Utd, Mansfield (L), Macclesfield, Altrincham (L), Stevenage, Forest Green, Wrexham					
◊ Wells	Dean	33	Defender	20	
Brentford, Hampton & R, Staines, MK Dons, Braintree, Stevenage, Boreham W					
◊ Wells	William	20	Defender		
Guiseley					
◊ Wesolowski	James	30	Midfielder	7	
Leicester, Cheltenham (L), Dundee Utd (L), Hamilton (L), Peterborough, Oldham, Shrewsbury, Guiseley					
◊ Westbrooke	Zain	21	Midfielder	10	
Brentford, Solihull M (L), Leyton Orient (L), Coventry					
◊ Weston	Myles	30	Midfielder	38	8
Charlton, Notts Co (L), Notts Co, Brentford, Gillingham, Southend, Wycombe, Ebbsfleet					
◊ Wharton	Patrick	18	Goalkeeper		
Tranmere					
◊ Wheeler	Nick	27	Midfielder	1	
Charlton, Lewis, Burgess Hill, Lewes, Tonbirdge A, Dagenham & R, Billericay, Woking					
◊ Whitaker	Dan	37	Midfielder	45	9
Macclesfield, Port Vale, Oldham, Chesterfield, Macclesfield					
◊ White	Harry	23	Forward	32	5
Gloucester, Barnsley, Kidderminster (L), Boreham W (L), Solihull M, Chester					
◊ White	Joe	19	Forward	3	1
Dagenham & R, Wealdstone (L), Stevenage					
◊ White	Jordan	26	Forward	48	7
Dunfermline, Clyde (L), Dumbarton (L), Drogheda, Clyde, Falkirk, Stirling (L), Stirling, Livingston, Wrexham, Barrow					

PLAYER DATABASE

SURNAME Clubs Played for	FIRST NAME	AGE	POSITION	2017-18 TOTAL Apps	Gls
◊ Whitehead	Danny	24	Midfielder	37	6
Stockport, West Ham, Accrington, Macclesfield (L), Wigan, Macclesfield (L), Cheltenham (L), Macclesfield (L), Macclesfield					
◊ Whitely	Corey	27	Forward	44	11
Tottenham, Waltham F, Cheshunt, Enfield T, Dagenham & R, Ebbsfleet United					
◊ Widdowson	Joe	29	Defender	44	
West Ham, Rotherham (L), Grimsby (L), Grimsby, Rochdale, Northampton, Bury, Morecambe (L), Dagenham & R (L), Dagenham & R, Leyton Orient					
◊ Wilde	Josh	26	Defender	37	
Sheffield U, Buxton, Gainsborough, North Ferriby, Halifax					
◊ Willard	Harley	20	Midfielder	3	
Southampton, Maidstone, Eastbourne (L), Welling (L)					
◊ Williams	Brett	30	Forward	46	10
Reading, Rotherham (L), Northampton, Woking (L), Aldershot, Stevenage, Forest Green, Torquay, Bromley, Torquay (L)					
◊ Williams	Callum	21	Defender	24	
Newcastle, Gateshead (L)					
◊ Williams	Marcus	32	Defender	8	
Scunthorpe, Reading, Peterborough (L), Sheffield U (L), Sheffield U, Scunthorpe (L), Scunthorpe, Guiseley, York (L)					
◊ Williams	Ryan		Midfielder	1	
Wrexham					
◊ Williams	Tyrone	23	Defender	14	1
Kidderminster, Hednesford (L), Solihull M					
◊ Williamson	Ben	29	Forward	37	10
Worthing, Jerez Ind., Bournemouth, Hyde, Port Vale (L), Port Vale, Gillingham, Cambridge U (L), Cambridge U, Eastleigh					
◊ Wilson	Lawrie		Defender	17	
Charlton, Colchester, Stevenage, Charlton, Rotherham (L), Bolton, Peterborough (L), Port Vale, Ebbsfleet					
◊ Wilson	Scott	25	Forward	37	14
Gloucester, Weston-S-M, Eastleigh, Macclesfield					
◊ Winfield	Dave	30	Defender	31	2
Aldershot, Salisbury (L), Wycombe, Shrewsbury, York, Wimbledon (L), Ebbsfleet					
◊ Wollacott	Jojo	21	Goalkeeper	2	
Bristol C, Bath (L), Woking (L), Truro (L)					
◊ Wood	Sam	31	Midfielder	37	
Brentford, Rotherham (L), Wycombe, Eastleigh					
◊ Woodards	Danny	34	Defender	40	1
Exeter, Crewe, MK Dons, Bristol R, Tranmere, Boreham W					
◊ Woods	Michael	28	Midfielder	42	11
Leeds, Chelsea, Notts Co (L), Yeovil, Doncaster, Harrogate T, Hartlepool					
◊ Woolfenden	Luke	19	Defender	26	1
Ipswich Town, Bromley					
◊ Worgan	Lee	34	Goalkeeper	53	
MK Dons, Wycombe (L), Rushden, Cardiff, Maidstone					

SURNAME Clubs Played for	FIRST NAME	AGE	POSITION	2017-18 TOTAL Apps Gls	
◊ Wraight East Thurrock, Maidstone	Tom	24	Forward	25	2
◊ Wright Fleetwood, AFC Fylde (L), Barrow (L), Wrexham	Akil	22	Defender	31	
◊ Wright Sutton U, Salisbury (L)	Tommy	21	Forward	46	15
◊ Wrightman Aldershot	Luca		Midfielder	2	
◊ Wynter Crystal Palace, Colchester (L), Portsmouth (L), Colchester, Maidstone	Alex	24	Defender	49	6
◊ Wynter Crystal Palace, BromleyHampton & R (L), Hampton & R	Ben	20	Defender	16	
◊ Wynter Arsenal, Bristol C, Cheltenham (L), Cheltenham, Telford (Lx2), Bromley, Woking	Jordan	24	Midfielder	31	
◊ Yates Crewe, Halifax (L), Morecambe, Burton (L), Port Vale, Northampton (L), Macclesfield (L)	Adam	35	Defender	7	
◊ Yeates Tottenham, Brighton (L), Swindon (L), Colchester (L), Hull (L), Leicester (L), Colchester, Middlesbrough, Sheffield U, Watford, Bradford, Oldham, Blackpool, Notts Co, Eastleigh	Mark	33	Midfielder	47	5
◊ York Nuneaton, Wrexham, Gateshead	Wesley	25	Forward	41	6
◊ Young Plymouth, Torquay	Luke	25	Midfielder	48	5
◊ Young Sheff Wed, Carlisle (L), Dover, Kidderminster, Chelmsford, Welling, Woking	Matt	24	Defender	41	2
◊ Young Woking	Reggie		Midfielder		
◊ Yussuf Tamworth, Burton Albion, Lincoln City, Oxford City, Mansfield Town, Crawley Town (L), Grimsby Town (L), Barrow, Solihull Moors	Adi	26	Forward	38	10
◊ Zanzala Derby County, Stevenage Borough (L), Chester (L), Accrington Stanley (L)	Offrande	21	Forward	5	
◊ Zebroski Cirencester, Plymouth, Millwall, Oxford U (L), Torquay (L), Wycombe, Torquay (L), Torquay, Bristol RCheltenham, Eastleigh, Newport Co, Eastleigh	Chris	31	Forward	39	10

Make sure of your 2019/20 edition of the Non-League Club Directory

To get your name on the mailing list for next season, either email your details to **mwpublishing@btconnect.com**
or send them to:

**MW Publishing
Rose-Bank
Kingsbridge
TQ7 2NR**

Don't be left standing on the terraces waiting for your copy to hit the shops, have it sent directly to you...

HOT OFF THE PRESS!